HUMAN ANATOMY AND PHYSIOLOGY

Third Edition

OF RELATED INTEREST FROM
THE BENJAMIN/CUMMINGS SERIES IN THE LIFE SCIENCES

Anatomy and Physiology

R. A. Chase
The Bassett Atlas of Human Anatomy (1989)

S. W. Langjahr and R. D. Brister
Coloring Atlas of Human Anatomy, second edition (1992)

E. N. Marieb
Human Anatomy Laboratory Manual (1992)

E. N. Marieb
The A&P Coloring Workbook: A Complete Study Guide to Anatomy and Physiology, fourth edition (1994)

E. N. Marieb
Essentials of Human Anatomy and Physiology, fourth edition (1994)

E. N. Marieb
Human Anatomy and Physiology Laboratory Manual, Brief Version, third edition (1992)

E. N. Marieb
Human Anatomy and Physiology Laboratory Manuals: Cat and Fetal Pig Versions, fourth edition (1993)

E. N. Marieb
Study Guide to Accompany Human Anatomy and Physiology, third edition (1995)

E. N. Marieb and Jon Mallatt
Human Anatomy (1992)

Alexander Spence
Basic Human Anatomy, third edition (1991)

Chemistry

George Sackheim
Introduction to Chemistry for Biology Students, fourth edition (1991)

General Biology

N. A. Campbell
Biology, third edition (1993)

N. A. Campbell, L. G. Mitchell, J. B. Reece
Biology, Concepts and Connections (1994)

Microbiology

I. E. Alcamo
Fundamentals of Microbiology, fourth edition (1994)

G. J. Tortora, B. R. Funke, and C. L. Case
Microbiology: An Introduction, fourth edition (1995)

HUMAN ANATOMY AND PHYSIOLOGY

Third Edition

Elaine N. Marieb, R.N., Ph.D.
Holyoke Community College

The Benjamin/Cummings Publishing Company, Inc.
Redwood City, California   Menlo Park, California   Reading, Massachusetts   New York
Don Mills, Ontario   Wokingham, U.K.   Amsterdam   Bonn   Sydney   Singapore   Tokyo   Madrid   San Juan

Executive Editor: Robin Heyden

Sponsoring Editor: Johanna Schmid

Developmental Editor: Elizabeth Maynard Schaefer

Marketing Manager: John Minnick

Production Supervisor: Anne Friedman

Assistant Editor: Natasha Banta

Editorial Assistant: Thor Ekstrom

Art Supervisor: Kelly Hall

Art Coordinators: Carol Ann Smallwood, Sandra Hall, and Roseann Viano

Text Designer: Jeanne Calabrese

Cover Designer: Yvo Riezebos

Dummy Artist: Brenn Lea Pearson

Photo Editor: Cecilia Mills

Photo Researcher: Mary Goljenboom/Ferret Research, Inc.

Illustrators: Nea Bisek, Martha Blake, Raychel Ciemma, Barbara Cousins, Charles W. Hoffman, Georg Klatt, Jeanne Koelling, Marshall Krasser, Stephanie McCann, Linda McVay, Ken Miller, Elizabeth Morales-Denney, Laurie O'Keefe, Kristin Otwell, Vincent Perez, Carla Simmons, Nadine Sokol, Webtech International (Jim Clark, Niño Paterson, and Jean-Paul Wehbe), Cyndie Wooley, and University of Medicine and Dentistry, Robert Wood Johnson Medical School.

Production Artists: Philip Dee, Valerie Felts, Mark J. Konrad, Steve McGuire, Abigail Rudner, and Denise Schmidt

Copyeditor: Mary Prescott

Proofreaders: Anita Wagner and Martha Ghent

Indexer: Katherine Pitcoff

Compositor: American Composition and Graphics, Inc.

Film Preparation: Northwestern Colorgraphics

Manufacturing Coordinators: Merry Free Osborn and Jenny Rossi

Film and Composition Manager: Lillian Hom

Film and Composition Coordinator: Vivian McDougal

This book is printed on recycled 45# Bulkton Matte paper. The cover is printed with vegetable-based inks.

About the cover
Delightful symbols of the human body in action, the importance of relationships, and our communication of this information to new generations, Olympic gold medal winner Evelyn Ashford and her daughter, Rana, are the perfect choice for the cover of the Third Edition of *Human Anatomy and Physiology.* © Annie Leibowitz/Contact Press Images.

Library of Congress Cataloging-in-Publication Data
Marieb, Elaine Nicpon
   Human anatomy and physiology / Elaine N. Marieb. —
     3rd ed. p.   cm. — (The Benjamin/Cummings series in
     the life sciences)
   Includes bibliographical references and index.
   ISBN 0-8053-4281-8
   1. Human physiology. 2. Human anatomy. I. Title.
   II. Series.
QP31.2.M36   1991
612—dc20   94-27422
                                   CIP

Addison-Wesley School Division   0-8053-4294-X

   4 5 6 7 8 9 10-RN-98 97 96

The Benjamin/Cummings Publishing Company, Inc.
390 Bridge Parkway
Redwood City, California 94065

About the Author

When Elaine Marieb walks into her classroom, she faces the same challenge all anatomy and physiology instructors do. She must communicate a vast amount of complex information to students in a way that stimulates their interest, not dampens it. Twenty-six years of teaching in both the laboratory and the classroom have enhanced her sensibilities about pedagogy and presentation. The insights gained from this experience are distilled in *Human Anatomy and Physiology*—a book that truly addresses the problems students encounter in this course.

Dr. Marieb began her teaching career at Springfield College, where she taught anatomy and physiology to physical education majors. She then joined the faculty of the Biological Science Division of Holyoke Community College in 1969 after receiving her Ph.D. in Zoology from the University of Massachusetts at Amherst. As a result of her contact with students at Holyoke Community College, many of whom were pursuing degrees in nursing, she developed a desire to better understand the relationship between the scientific study of the human body and clinical aspects of nursing practice. While continuing to teach full-time, Dr. Marieb earned an associate degree in nursing in 1980 from Holyoke Community College. She continued her nursing education, receiving a bachelor's degree in nursing from Fitchburg State College and then a master's degree with a clinical specialization in gerontological nursing from the University of Massachusetts in 1985. Dr. Marieb is currently teaching at Holyoke Community College, where she was honored with the Outstanding Educator Award for excellence in classroom instruction. She is also a 1994 recipient of the Benefactor Award from the National Council for Resource Development, American Association of Community Colleges. The award recognizes Dr. Marieb's ongoing sponsorship of student scholarships, faculty teaching awards, and other academic contributions to her community college.

Dr. Marieb is an accomplished author, with several successful textbooks and laboratory manuals to her credit. These publications are listed on the page facing the title page. This text—*Human Anatomy and Physiology*—is the culmination of her career as an educator and author.

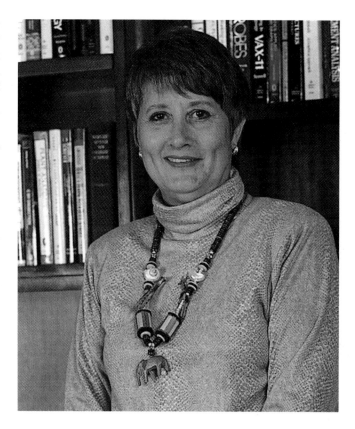

Preface to the Instructor

As a teacher, you know that teaching is not just the presentation of facts. You must provide information in a framework that encourages genuine understanding, devise new presentations to get students over conceptual hurdles, and help students apply what they have learned to new situations. All the while you hope that you can inspire in them a real love of the subject.

After many years of teaching human anatomy and physiology to nursing students, my curiosity about the clinical aspects of anatomy and physiology led me to the classroom—not as a teacher, but as a nursing student. When I sat on the other side of the desk among allied health students of all ages, it was easy to see how my explanations of anatomy and physiology could be improved. I became convinced that new approaches to many topics could excite and challenge students' natural curiosity, and I decided to write this book. I was very fortunate to have a publisher that shared my goal: to set new standards for pedagogical and visual effectiveness in an anatomy and physiology text.

SHAPING THE REVISION: MAKING THE NEW STANDARD EVEN BETTER

As I embarked on the revision process that would give birth to the third edition, I looked back to review how effectively our purpose to set the new standard for an anatomy and physiology text had been accomplished in the first two editions. At the same time, the book team at Benjamin/Cummings gathered feedback from adopters to determine the second edition's effectiveness as a teaching tool. This feedback included User Diary Reviews from schools all over the country, and market feedback in the form of comparative reviews, focus groups, and surveys. This information gathering indicated that we were still meeting our initial goals, and that those goals are still viable. It also provided us with a particularly valuable guide to what specific areas needed to be honed, reworked, or updated. Additionally, if positive feedback in the form of letters from faculty and students is a measure of such an accomplishment, we have succeeded! Thus reassured, my approach, now as then, is to explain the fundamental principles and unifying themes of anatomy and physiology, to reinforce these explanations with comfortable analogies and familiar examples, and to stress mechanisms and cause and effect relationships so that students will gain a knowledge of the integrated workings of the human body.

Now, as in the preparation of the earlier editions, reviewers' contributions have been invaluable in suggesting ways to make the book an even better teaching tool. Indeed, much of the actual work of this revision was driven by and based on this input. My efforts targeted streamlining and improving the clarity of some of the explanations, deleting nebulous phrases and terminology, and adding or polishing accompanying art (for example, redoing once again the bone art in Chapter 7, and guiding the creation of a magnificent new systems figure in Chapter 1). In certain instances, this "sculpting" process entailed substantial reorganization of chapters (the cardiovascular system, Chapters 19 and 20, for instance). In other cases, simplification of material was the major goal.

With this edition I decided to take a chance on introducing and running the gamut with certain amply substantiated information that has physiological or clinical significance for the student—namely, the topics of nitric oxide and G protein regulatory systems, heretofore considered "too new, too much, or too peripheral" for the A&P student audience. Although I continue to struggle with this issue, my personal belief is that students can master and appreciate this greater detail if they are led to it properly and it is presented understandably (ah—there's the rub, but I hope I've done it). Another major undertaking of this revision was to update factual material in all subject areas. The breadth of literature in areas that provide subject matter for an A&P course makes this a monumental task that demands painstaking selectivity. Although information changes even as a textbook goes to press, be assured that this intent and responsibility was carried out to the best of my ability.

NEW TO THE THIRD EDITION

To further enhance the text's educational value and visual effectiveness, the following additions have been incorporated into this third edition.

New Body Systems Figure (Figure 1.2). New to this edition is a beautifully rendered body systems figure. Organs of each body system are skillfully painted over photographs of anatomical models, computer manipulated, and presented in a composite blue-screened format. The images in this figure also provide the central art pieces that anchor the new *Making Connections* feature described next.

Making Connections Feature. The *Systems Interactions* figures of the earlier editions have been totally reconceived as three-part expositions (power pedagogy). The first part, *Systems Connections,* synthesizes for the student the "must-know" information about interactions between the system under consideration and all other body systems. The second part, *Closer Connections,* expands upon the most crucial or most intimate systems interactions with the system in question. This section allows important relationships with systems not yet described (in the chapter sequence) to be brought to the attention of the student, broadening his or her understanding of the system being considered and creating a base for future learning. The last section, *Clinical Connections,* gradually introduces the student to a group of patients (all hypothetical victims of a common bus accident) and provides the opportunity for students to use both current and past learning to deduce the patients' medical problems and predict appropriate therapy or the outcome of their treatment.

Key Figure Questions. In each chapter, questions have been added to selected figures to help the student interpret the figures, and to apply and integrate their past and present learning. Answers to these questions are provided in Appendix H.

Epilogue: A Day in the Life. Totally new in concept and presentation is our Epilogue. Its genesis is lodged in a couple of personally distressing observations. We A&P instructors spend a year taking the body apart and presenting it to students bit by bit, but we never put it back together again. Also motivating was the number of times students have come to me one year *after* completing the course to say something like "I didn't realize how much I really knew until I had to apply it to real-life situations." Hence, the goal of this feature is to put the body back together for students by allowing them to consider the seemingly simple, usual activities of daily life in a nonthreaten-ing way. To do this, we chronicle a day in the life of John, an A&P student, via a descriptive text accompanied by graphic-style art juxtaposed with a simulated computer printout detailing many of the physiological events going on in his body. The presentation emphasizes that this is not intended to be just *another chapter for students to master* at the end of the course, but rather is my gift to them—a touchstone to make the "forest" appear as they see how much they have actually learned, and how all of that information really applies to their own lives. Hopefully, it will engender a feeling of success and an overwhelming awe at the beautiful complexity of their own bodies.

New Appendices. Three new appendices are included in the third edition: Amino acid structures, a summary of the important functional groups in organic molecules, and tables of blood and urine values.

CHANGES IN THE THIRD EDITION.

In addition to the new material and features added, I have made the following changes to the third edition.

More Critical Thinking and Clinical Application Questions. The ability to solve problems is a significant goal for today's prenursing and pre–allied health professionals. To help them master this skill, more Critical Thinking and Clinical Application Questions (formerly called *Critical Thinking Questions*) have been added at the ends of chapters. These are identified by a stethoscope logo.

Added Boldface Terms, Pronunciations, and Word Roots. Because learning the language of anatomy and physiology is a formidable task for the new A&P student, more terms have been boldfaced. Virtually all boldface terms are accompanied by pronunciations the first time they are used, and in many cases their word root and word root meanings have also been supplied.

Earlier Introduction and Enhanced Treatment of Cell Signaling Mechanisms. Although Chapters 11 (Fundamentals of the Nervous System and Nervous Tissue) and 17 (The Endocrine System) treated cell signaling mechanisms briefly in earlier editions, little was said about G protein signaling mechanisms or novel chemical signals such as nitric oxide. As most well–read A&P instructors are aware, many and perhaps most cell signaling mechanisms have proven to be mediated by G proteins, and the influence of nitric oxide is widespread in the body. Hence, a new section on Cell-Environment

Interactions has been written into Chapter 3, and G protein receptor mechanisms and nitric oxide are introduced there. The importance and operation of G proteins are considered later in reference to neurotransmission (Chapter 11), vision and hearing (Chapter 16), and the endocrine system (Chapter 17). Nitric oxide is treated further in discussions of stroke (Chapter 12), memory (Chapter 15), blood pressure regulation (Chapter 20), and sexual arousal (Chapter 28).

Retouched Bone Art.   Because the art in the skeletal system chapters is often the only means available to students to learn bone anatomy, over 60% of the bone art was retouched to more clearly reveal concavities and protrusions and to make it even more lifelike.

Additional Art to Enhance Physiological Concepts.   Many new pieces of art have been added to illustrate physiological concepts. Some of these have a simple one-concept focus; others are illustrated flowcharts that follow pathways—a task that students are often asked to perform.

Updated Clinical Material.   Because information in this area changes quickly, much of the clinical material in the third edition has been updated, and several new clinical photos have been added.

Updated Closer Look Boxes.   Several of the *A Closer Look* boxes have been undated to reflect new information and new techniques relative to the topics discussed.

UNIFYING THEMES

The story of anatomy and physiology would not be coherent or logical without the development of unifying themes. Three integrating themes form the common thread that unifies, organizes, and sets the tone for the entire book.

Interrelationships of Body Organ Systems. The fact that nearly all regulatory mechanisms require interaction of several organ systems is continually emphasized. For example, Chapter 6, which describes the growth and maintenance of bone tissue, emphasizes the importance of muscle pull on bones to maintain bone strength; Chapter 21, which deals with the structure and function of lymphatic vessels and lymphoid tissues, discusses the vital importance of these organs both to body immunity and to maintaining blood circulation, an absolute necessity for life. The unique *Making Connections* feature (described above) is the culmination of this approach and should help students think of the body as a dynamic community of interdependent parts rather than as a number of isolated structural units. The wall

chart entitled "Physiological Interactions," available with the text, will also help students achieve an appreciation for the interrelationships of systems.

Homeostasis.   The normal and most desirable condition of body functioning is homeostasis. Its loss or destruction always leads to some type of pathology—temporary or permanent. Pathological conditions are introduced and integrated with the text material as appropriate. However, clinical examples are used only to clarify and illuminate normal functioning, not as an end in and of themselves. For example, Chapter 20, which deals with the structure and function of blood vessels, explains how the ability of healthy arteries to expand and recoil ensures continuous blood flow and proper circulation. Also discussed in this chapter, however, are the effects on homeostasis when arteries lose their elasticity: high blood pressure and all of its attendant problems. These homeostatic imbalances are indicated visually by a red seesaw symbol that has been tipped off balance. Whenever students see the unbalanced seesaw in art or text, the concept of disease as a loss of homeostasis is reinforced.

Complementarity of Structure and Function. Students are encouraged to understand the structure of an organ, a tissue, or a cell as a prerequisite to comprehending its function. The fundamental concepts of physiology are carefully explained and related to structural characteristics that promote or allow the various functions to occur. For example, the heart can act as a double blood pump because its chambers are interconnected by muscle bundles that coil like figure eights with no beginning and no end.

CONTENT AND ORGANIZATION

The material in this book is presented in five units encompassing a total of 30 chapters. Each unit is self-contained and its individual chapters can be assigned in any sequence without loss of continuity. Following is an overview of the book's organization.

Unit 1: Organization of the Body (Chapters 1–4).   Chapter 1 introduces the student to the basic organization of the body, defines homeostasis and explains the basis of control systems, and introduces the terminology that will be used thereafter in dealing with anatomical concepts. Chapter 2 provides students with an unintimidating treatment of chemistry, complete with all the background they need to comprehend physiological principles. Chapter 3 provides an up-to-date treatment of the cell and its organelles. The chapter also introduces the concept of membrane potential, which must be understood before the activity of excitable cells (muscle and nerve cells) makes sense. The tabular figures in Chapter 4 are a complete histology learning tool—a combination of photomicrographs, line art, and descriptions of structure, function, and location of body tissues.

Unit 2: Covering, Support, and Movement of the Body (Chapters 5–10).
This unit first considers skin and then the skeletal and muscular systems and their interactions in promoting body support, protection, and mobility. Chapter 5 provides comprehensive coverage of the protective and other functions of the skin. A thorough discussion of bone remodeling and its controls is found in Chapter 6. Chapter 9 provides a current and understandable presentation of muscle cell anatomy and physiology. Figure 9.11 (p. 262) on excitation-contraction coupling is a model of simplicity that accurately and understandably explains some difficult concepts.

Unit 3: Regulation and Integration of the Body (Chapters 11–17).
Unit 3 examines the two great regulatory systems of the body, the nervous system and the endocrine system. Chapter 11 sets the stage by focusing on the relationship between neuron anatomy and physiology. An illustrated table summarizing neuron structure and functional regions is included in this chapter. Chapter 13 contains an illustrated table on sensory receptors, including the latest information on these tiny "sentinels." These illustrated tables, plus those on cranial nerves in Chapter 13, are superb learning tools. Chapter 15, on neural integration, explores the various levels of motor and sensory integration, current rapidly changing theories about the operation of higher mental functions such as language and memory, and the cause and consequences of stroke. Chapter 16, The Special Senses, features illustrations not seen elsewhere. For example, Figure 16.18a (p. 519) is an exquisite depiction of rods and cones.

Unit 4: Maintenance of the Body (Chapters 18–27).
Unit 4 presents body systems and mechanisms that maintain homeostasis on a day-to-day basis—cardiovascular, lymphatic/immune, respiratory, digestive, and urinary systems and water, electrolyte, and acid-base balance of body fluids. In this new edition, there is more explanation of physiological concepts and more physiological art in the cardiovascular unit. As before, an illustrated table on the blood vessels spans 20 pages in Chapter 20. Chapter 22, on immunity, is a thorough treatment of an increasingly important and fast-moving field. It has been updated in the new edition.

Unit 5: Continuity (Chapters 28–30).
The final unit considers the reproductive system, sexual development, pregnancy, embryonic development, and basic concepts of heredity. The discussion in Chapter 28 of the hormonal regulation of the female

cycles has been praised as the clearest explanation in any text. Chapter 30 provides a substantial mini-exposition of the basic understandings of human genetics. Although this is considered optional information in many anatomy and physiology courses, we have chosen to retain this chapter in the third edition as many students express a great interest in this topic and it is my belief that it should be part of the knowledge base of any college-educated person.

SPECIAL FEATURES

Art and Photo Program.
Art plays a critical role in helping students visualize anatomical and physiological concepts. Writing this text has been a process of translating my knowledge about anatomy and physiology into words and illustrations. The developmental editor and I conceptualized and discussed the pedagogical value of each piece of new art before sending it to be rendered. Our team of medical illustrators read the manuscript, did additional research when necessary, and then provided realistic, highly accurate figures to depict the anatomy and devised innovative approaches to illustrate physiological concepts. Each illustration was carefully reviewed at every stage of its development to ensure accuracy.

The art program is full color throughout, and color is used not only in an aesthetic sense but in a functional sense as well. For example, the color protocol for the parts and organelles of the cell established in Chapter 3 is used throughout the book whenever cellular structures are shown. Thus, the nucleus is always illustrated in shades of purple and the mitochondria in orange. Likewise, ATP is signalled by a bright yellow sunburst whenever it appears.

Consistency of this nature encourages automatic learning on the part of students and continually reinforces their memory. In many figures, the body location or general structure of a body part is first illustrated in a simple orientation diagram, and then the structures of interest are shown in enlarged, detailed view. Light and scanning electron micrographs are used abundantly, and images produced by modern medical scanning techniques (CT, PET, and MRI) are inserted where appropriate to enhance the students' grasp of structure. The highly acclaimed Bassett photographs of dissected cadavers are sprinkled throughout the book.

Illustrated Tables.
The use of illustrations within tables is a highly effective and efficient method of helping students learn important information. Thus most chapters have at least one illustrated table. These tables run the gamut in level of complexity from the exceptionally complete tissue tables in Chapter 4 to the simple but highly effective table of orientation and directional terms in Chapter 1. The illustrated gross muscle anatomy tables in Chapter 10

are unique because, in addition to doing what all such tables do (summarizing the location, attachments, and general functions of the skeletal muscles), these tables include an essay overview of the functions of each group of muscles and describe how they interact and play against one another. The innovative and beautiful blood vessel tables in Chapter 20 do what no text has done before—they juxtapose art showing location of the vessels with flowcharts visually identifying the branching and distribution of those vessels.

Color Coding. Each body system has been assigned a specific color. For example, all chapters concerned with the cardiovascular system, Chapters 18–20, are identified by a red color tab at the top of the page. Thus, if you wish to quickly flip to the chapters on this system, you would simply open the book to the section identified by the red-edged pages. Likewise, all *Making Connections* features, which summarize interactions of the body's organ systems, and several tables and figures identify the organ systems by the same color codes. The table of contents also provides a guide to interpreting the color coding scheme.

Physical Education Applications. Because most students majoring in physical education (PE) take a course in human anatomy and physiology, this text describes physiological changes or demands during exercise. The text also explains the "why" of common sports injuries, and discusses other concerns of athletes. These PE applications are signified by a bicycle symbol preceding the sections.

"A Closer Look" Boxes. Many chapters of this book have special topic boxes. Some of these boxes deal with timely topics such as AIDS (p. 738), cocaine (p. 371), and steroid use by athletes (p. 559). Others describe recent medical advances such as the new technique of using skeletal muscle to repair a decompensated heart (p. 624) or in vitro fertilization (p. 1006). Some boxes are expanded discussions of important topics in the text such as the common language of neurons and immune cells (p. 716). In cases where topic boxes include timely information, care was taken to update them.

Life Span Approach. Most chapters close with a "Developmental Aspects" section that summarizes the embryonic development of organs of the system and then examines how they change throughout the life span. Diseases particularly common at certain periods of life are pointed out, and problems encountered by the elderly are emphasized. Implications for the elderly are particularly important to students in the health-related curricula because many, if not most, of their clients will be in that age group.

IN-TEXT LEARNING AIDS

A number of pedagogical devices have been incorporated into *Human Anatomy and Physiology* to enhance its utility as a learning tool.

Combined Chapter Outline and Objectives. Each chapter begins with an outline of the major topics of the chapter with specific objectives for each topic. Page references allow students to easily refer to pertinent text discussions.

Related Clinical Terms. At the end of each chapter, a list of clinical terms that are relevant to the content of the chapter is provided.

Chapter Summary. Thorough chapter summaries in a study outline format with page references help students review material they have just read.

Review Questions. A variety of question formats—multiple choice, matching, and short answer essay—are found at the end of each chapter. This set of questions provides an important tool for students to test their knowledge of the material. Answers to the multiple choice and matching questions can be found in Appendix H.

 Critical Thinking and Clinical Application Questions. These questions, identified by the stethoscope icon, are found at the end of every chapter and encourage the student to synthesize information and solve new problems.

Appendices. The appendices offer several useful references for the student. They include Appendix A: The Metric System; Appendix B: The Codon Sheet with amino acid abbreviations; Appendix C: Amino Acid Structures; Appendix D: Functional Groups in Organic Molecules; Appendix E: Some Important Metabolic Pathways; Appendix F: The Periodic Table; Appendix G: Reference Values for Selected Blood and Urine Studies; Appendix H: Answers to Multiple Choice, Matching, and Key Figure Questions.

Glossary. At the end of this book is an extensive glossary that includes both the definitions and phonetic pronunciations of key terms.

Word Roots. An expanded listing of word roots appears on the endpapers for easy reference.

THE INTEGRATED TEACHING PACKAGE

The teaching package that accompanies *Human Anatomy and Physiology* has been carefully developed to assist instructors and students in using and deriving the greatest benefit from this text. The package for this third edition includes previous offerings plus several new and exciting elements.

Instructor's Resource Guide.   Updated for the third edition, the Instructor's Resource Guide is designed to coincide with the way you prepare for lectures and teach anatomy and physiology. Each chapter contains lecture outlines, list of histology slides, lecture tips, critical thinking and application questions, and more. Also included are answers to all text questions, an extensive bibliography, and several case studies on how to use A.D.A.M., the A&P videodisc, and the Epilogue.

Testbank.   Completely revised and rewritten by Joseph Berger and Mary Healey of Springfield College, the new testbank now contains 4000 test questions including multiple choice, true/false, matching, short answer, and clinical questions. Each question has been assigned Learning Objectives from the text, a level of difficulty notation, the test answer, and a page reference to the text. In addition, we have added 60 line drawings to the testbank to help students visualize and identify various physiological processes. This testbank is available on a microcomputer test generation program for IBM PC and compatibles and Macintosh computers.

Overhead Acetate Transparencies.   The third edition package contains 350 full-color acetates. In addition to adding figure numbers to each acetate, we have used large, boldface type for easier viewing in large lecture halls. On all acetates the color has been enhanced for improved clarity.

Photo Atlas.   Authored by Robert A. Chase, M.D., Professor of Anatomy at Stanford University, *The Bassett Atlas of Human Anatomy* offers an extraordinary collection of full-color dissection photos that will be extremely useful to your students in their laboratories.

Human Dissection Slides.   Qualified adopters of *The Bassett Atlas of Human Anatomy* or the *Human Anatomy and Physiology* text or laboratory manuals can receive a set of 85 complimentary dissection slides taken from *The Bassett Atlas of Human Anatomy.*

Histology Slides.   These 135 full-color slides were photographed by Allen Bell of the University of New England and Victor Eroschenko of the University of Idaho.

A.D.A.M.   Recognizing the widespread desire for a more interactive learning experience, Benjamin/Cummings and A.D.A.M. Software, Inc. have joined forces to develop new multimedia products for college science and nursing courses that provide an interactive approach to understanding *Human Anatomy and Physiology.*

A.D.A.M. Standard—This new version of the Animated Dissection of Anatomy for Medicine multimedia product is designed for the undergraduate student. Easy to use, streamlined, with terminology correlated to Marieb *Human Anatomy and Physiology,* this product is available on IBM Windows and Macintosh platforms.

Cardiovascular Physiology Module—The first in a series of 13 CD-ROM modules featuring animations and interactive exercises to help students with the most important and complex physiological processes.

To make this new software easier to use there will be a number of links between the software and Marieb's third edition. Immediately available: End-of-chapter questions that can be answered by consulting A.D.A.M. are indicated by the "walking man" icon. Case studies written by instructors successfully using A.D.A.M. in their courses are included in the Instructor's Guide. The third edition of Marieb's *Study Guide* will feature an A.D.A.M. appendix to help students to use the software as they work through the *Study Guide* exercises.

For more information about the A.D.A.M. productline call our Life Sciences Hotline at 1-800-955-8398.

Toolkit Software.   This tutorial software, developed by Peter Zao of North Idaho College, is directly correlated to *Human Anatomy and Physiology,* third edition. The A&P Multimedia Notes section outlines each chapter and links highlighted key terms to definitions, selected figures, and the *Slice of Life* videodisc. The A&P Practice Exams section offers multiple-choice tests for students to complete, explanations of answers, and an optional feature that allows students to track their success throughout the Practice Exam. Two versions are available: an instructor's version with authoring features and animations, and a student version with animations. Available for IBM Windows (version 3.1 or greater).

Laboratory Manuals.   Elaine N. Marieb has authored three proven lab manuals that are written to complement this textbook: *Human Anatomy and Physiology Lab Manual: Brief Version,* third edition (1992); *Human Anatomy and Physiology Lab Manual: Cat Version,* fourth edition (1993); and *Human Anatomy and Physiology Lab Manual: Fetal Pig Version,* fourth edition (1993). One of these will meet the needs of your laboratory course, depending on the animal of dissection. The *Human Anatomy and Physiology Lab Manual: Brief Version* is designed for labs that use no major dissection animal. Responding to trends for less animal dissection, the greater expense of cadavers, cats, fetal pigs, and models, the need for greater precautions in labs utilizing blood and body fluids, and the increased use of computers in the lab, these manuals have restructured many of their approaches to laboratory studies and incorporate an exercise based on the commercially available physiology simulation, "Mechanical Properties of Active Muscle." Adopters of any of these manuals or *Human Anatomy and Physiology* will receive a complimentary copy of this award-winning computer simulation. The new editions of these manuals, scheduled for publication in 1996, will include directions for use of *Intellitool* software for specific exercises.

Student Study Guide.

Written by Elaine Marieb and revised in earlier editions with the help of contributions from Marie Fitzgerald of Holyoke Community College and Betsy Ott of Tyler Junior College, the new study guide (third edition) contains more multiple choice, clinical application, and critical thinking questions. The variety of exercises and learning tools that were so well-received in the first two editions—identification, matching, labeling, completion, and true/false questions; definitions, coloring exercises; and unique visualization exercises called *Incredible Journeys*—have been retained. With all the answers at the end of the book, this study guide is an ideal tool for students to review the basic concepts of anatomy and physiology.

In this edition of the study guide, the A.D.A.M. "walking man" icon has been added to selected pieces of art whose comprehension can be enhanced by using A.D.A.M. Also included is an appendix that explains the major features of A.D.A.M. and correlates specific text and study guide figures to pertinent anatomical structures in A.D.A.M.

Physiological Interactions Wall Chart.

Because student response has been so overwhelmingly positive to this unique study tool, we have continued to make available a poster with each copy of the third edition. This innovative wall chart reinforces the principal theme of the book—the interrelationships of body systems—and serves as a road map for students throughout the entire course.

The Human Cadaver Dissection Videotapes.

Scripted, developed, and produced by Rose Leigh Vines and Allan Hinderstein of California State University, Sacramento, these videos are highly acclaimed. The **Human Musculature Videotape** takes the student on an 18-minute tour of 38 muscles on a prosected cadaver. Ideal for the anatomy lab, each muscle's origin and insertion is also shown. The **Human Nervous System Videotape** points out areas of the brain, the cranial nerves, regions of the spinal cord and major nerves and plexuses arising from the cord. Because the video shows structures on a prosected cadaver that are usually difficult to see with models or drawings, this video is also ideally suited for the laboratory.

New to this edition is the **Human Cardiovascular System Videotape** which showcases heart anatomy, demonstrates how the heart valves function, and traces the major branches of the vascular system through the body.

Hormonal Action Videotape.

Developed and produced by Juanita Barrena and Rose Leigh Vines of California State University, Sacramento, and University Media Services, California State University, Sacramento, this dynamic 15-minute video entitled **Selected Actions of Hormones and Other Chemical Messengers** demonstrates three hormonal experiments that appear in the lab manuals under the title "Experiments in Hormonal Action." The first experiment examines the effect of pituitary hormones on egg production in the frog; the second looks at the effect of hyperinsulinism on the goldfish. The final experiment demonstrates the effects of epinephrine on the frog heart. Additionally, this exercise illustrates the effect of acetylcholine, a neurotransmitter, on heart rate and force, allowing the opposing effects of the sympathetic nervous system (mediated by epinephrine) and the parasympathic nervous system (mediated by acetylcholine) to be evaluated.

Anatomy and Physiology Videodisc.

This exciting teaching aid is completely new for the third edition. Combining photographs, filmclips, animations of physiological processes, and art from the text (broken into steps or animated where appropriate), it enables you to instantly illustrate the concepts you describe in lectures and labs. The videodisc is accompanied by a barcode manual that allows you to select and display material in any order.

The Anatomy Tutor.

Programmed by Dr. Marvin Branstrom of Cañada College, these student tutorials include one module for each system on a total of four discs for the Macintosh computer and use the HyperCard program. Designed to help the student review the anatomy of the body systems, each module has been class tested and reviewed for accuracy and ease of use.

The Physiology Tutor.

Also programmed by Dr. Marvin Branstrom of Cañada College, these modules provide a computerized review of physiology for the body systems. The Physiology Tutor is also a Macintosh program available in a four-disc package.

ACKNOWLEDGMENTS

I find it hard to believe that nearly three years have passed since I sat in front of my computer working on the second edition of *Human Anatomy and Physiology*. Here I am again, but it's the third edition this time. What is it they say about time flying when you're having fun? As I've said before, bringing the book to its final printed form requires the collaborative effort of many dedicated and skilled people. The names are different in many cases, but the roles are timeless and deserve honorable mention.

As in the first edition, our team of artists has been superb. Some of the names listed on page iv are familiar; some are new to this edition. It makes little difference; they are still making the body come alive and dance, and imbuing the students with a lasting imagery from their anatomy and physiology studies. Worthy of special mention is Vince Perez, the artist who painted the photographs in Figure 1.2 and gifted us with the inspired illustrations for the *Epilogue: A Day in the Life.* I love this artwork because it reinforces the idea that learning should be fun.

Cecilia Mills, head of photo research for this edition as well as the last, continues to make her own mark. She's amazing in her ability to ferret out photos and photo-micrographs that "fit" exactly the pedagogical and artistic goals. And then there's Kelly Hall, who coordinated the art for this edition and found such great artists. Kelly's organizational skills and her personal artistic competence and creativity were evident from the moment I began working with her. By always previewing and editing the art (sending it back for corrections if necessary), before she sent it on for my comments or approval, she removed most of the stress of a tight production schedule from my shoulders. I "luv ya," Kelly, don't lose the fire in your belly. My thanks also go to Carol Ann Smallwood, Pat Burner, and Hilair Chism who helped with the art program. Their attention to the seemingly millions of sniggling details was laudable.

One of the biggest bugaboos, for both A&P authors and their audiences, is the seemingly unruly growth of information in their field. Without editorial limitations, books tend to grow like topsy. Beth Schaefer, the developmental editor on this edition, with pencil raised like a lance, worked to hold off the "beast" and keep this edition from becoming unwieldy. More important personally was her willingness to be a "cognitive sounding board" for my ideas for text changes or new art, her careful attention to clarity of description, and our common desire to put out the best book possible. Mary Prescott, the manuscript copy editor, picked up the torch from Beth and competently polished the final draft of the manuscript.

Anne Friedman, production coordinator for the project, was as demanding as I in insisting on consistency of style, art-text coordination, and on the need to break the rules sometimes to get the best pedagogy. She is a publishing professional who has the scent of what constitutes good teaching. Not to be forgotten is the marketing manager, John Minnick. His relentless crusade to stay abreast of market changes in A&P was immensely helpful in the revision process. Additionally, his unabated and enthusiastic support of the book has been very gratifying personally.

I guess one would classify Sami Iwata, the assistant editor I worked closely with on this edition, as a jack-of-all-trades. It was her responsibility to find the most qualified and informed reviewers, to ensure that they received the manuscript in good order, and then see that I received the feedback while it was still usable (deadlines!!!). Sami is off (trekking in Nepal) now as I complete this edition, and the responsibility for coordinating the supplements is in the capable hands of Natasha Banta, new to the team.

Acquisitions editors are like chameleons—each special and unique in their own right. Jim Behnke signed the first edition of this book, Andy Crowley got it started, and Connie Spatz steered it to completion with love and skill. Melinda Adams supported the revision process in every way she could and had unwavering faith in my decisions and choices. Johanna Schmid, my present acquisitions editor, was a latecomer in this revision—decisions made earlier were already in progress. Hence, her major third edition role, which she assumed with enthusiasm, and for which I thank her, was to keep the book team working together like a well-oiled machine. Robin Heyden, executive editor, who assumed the added responsibilities of those early decisions, was already overburdened with the demands of her own position—nonetheless, she was a great leader with seemingly boundless energy.

As before, I also owe a tremendous debt of gratitude to my colleagues at Holyoke Community College, particularly Art Jackson and Ed Brown, both of whom kept me jumping with feedback and suggestions for "the next time around."

Finally, as ever, I want to thank my husband, Zeb, who keeps standing by me, despite my occasional short temper, lack of social time, and quick meals. With this edition, as with those that preceded it, we are rejoicing in its completion.

Now that the work of this edition is ending, I can look back on it and say quite truthfully that this time it really was a much easier experience than I expected! Without question, this speaks to the publishing excellence of my book team at Benjamin/Cummings. I think I have a "keeper" again and hope that you—my users—will too.

* * *

Thank you for taking the time to write to me with your thoughts on the second edition. Your suggestions, criticisms, and encouraging words provided much of the impetus for this revision. Again, the proof of the effectiveness of the third edition as a teaching tool will be its usefulness in the classroom. I hope you agree that our goals to set new standards for pedagogical effectiveness have been fulfilled. I would appreciate hearing from you about the ways this book might be improved still in future editions.

Elaine N. Marieb
Holyoke Community College
Department of Science, Engineering, and Math
303 Homestead Avenue
Holyoke, Massachusetts 01040

First Edition Reviewers

Focus Group Participants

Robert Agnew, *Northlake College*

Joe Anders, *North Harris County College*

Jennifer Breckler, *San Francisco State University*

Jean Cons, *College of San Mateo*

Carl Knight, *Eastfield College*

Sylvia Lianides, *West Valley College*

Jerri Lindsey, *Tarrant County Junior College*

Gordon Locklear, *Chabot College*

Gail Matson, *American River College*

Robert Nabors, Jr., *Tarrant County Junior College*

David Smith, *San Antonio College*

Greg Smith, *St. Mary's College*

Richard Symmons, *California State University at Hayward*

Manuscript and Art Reviewers

Thomas Adams, *Michigan State University*

Robert Agnew, *Northlake College*

Joe Anders, *North Harris County College*

Robert Anthony, *Triton College*

Delon Barfuss, *Georgia State University*

Wayne Becker, *University of Wisconsin at Madison*

John Benson, *Ohio University*

Frank Binder, *Marshall University*

Lanier Byrd, *Saint Philips College*

Gene Block, *University of Virginia*

Franklyn Bolander, *University of South Carolina*

Robert Boley, *University of Texas at Arlington*

Michael Bowes, *Humboldt State University*

James Boyson, *San Antonio College*

Jennifer Breckler, *San Francisco State University*

Alan Brush, *University of Connecticut*

Warren Burggren, *University of Massachusetts at Amherst*

Michael Burke, *University of Kansas*

Ray Burkett, *Shelby State College*

Kenneth Bynum, *University of North Carolina at Chapel Hill*

Colin Campbell, *Pima Community College*

Wayne Carley, *Lamar University*

Tom Cole, *Phillips College*

Richard Connett, *University of Rochester*

Darrell Davies, *Kalamazoo Valley Community College*

Scott Dunham, *Illinois Central College*

Klaus Elgert, *Virginia Technological Institute*

Victor Eroschenko, *University of Idaho*

Jim Ewig, *Towson State University*

Douglas Fonner, *Ferris State College*

John Frehn, *Illinois State University*

Anne Funkhauser, *University of the Pacific*

Gregory Garman, *Centralia College*

Stephen George, *Amherst College*

Carol Gerding, *Cuyahoga Community College*

Todd Gleeson, *University of Colorado at Boulder*

Judy Goodenough, *University of Massachusetts at Amherst*

Ann Hagan, *American University*

Ann Harmer, *Orange Coast College*

Deborah Hettinger, *Texas Lutheran College*

C.J. Hubbard, *Northern Illinois University*

Margaret Hudson, *Seattle University*

Karen Jones, RN, *Cardiovascular Surgery, Inc., Evansville, Indiana*

Donald Kisiel, *Suffolk Community College*

William Kleinelp, *Middlesex County College*

Carl Knight, *Eastfield College*

Robert Laird, *University of Central Florida*

Jerri Lindsey, *Tarrant County Junior College*

Alan Liss, *State University of New York at Binghamton*

Mark Lomolino, *University of Arizona*

Jon Mallatt, *Washington State University*

William Matthai, *Tarrant County Junior College*

Gary Matthews, *State University of New York at Stony Brook*

Esmail Meisami, *University of Illinois at Urbana-Champaign*

Doug Merrill, *Rochester Institute of Technology*

Lewis Milner, *North Central Technical College*

John Minnich, *University of Wisconsin at Milwaukee*

Robert Nabors, Jr., *Tarrant County Junior College*

Evan Oyakawa, *California State University at Los Angeles*

Harry Painter, *North Virginia Community College*

Arthur Reed, *University of Hawaii-Manoa*

Curtis Smith, *Mount Holyoke College*

Wendy Smith, *Northeastern University*

Phil Sokolove, *University of Maryland*

Richard Symmons, *California State University at Hayward*

Sunny Tripp, *University of Notre Dame*

Guy Van Cleave, *Modesto Junior College*

Edward Wallen, *University of Wisconsin at Parkside*

James Waters, *Humboldt State University*

Richard Welton, *Southern Oregon State College*

Glenn Yoshida, *Los Angeles Southwest College*

Yameen Zubairi, *Catonsville Community College*

Second Edition Reviewers

Focus Group Participants

Craig Clifford, *Northeastern State University*

William Despain, *North Central Technical College*

Gwen Eller, *Western Piedmont Community College*

Thomas Grittinger, *University of Wisconsin at Sheboygan*

Patricia Hedley, *Humber College*

Herbert House, *Elon College*

Earl Lindberg, *Davidson Community College*

Lewis Milner, *North Central Technical College*

Robert Nabors, Jr., *Tarrant County Junior College-South Campus*

Betsy Ott, *Tyler Junior College*

Ruby Pharr, *Western Piedmont Community College*

Jane Salisbury, *Edison State Community College*

David Smith, *San Antonio College*

Richard Symmons, *California State University at Hayward*

Larry Thiery, *Wilmar Community College*

Margaret Weck, *Lake Superior State College*

Glenn Yoshida, *Los Angeles Southwest College*

John Yrios, *Edgewood College*

Manuscript and Art Reviewers

Annie Bianchino, *California State University at Long Beach*

Charles Biggers, *Memphis State University*

Julia Bonner, *Northeast Iowa Community College*

Christine Bouwman, *Macomb Community College-South Campus*

Alan Brush, *University of Connecticut*

Ken Bynum, *University of North Carolina at Chapel Hill*

Clementine De Angelis, *Tarrant County Junior College-South Campus*

Augustine Di Giovanna, *Salisbury State University*

Cheryl Donlon, *Northeast Iowa Community College*

Debra Draves, *Contra Costa College*

Durwood Foote, *Tarrant County Junior College-Northeast Campus*

Sharon Fowler, *Dutchess Community College*

David Goldstein, *Wright State University*

Jon Hastings, *Northern Kentucky University*

Reinhold Hutz, *University of Wisconsin-Milwaukee*

Robert Hyde, *San Jose State University*

Bonnie Kalison, *Mesa Community College*

Joseph Keyes, *Sinclair Community College*

William Klopfenstein, *Sinclair Community College*

Anna Langford, *Sante Fe Community College*

Marianne Litvaitis, *University of New Hampshire*

Robert Loeschen, *California State University at Long Beach*

Katherine T. Mechlin, *Wright State University*

Anne Howard Millican, *Guilford Technical Community College*

Lewis Milner, *North Central Technical College*

Saundra Minckley, *Mesa Community College*

John Moorhead, *University of Colorado*

Robert Nabors, Jr., *Tarrant County Junior College-South Campus*

Betsy Ott, *Tyler Junior College*

Donald Puder, *College of Southern Idaho*

Arthur Reed, *University of Hawaii-Manoa*

Joe Reicherter, *State University of New York at Farmingdale*

George Spiegel, Jr., *Austin Community College*

Richard Symmons, *California State University at Hayward*

Donna Van Wynsberghe, *University of Wisconsin-Milwaukee*

James White, *Prairie State College*

Benjamin Wise, *Keene State College*

Willard Woodward, *Parkland College*

Third Edition Reviewers

Focus Group Participants

Al Bassinger, *Angelina College*

John Boothby, *San Jose State University*

Earl Bourne, *University of New Mexico*

Sandra Bruner, *Polk Community College*

Billie Fitch, *Green River Community College*

Richard Fredrickson, *Tacoma Community College*

Sherry King, *Trinity Valley Community College*

Ron McCune, *Crafton Hills College*

Lewis Milner, *North Central Technical College*

Kay Pauling, *Foothill Community College*

Jeff Robertson, *Tyler Junior College*

Adrian Rodriguez, *San Jose State University*

Henry Scurry, *Miami-Dade Community College*

John Searle, *College of San Mateo*

Lisa Shimeld, *Crafton Hills College*

Shirley Simon, *Catonsville Community College*

David Smith, *San Antonio College*

Richard Symmons, *California State University at Hayward*

Steve Williams, *Glendale Community College*

Peter Zao, *North Idaho College*

Manuscript and Art Reviewers

Mark Aronson, *Scott Community College*

Ralph Barclay, *Wayne State College*

Debra Barnes, *Contra Costa College*

Robert W. Bauman, Jr., *Amarillo College*

Robert Boettcher, *Lane Community College*

Alphonse Burdi, *University of Michigan*

Craig Clifford, *Northeastern State University*

Darwin Coy, *University of North Florida*

Jay Druecker, *Chadron State College*

Ralph Eckerlin, *Northern Virginia Community College*

Philip Fawley, *Westminster College*

Christina Fisher-Dark, *University of New England*

Kelleen Flaherty, *Indiana Vocational Technical College-Indianapolis*

Ross Hansen, *University of Sydney*

Vicki Harber, *University of Alberta*

Julie Hendricksen, *Pasco-Hernando Community College*

Henry Kermott, *Saint Olaf College*

Wesley Klein, *Lamar University-Orange*

Earl Lindberg, *Davidson Community College*

Elden Martin, *Bowling Green State University*

Zona McGuirt, *Georgia State University*

Dean Milligan, *University of Alaska-Anchorage*

William Milsom, *University of British Columbia*

Laney Mobley, *Kilgore College*

Michael Page, *Carson-Newman College*

Michael Postula, *Parkland College*

Donald Puder, *College of Southern Idaho*

Nancy Rauch, *Merritt College*

Carolyn Robertson, *Tarrant County Junior College-South Campus*

Cynthia Surmacz, *Bloomsburg University*

Richard Tsika, *University of Illinois at Urbana-Champaign*

Tony Waldrop, *University of Illinois at Urbana-Champaign*

Eugene Walton, *Tallahassee Community College*

Willard Woodward, *Parkland College*

Yameen Zubairi, *Catonsville Community College*

Preface to the Student

This book is written for you. In a way, it is written by you (students) because it incorporates your suggestions, the answers to questions most often asked, and explanatory approaches that have produced the greatest success in helping you learn about the human body. Human anatomy and physiology is more than just interesting—it is fascinating. To help get you involved in the study of this exciting subject, a number of special features are incorporated throughout the book.

The tone of this book is intentionally informal and unintimidating. There is absolutely no reason that you can't enjoy your learning task. This book is meant to be a guide to the understanding of your own body, not an encyclopedia of human anatomy and physiology. I have tried to be selective about the information included and have chosen facts that stress essential concepts. Physiological concepts are explained thoroughly; abundant analogies are used and examples are taken from familiar events whenever possible.

The illustrations and tables are designed with your learning needs in mind. The tables are summaries of important information in the text and should be valuable resources for reviewing for an exam. In all cases, the figures are referenced where their viewing would be most advantageous to help in understanding the text. Those depicting physiological mechanisms often use the flowchart format so that you can see where you've been and where you're going. Additionally, several *key figures* come equipped with questions that will help you to interpret the figures or to apply and integrate what you have learned. Special topic boxes, called *A Closer Look,* alert you to advances in medicine or present scientific information that can be applied to your daily life. The *Making Connections* feature, new to this edition, tries to do several things to aid your studies. The *Systems Connections* recaps the information that you should know when you complete each body system. *Closer Connections* is intended to broaden your horizon and enrich your understanding of the system being studied—you may or may not have covered all of its concepts. The *Clinical Connections* challenges you to use what you have learned to assess and predict clinical outcomes—in other words, to apply your learning. Please use this feature; it will help you to learn this subject.

Even closer to my heart is the second new feature written with you in mind—the *Epilogue: A Day in the Life.* This is my gift to you. My nursing students have told me two things that caused me to write this section: (1) Because of all the details of the course, they had problems seeing the whole picture, and (2) they learned so much but never realized it until they had to cope with the Medical-Surgical clinical rotation. I want you to realize your success. Furthermore I want you to be able to (1) put all the "trees" (individual facts learned about organs, etc.) back in the "forest" (understand the place of organs and organ systems in the scheme of body functioning) and (2) relate the commonplace events of your day to what you have learned. So—accompany John on his day when even the simplest things he does are interpreted by a computer printout of the most important events occurring in his body at the time. This feature can also be used to help you integrate your learning as you work your way through the course. The thing that it should *not* be is something more to learn. It should be fun and make you feel really good about what you have learned.

Each chapter begins with an outline of its major topics (and their page references), with specific learning objectives listed for each topic. Important terms within the chapter text are highlighted by being bold-faced (in dark type), and phonetic spellings are provided for terms that are likely to be unfamiliar to you. To use these phonetic aids, you will need to remember the following rules:

1. Syllables are separated by dashes.
2. Accent marks follow stressed syllables. The primary stress is shown by ' and secondary stress by ".
3. Unless otherwise noted, assume that vowels at the ends of syllables are long. Assume that all other vowels are short unless a bar, indicating a long vowel sound, appears above them.

For example, the phonetic spelling of "thrombophlebitis" is throm"bo-fleh-bi'tis. The fourth syllable (bi´) receives the greatest stress, and the first sylla-ble (throm˝) gets the secondary stress. The "o" in the second syllable and the "i" in the fourth syllable are long. A more complete explanation of the pronuncia-tion system can be found at the beginning of the glossary.

Any exam causes anxiety. To help you better pre-pare for an exam or comprehend the material you have just read, thorough summaries complete with page references are found at the ends of the chapters, as are review questions that use a combination of test-ing techniques (multiple choice, matching, short answer essay, critical thinking, and clinical applica-tions). Also remember that key figure questions are sprinkled throughout the chapter.

I hope that you enjoy *Human Anatomy and Phys-iology* and that this book makes learning about the body's structures and functions an exciting and rewarding process. Perhaps the best bit of advice I can give you is that memory depends on understanding. Thus, if you strive to achieve understanding instead of rote memorization, your memory will not fail you very often.

I would appreciate hearing from you about your experiences with this textbook or suggestions for improvements in future editions.

Elaine N. Marieb
Holyoke Community College
Department of Science, Engineering, and Math
303 Homestead Avenue
Holyoke, Massachusetts 01040

Detailed Contents

UNIT 2
COVERING, SUPPORT, AND MOVEMENT
OF THE BODY

5 The Integumentary System   **135**

6 Bones and Bone Tissue   **155**

UNIT 4
MAINTENANCE OF THE BODY

19 The Cardiovascular System: The Heart 612

20 The Cardiovascular System: Blood Vessels 643

23 The Respiratory System 743

UNIT 5
CONTINUITY

HUMAN ANATOMY AND PHYSIOLOGY
Third Edition

The Human Body:
An Orientation

CHAPTER OUTLINE AND STUDENT OBJECTIVES

An Overview of Anatomy and Physiology (pp. 3–5)

1. Define anatomy and physiology and describe their subdivisions.

2. Explain the principle of complementarity.

The Hierarchy of Structural Organization (pp. 5–7)

3. Name (in order of increasing complexity) the different levels of structural organization that make up the human body, and explain their relationships.

4. List the 11 organ systems of the body and briefly explain the major function(s) of each system.

Maintaining Life (pp. 5, 8–9)

5. List the functional characteristics common to humans (and other organisms) and explain the importance of each to maintaining life.

6. List the survival needs of the body.

Homeostasis (pp. 10–13)

7. Define homeostasis and explain its importance.

8. Define negative feedback and describe its role in maintaining body homeostasis.

9. Define positive feedback and explain why it usually causes homeostatic imbalance. Also note specific situations in which it contributes to homeostasis, or normal body function.

10. Describe the relationship between homeostatic imbalance and disease.

The Language of Anatomy (pp. 13–22)

11. Describe the anatomical position.

12. Use correct anatomical terminology to describe body directions, regions, and body planes or sections.

13. Locate and name the major body cavities and their subdivisions, and list the major organs in each cavity or subdivision.

14. Name the specific serous membranes and note their common function.

15. Name the nine regions or four quadrants of the abdominopelvic cavity and list the organs they contain.

As you make your way through this book, you will be learning about one of the most fascinating subjects possible—your own body. Such a study is not only highly personal, but timely as well. We live in the middle of an information blizzard, and news of some medical advance appears almost daily. If you are to appreciate emerging discoveries in genetic engineering, to understand new techniques for detecting and treating disease, and to make use of published facts on how to stay healthy, it is important to learn about the workings of your body. For those of you preparing for a career in the health sciences, the study of anatomy and physiology has added rewards because it provides the strong foundation needed to support your clinical experiences.

In this chapter we define and contrast anatomy and physiology and discuss the levels of organizational complexity in the human body. Then we review needs and functional processes common to all living organisms. Three essential concepts—the *complementarity of structure and function, hierarchy of structural organization,* and *homeostasis*—will form the bedrock for your study of the human body and will unify the topics discussed in this book. The final section of the chapter deals with the language of anatomy—the terminology that anatomists use when they describe the body or its parts.

AN OVERVIEW OF ANATOMY AND PHYSIOLOGY

Although many branches of science help us to understand the human body, the most critical concepts are embodied in two subdivisions of biology: anatomy and physiology. Anatomy and physiology are complementary sciences. **Anatomy** is the study of the structure of body parts and their relationships to one another. Anatomy has a certain appeal because it is concrete. Body structures can be seen, felt, and examined closely; it is not necessary to *imagine* what they look like. **Physiology** concerns the functioning of the body's structural machinery, that is, how the parts of the body work and carry out their life-sustaining activities. When all is said and done, physiology is explainable only in terms of the underlying anatomy.

Topics of Anatomy

Anatomy is a broad field with many subdivisions, each providing enough information to be a course in itself. **Gross,** or **macroscopic, anatomy** is the study of large body structures visible to the naked eye, such as the heart, lungs, and kidneys. Indeed, the term *anatomy* (derived from the Greek words meaning "to cut apart") is related most closely to gross anatomy because in such studies preserved animals or their organs are dissected (cut up) to be examined. Gross anatomy can be approached in different ways. In **regional anatomy,** all the structures (muscles, bones, blood vessels, nerves, etc.) in one particular region of the body, such as the abdomen or leg, are examined at the same time. In **systemic** (sis-tem′ik) * **anatomy,** the gross anatomy of the body is studied system by system. For example, when studying the cardiovascular system, you would examine the heart and the blood vessels of the entire body. Still another subdivision of gross anatomy is **surface anatomy.** This is the study of internal body structures as they relate to the overlying skin surface. You use surface anatomy when you identify the bulging muscles beneath a body builder's skin, and nurses use it when they locate the appropriate blood vessels in which to feel pulses and draw blood.

Microscopic anatomy concerns structures too small to be seen without the aid of a microscope. For most such studies, exceedingly thin slices, or sections, of body tissues are stained and mounted on slides to be examined under the microscope. Subdivisions of microscopic anatomy include *cellular anatomy,* or **cytology** (si-tol′o-je), which considers the cells of the body, and **histology** (his-tol′o-je), the study of tissues.

Developmental **anatomy** traces structural changes in an individual from conception through old age. **Embryology** (em″bre-ol′o-je), a subdivision of developmental anatomy, concerns only the developmental changes that occur before birth.

A number of highly specialized branches of anatomy are used primarily for medical diagnosis and scientific research. For example, in *pathological anatomy,* structural changes in the body caused by disease are studied on both gross and microscopic levels. *Radiographic anatomy* is the study of internal structures as they are visualized by X-ray images or specialized scanning procedures. Radiology is valuable to clinicians evaluating patients for certain bone disorders, tumors, and other conditions that cause anatomical changes. In *molecular biology,* the structure of biological molecules (chemical substances) is investigated. Molecular biology is actually a separate branch of biology, but it falls under the anatomy "umbrella" when we push anatomical studies to the subcellular level, where molecules provide the fundamental links between structure and function. As you can see, subjects of interest to anatomists range from easily seen structures down to the smallest molecule, and their study provides us with a static image of the architecture of the body and its parts.

As you will quickly learn, the most important "tools" for studying anatomy are observation, manipulation, and a mastery of anatomical terminology. A simple example will illustrate how these tools work together in an anatomical study. Let's assume that your topic is freely movable joints of the body. In the laboratory, you will be able to *observe* an animal joint, noting how its parts fit together. You can work the joint (*manipulate* it) to determine its range of motion. Then, using *anatomical terminology,* you can name its parts and describe their relationships so that other students (and your instructor) will have no trouble understanding you. The list of word roots (on the inside of the book cover) and the glossary will help you with this special vocabulary. Although most of your observations will be made with the naked eye or with the help of a microscope, medical technology has developed a number of sophisticated tools that can peer into the body without disrupting it. These include CT and MRI scans and other exciting medical imaging techniques discussed in *A Closer Look* on pp. 18–19.

Topics of Physiology

Like anatomy, physiology has several subdivisions. The most common subdivisions of physiology consider the operation of specific organ systems. For example, **renal physiology** concerns urine production and kidney function; **neurophysiology** explains the workings of the nervous system; and **cardiovascular physiology** examines the operation of the heart

---

*For the pronunciation guide rules, see the Preface to the Student, p. xvii.

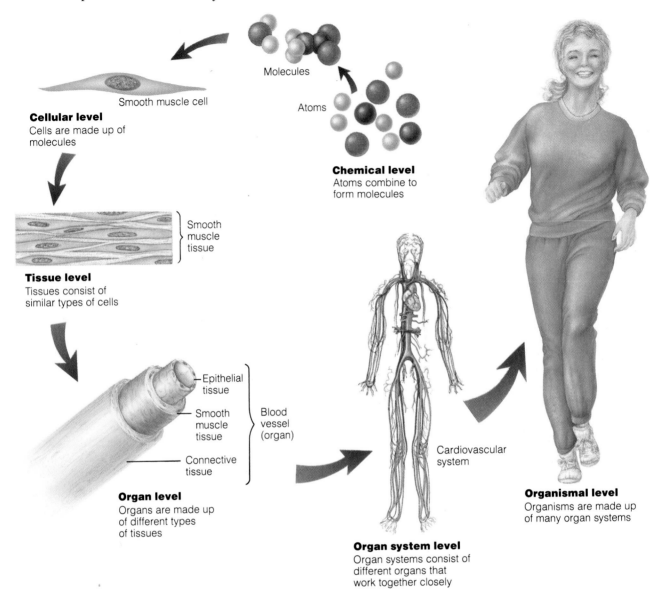

Molecules

Smooth muscle cell

Cellular level
Cells are made up of
molecules

Atoms

Chemical level
Atoms combine to
form molecules

**Smooth
muscle
tissue**

Tissue level
Tissues consist of
similar types of cells

Epithelial
tissue

Smooth
muscle
tissue

Blood
vessel
(organ)

Connective
tissue

Organ level
Organs are made up
of different types
of tissues

Cardiovascular
system

Organ system level
Organ systems consist of
different organs that
work together closely

Organismal level
Organisms are made up
of many organ systems

FIGURE 1.1
Levels of structural complexity. In this diagram, components of the cardiovascular
system are used to illustrate the various levels of structural complexity in a human being.

and blood vessels. While anatomy provides the static
image, physiology reveals the dynamic nature of the
workings of the living body.

Physiology often focuses on events at the cellular
or molecular level because the body's abilities
depend on the operation of its individual cells; and
cells' abilities ultimately depend on the chemical
reactions that go on within them. An in-depth understanding of physiology also rests on the principles of
physics, which help to explain electrical currents,
blood pressure, and the way muscles use bones to
cause body movements. Body functions such as nervous system activity, muscle contraction, digestion,
and many others are incomprehensible without an
understanding of the underlying chemistry and
physics. Thus, basic chemical and physical princi-

ples are presented in Chapter 2 and throughout the
book as needed to explain physiological topics.

Complementarity of Structure and Function

Although it is possible to study anatomy and physiology in isolation from one another, they are truly
inseparable sciences because function always reflects
structure; that is, what a structure can do depends on
its specific form. This is called the **principle of complementarity of structure and function.** For example,
bones can provide support and protection to body
organs because they contain hard mineral deposits;
blood flows in one direction through the heart

because the heart has valves that prevent backflow; and the lungs can serve as a site for gas exchange because the walls of their air sacs are extremely thin. The intimate relationship of anatomy and physiology is stressed throughout this book to make your learning more meaningful. In all cases, a description of the anatomy of a structure is accompanied by an explanation of its function, emphasizing the structural characteristics contributing to that function.

THE HIERARCHY OF STRUCTURAL ORGANIZATION

The human body exhibits many levels of structural complexity (Figure 1.1). The simplest level of the structural hierarchy is the *chemical level,* which we study in Chapter 2. At this level, **atoms,** tiny building blocks of matter, combine to form **molecules** such as water, sugar, and proteins. Molecules, in turn, associate in specific ways to form *organelles,* basic components of the microscopic cells. **Cells** are the smallest units of living things. The *cellular level* is examined in Chapter 3. Individual cells vary widely in size and shape, reflecting their unique functions in the body. All cells use nutrients and maintain their boundaries, but only certain cell types form the transparent lens of the eye, secrete mucus, or conduct nerve impulses.

The simplest living creatures are composed of single cells, but in complex organisms, such as human beings, the hierarchy continues on to the *tissue level.* **Tissues** consist of groups of similar cells that have a common function. The four basic tissue types in the human body are epithelium, muscle, connective tissue, and nervous tissue. Each tissue type has a characteristic role in the body, which we explore in detail in Chapter 4. Briefly, epithelium covers the body surface and lines its cavities; muscle causes movement; connective tissue supports the body and protects its organs; and nervous tissue provides a means of rapid internal communication by transmitting electrical impulses.

An **organ** is a structure composed of at least two tissue types (four is more commonplace) that performs a specific function for the body. At the *organ level,* extremely complex physiological processes become possible. Let's take the stomach for an example. Its lining is an epithelium that produces digestive juices; the bulk of its wall is composed of muscle that churns and mixes stomach contents (food); its connective tissue reinforces the soft muscular walls; and its nerve fibers increase digestive activity by stimulating the muscle to contract more vigorously and the glands to secrete more digestive juices. The liver, the brain, and a blood vessel are very different from the stomach, but they are organs as well. You can think of each organ of the body as a specialized functional center responsible for a necessary activity that no other organ can perform.

The next level of organization is the *organ system.* Organs that cooperate and work closely with one another to accomplish a common purpose are said to be part of a particular **organ system.** For example, organs of the cardiovascular system—mainly the heart and blood vessels—ensure that blood containing nutrients, oxygen, and other vital substances circulates continuously to all body cells. Organs making up the digestive system—the mouth, esophagus, stomach, intestine, and so forth—break down ingested food so that the nutrients can be absorbed into the blood. The digestive system also removes indigestible food residues from the body. Besides the cardiovascular and digestive systems, the other organ systems of the body are the integumentary, skeletal, muscular, nervous, endocrine, respiratory, lymphatic, urinary, and reproductive systems. Figure 1.2 provides a brief overview of the 11 organ systems, which we study in more detail in Units 2–5.

The highest level of organization is the **organism,** the living human being. The *organismal level* represents the sum total of all structural levels working in unison to promote life.

MAINTAINING LIFE

Functional Characteristics

Now that you're aware of the structural levels composing the human body, the question that naturally follows is, What does this highly organized human body do? Like all complex animals, human beings maintain their boundaries, move, respond to environmental changes, take in and digest nutrients, carry out metabolism, dispose of wastes, reproduce themselves, and grow. We will discuss each of these necessary life functions briefly here and in more detail in later chapters.

It cannot be emphasized too strongly that the multicellular state and the parceling out of vital body functions to several different organ systems result in interdependence of all body cells. No individual's organ systems work in isolation. Instead, they work together cooperatively to promote the well-being of the entire body. Because this theme is emphasized throughout this book, it is appropriate to identify the organ systems making the major contributions to each of the functional processes (Figure 1.3). As you read this section, you may want to refer back to the more detailed descriptions of the organ systems in Figure 1.2.

Maintenance of Boundaries

Every living organism must be able to **maintain its boundaries** so that its internal environment (inside) remains distinct from the external environment surrounding it (outside). In single-celled organisms, the boundary is an external limiting membrane that contains its contents and admits needed substances while

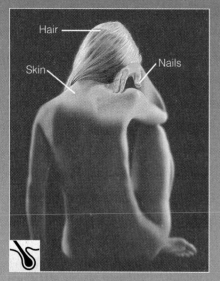

(a) Integumentary System
Forms the external body covering; protects deeper tissues from injury; synthesizes vitamin D; site of cutaneous (pain, pressure, etc.) receptors, and sweat and oil glands.

(b) Skeletal System
Protects and supports body organs; provides a framework the muscles use to cause movement; blood cells are formed within bones; stores minerals.

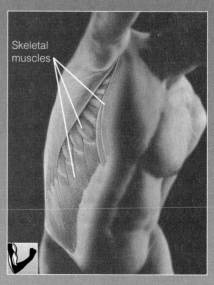

(c) Muscular System
Allows manipulation of the environment, locomotion, and facial expression; maintains posture; produces heat.

(d) Nervous System
Fast-acting control system of the body; responds to internal and external changes by activating appropriate muscles and glands.

(e) Endocrine System
Glands secrete hormones that regulate processes such as growth, reproduction, and nutrient use (metabolism) by body cells.

(f) Cardiovascular System
Bloods vessels transport blood which carries oxygen, carbon dioxide, nutrients, wastes, etc.; the heart pumps blood.

FIGURE 1.2
Summary of the body's organ systems. The structural components of each organ system are illustrated in the diagrammatic view. The major functions of the organ system are listed beneath each illustration. Note that the lymphatic system/immunity (**g**) is a functional system rather than an organ system in the true sense.

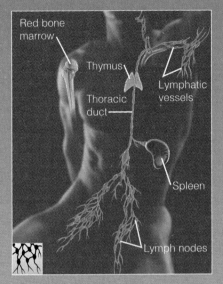

(g) Lymphatic System/Immunity
Picks up fluid leaked from blood vessels
and returns it to blood; disposes of debris
in the lymphatic stream; houses white blood
cells (lymphocytes) involved in immunity.
The immune response mounts the attack
against foreign substances within the body.

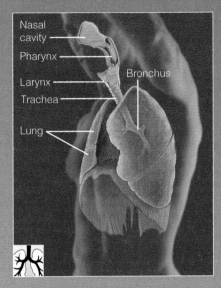

(h) Respiratory System
Keeps blood constantly supplied with oxygen and removes carbon dioxide; the
gaseous exchanges occur through the
walls of the air sacs of the lungs.

(i) Digestive System
Breaks down food into absorbable units
that enter the blood for distribution to body
cells; indigestible foodstuffs are eliminated
as feces.

(j) Urinary System
Eliminates nitrogenous wastes from the
body; regulates water, electrolyte, and acid-
base balance of the blood.

(k) Male Reproductive System
Overall function is production of offspring. Testes produce sperm and male sex hormone;
ducts and glands aid in delivery of sperm to the female reproductive tract. Ovaries produce
eggs and female sex hormones; remaining structures serve as sites for fertilization and
development of the fetus. Mammary glands of female breasts produce milk to nourish the
newborn.

(l) Female Reproductive System

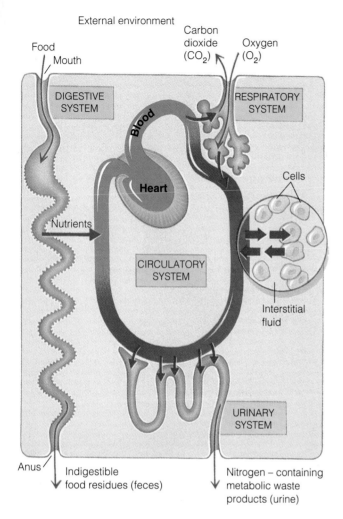

FIGURE 1.3
Examples of selected interrelationships among body organ systems. The digestive and respiratory systems, in contact with the external environment, take in nutrients and oxygen, respectively, which are then distributed by the blood to all body cells. Elimination from the body of metabolic wastes is accomplished by the urinary and respiratory systems.

restricting the entry of potentially damaging or unnecessary substances. Similarly, all the cells of our body are surrounded by a selectively permeable membrane. Additionally, the body as a whole is enclosed and protected by the integumentary system, or skin. The integumentary system plays an important role in protecting our internal organs from drying out (which would be fatal), bacterial invasion, and the damaging effects of an unbelievable number of chemicals and physical factors in the external environment.

Movement

Movement includes all the activities promoted by the muscular system, such as propelling ourselves from one place to another by walking, running, or swim-ming, and manipulating the external environment with our nimble fingers. The muscular system is aided by the skeletal system, which provides the bony framework that the muscles pull on as they work. Movement also occurs when substances such as blood, foodstuffs, and urine are propelled through internal organs of the cardiovascular, digestive, and urinary systems, respectively. On the cellular level, the muscle cell's ability to move by shortening is more precisely called **contractility.**

Responsiveness

Responsiveness, or **irritability,** is the ability to sense changes (stimuli) in the environment and then react or respond to them. For example, if you cut your hand on broken glass, a withdrawal reflex occurs—you involuntarily pull your hand away from the painful stimulus (the broken glass). It is not necessary to think about it—it just happens! Likewise, when carbon dioxide in your blood rises to dangerously high levels, chemical sensors respond by sending messages to brain centers controlling respiration, and your breathing rate is accelerated.

Because nerve cells are highly irritable and communicate rapidly with each other by conducting electrical impulses, the nervous system bears the major responsibility for responsiveness. However, all body cells exhibit irritability to some extent.

Digestion

Digestion is the process of breaking down ingested foodstuffs to simple molecules that can be absorbed into the blood for distribution to all body cells by the cardiovascular system. In a simple, one-celled organism such as an amoeba, the cell itself is the "digestion factory," but in the complex multicellular human body, the digestive system performs this function for the entire body.

Metabolism

Metabolism (mĕ-tab′o-lizm; "a state of change") is a broad term that encompasses all chemical reactions that occur within body cells. It includes breaking down complex substances into their simpler building blocks, synthesizing more complex cellular structures from simpler substances, and using nutrients and oxygen to produce (via *cellular respiration*) ATP, the energy-rich molecules that power cellular activities. Metabolism depends on the digestive and respiratory systems to make nutrients and oxygen available to the blood and on the cardiovascular system to distribute these needed substances throughout the body. Metabolism is regulated largely by hormones secreted by glands of the endocrine system.

Excretion

Excretion is the process of removing *excreta* (ek-skre'tah), or wastes, from the body. If the body is to continue to operate as we expect it to, it must get rid of nonuseful substances produced during digestion and metabolism. Several organ systems participate in excretion. For example, the digestive system rids the body of indigestible food residues in feces, and the urinary system disposes of nitrogen-containing metabolic wastes, such as urea and uric acid, in urine. Carbon dioxide, a by-product of cellular respiration, is carried in the blood to the lungs, where it leaves the body in exhaled air.

Reproduction

Reproduction can occur at the cellular or organismal level. In cellular reproduction the original cell divides, producing two identical daughter cells that may then be used for body growth or repair. Reproduction of the human organism, or making a whole new person, is the major task of the reproductive system. When a sperm unites with an egg, a fertilized egg forms, which then develops into a bouncing baby within the mother's body. The reproductive system is directly responsible for producing offspring, but its function is exquisitely regulated by hormones of the endocrine system.

Because males produce sperm and females produce eggs (ova), there is a division of labor in the reproductive process, and the reproductive organs of males and females are quite different (see Figure 1.2). Additionally, the female's reproductive structures provide the site for fertilization of eggs by sperm, then protect and nurture the developing fetus until birth.

Growth

Growth is an increase in size of a body part or the organism. It is usually accomplished by increasing the number of cells. However, individual cells also increase in size when not dividing. For true growth to occur, anabolic (constructive) activities must occur at a faster rate than catabolic (destructive) activities.

Survival Needs

The ultimate goal of all body systems is to maintain life. However, life is extraordinarily fragile and requires several factors. These factors, which we will call *survival needs,* include nutrients (food), oxygen, water, and appropriate temperature and atmospheric pressure.

Nutrients, taken in via the diet, contain the chemical substances used for energy and cell building. Most plant-derived foods are rich in carbohydrates, vitamins, and minerals, whereas most animal foods are rich in proteins and fats. Carbohydrates are the major energy fuel for body cells. Proteins and to a lesser extent fats are essential for building cell structures. Fats also cushion body organs, form insulating layers, and provide a reserve of energy-rich fuel. Selected minerals and vitamins are required for the chemical reactions that go on in cells and for oxygen transport in the blood. For example, the mineral calcium helps to make bones hard and is required for blood clotting.

All the nutrients in the world are useless unless **oxygen** is also available, because the chemical reactions that release energy from foods are *oxidative* reactions that require oxygen. Without oxygen, cells can survive for only a few minutes. Approximately 20% of the air we breathe is oxygen. It is made available to the blood and body cells by the cooperative efforts of the respiratory and cardiovascular systems.

Water accounts for 60% to 80% of body weight and is the single most abundant chemical substance in the body. It provides the watery environment necessary for chemical reactions and the fluid base for body secretions and excretions. Water is obtained chiefly from ingested foods or liquids and is lost from the body by evaporation from the lungs and skin and in body excretions.

If chemical reactions are to proceed at life-sustaining rates, **body temperature** must be maintained at around 37°C (98°F). As body temperature drops below this point, metabolic reactions become slower and slower, and finally stop. When body temperature is too high, chemical reactions proceed so rapidly that body proteins lose their characteristic shape and stop functioning. At either extreme, death occurs. Most body heat is generated by the activity of the skeletal muscles.

The force exerted on the surface of the body by the weight of air is referred to as **atmospheric pressure.** Breathing and exchanging oxygen and carbon dioxide in the lungs depend on appropriate atmospheric pressure. At high altitudes, where the atmospheric pressure is lower and the air is thin, gas exchange may be inadequate to support cellular metabolism. However, the bone marrow eventually compensates by forming more red blood cells.

The mere presence of these survival factors is not sufficient to maintain life. They must be present in appropriate amounts as well; excesses and deficits may be equally harmful. For example, oxygen is essential but extremely high levels of oxygen are toxic to body cells. Similarly, the food ingested must be of high quality and in proper amounts; otherwise, nutritional disease, obesity, or starvation are likely. Also, while the listed needs are the most crucial, they do not even begin to encompass all of the body's needs. For example, we can, if we must, live without gravity, but the quality of life suffers.

HOMEOSTASIS

When you think about the fact that your body contains trillions of cells in nearly constant activity, and that remarkably little usually goes wrong with it, you begin to appreciate what a marvelous machine your body is. Walter Cannon, an American physiologist of the early twentieth century, spoke of the "wisdom of the body," and he coined the word **homeostasis** (ho″-me-o-sta′-sis) to describe its ability to maintain relatively stable internal conditions even though there is continuous change in the outside world. Although the literal translation of homeostasis is "unchanging," the term does not really mean a static, or unchanging, state. Rather, it indicates a *dynamic* state of equilibrium, or a balance, in which internal conditions change and vary, but always within relatively narrow limits.

In general, the body is in homeostasis when its needs are adequately met and its functions are occurring smoothly. But maintaining homeostasis is much more complex than it appears at first glance. Virtually every organ system plays a role in maintaining the constancy of the internal environment. Adequate blood levels of vital nutrients must be continuously present, and heart activity and blood pressure must be constantly monitored and adjusted so that the blood is propelled with adequate force to reach all body tissues. Also, wastes must not be allowed to accumulate, and body temperature must be precisely controlled. A wide variety of chemical, thermal, and neural factors act and interact in complex ways—sometimes bolstering and sometimes impeding the body as it works to maintain its "steady rudder."

General Characteristics of Control Mechanisms

Communication within the body is essential for homeostasis. Communication is accomplished chiefly by the nervous and endocrine systems, which use electrical impulses delivered by nerves or bloodborne hormones respectively as information carriers. The details of how these two great regulating systems operate are the subjects of later chapters, but the basic characteristics of control systems that promote homeostasis are explained here.

Regardless of the factor or event being regulated—this is called the **variable**—all homeostatic control mechanisms have at least three interdependent components (Figure 1.4). The first component is a **receptor.** Essentially, it is some type of sensor that monitors the environment and responds to changes, called *stimuli,* by sending information (input) to the second element, the *control center.* The flow of information from the receptor to the control center occurs along the so-called *afferent pathway.* The **control center,** which determines the *set point* (the level or range) at which a variable is to be maintained, analyzes the input it receives and then determines the appropriate response.

FIGURE 1.4
Schematic representation of the elements of a control system. Communication between the receptor, control center, and effector is essential for normal operation of the system.

The third component is the **effector,** which provides the means for the control center's response (output) to the stimulus. Information flows from the control center to the effector along the *efferent pathway.* The results of the response then *feed back* to influence the stimulus, either depressing it (negative feedback) so that the whole control mechanism is shut off or enhancing it (positive feedback) so that the reaction continues at an even faster rate.

Now that we have examined the basic flow of information in control systems, we are ready to explain how negative and positive feedback mechanisms help maintain body homeostasis.

Negative Feedback Mechanisms

Most homeostatic control mechanisms are **negative feedback mechanisms**. In such systems, the net effect is that the output of the system decreases or shuts off the original stimulus or reduces its intensity. These mechanisms cause the variable to change in a direction *opposite* to that of the initial change, returning it to its "ideal" value; thus the name "negative" feedback mechanisms.

A frequently used example of a nonbiological negative feedback system is a home heating system connected to a temperature-sensing thermostat. The thermostat houses both the receptor and the control center. If the thermostat is set at 20°C (68°F), the heating system (effector) is triggered ON when the house temperature drops below that setting. As the furnace

? *(1) What is the control center in this example? (2) What is the stimulus for insulin release? (3) What is the response to insulin release?*

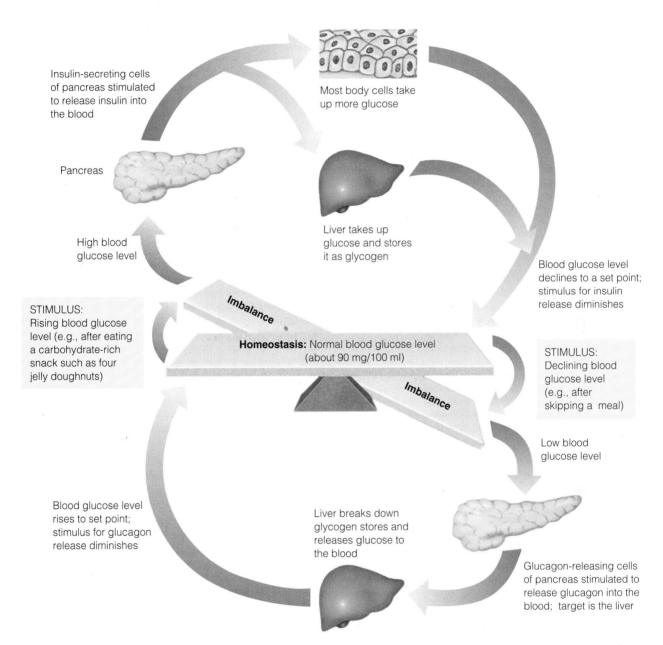

Insulin-secreting cells of pancreas stimulated to release insulin into the blood

Most body cells take up more glucose

Pancreas

Liver takes up glucose and stores it as glycogen

High blood glucose level

Blood glucose level declines to a set point; stimulus for insulin release diminishes

Imbalance

STIMULUS: Rising blood glucose level (e.g., after eating a carbohydrate-rich snack such as four jelly doughnuts)

Homeostasis: Normal blood glucose level (about 90 mg/100 ml)

STIMULUS: Declining blood glucose level (e.g., after skipping a meal)

Imbalance

Low blood glucose level

Blood glucose level rises to set point; stimulus for glucagon release diminishes

Liver breaks down glycogen stores and releases glucose to the blood

Glucagon-releasing cells of pancreas stimulated to release glucagon into the blood; target is the liver

FIGURE 1.5
Regulation of blood glucose levels by a negative feedback mechanism involving pancreatic hormones.

produces heat and the air is warmed, the temperature begins to rise, and when it reaches 20°C or slightly higher, the thermostat triggers the furnace OFF. This process results in a cycling of "furnace-ON" and "furnace-OFF" so that the temperature in the house stays very near the desired temperature of 20°C. Your body "thermostat," located in a part of your brain called the hypothalamus, operates in a similar fashion.

Regulation of body temperature by the hypothalamus illustrates only one of the many ways the nervous system maintains the constancy of the internal environment. Another type of neural control mechanism is seen in the *withdrawal reflex* referred to earlier, in which the hand is jerked quickly away from a painful stimulus such as broken glass. The endocrine system is equally important in the maintenance of homeostasis, however, and a good example of a hormonally controlled negative feedback mechanism is the control of blood glucose levels by pancreatic hormones (Figure 1.5).

To carry out normal metabolism, body cells must have continuous access to glucose, their major fuel for producing cellular energy, or ATP. Blood sugar levels are normally maintained around 90 milligrams (mg) of glucose per 100 milliliters (ml) of blood.* Let's assume that you have lost your willpower and have downed four jelly doughnuts. The doughnuts are quickly broken down to sugars by your digestive system, and as the sugars flood into the bloodstream, blood sugar levels spike upward, disrupting homeostasis. The rising glucose levels stimulate the insulin-producing cells of the pancreas, which respond by secreting insulin into the blood. Insulin accelerates the uptake of glucose by most body cells and encourages storage of excess glucose as glycogen in the liver and muscles so that a reserve supply of glucose is "put into the larder," so to speak. Consequently, blood sugar levels ebb back toward the normal set point, and the stimulus for insulin release diminishes.

Glucagon, the other pancreatic hormone, has the opposite effect. Its release is triggered as blood sugar levels decline below the set point. Suppose, for example, that you have skipped lunch and it is now about 2 P.M. Since your blood sugar level is running low, glucagon secretion is stimulated. Glucagon targets the liver, causing it to release its glucose reserves into the blood. Consequently, blood sugar levels increase back into the homeostatic range.

The body's ability to regulate its internal environment is fundamental, and all negative feedback mechanisms have the same goal: preventing sudden severe changes within the body. Body temperature and blood glucose levels are only two of the variables that need to be regulated. There are hundreds! Other negative feedback mechanisms regulate heart rate, blood pressure, the rate and depth of breathing, and blood levels of oxygen, carbon dioxide, and minerals. We will discuss many of these mechanisms when we consider the different organ systems of the body. Now, however, we will look at the other type of control mechanism—positive feedback.

Positive Feedback Mechanisms

In **positive feedback mechanisms,** the result or response of the mechanism enhances or exaggerates the original stimulus so that the activity (output) is accelerated. This feedback mechanism is said to be "positive" because the change that occurs proceeds in the *same* direction as the initial disturbance, causing the variable to deviate further and further from its original value or range. In contrast to negative feedback controls, which maintain some physiological function or keep blood chemicals within narrow ranges, positive feedback mechanisms usually control episodic (infrequent) events that do not require

*The metric system is described in Appendix A.

continuous adjustments. Typically, they set off a series of events that may be self-perpetuating and quite explosive. Because of these characteristics, positive feedback mechanisms are often referred to as *cascades* (from the Italian word meaning "to fall"). Because positive feedback mechanisms are likely to race out of control, they are rarely used to promote the moment-to-moment well-being of the body. However, there are at least two familiar examples of their use as homeostatic mechanisms—blood clotting and enhancement of labor contractions during birth.

Blood clotting is a normal response to laceration or damage to the lining of a blood vessel and is an excellent example of an important body function controlled by positive feedback. Basically, once vessel damage has occurred (1), blood elements called platelets immediately begin to cling to the injured site (2) and release chemicals that attract more platelets (3). This rapidly growing pile-up of platelets initiates the sequence of events that finally forms a clot (4) as related in Figure 1.6.

The positive feedback mechanism that intensifies labor contractions during the birth of a baby works in the following way. As the baby moves down into its mother's birth canal, the increased pressure on her cervix (the muscular outlet of the uterus) excites pressure receptors located there. The receptors send rapid nerve impulses to the brain, which responds by triggering the release of the hormone oxytocin. Oxytocin is transported in blood to the uterus, where it stimulates the muscles in the uterine wall to contract even more vigorously, forcing the baby still farther into the birth canal. This cyclic series of events causes the contractions to become both more frequent and more powerful, until the baby is finally born. At this point, the stimulus for oxytocin release (the pressure) ends, shutting off the positive feedback mechanism. (See also Figure 29.16, p. 1019.)

Homeostatic Imbalance

Homeostasis is so important that most disease is regarded as a result of its disturbance, a condition called **homeostatic imbalance.** As we age, our body organs and control systems become less efficient. As a result, the internal environment becomes less and less stable. These events place us at an ever greater risk for illness and produce the changes we associate with aging.

Another important source of homeostatic imbalance occurs in certain pathological situations when the usual negative feedback mechanisms are overwhelmed and destructive positive feedback mechanisms take over. Some instances of heart failure reflect this phenomenon.

Examples of homeostatic imbalance are provided throughout this book to enhance your understanding of normal physiological mechanisms. These homeo-

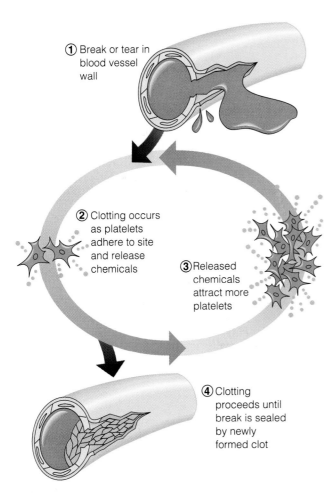

① Break or tear in blood vessel wall

② Clotting occurs as platelets adhere to site and release chemicals

③ Released chemicals attract more platelets

④ Clotting proceeds until break is sealed by newly formed clot

**FIGURE 1.6
Summary of the positive feedback mechanism
regulating blood clotting.**

static imbalance sections are preceded by the symbol to alert you to the fact that an abnormal condition is being described.

THE LANGUAGE OF ANATOMY

Although most of us are naturally curious about our bodies, our interest is sometimes dampened when we are confronted with the terminology used in the study of anatomy and physiology. Let's face it. You can't just pick up an anatomy and physiology book and read it as though it were a novel. Unfortunately, confusion is inevitable without such specialized terminology. For example, if you are looking at a ball,

"above" always means the area over the top of the ball. Other directional terms can also be used consistently because the ball is a totally symmetrical object, a sphere. All sides and surfaces are equivalent. The human body, of course, has many protrusions, bends, and unique landmarks. Thus, the question becomes: Above what? To prevent misunderstanding, anatomists have a universally accepted terminology that allows body structures to be located and identified precisely with a minimum of words. This language of anatomy is presented and explained next.

Anatomical Position and Directional Terms

To describe body parts and position accurately, we must have an initial reference point and use indications of direction. The anatomical reference point is a standard body position called the **anatomical position.** In the anatomical position, the body is erect with feet together. This position is easy to remember because it resembles "standing at attention," except that the palms face forward and the thumbs point away from the body. You can see the anatomical position in Figure 1.7. It is essential to understand the anatomical position because most of the directional terms used in this book refer to the body *as if it were in this position, regardless of its actual position.* Another point to remember is that the terms "right" and "left" refer to those sides of the person or the cadaver being viewed—not those of the observer.

Directional terms used by medical personnel and anatomists allow them to explain exactly where one body structure is in relation to another. For example, we could describe the relationship between the ears and the nose informally by stating, "The ears are located on each side of the head to the right and left of the nose." Using anatomical terminology, this condenses to, "The ears are lateral to the nose." Clearly, using anatomical terminology saves a good deal of description and is less ambiguous. Commonly used orientation and directional terms are defined and illustrated in Table 1.1 (p. 16). Although most of these terms are also used in everyday conversation, keep in mind that their anatomical meanings are very precise.

Regional Terms

The most fundamental divisions of our body are its *axial* and *appendicular* (ap"en-dik'u-lar) parts. The **axial part,** so named because it makes up the main *axis* of our body, consists of the head, neck, and trunk. The **appendicular part** consists of the *appendages,* or *limbs,* which are attached to the body's axis. **Regional terms** used to designate specific areas within the major body divisions are indicated in Fig-

? *As you study this figure, determine precisely where you would be injured if you (1) pulled a muscle in your* axillary *region, (2) cracked a bone in your* occipital *region, and (3) received a cut on a* digit.

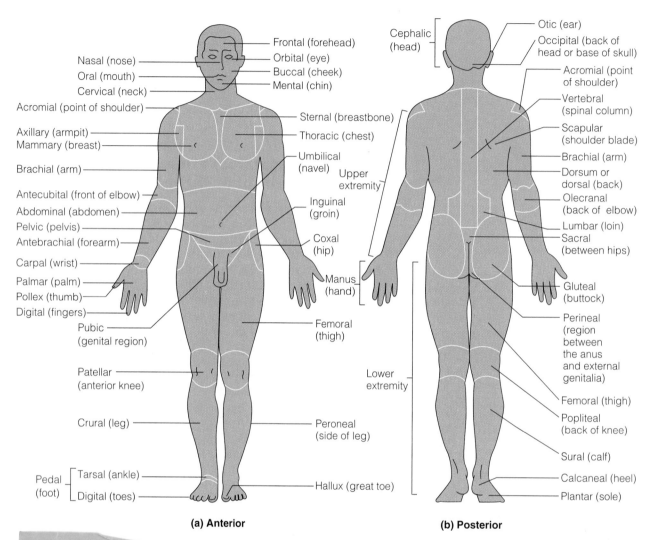

(a) Anterior

(b) Posterior

FIG...
Re...ecific body areas. The body is depicted in
ana... ...e raised slightly to show the plantar surface of the foot.

ure ... ...ach of these body
reg... ...heses) to orient you
to ... ...

Body Planes and Sections

In the study of anatomy, the body is often *sectioned* (cut) along a flat surface called a plane. The most frequently used body planes are sagittal, frontal, and transverse planes, which lie at right angles to one another (Figure 1.8). A section bears the name of the plane along which it is cut. Thus, a cut along a sagittal plane produces a sagittal section.

A **sagittal plane** (saj′i-tal; "arrow") lies vertically and divides the body into the right and left parts. The specific sagittal plane that lies exactly in the midline

is the **median plane,** or **midsagittal plane** (Figure 1.8a). All other sagittal planes, offset from the midline, are **parasagittal planes** (*para* = near).

Frontal planes, like sagittal planes, lie vertically. Frontal planes, however, divide the body into anterior and posterior parts (Figure 1.8b). A frontal plane is also called a **coronal plane** (kŏ-ro′nal; "crown").

A **transverse,** or **horizontal, plane** runs horizontally from right to left, dividing the body into superior and inferior parts (Figure 1.8c). Of course, many different transverse planes exist at every possible level from head to foot. A transverse section is also called a **cross section.** Cuts made along any plane that lies diagonally between the horizontal and the vertical are called **oblique sections.** Such sections are often confusing and difficult to interpret and are not used much.

(a) Median sagittal plane

Median sagittal
section through head

Brain

Nose

Tongue

Spinal
cord

Trachea

(b) Frontal (coronal) plane

Frontal section through torso

Heart

Right
lung

Left
lung

Liver   Stomach

Spleen

(c) Transverse plane

Posterior

Anterior

Transverse section through torso
(Superior view)

Spinal cord   Spleen

Aorta

Liver

Subcutaneous
fat layer

Stomach
content

FIGURE 1.8

Planes of the body. The left side of the figure illustrates three major planes of space (sagittal, frontal, and transverse) relative to humans in the anatomical position. Selected areas of the body, visualized using magnetic resonance imaging (MRI) scans of the body taken at corresponding planes, are illustrated in the center of the figure. Diagrams identifying body organs seen in the MRI scans are shown on the right.

Table 1.1 Orientation and Directional Terms

Term	Definition		Example
Superior (cranial)	Toward the head end or upper part of a structure or the body; above		The forehead is superior to the nose
Inferior (caudal)	Away from the head end or toward the lower part of a structure or the body; below		The navel is inferior to the breastbone
Anterior (ventral)*	Toward or at the front of the body; in front of		The breastbone is anterior to the spine
Posterior (dorsal)*	Toward or at the back of the body; behind		The heart is posterior to the breastbone
Medial	Toward or at the midline of the body; on the inner side of		The groin is medial to the thigh
Lateral	Away from the midline of the body; on the outer side of		The eye is lateral to the bridge of the nose
Intermediate	Between a more medial and a more lateral structure		The collarbone is intermediate between the breastbone and shoulder
Proximal	Closer to the origin of the body part or the point of attachment of a limb to the body trunk		The elbow is proximal to the wrist
Distal	Farther from the origin of a body part or the point of attachment of a limb to the body trunk		The knee is distal to the thigh
Superficial	Toward or at the body surface		The skin is superficial to the skeleton
Deep	Away from the body surface; more internal		The pelvis is deep to the buttock muscles

*Whereas the terms *ventral* and *anterior* are synonymous in humans, this is not the case in four-legged animals. *Ventral* specifically refers to the "belly" of a vertebrate animal and thus is the inferior surface of four-legged animals. Likewise, although the dorsal and posterior surfaces are the same in humans, the term *dorsal* specifically refers to an animal's back. Thus, the dorsal surface of four-legged animals is their superior surface.

The ability to interpret sections through the body, especially transverse sections, is increasingly important in the clinical sciences. New medical imaging devices (described on pp. 18–19) produce sectional images rather than three-dimensional images. It can be difficult to decipher an object's overall shape from sectioned material. A cross section of a banana, for example, looks like a circle and gives no indication of the whole banana's crescent shape. Likewise, sectioning the body or an organ along different planes often results in very different views. For example, a transverse section of the body trunk at the level of the kidneys would show kidney structure in cross section very nicely; a frontal section of the body trunk would show a different view of kidney anatomy; and a midsagittal section would miss the kidneys completely. It will take practice, but you will gradually learn to relate two-dimensional sections to three-dimensional shapes.

Body Cavities and Membranes

Within the axial portion of the body are two large cavities called the dorsal and ventral body cavities. They are closed to the outside and each contains internal organs.

Dorsal Body Cavity

The **dorsal body cavity** (Figure 1.9) is subdivided into a **cranial cavity,** within which the brain is encased by the skull, and a **vertebral,** or **spinal, cavity** which runs within the bony vertebral column and encloses the delicate spinal cord. Since the spinal cord issues from and is essentially a continuation of the brain, the cranial and spinal cavities are continuous with one another. The vital and very fragile nervous system organs housed by the dorsal body cavity are well protected by its hard bony walls.

Ventral Body Cavity

The more anterior and larger of the closed body cavities is the **ventral body cavity** (see Figure 1.9). Like the dorsal cavity, it has two major subdivisions, the *thoracic cavity* and the *abdominopelvic cavity.* The ventral body cavity houses a group of internal organs that are collectively called the **viscera** (vis′er-ah), or **visceral organs.**

The more superior subdivision, the **thoracic** (tho-ras′ik) **cavity,** is surrounded by the ribs and muscles of the chest. The thoracic cavity is further subdivided into lateral **pleural** (ploo′ral) **cavities,** each housing a lung, and the medial **mediastinum** (me″de-ah-sti′num). The mediastinum contains the **pericardial** (per″ĭ-kar′de-al) **cavity,** which encloses the heart, and the remaining thoracic organs (esophagus, trachea, and others).

The thoracic cavity is separated from the more inferior **abdominopelvic** (ab-dom′ĭ-no-pel′vic) **cavity** by the diaphragm, a dome-shaped muscle important in breathing. The abdominopelvic cavity, as its name suggests, has two parts. However, these regions are not

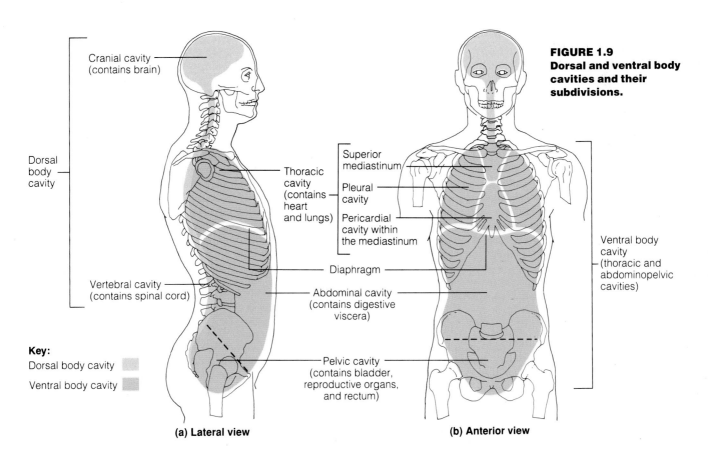

FIGURE 1.9
Dorsal and ventral body cavities and their subdivisions.

Cranial cavity (contains brain)

Dorsal body cavity

Thoracic cavity (contains heart and lungs)

Vertebral cavity (contains spinal cord)

Key:
Dorsal body cavity
Ventral body cavity

Superior mediastinum

Pleural cavity

Pericardial cavity within the mediastinum

Diaphragm

Abdominal cavity (contains digestive viscera)

Pelvic cavity (contains bladder, reproductive organs, and rectum)

Ventral body cavity (thoracic and abdominopelvic cavities)

(a) Lateral view   **(b) Anterior view**

Physicians have long sought ways to examine the body's internal organs for evidence of disease without subjecting the patient to the shock and pain of exploratory surgery, but until about 30 years ago, the magical but murky X ray was the only means of extracting information from within a living body. Produced by directing *X rays,* electromagnetic waves of very short wavelength, at the body, an **X ray** or **radiograph** is essentially a shadowy negative of the internal structures of the body. Dense structures absorb the X rays most and so appear as light areas on the radiograph. Hollow air-containing organs and fat, which absorb the X rays to a lesser extent, appear as dark areas. In a variation of radiography, X-ray images are viewed on a fluorescent screen, or **fluoroscope,** as they are being generated. What X rays do best is to visualize hard, bony structures and to locate abnormally dense structures (tumors, tuberculosis nodules) in the lungs.

The 1950s saw the advent of nuclear medicine, which uses radioisotopes to scan the body, and ultrasound techniques. In the 1970s, CT, PET, and MRI scanning techniques were introduced. These new imaging techniques not only reveal the structure of our "insides" but also wring out information about the private, and until now secret, workings of their molecules. The best known of the new imaging devices is **computed tomography (CT)** (formerly called **computerized axial tomography (CAT),** a refined version of X-ray equipment. As the patient is slowly moved through the doughnut-shaped CT machine, its X-ray tube rotates around the body and sends beams from all directions to a specific level of the patient's body. Since at any point in time its fan-shaped beam is confined to a "slice" of the body about as thick as a dime, CT ends the confusion resulting from images of overlapping structures seen in conventional X rays. The device's computer translates this information into a detailed, cross-sectional picture of each of the consecutive body regions scanned. CT's clarity has all but eliminated

exploratory surgery [see photo (a)]. CT scans are at the forefront of medical technology for evaluating most problems that affect the brain, as well as abdominal problems and certain skeletal problems.

Special high-speed CT devices are used in a technique called **dynamic spatial reconstruction (DSR),** which not only provides three-dimensional images of body organs from any angle but also allows their movements and changes in their internal volumes to be scrutinized at normal speed, in slow motion, and at a specific moment in time. Although DSR can be used to evaluate the lungs and certain other mobile organs, its greatest value has been to visualize the heart beating and blood flowing through blood vessels, allowing heart defects, constricted blood vessels, and the status of coronary bypass grafts to be evaluated.

Another computer-assisted X-ray technique is **digital subtraction angiography (DSA)** (*angiography* = "vessel pictures"). This technique provides an unobstructed view of diseased blood vessels. Its principle is simple: Conventional radiographs are taken before and after a contrast medium is injected into an artery. Then the computer subtracts the "before" image from the "after" image, eliminating all traces of body structures that obscure the vessel. DSA is often used to identify blockage of the arteries that supply the heart wall and the brain.

Just as the X ray spawned "big brothers," so too did nuclear medicine in the form of **positron emission tomography (PET).** The special advantage of PET is that its images send messages about *metabolic processes.* The patient is given an injection of radioisotopes that have been tagged to biological molecules (such as glucose) and is then positioned in the PET scanner. As the radioisotopes are absorbed by the most active brain cells, high-energy γ rays are produced. The computer analyzes the γ-ray emission and produces a picture of the brain's biochemical activity in vivid colors.

PET's greatest value has been its ability to provide insights into brain activity in people affected by mental illness, stroke, Alzheimer's disease, and epilepsy [see photo (b)]. One of its most exciting uses has been to determine which specific regions of the *healthy* brain are most active during certain tasks (e.g., speaking, listening to music, or figuring out a mathematical problem). Such information about brain metabolism was virtually unobtainable until the advent of PET.

Sonography, or **ultrasound imaging,** has some distinct advantages over the approaches examined so far. First, the equipment is inexpensive. Second, the high-frequency sound waves (ultrasound) used as its energy source seem to be safer than ionizing forms of radiation used in nuclear medicine with fewer adverse effects on living tissues. The body is probed with pulses of sound waves that, when reflected and scattered to different extents by body tissues, cause echoes. A computer analyzes these echoes to construct visual images of the outlines of body organs of interest. A single, hand-held device is used both to emit the sound and to pick up the echoes. This device is easy to move around the body, so sections can be scanned from many different body planes.

Because of its safety, ultrasound is the imaging technique of choice for obstetrics, i.e., for determining fetal age and position and locating the placenta [see photo (c)]. Because sound waves have very low penetrating power and rapidly dissipate in air, sonography is of little value for looking at air-filled structures (the lungs) or those surrounded by bone (the brain and spinal cord).

Magnetic resonance imaging (MRI) is a technique with tremendous appeal because it produces high-contrast images of our *soft* tissues, an area in which X rays and CT scans are weak. As initially developed, MRI primarily maps the element hydrogen. In our body, most of the hydrogen is in water. The technique subjects the body to magnetic fields up to 60,000 times stronger than that of the earth to pry

(a)

(b)

(c)

Three different methods for illuminating the body. (a) CT scan through the thorax showing the lungs flanking the heart. (b) PET scan of the brain of a patient who has suffered a stroke. The area of damage and reduced brain activity is the darkened area at the upper left of the photo. (c) Computer-enhanced ultrasound image of a fetus in utero; the head, trunk, and limbs are clearly visible.

information from the body's molecules. The patient lies in a chamber within a huge magnet. Hydrogen molecules spin like tops in the magnetic field, and their energy is further enhanced by radio waves. When the radio waves are turned off, the energy released is translated into a visual image.

Because MRI tends to distinguish body tissues from one another on the basis of differences in water content, it can differentiate between the fatty white matter and the more watery gray matter of the brain (see Figure 1.8a) and enable physicians to see the delicate nerve fibers in the spinal cord. Since dense structures do not show up at all in MRI, it peers easily into the skull and vertebral column. MRI is also particularly good at detecting tumors and degenerative disease of various kinds. Multiple sclerosis plaques do not show up well in CT scans, but are dazzlingly clear in MRI scans. MRI can also tune in on metabolic reactions, such as processes that generate energy-rich ATP molecules. A newer variation of MRI, called **magnetic resonance spectroscopy (MRS),** maps the distribution of elements other than hydrogen to reveal more about how disease changes body chemistry. Furthermore, advances in computer techniques are allowing MRI scans to be displayed in three dimensions and their use to guide laser surgery. In 1992 MRI technology leaped forward with the development of the **functional MRI,** which allows tracking of blood flow into the brain in real time. Until then, matching thoughts, deeds, and disease to corresponding brain activity had been the sole domain of PET. Since functional MRI does not require injections of tracer elements, it provides another, and perhaps more desirable, alternative to such studies.

Despite its advantages, the powerful magnetic field of MRI presents some thorny problems. For example, it can "suck" metal objects, such as implanted pacemakers and loose tooth fillings, through and from the body. Moreover, there is no convincing evidence that such strong mag-netic fields can be used without risk to the body, although the procedure is currently considered safe.

Although they are stunning, the pictures produced by the new imaging devices are abstractions assembled within the "mind" of a computer. They are artificially enhanced for sharpness and artificially colored to increase contrast (all colors are "phony"). The images are not inaccurate; they are, however, several steps removed from direct visual observation.

As you can see, medical science has some remarkable new diagnostic tools, and there is little question that they have made their mark. CT and PET scans now account for about 25% of imaging. Ultrasonography, because of its safety and low cost, has become the most widespread of the new techniques. The use of MRI scans is increasing rapidly. Even so, conventional X rays remain the workhorse of diagnostic imaging techniques and still account for over half of all imaging currently done.

physically separated by a muscular or membrane wall. Its superior portion, the **abdominal cavity,** contains the stomach, intestines, spleen, liver, and other organs. The inferior part, the **pelvic cavity,** contains the bladder, some reproductive organs, and the rectum. As Figure 1.9a reveals, the abdominal and pelvic cavities are not aligned with each other; rather, the bowl-shaped pelvis is tipped away from the perpendicular.

When the body is subjected to physical trauma (as often happens in an automobile accident), the most vulnerable abdominopelvic organs are those within the abdominal cavity. This is because the walls of the abdominal cavity are formed only by trunk muscles and are not reinforced by bone. The pelvic organs receive a somewhat greater degree of protection from the bony pelvis in which they reside. •

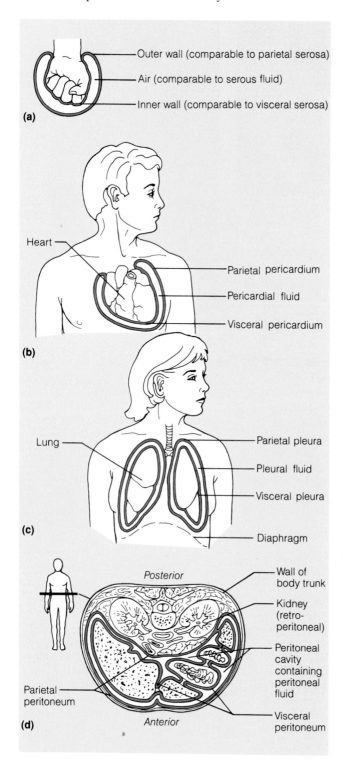

FIGURE 1.10
Serous membrane relationships. (a) A fist is thrust into a flaccid balloon to demonstrate the relationship between the parietal and visceral serous membrane layers. (b) The parietal pericardium is the outer layer lining the pericardial cavity; the visceral pericardium clings to the external heart surface. (c) The visceral pleura surrounding each lung is continuous with the parietal pleura that adheres to the walls of the thoracic cavity. (d) Transverse section through the body trunk at the level of the liver and kidneys. The parietal peritoneum lines the walls of the abdominopelvic cavity; the visceral peritoneum covers the external surfaces of most organs within the cavity. (However, some abdominal organs are retroperitoneal [behind the peritoneum]. This is true of the kidneys.)

Membranes in the Ventral Body Cavity

The walls of the ventral body cavity and the outer surfaces of the organs it contains are covered by an exceedingly thin, double-layered membrane, the **serosa** (se-ro′sah), or **serous membrane.** The part of the membrane lining the cavity walls is generally called the **parietal** (pah-ri′ĕ-tal) **serosa.** It folds in on itself to form the **visceral serosa,** covering the organs in the cavity. (Parietal comes from *parie,* meaning wall, and always pertains to the walls of a cavity; visceral comes from *viscus,* meaning an organ in a body cavity.)

You can visualize the relationship between the serosal layers by pushing your fist into a limp balloon (Figure 1.10a). The part of the balloon that clings closely to your fist can be compared to the visceral serosa clinging to the organ's external surface. The outer wall of the balloon represents the parietal serosa that lines the walls of the cavity. (However, unlike the balloon, it is never exposed but is always fused to the cavity wall.) In the body, the serous layers are separated not by air but by a thin, lubricating fluid, called **serous fluid,** which is secreted by both membranes. Although there is a potential space between the two membranes, they tend to lie very close to each other.

The slippery serous fluid allows the organs to slide without friction across the cavity walls and one another as they carry out their routine functions. This is extremely important for mobile organs such as the pumping heart and the churning stomach.

Specific serous membranes are named for the cavity and organs with which they are associated. For example, the *parietal pericardium* lines the pericardial cavity, while the *visceral pericardium* covers the heart within that cavity (Figure 1.10b). The *parietal pleura* (ploo′rah) lines the walls of the thoracic cavity, and the *visceral pleura* covers the lungs (Figure 1.10c). Finally, the *parietal peritoneum* (per″ĭ-to-ne′um) is associated with the walls of the abdominopelvic cavity, while the *visceral peritoneum* covers most of the organs within that cavity (Figure 1.10d).

Inflammation of the serous membranes is typically accompanied by a deficit of lubricating fluid. This leads to excruciating pain as the organs stick together and drag across one another, as anyone who has experienced *pleurisy* (inflammation of the pleurae) or *peritonitis* (inflammation of the peritonea) can attest. •

Other Body Cavities

In addition to the large closed body cavities, there are several smaller body cavities. Many of these are located in the head and most open to the body exterior:

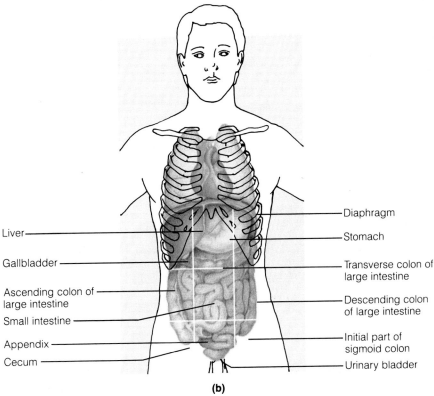

(a)

(b)

FIGURE 1.11
The nine abdominopelvic regions.
(a) Division of the abdominopelvic cavity into nine regions delineated by four planes. The superior transverse plane is just inferior to the ribs; the inferior transverse plane is just superior to the hip bones; and the parasagittal planes lie just medial to the nipples. **(b)** Anterior view of the abdominopelvic cavity showing the superficial organs.

1. **Oral and digestive cavities.** The oral cavity, commonly called the mouth, contains the teeth and tongue. This cavity is part of and continuous with the cavity of the digestive organs, which also opens to the exterior at the anus.

2. **Nasal cavity.** Located within and posterior to the nose, the nasal cavity is part of the passages of the respiratory system.

3. **Orbital cavities.** The orbital cavities (orbits) house the eyes and present them in an anterior position.

4. **Middle ear cavities.** The middle ear cavities carved into the temporal bone of the skull lie just medial to the eardrums. These cavities contain tiny bones that transmit sound vibrations to the organ of hearing in the inner ears.

5. **Synovial** (sĭ-no′ve-al) **cavities.** Synovial cavities are joint cavities. They are enclosed within fibrous capsules that surround freely movable joints of the body (such as the elbow and knee joints). Like the serous membranes of the ventral body cavity, membranes lining the synovial cavities secrete a lubricating fluid that reduces friction as the bones move across one another.

Abdominopelvic Regions and Quadrants

Since the abdominopelvic cavity is large and contains many organs, it is helpful to divide it into smaller areas for study. One division method, used primarily by anatomists, uses two transverse and two parasagittal planes. These planes, positioned like a tic-tac-toe grid on the abdomen, divide the cavity into nine **regions** (Figure 1.11):

*   The **umbilical region** is the centermost region deep to and surrounding the umbilicus (navel).

*   The **epigastric region** is located superior to the umbilical region (*epi* = upon, above; *gastric* = stomach).

*   The **hypogastric (pubic) region** is located inferior to the umbilical region (*hypo* = below).

*   The **right** and **left iliac,** or **inguinal** (ing′gwĭ-nal), **regions** are located lateral to the hypogastric region (*iliac* = superior part of the hip bone).

*   The **right** and **left lumbar regions** lie lateral to the umbilical region (*lumbus* = loin).

*   The **right** and **left hypochondriac regions** flank the epigastric region laterally (*chondro* = cartilage).

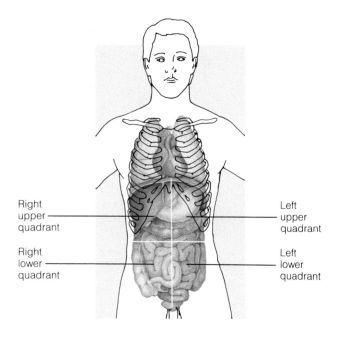

Right upper quadrant

Left upper quadrant

Right lower quadrant

Left lower quadrant

FIGURE 1.12
The four abdominopelvic quadrants. In this scheme, the abdominopelvic cavity is divided into four quadrants by two planes. The figure shows superficial organs within each quadrant.

Medical personnel usually use a simpler scheme to localize and describe the condition of the abdomino-pelvic cavity organs (Figure 1.12). In this scheme, one transverse and one median sagittal plane pass through the umbilicus at right angles. The resulting **quadrants** are named according to their positions from the subject's point of view: the **right upper quadrant (RUQ)**, **left upper quadrant (LUQ)**, **right lower quadrant (RLQ)**, and **left lower quadrant (LLQ)**.

CHAPTER SUMMARY

An Overview of Anatomy and Physiology (pp. 3–5)

1.   Anatomy is the study of body structures and their relationships; physiology is the science of how body parts function.

Topics of Anatomy (p. 3)
2.   Major subdivisions of anatomy include gross anatomy, microscopic anatomy, and developmental anatomy.

Topics of Physiology (pp. 3–4)
3.   Typically, physiology concerns the functioning of specific organs or organ systems. Examples include cardiac physiology, renal physiology, and muscle physiology.

4.   Physiology is explained by chemical and physical principles.

Complementarity of Structure and Function (pp. 4–5)
5.   Anatomy and physiology are inseparable: What a body can do depends on the unique architecture of its parts. This is called the complementarity of structure and function.

The Hierarchy of Structural Organization (pp. 5–7)

1.   The levels of structural organization of the body, from simplest to most complex, are: chemical, cellular, tissue, organ, organ system, and organismal.

2.   The 11 organ systems of the body are the integumentary, skeletal, muscular, nervous, endocrine, cardiovascular, lymphatic, respiratory, digestive, urinary, and reproductive systems. The immune system is a functional system closely associated with the lymphatic system.

Maintaining Life (pp. 5, 8–9)

Functional Characteristics (pp. 5, 8–9)
1.   All living organisms carry out certain vital functional activities necessary for life, including maintenance of boundaries, movement, responsiveness, digestion, metabolism, excretion, reproduction, and growth.

Survival Needs (p. 9)
2.   Survival needs include nutrients, water, oxygen, appropriate body temperature, and atmospheric pressure.

Homeostasis (pp. 10–13)

1.   Homeostasis is a dynamic equilibrium of the internal environment. All body systems contribute to homeostasis, but the nervous and endocrine systems are most important.

General Characteristics of Control Mechanisms (p. 10)
2.   Control systems of the body contain at least three elements: receptor(s), control center, and effector(s).

Negative Feedback Mechanisms (pp. 10–12)
3.   Negative feedback mechanisms reduce the original stimulus, and are essential for maintaining homeostasis. Body temperature, heart rate, breathing rate and depth, and blood levels of glucose and certain ions are regulated by negative feedback mechanisms.

Positive Feedback Mechanisms (p. 12)
4.   Positive feedback mechanisms intensify the initial stimulus, leading to an enhancement of the response. Positive feedback mechanisms rarely contribute to homeostasis, but blood clotting and labor contractions are regulated by such mechanisms.

Homeostatic Imbalance (pp. 12–13)
5.   With age, the efficiency of negative feedback mechanisms declines, and positive feedback mechanisms occur more frequently. These changes underlie certain disease conditions.

The Language of Anatomy (pp. 13–22)

Anatomical Position and Directional Terms (p. 13)
1.   In the anatomical position, the body is erect, facing forward, feet together, arms at sides with palms forward.

2.   Directional terms allow body parts to be located precisely. Terms used to describe body directions and orientation include: superior/inferior; anterior/ posterior; ventral/dorsal; medial/lateral; intermediate; proximal/distal; and superficial/deep.

Regional Terms (pp. 13–14)
3.   Regional terms are used to designate specific areas of the body (see Figure 1.7).

Body Planes and Sections (pp. 14–17)
4.   The body or its organs may be cut along planes, or imagi-

nary lines, to produce different types of sections. Frequently used planes are sagittal, frontal, and transverse.

Body Cavities and Membranes (pp. 17–21)

5. The body contains two major closed cavities: the dorsal cavity, subdivided into the cranial and spinal cavities; and the ventral cavity, subdivided into the superior thoracic cavity and the inferior abdominopelvic cavity.

6. The walls of the ventral cavity and the surfaces of the organs it contains are covered with thin membranes, the parietal and visceral serosae, respectively. The serosae produce a thin fluid that decreases friction during organ functioning.

7. There are several smaller body cavities. Most of these are in the head and open to the exterior.

Abdominopelvic Regions and Quadrants (pp. 21–22)

8. The abdominopelvic cavity may be divided by four planes into nine abdominal regions (epigastric, umbilical, hypogastric, right and left iliac, right and left lumbar, and right and left hypochondriac), or by two planes into four quadrants.

REVIEW QUESTIONS

Multiple Choice/Matching

(Some questions have more than one correct answer.)

1. The correct sequence of levels forming the structural hierarchy is (a) organ, organ system, cellular, chemical, tissue, organismal; (b) chemical, cellular, tissue, organismal, organ, organ system; (c) chemical, cellular, tissue, organ, organ system, organismal; (d) organismal, organ system, organ, tissue, cellular, chemical.

2. The structural and functional unit of life is (a) a cell, (b) an organ, (c) the organism, (d) a molecule.

3. Which of the following is a *major* functional characteristic of all organisms? (a) movement, (b) growth, (c) metabolism, (d) responsiveness, (e) all of these.

4. Two of these organ systems bear the major responsibility for ensuring homeostasis of the internal environment. Which two? (a) nervous system, (b) digestive system, (c) cardiovascular system, (d) endocrine system, (e) reproductive system.

5. In (a)–(e), a directional term [e.g., distal in (a)] is followed by terms indicating different body structures or locations (e.g., the elbow/the wrist). In each case, choose the structure or organ that matches the given directional term.
(a) distal: the elbow/the wrist
(b) lateral: the hip bone/the umbilicus
(c) superior: the nose/the chin
(d) anterior: the toes/the heel
(e) superficial: the scalp/the skull

 6. Assume that the body has been sectioned along a median sagittal plane, a frontal plane, or a transverse plane made at the level of each of the organs listed below. Which organs would not be visible in all three cases? (a) urinary bladder, (b) brain, (c) lungs, (d) kidneys, (e) small intestine, (f) heart.

7. Relate each of the following conditions or statements to either the dorsal body cavity or the ventral body cavity.
(a) surrounded by the bony skull and the vertebral column
(b) includes the thoracic and abdominopelvic cavities
(c) contains the brain and spinal cord
(d) contains the heart, lungs, and digestive organs

8. Which of the following relationships is *incorrect?* (a) visceral peritoneum/outer surface of small intestine, (b) parietal pericardium/outer surface of heart, (c) parietal pleura/wall of thoracic cavity.

 9. Which ventral cavity subdivision has no bony protection? (a) thoracic cavity, (b) abdominal cavity, (c) pelvic cavity.

Short Answer Essay Questions

10. According to the principle of complementarity, how does anatomy relate to physiology?

11. Construct a table that lists the 11 systems of the body, name two organs of each system (if appropriate), and describe the overall or major function of each system.

12. List and describe briefly five external factors that must be present or provided to sustain life.

13. Define homeostasis.

14. Compare and contrast the operation of negative and positive feedback mechanisms in maintaining homeostasis. Provide two examples of variables controlled by negative feedback mechanisms and one example of a process regulated by a positive feedback mechanism.

15. Describe and assume the anatomical position. Why is an understanding of this position important? What is the importance of directional terms?

16. Define plane and section.

17. Provide the anatomical term that correctly names each of the following body regions: (a) arm, (b) thigh, (c) chest, (d) fingers and toes, (e) anterior aspect of the knee.

 18. (a) Make a diagram showing the nine abdominopelvic regions, and name each region. Name two organs (or parts of organs) that could be located in each of the named regions. (b) Make a similar sketch illustrating how the abdominopelvic cavity may be divided into quadrants, and name each quadrant.

CRITICAL THINKING AND CLINICAL APPLICATION QUESTIONS

1. John has been suffering agonizing pain with each breath and has been informed by the physician that he has pleurisy. (a) Specifically, what membranes are involved in this condition? (b) What is their usual role in the body? (c) Explain why John's condition is so painful.

2. When at the clinic, Harry was told that blood would be drawn from his antecubital region. What body part was Harry asked to hold out? Later, the nurse came in and gave Harry a shot of penicillin in his gluteal region. Did Harry take off his shirt or drop his pants to receive the injection? Before Harry left, the nurse noticed that Harry had a nasty bruise on his cervical region. What part of his body was black and blue?

3. A man is behaving abnormally, and his physician suspects that he has a brain tumor. Which of the following medical imaging devices would best localize the tumor in the man's brain (and why)? conventional X-ray, DSA, PET, sonography, MRI.

4. When we begin to become dehydrated, we usually become thirsty, which causes us to drink fluids. Decide whether the thirst sensation is part of a negative or positive feedback control system and defend your choice.

2

Chemistry Comes Alive

CHAPTER OUTLINE AND STUDENT OBJECTIVES

PART 1: BASIC CHEMISTRY

Definition of Concepts: Matter and Energy (pp. 25–26)

1. Differentiate clearly between matter and energy and between potential energy and kinetic energy.

2. Describe the major energy forms.

Composition of Matter: Atoms and Elements (pp. 26–29)

3. Define chemical element and list the four elements that form the bulk of body matter.

4. List the subatomic particles; describe their relative masses, charges, and positions in the atom.

5. Define atom, atomic weight, isotope, and radioisotope.

How Matter Is Combined: Molecules and Mixtures (pp. 29–31)

6. Distinguish between a compound and a mixture. Define molecule.

7. Compare solutions, colloids, and suspensions.

Chemical Bonds (pp. 31–36)

8. Differentiate between ionic and covalent bonds. Contrast these bonds with hydrogen bonds.

9. Compare and contrast polar and nonpolar compounds.

Chemical Reactions (pp. 36–39)

10. Contrast synthesis, decomposition, and exchange reactions. Comment briefly on the nature of oxidation-reduction reactions and their importance.

11. Explain why chemical reactions in the body are often irreversible.

12. Describe factors that affect chemical reaction rates.

PART 2: BIOCHEMISTRY: THE COMPOSITION AND REACTIONS OF LIVING MATTER

Inorganic Compounds (pp. 39–42)

13. Explain the importance of water and salts to body homeostasis.

14. Define acid and base, and explain the concept of pH.

Organic Compounds (pp. 42–56)

15. Compare the building blocks, general structures, and biological functions of carbohydrates, lipids, proteins, and nucleic acids.

16. Explain the role of dehydration synthesis and hydrolysis in the formation and breakdown of organic molecules.

17. Compare the functional roles of neutral fats, phospholipids, and steroids in the body.

18. Describe the four levels of protein structure.

19. Describe the general mechanism of enzyme activity.

20. Describe the function of stress proteins.

21. Compare and contrast DNA and RNA.

22. Explain the role of ATP in cell metabolism.

Why study chemistry in an anatomy and physiology course? The answer is simple. The food you eat and the medicines you take when you are ill are composed of chemical substances. Indeed, your entire body is made up of chemicals, thousands of them, continuously interacting with one another at an incredible pace. Although it is possible to study anatomy without much reference to chemistry, chemical reactions underlie all physiological processes—movement, digestion, the pumping of your heart, and even your thoughts. This chapter presents the basics of chemistry and biochemistry (the chemistry of living material), providing the background you will need to understand body functions.

PART 1: BASIC CHEMISTRY

DEFINITION OF CONCEPTS: MATTER AND ENERGY

Matter

Matter is the "stuff" of the universe. More precisely, matter is anything that occupies space and has mass. For all practical purposes, we can consider mass to be the same as weight, and we will use these terms interchangeably. However, this usage is not quite accurate. The *mass* of an object, equivalent to the amount of matter in the object, remains constant wherever the object is. In contrast, the weight of an object varies with gravity. So while your mass is the same at sea level and on a mountaintop, you weigh just slightly less on that mountaintop. The science of chemistry studies the nature of matter, especially how its building blocks are put together and interact with one another.

States of Matter

Matter exists in *solid, liquid,* and *gaseous states.* Examples of each state are found in the human body. Solids, like bones and teeth, have a definite shape and volume. Liquids such as blood plasma and interstitial fluid have a definite volume, but they conform to the shape of their container. Gases have neither a definite shape nor a definite volume. The air we breathe is a gas.

Energy

Compared with matter, **energy** is less tangible. Energy has no mass and does not take up space. It can be measured only by its effects on matter. Energy is defined as the capacity to do work, or to put matter into motion. The greater the work done, the more energy expended doing it. A baseball player who has just hit the ball over the fence uses much more energy than a batter who just bunts the ball back to the pitcher.

Kinetic vs. Potential Energy

Energy exists in two forms, or work capacities, each transformable to the other. **Kinetic** (ki-net′ik) **energy** is energy in action. It does work by moving objects which in turn can do work by transferring their motion to other objects. For example, the push you give a swinging door sets it into motion. Kinetic energy is seen in the movement of the tiniest particles of matter (atoms) as well as in larger objects (a bouncing ball). **Potential energy** is stored or inactive energy that has the *potential,* or capability, to do work but is not presently doing so. The batteries in an unused toy have potential energy, as do your leg muscles when you sit still on the couch. When potential energy is released, it becomes kinetic energy and so is capable of doing work. For example, dammed water becomes a rushing torrent when the dam is opened, whereupon it can move a turbine at a hydroelectric plant, or charge a battery.

Actually, energy is a topic of physics, but matter and energy are inseparable. Matter is the substance, and energy is the mover of the substance. All living things are composed of matter and, to grow and function, they all require energy. It is the release and use of energy by living systems that gives us the elusive quality called "life." Thus, it is worth taking a brief detour to introduce the forms of energy used by the body as it does its work.

Forms of Energy

The body uses energy in several forms. **Chemical energy** is the form stored in the bonds of chemical substances. When the bonds are broken, the potential energy is released for use and becomes kinetic energy.

For example, some of the energy in the foods you eat is eventually converted into the kinetic energy of your moving arm. However, food fuels cannot be used to energize body activities directly. Instead, some of the energy stored in the foods that we eat is captured temporarily in the bonds of a chemical called **adenosine triphosphate** (ah-den′o-sēn tri″fos′fāt), or **ATP.** Later, ATP's bonds are broken and the stored energy is released as needed to do cellular work. Chemical energy in the form of ATP is the most fundamental form of energy in living systems because it is used to run all functional processes. (ATP is described more fully on p. 55.)

Electrical energy reflects the movement of charged particles. In your home, electrical energy is found in the flow of electrons along the household wiring. In your body, electrical currents are generated as charged particles called *ions* move across cell membranes. The nervous system uses electrical currents, called *nerve impulses,* to transmit messages from one part of the body to another. Electrical currents traveling across the heart stimulate it to contract (beat) and pump blood. Therefore, a strong electrical shock (which interferes with such currents) can cause death.

Mechanical energy is energy *directly* involved in moving matter. When you ride a bicycle, your legs provide the mechanical energy that moves the pedals.

Radiant energy, or **electromagnetic** (e-lek″tro-mag-net′ik) **energy,** is energy that travels in waves. These waves, which vary in length, are collectively called the *electromagnetic spectrum* and include visible light, infrared waves, radio waves, ultraviolet waves, and X rays (see Figure 16.13, p. 515). When light strikes the retinas of our eyes, it sets off a chain of reactions that eventually results in vision. Ultraviolet waves cause sunburn, but they also stimulate our body to make vitamin D. X rays have little to do with normal body functioning, but they are important in the study of anatomy and in medical diagnosis.

With few exceptions, energy can easily be converted from one form to another. For example, chemical energy (gasoline) that powers the motor of a speedboat is converted into the mechanical energy of the whirling propeller that allows the boat to skim across the water. Energy conversions are quite inefficient; some of the initial energy supply is always "lost" to the environment as heat. (It is not really lost because energy cannot be created or destroyed, but that part given off as heat is at least partly *unusable.*) You can easily demonstrate this principle. Electrical energy is converted into light energy in a light bulb, but if you touch a lit bulb, you will soon discover that some of the electrical energy is producing heat instead. Likewise, all energy conversions that occur in the body liberate heat. This heat makes us warm-blooded animals and contributes to our relatively high body temperature, which has an important influence on body functioning. For example, when matter is heated, its particles begin to move more quickly; that is, their kinetic energy increases. The higher the temperature, the faster the body's chemical reactions occur. We will learn more about this later.

COMPOSITION OF MATTER: ATOMS AND ELEMENTS

All matter is composed of fundamental substances called **elements.** Elements are unique substances that cannot be broken down into simpler substances by ordinary chemical methods. Among the well-known elements are oxygen, carbon, gold, silver, copper, and iron. At present, 110 elements are known, of which 92 occur in nature. The rest are made artificially in particle accelerator devices. Four elements—carbon, oxygen, hydrogen, and nitrogen—make up about 96% of body weight; 20 others are present in the body in lesser or trace amounts. The elements contributing to body mass and their importance are given in Table 2.1 (p. 28). The **periodic table,** a more complete listing of the known elements, is provided in Appendix F.

Each element is composed of more or less identical particles or building blocks, called **atoms.** The smallest atoms are less than 0.1 nanometer (nm) in diameter, and the largest only about five times as large. (1 nm = 0.0000001 [or 10^{-7}] centimeter [cm], or 40 billionths of an inch!)

Each element's atoms differ from those of all other elements and give the element its unique physical and chemical properties. *Physical properties* are those we can detect with our senses (such as color and texture) or measure (such as boiling point and freezing point). *Chemical properties* pertain to the

way atoms interact with other atoms (bonding behavior) and account for the facts that iron rusts, gasoline burns in air, animals can digest their food, and so on.

Each element is designated by a one- or two-letter chemical shorthand called an **atomic symbol,** usually the first letter(s) of the element's name. For example, C stands for carbon, O for oxygen, and Ca for calcium. In a few cases, the atomic symbol is taken from the Latin name for the element; for example, sodium is indicated by Na, from the Latin word *natrium.*

Atomic Structure

The word *atom* comes from the Greek word meaning "indivisible," and until this century atomic indivisibility was accepted as a scientific truth. We now know that atoms are clusters of even smaller particles called protons, neutrons, and electrons and that even those subatomic particles can be subdivided with high-technology tools. Even so, the old idea of atomic indivisibility is still helpful because an atom loses the unique properties of its element when it is split into its subatomic particles.

An atom's subatomic particles differ in mass, electrical charge, and position in the atom. An atom has a central **nucleus** containing protons and neutrons tightly bound together. The nucleus, in turn, is surrounded by orbiting electrons (Figure 2.1a). **Protons** (p^+) bear a positive electrical charge, while **neutrons** (n^0) are neutral. Thus, the nucleus is positively charged overall. Protons and neutrons are heavy subatomic particles and have approximately the same mass, which is arbitrarily designated as 1 **atomic mass unit** (1 amu). Since all of the heavy subatomic particles are concentrated in the nucleus, the nucleus is fantastically dense and accounts for nearly the entire mass (99.9%) of the atom. The tiny **electrons** (e^-) bear a negative charge equal in strength to the positive charge of the proton. However, an electron has only about 1/2000 the mass of a proton, and the mass of an electron is usually designated as 0 amu.

Because all atoms are electrically neutral, the number of protons an atom has must be precisely balanced by its number of electrons (the + and − charges will then cancel the effect of each other). Thus, hydrogen has one proton and one electron, and iron has 26 protons and 26 electrons. For any atom, the number of protons and electrons is always equal.

The **planetary model,** illustrated in Figure 2.1a, is a simplified (and now outdated) model of atomic structure. As you can see, it depicts electrons moving around the nucleus in fixed, generally circular orbits. But we can never determine the exact location of electrons at a particular time because they jump around following unknown trajectories. So, instead of speaking of discrete orbits, chemists talk about **orbitals**—regions around the nucleus in which a given electron or electron pair is likely to be found most of the time.

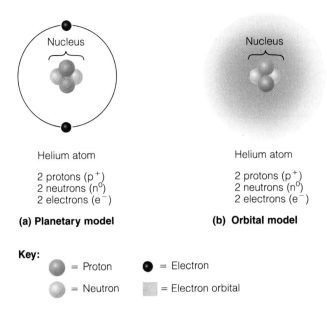

Helium atom

2 protons (p^+)
2 neutrons (n^0)
2 electrons (e^-)

(a) Planetary model

Helium atom

2 protons (p^+)
2 neutrons (n^0)
2 electrons (e^-)

(b) Orbital model

Key:

⬤ = Proton   ⬤ = Electron

⬤ = Neutron   ▦ = Electron orbital

FIGURE 2.1
The structure of an atom. The dense central nucleus contains the protons and neutrons. **(a)** In the planetary model of atomic structure, the electrons move around the nucleus in fixed orbits. **(b)** The orbital model recognizes that we never know exactly where electrons are; therefore electrons are shown as a cloud of negative charge (electron cloud).

This more modern model of atomic structure, called the **orbital model,** is more useful for predicting the chemical behavior of atoms. As illustrated in Figure 2.1b, the orbital model depicts *probable* regions of greatest electron density by denser shading (this is called the *electron cloud*). However, because of the simplicity of the planetary model, most descriptions of atomic structure in this text will use that model.

Hydrogen, with just one proton and one electron, is the simplest atom. You can visualize the spatial relationships in the hydrogen atom by imagining it

enlarged until its diameter equals the length of a football field. In that case, the nucleus could be represented by a lead ball the size of a gumdrop in the exact center of the sphere and its lone electron pictured as a fly buzzing about unpredictably within the sphere. This mental picture should serve as a reminder that most of the volume of an atom is empty space, and nearly all of its mass is concentrated in the central nucleus.

Identifying Elements

All protons are alike, regardless of the atom being considered. The same is true of all neutrons and all electrons. So what determines the unique properties of each element? The answer is that atoms of different elements are composed of *different numbers* of protons, neutrons, and electrons.

The simplest and smallest atom, hydrogen, has one proton, one electron, and no neutrons (Figure 2.2). Next is the helium atom, with two protons, two neutrons, and two orbiting electrons. Lithium follows with three protons, four neutrons, and three electrons. If we continued this step-by-step progression, we would get a graded series of atoms containing from 1 to 110 protons, an equal number of electrons, and a slightly larger number of neutrons at each step. However, all we really need to know to identify a particular element is its atomic number, mass number, and atomic weight. Taken together, these provide a fairly complete profile of each element.

Atomic Number

The **atomic number** of any atom is equal to the number of protons in the nucleus and is written as a subscript to the left of its atomic symbol. Hydrogen, with one proton, has an atomic number of 1 ($_1$H); helium, with two protons, has an atomic number of 2 ($_2$He); and so on. Since the number of protons is always

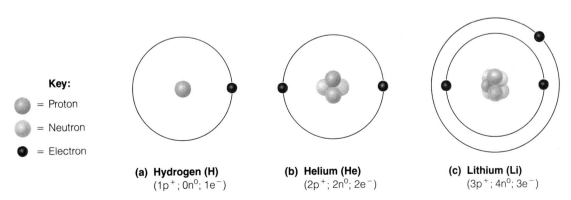

Key:

⬤ = Proton

⬤ = Neutron

⬤ = Electron

(a) Hydrogen (H)
($1p^+$; $0n^0$; $1e^-$)

(b) Helium (He)
($2p^+$; $2n^0$; $2e^-$)

(c) Lithium (Li)
($3p^+$; $4n^0$; $3e^-$)

FIGURE 2.2
Atomic structure of the three smallest atoms.

Table 2.1 Common Elements Composing the Human Body*

Element	Atomic symbol	Approx. % body mass[†]	Functions
Major (96.2%)			
Oxygen	O	65.0	A major component of both organic (carbon-containing) and inorganic (non-carbon-containing) molecules; as a gas, it is necessary for the production of cellular energy (ATP)
Carbon	C	18.5	A primary component of all organic molecules, which include carbohydrates, lipids (fats), proteins, and nucleic acids
Hydrogen	H	9.5	A component of all organic molecules; as an ion (proton), it influences the pH of body fluids
Nitrogen	N	3.2	A component of proteins and nucleic acids (genetic material)
Lesser (3.9%)			
Calcium	Ca	1.5	Found as a salt in bones and teeth; its ionic (Ca^{2+}) form is required for muscle contraction, conduction of nerve impulses, and blood clotting
Phosphorus	P	1.0	Part of calcium phosphate salts in bones and teeth; also present in nucleic acids; part of ATP
Potassium	K	0.4	Its ion (K^+) is the major positive ion (cation) in cells; necessary for conduction of nerve impulses and muscle contraction
Sulfur	S	0.3	Component of proteins, particularly muscle proteins
Sodium	Na	0.2	As an ion (Na^+), sodium is the major positive ion found in extracellular fluids (fluids outside of cells); important for water balance, conduction of nerve impulses, and muscle contraction
Chlorine	Cl	0.2	Ionic chlorine (Cl^-) is the most abundant negative ion (anion) in extracellular fluids
Magnesium	Mg	0.1	Present in bone; also an important cofactor in a number of metabolic reactions
Iodine	I	0.1	Needed to make functional thyroid hormones
Iron	Fe	0.1	Component of hemoglobin (which transports oxygen within red blood cells) and some enzymes
Trace (less than 0.01%)			
Chromium (Cr); Cobalt (Co); Copper (Cu); Fluorine (F); Manganese (Mn); Molybdenum (Mo); Selenium (Se); Silicon (Si); Tin (Sn); Vanadium (V); Zinc (Zn)			
These elements are referred to as *trace elements* because they are required in very minute amounts; many are found as part of enzymes or are required for enzyme activation			

*A listing of the elements by ascending order of atomic number appears in the periodic table, Appendix F.
[†]Percentage "wet" body mass; includes water.

equal to the number of electrons in an atom, the atomic number *indirectly* tells us the number of electrons in the atom as well. As explained shortly, this is important information indeed, because electrons determine the chemical behavior of atoms.

Mass Number

The **mass number** of an atom is the sum of the masses of its protons and neutrons. (The mass of the electrons is so small that it is ignored.) Hydrogen has only one proton in its nucleus, so its atomic and mass numbers are the same: 1. Helium, with two protons and two neutrons, has a mass number of 4. The mass number is usually indicated by a superscript to the left of the atomic symbol. Thus, helium can be described by the notation $^4_2$He. This simple notation allows us to deduce the total number and kinds of subatomic particles in any atom because it indicates the number of protons (the atomic number), the number of electrons (equal to the atomic number), and the number of neutrons (mass number minus atomic number).

From what we have said so far, it may appear as if each element has one, and only one, type of atom representing it. This is not the case. Nearly all known elements have two or more atomic variants called **isotopes** (i'so-tōps), which have the same atomic number but vary in their mass numbers (and therefore their

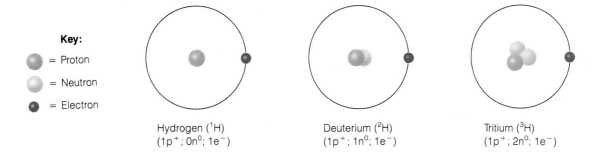

Key:
= Proton
= Neutron
= Electron

Hydrogen (^{1}H)
(1p$^+$; 0n^0; 1e$^-$)

Deuterium (^{2}H)
(1p$^+$; 1n^0; 1e$^-$)

Tritium (^{3}H)
(1p$^+$; 2n^0; 1e$^-$)

FIGURE 2.3
Isotopes of hydrogen.

weights). Another way of saying this is that all the isotopes of an element have the same number of protons (and electrons), but vary in the number of neutrons they contain. Earlier, when we said that hydrogen has a mass number of 1, we were speaking of ^{1}H, its most abundant isotope. Some hydrogen atoms have a mass of 2 or 3 amu (atomic mass units), which means that they have one proton and, respectively, one or two neutrons (Figure 2.3). Similarly, carbon exists in three isotopic forms: ^{12}C, ^{13}C, and ^{14}C. Each of the carbon isotopes has six protons (otherwise it would not be carbon), but the first has six neutrons, the second has seven, and the third has eight.

Atomic Weight

It would seem that atomic weight should be the same as atomic mass, and this would be so if atomic weight referred to the weight of a single atom. However, **atomic weight** is an average of the relative weights (mass numbers) of all the isotopes of an element, taking into account their relative abundance in nature. As a rule, the atomic weight of an element is approximately equal to the mass number of its most abundant isotope. For example, the atomic weight of hydrogen is 1.008, which reveals that its lightest isotope (^{1}H) is present in much greater amounts than its ^{2}H or ^{3}H forms.

Radioisotopes

The heavier isotopes of many elements are unstable, and their atoms decompose spontaneously into more stable forms. This process of atomic decay is called *radioactivity,* and isotopes that exhibit this behavior are called **radioisotopes** (ra″de-o-i′so-tōps). The disintegration of a radioactive nucleus may be compared to a tiny explosion. It occurs when *alpha* (α) *particles* (packets of 2p + 2n), *beta* (β) *particles* (electron-like negative particles), or *gamma* (γ) *rays* (electromagnetic energy) are ejected from the atomic nucleus. Why this happens is complex, and you only need to know that the dense nuclear particles are composed of even smaller particles called *quarks* that associate

in one way to form protons and in another way to form neutrons. Apparently, the nuclear "glue" that holds these quarks together is less effective in the heavier isotopes.

Radioisotopes may produce one or more forms of radiation and tend to gradually lose radioactive behavior. The time required for a radioisotope to lose one-half of its activity is called its *half-life.* The half-lives of radioisotopes vary dramatically from hours to thousands of years.

Because radioactivity can be detected with scanners, radioisotopes are valuable tools for biological research and medicine. Most radioisotopes used in the clinical setting are used for diagnosis, that is, to localize damaged or cancerous tissues. For example, iodine-131 is used to determine the size and activity of the thyroid gland and to detect thyroid cancer. The sophisticated PET scans described in *A Closer Look* on pp. 18–19 use radioisotopes to probe the workings of molecules deep within our bodies. All types of radioactivity, regardless of the purpose for which they are used, damage living tissue.

Alpha emission has the lowest penetrating power and is least damaging to living tissue; γ emission has the greatest penetrating power. Radium-226, cobalt-60, and certain other radioisotopes are used to destroy localized cancers. For example, radium is sometimes used to destroy uterine cancer.

HOW MATTER IS COMBINED: MOLECULES AND MIXTURES

Molecules and Compounds

Most atoms do not exist in the free state, but instead are chemically combined with other atoms. Such a combination of two or more atoms held together by chemical bonds is called a **molecule.** (The nature of the uniting chemical bonds is described shortly.)

If two or more atoms of the *same* element combine, the resulting substance is called a *molecule of that element.* When two hydrogen atoms bond, the product is a molecule of hydrogen gas and is written as H_2. Similarly, when two oxygen atoms combine, a molecule of oxygen gas (O_2) is formed. Sulfur atoms commonly combine to form molecules containing eight sulfur atoms (S_8).

When two or more *different* kinds of atoms bind, they form molecules of a **compound.** Two hydrogen atoms combine with one oxygen atom to form the compound water (H_2O), and four hydrogen atoms combine with one carbon atom to form the compound methane (CH_4). Notice again that molecules of methane and water are compounds, but molecules of hydrogen gas are not, because compounds always contain atoms of at least two different elements.

Compounds are chemically pure substances, and all of their molecules are identical. Thus, just as an atom is the smallest particle of an element that still exhibits the properties of the element, a molecule is the smallest particle of a compound that still displays the specific characteristics of the compound. This is an important concept because the properties of compounds are usually very different from those of the atoms they contain. Indeed, it is next to impossible to determine the atoms in a compound without analyzing it chemically.

Mixtures

Mixtures are substances composed of two or more components *physically intermixed.* Although most matter in nature exists in the form of mixtures, there are only three basic types: *solutions, colloids,* and *suspensions.*

Solutions

Solutions are *homogeneous* mixtures of two or more components that may be gases, liquids, or solids. Examples include the air we breathe (a mixture of gases), seawater (a mixture of salts, which are solids, and water), and rubbing alcohol (a mixture of two liquids, alcohol and water). The substance present in the greatest quantity is called the **solvent** (or dissolving medium); solvents are usually liquids. Substances present in smaller amounts are called **solutes.**

Water is the body's chief solvent. Most solutions in the body are *true solutions* containing gases, liquids, or solids dissolved in water. True solutions are usually transparent; examples are saline solution (table salt [NaCl] and water) and a mixture of glucose and water. The solutes of true solutions are minute, usually in the form of individual atoms and molecules. Consequently, they are not visible to the naked eye, do not settle out, and do not scatter light. If a beam of light is passed through a true solution, you will not see the path of light.

Expressing the Concentration of Solutions.

True solutions are often described in terms of their *concentration,* which may be specified in various ways. Solutions used in a college laboratory or a hospital are often described in terms of the **percent** (parts per 100 parts) of the solute in the solution. This designation always refers to the solute percentage, and unless otherwise noted, water is assumed to be the solvent.

Another way to express the concentration of a solution is in terms of its **molarity** (mo-lar′ĭ-te), or moles per liter, indicated by M. This method is more complicated, but is much more useful. To understand molarity, you must first understand what a mole is. A **mole** of any element or compound is equal to its atomic weight or **molecular weight** (sum of the atomic weights) weighed out in grams. This concept is easier than it seems, as illustrated by the following example.

Glucose is $C_6H_{12}O_6$, which indicates that it has 6 carbon atoms, 12 hydrogen atoms, and 6 oxygen atoms. To compute the molecular weight of glucose, you would look up the atomic weight of each of its atoms in the periodic table (see Appendix F) and compute its molecular weight as follows:

Atom	Number of Atoms		Atomic Weight		Total Atomic Weight
C	6	×	12.011	=	72.066
H	12	×	1.008	=	12.096
O	6	×	15.999	=	95.994
					180.156

Then, to make a *one-molar* solution of glucose, you would weigh out 180.156 grams (g), one gram molecular weight, of glucose and add enough water to make 1 liter (L) of solution. Thus, a one-molar solution (abbreviated 1.0 M) of a chemical substance is one gram molecular weight of the substance (or one gram atomic weight in the case of elemental substances) in 1 L (1000 ml) of solution.

The beauty of using the mole as the basis of preparing solutions is the precision of this measurement. One mole of any substance always contains exactly the same number of solute particles, that is, 6.02×10^{23}. This number is called **Avogadro's** (av″o-gad′rōz) **number.** So whether you weigh out 1 mole of glucose (180 g) or 1 mole of water (18 g) or 1 mole of methane (16 g), in each case you will have 6.02×10^{23} molecules of that substance.* This allows almost mind-boggling precision to be achieved.

*The important exception to this rule concerns molecules that ionize and break up into charged particles (ions) in water, such as salts, acids, and bases (see p. 39). For example, simple table salt (sodium chloride) breaks up into two types of charged particles; therefore, in a 1.0 M solution of sodium chloride, there are actually *2 moles* of solute particles in solution.

Colloids

Colloids (kol′oidz) are *heterogeneous* mixtures that often appear translucent or milky. Although the solute particles are larger than those in true solutions, they still do not settle out. However, they do scatter light, and the path of a light beam shining through a colloidal mixture is visible.

Colloids have many unique properties, including the ability of some to undergo **sol-gel transformations,** that is, to change reversibly from a fluid (sol) state to a more solid (gel) state. Jell-O, or any gelatin product, is a familiar example of a nonliving colloid that changes from a sol to a gel when refrigerated (and that will liquefy again if placed in the sun). Cytosol, the semifluid material in living cells, is also considered a colloid, and its sol-gel changes underlie many important cell functions, such as cell division.

Suspensions

Suspensions are *heterogeneous* mixtures with large, often visible solutes that tend to settle out. An example of a suspension is a mixture of sand in water. Blood is also a suspension in which the living blood cells are suspended in the fluid portion of blood, or blood plasma. If left to stand, the suspended cells settle out unless some means—mixing, shaking, or, in the body, circulation—is used to keep them in suspension.

As you can see, all three types of mixtures are found in both living and nonliving systems. In fact, living material is the most complex mixture of all, since it contains all three kinds of mixtures in complex interactions with one another.

Distinguishing Mixtures from Compounds

Now that we have examined the various mixtures, we are ready to "zero in" on how to distinguish mixtures and compounds from one another. Mixtures differ from compounds in several important ways:

1. The fact that no chemical bonding occurs between the components of a mixture is the chief difference between mixtures and compounds. The properties of atoms and molecules are not changed when they become part of a mixture. (Remember they are only "physically intermixed.")

2. The substances making up a mixture can be separated by physical means—straining, filtering, evaporation, and so on, depending on the nature of the mixture. Compounds, by contrast, can be separated into their constituent atoms only by chemical means (breaking bonds).

3. Some mixtures are homogeneous, whereas others are heterogeneous. To say that a substance is *homogeneous* means that a sample taken from any part of the substance will have exactly the same composition (in terms of the atoms or molecules it contains) as any other sample. A bar of 100% pure (elemental) iron is homogeneous, as are all compounds. *Heterogeneous* substances vary in their makeup from place to place. For example, iron ore is a heterogeneous mixture that contains iron as well as many other elements.

CHEMICAL BONDS

As noted earlier, when atoms combine with other atoms, they are held together by **chemical bonds.** A chemical bond is not a physical structure like a pair of handcuffs linking two people together. Instead, it represents an energy relationship between the electrons of the reacting atoms.

The Role of Electrons in Chemical Bonding

Electrons forming the electron cloud around the nucleus of an atom occupy regions of space called **electron shells** that consecutively surround the atomic nucleus. The atoms known so far can have electrons in seven shells (numbered 1 to 7 from the nucleus outward), but the actual number in any specific atom depends on the number of electrons that atom possesses. Each electron shell contains one or more orbitals.

It is important to understand that each electron shell represents a different **energy level,** because this prompts you to think of electrons as particles with a certain amount of potential energy. In general, the terms *electron shell* and *energy level* are used interchangeably.

The amount of potential energy an electron has depends first and foremost on the energy level it occupies because the attraction between the positively charged nucleus and negatively charged electrons is greatest closest to the nucleus and falls off with increasing distance. This statement explains why electrons farthest from the nucleus (1) have the greatest potential energy (it takes more energy to overcome the nuclear attraction and reach the more distant energy levels), and (2) are most likely to interact chemically with other atoms (they are least tightly held by their own atomic nucleus and most easily influenced by other atoms and molecules).

Each electron shell can hold a specific number of electrons. Shell 1, the shell immediately surrounding the nucleus, can accommodate only 2 electrons. Shell 2 holds a maximum of 8; shell 3 has room for 18 electrons. Subsequent shells hold larger and larger num-

(a) Chemically inert elements (valence shell complete)

Helium (He)
$(2p^+; 2n^0; 2e^-)$

Neon (Ne)
$(10p^+; 10n^0; 10e^-)$

Hydrogen (H)
$(1p^+; 0n^0; 1e^-)$

Carbon (C)
$(6p^+; 6n^0; 6e^-)$

Oxygen (O)
$(8p^+; 8n^0; 8e^-)$

Sodium (Na)
$(11p^+; 12n^0; 11e^-)$

(b) Chemically active elements (valence shell incomplete)

FIGURE 2.4
Chemically inert and reactive elements. (a) Helium and neon are chemically inert because in each case the outermost energy level (valence shell) is fully occupied by electrons. **(b)** Elements in which the valence shell is incomplete are chemically reactive. Such atoms tend to react with other atoms to gain, lose, or share electrons to fill their valence shells. (*Note:* To simplify the diagrams, each atomic nucleus is shown as a circle with the atom's symbol in it; individual protons and neutrons are not shown.)

bers of electrons. The shells tend to be filled with electrons consecutively. For example, shell 1 is completely filled before any electrons appear in shell 2.

When atoms form bonds, the important electrons are those in the atom's outermost energy level. Inner electrons usually do not take part in bonding because they are more tightly held by the atomic nucleus. When the outermost energy level of an atom either is filled to capacity or contains eight electrons, a stable state is reached. Such atoms are *chemically inert* (in-ert'), that is, unreactive. A group of elements called the *noble gases,* which include helium and neon, typify this condition (Figure 2.4a). However, atoms in which the outermost energy level contains fewer than eight electrons (Figure 2.4b) tend to gain, lose, or share electrons with other atoms to achieve stability.

A possible point of confusion must be addressed here. In atoms that have more than 20 electrons, the energy levels beyond shell 2 can contain *more* than eight electrons. However, the number of electrons that can participate in bonding is still limited to a total of eight. The term **valence** (va'lens) **shell** is used specifically to indicate an atom's outermost energy level *or that portion of it* containing the electrons that are chemically reactive. Hence, the key to chemical reactivity is the **octet** (ok-tet') **rule**, or **rule of eights.** Except for shell 1, which is filled with two electrons, atoms tend to interact in such a way that they have eight electrons in their valence shell.

Types of Chemical Bonds

Three major types of chemical bonds—*ionic, covalent,* and *hydrogen bonds*—result from attractive forces between atoms.

Ionic Bonds

Atoms are electrically neutral. However, electrons can be transferred from one atom to another and, when this happens, the precise balance of + and − charges is lost and charged particles called **ions** are formed. The atom that gains one or more electrons, the *electron acceptor,* acquires a net negative charge and is called an **anion** (an'i-on). The atom that loses electrons (the *electron donor*) acquires a net positive charge and is called a **cation** (kat'i-on). (It might help to think of the "t" in "cation" as a + sign.) Both anions and cations are formed whenever electron transfer between atoms occurs. Since opposite charges attract, these ions tend to stay close together. The result is an **ionic** (i-on'ik) **bond.**

One example of ionic bonding is the formation of sodium chloride (NaCl), by interaction of sodium and chlorine atoms (Figure 2.5). Sodium, with an atomic number of 11, has one electron in its valence shell, and it would be very difficult to attempt to fill this shell by adding seven more. However, if this single

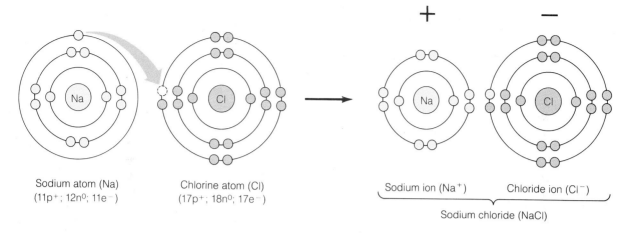

FIGURE 2.5
Formation of an ionic bond. Both sodium and chlorine atoms are chemically reactive because their valence shells are incompletely filled. Sodium gains stability by losing one electron, whereas chlorine becomes stable by gaining one electron. After electron transfer, sodium becomes a sodium ion (Na$^+$), and chlorine becomes a chloride ion (Cl$^-$). The oppositely charged ions attract each other.

electron is lost, shell 2 with eight electrons becomes the valence shell (outermost energy level containing electrons) and is full. Thus, by losing the lone electron in its third energy level, sodium achieves stability and becomes a cation (Na$^+$). On the other hand, chlorine, atomic number 17, needs only one electron to fill its valence shell. By accepting an electron, chlorine becomes an anion and achieves stability. When these two atoms interact, this is exactly what happens. Sodium donates an electron to chlorine, and the ions created in this exchange attract each other forming sodium chloride. Ionic bonds are commonly formed between atoms with one or two valence shell electrons (the metallic elements, such as sodium, calcium, and potassium) and atoms with seven valence shell electrons (such as chlorine, fluorine, and iodine). Most ionic compounds fall in the chemical category called *salts.*

In the dry state, ionic compounds such as sodium chloride do not exist as individual molecules. Instead, they form **crystals,** large arrays of cations and anions held together by ionic bonds (see Figure 2.11, page 39).

Sodium chloride is an excellent example of the difference in properties between a compound and its constituent atoms. Sodium is a silvery white metal, and chlorine in its molecular state is a poisonous green gas used to make bleach. However, sodium chloride is a white crystalline solid that we sprinkle on our food.

Covalent Bonds

Electrons do not have to be completely transferred for atoms to achieve stability. Instead, they may be *shared* so that each atom is able to fill its outer elec-

tron shell for at least part of the time. Electron sharing produces molecules in which the shared electrons constitute **covalent** (ko-va′lent) **bonds.**

Hydrogen with its single electron can fill its only shell (shell 1) by sharing a pair of electrons with another atom. When it shares with another hydrogen, a molecule of hydrogen gas is formed. The shared electron pair orbits around the molecule as a whole, satisfying the stability needs of each atom. Hydrogen can also share an electron pair with different kinds of atoms to form a compound (Figure 2.6a). Carbon has four electrons in its outermost shell, but needs eight to achieve stability, whereas hydrogen has one electron, but needs two. When a methane molecule (CH$_4$) is formed, carbon shares four pairs of electrons with four hydrogen atoms (one pair with each hydrogen). Again, the shared electrons orbit and "belong to" the whole molecule, ensuring the stability of each atom. When atoms share one pair of electrons, a *single covalent bond* is formed (indicated by a single line connecting the atoms, such as H—H). But in some cases, atoms share two or three electron pairs (Figure 2.6b and c), resulting in *double* or *triple covalent bonds* (indicated by double or triple lines such as O=O or N≡N).

Polar and Nonpolar Molecules.
In the covalent bonds discussed thus far, the shared electrons have been shared equally between the atoms of the molecule. The molecules formed are electrically balanced and are called **nonpolar molecules.** However, this is not always the case. When two or more atoms form covalent bonds, the resulting molecule always has a specific three-dimensional shape, with bonds formed at definite angles. A molecule's shape helps determine what other molecules or atoms it can interact with; it may also result in unequal electron pair shar-

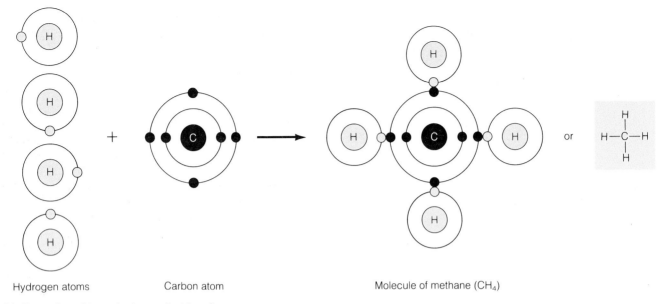

Hydrogen atoms   Carbon atom   Molecule of methane (CH₄)

(a) Formation of four single covalent bonds

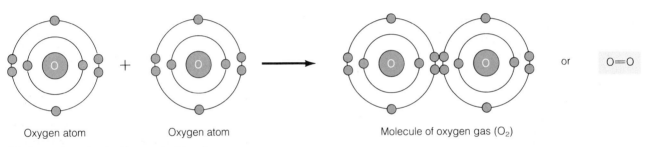

Oxygen atom   Oxygen atom   Molecule of oxygen gas (O₂)

(b) Formation of a double covalent bond

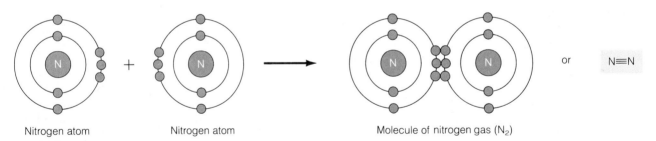

Nitrogen atom   Nitrogen atom   Molecule of nitrogen gas (N₂)

(c) Formation of a triple covalent bond

FIGURE 2.6
Formation of covalent bonds. The electron-sharing patterns of interacting atoms are shown to the left. In the shaded boxes to the far right, each covalent bond is indicated by a single line between the atoms that share an electron pair. **(a)** Formation of a molecule of methane; carbon shares four electron pairs with four hydrogen atoms. **(b)** Formation of a molecule of oxygen gas; each oxygen atom shares two electron pairs with its partner, forming a double covalent bond. **(c)** When a molecule of nitrogen gas is formed, the two nitrogen atoms share three electron pairs, forming a triple covalent bond.

ing and **polar molecules.** This is especially true in nonsymmetrical molecules that contain atoms with different electron-attracting abilities. The ability of atoms to attract electrons is related to their number of valence shell electrons and to atomic size. In general, *small* atoms with six or seven valence shell electrons, such as oxygen, nitrogen, and chlorine, attract electrons very strongly. This capability of electron-hungry atoms is called **electronegativity.** Conversely, most atoms with only one or two valence shell electrons tend to be **electropositive**; that is, their electron-attracting ability is so low that they usually lose their

(a) Carbon dioxide (CO₂)

(b) Water (H₂O)

FIGURE 2.7
Molecular models illustrating the three-dimensional structure of carbon dioxide and water molecules.

valence shell electrons to other atoms. Potassium and sodium, each with one valence shell electron, are good examples of electropositive atoms.

Carbon dioxide and water illustrate the importance of molecular shape and the relative electron-attracting abilities of atoms in determining whether a covalently bonded molecule is nonpolar or polar. Carbon dioxide (CO_2) is formed when carbon shares four electron pairs with two oxygen atoms (two pairs are shared with each oxygen). Oxygen is very electronegative and attracts the shared electrons much more strongly than does carbon. However, since the carbon dioxide molecule is linear (Figure 2.7a), the electron-pulling ability of one oxygen atom is offset by that of the other, like a tug-of-war at a standoff. As a result, the shared electrons are shared equally and carbon dioxide is a nonpolar compound.

On the other hand, a water molecule (H_2O) is V-shaped (Figure 2.7b). The two hydrogen atoms are located at the same end of the molecule, and oxygen is at the opposite end. This arrangement allows the oxygen atom to pull the shared electrons toward itself and away from the two hydrogen atoms. In this case, the electron pairs are *not* shared equally, but spend more time in the vicinity of oxygen. Since electrons are negatively charged, the oxygen end of the molecule is slightly more negative (indicated by δ [delta]⁻) and the hydrogen end slightly more positive (indicated by δ⁺). Because water has two poles of charge, it is a *polar molecule,* or **dipole** (di′pōl). Polar molecules orient themselves toward other dipoles or toward charged particles (such as ions and some proteins), and they play essential roles in chemical reactions in body cells. The polarity of water is particularly significant, as you will see later in this chapter.

Different types of molecules exhibit different degrees of polarity, and we can see a gradual change from ionic to nonpolar covalent bonding as summarized in Figure 2.8. Ionic bonds (complete electron transfer) and nonpolar covalent bonds (equal electron

sharing) are the extremes of a continuum, with various degrees of unequal electron sharing in between.

Hydrogen Bonds

Unlike the stronger ionic and covalent bonds, hydrogen bonds are too weak to bind atoms together to form molecules. Hydrogen bonds form when a hydrogen atom, already covalently linked to one electronegative atom (usually nitrogen or oxygen), is attracted by another electron-hungry atom, and forms a "bridge" between them. Hydrogen bonding is common between dipoles such as water molecules, because the slightly positive hydrogens of one molecule are attracted to the slightly negative oxygen atoms of other molecules (Figure 2.9). The tendency of water molecules to cling together and form films, referred to as *surface tension,* helps explain why water beads up into spheres when it sits on a hard surface.

? *Assume imaginary compound XY has a covalent polar bond. How does its charge distribution differ from that of XX molecules?*

FIGURE 2.8
Comparison of ionic, polar covalent, and nonpolar covalent bonds. This display compares the status of electrons involved in bonding and the electrical charge distribution in the molecules formed.

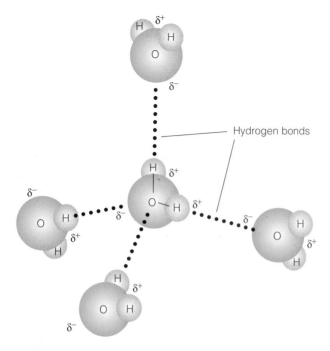

FIGURE 2.9
Hydrogen bonding between polar water molecules. The slightly positive ends (indicated by δ^+) of the water molecules become aligned with the slightly negative ends (indicated by δ^-) of other water molecules.

Hydrogen bonds are also important as *intramolecular bonds*, which bind different parts of a single large molecule together into a specific three-dimensional shape. Some large biological molecules, such as proteins and DNA, have numerous hydrogen bonds that help maintain and stabilize their structures.

CHEMICAL REACTIONS

As noted earlier, all particles of matter are in constant motion because of their kinetic energy. Movement of atoms or molecules in a solid is usually limited to vibration because the particles are united by fairly rigid bonds. But in liquids or gases, particles dart about randomly, sometimes colliding with one another and interacting to undergo chemical reactions. A **chemical reaction** occurs whenever chemical bonds are formed, rearranged, or broken.

Chemical Equations

Earlier, we discussed joining two hydrogen atoms to form hydrogen gas and combining four atoms of hydrogen and one atom of carbon to form methane. These reactions can be written in symbolic form as **chemical equations:**

$$H + H \rightarrow H_2 \text{ (hydrogen gas)}$$
(reactants)　　　(product)

and

$$4H + C \rightarrow CH_4 \text{ (methane)}$$

Notice that a number written as a *subscript* indicates that the atoms are joined by chemical bonds. But a number written as a *prefix* denotes the number of *unjoined* atoms or molecules. Hence, CH_4 reveals that four hydrogen atoms are bonded together with carbon to form the methane molecule, but 4H signifies four unjoined hydrogen atoms.

A chemical equation is like a sentence describing what happens in a reaction. It contains the following information: the number and kinds of reacting substances, or **reactants;** the chemical composition of the **product(s);** and, in balanced equations, the relative proportion of each reactant and product. In the preceding examples, reactants are atoms, as indicated by their atomic symbols (H, C). The product in each case is a molecule, as indicated by its **molecular formula** (H_2, CH_4). The equation for the formation of methane may be read as *either* "four atoms of hydrogen plus one atom of carbon yield one molecule of methane" *or* "four moles of hydrogen atoms plus one mole of carbon yield one mole of methane." Generally, using moles is more practical because it is impossible to measure out one atom or one molecule of anything!

Patterns of Chemical Reactions

Most chemical reactions exhibit one of three major patterns: they are either *synthesis, decomposition,* or *exchange reactions.*

When atoms or molecules combine to form a larger, more complex molecule, the process is called a **synthesis,** or **combination, reaction.** A synthesis reaction, which always involves bond formation, can be represented (using arbitrary letters) as

$$A + B \rightarrow AB$$

Synthesis reactions are the basis of constructive, or **anabolic,** activities in body cells, such as uniting small molecules called amino acids into large protein molecules (Figure 2.10a). Synthesis reactions are especially prominent in rapidly growing tissues.

A **decomposition reaction** occurs when a molecule is broken down into smaller molecules or its constituent atoms:

$$AB \rightarrow A + B$$

Essentially, decomposition reactions are reverse synthesis reactions; bonds are broken. Decomposition reactions underlie all degradative, or **catabolic,** processes that occur in body cells. For example, the bonds of large glycogen molecules are broken to release simpler molecules of glucose sugar (Figure 2.10b).

Exchange, or **displacement, reactions** involve both synthesis and decomposition; that is, bonds are both made and broken. In an exchange reaction, parts

Amino acids — Protein molecule

(a) Example of a synthesis reaction: amino acids are joined to form a protein molecule

Glycogen — Glucose molecules

(b) Example of a decomposition reaction: breakdown of glycogen to release glucose units

Glucose + Adenosine triphosphate (ATP)

Glucose phosphate + Adenosine diphosphate (ADP)

(c) Example of an exchange reaction: ATP transfers its terminal phosphate group to glucose to form glucose-phosphate

FIGURE 2.10

Patterns of chemical reactions. (a) In synthesis reactions, smaller particles (atoms, ions, or molecules) are bonded together to form larger, more complex molecules. **(b)** Decomposition reactions involve bond breaking. **(c)** In exchange, or displacement, reactions, bonds are both made and broken.

of the reactant molecules change partners, so to speak, producing different product molecules:

$$AB + C \rightarrow AC + B \quad \text{and} \quad AB + CD \rightarrow AD + CB$$

An exchange reaction occurs when ATP reacts with glucose and transfers its end phosphate group (indicated by a circled P in Figure 2.10c) to glucose, forming glucose-phosphate. At the same time, the ATP becomes ADP. This important reaction occurs when-

ever glucose enters a body cell and it effectively traps the glucose fuel molecule inside the cell.

Another group of very important chemical reactions in living systems are **oxidation-reduction reactions—redox reactions** for short. Oxidation-reduction reactions are hybrid reactions that can be classified as both decomposition and exchange reactions. They are decomposition reactions in that they are the basis of all reactions in which food fuels are catabolized for energy (that is, in which ATP is produced). They can also be viewed as a special type of exchange reaction because electrons are exchanged between the reactants. The reactant losing the electrons is referred to as the *electron donor* and is said to be **oxidized**; the reactant called the *electron acceptor* is said to become **reduced** as it takes up the transferred electrons. Redox reactions occur when ionic compounds are formed. (Recall that in the formation of NaCl [see Figure 2.5], sodium loses an electron to chlorine. Consequently, sodium is oxidized and becomes the sodium ion, and chlorine is reduced and becomes the chloride ion.) However, not all oxidation-reduction reactions involve complete transfer of electrons—some simply change the pattern of electron sharing in covalent bonds. For example, a substance is oxidized both by the loss of hydrogen atoms and by combining with oxygen. The common factor in these events is that electrons that formerly "belonged" to the reactant molecule are lost—either entirely (as hydrogen is removed and takes its electron with it) or relatively (the shared electrons spend more time in the vicinity of the very electronegative oxygen atom).

To understand the importance of oxidation-reduction reactions in living systems, take a look at the overall equation for *cellular respiration,* which represents the major pathway by which glucose is broken down for energy in body cells:

$$\underset{\text{glucose}}{C_6H_{12}O_6} + \underset{\text{oxygen}}{6O_2} \rightarrow \underset{\substack{\text{carbon}\\\text{dioxide}}}{6CO_2} + \underset{\text{water}}{6H_2O} + \underset{\substack{\text{cellular}\\\text{energy}}}{ATP}$$

As you can see, it is an oxidation-reduction reaction. Glucose is oxidized to carbon dioxide as it loses hydrogen atoms, and oxygen is reduced to water as it accepts the hydrogen atoms. This reaction is described in detail in Chapter 25, along with other topics of cellular metabolism.

Energy Flow in Chemical Reactions

Because all chemical bonds represent stored chemical energy, all chemical reactions ultimately result in net absorption or release of energy. Reactions that release energy are called **exergonic reactions.** These reactions yield products that have less energy than the initial reactants, but they also provide energy that can be harvested for other uses. With a few exceptions, most catabolic and oxidative reactions are exergonic. On the other hand, the products of energy-absorbing, or **endergonic,** reactions contain more potential energy in their chemical bonds than did the reactants. Energy is required to make the bonds of most large molecules in the body, and anabolic reactions are typically energy-absorbing endergonic reactions. Essentially this is a case of "one hand washing the other"—the energy released as fuel molecules are broken down (oxidized) is captured in ATP molecules and then used to synthesize the complex biological molecules the body needs to sustain life.

Reversibility of Chemical Reactions

All chemical reactions are theoretically reversible. If chemical bonds can be made, they can be broken, and vice versa. Reversibility is indicated by a double arrow. When the arrows differ in length, the longer arrow indicates the major direction in which the reaction proceeds:

$$A + B \rightleftharpoons AB$$

In this example, more product (AB) is made as the reaction goes on. Over time, the product accumulates and the reactants (A and B) decrease in amount.

When the arrows are of equal length, as in:

$$A + B \rightleftharpoons AB$$

neither the forward reaction nor the reverse reaction is dominant; that is, for each molecule of product (AB) formed, one product molecule breaks down, releasing the reactants A and B. Such a chemical reaction is said to be in a state of **chemical equilibrium.** Once chemical equilibrium is reached, there is no further *net change* in the amounts of reactants and products. Product molecules are still formed and broken down, but the situation already established when equilibrium is reached (such as greater numbers of product molecules) remains unchanged. This is analogous to the admission scheme used by many large museums in which tickets are sold according to time of entry. If 300 tickets are issued for the 9 A.M. admission, 300 people will be admitted when the doors open. Thereafter, when 6 people leave, 6 are admitted, and when another 15 people leave, 15 more are allowed in. Although there is a continual turnover, the museum contains about 300 art lovers throughout the day.

Although all chemical reactions are reversible in theory, many show so little tendency to go in the reverse direction that they are irreversible for all practical purposes. This is true of many biological reactions. Chemical reactions that release energy when going in one direction will not go in the opposite direction unless energy is put back into the system. For example, as mentioned above, when our cells break down glucose via the reactions of cellular respiration to yield carbon dioxide and water, some of the

energy released is trapped in the bonds of ATP. Since the cells need ATP's energy for various functions (and more glucose will be along with the next meal), this particular reaction is never reversed in our cells. Furthermore, if a product of a reaction is continuously removed from the reaction site, it is unavailable to take part in the reverse reaction. The carbon dioxide that is released as glucose is degraded leaves the cell, enters the blood, and is eventually removed from the body by the lungs.

Factors Influencing the Rate of Chemical Reactions

For atoms and molecules to react chemically, they must *collide* with enough force to overcome the repulsion between their electrons. Interactions between valence shell electrons—the basis of bond making and breaking—cannot occur long distance. The force of collisions depends on how fast the particles are moving. Solid, forceful collisions between rapidly moving particles are much more likely to cause reactions than are those in which the particles graze each other lightly.

Temperature

Increasing the temperature of a substance increases the kinetic energy of its particles and the force of their collisions. Therefore, chemical reactions proceed more quickly at higher temperatures. When the temperature drops, particle movement and reactions occur more slowly.

Particle Size

Smaller particles move faster than larger ones (at the same temperature) and therefore tend to collide more frequently and more forcefully. Hence, the smaller the reacting particles, the faster a chemical reaction goes at a given temperature and concentration.

Concentration

Chemical reactions progress most rapidly when the reacting particles are present in high concentration, because the larger the number of randomly moving particles in a given space, the greater the chance of successful collisions. As the concentration of the reactants declines, chemical equilibrium eventually occurs unless additional reactants are added or products are removed from the reaction site.

Catalysts

Although many chemical reactions that occur in nonliving systems can be speeded up simply by heating, drastic increases in body temperature are life threatening because important biological molecules are destroyed. Still, at normal body temperatures, most chemical reactions would proceed far too slowly to maintain life were it not for the presence of catalysts. **Catalysts** (kat′ah-lists) are substances that increase the rate of chemical reactions without themselves becoming chemically changed or part of the product. Molecules called **enzymes** (en′zīmz) are biological catalysts. The presence of enzymes is the single most important factor determining the rate of chemical reactions in living systems. Most, but not all, enzymes are proteins. Enzymes and their mode of action are described later in this chapter.

PART 2: BIOCHEMISTRY: THE COMPOSITION AND REACTIONS OF LIVING MATTER

Compounds contributing to body structure and function fall into one of two major classes: inorganic and organic compounds. **Organic compounds** contain carbon. All organic compounds are covalently bonded molecules, and many are large.

All other chemicals in the body are considered **inorganic compounds.** These include water, salts, and many acids and bases. Organic and inorganic compounds are equally essential for life. Trying to decide which is more valuable is like trying to decide whether the ignition system or the engine is more essential to the operation of a car!

INORGANIC COMPOUNDS

Water

Water, the most abundant and important inorganic compound in living material, makes up 60% to 80% of the volume of most living cells. The versatility of this vital fluid is incredible, as reflected in its properties (described next).

1.   High heat capacity. Water has a *high heat capacity;* that is, it absorbs and releases large amounts of heat before changing appreciably in temperature itself. Its abundance in the body prevents sudden changes in temperature caused by external factors, such as sun or wind exposure, or by internal conditions that cause rapid heat liberation, such as vigorous muscle activity. As part of blood, water redistributes heat among body tissues, ensuring temperature homeostasis.

2.   High heat of vaporization. When water evaporates, or vaporizes, it changes from a liquid to a gas (water vapor). The transformation requires that large

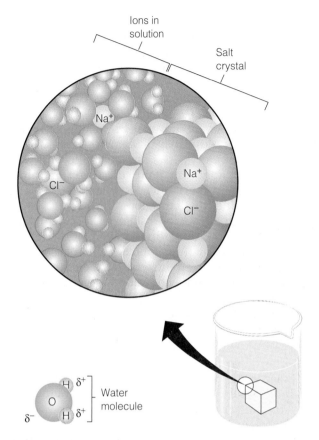

FIGURE 2.11
Dissociation of a salt in water. The slightly negative ends of the water molecules (δ^-) are attracted to Na$^+$, whereas the slightly positive ends of water molecules (δ^+) orient toward Cl$^-$, causing the ions to be pulled off the crystal lattice.

amounts of heat be absorbed to break the hydrogen bonds that hold water molecules together. This property is extremely beneficial when we sweat. As perspiration (mostly water) evaporates from our skin, large amounts of heat are removed from the body and lost to the external environment, providing an efficient cooling mechanism.

3.   Polarity/solvent properties. Water is an unparalleled solvent and suspension medium for both inorganic and organic molecules. Indeed, water is often called the **universal solvent.** Biochemistry is "wet chemistry": biological molecules do not react chemically unless they are in solution, and virtually all chemical reactions occurring in the body depend on water's solvent properties.

Because of their polar nature, water molecules orient themselves with their slightly negative ends toward the positive ends of the solutes, and vice versa, first attracting them, then surrounding them. This property of water explains why ionic compounds and other small reactive molecules (such as acids and bases) *dissociate* in water, their ions separating from each other and becoming evenly scattered in the water, forming true solutions (Figure 2.11).

Water also forms **hydration layers** (layers of water molecules) around large charged molecules such as proteins, shielding them from the effects of other charged substances in the vicinity and preventing them from settling out of solution. Such protein-water mixtures are *biological colloids.* Cerebrospinal fluid is an example of a colloid.

Water serves as the body's major transport medium because it is such an excellent solvent. Nutrients, respiratory gases, and metabolic wastes are carried throughout the body dissolved in blood plasma, and many metabolic wastes are excreted from the body in urine, another watery fluid.

Specialized molecules that act as body lubricants also use water as their dissolving medium. Such lubricating fluids include mucus, which eases feces through the bowel, and the serous fluids that reduce friction and prevent adhesions among visceral organs.

4. Reactivity. Water is an important *reactant* in many chemical reactions. For example, foods are digested to their building blocks by adding a water molecule to each bond to be broken. Such decomposition reactions are more specifically called **hydrolysis** (hi-drol′ĭ-sis; "water splitting") **reactions.** Conversely, when large carbohydrate or protein molecules are synthesized from smaller molecules, a water molecule is removed for every bond formed, in a reaction called **dehydration synthesis.**

5. Cushioning. Finally, by forming a resilient cushion around certain body organs, water helps protect them from physical trauma. The cerebrospinal fluid surrounding the brain exemplifies water's *cushioning* role.

Salts

A **salt** is an ionic compound containing cations other than H^+ and anions other than the hydroxyl ion (OH^-). As already noted, when salts are dissolved in water, they dissociate into their component ions (Figure 2.11). For example, sodium sulfate (Na_2SO_4) dissociates into two Na^+ ions and one SO_4^{2-} ion. This occurs easily because the ions are already formed. All that remains is for water to overcome the attraction between the oppositely charged ions. All ions are **electrolytes** (e-lek′tro-līts), substances that conduct an electrical current in solution. (Note that groups of atoms that bear an overall charge, such as sulfate, are called *polyatomic ions.*)

Salts of many metal elements, such as NaCl, Ca_2CO_3 (calcium carbonate), and KCl (potassium chloride), are common in the body. However, the most plentiful salts are the calcium phosphates that contribute to the hardness of bones and teeth. In their ionized form, salts play vital roles in body function. For instance, the electrolyte properties of ionic sodium and potassium are essential for nerve impulse

transmission and muscle contraction. Ionic iron forms part of the hemoglobin molecules that transport oxygen within red blood cells, and ionic zinc and copper are important to the activity of some enzymes. Other important functions of the elements found in body salts are summarized in Table 2.1 (page 28).

Maintaining proper ionic balance in our body fluids is one of the most critical homeostatic roles of the kidneys. When this balance is severely disturbed, virtually nothing in the body works. All the physiological activities listed above and thousands of others are disrupted and ultimately grind to a stop. •

Acids and Bases

Like salts, acids and bases are electrolytes; that is, they ionize and dissociate in water and can then conduct an electrical current. However, unlike salts, acids and some bases are covalently bonded molecules. Therefore, ions have to be formed before dissociation can occur.

Acids

Acids have sour taste, can react with many metals, and "burn" a hole in your rug. But the most useful definition of an acid for our purposes is that it is a substance that releases **hydrogen ions** (H^+) in detectable amounts. Since a hydrogen ion is just a hydrogen nucleus, or "naked" proton, acids are also defined as **proton donors.**

When acids dissolve in water, they release hydrogen ions (protons) and anions. It is the concentration of protons that determines the acidity of a solution. The anions have little or no effect on acidity. For example, hydrochloric acid (HCl), an acid produced by stomach cells that aids digestion, dissociates into a proton and a chloride ion:

$$HCl \longrightarrow \underset{\text{proton}}{H^+} + \underset{\text{anion}}{Cl^-}$$

Other acids found or produced in the body include acetic acid ($HC_2H_3O_2$, commonly abbreviated as HAc), the acidic portion of vinegar; and carbonic acid (H_2CO_3). The molecular formula for an acid is easy to recognize because the hydrogen is written first.

Bases

Bases have a bitter taste, feel slippery, and are **proton acceptors**—that is, they take up hydrogen ions (H^+) in detectable amounts. Common inorganic bases include the *hydroxides* (hi-drok′sīds), such as magnesium hydroxide (milk of magnesia) and sodium hydroxide (lye). Like acids, hydroxides dissociate when dissolved in water, but in this case **hydroxyl** (hi-drok′sil) **ions** (OH^-) and cations are liberated. For example, ionization of sodium hydroxide (NaOH) produces a hydroxyl ion and a sodium ion; the hydroxyl ion then binds to (accepts) a proton present in the solution. This produces water and simultaneously reduces the acidity (hydrogen ion concentration) of the solution:

$$NaOH \longrightarrow \underset{\text{cation}}{Na^+} + \underset{\text{hydroxyl ion}}{OH^-}$$

and then

$$OH^- + H^+ \longrightarrow \underset{\text{water}}{H_2O}$$

Bicarbonate ion (HCO_3^-), an important base in the body, is particularly abundant in blood. *Ammonia* (NH_3), a common waste product of protein breakdown in the body, is also a base. It has one pair of unshared electrons that strongly attracts protons. By accepting a proton, ammonia becomes an ammonium ion:

$$NH_3 + H^+ \longrightarrow \underset{\substack{\text{ammonium} \\ \text{ion}}}{NH_4^+}$$

pH: Acid-Base Concentration

The more hydrogen ions in a solution, the more acidic the solution is said to be. Conversely, the greater the concentration of hydroxyl ions (the lower the concentration of H^+), the more basic, or *alkaline* (al′kuh-lĭn), the solution becomes. The relative concentration of hydrogen ions in various body fluids is measured in concentration units called **pH** (pe-āch′) **units.**

The idea for a pH scale was devised by a Danish biochemist and part-time beer brewer named Sören Sörensen in 1909. He was searching for a convenient means of checking the acidity of his alcoholic product to prevent its spoilage by bacterial action. (Many bacteria are inhibited by acidic conditions.) The pH scale that resulted is based on the concentration of hydrogen ions in a solution, expressed in terms of moles per liter, or molarity. The pH scale runs from 0 to 14 and is logarithmic; that is, each successive change of one pH unit represents a tenfold change in hydrogen ion concentration (Figure 2.12). The pH of a solution is thus defined as the negative logarithm of the hydrogen ion concentration in moles per liter or $-\log[H^+]$.

At a pH of 7 (at which $[H^+]$ is $10^{-7}\ M$), the number of hydrogen ions exactly equals the number of hydroxyl ions, and the solution is *neutral*—neither acidic nor basic. Absolutely pure (distilled) water has a pH of 7. Solutions with a pH below 7 are acidic; the hydrogen ions outnumber the hydroxyl ions. The lower the pH, the more acidic the solution. A solution with a pH of 6 has ten times as many hydrogen ions as a solution with a pH of 7.

Solutions with a pH higher than 7 are alkaline, and the relative concentration of hydrogen ions decreases by a factor of 10 with each higher pH unit. Thus, solutions with pH values of 8 and 12 have,

Concentration in moles/liter

FIGURE 2.12

The pH scale and pH values of representative substances. The pH scale is based on the number of hydrogen ions in solution. The actual concentration of hydrogen ions ($[H^+]$) (expressed in moles per liter) and the corresponding hydroxyl concentration ($[OH^-]$) are indicated for each pH value noted. At a pH of 7, the concentrations of hydrogen and hydroxyl ions are equal and the solution is neutral.

respectively, 1/10 and 1/100,000 as many hydrogen ions as a solution of pH 7. Notice that as the hydrogen ion concentration decreases, the hydroxyl ion concentration rises, and vice versa. The approximate pH of several body fluids and of a number of common substances also appears in Figure 2.12.

Neutralization

When acids and bases are mixed, they react with each other in displacement reactions to form water and a salt. For example, when hydrochloric acid and sodium hydroxide interact, sodium chloride (a salt) and water are formed.

$$HCl + NaOH \longrightarrow H_2O + NaCl$$
$$\text{acid} \quad\quad \text{base} \quad\quad \text{water} \quad \text{salt}$$

This type of reaction is called a **neutralization reaction,** because the combining of H^+ and OH^- to form water neutralizes the solution. Although the salt formed in this reaction is written in molecular form (NaCl), remember that it actually exists as dissociated sodium and chloride ions when dissolved in water.

Buffers

Living cells are extraordinarily sensitive to even slight changes in the pH of the environment. In high concentrations, acids and bases are extremely damaging to living tissue. Homeostasis of acid-base balance is carefully regulated by the kidneys and lungs and by chemical systems (proteins and other types of molecules) called **buffers.** Buffers resist abrupt and large swings in the pH of body fluids by releasing hydrogen ions (acting as acids) when the pH begins to rise and by binding hydrogen ions (acting as bases) when the pH drops. Because blood comes into close contact with nearly every body cell, regulation of its pH is particularly critical. Normally, blood pH varies within a very narrow range (7.35 to 7.45). If blood pH varies from these limits by more than a few tenths of a unit, it may be fatal.

To comprehend how chemical buffer systems operate, you must thoroughly understand strong and weak acids and bases. The first important concept is that the acidity of a solution reflects *only* the free hydrogen ions, not those bound to anions. Consequently, acids that dissociate completely and irreversibly in water are called **strong acids,** because they can dramatically change the pH of a solution. Examples are hydrochloric acid and sulfuric acid. If we could count out 100 hydrochloric acid molecules and place them in 1 ml of water, we could expect to end up with 100 H^+, 100 Cl^-, and no undissociated hydrochloric acid molecules in that solution. Acids that do not dissociate completely, like carbonic acid (H_2CO_3) and acetic acid (HAc), are said to be **weak acids.** If we were to place 100 acetic acid molecules in 1 ml of water, the reaction would be something like this:

$$100\,HAc \longrightarrow 90\,HAc + 10\,H^+ + 10\,Ac^-$$

Because undissociated acids do not affect pH, the acetic acid solution is much less acidic than the HCl solution. Weak acids dissociate in a predictable way, and molecules of the intact acid are in dynamic equi-

librium with the dissociated ions. Consequently, the dissociation of acetic acid may also be written as:

$$HAc \rightleftharpoons H^+ + Ac^-$$

Viewing it from this perspective allows us to see that if H^+ (released by a strong acid) is added to the acetic acid solution, the equilibrium will shift to the left and some of the H^+ and Ac^- will recombine to form HAc. On the other hand, if a strong base is added and the pH begins to rise, the equilibrium shifts to the right and more of the HAc molecules dissociate to release H^+. This characteristic of weak acids allows them to play extremely important roles in the chemical buffer systems of the body.

The concept of strong and weak bases is more easily explained. Remember that bases are proton acceptors. Thus, **strong bases** are those, like hydroxides, that dissociate easily in water and quickly tie up H^+. On the other hand, sodium bicarbonate (commonly known as baking soda) ionizes incompletely and reversibly. Because it accepts relatively few protons, it is considered a **weak base.**

Now let's examine how one buffer system helps to maintain pH homeostasis of the blood. Although there are other chemical blood buffers, the **carbonic acid–bicarbonate system** is a very important one. Carbonic acid (H_2CO_3) dissociates reversibly, releasing bicarbonate ions (HCO_3^-) and protons (H^+):

$$\overset{\text{Response to rise in pH}}{\underset{\text{Response to drop in pH}}{H_2CO_3 \rightleftharpoons HCO_3^- + H^+}}$$

H^+ donor (weak acid) H^+ acceptor (weak base)   proton

The chemical equilibrium between carbonic acid (a weak acid) and bicarbonate ion (a weak base) resists changes in blood pH by shifting to the right or left as H^+ ions are added to or removed from the blood. As blood pH rises (i.e., becomes more alkaline due to the addition of a strong base), the equilibrium shifts to the right, forcing carbonic acid to dissociate more completely. Similarly, as blood pH begins to drop (i.e., becomes more acidic due to the addition of a strong acid), the equilibrium shifts to the left as more bicarbonate ions begin to bind with protons. As you can see, strong bases are replaced by a weak base (bicarbonate ion) and protons released by strong acids are tied up in a weak one (carbonic acid). In either case, the pH of the blood changes much less than it would in the absence of the buffering system. Acid-base balance and buffers are discussed in more detail in Chapter 27.

ORGANIC COMPOUNDS

Molecules unique to living systems—proteins, carbohydrates, lipids (fats), and nucleic acids—all contain carbon and hence are organic compounds. Although organic compounds are distinguished by the fact that they contain carbon and inorganic compounds are defined as compounds that lack carbon, there are a few irrational exceptions to this generalization that you should be aware of. Carbon dioxide, carbon monoxide, and carbides, for example, all contain carbon but are considered inorganic compounds.

What makes carbon so special that "living" chemistry depends on its presence? To begin with, no other *small* atom is so precisely **electroneutral.** The consequence of its electroneutrality is that carbon never loses or gains electrons; it always shares them. Furthermore, with four valence shell electrons, carbon forms four covalent bonds with other elements, as well as with other carbon atoms. As a result, carbon is found in long, chainlike molecules (common in fats), ring structures (typical of carbohydrates and steroids), and many other structures that are uniquely suited for specific roles in the body.

Carbohydrates

Carbohydrates, a group of molecules that includes sugars and starches, represent 1% to 2% of cell mass. Carbohydrates contain carbon, hydrogen, and oxygen, and generally the hydrogen and oxygen atoms occur in the same 2:1 ratio as in water. This ratio is reflected in the word *carbohydrate* (meaning "hydrated carbon").

A carbohydrate can be classified according to size and solubility as a monosaccharide ("one sugar"), disaccharide ("two sugars"), or polysaccharide ("many sugars"). Monosaccharides are the structural units, or building blocks, of the other carbohydrates. In general, the larger the carbohydrate molecule, the less soluble it is in water.

Monosaccharides

Monosaccharides (mon″o-sak′ah-rīdz), or *simple sugars,* are single-chain or single-ring structures containing from three to seven carbon atoms (Figure 2.13a). Usually, the carbon, hydrogen, and oxygen atoms occur in the ratio 1:2:1, so a general formula for a monosaccharide is $(CH_2O)_n$, where *n* is the number of carbons in the sugar. Glucose, for example, has six carbon atoms, and its molecular formula is $C_6H_{12}O_6$. Ribose, with five carbons, is $C_5H_{10}O_5$.

Monosaccharides are named generically according to the number of carbon atoms they contain. Most important in the body are the pentose (five-carbon) and hexose (six-carbon) sugars. For example, *deoxyribose* (de-ok″s̲i̲-ri′bōs), a pentose, is part of DNA, and *glucose,* a hexose, is blood sugar. Two other hexoses, *galactose* and *fructose,* are **isomers** (i′so-mers) of glucose. That is, they have the same molecular formula $(C_6H_{12}O_6)$, but their atoms are arranged differently, giving them different chemical properties (see Figure 2.13a). When ingested in the diet, galactose and fructose are often converted to glucose for use by the body cells.

Disaccharides

A **disaccharide** (di-sak′ah-rīd), or *double sugar,* is formed when two monosaccharides are joined together by **dehydration synthesis** (Figure 2.13b). In this synthesis reaction, a water molecule is lost as the bond is formed, as illustrated by the synthesis of sucrose (soo′krōs):

$$2C_6H_{12}O_6 \longrightarrow C_{12}H_{22}O_{11} + H_2O$$

glucose + fructose   sucrose   water

Notice that the molecular formula for sucrose contains two hydrogen atoms and one oxygen atom less than the total number of hydrogen and oxygen atoms in glucose and fructose, because a water molecule is released during bond formation.

Important disaccharides in the diet are *sucrose* (glucose + fructose), which is cane or table sugar; *lactose* (glucose + galactose), found in milk; and *maltose* (glucose + glucose), also called malt sugar (see Figure 2.13b). Since disaccharides are too large to pass through cell membranes, they must be digested to their simple sugar units to be absorbed from the digestive tract into the blood. This decomposition process is called **hydrolysis** and is essentially the reverse of dehydration synthesis. A water molecule is added to each bond, breaking the bonds and releasing the simple sugar units (see Figure 2.13b).

Polysaccharides

Polysaccharides (pol″e-sak′ah-rīdz) are long chains of simple sugars linked together by dehydration synthesis (Figure 2.13c). Such long, chainlike molecules made of many similar units are called **polymers.** Because polysaccharides are large, fairly insoluble molecules, they are ideal storage products. Another consequence of their large size is that they lack the sweetness of the simple and double sugars. Only two polysaccharides are of major importance to the body: starch and glycogen. Both are polymers of glucose. Only their degree of branching differs.

Starch is the storage carbohydrate formed by plants. The number of glucose units composing a starch molecule is high and variable. When we eat starchy foods such as grain products and potatoes, the starch must be digested to its glucose units to be absorbed. (We are unable to digest *cellulose,* another polysaccharide found in all plant products. However, it is important in providing the *bulk* that helps move feces through the colon.)

Glycogen (gli′ko-jen), the storage carbohydrate of animal tissues, is stored primarily in skeletal muscle and liver cells. Like starch, it is highly branched and is a very large molecule (see Figure 2.13c). When blood sugar levels drop precipitously, liver cells break down glycogen and release its glucose units to the blood. Since there are many branch endings from which glucose can be released simultaneously, body cells have almost instant access to glucose fuel.

(a) Monosaccharides

Glucose   Fructose   Galactose   Deoxyribose   Ribose

Glucose   +   Fructose   Dehydration synthesis / Hydrolysis H_2O Sucrose

Glucose   Glucose — Maltose

Galactose   Glucose — Lactose

(b) Disaccharides

(c) Portion of a polysaccharide molecule (glycogen)

Glycogen

FIGURE 2.13
Carbohydrate molecules.* **(a)** Monosaccharides important to the body. The hexose sugars glucose, fructose, and galactose are isomers: Their molecular formulas are all the same ($C_6H_{12}O_6$), but the arrangement of their atoms differs, as shown in this diagram. Deoxyribose ($C_5H_{10}O_4$) and ribose ($C_5H_{10}O_5$) are pentose sugars.

(b) Common disaccharides. Disaccharides are two monosaccharides linked together by dehydration synthesis, a process involving the removal of a water molecule at the bond site. The formation of sucrose ($C_{12}H_{22}O_{11}$) from glucose and fructose molecules is illustrated. In the reverse reaction (hydrolysis), sucrose is broken down to glucose and fructose by the addition of a

water molecule to the bond. Other important disaccharides are maltose ($C_{12}H_{22}O_{11}$) and lactose ($C_{12}H_{22}O_{11}$). **(c)** Simplified representation of part of a glycogen molecule. Glycogen is a polysaccharide formed from linked glucose units.
*(See footnote on facing page concerning the complete structure of these sugars.)

Carbohydrate Functions

The major function of carbohydrates in the body is to provide a ready, easily used source of cellular fuel. Most cells can use only a limited number of simple sugars, and glucose is at the top of the "cellular menu." As described in our earlier discussion of oxidation-reduction reactions (p. 37), glucose is broken down and oxidized within cells, and some of the bond energy released during glucose breakdown is trapped in the bonds of ATP molecules. When not immediately needed for ATP synthesis, dietary carbohydrates are converted to glycogen or fat and stored. Those of us who have gained weight from eating too many carbohydrate-rich snacks have a first-hand, personal awareness of this conversion process!

Small amounts of carbohydrates are used for structural purposes. For example, some sugars are found in our genes. Others are attached to the external surfaces of cells where they act as "road signs" to guide cellular interactions. When protein intake is inadequate, some sugars are converted by the liver into building blocks needed to produce proteins.

Lipids

Lipids are organic compounds that are insoluble in water but dissolve readily in other lipids and in organic solvents such as alcohol, chloroform, and ether. Like carbohydrates, all lipids contain carbon, hydrogen, and oxygen, but the proportion of oxygen in lipids is much lower. In addition, phosphorus is found in some of the more complex lipids. The lipids are a diverse group that includes *neutral fats, phospholipids* (fos"fo-lip′idz), *steroids* (stě′roidz), and a number of other lipoid substances. Table 2.2 gives the locations and functions of some lipids found in the body.

Neutral Fats

The **neutral fats** are commonly known as *fats* when solid or *oils* when liquid. A neutral fat is composed of two types of building blocks, *fatty acids* and *glycerol* (glis′er-ol) (Figure 2.14a). Fatty acids are linear chains of carbon and hydrogen atoms (hydrocarbon chains) with an organic acid group (—COOH)[†] at one end.

[†]Appendix D provides a listing of many of the functional groups of organic molecules.

---

[*]Notice that in Figure 2.13 the carbon (C) atoms present at each angle of the carbohydrate ring structures are not illustrated. For example, the illustrations below show the full structure of glucose on the left and the shorthand structure on the right. This shorthand is used for all organic ringlike structures illustrated in this chapter.

Glycerol is a modified simple sugar (a sugar alcohol). Fat synthesis involves the attachment of three fatty acid chains to a single glycerol molecule by dehydration synthesis, resulting in an E-shaped molecule. Because of the 3:1 fatty acid to glycerol ratio, the neutral fats are also called **triglycerides** (tri-glis′er-īdz) or **triacylglycerols** (tri-as"il-glis′er-olz; *acyl* = acid). The glycerol backbone is the same in all neutral fats, but the fatty acid chains vary. This results in different kinds of neutral fats. The neutral fats are large molecules, often consisting of hundreds of atoms, and ingested fats and oils must be broken down to their building blocks before they can be absorbed. Neutral fats are the body's most concentrated source of usable energy fuel, and when they are oxidized they yield large amounts of energy.

The hydrocarbon chains make neutral fats nonpolar molecules. Since polar and nonpolar molecules do not interact, oil (or fats) and water do not mix. Consequently, neutral fats are well suited for storing energy fuel in the body. Deposits of neutral fats are found primarily beneath the skin, where they insulate the deeper body tissues from heat loss and protect them from mechanical trauma. Women are usually better English Channel swimmers than men; this is attributed partly to their thicker subcutaneous fatty layer, which helps insulate them from the bitterly cold water of the channel.

The length of a neutral fat's fatty acid chains and their degree of saturation determine how solid a neutral fat is at a given temperature. Fatty acid chains with only single covalent bonds between carbon atoms are referred to as **saturated.** Fatty acids that contain one or more double bonds between carbon atoms are said to be **unsaturated, monounsaturated** and **polyunsaturated** respectively. Neutral fats with short fatty acid chains and/or unsaturated fatty acids are liquid at room temperature and are typical of plant lipids. We are familiar with these unsaturated fats as oils used for cooking. Olive and peanut oils are rich in monounsaturated fats. Corn, soybean, and safflower oils are examples of oils containing a high percentage of polyunsaturated fatty acids. Longer fatty acid chains and/or more saturated fatty acids are common in animal fats such as butter fat and the fat of meats, which are solid at room temperature.

Phospholipids

Phospholipids are modified triglycerides with a phosphorus-containing group and two, rather than three, fatty acid chains (Figure 2.14b). The phosphorus-containing group gives phospholipids their distinctive chemical properties. Although the hydrocarbon portion (the "tail") of the molecule is nonpolar and interacts only with nonpolar molecules, the phosphorus-containing part (the "head") is polar and attracts other polar or charged particles, such as water

Table 2.2 Representative Lipids Found in the Body

Lipid type	Location/function
Neutral fats (triglycerides)	In fat deposits (subcutaneous tissue and around organs); protects and insulates body organs; the major source of *stored* energy in the body
Phospholipids (phosphatidyl choline; cephalin; others)	Chief component of cell membranes; may participate in the transport of lipids in plasma; prevalent in nervous tissue
Steroids:	
Cholesterol	The structural basis for manufacture of all body steroids
Bile salts	Breakdown products of cholesterol; released by the liver into the digestive tract, where they aid fat digestion and absorption
Vitamin D	A fat-soluble vitamin produced in the skin on exposure to UV radiation; necessary for normal bone growth and function
Sex hormones	Estrogen and progesterone (female hormones) and testosterone (a male hormone) are produced in the gonads and are necessary for normal reproductive function
Adrenal cortical hormones	Cortisol, a glucocorticoid, is a metabolic hormone necessary for maintaining normal blood glucose levels; aldosterone helps to regulate salt and water balance of the body by targeting the kidneys
Other lipoid substances:	
Fat-soluble vitamins:	
A	Found in orange-pigmented vegetables and fruits; converted in the retina to retinal, a part of the photoreceptor pigment involved in vision
E	Found in plant products such as wheat germ and green leafy vegetables; claims have been made (but not proved in humans) that it promotes wound healing and contributes to fertility; may help to neutralize highly reactive particles called free radicals believed to be involved in triggering some types of cancer
K	Made available to humans largely by the action of intestinal bacteria; also prevalent in a wide variety of foods; necessary for proper clotting of blood
Eicosanoids (prostaglandins; leukotrienes; thromboxanes)	Group of molecules derived from fatty acids found in all cell membranes; the potent prostaglandins have diverse effects, including stimulation of uterine contractions, regulation of blood pressure, control of gastrointestinal tract motility, and secretory activity; both prostaglandins and leukotrienes are involved in inflammation; thromboxanes are powerful vasoconstrictors
Lipoproteins	Lipoid and protein-based substances that transport fatty acids and cholesterol in the bloodstream; major varieties are high-density lipoproteins (HDLs) and low-density lipoproteins (LDLs)

or ions. As you will see in Chapter 3, cells use this unique characteristic of phospholipids in building their membranes. Some biologically important phospholipids and their functions are listed in Table 2.2.

Steroids

The structure of steroids differs quite a bit from that of fats. **Steroids** are basically flat molecules formed of four interlocking hydrocarbon rings. Like neutral fats, steroids are fat soluble and contain little oxygen. The single most important steroid is *cholesterol* (ko-les′ter-ol) (Figure 2.14c). We ingest cholesterol in animal products such as eggs, meat, and cheese, and our liver produces a certain amount.

Cholesterol has earned "bad press" because of its role in arteriosclerosis, but it is absolutely essential for human life. Cholesterol is found in cell membranes and is the raw material of vitamin D, steroid hormones, and bile salts. Although steroid hormones are present in the body in only small quantities, they are vital to homeostasis. Without sex hormones, reproduction would be impossible, and a total lack of the corticosteroids produced by the adrenal gland is fatal.

Eicosanoids

The **eicosanoids** (i-ko′sah-noyds) are diverse lipids chiefly derived from a 20-carbon fatty acid (arachidonic acid) found in all cell membranes. Most impor-

(a) Formation of a triglyceride

(b) Phospholipid molecule (phosphatidyl choline)

(c) Cholesterol

FIGURE 2.14

Lipids. (a) The neutral fats, or triglycerides, are synthesized by dehydration synthesis. In this process, three fatty acid chains are attached to a single glycerol molecule, and a water molecule is lost at each bond site. **(b)** Structure of a typical phospholipid molecule. Two fatty acid chains and a phosphorus-containing group are attached to the glycerol backbone. In the commonly used schematic to the right, the polar end ("head") is depicted as a sphere, and the nonpolar end ("tail") is depicted as two wavy lines. **(c)** The generalized structure of cholesterol. Cholesterol is the basis for all steroids formed in the body. The steroid nucleus is shaded.

tant of these are the *prostaglandins* and their relatives, which play roles in various body processes (Table 2.2) including blood clotting, inflammation, and labor contractions.

Proteins

Protein composes 10% to 30% of cell mass and is the basic structural material of the body. However, not all proteins are construction materials; many play vital roles in cell function. Proteins, which include enzymes

(biological catalysts), hemoglobin of the blood, and contractile proteins of muscle, have the most varied functions of any molecules in the body. All proteins contain carbon, oxygen, hydrogen, and nitrogen, and many contain sulfur and phosphorus as well.

Amino Acids and Peptide Bonds

The building blocks of proteins are molecules called **amino acids,** of which there are 20 common types (see Appendix C). All amino acids have two impor-

(a) Generalized structure of all amino acids

(b) Glycine (the simplest amino acid)

(c) Aspartic acid (an acidic amino acid)

(d) Lysine (a basic amino acid)

(e) Cysteine (a sulfur-containing amino acid)

FIGURE 2.15
Amino acid structures. (a) Generalized structure of amino acids. All amino acids have both an amine (—NH₂) group and an acid (—COOH) group; they differ only in the atomic makeup of their R groups (green).

(b)–(e) Specific structures of four amino acids. **(b)** The simplest (glycine) has an R group consisting of a single hydrogen atom. **(c)** An acid group in the R group, as in aspartic acid, makes the amino acid more acidic. **(d)** An amine group in the R group, as

in lysine, makes the amino acid more basic. **(e)** The presence of a sulfhydryl (—SH) group in the R group of cysteine suggests that this amino acid is likely to participate in intramolecular bonding.

tant functional groups: a basic group called an *amine* (ah'mēn) *group* (—NH₂), and an organic *acid group* (—COOH). An amino acid may therefore act either as a base (proton acceptor) or an acid (proton donor). In fact, all amino acids are identical except for a single group of atoms called their *R group.* Differences in the numbers and arrangement of the atoms making up the R group make each amino acid unique in its chemical behavior (Figure 2.15).

Proteins are long chains of amino acids joined together by dehydration synthesis, with the amine end of one amino acid linked to the acid end of the next. The resulting bond produces a characteristic arrangement of linked atoms and is called a *peptide bond* (Figure 2.16). Two united amino acids form a *dipeptide,* three a *tripeptide,* and ten or more a *polypeptide.* Polypeptides containing more than 50 amino acids are called proteins; however, most proteins are **macromolecules,** large, complex molecules containing from 100 to over 1000 amino acids.

Because each type of amino acid has distinct properties, the sequence in which they are bound together produces proteins that vary widely in both structure and function. We can think of the 20 amino acids as a 20-letter "alphabet" used in specific combinations to form "words" (proteins). Just as a change in one letter can produce a word with an entirely different meaning (flour → floor) or is nonsensical (flour → fllur), changes in the kinds or positions of amino acids can produce proteins with different functions or proteins that are nonfunctional. Nevertheless, there are thousands of different proteins in the body, each with distinct functional properties, and all constructed from different combinations of the 20 amino acids.

Structural Levels of Proteins

Proteins can be described in terms of four structural levels. The linear sequence of amino acids composing the polypeptide chain is called the *primary structure* of a protein. This structure, which resembles a strand of amino acid "beads," is the backbone of the protein molecule (Figure 2.17a).

Proteins do not normally exist as simple, linear chains of amino acids. Instead, they twist or fold upon themselves to form a more complex *secondary structure.* The most common type of secondary structure is the **alpha (α) helix,** which resembles a "Slinky" (Figure 2.17b). The α helix is formed by coil-

FIGURE 2.16
Amino acids are linked together by dehydration synthesis. The acid group of one amino acid is bonded to the amine group of the next, with loss of a water molecule. The bond formed is called a peptide bond. Peptide bonds are broken when water is added to the bond (i.e., during hydrolysis).

ing of the primary chain and is stabilized by hydrogen bonds formed between NH and CO groups of amino acids in the primary chain, which are approximately four amino acids apart. Hydrogen bonds in α helices always link different parts of the *same* chain together. In another type of secondary structure, the **beta (β)-pleated sheet,** the primary polypeptide chains do not coil, but are linked side by side by hydrogen bonds to form a pleated, ribbonlike structure (Figure 2.17c). Notice that in this type of secondary structure, the

hydrogen bonds may link together *different polypeptide* chains as well as *different parts* of the same chain that has folded back on itself in accordion-like fashion. A given polypeptide chain may exhibit both types of secondary structure at various places along its length.

Many proteins have *tertiary* (ter′she-a″re) *structure,* the next higher level of complexity, which is superimposed on secondary structure. To achieve this level of structure, α-helical or β-pleated regions of the

(a) **Primary structure (polypeptide strand)**

(b) **Secondary structure (∝ helix)**

(c) **Secondary structure (β pleated sheet)**

∝ helix

(d) **Tertiary structure**

Heme group

(e) **Quaternary structure (hemoglobin molecule)**

FIGURE 2.17
Levels of protein structure. (a) Primary structure. Amino acids are linked together to form a polypeptide strand. **(b)** Secondary structure—the α helix. The primary chain is coiled upon itself to form a spiral structure that is maintained by hydrogen bonds (indicated by dotted lines).

(c) Secondary structure—the β-pleated sheet. Two or more primary chains are linked side by side by hydrogen bonds to form an undulating ribbonlike structure. **(d)** Tertiary structure is superimposed on folded secondary structure (in this example on α-helical regions) to form a basically spherical molecule that is maintained by

intramolecular bonds. The molecule shown is a beta chain, one of the four polypeptide chains of hemoglobin. **(e)** Quaternary structure of hemoglobin. Hemoglobin is formed from four polypeptide chains that are linked together in a specific manner.

Table 2.3 Representative Types of Proteins in the Body

Classification according to: Overall structure	General function	Examples from the body
Fibrous	Structural framework/ mechanical support	*Collagen*, found in all connective tissues, is the single most abundant protein in the body. It is responsible for the tensile strength of bones, tendons, and ligaments.
		Keratin is the structural protein of hair and nails and the waterproofing material of skin.
		Elastin is found, along with collagen, where durability and flexibility are needed, such as in the ligaments that bind bones together.
		Spectrin internally reinforces and stabilizes the surface membrane of some cells, particularly red blood cells. *Dystrophin* reinforces and stabilizes the surface membrane of muscle cells.
	Movement	*Actin* and *myosin*, contractile proteins, are found in substantial amounts in muscle cells, where they cause muscle cell shortening (contraction); they also function in cell division in all cell types. Actin is important in intracellular transport, particularly in nerve cells.
Globular	Catalysis	*Protein enzymes* are essential to virtually every biochemical reaction in the body; they increase the rates of chemical reactions by at least a millionfold. Examples include salivary amylase (in saliva), which catalyzes the breakdown of starch, and oxidase enzymes, which act to oxidize food fuels.
	Transport	*Hemoglobin* transports oxygen in blood, and *lipoproteins* transport lipids and cholesterol. Other transport proteins in the blood carry iron, hormones, or other substances.
	Regulation of pH	Many plasma proteins, such as *albumin*, function reversibly as acids or bases, thus acting as buffers to prevent wide swings in blood pH.
	Regulation of metabolism	*Peptide* and *protein hormones* help to regulate metabolic activity, growth, and development. For example, *growth hormone* is an anabolic hormone necessary for optimal growth; *insulin* helps regulate blood sugar levels.
	Body defense	*Antibodies* (immunoglobulins) are specialized proteins released by immune cells that recognize and inactivate foreign substances (bacteria, toxins, some viruses). *Complement proteins*, which circulate in blood, enhance both immune and inflammatory responses. *Stress proteins* aid folding of new proteins in both healthy and damaged cells.

polypeptide chain fold upon one another to produce a compact ball-like, or globular, molecule. For example, the tertiary structure (and underlying secondary structure) of a beta polypeptide chain of hemoglobin, the oxygen-binding protein found in red blood cells, is shown in Figure 2.17d. This highly specific structure is maintained by both covalent and hydrogen bonds between amino acids that are often widely separated in the primary chain. When two or more polypeptide chains are arranged, or aggregate, in a regular manner to form a complex protein, the protein has *quaternary* (kwah′ter-na″re) *structure.* Hemoglobin (Figure 2.17e) exhibits this structural level.

In all cases, the ultimate overall structure of any protein is specified by its primary structure. This reflects the fact that the types and relative positions of amino acids in the protein backbone determine where bonds can form to produce coiled or folded structures that achieve higher levels of complexity.

Fibrous and Globular Proteins

The overall structure of a protein dictates its biological function. For example, the abilities of hemoglobin to transport oxygen and of antibodies to bind to bacteria (and thus defend the body against them) are determined by the unique structures of these proteins. In general, proteins are classified according to their overall appearance and shape as either fibrous or globular.

Fibrous proteins have an extended, strandlike appearance. Most exhibit only one type of secondary structure, but some display quaternary structure as well. For example, *collagen* (kol′ah-jen) is a triple helix of three polypeptide chains that form a strong ropelike structure. Fibrous proteins are linear, insoluble in water, and very stable—all qualities ideally suited for providing mechanical support and tensile strength to the body's tissues. Besides collagen, which is the single most abundant protein in the body, the fibrous proteins include keratin, elastin, and the contractile proteins of muscle (Table 2.3). Because fibrous proteins are the chief building materials of the body, they are also known as **structural proteins.**

Globular proteins are compact, spherical proteins that have at least tertiary structure (with both helical and pleated sheet regions contributing to their secondary structures in most cases); some also exhibit quaternary structure. The globular proteins are water soluble, mobile, chemically active molecules, and they play crucial roles in virtually all biological processes. Consequently, some refer to this group as **functional proteins.** Some of these proteins (antibodies) help to provide immunity, others (protein-based hormones) regulate growth and development, and still others (enzymes) are catalysts that oversee just about every chemical reaction in the body. The roles of these and selected other proteins found in the body are summarized in Table 2.3.

Protein Denaturation

Fibrous proteins are exceptionally stable, but globular proteins are quite the opposite. The activity of a protein depends on its specific three-dimensional structure, and intramolecular bonds, particularly hydrogen bonds, are critically important in maintaining that structure. However, hydrogen bonds are fragile and easily disrupted by many chemical and physical factors, such as excessive acidity or heat. Although individual proteins vary in their sensitivity to environmental conditions, hydrogen bonds begin to break as the temperature or pH rises above normal (physiological) levels, causing proteins to unfold and lose their specific three-dimensional shape. In this condition, a protein is said to be **denatured.** Fortunately, the disruption is reversible in most cases, and the "scrambled" protein regains its native structure when desirable conditions are restored. However, if the temperature or pH change is so extreme that protein structure is damaged beyond repair, the protein is *irreversibly denatured.* The coagulation of egg white (primarily albumin protein) that occurs when you boil or fry an egg is an example of irreversible protein denaturation. There is no way to restore the white, rubbery protein to its original translucent form.

When globular proteins are denatured, they can no longer perform their physiological roles. This is because their function depends on the presence of specific arrangements of atoms, called **active sites,** on their surfaces. The active sites are regions that fit and interact chemically with other molecules of complementary shape and charge. Since atoms contributing to an active site may actually be very far apart in the primary chain, disruption of intramolecular bonds separates them and destroys the active site (Figure 2.18). Hemoglobin becomes totally unable to bind and transport oxygen when blood pH is too acidic, because the structure needed for function has been destroyed.

Most body proteins are described in conjunction with the organ systems or functional processes to which they are closely related. However, two groups of proteins—enzymes and stress proteins—are intimately involved in the normal functioning of all cells, and so these incredibly complex molecules are considered here.

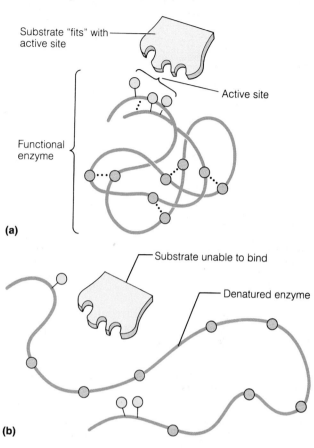

? *What event, which is possible in situation **(a)**, can no longer occur in situation **(b)**?*

Substrate "fits" with active site

Active site

Functional enzyme

(a)

Substrate unable to bind

Denatured enzyme

(b)

FIGURE 2.18

Denaturation of a globular protein such as an enzyme.
(a) The molecule's globular structure is maintained by intramolecular bonds. Atoms composing the active site of the enzyme are shown as stalked particles. The substrate, or interacting molecule, has a corresponding binding site, and the two sites fit together precisely. **(b)** Breaking the intramolecular bonds that maintain the secondary and tertiary structure of the enzyme results in a linear molecule, with atoms of the former active site widely separated. Enzyme-substrate binding can no longer occur.

Enzymes and Enzyme Activity

Characteristics of Enzymes. **Enzymes** are globular proteins that act as biological catalysts. *Catalysts* are substances that regulate and accelerate the rate of biochemical reactions but are not used up or changed in those reactions. Enzymes cannot force chemical reactions to occur between molecules that would not otherwise react; they can only increase the speed of reaction. We might think of enzymes as molecular "bellows" used to fan a sluggish fire into flaming activity, because without enzymes, biochemical reactions proceed so slowly that for practical pur-

(a) **Noncatalyzed reaction**

(b) **Enzyme-catalyzed reaction**

FIGURE 2.19
Comparison of the energy barrier in a noncatalyzed reaction and in the same reaction catalyzed by an enzyme. In each case, the reacting particles, indicated simply by a ball, must achieve a certain energy level before they can interact. The amount of energy that must be absorbed to reach that state and overcome the energy barrier, represented by the peak, is called activation energy. In **(a)**, the noncatalyzed reaction, the amount of activation energy needed is much higher than that needed in **(b)**, the enzyme-catalyzed reaction.

poses they do not occur at all. Enzymes increase reaction rates by a factor of about 1 million!

Some enzymes are purely protein. In other cases, the functional enzyme consists of two parts, collectively called a **holoenzyme**—an **apoenzyme** (the protein portion) and a **cofactor.** Depending on the enzyme, the cofactor may be an ion of a metal element such as copper or iron, or an organic molecule needed to assist the reaction in some particular way. Most organic cofactors are derived from vitamins (especially the B complex vitamins); this type of cofactor is more precisely called a **coenzyme.**

Each enzyme is highly specific; that is, it controls only a single chemical reaction or a small group of related reactions. The presence of specific enzymes thus determines not only which reactions will be speeded up, but also which reactions will occur—no enzyme, no reaction. This also means that the possibility of unwanted or unnecessary chemical reactions occurring is eliminated. Most enzymes are named for the type of reaction they catalyze. Enzymes called *hydrolases* (hi′droh-lās-es) add water during hydrolysis reactions; *oxidases* (ok′si-dās-es) add oxygen; and so on. Most enzyme names can be recognized by the suffix *-ase.*

Some enzymes are produced in an inactive form that must be activated in some way before they can function. For example, digestive enzymes produced in the pancreas are activated when they reach the small intestine, where they actually do their work. If they were produced in active form, the pancreas would digest itself. Sometimes, enzymes are inactivated immediately after they have performed their catalytic function. This is true of enzymes that promote blood clot formation when the wall of a blood vessel is damaged. Once the clotting process is trig-

gered, those enzymes are inactivated. Otherwise, you would have blood vessels full of solid blood instead of one protective blood clot.

Mechanism of Enzyme Activity. How do enzymes perform their catalytic role? As we said earlier, a chemical reaction cannot occur unless the interacting molecules reach a certain energy level, which is reflected in their speed of movement. More precisely, every reaction requires that a certain amount of energy, called **activation energy,** be absorbed to "prime" the reaction. The activation energy pushes the reactants to an energy level where their random collisions are forceful enough to ensure interaction. This is true regardless of whether the overall reaction is ultimately energy absorbing or energy releasing.

One obvious way to increase molecular energy is to increase the temperature, but in living systems this would result in protein denaturation. (This is why a high fever can be a serious event.) Enzymes allow reactions to occur without abnormal increases in body temperature, and they do this by decreasing the amount of activation energy required (Figure 2.19). Exactly how enzymes accomplish this remarkable feat is not fully understood. However, we know that they decrease the randomness of reactions by binding the reacting molecules temporarily to the enzyme surface and presenting them to each other in the proper position for chemical interaction to occur.

Three basic steps appear to be involved in the mechanism of enzyme action (Figure 2.20).

1. The enzyme must first bind with the substance(s) on which it acts. These substances are called the

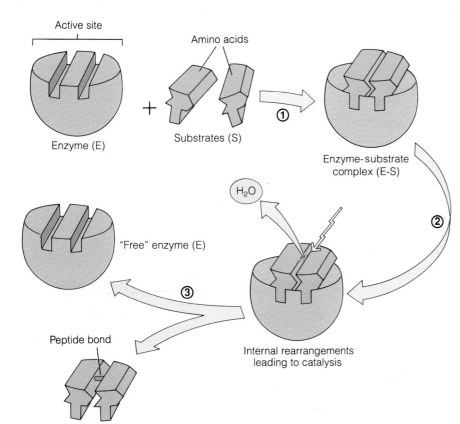

Active site

Amino acids

Enzyme (E)

Substrates (S)

①

Enzyme-substrate complex (E-S)

②

"Free" enzyme (E)

H_2O

③

Internal rearrangements leading to catalysis

Peptide bond

Dipeptide product (P)

FIGURE 2.20

Mechanism of enzyme action. Each enzyme is highly specific in terms of the reaction(s) it can catalyze and bonds properly to only one or a few substrates. In this example, the enzyme catalyzes the formation of a dipeptide from specific amino acids.

Step 1: The enzyme-substrate complex (E-S) is formed.

Step 2: Internal rearrangements occur. In this case, energy is absorbed (indicated by the yellow arrow) as a water molecule is removed and a peptide bond is formed.

Step 3: The enzyme releases the product (P) of the reaction, the dipeptide. The "free" enzyme has not changed in the course of the reaction and is now available to catalyze another such reaction.

Summary: $E + S \rightarrow E\text{-}S \rightarrow P + E$

substrates of the enzyme. Substrate binding occurs at a particular site on the enzyme's surface known as the **active site.** Substrate binding causes the active site to undergo a structural change that allows the substrate and the active site to fit together very precisely. This idea of the dynamic process of enzyme recognition of the proper substrate is called the *induced-fit model.*

2. The enzyme-substrate complex undergoes an internal rearrangement that forms the product.

3. The enzyme releases the product of the reaction. This step shows the catalytic role of the enzyme: If the enzyme became part of the product, it would be a reactant and not a catalyst.

Since the unaltered enzymes can act again and again, cells need only small amounts of each enzyme. Catalysis occurs with incredible speed; most enzymes can catalyze millions of reactions per minute.

Stress Proteins

In the 1970s, scientists discovered that cells subjected to high temperature began to crank out large amounts of proteins originally named **heat-shock proteins (hsp)** that seem to protect them from the destructive effects of heat. Subsequent studies revealed that hsp are also produced in response to a variety of traumatizing stimuli—for example, in the cells of feverish children and in the oxygen-deprived cells of a heart attack patient. As a result, the defensive proteins are now called **stress proteins.** As it turned out, most agents eliciting stress protein synthesis denature proteins. Although the sequence of amino acids in a protein determines the precise way the protein folds, the folding process also requires that stress proteins act as "molecular chaperones" to ensure that the folding is quick and accurate. As stressed and damaged cells accumulate denatured proteins, the "alarm sounds" and the cells synthesize more stress proteins to replace the denatured proteins. In addition, it is now clear that the stress proteins orchestrate the folding process during which proteins achieve their functional 3-D shapes in nontraumatized cells.

Nucleic Acids (DNA and RNA)

The **nucleic** (nu-kle′ic) **acids** include two major classes of molecules, **deoxyribonucleic** (de-ok″sĭ-ri″bo-nu-kle′ik) **acid (DNA)** and **ribonucleic acid (RNA).** Nucleic acids, composed of carbon, oxygen, hydrogen, nitrogen, and phosphorus, are the largest molecules in the body. Their structural units, called **nucleotides,** are quite complex. Each nucleotide con-

FIGURE 2.21
Structure of DNA. (a) The unit of DNA is the nucleotide, which is composed of a deoxyribose sugar molecule linked to a phosphate group, with a base attached to the sugar. Two nucleotides, linked by hydrogen bonds between their complementary bases, are illustrated. **(b)** DNA is a coiled double polymer of nucleotides (a double helix). The backbones of the ladderlike molecule are formed by alternating sugar and phosphate units. The rungs are formed by the binding together of complementary bases (A-T and G-C) by hydrogen bonds (shown by dotted lines). **(c)** Computer-generated image of a DNA molecule.

sists of three components joined together by dehydration synthesis (Figure 2.21a): a nitrogen-containing base, a pentose sugar, and a phosphate group. Five major varieties of nitrogen-containing bases can contribute to nucleotide structure: **adenine** (ad′ĕ-nēn), abbreviated A; **guanine** (gwan′ēn), G; **cytosine** (si′to-sēn), C; **thymine** (thi′mēn), T; and **uracil** (u′rah-sil), U. Adenine and guanine are large, two-ring bases (called purines), whereas cytosine, thymine, and uracil are smaller, single-ring bases (called pyrimidines).

Although DNA and RNA are both composed of nucleotides, they differ in many respects. Typically, DNA is found in the nucleus (control center) of the cell, where it constitutes the genetic material, or genes. DNA has two fundamental roles: It replicates (reproduces) itself before a cell divides, ensuring that the genetic information in the descendent cells is identical, and it provides instructions for building

Table 2.4 Comparison of DNA and RNA		
Characteristic	**DNA**	**RNA**
Major cellular site	Nucleus	Cytoplasm (cell area outside the nucleus)
Major function	Is the genetic material; directs protein synthesis; replicates itself before cell division	Carries out the genetic instructions for protein synthesis
Sugar	Deoxyribose	Ribose
Bases	Adenine, guanine, cytosine, thymine	Adenine, guanine, cytosine, uracil
Structure	Double strand coiled into a double helix	Single straight or folded strand

every protein in the body. By providing the information for protein synthesis, DNA determines what type of organism you will be—frog, human, oak tree—and directs your growth and development. Although we have said that enzymes govern all chemical reactions, remember that enzymes, too, are proteins formed at the direction of DNA. RNA is located chiefly outside the nucleus and can be considered a "molecular slave" of DNA. That is, RNA carries out the orders for protein synthesis issued by DNA. [Viruses in which RNA (rather than DNA) is the genetic material are an exception to this generalization.]

DNA is a long, double-stranded polymer—a double chain of nucleotides (Figure 2.21b and c). The bases in DNA are A, G, C, and T, and its pentose sugar is *deoxyribose* (as reflected in its name). Its two nucleotide chains are held together by hydrogen bonds between the bases, so that a ladderlike molecule is formed. Alternating sugar and phosphate molecules of each chain form the *backbones* or "uprights" of the "ladder," while the joined bases form the "rungs." Bonding of the bases is very specific: A always bonds to T, and G always bonds to C. A and T are therefore called **complementary bases,** as are C and G. A specific base sequence (say, ATGA) on one nucleotide strand would necessarily be bonded to a complementary base sequence (TACT) on the other strand. The whole molecule is coiled into a spiral staircase–like structure called a **double helix.**

RNA molecules are single strands of nucleotides. RNA bases include A, G, C, and U (U replaces the T found in DNA), and its sugar is *ribose* instead of deoxyribose. The three varieties of RNA are distinguished by their relative size and shape, and each has a specific role to play in carrying out DNA's instructions. We discuss DNA replication and the relative roles of DNA and RNA in protein synthesis in Chapter 3. Table 2.4 compares DNA and RNA.

Adenosine Triphosphate (ATP)

Although glucose is the most important cellular fuel, none of the chemical energy contained in its bonds is used directly to power chemical reactions. As mentioned earlier, the energy released during glucose breakdown is captured and stored as small "packets" of energy in the bonds of **adenosine triphosphate** or **ATP**. ATP synthesis is an all-important cellular function because it provides a form of chemical energy that is usable by all body cells.

Structurally, ATP is an adenine-containing RNA nucleotide to which two additional phosphate groups have been added (Figure 2.22). The "extra" phosphate groups are attached by unique chemical bonds called **high-energy phosphate bonds.** Rupturing these high-energy bonds by hydrolysis liberates energy that can be used immediately to power a particular cellular activity. ATP can be compared to a tightly coiled spring ready to uncoil with tremendous energy when the "catch" is released. An advantage of having ATP as the "energy currency" of the cell is that the amount of energy released by breaking its high-energy bonds corresponds closely to that needed to drive most biochemical reactions. As a result, cells are protected from excessive energy release that might be damaging, and energy squandering is kept to a minimum.

FIGURE 2.22
Structure of ATP (adenosine triphosphate). ATP is an adenine nucleotide to which two additional phosphate groups have been attached by high-energy phosphate bonds. (The high-energy phosphate bonds are indicated by the wavy lines.) When the terminal phosphate group is cleaved off, energy is released to do useful work and ADP (adenosine diphosphate) is formed. When the terminal phosphate group is cleaved off ADP, a similar amount of energy is released and AMP (adenosine monophosphate) is formed.

FIGURE 2.23
Three examples of how ATP drives cellular work. The high-energy bonds of ATP are like coiled springs that release energy for use by the cell when they are broken. **(a)** ATP drives the transport of certain solutes (amino acids, for example) across cell membranes. **(b)** ATP activates contractile proteins in muscle cells so that the cells can shorten and perform mechanical work. **(c)** ATP provides the energy required to drive endergonic (energy-absorbing) chemical reactions.

Cleaving the terminal phosphate bond of ATP yields a molecule with two phosphate groups—*adenosine diphosphate (ADP)* and an inorganic phosphate group, indicated by P_i—accompanied by release of energy:

$$ATP \underset{H_2O}{\overset{H_2O}{\rightleftharpoons}} ADP + P_i + Energy$$

As ATP's bonds are broken by hydrolysis to provide energy for cellular needs, ADP accumulates. Sometimes, the second high-energy phosphate bond is also cleaved, liberating a similar amount of energy and producing adenosine monophosphate (AMP). ATP supplies are replenished as glucose and other fuel molecules are oxidized and their bond energy is released. The same amount of energy that is liberated when ATP's terminal phosphates are cleaved off must be captured and used to reverse the reaction to reattach phosphates and re-form the high-energy bonds. Without ATP, molecules cannot be made or degraded, cells cannot transport substances across their membrane boundaries, muscles cannot shorten to tug on other structures, and life processes cease (Figure 2.23).

RELATED CLINICAL TERMS

Acidosis (as"ĭ-do'sis; *acid* = sour, sharp) A condition of acidity or low pH (below 7.35) of the blood; high hydrogen ion concentration.

Alkalosis (al"kah-lo'sis) A condition of basicity or high pH (above 7.45) of the blood; low hydrogen ion concentration.

Heavy metals Metals with toxic effects on the body, including arsenic, mercury, and lead; iron, also included in this group, is toxic in high concentrations.

Ionizing radiation Radiation that causes atoms to ionize, e.g., radioisotopes and X rays.

Ketosis (ke-to'sis) A form of acidosis resulting from excessive ketones (breakdown products of fats) in the blood; common during starvation and acute attacks of diabetes mellitus.

Radiation sickness Disease resulting from exposure of the body to radioactivity; digestive system organs are most affected.

CHAPTER SUMMARY

PART 1: BASIC CHEMISTRY

Definition of Concepts: Matter and Energy (pp. 25–26)

Matter (p. 25)
1. Matter is anything that takes up space and has mass. Energy is the capacity to do work or put matter into motion.

Energy (pp. 25–26)
2. Energy exists as potential energy (stored energy or energy

of position) and kinetic energy (active or working energy).

3. Forms of energy involved in body functioning are chemical, electrical, radiant, and mechanical. Of these, chemical (bond) energy is most important.

4. Energy may be converted from one form to another, but some energy is always unusable (lost as heat) in such transformations.

Composition of Matter: Atoms and Elements (pp. 26–29)

1. Elements are unique substances that cannot be decomposed into simpler substances by ordinary chemical methods. Four elements (carbon, hydrogen, oxygen, and nitrogen) make up 96% of body weight.

Atomic Structure (pp. 26–27)

2. The building blocks of elements are atoms.

3. Atoms are composed of positively charged protons, negatively charged electrons, and uncharged neutrons. Protons and neutrons are located in the atomic nucleus; electrons are outside the nucleus in the electron shells. In any atom, the number of electrons equals the number of protons.

Identifying Elements (pp. 27–29)

4. Atoms may be identified by their atomic number (p^+) and mass number ($p^+ + n^0$). The notation ^4_2He means that helium (He) has an atomic number of 2 and a mass number of 4.

5. Isotopes of an element differ in the number of neutrons they contain. The atomic weight of any element is approximately equal to the mass number of its most abundant isotope.

Radioisotopes (p. 29)

6. Many heavy isotopes are unstable (radioactive) and decompose to more stable forms by emitting α or β particles or γ rays. Radioisotopes are useful in medical diagnosis and treatment and in biochemical research.

How Matter Is Combined: Molecules and Mixtures (pp. 29–31)

Molecules and Compounds (pp. 29–30)

1. A molecule is the smallest unit resulting from the chemical bonding of two or more atoms. If the atoms are different, they form a molecule of a compound.

Mixtures (pp. 30–31)

2. Mixtures are physical combinations of solutes in a solvent. The components of a mixture retain their individual properties.

3. The types of mixtures, in order of increasing solute size, are solutions, colloids, and suspensions.

4. Solution concentrations are typically designated in terms of percent or molarity.

Distinguishing Mixtures from Compounds (p. 31)

5. Compounds are homogeneous; their elements are chemically bonded. Mixtures may be homogeneous or heterogeneous; their components are physically combined and separable.

Chemical Bonds (pp. 31–36)

The Role of Electrons in Chemical Bonding (pp. 31–32)

1. Electrons of an atom occupy areas of space called electron shells or energy levels. Electrons in the shell farthest from the nucleus (valence shell) are most energetic.

2. Chemical bonds are energy relationships between valence shell electrons of the reacting atoms. Atoms with a full valence shell or eight valence shell electrons are chemically unreactive (inert); those with an incomplete valence shell interact with other atoms to achieve a stable electronic configuration.

Types of Chemical Bonds (pp. 32–36)

3. Ionic bonds are formed when valence shell electrons are completely transferred from one atom to another.

4. Covalent bonds are formed when atoms share electron pairs. If the electron pairs are shared equally, the molecule is nonpolar; if they are shared unequally, it is polar (a dipole).

5. Hydrogen bonds are weak bonds formed between hydrogen and nitrogen or hydrogen and oxygen. They bind together different molecules (e.g., water molecules) or different parts of the same molecule (as in protein molecules).

Chemical Reactions (pp. 36–39)

Chemical Equations (p. 36)

1. Chemical reactions involve the formation, breaking, or rearrangement of chemical bonds.

Patterns of Chemical Reactions (pp. 36–37)

2. Chemical reactions include synthesis, decomposition, and exchange reactions. Oxidation-reduction reactions may be considered a special type of exchange (or catabolic) reaction.

Energy Flow in Chemical Reactions (pp. 37–38)

3. Bonds are energy relationships and there is a net loss or gain of energy in every chemical reaction.

4. In exergonic reactions, energy is liberated; in endergonic reactions, energy is absorbed.

Reversibility of Chemical Reactions (p. 38)

5. If reaction conditions remain unchanged, all chemical reactions eventually reach a state of chemical equilibrium in which the reaction proceeds in both directions at the same rate.

6. All chemical reactions are theoretically reversible, but many biological reactions go only in one direction because of energy requirements and/or the removal of reaction products.

Factors Influencing the Rate of Chemical Reactions (pp. 38–39)

7. Chemical reactions occur only when particles collide and valence shell electrons interact.

8. The smaller the reacting particles, the greater their kinetic energy and hence the faster the reaction rate. Increasing the temperature or concentration of the reactants, as well as the presence of catalysts, increases chemical reaction rates.

PART 2: BIOCHEMISTRY: THE COMPOSITION AND REACTIONS OF LIVING MATTER

Inorganic Compounds (pp. 39–42)

1. Most inorganic compounds do not contain carbon. Those found in the body include water, salts, and inorganic acids and bases.

Water (pp. 39–40)

2. Water is the single most abundant compound in the body. It absorbs and releases heat slowly, acts as a universal solvent, participates in chemical reactions, and cushions body organs.

Salts (p. 40)

3. Salts are ionic compounds that dissolve in water and act as electrolytes. Calcium and phosphorus salts contribute to the hardness of bones and teeth. Ions of salts are involved in many physiological processes.

Acids and Bases (pp. 40–42)

4.   Acids are proton donors; in water, they ionize and dissociate, releasing hydrogen ions (which account for their properties) and anions.

5.   Bases are proton acceptors. The most important inorganic bases are the hydroxides; bicarbonate ion and ammonia are important bases in the body.

6.   pH is a measure of hydrogen ion concentration of a solution (in moles per liter). A pH of 7 is neutral; a higher pH is alkaline, and a lower pH is acidic. Normal blood pH is 7.35–7.45. Buffers help to prevent excessive changes in the pH of body fluids.

Organic Compounds (pp. 42–56)

1.   Organic compounds contain carbon. Those found in the body include carbohydrates, lipids, proteins, and nucleic acids, all of which are synthesized by dehydration synthesis and digested by hydrolysis. All of these biological molecules contain C, H, and O. Proteins and nucleic acids also contain N.

Carbohydrates (pp. 43–45)

2.   Carbohydrate building blocks are monosaccharides, the most important of which are hexoses (glucose, fructose, galactose) and pentoses (ribose, deoxyribose).

3.   Disaccharides (sucrose, lactose, maltose) and polysaccharides (starch, glycogen) are composed of linked monosaccharide units.

4.   Carbohydrates, particularly glucose, are the major energy fuel for forming ATP. Excess carbohydrates are stored as glycogen or converted to fat for storage.

Lipids (pp. 45–47)

5.   Lipids dissolve in fats or organic solvents, but not in water.

6.   Neutral fats, composed of fatty acid chains and glycerol, are found chiefly in fatty tissue; they serve as insulation and reserve body fuel.

7.   Phospholipids are modified phosphorus-containing neutral fats that have polar and nonpolar portions. They are found in all plasma membranes.

8.   The steroid cholesterol is found in cell membranes and is the basis of steroid hormones, bile salts, and vitamin D.

Proteins (pp. 47–53)

9.   The unit of proteins is the amino acid; 20 common amino acids are found in the body.

10.   Many amino acids joined by peptide bonds form a polypeptide. A protein (one or more polypeptides) is distinguished by the number and sequence of amino acids in its chain(s) and by the complexity of its three-dimensional structure.

11.   Fibrous proteins, such as keratin and collagen, have secondary (α helix or β-pleated sheet) and perhaps quaternary structure.

12.   Globular proteins (e.g., enzymes, some hormones, antibodies, hemoglobin) achieve tertiary or quaternary structure and are generally spherical, soluble molecules.

13.   Proteins are denatured by extremes of temperature or pH.

Denatured globular proteins are unable to perform their usual function.

14.   Enzymes, biological catalysts, increase the rate of chemical reactions by decreasing the amount of activation energy needed. They do this by combining with the reactants and holding them in the proper position to interact. Many enzymes require cofactors to function.

15.   Stress proteins orchestrate folding of proteins into their functional 3-D shape. They are synthesized in greater amounts when cells are stressed by environmental factors and begin to accumulate denatured proteins.

Nucleic Acids (DNA and RNA) (pp. 53–55)

16.   Nucleic acids include deoxyribonucleic acid (DNA) and ribonucleic acid (RNA). The structural unit of nucleic acids is the nucleotide, which consists of a nitrogenous base (adenine, guanine, cytosine, thymine, or uracil), a sugar (ribose or deoxyribose), and a phosphate group.

17.   DNA is a double-stranded helix: it contains deoxyribose and the bases A, G, C, and T. DNA specifies protein structure and replicates itself exactly before cell division.

18.   RNA is single-stranded; it contains ribose and the bases A, G, C, and U. RNA is involved in carrying out DNA's instructions for protein synthesis.

Adenosine Triphosphate (ATP) (pp. 55–56)

19.   ATP is the universal energy compound of body cells. Some of the energy liberated by the breakdown of glucose and other food fuels is captured in the bonds of ATP molecules and transferred to energy-consuming reactions.

REVIEW QUESTIONS

Multiple Choice/Matching

1.   Which of the following forms of energy are in use during vision? (a) chemical, (b) electrical, (c) mechanical, (d) radiant.

2.   All of the following are examples of the four major elements contributing to body mass except (a) hydrogen, (b) carbon, (c) nitrogen, (d) sodium, (e) oxygen.

3.   The mass number of an atom is (a) equal to the number of protons it contains, (b) the sum of its protons and neutrons, (c) the sum of all of its subatomic particles, (d) the average of the mass numbers of all of its isotopes.

4.   A deficiency in this element can be expected to reduce the hemoglobin content of blood: (a) Fe, (b) I, (c) F, (d) Ca, (e) K.

5.   Which set of terms best describes a proton? (a) negative charge, massless, in the orbital; (b) positive charge, 1 amu, in the nucleus; (c) uncharged, 1 amu, in the nucleus.

6.   The subatomic particles responsible for the chemical behavior of atoms are (a) electrons, (b) ions, (c) neutrons, (d) protons.

7.   Which of the following are molecules of a compound? (a) N_2, (b) C, (c) $C_6H_{12}O_6$, (d) NaOH, (e) S_8.

8.   Which of the following does *not* describe a mixture? (a) Properties of its components are retained, (b) chemical bonds are formed, (c) components can be separated physically, (d) includes both heterogeneous and homogeneous examples.

9. A mixture that is homogeneous and transparent and does not scatter light is (a) a true solution, (b) a colloid, (c) a compound, (d) a suspension.

10. When a pair of electrons are shared between two atoms, the bond formed is called (a) a single covalent bond, (b) a double covalent bond, (c) a triple covalent bond, (d) an ionic bond.

11. Molecules formed when electrons are shared unequally are (a) salts, (b) polar molecules, (c) nonpolar molecules.

12. Which of the following covalently bonded molecules are polar?

(a) $H—Cl$ (b) $H—\overset{\displaystyle H}{\underset{\displaystyle H}{\overset{|}{\underset{|}{C}}}}—H$ (c) $Cl—\overset{\displaystyle H}{\underset{\displaystyle Cl}{\overset{|}{\underset{|}{C}}}}—Cl$ (d) $N{=}N$

13. Identify each reaction as (a) a synthesis reaction, (b) a decomposition reaction, or (c) an exchange reaction.

(1) $2\,Hg + O_2 \rightarrow 2\,HgO$

(2) $HCl + NaOH \rightarrow NaCl + H_2O$

14. Factors that accelerate the rate of chemical reactions include all but (a) the presence of catalysts, (b) increasing the temperature, (c) decreasing the temperature, (d) increasing the concentration of the reactants.

15. Which of the following molecules is an inorganic molecule? (a) sucrose, (b) cholesterol, (c) collagen, (d) sodium chloride.

16. Water's importance to living systems reflects (a) its polarity and solvent properties, (b) its high heat capacity, (c) its high heat of vaporization, (d) its chemical reactivity, (e) all of these.

17. Acids (a) release hydroxyl ions when dissolved in water, (b) are proton acceptors, (c) cause the pH of a solution to rise, (d) release protons when dissolved in water.

18. A chemist, during the course of an analysis, runs across a chemical that he determines to be composed of carbon, hydrogen, and oxygen in the proportion 1:2:1 and to have six-sided molecular shape. It is probably (a) a pentose, (b) an amino acid, (c) a fatty acid, (d) a monosaccharide, (e) a nucleic acid.

19. A neutral fat consists of (a) glycerol plus up to three fatty acids, (b) a sugar-phosphate backbone to which two amino groups are attached, (c) two to several hexoses, (d) amino acids that have been thoroughly saturated with hydrogen.

20. A chemical has an amine group and an organic acid group. It does not, however, have any peptide bonds. It is (a) a monosaccharide, (b) an amino acid, (c) a protein, (d) a fat.

21. The lipid(s) used as the basis of vitamin D, sex hormones, and bile salts is/are (a) neutral fats, (b) cholesterol, (c) phospholipids, (d) prostaglandin.

22. Enzymes are organic catalysts that (a) alter the direction in which a chemical reaction proceeds, (b) determine the nature of the products of a reaction, (c) increase the speed of a chemical reaction, (d) are essential raw materials for a chemical reaction that are converted into some of its products.

Short Answer Essay Questions

23. Define or describe energy, and explain the relationship between potential and kinetic energy.

24. Some energy is lost in every energy conversion. Explain the meaning of this statement. (Direct your response to answer-

ing the question, Is it really lost? If not, what then?)

25. Provide the atomic symbol for each of the following elements: (a) calcium, (b) carbon, (c) hydrogen, (d) iron, (e) nitrogen, (f) oxygen, (g) potassium, (h) sodium.

26. Consider the following information about three atoms:

$$^{12}_{6}C \qquad ^{13}_{6}C \qquad ^{14}_{6}C$$

(a) How are they similar to one another? (b) How do they differ from one another? (c) What are the members of such a group of atoms called? (d) Using the planetary model, draw the atomic configuration of $^{12}_{6}C$ showing the relative position and numbers of its subatomic particles.

27. How many moles of aspirin, $C_9H_8O_4$, are there in a bottle containing 450 g by weight? (*Note:* The approximate atomic weights of its atoms are $C = 12$, $H = 1$, and $O = 16$.)

28. Given the following types of atoms, decide which type of bonding, ionic or covalent, is most likely to occur: (a) two oxygen atoms; (b) four hydrogen atoms and one carbon atom; (c) a potassium atom ($^{39}_{19}K$) and a fluorine atom ($^{19}_{9}F$).

29. What are hydrogen bonds and how are they important in the body?

30. The following equation, which represents the oxidative breakdown of glucose by body cells, is a reversible reaction.

$$glucose + oxygen \rightarrow carbon\ dioxide + water + ATP$$

(a) How can you indicate that the reaction is reversible? (b) How can you indicate that the reaction is in chemical equilibrium? (c) Define chemical equilibrium.

31. (a) Differentiate clearly between primary, secondary, and tertiary protein structure. (b) What level of structure do most fibrous proteins achieve? (c) How do globular proteins relate to the structural levels?

32. Dehydration and hydrolysis reactions are essentially opposite reactions. How are they related to the synthesis and degradation (breakdown) of biological molecules?

33. Describe the mechanism of enzyme activity. In your discussion, explain how enzymes decrease activation energy requirements.

34. Explain the importance of stress proteins.

 ## CRITICAL THINKING AND CLINICAL APPLICATION QUESTIONS

1. As Ben jumped on his bike and headed for the fresh-water lake, his mother called after him "Don't swim if we have an electrical storm—it looks threatening." This was a valid request. Why?

2. Some antibiotics act by binding to certain essential enzymes in the target bacteria. (a) How might these antibiotics influence the chemical reactions controlled by the enzymes? (b) What is the anticipated effect on the bacteria? On the person taking the antibiotic prescription?

3. Mrs. Roberts, in a diabetic coma, has just been admitted to Noble Hospital. Her blood pH indicates that she is in severe acidosis, and measures are quickly instituted to bring her blood pH back within normal limits. (a) Define pH and note the normal pH of blood. (b) Why is severe acidosis problematic?

3

Cells:
The Living Units

CHAPTER OUTLINE AND STUDENT OBJECTIVES

Overview of the Cellular Basis of Life (pp. 60–61)

1. Define cell.

2. List the three major regions of a generalized cell and indicate the general function of each region.

The Plasma Membrane: Structure (pp. 61–65)

3. Describe the chemical composition of the plasma membrane.

4. Compare the structure and function of tight junctions, desmosomes, and gap junctions.

The Plasma Membrane: Functions (pp. 65–75)

5. Relate plasma membrane structure to active and passive transport mechanisms. Differentiate clearly between these transport processes relative to energy source, substances transported, direction, and mechanism.

6. Define membrane potential and explain how the resting membrane potential is maintained.

7. Describe the role of the plasma membrane glycocalyx in cells' interactions with their environment.

The Cytoplasm (pp. 75–84)

8. Describe the composition of the cytosol; define inclusions and list several types.

9. Discuss the structure and function of mitochondria.

10. Discuss the structure and function of ribosomes, the endoplasmic reticulum, and the Golgi apparatus; note functional interrelationships among these organelles.

11. Compare the functions of lysosomes and peroxisomes.

12. Name and describe the structure and function of cytoskeletal elements.

13. Describe the roles of centrioles in mitosis and in formation of cilia and flagella.

The Nucleus (pp. 84–86)

14. Describe the chemical composition, structure, and function of the nuclear membrane, nucleolus, and chromatin.

Cell Growth and Reproduction (pp. 86–95)

15. List the phases of the cell life cycle and describe the events of each phase.

16. Describe the process of DNA replication. Explain the importance of this process.

17. Define gene and explain the function of genes. Also explain the meaning of "genetic code."

18. Name the two phases of protein synthesis and describe the roles of DNA, mRNA, tRNA, and rRNA in each phase. Contrast triplets, codons, and anticodons.

Extracellular Materials (pp. 95–96)

19. Name and describe the composition of extracellular materials.

Developmental Aspects of Cells (pp. 96–98)

20. Discuss some of the theories of cell aging.

All living organisms are cellular in nature, from one-celled "generalists" like amoebas to complex multicellular organisms such as humans, dogs, or trees. Just as bricks and timbers are the structural units of a house, **cells** are the structural units of all living things. The human body has 50 to 60 trillion of these tiny building blocks.

This chapter focuses on structures and functions shared by all of our cells. Specialized cells and their unique functions are considered in detail in later chapters.

OVERVIEW OF THE CELLULAR BASIS OF LIFE

The English scientist Robert Hooke first observed plant cells with a crude microscope in the late 1600s. However, it was not until the mid-1800s that two German scientists, Matthias Schleiden and Theodor Schwann, were bold enough to assert that all living things are composed of cells. The German pathologist Rudolf Virchow extended this idea by contending that cells arise only from other cells. Virchow's proclamation was a landmark in biological history because it challenged the widely accepted *theory of spontaneous generation,* which held that organisms arise spontaneously from garbage or other nonliving matter. Since the late 1800s, cell research has been exceptionally fruitful, and our present understanding of the cell provides us with four concepts collectively known as the **cell theory:**

1. A cell is the basic structural and functional unit of living organisms. So, when you define the properties of a cell you are in fact defining the properties of life.

2. The activity of an organism is dependent on both the individual and collective activities of its cells.

3. According to the **principle of complementarity,** the biochemical activities of cells are determined and made possible by the specific subcellular structures of cells.

4. Continuity of life has a cellular basis.

All of these concepts will be expanded on, but for now let us consider the idea that the cell is the minimum amount of matter that is alive. This means that the cell is the fundamental unit from which the biological hierarchy is fashioned and on which life processes depend. Whatever its form, however it behaves, the cell is the microscopic package that contains all the parts necessary to survive in an ever-changing world. Indeed, loss of cellular homeostasis underlies virtually every disease that can confront us.

Perhaps the most striking property of a cell is its complex organization. Chemically, cells are composed chiefly of carbon, hydrogen, nitrogen, oxygen, and trace amounts of several other elements. These substances are found in the air around us and the ground beneath our feet, but within the cell they take on the special characteristics of life. Life, then, relates to the way living matter is organized and carries out metabolic processes—considerations far beyond chemical composition.

The trillions of cells in the human body include some 200 different types that are amazingly diverse in shape, size, and function. The spherical fat cells, disc-shaped red blood cells, branching nerve cells, and cubelike cells of kidney tubules are just a few examples of the shapes cells take. Depending on type, cells also vary greatly in length—ranging from 2 micrometers (1/12,000 of an inch) in the smallest cells to over a meter in the nerve cells that cause you to wiggle your toes. A cell's shape reflects its function. For example, the flat, tilelike epithelial cells that line the inside of your cheek fit closely together, forming a living barrier that protects underlying tissues from bacterial invasion.

Although no one cell type is exactly like all others, cells *do* have the same basic parts and there are certain functions common to all cells. Thus, it is possible to speak of a **generalized,** or **composite, cell** as a mental aid for introducing cell parts and components (Figure 3.1). Human cells have three major parts: a nucleus, cytoplasm (with cytoplasmic organelles), and a plasma membrane. The *nucleus* (nu′kle-us), which controls cell activities, is usually centrally located. The nucleus is surrounded by *cytoplasm* (si′to-plazm), which is packed with *organelles* (or″gah-nelz′), small structures that perform specific functions in the cell. The cytoplasm is enclosed by the *plasma membrane,* which forms the outer cell boundary. Functions of the various cell structures are summarized in Table 3.2 (p. 76) and described in detail later in the chapter.

THE PLASMA MEMBRANE: STRUCTURE

The flexible **plasma membrane** defines the extent of the cell and acts as a fragile barrier. (The term *cell membrane* is often used instead, but since nearly all cellular organelles are membranous, we will specifically designate the cell's surface or outer limiting membrane as the plasma membrane.) Although the plasma membrane is important in maintaining the integrity of the cell, it is much more than a passive envelope. As you will see, its unique structure allows it to play a dynamic role in many cellular activities.

The Fluid Mosaic Model

The **fluid mosaic model** of membrane structure (Figure 3.2) depicts the plasma membrane as an exceedingly thin (7–8 nm) but stable structure composed of a double layer, or bilayer, of phospholipid molecules with protein molecules dispersed in it. The proteins, which float in the fluid lipid bilayer, form a constantly changing mosaic pattern; hence the name of the model.

The lipid bilayer, constructed largely of phospholipids, forms the basic "fabric" of the membrane and is relatively impermeable to most water-soluble molecules. As explained in Chapter 2, phospholipids are lollipoplike molecules with a polar phosphorus-containing *"head,"* attached to a nonpolar *"tail"* made of two hydrocarbon fatty acid chains. The polar head interacts with water and is said to be **hydrophilic** (hi″dro-fil′ik), literally, "water loving" (*hydro* = water; *phil* = like, love). The nonpolar tail interacts only with other nonpolar substances, avoiding water and charged particles; this end is **hydrophobic** (hi″dro-fo′bik; *phob* = dislike, fear). Because of these phospholipid properties, all biological membranes share a common basic structure: They are "sandwiches" composed of two parallel sheets of phospholipid molecules lying tail to tail, with their polar heads exposed to water inside and outside the cell. This self-orienting property of phospholipids allows a biological membrane to self-assemble into closed, generally spherical, structures. It also enables a cell to reseal (repair) itself quickly when torn.

? *As you can see in this diagram of the cell, most organelles are membrane bound. What possible advantage does such a situation provide?*

Basal body
Nucleolus
Nucleus
Chromatin
Nuclear envelope
Centriole
Vacuole
Microtubules
Lysosome
Golgi apparatus
Secretion being released from cell by exocytosis
Cytosol
Peroxisome

Flagellum
Smooth endoplasmic reticulum
Rough endoplasmic reticulum
Plasma membrane
Ribosomes
Microvilli
Mitochondrion
Microfilament

FIGURE 3.1
Structure of the generalized cell. No cell is exactly like this one, but this composite illustrates features common to many human cells. Note that the organelles are not drawn to the same scale in this illustration.

The inner and outer layers of the membrane differ somewhat in the specific kinds of phospholipids they contain. About 10% of the externally facing phospholipid molecules have attached sugar groups (see Figure 3.2) and are called *glycolipids* (gli″ko-lip′idz). The membrane also contains substantial amounts of cholesterol. Cholesterol stabilizes the lipid membrane by wedging its platelike hydrocarbon rings between the phospholipid tails and immobilizing parts of them. Since this also prevents the phospholipids from aggregating, it helps keep the membrane fluid.

There are two distinct populations of membrane proteins, integral and peripheral (see Figure 3.2). Proteins make up about half of the membrane by weight and are responsible for most of the specialized functions of the plasma membrane (Figure 3.3). **Integral proteins** are firmly inserted in the lipid bilayer. Some face the aqueous environment on one membrane side only; those that face the external environment are usually receptors for hormones or other chemical messengers. Most, however, are *transmembrane proteins* that span the entire width of the membrane and protrude on both sides. Whether they extend entirely

through the membrane or not, all integral proteins have both hydrophobic and hydrophilic regions. This structural feature allows them to interact with the nonpolar tails of the lipids buried in the membrane interior and with water inside and outside the cell. Transmembrane proteins are mainly involved in transport functions (see Figure 3.3). Some cluster together to form channels, or pores, through which small, water-soluble molecules or ions can move, thus bypassing the lipid part of the membrane. Others act as carriers that bind to a substance and move it through the membrane.

Peripheral proteins are not embedded in the lipid at all. Instead, they are usually appended to exposed parts of integral proteins on the internal aspect of the membrane. Some peripheral proteins are enzymes. Others are involved in mechanical functions, such as the changes in cell shape that occur during cell division and the contraction of muscle cells.

Branching sugar groups are attached to most of the proteins that abut the extracellular space. The term **glycocalyx** (gli″ko-kal′iks; "sugar cup") is used to describe the fuzzy, somewhat sticky carbohydrate-

? *Some membrane proteins float freely in the lipid phase of the membrane. Others are secured in specific locations. According to this diagram, what would serve as the anchoring structures in the latter case?*

FIGURE 3.2
Structure of the plasma membrane according to the fluid mosaic model.

rich area at the cell surface; you can think of your cells as being "sugar-coated." The glycocalyx is also enriched by glycoproteins that have been secreted by the cell and then cling to its surface, and by the glycolipids mentioned above. The stickiness of the glycocalyx helps bind adjacent cells together. Because every cell type has a different pattern of sugars in its glycocalyx, the glycocalyx provides highly specific biological markers by which cells recognize each other. For example, a sperm recognizes the ovum (egg cell) by the unique nature of the ovum's glycocalyx, liver phagocytes that dispose of aging red blood cells recognize their "prey" because such blood cells have fewer sugars in their glycocalyx, and cells of the immune system identify bacteria and virus particles by binding to certain membrane glycoproteins. These matters are discussed in greater detail on p. 74.

Definite changes in the glycocalyx occur in a cell that is becoming transformed into a cancerous cell.

In fact, a cancer cell's glycocalyx may change almost continuously, allowing it to keep ahead of immune system recognition mechanisms and avoid destruction. (Cancer is discussed later in this chapter.) •

The plasma membrane is a dynamic fluid structure that is in a constant state of flux. It's consistency is like that of olive oil. The lipid molecules are free to move laterally (side to side), but their polar-nonpolar interactions prevent them from flip-flopping or moving from one lipid layer to the other. Some of the proteins float freely, while others, particularly the peripheral proteins, are more restricted in their movements. These restricted proteins appear to be "tethered" to intercellular structures that make up the *cytoskeleton.* This anchoring network helps to support the cytoplasmic side of the plasma membrane; without it, the membrane would break up into many tiny sacs.

Transport proteins (a) A protein that spans the membrane may provide a hydrophilic channel across the membrane that is selective for a particular solute. (b) Some transport proteins hydrolyze ATP as an energy source to actively pump substances across the membrane.

(a) **(b)** ATP

Enzymes A protein built into the membrane may be an enzyme with its active site exposed to substances in the adjacent solution. In some cases, several enzymes in a membrane act as a team that catalyzes sequential steps of a metabolic pathway as indicated (right to left) here.

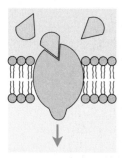

Proteins as receptor sites A membrane protein exposed to the outside of the cell may have a binding site that complements the shape of a chemical messenger, such as a hormone. If the receptor protein spans the membrane, the external signal may induce a conformational change in the protein that initiates a chain of chemical reactions in the cell.

Cell adhesion Membrane proteins of adjacent cells may be hooked together in various kinds of intercellular junctions. Some membrane proteins of this group provide temporary binding sites that guide cell migration and other cell-to-cell interactions.

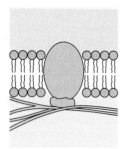

Attachment to the cytoskeleton Elements of the cytoskeleton (cell's internal supports) may be attached to membrane proteins, a function that is important in maintaining cell shape and in fixing the location of certain membrane proteins.

FIGURE 3.3
Some functions of membrane proteins. A single protein may perform some combination of these tasks; for example, a receptor protein may also be secured in a specific location on the cell exterior by its attachments to the cytoskeleton.

Specializations of the Plasma Membrane

Microvilli

Microvilli (mi″kro-vil′i; "little shaggy hairs") are minute, fingerlike extensions of the plasma membrane that project from a free, or exposed, cell surface (see Figure 3.1). They increase the plasma membrane surface area tremendously and are most often found on the surface of absorptive cells such as kidney tubule and intestinal cells. Microvilli have a core of actin filaments. Actin is a contractile protein, but in microvilli it appears to function as a mechanical "stiffener."

Membrane Junctions

Although certain cell types—blood cells, sperm cells, and some phagocytic cells—are "footloose" within the body, many cells, particularly those of epithelial tissues, are knit into tight communities. Typically, three factors act to bind cells closely together. First, there are adhesive glycoproteins in the glycocalyx. Second, the plasma membranes of adjacent cells are wavy and fit together in a tongue-and-groove fashion. Third, and most important, are the special membrane junctions described next.

Tight Junctions. In **tight junctions,** protein molecules in adjacent plasma membranes fuse together tightly like a zipper, forming an impermeable junction that encircles the cell (Figure 3.4a). Tight junctions prevent molecules from passing through the extracellular space between adjacent cells of an epithelial membrane. For example, tight junctions between epithelial cells lining the digestive tract keep digestive enzymes and microorganisms in the intestine from seeping into the bloodstream.

Desmosomes. Desmosomes (des′mo-sōmz; "binding bodies") are mechanical couplings or adhesive spots scattered like rivets along the sides of abutting cells that prevent their separation. Desmosomes have a complicated structure (Figure 3.4b). On the cytoplasmic face of each plasma membrane is a buttonlike thickening called a *plaque.* Adjacent cells do not actually touch, but are held together by thin *linker proteins* which extend from the plaques to span the intercellular space. Thicker keratin filaments (which form part of the cytoskeleton) extend from the cytoplasmic side of the plaque across the width of the cell to anchor to the plaque on its opposite side. Thus, desmosomes not only bind adjacent cells together, they also contribute to a continuous network of strong "guy-wires," many of which extend from cell to cell. This arrangement helps to distribute tension throughout a cellular sheet and reduces its chance of tearing when it is exposed to pulling forces. Desmosomes are abundant in tissues

FIGURE 3.4
Cell junctions. An epithelial cell is shown joined to adjacent cells by three common types of cell junctions: tight junctions, desmosomes, and gap junctions. Each junction type is also illustrated by a corresponding transmission electron micrograph: (**a**) tight junction (29,000×); (**b**) desmosome (72,000×); (**c**) gap junction (134,000×).

subjected to great mechanical stress, such as skin, heart muscle, and the neck of the uterus.

Gap Junctions. The basic function of **gap junctions** is to allow direct passage of chemical substances between adjacent cells. At gap junctions, the adjacent plasma membranes are very close, and the cells are connected by hollow cylinders, called *connexons* (kŏ-nek′sonz), composed of transmembrane proteins. Ions, sugars, and other small molecules pass through these channels from one cell to the next (Figure 3.4c). Gap junctions between embryonic cells are vital in distributing nutrients before the circulatory system is established. In adult tissues, gap junctions exist in electrically excitable tissues, such as the heart and smooth muscle, where passage of ions from cell to cell helps synchronize their electrical activity and contraction.

THE PLASMA MEMBRANE: FUNCTIONS

Membrane Transport

Our cells are continuously bathed in an extracellular fluid called **interstitial** (in″ter-stish′al) **fluid** that is derived from the blood. Interstitial fluid can be thought of as a rich, nutritious, and rather unusual "soup." It contains thousands of ingredients, including amino acids, sugars, fatty acids, vitamins, regulatory substances such as hormones and neurotransmitters, salts, and waste products. To remain healthy, each cell must extract from this soup the exact amounts of the substances it needs at specific times and reject the rest.

The plasma membrane is a **selectively,** or **differentially, permeable** barrier, meaning that it allows some

FIGURE 3.5
Diffusion. Molecules in solution move continuously and collide constantly with other molecules. As a result, molecules tend to move away from areas of their highest concentration and become evenly distributed, as illustrated by the diffusion of sugar molecules in a cup of coffee.

substances to pass while excluding others. Thus, it allows nutrients to enter the cell, but keeps many undesirable substances out. At the same time, valuable cell proteins and other substances are kept within the cell, and wastes are allowed to pass out of it.

Selective permeability is a characteristic of healthy, intact cells. When the cell (or its plasma membrane) is severely damaged, the membrane becomes permeable to virtually everything, and substances flow into and out of cells freely. This phenomenon is evident when someone has been severely burned. Precious fluids, proteins, and ions "weep" from the dead and damaged cells of the burned areas. •

Movement of substances through the plasma membrane happens in essentially two ways—passively or actively. In **passive processes,** substances penetrate the membrane without any energy input from the cell. In **active processes,** the cell provides the metabolic energy (ATP) that drives the transport process to move the substance across the membrane. The various transport processes that occur in cells are summarized in Table 3.1. Now let's examine how each of these types of membrane transport works.

Passive Processes: Diffusion

Diffusion (di-fu'zhun) is an important means of passive membrane transport for every cell of the body. (By contrast, the other passive transport process, *filtration,* generally occurs only across capillary walls.) **Diffusion** is the tendency of molecules or ions to scatter evenly throughout the environment (Figure 3.5). Recall that all molecules possess kinetic energy and are in constant motion (see Chapter 2, p. 25). As molecules move about randomly at high speeds, they collide and ricochet off one another, changing direction with each collision. Since the overall effect of this erratic movement is that molecules move away from areas where they are in greater concentration to areas where their concentration is lower, we say that molecules diffuse *along,* or *down,* their **concentration gradient.** The greater the difference in concentration between the two areas, the faster the net diffusion of the particles.

Because the driving force (energy source) is the kinetic energy of the molecules themselves, the speed of diffusion is also influenced by the size of molecules (the smaller, the faster) and by temperature (the warmer, the faster). In a closed container, diffusion will eventually produce a uniform mixture of the different kinds of molecules. In other words, the system reaches equilibrium, with molecules moving equally in all directions (no net movement). Examples of diffusion are familiar to everyone. When you peel onions, you get teary-eyed because the cut onion releases volatile substances that diffuse through the air, dissolve in the fluid film covering your eyes, and form irritating sulfuric acid.

Because of its hydrophobic interior, the plasma membrane is a physical barrier to free diffusion. However, a molecule will diffuse passively through the plasma membrane if it is (1) lipid soluble, (2) small enough to pass through membrane pores, or (3) assisted by a carrier molecule. The unassisted diffusion of lipid-soluble or very small particles is called *simple diffusion.* A special name is given to the unassisted diffusion of water; it is called *osmosis* (oz-mo'-sis; *osmos* = pushing). Assisted diffusion is known as *facilitated diffusion.*

Simple Diffusion. Substances that are nonpolar and lipid soluble move easily into and out of the cell by diffusing directly through the lipid bilayer (Figure 3.6a). Such substances include oxygen, carbon dioxide, fats, urea, and alcohol. Since oxygen is always in higher concentration in the blood than in tissue cells, oxygen continuously moves into the cells, whereas carbon dioxide (in higher concentration within the cells) diffuses from cells into the blood. Most water-soluble particles are unable to diffuse through the lipid bilayer because they are repelled by its core of nonpolar hydrocarbon chains.

Polar and charged particles that are insoluble in the lipid bilayer can diffuse through the membrane if they are small enough to pass through the water-filled pores constructed by the channel proteins (Figure 3.6a). Pore size varies, but it is estimated to be no more than 0.8 nm in diameter, and the channels tend to be selective. For example, sodium channels allow only sodium ions to pass. Additionally, while some pores are always open, others can be opened or closed in response to various chemical or electrical signals.

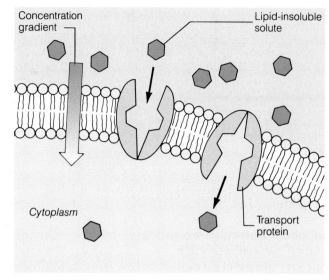

(a) Simple diffusion

(b) Facilitated diffusion

FIGURE 3.6
Diffusion through the plasma membrane. (a) Simple diffusion. As depicted on the left, fat-soluble molecules diffuse directly through the lipid bilayer of the

plasma membrane, in which they can dissolve. On the right, small polar or charged particles (water molecules or small ions) are shown diffusing through the membrane channels constructed by channel proteins.

(**b**) Facilitated diffusion moves large, lipid-insoluble molecules (e.g., glucose) across the membrane. The substance to be transported binds to a transmembrane carrier protein.

Osmosis. The diffusion of a solvent, such as water, through a selectively permeable membrane like the plasma membrane is called **osmosis.** Since water is highly polar, it is restricted from passing through the lipid bilayer, but it is small enough to move easily through the pores of most plasma membranes. Osmosis occurs whenever there is a difference in water concentration on the two sides of the membrane. We will use some examples from nonliving systems to illustrate the process of osmosis and then describe osmosis across living membranes.

If distilled water is present on both sides of a selectively permeable membrane, no net osmosis occurs, even though water molecules continue to move in both directions through the membrane. If, however, the solute concentration on the two sides of the membrane differs, water concentration differs as well, because as solute concentration increases, water concentration decreases. The extent to which water's concentration is decreased by solutes *depends on the number not the type* of solute particles in a solution, because one molecule or one ion of solute (theoretically) displaces one water molecule. The total concentration of all solute particles in a solution is referred to as the solution's **osmolarity** (oz″mo-lar′ĭ-te). When equal volumes of solutions of different osmolarity are separated by a membrane that is permeable to *all* molecules in the system, net diffusion of both solute and water occurs, each moving down its own concentration gradient (Figure 3.7a). Eventually, equilibrium will be reached, and the water and solute concentrations will be the same in both compartments. If we consider the same system, but make

the membrane impermeable to the solute molecules, we see quite a different result (Figure 3.7b). Water quickly diffuses from compartment 1 into compartment 2 and continues to do so until its concentration (and that of the solution) is the same on both sides of the membrane. Notice that in this case equilibrium results from the movement of water alone (the solutes are prevented from moving) and leads to dramatic changes in the volumes of the two compartments.

The last example considered is similar to the osmotic events that occur across plasma membranes of living cells, with one major difference. In our examples, the volumes of the compartments are infinitely expandable and the effect of pressure exerted by the added weight of the higher fluid column is not considered. In living plant cells, which have rigid cell walls external to their plasma membranes, this is not the case. As water diffuses into the cell, the point is finally reached where the **hydrostatic pressure** (the back pressure exerted by water against the membrane) within the cell is equal to its **osmotic pressure**—its tendency to resist further (net) water entry. As a rule, the higher the amount of nondiffusible (or nonpenetrable) solutes within the cell, the higher the osmotic pressure and the greater the hydrostatic pressure that must be developed to resist further net water entry.

However, such major changes in hydrostatic (and osmotic) pressures do not occur in living animal cells, which lack rigid cell walls and are surrounded only by flexible plasma membranes. Osmotic imbalances cause animal cells to swell or shrink (due to net water gain or loss) until the solute concentration on

FIGURE 3.7
Influence of membrane permeability on diffusion and osmosis. **(a)** In this system, the membrane is permeable to both water and solute (sugar) molecules. Water moves from the solution with lower osmolarity (compartment 1) to the solution with greater osmolarity (compartment 2). The solute moves along its own concentration gradient in the opposite direction. When the system comes to equilibrium (right), the solutions have the same osmolarity and volume. **(b)** This system is identical to that in (a) except that the membrane is impermeable to the solute. Water moves by osmosis from compartment 1 to compartment 2, until its concentration and that of the solutions are identical. Since the solute is prevented from moving, the volume of the solution in compartment 2 increases.

both sides of the plasma membrane is the same (reaches equilibrium), or the membrane is stretched to its breaking point. This leads us to the important concept of *tonicity* (to-nis′ĭ-te). As noted, many molecules, particularly intracellular proteins and selected ions, are prevented from diffusing through the plasma membrane. Consequently, any changes in their concentration produce changes in water concentration on the two sides of the membrane and result in net loss or gain of water by the cell. The ability of a solution to change the tone or shape of cells by altering their internal water volume is called **tonicity** (*tono* = tension). Solutions with concentrations of nonpenetrating solutes equal to those found in cells (0.9% saline or 5% glucose) are **isotonic** (literally, "the same tonicity"). Cells exposed to such solutions retain their normal shape, and exhibit no net loss or gain of water (Figure 3.8a). As you might expect, extracellular fluids of the body and most intravenous solutions (solutions infused into the body via a vein) are isotonic. Solutions that have a higher concentration of nonpenetrating solutes than the cell are **hypertonic.** Cells immersed in hypertonic solutions lose water by osmosis, which causes them to shrink, or *crenate* (kre′nāt) (Figure 3.8b). Solutions that are more dilute (contain fewer nonpenetrating solutes) than cells are called **hypotonic.** Cells placed in hypotonic solutions plump up rapidly as water rushes into them (Figure 3.8c). Distilled water represents the most extreme example of hypotonicity. Because it contains *no* solutes, water continues to enter cells until they finally burst or *lyse.*

Hypertonic solutions are sometimes infused intravenously into the bloodstream of edematous patients (those swollen because of water retained in their tissues) to draw the excess water out of the extracellular space and move it into the bloodstream so that it can be eliminated by the kidneys. Hypotonic solutions may be used (with care) to rehydrate the tissues of extremely dehydrated patients. In less extreme cases of dehydration, drinking hypotonic fluids usually does the trick. (Many fluids that healthy humans tend to drink regularly, such as tea, colas, apple juice, and sports drinks, are hypotonic.) •

Notice that osmolarity and tonicity are not the same. The key factor in determining tonicity is the nonpenetrating solutes, whereas osmolarity considers the total solute spectrum. Osmolarity is expressed as osmoles per liter (osmol/L); 1 osmol is equal to 1 mole of nonionizing molecules.* A 0.3 osmol/L solution of NaCl is isotonic because sodium ions are usually prevented from diffusing freely through the plasma membrane. But if the cell is immersed in a 0.3 osmol/L solution of a penetrating solute, the solute will enter the cell and water will follow. The cell will then swell and burst, just as if it had been placed in pure water.

Osmotic water flows are extremely important in determining the distribution of water in the various fluid-containing compartments of the body (cells, interstitial fluid, blood, etc.). In general, osmosis continues until pressures acting at the membrane (osmotic and hydrostatic pressures) are equal. For example, water is forced out of capillary blood by the hydrostatic pressure of the blood against the capillary wall, but the presence in the blood of solutes that are

*Osmolarity (Osm) is determined by multiplying molarity (*M*) by the number of particles resulting from ionization. For example, since NaCl ionizes to Na$^+$ + Cl$^-$, a 1 *M* solution of NaCl is a 2 Osm solution. For substances that do not ionize (e.g., glucose), molarity and osmolarity are the same.

too large to cross the capillary membrane draws water back into the bloodstream. As a result, very little net loss of plasma fluid occurs.

Facilitated Diffusion.   Certain molecules, notably glucose, are both lipid insoluble and too large to pass through plasma membrane pores. However, they move through the membrane very rapidly by a passive transport process called **facilitated diffusion,** in which they combine with protein *carrier* molecules in the plasma membrane and are released into the cytoplasm. Just how this translocation is achieved is still a puzzle, but biologists are fairly sure that the carrier does not "flip-flop" or physically move across the membrane like a ferryboat. The most popular model, shown in Figure 3.6b, suggests that changes in the shape of the carrier allow it to first envelop and then release the transported substance, shielding it en route from the nonpolar regions of the membrane. Hence, the binding site is moved from one face of the membrane to the other by changes in the shape of the carrier protein.

The diffusion processes previously described are not very selective. In those processes, whether a molecule can pass through the membrane or not depends chiefly on its size or solubility in lipid, not on its unique structure. Facilitated diffusion, on the other hand, is highly selective; the carrier for glucose combines specifically with glucose, much in the way an enzyme binds to its specific substrate. Although it is presumed that the cell does not use ATP to drive facilitated diffusion, it does provide assistance in the form of protein carrier molecules. (However, as glucose enters the cytoplasm, it immediately undergoes a coupled reaction with ATP that produces glucose phosphate, as shown in Figure 2.10c. Thus, glucose transport may in fact prove to be an example of an active transport process.) As in any diffusion process, glucose is transported down its concentration gradient. Glucose is normally in higher concentrations in the blood than in the cells, where it is rapidly used for ATP synthesis, so within the body glucose transport is typically unidirectional—into the cells. Carrier-mediated transport is limited by the number of receptors present. For example, when all the glucose carriers are "engaged," they are said to be *saturated,* and glucose transport is occurring at its maximum rate.

Oxygen, water, and glucose are vitally important to cellular homeostasis. Thus, their passive transport by diffusion represents a tremendous saving of cellular energy. Indeed, if all these substances (and carbon dioxide) had to be transported actively, cell expenditures of ATP would increase exponentially!

Passive Processes: Filtration

Filtration is the process by which water and solutes are forced through a membrane or capillary wall by *fluid,* or *hydrostatic* pressure. Like diffusion, filtration is a passive transport process and involves a gradient. In filtration, however, the gradient is a **pressure gradient** that actually pushes solute-containing fluid (filtrate) from the higher-pressure area to the lower-pressure area. We have already mentioned that in the body the hydrostatic pressure exerted by blood forces fluid from the capillaries, and this fluid contains solutes that are vital to the tissues. Filtration also provides the fluid ultimately excreted by the kidneys as urine. Filtration is not a selective process; only blood cells and protein molecules too large to pass through the membrane pores are held back.

(a)

(b)

(c)

FIGURE 3.8
The effect of solutions of varying tonicities on living red blood cells.
(**a**) In isotonic solutions (same solute/water concentrations as inside cells), cells retain their normal size and shape. (**b**) When in a hypertonic solution (containing more solutes than are present inside the cells), the cells lose water and shrink (crenate). (**c**) In a hypotonic solution (containing fewer solutes than are present inside the cell), the cells take in water by osmosis until they become bloated and may burst (lysis).

Table 3.1 Membrane Transport Processes

Process	Energy source	Description	Examples
Passive processes			
Simple diffusion	Kinetic energy	Net movement of particles (ions, molecules, etc.) from an area of their higher concentration to an area of their lower concentration, that is, along their concentration gradient	Movement of fats, oxygen, carbon dioxide through the lipid portion of the membrane, and ions through protein channels under certain conditions
Osmosis	Kinetic energy	Simple diffusion of water through a selectively permeable membrane	Movement of water into and out of cells via membrane pores
Facilitated diffusion	Kinetic energy	Same as simple diffusion, but the diffusing substance is attached to a lipid-soluble membrane carrier protein	Movement of glucose into cells
Filtration	Hydrostatic pressure	Movement of water and solutes through a semipermeable membrane from a region of higher hydrostatic pressure to a region of lower hydrostatic pressure, that is, along a pressure gradient	Movement of water, nutrients, and gases through a capillary wall; formation of kidney filtrate
Active processes			
Active transport (solute pumping)	ATP (cellular energy)	Movement of a substance through a membrane against a concentration (or electrochemical) gradient; requires a membrane carrier protein	Movement of amino acids and most ions across the membrane
Bulk transport			
• Exocytosis	ATP	Secretion or ejection of substances from a cell; the substance is enclosed in a membranous vesicle, which fuses with the plasma membrane and ruptures, releasing the substance to the exterior	Secretion of neurotransmitters, hormones, mucus, etc.; ejection of cell wastes
• Phagocytosis (endocytosis)	ATP	"Cell eating": A large external particle (proteins, bacteria, dead cell debris) is surrounded by a "seizing foot" and becomes enclosed in a plasma membrane sac	In the human body, occurs primarily in protective phagocytes (some white blood cells, macrophages)
• Pinocytosis (endocytosis)	ATP	"Cell drinking": Plasma membrane sinks beneath an external fluid droplet containing small solutes; membrane edges fuse, forming a fluid-filled vesicle	Occurs in most cells; important for taking in solutes by absorptive cells of the kidney and intestine
• Receptor-mediated endocytosis	ATP	Selective endocytosis process; external substance binds to membrane receptors, and coated pits are formed	Means of intake of some hormones, cholesterol, iron, and other molecules

Active Processes

Whenever a cell uses its energy from ATP to move substances across the membrane, the process is referred to as *active.* Substances moved across the plasma membrane by active means are usually unable to pass in the necessary direction by any of the passive diffusion processes. They may be too large to pass through the pores, unable to dissolve in the bilipid membrane core, or required to move against rather than with a concentration gradient. There are two major mechanisms of active membrane transport: active transport and bulk transport.

Active Transport. Active transport, or **solute pumping,** is similar to facilitated diffusion in that both processes require carrier proteins that combine *specifically* and *reversibly* with the transported substances.

However, facilitated diffusion always honors concentration gradients because its driving force is kinetic energy. In contrast, the enzymelike protein carriers or **solute pumps** that mediate active transport move solutes, most importantly amino acids and ions (such as Na^+, K^+, and Ca^{2+}), "uphill" *against* their concentration gradients. To do this work, cells must harness the energy of ATP supplied by cellular metabolism. Although the exact mechanism of active transport is not fully understood, the energized protein carrier is believed to change its conformation in a manner that moves the bound solute across the membrane.

Many active transport systems are *coupled systems;* that is, they move more than one substance at a time. If the two transported substances are moved in the same direction, the system is a *symport* (*sym* = same) *system;* if the transported substances "wave to each other" as they cross the membrane in opposite directions, it is called an *antiport* (*anti* = opposite, against) *system.* Additionally, active transport processes are distinguished according to the source of energy that drives the transport process. In **primary active transport,** the energy is provided directly by hydrolysis of ATP, whereas in **secondary active transport,** transport is driven indirectly by passive ion gradients created by operation of primary active transport pumps. Let's examine these processes more carefully.

The most investigated example of a primary active transport system is the operation of the sodium-potassium pump, actually an enzyme called **Na^+-K^+ ATPase.** The concentration of K^+ inside the cell is generally 10–20 times higher than that outside, and the reverse is true of Na^+. These ionic concentration differences are essential for irritable cells like muscle and nerve cells to function normally and for all body cells to maintain their normal fluid volume. Because Na^+ and K^+ leak slowly but continuously through the plasma membrane along their concentration gradients (and cross more rapidly in stimulated muscle and nerve cells), the Na^+-K^+ pump operates more or less continuously as an antiport that simultaneously drives Na^+ out of the cell against a steep gradient and pumps K^+ back in (Figure 3.9). Other examples of primary active transport are seen in the calcium pumps that actively sequester ionic calcium from the intracellular fluid into specific organelles.

A single ATP-powered pump, such as the Na^+-K^+ pump that maintains the sodium gradient, can indirectly drive the transport of several other solutes (secondary active transport). By moving sodium across the plasma membrane against its concentration gradient, the pump stores energy (in the ion gradient). Then, just as water pumped uphill can do work (turn a turbine for instance) as it flows back down, a substance pumped across a membrane can do work as it leaks back. Thus, as sodium diffuses back into the cell with the help of a carrier protein (facilitated diffusion), other substances are "dragged along" or

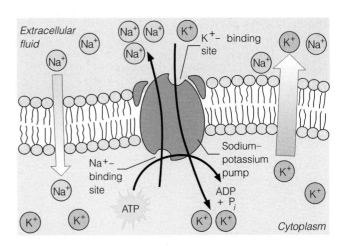

FIGURE 3.9
Operation of the sodium-potassium pump, an antiport pump (Na^+-K^+ ATPase). Hydrolysis of a molecule of ATP provides energy for a "pump" protein to move three sodium ions out of the cell and two potassium ions into the cell. Both ions are moved against their concentration gradients, indicated by colored arrows moving through the membrane (yellow arrow = Na^+ gradient; green arrow = K^+ gradient). Hence, this pump is an *antiport.*

cotransported by the same carrier proteins. For example, a variety of amino acids, some sugars, and many ions are cotransported in this way into cells lining the small intestine. Though the cotransported substances both move passively, sodium has to be pumped back into the lumen of the intestine to maintain its diffusion gradient. Ion gradients can also be used to drive antiport systems such as those that help to regulate intracellular pH by using the sodium gradient to expel hydrogen ions (H^+).

Regardless of whether the energy is provided directly or indirectly for the active transport process, each membrane pump transports only specific substances. Hence, solute pumping provides a way for the cell to be very selective in cases where substances cannot pass by diffusion. (No pump—no transport.)

Bulk Transport. Large particles and macromolecules are transported through plasma membranes by **bulk transport.** Like solute pumping, bulk transport is energized by ATP. The two major kinds of bulk transport are exocytosis and endocytosis.

Exocytosis (ek″so-si-to′sis; "out of the cell") is a mechanism that moves substances from the cell interior into the extracellular space. It accounts for hormone secretion, neurotransmitter release, mucus secretion, and, in some cases, ejection of wastes. In exocytosis, the substance or cell product to be released is first enclosed within a membranous sac called a *vesicle.* The vesicle migrates to the plasma membrane, fuses with it, and then ruptures, spilling

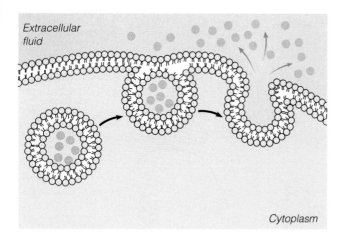

FIGURE 3.10
Exocytosis. The membrane-bounded vesicle containing the substance to be secreted migrates to the plasma membrane, and the two membranes fuse. The fused site opens and releases the contents of the secretory vesicle into the intercellular space.

the sac contents out of the cell (Figure 3.10). The mechanism involves a "docking" process in which proteins on the vesicles recognize certain plasma membrane proteins and bind with them, bringing the two membranes close enough to fuse. As described shortly, membrane material added by exocytosis is removed by endocytosis—its mirror image process.

Endocytosis (en″do-si-to′sis; "into the cell") provides a means for large particles or macromolecules to enter cells. The substance to be taken into the cell is progressively enclosed by an infolding portion of the plasma membrane. Once the membranous vesicle is formed, it pinches off from the plasma membrane and moves into the cytoplasm, where its contents are digested. Three types of endocytosis are recognized: phagocytosis, pinocytosis, and receptor-mediated endocytosis.

In **phagocytosis** (fag″o-si-to′sis), literally, "cell eating," parts of the plasma membrane and cytoplasm protrude and flow around some relatively large or solid material, such as a clump of bacteria or cell debris, and engulf it (Figure 3.11a). The membranous vesicle thus formed is called a **phagosome** (fag′o-sōm; "eaten body"). In most cases, the phagosome becomes fused with a *lysosome* (li′so-sōm), a specialized cell structure containing digestive enzymes (see Figure 3.17, p. 80), and its contents are digested.

Phagocytic cells in the human body include macrophages and some white blood cells. These phagocytic "professionals" help to police and protect the body by ingesting and disposing of bacteria, other foreign substances, and dead tissue cells. Most phagocytes have the ability to move about by **amoeboid** (ah-me′boyd; "changing shape") **motion;** that is, the flowing of their cytoplasm into temporary pseudopods (soo′do-pahdz; *pseudo* = false, *pod* = foot) allows them to creep along.

? *Phagocytic cells gather in the air sacs of the lungs, especially in the lungs of smokers. What is the connection?*

(a) Phagocytosis

(b) Pinocytosis

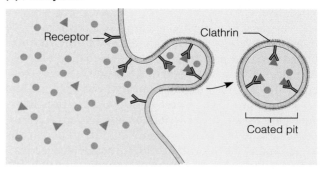

(c) Receptor-mediated endocytosis

FIGURE 3.11
Three types of endocytosis.

Just as we can say that cells eat, we can also say that they drink. **Pinocytosis** (pin″o-si-to′sis) is "cell drinking" (Figure 3.11b). In pinocytosis, a bit of infolding plasma membrane surrounds a droplet of external fluid containing dissolved molecules. This droplet enters the cell in a tiny membranous *pinocytotic vesicle.* Unlike phagocytosis, pinocytosis is a routine activity of most cells. It is particularly important in cells that function in nutrient absorption, such as cells that line the intestines.

In both phagocytosis and pinocytosis, bits of the plasma membrane are removed when the membranous sacs are internalized. However, since these membranes are recycled back to the plasma membrane by exocytosis, the surface area of the plasma membrane remains remarkably constant.

Unlike phagocytosis and pinocytosis, which are often nonspecific ingestion processes, **receptor-mediated endocytosis** is exquisitely selective (Figure 3.11c). The receptors are plasma membrane proteins that bind only with certain substances. Both the receptors and attached material are internalized in a small vesicle called a *coated pit,* a term that refers to the bristlelike *clathrin* (kla′thrin; "lattice") protein coating on the cytoplasmic face of the vesicle.

Substances taken up by receptor-mediated endocytosis include the hormone insulin, low-density lipoproteins (such as cholesterol attached to a transport protein), and iron. When the coated pit combines with a lysosome, the hormone (or cholesterol or iron) is released, and the membranes containing the attached receptors are recycled back to the plasma membrane.

In an inherited disease called *familial hypercholesterolemia,* the protein receptors for receptor-mediated cholesterol uptake are missing. As a result, cholesterol is unable to enter body cells and accumulates in the blood. Untreated, it contributes to early development of atherosclerosis and an exponentially increased risk of coronary artery disease. •

Generation and Maintenance of a Resting Membrane Potential

As you're now aware, the plasma membrane is more permeable to some molecules than to others. This differential permeability can lead to dramatic osmotically induced changes in cell tone, but that is not its only consequence. An equally important result is the generation of a **membrane potential,** or voltage, across the membrane. A *voltage* is electrical potential energy resulting from the separation of oppositely charged particles. In regard to cells, the oppositely charged particles are ions, and the barrier that keeps them apart is the plasma membrane.

In their resting state, all body cells exhibit a **resting membrane potential** that typically ranges from −20 to −200 millivolts (mV), depending on the organism and cell type. Hence, all cells are said to be **polarized.** The sign before the voltage indicates that the inside of the cell is negative compared to its outside. This voltage (or charge separation) exists only at the membrane, however, because if we were to add up all the negative and positive charges in the cell cytoplasm, we would find that the cell interior is electrically neutral. Likewise, the positive and negative charges in the extracellular fluid balance exactly.

So how does the resting membrane potential come about, and how is it maintained? Although many different kinds of ions are found both inside cells and in the extracellular fluid, the resting membrane potential is determined mainly by concentration gradients of sodium ions and potassium ions and

(1) Which ion(s) is/are being pumped against its concentration gradient? (2) Which ion(s) is/are being pumped against its electrical gradient?

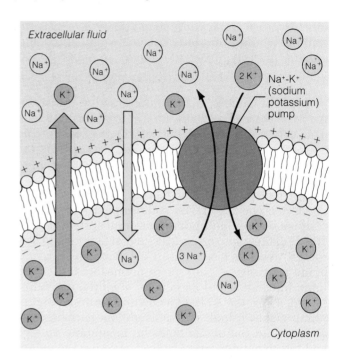

FIGURE 3.12

Summary of forces that generate and maintain membrane potentials. The ionic imbalances that produce the membrane potential reflect passive diffusion of ions (sodium diffuses into the cell more slowly than potassium diffuses out of the cell because of differential membrane permeability to these two ions) and the active transport of sodium and potassium ions (in a ratio of 3:2) by the Na⁺-K⁺ pump. The net effect is that the outside membrane face becomes more electrically positive (more positive ions build up) than the inside, which is relatively more negative.

by the differential permeability of the plasma membrane to those ions. As mentioned before and illustrated in Figure 3.12, body cells have a predominance of K⁺ inside and are surrounded by extracellular fluid containing relatively more Na⁺. At rest, the plasma membrane is slightly permeable to K⁺, but nearly impermeable to Na⁺. As you can see, potassium diffuses out of the cell along its concentration gradient. Sodium is strongly attracted to the cell interior by its concentration gradient, but because sodium permeability is much lower than that of potassium, sodium influx is less and so is inadequate to balance potassium outflow. The result of this unequal Na⁺-K⁺ diffusion across the membrane is a relative loss (deficit) of positive ions within the cell, which establishes the resting membrane potential. Although it is tempting to believe that massive flows of ions occur to generate the resting potential, this is not the case. Surprisingly, the number of ions producing the membrane potential is so small that it does not change ion concentrations in any significant way.

In the polarized state, sodium and potassium concentrations are *not* at equilibrium, and if only passive forces were at work, sodium and potassium concentrations would eventually become equal inside and outside the cell. Instead, a *steady state* exists that maintains the ionic distribution of the polarized state. This steady state results from both passive and active processes—namely, diffusion and active transport. As we have seen, potassium and sodium ions leak passively according to their driving forces, but the active transport rate is equal to, and depends on, the rate of diffusion of sodium ions into the cell. If more sodium enters, more is pumped out. (This is like being in a leaky boat. The more water that comes in, the faster you bail!) The sodium-potassium pump couples sodium and potassium transport, and each "turn" of the pump ejects $3Na^+$ out of the cell and carries $2K^+$ back in (see Figure 3.12). Because the membrane is always slightly more permeable to K^+, the ionic imbalance and membrane potential are maintained. Thus, the ATP-dependent sodium-potassium pump makes it look as if cells are not permeable to sodium and maintains both the membrane voltage and the osmotic balance. Indeed, if sodium were not continuously removed from cells, so much would accumulate intracellularly that an osmotic gradient would be established that would draw water into the cells, causing them to burst.

Before leaving this topic, we must add a detail or two to our earlier discussion of diffusion. We said that solutes diffuse down their concentration gradients. This is true for uncharged solutes, but only partially true for ions or other charged molecules. Because the plasma membrane has a voltage, its negatively and positively charged faces can help or hinder diffusion driven by a concentration gradient. It is more correct to say that ions diffuse according to **electrochemical gradients,** thereby recognizing the effect of both concentration (chemical) and electrical forces. Consequently, if we take a second look at the diffusion of K^+ and Na^+ across the plasma membrane, we see that while diffusion of K^+ is facilitated by the membrane's greater permeability to it and by its concentration gradient, its diffusion is resisted somewhat by the positivity of the cell exterior. On the other hand, Na^+ is drawn into the cell by a steep electrochemical gradient; the limiting factor is the membrane's relative impermeability to it. As will be described in some detail in later chapters, "upsetting" the resting membrane potential by transient opening of ion (Na^+ and K^+) channels in the plasma membrane is a normal means of activating neurons and muscle cells.

Cell-Environment Interactions

Cells are biological minifactories and, like other factories, they receive and send orders from and to the outside community. But *how* does a cell interact with its environment, and what activates it to synthesize proteins or carry out its other homeostatic functions?

Although we tend to think mainly of cells interacting with other cells, in many cases cells respond to extracellular chemicals, such as hormones and neurotransmitters distributed in body fluids. Cells also interact with molecules in the substratum that act as "signposts" to guide cell migration during development (and repair).

Regardless of whether cells interact directly or indirectly, the glycocalyx is involved. The best understood of the participating glycocalyx molecules fall into two large families—adhesion molecules and membrane receptors (see Figure 3.3).

Roles of Cell Adhesion Molecules

Thousands of **cell adhesion molecules (CAMs)** are found on almost every cell in the body. CAMs play key roles in embryonic development and wound repair (where cell mobility is important) and in immunity. These sticky glycoproteins are (1) the molecular "Velcro" cells use to anchor themselves to molecules in the extracellular space and to each other, (2) the "arms" that migrating cells use to haul themselves past one another, and (3) the SOS signals (in the form of selectin CAMS sticking out from the blood vessel lining) that rally protective white blood cells to a nearby infected or injured area.

Roles of Membrane Receptors

The **membrane receptors** are a huge and diverse group of integral proteins and glycoproteins that serve as binding sites. Some of these receptors function in *contact signaling,* the means by which cells recognize other cells. Contact signaling is particularly important for normal development and immunity. Some bacteria and other infectious agents also use contact signaling to identify "preferred" target tissues or organs. However, most membrane-bound receptors are involved in *chemical signaling,* and this group will receive the bulk of our attention.

Signaling chemicals that bind specifically to membrane receptors are called **ligands.** Among these ligands are most *neurotransmitters* (nervous system signals), *hormones* (endocrine system signals), and *paracrines* (chemicals that act locally and are rapidly destroyed). When a ligand binds to a receptor, the receptor's structure changes. Different cells respond in different ways to the same ligand. Acetylcholine, for instance, stimulates skeletal muscle cells to contract, but it inhibits heart muscle. Thus, target cell response depends on the internal machinery that the receptor is linked to, not the specific ligand that binds to it. Though cell responses to receptor binding vary widely, there is a fundamental similarity. Cell proteins are always altered in some way—muscle proteins change shape to generate force, enzymes are activated or inactivated, and channel proteins open and close ion channels, etc.

Some membrane receptor proteins are *catalytic proteins* that function as enzymes. *Channel-linked receptors,* common in muscle and nerve cells, respond to ligands by transiently opening or closing the associated ion channels, which in turn changes the excitability of the cell (see the discussion of membrane potentials on p. 73). Still other receptors are coupled to enzymes or ion channels by a regulatory molecule called a G protein. Since nearly every cell in the body displays at least some of these receptors, we will spend a bit more time with them.

G protein-linked receptors exert their effect indirectly through **G protein,** which acts as a middleman to activate (or inactivate) a membrane bound enzyme or ion channel (Figure 3.13). As a result, one or more intracellular chemical signals, commonly called **second messengers,** are generated and connect plasma membrane events to the internal metabolic machinery of the cell. Two very important second messengers are **cyclic AMP** and ionic calcium, which typically activate protein kinase enzymes. By transferring phosphate groups from ATP to other proteins, the protein kinases, in turn, can activate a whole series of enzymes (including some other kinases) which bring about the desired cellular activity. Since a single enzyme can catalyze hundreds of reactions, the amplification effect of such a chain of events is tremendous. These and other receptor systems are described in greater detail in Chapter 17.

Before leaving this topic, one more signaling molecule must be mentioned, even though it doesn't "fit" any of the mechanisms described. *Nitric oxide (NO),* made of a single atom of nitrogen and one of oxygen, is one of nature's simplest molecules, an environmental pollutant, and the first gas known to act as a biological messenger. Because of its tiny size, it slips into and out of cells easily. Its one unpaired electron makes it a highly reactive free radical that reacts with headspinning speed with other key molecules to spur cells into a broad array of activities. You will be hearing more about NO in later (neural, cardiovascular, and immune) chapters.

THE CYTOPLASM

Cytoplasm (*cyto* = cell; *plasm* = shaped, molded) is the cellular material inside the plasma membrane and outside the nucleus. It is the major functional area, the site where most cellular activities are accomplished. Although early microscopists thought that the cytoplasm was a structureless gel, the electron microscope has revealed that it consists of three major elements: the cytosol, organelles, and inclusions (Table 3.2).

The **cytosol** is the viscous, semitransparent fluid substance of the cytoplasm within which the other elements are suspended. Dissolved in the cytosol,

FIGURE 3.13
Model of a G protein–linked receptor mechanism.

which is largely water, are soluble proteins, salts, sugars, and a variety of other solutes. Hence, the cytosol is a complex mixture with properties of both a colloid and a true solution.

The **organelles,** described in detail shortly, are the metabolic machinery of the cell. Each type of organelle is "engineered" to carry out a specific function for the cell as a whole; some synthesize proteins, others package those proteins, and so on.

Inclusions are not functioning units, but instead are chemical substances that may or may not be present, depending on the specific cell type. Examples include stored nutrients, such as the glycogen granules abundant in liver and muscle cells; lipid droplets common in fat cells; pigment (melanin) granules seen in certain cells of the skin and hairs; and crystals of various types.

Cytoplasmic Organelles

The cytoplasmic organelles, literally, "little organs," are specialized cellular compartments, each performing its own job to maintain the life of the cell. Most organelles are bounded by a membrane similar in composition to the plasma membrane (but without a glycocalyx), which enables them to maintain an internal environment quite different from that of the surrounding cytosol. This compartmentalization is crucial to cell functioning; without it, thousands of enzymes would be randomly mixed and biochemical activity would be chaotic. Besides providing "splendid isolation," the organelle membranes unite them

Table 3.2 Parts of the Cell: Structure and Function

Cell part	Structure	Functions
Plasma membrane (Figure 3.2)	Membrane composed of a double layer of lipids (phospholipids, cholesterol, etc.) within which proteins are embedded; proteins may extend entirely through the lipid bilayer or protrude on only one face; externally facing proteins and some lipids have attached sugar groups	Serves as an external cell barrier; acts in transport of substances into or out of the cell; maintains a resting potential that is essential for functioning of excitable cells; externally facing proteins act as receptors (for hormones, neurotransmitters, etc.) and in cell-to-cell recognition
Cytoplasm	Cellular region between the nuclear and plasma membranes; consists of fluid **cytosol**, containing dissolved solutes, **inclusions** (stored nutrients, secretory products, pigment granules), and **organelles**, the metabolic machinery of the cytoplasm	
Cytoplasmic organelles • Mitochondria (Figure 3.14)	Rodlike, double-membrane structures; inner membrane folded into projections called cristae	Site of ATP synthesis; powerhouse of the cell
• Ribosomes (Figure 3.15)	Dense particles consisting of two subunits, each composed of ribosomal RNA and protein; free or attached to rough ER	The sites of protein synthesis
• Rough endoplasmic reticulum (rough ER) (Figure 3.15)	Membrane system enclosing a cavity, the cisterna, and coiling through the cytoplasm; externally studded with ribosomes	Sugar groups are attached to proteins within the cisternae; proteins are bound in vesicles for transport to the Golgi apparatus and other sites; external face synthesizes phospholipids and cholesterol
• Smooth endoplasmic reticulum (smooth ER) (Figure 3.15)	Membranous system of sacs and tubules; free of ribosomes	Site of lipid and steroid synthesis, lipid metabolism, and drug detoxification
• Golgi apparatus (Figure 3.16)	A stack of smooth membrane sacs and associated vesicles close to the nucleus	Packages, modifies, and segregates proteins for secretion from the cell, inclusion in lysosomes, and incorporation into the plasma membrane
• Lysosomes (Figure 3.18)	Membranous sacs containing acid hydrolases	Sites of intracellular digestion
• Peroxisomes (Figure 3.1)	Membranous sacs of oxidase enzymes	The enzymes detoxify a number of toxic substances; the most important enzyme, catalase, breaks down hydrogen peroxide
• Microfilaments (Figure 3.20)	Fine filaments of the contractile protein actin	Involved in muscle contraction and other types of intracellular movement; help form the cell's cytoskeleton
• Intermediate filaments (Figure 3.20)	Protein fibers; composition varies	The stable cytoskeletal elements; resist mechanical forces acting on the cell
• Microtubules (Figures 3.20, 3.21, 3.22)	Cylindrical structures composed of tubulin proteins	Support the cell and give it shape; involved in intracellular and cellular movements; form centrioles
• Centrioles (Figure 3.21)	Paired cylindrical bodies, each composed of nine triplets of microtubules	Organize a microtubule network during mitosis to form the spindle and asters; form the bases of cilia and flagella
• Cilia (Figure 3.22)	Short, cell surface projections; each cilium composed of nine pairs of microtubules surrounding a central pair	Move in unison, creating a unidirectional current that propels substances across cell surfaces
• Flagella (Figure 3.1)	Like cilium, but longer; only example in humans is the sperm tail	Propels the cell
Nucleus (Figure 3.23)	Largest organelle; surrounded by the nuclear envelope; contains fluid nucleoplasm, nucleoli, and chromatin	Control center of the cell; responsible for transmitting genetic information and providing the instructions for protein synthesis
• Nuclear envelope (Figure 3.23)	Double-membrane structure; pierced by the pores; outer membrane continuous with the cytoplasmic ER	Separates the nucleoplasm from the cytoplasm and regulates passage of substances to and from the nucleus
• Nucleoli (Figure 3.23)	Dense spherical (non-membrane-bounded) bodies; composed of ribosomal RNA and proteins	Site of ribosome subunit manufacture
• Chromatin (Figures 3.23, 3.24)	Granular, threadlike material composed of DNA and histone proteins	DNA constitutes the genes

into an interactive intracellular system called the *endomembrane system* (see p. 81). Now, let us consider what goes on in each of the workshops of our cellular factory.

Mitochondria

Mitochondria (mi″to-kon′dre-ah) are usually depicted as tiny threadlike (*mitos* = thread) or sausage-shaped organelles (Figure 3.14), but in living cells they squirm, elongate, and change shape almost continuously. Mitochondria are the "power plants" of a cell because they provide most of its ATP supply. The density of mitochondria in a particular cell reflects that cell's energy requirements, and mitochondria are generally clustered "where the action is." Busy cells like muscle and liver cells have hundreds of mitochondria, whereas cells that are relatively inactive (such as lymphocytes) have just a few.

Mitochondria are actually enclosed by *two* membranes, each with the general structure of the plasma membrane. The outer membrane is smooth and featureless, but the inner membrane folds inward forming shelflike *cristae* (kris′te; "crests"). The cristae protrude into the matrix, the gel-like substance within the mitochondrion. Nutrients (glucose and others) are processed and broken down to water and carbon dioxide by teams of enzymes, some dissolved in the mitochondrial matrix and others forming part of the crista membrane.

As glucose breaks down, some of the energy released is captured and used to attach phosphate groups to ADP molecules to form ATP. This multistep mitochondrial process is generally referred to as *aerobic* (a-er-o′bik) *cellular respiration* because it requires oxygen. It is described in detail in Chapter 25. The matrix also contains spherical particles of calcium phosphate called *matrix granules*. The matrix granules are evidence of another mitochondrial function—storing and releasing calcium ions. Since ionic calcium is an intracellular signal for so many cellular events (including muscle contraction and secretion), its concentration in the cytosol is usually kept at low levels.

Mitochondria contain DNA and RNA and are self-replicating organelles. Although mitochondrial DNA directs the synthesis of some 13 of the proteins required for mitochondrial function, the DNA of the nucleus encodes the remaining 50 or so proteins needed to carry out cellular respiration. When cellular requirements for ATP increase, the mitochondria simply pinch in half (a process called *fission*) to increase their number, then grow to their former size. Intriguingly, mitochondria are very similar to a specific group of bacteria (purple bacteria phylum). It is now widely believed that mitochondria arose from bacteria that invaded the ancient ancestors of our cells and eventually surrendered their independence.

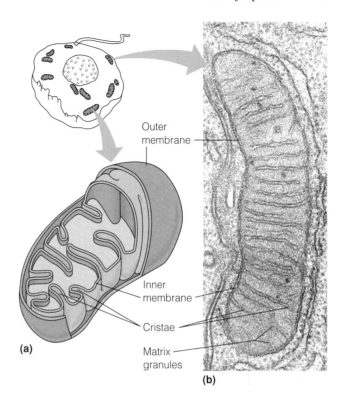

Outer membrane

Inner membrane

Cristae

Matrix granules

(a)

(b)

FIGURE 3.14
Mitochondrion. (**a**) Diagrammatic view of a longitudinally sectioned mitochondrion. (**b**) Electron micrograph of a mitochondrion (approx. 44,880 ×).

Ribosomes

Ribosomes (ri′bo-sōmz) are small, dark-staining granules composed of proteins and one variety of RNA (specifically called *ribosomal RNA*). Each ribosome has two globular subunits that fit together and roughly resemble an acorn when the small unit sits atop the larger one (see Figure 3.15c). Ribosomes are sites of protein synthesis, a function we discuss in detail later in this chapter.

Some ribosomes float freely in the cytoplasm; others are attached to membranes, forming a complex called the *rough endoplasmic reticulum*. These two ribosomal populations appear to divide the chore of protein synthesis. *Free ribosomes* make soluble proteins that will function in the cytosol, whereas *membrane-bound ribosomes* are chiefly involved in synthesizing protein products destined for cellular membranes or for export from the cell. Ribosomes can switch back and forth between these two functions, attaching to and detaching from the membranes of the endoplasmic reticulum, according to the type of protein they are making at a given time.

(a)

(b) Smooth ER   Rough ER with bound ribosomes

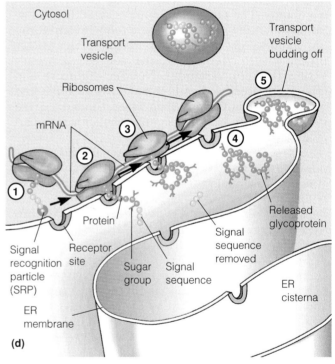

(d)

FIGURE 3.15
The endoplasmic reticulum. (**a**) Three-dimensional diagram of the rough ER in a liver cell; its connections to smooth ER areas are also illustrated. (**b**) Electron micrograph of smooth and rough endoplasmic reticulum (approx. 26,500×). (**c**) Diagram of a ribosome showing the large and small subunits. (**d**) Enlarged view of a portion of the rough ER membrane bearing ribosomes and the ER cisterna where sugar groups are attached to newly synthesized proteins. According to the signal hypothesis of protein synthesis: (1) Presence of a short signal sequence on a newly forming protein causes the mRNA-ribosome complex to be directed to the rough ER by a signal recognition particle (SRP). (2) Once attached to the ER receptor site, the SRP is released and the signal sequence is inserted through the ER membrane into the cisterna. (3) The signal sequence is clipped off by an enzyme and as protein synthesis continues, sugar groups may be added to the protein. (4) In this example, the completed protein is released and folds into its 3-D conformation, a process aided by stress proteins. Some proteins are only partially translocated and

remain embedded in the membrane. (5) Protein is enclosed within a membranous transport vesicle that pinches off the ER. The transport vesicles make their way to the cell's Golgi apparatus where further processing of the proteins occurs (see Figure 3.16).

Endoplasmic Reticulum

The **endoplasmic reticulum** (en″do-plaz′mik re-tik′u-lum), or **ER,** is literally the "network within the cyto-plasm." As shown in Figure 3.15, it is an extensive system of interconnected tubes and parallel membranes enclosing fluid-filled cavities, or *cisternae*

(sis-ter′ne), that coils and twists through the cytosol. The ER is continuous with the nuclear membrane and accounts for about half of the cell's membranes. There are two distinct varieties of ER: rough ER and smooth ER. One variety or the other may predominate in a given cell type, depending on the specific functions of the cell.

Golgi apparatus

Cis face:
"Receiving" side of Golgi apparatus

Transport vesicle from smooth ER

New vesicles forming

Transport vesicle from the Golgi

Trans face:
"Shipping" side of Golgi apparatus

Plasma membrane

FIGURE 3.16
Golgi apparatus. (**a**) Three-dimensional diagrammatic view of the Golgi apparatus.
(**b**) Electron micrograph of the Golgi apparatus (approx. 27,000×). Notice the vesicles in the process of pinching off from the membranous Golgi apparatus.

Rough Endoplasmic Reticulum.   The external surface of the **rough ER** is studded with ribosomes (Figure 3.15). Proteins assembled on these ribosomes thread their way into the watery environment of the ER cisternae where various fates await them (as described shortly). The rough ER has several functions. Its ribosomes manufacture all proteins that are secreted from cells. Thus, the rough ER is particularly abundant and well developed in most secretory cells, antibody-producing plasma cells, and liver cells, which produce most blood proteins. The rough ER can also be considered the cell's "membrane factory" because the integral proteins, phospholipids, and cholesterol that form part of all cellular membranes are manufactured there. The enzymes needed to catalyze lipid synthesis have their active sites on the external (cytosolic) face of the ER membrane, where the needed substrates are readily available.

Now that we have provided an overview of ER functions, we will examine the sequence of events that occurs there as proteins are synthesized by its resident ribosomes. When a short "leader" peptide segment called a *signal sequence* is present in the protein being synthesized, the associated ribosome attaches to the membrane of the rough ER. This signal sequence (with its attached "cargo" of the ribosome and messenger RNA) is guided to the appropriate receptor sites on the ER membrane by a *signal-recognition particle (SRP),* which cycles between the ER and the cytosol. The subsequent events occurring at the ER are described in detail in Figure 3.15d.

Smooth Endoplasmic Reticulum.   The **smooth ER** (see Figures 3.1 and 3.15) is a continuation of the rough ER and consists of tubules arranged in a branching network. It plays no role in protein synthesis. Instead, its enzymes (all integral proteins forming part of its membranes) catalyze reactions involved with (1) lipid metabolism and synthesis of cholesterol and of the lipid components of lipoproteins (in liver cells); (2) synthesis of steroid-based hormones such as sex hormones (testosterone-synthesizing cells of the testes are full of smooth ER); (3) absorption, synthesis, and transport of fats (in intestinal cells); and (4) detoxification of drugs (in the liver and kidneys). Additionally, skeletal and cardiac muscle cells have an elaborate smooth ER (called the sarcoplasmic reticulum) that plays an important role in calcium ion storage and release during muscle contraction. Except for the examples given above, most body cells contain little, if any, true smooth ER.

Golgi Apparatus

The **Golgi** (gol'je) **apparatus** consists of flattened membranous sacs, stacked like dinner plates, associated with swarms of tiny membranous vesicles (Figure 3.16). The Golgi apparatus is probably the principal "traffic director" for cellular proteins: Its major function is to modify, concentrate, and package the proteins and membranes made at the rough ER in specific ways, depending on their ultimate destination. The transport vesicles that bud off from the rough ER

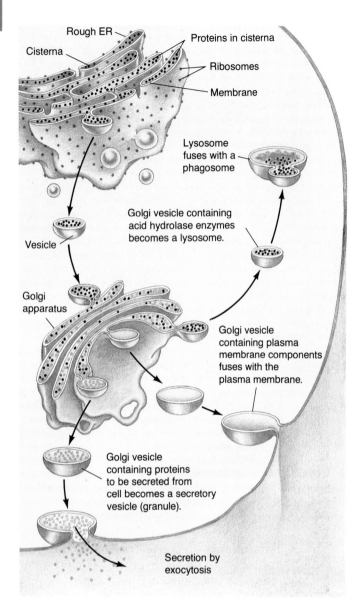

Rough ER

Cisterna

Proteins in cisterna

Ribosomes

Membrane

Lysosome fuses with a phagosome

Golgi vesicle containing acid hydrolase enzymes becomes a lysosome.

Vesicle

Golgi apparatus

Golgi vesicle containing plasma membrane components fuses with the plasma membrane.

Golgi vesicle containing proteins to be secreted from cell becomes a secretory vesicle (granule).

Secretion by exocytosis

FIGURE 3.17
Role of the Golgi apparatus in packaging proteins for cellular use and for secretion. The sequence of events from protein synthesis on the rough ER to the final distribution of those proteins. Protein-containing vesicles pinch off the rough ER and migrate to fuse with the membranes of the Golgi apparatus. Within the Golgi compartments, the proteins are modified; they are then accumulated in different Golgi vesicle types, depending on their ultimate destination.

migrate to and fuse with the membranes at the *cis face,* the "receiving" side of the Golgi apparatus (Figures 3.16 and 3.17). Inside the apparatus, glycoproteins are modified: Some sugar groups are trimmed while others are added, and in some cases, phosphate groups are added. The various proteins are "tagged" for delivery to a specific address, sorted, and accumulated in at least three distinct types of vesicles attached to the *trans face* (the "shipping" side) of the Golgi stack.

Vesicles containing proteins destined for export pinch off from the trans face as **secretory vesicles,** or **granules,** which migrate to the plasma membrane and discharge their contents from the cell by exocytosis. Specialized secretory cells such as the enzyme-producing cells of the pancreas have a very prominent Golgi apparatus. In addition to its packaging-for-release function, the Golgi apparatus pinches off vesicles containing lipids and transmembrane proteins destined for the plasma membrane or other membranous organelles and packages hydrolytic (digestive) enzymes into membranous sacs called *lysosomes* that remain in the cell.

Lysosomes

Lysosomes ("disintegration bodies") are spherical membranous bags containing digestive enzymes (Figure 3.18). As you might guess, lysosomes are large and abundant in phagocytes. Lysosomal enzymes can digest all varieties of biological molecules. They work best in acidic conditions (approximately pH 5) and thus are called *acid hydrolases* (hi″drah-la′siz). The lysosomal membrane is adapted to serve lysosomal functions in two important ways: (1) It contains hydrogen ion (proton) "pumps" that gather hydrogen ions from the surrounding cytosol to maintain the organelle's low internal pH, and (2) it retains the dangerous acid hydrolases, while permitting the final products of digestion to escape so that they can be used by the cell or excreted. Hence, lysosomes provide sites where digestion can proceed *safely* within a cell. Lysosomes function as a cell's "demolition sites" for (1) digestion of particles ingested by endocytosis, particularly important in rendering ingested bacteria, viruses, and toxins harmless to the cell; (2) degradation of worn-out or nonfunctional organelles; (3) metabolic functions, such as the breakdown of stored glycogen and the release of thyroid hormone from its storage form in thyroid cells; and (4) degradation of nonuseful tissues, such as the webs between the fingers and toes of a developing fetus and the uterine lining during menstruation. Breakdown of bone to release calcium ions into the blood also reflects lysosomal activity.

The lysosomal membrane is ordinarily quite stable, but it becomes fragile when the cell is injured or deprived of oxygen and when excessive amounts of vitamin A are present. Lysosomal rupture results in self-digestion of the cell, a process called *autolysis* (aw″-tol′ĭ-sis). Autolysis is the basis for "desirable destruction" processes (see point 4 above), and for certain *autoimmune* diseases such as rheumatoid arthritis (see Chapter 8).

Inherited deficiencies of certain of the lysosomal enzymes can lead to abnormal accumulation of metabolic waste products. For example, in *Tay-Sachs disease,* a condition seen mostly in Jews from Central Europe, the lysosomes lack an enzyme needed to break down a specific glycolipid abundant in nerve

FIGURE 3.18
Lysosomes. Electron micrograph of a cell containing lysosomes
(12,000×).

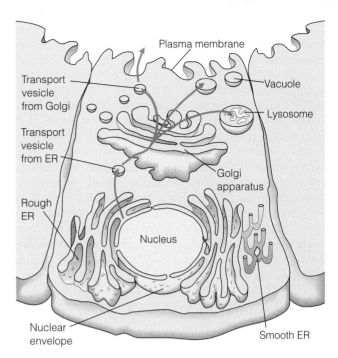

FIGURE 3.19
The endomembrane system.

cell membranes. As a result, the lysosomes of nerve cells become swollen with the undigested lipids, which interfere with nervous system functioning. Affected infants typically have doll-like features and pink translucent skin. At 3 to 6 months of age, the first signs of disease appear (listlessness, motor weakness). These progress to mental retardation, seizures, blindness, and ultimately death within a year and a half. •

Peroxisomes

Peroxisomes (pĕ-roks′ĭ-sōmz) are membranous sacs containing powerful oxidase enzymes that use molecular oxygen (O_2) to detoxify a number of harmful or toxic substances, including alcohol and formaldehyde. However, their most important function is to "disarm" dangerous free radicals. **Free radicals** are highly reactive chemicals with unpaired electrons that can scramble the structure of proteins, lipids, and nucleic acids. Although free radicals and hydrogen peroxide are normal by-products of cellular metabolism, if allowed to accumulate, they can have devastating effects on cells. Peroxisomes act on free radicals such as superoxide ion (O_2^-) and hydroxyl radical by converting them to hydrogen peroxide (H_2O_2). This function is indicated in the naming of these organelles as *peroxisomes* (literally, "peroxide

bodies"). The enzyme *catalase* (kat′ah-lās) then reduces excess hydrogen peroxide to water. Peroxisomes are especially numerous in liver and kidney cells, which are very active in detoxification.

Although peroxisomes look like small lysosomes (see Figure 3.1), they do not arise by budding from the Golgi apparatus. Instead, they appear to be self-replicating organelles formed by a simple pinching in half of preexisting peroxisomes.

Summary of Interactions in the Endomembrane System

The **endomembrane system** (Figure 3.19) is a system of organelles (most described above) that work together mainly (1) to produce, store, and export biological molecules, and (2) to degrade potentially harmful substances. It includes the ER, Golgi apparatus, secretory vesicles, and lysosomes, as well as the nuclear membrane—that is, all of the membranous organelles or elements that (1) are continuous structurally or (2) arise or interact via forming or fusing transport vesicles. There are continuities between the nuclear envelope (itself an extension of the rough ER) and the rough and smooth ER. Additionally, the plasma membrane, though not actually an *endo* membrane, is functionally part of this system. Besides these direct structural connections, there is a wide variety of indirect interactions (indicated by the arrows on the figure) among the members of the system. As you've seen, some of the vesicles "born" in the ER migrate to and fuse with the Golgi apparatus or the plasma membrane. Likewise, vesicles arising from the Golgi apparatus can become part of the plasma membrane, secretory vesicles, or lysosomes. Just how these vesicles recognize their destination or incorporate themselves into another membrane is still a question. Recently a number of "hooks" have been identified that help the vesicles grasp and then fuse into cellular membranes. At least one variety of hooks is a group of soluble attachment proteins, fancifully named SNAPs. Others are membrane proteins referred to as SNAREs (short for SNAP receptors). The idea is that every vesicle bears a specific SNARE protein (a v-SNARE) that will bind only with a particular t-SNARE, which is part of the target membrane with which it will ultimately fuse. Thus, v-SNAREs are like zip codes that send the vesicle to a particular address (t-SNARE site).

The figure also reveals another interesting point: cell products that initially enter the ER cisternae can be secreted to the cell exterior or enter its nucleus without ever actually crossing a cellular membrane. Since the endomembrane system meanders through a good part of the cytosol and thus could (conceivably) hinder intracellular transport, this is an important point indeed.

Cytoskeleton

The **cytoskeleton,** literally, "cell skeleton," is an elaborate series of rods running through the cytosol (Figure 3.20). This network acts as a cell's "bones" and "muscles" by supporting cellular structures and providing the machinery to generate various cell movements. The three types of rods in the cytoskeleton are *microtubules, microfilaments,* and *intermediate filaments.* None of these is membrane covered.

Microtubules (mi″kro-tu′būlz), the elements with the largest diameter, are hollow tubes made of spherical protein subunits called *tubulins.* All microtubules originate in a small region of cytoplasm near the nucleus called the *centrosome* or *cell center.* This radiating collection of stiff microtubules determines the overall shape of the cell, as well as the distribution of cellular organelles. Mitochondria, lysosomes, and secretory granules are arranged along the microtubules like ornaments hanging from the limbs of a Christmas tree. These attached organelles are continually pulled along the microtubules and repositioned by **motor proteins** (*kinesin, dynein,* and others) that act like train engines on the microtubular "railroad tracks." Microtubules are remarkably dynamic or-ganelles, constantly growing out from the cell center, disassembling spontaneously, then reassembling.

Microfilaments (mi″kro-fil′ah-ments) are thin strands of the contractile protein *actin* ("ray"). Each cell appears to have its own arrangement of microfilaments; thus, no two cells are alike. However, nearly all cells have a fairly dense cross-linked network of microfilaments attached to the cytoplasmic side of their plasma membranes that braces and strengthens the cell surface. Most microfilaments are involved in cell motility or changes in cell shape. You could say that cells move when they get their act(in) together. For example, actin microfilaments interact with **myosin** (mi′o-sin), a motor protein, to generate contractile forces within the cell, and to form the cleavage furrow that pinches a cell in two during cell division. Microfilaments which attach to CAMs (see p. 74) in the glycocalyx are responsible for the crawling movements of ameboid motion (see p. 72), and the

FIGURE 3.20
Cytoskeleton. Scanning electron micrograph of a portion of a cell's cytoskeleton (51,000 ×); diagrammatic views of the cytoskeletal element types are shown below the SEM.

membrane changes that accompany endocytosis and exocytosis. Except in muscle cells, where they are highly developed and permanent, microfilaments are labile. That is, they are constantly breaking down and re-forming from smaller subunits when and where their services are needed.

Intermediate filaments are tough, insoluble protein fibers, with a diameter between those of microfilaments and microtubules. Constructed like woven ropes, intermediate filaments are the most stable and permanent of the cytoskeletal elements and have high tensile strength. They act as internal guy wires to resist pulling forces on the cell, and they play a role in forming desmosomes (the adhesive junctions described on p. 64). The protein composition of intermediate filaments varies in different cell types, which has led to numerous names for these cytoskeletal elements. For example, they are called neurofilaments in nerve cells and keratin filaments (or tonofilaments) in epithelial cells.

Some researchers believe that an additional fine, weblike element, which they have called the *microtrabecular lattice,* weaves its way through the cytosol, interconnecting the other cytoskeletal elements and giving the cytosol its gel-like consistency. They suggest that this lattice suspends free ribosomes and probably serves as an attachment point for soluble enzymes that catalyze multistep chemical reactions in the cytosol. However, this element has been difficult to study and illustrate, and its presence is still hotly disputed.

Centrosome and Centrioles

As mentioned above, many microtubules appear to be anchored at one end in a region near the nucleus called the **centrosome** or **cell center**. The centrosome, which acts as a *microtubule-organizing center,* has few distinguishing marks other than the fact that it contains paired organelles called **centrioles**. The centrioles are small, barrel-shaped bodies oriented at right angles to each other (Figure 3.21). Each centriole consists of an array of nine *triplets* of stabilized microtubules, arranged to form a hollow tube. Centrioles are best known for their role of organizing the mitotic spindle (see Figure 3.28) in cell division. They also form the basis of two types of motile cellular projections: cilia and flagella.

Cilia and Flagella

Cilia (sil'e-ah; "eyelashes") are whiplike, motile cellular extensions that occur, typically in large numbers, on the exposed surfaces of certain cells. Ciliary action is very important in moving substances in one direction across cell surfaces. For example, ciliated cells that line the respiratory tract propel mucus laden with dust particles and bacteria upward away from the lungs.

When a cell is about to form cilia, the centrioles multiply and line up beneath the plasma membrane

FIGURE 3.21
Centrioles. (a) Three-dimensional view of a centriole pair oriented at right angles, as they are usually seen in the cell. The centrioles are located in a nonconspicuous region to one side of the nucleus called the centrosome, or cell center. (b) An electron micrograph showing a cross section of a centriole (approx. 150,000 ×). Notice that it is composed of nine microtubule triplets.

at the free cell surface. Microtubules then begin to "sprout" from each centriolar region and exert pressure on the plasma membrane, forming the ciliary projections. When the projections formed by centrioles are substantially longer, they are called **flagella** (flah-jel'ah). The single example of a flagellated cell in the human body is a sperm, which has one propulsive flagellum, commonly called a "tail." Notice that cilia *propel other substances* across a cell's surface, whereas a flagellum *propels the cell itself.*

Centrioles forming the bases of cilia and flagella are commonly referred to as **basal** (ba'sal) **bodies** (Figure 3.22a), since they were thought to be different from the structures seen in the centrosome. We now know that centrioles and basal bodies are identical structures. However, the "9 + 2" pattern of microtubules in the cilium or flagellum itself differs

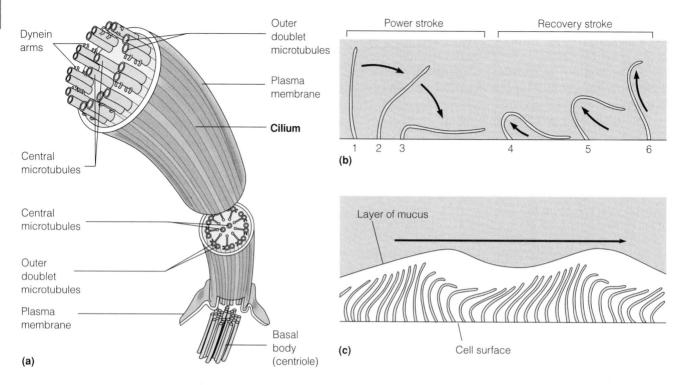

FIGURE 3.22
Cilia structure and function. (a) Three-dimensional diagram of a cross section through a cilium, showing its nine pairs of peripheral microtubules and one central microtubule pair. **(b)** Diagram of the phases of ciliary motion. 1–3 are part of the power (propulsive) stroke; 4–6 are phases of the recovery (nonpropulsive) stroke when the cilium is resuming its initial position. **(c)** A representation of the traveling wave created by the activity of many cilia acting together to propel mucus across the cell surfaces.

slightly from that of a centriole (nine microtubule *triplets*).

Just how the activity of the cilia is coordinated is not understood. However, function follows structure, and microtubules are definitely involved. The core of each cilium contains nine *doublets,* or pairs, of microtubules encircling one central pair (Figure 3.22a). Extending from the doublets are arms composed of the motor protein *dynein.* Ciliary movement is generated when the dynein side arms grip adjacent doublets and start to crawl along their length, much like cats dig in their claws to climb a tree. The collective bending action of all the doublets causes the cilium to bend.

As a cilium moves, it alternates rhythmically between a propulsive *power stroke,* when it is nearly straight and moves in an arc, and a *recovery stroke,* when it bends and returns to its initial position (Figure 3.22b). With these two strokes, the cilium produces a pushing motion in a single direction. However, cilia do not act independently of each other. Instead, the activity of the entire group of cilia in a particular region is coordinated so that the bending of one cilium is quickly followed by the bending of the next and then the next, creating a current at the cell surface that brings to mind the *traveling waves* that pass across a field of grass on a windy day (Figure 3.22c).

THE NUCLEUS

Anything that works, works best when it is controlled. For cells, the control center is the gene-containing **nucleus** (*nucle* = pit, kernel). The nucleus can be compared to a computer, design department, construction boss, and board of directors—all rolled into one unique organelle. While most cells have only one nucleus, some, including skeletal muscle cells, bone destruction cells, and some liver cells, are *multinucleate* (mul″tĭ-nu′kle-āt); that is, they have many nuclei. The presence of more than one nucleus usually signifies that a larger-than-usual cytoplasmic mass must be regulated. With one exception, all of our body cells are *nucleated.* The exception is mature red blood cells, whose nuclei are ejected before the cells enter the bloodstream. These *anucleate* (a-nu′kle-āt; *a* = without) cells cannot reproduce and therefore live in the bloodstream for only three to four months before they begin to deteriorate. Without a nucleus, a cell cannot make any more proteins, and when its enzymes and cell structures start to break down (as all eventually do), they cannot be replaced.

The nucleus, averaging 5 μm in diameter, is the largest organelle in the cell. While most often spherical or oval, its shape usually conforms to the shape of

FIGURE 3.23
The nucleus. (a) Three-dimensional diagrammatic view of the nucleus, showing the continuity of its double membrane with the ER. (b) Transmission electron micrograph (9500×) of the nucleus showing nuclear envelope, nuclear pores, a nucleolus, and condensed chromatin regions.

the cell. If a cell is elongated, for example, the nucleus may be elongated as well. The nucleus has three distinct regions or structures: the *nuclear envelope (membrane), nucleoli,* and *chromatin* (Figure 3.23).

The nuclear envelope encloses a jellylike colloidal fluid called **nucleoplasm** (nu′kle-o-plazm″), within which nucleoli and chromatin are suspended. Like the cytosol, the nucleoplasm contains salts, nutrients, and other needed chemicals.

Nuclear Envelope

The nucleus is bounded by the **nuclear envelope,** which is a *double* nuclear membrane barrier (each membrane is a phospholipid bilayer) similar to the mitochondrial membrane. Between the two membranes is a fluid-filled space called the *perinuclear* (per″ĭ-nu′kle-ar) *cisterna.* The outer nuclear membrane is continuous with the ER of the cytoplasm and is studded with ribosomes on its external face.

At various points, the two layers of the nuclear envelope fuse, and **nuclear pores** penetrate these regions. Like other cellular membranes, the nuclear envelope is selectively permeable, but the passage of substances is much freer than elsewhere because of its relatively large pores. Protein molecules imported from the cytoplasm and RNA molecules exported from the nucleus pass easily through the pores.

Nucleoli

Nucleoli (nu-kle′o-li; "little nuclei") are dark-staining spherical bodies found within the nucleus (see Figure 3.23). They are not membrane bounded. Typically, there are one or two nucleoli per cell, but there may be more. Nucleoli are "ribosome-producing machines"; consequently, they are usually very large in growing cells that are actively making large amounts of tissue proteins. Nucleoli are associated with chromatin regions containing the DNA that issues genetic instructions for synthesizing ribosomal RNA (rRNA). Such DNA segments are called *nucleolar organizer regions.* As molecules of rRNA are synthesized within a nucleolus, they combine with pro-

(a)

(b)

FIGURE 3.24
Chromatin. (**a**) Electron micrograph of chromatin fibers, which have the appearance of beads on a string (216,000×). (**b**) A proposed model for the structure of a chromatin fiber. The DNA molecule winds around spherical particles called nucleosomes; each nucleosome is composed of eight histone proteins.

teins to form the two kinds of ribosomal subunits. (The proteins are manufactured on ribosomes in the cytoplasm and "imported" into the nucleus.) These subunits leave the nucleus through the nuclear pores and enter the cytoplasm, where they are assembled into functional ribosomes.

Chromatin

Seen through a light microscope, **chromatin** (kro′-mah-tin) appears as a fine, unevenly stained network, but special techniques reveal it as a system of bumpy threads weaving their way through the nucleoplasm (Figure 3.24a). Chromatin is composed of approximately equal amounts of DNA, which constitutes our genetic material, and globular **histone** (his′tōn) **proteins. Nucleosomes** (nu′kle-o-sōmz; "nuclear bodies"), the fundamental units of chromatin, are spherical clusters of eight histone proteins connected like beads on a string by a DNA molecule that winds around each of them (Figure 3.24b). In addition to providing a physical means for packing the very long DNA molecules in a compact orderly way, the histones play an important role in gene regulation. For example, changes in the shape of the histones in a nondividing cell expose different DNA segments, or

genes, so that they can "dictate" the specifications for protein synthesis. Such active chromatin segments, referred to as *extended chromatin,* are not usually visible under the light microscope. The nonactive *condensed chromatin* segments are darker staining and so are more easily detected. When a cell is preparing to divide, the chromatin threads coil and condense enormously to form short, barlike bodies called *chromosomes* ("colored bodies") (Figure 3.25). Chromosomes are moved extensively during cell division (pp. 90–91). Their compactness avoids entanglement and breakage of the delicate chromatin strands during such movements. The functions of DNA and the mechanism of cell division are described in the next section.

CELL GROWTH AND REPRODUCTION

The Cell Life Cycle

The **cell life cycle** is the series of changes a cell goes through from the time it is formed until it reproduces itself. The cycle encompasses two major periods: *interphase,* in which the cell grows and carries on its

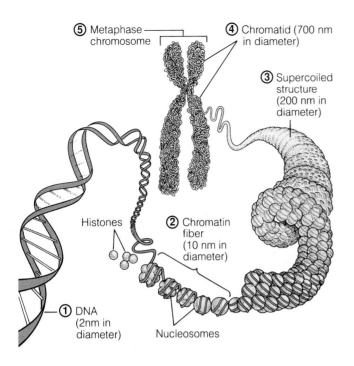

FIGURE 3.25
Chromosome structure. The ascending levels of structural complexity (coiling) from the DNA helix to the metaphase chromosome are indicated in numeric order. (Metaphase is a stage of nuclear division that occurs *before* the genetic material is distributed to the daughter cells.)

For most of G_1, virtually no activities directly related to cell division occur; however as G_1 ends the centrioles start to replicate in preparation for cell division. During the next phase, the **S (synthetic) phase,** DNA replicates itself, ensuring that the two future cells will receive identical copies of the genetic material. New histones are made and assembled into chromatin. (We will describe DNA replication next.) The final phase of interphase, called G_2 **(growth 2),** is very brief. During this period, enzymes and other proteins needed for division are synthesized and moved to their proper sites. By the end of G_2, centriole replication (begun in G_1) is complete. Throughout the S and G_2 phases, the cell continues to grow and carries on with business as usual.

DNA Replication.   Before a cell can divide, its DNA must be replicated exactly, so that identical copies of the cell's genes can be passed on to each of its offspring. The precise trigger for DNA synthesis is unknown, but once it begins it is an all-or-none phenomenon. The replication process begins simultane-

usual activities, and *cell division,* or the *mitotic phase,* during which it reproduces (Figure 3.26).

Interphase

Interphase includes the total period from cell formation to cell division. Early cytologists, unaware of the constant molecular activity in cells and impressed by the obvious movements of cell division, called interphase the resting phase of the cell cycle. (The term *interphase* reflects this idea that it is merely a stage *between* cell divisions.) However, this is grossly misleading, because during interphase a cell is carrying out all its routine activities and is "resting" only from dividing. Perhaps a more accurate name for this phase would be *metabolic phase* or *growth phase.*

In addition to carrying on its life-sustaining reactions, an interphase cell prepares for the next cell division. Interphase is divided into G_1, S, and G_2 subphases. During G_1 **(growth 1),** the first portion of interphase, cells are metabolically active, synthesize proteins rapidly, and grow vigorously. This is the most variable phase in terms of length. Cells with rapid division rates have a G_1 phase lasting minutes to hours; those that divide more slowly can be in this phase for days or even years. Cells that permanently cease dividing are said to be in the G_0 **phase.**

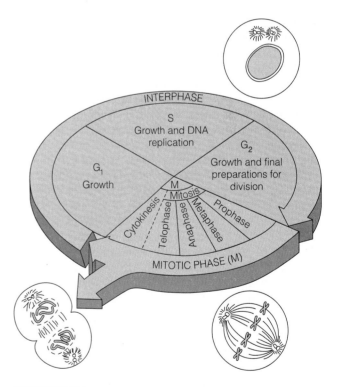

FIGURE 3.26
The cell cycle. During G_1, cells grow rapidly and carry out their routine functions; the centrioles begin to replicate as this phase ends. The S phase begins when DNA synthesis starts, and it ends when the DNA has replicated. In the short G_2 phase, materials needed for cell division are synthesized and growth continues. During the M phase (cell division), mitosis and cytokinesis occur, producing two daughter cells. The length of the cell cycle varies with different cell types, but the G_1 phase is the longest and most variable phase in all cells.

ously on several chromatin threads and continues until all of the DNA has been replicated.

The process begins with uncoiling of the DNA helices. A *helicase* enzyme untwists the double helix and gradually separates the DNA molecule into its two complementary nucleotide chains (Figure 3.27). The site of separation is called a *replication bubble;* the Y-shaped region at each end of the replication bubble is called a *replication fork.* Each freed nucleotide strand then serves as a *template,* or set of instructions, for building a new complementary nucleotide strand from DNA nucleosides in the nucleoplasm. Although the DNA building blocks are *nucleotides* the substrates for DNA synthesis are *nucleosides,* which differ by having not one but three phosphate groups. As in ATP, their terminal phosphates are secured by high-energy bonds, and as each nucleoside joins the growing nucleotide chain, hydrolysis of its terminal phosphates provides the energy to drive the polymerization process. A pretty neat system indeed.

Several enzymes are involved in DNA synthesis. *DNA polymerases,* the enzymes that position and then link the DNA nucleotides together, work only in one direction. Consequently, one strand, the *leading strand,* is synthesized continuously following the movement of the replication fork. The other strand, called the *lagging strand,* is constructed in segments in the opposite direction. The segments are linked together later.

Recall that nucleotide base pairing is always complementary: *adenine* (*A*) always bonds to *thymine* (*T*), and *guanine* (*G*) always bonds to *cytosine* (*C*) (see p. 55). Such specific base pairing ensures the precision of DNA replication: The order of the nucleotides on the template strand determines the order on the new strand being built. For example, a TACTGC sequence on a template strand would bond to new nucleotides with the order ATGACG; and the comparable region on the other template strand, which has the base sequence ATGACG, bonds to new nucleotides with the order TACTGC. The end result is that two DNA molecules are formed from and are identical to the original DNA helix, and each consists of one old and one newly assembled nucleotide strand. This mechanism of DNA replication is referred to as **semiconservative replication.** As soon as replication ends, histones associate with the DNA, completing the formation of two new chromatin strands. The chromatin strands condense to form **chromatids** (see Figure 3.25) and are united by a centromere. The chromatids remain attached until the cell has entered the anaphase stage of mitotic cell division. They are then distributed to the daughter cells, as next described, ensuring that each has identical genetic information.

Cell Division

Cell division is essential for body growth and tissue repair. Cells that continually wear away, such as cells of the skin and intestinal lining, reproduce them-

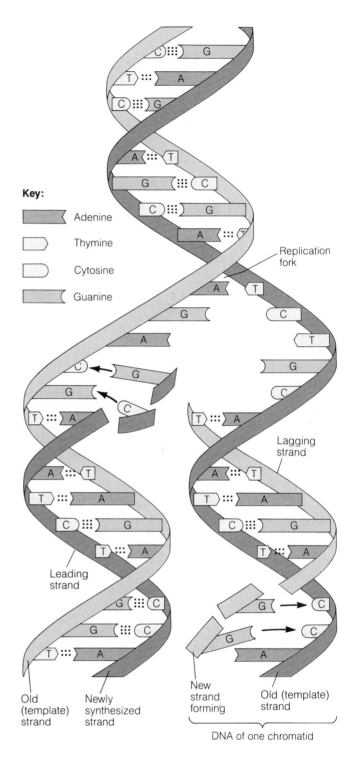

Key:
- Adenine
- Thymine
- Cytosine
- Guanine

Replication fork

Lagging strand

Leading strand

Old (template) strand

Newly synthesized strand

New strand forming

Old (template) strand

DNA of one chromatid

FIGURE 3.27
Replication of DNA. The DNA helix uncoils, and the hydrogen bonds between its base pairs are broken. Then each nucleotide strand of the DNA acts as a template for the construction of a complementary nucleotide strand, as illustrated in the bottom portion of the diagram. Because the DNA polymerases (not illustrated) work in one direction only, the two new strands (leading and lagging) are synthesized in opposite directions. After replication is completed, two DNA molecules exist, each identical to the original DNA molecule and to one another. Each DNA molecule formed consists of one old (template) strand and one newly assembled strand and constitutes a chromatid of a chromosome.

selves almost continuously. Others, such as liver cells, divide more slowly (maintaining the organ they compose at a particular size), but retain the ability to reproduce quickly if the organ is damaged. Cells of nervous tissue and skeletal and heart muscle totally lose their ability to divide when they are fully mature, and repairs are made with inelastic scar tissue (a fibrous type of connective tissue).

Control of Cell Division.   The signals that prod cells to divide are poorly understood, but we know that *surface-volume relationships* are important. The amount of nutrients a growing cell requires is directly related to its volume, but as a cell increases in volume, its surface area does not increase proportionately. Volume increases with the cube of cell radius, whereas surface area increases with the square of the radius. Thus, a 64-fold increase in cell volume is accompanied by only a 16-fold increase in surface area. Consequently, the surface area of the plasma membrane becomes inadequate for nutrient and waste exchange when a cell reaches a certain critical size. Cell division solves this problem because the smaller daughter cells once again have a favorable surface-volume relationship. These surface-volume relationships explain why most cells are microscopic in size. Other mechanisms that help to determine when cells divide include chemical signals released by other cells in the area or the availability of space. Normal cells stop proliferating when they begin touching, a phenomenon called *contact inhibition.* Cancer cells escape many of the normal controls of cell division and divide wildly, which makes them dangerous to their host (see *A Closer Look* on p. 96).

While the precise trigger for cell division is still unknown, one thing is sure—a number of "switches" are involved. For example, a crucial checkpoint occurs late in G_1. If all systems are "go" at this point, the cell enters the S phase, replicates its DNA, and begins the sequence of tasks necessary to divide. A second checkpoint occurs late in G_2 when a threshold amount of a protein complex called **MPF** is required to give the "OK" signal to enter the mitotic (M) phase. (Although originally called *maturation promoting factor,* it may be more helpful to remember MPF as *M-phase promoting factor.*) Activated MPF consists of a pair of proteins; either protein alone is useless. One of these proteins, called the *cell division cycle* (cdc_2) protein, is constant and always there. The other is one of a family of proteins called *cyclins,* because their levels rise and fall during each cycle. In response to some (as yet) unidentified signals, a new batch of cyclins is created *en masse* and is then destroyed in the twinkling of an eye at the end of mitosis. As the cdc_2 and cyclin proteins clasp together, they initiate enzymatic cascades that phosphorylate other proteins required to direct or perform the tasks of the various stages of cell division.

Events of Cell Division.   In most body cells, cell division or the **M (mitotic) phase** of the cell life cycle

(see Figure 3.26) involves two distinct events: *mitosis* (mi-to′sis), or division of the nucleus, and *cytokinesis* (si″to-ki-ne′sis), or division of the cytoplasm. A somewhat different process of nuclear division called *meiosis* (mi-o′sis) produces sex cells (ova and sperm) with only half the number of genes found in other body cells. (Then when two sex cells combine in fertilization, the full complement of genetic material is restored.) The details of meiosis are discussed in Chapter 28. Here we concentrate on mitotic cell division.

Mitosis.   Mitosis (*mit* = thread; *osis* = process) is the series of events that parcel out the replicated DNA of the mother cell to two daughter cells. (Use of the terms *mother cell* and *daughter cells* has a long history and carries no sexual implications.) Mitosis is described in terms of four phases: **prophase, metaphase, anaphase,** and **telophase,** but it is actually a continuous process, with one phase merging smoothly into the next. Its duration varies according to cell type, but it typically takes about 2 hours from start to finish. Mitosis is described in detail in Figure 3.28.

Cytokinesis.   Division of the cytoplasm, or **cytokinesis** (*kines* = movement), begins during late anaphase or early telophase (see Figure 3.28). The plasma membrane over the center of the cell (the spindle equator) is drawn inward to form a **cleavage furrow** by the activity of a *contractile ring* made of microfilaments. The cleavage furrow deepens until the original cytoplasmic mass is pinched into two parts, so that at the end of cytokinesis there are two daughter cells. Each is smaller and has less cytoplasm than the mother cell, but is *genetically* identical to it. The daughter cells then enter the interphase portion of their life cycle and grow and carry out normal cell activities until it is their turn to divide.

Protein Synthesis

In addition to directing its own replication, DNA serves as the master blueprint for protein synthesis. Although cells also make lipids and carbohydrates, DNA does not dictate the structure of those molecules; it specifies *only* the structure of protein molecules, including the enzymes that catalyze the synthesis of all classes of biological molecules. Most of the metabolic machinery of the cell is concerned in some way with protein synthesis. This should not be surprising, since structural proteins constitute most of the dry cell material, and functional proteins direct and underlie all cellular activities. Basically, cells are miniature protein factories that synthesize the huge variety of proteins that determine the chemical and physical nature of cells—and therefore of the body as a whole.

Proteins, you will recall, are composed of polypeptide chains, which in turn are made up of amino acids (see pp. 47–48). For purposes of this dis-

FIGURE 3.28
The stages of mitosis. These particular cells are from an early embryo of a whitefish. (Micrographs approx. 600×.) For simplicity, only four chromosomes are drawn.

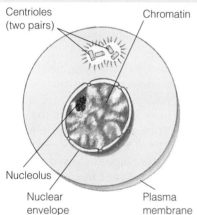

Centrioles (two pairs)   Chromatin

Nucleolus

Nuclear envelope   Plasma membrane

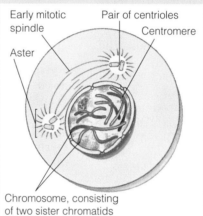

Early mitotic spindle   Pair of centrioles
                         Centromere
Aster

Chromosome, consisting of two sister chromatids

Fragments of nuclear envelope   Polar microtubules
                                 Kinetochore

Kinetochore microtubules   Spindle pole

Interphase

Interphase is the period of a cell's life when it is carrying out its normal metabolic activities and growing. During interphase, the chromosomal material is seen in the form of diffuse (extended) chromatin, and the nuclear membrane and nucleolus are intact and visible. Microtubule arrays (asters) are seen extending from the centrosomes. During various periods of this phase, the centrioles begin replicating (G_1 through G_2), DNA is replicated (S), and the final preparations for mitosis are completed (G_2). The centriole pair finishes replicating into two pairs during G_2.

Early prophase

Prophase, the first and longest phase of mitosis, begins when the chromatin threads start to coil and condense, forming barlike *chromosomes* that are visible with a light microscope. Since DNA replication has occurred during interphase, each chromosome is actually made up of two identical chromatin threads, now called *chromatids*. The chromatids of each chromosome are held together by a small, but-tonlike body called a *centromere*. After the chromatids separate, each will be considered a new chromosome.

As the chromosomes appear, the nucleoli disappear, and the cytoskeletal microtubules disassemble. The centriole pairs separate from one another. The centrioles act as focal points for growth of a new assembly of microtubules called the **mitotic spindle.** As these microtubules lengthen, they push the centrioles farther and farther apart, propelling them toward opposite ends (poles) of the cell.

Late prophase

While the centrioles are still moving away from each other, the nuclear membrane fragments, allowing the spindle to occupy the center of the cell and to interact with the chromosomes. The centrioles also cause the *asters,* microtubules to radiate outward from the ends of the spindle and anchor it to the plasma membrane. Meanwhile, some of the growing spindle microtubules attach to special protein complexes, called *kinetochores (ki-ne'to-korz),* on each chromosome's centromere. Such microtubules are called *kinetochore microtubules.* The remaining spindle microtubules, which do not attach to any chromosomes, are called *polar,* or *nonkinetochore, microtubules.* The kinetochore microtubules pull on each chromosome from both poles, resulting in a tug-of-war that ultimately draws the chromosomes to the middle of the cell.

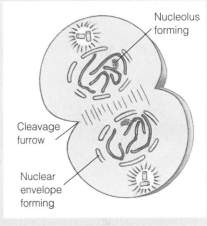

Metaphase plate

Spindle

Daughter chromosomes

Nucleolus forming

Cleavage furrow

Nuclear envelope forming

Metaphase

Metaphase is the second phase of mitosis. The chromosomes cluster at the middle of the cell, with their centromeres precisely aligned at the exact center, or *equator*, of the spindle. This arrangement of the chromosomes along a plane midway between the poles is called the *metaphase plate.*

Anaphase

Anaphase, the third phase of mitosis, begins abruptly as the centromeres of the chromosomes split, and each chromatid now becomes a chromosome in its own right. The kinetochore fibers shorten (probably due to their disassembly at their kinetochore ends) and, like a recoiling rubber band, gradually pull each chromosome toward the pole it faces. The polar microtubules slide past each other (a process presumed to be driven by kinesin motor molecules), lengthen and push the two poles of the cell apart causing the whole cell to elongate. Anaphase is easy to recognize because the moving chromosomes look V-shaped. The centromeres, which are attached to the kinetochore microtubules, lead the way, and the chromosomal "arms" dangle behind them. Anaphase is the shortest stage of mitosis; it typically lasts only a few minutes.

This process of moving and separating the chromosomes is helped by the fact that the chromosomes are short, compact bodies. Diffuse chromatin threads would tangle, trail, and break, which would damage the genetic material and result in its imprecise "parceling out" to the daughter cells.

Telophase and cytokinesis

Telophase begins as soon as chromosomal movement stops. This final phase is like prophase in reverse. The identical sets of chromosomes at the opposite poles of the cell uncoil and resume their threadlike extended chromatin form. A new nuclear membrane, derived from the rough ER, reforms around each chromatin mass. Nucleoli reappear within the nuclei, and the spindle breaks down and disappears. Mitosis is now ended. The cell, for just a brief period, is a binucleate cell (has two nuclei) and each new nucleus is identical to the original mother nucleus.

As a rule, as mitosis draws to a close, *cytokinesis* occurs, completing the division of the cell into two daughter cells. Cytokinesis occurs as a ring of peripheral microfilaments (not shown) contracts at the *cleavage furrow* and squeezes the cells apart.

cussion, we can define a **gene** as a segment of a DNA molecule that carries instructions for one polypeptide chain. However, selected genes specify the structure of certain varieties of RNA as their final product.

The four nucleotide bases (A, G, T, and C) are the "letters" of the genetic dictionary, and the information of DNA is found in the sequence of these bases. Each sequence of three bases, called a **triplet,** can be thought of as a "word" that specifies a particular amino acid. For example, the triplet AAA calls for the amino acid phenylalanine, while CCT calls for glycine. The sequence of the triplets in each gene forms a "sentence" that tells exactly how a particular polypeptide is to be made; it tells the number, kinds, and order of amino acids needed to build that protein. Variations in the arrangement of A, T, C, and G allow our cells to make all the different kinds of proteins needed. Even an unusually "small" gene has an estimated 2100 base pairs in sequence. Since the ratio between DNA bases in the gene and amino acids in the polypeptide is 3:1, the polypeptide specified by such a gene would be expected to contain 700 amino acids. Actually, the situation is not quite this simple because most genes of higher organisms contain **exons,** amino acid–specifying informational sequences, separated by **introns.** Introns are noncoding segments that range from 60 to 100,000 nucleotides long. Since a single gene may have as many as 50 introns, most genes are much larger than you might expect.

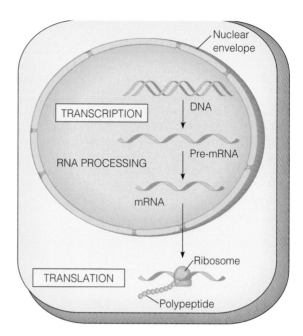

FIGURE 3.29
Simplified scheme of information flow from the DNA gene to protein structure. Information flows from DNA to mRNA during transcription. (The RNA is first synthesized as pre-mRNA, which is processed by enzymes before leaving the nucleus.) During translation, information flows from mRNA to synthesize a protein as amino acids are joined together in the designated order.

The Role of RNA

By itself, DNA is rather like a strip of magnetic recording tape: The information it contains cannot be expressed without a decoding mechanism. Furthermore, polypeptides are manufactured at ribosomes in the cytoplasm, but in interphase cells DNA never leaves the nucleus. So, DNA requires not only a decoder, but a messenger as well. The decoding and messenger functions are carried out by the second type of nucleic acid: RNA.

As you learned in Chapter 2, RNA differs from DNA in being single stranded and in having the sugar ribose instead of deoxyribose and the base uracil (U) instead of thymine (T). Three forms of RNA act together to carry out DNA's instructions for polypeptide synthesis: (1) **transfer RNA (tRNA),** small and roughly cloverleaf-shaped molecules; (2) **ribosomal RNA (rRNA),** which forms part of the ribosomes; and (3) **messenger RNA (mRNA),** relatively long nucleotide strands resembling "half-DNA" molecules, or one of the two strands of a DNA molecule.

All three types of RNA are formed on the DNA in the nucleus in much the same way as DNA replicates itself: The DNA helix separates and one of its strands serves as a template for synthesis of a complementary RNA strand. Once formed, the RNA molecule is released from the DNA template strand and migrates

into the cytoplasm. Its job done, DNA simply recoils into its helical, inactive form. Most of the nuclear DNA codes for the synthesis of short-lived mRNA, so named because it carries the "message" containing the instructions for building a polypeptide from the gene to the ribosomes. Thus, the end product of most genes is a polypeptide. Relatively small amounts of the DNA code for the synthesis of rRNA (the nucleolar organizer regions mentioned previously) and tRNA, both of which are long-lived and stable types of RNA. Since rRNA and tRNA do not carry codes for synthesizing other molecules, they are the final products of the genes that code for them. Ribosomal RNA and tRNA act together to "translate" the message carried by mRNA.

The rules by which the base sequence of a DNA gene are translated into protein structure (amino acid sequence) are referred to as the **genetic code.** Essentially, polypeptide synthesis involves two major steps: (1) *transcription,* in which DNA's information is encoded in mRNA, and (2) *translation,* in which the information carried by mRNA is decoded and used to assemble polypeptides. These steps are summarized simply in Figure 3.29 and described in more detail next.

Transcription

The word *transcription* often refers to one of the jobs done by a secretary—converting notes taken in shorthand into a longhand or typewritten copy. In other words, the same information is transformed, or transferred, from one form (or format) to another. In cells, **transcription** involves the transfer of information from a DNA gene's base sequence to the complementary base sequence of an mRNA molecule. The form is different, but the same information is being conveyed. Once the mRNA molecule is made, it detaches and leaves the nucleus. Only DNA and mRNA are involved in the transcription process.

Let us follow the transcription process when a particular polypeptide is to be made.

Making the mRNA Complement.

The process begins when *RNA polymerase,* the enzyme that oversees the synthesis of mRNA, binds to a special DNA site adjacent to the "start" sequence, called the promoter. Once bound, the polymerase opens up the DNA helix and the DNA segment coding for that protein is uncoiled. One DNA nucleotide strand, called the *sense strand,* serves as the template for the construction of a complementary mRNA molecule (see Figure 3.30, step 1). For example, if a particular DNA triplet sequence is AGC, the mRNA sequence synthesized at that site will be UCG. While each three-base sequence on DNA is called a triplet, the corresponding three-base sequence on mRNA is called a **codon,** reflecting the fact that it is the coded information of mRNA that is actually used in protein synthesis.

Since there are four kinds of RNA (or DNA) nucleotides, there are 4^3, or 64, possible codons. Three of these 64 codons are "stop signs" that specify the termination of a polypeptide; all the rest code for amino acids. Because there are only about 20 amino acids, some are specified by more than one codon. This redundancy in the genetic code helps protect against problems due to transcription (and translation) errors. A few examples of mRNA codons and the amino acids they specify are provided in Figure 3.31. A complete codon list is provided in Appendix B.

Editing of mRNA.

Although it would appear that translation can begin as soon as the complementary messenger is made, the process is a bit more complex. As mentioned before, mammalian DNA (like ours) has coding regions (exons) separated by noninformational regions (introns). Since the DNA gene is transcribed sequentially, the mRNA initially made, called pre-mRNA, is littered with intron "nonsense." Before the newly formed RNA can be used as a messenger, it must be edited (see Figure 3.29)—sections of the pre-mRNA corresponding to introns must be removed and the remaining exon-coded sections spliced together in the order in which they occurred in the DNA gene. This splicing process is mediated by RNA-

protein complexes called *small ribonucleoproteins,* or *snRNPs.* SnRNPs (pronounced "snurps") work together in assemblies called *spliceosomes* (spli'so-sōmz) to produce the functional mRNA that directs translation at the ribosome.

Translation

A translator takes a message in one language and restates it in another. In the **translation** step of protein synthesis, the language of nucleic acids (base sequence) is translated into the language of proteins (amino acid sequence). The process of translation occurs in the cytoplasm and involves all three varieties of RNA (see Figure 3.30, steps 2–5).

When the mRNA molecule carrying instructions for a particular protein reaches the cytoplasm, it binds to a small ribosomal subunit by base pairing to rRNA. Then transfer RNA comes into the picture. As its name suggests, tRNA has the job of transferring amino acids to the ribosome. There are approximately 20 different types of tRNA, each capable of binding with a specific amino acid. The attachment process is controlled by a synthetase enzyme in each case and is activated by ATP. Once the tRNA molecule has picked up its amino acid, it migrates to the ribosome, where it maneuvers the amino acid into the proper position, as specified by the codons on the mRNA strand. This is a bit more complex than it seems. Not only must tRNA bring an amino acid to the protein synthesis site, but it must also "recognize" the codon calling for that amino acid.

The structure of the tiny tRNA molecule is well suited for its dual function. The amino acid is bound to one end of tRNA, at a region called the "tail." At the other end, the "head," is its **anticodon** (an"ti-ko'don), a specific three-base sequence complementary to the mRNA codon calling for the amino acid carried by that particular tRNA. Since tRNA anticodons are able to form hydrogen bonds with complementary codons, the tiny tRNAs serve as the links between the languages of nucleic acids and proteins. Thus, if the mRNA codon is UUU, which specifies phenylalanine, the tRNAs carrying phenylalanine will have the anticodon AAA, which can bind to the correct codons.

The translation process begins when the first, or "initiator," mRNA codon, usually AUG (see Figure 3.31), is recognized and bound by the anticodon (UAC) of a tRNA carrying the amino acid methionine. This stimulates a large ribosomal subunit to bind and results in the formation of a functional ribosome with mRNA positioned in the "groove" between the two ribosomal subunits.

The ribosome is more than just a passive attachment site for mRNA and tRNA. Besides its binding site for mRNA, it has two binding sites for tRNA (A site for incoming tRNA and P site for outgoing tRNA), and its function in translation is to coordinate the coupling of codons and anticodons. Once the first

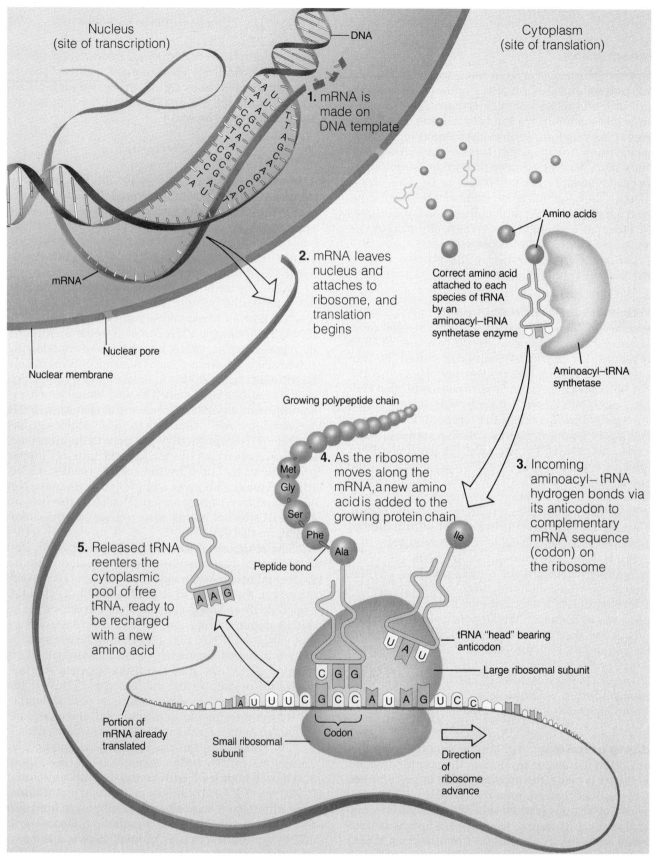

FIGURE 3.30

Protein synthesis. (1) *Transcription*. The DNA segment, or gene, specifying one polypeptide uncoils, and one strand acts as a template for the synthesis of a complementary mRNA molecule. (2–5) *Translation*. Messenger RNA from the nucleus attaches to a small ribosomal subunit in the cytoplasm (2). Transfer RNA transports amino acids to the mRNA strand and recognizes the mRNA codon calling for its amino acid by base pairing with it (via its anticodon). The ribosome then assembles and translation begins (3). The ribosome moves along the mRNA strand as each codon is read sequentially (4). As each amino acid is bound to the next by a peptide bond, its tRNA is released (5). The polypeptide is released when the stop codon is read. (For simplicity, the mRNA editing that occurs in phase 1 is not shown.)

Triplets

DNA base sequence (triplets) of the "gene" coding for the synthesis of a particular polypeptide chain

Codons

Base sequence (codons) of the transcribed mRNA

Consecutive base sequences of tRNA *anticodons* capable of recognizing the mRNA codons "calling for" the amino acids they transport

Amino acid sequence of the polypeptide chain

FIGURE 3.31
Information transfer from DNA to RNA. Information is transferred from the DNA of the gene to the complementary messenger RNA molecule, whose codons are then "read" by transfer RNA anticodons. Notice that the "reading" of the mRNA by tRNA anticodons reestablishes the base (triplet) sequence of the DNA genetic code (except that T is replaced by U).

tRNA has been positioned on a codon as just described, the ribosome moves the mRNA strand along, bringing the next codon into position to be "read" by another tRNA. As successive amino acids are brought to their proper positions, peptide bonds are formed between them and the polypeptide chain becomes longer and longer. When each amino acid is bonded to the next, its tRNA is released from the P site and moves away from the ribosome to pick up another amino acid. As mRNA is progressively read, its initial portion is moved off the ribosome and may become attached successively to several other ribosomes, all reading the same message simultaneously. Such a multiple ribosome-mRNA complex is called a *polyribosome,* and it provides an efficient system for producing many copies of the same protein. The mRNA strand continues to be read sequentially until its last codon, the *terminal codon,* or *stop codon* (see Figure 3.31), enters the ribosomal groove. The terminal codon is the "period" at the end of the mRNA sentence that triggers the release of the completed polypeptide chain from the ribosome. The ribosome then dissociates into its subunits, if not engaged by another mRNA molecule.

The genetic information of a cell is translated into the production of proteins via a sequence of information transfer that is completely directed by complementary base pairing. Notice that if the anticodons of all the tRNAs reading the mRNA codons could be aligned at the same time, the DNA base sequence would be reestablished, except that T of DNA is represented by U in tRNA. Thus, the transfer of information goes from DNA base sequence (triplets) to the complementary base sequence of mRNA (codons) and back to the DNA base sequence (anticodons).

EXTRACELLULAR MATERIALS

Many substances contributing to body mass are found outside the cells. These substances are referred to collectively as **extracellular materials.** One class of extracellular materials is *body fluids,* represented by interstitial fluid, blood plasma, and cerebrospinal fluid. These extracellular fluids are important as transport and dissolving media. *Cellular secretions,* also extracellular materials, include substances that aid in digestion (intestinal and gastric fluids) and that act as lubricants (saliva, mucus, and serous fluids).

By far the most abundant of the extracellular materials is the *extracellular matrix.* Most body cells are in contact with a jellylike substance composed of proteins and polysaccharides. These molecules are secreted by the cells and self-assemble into an organized mesh in the extracellular space, where they serve as a universal "cell glue" that helps to hold

A CLOSER LOOK | Cancer—The Intimate Enemy

The word **cancer** elicits dread in nearly everyone. Why does cancer strike some and not others? Are its "seeds" part of our genetic dowry?

Research has revealed a surprisingly close relationship between cancer and fundamental life processes. Although formerly perceived as an example of rapid disorganized cell growth, this disease is now known to be a logical, coordinated process in which a precise sequence of tiny alterations changes a normal cell into a killer. Let's take a closer look at what cancer really is.

When cells fail to honor normal controls of cell division and multiply excessively, an abnormal mass of proliferating cells called a *neoplasm* (literally, "new growth") results. Neoplasms are classified as benign or malignant. A **benign** ("kindly") **neoplasm**, commonly called a *tumor,* is strictly a local affair. These compact neoplasms, which are often encapsulated, tend to grow slowly and seldom kill their hosts if they are removed before they compress vital organs. In contrast, **malignant (cancerous) neoplasms** are nonencapsulated masses that grow more relentlessly and may become killers. Their cells, which usually resemble immature (undifferentiated) cells, invade their surroundings rather than pushing them aside, as reflected in the name *cancer,* from the Latin word for "crab." Malignant cells can also break away from the parent mass, the *primary tumor,* and travel via blood or lymph to other body organs, where they form *sec-ondary cancer masses.* This capability, called **metastasis** (mĕ-tas'tah-sis), and invasiveness distinguish cancer cells from the cells of benign neoplasms. Cancer cells consume an exceptional amount of the body's nutrients, leading to loss of weight and tissue wasting that contribute to death.

Mechanisms of Carcinogenesis. But, what causes **transformation**—the changes that convert a normal cell to a cancerous one? It is well known that some physical factors (radiation, mechanical trauma), certain viral infections, and many chemicals (tobacco tars, saccharine, some natural food chemicals) can act as **carcinogens** (cancer-causers). What all of these factors have in common is that they all cause mutations—changes in DNA that alter the expression of certain genes. However, not all carcinogens get the chance to do damage because most are eliminated by peroxisomal or lysosomal enzymes or by the immune system. Furthermore, one mutation "doesn't do it"—apparently it takes a sequence of several genetic changes to change a normal cell to a full-fledged cancer cell. A clue to the role of genes was provided by the discovery of **oncogenes** (Greek *onco* = tumor), or cancer-causing genes in rapidly spreading cancers. Later, **proto-oncogenes,** benign forms of oncogenes in normal cells, were discovered. Proto-oncogenes code for proteins that are essential for cell division, growth, and cellular adhesion, among other things. However, many have fragile sites that break when exposed to carcinogens, causing their conversion to oncogenes. Examples of problems that might result from this "betrayal" are loss of an enzyme that controls an important metabolic process, and "switching on" of additional (or dormant) genes that allow cells to become invasive and metastasize (capabilities present in embryonic cells and cancer cells but not adult cells).

Oncogenes have been detected in only 15% to 20% of human cancers, so investigators were not too surprised by the more recent discovery of **tumor suppressor genes,** or **anti–oncogenes,** such as p53 and p16, which work to suppress cancer. These genes influence processes that inactivate carcinogens, aid DNA repair, or enhance the ability of the immune system to destroy cancer cells. Whatever genetic factor is at work, the "seeds" of cancer do appear to be in our own genes; thus cancer is an intimate enemy indeed.

A model of some of the mutations known to occur in colorectal cancer, one of the best-understood human cancers, appears in the accompanying flowchart. As with most cancers, the development of a metastasizing colon cancer is a gradual process. One of the first signs is the appearance of a polyp, a small benign growth consisting of apparently normal mucosa cells. As cell division continues, the growth enlarges, becoming an adenoma. As various tumor-suppressor genes are inactivated and the *RAS*

---

body cells together. In connective tissues the extracellular matrix is particularly abundant—so much so, in some cases, that it (rather than living cells) accounts for the bulk of that tissue type. Depending on the structure to be formed, connective tissue extracellular matrix may be soft, tough and ropelike, or rock-hard. In the next chapter, we will pay a good deal of attention to the matrix of specialized connective tissues.

DEVELOPMENTAL ASPECTS OF CELLS

We all begin life as a single cell, the fertilized egg, from which arise all the cells of our body. Very early in development, cells begin to specialize, some forming liver cells, some nerve cells, and others becoming the transparent lens of the eye. Since all our cells carry the same genes, how can one cell be so different from another? This is a fascinating question. Appar-

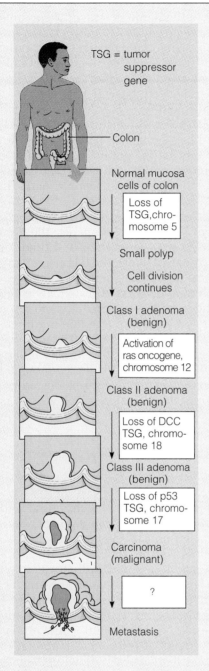

TSG = tumor suppressor gene

Colon

Normal mucosa cells of colon

Loss of TSG, chromosome 5

Small polyp

Cell division continues

Class I adenoma (benign)

Activation of ras oncogene, chromosome 12

Class II adenoma (benign)

Loss of DCC TSG, chromosome 18

Class III adenoma (benign)

Loss of p53 TSG, chromosome 17

Carcinoma (malignant)

?

Metastasis

oncogene is mobilized, the mutations pile up and the adenoma becomes increasingly abnormal. The final consequence is colon carcinoma (cancer). Colon cancer metastasis is common, its genetic trigger is not yet known.

Cancer Prevalence, Types, and Management.
Almost half of all Americans develop cancer in their lifetime and a fifth of us will die of it. Cancer can arise from almost any cell type, but the most common cancers originate in the skin, lung, colon, breast, male prostate gland, and urinary bladder (in that order).

Many forms of cancer are preceded by observable structural changes in the tissue called *preneoplastic lesions.* An example is the development of *leukoplakia,* white patches in the mouth that may result from chronic irritation of badly fitting dentures or heavy smoking. Although these lesions sometimes progress to cancer, in many cases they remain stable or even revert to a normal condition if the environmental stimulus is removed.

Cancer management techniques vary, but the usual sequence is:

1. Diagnosis. Screening procedures, such as self-examination of one's breasts or testicles for lumps, and checking fecal samples for blood, aid in early detection of cancers. However, most cancers are diagnosed only after they have begun to cause symptoms (pain, bloody discharge, lump, etc.) and the diagnostic method most used is the biopsy. In a biopsy, a sample of the primary tumor is removed surgically (or by scraping) and examined microscopically for structural changes typical of malignant cells.

2. Staging. Several techniques (physical and histological examinations, lab tests, and imaging techniques) are used to determine the extent of the disease (size of the neoplasm, degree of metastasis, etc.). Then, the cancer is assigned a stage from 1 to 4 according to the probability of cure (stage 1 has the best probability, stage 4 the worst).

3. Treatment. Most cancers are removed surgically if possible. To destroy metastasized cells, surgery is commonly followed by radiation therapy (X irradiation and/or treatment with radioisotopes) and chemotherapy (treatment with cytotoxic drugs).

Treatment cures about half of all cancer cases. However, some cancers have very low survival rates; these include cancers of the lungs, digestive organs, and ovaries. The newest research seeks to fix defective tumor-suppressor genes and oncogenes in cancer cells.

Cancer treatments can be extremely distressing because most target all rapidly dividing cells in the body, including normal ones. For example, chemotherapy causes nausea, vomiting, and hair loss.

There are many still-unproved cancer treatments "in the wings," so to speak. *Differentiation therapy* uses drugs to force cancer cells from their immature uncontrolled state toward a more normal specialized form. Immunotherapy uses antibodies, protein molecules that act in the immune response, to immobilize cancer cells. *Monoclonal antibodies,* made by genetic engineering techniques, respond to a single protein on a cancerous cell. These "silver bullets" are being used to deliver cytotoxic drugs exclusively to the cancer cells.

ently, cells in various regions of the embryo are exposed to different chemical signals that channel them into specific pathways of development. When the embryo consists of just a few cells, slight differences in oxygen and carbon dioxide concentrations between the more superficial and the deeper cells may be the major signals. But as development continues, cells release chemicals that influence development of neighboring cells by switching some of their genes "on" or "off." Some genes are active in all cells;

for example, all cells have to carry out protein synthesis and make ATP. However, genes for enzymes that catalyze the synthesis of specialized products such as hormones or neurotransmitters are activated only in certain cell populations—only cells of the thyroid gland can produce thyroxine. Hence, the secret of cell specialization lies in the kinds of proteins made and reflects differential gene activation in different cell types. Cell specialization leads to *structural* variation —different organelles come to predominate in different cells. For example, muscle cells make tremendous quantities of actin and myosin, and their cytoplasm fills with microfilaments; liver and phagocytic cells produce more lysosomal enzymes and lysosomes. The development of specific and distinctive features in cells is called **cell differentiation**.

During early development, cell death and destruction are normal events. Nature takes a few chances. More cells than are needed are produced and excesses are eliminated. This is particularly true in the nervous system. Most organs are well formed and functional long before birth, but the body continues to grow and enlarge by forming new cells throughout childhood and adolescence. Once adult size has been reached, cell division is important mainly to replace short-lived cells and repair wounds.

During young adulthood, cell numbers remain fairly constant. However, local changes in the rate of cell division are fairly common. For example, when one is anemic, bone marrow undergoes **hyperplasia** (hi″per-pla′ze-ah), or accelerated growth (*hyper* = over; *plas* = grow), so that red blood cells are produced at a faster rate. If the anemia is remedied, the excessive marrow activity ceases. **Atrophy** (at′ro-fe), a decrease in size of an organ or body tissue, can result from loss of normal stimulation. Muscles that lose their nerve supply atrophy and waste away, and lack of exercise leads to thinned, brittle bones.

Cell aging occurs and is a complex process with many causes. The *wear-and-tear theory* attributes aging to little chemical insults that have cumulative effects throughout life. For example, environmental toxins such as pesticides, alcohol, and bacterial toxins may damage cell membranes, poison enzyme systems, or cause "mistakes" in DNA replication. Temporary lack of oxygen, which occurs increasingly with age as our blood vessels clog with fatty materials, leads to accelerated rates of cell death throughout the body. X rays and other types of radiation, as well as some chemicals, can generate huge numbers of free radicals, which can overwhelm the peroxisomal enzymes. Vitamins C and E and beta carotene appear to act as antioxidants in the body and may help to prevent excessive free radical formation. Attack comes from within as well. With age, glucose (blood sugar) becomes party to cross linking our proteins together, which severely disrupts protein function.

Another theory of cell aging attributes it to progressive disorders in the immune system. According to this theory, cell damage results from (1) autoimmune responses in which the immune system turns against one's own tissues, and (2) a progressive weakening of the immune response, so that the body is less and less able to get rid of cell-damaging pathogens.

Perhaps the most widely accepted theory of cell aging is the *genetic theory,* which suggests that cessation of mitosis and cell aging are "programmed into our genes." One interesting notion here is that a *telomere clock* determines the number of times a cell can divide. Telomeres (*telo* = end; *mer* = part) are strings of nucleotides that cap the end of chromosomes, protecting them from fraying or fusing with other chromosomes. In human telomeres, the base sequence TTAGGG is repeated a thousand times or more (like a DNA stutter). Though the telomeres carry no genes, they appear to be vital for chromosomal survival, because each time DNA is replicated, 50 to 100 of the end nucleotides are lost and the telomere gets a bit shorter. When telomeres reach a certain minimum length, the stop-division signal is given. The idea that cell longevity depends on telomeres integrity is supported by the 1994 discovery of *telomerase,* an enzyme believed to protect telomeres from degrading. Pegged as the "immortality enzyme," telomerase is almost universally found in cancer cells, but not in other cell types.

*   *   *

We have described the cell, the structural and functional unit that fashions and maintains our bodies, from the vantage point of the generalized cell. One of the wonders of the cell is the disparity between its minute size and its extraordinary activity, which reflects the amazing diversity of its organelles. The evidence for division of labor and functional specialization among organelles is inescapable: Only ribosomes synthesize proteins, and intracellular digestion is the bailiwick of lysosomes. Membranes compartmentalize most organelles, allowing them to work without hindering or being hindered by other cell activities, and the plasma membrane regulates molecular traffic across the cell's boundary. Now that you know what cells have in common, you are ready to explore how they differ in the various body tissues.

RELATED CLINICAL TERMS

Anaplasia (an″ah-pla′ze-ah; *an* = without, not; *plas* = to grow) Abnormalities in cell structure; e.g., cancer cells typically lose the appearance of the parent cells and come to resemble undifferentiated or embryonic cells.

Dialysis (di-al′ĭ-sis; *dialys* = separate, break apart) The process of separating smaller solute molecules from larger ones in a solution by means of diffusion through a selectively permeable membrane; used by the artificial kidney to cleanse the blood of metabolic wastes, such as urea, and excess ions.

Dysplasia (dis-pla′ze-ah; *dys* = abnormal) A change in cell size, shape, or arrangement due to chronic irritation or inflammation (infections, etc.).

Hypertrophy (hi-per′tro-fe) Growth of an organ or tissue due to an increase in the size of its cells. Hypertrophy is a normal response of skeletal muscle cells when they are challenged to lift excessive weight; differs from hyperplasia, which is an increase in size due to increase in cell number.

Liposomes (lip′o-sōmz) Hollow microscopic sacs formed of phospholipids that can be filled with a variety of drugs. Serve as multi-purpose vehicles for drugs, genetic material, and cosmetics.

Mutation A change in DNA base sequence leading to incorporation of "incorrect" amino acids in particular positions in the resulting protein; the affected protein may remain unimpaired or may function abnormally or not at all, leading to disease.

Necrosis (nĕ-kro′sis; *necros* = death; *osis* = process) Death of a cell or group of cells due to injury or disease.

CHAPTER SUMMARY

Overview of the Cellular Basis of Life (pp. 60–61)

1. All living organisms are composed of cells—the basic structural and functional units of life.

2. The principle of complementarity states that the biochemical activity of cells reflects the operation of organelles.

3. Cells vary widely in both shape and size.

4. The generalized cell is a concept that typifies all cells. The generalized cell has three major regions—the nucleus, cytoplasm, and plasma membrane.

The Plasma Membrane: Structure (pp. 61–65)

1. The plasma membrane encloses cell contents, mediates exchanges with the extracellular environment, and plays a role in cellular communication.

The Fluid Mosaic Model (pp. 61–64)
2. The fluid mosaic model depicts the plasma membrane as a fluid bilayer of lipids (phospholipids, cholesterol, and glycolipids) within which proteins are inserted.

3. The lipids have both hydrophilic and hydrophobic regions that organize their aggregation and self-repair. The lipids form the structural part of the plasma membrane.

4. Most proteins are integral transmembrane proteins that extend entirely through the membrane. Some, appended to the integral proteins, are peripheral proteins.

5. Proteins are responsible for most specialized membrane functions; i.e., some are enzymes, some are receptors, and others mediate membrane transport functions. Externally facing glycoproteins contribute to the glycocalyx.

Specializations of the Plasma Membrane (pp. 64–65)
6. Microvilli are extensions of the plasma membrane that typically increase its surface area for absorption.

7. Membrane junctions join cells together and may aid or inhibit movement of molecules between or past cells. Tight junctions are impermeable junctions; desmosomes mechanically couple cells into a functional community; gap junctions allow joined cells to communicate.

The Plasma Membrane: Functions (pp. 65–75)

Membrane Transport (pp. 65–73)
1. The plasma membrane acts as a selectively permeable barrier. Substances are moved across the plasma membrane by passive processes, which depend on the kinetic energy of molecules or on pressure gradients, and by active processes, which depend on the provision of cellular energy (ATP).

2. Diffusion is the movement of molecules (driven by kinetic energy) down a concentration gradient. Fat-soluble solutes can diffuse directly through the membrane by dissolving in the lipid. Charged small molecules or ions move by diffusion through the membrane if they are small enough to pass through the protein channels. Some protein channels are selective.

3. Osmosis is the diffusion of a solvent, such as water, through a selectively permeable membrane. Water diffuses through the membrane pores from a solution of lesser osmolarity to a solution of greater osmolarity.

4. The presence of impermeable solutes leads to changes in cell tone that may cause cell swelling or shrinkage. Net osmosis ceases when the solute concentration on both sides of the plasma membrane reaches equilibrium.

5. Solutions that cause a net loss of water from cells are hypertonic; those causing net water gain are hypotonic; those causing neither gain nor loss of cellular water are isotonic.

6. Facilitated diffusion is the passive movement of certain solutes across the membrane by their combination with a membrane carrier protein. As with other diffusion processes, it is driven by kinetic energy, but the carriers are selective.

7. Filtration occurs when a filtrate is forced across a membrane by hydrostatic pressure. It is nonselective and limited only by pore size. The pressure gradient is the driving force.

8. Active transport (solute pumping) depends on a carrier protein and ATP. Substances transported (amino acids and ions) move against concentration or electrical gradients. Many such systems (pumps) are coupled, i.e., cotransported substances move in the same (symport) or opposite (antiport) directions across the membrane.

9. Endocytotic processes also require that ATP be provided. If the substance is particulate, the process is called phagocytosis; if the substance is dissolved molecules, the process is pinocytosis. Receptor-mediated endocytosis is selective; engulfed particles (minerals, cholesterol, and some hormones) attach to receptors on the membrane before endocytosis occurs.

Generation and Maintenance of a Resting Membrane Potential (pp. 73–74)
10. All cells in the resting stage exhibit a voltage across their membrane, called the resting membrane potential.

11. The membrane potential is generated by concentration gradients of and differential permeability of the plasma membrane to sodium and potassium ions. Sodium is in high extracellular–low intracellular concentration, and the membrane is poorly permeable to it. Potassium is in high concentration in the cell and low concentration in the extracellular fluid. The membrane is more permeable to potassium than to sodium.

12. The greater outward diffusion of potassium (than inward diffusion of sodium) leads to a charge separation at the membrane (inside negative). This charge separation is maintained by the operation of the sodium-potassium pump.

13. Because of the membrane potential, both concentration and electrical gradients determine the ease of an ion's diffusion.

Cell-Environment Interactions (pp. 74–75)
14. Cells interact directly and indirectly with other cells. Indirect interactions involve extracellular chemicals carried in body fluids or forming part of the extracellular matrix.

15. Molecules of the glycocalyx are intimately involved in cell-environment interactions. Most are cell adhesion molecules or membrane receptors.

16. Activated membrane receptors act as catalysts, regulate channels, or like G protein–linked receptors, act through second messengers such as cyclic AMP and Ca^{2+}. Ligand binding results in changes in protein structure or function within the targeted cell.

17. Nitric oxide is a highly reactive gas that plays a number of biological roles in neural, cardiovascular, and immune functioning.

The Cytoplasm (pp. 75–84)

1. The cytoplasm, the cellular region between the nuclear and plasma membranes, consists of the cytosol (fluid cytoplasmic environment), inclusions (nonliving nutrient stores, pigment granules, crystals, etc.), and cytoplasmic organelles.

Cytoplasmic Organelles (pp. 75–84)

2. The cytoplasm is the major functional area of the cell. These functions are mediated by cytoplasmic organelles.

3. Mitochondria are sites of ATP formation. Their internal enzymes carry out the oxidative reactions of cellular respiration.

4. Ribosomes, composed of two subunits containing ribosomal RNA and proteins, are the sites of protein synthesis. They may be free or attached to membranes.

5. The rough endoplasmic reticulum is a ribosome-studded membrane system. Its cisternae act as sites for protein modification. Its external face acts in phospholipid and cholesterol synthesis. Vesicles pinched off from the ER transport the proteins to other cell sites.

6. The smooth endoplasmic reticulum synthesizes lipid and steroid molecules. It also acts in fat metabolism and in drug detoxification. In muscle cells, it is a calcium ion depot.

7. The Golgi apparatus is a membranous system close to the nucleus that packages protein secretions for export, packages enzymes into lysosomes for cellular use, and modifies proteins destined to become part of cellular membranes.

8. Lysosomes are membranous sacs of acid hydrolases packaged by the Golgi apparatus. Sites of intracellular digestion, they degrade worn-out organelles, and tissues that are no longer useful, and release ionic calcium from bone.

9. Peroxisomes are membranous sacs containing oxidase enzymes that protect the cell from the destructive effects of free radicals and other toxic substances by converting them to hydrogen peroxide, and then water.

10. The cytoskeleton includes microfilaments, intermediate filaments, microtubules, and the microtrabecular lattice. Microfilaments, formed of contractile proteins, are important in cell motility or movement of cell parts. Microtubules organize the cytoskeleton and are important in intracellular transport. Intermediate filaments help cells resist mechanical stress. A microtrabecular lattice may connect other elements and provide attachment sites for ribosomes and soluble enzymes.

11. Centrioles form the mitotic spindle and are the basis of cilia and flagella.

The Nucleus (pp. 84–86)

1. The nucleus is the control center of the cell. Most cells have a single nucleus. Without a nucleus, a cell cannot divide or synthesize more proteins; thus, it is destined to die.

2. The nucleus is surrounded by the nuclear envelope, a double membrane penetrated by fairly large pores.

3. Chromatin is a complex network of slender threads containing histone proteins and DNA. The chromatin units are called nucleosomes. When a cell begins to divide, the chromatin coils and condenses.

4. Nucleoli are nuclear sites of ribosome subunit synthesis.

Cell Growth and Reproduction (pp. 86–95)

The Cell Life Cycle (pp. 86–89)

1. The cell life cycle is the series of changes that a cell goes through from the time it is formed until it divides.

2. Interphase is the nondividing phase of the cell life cycle. Interphase consists of G_1, S, and G_2 subphases. During G_1, the cell grows vigorously and centriole replication begins; during the S phase, DNA is replicated; and during G_2, the final preparations for division are made.

3. DNA replication occurs before cell division. The DNA helix uncoils, and each DNA nucleotide strand acts as a template for the formation of a complementary strand from DNA nucleosides present in the nucleus. Base pairing provides the guide for the proper positioning of the nucleotides.

4. The products of the semiconservative replication of a DNA molecule are two DNA molecules identical to the parent molecule, each formed of one "old" and one "new" strand.

5. Cell division, essential for body growth and repair, occurs during the M phase. Cell division is stimulated by certain chemicals (including MPF) and increasing cell size. Lack of space and inhibitory chemicals deter cell division. Cell division consists of two distinct phases: mitosis and cytokinesis.

6. Mitosis, consisting of prophase, metaphase, anaphase, and telophase, results in the parceling out of the replicated chromosomes to two daughter nuclei, each genetically identical to the mother nucleus. Cytokinesis, which usually follows mitosis, divides the cytoplasmic mass into two parts.

7. Cancer is the consequence of uncontrolled cell division in which the cells produced often change structurally (dedifferentiate), become invasive, and metastasize. Cancers result from changes in DNA that are promoted in most cases by environmental factors. Methods of treatment include surgery, radiotherapy, and chemotherapy.

Protein Synthesis (pp. 89–95)

8. A gene is defined as a DNA segment that provides the instructions for the synthesis of one polypeptide chain. Since the major structural materials of the body are proteins, and since all enzymes are proteins, this amply covers the synthesis of all biological molecules.

9. The base sequence of DNA provides the information for protein structure. Each three-base sequence (triplet) calls for a particular amino acid to be built into a polypeptide chain.

10. The three varieties of RNA are synthesized on single strands of the DNA template. RNA nucleotides are joined following base-pairing rules.

11. Ribosomal RNA forms part of the protein synthesis sites; messenger RNA carries instructions for making a polypeptide chain from the DNA to the ribosomes; transfer RNA ferries amino acids to the ribosomes and recognizes codons on the mRNA strand specifying its amino acid.

12. Protein synthesis involves (1) transcription, synthesis of a

complementary mRNA, and (2) translation, "reading" of the mRNA by tRNA and peptide bonding of the amino acids into the polypeptide chain. Ribosomes coordinate translation.

13. In mammalian cells, introns (noncoding segments) must be removed from the pre-MRNA before it can be used for translation.

Extracellular Materials (pp. 95–96)

1. Substances found outside the cells are called extracellular materials. These include body fluids, cellular secretions, and extracellular matrix. Extracellular matrix is particularly abundant in connective tissues.

Developmental Aspects of Cells (pp. 96–98)

1. The first cell of an organism is the fertilized egg. Early in development, cell specialization begins and reflects differential gene activation.

2. During adulthood, cell numbers remain fairly constant; cell division occurs primarily to replace lost cells.

3. Cellular aging may reflect chemical insults, progressive disorders of immunity, and/or a genetically programmed decline in the rate of cell division with age.

REVIEW QUESTIONS

Multiple Choice/Matching

1. The smallest unit capable of life by itself is (a) the organ, (b) the organelle, (c) the tissue, (d) the cell, (e) the nucleus.

2. The most abundant types of lipid found in the plasma membranes are (choose two) (a) cholesterol, (b) neutral fats, (c) phospholipids, (d) fat-soluble vitamins.

3. Membrane junctions that allow nutrients or ions to flow from cell to cell are (a) desmosomes, (b) gap junctions, (c) tight junctions, (d) all of these.

4. A person drinks a six-pack of beer and has to make several trips to the bathroom. This increase in urination reflects an increase in what process occurring in the kidneys? (a) diffusion, (b) osmosis, (c) dialysis, (d) filtration.

5. The term used to describe the type of solution in which cells will lose water to their environment is (a) isotonic, (b) hypertonic, (c) hypotonic, (d) catatonic.

6. Osmosis always involves (a) a differentially permeable membrane, (b) a difference in solvent concentration, (c) diffusion, (d) active transport, (e) a, b, and c.

7. A physiologist observes that the concentration of sodium inside a cell is decidedly lower than that outside the cell. Yet sodium does diffuse easily across the plasma membrane of such cells when they are dead, but *not* when they are alive. Which of the following terms applies best to this cellular function that is lacking in dead cells? (a) osmosis, (b) diffusion, (c) active transport (solute pumping), (d) dialysis.

8. The solute-pumping variety of active transport is accomplished by (a) pinocytosis, (b) phagocytosis, (c) electrical forces in the cell membrane, (d) conformational-positional changes in carrier molecules in the plasma membrane.

9. The endocytotic process in which particulate matter is engulfed and brought into the cell is called (a) phagocytosis, (b) pinocytosis, (c) exocytosis.

10. The nuclear substance composed of histone proteins and DNA is (a) chromatin, (b) the nucleolus, (c) nuclear sap, or nucleoplasm, (d) nuclear pores.

11. The information sequence that determines the nature of a protein is the (a) nucleotide, (b) gene, (c) triplet, (d) codon.

12. Mutations may be caused by (a) X rays, (b) certain chemicals, (c) radiation from ionizing radioisotopes, (d) all of these.

13. The phase of mitosis during which centrioles reach the poles and chromosomes attach to the spindle is (a) anaphase, (b) metaphase, (c) prophase, (d) telophase.

14. Final preparations for cell division are made during the life cycle subphase called (a) G_1, (b) G_2, (c) M, (d) S.

15. The RNA synthesized on one of the DNA strands is (a) mRNA, (b) tRNA, (c) rRNA, (d) all of these.

16. The RNA species that carries the coded message, specifying the sequence of amino acids in the protein to be made, from the nucleus to the cytoplasm is (a) mRNA, (b) tRNA, (c) rRNA, (d) all of these.

17. If DNA has a sequence of AAA, then a segment of mRNA synthesized on it will have a sequence of (a) TTT, (b) UUU, (c) GGG, (d) CCC.

18. A nerve cell and a lymphocyte are presumed to differ in their (a) specialized structure, (b) suppressed genes and embryonic history, (c) genetic information, (d) a and b, (e) a and c.

Short Answer Essay Section

19. (a) Name the organelle that is the major site of ATP synthesis. (b) Name three organelles involved in protein synthesis and/or modification. (c) Name two organelles that contain enzymes, and describe their relative functions.

20. Explain why mitosis can be thought of as cellular immortality.

21. If a cell loses or ejects its nucleus, what is its fate and why?

22. The external faces of some of the proteins in the plasma membrane have carbohydrate groups attached to them. What role do such "sugar-coated" proteins play in the life of the cell?

23. Cells are living units. However, three classes of nonliving substances are found outside the cells. What are these classes, and what functional roles do they play?

24. Comment on the role of the sodium-potassium pump in maintaining a cell's resting membrane potential.

 CRITICAL THINKING AND CLINICAL APPLICATION QUESTIONS

1. Explain why limp celery becomes "crisp" and the skin of your fingertips wrinkles when placed in tap water. (The principle is exactly the same.)

2. A "red-hot" bacterial infection of the intestinal tract irritates the intestinal cells and interferes with digestion. Such a condition is often accompanied by diarrhea, which causes loss of body water. On the basis of what you have learned about osmotic water flows, explain why diarrhea may occur.

3. Two examples of chemotherapeutic drugs (drugs used to treat cancer) and their cellular actions are listed below. Explain why each drug could be fatal to a cell.
• Vincristine: Damages the mitotic spindle.
• Adriamycin: Binds to DNA and blocks mRNA synthesis.

4

Tissue:
The Living Fabric

CHAPTER OUTLINE AND STUDENT OBJECTIVES

Epithelial Tissue (pp. 103–112)

1. List several structural and functional characteristics of epithelial tissue.

2. Classify the different epithelia.

3. Name and describe the various types of epithelia; also indicate their chief function(s) and location(s).

4. Compare endocrine and exocrine glands relative to their structure, product(s), and mode of secretion.

5. Describe how multicellular exocrine glands are classified structurally and functionally.

Connective Tissue (pp. 112–124)

6. Describe common characteristics of connective tissue.

7. List the structural elements of connective tissue and describe each element.

8. Describe the types of connective tissue found in the body, and indicate their characteristic functions.

Epithelial Membranes (p. 124)

9. Describe the structure and function of cutaneous, mucous, serous, and synovial membranes.

Muscle Tissue (pp. 124–126)

10. Compare and contrast the structures and body locations of the three types of muscle tissue.

Nervous Tissue (p. 126)

11. Note the general characteristics of nervous tissue.

Tissue Repair (pp. 126–131)

12. Describe the process of tissue repair involved in normal healing of a superficial wound.

Developmental Aspects of Tissues (pp. 131–132)

13. Indicate the embryonic derivation of each tissue class.

14. Briefly describe tissue changes that occur with age, and indicate possible causes of such changes.

Unicellular (one-cell) organisms, such as amoebas, are rugged individualists. They alone obtain and digest their food, carry out gas exchange, and perform all the other activities necessary to keep themselves alive and healthy. But in the multicellular human body, cells do not operate independently. Instead, they form tight cell communities that live and work together.

Individual cells are specialized, with each type performing specific functions that help maintain homeostasis and benefit the body as a whole. The specialization of our cells is obvious: Muscle cells look and act quite differently from skin cells, which in turn are easily distinguished from cells of the brain. Cell specialization allows the various parts of the body to function in very sophisticated ways, but this division of labor also has certain hazards. When a particular group of cells is indispensable, its loss can severely disable or even destroy the body.

Groups of closely associated cells that are similar in structure and perform a common or related function are called **tissues** (*tissu* = woven). Four primary tissue types interweave to form the "fabric" of the body. These basic tissues are epithelial (ep″i-the′le-ul), connective, muscle, and nervous tissue, and each has numerous subclasses or varieties. If we had to assign a single term to each primary tissue type that would best describe its general role, the terms would most likely be *covering* (epithelial), *support* (connective), *movement* (muscle), and *control* (nervous). However, these terms reflect only a fraction of the functions that each tissue performs.

As explained in Chapter 1, tissues are organized into organs such as the kidneys and the heart. Most organs contain representatives of all four tissue types, and the arrangement of the tissues determines the organ's structure and capabilities. The study of tissues, or **histology,** complements the study of gross anatomy. Together they provide the structural basis for understanding organ physiology. Furthermore, learning the characteristic patterns of each tissue type will allow you to predict the function of an organ once its structure is known, and vice versa.

EPITHELIAL TISSUE

Epithelial tissue, or an **epithelium** (plural = epithelia), is a sheet of cells that covers a body surface or lines a body cavity (*epithe* = laid on, covering). It occurs in the body as (1) *covering and lining epithelium* and (2) *glandular epithelium.* Covering and lining epithelium is found as the outer layer of the skin, dipping into and lining the open cavities of the digestive and respiratory systems, lining blood vessels and the heart, and covering the walls and organs of the closed ventral body cavity. Glandular epithelium fashions the glands of the body.

Epithelia form the boundaries between different environments. For example, the epidermis of the skin lies between the inside and the outside of the body and epithelium lining the urinary bladder separates underlying cells of the bladder wall from urine. Furthermore, nearly all substances received or given off by the body must pass through an epithelium.

In its role as an interface tissue, epithelium accomplishes many functions, including (1) protection, (2) absorption, (3) filtration, (4) excretion, (5) secretion, and (6) sensory reception. Each of these functions is described in detail later, but briefly, the epithelium of the skin protects underlying tissues from mechanical and chemical injury and bacterial invasion and contains nerve endings that respond to various stimuli acting at the skin surface (pressure, heat, etc.); that lining the digestive tract is specialized to absorb substances; and that found in the kidneys performs nearly the whole functional "menu"— excretion, absorption, secretion, and filtration. Secretion is the specialty of glands.

Special Characteristics of Epithelium

Epithelial tissues have many characteristics that distinguish them from other tissue types.

1. Cellularity. Epithelial tissue is composed almost entirely of close-packed cells. Only a tiny amount of extracellular material lies in the narrow spaces between them.

2. Specialized contacts. Epithelial cells fit close together to form continuous sheets. Adjacent cells are bound together at many points by lateral contacts, including *tight junctions* and *desmosomes* (see Chapter 3, p. 64).

3. Polarity. All epithelia have a free surface, called the **apical surface,** which is exposed to the body exterior or the cavity of an internal organ, and an attached **basal surface.** All epithelia exhibit *polarity,* meaning that cells near the apical surface differ from those at the basal surface. Although some apical surfaces are smooth and slick, most have **microvilli,** fingerlike extensions of the plasma membrane. Microvilli tremendously increase the exposed surface area, and in epithelia that absorb or secrete substances (those lining the intestine or kidney tubules, for instance), the microvilli are often so dense that the cell apices have a fuzzy appearance called a *brush border.* Some epithelia, such as that lining the trachea, have motile **cilia** that propel substances along their free surface.

4. Basement membrane. At the border between the epithelium and the connective tissue deep to it is a thin supporting sheet called the **basal lamina** (lam'ĭ-nah; "sheet"). This noncellular, adhesive sheet consists largely of glycoproteins secreted by the epithelial cells. Functionally, the basal lamina acts as a selective filter; that is, it determines which molecules diffusing from blood vessels in the underlying connective tissue will be allowed to enter the epithelium. The basal lamina also acts as a scaffolding along which epithelial cells can migrate to repair a wound. Luckily, infections and toxins that destroy epithelial cells usually leave the basal lamina in place, for without this lamina, epithelial regeneration is difficult or impossible.

Directly deep to the basal lamina is the **reticular lamina,** a similar layer of extracellular material containing a fine network of collagen protein fibers. Together the two laminae form the **basement membrane.** The basement membrane reinforces the epithelial sheet, helping it to resist stretching and tearing forces, and defines the epithelial boundary. An important characteristic of cancerous epithelial cells is their failure to respect this boundary, which they penetrate to invade the tissues beneath. •

5. Innervated but avascular. Although epithelium is *innervated* (supplied by nerve fibers), it is *avascular* (contains no blood vessels). Epithelial cells are nourished by substances diffusing from blood vessels in the underlying connective tissue.

6. Regeneration. Epithelium has a high regenerative capacity. Some epithelia are exposed to friction and their surface cells removed by abrasion. Others are damaged by hostile substances in the external environment (bacteria, acids, smoke). As long as epithelial cells receive adequate nutrition, they can replace lost cells rapidly by cell division.

Classification of Epithelia

In classifying the many varieties of epithelium, each epithelium is given two names. The first name indicates the number of cell layers present; the second describes the shape of its cells (Figure 4.1). Based on the number of cell layers, there are simple and stratified epithelia. **Simple epithelia,** composed of a single cell layer, are typically found where absorption and filtration occur and where the thinness of the epithelial barrier helps to speed these processes. **Stratified epithelia,** consisting of two or more cell layers

(a)

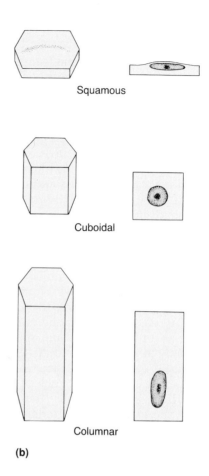

(b)

FIGURE 4.1
Classification of epithelia. **(a)** Classification on the basis of number of layers. **(b)** Classification on the basis of cell shape. For each category, a whole cell is shown on the left and a longitudinal section is shown on the right.

stacked one on top of the other, are common in high-abrasion areas where protection is important, such as the skin surface and the lining of the mouth.

In cross section, all epithelial cells have six (somewhat irregular) sides. This polyhedral shape allows the cells to be so closely packed that an apical surface view of an epithelial sheet looks like a honeycomb. However, epithelial cells vary in height, and on that basis, there are three common shapes of epithelial cells. **Squamous** (skwa'mus) **cells** are flattened and scalelike (*squam* = scale); **cuboidal** (ku-boi'dahl) **cells** are approximately as tall as they are wide; and **columnar** (kŏ-lum'nar) **cells** are tall and column shaped. In each case, the shape of the nucleus conforms to that of the cell. The nucleus of a squamous cell is disc shaped; that of a cuboidal cell is spherical; and a columnar cell nucleus is elongated from top to bottom and is usually located close to the cell base. Keep nuclear shape in mind when you attempt to identify epithelial types.

The simple epithelia are easy to classify by cell shape, because all the cells in the layer have the same shape. There are four major classes of simple epithelia: simple squamous, simple cuboidal, simple columnar, and a highly modified simple epithelium called pseudostratified (*pseudo* = false), which looks like it has several layers.

There are also four major classes of stratified epithelia: stratified squamous, stratified cuboidal, stratified columnar, and a modified stratified squamous epithelium called transitional epithelium (Figure 4.2). In terms of body distribution and abundance, only stratified squamous and transitional epithelia are significant. In stratified epithelia, cell shape varies in the different layers. Thus, to avoid ambiguity, stratified epithelia are named according to the shape of the cells at the apical or free surface. For example, the apical cells of a stratified squamous epithelium are squamous cells, but its basal cells are cuboidal or columnar.

As you read about the individual epithelial classes and study their illustrations in Figure 4.2, try to pick out the individual cells within each epithelium. This is not always easy. Tissues are three-dimensional, but their structure is studied using stained tissue sections viewed through a microscope. Depending on the precise plane of the cut made to prepare the tissue slides, the nucleus of a particular cell may or may not be visible, and (frustratingly) the boundaries between epithelial cells are often indistinct.

Simple Epithelia

The simple epithelia are most concerned with absorption, secretion, and filtration. Because they are usually very thin, protection is not one of their "specialties."

Simple Squamous Epithelium.

The cells of a **simple squamous epithelium** are flattened laterally, and their cytoplasm is sparse (Figure 4.2a). In a surface view, the close-fitting cells resemble a tiled floor;

when cut perpendicular to their free surface, the cells resemble fried eggs seen from the side, with their cytoplasm wisping out from the slightly bulging nucleus. Thin and often permeable, this epithelium is found where filtration or the exchange of substances by rapid diffusion is a priority. In the kidneys, simple squamous epithelium forms part of the filtration membrane; in the lungs, it forms the walls of the air sacs across which gas exchange occurs.

Two simple squamous epithelia in the body have special names that reflect their location. **Endothelium** (en″do-the′-le-um; "inner covering") provides a slick, friction-reducing lining in lymphatic vessels as well as in all hollow organs of the cardiovascular system—blood vessels and the heart. The walls of capillaries consist exclusively of endothelium, where its exceptional thinness encourages the efficient exchange of nutrients and wastes between the bloodstream and surrounding tissue cells. **Mesothelium** (mez″o-the′le-um; "middle covering") is the epithelium found in serous membranes lining the ventral body cavity and covering its organs. (The serous membranes are described in more detail on p. 124.)

Simple Cuboidal Epithelium.

Simple cuboidal epithelium consists of a single layer of cubical cells (Figure 4.2b). The spherical nuclei stain darkly, causing the layer to look like a string of beads when viewed microscopically. Important functions of simple cuboidal epithelium are secretion and absorption. In glands, it forms both the secretory portions and some of the small ducts that deliver secretions to their destinations. Some simple cuboidal epithelium in the kidney tubules has dense microvilli, betraying its active role in absorption.

Simple Columnar Epithelium.

Simple columnar epithelium is seen as a single layer of tall, closely packed cells, aligned like soldiers in a row (Figure 4.2c). This epithelial type lines the digestive tract from the stomach to the rectum. Columnar cells are mostly associated with absorption and secretion, and the digestive tract lining has two distinct modifications that reflect that dual function: (1) dense microvilli on the apical surface of absorptive cells and (2) **goblet cells** that secrete a protective lubricating mucus. The goblet cells, named for their "goblet" shape, contain "cups" of mucus that occupy most of the apical cell volume (see Figure 4.3).

Some simple columnar epithelia display cilia on their free surfaces. This more unusual variety, called **simple ciliated columnar epithelium,** lines the uterine tubes and limited areas of the respiratory tract.

Pseudostratified Columnar Epithelium.

The cells of **pseudostratified** (soo″do-stra′ti-fid) **columnar epithelium** are varied in height (Figure 4.2d). All of its cells rest on the basement membrane, but only the tallest reach the apical surface of the epithelium.

(a) Simple squamous epithelium

Description: Single layer of flattened cells with disk-shaped central nuclei and sparse cytoplasm; the simplest of the epithelia.

Location: Air sacs of lungs; kidney glomeruli; lining of heart, blood vessels, and lymphatic vessels; lining of ventral body cavity (serosae).

Function: Allows passage of materials by diffusion and filtration in sites where protection is not important; secretes lubricating substances in serosae.

Photomicrograph: Simple squamous epithelium forming walls of alveoli (air sacs) of the lung (280 ×).

Nucleus

Simple squamous epithelial cell

FIGURE 4.2
Epithelial tissues. Simple epithelium **(a)**.

(b) Simple cuboidal epithelium

Description: Single layer of cubelike cells with large, spherical central nuclei.

Location: Kidney tubules; ducts and secretory portions of small glands; ovary surface.

Function: Secretion and absorption.

Photomicrograph: Simple cuboidal epithelium in kidney tubules (260X)

Simple cuboidal epithelial cells

Basement membrane

Connective tissue

(c) Simple columnar epithelium

Description: Single layer of tall cells with *oval* nuclei; some cells bear cilia; layer may contain mucus-secreting glands (goblet cells).

Location: Nonciliated type lines most of the digestive tract (stomach to anal canal), gallbladder and excretory ducts of some glands; ciliated variety lines small bronchi, uterine tubes, and some regions of the uterus.

Function: Absorption; secretion of mucus, enzymes, and other substances; ciliated type propels mucus (or reproductive cells) by ciliary action.

Photomicrograph: Simple columnar epithelium of the stomach mucosa (280 ×).

Connective tissue

Simple columnar epithelial cell

Basement membrane

FIGURE 4.2
(continued) Simple epithelia (**b** and **c**).

(d) Pseudostratified epithelium

Description: Single layer of cells of differing heights, some not reaching the free surface; nuclei seen at different levels; may contain goblet cells and bear cilia.

Location: Nonciliated type in ducts of large glands, parts of male urethra; ciliated variety lines the trachea, most of the upper respiratory tract.

Function: Secretion, particularly of mucus; propulsion of mucus by ciliary action.

Photomicrograph: Pseudostratified ciliated columnar epithelium lining the human trachea (430×).

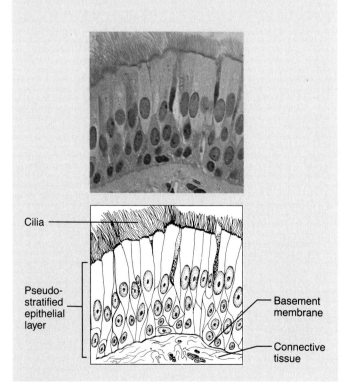

Cilia

Pseudo-stratified epithelial layer

Basement membrane

Connective tissue

(e) Stratified squamous epithelium

Description: Thick membrane composed of several cell layers; basal cells are cuboidal or columnar and metabolically active; surface cells are flattened (squamous); in the keratinized type, the surface cells are full of keratin and dead; basal cells are active in mitosis and produce the cells of the more superficial layers.

Location: Nonkeratinized type forms the moist linings of the esophagus, mouth, and vagina; keratinized variety forms the epidermis of the skin, a dry membrane.

Function: Protects underlying tissues in areas subjected to abrasion.

Photomicrograph: Stratified squamous epithelium lining of the esophagus (173×).

Stratified squamous epithelium

Nuclei

Basement membrane

Connective tissue

FIGURE 4.2

(continued) Simple epithelium **(d)** and stratified epithelium **(e)**.

(f) Stratified cuboidal epithelium

Description: Generally two layers of cube-like cells.

Location: Largest ducts of sweat glands, mammary glands, and salivary glands.

Function: Protection.

Photomicrograph: Stratified cuboidal epithelium forming a salivary gland duct (400×).

Cuboidal epithelial cells

Duct lumen

(g) Stratified columnar epithelium

Description: Several cell layers; basal cells usually cuboidal; superficial cells elongated and columnar.

Location: Rare in the body; small amounts in male urethra and in large ducts of some glands.

Function: Protection; secretion.

Photomicrograph: Stratified columnar epithelium lining of the male urethra (360×).

Stratified columnar epithelium

Underlying connective tissue

Basement membrane

FIGURE 4.2
(continued) Stratified epithelia (**f** and **g**).

(h) Transitional epithelium

Description: Resembles both stratified squamous and stratified cuboidal; basal cells cuboidal or columnar; surface cells dome-shaped or squamous-like, depending on degree of organ stretch.

Location: Lines the ureters, bladder, and part of the urethra.

Function: Stretches readily and permits distension of urinary organ by contained urine.

Photomicrograph: Transitional epithelium lining of the bladder, relaxed state (170×); note the bulbous, or rounded, appearance of the cells at the surface; these cells flatten and become elongated when the bladder is filled with urine.

Basement membrane

Connective tissue

Transitional epithelium

FIGURE 4.2
(continued) Stratified epithelium **(h)**.

The cell nuclei are located at different levels above the basement membrane, giving the false (pseudo) impression that several cell layers are present, hence "pseudostratified." This epithelium, like simple columnar variety, functions in secretion or absorption. A ciliated version containing goblet cells (more precisely called **pseudostratified ciliated columnar epithelium**) lines most of the respiratory tract. The mucus produced by the cells traps inhaled dust and other debris, and the motile cilia act to propel it superiorly away from the lungs.

Stratified Epithelia

Stratified epithelia consist of two or more cell layers. They regenerate from below; that is, the basal cells divide and push apically to replace the older surface cells. Considerably more durable than the simple epithelia, the major (but not the only) function of stratified epithelia is protection.

Stratified Squamous Epithelium. Stratified **squamous epithelium** is the most widespread stratified epithelium (Figure 4.2e). Composed of several layers, it is thick and well suited for its protective role in the body. Its free surface cells are squamous; cells of the deeper layers are cuboidal or, less commonly, columnar. This epithelium is found in areas subjected to wear and tear, and its surface cells are constantly being rubbed away and replaced by mitotic division of the cells of its basal layer. Since epithelium depends on diffusion of nutrients from a deeper connective tissue layer, the epithelial cells farther from the basement membrane are less viable; those at the apical surface are often flattened and atrophied.

Stratified squamous epithelium forms the external part of the skin and extends a short distance into every body opening directly continuous with the skin. Therefore, it also covers the tongue and lines the mouth, pharynx, esophagus, anal canal, and vagina. The outer layer, or *epidermis,* of the skin is *keratinized* (ker'ah-tin"īzd), meaning its surface cells contain *keratin,* a tough protective protein. (The epidermis is discussed in Chapter 5.) The other stratified squamous epithelia of the body are *nonkeratinized.*

Stratified Cuboidal and Columnar Epithelia. Stratified cuboidal and stratified columnar epithelia are rare types of tissue, forming little else than the large ducts of some glands. (Specific locations are mentioned in Figure 4.2f and g.)

Transitional Epithelium. Transitional epithelium forms the lining of urinary organs, which are subjected to considerable stretching and varying internal pressure as they fill with urine (Figure 4.2h). Cells of its basal layer are cuboidal or columnar. The apical cells vary in appearance, depending on the degree of distension of the organ. When the organ is not stretched, the membrane is many-layered and the superficial cells are rounded and domelike. When the organ is distended with urine, the epithelium thins (undergoes a transition) from about six cell layers to three, and its apical cells flatten and become squamouslike. The ability of transitional cells to change their shape allows a greater volume of urine to flow through a tubelike organ. In the bladder, it allows more urine to be stored.

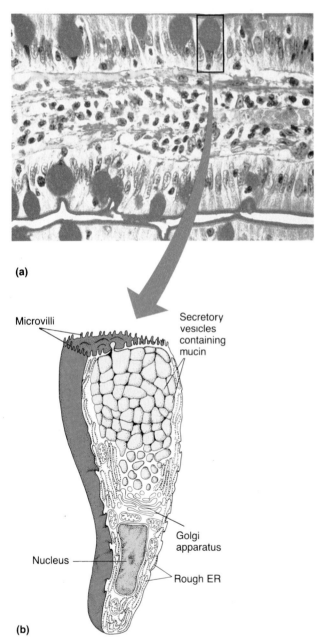

(a)

(b)

FIGURE 4.3
Goblet cells, examples of unicellular exocrine glands.
(a) Photomicrograph of simple columnar (intestinal) epithelium with goblet cells (approx. 300 ×). **(b)** Diagram of the fine structure of a goblet cell. Notice the abundant rough endoplasmic reticulum (ER) responsible for synthesizing the protein mucin and the large Golgi apparatus, which is involved in packaging the mucin secretion in vesicles.

Glandular Epithelia

A **gland** consists of one or more cells that make and secrete a particular product. This product, called a *secretion,* is an aqueous (water-based) fluid that usually contains proteins. Secretion is an active process whereby glandular cells obtain needed substances from the blood and transform them chemically into a product that is then discharged from the cell. More specifically, the protein product is made in the rough ER, packaged into secretory granules by the Golgi apparatus, and ultimately released from the cell by exocytosis (recall p. 72 and Figure 3.17, p. 80). Hence, gland cells that secrete proteins almost always have secretory granules in their apical cytoplasm. Notice that the term *secretion* can refer to both the gland's *product* and the *process* of making and releasing that product.

Glands are classified as *endocrine* (en'do-krin; "internal secretion") or *exocrine* (ek'so-krin; "external secretion"), depending on their route of secretion, and as *unicellular* ("one-celled") or *multicellular* ("many-celled") depending on their cell number. During embryonic development, most multicellular epithelial glands form by invagination from an epithelial sheet and at least initially have ducts, tubelike connections to the epithelial sheet.

Endocrine Glands

Because **endocrine glands** eventually lose their ducts, they are often called **ductless glands.** They produce **hormones,** regulatory chemicals which they secrete directly into the extracellular space. The hormones enter the blood or lymphatic fluid. Since not all endocrine glands are epithelial derivatives, we defer consideration of their structure and function to Chapter 17.

Exocrine Glands

Exocrine glands are far more numerous than endocrine glands, and many of their products are familiar. The multicellular glands secrete their products through a **duct** onto body surfaces or into body cavities. Exocrine glands are a diverse lot. They include mucous, sweat, oil, and salivary glands, the liver (which secretes bile), the pancreas (which synthesizes digestive enzymes), and many others.

Unicellular Exocrine Glands. Unicellular **exocrine glands** are single cells interposed in an epithelial sheet between cells with other functions. They have no ducts. In humans, all such glands produce **mucin** (mu'sin), a complex glycoprotein that dissolves in water when secreted. Once dissolved, mucin forms **mucus,** a slimy coating that both protects and lubricates surfaces. The only important unicellular glands in humans are the **goblet cells** found scattered among the columnar epithelial cells lining

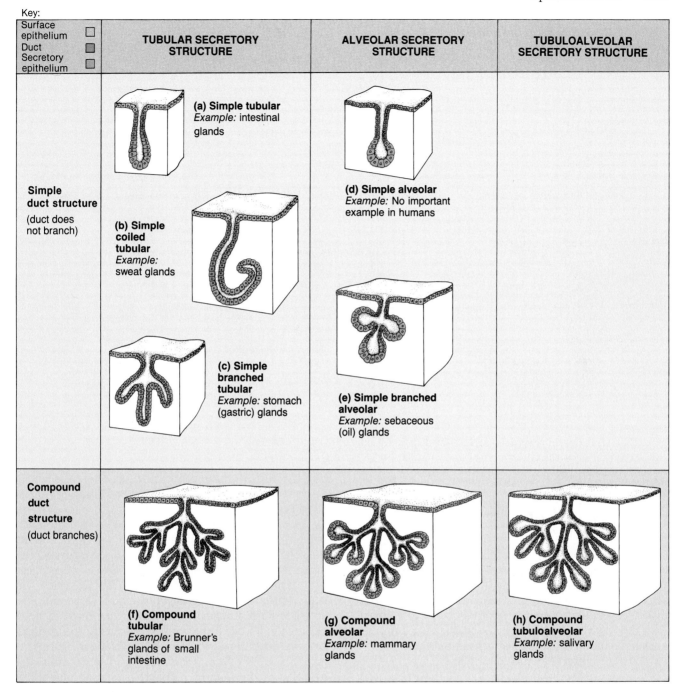

FIGURE 4.4
Types of multicellular exocrine glands. Multicellular glands are classified according to duct type (simple or compound) and the structure of their secretory units (tubular, alveolar, or tubuloalveolar).

the intestinal and respiratory tracts (Figure 4.3). Although unicellular glands probably outnumber multicellular glands, unicellular glands are the less well known of the two gland types.

Multicellular Exocrine Glands. **Multicellular exocrine glands** have two common structural elements: an epithelium-derived *duct* and a *secretory unit* consisting of secretory cells. Furthermore, in all but the simplest glands, *supportive connective tissue*

surrounds the secretory unit and supplies it with blood vessels and nerve fibers. Often, the connective tissue forms a *fibrous capsule* that extends into the gland proper and divides the gland into lobes.

Multicellular glands are divided into two major categories on the basis of their duct structures (Figure 4.4). **Simple glands** have a single unbranched duct, whereas **compound glands** have a branched duct. The glands can be further described according to the structure of their secretory parts as (1) **tubular** if the

? *Which of the three gland types illustrated would have the highest rate of cellular mitosis? Why?*

(a) Merocrine gland **(b) Holocrine gland** **(c) Apocrine gland**

FIGURE 4.5
Modes of secretion in exocrine glands. **(a)** Merocrine glands secrete their products by exocytosis. **(b)** In holocrine glands, the entire secretory cell ruptures, releasing secretions and dead cell fragments. **(c)** In apocrine glands, the apex of each secretory cell pinches off and releases its secretions.

secretory cells form a tube; (2) **alveolar** (al-ve′o-lar) if the secretory cells form small, flasklike sacs *(alveolus* = small hollow cavity); and (3) **tubuloalveolar** if they contain both tubular and alveolar secretory units. Terms denoting duct and secretory part structure are combined to describe the gland fully. It should be noted that the term **acinar** (as′ĭ-nar; "berrylike") is used interchangeably with alveolar.

Since multicellular glands secrete their products in different ways, they can also be classified functionally. Most exocrine glands are **merocrine** (mer′o-krin) **glands,** which secrete their products by exocytosis as they are produced. The secretory cells are not altered in any way. The pancreas, most sweat glands, and salivary glands belong to this class (Figure 4.5a).

Secretory cells of **holocrine** (hol′o-krin) **glands** accumulate their products within them until they rupture. (They are replaced by the division of underlying cells.) Since holocrine gland secretions include the synthesized product plus dead cell fragments (*holos* = all), you could say that their cells "die for their cause." Sebaceous (oil) glands of the skin are the only true example of holocrine glands (Figure 4.5b).

Apocrine (ap′o-krin) **glands** also accumulate their products, but in this case accumulation occurs only just beneath the free surface. Eventually, the apex of the cell pinches off (*apo* = from, off) and the secretion is released. The cell repairs its damage and repeats the process again and again (Figure 4.5c). There is some controversy over whether humans have apocrine glands, but apocrine glands are definitely present in other animals. The only possibilities in humans are the mammary glands, but cytoplasmic loss is slight and many histologists classify mammary glands as merocrine glands.

CONNECTIVE TISSUE

Connective tissue is found everywhere in the body. It is the most abundant and widely distributed of the primary tissues, but its amount in particular organs varies greatly. For example, skin consists primarily of connective tissue, while the brain contains very little.

Connective tissue does much more than *connect* body parts; it has many forms and many functions. Its chief subclasses are connective tissue proper, cartilage, bone, and blood. Its major functions include (1) *binding and support,* (2) *protection,* (3) *insulation,* and as blood, (4) *transportation* of substances within the body. For example, tough ropelike connective tis-

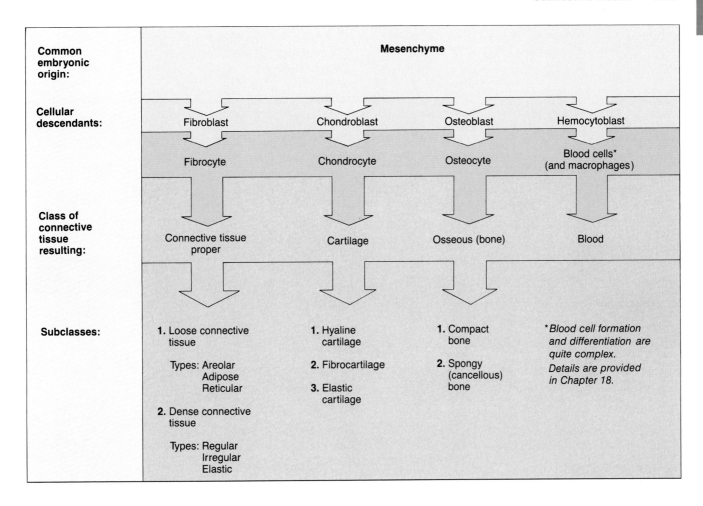

FIGURE 4.6
Major classes of connective tissue. All these classes arise from the same embryonic tissue type (mesenchyme).

sue structures connect muscle to bone (tendons), and fine, resilient connective tissue invades soft organs and supports and binds their cells together. Bone and cartilage support and protect body organs by providing the hard "underpinnings" of the skeleton; fat cushions insulate and protect body organs as well as providing reserve energy fuel.

Common Characteristics of Connective Tissue

Despite their many and varied functions in the body, connective tissues have certain common properties that set them apart from other primary tissues:

1. **Common origin.** All connective tissues arise from **mesenchyme,** an embryonic tissue derived from the mesoderm germ layer, and hence have a common kinship (Figure 4.6). The embryonic germ layers are described later in this chapter (p. 131).

2. **Degrees of vascularity.** Unlike epithelium, which is avascular, and muscle and nervous tissue, which

have a rich vascular supply, connective tissues run the entire gamut of vascularity. Cartilage is avascular; dense connective tissue is poorly vascularized; and the other types have a rich supply of blood vessels.

3. **Extracellular matrix.** Whereas all other primary tissues are composed mainly of cells, connective tissues are composed largely of nonliving **extracellular matrix** (ma′triks; "womb"), which separates, often widely, the living cells of the tissue. Because of this matrix, connective tissue is able to bear weight, withstand great tension, and endure abuses, such as physical trauma and abrasion, that no other tissue could withstand.

Structural Elements of Connective Tissue

In any type of connective tissue, three elements must be considered: *ground substance, fibers,* and *cells.* The ground substance and fibers make up the extracellular matrix. (Note that some authors use the term *matrix* to indicate the ground substance only.)

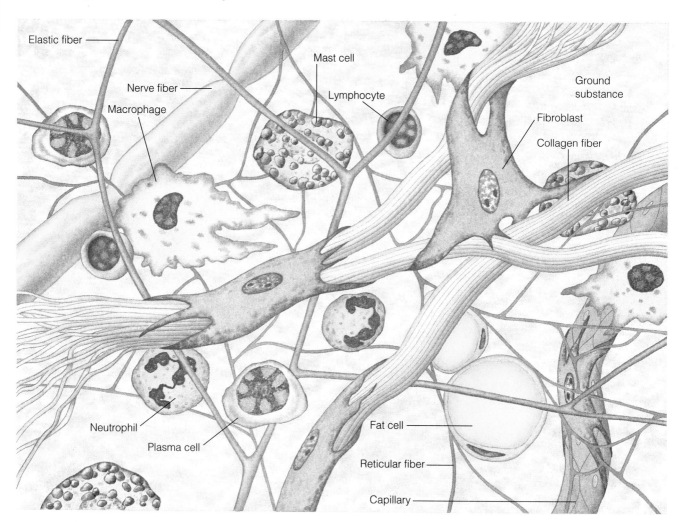

FIGURE 4.7
Areolar connective tissue: A prototype (model) connective tissue. This tissue
underlies epithelia and surrounds capillaries. Note the various cell types and the three classes of
fibers (collagen, reticular, elastic) embedded in the ground substance.

The properties of the cells and the composition and arrangement of extracellular matrix elements vary tremendously, giving rise to an amazing diversity of connective tissues, each uniquely adapted to perform its specific function in the body. For example, the matrix can be delicate and fragile to form a soft "packing" around an organ, or it can form "ropes" (tendons and ligaments) of incredible strength. Nonetheless, connective tissues have a common structural plan, and in describing the general characteristics of connective tissues below, we use *areolar* (ah-re'o-lar) *connective tissue* as our *prototype,* or model for this group of tissues (Figure 4.7). All other subclasses are simply variants of this common tissue type.

Ground Substance

Ground substance is an amorphous (unstructured) material that fills the space between the cells and contains the fibers. It is composed of *interstitial fluid, cell adhesion proteins,* and *proteoglycans* (pro"te-o-gli'kanz). Cell adhesion proteins, a group that includes *fibronectin, anchorin,* and *laminin,* serve mainly as a connective tissue "glue" that allows connective tissue cells to attach themselves to matrix elements. The proteoglycans consist of a protein "core" to which *glycosaminoglycans* (gli"kos-ah-me"no-gli'kanz) (GAGs) are attached. The strandlike GAGs, large, negatively charged polysaccharides, stick out from the core protein like the fibers of a bottle brush. The GAGs intertwine and trap water, forming a substance that varies from a fluid to a semistiff hydrated gel. Important examples of GAGs in connective tissues are *chondroitin sulfates, keratan sulfates,* and *hyalouronic* (hi"ah-lu-ron'ik) *acid.* The relative amounts and kinds of GAGs help determine the mechanical and chemical properties of the matrix. For example, the higher its GAG content, the stiffer the ground substance is.

The ground substance holds fluid and functions as a molecular "sieve," or medium, through which nutrients and other dissolved substances can diffuse between the blood capillaries and the cells. The fibers embedded in the ground substance impede diffusion somewhat and make it less pliable.

Fibers

The *fibers* of connective tissue provide support. Three types of fibers are found in connective tissue matrix: collagen, elastic, and reticular fibers. Of these, collagen fibers are by far the most abundant.

Collagen fibers are constructed primarily of the fibrous protein *collagen.* Collagen molecules are secreted into the extracellular space, where they assemble spontaneously into cross-linked fibers. Collagen fibers are extremely tough and provide high tensile strength (that is, the ability to resist longitudinal stress) to the matrix. Indeed, stress tests show that collagen fibers are stronger than steel fibers of the same size! When fresh, they have a glistening white appearance; they are therefore also called *white fibers.*

Elastic fibers are formed largely from another fibrous protein, *elastin.* Elastin has a randomly coiled structure that allows it to stretch and recoil like a rubber band. The presence of elastin in the matrix gives it a rubbery, or resilient, quality. Connective tissue can stretch only so much before its thick, ropelike collagen fibers become taut. Then, when the tension lets up, elastic fibers snap the connective tissue back to its normal length and shape. Elastic fibers are found where greater elasticity is needed, for example, in the skin, lungs, and blood vessel walls. Since fresh elastic fibers appear yellow, they are sometimes called *yellow fibers.*

Reticular fibers are fine collagenous fibers (with a slightly different chemistry and form) and are continuous with collagen fibers. They branch extensively, forming delicate networks (*reticul* = network) that surround small blood vessels and support the soft tissue of organs. They are particularly abundant where connective tissue abuts other tissue types, for example, in the basement membrane of epithelial tissues, and around capillaries, where they form fuzzy "nets."

Cells

Each major class of connective tissue has a fundamental cell type that exists in immature and mature forms (see Figure 4.6). The undifferentiated cells, indicated by the suffix *blast* (literally, "bud," or "sprout," but meaning "forming"), are actively mitotic cells that secrete both the ground substance and the fibers characteristic of their particular matrix. The primary blast cell types by connective tissue class are (1) connective tissue proper: **fibroblast;** (2) cartilage: **chondroblast** (kon'dro-blast); (3) bone: **osteoblast** (os'te-o-blast"); and (4) blood: **hemocytoblast** (he"mo-si'to-blast) or **hematopoietic stem cell.**

Once the matrix has been synthesized, the blast cells assume their less active, mature mode, indicated by the suffix *cyte* (see Figure 4.6). The mature cells maintain the health of the matrix. However, if the matrix is injured, they can easily revert to their more active state to repair and regenerate the matrix. (The hemocytoblast, the blood-forming stem cell found in bone marrow, always remains actively mitotic.)

Additionally, connective tissue is "home" to an assortment of other cell types, such as nutrient-storing *fat cells* and mobile cells that migrate into the connective tissue matrix from the bloodstream. The latter include **white blood cells** (neutrophils, eosinophils, lymphocytes) and other cell types concerned with tissue response to injury, such as *mast cells, macrophages* (mak'ro-fāj-es), and antibody-producing **plasma cells.** This wide variety of cells is particularly obvious in our prototype, areolar connective tissue (Figure 4.7).

Although all of these accessory cell types are described in later chapters, mast cells and macrophages are so significant to overall body defense that they deserve a brief mention here. The oval **mast cells** are typically found clustered in tissue spaces deep to an epithelium or along blood vessels. These cells act as "sensitive sentinels" to detect foreign substances (e.g., bacteria, fungi) and initiate local inflammatory responses against them. In the mast cell cytoplasm are conspicuous secretory granules containing (1) *heparin* (hep'ah-rin) and (2) *histamine* (his'tah-mēn). Heparin is an anticoagulant (a chemical that prevents blood clotting) when free in the bloodstream, but its significance in human mast cells is uncertain. Histamine, released during inflammatory reactions, makes the capillaries leaky. (The inflammatory process is discussed in Chapter 22.)

Macrophages (*macro* = large; *phago* = eat) are large, irregularly shaped cells that avidly phagocytize a broad variety of foreign materials, ranging from foreign molecules to entire bacteria to dust particles. Macrophages also engulf and dispose of dead tissue cells, and they are central actors in the immune system. In connective tissues, they may be fixed (attached to the connective tissue fibers) or they may migrate freely through the matrix.

Macrophages are peppered throughout loose connective tissue, bone marrow, and lymphatic tissue. Those in certain sites are given specific names. They are called *histiocytes* (his'te-o-sitz") in loose connective tissue, *Kupffer* (koop'fer) *cells* in the liver, and *microglial* (mi-krog'le-ul) *cells* in the brain. Although all these cells are phagocytes, some have selective appetites. For example, macrophages of the spleen primarily dispose of aging red blood cells; but they will not turn down other "delicacies" that come their way.

Types of Connective Tissue

As noted, all classes of connective tissue consist of living cells surrounded by a matrix. Their major differences reflect cell type, fiber type, and the proportion of the matrix contributed by fibers. Collectively, these three factors determine not only the major connective tissue classes but also their subclasses and types. The connective tissues described in this section are illustrated in Figure 4.8. Since the mature connective tissues arise from a common embryonic tissue, it is appropriate to describe this here as well.

Embryonic Connective Tissue: Mesenchyme

Mesenchyme (mes'en-kīm), or **mesenchymal tissue,** is the first definitive tissue formed from the mesoderm germ layer (Figure 4.13, p. 131). Mesenchyme is composed of star-shaped mesenchymal cells and a fluid ground substance containing fine fibrils (Figure 4.8a). It arises during the early weeks of embryonic development and eventually differentiates (specializes) into all other connective tissues. However, it appears that some mesenchymal cells remain in the tissues and provide a source of new cells in mature connective tissues.

Mucous connective tissue is a temporary tissue, derived from mesenchyme and similar to it. *Wharton's jelly,* which supports the umbilical cord of the fetus, is the best example of this scant embryonic tissue.

Connective Tissue Proper

Connective tissue proper has two subclasses: the **loose connective tissues** (areolar, adipose, and reticular) and **dense connective tissues** (dense regular, dense irregular, and elastic). Except for bone, cartilage, and blood, all mature connective tissues belong to this class.

Areolar Connective Tissue.

Areolar connective tissue has a semifluid or gelatinous ground substance formed primarily of hyaluronic acid in which all three fiber types are loosely dispersed (Figure 4.8b). **Fibroblasts,** flat, branching cells that appear spindle shaped in profile, are the predominant cell type of this tissue. Numerous macrophages are also seen and present a formidable barrier to invading microorganisms. Fat cells appear singly or in small clusters, and occasional mast cells are identified easily by the large, darkly stained cytoplasmic granules that often obscure their nuclei. Other cell types are scattered throughout.

Perhaps the most obvious structural feature of this tissue is the loose arrangement of its fibers, which account for only small portions of the matrix. The rest of the matrix, occupied by ground substance, appears to be empty space when viewed through the microscope; in fact, the Latin term *areola* means "a small open space." Essentially all body cells obtain their nutrients from and release their wastes into this "tissue fluid." However, its high content of hyaluronic acid makes the ground substance quite viscous, which may hinder the movement of cells through it. Some white blood cells, which protect the body from disease-causing microorganisms, secrete the enzyme hyaluronidase, to liquefy the ground substance and ease their passage. (Unhappily, some potentially harmful bacteria have the same capability.) Because of its loose nature, areolar connective

Text continues on p. 122

Embryonic connective tissue

(a) Mesenchyme

Description: Embryonic connective tissue; gel-like ground substance containing fine fibers; star-shaped mesenchymal cells.

Location: Primarily in embryo.

Function: Gives rise to all other connective tissue types.

Photomicrograph: Mesenchymal tissue, an embryonic connective tissue (475×); the clear-appearing background is the fluid ground substance of the matrix; notice the fine, sparse fibers.

Mesenchymal cell

Ground substance

Fibers

FIGURE 4.8
Connective tissues

Connective tissue proper: Loose connective tissue (b to d)

(b) Areolar connective tissue

Description: Gel-like matrix with all three fiber types; cells: fibroblasts, macrophages, mast cells, and some white blood cells.

Location: Widely distributed under epithelia of body, e.g., forms lamina propria of mucous membranes; packages organs; surrounds capillaries.

Epithelium

Lamina propria

Function: Wraps and cushions organs; its macrophages phagocytize bacteria; plays important role in inflammation; holds and conveys tissue fluid.

Photomicrograph: Areolar connective tissue, a soft packaging tissue of the body (170×).

Mast cell

Fibroblast

Fibers of matrix

(c) Adipose tissue

Description: Matrix as in areolar, but very sparse; closely packed adipocytes, or fat cells, have nucleus pushed to the side by large fat droplet.

Location: Under skin; around kidneys and eyeballs; in bones and within abdomen; in breasts.

Function: Provides reserve food fuel; insulates against heat loss; supports and protects organs.

Photomicrograph: Adipose tissue from the subcutaneous layer under the skin (500×).

Nuclei of fat cells

Vacuole containing fat droplet

FIGURE 4.8
(continued)

Connective tissue proper: Dense connective tissue (e and f)

(d) Reticular connective tissue

(e) Dense regular connective tissue

Description: Network of reticular fibers in a typical loose ground substance; reticular cells predominate.

Description: Primarily parallel collagen fibers; a few elastin fibers; major cell type is the fibroblast.

Location: Lymphoid organs (lymph nodes, bone marrow, and spleen).

Location: Tendons, most ligaments, aponeuroses.

Spleen

Shoulder joint

Ligament

Tendon

Function: Fibers form a soft internal skeleton that supports other cell types.

Function: Attaches muscles to bones or to muscles; attaches bones to bones; withstands great tensile stress when pulling force is applied in one direction.

Photomicrograph: Dark-staining network of reticular connective tissue fibers forming the internal skeleton of the spleen (625×).

Photomicrograph: Dense regular connective tissue from a tendon (200×).

Reticular cell

Blood cells

Reticular fibers

Collagen fibers

Nuclei of fibroblasts

FIGURE 4.8
(continued)

Cartilage: (g to i)

(f) Dense irregular connective tissue

(g) Hyaline cartilage

Description: Primarily irregularly arranged collagen fibers; some elastic fibers; major cell type is the fibroblast.

Description: Amorphous but firm matrix; collagen fibers form an imperceptible network; chondroblasts produce the matrix and when mature (chondrocytes) lie in lacunae.

Location: Dermis of the skin; submucosa of digestive tract; fibrous capsules of organs and of joints.

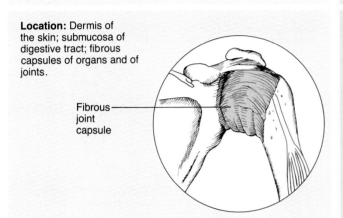

Fibrous joint capsule

Location: Forms most of the embryonic skeleton; covers the ends of long bones in joint cavities; forms costal cartilages of the ribs; cartilages of the nose, trachea, and larynx.

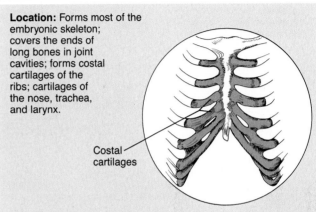

Costal cartilages

Function: Able to withstand tension exerted in many directions; provides structural strength.

Function: Supports and reinforces; has resilient cushioning properties; resists compressive stress.

Photomicrograph: Dense irregular connective tissue from the dermis of the skin (475×).

Collagen fibers

Nuclei of fibroblasts

Photomicrograph: Hyaline cartilage from the trachea (475×).

Chondrocyte in lacuna

Matrix

FIGURE 4.8
(continued)

(h) Elastic cartilage

Description: Similar to hyaline cartilage, but more elastic fibers in matrix.

Location: Supports the external ear (pinna); epiglottis.

Function: Maintains the shape of a structure while allowing great flexibility.

Photomicrograph: Elastic cartilage from the human ear pinna; forms the flexible skeleton of the ear (250x).

Elastic
fibers

Chondrocytes
in lacuna

(i) Fibrocartilage

Description: Matrix similar but less firm than in hyaline cartilage; thick collagen fibers predominate.

Location: Intervertebral discs; pubic symphysis; discs of knee joint.

Function: Tensile strength with the ability to absorb compressive shock.

Photomicrograph: Fibrocartilage of an intervertebral disc (500x).

Chondrocyte

Lacuna

Collagen
fibers

FIGURE 4.8
(continued)

Others: (j and k)

(j) Bone (osseous tissue)

Description: Hard, calcified matrix containing many collagen fibers; osteocytes lie in lacunae. Very well vascularized.

Location: Bones

Function: Bone supports and protects (by enclosing); provides levers for the muscles to act on; stores calcium and other minerals and fat; marrow inside bones is the site for blood cell formation (hematopoiesis).

Photomicrograph: Cross-sectional view of bone (100×).

Osteocytes in lacunae

(k) Blood

Description: Red and white blood cells in a fluid matrix (plasma).

Location: Contained within blood vessels.

Function: Transport of respiratory gases, nutrients, wastes, and other substances.

Photomicrograph: Smear of human blood (1000×); two white blood cells (neutrophil in upper left and lymphocyte in lower right) are seen surrounded by red blood cells.

FIGURE 4.8
(continued)

tissue provides a reservoir of water and salts for surrounding body tissues, always holding approximately as much fluid as there is in the entire bloodstream. When a body region is inflamed, the areolar tissue in the area soaks up excess fluids like a sponge, and the affected area swells and becomes puffy, a condition called **edema** (ĕ-de'mah).

Areolar connective tissue serves as a kind of universal packing material between other tissues. The most widely distributed connective tissue in the body, it binds body parts together while allowing them to move freely over one another; wraps small blood vessels and nerves; surrounds glands; and forms the subcutaneous tissue, which cushions and attaches the skin to underlying structures. It is present in all mucous membranes as the *lamina propria.* (As described on p. 124, mucous membranes line body cavities open to the exterior.)

Adipose (Fat) Tissue.

Adipose (ad'ĭ-pōs) **tissue** is basically an areolar connective tissue in which the nutrient-storing function is greatly increased. Consequently, **adipocytes** (ad'ĭ-po-sītz), commonly called adipose or fat cells, predominate. A glistening oil droplet (almost pure neutral fat) occupies most of a fat cell's volume and compresses the nucleus, displacing it to one side. Only a thin rim of surrounding cytoplasm is seen. Since the oil-containing region looks empty, and the thin cytoplasm containing the bulging nucleus looks like a ring with a seal, fat cells have been called "signet ring" cells (Figure 4.8c). Mature adipocytes are among the largest cells in the body and are incapable of cell division. As they take up or release fat, they become plumper or more wrinkled looking, respectively.

Compared to other connective tissues, adipose tissue is very cellular. The adipose cells, which account for about 90% of the tissue's mass, are packed closely together, giving a chicken wire appearance to the tissue. Adipose tissue is richly vascularized, indicating its high metabolic activity. Without the fat stores in our adipose tissue, we could not live for more than a few days without eating. Adipose tissue is certainly abundant: It constitutes 18% of an average person's body weight (15% in men and 22% in women). Indeed, a chubby person's body can be 50% fat without being morbidly obese.

Adipose tissue may develop almost anywhere areolar tissue is plentiful, but it usually accumulates in subcutaneous tissue, where it also acts as a shock absorber and as insulation. Since fat is a poor conductor of heat, it helps prevent heat loss from the body. Other sites of fat accumulation include the bone marrow, around the kidneys, behind the eyeballs, and genetically determined fat depots such as the abdomen and hips.

Reticular Connective Tissue.

Reticular connective tissue resembles areolar connective tissue but the only fibers in its matrix are reticular fibers. The interwoven reticular fibers form a delicate network along which fibroblasts called **reticular cells** lie scattered (Figure 4.8d). Although reticular fibers are widely distributed in the body, reticular tissue is limited to certain sites. It forms a labyrinthlike **stroma,** (literally, "bed" or "mattress"), or internal framework, that can support many free blood cells (largely lymphocytes) in lymph nodes, the spleen, and bone marrow.

Dense Regular Connective Tissue.

Dense regular connective tissue is one variety of the dense connective tissues, all of which have fibers as their predominant element. For this reason, the dense connective tissues are often referred to as **dense fibrous connective tissues.**

Dense regular connective tissue contains closely packed bundles of collagen fibers running in the same direction, parallel to the direction of pull. This results in a white, flexible tissue with great resistance to tension (pulling forces) where the tension is exerted in a single direction. Crowded among the collagen fibers are rows of fibroblasts that continuously manufacture fibers and scant ground substance. As seen in Figure 4.8e, collagen fibers are slightly wavy. This allows the tissue to stretch a little, but once the fibers are straightened out, there is no further "give" to this tissue. Unlike our "model" (areolar) connective tissue, this tissue has relatively few cells other than fibroblasts and it is poorly vascularized.

With its enormous tensile strength, dense regular connective tissue forms the *tendons,* cords that attach muscles to bones, and flat, sheetlike tendons called *aponeuroses* (ap"o-nu-ro'sēz) that attach muscles to other muscles or to bones. Dense regular connective tissue also forms the *ligaments* that bind bones together at joints. Ligaments contain more elastic fibers than tendons and thus are slightly more stretchy. A few ligaments of the body, such as the *ligamenta nuchae* and *flava* connecting adjacent vertebrae, are highly elastic. Their content of elastic fibers is so high that the connective tissue in those structures is referred to as *elastic connective tissue* to distinguish it from the dense variety in which collagen fibers predominate.

Dense Irregular Connective Tissue.

Dense irregular connective tissue has the same structural elements as the regular variety. However, the bundles of collagen fibers are much thicker and they are interwoven and arranged irregularly; that is, they run in more than one plane (Figure 4.8f). This type of tissue forms sheets in body areas where tension is exerted from many different directions. It is found in the skin as the *dermis,* and it forms fibrous joint capsules and the fibrous coverings that surround some organs (testes, kidneys, bones, cartilages, muscles, and nerves).

Cartilage

Cartilage (kar′tĭ-lij) has qualities intermediate between dense connective tissue and bone. It is tough but flexible, providing a resilient rigidity to the structures it supports. Cartilage is avascular and devoid of nerve fibers. Its ground substance contains large amounts of the GAG chrondroitin sulfate, as well as hyaluronic acid. It also contains an abundance of *chondronectin*, a major adhesion protein. The ground substance is heavily invested with firmly bound collagen fibers and, in some cases, elastic fibers, and is usually quite firm. Cartilage matrix also contains an exceptional amount of tissue fluid; in fact, cartilage is up to 80% water! The movement of tissue fluid in its matrix enables cartilage to rebound after being compressed (see *A Closer Look*, p. 130) and also helps to keep the cartilage cells well nourished.

The surfaces of most cartilage structures are surrounded by a well-vascularized dense irregular connective tissue membrane called a **perichondrium** (per″ĭ-kon′dre-um; *peri* = around, *chondro* = cartilage), from which the nutrients diffuse through the matrix to the chondrocytes. This mode of nutrient delivery limits cartilage thickness.

Chondroblasts, the predominant cell type in growing cartilage, produce new matrix by two mechanisms. In **interstitial growth,** the growth process most apparent during the initial phase of cartilage formation, the chondroblasts within the cartilage divide and secrete new matrix. This causes growth from within the cartilage piece. In **appositional growth,** chondroblasts located deep to the perichondrium secrete new matrix elements on the superficial face of the cartilage structure. Both growth processes continue until the bony skeleton stops growing at the end of adolescence. Because the firm cartilage matrix prevents the cells from becoming widely separated, **chondrocytes,** or mature cartilage cells, are typically found in small groups within common cavities called **lacunae** (lah-ku′ne; "pits").

Because of the avascular nature of cartilage and the fact that aging cartilage cells lose their ability to divide, cartilages heal slowly when injured. This phenomenon is excruciatingly familiar to those experiencing sports injuries. During later life, cartilages tend to calcify or even ossify (become bony). In such cases, the chondrocytes are poorly nourished and die. •

There are three varieties of cartilage: *hyaline cartilage, elastic cartilage,* and *fibrocartilage.*

Hyaline Cartilage.
Hyaline (hi′ah-līn) **cartilage,** or *gristle,* is the most abundant cartilage type in the body. Although it contains large numbers of collagen fibers, they are not apparent and the matrix appears amorphous and glassy (*hyalin* = glass) blue-white (Figure 4.8g) when viewed by the unaided eye.

Hyaline cartilage provides firm support with some pliability. It covers the ends of long bones as *articular cartilage,* providing springy pads that absorb compression at joints. Hyaline cartilage also supports the tip of the nose, connects the ribs to the sternum, and forms most of the larynx and supporting cartilages of the trachea and bronchial tubes. Most of the embryonic skeleton is formed of hyaline cartilage before bone is formed. Hyaline cartilage persists during childhood as the *epiphyseal* (e″pĭ-fis′e-ul) *plates,* actively growing regions near the end of long bones that provide for continued growth in length.

Elastic Cartilage.
Histologically, **elastic cartilage** (Figure 4.8h) is nearly identical to hyaline cartilage. However, there are many more elastin fibers in elastic cartilage, which gives this tissue a greater tolerance for repeated bending. It is found where strength and exceptional ability to stretch are needed. Elastic cartilage forms the "skeletons" of the external ear and the epiglottis. The epiglottis is the flap that covers the opening to the respiratory passageway when we swallow, preventing food or fluids from entering the lungs.

Fibrocartilage.
Fibrocartilage is often found where hyaline cartilage meets a true ligament or a tendon. Fibrocartilage is a perfect structural intermediate between hyaline cartilage and dense regular connective tissues. It consists of rows of chondrocytes (a cartilage feature) alternating with rows of thick collagen fibers (a feature of dense regular connective tissue) (Figure 4.8i). Because it is compressible and resists tension well, fibrocartilage is found where strong support and the ability to withstand heavy pressure are required. For example, the intervertebral discs (resilient cushions between the bony vertebrae) and the spongy cartilages of the knee are fibrocartilage structures.

Bone (Osseous Tissue)

Because of its rocklike hardness, **bone,** or **osseous** (os′e-us) **tissue,** has an exceptional ability to support and protect softer tissues. Bones of the skeleton also provide cavities for fat storage and synthesis of blood cells. Bone matrix is similar to that of cartilage but is harder and more rigid because, in addition to its more abundant collagen fibers, bone has an added matrix element—inorganic calcium salts (bone salts).

Osteoblasts produce the organic portion of the matrix; then, bone salts are deposited on and between the fibers. Mature bone cells, or **osteocytes,** reside in the lacunae within the matrix they have made (Figure 4.8j). Unlike cartilage, the next firmest connective tissue, bone is very well supplied by invading blood vessels. We will consider the structure, growth, and metabolism of bone further in Chapter 6.

Blood

Blood, the fluid within blood vessels, is the most atypical connective tissue. It is classified as a connective tissue because it consists of *blood cells,* surrounded by a nonliving fluid matrix called *blood plasma* (Figure 4.8k). The "fibers" of blood are soluble protein molecules that become visible only during blood clotting. Blood functions as the transport vehicle for the cardiovascular system, carrying nutrients, wastes, respiratory gases, and many other substances throughout the body. Blood is considered in detail in Chapter 18.

EPITHELIAL MEMBRANES

Now that we have described both connective and epithelial tissues, we can consider the complex epithelial membranes that incorporate both types of tissue. Our previous classification of epithelia by cell shape and arrangement allows each individual epithelium to be described precisely, but it reveals nothing about the tissue's location in the body. Here we will describe the covering and lining epithelia using terms that indicate their special locations in the body and/or their general functional qualities.

There is tremendous variety in the way the term "epithelial membrane" is used. Here, **epithelial membrane** is defined as a continuous multicellular sheet composed of at least two primary tissue types: an epithelium bound to an underlying layer of connective tissue proper. Hence, epithelial membranes can be considered to be simple organs. Most of the covering and lining epithelia take part in forming one or more of the three common types of epithelial membranes: *cutaneous, mucous,* or *serous.*

Cutaneous Membrane

The **cutaneous** (ku-ta′ne-us; *cutis* = skin) **membrane** is your skin (Figure 4.9a). It is an organ system consisting of a keratinized stratified squamous epithelium (epidermis) firmly attached to a thick layer of dense irregular connective tissue (dermis). Unlike other epithelial membranes, the cutaneous membrane is exposed to the air and is a dry membrane. Chapter 5 is devoted to this unique organ system.

Mucous Membranes

Mucous membranes, or **mucosae** (mu-ko′se), line body cavities that are open to the exterior, such as those of the hollow organs of the digestive, respiratory, and urogenital tracts (Figure 4.9b). In all cases, they are "wet," or moist, membranes bathed by secretions or, in the case of the urinary mucosa, urine. Notice that the term *mucosa* refers to the location of

the epithelial membrane, *not* its cell composition, which varies. However, most mucosae contain either stratified squamous or simple columnar epithelia.

Mucous membranes are often adapted for absorption and secretion. Although many mucosae secrete mucus, this is not a requirement. The mucosae of both the digestive and respiratory tracts secrete copious amounts of protective lubricating mucus; that of the urinary tract does not.

All mucous membranes consist of an epithelial sheet directly underlain by a layer of loose connective tissue called the **lamina propria** (lam′ĭ-nah pro′preah; "one's own layer"). In some mucosae, the lamina propria rests on a third (deeper) layer of smooth muscle cells. These variations in specific mucosae are covered in later chapters.

Serous Membranes

Serous membranes, or **serosae** (se-ro′se), are the moist membranes found in closed ventral body cavities (Figure 4.9c). Each serosa consists of a *parietal layer* that lines the cavity wall and then reflects back as the *visceral layer* to cover the outer surface(s) of organs within the cavity. Each of these layers consists of simple squamous epithelium (mesothelium) resting on a thin layer of loose connective (areolar) tissue. The mesothelial cells enrich the fluid that filters from the capillaries in the associated connective tissue with hyaluronic acid to produce thin, clear *serous fluid* that lubricates the facing surfaces of the parietal and visceral layers, so that they slide across each other easily. This reduces friction and prevents organs from sticking to the cavity walls and to each other.

The serosae are named according to their site and specific organ associations. For example, the serosa lining the thoracic wall and covering the lungs is the **pleura;** that enclosing the heart is the **pericardium;** and those of the abdominopelvic cavity and viscera are the **peritoneums.**

MUSCLE TISSUE

Muscle tissues are highly cellular, well-vascularized tissues that are responsible for most types of body movement. Because of their elongated shape, which enhances their shortening (contractile) function, muscle cells are called **muscle fibers.** Muscle cells possess **myofilaments,** elaborate versions of the *actin* and *myosin* filaments that bring about movement or contraction in all cell types. There are three kinds of muscle tissue: skeletal, cardiac, and smooth.

Skeletal muscle is packaged by connective tissue sheets into organs called *skeletal muscles* that are attached to the bones of the skeleton. These muscles

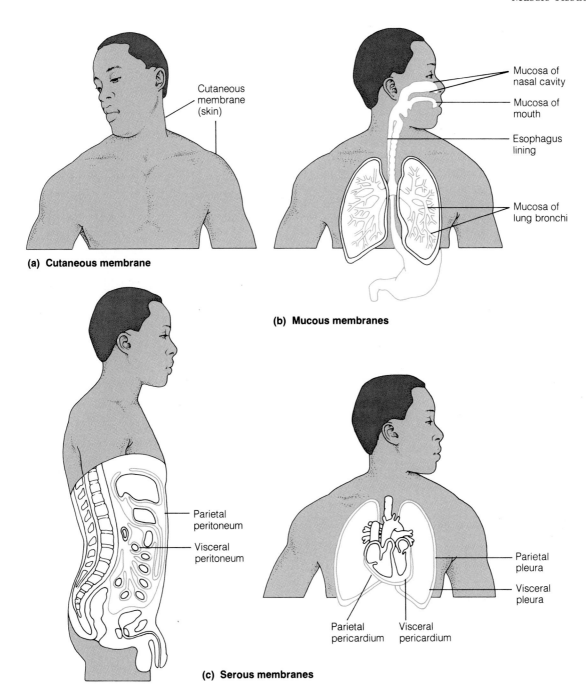

(a) Cutaneous membrane

(b) Mucous membranes

(c) Serous membranes

FIGURE 4.9
Classes of epithelial membranes. (a) Cutaneous membrane, or skin. (b) Mucous
membranes line body cavities that are open to the exterior. (c) Serous membranes line ventral
body cavities that are closed to the exterior.

form the flesh of the body, and as they contract, they pull on bones or skin, causing gross body movements or facial expressions. Skeletal muscle cells are long, cylindrical cells that contain many nuclei. Their obvious banded, or *striated,* appearance reflects the precise alignment of their myofilaments (Figure 4.10a).

Cardiac muscle occurs in the walls of the heart; it is found nowhere else in the body. Its contractions propel blood through the blood vessels to all parts of the body. Like skeletal muscle cells, cardiac muscle cells are striated. However, they differ structurally in that cardiac cells (1) are uninucleate and (2) are branching cells that fit together tightly at unique junctions called **intercalated** (in-ter′kah-la″ted) **discs** (Figure 4.10b).

Smooth muscle is so named because its fibers have no externally visible striations. Individual smooth muscle cells are spindle shaped and contain one centrally located nucleus (Figure 4.10c). Smooth muscle occurs mainly in the walls of hollow organs (digestive and urinary tract organs, uterus, and blood vessels). It generally acts to propel (squeeze) substances through these organs by alternately contracting and relaxing.

Since skeletal muscle contraction is under our conscious control, skeletal muscle is often called **voluntary muscle,** while the other two types are called **involuntary muscle.** Skeletal muscle and smooth muscle are described in detail in Chapter 9; cardiac muscle is discussed in Chapter 19.

NERVOUS TISSUE

Nervous tissue makes up the nervous system—the brain, spinal cord, and nerves—which regulates and controls body functions. It is composed of two major cell types. **Neurons** are highly specialized nerve cells that generate and conduct nerve impulses (Figure 4.11, on p. 128). Typically, they are branching or stellate cells. The cytoplasmic extensions, or processes, allow them to transmit electrical impulses over substantial distances within the body. The balance of nervous tissue consists of various types of **supporting cells,** nonconducting cells that support, insulate, and protect the delicate neurons. A more complete discussion of nervous tissue appears in Chapter 11.

TISSUE REPAIR

The body has many techniques for protecting itself from uninvited "guests" or injury. Intact mechanical barriers such as the skin and mucosae, the ciliary activity of epithelial cells lining the respiratory tract, and a strong acid (chemical barrier) produced by stomach glands represent three defenses exerted at the body's external boundaries. When tissue injury

(a) Skeletal muscle

Description: Long, cylindrical, multinucleate cells; obvious striations.

Location: In skeletal muscles attached to bones or occasionally to skin.

Function: Voluntary movement; locomotion; manipulation of the environment; facial expression. Voluntary control.

Photomicrograph: Skeletal muscle (approx. 30x). Notice the obvious banding pattern and the fact that these large cells are multinucleate.

Nuclei

Muscle fiber

FIGURE 4.10
Muscle tissues.

Text continues on p. 128

(b) Cardiac muscle

Description: Branching, striated, generally uninucleate cells that interdigitate at specialized junctions (intercalated discs).

Location: The walls of the heart.

Function: As it contracts, it propels blood into the circulation; involuntary control.

Photomicrograph: Cardiac muscle (250x); notice the striations, branching of fibers, and the intercalated discs.

Inter-
calated
disc

Nucleus

(c) Smooth muscle

Description: Spindle-shaped cells with central nuclei; cells arranged closely to form sheets; no striations.

Location: Mostly in the walls of hollow organs.

Function: Propels substances or objects (foodstuffs, urine, a baby) along internal passageways; involuntary control.

Photomicrograph: Sheet of smooth muscle (approx. 300x).

Smooth
muscle
cell

Nuclei

FIGURE 4.10
(continued)

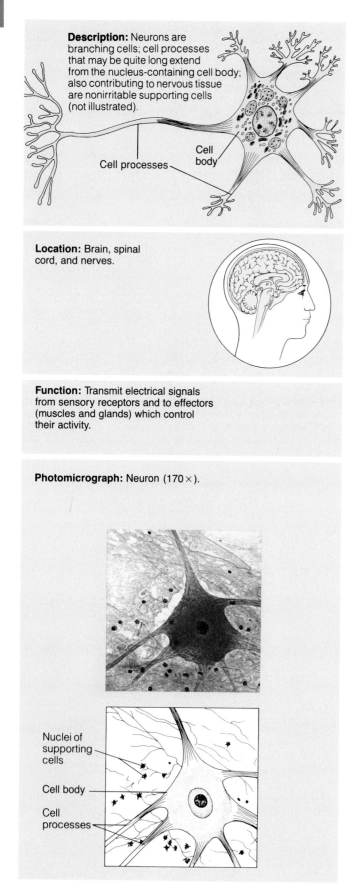

Description: Neurons are branching cells; cell processes that may be quite long extend from the nucleus-containing cell body; also contributing to nervous tissue are nonirritable supporting cells (not illustrated).

Cell processes

Cell body

Location: Brain, spinal cord, and nerves.

Function: Transmit electrical signals from sensory receptors and to effectors (muscles and glands) which control their activity.

Photomicrograph: Neuron (170×).

Nuclei of supporting cells

Cell body

Cell processes

FIGURE 4.11
Nervous tissue.

occurs these barriers are penetrated; this stimulates the body's inflammatory and immune responses, which wage their battles largely in the connective tissues of the body. The inflammatory response is a relatively nonspecific reaction that occurs whenever and wherever tissues are injured. Essentially, inflammation represents an offensive action that develops quickly and acts to limit damage, eliminate the harmful agent, prevent further injury, and restore the tissue to a healthy condition. The immune response, on the other hand, is extremely specific, but takes longer to swing into action. Cells of the immune system, programmed to identify foreign substances such as microorganisms, toxins, and cancer cells, mount a vigorous attack against specific recognized invaders, either by interacting directly with them or by releasing antibodies into the blood and other body fluids. The inflammatory and immune responses are considered in detail in Chapter 22.

Steps of Tissue Repair

Tissue repair requires that cells divide and crawl (migrate), activities initiated by growth factors (wound hormones) released by injured cells. It occurs in two major ways: by regeneration and by fibrosis. Which of these occurs depends on (1) the type of tissue damaged and (2) the severity of the injury. **Regeneration** is replacement of destroyed tissue with the same kind of tissue, whereas **fibrosis** involves proliferation of fibrous connective tissue called **scar tissue.** In skin, the tissue we will use as our example, repair involves both activities.

1. *Inflammation sets the stage.*   Figure 4.12 illustrates the process of tissue repair of a skin wound, showing both regeneration and fibrosis. The process begins while the inflammatory reaction, the body's response to tissue injury, is still going on. Let us briefly examine what has happened up to this point. Tissue injury sets the following inflammatory events into motion. First, because of the release of histamine and other inflammatory chemicals by injured tissue cells, macrophages, mast cells, and others, the capillaries dilate and become very permeable. This allows white blood cells and plasma fluid rich in clotting proteins, antibodies, and other substances to seep into the injured area. Then, the leaked clotting proteins construct a clot, which stops the loss of blood, holds the edges of the wound together, and effectively "walls off," or isolates, the injured area, preventing bacteria, toxins, or other harmful substances from spreading to surrounding tissues (Figure 4.12a). The portion of the clot exposed to air quickly dries and hardens, forming a scab. The inflammatory events leave excess fluid, bits of destroyed cells, and other debris in the area. Most of this material is eventually removed from the area by lymphatic vessels or phagocytized by macrophages. At this point, the first step of tissue repair, organization, begins to occur.

2. Organization restores the blood supply.
Organization is the process during which the temporary blood clot is replaced by granulation tissue (Figure 4.12b). **Granulation tissue** is a delicate pink tissue composed of several elements. Thin, extremely permeable capillaries bud from intact capillaries nearby and enter the damaged area, laying down a new capillary bed; they protrude nublike from the surface of the granulation tissue, giving it a granular appearance. These capillaries are fragile and bleed freely, as demonstrated when someone "picks at" a scab. Also present in granulation tissue are scattered macrophages and proliferating fibroblasts that synthesize new collagen fibers to bridge the gap permanently. As organization continues, macrophages digest and remove the original blood clot. The granulation tissue, destined to become scar tissue (a permanent fibrous tissue patch), is highly resistant to infection, because it produces bacterium-inhibiting substances.

3. Regeneration and/or fibrosis effects permanent repair.
While organization is going on, the surface epithelium begins to regenerate (see Figure 4.12b), growing across the granulation tissue just beneath the scab, which soon detaches. As the fibrous tissue beneath matures and contracts, the regenerating epithelium thickens until it finally resembles that of the adjacent skin (Figure 4.12c). The end result is a fully regenerated epithelium, and an underlying region of scar tissue. The scar may be invisible, or visible as a thin white line, depending on the severity of the wound.

Factors Affecting the Repair Process

Many factors influence the repair process. Included among these are (1) the type of tissue injured; (2) the type of injury and immediate care given to the injured site; (3) nutrition; (4) adequacy of blood supply; (5) state of health; and (6) age. Of these, we will discuss only the influence of tissue type. Relative to the other factors it is sufficient to say that the more minor the injury (and the sooner it is cared for), the better one's nutrition, circulatory efficency, and health, and the younger one's age, the more satisfactory the healing process will be.

Tissue Type

The ability of the different tissue types to regenerate varies widely. Epithelial tissues such as the skin epidermis and mucous membranes regenerate beautifully. So, too, do bone and most fibrous connective tissues. Smooth muscle and dense regular connective

(1) What is the makeup of granulation tissue formed at the injured site? **(2)** Where do the new capillaries that invade the injured area come from? **(3)** How would this pictorial series look different if repair by regeneration was not possible?

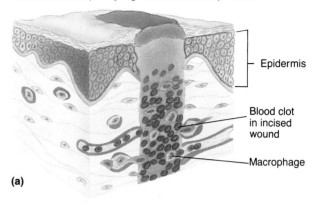

Epidermis

Blood clot in incised wound

Macrophage

(a)

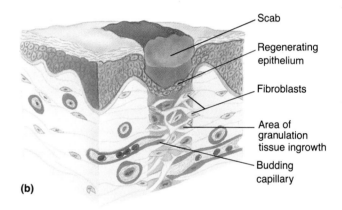

Scab

Regenerating epithelium

Fibroblasts

Area of granulation tissue ingrowth

Budding capillary

(b)

Regenerated epithelium

Fibrosed area

(c)

FIGURE 4.12
Tissue repair of a nonextensive skin wound: regeneration and fibrosis. **(a)** Severed blood vessels bleed. Inflammatory chemicals are released, and local blood vessels dilate and become more permeable, allowing white blood cells, fluid, clotting proteins, and other plasma proteins to invade the injured site. Clotting proteins initiate clotting; surface dries and forms a scab. **(b)** Granulation tissue is formed. Capillary buds invade the clot, restoring a vascular supply. Fibroblasts invade the region and secrete soluble collagen, which constructs collagen fibers that bridge the gap. Macrophages phagocytize dead and dying cell debris. Surface epithelial cells proliferate and migrate over the granulation tissue. **(c)** Approximately one week later, the fibrosed area (scar) has contracted and regeneration of the epithelium is in progress. The scar tissue may or may not be visible beneath the epidermis.

A CLOSER LOOK | Cartilage—Strong Water

It's match point. Argosy tosses the tennis ball into the air, arches back, and then smashes it over the net into the opposite service court. Belsky backpedals rapidly, and then dives wildly in an attempt to return the shot. Tennis anyone? Not without healthy cartilage, the tissue that forms the framework for building most bones and fashions the spongy cushions of our movable joints.

The cartilages of professional tennis players, like Pete Sampras, should be well nourished because of the tremendous physical demands placed on body joints by this sport.

Cartilage is *resilient:* if you push on it and then ease the pressure, it bounces back. This resilience allows the articular cartilages at the ends of our bones to cushion the impact of various activities, such as lifting heavy objects, striking a tennis ball, sprinting, jogging, or jumping. Once an action is complete, the cartilage tissue springs back to await the next movement.

Another important feature of cartilage tissue is its *rapid growth,* which enables it to keep pace with the rapid growth of the embryo. Indeed, most of the embryo's "bones" originate as cartilage models that are only gradually replaced by bone tissue. During childhood, growth plates of cartilage remain in most bones and provide for skeletal growth. Throughout life, broken bones are repaired by cartilage before new bone tissue is in place—much like replaying a tape of embryonic events.

Although embryonic cartilage-forming tissue is initially sprayed with capillaries, these soon disappear, so that the increasingly crowded cartilage cells have no direct supply of oxygen and nutrients. They receive all their oxygen and nutrients from surrounding vessels in the perichondrium.

Cartilage performs its crucial functions even though it lacks structures common in other body tissues. It has no nerves, blood vessels, or lymphatics. The exceptional resilience and rapid growth properties of cartilage are determined not by its cells but by the elaborate network of giant molecules the cells deposit around themselves. Like all connective tissues, its matrix includes proteogly-cans (proteins that are attached to large polysaccharide molecules called GAGs and so form some of the largest modified proteins made by any living cells), abundant collagen fibers, and huge volumes of water. Indeed, the structuring of water is responsible for this tissue's functional characteristics. The collagen fibers in cartilage form a framework much like the steel girders supporting a bridge. Within this mesh are the central organizing molecules of the matrix, hyaluronic acid molecules. Up to 100 glycoproteins are attached to and extend from each hyaluronic acid molecule; around these cores are proteoglycans (typically containing the GAG chondroitin sulfate). The sugars and negative charges of these gigantic proteoglycans in cartilage avidly attract the polar water molecules, which form interacting "water shells" around them. Thus, its proteoglycans structure massive amounts of water—many times their own weight—and water becomes the chief component of cartilage.

In the developing embryo, this contained water "saves space" for the development of the long bones of the body. Throughout life, it gives the cartilage its resilience, or springiness. When pressure is applied to cartilage, water is forced away from the negatively charged areas. Then, as the charged areas are pressed closer and closer together, they repel one another and resist further compression. When the pressure is released, water molecules rush back to their original sites, causing the cartilage to spring back forcefully to its original shape. These events also play a vital role in the nourishment of joint cartilage: The flow of liquids that occurs when it is alternately compressed and released carries nutrients to the cartilage cells. This explains the observation that long periods of inactivity can weaken joint cartilage.

Like all body cells, chondrocytes age and seem to respond to some programmed biological clock. Proteoglycans produced by aging chondrocytes are distinctly different from those of young cells: In elderly people these differences may account for some forms of osteoarthritis in which the cartilage thins and becomes less resilient. If the pressure on the joint exceeds the ability of the aging cartilage to respond, the cartilage can fragment, leading to the swelling and pain of osteoarthritis. The aging-chondrocyte theory raises the possibility that arthritis could be prevented or reversed by transplanting sheets of chrondrocytes to joint surfaces. Indeed, such "chondrocyte grafts" are being tested in humans for their effectiveness in resurfacing human knee joints.

The unique properties of cartilage suggest some other interesting research prospects. Tumors require a rich blood supply and are known to release a factor that causes blood vessels to proliferate at the tumor site. Viable cartilage, on the other hand, contains a substance that specifically excludes blood vessels. Could this substance be applied to a growing tumor to throttle its blood supply and kill it? We do not yet know, but the race to isolate the blood vessel–inhibiting factor is now on.

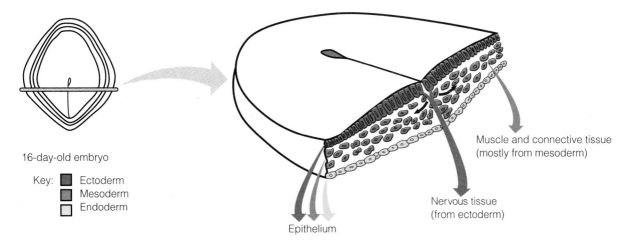

16-day-old embryo

Key: ■ Ectoderm
■ Mesoderm
□ Endoderm

Muscle and connective tissue
(mostly from mesoderm)

Nervous tissue
(from ectoderm)

Epithelium

FIGURE 4.13
Embryonic germ layers and the primary tissue types
they produce. The three embryonic layers collectively form the
very early embryonic body.

tissue have a very limited regenerative capacity, and skeletal muscle and cartilage regenerate poorly, if at all. Cardiac muscle and nervous tissue in the brain and spinal cord have essentially no regenerative ability; they can be replaced only by scar tissue.

In nonregenerating tissues, fibrosis totally replaces the lost tissue. Over a period of months, the mass of fibrous tissue shrinks and becomes more and more compact. The resulting scar appears as a pale, often shiny area. It is composed mostly of collagen fibers and contains few cells or capillaries. Scar tissue is very strong, but it lacks the flexibility and elasticity of most normal tissues. Also, it cannot perform the normal functions of the tissue it has replaced.

If scar tissue forms in the wall of the urinary bladder, heart, or other muscular organ, it may severely hamper organ function. The normal shrinking of scar tissue reduces the internal volume of an organ and may cause abnormal flow patterns through hollow organs. Scar tissue hampers muscle's ability to contract and may also interfere with its normal excitation by the nervous system. In the heart, these problems may result in progressive heart failure. In some cases, particularly following abdominal sur-gery, *adhesions* form as the newly forming scar tissue connects adjacent organs together. Adhesions in the abdominal cavity can prevent the normal shifting about of loops of the intestine, dangerously obstructing the flow of foodstuffs through it. Adhesions can also restrict heart movements and immobilize joints. •

The repair process described above follows healing of a wound (cut, scrape, puncture) that breaches an epithelial barrier. In pure *infections* (a pimple or sore throat), by contrast, healing is solely by regeneration. There is usually no clot formation or scarring. Only severe (destructive) infections lead to scarring.

DEVELOPMENTAL ASPECTS OF TISSUES

One of the first events of embryonic development is the formation of the three **primary germ layers,** which lie one atop the next like a three-layered cellular pancake. From superficial to deep, these layers are the **ectoderm, mesoderm** (mez'o-derm), and **endoderm** (Figure 4.13). These primary germ layers then begin to specialize to form the four primary tissues from which all body organs are derived. Epithelial tissues are formed from all three germ layers: most mucosal epithelia from endoderm; endothelium and mesothelium from mesoderm; and the epidermis from ectoderm. Muscle and connective tissues develop from mesoderm, and nervous tissue arises from ectoderm.

By the end of the second month of development, the primary tissues have appeared, and all major organs are laid down, at least in rudimentary form. In general, tissue cells remain mitotic and provide for the rapid growth that occurs throughout the embryonic and fetal periods. Most tissue cells, except neurons, continue to undergo mitosis until adult body size is achieved. Cellular division then slows greatly, although many tissues retain regenerative capability. In adulthood, only epithelia and blood-forming tissues are highly mitotic. Some tissues that regenerate through life, such as the glandular cells of the liver, accomplish this through division of their mature (specialized) cells. Others, like the epidermis of the skin and cells lining the intestine, have *stem cells,* relatively undifferentiated cells that divide as necessary to produce new cells.

Given good nutrition, good circulation, and relatively infrequent wounds and infections, our tissues normally function efficiently through youth and middle age. But with increasing age, the epithelia thin and are more easily breached. The amount of collagen in the body declines, making tissue repair less efficient, and bone, muscle, and nervous tissues begin to atrophy. These events are due in part to decreased circulatory efficiency, which reduces delivery of nutrients to the tissues, but in some cases, diet is a contributing factor. As their income declines or as chewing becomes more difficult, older people tend to eat soft foods, which may be low in protein and vitamins. As a result, tissue health suffers.

As we have seen, body cells combine to form four discrete tissue types: epithelial, connective, muscle, and nervous tissues. The cells making up each of these tissues share certain features but are by no means identical. They "belong" together because they have basic functional similarities. The connective tissues assume many guises, but perhaps the most versatile cells are those of epithelium: They protect our outer and inner surfaces, permit us to obtain oxygen, allow our kidneys to excrete wastes, and absorb vital nutrients into the blood. The important concept to carry away with you is that tissues, despite their unique abilities, cooperate to keep the body safe, healthy, and whole.

RELATED CLINICAL TERMS

Adenoma (ad″ĕ-no′mah; *aden* = gland, *oma=* tumor) Any neoplasm of glandular epithelium, benign or malignant. The malignant type is more specifically called *adenocarcinoma.*

Autopsy (aw′top-se) Examination of the body, its organs, and its tissues after death to determine the actual cause of death; also called postmortem examination and necropsy.

Carcinoma (kar″sĭ-no′mah; *karkinos* = crab, cancer) Cancer arising in an epithelium.

Fat embolism Freely floating fat globule in the bloodstream; may result from extensive injury to fatty subcutaneous tissue or a bone fracture in which the fat in the bone marrow cavity is released; the danger is that the fatty masses may obstruct blood circulation to vital organs (heart, lungs, brain).

Healing by first intention The simplest type of healing; occurs when the edges of the wound are brought together by sutures, staples, or other means used to close surgical incisions; only small amounts of granulation tissue need be formed.

Healing by second intention The wound edges remain separated, and the gap is bridged by granulation tissue; the manner in which unattended wounds heal (slower than in healing by first intention); more granulation tissue is formed, and a greater degree of epithelial proliferation occurs than in wounds in which the edges are brought together; larger scars result.

Keloid (ke′loid) Abnormal proliferation of connective tissue during healing of skin wounds; results in large, unsightly mass of scar tissue at the skin surface.

Lesion (le′zhun; "wound") Any injury, wound, or infection that affects tissue over an area of a definite size (as opposed to widely spread throughout the body).

Marfan's syndrome Genetic disease resulting in abnormalities of connective tissues due to a defect in fibrillin, a protein that helps provide the scaffolding between cells. Clinical signs include excessive height, loose-jointedness, long spiderlike fingers, visual problems, and a weakened heart and blood vessels due to poor connective tissue reinforcement.

Pathology (pah-thol′o-je) Scientific study of changes in organs and tissues produced by disease.

Pus A collection of tissue fluid, bacteria, dead and dying tissue cells, white blood cells, and macrophages in an inflamed area.

Sarcoma (sar-ko′mah; *sarkos* = flesh; *oma* = tumor) Cancer arising in the mesenchyme-derived tissues, that is, in connective tissues and muscle.

Scurvy A nutritional deficiency caused by lack of adequate vitamin C to synthesize collagen; signs and symptoms include blood vessel disruption, delay in wound healing, weakness of scar tissue, and loosening of teeth.

CHAPTER SUMMARY

Cells of the multicellular body aggregate to form tissues, collections of similar cells that are specialized to perform a specific function for the body. The four primary tissue types are epithelial, connective, muscle, and nervous tissues.

Epithelial Tissue (pp. 103–112)

1. Epithelial tissue is the covering, lining, and glandular tissue of the body. Its functions include protection, absorption, secretion, filtration, and sensory reception.

Special Characteristics of Epithelium (p. 103)

2. Epithelial tissues exhibit a huge degree of cellularity, specialized lateral contacts, polarity, avascularity, a basement membrane, and high regenerative capacity.

Classification of Epithelia (pp. 103-110)

3. Epithelium is classified by arrangement as simple (one layer) or stratified (more than one) and by cell shape as squamous, cuboidal, or columnar. The terms denoting cell shape and arrangement are combined to describe the epithelium fully.

4. Simple squamous epithelium consists of a single layer of squamous cells. Highly adapted for filtration and exchange of substances. Forms walls of air sacs of the lungs and lines blood vessels. Contributes to serosae as mesothelium and forms the lining of all hollow circulatory system organs as endothelium.

5. Simple cuboidal epithelium is commonly active in secretion and absorption. Found in glands and in kidney tubules.

6. Simple columnar epithelium, specialized for secretion and absorption, consists of a single layer of tall columnar cells that exhibit microvilli and often goblet cells. Lines most of the digestive tract.

7. Pseudostratified columnar epithelium is a simple columnar epithelium that appears stratified. Its ciliated variety, rich in goblet cells, lines most of the upper respiratory passages.

8. Stratified squamous epithelium is multilayered; cells at the free edge are squamous. It is adapted to resist abrasion. It lines the esophagus; its keratinized variety forms the skin epidermis.

9. Stratified cuboidal and stratified columnar epithelia are rare in the body, and are found chiefly in ducts of large glands.

10. Transitional epithelium is a modified stratified squamous epithelium, adapted for responding to stretch. Lines hollow urinary system organs.

Glandular Epithelia (pp. 110–112)

11. A gland is one or more cells specialized to secrete a particular product.

12. On the basis of route of secretion and type of product, glands are classified as exocrine or endocrine. Glands are classified structurally as unicellular or multicellular.

13. Multicellular exocrine glands are classified according to duct structure as simple or compound, and according to the structure of their secretory parts as tubular, alveolar, and tubuloalveolar.

14. Multicellular exocrine glands are classified functionally as merocrine, holocrine, or apocrine.

Connective Tissue (pp. 112–124)

1. Connective tissue is the most abundant and widely distributed tissue of the body. Its functions include support, protection, binding, insulation, and transportation (blood).

Common Characteristics of Connective Tissue (p. 113)

2. Connective tissues originate from embryonic mesenchyme and exhibit matrix. Depending on type, a connective tissue may be well vascularized (most), poorly vascularized (dense connective tissue), or avascular (cartilage).

Structural Elements of Connective Tissue (pp. 113–115)

3. The structural elements of all connective tissues are extracellular matrix and cells.

4. Extracellular matrix consists of ground substance and fibers. It may be fluid, gel-like, or firm.

5. Each connective tissue type has a primary cell type that can exist as a mitotic, matrix-secreting cell (blast) or as a mature cell (cyte) responsible for maintaining the matrix. The chief cell type of connective tissue proper is the fibroblast; that of cartilage is the chondroblast; that of bone is the osteoblast; and that of blood-forming tissue is the hemocytoblast or hematopoietic stem cell.

Types of Connective Tissue (pp. 115–124)

6. Embryonic connective tissue is called mesenchyme.

7. Connective tissue proper consists of loose and dense varieties. The loose connective tissues are:

- areolar: semifluid ground substance; all three fiber types loosely interwoven; contains a variety of cells; forms a soft packing around body organs and the lamina propria; the prototype.

- adipose: consists largely of adipocytes; scant matrix; insulates and protects body organs; provides reserve energy fuel.

- reticular: finely woven reticular fibers in soft ground substance; the stroma of lymphoid organs and bone marrow.

8. Dense connective tissue proper includes:

- dense regular: dense parallel bundles of collagen fibers; few cells, little ground substance; high tensile strength; forms tendons, ligaments, aponeuroses; in cases where this tissue contains numerous elastic fibers (as well as collagen fibers) called elastic connective tissue.

- dense irregular: like regular variety, but fibers are arranged in different planes; resists tension exerted from many different directions; forms the dermis of the skin and organ capsules.

9. Cartilage exists as:

- hyaline: firm ground substance containing collagen fibers; resists compression well; found in fetal skeleton, at articulating surfaces of bones, and trachea; most abundant type.

- elastic cartilage: elastic fibers predominate; provides flexible support of the external ear and epiglottis.

- fibrocartilage: coarse parallel collagen fibers; provides support with compressibility; forms intervertebral discs and knee cartilages.

10. Bone (osseous tissue) consists of a firm, collagen-containing matrix embedded with calcium salts, which confer rigidity; forms the bony skeleton.

11. Blood consists of blood cells in a fluid matrix (plasma).

Epithelial Membranes (p. 124)

1. Epithelial membranes are simple organs, consisting of an epithelium bound to an underlying connective tissue layer. Include the mucosae, serosae, and the cutaneous membrane.

Muscle Tissue (pp. 124–126)

1. Muscle tissue consists of elongated cells (fibers) specialized to contract and cause movement.

2. Based on structure and function, there are:

- skeletal muscle: attached to and moves the bony skeleton.

- cardiac muscle: forms the walls of the heart; pumps blood.

- smooth muscle: in the walls of hollow organs; propels substances through the organs.

Nervous Tissue (p. 126)

1. Nervous tissue forms organs of the nervous system. It is composed of neurons and supporting cells.

2. Neurons are branching cells that receive and transmit electrical impulses; involved in body regulation.

Tissue Repair (pp. 126–131)

1. Inflammation is the body's response to injury. Tissue repair begins during the inflammatory process. It may lead to regeneration, fibrosis, or both.

2. Tissue repair begins with organization, during which the blood clot is replaced by granulation tissue. If the wound is small and the damaged tissue is actively mitotic, the tissue will regenerate and cover the fibrous tissue. When a wound is extensive or the damaged tissue amitotic, it is repaired only by fibrous connective (scar) tissue.

Developmental Aspects of Tissues (pp. 131–132)

1. All body tissues develop from one or more of the three primary germ layers that appear in the embryo. Epithelium arises from all three germ layers (ectoderm, mesoderm, endoderm); muscle and connective tissue from mesoderm; and nervous tissue from ectoderm.

2. The decrease in mass and viability seen in most body tissues during old age often reflects circulatory deficits or poor nutrition.

REVIEW QUESTIONS

Multiple Choice/Matching

1. Use the key to classify each of the following described tissue types into one of the four major tissue categories.

Key: **(a)** connective tissue   **(c)** muscle
       (b) epithelium   **(d)** nervous tissue

_____ Tissue type composed largely of nonliving extracellular matrix; important in protection and support
_____ The tissue immediately responsible for body movement
_____ The tissue that allows us to be aware of the external environment and to react to it; specialized for communication
_____ The tissue that lines body cavities and covers surfaces

2. An epithelium that has several layers, with a layer of flattened cells most superficial, is called (choose all that apply): (a) ciliated, (b) columnar, (c) stratified, (d) simple, (e) squamous.

3. Match the epithelial types named in column B with the appropriate description(s) in column A.

Column A	Column B
_____ Lines most of the digestive tract	**(a)** pseudostratified ciliated columnar
_____ Lines the esophagus	**(b)** simple columnar
_____ Lines much of the respiratory tract	**(c)** simple cuboidal
_____ Forms the walls of the air sacs of the lungs	**(d)** simple squamous
_____ Found in urinary tract organs	**(e)** stratified columnar
_____ Endothelium and mesothelium	**(f)** stratified squamous
	(g) transitional

4. The gland type that secretes products such as milk, saliva, bile, or sweat through a duct is (a) an endocrine gland, (b) an exocrine gland.

5. The membranous lining of the body cavities open to the exterior is (a) endothelium, (b) cutaneous membrane, (c) mucous membrane, (d) serous membrane

6. Scar tissue is a variety of (a) epithelium, (b) connective tissue, (c) muscle tissue, (d) nerve tissue, (e) all of these.

Short Answer Essay Questions

7. Define tissue.

8. Name four important functions of epithelial tissue and provide at least one example of a tissue that exemplifies each function.

9. Describe the criteria used to classify covering and lining epithelia.

10. Explain the functional classification of multicellular exocrine glands and supply an example for each class.

11. Name four important functions of connective tissue and provide examples from the body that illustrate each function.

12. Name the primary cell type in connective tissue proper; in cartilage; in bone.

13. Name the two major components of matrix and, if applicable, subclasses of each component.

14. Matrix is extracellular. How does the matrix get to its characteristic position?

15. Name the specific connective tissue type found in the following body locations: (a) forming the soft packing around organs, (b) supporting the ear pinna, (c) forming "stretchy" ligaments, (d) first connective tissue in the embryo, (e) forming the intervertebral discs, (f) covering the ends of bones at joint surfaces; (g) main component of subcutaneous tissue.

16. What is the function of macrophages?

17. Compare and contrast skeletal, cardiac, and smooth muscle tissue relative to structure, body location, and specific function.

18. Differentiate clearly between the roles of neurons and the supporting cells of nervous tissue.

19. Describe the process of tissue repair, making sure you indicate factors that influence this process.

20. Name the three embryonic germ layers, and indicate which primary tissue classes derive from each layer.

 CRITICAL THINKING AND CLINICAL APPLICATION QUESTIONS

1. John has sustained a severe injury during football practice and is told that he has a torn knee cartilage. Can John expect a quick, uneventful recovery? Explain your response.

2. The epidermis (epithelium of the cutaneous membrane or skin) is a keratinized stratified squamous epithelium. Explain why that epithelium is much better suited for protecting the body's external surface than a mucosa consisting of a simple columnar epithelium would be.

3. Your friend is trying to convince you that if the ligaments binding the bones together at your freely movable joints (such as your knee, shoulder, and hip joints) contained more elastic fibers, you would be much more flexible. Although there is *some* truth to this statement, such a condition would present some serious problems. Why?

4. In adults, over 90% of all cancers are either adenomas (adenocarcinomas) or carcinomas. In fact, cancers of the skin, lung, colon, breast, and prostate are all in these categories. Which one of the four basic tissue types gives rise to most cancers? Why do you think this is so?

The Integumentary System

5

CHAPTER OUTLINE AND STUDENT OBJECTIVES

The Skin (pp. 135–140)

1. Name the specific tissue types composing the epidermis and dermis. List the major layers of each and describe the function of each layer.

2. Describe the factors that normally contribute to skin color. Briefly describe how changes in skin color may be used as clinical signs of certain disease states.

Appendages of the Skin (pp. 141–145)

3. List the parts of a hair follicle and explain the function of each part. Also describe the functional relationship of arrector pili muscles to the hair follicle.

4. Explain the basis of hair color. Describe the distribution, growth, and replacement of hairs and the changing nature of hair during the life span.

5. Compare the structure and most common locations of sweat and oil glands. Also compare the composition and functions of their secretions.

6. Compare and contrast eccrine and apocrine glands.

7. Describe the structure of nails.

Functions of the Integumentary System (pp. 145–146)

8. Describe how the skin accomplishes at least five different functions.

Homeostatic Imbalances of Skin (pp. 146–149)

9. Explain why serious burns are life-threatening. Describe how to determine the extent of a burn and differentiate between first-, second-, and third-degree burns.

10. Summarize the characteristics and warning signs of skin cancers.

Developmental Aspects of the Integumentary System (pp. 149–152)

11. Briefly describe the changes that occur in the skin from birth to old age. Attempt to explain the causes of such changes.

---

ould you be enticed by an advertisement for a coat that is waterproof, stretchable, washable, and permanent-press, that invisibly repairs small cuts, rips, and burns, and that is guaranteed to last a lifetime with reasonable care? Sounds too good to be true, but you already have such a coat—your skin. The skin and its derivatives (sweat and oil glands, hairs, and nails) make up a very complex set of organs that serves several functions, mostly protective. Together, these organs form the **integumentary** (in-teg″u-men′tar-e) **system.**

THE SKIN

The skin ordinarily receives very little respect from its inhabitants, but architecturally it is a marvel. It covers the entire body, has a surface area of 1.5–2 square meters, weighs approximately 4 kg (9 pounds), and accounts for about 7% of total body weight in the average adult. It has been estimated that every square centimeter (cm) of the skin contains 70 cm of blood vessels, 55 cm of nerves, 100 sweat glands, 15 oil glands, 230 sensory receptors, and about half a million cells that are constantly dying and being replaced. The skin is also called the **integument,** which simply means "covering," but its functions go well beyond serving as a large, opaque bag for the body contents. It is pliable yet tough, allowing it to take constant punishment from external agents. Without our skin, we would quickly fall prey to bacteria and perish from water and heat loss.

The skin, which varies in thickness from 1.5 to 4.0 millimeters (mm) or more in different parts of the body, is composed of two distinct regions, the *epidermis* (ep″ĭ-der′mis) and the *dermis* (Figure 5.1). The epidermis (*epi* = upon), composed of epithelial cells, is the outermost protective shield of

(1) Given that epithelia are avascular, which epidermal layer would be expected to have the best-nourished cells? (2) What cell component of the hypodermis makes it a good shock absorber and insulator?

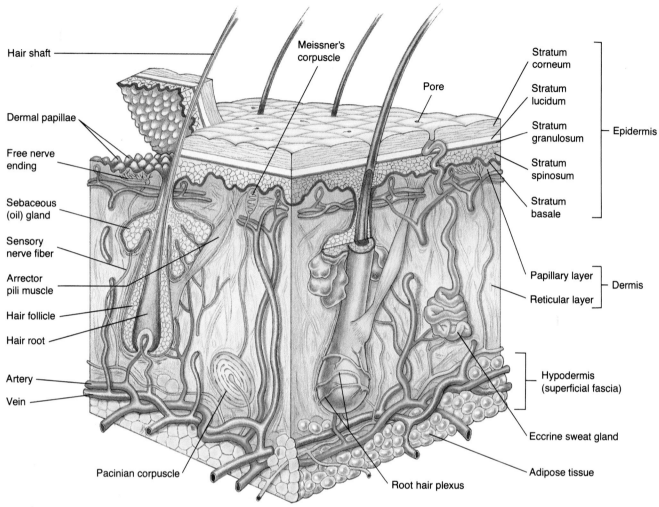

Hair shaft

Meissner's corpuscle

Pore

Stratum corneum

Stratum lucidum

Stratum granulosum

Epidermis

Stratum spinosum

Stratum basale

Dermal papillae

Free nerve ending

Sebaceous (oil) gland

Sensory nerve fiber

Arrector pili muscle

Hair follicle

Hair root

Artery

Vein

Papillary layer

Reticular layer

Dermis

Hypodermis (superficial fascia)

Eccrine sweat gland

Adipose tissue

Pacinian corpuscle

Root hair plexus

FIGURE 5.1
Skin structure. Three-dimensional view of the skin and underlying subcutaneous tissue. The epidermal and dermal layers have been pulled apart at the left corner to reveal the dermal papillae.

the body. The underlying dermis, making up the bulk of the skin, is a tough leathery layer composed of fibrous connective tissue. Only the dermis is vascularized; nutrients reach the epidermis by diffusing through the tissue fluid from blood vessels in the dermis.

The subcutaneous tissue just deep to the skin is known as the **hypodermis** or **superficial fascia.** Strictly speaking, the hypodermis is not considered part of the skin, but it shares some of the skin's protective functions. The hypodermis consists of mostly adipose plus some areolar connective tissue. Besides storing fat, the hypodermis anchors the skin to the underlying structures (mostly to muscles) and allows the skin to slide relatively freely over those structures. Sliding skin protects us by ensuring that many

blows just glance off our bodies. Because of its fatty composition, the hypodermis can also act as a shock absorber and insulate the deeper body tissues from heat loss. The hypodermis thickens markedly when one gains weight. In females, this "extra" subcutaneous fat accumulates first in the thighs and breasts, but in males it first accumulates in the anterior abdomen (as a "beer belly").

Epidermis

Structurally, the **epidermis** is a thick keratinized stratified squamous epithelium consisting of four distinct cell types and four or five distinct layers.

Cells of the Epidermis

The cells populating the epidermis include *keratinocytes, melanocytes, Merkel cells,* and *Langerhans' cells* (Figure 5.2). Since most epidermal cells are keratinocytes, we discuss them first. The chief role of **keratinocytes** (kĕ-rat′ĭ-no-sītz″; "keratin cells") is to produce **keratin,** the fibrous protein that gives the epidermis its protective properties (*kera* = horn in Greek). Tightly connected to one another by desmosomes, the keratinocytes arise in the deepest part of the epidermis from a basal layer of cells that undergo almost continuous mitosis. As the keratinocytes are pushed toward the skin surface by the production of new cells beneath them, they manufacture the keratin that eventually dominates their cell contents. By the time the keratinocytes reach the free (apical) surface of the skin, they are dead, scalelike structures that are little more than keratin-filled plasma membranes. Millions of these dead cells rub off every day, giving us a totally new epidermis every 35 to 45 days—the time from the "birth" of a keratinocyte to its final wearing away. In healthy epidermis, the production of new cells balances cell loss at the skin surface. In body areas regularly subjected to friction, such as the hands and feet, both cell production and keratin formation are accelerated. Growth of the epidermis is controlled, at least in part, by a protein hormone called **epidermal growth factor (EGF).**

Melanocytes (mel′ah-no-sītz), the specialized epithelial cells that synthesize the pigment **melanin** (mel′ah-nin; *melan* = black), are found in the deepest layer of the epidermis. The spider-shaped melanocytes have numerous branching processes that touch all the keratinocytes in the basal layer (Figure 5.2). As melanin is made in membrane-lined granules called *melanosomes,* it is moved to the ends of these processes and then is periodically shed. The keratinocytes nearby engulf sloughed off materials, ingesting the pigment. The melanin granules accumulate on the superficial, or "sunny," side of the keratinocyte nucleus, forming a pigment shield that protects the nucleus from the destructive effects of ultraviolet (UV) radiation in sunlight. Since all humans have the same relative number of these cells, individual and racial differences in skin coloring are probably due to differences in melanocyte activity or the speed of melanin breakdown within the keratinocytes.

The star-shaped **Langerhans'** (lahng′er-hanz) **cells,** which arise from bone marrow and migrate to the epidermis, are macrophages that help to activate our immune system as described later in this chapter (p. 145). Their slender processes extend among the keratinocytes, forming a more or less continuous network (Figure 5.2).

Merkel cells are present in small numbers at the epidermal-dermal junction. Shaped like a hemisphere (Figure 5.2), each Merkel cell is intimately

Why are the desmosomes connecting the keratinocytes so important?

FIGURE 5.2

Diagram showing the main features—layers and relative distribution of the different cell types—in epidermis of thin skin. The keratinocytes (pink) form the bulk of the epidermis. Less numerous are the melanocytes (gray), which produce the pigment melanin; Langerhans' cells (blue), which function as macrophages; and Merkel cells (purple). A sensory nerve ending (yellow), extending to the Merkel cell from the dermis (tan), is shown associated with the Merkel cell forming a Merkel disc (touch receptor). Notice that the keratinocytes, but not the other cell types, are joined by numerous desmosomes (indicated by connections between membranes of adjacent cells). The stratum lucidum, present in thick skin, is not illustrated here.

associated with a disclike sensory nerve ending. The combination, called a *Merkel disc,* is believed to function as a sensory receptor for touch.

Layers of the Epidermis

In **thick skin,** which covers the palms, fingertips, and soles of the feet, the epidermis consists of five layers, or *strata* (stra′-tah; "bed sheets") (see Figures 5.1 and

Stratum corneum—

Stratum lucidum—

Stratum granulosum—

Stratum spinosum—

Stratum basale—

Dermis—

FIGURE 5.3
Photomicrograph showing layers of the skin (150×).
From *Gray's Anatomy,* Henry Gray. Churchill Livingstone, UK.

5.3). From deep to superficial, these layers are: stratum basale, stratum spinosum, stratum granulosum, stratum lucidum, and stratum corneum. In **thin skin,** which covers the rest of the body, the stratum lucidum is absent and the other four strata are thinner (Figure 5.2).

Stratum Basale (Basal Layer).

The **stratum basale** (stra′tum ba-să′le), the deepest epidermal layer, is firmly attached to the underlying dermis along a wavy borderline. For the most part, it consists of a single row of cells, mostly stem cells representing the youngest keratinocytes. The many mitotic nuclei seen in this layer reflect the rapid division of these cells and account for its alternate name, **stratum germinativum** (stra′tum jer′mĭ-nă″tiv-um; "germinating layer").

Some 10% to 25% of the cells in the stratum basale are melanocytes, and their branching processes extend among the surrounding cells reaching well into the more superficial stratum spinosum layer. Occasional Merkel cells are also seen in this stratum.

Stratum Spinosum (Spiny Layer).

The **stratum spinosum** (spi′no-sum) is several cell layers thick. These cells contain thick bundles of intermediate filaments called *tonofilaments* ("tension filaments"). Tonofilaments consist of a tension-resisting protein called *prekeratin.* The keratinocytes in this layer are somewhat flattened and irregular in shape. In typical histological preparations, they display

minute spiney projections, hence they are often called *prickle cells.* However, these spines do not exist in the living cells. They appear during tissue preparation because the cells shrink while their numerous desmosomes "hold tight." Scattered among the keratinocytes are Langerhans' cells, which are most abundant in this epidermal layer.

Stratum Granulosum (Granular Layer).

The thin **stratum granulosum** (gran″u-lo′sum) consists of three to five layers of flattened keratinocytes. Along with abundant tonofilaments, these cells contain *keratohyaline granules* and *lamellated granules.* The keratohyaline (ker″ah-to-hi′ah-lin) granules contribute to the formation of keratin in the higher strata, as described below. The lamellated (lam′ĭ-la-ted; "plated") granules contain a waterproofing glycolipid that is secreted into the extracellular space and is a major factor slowing water loss across the epidermis. The plasma membranes of these cells also thicken, so that they become more resistant to destruction. You might say that the keratinocytes are "toughening up" to make the outer strata the strongest skin region.

Like all epithelia, the epidermis relies on capillaries in the underlying connective tissue (the dermis) for its nutrients. Above the stratum granulosum, the epidermal cells are too far from the dermal capillaries to receive adequate nourishment, so they die. This is a completely normal sequence of events.

Stratum Lucidum (Clear Layer).

Through the light microscope, the **stratum lucidum** (loo′sid-um) appears as a thin translucent band just above the stratum granulosum. It consists of a few rows of flattened dead keratinocytes with indistinct boundaries. Here, or in the stratum corneum above, the "gummy" substance of the keratohyalin granules becomes intimately associated with parallel arrays of tonofilaments in the cells. This keratohyalin-tonofilament combination forms the keratin fibrils. As mentioned before, the stratum lucidum is present only in thick skin.

Stratum Corneum (Horny Layer).

The outermost layer, the **stratum corneum** (kor′ne-um), is a broad zone 20 to 30 cell layers thick. It accounts for up to three-quarters of the epidermal thickness. Keratin and the thickened plasma membranes of cells in the stratum corneum protect the skin against abrasion and penetration. Additionally, the glycolipid between its cells helps keep this layer waterproof. Hence, the stratum corneum provides a durable "overcoat" for the body, protecting deeper cells from the hostile external environment (air) and from water loss and rendering the body relatively insensitive to biological, chemical, and physical assaults. It is amazing that a layer of dead cells can still play so many roles.

The shingle-like cell remnants of the stratum corneum are referred to as *cornified,* or *horny cells* (*cornu* = horn). They are familiar to everyone as the dandruff shed from the scalp and the flakes that slough off dry skin. (The average person sheds 18 kg [40 pounds] of these skin flakes in a lifetime.) The common saying "Beauty is only skin deep" is especially interesting in light of the fact that nearly everything we see when we look at someone is dead!

Dermis

The **dermis** (*derm* = skin), the second major skin region, is a strong but flexible connective tissue layer. The cell types found in the dermis are typical of those found in any connective tissue proper: fibroblasts, macrophages, and occasional mast cells and white blood cells. So too is its semifluid matrix heavily embedded with collagen, elastin, and reticular fibers. The dermis binds the entire body together like a body stocking. It is your "hide" and corresponds exactly to animal hides used to make highly prized leather products.

The dermis is richly supplied with nerve fibers (many equipped with sensory receptors), blood vessels, and lymphatic vessels. The major portions of hair follicles, as well as oil and sweat glands, are derived from epidermal tissue but reside in the dermis, as will be described later.

The dermis has two major layers: the papillary and reticular layers (see Figure 5.1). The thin superficial **papillary** (pap′il-er-e) **layer** is connective tissue in which the fibers form a loosely woven mat that is heavily invested with blood vessels. Its superior surface is thrown into nipplelike projections called **dermal papillae** (pah-pil′e; *papill* = nipple) that indent the overlying epidermis (see Figure 5.1). Many dermal papillae contain capillary loops; others house free (bare) nerve endings (pain receptors) and touch receptors called *Meissner's corpuscles* (mīs′nerz kor′pus′lz). On the palms of the hands and soles of the feet, the papillae lie atop larger mounds called *dermal ridges* which, in turn, produce conspicuous looped and whorled ridges on the epidermal surface. These *epidermal ridges* increase friction and enhance the gripping ability of the fingers and feet. Their patterns are genetically determined and unique to each individual. Because sweat pores open along the crests of the epidermal ridges, the fingertips leave identifying films of sweat called **fingerprints** on almost anything they touch.

The deeper **reticular layer,** which accounts for about 80% of the dermis, is typical dense irregular connective tissue. Its extracellular matrix contains thick bundles of interlacing collagen fibers that run in various planes; however, most run parallel to the skin surface. Separations, or less dense regions, between these bundles form *lines of cleavage,* or *tension lines,* in the skin. The cleavage lines tend to run longitudinally in the skin of the head and limbs and in circular patterns around the neck and trunk. Cleavage lines are important to both surgeons and their patients. When an incision is made *parallel* to these lines, the skin tends to gape less and heals more readily than when the incision is made *across* cleavage lines.

The collagen fibers of the dermis give skin a strength and resiliency, which prevents most jabs and scrapes from penetrating the dermis. In addition, collagen binds water, helping to maintain the hydration of the skin. Elastin fibers provide the stretch-recoil properties of skin.

Extreme stretching of the skin, such as occurs during pregnancy, can tear the dermis. Dermal tearing is indicated by silvery white scars called *striae* (stri′e; "streaks"), commonly called "stretch marks." Short-term but acute trauma (as from a burn or wielding a hoe) can cause a **blister,** the separation of the epidermal and dermal layers by a fluid-filled pocket. ●

In addition to the epidermal ridges and tension lines, a third type of skin marking, *flexure lines,* reflects dermal modifications. These markings are especially obvious on the wrists, palms, soles of the feet, fingers, and toes. Flexure lines are dermal folds that typically occur at or near joints, where the dermis is tightly secured to deeper structures. Since the skin cannot slide easily to accommodate joint movement in such regions, the dermis folds and deep skin creases form.

Skin Color

Three pigments contribute to skin color: melanin, carotene, and hemoglobin. Of these, only melanin is made in the skin. **Melanin,** a polymer made of tyrosine amino acids, ranges in color from yellow to reddish-brown to black. Its synthesis depends on an enzyme in melanocytes called tyrosinase (ti-ro′sĭ-nās) and, as noted earlier, it passes from melanocytes to the basal keratinocytes. Racial differences in skin coloring reflect the relative kind and amount of melanin made. Melanocytes of black- and brown-skinned people produce much more and darker melanin than those of fair-skinned individuals, and their keratinocytes retain it longer. *Freckles* and *pigmented moles* are local accumulations of melanin. Melanocytes are stimulated to greater activity when we expose our skin to sunlight. Prolonged sun exposure causes a substantial melanin buildup, which helps protect DNA of viable skin cells from UV radiation. In all but the darkest people, this response causes visible darkening of the skin (a tan).

Despite melanin's protective effects, excessive sun exposure eventually damages the skin. It causes clumping of elastin fibers leading to "leathery skin," temporarily depresses the immune system, and can alter the DNA of skin cells and in this way lead to skin cancer. The fact that dark-skinned people seldom have skin cancer attests to melanin's amazing effectiveness as a natural sunscreen.

Ultraviolet radiation has other consequences as well. Many chemicals induce photosensitivity; that is, they heighten the skin's sensitivity to UV radiation, setting up sun worshippers for a skin rash the likes of which they would rather not see. Such substances include some antibiotic and antihistamine drugs, many chemicals in perfumes and detergents, and a chemical found in limes and celery. Small, itchy, blisterlike lesions erupt all over the body; then the peeling begins, in sheets! •

Carotene (kar′o-tēn) is a yellow to orange pigment found in certain plant products, such as carrots, and is a rich source of vitamin A. It tends to accumulate in the stratum corneum and in fatty tissue of the hypodermis. Its color is most obvious in the palms and soles, where the stratum corneum is thickest, and most intense when large amounts of carotene-rich foods are eaten. However, the yellowish tinge of the skin of some Asian peoples is due to variations in melanin, not to carotene.

The pinkish hue of fair skin reflects the crimson color of oxygenated **hemoglobin** (he′mo-glo″bin) in the red blood cells circulating through the dermal capillaries. Since Caucasian skin contains only small amounts of melanin, the epidermis is nearly transparent and allows hemoglobin's color to show through.

When hemoglobin is poorly oxygenated, both the blood and the skin of light-skinned people appear blue. This condition is called *cyanosis* (si″ah-no′-sis; *cyan* = dark blue). Skin often becomes cyanotic when blood is inadequately oxygenated as during heart failure and severe respiratory disorders. In dark-skinned individuals, the skin does not appear cyanotic because of the masking effects of melanin, but cyanosis is apparent in their mucous membranes and nail beds (the same sites where the red cast of normally oxygenated blood is visible).

The skin color of some people is also influenced by emotional stimuli, and many alterations in skin color signal certain disease states:

- *redness, or erythema* (er″ĭ-the′mah): Reddened skin may indicate embarrassment (blushing), fever, hypertension, inflammation, or allergy.

- *pallor, or blanching:* Under certain types of emotional stress (fear, anger, and others), some people become pale. Pale skin may also signify anemia or low blood pressure.

- *jaundice (jawn′dis), or yellow cast:* An abnormal yellow skin tone usually signifies a liver or biliary disorder, in which excess bile pigments are present in the blood and are deposited in body tissues. (Normally, the liver cells secrete the bile pigments [bilirubin] as a component of bile.)

- *bronzing:* A bronze, almost metallic appearance of the skin is a sign of Addison's disease, hypofunction of the adrenal cortex.

- *black-and-blue marks, or bruises:* Black-and-blue marks reveal where blood has escaped from the circulation and clotted beneath the skin. Such clotted blood masses are called *hematomas* (he″mah-to′mah; "blood swelling"). Unusual susceptibility to bruising may signify a deficiency of vitamin C or *hemophilia* (bleeders' disease). •

APPENDAGES OF THE SKIN

Along with the skin itself, the integumentary system includes several derivatives of the epidermis. These **skin appendages** include the hair and hair follicles, sebaceous (oil) glands, sweat glands, and nails. Each of these plays a unique role in maintaining body homeostasis.

Hairs and Hair Follicles

Although hair serves other mammals by keeping them warm, our body hair is far less useful. The main function of our sparse body hair is to sense insects on the skin before they sting us. That on the head guards the head against physical trauma, heat loss, and sunlight. Eyelashes shield the eyes and nose hairs filter large particles like lint and insects from the air we inhale.

Structure of a Hair

Hairs, or **pili** (pi′li), are flexible strands produced by hair follicles that consist largely of keratinized cells. The **hard keratin** that dominates hairs has two advantages over the **soft keratin** that is found in typical epidermal cells: (1) It is tougher and more durable, and (2) its individual cells do not flake off.

The chief regions of a hair are the *shaft,* which projects from the skin (Figure 5.4), and the *root,* the part embedded in the skin (Figure 5.5a). The shape of the shaft determines whether hair is straight or curly. If the shaft is flat and ribbonlike in cross section, the hair is kinky; if it is oval, the hair is wavy; if it is perfectly round, the hair is straight.

A hair has three concentric layers of keratinized cells (Figure 5.5b). Its central core, the *medulla* (mĕ-dul′ah; "middle"), consists of large cells that are partially separated by air spaces. The medulla is absent in fine hairs. The *cortex,* a bulky layer surrounding the medulla, consists of several layers of flattened cells. The outermost **cuticle** is formed from a single layer of cells that overlap one another from below like shingles on a roof (Figure 5.4). This arrangement helps to keep neighboring hairs apart so that the hair does not mat. The most heavily keratinized part of the hair, the cuticle, provides strength and helps keep the inner layers tightly compacted. Because it is subjected to the most abrasion, the cuticle tends to wear away at the tip of the hair shaft, allowing the keratin fibrils in the cortex and medulla to frizz out, creating "split ends."

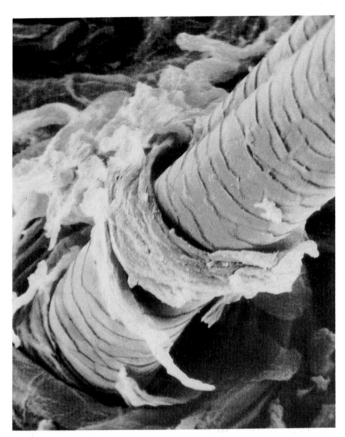

FIGURE 5.4
Scanning electron micrograph showing a hair shaft emerging from a follicle at the epidermal surface. Notice how the scalelike cells of the cuticle overlap one another (1500×).

Hair pigment is made by melanocytes at the base of the hair follicle and transferred to the cortical cells. Various proportions of melanins of different colors (yellow, rust, brown, and black) combine to produce hair color from blond to pitch black. Gray or white hair results from decreased melanin production (mediated by delayed-action genes) and from the replacement of melanin by air bubbles in the hair shaft.

Structure of a Hair Follicle

Hair follicles (*folli* = bag) extend from the epidermal surface into the dermis. In the scalp, they may even extend into the hypodermis. The deep end of the follicle is expanded, forming a **hair bulb** (Figure 5.5c). A knot of sensory nerve endings called a **root hair plexus** wraps around each hair bulb (see Figure 5.1), and bending the hair stimulates these endings. Consequently, our hairs act as sensitive touch receptors. (Feel the "tickle" as you run your hand over the hairs on your forearm.)

A *papilla,* a nipplelike bit of dermal tissue containing a knot of capillaries, protrudes into the hair bulb and supplies nutrients to the growing hair. Except for its specific location, this papilla is similar to the dermal papillae underlying other epidermal regions.

The wall of a hair follicle is actually a compound structure composed of an outer **connective tissue root sheath,** derived from the dermis, and an inner **epithelial root sheath,** formed mainly by an invagination of the epidermis (Figure 5.5c and d). The epithelial root sheath, which has external and internal parts, thins as it approaches the hair bulb, so that only a single layer of stratum basale cells remains to wind around the papilla. However, the stem cells that comprise the **hair matrix,** or actively dividing germinal area of the hair bulb which produces the hair, originate in a region called the *hair bulge* located a fraction of a millimeter above the hair bulb. When chemical signals diffusing from the papilla reach the hair bulge, some of its cells begin to migrate toward the papilla, where they divide to produce the hair cells. As new hair cells are produced by the matrix, the older part of the hair is pushed upward, and its fused cells become increasingly keratinized and die.

Associated with each hair follicle is a bundle of smooth muscle cells called an **arrector pili** (ah-rek′-tor pi′li; "raiser of hair") muscle. As you can see in Figure 5.5e, most hair follicles approach the skin surface at a slight angle, or obliquely. The arrector pili muscles are attached in such a way that their contraction pulls the hair follicle into an upright position and dimples the skin surface to produce goose bumps in response to cold external temperatures or fear. Although this "hair-raising" response is not very useful to humans, with our short sparse hairs, it is an important heat retention and protection mechanism in other animals. Furry animals can stay warmer by trapping a layer of insulating air in their fur; and a scared animal with its hair on end looks larger and more formidable to its enemy.

Distribution, Types, and Growth of Hair

Millions of hairs are scattered over nearly all of the body. There are about 100,000 of them in the scalp and another 30,000 in a man's beard. Only the lips, nipples, parts of the external genitalia, and thick-skin areas such as the palms of the hands and soles of the feet totally lack hair.

Hairs come in various sizes and shapes, but as a rule, they can be classified as vellus or terminal. The body hair of children and adult females is of the pale, fine **vellus** (vel′us; *vell* = wool, fleece) **hair** variety. The coarser, often longer hair of the eyebrows and scalp is **terminal hair;** terminal hair may also be darker. At puberty, terminal hairs appear in the axillary and pubic regions of both sexes and on the face and chest (and, typically, the arms and legs) of males. These terminal hairs grow in response to the stimulating effects of male sex hormones called *androgens* (of which *testosterone* is the most important).

Hair growth and density are influenced by many factors, but most importantly by nutrition and hormones. As a rule, poor nutrition means poor hair growth. On the other hand, conditions that increase

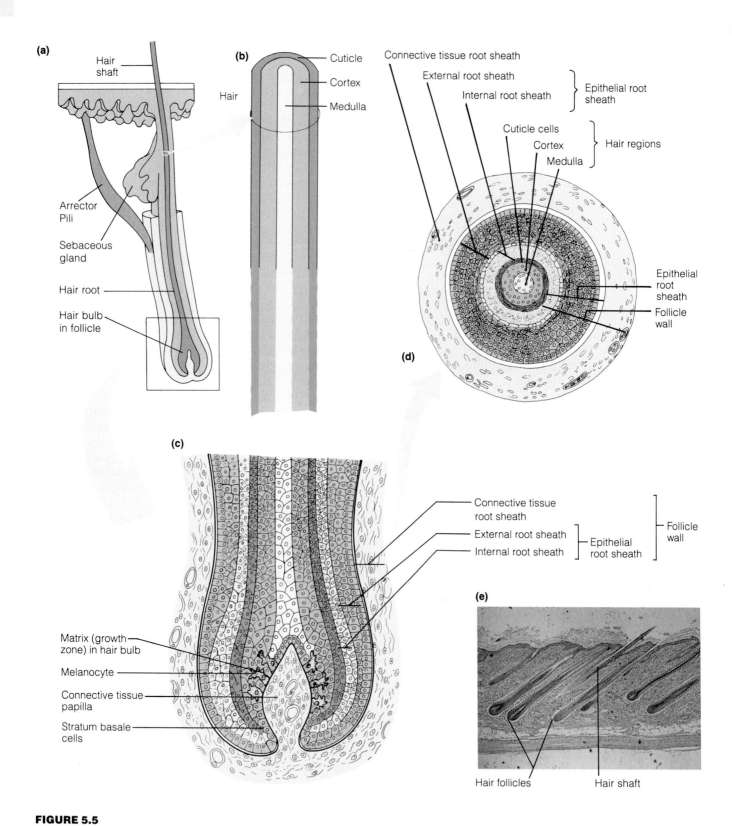

(a)
Hair shaft

Arrector Pili

Sebaceous gland

Hair root

Hair bulb in follicle

(b)
Cuticle

Cortex

Medulla

Hair

Connective tissue root sheath

External root sheath

Internal root sheath } Epithelial root sheath

Cuticle cells

Cortex

Medulla } Hair regions

Epithelial root sheath

Follicle wall

(d)

(c)

Connective tissue root sheath

External root sheath

Internal root sheath } Epithelial root sheath } Follicle wall

Matrix (growth zone) in hair bulb

Melanocyte

Connective tissue papilla

Stratum basale cells

(e)

Hair follicles   Hair shaft

FIGURE 5.5
Structure of a hair and hair follicle. (a) Longitudinal section of a hair within its follicle.
(b) Enlarged longitudinal section of a hair. (c) Enlarged longitudinal view of the expanded hair bulb of the follicle which encloses the matrix, actively dividing epithelial cells that produce the hair. (d) Cross section of a hair and hair follicle. (e) Photomicrograph of scalp tissue showing numerous hair follicles (24×).

the local dermal blood flow (such as chronic physical irritation or inflammation) may enhance local hair growth. Many old-time bricklayers who carried their hod on one shoulder all the time developed one hairy shoulder. As noted, testosterone also encourages hair growth, and when male hormones are present in large amounts, terminal hair growth is luxuriant. Hair growth in certain body areas that is seen as undesirable (such as on a woman's upper lip) may be arrested by *electrolysis* treatments, which use electricity to destroy the hair roots.

In women, small amounts of androgens are normally produced by both the ovaries and the adrenal glands. Excessive hairiness, or *hirsutism* (her'soot-izm; *hirsut* = hairy), as well as other signs of masculinization, may result from an adrenal gland tumor that secretes abnormally large amounts of androgens. Since few women want a beard or hairy chest, such tumors are surgically removed as soon as possible. •

The rate of hair growth varies from one body region to another and with sex and age, but it averages about 2 mm per week. Each follicle goes through *growth cycles* (Figure 5.6). In each cycle, an active growth phase is followed by a resting phase, when the matrix is inactive and the follicle base and hair bulb atrophy somewhat. After the resting phase, the matrix proliferates again and forms a new hair to replace the old one that has fallen out or will be pushed out by the new hair.

The life span of hairs varies. The follicles of the scalp remain active for years (the average is four years) before becoming inactive for a few months. Because only a small percent of the hair follicles are in the shedding phase at any one time, we lose an average of 90 scalp hairs daily. The follicles of the eyebrow hairs remain active for only three to four months, which explains why your eyebrows are never as long as the hairs on your head.

Hair Thinning and Baldness

Given ideal conditions, hair grows fastest from the teen years to the 40s; then its growth slows. The declining rate of hair growth that begins in the fourth decade reflects a natural age-related atrophy of hair follicles. The fact that hairs are not replaced as fast as they are shed leads to hair thinning and some degree of baldness, or **alopecia** (al″o-pe′she-ah), in both sexes. Much less dramatic in women, the process usually begins at the anterior hairline and progresses posteriorly. Coarse terminal hairs are replaced by vellus hairs, and the hair becomes increasingly wispy.

True, or *frank, baldness* is a different story entirely. The most common type of frank baldness, **male pattern baldness,** is a genetically determined, sex-influenced condition. It is thought to be caused by a delayed-action gene that "switches on" in adulthood and changes the response of the hair follicles to testosterone. As a result, the follicular growth cycles

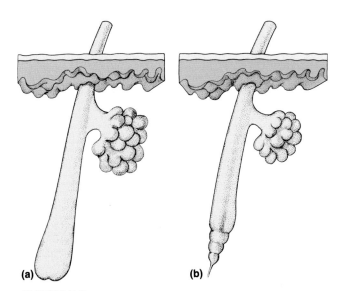

FIGURE 5.6
Overall shape of (a) an active and (b) a resting hair follicle. The hair is shed during or just after the resting phase.

become so short that many hairs never even emerge from their follicles before shedding, and those that do are fine vellus hairs that look like peach fuzz in the "bald" area. Until recently, the only cure for male pattern baldness has been drugs that inhibit testosterone production, but they also cause loss of sex drive—a trade-off few men would select. Quite by accident, it was discovered that minoxidil, a drug used to reduce high blood pressure by causing blood vessels to dilate, has an interesting side effect in some bald men; it stimulates hair regrowth. Although its results are variable, minoxidil is available in ointment form for application to the scalp.

Hair thinning can be induced by a number of other factors that lengthen follicular resting periods and upset the normal balance between the rates of hair loss and replacement. Outstanding examples are stressors, such as acutely high fever, surgery, or severe emotional trauma, and certain drugs (excessive vitamin A, some antidepressants, and most chemotherapy drugs). Protein-deficient diets and lactation lead to hair thinning because new hair growth stops when protein needed for keratin synthesis is not available or is being used for milk production. In all of these cases, hair regrows if the cause of thinning is removed or corrected. However, hair loss due to prolonged physical trauma, excessive radiation, or genetic factors is permanent. •

Nails

A **nail** is a scalelike modification of the epidermis that forms a clear protective covering on the dorsum of the distal part of a finger or toe (Figure 5.7). Nails, which correspond to the hoofs or claws of other animals, are particularly useful as "tools" to help pick up

FIGURE 5.7
Structure of a nail. Longitudinal section of the distal part of a finger showing nail parts. The nail matrix that forms the nail lies beneath the lunula; the epidermis of the nail bed underlies the nail.

small objects and to scratch an itch. Like hairs, nails contain hard keratin. Each nail has a *free edge,* a *body* (visible attached portion), and a proximal *root* (embedded in the skin). The deeper layers of the epidermis extend beneath the nail as the *nail bed;* the nail itself corresponds to the superficial keratinized layers. The thickened proximal portion of the nail bed, called the **nail matrix,** is responsible for nail growth. As the nail cells produced by the matrix become heavily keratinized, the nail body slides distally over the nail bed.

Nails normally appear pink because of the rich bed of capillaries in the underlying dermis. However, the region that lies over the thickened nail matrix appears as a white crescent called the *lunula* (lu'nu-lah; "little moon"). The proximal and lateral borders of the nail are overlapped by skin folds, called *nail folds.* The proximal nail fold projects onto the nail body as the *cuticle* or *eponychium* (ep"o-nik'e-um; "on the nail").

Sweat (Sudoriferous) Glands

Sweat glands, also called **sudoriferous** (su"do-rif'er-us; *sudor* = sweat) **glands,** are distributed over the entire skin surface except the nipples and parts of the external genitalia. Their number is staggering—more than 2.5 million per person. There are two types of sweat glands: eccrine and apocrine.

Eccrine (ek'-rin; "secreting") **sweat glands** are far more numerous and are particularly abundant on the palms, soles of the feet, and forehead. Each is a simple, coiled, tubular gland. The secretory part lies coiled in the dermis; the duct extends to open in a funnel-shaped **pore** (*por* = channel) at the skin surface (see Figure 5.1). (These sweat pores are different from the so-called "pores" of one's complexion, which are actually the external outlets of hair follicles.)

Eccrine gland secretion, commonly called **sweat,** is a hypotonic filtrate of the blood, which passes through the secretory cells of the sweat glands and is released by exocytosis. It is 99% water, with some salts (mostly sodium chloride), antibodies, traces of metabolic wastes (urea, uric acid, ammonia), lactic acid, and vitamin C. The exact composition depends on heredity and diet. Small amounts of ingested drugs may also be excreted by this route. Normally, sweat is acidic with a pH between 4 and 6.

Sweating is regulated by the sympathetic division of the autonomic nervous system, over which we have little control. Its major role is to assist in thermoregulation and prevent overheating of the body. Heat-induced sweating begins on the forehead and then spreads inferiorly over the rest of the body. Emotionally induced sweating—the so-called "cold sweat" brought on by fright, embarrassment, or nervousness—begins on the palms, soles, and axillae (armpits) and then spreads to other body areas.

Apocrine (ap'o-krin) **sweat glands*** are largely confined to the axillary and anogenital areas. They are larger than eccrine glands, and their ducts empty into hair follicles. Apocrine secretion contains the same basic components as true sweat, plus some fatty substances and proteins. Consequently, it is quite viscous and sometimes has a milky or yellowish color. The secretion is odorless, but when its organic molecules are decomposed by bacteria on the skin, it takes on a musky and generally unpleasant odor, the basis of body odor.

Apocrine glands begin to function at puberty under the influence of androgens. Although their output certainly increases on hot days, apocrine glands have little role to play in thermoregulation. Their precise function is not yet known, but they are activated by sympathetic nerve fibers during pain and stress. Since their activity is increased by sexual foreplay, and they enlarge and recede with the phases of a woman's menstrual cycle, they may be analogous to the sexual scent glands of other animals.

Ceruminous (sĕ-roo'mĭ-nus; *cera* = wax) **glands** are modified apocrine glands found in the lining of the external ear canal. They secrete a rather sticky substance called *cerumen,* or earwax, that is thought to deter insects and block entry of foreign material.

Mammary glands, another variety of specialized sweat glands, secrete milk. Although they are properly part of the integumentary system, we consider the mammary glands in Chapter 28, along with female reproductive organs.

---

*The term apocrine sweat glands is a misnomer. These glands were originally thought to release their product by the apocrine mode (in which the apical surface pinches off) and were named accordingly. Subsequent studies proved them to be merocrine glands, which release their product by exocytosis like the eccrine sweat glands.

Sebaceous (Oil) Glands

The **sebaceous** (se-ba′shus) **glands,** or **oil glands** (see Figure 5.1), are simple alveolar glands found all over the body except on the palms and soles. They are small on the body trunk and limbs, but quite large on the face, neck, and upper chest. These glands secrete an oily secretion called **sebum** (se′bum; *seb* = grease). The central cells of the alveoli accumulate lipids until they become so engorged that they burst, so functionally these glands are *holocrine glands.* The accumulated lipids and cell fragments constitute sebum. Sebum is usually secreted into a hair follicle, or occasionally to a pore on the skin surface. Sebum softens and lubricates the hair and skin, prevents hair from becoming brittle, and slows water loss from the skin when the external humidity is low. Perhaps even more important is its *bactericidal* (bacterium-killing) action.

The secretion of sebum is stimulated by hormones, especially androgens. These glands are relatively inactive during childhood but are activated in both sexes during puberty, when androgen production begins to rise.

If a sebaceous gland duct becomes blocked by accumulated sebum, a *whitehead* appears on the skin surface. If the material oxidizes and dries, it darkens to form a *blackhead. Acne* is an active inflammation of the sebaceous glands accompanied by "pimples" (pustules or cysts) on the skin. It is usually caused by bacterial infection, particularly by staphylococcus, and can be mild or extremely severe, leading to permanent scarring. **Seborrhea** (seb″o-re′ah), known as "cradle cap" in infants, is caused by overactivity of the sebaceous glands. It begins on the scalp as pink, raised lesions that gradually become yellow to brown and begin to slough off oily scales. Careful washing to remove the excessive oil often helps. •

FUNCTIONS OF THE INTEGUMENTARY SYSTEM

The skin and its derivatives perform a variety of functions that affect body metabolism, and prevent external factors such as bacteria, abrasion, temperature, and chemicals from upsetting body homeostasis.

Protection

The skin constitutes at least three types of barriers: chemical, physical, and biological.

The **chemical barriers** include skin secretions and melanin. Although the skin's surface is always teeming with bacteria, the low pH of skin secretions, or the so-called **acid mantle,** retards their multiplication. In addition, many bacteria are killed outright by bactericidal substances in sebum. As discussed earlier, melanin provides a chemical pigment shield to prevent ultraviolet damage to the viable skin cells.

Physical, or **mechanical, barriers** are provided by the continuity of skin and the hardness of its keratinized cells. As a physical barrier, the skin is a remarkable compromise. A thicker epidermis would certainly be more impenetrable, but we would pay the price in loss of suppleness and agility. Epidermal continuity works hand in hand with the acid mantle to ward off bacterial invasion. The extracellular glycolipids effectively block the diffusion of water and water-soluble substances between cells, preventing both their loss from and entry into the body through the skin. Substances that do penetrate the skin in limited amounts include (1) *lipid-soluble substances,* such as oxygen, carbon dioxide, fat-soluble vitamins (A, D, E, and K), and steroids; (2) *oleoresins* (o″le-o-rez′inz) of certain plants, such as poison ivy and poison oak; (3) *organic solvents,* such as acetone, dry-cleaning fluid, and paint thinner, which dissolve the cell lipids; and (4) *salts of heavy metals,* such as lead, mercury, and nickel.

Organic solvents and heavy metals are devastating to the body and can be lethal. Absorption of organic solvents through the skin into the bloodstream can cause the kidneys to shut down and can also cause brain damage. Absorption of lead results in anemia and neurological defects. These substances should never be handled with bare hands. •

Biological barriers include the Langerhans' cells of the epidermis and the macrophages in the dermis. The Langerhans' cells are active elements of the immune system. For the immune response to be activated, the foreign substances, or *antigens,* must be presented to specialized white blood cells called lymphocytes. In the epidermis, it is the Langerhans' cells that play this role. Dermal macrophages constitute a second line of defense to dispose of viruses and bacteria that have managed to penetrate the epidermis. They, too, act as antigen "presenters."

Body Temperature Regulation

Even when we exercise vigorously, and even when the environmental temperature is high or low, body temperature remains within homeostatic limits. Like car engines, we need to get rid of the heat generated by our internal reactions. As long as the external temperature is lower than body temperature, the skin surface loses heat to the air and to cooler objects in its environment, just as a car radiator loses heat to the air and other nearby engine parts.

Under normal resting conditions, and as long as the environmental temperature is below 31°–32°C (88° –90°F), sweat glands continuously secrete unnoticeable amounts of sweat (about 500 ml [0.5 L] of sweat per day). This inconspicuous water loss is referred to as *insensible perspiration.* When body temperature rises, the dermal blood vessels dilate and the sweat glands are stimulated into vigorous secretory activity. Sweat output increases dramatically and noticeably (*sensible perspiration*) and can account for the loss of up to 12 L of body water in one day. Evaporation of sweat from the skin surface dissipates body heat and cools the body, thus preventing overheating.

When the external environment is cold, dermal blood vessels constrict. This causes the warm blood to bypass the skin temporarily and allows skin temperature to drop to that of the external environment. Once this has happened, further passive heat loss from the body is slowed. This conserves body heat and helps maintain homeostatic body temperature. Body temperature regulation is discussed in greater detail in Chapter 25.

Cutaneous Sensation

The skin is richly supplied with **cutaneous sensory receptors,** which are actually part of the nervous system. The cutaneous receptors are classified as *exteroceptors* (ek"ster-o-sep'torz) because they respond to stimuli arising outside the body. For example, Meissner's corpuscles (in the dermal papillae) allow us to become aware of a caress or the feel of our clothing against our skin, whereas Pacinian receptors (in the deeper dermis or hypodermis) alert us to bumps or contacts involving deep pressure. Root hair plexuses report on wind blowing through our hair and a playful tug on a pigtail. Painful stimuli (irritating chemicals, extreme heat or cold, and others) are sensed by bare nerve endings that meander throughout the skin. Detailed discussion of these cutaneous receptors is deferred to Chapter 13, but those mentioned above are illustrated in Figure 5.1.

Metabolic Functions

When sunlight bombards the skin, modified cholesterol molecules in epidermal cells are converted to a vitamin D precursor. This precursor is absorbed into the dermal capillaries and transported to other body areas to play various roles in calcium metabolism. For example, calcium cannot be absorbed from the digestive tract without vitamin D.

Surprising results of recent studies indicate that besides synthesizing vitamin D, the epidermis has a host of other metabolic functions. It is able to make chemical conversions that supplement those of the liver—for example, keratinocyte enzymes can render harmless many cancer-causing chemicals (carcinogens) that begin to penetrate the epidermis. Conversely, they can convert some innocuous chemicals into carcinogens. Keratinocytes also activate some steroid hormones; for example, they can transform cortisone applied topically to irritated skin into hydrocortisone, a potent anti-inflammatory drug. Skin cells also make several biologically important proteins

(see p. 151) and collagenase, an enzyme that aids the natural turnover of collagen (and deters wrinkles).

Blood Reservoir

The skin vascular supply is quite extensive and can hold large volumes of blood (about 5% of the body's entire blood volume). When other body organs, such as vigorously working muscles, need a greater blood supply, the nervous system constricts the dermal blood vessels. This shunts more blood into the general circulation, making it available to the muscles and other body organs.

Excretion

Limited amounts of nitrogen-containing wastes (ammonia, urea, and uric acid) are eliminated from the body in sweat, although most such wastes are excreted in urine. Profuse sweating is an important avenue for water and sodium chloride loss.

HOMEOSTATIC IMBALANCES OF SKIN

When skin rebels, it is quite a visible revolution. Loss of homeostasis in body cells and organs reveals itself on the skin in ways that are sometimes almost too incredible to believe. The skin can develop more than 1000 different conditions and ailments. The most common skin disorders are bacterial, viral, or yeast infections; a number of these are summarized in Related Clinical Terms on p. 152. Less common, but far more damaging to body well-being, are burns and skin cancer, considered next. •

Burns

Burns are a devastating threat to the body primarily because of their effects on the skin. A burn is tissue damage inflicted by intense heat, electricity, radiation, or certain chemicals, all of which denature cell proteins and cause cell death in the affected areas. Over 2 million Americans are treated for burns each year and approximately 12,000 of them die as a result of their burns.

The immediate threat to life resulting from severe burns is a catastrophic loss of body fluids containing proteins and electrolytes. As fluid seeps from the burned surfaces, dehydration and electrolyte imbalance result. These, in turn, lead to renal shutdown and circulatory shock (inadequate blood circulation due to reduced blood volume). To save the patient, the lost fluids must be replaced immediately. In adults, the volume of fluid lost can be estimated by computing the percentage of body surface burned (extent of the burns) using the **rule of nines.** This

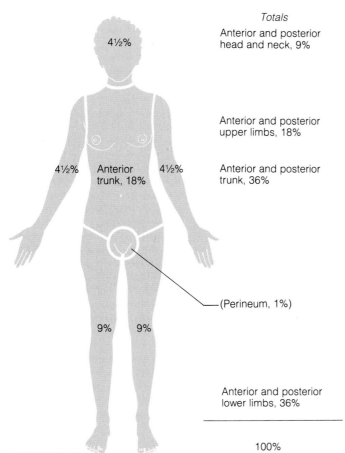

Totals

Anterior and posterior head and neck, 9%

4½%

Anterior and posterior upper limbs, 18%

4½%   Anterior trunk, 18%   4½%

Anterior and posterior trunk, 36%

(Perineum, 1%)

9%   9%

Anterior and posterior lower limbs, 36%

100%

FIGURE 5.8
Estimating the extent of burns by using the rule of nines. The surface area values for the anterior body surface are indicated on the human figure. Total surface area (anterior and posterior body surfaces) for each body region is indicated to the right of the figure.

method divides the body into 11 areas, each accounting for 9% of total body area, plus an additional area surrounding the genitals accounting for 1% of body surface area (Figure 5.8). This method is only approximate, so special tables are used when greater accuracy is desired (as for children, whose body proportions change rapidly).

In addition to fluid and electrolyte replacement, burn patients need thousands of extra food calories daily to replace lost proteins and allow tissue repair. No one can eat enough food to provide these calories, so burn patients are given supplementary nutrients through gastric tubes and intravenous (IV) lines. After the initial crisis has passed, infection becomes the main threat and is the leading cause of death in burn victims. Burned skin is sterile for about 24 hours. Thereafter, bacteria, fungi, and other pathogens can easily invade areas where the skin barrier is destroyed, and they multiply rapidly in the nutrient-rich environment of dead tissues and protein-containing fluid. Adding to this problem is the fact that the immune system becomes deficient within one to two days after severe burn injury.

Burns are classified according to their severity (depth) as first-, second-, or third-degree burns. In **first-degree burns,** only the epidermis is damaged. Symptoms include localized redness, swelling, and pain. Generally, first-degree burns heal in two to three days without special attention. Sunburn is usually a first-degree burn. **Second-degree burns** injure the epidermis and the upper region of the dermis. Symptoms mimic those of first-degree burns, but blisters also appear. Since sufficient numbers of epithelial cells are still present, skin regeneration occurs with little or no scarring within three to four weeks if care is taken to prevent infection. First- and second-degree burns are referred to as **partial-thickness burns.**

Third-degree burns involve the entire thickness of the skin; these burns are also called **full-thickness burns.** The burned area appears blanched (gray-white), cherry red, or blackened, and initially there is little or no edema. Since the nerve endings in the area have been destroyed, the burned area is not painful. Although skin regeneration might eventually occur by the proliferation of epithelial cells at the edges of the burn, it is usually impossible to wait this long because of fluid loss and infection. Thus, skin grafting is usually necessary.

To prepare the burned area for grafting, the *eschar* (es'kar), or burned skin, must first be debrided (removed). To prevent infection and fluid loss, the area is then flooded with antibiotics and covered temporarily with a synthetic membrane, animal (pig) skin, cadaver skin, or "living bandage" made from the thin amniotic sac membrane that surrounds a fetus. Then healthy skin is transplanted to the burned site. Unless the graft is taken from a donor site on the patient, however, there is a good chance that it will be rejected (destroyed) by the patient's immune system. (See Organ Transplants and Prevention of Rejection on p. 731.) Even if the graft "takes," or is successful, extensive scar tissue often forms in the burned areas.

An exciting technique is eliminating many of the traditional problems of skin grafting. Synthetic skin made of a plastic "epidermis" bound to a spongy "dermal" layer composed of collagen and ground cartilage is applied to the debrided area. In time, the artificial dermis is invaded by blood vessels and by fibroblasts that produce collagen fibers. The newly formed collagen fibers replace those of the synthetic dermis, which naturally degrade. While dermal reconstruction is going on, tiny bits of epidermal tissue are harvested from unburned parts of the patient's body. The cells are isolated and then coaxed to proliferate in test tubes. Once the new dermis is complete (usually in two to three months), sheets of smooth, pink, bottle-grown epidermis are grafted on the dermal surface to seed new epidermal growth. This eventually forms a completely new epidermis. A similar commercial product (*Testskin*) is being used to test the effects of cosmetics and other chemicals on

A CLOSER LOOK | Vampires: Where(wolf) Art Thou?

Stories of vampires and werewolves are part of the folklore of many countries. Although many aspects of vampire legends derive from the "behavior" of bloated corpses that shift in their graves (the "undead"), other aspects may be based on living people with rare skin conditions. One likely condition is **porphyria** (por-fēr′e-ă; "purple"), an inherited disease. People with this condition cannot make some of the enzymes that catalyze the biochemical pathway resulting in *heme* formation. Heme is the iron-containing part of hemoglobin, the molecule that carries oxygen in red blood cells. Without these enzymes, the intermediate products of this pathway, called **porphyrins,** build up, spill into the circulation, and eventually cause lesions throughout the body—especially when exposed to rays of sunlight.

Unfortunate victims who were once shunned as vampires or werewolves, and many mentally ill people (including the Dutch painter Vincent

van Gogh), may actually have had this disease. Porphyria affects about 1 of every 25,000 people and is actually a group of diseases characterized by five Ps: (1) *puberty* (the time that symptoms typically appear), (2) *psychiatric abnormalities,* (3) *pain,* (4) *polyneuropathy* (different neurological defects), and (5) *photosensitivity* (sensitivity to light) in many cases. Symptoms tend to come and go and are aggravated by exposure to alcohol and many other chemicals, including some in garlic which severely aggravates porphyria symptoms.

Sunlight creates all kinds of nasty damage in porphyria victims (a reason, perhaps, why vampires were said to hide in dark basements and coffins during daylight hours). Light breaks down porphyrins to free radicals and other destructive chemicals, and sun-exposed skin becomes lesioned and scarred. The fingers, toes, and nose are often mutilated, and the teeth grow prominent as the gums degenerate (the basis of the large

vampire "fangs"?). Rampant growth of hair causes the sufferer's face to become "wolflike" and the hands to resemble paws. One treatment for porphyria is to inject heme molecules extracted from healthy red blood cells. Heme injections were not available in the Middle Ages, so (perhaps) the next best thing would be to drink blood, as vampires were said to do.

human skin and is rapidly replacing the use of animals for such tests.

In general, burns are considered critical if any of the following conditions exists: (1) over 25% of the body has second-degree burns, (2) over 10% of the body has third-degree burns, or (3) there are third-degree burns of the face, hands, or feet. Facial burns introduce the possibility of burned respiratory passageways, which can swell and cause suffocation. Burns at joints are also troublesome because scar tissue formation can severely limit joint mobility.

Skin Cancer

Most tumors that arise in the skin are benign and do not spread (metastasize) to other body areas. (A wart, a neoplasm caused by a virus, is one example.) However, some skin tumors are malignant, or cancerous, and invade other body areas. A crucial risk factor for skin cancer, especially in those with fair skin, is overexposure to the ultraviolet radiation in sunlight, which appears to disable gene p53 (a tumor suppressor gene). In limited numbers of cases, however, frequent irritation of the skin by infections, chemicals, or physical trauma seems to be a predisposing factor.

Basal Cell Carcinoma

Basal cell carcinoma (kar″sĭ-no′mah) is the least malignant and most common skin cancer. Cells of the stratum basale proliferate, invading the dermis and hypodermis. The cancer lesions occur most often on sun-exposed areas of the face and appear as shiny, dome-shaped nodules that later develop a central ulcer with a "pearly" beaded edge (Figure 5.9a). Basal cell carcinoma is relatively slow-growing, and metastasis seldom occurs before it is noticed. Full cure by surgical excision is the rule in 99% of cases.

Squamous Cell Carcinoma

Squamous cell carcinoma arises from the keratinocytes of the stratum spinosum. The lesion appears as a scaly reddened papule (small, rounded elevation) that arises most often on the scalp, ears, dorsum of the hands, and lower lip. It tends to grow rapidly and metastasize to adjacent lymph nodes if not removed. If it is caught early and removed surgically or by radiation therapy, the chance of complete cure is good.

(a)

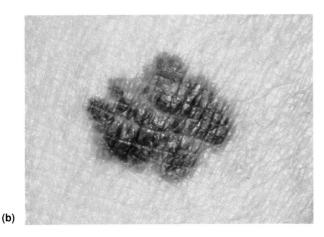

(b)

FIGURE 5.9
Photographs of skin cancers. (a) Basal cell carcinoma.
(b) Malignant melanoma typically begins as a small, irregular brown lesion.

Malignant Melanoma

Malignant melanoma (mel″ah-no′mah), cancer of melanocytes, is the most dangerous skin cancer. It accounts for only about 5% of skin cancers, but its incidence is increasing rapidly. Melanoma can begin wherever there is pigment. Most such cancers appear spontaneously, but about one-third develop from pigmented moles. It usually appears as a spreading brown to black patch (Figure 5.9b) that metastasizes rapidly to surrounding lymph and blood vessels. The chance for surviving melanoma is not high, but early detection helps. The usual therapy for malignant melanoma is wide surgical excision accompanied by chemotherapy.

The American Cancer Society suggests that sun worshippers periodically examine their skin for new moles or pigmented spots, and apply the **ABCD rule** for recognizing melanoma. **A. Asymmetry:** the two sides of the pigmented spot or mole do not match; **B. Border irregularity:** the borders of the lesion are not smooth but exhibit indentations; **C. Color:** the pigmented spot contains areas of different colors (blacks, browns, tans, and sometimes blues and reds); **D. Diameter:** the spot is larger than 6 mm in diameter (the size of a pencil eraser).

DEVELOPMENTAL ASPECTS OF THE INTEGUMENTARY SYSTEM

The epidermis develops from the embryonic ectoderm and the dermis and hypodermis develop from the mesoderm germ layer. By the fourth month of development, the skin is fairly well formed: The epidermis has all its strata, dermal papillae are obvious, and rudimentary epidermal derivatives are present. During the fifth and sixth months, the fetus is covered with a downy coat of delicate hairs called the **lanugo** (*lah-nu′go;* "wool") **coat.** This hairy cloak is shed by the seventh month, and vellus hairs make their appearance.

When a baby is born, its skin is covered with **vernix caseosa** (ver′niks kă-se-o′sah; "varnish of cheese"), a white, cheesy-looking substance produced by the sebaceous glands that protects the fetus's skin while inside the water-filled sac (the amnion). The newborn's skin is very thin and often has accumulations in the sebaceous glands on the forehead and nose that appear as small white spots called *milia* (mil′e-ah). These normally disappear by the third week after birth. During infancy and childhood, the skin thickens, and more subcutaneous fat is deposited.

During adolescence, the skin and hair become oilier as sebaceous glands are activated, and acne may appear. Acne generally subsides in early adulthood, and skin reaches its optimal appearance when we reach our 20s and 30s. Thereafter, the skin starts to show the effects of cumulative environmental assaults (abrasion, wind, sun, chemicals). Scaling and various kinds of skin inflammation, or **dermatitis** (der″mah-ti′tis), become more common.

As old age approaches, the rate of epidermal cell replacement slows, the skin thins, and its susceptibility to bruises and other types of injury increases. All of the lubricating substances produced by the skin glands that make young skin so soft start to become deficient. As a result, the skin becomes dry and itchy. However, those with naturally oily skin seem to postpone this dryness until later in life. Elastic fibers begin to clump and degenerate, and collagen fibers become fewer and stiffer as they link together. These alterations of dermal fibers are hastened by prolonged exposure to the sun and wind. The hypodermal fat layer diminishes, leading to the intolerance to cold so common in elderly people. The decreasing elasticity of the skin, along with the loss of subcutaneous tissue, inevitably leads to wrinkling. Decreasing numbers of melanocytes and Langerhans' cells enhance the risk and incidence of skin cancer in this age group. As a rule, redheads and fair-haired individu-

Making Connections

Systems Connections: Homeostatic Interrelationships Between the Integumentary System and Other Body Systems

Endocrine System

• Skin protects endocrine organs; converts some hormones to their active forms

• Androgens produced by the endocrine system activate sebaceous glands and are involved in regulation of hair growth

Cardiovascular System

• Skin protects cardiovascular organs; prevents fluid loss from body; serves as blood reservoir

• Cardiovascular system transports oxygen and nutrients to skin and removes wastes from skin; provides substances needed by skin glands to make their secretions

Lymphatic System/Immunity

• Skin protects lymphatic organs; prevents pathogen invasion; Langerhans' cells help activate the immune response

• Lymphatic system prevents edema by picking up excessive leaked fluid; immune system protects skin cells

Respiratory System

• Skin protects respiratory organs

• Respiratory system furnishes oxygen to skin cells and removes carbon dioxide via gas exchange with blood

Skeletal System

• Skin protects bones; skin synthesizes vitamin D bones need for normal calcium absorption and deposit of bone (calcium) salts which make bones hard

• Skeletal system provides support for skin

Muscular System

• Skin protects muscles

• Active muscles generate large amounts of heat which increase blood flow to the skin and may promote activation of sweat glands of skin

Nervous System

• Skin protects nervous system organs; cutaneous sensory receptors located in skin (see Figure 5.1)

• Nervous system regulates diameter of blood vessels in skin; activates sweat glands, contributing to thermoregulation; interprets cutaneous sensation; activates arrector pili muscles

Digestive System

• Skin protects digestive organs; provides vitamin D needed for calcium absorption; performs some of the same chemical conversions as liver cells

• Digestive system provides needed nutrients to the skin

Urinary System

• Skin protects urinary organs; excretes salts and some nitrogenous wastes in sweat

• Urinary system activates vitamin D precursor made by keratinocytes

Reproductive System

• Skin protects reproductive organs; cutaneous receptors respond to erotic stimuli; highly modified sweat glands (mammary glands) produce milk. During pregnancy, skin stretches to accommodate growing fetus; changes in skin pigmentation may occur.

Closer Connections: The Integumentary System and Interrelationships with the Nervous, Cardiovascular, and Lymphatic / Immune Systems

First and foremost, our skin is a barrier. Like the skin of a grape, it keeps its contents juicy and whole. The skin, however, is a master at self (wound) repair, and interacts intimately with other body systems by making vitamin D (necessary for hard bones) and other potent molecules, all the while protecting deeper tissues from damaging external agents. Perhaps the most crucial roles of the skin in terms of overall body homeostasis are those it plays with the nervous, cardiovascular, and lymphatic systems. These interactions are detailed next.

Nervous System

The skin houses the tiny sensory receptors that provide a great deal of information about our external environment—its temperature, the pressure exerted by objects, and the presence of dangerous substances. What if we stepped on broken glass or hot pavement but did not have neural monitors in our skin? If we did not actually see, hear, taste, or smell such a damaging event, no reports would be sent to the nervous system. Consequently, the nervous system would be left "in the dark," unable to evaluate the need for a response and to order the steps needed to protect us from further damage or to get first aid. Thus, the whole body benefits from the skin's interaction with the nervous system.

Nervous and Cardiovascular System

Skin provides the site both for sensing external temperature and for responding to temperature changes. Dermal blood vessels (cardiovascular system

organs) and sweat glands (controlled by the nervous system) play crucial roles in thermoregulation. So too do blood and the hot and cold receptors in the skin. When we are chilled, our blood loses heat to internal organs and cools. This alerts the nervous system to retain heat by constricting blood vessels. When body and blood temperature rises, dermal vessels dilate and sweating begins. Thermoregulation is vital: When the body overheats, life-threatening changes occur. Chemical reactions speed up and, if excessive, vital proteins are destroyed and cells die. Cold causes the opposite effect; cellular activity slows and ultimately stops.

Lymphatic System/Immunity

The role of the skin in immunity is very complex. Keratinocytes in the skin manufacture interferons (proteins that block viral infection) and other proteins important to the immune response. Langerhans' cells in the skin interact with antigens (foreign substances) that have penetrated the stratum corneum. The Langerhans' cells then migrate to lymphatic organs, where they present bits of the antigens to cells that will mount the immune response against them. This "messenger" function alerts the immune system early on to the presence of pathogens.

Even a mild sunburn disrupts the normal immune response because UV radiation disables the skin's presenter cells. This may explain why many people infected by the cold sore virus tend to have a cold sore eruption after sun exposure.

Clinical Connections

Integumentary System

A terrible collision between a trailer truck and a bus has occurred on Route 91. Several of the passengers are rushed to area hospitals for treatment. A few of these people will be followed in clinical case studies, which will continue from system to system.

Case study 1: Examination of Mrs. DeStephano, a 45-year-old woman, reveals several impairments of homeostasis. Relative to her integumentary system, the following comments are noted on her chart:

• Epidermal abrasions of the right arm and shoulder
• Severe lacerations of the right cheek and temple
• Cyanosis apparent

The lacerated areas are cleaned, sutured, and bandaged by the emergency room (ER) personnel and Mrs. DeStephano is admitted for further tests.

Relative to her signs:
1. What protective mechanisms are impaired or deficient in the abraded areas?

2. Assuming that bacteria are penetrating the dermis in these areas, what remaining skin defense mechanisms might act to prevent further bacterial invasion?

3. What benefit is conferred by suturing the lacerations? (Hint: see Chapter 4, p. 132)

4. Mrs. DeStephano's cyanotic skin may hint at what additional problem (and impairment of what body systems or functions)?

als, who have less melanin to begin with, show age-related changes more rapidly than do those with darker skin and hair.

By the age of 50 years, the number of active hair follicles is less than one-third and continues to decline, resulting in hair thinning. Hair loses its luster in old age, and the delayed-action genes responsible for graying and male pattern baldness become activated.

Although there is no known way to avoid the aging of the skin, one of the best ways to slow the process is to shield your skin from the sun by means of sunscreens and protective clothing. Remember, the same sunlight that produces that fashionable tan also causes the sagging, blotchy, wrinkled skin of old age.

Good nutrition, plenty of fluids, and cleanliness may delay the process.

* * *

The skin is only about as thick as a paper towel—not too impressive as organ systems go. Yet, when it is severely damaged, nearly every body system reacts. Metabolism accelerates or may be impaired, immune system changes occur, bones may soften, the cardiovascular system may fail—the list goes on and on. On the other hand, when the skin is intact and performing its many functions, the body as a whole benefits. Homeostatic interrelationships between the integumentary system and other organ systems are summarized in *Making Connections* on pp. 150–151.

RELATED CLINICAL TERMS

Albinism (al′bĭ-nizm; *alb* = white) Inherited condition in which melanocytes do not synthesize melanin owing to a lack of tyrosinase. An albino's skin is pink; the hair pale or white.

Boils and carbuncles (kar′bung-klz) Inflammation of hair follicles and sebaceous glands in which the infection has spread to the underlying dermis; common on dorsal neck; carbuncles are composite boils; common cause is bacterial infection (often *Staphylococcus aureus*).

Callus Gross thickening of the epidermis caused by persistent friction, as from a poorly fitting shoe.

Cold sores (fever blisters) Small fluid-filled blisters that itch and smart; usually occur around the lips and in oral mucosa of mouth; caused by a herpes simplex infection. The virus localizes in a cutaneous nerve, where it remains dormant until activated by emotional upset, fever, or UV radiation.

Contact dermatitis Itching, redness, and swelling, progressing to blister formation; caused by exposure of the skin to chemicals (e.g., poison ivy) that provoke an allergic response in sensitive individuals.

Decubitus (de-ku′bĭ-tus) **ulcer** Localized breakdown and ulceration of skin due to interference with its blood supply. Usually occurs over a bony prominence, such as the hip or heel, that is subjected to continuous pressure; also called a bedsore.

Dermatology The branch of medicine that studies and treats disorders of the skin.

Epidermolysis bullosa (EB) A group of hereditary disorders characterized by inadequate or faulty synthesis of keratin and/or collagen that results in lack of cohesion between layers of the skin and mucosa; a simple touch causes layers to separate and blister. For this reason, EB victims are called "touch-me-nots." When skin blisters and erosions are limited to the feet and hands, the ends of the digits may become fused together by scar tissue; in the most severe cases fatal blistering occurs in major vital organs. Because the blisters rupture easily, victims suffer frequent infections; treatments are aimed at relieving the symptoms and preventing infection.

Impetigo (im″pĕ-ti′go; *impet* = an attack) Pink, water-filled, raised lesions (common around the mouth and nose) that develop a yellow crust and eventually rupture; caused by staphylococcus infection; contagious; common in school-age children.

Mongolian spot Blue-black spot appearing in the skin of the sacral region; results from the unusual presence of a cluster of melanocytes in the dermis; the light-scattering effect of the epidermis causes these dermal melanin-containing regions to appear blue; disappears with age.

Port wine stain Most noticeable of birthmarks; pink to deep red blotches on the skin resulting from an abnormally dense network of blood vessels beneath the skin surface. Tend to darken with age and become nodular; removed by laser therapy.

Psoriasis (so-ri′ah-sis) A chronic condition characterized by reddened epidermal lesions covered with dry silvery scales; when severe, may be disfiguring and debilitating; cause is unknown; may be hereditary in some cases; attacks often triggered by trauma, infection, hormonal changes, and stress.

Ringworm Common name designating a number of highly contagious fungus infections of the skin that may or may not appear ring-shaped. The causative fungi feed on dead skin and wastes in sweat, and tend to localize in warm, often damp, body folds (axillae, genital area, between toes [a form called **athlete's foot**]). The red, scaly itchy lesions often become ring-shaped as the infection spreads. Treated with antifungal drugs.

Vitiligo (vit″ĭ-li′go; *viti* = a vine, winding) The most prevalent skin pigmentation disorder; characterized by a loss of melanocytes and uneven dispersal of melanin, i.e., unpigmented skin regions (light spots) surrounded by normally pigmented areas; thought to be an autoimmune disease.

CHAPTER SUMMARY

The Skin (pp. 135–140)

1. The skin, or integument, is composed of two discrete tissue layers, an outer epidermis and a deeper dermis, resting on subcutaneous tissue, the hypodermis.

Epidermis (pp. 136–139)

2. The epidermis is an avascular, keratinized stratified squamous epithelial sheet. Most epidermal cells are keratinocytes. Scattered among the keratinocytes in the deepest epidermal layers are melanocytes, Merkel cells, and Langerhans' cells.

3. From deep to superficial, the strata, or layers of the epidermis, are the basale, spinosum, granulosum, lucidum, and corneum. The stratum lucidum is absent in thin skin. The

actively mitotic stratum basale (germinativum) is the source of new cells for epidermal growth. The most superficial layers are increasingly keratinized and less viable. The stratum corneum consists of fully keratinized, dead cells that continuously slough off.

Dermis (p. 139)

4. The dermis, composed mainly of dense, irregular connective tissue, is well supplied with blood vessels, lymphatic vessels, and nerves. Cutaneous receptors, glands, and hair follicles reside within the dermis.

5. The more superficial papillary layer exhibits dermal papillae that protrude into the epidermis above and the epidermal ridges that produce fingerprints.

6. In the deeper thicker reticular layer, the connective tissue fibers are much more densely interwoven. Less dense regions between the bundles produce cleavage, or tension, lines in the skin. Points of tight dermal attachment to the hypodermis produce dermal folds, or flexure lines.

Skin Color (pp. 139–140)

7. Skin color reflects the amount of pigments (melanin and/or carotene) in the skin and the oxygenation level of hemoglobin in blood.

8. Melanin production is stimulated by exposure to ultraviolet radiation in sunlight. Melanin, produced by melanocytes and transferred to keratinocytes, protects the keratinocyte nuclei from the damaging effects of UV radiation.

9. Skin color is affected by emotional state. Alterations in normal skin color (jaundice, bronzing, erythema, and others) may indicate certain disease states.

Appendages of the Skin (pp. 140–145)

1. Skin appendages, which derive from the epidermis, include hairs and hair follicles, nails, and glands (sweat and sebaceous).

Hairs and Hair Follicles (pp.140–143)

2. A hair, produced by a hair follicle, consists of heavily keratinized cells. A typical hair consists of a central medulla, a cortex, and an outer cuticle and has root and shaft portions. Hair color reflects the amount and kind of melanin present.

3. A hair follicle consists of an inner epidermal root sheath, enclosing the matrix (region of the hair bulb that produces the hair), and an outer connective tissue sheath derived from the dermis. A hair follicle is richly vascularized and well supplied with nerve fibers. Arrector pili muscles pull the follicles into an upright position and produce goose bumps.

4. Except for hairs of the scalp and around the eyes, hairs formed initially are fine vellus hairs; at puberty, under the influence of androgens, coarser, darker terminal hairs appear.

5. The rate of hair growth varies in different body regions and with sex and age. Differences in life span of hairs account for differences in length on different body regions. Hair thinning reflects factors that lengthen follicular resting periods, age-related atrophy of hair follicles, and a delayed-action gene.

Nails (pp. 143–144)

6. A nail is a scalelike modification of the epidermis that covers the dorsum of a finger (or toe) tip. The actively growing region is the nail matrix.

Sweat (Sudoriferous) Glands (p. 144)

7. Eccrine sweat glands, with a few exceptions, are distributed over the entire body surface. Their primary function is thermoregulation. They are simple coiled tubular glands that secrete a salt solution containing small amounts of other solutes. Their ducts usually empty to the skin surface via pores.

8. Apocrine sweat glands are found primarily in the axillary and anogenital areas. Their secretion is similar to eccrine secretion, but it also contains proteins and fatty substances on which bacteria thrive. The role of apocrine glands is still not fully known, but they may function as scent glands.

Sebaceous (Oil) Glands (p. 145)

9. Sebaceous glands occur all over the body surface except for the palms and soles. They are simple alveolar glands; their oily holocrine secretion is called sebum. Sebaceous gland ducts usually empty into hair follicles.

10. Sebum lubricates the skin and hair, prevents water loss from the skin, and acts as a bactericidal agent. Sebaceous glands are activated (at puberty) and controlled by androgens.

Functions of the Integumentary System (pp. 145–146)

1. Protection. The skin protects by chemical barriers (the antibacterial nature of sebum and the acid mantle, and melanin), physical barriers (the hardened keratinized surface), and biological barriers (phagocytes).

2. Body Temperature Regulation. The skin vasculature and sweat glands, regulated by the nervous system, play an important role in maintaining body temperature homeostasis.

3. Cutaneous Sensation. Cutaneous sensory receptors respond to temperature, touch, pressure, and pain stimuli.

4. Metabolic Functions. Vitamin D is synthesized from cholesterol by epidermal cells. Skin cells also play a role in some chemical conversions.

5. Blood Reservoir. The extensive vascular supply of the dermis allows the skin to act as a blood reservoir.

6. Excretion. Sweat contains small amounts of nitrogenous wastes and plays a minor role in excretion.

Homeostatic Imbalances of Skin (pp. 146–149)

1. The most common skin disorders result from infections.

Burns (pp. 146–148)

2. In severe burns, the initial threat is loss of protein- and electrolyte-rich body fluids, which may lead to circulatory collapse. The second threat is overwhelming bacterial infection.

3. The extent of a burn may be evaluated by using the rule of nines. The severity of burns is indicated by the terms first degree, second degree, and third degree. Third-degree burns require grafting for successful recovery.

Skin Cancer (pp. 148–149)

4. The most common cause of skin cancer is exposure to ultraviolet radiation.

5. Basal cell carcinoma and squamous cell carcinoma are cured if they are removed before metastasis. Malignant melanoma, a cancer of melanocytes, is fairly rare, but usually fatal.

Developmental Aspects of the Integumentary System (pp. 149–152)

1. The epidermis develops from embryonic ectoderm; the dermis (and hypodermis) develop from mesoderm.

2. The fetus exhibits a downy lanugo coat. Fetal sebaceous glands produce vernix caseosa, which helps protect the fetus's skin from its watery environment.

3. A newborn's skin is thin. During childhood the skin thickens and more subcutaneous fat is deposited. At puberty, sebaceous glands are activated and terminal hairs appear.

4. In old age, the rate of epidermal cell replacement declines and the skin and hair thin. Skin glands become less active. Loss of collagen and elastin fibers and subcutaneous fat leads to wrinkling; delayed-action genes cause graying and balding.

REVIEW QUESTIONS

Multiple Choice/Matching

1. Which epidermal cell type is most numerous? (a) keratinocyte, (b) melanocyte, (c) Langerhans' cell, (d) Merkel cell.

2. Which is probably a macrophage? (a) a keratinocyte, (b) a melanocyte, (c) a Langerhans' cell, (d) a Merkel cell.

3. The epidermis provides a physical barrier due largely to the presence of (a) melanin, (b) carotene, (c) collagen, (d) keratin.

4. Skin color is determined by (a) the amount of blood, (b) pigments, (c) oxygenation level of the blood, (d) all of these.

5. The sensations of touch and pressure are picked up by receptors located in (a) the stratum germinativum, (b) the dermis, (c) the hypodermis, (d) the stratum corneum.

6. Which is not a true statement about the papillary layer of the dermis? (a) It produces the pattern for fingerprints, (b) it is most responsible for the toughness of the skin, (c) it contains nerve endings that respond to stimuli, (d) it is highly vascular.

7. Skin surface markings that reflect points of tight dermal attachment to underlying tissues are called (a) tension lines, (b) papillary ridges, (c) flexure lines, (d) epidermal papillae.

8. Which of the following is not an epidermal derivative? (a) hair, (b) sweat gland, (c) sensory receptor, (d) sebaceous gland.

9. You can cut hair without feeling pain because (a) there are no nerves associated with hair, (b) the shaft of the hair consists of dead cells, (c) hair follicles develop from epidermal cells and the epidermis lacks a nerve supply, (d) hair follicles have no source of nourishment and therefore cannot respond.

10. An arrector pili muscle (a) is associated with each sweat gland, (b) can cause the hair to stand up straight, (c) enables each hair to be stretched when wet, (d) provides new cells for continued growth of its associated hair.

11. The product of this type of sweat gland includes protein and lipid substances that become odoriferous as a result of bacterial action: (a) apocrine gland, (b) eccrine gland, (c) sebaceous gland, (d) pancreatic gland.

12. Sebum (a) lubricates the surface of the skin and hair, (b) consists of dead cells and fatty substances, (c) in excess may cause seborrhea, (d) all of these.

13. The "rule of nines" is helpful clinically in (a) diagnosing skin cancer, (b) estimating the extent of a burn, (c) estimating how serious a cancer is, (d) preventing acne.

Short Answer Essay Questions

14. Which epidermal cells are also called prickle cells? Which contain keratohyalin and lamellated granules?

15. Is a bald man really hairless? Explain.

16. Both newborn infants and aged individuals have very little subcutaneous tissue. How does this affect their sensitivity to cold environmental temperature?

17. You go to the beach to swim on an extremely hot, sunshiny summer afternoon. Describe two ways in which your integumentary system acts to preserve homeostasis during your outing.

18. Distinguish clearly between first-, second-, and third-degree burns.

19. Describe the process of hair formation, and list several factors that may influence (a) growth cycles and (b) hair texture.

20. What is cyanosis and what does it reflect?

21. Why does skin wrinkle and what factors accelerate the wrinkling process?

22. Explain each of these familiar phenomena in terms of what you learned in this chapter: (a) pimples, (b) dandruff, (c) greasy hair and "shiny nose," (d) stretch marks from gaining weight, (e) freckles, (f) leaving fingerprints.

23. Count Dracula, the most famous vampire, rumored to have killed at least 200,000 people, was based on a real person who lived in eastern Europe about 600 years ago. He was indeed a "monster," even though he was not a real vampire. The historical Count Dracula may have suffered from which of the following? (a) porphyria, (b) EB, (c) halitosis, (d) vitiligo. Explain your answer.

24. Why are there no skin cancers that originate from stratum corneum cells?

CRITICAL THINKING AND CLINICAL APPLICATION QUESTIONS

1. Dean, a 40-year-old aging beach boy, is complaining to you that his sun tan made him popular when he was young, but now his face is all wrinkled, and he has several darkly pigmented moles that are growing rapidly and are as big as large coins. He shows you the moles, and immediately you think "ABCD." What does that mean and why should he be concerned?

2. Victims of third-degree burns demonstrate the vital functions performed by the skin. What are the two most important problems encountered clinically with such patients? Explain each in terms of the absence of skin.

3. A 30-year-old mental patient named Thelma has an abnormal growth of hair on the dorsum of her right index finger. The orderly comments that she gnaws on that finger continuously. What do you think is the relationship between Thelma's gnawing activity and her "hairy" finger?

4. A model is concerned about a new scar on her abdomen. She tells her surgeon that there is practically no scar from the appendix operation done when she was 16, but this new gallbladder scar is "gross." Her appendectomy scar is small and obliquely located on the inferior abdominal surface—it is very indistinct. By contrast, the gallbladder scar is large and lumpy and runs at right angles to the central axis of the body trunk. Can you explain why the scars are so different?

Bones and Skeletal Tissues

6

CHAPTER OUTLINE AND STUDENT OBJECTIVES

Skeletal Cartilages (pp. 155–156)

1. Explain the functional properties of each of the three types of cartilage tissue.
2. Locate the major cartilages of the adult skeleton.
3. Explain how cartilage grows.

Functions of Bones (p. 156)

4. List and describe five important functions of bones.

Classification of Bones (pp. 156–158)

5. Compare and contrast the structure of the four bone classes and provide examples of each class.

Bone Structure (pp. 158–163)

6. Describe the gross anatomy of a typical long bone and flat bone. Indicate the locations and functions of red and yellow marrow, articular cartilage, periosteum, and endosteum.
7. Distinguish clearly between the several types of bone markings and note their relative functions.
8. Describe the histology of compact and spongy bone.
9. Discuss the chemical composition of bone and the relative advantages conferred by its organic and its inorganic components.

Bone Development (Osteogenesis) (pp. 163–166)

10. Compare and contrast the two types of bone formation: intramembranous and endochondral ossification.
11. Describe the process of long bone growth that occurs at the epiphyseal plates.

Bone Homeostasis: Remodeling and Repair (pp. 166–171)

12. Compare the locations and functions of the osteoblasts, osteocytes, and osteoclasts in bone remodeling.
13. Explain how hormonal controls and physical stress regulate bone remodeling.
14. Describe the steps of fracture repair.

Homeostatic Imbalances of Bone (p. 172)

15. Contrast the disorders of bone remodeling seen in osteoporosis, osteomalacia, and Paget's disease.

Developmental Aspects of Bones: Timing of Events (pp. 172–173)

16. Describe the timing and cause of changes in bone architecture and bone mass throughout life.

A t one time or another, all of us have heard expressions like "bone tired," "dry as a bone," and "bag of bones,"—pretty unflattering and inaccurate images of one of our most phenomenal tissues and our main skeletal elements. Our brains, not our bones, convey feelings of fatigue, and bones are far from dry. As for "bag of bones," they are indeed more prominent in some of us, but without them to form our internal skeleton we would creep along the ground like slugs, lacking any defined shape or form. Along with its bones, the skeleton contains cartilages. Though not as strong as bones, the cartilages are more resilient. In this chapter, we discuss briefly the main locations of skeletal cartilages. However, the major focus here is on the gen-eral structure and function of bone tissue and on the dynamics of its formation and remodeling throughout life. Individual bones that fashion the skeleton and joints that allow skeletal mobility are the topics of Chapters 7 and 8.

SKELETAL CARTILAGES

Although our skeleton is initially made up of carti-lages and fibrous membranes, most of these early supports are soon replaced by bone. The few carti-lages that remain in the adult skeleton are found mainly in regions where more resilient skeletal tis-sues are needed, as described below.

Basic Structure, Types, and Locations

A **skeletal cartilage** is made of some variety of *cartilage tissue,* which typically consists largely of water. (As described in *A Closer Look* on p. 130, the high water content of cartilage accounts for its resilience, that is, its ability to spring back to its original shape after being compressed.) The cartilage, which contains no nerves or blood vessels, is surrounded by a dense connective tissue membrane, called a *perichondrium* (per"ĭ-kon'drĭ-um; "around the cartilage"). The perichondrium acts like a girdle to resist outward expansion when the cartilage is compressed.

As described in Chapter 4, there are three types of cartilage tissue in the body: hyaline, elastic, and fibrocartilage. All three types have the same basic components—cells called *chondrocytes,* encased in small cavities (lacunae) within an *extracellular matrix* containing a jellylike ground substance and fibers. The skeletal cartilages contain representatives from all three tissue groups.

Hyaline Cartilages

The chondrocytes of the **hyaline cartilages** appear spherical (see Figure 4.8g) and the only fiber type in their matrix is collagen fibers. Hyaline cartilages, which look like frosted glass when freshly exposed, provide support with flexibility and resilience. They are the most abundant skeletal cartilages. As depicted in Figure 6.1, they include (1) **articular cartilages,** which cover the bone ends at movable joints; (2) **costal cartilages,** which connect the ribs to the sternum (breastbone); (3) **laryngeal cartilages,** which form the skeleton of the larynx (voicebox); (4) **tracheal** and **bronchial cartilages,** which reinforce other passageways of the respiratory system; and (5) **nasal cartilages,** which support the external nose.

Elastic Cartilages

Elastic cartilage tissue looks very much like hyaline cartilage (see Figure 4.8h). However, it contains more stretchy elastic fibers, and so is better able to stand up to repeated bending. The flexible **elastic cartilages** are found in only two skeletal locations (Figure 6.1)—supporting the external ear, and forming the epiglottis (the flap that bends to cover the opening of the larynx when we swallow, preventing food and fluids from entering the lungs).

Fibrocartilages

In fibrocartilage tissue, roughly parallel rows of chondrocytes alternate with thick collagen fibers (see Figure 4.8i). This tissue is highly compressible and has great tensile strength. **Fibrocartilages** occur in sites that are subjected to both heavy pressure and stretch, such as the padlike cartilages (menisci) of the knee and the discs between the vertebrae of the spine.

Growth of Cartilage

Cartilage grows in two ways—by appositional (ap'o-zish'un-al) growth and by interstitial (in"ter-stish'al) growth. In **appositional growth** (literally, "growth from outside"), cartilage-forming cells in the surrounding perichondrium secrete the new matrix against the existing cartilage tissue. In **interstitial growth** ("growth from within"), the lacunae-bound chondrocytes inside the cartilage divide and secrete new matrix, expanding the cartilage from within. Typically, cartilage growth ends during adolescence when the skeleton itself stops growing.

Under certain conditions, calcium salts may be deposited in the matrix of cartilage. Such calcification occurs during normal *bone growth* (p. 165) and during aging. Note, however, that calcified cartilage is *not* bone; cartilage and bone are always distinct tissues.

FUNCTIONS OF BONES

Besides contributing to body shape and form, our bones perform several important functions for the body:

1. **Support.** Bones provide a hard framework that supports the body and cradles its soft organs. For example, bones of lower limbs act as pillars to support the body trunk when we stand, and the rib cage supports the thoracic wall.

2. **Protection.** The fused bones of the skull provide a snug enclosure for the brain. The vertebrae surround the spinal cord, and the rib cage helps protect the vital organs of the thorax.

3. **Movement.** Skeletal muscles, which are attached to bones by tendons, use the bones as levers to move the body and its parts. As a result, we can walk, grasp, and breathe. The arrangement of bones and the design of joints determine the types of movement possible.

4. **Mineral storage.** Bone serves as a reservoir for minerals, the most important of which are calcium and phosphate. The stored minerals can be released into the bloodstream as ions for distribution to all parts of the body as needed. Indeed, "deposits" and "withdrawals" of minerals to and from the bones go on almost continuously.

5. **Blood cell formation.** The bulk of blood cell formation, or *hematopoiesis* (hem"ah-to-poi-e'sis), occurs within the marrow cavities of certain bones.

CLASSIFICATION OF BONES

Bones come in many sizes and shapes. For example, the tiny pisiform bone of the wrist is the size and shape of a pea, whereas the femur (thigh bone) is nearly 2 feet long in some people and has a large ball-shaped head. The unique shape of each bone fulfills a

- ■ Hyaline cartilages
- ■ Elastic cartilages
- ■ Fibrocartilages

FIGURE 6.1
Cartilages in the adult skeleton and body. The cartilages that support the respiratory tubes and larynx are drawn separately at right.

particular need. The femur, for example, must withstand great weight and pressure, and its hollow cylindrical design provides maximum strength with minimum weight.

Bones are classified by their shape as long, short, flat, and irregular bones (Figure 6.2). Bones of different shapes contain different proportions of the two basic types of osseous tissue: compact and spongy bone. **Compact,** or **dense, bone** looks smooth and homogeneous. **Spongy,** or **cancellous, bone** is composed of small needlelike or flat pieces of bone called **trabeculae** (trah-bek′u-le; "little beams") and has a good deal of open space. The trabeculae form a network, and the spaces between the trabeculae are filled with red or yellow bone marrow in living bones. We will describe these bone textures in more detail when we discuss the microscopic structure of bone.

1. Long bones. As their name suggests, long bones are considerably longer than they are wide. A long bone consists of a shaft plus two ends. It is constructed primarily of compact bone, but may contain

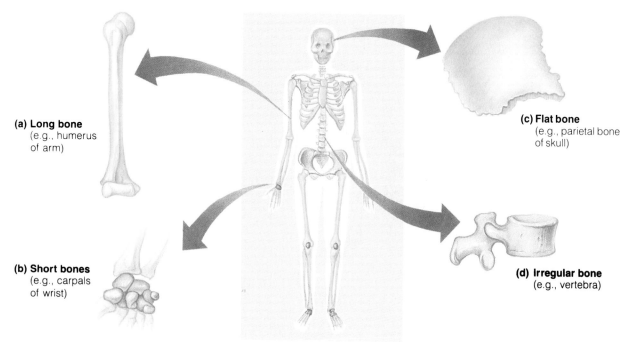

(a) Long bone
(e.g., humerus of arm)

(b) Short bones
(e.g., carpals of wrist)

(c) Flat bone
(e.g., parietal bone of skull)

(d) Irregular bone
(e.g., vertebra)

FIGURE 6.2
Classification of bones on the basis of shape.

substantial amounts of spongy bone in its interior. All bones of the limbs, except the patella and those of the wrist and ankle, are long bones (see Figure 6.2). Notice that this bone classification reflects the elongated shape of these bones, *not* their overall size. The three bones in each of your fingers are long bones, even though they are very small.

2. **Short bones.** Short bones are roughly cubelike. They contain mostly spongy bone; compact bone provides just their thin surface layer. The bones of the wrist and ankle are short bones (see Figure 6.2).

The **sesamoid** (ses'ah-moid; "shaped like a sesame seed") **bones** are a special type of short bone embedded within a tendon (for example, the kneecap, or patella). They vary in size and number in different individuals. Some clearly act to alter the direction of pull of a tendon; the function of others is not known.

3. **Flat bones.** Flat bones are thin, flattened, and usually a bit curved. They have two roughly parallel compact bone surfaces, with a layer of spongy bone between. The sternum (breastbone), ribs, and most skull bones are flat bones (see Figure 6.2).

4. **Irregular bones.** Bones that fit none of the preceding classes are called irregular bones. Irregular bones include the vertebrae and the hip bones (see Figure 6.2). All of these bones have complicated shapes and consist mainly of spongy bone enclosed by thin layers of compact bone.

BONE STRUCTURE

Bones are *organs.* (Recall that an organ contains several different tissues.) Although bone (osseous) tissue dominates bones, they also contain nervous tissue in their nerves, cartilage in their articular cartilages, fibrous connective tissue lining their cavities, and muscle and epithelial tissues in their blood vessels. We will consider bone anatomy at three structural levels: the gross, microscopic, and chemical levels.

Gross Anatomy

Structure of a Typical Long Bone

With few exceptions, all long bones have the same general structure (Figure 6.3).

Diaphysis. The tubular **diaphysis** (di-af'ĭ-sis; *dia* = through, *physis* = growth), or *shaft,* constitutes the long axis of the bone. It is constructed of a relatively thick *collar* of compact bone that surrounds a central **medullary cavity** (med'u-lar-e; "middle") or *marrow cavity.* In adults, the medullary cavity contains fat (yellow marrow) and is also called the **yellow bone marrow cavity.**

Epiphyses. The **epiphyses** (e-pif'ĭ-sez) are the bone ends (*epi* = upon). In many cases, they are more expanded than the diaphysis. Compact bone forms the exterior of epiphyses, their interior contains

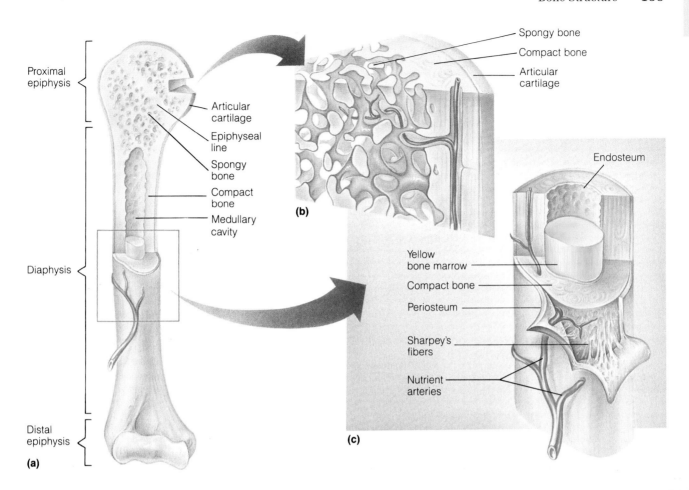

FIGURE 6.3
The structure of a long bone (humerus of arm). (a) Anterior view with bone sectioned frontally to show the interior at the proximal end. **(b)** Enlarged, three-dimensional view of spongy bone and compact bone of the epiphysis of (a). **(c)** Enlarged cross-sectional view of the shaft (diaphysis) of (a). Note that the external surface of the diaphysis is covered by periosteum, but the articular surface of the epiphysis is covered with hyaline cartilage.

spongy bone. The joint surface of each epiphysis is covered with a thin layer of **articular** (hyaline) **cartilage,** which cushions the opposing bone ends during joint movement and absorbs stress. Between the diaphysis and each epiphysis of an adult long bone is an **epiphyseal line.** This line is a remnant of the epiphyseal plate, a disclike region of hyaline cartilage that grows during childhood to lengthen the bone (p. 165).

Membranes. Both the internal and the external bone surfaces are associated with membranes. The outer surface of the diaphysis is covered and protected by glistening white, double-layered membrane called the **periosteum** (per″e-os′te-um; *peri* = around, *osteo* = bone). The outer *fibrous layer* of the periosteum is dense irregular connective tissue. The inner *osteogenic layer,* abutting the bone surface, consists primarily of bone-forming cells, or **osteoblasts** (os′te-o-blasts; "bone germinators"), and bone-destroying cells, or **osteoclasts** ("bone breakers").

The periosteum is richly supplied with nerve fibers, lymphatic vessels, and blood vessels, which enter the bone of the shaft via a **nutrient foramen** (fo-ra′min; "opening"). It is secured to the underlying bone by **Sharpey's fibers** (Figure 6.3), tufts of collagen fibers that extend from the fibrous layer into the bone matrix. The periosteum also provides an insertion or anchoring point for tendons and ligaments, and at these points the Sharpey's fibers are exceptionally dense.

Internal bone surfaces are covered with a delicate connective tissue membrane called the **endosteum** (en-dos′te-um; "within the bone"). The endosteum (Figure 6.3) covers the trabeculae of spongy bone in the marrow cavities and lines the canals that pass through compact bone. Like the periosteum, the endosteum contains both osteoblasts and osteoclasts.

Structure of Short, Irregular, and Flat Bones

Short, irregular, and flat bones share a simple design: They consist of thin plates of periosteum-covered compact bone on the outside and endosteum-covered spongy bone within. These bones are not cylindrical

Flat bone of skull

Spongy bone
(diploë)

Compact bone

FIGURE 6.4
Structure of a flat bone. Flat bones, such as most bones of the
skull, consist of a layer of spongy bone (the diploë) sandwiched
between two thin layers of compact bone.

and so they have no shaft or epiphyses. They contain
bone marrow (between their trabeculae), but no marrow cavity is present.

Figure 6.4 shows a typical flat bone of the skull.
In flat bones, the internal layer of spongy bone is
called the **diploë** (dip′lo-e) and the whole arrangement resembles a stiffened sandwich.

Location of Hematopoietic Tissue in Bones

Because the hematopoietic tissue, **red marrow,** is typically found within the cavities of spongy bone of
long bones and in the diploë of flat bones, these cavities are often referred to as **red marrow cavities.** In
newborn infants, the medullary cavity and all areas of
spongy bone contain red bone marrow. In most adult
long bones, the fat-containing medullary cavity
extends well into the epiphysis, and little red marrow
is present in the spongy bone cavities. Hence, blood
cell production in adult long bones routinely occurs
only in the head of the femur and humerus (the long
bone of the arm). Much more important and more
active in hematopoiesis is the red marrow found in
the diploë of flat bones (such as the sternum) and in
some irregular bones (such as the hip bone). These are
the sites routinely used for obtaining red marrow
samples when problems with the blood-forming tissue are suspected. However, yellow marrow of the
medullary cavity can revert to red marrow if a person
becomes very anemic and needs enhanced red blood
cell production.

Microscopic Structure of Bone

Compact Bone

Observed with the unaided eye, compact bone
appears very dense. However, a microscope reveals
that it is riddled with canals and passageways that
serve as conduits for nerves, blood vessels, and lymphatic vessels (Figure 6.5). The structural unit of
compact bone is called the **osteon** (os′te-on) or **Haversian** (ha-ver′shan) **system.** Each osteon is an elongated cylinder oriented parallel to the long axis of the
bone. Functionally, osteons can be thought of as tiny
weight-bearing pillars. As shown in the "exploded
view" in Figure 6.6, an osteon is a group of hollow
tubes of bone matrix, one placed outside the next like
the growth rings of a tree trunk. Each of the matrix
tubes is a **lamella** (lah-mel′ah; "little plate"), so compact bone is often called **lamellar bone.** Although all
of the collagen fibers in a particular lamella run in a
single direction, the collagen fibers in adjacent lamellae always run in opposite directions. This alternating pattern is beautifully designed to withstand tor-
sion stresses—the adjacent lamellae in an osteon
reinforce one another to resist twisting.

Running through the core of each osteon is a
canal, called the **central,** or **Haversian, canal.** This
canal contains small blood vessels and nerve fibers
that serve the needs of the osteon's cells. Canals of a
second type called **perforating,** or **Volkmann's** (folk′-
mahnz), **canals,** lie at right angles to the long axis of
the bone, connecting the vascular and nerve supplies
of the periosteum to those in the central canals and
the medullary cavity (see Figure 6.5a). Like all internal bone cavities, both canal types are lined with
endosteum.

Spider-shaped **osteocytes** (mature bone cells)
occupy small cavities, or **lacunae** (lah-ku′ne), at the
junctions of the lamellae. Hairlike canals called
canaliculi (kan″ah-lik′u-li) connect the lacunae to
each other and to the central canal. The manner in
which these canaliculi are formed is interesting. In
forming bone, osteoblasts secreting the bone matrix
maintain contact with one another by tentaclelike projections containing gap junctions. Then, as the matrix
hardens and the maturing cells become trapped
within it, an entire system of tiny canals (filled with
tissue fluid and containing the osteocyte extensions)
is formed. The canaliculi tie all the osteocytes in an
osteon together, permitting nutrients and wastes to be
easily relayed from one osteocyte to the next throughout the osteon. Although bone matrix is hard and
impermeable to nutrients, its canaliculi and cell-to-
cell relays allow bone cells to be very well nourished.
Osteocytes function to maintain the bone matrix. If
they die, the surrounding matrix is resorbed.

Between intact osteons lie incomplete lamellae
called **interstitial** (in″ter-stish′al) **lamellae.** These fill
the gaps between forming osteons or are remnants of

(a)

(b)

FIGURE 6.5
Microscopic structure of compact bone. (a) Diagrammatic view of a pie-shaped segment of compact bone, illustrating its structural units (osteons). The inset shows a more highly magnified view of a portion of one osteon. Note the position of osteocytes in lacunae (cavities in the matrix). **(b)** Photomicrograph of a cross-sectional view of one osteon and portions of others (90×).

osteons that have been cut through by bone remodeling (discussed later). Additionally, there are **circumferential lamellae,** located just deep to the periosteum, that extend around the circumference of the shaft. Circumferential lamellae effectively resist twisting of the long bone as a whole.

Spongy Bone

In contrast to compact bone, spongy bone, consisting of trabeculae, looks like a poorly organized tissue (see Figure 6.4 and Figure 6.3b). However, the arrangement of the trabeculae is far from haphazard. Instead, the trabeculae align precisely along lines of stress and help the bone to resist that stress as much as possible. Thus, the tiny bone struts are as carefully positioned as the flying buttresses that support the walls of a Gothic cathedral.

Only a few cell layers thick, trabeculae contain irregularly arranged lamellae and osteocytes interconnected by canaliculi. No osteons are present. Nutrients reach the osteocytes of spongy bone by diffusing through the canaliculi from the marrow spaces between the trabeculae.

Chemical Composition of Bone

Bone has both organic and inorganic components. Its *organic components* include the cells, osteoblasts, osteocytes, and osteoclasts, and **osteoid** (os′te-oid), the organic part of the matrix. Osteoid, which makes up approximately one-third of the matrix, includes proteoglycans, glycoproteins, and collagen fibers, all of which are made and secreted by osteoblasts. These organic substances, particularly collagen, not only

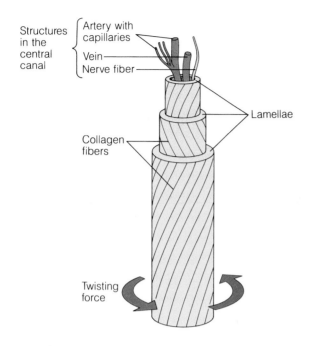

Structures in the central canal
- Artery with capillaries
- Vein
- Nerve fiber

Lamellae

Collagen fibers

Twisting force

FIGURE 6.6
Diagram of a single osteon. In this view, the osteon is drawn as if pulled out like a telescope to illustrate the individual lamellae composing it. The slanted lines within each lamella indicate the direction in which its collagen fibers run within the matrix.

contribute to a bone's structure, but also are responsible for the bone's flexibility and great tensile strength, that is, its ability to resist stretch and twisting.

The *inorganic components* of bone (65% by mass) consist of **hydroxyapatites** (hi-drok"se-ap'ah-tītz), or *mineral salts,* largely calcium phosphates. Calcium salts are present in the form of tiny crystals that lie in and around the collagen fibers in the extracellular matrix. They account for the most notable characteristic of bone—its exceptional hardness, which allows it to resist compression. The proper combination of organic and inorganic matrix elements allows bones to be exceedingly durable and strong without being brittle. It is surprising to learn that healthy bone is half as strong as steel in resisting compression and fully as strong as steel in resisting tension.

Because of bone salts, bones persist long after death and provide an enduring "monument." In fact, skeletal remains many centuries old have revealed the shapes, sizes, races, and sexes of ancestral peoples and have allowed us to know the kinds of work they did and many of the ailments they suffered (arthritis and others).

Bone Markings

The external surfaces of bones are rarely smooth and featureless. Instead, they display bulges, depressions, and holes, which serve as sites of muscle, ligament,

Table 6.1 Bone Markings	
Name of bone marking	**Description**
Projections that are sites of muscle and ligament attachment	
Tuberosity (too"bĕ-ros'ĭ-te)	Large rounded projection; may be roughened
Crest	Narrow ridge of bone; usually prominent
Trochanter (tro-kan'ter)	Very large, blunt, irregularly shaped process (The only examples are on the femur.)
Line	Narrow ridge of bone; less prominent than a crest
Tubercle (too'ber-kl)	Small rounded projection or process
Epicondyle (ep"ĭ-kon'dīl)	Raised area on or above a condyle
Spine	Sharp, slender, often pointed projection
Projections that help to form joints	
Head	Bony expansion carried on a narrow neck
Facet	Smooth, nearly flat articular surface
Condyle (kon'dīl)	Rounded articular projection
Ramus (ra'mus)	Armlike bar of bone
Depressions and openings allowing blood vessels and nerves to pass	
Meatus (me-a'tus)	Canal-like passageway
Sinus	Cavity within a bone, filled with air and lined with mucous membrane
Fossa (fos'ah)	Shallow, basinlike depression in a bone, often serving as an articular surface
Groove	Furrow
Fissure	Narrow, slitlike opening
Foramen (fo-ra'men)	Round or oval opening through a bone

and tendon attachment, as points of articulation, or as conduits for blood vessels and nerves. These *markings* are named in different ways. Projections that grow outward from the bone surface include heads, trochanters, spines, and others, and each has certain distinguishing features and functions. Depressions and openings are termed fossae, sinuses, foramina, and grooves. The most important types of bone markings are described in Table 6.1. You should familiarize yourself with these terms because you will encounter them again as identifying marks of the individual bones described in Chapter 7 and studied in the lab.

BONE DEVELOPMENT (OSTEOGENESIS)

Osteogenesis (os"te-o-jen'ĕ-sis) and **ossification** are synonyms indicating the process of bone formation (*os* = bone, *genesis* = beginning). In embryos this process leads to the *formation of the bony skeleton. Bone growth,* another form of ossification, goes on until early adulthood as we continue to increase in size. Bones are capable of growing in thickness throughout life. However, ossification in adults serves mainly for *remodeling* and repair of bones.

Formation of the Bony Skeleton

At six weeks, the skeleton of a human embryo is constructed entirely from fibrous membranes and hyaline cartilage. Bone tissue begins to develop at about this time and eventually replaces most of the existing fibrous or cartilage structures. When a bone develops from a fibrous membrane, the process is called *intramembranous ossification,* and the bone is called a **membrane bone.** Bone formation that occurs by replacing hyaline cartilage structures is called *endochondral ossification* (*endo* = within; *chondro* = cartilage), and the resulting bone is called a **cartilage,** or **endochondral, bone.**

Intramembranous Ossification

Intramembranous ossification results in the formation of most bones of the skull and the clavicles. Notice that all bones formed by this route are flat bones. Fibrous connective tissue membranes formed by *mesenchymal cells* serve as the initial supporting structures on which ossification occurs. Essentially, the process involves the following steps (Figure 6.7).

1. **Formation of bone matrix within the fibrous membrane.** Starting around the eighth week of development, certain mesenchymal cells in the fibrous membrane cluster and then differentiate into osteoblasts, which begin secreting organic bone matrix (osteoid). Within a few days, the osteoid is mineralized and converted to a true bone matrix. Once trapped in lacunae, the osteoblasts become mature bone cells or osteocytes. This process may begin at several sites, but typically one major *ossification center* appears in the center of the membrane.

2. **Formation of woven bone and the periosteum.** As the deposits of osteoid accumulate, they extend and fuse together, forming a delicate network of trabeculae that encloses local blood vessels. This early membrane bone is referred to as **woven bone** because its collagen fibers are arranged irregularly and tend to form networks (rather than lamellae as in the mature spongy bone formed later). At the same time, a layer of vascular mesenchyme condenses just external to the woven bone and then becomes the periosteum.

FIGURE 6.7
The stages in intramembranous ossification. The unnumbered top diagram illustrates the composition of the fibrous membrane as intramembranous ossification begins. Events depicted in diagrams 1 through 3 correspond to the description on this page. Note that diagrams 2 and 3 represent much lower magnification than the diagrams preceding them.

3. **Formation of compact bone plates.** Once the periosteum forms, the adjacent trabeculae grow thicker and thicker until they become continuous plates of bone. Initially, this bone collar, like the bone formed within the membrane, is woven bone. Later, the plates of woven bone are replaced with mature compact (lamellar) bone. However, the trabeculae in the center of the bone remain distinct, so spongy bone is produced there. When the vascular tissue within the spongy bone differentiates into red marrow, the formation of the diploë is complete. The final result is a flat bone, as depicted earlier in Figure 6.4 (p. 160).

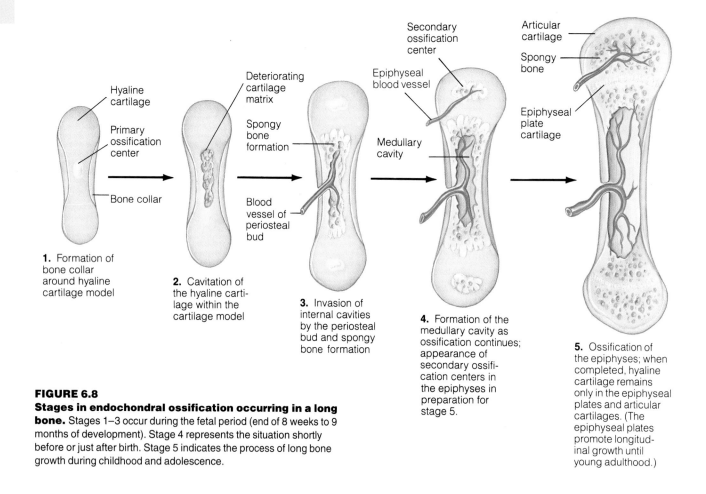

FIGURE 6.8
Stages in endochondral ossification occurring in a long bone. Stages 1–3 occur during the fetal period (end of 8 weeks to 9 months of development). Stage 4 represents the situation shortly before or just after birth. Stage 5 indicates the process of long bone growth during childhood and adolescence.

Hyaline cartilage
Primary ossification center
Bone collar

1. Formation of bone collar around hyaline cartilage model

Deteriorating cartilage matrix
Spongy bone formation
Blood vessel of periosteal bud

2. Cavitation of the hyaline cartilage within the cartilage model

3. Invasion of internal cavities by the periosteal bud and spongy bone formation

Secondary ossification center
Epiphyseal blood vessel
Medullary cavity

4. Formation of the medullary cavity as ossification continues; appearance of secondary ossification centers in the epiphyses in preparation for stage 5.

Articular cartilage
Spongy bone
Epiphyseal plate cartilage

5. Ossification of the epiphyses; when completed, hyaline cartilage remains only in the epiphyseal plates and articular cartilages. (The epiphyseal plates promote longitudinal growth until young adulthood.)

Endochondral Ossification

Most bones of the skeleton form by the process of **endochondral** (en″do-kon′dral) **ossification,** which uses hyaline cartilage "bones" as models, or patterns, for bone construction. The process begins late in the second month of development and is more complex than intramembranous ossification because the hyaline cartilage must be broken down as ossification proceeds. We will use a forming long bone as our example.

The formation of a long bone typically begins at a **primary ossification center** at the center of the hyaline cartilage shaft. First, the perichondrium (the fibrous connective tissue membrane covering the hyaline cartilage "bone") becomes infiltrated with blood vessels, converting it to a vascularized periosteum. As a result of the change in nutrition, the underlying mesenchymal (osteoprogenitor) cells specialize into osteoblasts. The stage is now set for ossification to begin, as illustrated in Figure 6.8 and described next.

1. A bone collar forms around the shaft of the hyaline cartilage model. Osteoblasts of the newly "converted" periosteum secrete osteoid against the hyaline cartilage shaft, encasing it externally in a bone *collar.*

2. The hyaline cartilage in the center of the shaft calcifies. As the bone collar forms externally, the chondrocytes within the shaft hypertrophy (enlarge) and signal the surrounding cartilage matrix to calcify. Because calcified cartilage matrix is impermeable to diffusing nutrients, the chondrocytes die and the matrix they maintained begins to deteriorate. Although this opens up cavities and weakens the shaft, the deteriorating hyaline cartilage model is stabilized externally by the bone collar. Elsewhere, the cartilage remains healthy and continues to grow briskly, causing the entire cartilage bone to elongate.

3. The periosteal bud invades the internal cavities and spongy bone forms. In the third month of development, the forming cavities are quickly invaded by a collection of elements called the **periosteal bud.** Most importantly, the bud contains a nutrient artery and vein, lymphatics, nerve fibers, red marrow elements, osteoblasts, and osteoclasts. The entering osteoblasts secrete osteoid around the remaining fragments of hyaline cartilage, forming bone-covered cartilage trabeculae—the earliest form of spongy bone in a developing long bone.

4. The medullary cavity forms. As the primary ossification center enlarges, spreading proximally and distally, osteoclasts break down the newly formed spongy bone and open up a medullary cavity in the center of the shaft. The formation of this cavity is the final step in ossification of the shaft. Throughout the fetal period, the rapidly growing epiphyses consist only of cartilage, and the hyaline cartilage models continue to elongate by division of viable cartilage cells at the epiphyses. Since cartilage is calcifying, breaking down, and being replaced by bony spicules on the epiphyseal surfaces facing the medullary cavity, ossification "chases" cartilage formation along the length of the shaft.

5. **The epiphyses ossify.** When we are born, most of our long bones have a bony diaphysis surrounding remnants of spongy bone, a widening medullary cavity, and two cartilaginous epiphyses. Shortly before or after birth, **secondary ossification centers** appear in one or both epiphyses, and the epiphyses gain bony tissue. The cartilage in the center of the epiphysis calcifies and deteriorates, opening up cavities that allow entry of a periosteal bud. Then bone matrix is secreted around the remaining cartilage fragments by the entering osteoblasts. (In short bones, only the primary ossification center is formed, while most irregular bones develop from several distinct ossification centers.)

Secondary ossification reproduces almost exactly the events of primary ossification, except that the spongy bone in the interior is retained and no medullary cavity forms in the epiphyses. When secondary ossification is complete, hyaline cartilage remains only at two places: (1) on the epiphyseal surfaces, as the *articular cartilages,* and (2) at the junction of the diaphysis and epiphysis, where it forms the **epiphyseal plates,** or *growth plates.*

Bone Growth

During infancy and youth, long bones lengthen entirely by interstitial growth of the epiphyseal plates, and all bones grow in thickness by appositional growth. Most bones stop growing during adolescence or in early adulthood. However, some facial bones, such as those of the nose and lower jaw, continue to grow almost imperceptibly throughout life.

Growth in Length of Long Bones

The process of longitudinal bone growth mimics many of the events of endochondral ossification. The hyaline cartilage of the epiphyseal plate abutting the shaft organizes into a pattern that allows fast, efficient growth (Figure 6.9). The cartilage cells here form tall columns, like coins in a stack. The cells at the "top" (epiphyseal side) of the stack (zone 1) divide quickly, increasing the thickness of the epiphyseal plate and pushing the epiphysis away from the diaphysis, causing the entire long bone to lengthen (see left side of

(1) What tissue is responsible for growth in length of a long bone? (2) Why are the cartilage cells in zone 2 dying?

1. Cells undergo mitosis

2. Older cells enlarge; matrix becomes calcified

3. Dead cartilage cells; matrix begins deteriorating

4. Ossification is occurring

Calcified cartilage spicule

Osteoblast depositing osseous tissue

Osseous tissue covering cartilage spicules

FIGURE 6.9

Growth in length of a long bone. The region of the epiphyseal plate closest to the epiphysis (distal face) contains resting cartilage cells. As shown in the photomicrograph (250×), the cells of the epiphyseal plate proximal to the resting cartilage area are arranged in four functionally different layers. **(1)** Consecutive layers of mitotic cartilage cells. **(2)** Cartilage cells undergoing hypertrophy, followed by calcification of their matrix. **(3)** An area of dead cartilage cells; matrix begins to deteriorate. **(4)** On the face of the epiphyseal plate next to the medullary cavity, ossification is occurring as osteoblasts deposit bone matrix around the cartilage remnants, forming bony trabeculae.

Figure 6.10, p. 166). Meanwhile, the older chondrocytes closer to the shaft (zone 2 in Figure 6.9) enlarge, and the surrounding cartilage matrix calcifies. Subsequently, these chondrocytes die and their matrix deteriorates (zone 3). This leaves long spicules of calcified cartilage at the epiphysis-diaphysis junction (zone 4), which look like stalactites hanging from the roof of a cave. The cartilage spicules are quickly covered with bone matrix by osteoblasts, forming spongy bone that is eventually digested by osteoclasts. Thus, the medullary cavity also grows longer as the long bone lengthens.

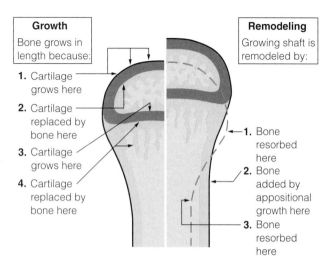

What do you think a long bone would look like at the end of adolescence if remodeling did not occur?

Growth

Bone grows in length because:

1. Cartilage grows here

2. Cartilage replaced by bone here

3. Cartilage grows here

4. Cartilage replaced by bone here

Remodeling

Growing shaft is remodeled by:

1. Bone resorbed here

2. Bone added by appositional growth here

3. Bone resorbed here

FIGURE 6.10
Long bone growth and remodeling during youth. The events indicated at the left depict the process of endochondral ossification that occurs at the articular cartilages and epiphyseal plates as the bone grows in length. The events indicated at the right reveal the process of bone remodeling that occurs during long bone growth to maintain proper bone proportions.

Longitudinal growth is accompanied by almost continuous remodeling of the epiphyseal ends to maintain the proper proportions between the diaphysis and epiphyses (see Figure 6.10). Bone remodeling, involving both new bone formation and bone resorption (destruction), is described in more detail on pp. 168–170 in conjunction with the changes that occur in adult bones.

During childhood and the teen years, the epiphyseal plate maintains a constant thickness because the rate of cartilage growth on its epiphyseal face is balanced by its replacement with bony tissue on its diaphyseal face. As adolescence draws to an end, the cartilage cells of the epiphyseal plates divide less often and the plates become thinner and thinner until they are entirely replaced by bone tissue. Longitudinal bone growth ends when the bone of the epiphysis and diaphysis fuses. This process, called *epiphyseal plate closure,* happens at about 18 years of age in females and 21 years of age in males. However, a bone can still increase in diameter or thickness by appositional growth if it is severely stressed by excessive muscle activity or body weight.

Appositional Growth

Growing bones must widen as they lengthen. As with cartilages, bones increase in thickness or, in the case of long bones, diameter, by the process of appositional growth. *Appositional* means "placed next to,"

which describes the process fairly well. The osteoblasts beneath the periosteum form new osteons on the external bone surface. This increase in compact bone thickness is usually accompanied by bone destruction by osteoclasts on the endosteal surface of the bone collar (see Figure 6.10). However, there is normally slightly less breaking down than building up. This unequal process produces a thicker and stronger bone but prevents it from becoming too heavy.

Hormonal Regulation of Bone Growth During Youth

The growth of bones that occurs throughout childhood and ends in early adulthood is exquisitely controlled by a symphony of hormones. During infancy and childhood, the single most important stimulus of epiphyseal plate activity is *growth hormone* released by the anterior pituitary gland. Growth hormone acts indirectly, prodding the liver to release growth factors called *somatomedins,* which in turn stimulate growth of the epiphyseal plate cartilage. Thyroid hormones (T_3 and T_4) modulate the activity of growth hormone, ensuring that the skeleton has proper proportions as growth occurs. At puberty, male and female sex hormones (testosterone and estrogens, respectively) are released in increasing amounts. Initially these sex hormones promote the growth spurt typical of the adolescent, as well as the masculinization or feminization of specific parts of the skeleton. Later they induce epiphyseal plate closure, ending longitudinal bone growth.

Excesses or deficits of any of these hormones can result in obvious skeletal malproportion. For example, hypersecretion of growth hormone in children results in excessive height (gigantism), and deficits of growth hormone or thyroid hormone result in characteristic types of dwarfism. Hormone activity is considered in detail in Chapter 17.

BONE HOMEOSTASIS: REMODELING AND REPAIR

Bones appear to be the most lifeless of body organs, and may even summon images of a graveyard. But as you have just learned, appearances can be deceiving. Bone is a very dynamic and active tissue. Unlike predominantly cellular tissues, in which renewal takes place mainly at the cellular level, bone is renewed, or revitalized, at the tissue level. Large volumes of bone are removed and replaced, and bone architecture continually changes. Every week we recycle 5% to 7% of our bone mass, and as much as half a gram of calcium may enter or leave the adult skeleton each day! And when we break bones—the commonest disorder of bone homeostasis—they undergo a remarkable process of self-repair that we will describe shortly.

A CLOSER LOOK | Them Bones, Them Bones Goin' to Walk Around—Clinical Advances in Bones Repair

Although bones have remarkable self-regenerative powers, some conditions frustrate even their most heroic efforts. Outstanding examples include massive shattering (as in automobile accidents), inadequate circulation in old bones, severe bone atrophy, and certain birth defects. However, recent medical advances are allowing us to deal with some problems that bones cannot handle themselves. Let's take a look.

1. **Electrical stimulation of fracture sites** has dramatically increased the rapidity and completeness of bone healing in large or slowly healing fractures. For years it's been known that bone tissue is deposited in regions of negative charge and absorbed in areas of positive charge, but just how electricity promotes healing was not known until recently. It appears that the electrical fields prevent parathyroid hormone (PTH) from stimulating osteoclasts at the fracture site, thus allowing increased formation and accumulation of bony tissue.

2. **Ultrasound treatments.** Ultrasound, one of the imaging techniques described in Chapter 1, also helps speed human bone repair. Daily treatments reduce the healing time of broken arms and shinbones by 25% to 35%.

3. The **free vascular fibular graft technique** uses pieces of the fibula to replace missing or severely damaged bone. The fibula is a nonessential sticklike bone of the leg that does not bear weight in humans; it primarily stabilizes the ankle. In the past, extensive bone grafts usually failed because an adequate blood supply could not reach their interior, necessitating eventual amputation. This new technique transplants normal blood vessels along with the bone section, and has been used successfully to construct a radius (forearm bone) for a

child born without one and to replace long bones destroyed by osteomalacia or accidental trauma. Subsequent remodeling of the bones leads to an almost perfect replica of the normally present bone.

The illustration shows the external fixator apparatus used to stabilize an implanted fibular graft in the tibia, a much larger bone. The arrow points to the site of anastomosis (joining) of the blood vessels of the patient's tibia and the graft.

4. **Bone substitutes.** Desperate for bone fillers, surgeons have traditionally resorted to using synthetic materials or crushed bone from cadavers. Crushed bone induces the body to form new bone of its own and, when mixed with water, it can be molded to the shape of the desired bone or packed into small, difficult-to-reach spaces. Thus, it avoids the often

painful and time-consuming procedure of bone transplantation or grafting. The same can be said for most synthetic bone substitutes; however, both approaches have shortcomings. Cadaveric bone carries with it a small (but real) risk of hepatitis or HIV infection. Additionally, as foreign tissue, it may induce rejection by mobilizing the immune system. Synthetics tend to provoke inflammation, which hinders healing and promotes infection.

Currently in clinical trials is a particularly exciting bone "stand-in" called **sea bone** (made from coral), which avoids both problems. The coral is heat treated to kill the living coral cells and convert its mineral structure (of calcium carbonates) to hydroxyapatite, the salt in human bone. The brittle coral graft is then carved to the desired shape, coated with naturally occurring bone growth–enhancing proteins, called *bone morphogenic protein (BMP),* and then implanted. Osteoblasts and blood vessels migrate from the adjacent natural bone into the maze of interconnected channels provided by the coral scaffolding, filling them and forming a permanent graft. Typically, 50% of the graft channels are filled in by bone in just three months.

Research on bone replacement materials has also produced **artificial bone** made of a biodegradable ceramic substance known as TCP. TCP is soft enough to be shaped, but it is not very strong. Its biggest application has been to replace parts of non-weight-bearing bones, such as skull bones. Since the material is porous, osteoblasts enter it and lay down bone matrix. In most instances, the TCP has been completely degraded and replaced by new bone within two years.

Bone Remodeling

In the adult skeleton, bone deposit and bone resorption (removal) occur at one time or another at all periosteal and endosteal surfaces. Together, the two processes constitute **bone remodeling,** and they are coupled and coordinated by "packets" of osteoblasts and osteoclasts called *remodeling units.* In healthy young adults, total bone mass remains constant, an indication that the rates of bone deposit and resorption are essentially equal. The remodeling process is not uniform however, and some bones (or bone areas) are very actively remodeled while others are not. For example, the distal part of the femur, or thigh bone, is fully replaced every five to six months, whereas its shaft is altered much more slowly.

Bone deposit occurs where bone is injured or added bone strength is required. For optimal bone deposit, a healthy diet rich in proteins, vitamin C (for collagen synthesis), vitamin A, and several minerals (calcium, phosphorus, magnesium, and manganese, to name a few) is essential.

Sites of new matrix deposit are revealed by the presence of an **osteoid seam,** an unmineralized band of gauzy-looking bone matrix about 10 to 12 μm wide. Between the osteoid seam and the older mineralized bone, there is an abrupt transition called the **calcification front.** Because the osteoid seam is always of constant width and the change from unmineralized to mineralized matrix is sudden, some authorities theorize that the osteoid must "mature" before it can be calcified. This maturation is under the control of the osteoblasts that secrete the osteoid and appears to involve several biochemical changes that occur over a period of 10 to 12 days. The precise trigger for calcification of the matrix is still controversial. However, one critical factor for the precipitation of calcium salts is the product of the local concentrations of calcium and phosphate (P_i) ions (the $Ca^{2+} \cdot P_i$ product). When this product reaches a certain level, tiny crystals of hydroxyapatite form spontaneously. These so-called *crystallization nuclei* grow rapidly and then catalyze further crystallization of calcium salts in the area. Other factors believed to be involved are matrix proteins (such as osteonectin and osteocalcin) that bind and concentrate calcium, and a rich supply of the enzyme **alkaline phosphatase.** This enzyme is essential for mineralization, but whether it directly stimulates calcium salt deposit or acts indirectly by blocking the action of calcification inhibitors is still a mystery. In any case, the plasma membranes of osteoblasts bear the enzyme, and in rapidly growing bones the osteoblasts (and chondroblasts as well) exhibit *matrix vesicles,* tiny membranous protrusions containing alkaline phosphatase that eventually pinch off and enter the matrix. Once the proper conditions are present, calcium salt precipitation occurs simultaneously and with great precision throughout the "matured" matrix, i.e., the calcium salt crystals

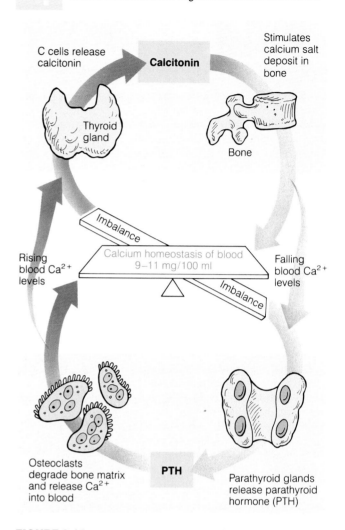

What is the result of the negative feedback of calcitonin?

FIGURE 6.11
Hormonal controls of ionic calcium levels in the blood. PTH and calcitonin operate in negative feedback control systems that influence each other.

pack together in a highly organized pattern that reduces the risk of cracks in a stressed bone.

Bone resorption is accomplished by osteoclasts, giant multinucleate cells that are believed to arise from *hematopoietic stem cells* (possibly the same cells that differentiate into macrophages). Osteoclasts secrete (1) lysosomal enzymes (and perhaps other catabolic enzymes) that digest the organic matrix, and (2) metabolic acids (carbonic, lactic, and others) that convert the calcium salts into soluble forms that pass easily into solution. Osteoclasts may also phagocytize the demineralized matrix. Osteoclasts have a clear *ruffled border,* a region rich in actin filaments that anchors them to the surface being digested. As the organic matrix is degraded and the mineral salts are leached out and dissolved by the acids, the released calcium (and phosphate) ions enter the interstitial fluid and then the blood.

Control of Remodeling

The extensive remodeling that goes on continuously in the skeleton is regulated by two control loops. One is a negative feedback hormonal mechanism; the other involves mechanical and gravitational forces acting on the skeleton.

Hormonal Effects. The hormonal mechanism reflects the interaction of **parathyroid hormone (PTH),** produced by the parathyroid glands, and **calcitonin** (kal″sĭ-to′nin), produced by parafollicular cells (C cells) of the thyroid gland (Figure 6.11). PTH is released when blood levels of ionic calcium decline. It stimulates osteoclasts to resorb bone, which causes calcium release from bone matrix. The osteoclasts are no "respecters" of matrix age. When activated, they break down both old and fairly new matrix. Only osteoid, which lacks calcium salts, escapes digestion. As blood concentrations of calcium increase, the stimulus for PTH release ends.

Calcitonin, secreted when blood calcium levels rise, inhibits bone resorption and encourages calcium salt deposit in bone matrix, effectively reducing blood calcium levels. As blood calcium levels fall, calcitonin release wanes as well.

The hormonal controls act to maintain blood calcium homeostasis, rather than the skeleton's strength or well-being. In fact, if blood calcium levels are low for an extended time, the bones will become so demineralized that they develop large, "punched out"-looking holes. Thus, the bones serve as a storehouse from which ionic calcium is drawn as needed to meet the body's needs.

Ionic calcium (Ca^{2+}) is necessary for an amazing number of physiological processes, including transmission of nerve impulses, contraction of muscles, blood coagulation, secretion by glands and nerve cells, and cell division. The human body contains about 1200–1400 g of calcium, over 99% of which is present as bone minerals. Most of the balance is intracellular, that is, within body cells. Less than 1.5 g is present in blood, and blood Ca^{2+} levels are normally maintained within the very narrow range of 9–11 mg per 100 ml of blood by the hormonal control loop. Calcium is absorbed from the intestine under the control of vitamin D metabolites. The daily requirement of calcium is 1200 mg during the time when bones are still growing and increasing mass (from birth to the age of 25).

Minute changes from the homeostatic range for blood calcium can lead to severe neuromuscular problems ranging from hyperexcitability to inability to function. In addition, sustained *hypercalcemia* (hi″per-kal-se′me-ah), high blood levels of Ca^{2+}, can lead to undesirable deposition of calcium salts in the

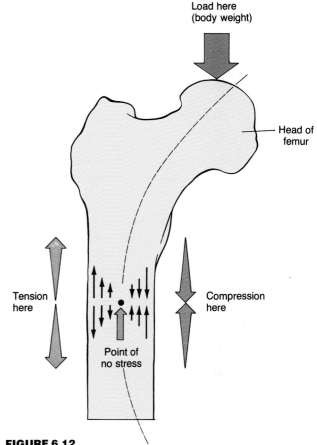

FIGURE 6.12
Bone anatomy and stress. Because the load placed on most bones is off center, bones are subjected to bending stress. Using the femur of the thigh as an example, we show that body weight is transmitted to the head of the femur and threatens to bend the bone along the indicated arc. This bending compresses the bone on one side (converging arrows) and stretches it, promoting tension on the other side (diverging arrows). Because these two forces cancel each other internally (at the point of no stress), much less bone material is needed internally than peripherally.

blood vessels, kidneys, and other soft organs, which may hamper the functioning of these organs. •

Mechanical Factors. The second mechanism that regulates bone remodeling promotes skeletal reshaping in response to mechanical stress (muscle pull) and gravity. Unlike the hormonal mechanism, this set of controls serves the needs of the skeleton itself, keeping the bones strong where stressors are acting. *Wolff's law*—accepted by some, but not all, scientists—holds that a bone grows or remodels in response to the forces or stresses placed on it. Perhaps the very first concept to understand is that a bone's anatomy reflects the common stresses placed on it. For example, most long bones are loaded (stressed) by bending, a combination of *compression* and *tension* (stretch) forces acting on opposite sides of the shaft (Figure 6.12). But since both forces are minimal toward the center of the bone (they cancel each other out), the bone can "hollow out" for lightness without jeopardy. Other phenomena explained by this theory include the facts that (1) long bones are thickest midway along the shaft, exactly where bending stresses are greatest (bend a stick and it will split near the middle); (2) curved bones are thickest where they are most likely to buckle; (3) the trabeculae of spongy bone form trusses, or struts, along lines of compression; and (4) large, bony projections occur where heavy, active muscles attach. (The bones of weight lifters have enormous thickenings at the insertion sites of the most used muscles, and the foot bones of young ballet dancers gradually thicken in response to the intense pressure of dancing *en pointe*.) Wolff's law also explains the featureless bones of the fetus and the atrophied bones of bedridden people—situations in which the bones are not stressed.

How do mechanical forces communicate with the cells responsible for bone remodeling? We know that deforming a bone produces an electrical current proportional to the applied force. Since compressed and stretched regions are oppositely charged, it has been suggested that electrical signals direct the remodeling process. This principle and some of the devices currently used to speed bone repair and the healing of fractures are discussed in *A Closer Look* on p. 167. In the final analysis, the mechanisms by which bone responds to mechanical stimuli are still uncertain. What is certain is that heavy usage leads to heavy bones (or bony areas) and nonuse leads to bone wasting.

The skeleton is continuously subjected to both hormonal influences and mechanical forces. At the risk of constructing too large a building on too small a foundation, one can speculate that PTH (along with calcitonin during youth) is the major determinant of *whether* and *when* remodeling will occur in response to changing blood calcium levels, while mechanical and gravitational forces determine *where* remodeling occurs. For example, if bone must be resorbed to increase blood calcium levels, PTH is released and targets the osteoclasts. However, mechanical forces determine *which* osteoclasts are most sensitive to PTH stimulation, so that bone in the least stressed areas (which is temporarily dispensable) is broken down.

Repair of Fractures

Despite their remarkable strength, bones are susceptible to **fractures,** or breaks, all through life. During youth, most fractures result from exceptional trauma that twists or smashes the bones (sports injuries, automobile accidents, and falls, for example). In old age, bones thin and weaken, and fractures occur with increased frequency. The common types of fractures are explained in Table 6.2.

A fracture is treated by *reduction,* the realignment of the broken bone ends. In **closed reduction,** the bone ends are coaxed back into their normal position by the physician's hands. In **open reduction,** surgery is performed and the bone ends are secured together with pins or wires. After the broken bone is reduced, it is immobilized by a cast or by traction to allow the healing process to begin. The healing time of a simple fracture is 8–12 weeks, but it is much longer for large, weight-bearing bones and for bones of elderly people (because of their poorer circulation).

The repair process in a simple fracture can be described in terms of four major phases as illustrated in Figure 6.13 and described next.

1. **Hematoma formation.** When a bone breaks, blood vessels in the bone itself, and perhaps in surrounding tissues, are torn and hemorrhage. As a result, a **hematoma** (he″mah-to′mah), a mass of clotted blood, forms at the fracture site. Shortly after, bone cells deprived of nutrition begin to die, and the tissue at the fracture site becomes swollen, painful, and obviously inflamed.

2. **Fibrocartilaginous callus formation.** The next event is formation of soft *granulation tissue,* which occurs over the next 3 to 4 weeks. As described in Chapter 4, several events help to form the granulation tissue, initially called the *soft callus* (kal′us; "hard skin"): Capillaries grow into the hematoma and phagocytic cells invade the area and begin to clean up the debris. Meanwhile, fibroblasts and osteoblasts migrate into the fracture site from the nearby periosteal and endosteal membranes and begin reconstructing the bone. The fibroblasts produce collagen fibers that span the break and connect the broken bone ends, and some differentiate into chondroblasts that secrete cartilage matrix. Within this mass of repair tissue, osteoblasts begin forming spongy bone, but those farthest from the capillary supply secrete an externally bulging cartilaginous matrix that later calcifies. This entire mass of repair tissue, now called the **fibrocartilaginous callus,** splints the broken bone. The portion that directly connects the broken bone ends is called the **internal callus;** the part protruding from the outer bone surface is the **external callus.**

3. **Bony callus formation.** Osteoblasts and osteoclasts continue to migrate inward and multiply rapidly in the fibrocartilaginous callus, which, as a result of their labors, is gradually converted to a **bony (hard) callus** of spongy (actually, woven) bone. Bony callus formation begins 3–4 weeks after injury and continues until a firm bony union is formed 2–3 months later.

4. **Remodeling.** Beginning during bony callus formation and continuing for several months thereafter, the bony callus is remodeled. The excess material on the outside of the bone shaft and within the medullary cavity is removed, and compact bone is laid down to reconstruct the shaft. The final structure of the remodeled area resembles that of the original unbroken bony region because it responds to the same set of mechanical stimuli.

Table 6.2 Common Types of Fractures

Fracture type	Illustration	Description	Comments
Simple		Bone breaks cleanly, but does not penetrate the skin	Sometimes called a closed fracture
Compound		Broken ends of the bone protrude through soft tissues and the skin	More serious than a simple fracture; may result in a severe bone infection (osteomyelitis), requiring massive doses of antibiotics
Comminuted		Bone fragments into many pieces	Particularly common in the aged, whose bones are more brittle
Compression		Bone is crushed	Common in porous bones (i.e., osteoporotic bones)
Depressed		Broken bone portion is pressed inward	Typical of skull fracture
Impacted		Broken bone ends are forced into each other	Commonly occurs when one falls and attempts to break the fall with outstretched arms; also common in hip fractures
Spiral		Ragged break occurs when excessive twisting forces are applied to a bone	Common sports fracture
Greenstick		Bone breaks incompletely, much in the way a green twig breaks	Common in children, whose bones have relatively more organic matrix and are more flexible than those of adults

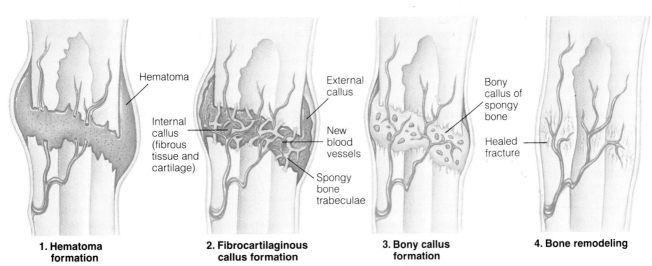

1. Hematoma formation

Hematoma

Internal callus (fibrous tissue and cartilage)

2. Fibrocartilaginous callus formation

External callus

New blood vessels

Spongy bone trabeculae

3. Bony callus formation

Bony callus of spongy bone

Healed fracture

4. Bone remodeling

FIGURE 6.13
Stages in the healing of a bone fracture.

HOMEOSTATIC IMBALANCES OF BONE

Imbalances between bone formation and bone resorption underlie nearly every disease that influences the adult skeleton.

Osteoporosis

For most of us, the phrase "abnormal bone remodeling" quickly brings to mind the stereotype of a hunched-over old woman shuffling behind her walker. **Osteoporosis** (os"te-o-po-ro'sis) refers to a group of diseases in which bone resorption outpaces bone deposit. Although the bone mass is reduced, the chemical composition of the matrix remains normal. Osteoporotic bones become more porous and lighter. For example, even though osteoporosis affects the entire skeleton, the spongy bone of the spine is most vulnerable, and compression fractures of the vertebrae are common. The femur (thigh bone), particularly its neck, is also very susceptible to fracture (called a *broken hip*), in people with osteoporosis.

Osteoporosis occurs most often in the aged, particularly in postmenopausal women. Estrogen helps to maintain the health and normal density of a woman's skeleton by mediating PTH activity. After menopause, however, estrogen secretion wanes and estrogen deficiency is strongly implicated in osteoporosis in older women. Other factors that may contribute to age-related osteoporosis include insufficient exercise to stress the bones, a diet poor in calcium and protein, abnormalities of vitamin D and calcitonin metabolism, smoking (which reduces estrogen levels), and hormone-related conditions (such as the intake of corticosteroid drugs, hyperthyroidism, and diabetes mellitus). In addition, osteoporosis can occur at any age as a result of immobility. The condition is usually treated with supplemental calcium and vitamin D, increased weight-bearing exercise, and use of low-heeled shoes to decrease stress on the spine. However, in many cases, *estrogen replacement therapy (ERT)* offers the best protection against osteoporotic bone fractures. Frustratingly, these treatments can only slow the loss of bone, not reverse it. Particularly exciting is the recent finding that *etidronate,* a drug that suppresses osteoclast activity and has been used to treat Paget's disease (described below), shows promise in reversing osteoporosis in the spine.

With some forethought and planning, osteoporosis can be prevented (or at least delayed). The first requirement is to get enough calcium while your bones are still increasing in density (long bones reach their peak density between the ages of 35 and 40; bones with relatively more spongy bone are densest between the ages of 25 and 30). Second, drinking fluoridated water hardens bones (as well as teeth). Finally, getting plenty of weight-bearing exercise (walking, jogging, tennis, etc.) during youth and throughout life will increase bone mass above normal values and provide a greater "buffer" against age-related bone loss.

Osteomalacia and Rickets

Osteomalacia (os"te-o-mah-la'she-ah; "soft bones") includes a number of disorders in which the bones are inadequately mineralized. Osteoid is produced, but since calcium salts are not deposited, bones soften and weaken. Weight-bearing bones, particularly in the legs and pelvis, may fracture or bend and deform. The main symptom is pain when weight is put on the affected bones.

Rickets, the analogous disease in children, is accompanied by many of the same signs and symptoms, such as bowed legs and a deformed pelvis. Additionally, malformities of the skull and rib cage are common. However, since bones are still growing rapidly, the condition is much more severe. Because the epiphyseal plates cannot be calcified, they continue to widen, and the ends of long bones become visibly enlarged.

Osteomalacia and rickets are caused by insufficient calcium in the diet or vitamin D deficiency. Hence, drinking vitamin D–fortified milk and exposing the skin to sunlight usually cure these disorders.

Paget's Disease

Paget's (paj'ets) **disease** is characterized by excessive and abnormal bone formation and resorption. Newly formed bone, called *Pagetic bone,* is hastily made and has an abnormally high ratio of woven bone to compact bone. This, along with reduced bone mineralization, makes bones soft and weak. Late in the disease, osteoclast activity wanes, but osteoblasts continue to "work," often forming irregular bone thickenings or filling the marrow cavity with Pagetic bone.

Paget's disease may affect any part of the skeleton, but it is usually a localized condition. The spine, pelvis, femur, and skull are most often involved and become increasingly deformed and painful. The condition is rarely seen before the age of 40 years. Its cause is unknown, but it may be initiated by a virus. One drug therapy for this ailment is etidronate. •

DEVELOPMENTAL ASPECTS OF BONES: TIMING OF EVENTS

It can be said that the bones are on a precise schedule from the time they form until death. The mesoderm germ layer gives rise to embryonic mesenchymal cells, which in turn produce the membranes and cartilages that form the embryonic skeleton. These structures then ossify according to an amazingly predictable timetable that allows fetal age to be determined easily from X rays or sonograms of the fetal skeleton. Although each bone has its own developmental schedule, most long bones begin ossifying by 8 weeks, and exhibit obvious primary ossification centers by 12 weeks (Figure 6.14). Before this, blood cells are formed in the fetal liver and spleen. But once ossification begins, red marrow within the developing bones takes over the chore of hematopoiesis.

At birth, most long bones of the skeleton are well ossified except for their epiphyses. After birth, secondary ossification centers develop in a predictable sequence from infancy to the preschool years. The epiphyseal plates persist and provide for long bone growth during childhood and the sex hormone–mediated growth spurt at adolescence. All bones are relatively featureless at birth, but as the child uses his or her muscles more and more, the bone markings develop and become increasingly prominent. By the age of 25 years, nearly all bones are completely ossified and skeletal growth ceases.

In children and adolescents, the rate of bone formation exceeds the rate of bone resorption; in young adults, these processes are in balance; in old age, resorption predominates. Beginning in the fourth decade of life, the mass of both compact and spongy bone decreases with age; the only exception appears to be in bones of the skull. Among young adults, skeletal mass is generally greater in males than in females, and in blacks than in whites. As we age, the rate of bone loss is faster in whites than in blacks (who have greater bone density to begin with) and in females than in males.

As bone mass declines with age, qualitative changes also occur. An increasing number of osteons remain incompletely formed and mineralization is less complete. The amount of nonviable compact bone increases, reflecting a diminished blood supply to the bones in old age.

FIGURE 6.14
Primary ossification centers in the skeleton of a 12-week-old fetus are indicated by the darker areas.

* * *

Skeletal cartilages and bones—their architecture, composition, and dynamic nature—have been examined in some detail in this chapter. We have also discussed the role of bones in maintaining overall body homeostasis, as summarized in *Making Connections.* Now we are ready to look at how the bones are assembled into the skeleton and contribute to its functions, both collectively and individually.

RELATED CLINICAL TERMS

Achondroplasia (a-kon″dro-pla′ze-ah; *a* = without; *chondro* = cartilage; *plasi* = mold, shape) A congenital condition involving defective cartilage growth and a deficient ability to form endochondral bones; results in dwarfism.

Bony spur Abnormal projection from a bone due to bone overgrowth; common in aging bones.

Metastatic calcification Deposit of bone salts in tissues that do not normally become calcified; a consequence of sustained hypercalcemia resulting from hyperparathyroidism or other bone-demineralizing conditions.

Osteitis (os″te-i′tis; *itis* = inflammation) Inflammation of bony tissue.

Osteomyelitis (os″te-o-mi″ĕ-li′tis) Inflammation of bone caused by pus-forming bacteria that enter the body via a wound (e.g., compound bone fracture), or spread from an infection near the bone; most commonly affects the long bones of the limbs, causing acute pain and fever; may result in joint stiffness, bone destruction, and shortening of a limb (if a long bone growth plate is destroyed); treatment involves antibiotic therapy, draining of any abscesses (local collections of pus) formed, and removal of dead bone fragments (which prevent healing if allowed to remain).

Osteosarcoma (os′te-o-sar-ko′mah) A form of bone cancer typically arising in a long bone of a limb and most often in those between 10 and 25 years of age. Grows aggressively, eroding the bone; tends to metastasize to the lungs and most deaths result from secondary lung tumors. Signs include visible swelling accompanied by pain; usual treatment is amputation of the affected bone or limb, followed by chemotherapy. Survival rate is about 50% if detected early.

Making Connections

Systems Connections: Homeostatic Interrelationships Between the Skeletal System and Other Body Systems

Endocrine System

• Skeletal system provides some bony protection; stores calcuim needed for second messenger signaling mechanisms

• Hormones regulate uptake and release of calcium from bone; hormones promote long bone growth and maturation

Cardiovascular System

• Bone marrow cavities provide site for blood cell formation; matrix stores calcium needed for cardiac muscle activity

• Cardiovascular system delivers nutrients and oxygen to bones; carries away wastes

Lymphatic System/Immunity

• Skeletal system provides some protection to lymphatic organs; bone marrow is site of origin for lymphocytes involved in immune response

• Lymphatic system drains leaked tissue fluids; immune cells protect against pathogens

Respiratory System

• Skeletal system protects lungs by enclosure (rib cage)

• Respiratory system provides oxygen; disposes of carbon dioxide

Digestive System

• Skeletal system provides some bony protection to intestines, pelvic organs, and liver

• Digestive system provides nutrients needed for bone health and growth

Urinary System

• Skeletal system protects pelvic organs (bladder, etc.)

• Urinary system activates vitamin D; disposes of nitrogenous wastes

Reproductive System

• Skeletal system protects some reproductive organs by enclosure

• Gonads produce hormones that influence form of skeleton and epiphyseal closure

Integumentary System

• Skeletal system provides support for body organs including the skin

• Skin provides vitamin D needed for proper calcium absorption and use

Muscular System

• Skeletal system provides levers plus calcium for muscle activity

• Muscle pull on bones increases bone strength and viability; helps determine bone shape

Nervous System

• Skeletal system protects brain and spinal cord; depot for calcium ions needed for neural function

• Nerves innervate bone and joint capsules providing for pain and joint sense

Closer Connections: The Skeletal System and Interrelationships with the Muscular, Endocrine, and Integumentary Systems

Our skeleton supports us, protects our "innards" (the protection our brain gets from the skull is indispensable), gives us stature (for some reason, tall people get more respect), contributes to our shape (women *are* shaped differently than men), and allows us to move. Obviously, the skeletal system has important interactions with many other body systems, not the least of which are the endocrine and integumentary systems. However, its most intimate and mutually beneficial relationship is with the muscular system. Thus, we will consider that first.

Muscular System

The codependence of the skeletal and muscular systems is striking—as one system goes, so goes the other. If we participate in weight-bearing exercise (run, play tennis, do aerobics) regularly, our muscles become more efficient, and exert more force on our bones. As a result, our bones stay healthy and strong, and increase their mass to assume the added stress.

Since both spongy and compact bone reach peak density during mid-life, weight-bearing exercise during youth is important, especially in females who have less bone mass and lose it faster than males.

Regular exercise also stretches the connective tissues binding bones to muscles and to other bones, and reinforcing joints. Since this increases overall flexibility, we have fewer injuries, allowing us to stay active well into old age. (Pain makes couch potatoes.)

Endocrine System

Although mechanical factors are undeniably important in shaping the skeleton and helping to keep it strong, hormones acting individually and in concert direct skeletal growth during youth, and enhance (or impair) skeletal strength in adults. Growth hormone is essential for normal skeletal growth and maintenance throughout life, whereas thyroid and sex hormones ensure that normal skeletal proportions are established during childhood and adolescence. Conversely, PTH and calcitonin serve not the skeleton but a different master—homeostasis of blood calcium levels. Regardless of the precise skeletal aspect governed by hormones, any interference with their normal functioning is soon apparent as skeletal abnormality or malproportion.

Integumentary System

Under normal circumstances, the skeletal system is absolutely dependent on the integumentary system (the skin) for the calcium that keeps the bones hard and strong. The relationship is indirect to be sure: In the presence of sunlight, skin cells make a vitamin D precursor. It enters the blood, is activated, and (among its other roles) forms part of the carrier system that absorbs calcium from ingested foods into the blood. Because calcium is required for so many body functions (see p. 169), and bones provide the "calcium bank," the bones become increasingly soft and weak in the absence of vitamin D because no daily rations of calcium are allowed to enter the blood from the digestive tract.

Clinical Connections

Skeletal System

Case study: Remember Mrs. DeStephano? When we last heard about her she was being admitted for further studies. Relative to her skeletal system, the following notes have been added to her chart.

• Fracture of superior region of right tibia (shinbone of leg); skin lacerated; area cleaned and protruding bone fragments subjected to internal reduction and casted

• Nutrient artery of tibia damaged

• Medial meniscus (hyaline cartilage disc) of right knee joint crushed; knee joint inflamed and painful

Relative to these notes:
1. What type of fracture does Mrs. DeStephano have?

2. What problems can be predicted with such fractures and how are they treated?

3. What is internal reduction? Why was a cast applied?

4. Given an uncomplicated recovery, approximately how long should it take before Mrs. DeStephano has a good solid bony callus?

5. What complications might be predicted by the fact that the nutrient artery is damaged?

6. What new techniques might be used to enhance fracture repair if healing is delayed or impaired?

7. How likely is it that Mrs. DeStephano's knee cartilage will regenerate? Why? What measures will probably have to be taken to remedy this problem?

Pathologic fracture Fracture occurring in a diseased bone and involving slight or no physical trauma.

Traction Placing sustained tension on a body region to keep the parts of a fractured bone in proper alignment; also keeps the bone immobilized by preventing spasms of skeletal muscles, which would separate the fractured bone ends or crush the spinal cord in the case of vertebral column fractures.

CHAPTER SUMMARY

Skeletal Cartilages (pp. 155–156)

Basic Structure, Types, and Locations (p. 155)

1. A skeletal cartilage, formed from some type of cartilage tissue, contains large amounts of water, which accounts for its resilience. It lacks nerve fibers, and is avascular and surrounded by a fibrous perichondrium that resists expansion.

2. Typical cartilage tissue exhibits chondrocytes housed in lacunae (cavities) within the extracellular matrix (ground substance and fibers).

3. Hyaline cartilages appear glassy; the fibers are collagenic. They provide support with flexibility and resilience and are the most abundant skeletal cartilages, accounting for the articular, costal, respiratory, and nasal cartilages.

4. Elastic cartilages contain abundant elastic fibers and are more flexible than hyaline cartilages. They support the outer ear and epiglottis.

5. Fibrocartilages are the most compressible cartilages, and have great resistance to stretch. They form vertebral discs and knee joint cartilages.

Growth of Cartilage (p. 156)

6. Cartilages grow from within (interstitial growth) and by addition of new cartilage tissue at the periphery (appositional growth).

Functions of Bones (p. 156)

1. Bones protect and support body organs; provide levers for muscles to pull on; store calcium, and other minerals; and are the site of blood cell production.

Classification of Bones (pp. 156–158)

1. Bones are classified as long, short, flat, or irregular on the basis of their shape and the proportion of compact or spongy bones they contain.

Bone Structure (pp. 158–163)

Gross Anatomy (pp. 158–160)

1. A long bone is composed of a diaphysis and two epiphyses. The medullary cavity of the diaphysis contains yellow marrow; the epiphyses contain spongy bone. The epiphyseal line is the remnant of the epiphyseal plate. Periosteum covers the diaphysis; endosteum lines medullary cavities and the spaces of spongy bone. Hyaline cartilage covers articular surfaces.

2. Flat bones consist of two thin plates of compact bone enclosing a diploë (spongy bone layer). Short and irregular bones resemble flat bones structurally.

3. In adults, hematopoietic tissue is found within the diploë of flat bones and occasionally within the epiphyses of long bones. In infants red marrow is also found in the medullary cavity.

Microscopic Structure of Bone (pp. 160–161)

4. The structural unit of compact bone is the osteon, consisting of a central canal surrounded by concentric lamellae of bone matrix. Osteocytes, embedded in lacunae, are connected to each other and the central canal by canaliculi.

5. Spongy bone has slender trabeculae containing irregularly arranged lamellae, which enclose (red marrow–filled) cavities.

Chemical Composition of Bone (pp. 161–162)

6. Bone is composed of living cells (osteoblasts, osteocytes, and osteoclasts) and matrix. The matrix includes organic substances that are secreted by osteoblasts and give the bone tensile strength. Its inorganic components are hydroxyapatites (calcium salts), which make bone hard.

Bone Markings (p. 162)

7. Bone markings are important anatomical landmarks that reveal sites of muscle attachment, points of articulation, and sites of blood vessels and nerve passage.

Bone Development (Osteogenesis) (pp. 163–166)

Formation of the Bony Skeleton (pp. 163–165)

1. Intramembranous ossification forms the clavicles and most skull bones. The ground substance of the bone matrix is deposited between collagen fibers within the fibrous membrane to form spongy bone. Eventually, compact bone plates enclose the diploë.

2. Most bones are formed by endochondral ossification of a hyaline cartilage model. Osteoblasts beneath the periosteum secrete bone matrix on the cartilage model, forming the bone collar. Deterioration of the cartilaginous matrix opens up cavities, allowing periosteal bud entry. Bone matrix is deposited around the cartilage remnants, but is later broken down.

Bone Growth (pp. 165–166)

3. Long bones increase in length by interstitial growth of the epiphyseal plate cartilage and its replacement by bone.

4. Appositional growth increases bone diameter/thickness.

Bone Homeostasis: Remodeling and Repair (pp. 166–171)

Bone Remodeling (pp. 168–170)

1. New bone is continually deposited and resorbed in response to hormonal and mechanical stimuli. Together these processes constitute bone remodeling.

2. An osteoid seam appears at areas of new bone formation; calcium salts are deposited 10 to 12 days later.

3. Multinucleate osteoclasts secrete catabolic enzymes and acids on bone surfaces to be resorbed.

4. Bone remodeling involves hormonal and mechanical controls. The hormonal mechanism serves blood calcium homeostasis. When blood calcium levels decline, PTH is released and stimulates osteoclasts to digest bone matrix, releasing ionic calcium. When blood calcium levels rise, calcitonin is released, stimulating removal of calcium from the blood. Mechanical stress and gravity acting on the skeleton help maintain skeletal strength. Bones thicken, develop heavier prominences, or rearrange their trabeculae in sites where stressed.

Repair of Fractures (pp. 170–171)

5. Fractures are treated by open or closed reduction. The healing process involves formation of a hematoma, a fibrocartilaginous callus, a bony callus, and bone remodeling, in succession.

Homeostatic Imbalances of Bone (p. 172)

1. Imbalances between bone formation and resorption underlie all skeletal disorders.

2. Osteoporosis is any condition in which bone breakdown outpaces bone formation, causing bones to become porous and weaken. Postmenopausal women are particularly susceptible.

3. Osteomalacia and **rickets** occur when bones are inadequately mineralized. The bones become soft and deformed. The most frequent cause is inadequate vitamin D.

4. Paget's disease is characterized by excessive and abnormal bone remodeling.

Developmental Aspects of Bones: Timing of Events (pp. 172–173)

1. Osteogenesis occurs in a predictable and precisely timed manner.

2. Longitudinal long bone growth continues until the end of adolescence. Skeletal mass increases dramatically during puberty and adolescence, when formation exceeds resorption.

3. Bone mass is relatively constant in young adulthood, but beginning in the 40s, bone resorption exceeds formation.

REVIEW QUESTIONS

Multiple Choice/Matching

1. Which is a function of the skeletal system? (a) support, (b) hematopoietic site, (c) storage, (d) providing levers for muscle activity, (e) all of these.

2. A bone that has essentially the same width, length, and height is most likely (a) a long bone, (b) a short bone, (c) a flat bone, (d) an irregular bone.

3. The shaft of a long bone is properly called the (a) epiphysis, (b) periosteum, (c) diaphysis, (d) compact bone.

4. Sites of hematopoiesis include all but (a) red marrow cavities of spongy bone, (b) the diploë of flat bones, (c) medullary cavities in bones of infants, (d) medullary cavities in bones of a healthy adult.

5. An osteon has (a) a central canal carrying blood vessels, (b) concentric lamellae, (c) osteocytes in lacunae, (d) canaliculi that connect lacunae to the central canal, (e) all of these.

6. The organic portion of matrix is important in providing *all but* (a) tensile strength, (b) hardness, (c) ability to resist stretch, (d) flexibility.

7. The flat bones of the skull develop from (a) areolar tissue, (b) hyaline cartilage, (c) fibrous connective tissue, (d) compact bone.

8. The remodeling of bone is a function of which of these cells? (a) chondrocytes and osteocytes, (b) osteoblasts and osteoclasts, (c) chondroblasts and osteoclasts, (d) osteoblasts and osteocytes.

9. Bone growth during childhood and in adults is regulated and directed by (a) growth hormone, (b) thyroxine, (c) sex hormones, (d) mechanical stress, (e) all of these.

10. Where within the epiphyseal plate are the *dividing* cartilage cells located? (a) nearest the shaft, (b) in the marrow cavity, (c) farthest from the shaft, (d) in the primary ossification center.

11. Wolff's law is concerned with (a) calcium homeostasis of the blood, (b) the thickness and shape of a bone being determined by mechanical and gravitational stresses placed on it, (c) the electrical charge on bone surfaces.

12. Formation of the bony callus in fracture repair is followed by (a) hematoma formation, (b) fibrocartilaginous callus formation, (c) bone remodeling to convert woven bone to compact bone, (d) formation of granulation tissue.

13. A fracture in which the bone ends are incompletely separated is (a) greenstick, (b) compound, (c) simple, (d) comminuted, (e) compression.

14. The disorder in which bones are porous and thin but bone composition is normal is (a) osteomalacia, (b) osteoporosis, (c) Paget's disease.

Short Answer Essay Questions

15. Compare bone to cartilage tissue relative to its resilience, speed of regeneration, and access to nutrients.

16. Describe in proper order the events of endochondral ossification.

17. Compare compact and spongy bone in macroscopic appearance, microscopic structure, and relative location.

18. As we grow, our long bones increase in diameter, but the thickness of the bony collar of the shaft remains relatively constant. Explain this phenomenon.

19. Describe the process of new bone formation in an adult bone. Use the terms *osteoid seam* and *calcification front* in your discussion.

20. Compare and contrast controls of bone remodeling exerted by hormones and mechanical/gravitational forces relative to the actual purpose of each control system and changes in bone architecture that might occur.

21. (a) During what period of life does skeletal mass increase dramatically? Begin to decline? (b) Why are fractures most common in elderly individuals? (c) Why are greenstick fractures most common in children?

CRITICAL THINKING AND CLINICAL APPLICATION QUESTIONS

1. Following a motorcycle accident, a 22-year-old man was rushed to the emergency room. X rays revealed a spiral fracture of his right tibia (main bone of the leg). Two months later, X rays revealed good bony callus formation. What is bony callus?

2. A mother brought her four-year-old daughter to the doctor, complaining that her daughter didn't "look right." The child's forehead was enlarged, her rib cage was knobby, and her lower limbs were bent and deformed. X rays revealed very thick epiphyseal plates. The mother was advised to increase dietary amounts of vitamin D and milk and to "shoo" the girl outside to play in the sun. Based on the child's signs and symptoms, what disease do you think she has? Explain the doctor's instructions.

3. You overhear some anatomy students imagining out loud what their bones would look like if they had compact bone on the inside and spongy bone on the outside, instead of the other way around. You tell them that such imaginary bones would be poorly designed mechanically and would break easily. Explain your reason for saying this.

4. Why do you think wheelchair-bound people with paralyzed lower limbs have thin, weak leg and thigh bones?

5. Jock went to weight-lifting camp in the summer between seventh and eighth grade. He noticed that the camp trainer put tremendous pressure on him and his friends to improve their strength. After an especially vigorous workout, Jock's arm felt extremely sore and weak around the elbow. He went to the camp doctor, who took X rays and then told him that the injury was serious, for the "end of his upper arm bone was starting to twist off." What had happened? Could the same thing happen to Jock's 23-year-old sister, Trixie, who was also starting a program of weight lifting?

7

The Skeleton

The word **skeleton** comes from the Greek word meaning "dried up body" or "mummy," a rather unflattering description. Nonetheless, the internal human framework is a triumph of design and engineering that puts any skyscraper to shame. It is strong, yet light, and is almost perfectly adapted for the protective, locomotor, and manipulative functions it performs.

Our skeleton's present form was shaped more than 3 million years ago, when ancestors of human beings first stood erect on hind legs. As opposed to animals that walk on all fours, our upright stance increases the ability of our skeletal muscles to resist the pull of gravity. The skeleton has its flaws, to be sure: that S-shaped or swayback spine required for the upright posture burdens many of us with lower back pain. However, this structural imperfection is offset by the skeleton's capacity to respond to most demands we place on it.

The skeleton, composed of bones, cartilages, joints, and ligaments, accounts for about 20% of body mass (about 30 pounds' worth in a 160-pound person). Bones make up the bulk of the skeleton. Cartilages occur only in isolated areas, such as the nose, parts of the ribs, and the joints. Ligaments connect bones and reinforce joints, allowing required movements while restricting motions in other directions. Joints, the junctions between bones, provide for the remarkable mobility of the skeleton without impairing its immense strength. They are discussed separately in Chapter 8.

For descriptive purposes, the 206 named bones of the human skeleton are grouped into the axial and appendicular skeletons (see Figure 7.1). The **axial skeleton** forms the long axis of the body and includes the bones of the skull, vertebral column, and rib cage. The **appendicular** (ap″en-dik′u-lar) **skeleton** consists of the bones of the upper and lower limbs and the girdles (shoulder bones and hip bones) that attach the limbs to the axial skeleton.

PART 1: THE AXIAL SKELETON

The axial skeleton is structured from 80 bones segregated into three major regions: the *skull, vertebral column,* and *bony thorax* (Figure 7.1). This part of the skeleton supports the head, neck, and trunk, and it protects the brain, spinal cord, and the organs in the thorax.

THE SKULL

The **skull** is the body's most complex bony structure. It is formed by two sets of bones, the *cranial bones* and the *facial bones,* 22 in all. The tiny bones of the middle ear cavity are sometimes counted as skull bones, too, but since they are involved in hearing, we will consider them with the special senses in Chapter 16. Besides furnishing a site for attachment of head muscles, the cranial bones, or **cranium** (kra′ne-um), enclose and protect the fragile brain and the organs of hearing and equilibrium. The facial bones (1) form the framework of the face, (2) provide cavities for the sense organs of sight, taste, and smell, (3) provide openings for passage of air and food, (4) secure the teeth, and (5) anchor the facial muscles of expression, which we use to show our feelings. As you will see,

the individual skull bones are well suited to their assignments (see Table 7.1 on pp. 188–189).

Most skull bones are flat bones. Except for the mandible, which is connected to the rest of the skull by a freely movable joint, all bones of the adult skull are firmly united by interlocking joints called **sutures** (soo′cherz). The suture lines have a tortuous or serrated appearance, particularly obvious on the external bone surfaces. The major skull sutures, the *coronal, sagittal, squamosal,* and *lambdoidal sutures,* connect cranial bones (see Figures 7.2b and 7.3a). Most other skull sutures connect facial bones and are named according to the specific bones they connect.

Overview of Skull Geography

It is worth spending a few moments on basic skull "geography" before describing the individual bones. With the lower jaw removed, the skull resembles a lopsided, hollow, bony sphere. The facial bones form its anterior aspect, and the cranium forms the rest of the skull (see Figure 7.3a). The cranium can be divided into a *vault* and a *base.* The *cranial vault,* also called the *calvaria* (kal-va′re-ah) or skullcap, forms the superior, lateral, and posterior aspects of the skull, as well as the forehead. The *cranial base,* or *floor,* forms the skull's inferior aspect. Internally, prominent bony ridges divide the base into three distinct "steps" or fossae—the *anterior, middle,* and *posterior cranial fossae* (see Figure 7.4c). The brain sits snugly in these cranial fossae, completely enclosed by the cranial vault. Overall, the brain is said to occupy the *cranial cavity.*

In addition to the large cranial cavity, the skull has many smaller cavities. These include the middle and inner ear cavities (carved into the lateral side of its base) and, anteriorly, the nasal cavity and the orbits. The *orbits* house the eyeballs. Several bones of the skull contain air-filled sinuses. The sinuses in bones surrounding the nasal cavity are referred to as the *paranasal sinuses.* The sinuses lighten the skull and have additional roles that we will describe shortly.

Moreover, the skull has about 85 named openings (foramina, canals, fissures, etc.). The most important are those that provide openings for the spinal cord, the major blood vessels serving the brain (internal carotid arteries and internal jugular veins), and the cranial nerves (numbered I through XII), which transmit impulses to and from the brain.

As you read about the bones of the skull, locate each bone on the different skull views in Figures 7.2 to 7.4. The skull bones and their important markings are also summarized in Table 7.1. The color-coded dot beside a bone's name in the table corresponds to the color of that bone in the figures.

Which of the following bones is not part of the appendicular skeleton?
Humerus, vertebra, femur, tibia, clavicle, rib, scapula, ulna, sternum?

Skull

Cranium

Facial bones

Bony thorax
(ribs and
sternum)

Vertebral
column

Clavicle

Scapula

Sternum

Rib

Humerus

Vertebra

Radius

Ulna

Carpals

Phalanges

Metacarpals

Femur

Patella

Tibia

Fibula

Tarsals

Metatarsals

Phalanges

Bones of
pectoral
girdle

Upper
limb

Bones of
pelvic
girdle

Lower
limb

(a) Anterior view

(b) Posterior view

FIGURE 7.1
The human skeleton. The bones of the axial skeleton are shaded green; the bones of the
appendicular skeleton are shaded gold.

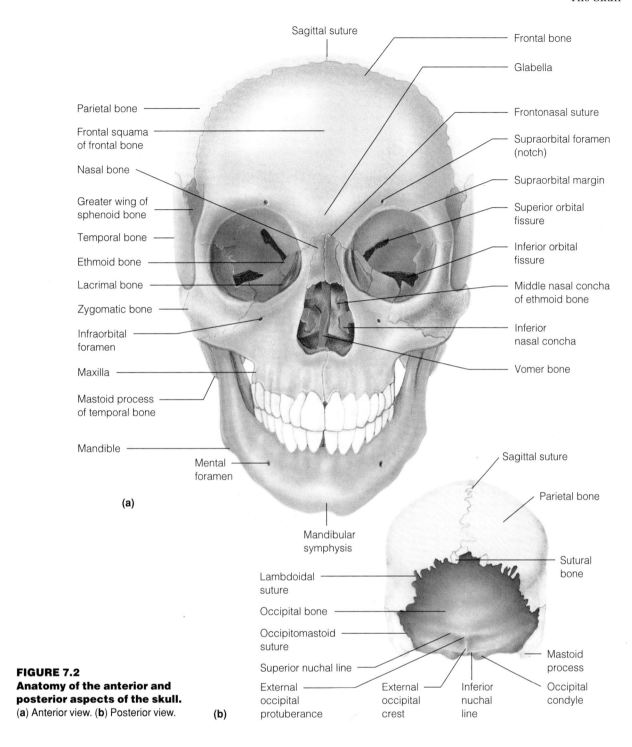

FIGURE 7.2
Anatomy of the anterior and posterior aspects of the skull. (a) Anterior view. (b) Posterior view.

Cranium

The eight cranial bones are the paired parietal and temporal bones and the unpaired frontal, occipital, sphenoid, and ethmoid bones. Together, these construct the brain's protective bony "helmet." Because its superior aspect is curved, the cranium is self-bracing. This allows the bones to be thin, and, like an eggshell, the cranium is remarkably strong for its weight.

Frontal Bone

The **frontal bone** (Figures 7.2a, 7.3, and 7.4b) forms the anterior portion of the cranium, the forehead, roofs of the orbits, and most of the anterior cranial fossa. It articulates posteriorly with the paired parietal bones via the prominent *coronal suture.*

The anteriormost vertical part of the frontal bone is the **frontal squama,** commonly called the *forehead.*

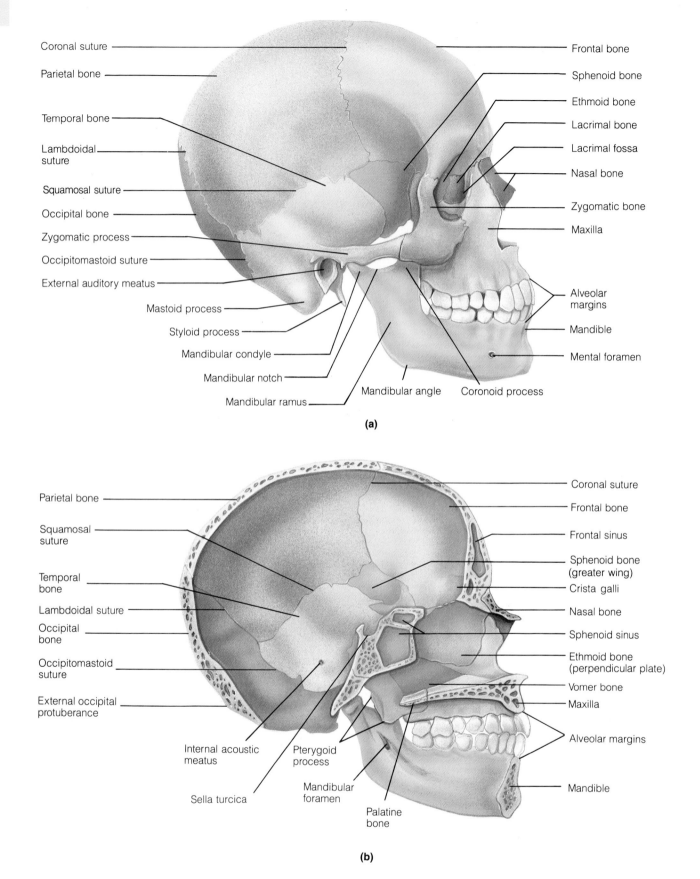

Coronal suture

Parietal bone

Temporal bone

Lambdoidal suture

Squamosal suture

Occipital bone

Zygomatic process

Occipitomastoid suture

External auditory meatus

Mastoid process

Styloid process

Mandibular condyle

Mandibular notch

Mandibular ramus

Mandibular angle

Coronoid process

Frontal bone

Sphenoid bone

Ethmoid bone

Lacrimal bone

Lacrimal fossa

Nasal bone

Zygomatic bone

Maxilla

Alveolar margins

Mandible

Mental foramen

(a)

Parietal bone

Squamosal suture

Temporal bone

Lambdoidal suture

Occipital bone

Occipitomastoid suture

External occipital protuberance

Internal acoustic meatus

Sella turcica

Pterygoid process

Mandibular foramen

Palatine bone

Coronal suture

Frontal bone

Frontal sinus

Sphenoid bone (greater wing)

Crista galli

Nasal bone

Sphenoid sinus

Ethmoid bone (perpendicular plate)

Vomer bone

Maxilla

Alveolar margins

Mandible

(b)

FIGURE 7.3
Anatomy of the lateral aspects of the skull. (a) External anatomy of the right lateral aspect of the skull. (b) Midsagittal view of the skull showing the internal anatomy of the left side of the skull.

How does Figure 7.4b illustrate the fact that the sphenoid bone is the keystone bone of the cranium?

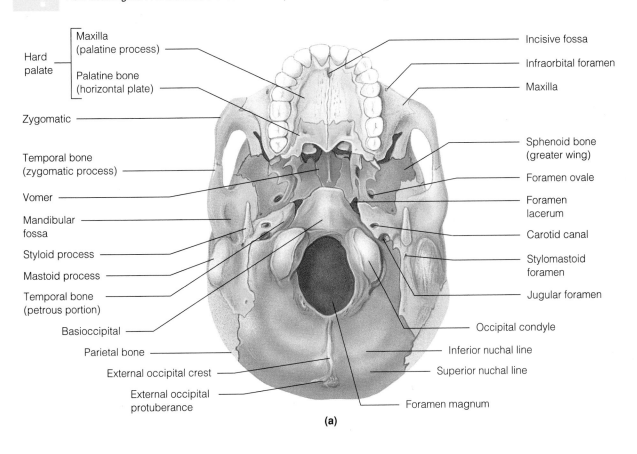

Hard palate
- Maxilla (palatine process)
- Palatine bone (horizontal plate)

Zygomatic

Temporal bone (zygomatic process)

Vomer

Mandibular fossa

Styloid process

Mastoid process

Temporal bone (petrous portion)

Basioccipital

Parietal bone

External occipital crest

External occipital protuberance

Incisive fossa

Infraorbital foramen

Maxilla

Sphenoid bone (greater wing)

Foramen ovale

Foramen lacerum

Carotid canal

Stylomastoid foramen

Jugular foramen

Occipital condyle

Inferior nuchal line

Superior nuchal line

Foramen magnum

(a)

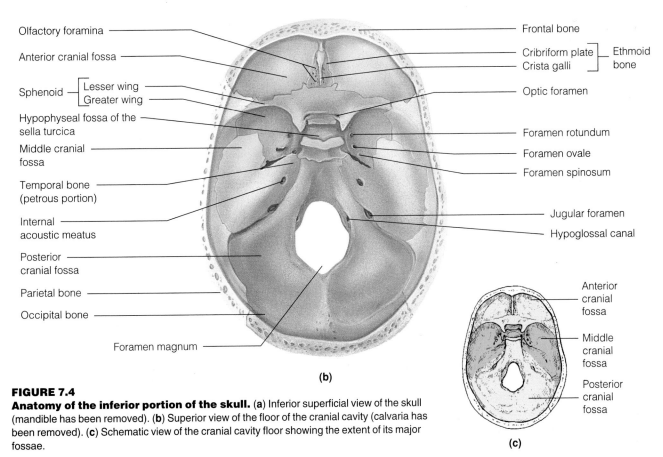

Olfactory foramina

Anterior cranial fossa

Sphenoid
- Lesser wing
- Greater wing

Hypophyseal fossa of the sella turcica

Middle cranial fossa

Temporal bone (petrous portion)

Internal acoustic meatus

Posterior cranial fossa

Parietal bone

Occipital bone

Foramen magnum

Frontal bone

Cribriform plate   Ethmoid
Crista galli   bone

Optic foramen

Foramen rotundum

Foramen ovale

Foramen spinosum

Jugular foramen

Hypoglossal canal

(b)

Anterior cranial fossa

Middle cranial fossa

Posterior cranial fossa

(c)

FIGURE 7.4
Anatomy of the inferior portion of the skull. (a) Inferior superficial view of the skull (mandible has been removed). **(b)** Superior view of the floor of the cranial cavity (calvaria has been removed). **(c)** Schematic view of the cranial cavity floor showing the extent of its major fossae.

The frontal squama ends inferiorly at the **supraorbital margins,** the thickened superior margins of the orbits that lie under the eyebrows. From here, the frontal bone extends posteriorly, forming the superior wall of the **orbits** and most of the **anterior cranial fossa** (see Figure 7.4b and c). This fossa supports the frontal lobes of the brain. Each supraorbital margin is pierced by a **supraorbital foramen (notch),** which allows the supraorbital artery and nerve to pass to the forehead region.

The smooth portion of the frontal bone between the orbits is the **glabella** (glah-bel′ah). Just inferior to this the frontal bone meets the nasal bones at the *frontonasal suture* (Figure 7.2a). The areas lateral to the glabella are riddled internally with sinuses, called the **frontal sinuses** (see Figures 7.3b and 7.11).

Parietal Bones and the Major Sutures

The two **parietal bones** are large, curved, rectangular bones that form most of the superior and lateral aspects of the skull; hence they form the bulk of the cranial vault. The four largest sutures of the skull occur where the parietal bones articulate (form a joint) with other cranial bones:

1. The **coronal** (kŏ-ro′nul) **suture,** where the parietal bones meet the frontal bone anteriorly (Figure 7.3).

2. The **sagittal suture,** where the two parietal bones meet at the cranial midline (see Figure 7.2).

3. The **lambdoidal** (lam-doi′dul) **suture,** where the parietal bones meet the occipital bone posteriorly (see Figures 7.2b and 7.3).

4. The **squamosal suture** (one on each side), where a parietal and temporal bone meet on the lateral aspect of the skull (see Figure 7.3).

Occipital Bone

The **occipital** (ok-sip′ĭ-tal) **bone** forms most of the posterior wall and base of the skull externally. It articulates anteriorly with the paired parietal and temporal bones via the *lambdoidal* and *occipitomastoid sutures,* respectively (Figure 7.3). It also joins with the sphenoid bone in the cranial floor via its narrowed band called the *basioccipital* (ba″ze-ok-sih′-pih-tul) (Figure 7.4a). Internally, the occipital bone forms the walls of the **posterior cranial fossa** (Figure 7.4b and c), which supports the cerebellum of the brain. In the base of the occipital bone is the **foramen magnum,** literally, "large hole." Through this opening, the inferior part of the brain (the medulla oblongata) connects with the spinal cord. The foramen magnum is flanked laterally by the paired **hypoglossal canals** (Figure 7.4b), through which nerves of the same name pass, and by two **occipital condyles** (see Figure 7.4a). The rockerlike occipital condyles articulate with the first vertebra of the spinal column in a way that permits a nodding movement of the head.

Just superior to the foramen magnum is a median protrusion called the **external occipital protuberance** (see Figures 7.2b, 7.3b, and 7.4a). You can feel this knoblike projection just below the most bulging part of your posterior skull. A number of inconspicuous ridges, the *external occipital crest* and the *superior* and *inferior nuchal* (nu′kal) *lines* mark the occipital bone near the foramen magnum. The external occipital crest secures the *ligamentum nuchae* (lig″ah-men′- tum noo′ke; *nu′ke* = of the neck), a large ligament that connects the vertebrae of the neck to the skull. The nuchal lines, and the bony regions between them, anchor many neck and back muscles. The superior nuchal line marks the upper limit of the neck.

Temporal Bones

The two **temporal bones** lie inferior to the parietal bones and meet them at the squamosal sutures (see Figure 7.3). The temporal bones form the inferolateral aspects of the skull and parts of the cranial floor. The use of the terms *temple* and *temporal,* from the Latin word *temporum,* meaning "time," came about because gray hairs, a common sign of time's passing, usually appear first in the temple areas.

Each temporal bone has a complicated shape and is described in terms of its four major regions, the *squamous, tympanic, mastoid,* and *petrous regions.* The flaring **squamous region** abuts the squamosal suture. It has a barlike **zygomatic process** that meets the zygomatic bone of the face anteriorly. Together, these two bones form the **zygomatic arch,** which you can feel as the projection of your cheek (*zygoma* = cheekbone). The small, oval **mandibular** (man-dib′u-lar) **fossa** on the inferior surface of the zygomatic process receives the condyle of the mandible (lower jawbone), forming the freely movable *temporomandibular joint.*

The **tympanic** (tim-pan′ik; "eardrum") **region** (Figure 7.5) of the temporal bone surrounds the **external auditory (acoustic) meatus,** or external ear canal, through which sound enters the ear. The external auditory meatus and the eardrum at its deep end are part of the *external ear* structures. In a dried skull, the eardrum has been removed; thus, part of the middle ear cavity deep to the external meatus can also be seen. Below the external auditory meatus is the needlelike **styloid** (sti′loid; "stakelike") **process,** an attachment point for several muscles of the neck and for a ligament that secures the hyoid bone in the neck region (see Figure 7.12).

The **mastoid** (mas′toid) **region** of the temporal bone exhibits the conspicuous **mastoid process,** an anchoring site for some neck muscles (see Figures 7.3a, 7.4a, and 7.5). The mastoid process can be felt as a lump just posterior to the ear. The **stylomastoid foramen,** between the styloid and mastoid processes, allows the facial nerve to leave the skull (see Figure 7.4a).

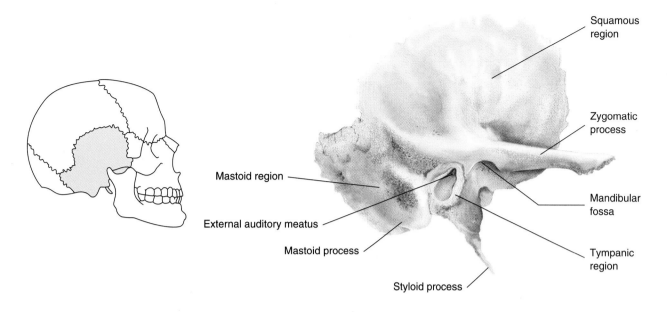

Squamous region

Zygomatic process

Mastoid region

Mandibular fossa

External auditory meatus

Mastoid process

Tympanic region

Styloid process

FIGURE 7.5
The temporal bone. Right superficial view.

The mastoid process is full of air cavities, the **mastoid sinuses,** or **air cells.** Its position adjacent to the middle ear cavity (a high-risk area for infections spreading from the throat) makes it extremely susceptible to infection itself. A mastoid sinus infection, or *mastoiditis,* is notoriously difficult to treat. Since the mastoid air cells are separated from the brain by only a very thin bony plate, mastoid infections may spread to the brain as well. Surgical removal of the mastoid process was once the best way to prevent life-threatening brain inflammations in people susceptible to repeated bouts of mastoiditis. Today, antibiotic therapy is the treatment of choice. •

The inferior, deep **petrous** (pet′rus; "rocky") **region** of the temporal bone (see Figure 7.4) looks like a miniature mountain ridge between the occipital bone posteriorly and the sphenoid bone anteriorly. The posterior slope of this ridge lies in the posterior

cranial fossa; the anterior slope is in the middle cranial fossa. Together, the sphenoid bone and the petrous portions of the temporal bones construct the **middle cranial fossa** (see Figure 7.4b and c), which supports the temporal lobes of the brain. Housed within the petrous region are the *middle* and *inner ear cavities,* which contain the sensory receptors for hearing and balance.

Several foramina penetrate the bone of the petrous region (see Figure 7.4a). The large **jugular foramen** at the junction of the occipital and petrous temporal bones allows passage of the internal jugular vein and three cranial nerves. The **carotid** (kar-rot′id) **canal,** just anterior to the jugular foramen, transmits the internal carotid artery through the petrous temporal bone. The two internal carotid arteries supply blood to over 80% of the cerebral hemispheres of the brain; their closeness to the inner ear cavities

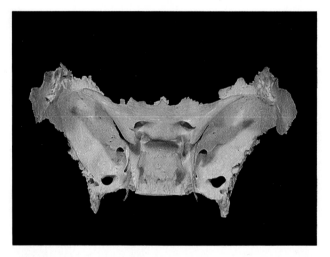

Optic foramen
Lesser wing
Superior orbital fissure
Foramen rotundum
Foramen ovale
Foramen spinosum
Body of sphenoid
Greater wing
Sella turcica

(a) Superior view

Body of sphenoid
Greater wing
Superior orbital fissure
Foramen rotundum
Pterygoid processes

(b) Posterior view

FIGURE 7.6
The sphenoid bone. (a) Superior view. (b) Posterior view.

explains why, during excitement or exertion, we sometimes hear our rapid pulse as a thundering sound in the head. The **foramen lacerum** (la′ser-um), a jagged opening (*lacerum* = torn or lacerated) between the petrous temporal bone and the sphenoid bone, is a short passageway for a number of small nerves and blood vessels. Because the carotid canal enters the posterosuperior aspect of the canal-like foramen lacerum, the internal carotid artery actually enters the middle cranial fossa through this opening. The foramen lacerum is almost completely closed by cartilage in a living person, but it is conspicuous in a dried skull, and students usually ask its name. The **internal acoustic meatus,** positioned superolateral to the jugular foramen (see Figures 7.3b and 7.4b), transmits cranial nerves VII and VIII.

Sphenoid Bone

The butterfly-shaped **sphenoid** (sfe′noid) **bone** spans the width of the middle cranial fossa (see Figure 7.4b). The sphenoid is considered the keystone of the cranium because it articulates as a central wedge with all other cranial bones. It consists of a central body and three pairs of processes: the greater wings, lesser wings, and pterygoid (ter′ĭ-goid) processes (Figure 7.6). Within the **body** of the sphenoid are the paired **sphenoid sinuses** (see Figures 7.3b and 7.11). The superior surface of the body bears a saddlelike depression, the **sella turcica** (sel′ah ter′si-kah), commonly called the "Turk's saddle." The seat of this saddle, called the *hypophyseal fossa,* forms a snug enclosure for the pituitary gland (hypophysis). The

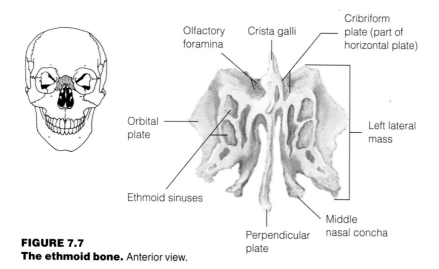

Olfactory foramina
Crista galli
Cribriform plate (part of horizontal plate)
Orbital plate
Left lateral mass
Ethmoid sinuses
Middle nasal concha
Perpendicular plate

FIGURE 7.7
The ethmoid bone. Anterior view.

greater wings project laterally from the body, forming parts of (1) the middle cranial fossa (see Figure 7.4b and c), (2) the dorsal walls of the orbits (see Figure 7.2), and (3) the external wall of the skull, where they are seen as flag-shaped, bony areas medial to the zygomatic arch (see Figure 7.3a). The **lesser wings** form part of the floor of the anterior cranial fossa (see Figure 7.4b and c) and a portion of the medial walls of the orbits. The trough-shaped **pterygoid processes** project inferiorly from the body (see Figure 7.6b). They form part of the lateral walls of the nasopharynx and anchor the pterygoid muscles, which are important in chewing.

A number of openings in the sphenoid bone are visible in Figures 7.4b and 7.6. The **optic foramina** lie anterior to the sella turcica; they allow the optic nerves and the ophthalmic arteries to pass. On each side of the sphenoid body is a crescent-shaped series of four openings. The anteriormost of these, the **superior orbital fissure,** is a long slit between the greater and lesser wings. It allows cranial nerves that control eye movements (III, IV, VI) to enter the orbit. This fissure is most obvious in an anterior view of the skull (see Figure 7.2). The foramen rotundum and foramen ovale provide passageways for branches of cranial nerve V to reach the face. The **foramen rotundum** is at the base of the greater wing and is usually oval, despite its name meaning "round opening." The **foramen ovale** (o-vă'le), a large, oval foramen posterior to the foramen rotundum, is visible in an inferior view of the skull (see Figure 7.4a). Posterolateral to the foramen ovale is the small **foramen spinosum** (Figure 7.4b); it transmits the *middle meningeal artery,* which serves the internal faces of some of the cranial bones.

Ethmoid Bone

Like the temporal and sphenoid bones, the **ethmoid bone** has a complex shape (Figure 7.7). Lying between the sphenoid and the nasal bones of the face, it is the most deeply situated bone of the skull. It forms most of the bony area between the nasal cavity and the orbit.

The superior surface of the ethmoid, the **horizontal plate** (see also Figure 7.4b), helps form the roof of the nasal cavities and the floor of the anterior cranial fossa. The paired **cribriform** (krib'rĭ-form; "perforated like a sieve") **plates,** which form the bulk of the horizontal plate, are punctured by tiny holes called *olfactory foramina* that allow the olfactory nerves to pass from the smell receptors in the nasal cavities to the brain. In the midline, between the two cribriform plates, is a triangular projection called the **crista galli** (kris'tah gah'le; "rooster's comb"). The outermost covering of the brain (the dura mater) attaches to the crista galli and helps secure the brain in the cranial cavity. The **perpendicular plate** of the ethmoid bone projects inferiorly and forms the superior part of the nasal septum (see Figure 7.3b). Flanking the perpendicular plate on each side is a **lateral mass** riddled with the **ethmoid sinuses** (see Figures 7.7 and 7.11) for which the bone is named (*ethmos* = sieve). Extending medially from the lateral masses are the delicately coiled **superior** and **middle nasal conchae** (kong'ke; *concha* = shell), or **turbinates,** which protrude into the nasal cavity (Figures 7.7 and 7.10a). The lateral surfaces of the ethmoid's lateral masses are called **orbital plates** because they contribute to the medial walls of the orbits.

Sutural Bones

Sutural bones, also called **Wormian bones,** are tiny irregularly shaped bones or bone clusters that appear in the sutures of the cranium, most often in the lambdoidal suture (see Figure 7.2b). Their number varies, and not all skulls exhibit them. Sutural bones probably represent additional ossification centers that appeared when the skull was expanding very rapidly during fetal development.

Table 7.1 Bones of the Skull

Bone*	Comments	Important markings
CRANIAL BONES		
○ **Frontal** (1) (Figures 7.2a, 7.3, and 7.4b)	Forms forehead; superior part of orbits and anterior cranial fossa; contains sinuses	**Supraorbital foramina (notches):** allow the supraorbital arteries and nerves to pass
○ **Parietal** (2) (Figures 7.2 and 7.3)	Forms most of the superior and lateral aspects of the skull	
● **Occipital** (1) (Figures 7.2b, 7.3, and 7.4)	Forms posterior aspect and most of the base of the skull	**Foramen magnum:** allows the spinal cord to issue from the brain stem to enter the vertebral canal
		Hypoglossal canal: allows passage of the hypoglossal nerve (cranial nerve XII)
		Occipital condyles: articulate with the atlas (first vertebra)
		External occipital protuberance and **nuchal lines:** sites of muscle attachment
		External occipital crest: attachment site of ligamentum nuchae
○ **Temporal** (2) (Figures 7.3, 7.4, and 7.5)	Forms inferolateral aspects of the skull and contributes to the middle cranial fossa; has squamous, mastoid, tympanic, and petrous regions	**Zygomatic process:** helps to form the zygomatic arch, which forms the prominence of the cheek
		Mandibular fossa: articular point of the mandibular condyle
		External auditory (acoustic) meatus: canal leading from the external ear to the eardrum
		Styloid process: attachment site for hyoid bone and several neck muscles
		Mastoid process: attachment site for several neck muscles
		Stylomastoid foramen: allows cranial nerve VII (facial nerve) to pass
		Jugular foramen: allows passage of the internal jugular vein and cranial nerves IX, X, and XI
		Internal acoustic meatus: allows passage of cranial nerves VII and VIII
		Carotid canal: allows passage of the internal carotid artery
○ **Sphenoid** (1) (Figures 7.2a, 7.3, 7.4b, and 7.6)	Keystone of the cranium; contributes to the middle cranial fossa and orbits; main parts are the body, greater wings, lesser wings, and pterygoid processes	**Sella turcica:** hypophyseal fossa portion is the seat of the pituitary gland
		Optic foramina: allow passage of cranial nerve II and the ophthalmic arteries
		Superior orbital fissures: allow passage of cranial nerves III, IV, VI, and part of V (ophthalmic division)
		Foramen rotundum: allows passage of the maxillary division of cranial nerve V
		Foraman ovale: allows passage of the mandibular division of cranial nerve V
		Foramen spinosum: allows passage of the middle meningeal artery

Table 7.1 continued

Bone*	Comments	Important markings
● **Ethmoid** (1) (Figures 7.2a, 7.3, 7.4b, 7.7 and 7.10)	Helps to form the anterior cranial fossa; forms part of the nasal septum and the lateral walls and roof of the nasal cavity; contributes to the medial wall of the orbit	**Crista galli:** attachment point for the falx cerebri, a dural membrane fold **Cribriform plates:** allow passage of nerve fibers of the olfactory (cranial nerve I) nerves **Superior** and **middle nasal conchae:** form part of lateral walls of nasal cavity; increase turbulence of air flow
Ear ossicles (malleus, incus, and stapes) (2 each)	Found in middle ear cavity; involved in sound transmission; see Chapter 16	
FACIAL BONES		
● **Mandible** (1) (Figures 7.2a, 7.3, and 7.8a)	The lower jaw	**Coronoid processes:** insertion points for the temporalis muscles **Mandibular condyles:** articulate with the temporal bones in freely movable joints (temporomandibular joints) **Mandibular symphysis:** medial fusion point of the mandibular bones **Alveoli:** sockets for the teeth **Mandibular foramina:** permit the alveolar nerves to pass **Mental foramina:** allow blood vessels and nerves to pass to the chin and lower lip
● **Maxilla** (2) (Figures 7.2a, 7.3, 7.4, and 7.8b)	Keystone bones of the face; form the upper jaw and parts of the hard palate, orbits, and nasal cavity walls	**Alveoli:** sockets for the teeth **Zygomatic processes:** help form the zygomatic arches **Palatine processes:** form the anterior hard palate **Frontal processes:** form part of lateral aspect of bridge of nose **Incisive fossa:** permits blood vessels and nerves to pass through hard palate (fused palatine processes) **Inferior orbital fissures:** permit maxillary branch of cranial nerve V, the zygomatic nerve, and blood vessels to pass **Infraorbital foramen:** allows passage of infraorbital nerve to skin of face
● **Zygomatic** (2) (Figures 7.2a, 7.3a, and 7.4a)	Form the cheek and part of the orbit	
● **Nasal** (2) (Figures 7.2a and 7.3)	Construct the bridge of the nose	
● **Lacrimal** (2) (Figures 7.2a and 7.3a)	Form part of the medial orbit wall	**Lacrimal fossa:** houses the lacrimal sac, which helps to drain tears into the nasal cavity
○ **Palatine** (2) (Figures 7.3b, 7.4a, and 7.8c)	Form posterior part of the hard palate and a small part of nasal cavity and orbit walls	
● **Vomer** (1) (Figures 7.2a and 7.10)	Part of the nasal septum	
● **Inferior nasal concha** (2) (Figures 7.2a and 7.10a)	Form part of the lateral walls of the nasal cavity	

*The color-coded dot beside each bone name corresponds to the bone's color in Figures 7.2 to 7.10. The number in parentheses ( ) following each bone name denotes the total number of such bones in the body.

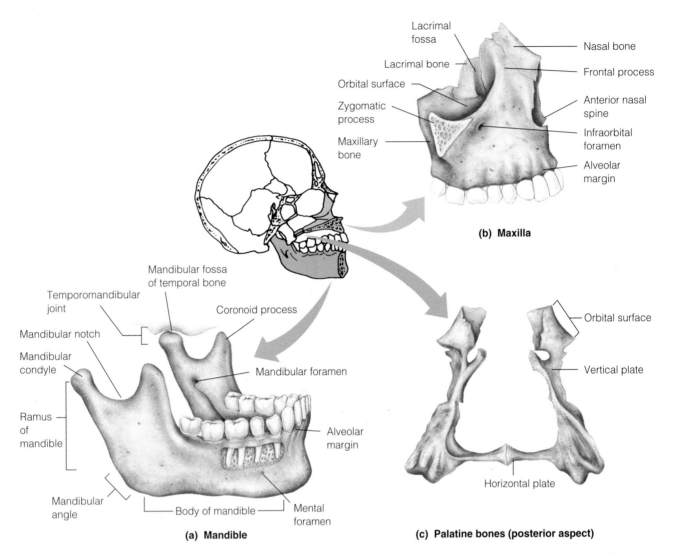

(b) Maxilla

(a) Mandible

(c) Palatine bones (posterior aspect)

FIGURE 7.8
Detailed anatomy of some isolated facial bones. **(a)** The mandible (and its articulation with the temporal bone). **(b)** The maxilla (and its articulations with the nasal and lacrimal bones). **(c)** Posterior view of the palatine bones. Note that the mandible, maxillae, and palatine bones are not drawn in proportion to one another.

Facial Bones

The facial skeleton is made up of 14 bones (see Figures 7.2a and 7.3a), of which only the mandible and the vomer are unpaired. The maxillae, zygomatics, nasals, lacrimals, palatines, and inferior conchae are paired bones. As a rule, the facial skeleton of men is more elongated than that of women; therefore, women's faces tend to be rounder and less angular.

Mandible

The U-shaped **mandible** (man′dĭ-bl), or lower jawbone (Figures 7.2, 7.3, and 7.8a), is the largest, strongest bone of the face. It has a *body,* which forms the chin, and two upright *rami* (*rami* = branches). Each ramus meets the body posteriorly at a **mandibular angle.** At the superior margin of each ramus are two processes

separated by the **mandibular notch.** The anterior **coronoid** (kor′o-noid; "crown-shaped") **process** is an insertion point for the large temporalis muscle that elevates the lower jaw during chewing. The posterior **mandibular condyle** articulates with the mandibular fossa of the temporal bone, forming the *temporomandibular joint* on the same side.

The mandibular **body** anchors the lower teeth. Its superior border, called the **alveolar** (al-ve′o-lar) **margin**, contains the sockets (*alveoli*) in which the teeth are embedded. In the midline of the mandibular body is a slight depression, the **mandibular symphysis** (sim′fih-sis), which indicates the line of fusion of the two mandibular bones during infancy (see Figure 7.2a).

Large **mandibular foramina,** one on the medial surface of each ramus, permit the nerves responsible for tooth sensation to pass to the teeth in the lower jaw. Dentists inject Novocain into these foramina to prevent pain while working on the lower teeth. The **mental foramina,** openings on the lateral aspects of the mandibular body, allow blood vessels and nerves to pass to the chin (*ment* = chin) and lower lip.

Maxillary Bones

The **maxillary bones,** or **maxillae** (mak-sil′le) (see Figures 7.2 to 7.4 and 7.8b), are fused medially. They form the upper jaw and the central portion of the facial skeleton. All facial bones except the mandible articulate with the maxillae. Hence, the maxillae are considered the keystone bones of the facial skeleton.

The maxillae carry the upper teeth in their **alveolar margins.** The **palatine** (pa′lah-tīn) **processes** of the maxillae project posteriorly from these margins and fuse medially, forming the anterior two-thirds of the hard palate, or bony roof of the mouth (see Figures 7.3b and 7.4a). Just posterior to the teeth is a midline foramen, called the **incisive fossa,** which serves as a passageway for blood vessels and nerves.

The **frontal processes** extend superiorly to the frontal bone, forming part of the lateral aspects of the bridge of the nose (see Figures 7.2a and 7.8b). The regions that flank the nasal cavity laterally contain the **maxillary sinuses** (see Figure 7.11), the largest of the paranasal sinuses. They extend from the orbits to the upper teeth. Laterally, the maxillae articulate with the zygomatic bones via their **zygomatic processes.**

The **inferior orbital fissure** is located deep within the orbit (see Figure 7.2a) at the junction of the maxilla with the greater wing of the sphenoid. It permits the zygomatic nerve, the maxillary nerve (a branch of cranial nerve V), and blood vessels to pass to the face. Just below the eye socket on each side is an **infraorbital foramen** that allows the infraorbital nerve and artery to reach the face.

Zygomatic Bones

The irregularly shaped **zygomatic bones** (see Figures 7.2a and 7.3a) are commonly called the cheekbones. They articulate with the zygomatic processes of the temporal bones posteriorly and with the zygomatic processes of the maxillae anteriorly. The zygomatic bones form the prominences of the cheeks and part of the inferolateral margins of the orbits.

Nasal Bones

The thin, basically rectangular **nasal** (na′zal) **bones** are fused medially, forming the bridge of the nose (see Figures 7.2a and 7.3a). They articulate with the frontal bone superiorly, the maxillary bones laterally, and the perpendicular plate of the ethmoid bone posteriorly. Inferiorly they attach to the cartilages that form most of the skeleton of the external nose (see Figure 6.1, p. 157.)

Lacrimal Bones

The delicate fingernail-shaped **lacrimal** (lak′rĭ-mal) **bones** contribute to the medial walls of each orbit (see Figures 7.2a and 7.3a). They articulate with the frontal bone superiorly, the ethmoid bone posteriorly, and the maxillae anteriorly. Each lacrimal bone has an anterior groove that helps form a **lacrimal fossa.** The lacrimal fossa houses the *lacrimal sac,* part of the passageway that permits tears to drain from the eye surface into the nasal cavity (*lacrima* = tears).

Palatine Bones

The **horizontal plates** of the L-shaped **palatine bones** complete the posterior portion of the hard palate (see Figures 7.3b, 7.4a, and 7.8c). Projecting superiorly from the horizontal plate of each palatine bone is a **vertical plate** that forms part of the posterolateral wall of the nasal cavity and a small part of the orbit.

Vomer

The slender, plow-shaped **vomer** (vo′mer) is located within the nasal cavity, where it forms part of the nasal septum (see Figures 7.2a and 7.10b). It will be discussed later in connection with the nasal cavity.

Inferior Nasal Conchae

The paired **inferior nasal conchae** are thin, curved bones in the nasal cavity. They project medially from the lateral walls of the nasal cavity, just inferior to the middle nasal conchae of the ethmoid bone (see Figures 7.2a and 7.10a). They are the largest of the three pairs of conchae, and like the others, they form part of the lateral walls of the nasal cavity.

Special Characteristics of the Orbits and Nasal Cavity

Two restricted skull regions, the orbits and the nasal cavity, are formed from an amazing number of bones. In fact, it is sometimes difficult to comprehend how the many parts form the whole. Thus, even though the individual bones forming these structures have been described, a brief summary is provided here to pull the parts together.

The Orbits

The **orbits** are bony cavities within which the eyes are firmly encased and cushioned by fatty tissue. The muscles that move the eyes and the tear-producing lacrimal glands are also housed within the orbits. The walls of each orbit are formed by parts of seven bones—the frontal, sphenoid, zygomatic, maxilla, palatine, lacrimal, and ethmoid bones. Their relationships are shown in Figure 7.9. Also seen in the orbits

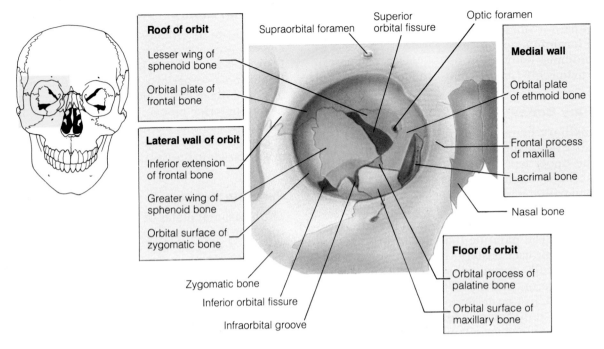

FIGURE 7.9
Special anatomical characteristics of the orbits. The contribution of each of the seven bones forming the orbit is illustrated.

are the superior and inferior orbital fissures and the optic foramina, described earlier.

The Nasal Cavity

The **nasal cavity** is constructed of bone and hyaline cartilage (Figure 7.10a). The *roof* of the nasal cavity is formed by the cribriform plates of the ethmoid. The *lateral walls* are shaped by the superior and middle conchae of the ethmoid bone, the vertical plates of the palatine bones, and the inferior nasal conchae. The depressions under cover of the conchae on the lateral walls are called *meatuses* (*meatus* = passage), so there are superior, middle, and inferior meatuses. The *floor* of the nasal cavity is formed by the palatine processes of the maxillae and the palatine bones. The nasal cavity is divided into right and left parts by the *nasal septum*. The bony portion of the septum is formed by the vomer inferiorly and the perpendicular plate of the ethmoid bone superiorly (Figure 7.10b). *Septal cartilage* completes the septum anteriorly.

The nasal septum and conchae are covered with a mucus-secreting mucosa. This mucosa moistens and warms the entering air and helps cleanse it of debris. The scroll-shaped conchae increase the surface area to enhance the turbulence of air flow through the nasal cavity and, thus, encourage trapping of airborne particles (dust, pollen, bacteria) in the sticky mucus.

Paranasal Sinuses

Five skull bones—the frontal, sphenoid, ethmoid, and paired maxillary bones—contain mucosa-lined, air-filled sinuses that cause them to look rather moth-eaten in an X ray. As noted previously, these sinuses are called **paranasal sinuses,** because they cluster around the nasal cavity (Figure 7.11). The paranasal sinuses lighten the skull and enhance the resonance of the voice. Small openings connect the sinuses to the nasal cavity. These passageways act as "two-way streets"; air enters the sinuses from the nasal cavity and mucus formed by the sinus mucosae drains into the nasal cavity. The mucosae of the sinuses also help to warm and humidify inspired air.

The Hyoid Bone

Though not really part of the skull, the **hyoid** (hi'oid; "U-shaped") **bone** (Figure 7.12) is intimately related to the mandible and temporal bones. The hyoid bone is unique in that it is the only bone of the body that does not articulate directly with any other bone. Instead, it lies just inferior to the mandible in the anterior neck, anchored by the narrow *stylohyoid ligaments* to the styloid processes of the temporal bones. Horseshoe-shaped, with a *body* and two pairs of *horns,* or *cornua,* the hyoid bone acts as a movable base for the tongue. Its body and greater horns are

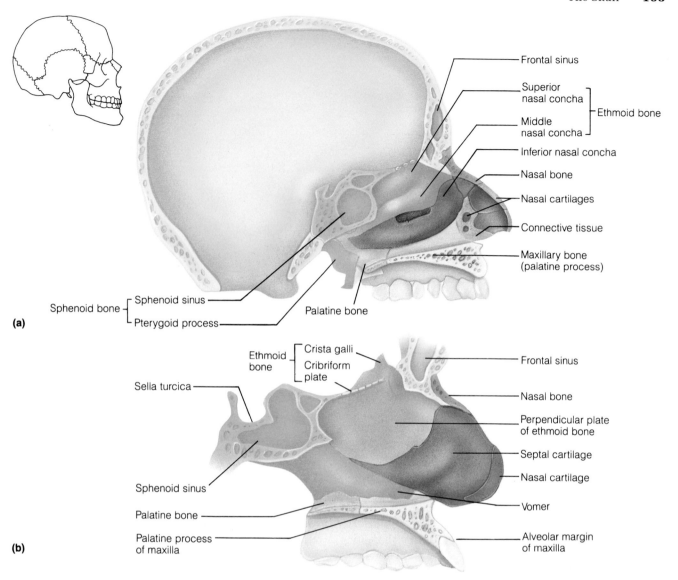

(a)

Frontal sinus

Superior nasal concha

Middle nasal concha

⎤ Ethmoid bone

Inferior nasal concha

Nasal bone

Nasal cartilages

Connective tissue

Maxillary bone (palatine process)

Sphenoid bone ⎡ Sphenoid sinus
⎣ Pterygoid process

Palatine bone

(b)

Ethmoid bone ⎡ Crista galli
⎣ Cribriform plate

Frontal sinus

Sella turcica

Nasal bone

Perpendicular plate of ethmoid bone

Septal cartilage

Nasal cartilage

Sphenoid sinus

Palatine bone

Vomer

Palatine process of maxilla

Alveolar margin of maxilla

FIGURE 7.10
Special anatomical characteristics of the nasal cavity. (a) Bones forming the left lateral wall of the nasal cavity. (b) The contribution of the ethmoid, vomer, and cartilage to the nasal septum.

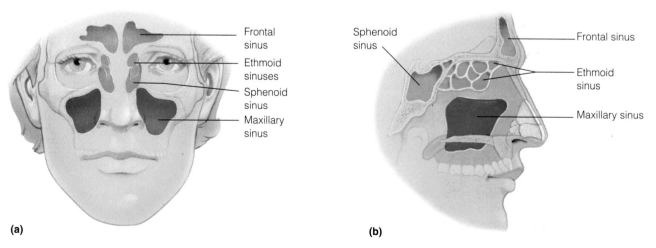

(a)

Frontal sinus

Ethmoid sinuses

Sphenoid sinus

Maxillary sinus

(b)

Sphenoid sinus

Frontal sinus

Ethmoid sinus

Maxillary sinus

FIGURE 7.11
Paranasal sinuses. (a) Anterior view. (b) Medial view.

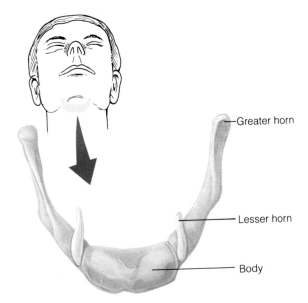

FIGURE 7.12
Anatomical location and structure of the hyoid bone. The hyoid bone is suspended in the mid-anterior neck by ligaments attached to the lesser horns (cornua) and the styloid processes of the temporal bones.

attachment points for neck muscles that raise and lower the larynx during swallowing and speech.

THE VERTEBRAL COLUMN

General Characteristics

Some people think of the **vertebral column** as a rigid supporting rod, but this picture is inaccurate. The vertebral column, also called the **spine**, is formed from 26 irregular bones connected in such a way that a flexible, curved structure results (Figure 7.13). Serving as the axial support of the trunk, the spine extends from the skull, which it supports, to its anchoring point in the pelvis, where it transmits the weight of the trunk to the lower limbs. Running through its central cavity is the delicate spinal cord, which it surrounds and protects. Additionally, the vertebral column provides attachment points for the ribs and for the muscles of the back. In the fetus and infant, the vertebral column typically consists of 33 separate bones, or **vertebrae** (ver′tĕ-bre). Nine of these eventually fuse to form two composite bones, the sacrum and the tiny coccyx. The remaining 24 bones persist as individual vertebrae separated by intervertebral discs.

Ligaments

Like a tall, tremulous TV transmitting tower, the vertebral column cannot possibly stand upright by itself. It must be held in place by an elaborate system of cablelike supports. In the case of the TV tower, the supports are steel guy wires; for the vertebral column,

Why would it be anatomically "stupid" to have the sturdiest vertebrae in the cervical instead of the lumbar region of the spine?

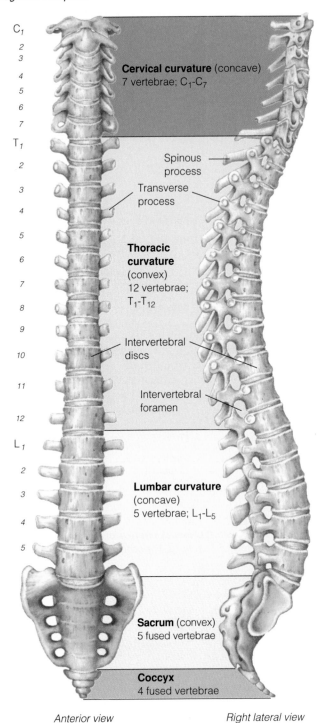

Anterior view   Right lateral view

FIGURE 7.13
The vertebral column. Notice the curvatures in the lateral view. (The terms *convex* and *concave* refer to the curvature of the posterior aspect of the vertebral column.)

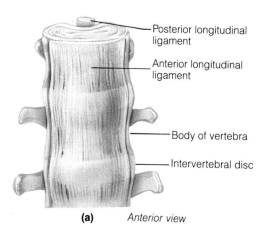

Posterior longitudinal ligament

Anterior longitudinal ligament

Body of vertebra

Intervertebral disc

(a)   *Anterior view*

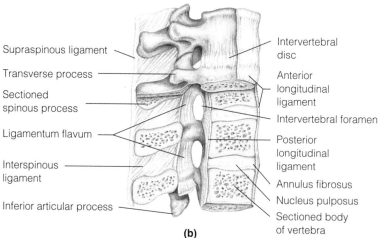

Supraspinous ligament

Transverse process

Sectioned spinous process

Ligamentum flavum

Interspinous ligament

Inferior articular process

Intervertebral disc

Anterior longitudinal ligament

Intervertebral foramen

Posterior longitudinal ligament

Annulus fibrosus

Nucleus pulposus

Sectioned body of vertebra

(b)

FIGURE 7.14
Ligaments and fibrocartilage discs uniting the vertebrae. (a) Anterior view of portions of three articulated vertebrae, showing the difference in width of the anterior and posterior longitudinal ligaments. **(b)** Median section of vertebrae, illustrating the ligaments and the composition of the discs. **(c)** Superior view of a sectioned herniated disc (slipped disc).

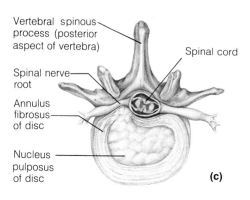

Vertebral spinous process (posterior aspect of vertebra)

Spinal cord

Spinal nerve root

Annulus fibrosus of disc

Nucleus pulposus of disc

(c)

straplike ligaments and the trunk muscles assume this role. The reinforcing muscles are discussed in Chapter 10. The major supporting ligaments are the **anterior** and **posterior longitudinal ligaments** (Figure 7.14). These run as continuous bands down the front and back surfaces of the spine from the neck to the sacrum. The broad anterior ligament is strongly attached to both the bony vertebrae and the discs. Along with its supporting role, it prevents hyperextension of the spine (bending too far backward). The posterior ligament, which resists hyperflexion of the spine (bending too sharply forward), is narrow and relatively weak. It attaches only to the discs. Short ligaments (ligamenta flava and others) connect each vertebra to those immediately above and below.

Intervertebral Discs

Each **intervertebral disc** is a cushionlike pad composed of an inner semifluid **nucleus pulposus** (pulpo′sus; "pulp"), which acts like a rubber ball to give the disc its elasticity and compressibility, and a strong outer ring of fibrocartilage, the **annulus fibrosus** (an′u-lus fi-bro′sus), which surrounds the nucleus pulposus and limits its expansion (see Figure 7.14b). The annulus fibrosus also holds together successive vertebrae. The discs act as shock absorbers during walking, jumping, and running, and they allow the spine to flex and extend, and to a lesser extent to bend laterally. At points of compression, the discs flatten and bulge out a bit from the intervertebral spaces. The discs are thickest in the lumbar and cervical regions, which enhances the flexibility of these regions. Collectively the discs account for about 25% of the length of the vertebral column.

Severe or sudden physical trauma to the spine—for example, from bending forward while lifting a heavy object—may result in herniation of one or more discs. A **herniated disc** (commonly called a *slipped disc*) usually involves rupture of the annulus fibrosus followed by protrusion of the spongy nucleus pulposus (see Figure 7.14c). If the protrusion presses on the spinal cord or on spinal nerves exiting from the cord, numbness, excruciating pain, or even destruction of these nervous system structures may result. Herniated discs are generally treated with bed rest, traction, and painkillers. If this fails, the protruding disc may have to be removed surgically. For those preferring to avoid surgery, a still-accepted last step in conservative (nonsurgical) therapy is to inject chymopapain to enzymatically digest the protruding portion of the disc. •

Divisions and Curvatures

The vertebral column is about 70 cm (28 inches) long in an average adult and has five major divisions (see Figure 7.13). The 7 vertebrae of the neck are the *cervical* (ser′vi-kal) *vertebrae,* the next 12 are the *thoracic* (tho-ras′ik) *vertebrae,* and the 5 supporting the lower back are the *lumbar* (lum′bar) *vertebrae.* (Remembering common meal times—7 AM, 12 noon, and 5 PM—may help you recall the number of bones in these three regions of the spine.) Inferior to the lumbar vertebrae is the *sacrum* (sa′krum), which articulates with the pelvis. The terminus of the vertebral column is the tiny *coccyx* (kok′siks). The number of cervical vertebrae is constant in all humans. Variations in the number of vertebrae in other regions occur in about 5% of people.

When you view the vertebral column from the side, you can see the four curvatures that give it its S, or springlike, shape. The **cervical** and **lumbar curvatures** are concave posteriorly; the **thoracic** and **sacral curvatures** are convex posteriorly. These curvatures increase the resilience and flexibility of the spine, making it function like a spring rather than a rigid rod.

There are several types of abnormal spinal curvatures. Some are congenital (present at birth); others result from disease, poor posture, or unequal muscle pull on the spine. *Scoliosis* (sko″le-o′sis), literally "twisted disease," is an abnormal *lateral* curvature that occurs most often in the thoracic region. It is quite common during late childhood, particularly in girls, for some unknown reason. The most severe cases result from abnormal vertebral structure, lower limbs of unequal length, or muscle paralysis. If muscles on one side of the body are nonfunctional, those of the opposite side exert an unopposed pull on the spine and force it out of alignment. Severe cases must be treated (with body braces or surgically) before growth ends if permanent deformity and breathing difficulties are to be avoided.

Kyphosis (ki-fo′sis), or hunchback, is a *dorsally* exaggerated *thoracic* curvature. It is particularly common in aged individuals because of osteoporosis, but may also reflect tuberculosis of the spine, rickets, or osteomalacia. *Lordosis,* or swayback, is an accentuated *lumbar* curvature. It, too, can result from spinal tuberculosis or rickets. Temporary lordosis is common in those carrying a "large load up front," such as men with "potbellies" and pregnant women, who automatically throw back their shoulders, accentuating their lumbar curvature, in an attempt to preserve their center of gravity. •

General Structure of Vertebrae

All vertebrae have a common structural pattern (Figure 7.15). Each vertebra consists of a discoid weight-bearing **body,** or **centrum,** anteriorly and a **vertebral arch** posteriorly. Together, the body and vertebral arch enclose an opening called the **vertebral foramen.** Successive vertebral foramina of the articulated vertebrae form the **vertebral canal,** through which the spinal cord passes.

The vertebral arch is a composite structure formed by two pedicles and two laminae. The **pedicles,** short bony cylinders projecting posteriorly from the vertebral body, form the sides of the vertebral arch. The **laminae** (lam′ĭ-ne) are flattened plates that fuse in the median plane, completing the arch posteriorly. Seven processes project from the vertebral

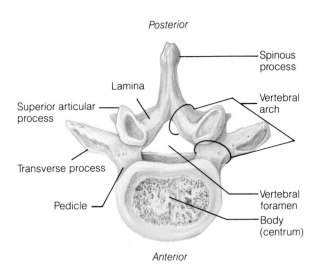

FIGURE 7.15
Structure of a typical vertebra. Superior view (inferior articulating surfaces not shown).

arch. The **spinous process** is a single midline posterior projection arising at the junction of the two laminae. The two **transverse processes** issue from the lateral aspects of the vertebral arch at the junctions of the pedicles and laminae. Both the spinous process and the transverse processes are attachment sites for muscles that move the vertebral column and for the ligaments that stabilize it. The **superior** and **inferior articular processes** are paired processes protruding upward and downward, respectively, from the pedicle-lamina junction on each side. The joint surfaces of the articular processes, called *facets* ("little faces"), are covered with hyaline cartilage. The inferior articular processes of each vertebra form movable joints with the superior articular processes of the vertebra immediately below. Thus, successive vertebrae join both at their bodies and at their articular processes.

The pedicles have notches on their superior and inferior borders, providing openings between adjacent vertebrae called **intervertebral foramina** (see Figure 7.13). The spinal nerves issuing from the spinal cord pass through these foramina.

Regional Vertebral Characteristics

In addition to the common structural features just described, vertebrae in the different regions of the spine have modifications that reflect their specific functions and movements allowed. The regional vertebral characteristics described in this section are illustrated and summarized in Table 7.2 on p. 199.

Cervical Vertebrae

The seven **cervical vertebrae,** identified as C_1–C_7, are the smallest, lightest vertebrae. The first two (C_1 and C_2) are atypical and we will skip them for the moment. The "typical" cervical vertebrae (C_3–C_7) have the following distinguishing features:

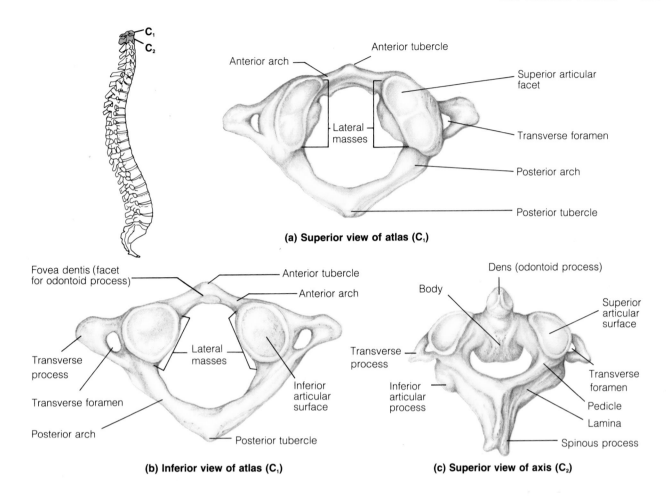

(a) Superior view of atlas (C₁)

(b) Inferior view of atlas (C₁)

(c) Superior view of axis (C₂)

FIGURE 7.16
The first and second cervical vertebrae.

1. The body is oval—broader from side to side than in the anteroposterior dimension.

2. Except in C_7, the spinous process is short, projects directly back, and is *bifid* (bi′fid), or split at its tip.

3. The vertebral foramen is large and generally triangular.

4. Each transverse process contains a **transverse foramen** through which the vertebral blood vessels pass to service the brain.

The spinous process of C_7 is not bifid and is much larger than those of the other cervical vertebrae (see Figure 7.17a). Because its spinous process is visible through the skin, C_7 can be used as a landmark for counting the vertebrae and is called the **vertebra prominens** ("prominent vertebra").

The first two cervical vertebrae, the atlas and the axis, have no intervertebral disc between them, and they are highly modified, reflecting their special functions. The **atlas** (C_1) has no body and no spinous process (Figure 7.16a and b). Essentially, it is a ring of bone consisting of *anterior* and *posterior arches* and a *lateral mass* on each side. Each lateral mass has articular surfaces on both its superior and inferior surfaces. The superior articular facets receive the occipital condyles of the skull; thus, they "carry" the skull, just as Atlas supported the heavens in Greek mythology. These joints allow you to nod "yes." The inferior articular surfaces form joints with the axis (C_2) below.

The **axis**, which has a body, spine, and the other typical vertebral processes, is not as specialized as the atlas. In fact, its only unusual feature is the knoblike **dens** (denz; "tooth"), or **odontoid** (o-don′-toid) **process,** projecting superiorly from its body. The dens is actually the "missing" body of the atlas, which fuses with the axis during embryonic development. Cradled in the anterior arch of the atlas by the transverse ligaments (see Figure 7.17a), the dens acts as a pivot for the rotation of the atlas. Hence, this joint allows you to rotate your head from side to side to indicate "no."

In rare cases of severe head trauma in which the skull is driven inferiorly toward the spine, the dens may be forced into the brain stem, causing death. This is the most serious potential consequence of automobile accidents in which the superior aspect of the skull is hit head-on. •

(a) Cervical vertebrae

- Dens of axis
- Transverse ligament of atlas
- C_1 (atlas)
- C_2 (axis)
- C_3
- Inferior articular process
- Bifid spinous process
- Transverse processes
- C_7 (vertebra prominens)

(b) Thoracic vertebrae

- Transverse process
- Lamina
- Spinous process
- Superior articular process
- Articular facet for tubercle of rib
- Body
- Intervertebral disc
- Pedicle
- Demifacet for head of rib
- Inferior articular process

(c) Lumbar vertebrae

- Superior articular process
- Transverse process
- Spinous process
- Body
- Pedicle
- Intervertebral disc
- Inferior articular processes

FIGURE 7.17
Posterolateral views of articulated vertebrae. Notice the bulbous tip on the spinous process of C_7, the vertebra prominens.

Thoracic Vertebrae

The 12 **thoracic vertebrae** (T_1–T_{12}) all articulate with the ribs (see Table 7.2 and Figure 7.17b). However, the first looks much like C_7, and the last four show a progression toward lumbar vertebral structure. The thoracic vertebrae increase in size from the first to the last. Unique characteristics of these vertebrae include the following:

1. The body is roughly heart shaped. It typically bears two *facets*, or more typically, *demifacets* (half-facets), on each side, one at the superior edge and the other at the inferior edge. The demifacets receive the heads of the ribs. (However, the bodies of T_{10}–T_{12} vary from this pattern by having only a single demifacet for their respective ribs.)

2. The vertebral foramen is circular.

3. The spinous process is long and points sharply inferiorly.

4. With the exception of T_{11} and T_{12}, the transverse processes have facets that articulate with the *tubercles* of the ribs.

Lumbar Vertebrae

The lumbar region of the vertebral column, commonly called the small of the back, receives the most stress. The enhanced weight-bearing function of the five **lumbar vertebrae** (L_1–L_5) is reflected in their sturdier structure. Their bodies are massive and kid-

Table 7.2 Regional Characteristics of Cervical, Thoracic, and Lumbar Vertebrae

Characteristic	Cervical (3–7)	Thoracic	Lumbar
Body	Small, wide side to side	Larger than cervical; heart shaped; bears two costal demifacets	Massive; kidney shaped
Spinous process	Short; bifid; projects directly posteriorly	Long; sharp; projects inferiorly	Short; blunt; projects directly posteriorly
Vertebral foramen	Triangular	Circular	Triangular
Transverse processes	Contain foramina	Bear facets for ribs (except T_{11} and T_{12})	No special features
Superior and inferior articulating processes	Superior facets directed superoposteriorly	Superior facets directed posteriorly	Superior facets directed posteromedially (or medially)
	Inferior facets directed inferoanteriorly	Inferior facets directed anteriorly	Inferior facets directed anterolaterally (or laterally)
Movements allowed	Flexion and extension of spine; lateral flexion; rotation	Rotation; some lateral flexion	Flexion and extension; some lateral flexion
Superior view			
Right lateral view			

ney shaped (see Table 7.2 and Figure 7.17c). Other characteristics typical of these vertebrae include the following:

1. The pedicles and laminae are shorter and thicker than those of other vertebrae.

2. The spinous processes are short, flat, and hatchet shaped and are easily seen when a person bends forward. They project directly backward, an

adaptation for the attachment of the large back muscles.

3. The vertebral foramen is triangular.

4. The orientation of the facets of the articular processes of the lumbar vertebrae differs substantially from that of the other vertebra types (see Table 7.2). These modifications lock the lumbar vertebrae together and provide stability by preventing rotation of the lumbar spine.

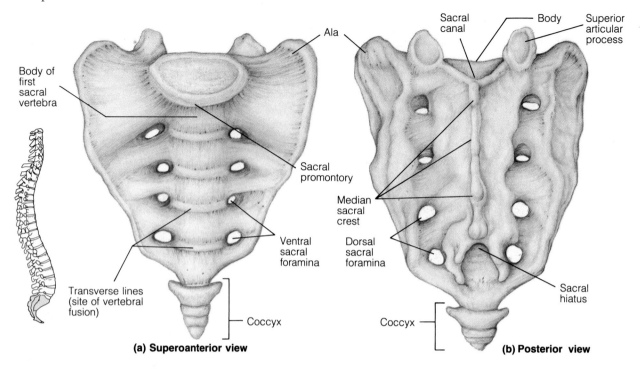

(a) Superoanterior view

(b) Posterior view

FIGURE 7.18
The sacrum and coccyx.

Sacrum

The triangular **sacrum** (Figure 7.18), which shapes the posterior wall of the pelvis, is formed by five fused vertebrae (S_1–S_5) in adults. It strengthens and stabilizes the pelvis. It articulates superiorly (via its **superior articular processes**) with L_5 and inferiorly with the coccyx. Laterally, the sacrum's two winglike **alae** (fused remnants of the transverse processes of S_1–S_5) articulate with the two hip bones to form the **sacroiliac** (sa″kro-il′e-ak) **joints** of the pelvis.

The **sacral promontory** (prom′on-tor″e), the anterosuperior margin of the first sacral vertebra, bulges forward into the pelvic cavity. The body's center of gravity lies about 1 cm posterior to this marking and, as you will see, the sacral promontory is an important anatomical landmark for obstetricians. Four ridges, the **transverse lines** of vertebral fusion, cross its concave anterior aspect, and **sacral foramina** penetrate the sacrum at the lateral ends of these ridges. The sacral foramina transmit blood vessels and nerves.

Dorsally, the median sacral surface is roughened by the **median sacral crest** (the fused spinous processes of the sacral vertebrae). The vertebral canal continues inside the sacrum as the **sacral canal.** Since the laminae of the fifth (and sometimes the fourth) sacral vertebrae fail to fuse medially, an enlarged external opening called the **sacral hiatus** (hi-a′tus; "gap") is obvious at the inferior end of the sacral canal.

Coccyx

The **coccyx,** our vestigial tailbone, is a small triangular bone (see Figure 7.18). It consists of four (or in some cases three or five) vertebrae fused together. The coccyx articulates superiorly with the sacrum. (The name *coccyx* comes from the Greek word meaning "cuckoo" and was so named because of its fancied resemblance to a bird's beak.) Except for the slight support the coccyx affords the pelvic organs, it is a nearly useless bone. Occasionally, a baby is born with an unusually long coccyx. In many such cases, this extraneous bony "tail" is discreetly snipped off by the physician.

THE BONY THORAX

Anatomically, the thorax is the chest, and its bony "underpinnings" are called the **bony thorax** or **thoracic cage.** Elements forming the bony thorax include the thoracic vertebrae dorsally, the ribs laterally, and the sternum and costal cartilages anteriorly. The costal cartilages secure the ribs to the sternum (Figure 7.19a). Basically a cone with its broad dimension inferiorly, the bony thorax forms a protective cage around the vital organs of the thoracic cavity (heart, lungs, and great blood vessels), supports the shoulder girdles and upper limbs, and provides attachment points for the muscles of the back, chest, and shoulders. In addition, the *intercostal spaces* between the

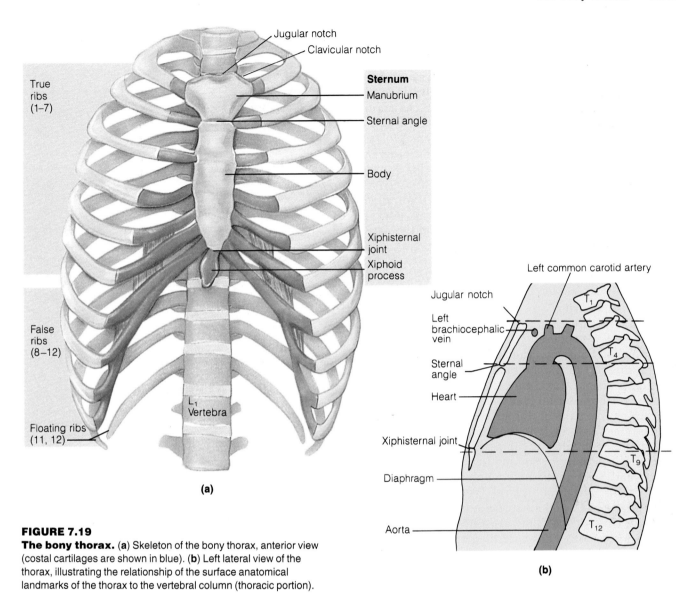

FIGURE 7.19
The bony thorax. (a) Skeleton of the bony thorax, anterior view
(costal cartilages are shown in blue). **(b)** Left lateral view of the
thorax, illustrating the relationship of the surface anatomical
landmarks of the thorax to the vertebral column (thoracic portion).

ribs are occupied by the intercostal muscles, which
lift and depress the thorax during breathing.

Sternum

The **sternum** (breastbone) lies in the anterior midline
of the thorax. Vaguely resembling a dagger, it is a flat
bone approximately 15 cm (6 inches) long. It results
from the fusion of three bones: the manubrium, the
body, and the xiphoid process. The **manubrium**
(mah-nu′bre-um), the superior portion, is shaped like
the knot in a necktie. It articulates via its **clavicular**
(klah-vik′u-lar) **notches** with the clavicles (collarbones) laterally; it also articulates with the first two
pairs of ribs. The **body,** or midportion, forms the bulk
of the sternum. The sides of the body are notched
where it articulates with the cartilages of the second
to seventh ribs. The **xiphoid** (zif′oid; "swordlike")

process forms the inferior end of the sternum. This
small, variably shaped process is a plate of hyaline
cartilage in youth, but it is usually ossified in adults.
The xiphoid process articulates only with the sternal
body and serves as an attachment point for the
diaphragm and some abdominal muscles.

In some people, the xiphoid process projects dorsally. This may present a problem because blows
to the chest can push such a xiphoid into the heart or
liver (both immediately deep to the xiphoid process),
causing massive hemorrhage. •

The sternum has three important anatomical
landmarks: the jugular notch, the sternal angle, and
the xiphisternal joint (see Figure 7.19). The easily palpated **jugular (suprasternal) notch** is visible as a
central indentation in the upper border of the
manubrium. It is generally in line with the disc
between the second and third thoracic vertebrae and

the point where the left common carotid artery issues from the aorta (see Figure 7.19b). The manubrium joins the sternal body at a cartilaginous joint that acts like a hinge, allowing the sternal body to swing forward when we inhale. The sternum is slightly angled at this joint, and this **sternal angle** can be felt as a horizontal ridge (or as a depression) across the front of the sternum. The sternal angle lies at the same level as the disc between the fourth and fifth thoracic vertebrae and at the level of the second pair of ribs. It provides a handy reference point for finding the second rib and thus for counting the ribs during a physical examination. The **xiphisternal** (zif″ĭ-ster′nul) **joint** is the point where the sternal body and xiphoid process fuse. It lies opposite the ninth thoracic vertebra.

Ribs

Twelve pairs of **ribs** form the flaring sides of the thoracic cage (Figure 7.19a). All ribs attach posteriorly to the thoracic vertebrae and curve inferiorly toward the anterior body surface. The superior seven rib pairs attach directly to the sternum by individual costal cartilages (bars of hyaline cartilage). These are the **true** or **vertebrosternal** (ver″tĕ-bro-ster′nal) **ribs.** The remaining five pairs of ribs are called **false ribs;** they either attach indirectly to the sternum or lack a sternal attachment entirely. Rib pairs 8–10 attach to the sternum indirectly by joining to each other via the costal cartilages immediately above; these ribs are also called **vertebrochondral** (ver″tĕ-bro-kon′dral) **ribs.** Rib pairs 11 and 12 are called **vertebral ribs** or **floating ribs** because they have no anterior attachments. Instead, their costal cartilages lie embedded in the muscles of the lateral body wall. The ribs increase in length from the first to the seventh pairs, then decrease in length from pair 8 to pair 12.

A typical rib is a bowed flat bone (Figure 7.20). The bulk of a rib is simply called the *shaft.* Its superior border is smooth, but its interior border is sharp and thin and has a *costal groove* on its inner face that lodges the intercostal nerves and blood vessels. In addition to the shaft, each rib has a head, neck, and tubercle. The wedge-shaped *head,* the posteriormost end, has two facets: One articulates with the demifacet on the body of the same-numbered thoracic vertebra, the other with that on the body of the vertebra immediately superior. The *neck* is the constricted portion of the rib beyond the head. Lateral to this, the knoblike *tubercle* articulates with the transverse process of the same-numbered thoracic vertebra. Beyond the tubercle, the shaft angles sharply forward (at the angle of the rib) and then extends to attach to its costal cartilage anteriorly. The costal cartilages provide secure but flexible rib attachments to the sternum.

The first pair of ribs is quite atypical. They are flattened superiorly to inferiorly and are quite broad. There are also other exceptions to the typical rib pattern. Ribs 1 and 10–12 articulate with only one verte-

(a)

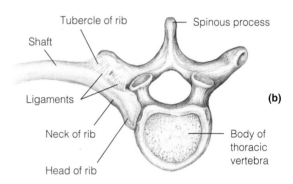

(b)

FIGURE 7.20
Structure of a "typical" true rib and its articulations.
(**a**) Vertebral and sternal articulations of a typical true rib. (**b**) Superior view of the articulation between a rib and a thoracic vertebra.

bral body, and ribs 11 and 12 do not articulate with transverse processes of the corresponding vertebrae. Except for the first rib, which lies deep to the clavicle, the ribs are easily felt in people of normal weight.

PART 2: THE APPENDICULAR SKELETON

Bones of the limbs and their girdles are collectively called the **appendicular skeleton,** because they are *appended to* the axial skeleton that forms the longitudinal axis of the body (see Figure 7.1). The yokelike *pectoral* (pek′tor-al; "chest") *girdles* attach the upper limbs to the body trunk. The more sturdy *pelvic girdle* secures the lower limbs. Although the bones of the upper and lower limbs differ in their functions and mobility, they have the same fundamental plan: Each limb is composed of three major segments connected together by movable joints.

Whereas the axial skeleton provides the central (axial) support for the body and protects internal organs, the appendicular skeleton enables us to carry out the movements typical of our freewheeling and manipulative life-style. Each time we take a step, throw a ball, or pop a caramel into our mouth, we are making good use of our appendicular skeleton.

THE PECTORAL (SHOULDER) GIRDLE

The **pectoral,** or **shoulder, girdle** consists of two bones, the anterior *clavicle* (klav′ĭ-kl) and the posterior *scapula* (skap′u-lah) (Figure 7.21 and Table 7.4 on p. 216). The paired pectoral girdles and their associated muscles form your shoulders. Although the term *girdle* usually signifies a beltlike structure encircling the body, a single pectoral girdle, or even the pair, does not quite satisfy this description. Anteriorly, the medial end of each clavicle joins the sternum; the distal ends of the clavicles meet the scapulae laterally. However, the scapulae fail to complete the ring posteriorly, because their medial borders do not join each other or the axial skeleton. Instead, the scapulae are attached to the thorax and vertebral column only by the muscles that clothe their surfaces.

The pectoral girdles attach the upper limbs to the axial skeleton and provide attachment points for many of the muscles that move the upper limbs. These girdles are very light and allow the upper limbs a degree of flexibility and mobility not seen anywhere else in the body. This is due to the following factors:

1. Since only the clavicle attaches to the axial skeleton, the scapula can move quite freely across the thorax, allowing the arm to move with it.

2. The socket of the shoulder joint (the scapula's glenoid cavity) is shallow and poorly reinforced, so it does not restrict the movement of the humerus (arm bone). Although this arrangement is good for flexibility, it is bad for stability: Shoulder dislocations are fairly common.

Clavicles

The **clavicles,** or collarbones, are slender, doubly curved long bones that can be felt along their entire course as they extend horizontally across the superior thorax (Figure 7.21a–c). Each clavicle is cone shaped at its medial **sternal end,** which attaches to the sternal manubrium, and flattened at its lateral **acromial** (ah-kro′me-al) **end,** where it articulates with the acromion of the scapula. The medial two-thirds of the clavicle is convex anteriorly; its lateral third is concave anteriorly. Its superior surface is smooth, but its inferior surface is ridged and grooved.

Besides providing attachment points for many thoracic and shoulder muscles, the clavicles act as anterior braces: They hold the scapulae and the upper limbs laterally away from the narrower superior part of the thorax. This bracing function becomes immediately obvious when a clavicle is fractured: The entire shoulder region collapses medially. The clavicles also transmit compression forces from the upper limbs to the axial skeleton. However, they are not very strong and are likely to fracture, for example, when a person uses outstretched arms to break a fall. The way the clavicle is curved ensures that it will fracture anteriorly (outward) rather than collapse posteriorly (inward), which would damage the subclavian artery that serves the upper limb. The clavicles are exceptionally sensitive to muscle pull and become noticeably larger and stronger in those who perform manual labor involving the shoulder and arm muscles.

Scapulae

The **scapulae,** or *shoulder blades,* are thin, triangular flat bones (Figure 7.21d–f). Interestingly, their name derives from a word meaning "spade" or "shovel," for ancient cultures made spades from the shoulder blades of animals. The scapulae lie on the dorsal surface of the rib cage, between ribs 2 and 7. Each scapula has three borders. The *superior border* is the shortest, sharpest border. The *medial,* or *vertebral, border* parallels the vertebral column. The *lateral,* or *axillary, border* abuts the armpit and has a small, shallow fossa, the **glenoid** (gle′noid) **cavity.** The glenoid cavity articulates with the humerus of the arm, forming the relatively unstable shoulder joint. Like all triangles, the scapula has three *angles.* The superior scapular border meets the medial border at the *superior angle* and the lateral border at the *lateral angle.* The medial and lateral borders join at the *inferior angle.* The inferior angle moves extensively as the arm is raised and lowered, and is an important landmark for studying scapular movements.

The anterior, or costal, surface of the scapula is concave and relatively featureless. Its posterior surface bears a sharp, prominent **spine** that is easily felt through the skin. The spine ends laterally in an enlarged, roughened anterior projection called the **acromion** (ah-kro′me-on), which forms the "point of the shoulder." The acromion articulates with the acromial end of the clavicle, forming the **acromioclavicular joint.** Each acromioclavicular joint is only about the size of a big toe joint. Projecting anteriorly from the superior scapular border is the **coracoid** (kor′ah-coid) **process;** *corac* means "beaklike," but the coracoid process looks more like a bent little finger. The coracoid process helps to anchor the biceps muscle of the arm. It is bounded by the **suprascapular notch** (a nerve passage) medially and by the glenoid fossa laterally.

Several large but shallow depressions, or fossae, appear on both sides of the scapula. These fossae are

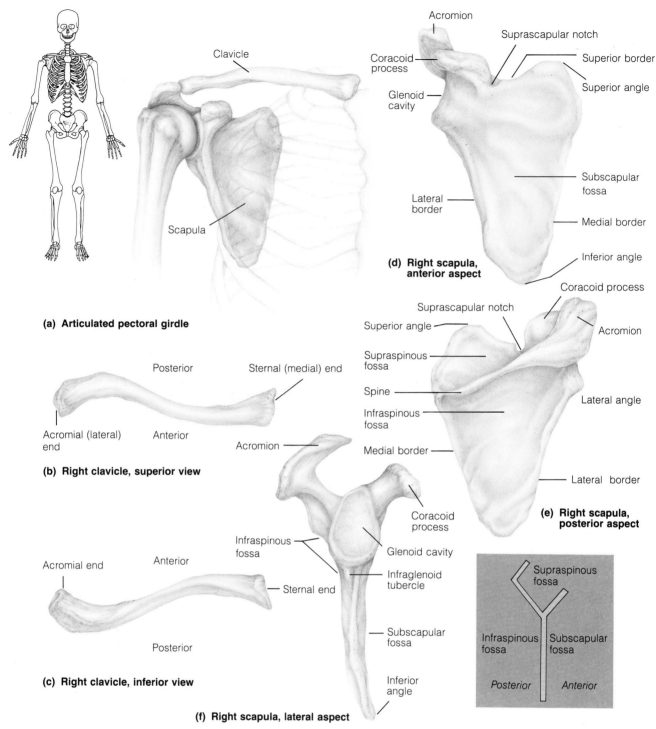

(a) **Articulated pectoral girdle**

(b) **Right clavicle, superior view**

Posterior

Sternal (medial) end

Acromial (lateral) end

Anterior

(c) **Right clavicle, inferior view**

Acromial end

Anterior

Sternal end

Posterior

(d) **Right scapula, anterior aspect**

Acromion

Coracoid process

Glenoid cavity

Lateral border

Suprascapular notch

Superior border

Superior angle

Subscapular fossa

Medial border

Inferior angle

(e) **Right scapula, posterior aspect**

Coracoid process

Suprascapular notch

Superior angle

Supraspinous fossa

Spine

Infraspinous fossa

Medial border

Acromion

Lateral angle

Lateral border

(f) **Right scapula, lateral aspect**

Acromion

Infraspinous fossa

Coracoid process

Glenoid cavity

Infraglenoid tubercle

Subscapular fossa

Inferior angle

Supraspinous fossa

Infraspinous fossa

Subscapular fossa

Posterior

Anterior

FIGURE 7.21
Bones of the pectoral girdle. View (f) is accompanied by a schematic representation of its orientation.

named according to location. For example, the **infra-spinous** and **supraspinous fossae** are respectively below and above the spine, and the **subscapular fossa** is the concavity of the entire anterior scapular surface.

THE UPPER LIMB

Thirty separate bones form the skeletal framework of each upper limb (see Figures 7.22 to 7.24, and Table 7.4 on p. 216). Each of these bones may be described regionally as a bone of the arm, forearm, or hand.

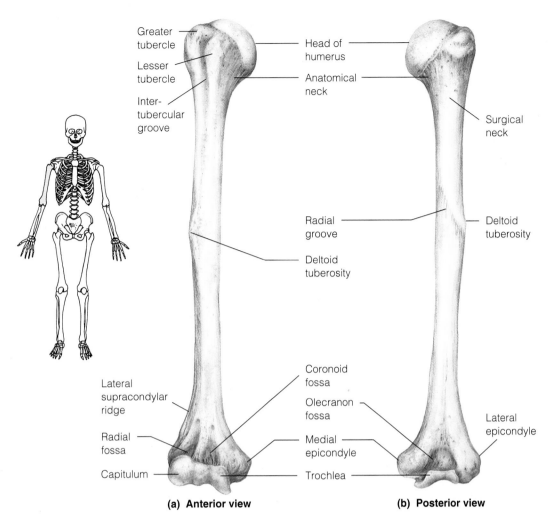

Greater
tubercle

Lesser
tubercle

Inter-
tubercular
groove

Head of
humerus

Anatomical
neck

Surgical
neck

Radial
groove

Deltoid
tuberosity

Deltoid
tuberosity

Lateral
supracondylar
ridge

Radial
fossa

Capitulum

Coronoid
fossa

Olecranon
fossa

Medial
epicondyle

Trochlea

Lateral
epicondyle

(a) Anterior view   **(b) Posterior view**

FIGURE 7.22
The humerus of the arm. (**a**) Anterior view of the right humerus. (**b**) Posterior view of the right humerus.

(Recall that anatomically the "arm" is only that part of the upper limb between the shoulder and elbow.)

Arm

The **humerus** (hu'mer-us), the sole bone of the arm, is a typical long bone (Figure 7.22). The largest, longest bone of the upper limb, it articulates with the scapula at the shoulder and with the radius and ulna (forearm bones) at the elbow.

At the proximal end of the humerus is its smooth, hemispherical **head,** which fits into the glenoid cavity of the scapula in a manner that allows the arm to hang freely at one's side. Immediately below the head is a slight constriction, the **anatomical neck.** Just inferior to the anatomical neck are the lateral **greater tubercle** and medial **lesser tubercle,** separated by the **intertubercular,** or **bicipital** (bi-sip'ĭ-tal), **groove.** The tubercles serve as muscle attachment points; the intertubercular groove guides a tendon of the biceps

muscle of the arm to its attachment point at the rim of the glenoid cavity. Just distal to the tubercles is the **surgical neck,** so named because it is the most frequently fractured part of the humerus. About midway down the shaft on its lateral side is the **deltoid tuberosity,** the roughened V-shaped attachment site of the fleshy deltoid muscle of the shoulder. A **radial groove** runs obliquely down the posterior aspect of the shaft, marking the course of the radial nerve, an important nerve of the upper limb.

At the distal end of the humerus are two condyles, a medial pulley-shaped **trochlea** (trok'le-ah) and a lateral ball-like **capitulum** (kah-pit'u-lum), which articulate with the ulna and radius, respectively. The condyle pair is flanked by the **medial** and **lateral epicondyles.** The ulnar nerve runs behind the medial epicondyle and is responsible for the painful, tingling sensation you experience when you hit your "funny bone." Superior to the trochlea on the anterior surface is the **coronoid fossa;** on the posterior surface

What bone markings would you examine to determine whether you were looking at a right or left ulna?

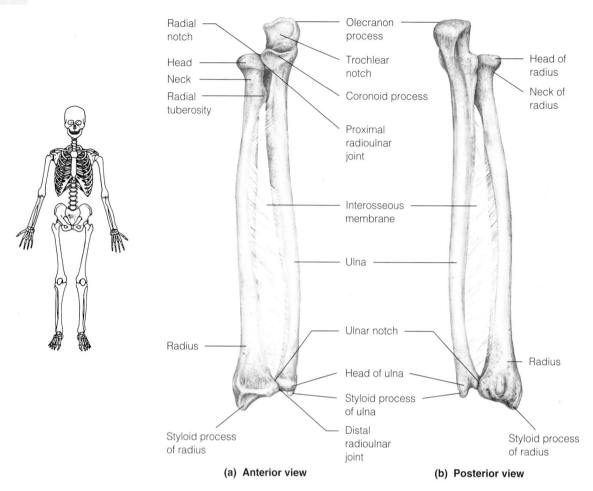

(a) Anterior view   **(b) Posterior view**

FIGURE 7.23
Bones of the forearm. (a) Anterior view of the radius and ulna of the right forearm, anatomical position. Interosseous membrane also shown. (b) Posterior view of the radius and ulna of the right forearm.

is the deeper **olecranon** (o-lek′rah-non) **fossa.** These two depressions allow the corresponding processes of the ulna to move freely when the elbow is flexed and extended. A small **radial fossa,** lateral to the coronoid fossa, receives the head of the radius when the elbow is flexed.

Forearm

Two parallel long bones, the radius and the ulna, form the skeleton of the forearm, or *antebrachium* (an″te-bra′ke-um) (Figure 7.23). Unless a person's forearm muscles are very bulky, these bones are easily palpated along their entire length. Their proximal ends articulate with the humerus; their distal ends form joints with bones of the wrist. The radius and ulna articulate with each other both proximally and distally at small **radioulnar** (ra″de-o-ul′nar) **joints,** and they are connected along their entire length by a flexible **interosseous** (in″ter-os′e-us) **membrane.** In

the anatomical position, the radius lies laterally (on the thumb side) and the ulna medially. However, when you rotate your forearm so that the palm faces posteriorly (a movement called pronation), the distal end of the radius crosses over the ulna and the two bones form an X (see Figure 8.7a, p. 233).

Ulna

The **ulna** (ul′nah; "elbow") is slightly longer than the radius. It has the main responsibility for forming the elbow joint with the humerus. Its proximal end looks like the "business end" of a monkey wrench; it bears two prominent processes, the **olecranon** (elbow) and **coronoid processes,** separated by a deep concavity, the **trochlear notch** (see Figure 7.23). Together, these two processes grip the trochlea of the humerus, forming a stable hinge joint that allows the forearm to be bent upon the arm (flexed) or extended. When the arm is fully extended, the olecranon process "locks"

FIGURE 7.24
Bones of the hand. (a) Ventral view of the right hand, illustrating the anatomical relationships
of the carpals, metacarpals, and phalanges. (b) X ray of the right hand. Notice the white bar on
the proximal phalanx of finger 4, showing the position at which a ring would be worn.

into the olecranon fossa, keeping the forearm from
hyperextending (moving posteriorly beyond the
elbow joint). The posterior olecranon process forms
the angle of the elbow when the forearm is flexed and
is the bony part that rests on the table when you lean
on your elbows. Laterally on the coronoid process is a
small depression, the **radial notch,** which articulates
with the head of the radius.

The ulnar shaft narrows as it runs distally to its
knoblike **head.** Medial to the head is a **styloid
process,** from which a ligament extends to the wrist.
Laterally, the head articulates with the radius at the
distal radioulnar joint. The ulnar head is separated
from the bones of the wrist by a disc of fibrocartilage
and plays little or no role in hand movements.

Radius

The **radius** ("rod") is thin at its proximal end and
widened distally—the opposite of the ulna. The **head**
of the radius is shaped like the head of a nail (see Figure 7.23). The superior concave surface of the head
articulates with the capitulum of the humerus. Medially, the head articulates with the radial notch of the

ulna. Just inferior to the head is a rough projection,
the **radial tuberosity,** which anchors the biceps muscle of the arm. Distally, where the radius is expanded,
it has a medial **ulnar notch,** which articulates with
the ulna, and a lateral **styloid process** (an anchoring
site for ligaments that run to the hand). Between these
two markings, the radius is concave where it articulates with carpal bones of the wrist. While the ulna
contributes more heavily than the radius to the elbow
joint, the radius is the major forearm bone contributing to the wrist joint. When the radius moves, the
hand moves with it.

Hand

The skeleton of the hand (Figure 7.24) includes the
bones of the carpus (wrist); the bones of the metacar-
pus (palm); and the phalanges (bones of the fingers).

Carpus (Wrist)

A "wrist" watch is actually worn on the distal forearm (over the lower ends of the radius and ulna), not
on the "wrist" at all. The true wrist, or **carpus,** is the

proximal portion of the structure we generally call our "hand." The carpus consists of a group of eight marble-size short bones, or **carpals** (kar′palz), closely united by ligaments. Because gliding movements occur between these bones, the carpus as a whole is quite flexible. The carpals are arranged in two irregular rows of four bones each (Figure 7.24). In the proximal row (lateral to medial) are the **scaphoid** (skaf′oid), **lunate** (lu′nāt), **triquetral** (tri-kwe′trul), and **pisiform** (pi′sĭ-form). Only the scaphoid and lunate articulate with the radius to form the wrist joint. The carpals of the distal row (lateral to medial) are the **trapezium** (trah-pe′ze-um), **trapezoid** (tra′-peh-zoid), **capitate,** and **hamate** (ham′āt). There are numerous memory-jogging phrases to help you recall the carpals in the order given above. If you don't have one, try: **S**ally **l**eft **t**he **p**arty **t**o **t**ake **C**athy **h**ome. As with all such devices, the first letter of each word is the first letter of the term you need to remember.

The carpus is concave anteriorly and a ligament spans this concavity, forming the notorious *carpal tunnel.* Besides the median nerve (which supplies the lateral side of the hand), several long muscle tendons crowd into this tunnel. Overuse and inflammation of the tendons cause them to swell, compressing the median nerve, which causes numbness of the areas served. Those who work at computer keyboards all day are particularly susceptible to this nerve impairment, called *carpal tunnel syndrome.* •

Metacarpus (Palm)

Five **metacarpal bones** radiate from the wrist like spokes to form the palm of the hand (see Figure 7.24). These small long bones are not named, but instead are numbered 1 to 5 from thumb to little finger. The **bases** of the metacarpals articulate with the carpals proximally and each other laterally; their bulbous **heads** articulate with the proximal phalanges of the fingers. When you clench your fist, the heads of the metacarpals become prominent as your *knuckles.* Metacarpal 1, associated with the thumb, is the shortest and most mobile. It occupies a more anterior position than the other metacarpals. Consequently, the joint between metacarpal 1 and the trapezium is a unique saddle joint that allows *opposition,* the action of touching your thumb to the tips of your other fingers.

Phalanges (Fingers)

The **fingers,** or **digits** of the upper limb, are numbered 1 to 5 beginning with the thumb, or **pollex** (pol′eks). In most people, the third finger is the longest. Each hand contains 14 miniature long bones called **phalanges** (fah-lan′jēz). Except for the thumb, each finger has three phalanges: *distal, middle,* and *proximal.* The thumb has no middle phalanx. (Phalanx [fa′langks] is the singular term for phalanges.)

THE PELVIC (HIP) GIRDLE

The **pelvic girdle,** or **hip girdle,** attaches the lower limbs to the axial skeleton, transmits the weight of the upper body to the lower limbs, and supports the visceral organs of the pelvis (Figure 7.25 and Table 7.4). While the pectoral girdle moves somewhat freely across the thorax and allows the upper limb a high degree of mobility, the pelvic girdle is secured to the axial skeleton by some of the strongest ligaments in the body, and its sockets, which articulate with the thigh bones, are deep and cuplike and heavily reinforced by ligaments. Thus, even though both the shoulder and hip joints are ball-and-socket joints, very few of us can wheel our legs and arms about with the same degree of freedom.

The pelvic girdle is formed by a pair of **coxal** (*coxa* = hip) **bones** (Figure 7.25), each also called an **os coxae** (ahs kok′se), or **hip bone.** Each coxal bone unites with its partner anteriorly and with the sacrum posteriorly. The deep, basinlike structure formed by the coxal bones, together with the sacrum and coccyx, is called the **bony pelvis.**

Each large, irregularly shaped coxal bone consists of three separate bones during childhood: the ilium, ischium, and pubis. In adults, these bones are firmly fused and their boundaries are indistinguishable. Their names are retained, however, to refer to different regions of the composite coxal bone. At the point of fusion of the ilium, ischium, and pubis is a deep hemispherical socket called the **acetabulum** (as″ĕ-tab′u-lum; "vinegar cup") on the lateral surface of the pelvis (see Figure 7.25b). The acetabulum articulates with the head of the femur, or thigh bone, at this *hip joint.*

Ilium

The **ilium** (il′e-um; "flank") is a large flaring bone that forms the major portion of a coxal bone. It consists of a **body** and a superior winglike portion called the **ala** (a′lah). When you rest your hands on your hips, you are resting them on the thickened superior margins of the alae, the **iliac crests.** Each iliac crest terminates anterosuperiorly in the blunt **anterior superior iliac spine** and posterosuperiorly in the sharp **posterior superior iliac spine.** Located below these are the less prominent **anterior** and **posterior inferior iliac spines.** All of these spines are attachment points for the muscles of the trunk, hip, and thigh. The anterior superior iliac spine is an especially important anatomical landmark; it is easily felt through the skin and may be visible (Figure 7.26a). The posterior superior iliac spine is difficult to palpate, but its position is revealed by a skin dimple in the sacral region (Figure 7.26b). Just inferior to the posterior inferior iliac spine, the ilium indents deeply to form the **greater sciatic** (si-at′ik) **notch,** through which the thick cordlike sciatic nerve passes to enter the thigh. The broad posterolateral surface of the ilium, the **gluteal**

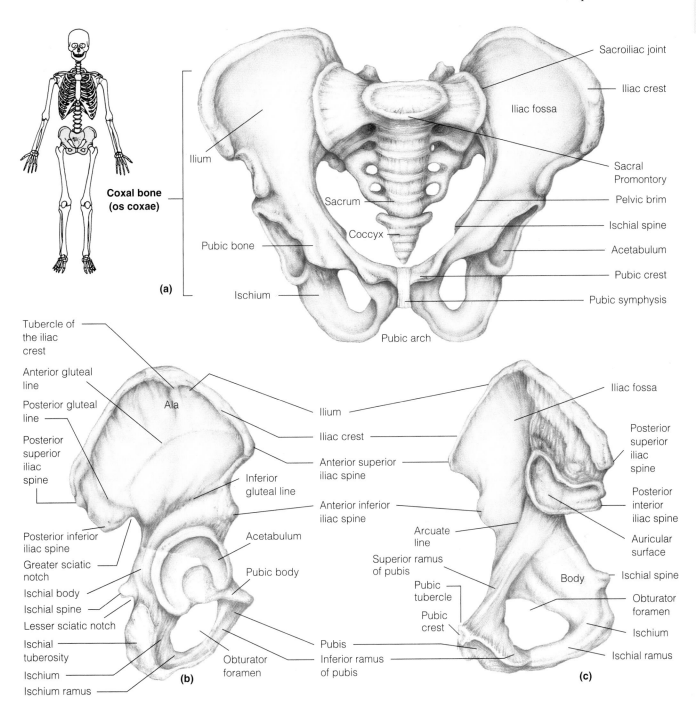

FIGURE 7.25
Bones of the pelvic girdle. (**a**) Articulated pelvis showing the
two coxal bones and the sacrum. (**b**) Lateral view of right coxal bone
showing the point of fusion of the ilium (gold), ischium (blue), and
pubic (pink) bones at the acetabulum. (**c**) Right os coxae, medial
view.

(gloo′te-al) **surface,** is crossed by three ridges, the
posterior, anterior, and **inferior gluteal lines,** to
which the gluteal (buttock) muscles attach.

The medial surface of the iliac ala is slightly concave, and this concavity is referred to as the **iliac
fossa.** Its posteriormost region, the roughened **auricu-**

lar (aw-rik′u-lar; "ear-shaped") **surface,** articulates
with the sacrum, forming the *sacroiliac joint.* The
weight of the body is transmitted from the spine to the
pelvis through the sacroiliac joints. Running inferiorly and anteriorly from the auricular surface is a
prominent ridge called the **arcuate** (ar′ku-at) **line.**

(a)

(b)

FIGURE 7.26
Surface anatomy of the pelvis. (a) Anterior view; the protrusion created by the left anterior superior iliac spine is indicated by the black arrow. **(b)** Posterior view illustrating the position of the posterior superior iliac spines. The attachment of the deep fascia to the posterior spines creates skin dimples at the level of the second sacral vertebra (see black arrows).

Together with the sacral promontory, the arcuate line defines the **pelvic brim.** The pelvic brim is the superior margin of the *true pelvis,* which we will discuss shortly. Anteriorly, the body of the ilium joins the ischium and pubic bones.

Ischium

The **ischium** (is'ke-um; "hip") forms the posteroinferior part of the hip bone (see Figure 7.25). Roughly L- or arc-shaped, it has a thicker, superior **body** adjoining the ilium and a thinner, inferior **ramus** (*ramus =* branch). The ramus joins the pubis anteriorly. Three important markings on the ischium are the ischial spine, the lesser sciatic notch, and the ischial tuberosity. The **ischial spine** projects medially into the pelvic cavity and serves as a point of attachment of a major (*sacrospinous*) ligament. Just inferior to the ischial spine is the **lesser sciatic notch.** A number of nerves and blood vessels pass through this notch to the perineum (anogenital area). The inferior surface of the ischial body is rough and grossly thickened as the **ischial tuberosity** (see Figure 7.25b). When we sit, our weight is borne entirely by the ischial tuberosities, which are the strongest parts of the hip bones. A massive ligament runs from the sacrum to each ischial tuberosity. This sacrotuberous ligament (not illustrated) helps hold the pelvis together.

Pubis

The **pubis** (pu'bis), or **pubic bone,** forms the anterior portion of the os coxa (see Figure 7.25). In the anatomical position, it lies nearly horizontally and the bladder rests upon it. Essentially, the pubis is V-shaped with **superior** and **inferior rami** issuing from a flattened medial **body.** The body of the pubis lies medially and its anterior border is thickened to form a **pubic crest.** At the lateral end of the pubic crest is the **pubic tubercle,** one of the attachments for the inguinal ligament. As the two rami of the pubic bone run laterally to join with the body and ramus of the ischium, they define a large opening in the os coxa, the **obturator** (ob"tu-ra'tor) **foramen,** through which a few blood vessels and nerves pass. Although the obturator foramen is large, it is nearly closed by a fibrous membrane in life (*obturator =* closed up).

The bodies of the two pubic bones are joined by a fibrocartilage disc, forming the midline **pubic symphysis** joint. Inferior to this joint, the inferior pubic rami angle laterally, forming an inverted V-shaped arch called the **pubic arch** (Figure 7.25). The acuteness of the pubic arch helps to differentiate the male from the female pelvis (Table 7.3).

Pelvic Structure and Childbearing

So striking are the differences between the male and female pelves that a trained anatomist can immediately determine the sex of a skeleton from a casual examination of the pelvis. The female pelvis reflects modifications for childbearing: It tends to be wider, shallower, lighter, and rounder than that of a male. Not only must the female pelvis accommodate a growing fetus, but it must be large enough to allow the infant's relatively large head to exit at birth. The major differences between the "typical" male and female pelves are summarized and illustrated in Table 7.3.

The pelvis is said to have a false (greater) pelvis and a true (lesser) pelvis. The **false pelvis** is that portion superior to the pelvic brim; it is bounded by the

Table 7.3 Comparison of the Female and Male Pelves

Characteristic	Female	Male
General structure and functional modifications	Tilted forward; adapted for childbearing; true pelvis defines the birth canal; cavity of the true pelvis is broad, shallow, and has a greater capacity	Tilted less far forward; adapted for support of a male's heavier build and stronger muscles; cavity of the true pelvis is narrow and deep
Bone thickness	Less; bones lighter, thinner, and smoother	Greater; bones heavier and thicker, and markings are more prominent
Acetabula	Smaller; farther apart	Larger; closer
Pubic angle/arch	Broad (80° to 90°); more rounded	Angle is more acute (50° to 60°)
Anterior view		
Sacrum	Wider; shorter; sacral curvature is accentuated	Narrow; longer; sacral promontory more ventral
Coccyx	More movable; straighter	Less movable; curves ventrally
Left lateral view		
Pelvic inlet (brim)	Wider; oval from side to side	Narrow; basically heart shaped
Pelvic outlet	Wider; ischial tuberosities shorter, farther apart and everted	Narrower; ischial tuberosities longer, sharper, and point more medially
Posteroinferior view		

Pelvic brim

alae of the ilia laterally and the lumbar vertebrae posteriorly. The false pelvis is really part of the abdomen and helps support the abdominal viscera. It does not restrict childbirth in any way. The **true pelvis** is the region inferior to the pelvic brim that is almost entirely surrounded by bone. It forms a deep "bowl" containing the pelvic organs. Its dimensions, particularly those of its *inlet* and *outlet,* are critical to the uncomplicated delivery of a baby, and they are carefully measured by an obstetrician.

The **pelvic inlet** is the **pelvic brim,** and its widest dimension is from right to left along the frontal plane (see Table 7.3). As labor begins, an infant's head typically enters the inlet with the forehead facing one ilium and the occipital region facing the other. A sacral promontory that is particularly large can impair the infant's entry into the true pelvis. The **pelvic outlet,** illustrated in the photos at the bottom of Table 7.3, is the inferior margin of the true pelvis. It is bounded anteriorly by the pubic arch, laterally by the ischia, and posteriorly by the sacrum and coccyx. Since both the coccyx and the ischial spines protrude into the outlet opening, a sharply angled coccyx or large sharp spines can cause problems in childbirth. The largest dimension of the outlet is the anteroposterior diameter. Generally, as the baby's head passes through the inlet, it rotates so that the forehead faces posteriorly and the occiput anteriorly. Thus, during birth, the infant's head makes a quarter turn to follow the widest dimensions of the true pelvis.

THE LOWER LIMB

The lower limbs carry the entire weight of the erect body and are subjected to exceptional forces when we jump or run. Thus, it is not surprising that the bones of the lower limbs are thicker and stronger than comparable bones of the upper limbs. Whereas the lighter bones of the upper limbs are adapted for flexibility and mobility, the more massive bones of the lower limbs are specialized for stability and weight bearing. The three segments of each lower limb are the thigh, the leg, and the foot (see Table 7.4 on p. 217).

Thigh

The **femur** (fe'mur; "thigh"), the single bone of the thigh (Figure 7.27), is the largest, longest, strongest bone in the body. Its durable anatomy reflects the fact that the stress on the femur during vigorous jumping can reach 280 kg/cm² (about 2 tons per square inch)! The femur is clothed by bulky muscles that prevent us from palpating its course down the length of the thigh. Its length is roughly one-quarter of a person's height. Proximally, the femur articulates with the hip bone and then courses medially as it descends toward the knee. This arrangement allows the knee joints to be closer to the body's center of gravity and provides

for better balance. The medial course of the two femurs is more pronounced in women because of their wider pelvis.

The ball-like **head** of the femur has a small central pit called the **fovea capitis** (fo've-ah kă'pĭ-tis). A short ligament, the *ligament of the head of the femur*, also called the *ligamentum teres* (te'rēz), runs from this pit to the acetabulum, where it helps secure the femur. The head is carried on a *neck* that angles laterally to join the shaft. This arrangement reflects the fact that the femur articulates with the side (rather than the inferior aspect) of the pelvis. The neck is the weakest part of the femur. At the junction of the shaft and neck are the lateral **greater trochanter** (trokan'ter) and posteromedial **lesser trochanter,** which serve as sites of thigh and buttock muscle attachment. The two trochanters are connected by the **intertrochanteric line** anteriorly and by the prominent **intertrochanteric crest** posteriorly. Inferior to the intertrochanteric crest on the posterior femur surface is the **gluteal tuberosity,** which blends into a long vertical ridge, the **linea aspera** (lin'e-ah as'per-ah; "rough line"), distally. Both markings are sites of muscle attachment. Except for the linea aspera, the femur shaft is smooth and rounded.

Distally, the femur broadens and terminates in the wheel-like **lateral** and **medial condyles,** which articulate with the tibia of the leg. Between the condyles on the posterior aspect of the femur is the deep, U-shaped **intercondylar notch.** The **medial** and **lateral epicondyles** (sites of muscle attachment) flank the condyles superiorly. Just superior to the medial epicondyle is the *adductor tubercle*. The smooth **patellar surface,** between the condyles on the anterior femoral surface, articulates with the **patella** (pahtel'ah), or **kneecap** (see Figures 7.27a and 7.1).

The patella is a triangular sesamoid bone enclosed in the (quadriceps) tendon that secures the anterior thigh muscles to the tibia. It guards the knee joint anteriorly and improves the leverage of the thigh muscles acting across the knee joint.

Leg

Two parallel bones, the tibia and fibula, form the skeleton of the leg, the region of the lower limb between the knee and the ankle (Figure 7.28). These two bones are connected by an interosseous membrane and articulate with each other both proximally and distally. However, unlike the joints between the radius and ulna of the forearm, the **tibiofibular** (tib"e-o-fib'u-lar) **joints** of the leg allow essentially no movement. The bones of the leg thus form a less flexible but stronger and more stable limb than those of the forearm. The large medial tibia articulates proximally with the femur to form the modified hinge joint of the knee and distally with the talus bone of the foot at the ankle. The fibula, by contrast, does not contribute to the knee joint and merely helps stabilize the ankle joint.

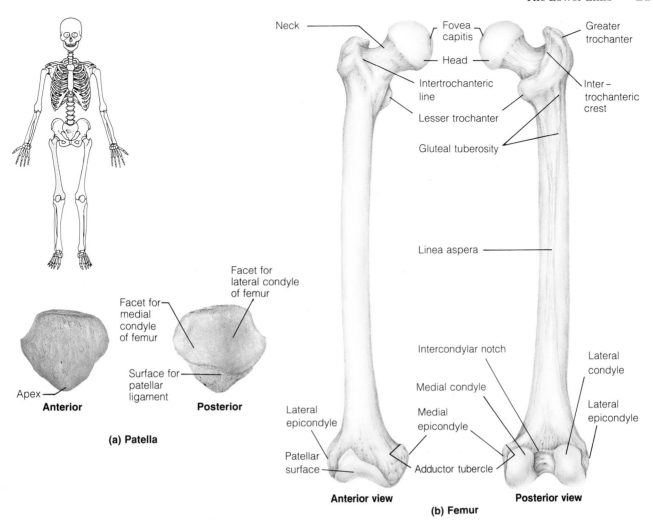

FIGURE 7.27
Bones of the right thigh and knee. (a) The patella (kneecap). (b) The femur (thigh bone).

Tibia

The **tibia** (tib'e-ah), or *shinbone,* receives the weight of the body from the femur and transmits it to the foot. Next to the femur, it is the largest, strongest bone in the body. At its broad proximal end are the concave **medial** and **lateral condyles;** these are separated by an irregular projection, the **intercondylar eminence,** which varies in size and may even be absent. The tibial condyles articulate with the corresponding condyles of the femur. The lateral tibial condyle bears a facet that indicates the site of the *proximal tibiofibular joint.* Just inferior to the condyles on the anterior surface is the large, rough **tibial tuberosity,** to which the patellar ligament attaches.

The tibial shaft is triangular in cross section. Its anterior border is the sharp **anterior crest.** Neither this crest nor the tibia's medial surface is covered by muscles, so they can be felt just deep to the skin along their entire length. The anguish of a "bumped" shin is

an experience familiar to nearly everyone. The distal end of the tibia is blunt where it articulates with the talus bone of the foot. Medial to that joint surface is an inferior projection, the **medial malleolus** (mah-le'o-lus), which forms the inner, or medial, bulge of the ankle. The **fibular notch,** found on the lateral surface of the tibia, participates in the *distal tibiofibular joint.*

Fibula

The **fibula** (fib'u-lah) is a sticklike bone with slightly expanded ends. It articulates proximally and distally with the lateral aspects of the tibia. Its upper end is its **head;** its lower end is the **lateral malleolus.** The lateral malleolus forms the conspicuous lateral ankle bulge and articulates with the talus. The fibular shaft is heavily ridged and appears to have been twisted a quarter turn. The fibula does not bear weight, but several muscles originate from it.

FIGURE 7.28
The tibia and fibula of the right leg.

(a) Anterior view   (b) Posterior view

Foot

The skeleton of the foot includes the bones of the tarsus, the bones of the metatarsus, and the phalanges, or toe bones (Figure 7.29). The foot has two important functions: It supports our body weight and it acts as a lever to propel the body forward when we walk and run. A single bone could serve both purposes but it would adapt poorly to uneven surfaces. Segmentation makes the foot pliable, avoiding this problem.

Tarsus

The **tarsus** is made up of seven **tarsal** (tar'sal) **bones** that form the proximal half of the foot. It corresponds to the carpus of the hand. Body weight is carried primarily by the two largest, most posterior tarsals: the **talus** (ta'lus; "ankle"), which articulates with the tibia and fibula superiorly, and the strong **calcaneus** (kal-ka'ne-us; "heel bone"), which forms the heel of the foot and carries the talus on its superior surface. The thick *calcaneal,* or *Achilles, tendon* of the calf muscles attaches to the posterior surface of the calcaneus. The part of the calcaneus that touches the ground is the *tuber calcanei* (kal-ka'ne-i), the calcaneal tuberosity. The remaining tarsals are the lateral **cuboid,** the medial **navicular** (nah-vik'u-lar), and most anteriorly

the **medial, intermediate,** and **lateral cuneiform** (ku-ne'I-form) **bones.** The cuboid and cuneiform bones articulate with the metatarsal bones anteriorly.

Metatarsus

The **metatarsus** consists of five small long bones called **metatarsal bones.** These are numbered 1 to 5 beginning with the medial (great toe) side of the foot. The first metatarsal is short and thick and its plantar surface rests on paired sesamoid bones (not shown), which play an important role in supporting the weight of the body. The arrangement of the metatarsals is more parallel than that of the metacarpals of the hands. Distally, where the metatarsals articulate with the proximal phalanges of the toes, the enlarged head of the first metatarsal forms the "ball" of the foot.

Phalanges (Toes)

The 14 phalanges of the toes are a good deal smaller than those of the fingers and thus less nimble. But their general structure and arrangement are the same. There are three phalanges in each digit except for the great toe, the **hallux.** The hallux has only two, proximal and distal.

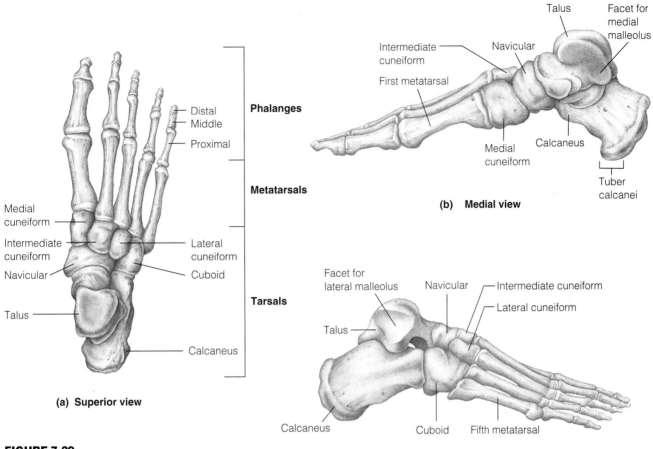

Phalanges
- Distal
- Middle
- Proximal

Metatarsals

Medial cuneiform

Intermediate cuneiform

Navicular

Lateral cuneiform

Cuboid

Tarsals

Talus

Calcaneus

(a) Superior view

Intermediate cuneiform

First metatarsal

Talus

Navicular

Facet for medial malleolus

Medial cuneiform

Calcaneus

Tuber calcanei

(b)   Medial view

Facet for lateral malleolus

Navicular

Intermediate cuneiform

Lateral cuneiform

Talus

Calcaneus

Cuboid

Fifth metatarsal

(c)   Lateral view

FIGURE 7.29
Bones of the right foot.

Arches of the Foot

A segmented structure can hold up weight only if it is arched. The foot has three arches: two *longitudinal arches* (the *medial* and *lateral*) and one *transverse arch* (Figure 7.30). These arches are maintained by the interlocking shape of the foot bones, by strong ligaments, and by the pull of some tendons during muscle activity. The ligaments and muscle tendons provide a certain amount of springiness. In general, the arches "give" when weight is applied to the foot and spring back when the weight is removed.

If you examine your wet footprints, you will see that the medial margin from the heel to the head of the first metatarsal leaves no print. This is because the **medial longitudinal arch** curves well above the ground. The talus bone serves as the keystone of the medial arch, which originates at the calcaneus, rises to the talus, and then descends to the three medial metatarsals. The **lateral longitudinal arch** is very low. It elevates the lateral part of the foot just enough to redistribute some of the weight to the calcaneus and the head of the fifth metatarsal (to the ends of the arch). The cuboid is the keystone bone of the lateral arch. The longitudinal arches serve as pillars for the **transverse arch,** which runs obliquely from one side

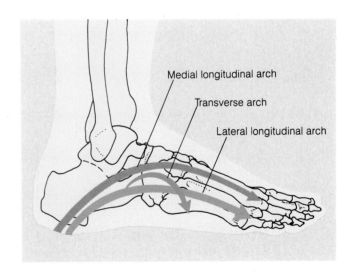

Medial longitudinal arch

Transverse arch

Lateral longitudinal arch

FIGURE 7.30
Arches of the foot.

Table 7.4 Bones of the Appendicular Skeleton

Body region	Bones*	Illustration	Location	Markings
PART I: Bones of the Pectoral Girdle and Upper Limb				
Pectoral girdle (Figure 7.21)	Clavicle (2)		Superoanterior thorax; articulates medially with sternum and laterally with scapula	Acromial end; sternal end
	Scapula (2)		Posterior thorax; forms part of the shoulder; articulates with humerus and clavicle	Glenoid cavity; spine; acromion; coracoid process; infraspinous, supraspinous, and subscapular fossae
Free upper limb Arm	Humerus (2)		Sole bone of arm; between scapula and elbow	Head; greater and lesser tuberosities; (Figure 7.22) intertubercular groove; deltoid tuberosity; trochlea; capitulum; coronoid and olecranon fossae; radial groove; epicondyles
Forearm (Figure 7.23)	Ulna (2)		Medial bone of forearm between elbow and wrist; forms elbow joint	Coronoid process; olecranon process; radial notch; trochlear notch; styloid process; head
	Radius (2)		Lateral bone of forearm; carries wrist	Radial tuberosity; styloid process; head; ulnar notch
Hand (Figure 7.24)	8 Carpals (16) (scaphoid, lunate, triquetral, pisiform, trapezium, trapezoid, capitate, hamate)		Form a bony crescent at the wrist; arranged in two rows of four bones each	
	5 Meta-carpals (10)		Form the palm; one in line with each digit	
	14 Phalanges (28) (distal, middle, proximal)		Form the fingers; three in digits 2–5; two in digit 1 (the thumb)	

Anterior view–right side of body

Table 7.4 continued

Body region	Bones*	Illustration	Location	Markings
PART II: Bones of the Pelvic Girdle and Lower Limb				
Pelvic girdle (Figure 7.25)	Coxal (2)		Each coxal bone is formed by the fusion of an ilium, ischium, and pubic bones; the coxal bones fuse anteriorly at the pubic symphysis and form sacroiliac joints with the sacrum posteriorly; girdle consisting of both coxal bones is basinlike	Iliac crest; anterior and posterior iliac spines; auricular surface; greater and lesser sciatic notches; obturator foramen; ischial tuberosity and spine; acetabulum; pubic arch; pubic crest; pubic tubercle
Free lower limb Thigh (Figure 7.27b)	Femur (2)		Sole bone of thigh; between hip joint and knee; largest bone of the body	Head; greater and lesser trochanters; neck; lateral and medial condyles and epicondyles; adductor tubercle; gluteal tuberosity; linea aspera
Kneecap (Figure 7.27a)	Patella (2)		A sesamoid bone lodged in the tendon fo the quadriceps (anterior thigh) muscles	
Leg (Figure 7.28)	Tibia (2)		Larger and more medial bone of leg; between knee and foot	Medial and lateral condyles; tibial tuberosity; anterior crest; medial malleolus
	Fibula (2)		Lateral bone of leg; sticklike	Head; lateral malleolus
Foot (Figure 7.29)	7 Tarsals (14) (talus, calcaneus, navicular, cuboid, and lateral, intermediate, and medial cuneiforms)		Seven bones forming the proximal part of the foot; the talus articulates with the leg bones at the ankle joint; the calcaneus, the largest tarsal, forms the heel	
	5 Metatarsals (10)		Five bones numbered 1–5 from the great toe	
	14 Phalanges (28) (distal, middle, proximal)		Form the toes; three in digits 2–5, two in digit 1 (the great toe)	

Anterior view of pelvic girdle and left lower limb

*The number in parentheses ( ) following the bone name denotes the total number of such bones in the body.

of the foot to the other, following the line of the joints between the tarsals and metatarsals. Together, the arches of the foot form a half-dome that distributes about half our standing and walking weight to the heel bones and half to the heads of the metatarsals.

Standing immobile for extended periods places excessive strain on the tendons and ligaments of the feet (because the muscles are inactive) and can result in fallen arches, or "flat feet," particularly if one is overweight. Running on hard surfaces can also cause arches to fall unless one wears shoes that give proper arch support. •

DEVELOPMENTAL ASPECTS OF THE SKELETON

The membrane bones of the skull start to ossify at the beginning of fetal development. The rapid deposit of bone matrix at the ossification centers produces cone-shaped protrusions in the developing bones. The skull bones of newborn infants are still incomplete and are connected by as yet unossified remnants of fibrous membranes called **fontanels** (fon"tah-nelz') (Figure 7.31). The fontanels allow the infant's head to be compressed slightly during birth, and they accommodate brain growth in the fetus and infant. A baby's pulse can be felt surging in these "soft spots"; hence their name (*fontanel* = little fountain). The large, diamond-shaped *anterior fontanel* is palpable for 1½ to 2 years after birth. The others are replaced by bone by the end of the first year.

At birth, the skull bones are very thin. The frontal bone and the mandible begin as paired bones that fuse medially during childhood. The tympanic part of the temporal bone is merely a C-shaped ring in the newborn.

Several congenital abnormalities may distort the axial skeleton, but perhaps the most common is *cleft palate,* a condition in which the palatine processes of the maxillae or the palatine bones (or both) fail to fuse medially. The persistent opening between the oral and nasal cavities interferes with sucking and can lead to aspiration (inhalation) of food into the lungs and *aspiration pneumonia.*

The skeleton changes throughout life, but the changes in childhood are most dramatic. At birth, the baby's cranium is huge relative to its face. The maxillae and mandible are foreshortened, and the contours of the face are flat (Figure 7.31). The rapid growth of the cranium before and after birth is related to the growth of the brain. By nine months after birth, the skull is already half of its adult size (volume). By two years, it is three-quarters of its adult size, and by eight to nine years, the skull has almost reached adult proportions. However, between the ages of 6 and 11, the head appears to enlarge substantially as the face literally grows out from the skull. The jaws increase in size and mass and the cheekbones and nose become more prominent. These facial changes are correlated with the expansion of respiratory passages and development of the permanent teeth. Figure 7.32 tracks how differential bone growth alters body proportions throughout life.

Two of the four spinal curvatures are present at birth: the thoracic and sacral curvatures. Both of these so-called **primary curvatures** are convex posteriorly, and an infant's spine is arched, like that of a four-legged animal. The **secondary curvatures**—cervical and lumbar—are convex anteriorly and are associated with a child's development. They result from reshaping of the intervertebral discs rather than from modifications of the bony vertebrae. The cervical curvature actually develops before birth, but becomes pro-

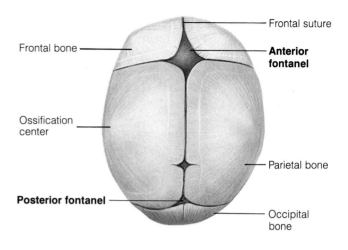

(a) Superior view

Frontal suture — Frontal bone — **Anterior fontanel** — Ossification center — **Posterior fontanel** — Parietal bone — Occipital bone

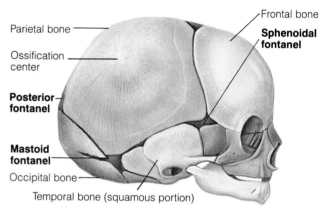

(b) Lateral view

Parietal bone — Ossification center — **Posterior fontanel** — **Mastoid fontanel** — Occipital bone — Temporal bone (squamous portion) — Frontal bone — **Sphenoidal fontanel**

**FIGURE 7.31
The fetal skull.**

nounced when the baby begins to lift its head independently (at about 3 months). The lumbar curvature develops when the baby begins to walk (at about 12 months). The lumbar curvature positions the weight of the trunk over the body's center of gravity and provides optimal balance when standing.

Vertebral problems (scoliosis or lordosis) may appear during the early school years, when rapid growth of the limb bones stretches many muscles. During the preschool years, lordosis is often present, but this is usually rectified as the abdominal muscles become stronger and the pelvis tilts forward. The thorax becomes broader and flatter laterally, but a true "military posture" (head erect, shoulders back, abdomen in, and chest out) does not develop until adolescence. Vertebral curvatures and posture are not under voluntary control, but are influenced by muscle strength and general health. A child typically adopts the posture that keeps his or her body parts in proper balance.

Like the axial skeleton, the appendicular skeleton can suffer from a number of congenital abnormalities. One that is fairly common and quite severe is *dyspla-*

sia (dis-pla'ze-ah; "bad formation") *of the hip.* The acetabulum forms incompletely and the head of the femur tends to slip out of it. Early diagnosis and treatment are essential to prevent permanent crippling.

During youth, growth of the skeleton not only increases overall body height and size, but changes body proportions as well (Figure 7.32). The **upper-lower (UL) body ratio** changes with age. The *lower segment* is the distance from the top of the pelvic girdle to the ground; the *upper segment* is the difference between the lower segment measurement and total height. At birth, the UL ratio is 1.7 to 1; that is, the head and trunk are approximately 1½ times as long as the lower limbs. The lower limbs grow more rapidly than the trunk from this time on, and by the age of ten, the UL ratio is approximately 1 to 1 and changes little thereafter. During puberty, the female pelvis broadens in preparation for childbearing, and the entire male skeleton becomes more robust. Once adult height is reached, a healthy skeleton changes very little until late middle age.

Old age affects many parts of the skeleton, especially the spine. The water content of the intervertebral discs declines (as it does in other tissues throughout the body). As the discs become thinner and less elastic, the risk of disc herniation increases. By 55 years, a loss of several centimeters in stature is common. Further shortening of the trunk can be produced by osteoporosis of the spine or by kyphosis (called "dowager's hump" in the elderly). What was done during youth may be undone in old age as the vertebral column gradually resumes its initial arc shape.

The thorax becomes more rigid with age, largely because the costal cartilages ossify. This loss of rib cage elasticity tends to cause shallow breathing, which leads to less efficient gas exchange.

All bones, you will recall, lose mass with age. Although cranial bones lose less mass than most, changes in facial contours of the aged are common. As the bony tissue of the jaws declines, the jaws appear foreshortened once again and the bony structure of the face becomes more childlike. As bones become more

Human fetus   Human adult

(a)

Newborn   2   5   15   Adult

Age in years

FIGURE 7.32

Differences in the growth rates for some parts of the body compared to others determine body proportions.

(a) Differential growth transforms the rounded, foreshortened skull of a newborn to the sloping skull characteristic of adults. (b) During growth of a human, the arms and legs grow faster than the head and trunk, as can be seen in this conceptualization of different-aged individuals all drawn at the same height.

porous, they become more susceptible to fracture, especially the vertebrae and the neck of the femur.

*   *   *

Our skeleton is a marvelous substructure, to be sure, but it is much more than that. It is a protector and supporter of other body systems, and without it (and the joints considered in Chapter 8), our muscles would be almost useless. The homeostatic relationships between the skeletal system and other body systems are illustrated in *Making Connections* in Chapter 6 (pp. 174–175).

RELATED CLINICAL TERMS

Bunion (halux valgus) A deformity of the great toe involving lateral displacement of the great toe and medial displacement of metatarsal 1; caused by wearing tight, improperly fitted shoes or, more rarely, by genetic factors; results in great toe inflammation, calluses, and bone spurs.

Chiropractic (ki"ro-prak'tik) A system of treating disease by manipulating the vertebral column based on the theory that most diseases are due to pressure on nerves caused by faulty bone alignment; a specialist in this field is a chiropractor.

Clubfoot A relatively common congenital defect in which the soles of the feet face medially and the toes point inferiorly; may be genetically induced or reflect an abnormal position of the foot during fetal development.

Colles' fracture Fracture of the radius, typically about 1 cm proximal to the wrist; usually results from forceful trauma, such as falling on outstretched hands; since the ulna plays no part in forming the wrist joint, the radius receives the brunt of the force.

Laminectomy Surgical removal of a vertebral lamina; most often done to relieve the symptoms of a ruptured disc.

Orthopedist or **orthopedic surgeon** A physician who specializes in restoring lost skeletal system function or repairing damage to bones and joints.

Ostealgia (os"te-al'je-ah) Pain in a bone.

Pelvimetry Measurement of the dimensions of the inlet and outlet of the pelvis, usually to determine whether the pelvis is of adequate size to allow normal delivery of a baby.

Podiatrist A specialist in foot disorders.

Prolapsed disc A herniated disc.

Spina bifida (spi′nah bĭ′fĭ-dah; "cleft spine") Congenital defect of the vertebral column in which the vertebral laminae fail to fuse medially; ranges in severity from inconsequential to severe conditions that impair neural functioning and encourage nervous system infections.

Spinal fusion Surgical procedure involving insertion of bone chips (or crushed bone) to immobilize and stabilize a specific region of the vertebral column, particularly in cases of vertebral fracture and herniated discs.

CHAPTER SUMMARY

1. The axial skeleton forms the longitudinal axis of the body. Its principal subdivisions are the skull, vertebral column, and thorax. It provides support and protection (by enclosure).

2. The appendicular skeleton consists of the bones of the pectoral and pelvic girdles and the limbs. It allows mobility for manipulation and locomotion.

PART 1: THE AXIAL SKELETON

The Skull (pp. 179–194)

1. The skull is formed by 22 bones. The cranium forms the vault and base of the skull, which protect the brain. The facial skeleton provides openings for the respiratory and digestive passages and attachment points for facial muscles.

2. With the exception of the temporomandibular joints, all bones of the adult skull are joined by immovable sutures.

3. **Cranium.** The eight bones of the cranium include the paired parietal and temporal bones and the single frontal, occipital, ethmoid, and sphenoid bones (see Table 7.1).

4. **Facial Bones.** The 14 bones of the face include the paired maxillae, zygomatics, nasals, lacrimals, palatines, and inferior conchae and the single mandible and vomer bones (Table 7.1).

5. **Orbits and Nasal Cavity.** Both the orbits and the nasal cavities are complicated bony regions formed of several bones.

6. **Paranasal Sinuses.** Paranasal sinuses occur in the frontal, ethmoid, sphenoid, and maxillary bones.

7. **Hyoid Bone.** The hyoid bone, supported in the neck by ligaments, serves as an attachment point for the tongue, pharynx muscles, and larynx.

The Vertebral Column (pp. 194–200)

1. **General Characteristics.** The vertebral column includes 24 movable vertebrae (7 cervical, 12 thoracic, and 5 lumbar) and the sacrum and coccyx.

2. The fibrocartilage intervertebral discs act as shock absorbers and provide flexibility to the vertebral column.

3. The primary curvatures of the vertebral column are the thoracic and sacral; the secondary curvatures are the cervical and lumbar.

4. **General Structure of Vertebrae.** With the exception of C_1 and C_2, all vertebrae have a body, two transverse processes, two superior and two inferior articular processes, a spinous process, and a vertebral arch.

5. **Regional Vertebral Characteristics.** Special features distinguish the regional vertebrae (see Table 7.2, p. 199).

The Bony Thorax (pp. 200–203)

1. The bones of the thorax include the 12 rib pairs, the sternum, and the thoracic vertebrae. The bony thorax protects the organs of the thoracic cavity.

2. **Sternum.** The sternum consists of the fused manubrium, body, and xiphoid process.

3. **Ribs.** The first seven rib pairs are called true ribs; the rest are called false ribs. Ribs 11 and 12 are floating ribs.

PART 2: THE APPENDICULAR SKELETON

The Pectoral (Shoulder) Girdle (pp. 203–204)

1. Each pectoral girdle consists of one clavicle and one scapula. The pectoral girdles attach the upper limbs to the axial skeleton.

2. **Clavicles.** The clavicles hold the scapulae laterally away from the thorax. The sternoclavicular joints are the only attachment points of the pectoral girdle to the axial skeleton.

3. **Scapulae.** The scapulae articulate with the clavicles and with the humerus bones of the arms.

The Upper Limb (pp. 204–208)

1. Each upper limb consists of 30 bones and is specialized for mobility.

2. **Arm/Forearm/Hand.** The skeleton of the arm is composed solely of the humerus; the skeleton of the forearm is composed of the radius and ulna; and the skeleton of the hand consists of the carpals, metacarpals, and phalanges.

The Pelvic (Hip) Girdle (pp. 208–212)

1. The pelvic girdle, a heavy structure specialized for weight bearing, is composed of two coxal bones that secure the lower limbs to the axial skeleton. Together with the sacrum, the coxal bones form the basinlike bony pelvis.

2. Each coxal bone consists of three fused bones: ilium, ischium, and pubis; the acetabulum occurs at the point of fusion.

3. **Ilium/Ischium/Pubis.** The ilium is the superior flaring portion of the os coxa. Each ilium forms a secure joint with the sacrum posteriorly. The ischium is a curved bar of bone; we sit on the ischial tuberosities. The V-shaped pubic bones articulate anteriorly at the pubic symphysis.

4. **Pelvic Structure and Childbearing.** The male pelvis is deep and narrow with larger, heavier bones than those of the female. The female pelvis, which forms the birth canal, is shallow and wide.

The Lower Limb (pp. 212–217)

1. Each lower limb consists of the thigh, leg, and foot and is specialized for weight bearing and locomotion.

2. **Thigh.** The femur is the sole bone of the thigh. Its ball-shaped head articulates with the acetabulum.

3. **Leg.** The bones of the leg are the tibia, which participates in forming both the knee and ankle joints, and the fibula.

4. **Foot.** The bones of the foot include the tarsals, metatarsals, and phalanges. The most important tarsals are the calcaneus (heel bone) and the talus, which articulates with the tibia superiorly.

5. The foot is supported by three arches that distribute body weight to the heel and ball of the foot.

Developmental Aspects of the Skeleton (pp. 218–219)

1. Fontanels, which allow brain growth and ease birth passage, are present in the skull at birth. Growth of the cranium after birth is related to brain growth; increase in size of the facial skeleton follows tooth development and enlargement of respiratory passageways.

2. The vertebral column is C-shaped at birth (thoracic and sacral curvatures are present); the secondary curvatures form when the baby begins to lift its head and walk.

3. Long bones continue to grow in length until late adolescence. The UL ratio changes from 1.7:1 to 1:1 by the age of ten.

4. Changes in the female pelvis (preparatory for childbirth) occur during puberty.

5. Once at adult height, the skeleton changes little until late middle age. With old age, the intervertebral discs thin; this, along with osteoporosis, leads to a gradual loss in height. Loss of bone mass predisposes elderly individuals to fractures.

REVIEW QUESTIONS

Multiple Choice/Matching

1. Using the letters from column B, match the bone descriptions in column A. (Note that some require more than a single choice.)

Column A	Column B
____ (1) connected by the coronal suture	**(a)** ethmoid
____ (2) keystone bone of cranium	**(b)** frontal
____ (3) keystone bone of the face	**(c)** mandible
____ (4) form the hard palate	**(d)** maxillary
____ (5) allows the spinal cord to pass	**(e)** occipital
____ (6) forms the chin	**(f)** palatine
____ (7) contain paranasal sinuses	**(g)** parietal
____ (8) contains mastoid sinuses	**(h)** sphenoid
	(i) temporal

 2. Match the key terms with the bone descriptions that follow.

Key: **(a)** clavicle **(b)** ilium **(c)** ischium **(d)** pubis **(e)** sacrum **(f)** scapula **(g)** sternum

____ (1) bone of the axial skeleton to which the pectoral girdle attaches
____ (2) markings include glenoid fossa and acromion
____ (3) features include the ala, crest, and greater sciatic notch
____ (4) doubly curved; acts as a shoulder strut
____ (5) pelvic girdle bone that articulates with the axial skeleton
____ (6) the "sit-down" bone
____ (7) anteriormost bone of the pelvic girdle
____ (8) part of the vertebral column

3. Use key choices to identify the bone descriptions that follow.

Key: **(a)** carpals **(b)** femur **(c)** fibula **(d)** humerus **(e)** radius **(f)** tarsals **(g)** tibia **(h)** ulna

____ (1) articulates with the acetabulum and the tibia
____ (2) forms the lateral aspect of the ankle
____ (3) bone that "carries" the hand
____ (4) the wrist bones
____ (5) end shaped like a monkey wrench
____ (6) articulates with the capitulum of the humerus
____ (7) largest bone of this "group" is the calcaneus

Short Answer Essay Questions

 4. Name the cranial and facial bones and compare and contrast the functions of the cranial and facial skeletons.

5. How do the relative proportions of the cranium and face of a fetus compare with those of an adult skull?

6. Name and diagram the normal vertebral curvatures. Which are primary and which are secondary curvatures?

7. List at least two specific anatomical characteristics each for typical, cervical, thoracic, and lumbar vertebrae that would allow *anyone* to identify each type correctly.

8. (a) What is the function of the intervertebral discs? (b) Distinguish between the annulus fibrosis and nucleus pulposus regions of a disc. (c) Which provides durability and strength? (d) Which provides resilience? (e) Which herniates in a "slipped" disc?

9. Name the major components of the bony thorax.

10. (a) What is a true rib? A false rib? (b) Is a floating rib a true rib or a false rib? (c) Why are floating ribs easily broken?

11. The major function of the shoulder girdle is flexibility. What is the major function of the pelvic girdle? Relate these functional differences to anatomical differences seen in these girdles.

12. List three important differences between the male and female pelvis.

13. Describe the function of the arches of the foot.

14. Briefly describe the anatomical characteristics and impairment of function seen in cleft palate and hip dysplasia.

15. Compare a young adult skeleton to that of an extremely aged person relative to bone mass in general and the bony structure of the skull, thorax, and vertebral column in particular.

 ### CRITICAL THINKING AND CLINICAL APPLICATION QUESTIONS

1. Malcolm was rushed to the emergency room after trying to break a fall with outstretched arms. The physician took one look at his shoulder and saw that he had a broken clavicle (and no other injury). Describe the position of Malcolm's shoulder. Malcolm was worried about injury to the main blood vessels to his arm (the subclavian vessels), but was told such injury was unlikely. Why could the doctor predict this with assurance?

2. An exhausted biology student was attending a lecture; after 30 minutes or so, he lost interest and began to doze. As the lecture ended, the hubbub aroused him and he let go with a tremendous yawn. To his great distress, he couldn't close his mouth—his lower jaw was "stuck" open. What do you think had happened?

3. Ralph had polio as a boy and was partially paralyzed in one lower limb for over a year. Although no longer paralyzed, he now has a severe lateral curvature of the lumbar spine. Explain what has happened and identify his condition.

4. Mary's grandmother slipped on a scatter rug and fell heavily to the floor. Her left lower limb was laterally rotated and noticeably shorter than the right, and when she attempted to get up, she winced with pain. Mary surmised that her grandmother might have "fractured her hip," which later proved to be true. What bone was probably fractured and at what site? Why is a "fractured hip" a common type of fracture in the elderly?

8

Joints

CHAPTER OUTLINE AND STUDENT OBJECTIVES

1. Define joint or articulation.

Classification of Joints (pp. 222–223)

2. Classify joints structurally and functionally.

Fibrous Joints (pp. 223–225)

3. Describe the general structure of fibrous joints. Name and give an example of each of the three common types of fibrous joints.

Cartilaginous Joints (p. 226)

4. Describe the general structure of cartilaginous joints. Name and give an example of each of the two common types of cartilaginous joints.

Synovial Joints (pp. 226–240)

5. Describe the structural characteristics shared by all synovial joints.

6. List three natural factors that stabilize synovial joints.

7. Compare the structures and functions of bursae and tendon sheaths.

8. Name and describe (or perform) the common body movements.

9. Name six types of synovial joints based on the movement(s) allowed. Provide examples of each type.

10. Describe the elbow, knee, hip, and shoulder joints. Consider in each case the articulating bones, anatomical characteristics of the joint, movements allowed, and relative joint stability.

Homeostatic Imbalances of Joints (pp. 240–244)

11. Name the most common joint injuries and discuss the symptoms and problems associated with each.

12. Compare and contrast osteoarthritis, rheumatoid arthritis, and gouty arthritis with respect to the population affected, possible causes, structural joint changes, disease outcome, and therapy.

Developmental Aspects of Joints (p. 244)

13. Discuss briefly the factors that promote or disturb joint homeostasis.

Joints, or **articulations,** are sites where two or more bones meet. Our joints have two fundamental functions: They hold our skeleton together and they give it mobility. The graceful movements of a ballet dancer and the rough-and-tumble grapplings of football players attest to the great variety of motion allowed by joints. Nevertheless, the bone-binding function of joints is just as important as their role in providing mobility. The rigid joints of the skull, for example, make it a secure enclosure for our vital "gray matter." Joints are the weakest parts of any skeleton. Even so, their structure enables them to resist crushing, tearing, and various forces that threaten to force them out of alignment.

CLASSIFICATION OF JOINTS

Joints may be classified structurally or functionally. The *structural classification* focuses on the material binding the bones together and whether or not a joint cavity is present. Structurally, there are *fibrous, cartilaginous,* and *synovial joints* (Table 8.1).

The *functional classification* is based on the amount of movement allowed at the joint. On this basis, there are **synarthroses** (sin″ar-thro′sēz), which are immovable joints (*syn* = together; *arthro* = joint); **amphiarthroses** (am″fe-ar-thro′sēz), slightly movable joints (*amphi* = on both sides); and **diarthroses** (di″ar-thro′sēz), or freely movable joints (*dia* = through, apart). Freely movable joints predominate in the limbs, whereas immovable and slightly movable joints are largely restricted to the axial skeleton, where firm bony attachments and protection of enclosed organs are priorities.

In general, fibrous joints are immovable, and all synovial joints are freely movable. However, cartilaginous joints have both rigid and slightly movable examples. Since the structural categories are more clear-cut, we will use the structural classification for the present discussion, indicating functional properties where appropriate. The specific characteristics of selected body joints are summarized in Table 8.2 (pp. 224–225).

FIBROUS JOINTS

In **fibrous joints,** the bones are joined by fibrous tissue; no joint cavity is present. The amount of movement allowed depends on the length of the fibers uniting the bones. Although a few fibrous joints are slightly movable, most are synarthrotic and permit essentially no movement. The three types of fibrous joints are *sutures, syndesmoses,* and *gomphoses.*

Sutures

Sutures, literally "seams," occur only between bones of the skull (Figure 8.1a). The wavy articulating bone edges interdigitate by either overlapping or interlocking, and the junction is completely filled by very short connective tissue fibers that penetrate into the articulating bones. The result is nearly rigid splices that bind the bones tightly together. During adulthood, the fibrous tissue becomes ossified and the

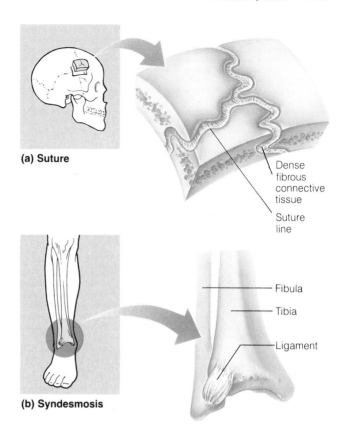

(a) Suture

Dense fibrous connective tissue

Suture line

Fibula

Tibia

Ligament

(b) Syndesmosis

FIGURE 8.1

Fibrous joints. Sutures, syndesmoses, and gomphoses are the three fibrous joint types (gomphoses are not illustrated here). **(a)** In sutures of the skull interconnecting connective tissue fibers are very short, and the bone edges interlock so that the joint is immovable (synarthrotic). **(b)** In the syndesmosis at the distal tibiofibular joint, the fibrous tissue (ligament) connecting the bones is longer than that in sutures; "give," but no true movement, is permitted.

Table 8.1 Summary of Joint Classes			
Structural class	Structural characteristics	Types	Mobility
Fibrous	Bone ends/parts united by collagenic fibers	(1) Suture (short fibers)	Immobile (synarthrosis)
		(2) Syndesmosis (longer fibers)	Slightly mobile (amphiarthrosis) and immobile
		(3) Gomphosis (periodontal ligament)	Immobile
Cartilaginous	Bone ends/parts united by cartilage	(1) Synchondrosis (hyaline cartilage)	Immobile
		(2) Symphysis (fibrocartilage)	Slightly movable
Synovial	Bone ends/parts covered with articular cartilage and enclosed within an articular capsule lined with synovial membrane	(1) Plane (2) Hinge (3) Pivot (4) Condyloid (5) Saddle (6) Ball and socket	Freely movable (diarthrosis; movements depend on design of joint)

Table 8.2 Structural and Functional Characteristics of Body Joints

Illustration	Joint	Articulating bones	Structural type*	Functional type; movements allowed
	Skull	Cranial and facial bones	Fibrous; suture	Synarthrotic; no movement
	Temporomandibular	Temporal bone of skull and mandible	Synovial; modified hinge† (contains articular disc)	Diarthrotic; gliding and uniaxial rotation; slight lateral movement, elevation, depression, protraction, retraction
	Atlanto-occipital	Occipital bone of skull and atlas	Synovial; condyloid	Diarthrotic; biaxial; flexion, extension, abduction, adduction, circumduction
	Atlantoaxial	Atlas (C_1) and axis (C_2)	Synovial; pivot	Diarthrotic; uniaxial; rotation of the head
	Intervertebral	Between adjacent vertebral bodies	Cartilaginous; symphysis	Amphiarthrotic; slight movement
	Intervertebral	Between articular processes	Synovial; plane	Diarthrotic; gliding
	Vertebrocostal	Vertebrae (transverse processes or bodies) and ribs	Synovial; plane	Diarthrotic; gliding
	Sternoclavicular	Sternum and clavicle	Synovial; shallow saddle (contains articular disc)	Diarthrotic; multiaxial (allows clavicle to move in all axes)
	Sternocostal	Sternum and rib 1	Cartilaginous; synchondrosis	Synarthrotic; no movement
	Sternocostal	Sternum and ribs 2–7	Synovial; double plane	Diarthrotic; gliding
	Acromioclavicular	Acromion process of scapula and clavicle	Synovial; plane	Diarthrotic; gliding; elevation, depression, protraction, retraction
	Shoulder (glenohumeral)	Scapula and humerus	Synovial; ball and socket	Diarthrotic; multiaxial; flexion, extension, abduction, adduction, circumduction, rotation
	Elbow	Ulna (and radius) with humerus	Synovial; hinge	Diarthrotic; uniaxial; flexion, extension
	Radioulnar (proximal)	Radius and ulna	Synovial; pivot	Diarthrotic; uniaxial; rotation around the long axis of forearm to allow pronation and supination
	Radioulnar (distal)	Radius and ulna	Synovial; pivot (contains articular disc)	Diarthrotic; uniaxial; rotation (convex head of ulna rotates in ulnar notch of radius)
	Wrist (radiocarpal)	Radius and proximal carpals	Synovial; condyloid	Diarthrotic; biaxial; flexion extension, abduction, adduction, circumduction
	Intercarpal	Adjacent carpals	Synovial; plane	Diarthrotic; gliding
	Carpometacarpal of digit 1 (thumb)	Carpal (trapezium) and metacarpal 1	Synovial; saddle	Diarthrotic; biaxial; flexion, extension, abduction, adduction, circumduction, opposition
	of digits 2–5	Carpal(s) and metacarpal(s)	Synovial; plane	Diarthrotic; gliding
	Knuckle (metacarpophalangeal)	Metacarpal and proximal phalanx	Synovial; condyloid	Diarthrotic; biaxial; flexion, extension, abduction, adduction, circumduction
	Finger (interphalangeal)	Adjacent phalanges	Synovial; hinge	Diarthrotic; uniaxial; flexion; extension

Table 8.2 continued

Illustration	Joint	Articulating bones	Structural type*	Functional type; movements allowed
	Sacroiliac	Sacrum and coxal bone	Synovial; plane	Diarthrotic; little to no movement, slight gliding possible (more during pregnancy)
	Pubic symphysis	Pubic bones	Cartilaginous; symphysis	Amphiarthrotic; slight movement (enhanced during pregnancy)
	Hip (coxal)	Coxal bone and femur	Synovial; ball and socket	Diarthrotic; multiaxial; flexion, extension, abduction, adduction, rotation, circumduction
	Knee (tibiofemoral)	Femur and tibia	Synovial; modified hinge†	Diarthrotic; biaxial; flexion, extension, some rotation allowed
	Knee (femoropatellar)	Femur and patella	Synovial; plane	Diarthrotic; gliding
	Tibiofibular	Tibia and fibula (proximally)	Synovial; plane	Diarthrotic; gliding
	Tibiofibular	Tibia and fibula (distally)	Fibrous; syndesmosis	Synarthrotic; slight "give" during dorsiflexion
	Ankle	Tibia and fibula with talus	Synovial; hinge	Diarthrotic; uniaxial; flexion, extension
	Intertarsal	Adjacent tarsals	Synovial; plane	Diarthrotic; gliding
	Tarsometatarsal	Tarsal(s) and metatarsal(s)	Synovial; plane	Diarthrotic; gliding
	Metatarsopha-langeal	Metatarsal and proximal phalanx	Synovial; condyloid	Diarthrotic; biaxial; flexion, extension, abduction, adduction, circumduction
	Toe (interphalan-geal)	Adjacent phalanges	Synovial; hinge	Diarthrotic; uniaxial; flexion; extension

*Fibrous joints indicated by orange circles; cartilaginous joints indicated by blue circles; synovial joints indicated by purple circles.
†These modified hinge joints are structurally bicondylar.

skull bones fuse into a single unit. The suture joints are then more precisely called **synostoses** (sin"os-to'-sēz), literally, "bony junctions." Since any movement of the cranial bones would severely damage the brain, the immovable nature of sutures is an exquisite adaptation for their protective function.

Syndesmoses

Syndesmoses (sin"des-mo'sēz) are fibrous joints in which the bones are connected by a cord or sheet of fibrous tissue, called a *ligament* (*syndesmos* = ligament) or an *interosseous membrane,* respectively. Although the connecting fibers are always longer than those in sutures, they vary quite a bit in length. Since the amount of movement possible increases with increasing length of the connecting fibers, slight to considerable movement is possible. For example, the ligament connecting the distal ends of the tibia and fibula is quite short (Figure 8.1b), and this tibiofibular joint is only slightly more resilient than a

suture, a characteristic best described as "give." True movement is still prevented, so the joint is classed functionally as an immovable joint, or synarthrosis. (Note, however, that some authorities classify this joint as an amphiarthrosis). On the other hand, the interosseous membrane connecting the radius and ulna along their length (Figure 7.23a, p. 206) is sufficiently broad and flexible to permit the ample movements of supination and pronation (rotation of the radius around the ulna).

Gomphoses

A **gomphosis** (gom-fo'sis) is a peg-in-socket fibrous joint. It is represented solely by the articulation of a tooth with its bony alveolar socket. The term *gomphosis* comes from the Greek *gompho,* meaning "nail" or "bolt," and refers to the way teeth are embedded in their sockets (as if hammered in). The fibrous connection in this case is the short **periodontal ligament** (see Figure 24.11 on p. 800).

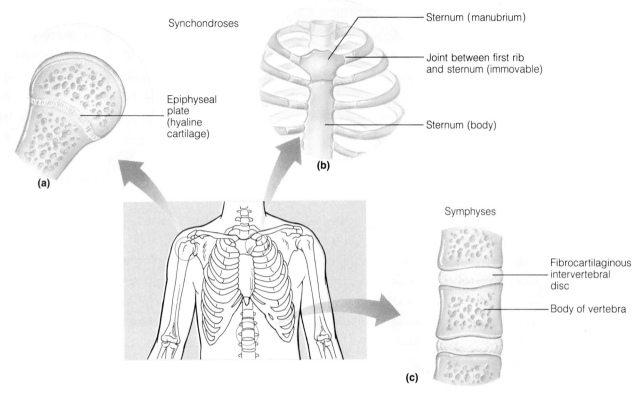

FIGURE 8.2
Cartilaginous joints. (a) The epiphyseal plate seen in a growing long bone is a temporary synchondrosis; the shaft and epiphysis are connected by hyaline cartilage that is later completely ossified. (b) The sternocostal joint between rib 1 and the manubrium of the sternum is an immovable hyaline cartilage joint, or synchondrosis. (c) The intervertebral joints, in which the vertebrae are connected by fibrocartilaginous discs, are symphyses.

CARTILAGINOUS JOINTS

In **cartilaginous** (kar″ti-laj′ĭ-nus) **joints,** the articulating bones are united by cartilage (Figure 8.2). Like fibrous joints, they lack a joint cavity. The two types of cartilaginous joints are *synchondroses* and *symphyses.*

Synchondroses

A bar or plate of *hyaline cartilage* unites the bones at a **synchondrosis** (sin″kon-dro′sis; "junction of cartilage"). During youth, virtually all synchondroses provide sites and means for bone growth, while contributing to skeletal flexibility. Once bone growth ends, however, almost all synchondroses become ossified and immovable (synarthrotic).

Although a few synchondroses occur in cartilaginous areas of the skull, the most common examples are the epiphyseal plates connecting the diaphysis and epiphysis regions in long bones (Figure 8.2a). Epiphyseal plates are temporary joints and eventually become synostoses. The joint between the first rib and the manubrium of the sternum is another example of a synarthrotic hyaline cartilage joint that eventually ossifies (Figure 8.2b).

Symphyses

In **symphyses** (sim′fih-sēz; "growing together") the articular surfaces of the bones are covered with articular (hyaline) cartilage, which in turn is fused to an intervening pad, or plate, of *fibrocartilage.* Since fibrocartilage is compressible and resilient, it acts as a shock absorber and permits a limited amount of movement at the joint. Symphyses are amphiarthrotic joints designed for strength with flexibility. Examples include the intervertebral joints (Figure 8.2c) and the pubic symphysis of the pelvis (see Table 8.2).

SYNOVIAL JOINTS

Synovial joints are those in which the articulating bones are separated by a fluid-containing joint cavity. This arrangement permits substantial freedom of movement, and all synovial joints are freely movable diarthroses. All joints of the limbs—indeed, most joints of the body—fall into this class.

General Structure

Typically, synovial joints have five distinguishing features (Figure 8.3a):

1. **Articular cartilage.** Glassy-smooth articular (hyaline) cartilage covers the opposing bone surfaces. These spongy cushions absorb compression placed on the joint and thereby keep the bone ends from being crushed.

2. **Joint cavity.** A feature unique to synovial joints, the joint cavity is more a potential space than a real one because it is filled with synovial fluid.

3. **Articular capsule.** The joint cavity is enclosed by a double-layered articular (joint) capsule. The external layer is a tough, flexible **fibrous capsule** that is continuous with the periostea of the articulating bones.

4. **Synovial membrane.** A synovial membrane, composed of loose connective tissue, lines the fibrous capsule internally and covers all internal joint surfaces that are not hyaline cartilage.

5. **Synovial fluid.** A small amount of slippery synovial fluid occupies all free spaces within the joint capsule. This fluid is derived largely by filtration from blood flowing through the capillaries in the synovial membrane. Synovial fluid has a viscous, egg-white consistency (*ovum* = egg) due to its content of hyaluronic acid secreted by the cells of the synovial membrane, but it thins and becomes less viscous as it warms during joint activity. Synovial fluid, which is also found *within* the articular cartilages, provides a slippery weight-bearing film that reduces friction between the cartilages. A mechanism called **weeping lubrication** squeezes synovial fluid into and out of the cartilages during normal movements, lubricating their free surfaces and nourishing their cells. The synovial fluid is forced from the cartilages when a joint is compressed. Then as pressure on the joint is relieved, synovial fluid seeps back into the articular cartilages like water into a sponge, ready to be squeezed out again the next time the joint is loaded (put under pressure). Synovial fluid also contains phagocytic cells that rid the joint cavity of microbes or cellular debris.

Besides the basic components described above, some synovial joints are reinforced and strengthened by a number of ligaments. Most often, the ligaments are **intrinsic,** or **capsular;** that is, they are thickened parts of the fibrous capsule. In other cases, they remain distinct and are found outside the capsule **(extracapsular ligaments)** or deep to it **(intracapsular ligaments).** Since intracapsular ligaments are covered with synovial membrane, they do not actually lie within the joint cavity.

Certain synovial joints have other structural features. Some, such as the hip and knee joints, have cushioning *fatty pads* between the fibrous capsule and the synovial membrane or bone. Others have discs or wedges of fibrocartilage separating the articular surfaces of the bones. Where present, these so-called **articular discs,** or **menisci** (mĕ-nis′ki; "crescents"), extend inward from the articular capsule and divide the synovial cavity into two separate cavities (see Figure 8.12). The articular discs improve the fit between the articulating bone ends, making the joint more stable. Articular discs occur in the knee, jaw, and a few other joints (see Table 8.2).

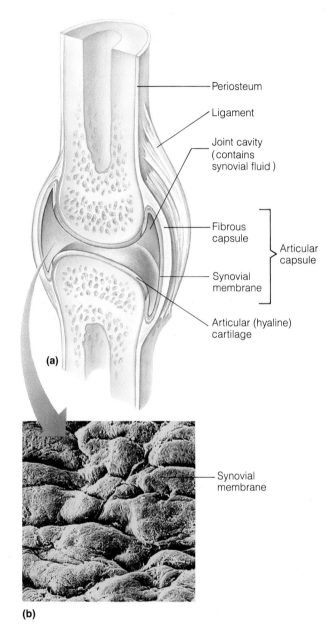

Synovial joints are most closely related to which of the following terms? protection; mobility; support.

(a)

(b)

FIGURE 8.3
General structure of a synovial joint. (a) The articulating bone ends are covered with articular cartilage and enclosed within an articular capsule. The exterior portion of the articular capsule, the fibrous capsule, is continuous with the periostea of the bones. Internally, the fibrous capsule is lined with a smooth synovial membrane that secretes synovial fluid. Typically, the joint is reinforced by ligaments. (b) Scanning electron micrograph (×7) of the synovial membrane from a knee joint.

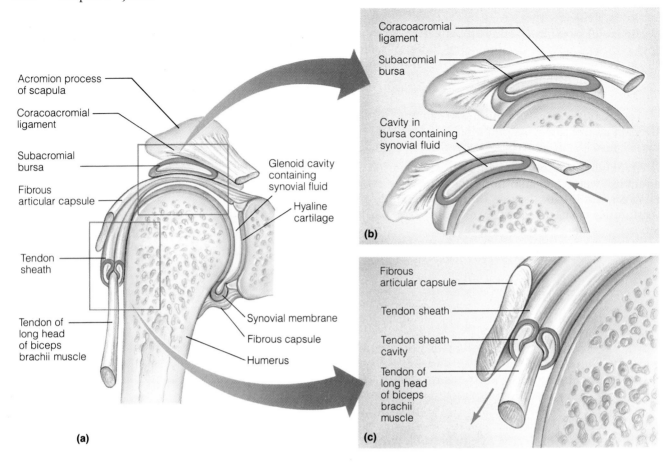

FIGURE 8.4
Friction-reducing structures: Bursae and tendon sheaths. (a) Frontal section through the right shoulder joint showing the saclike bursa and the tendon sheath around a muscle tendon. (b) Enlargement of part (a), showing the manner in which a bursa eliminates friction where a tendon (or other structure) is liable to rub against a bone. The synovial fluid within the bursa acts as a lubricant that allows its walls to slide easily across each other. (c) Enlarged three-dimensional view of the tendon sheath wrapped around the tendon of the biceps brachii muscle.

Bursae and Tendon Sheaths

Bursae and tendon sheaths are not strictly part of synovial joints, but they are often found closely associated with them (Figure 8.4). Essentially bags of lubricant, they act as "ball bearings" to reduce friction between adjacent structures during joint activity. **Bursae** (ber′se), from the Latin word meaning "purse," are flattened fibrous sacs lined with synovial membrane and containing a thin film of synovial fluid. They are common in sites where ligaments, muscles, skin, or muscle tendons overlie and rub against bone. Many people have never heard of a bursa, but most have heard of bunions (bun′yunz). A *bunion* is an enlarged bursa at the base of the big toe, swollen from rubbing of a tight or poorly fitting shoe.

Most bursae are present from birth, but additional ones, called *false bursae,* may develop at any site where there is excessive motion, and they function in the same manner as true bursae. A **tendon sheath** is essentially an elongated bursa that wraps completely around a tendon subjected to friction, like a bun around a hot dog.

Factors Influencing the Stability of Synovial Joints

Since joints are constantly stretched and compressed, they must be stabilized so that they do not dislocate (come out of alignment). The stability of a synovial joint depends chiefly on three factors: the nature of the articular surfaces; the number and positioning of ligaments; and muscle tone.

Articular Surfaces

The shapes of articular surfaces determine what movements are possible at a joint, but surprisingly, articular surfaces play a minimal role in joint stability. Many joints have shallow sockets or noncomplementary articulating surfaces ("misfits") that contribute little to or actually hinder joint stability. But when articular surfaces are large and fit snugly together, or when the socket is deep, stability is vastly improved. The ball and deep socket of the hip joint provide the best example of a joint made extremely stable by the shape of its articular surfaces.

Ligaments

The capsules and ligaments of synovial joints unite the bones, help to direct bone movement, and prevent excessive or undesirable motion. As a rule, the more ligaments a joint has, the stronger it is. However, when other stabilizing factors are inadequate, undue tension is placed on the ligaments and they stretch. Stretched ligaments stay stretched, like taffy, and a ligament can stretch only about 6% of its length before it snaps. Thus, when ligaments are the major means of bracing or strengthening a joint, the joint is not very stable.

Muscle Tone

For most joints, the muscle tendons that cross the joint are the most important stabilizing factor. These tendons are kept taut at all times by the tone of their muscles. (Muscle tone is defined as low levels of contractile activity in relaxed muscles that keep the muscles healthy and ready to react to stimulation.) Muscle tone is extremely important in reinforcing the shoulder and knee joints and arches of the foot.

The articular capsule and ligaments are richly supplied with sensory nerve endings that monitor the position of the joints and help to maintain muscle tone. Stretching of these structures sends nerve impulses to the central nervous system, resulting in reflexive contraction of muscles surrounding the joint.

Movements Allowed by Synovial Joints

Every skeletal muscle of the body is attached to bone or other connective tissue structures at no fewer than two points. The muscle's **origin** is attached to the immovable (or less movable) bone. Its other end, the **insertion,** is attached to the movable bone. Body movement occurs when muscles contract across joints and their insertion moves toward their origin. The movements can be described in directional terms relative to the lines, or *axes,* around which the body part moves and the planes of space along which the movement occurs, that is, along the transverse, frontal, or sagittal plane. (These planes were described in Chapter 1.)

Range of motion allowed by synovial joints varies from **nonaxial movement** (slipping movements only, since there is no axis around which movement can occur) to **uniaxial movement** (movement in one

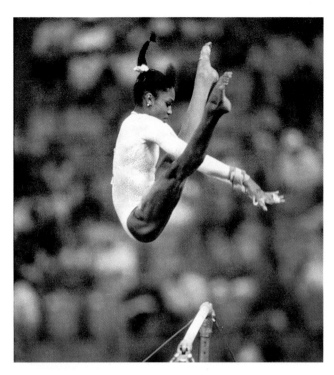

FIGURE 8.5
An example of extraordinary range of motion. Betty Okino, a U.S. gymnast in the 1992 Olympics, has hip joints nearly as flexible as her shoulder joints.

plane) to **biaxial movement** (movement in two planes) to **multiaxial movement** (movement in or around all three planes of space and axes). Range of motion varies greatly in different people. In some, such as trained gymnasts or acrobats, range of joint movement may be extraordinary (Figure 8.5). The ranges of motion at the major joints are given in Table 8.2.

There are three general types of movements: *gliding, angular movements,* and *rotation.* The most common body movements allowed by synovial joints are described next and illustrated in Figure 8.6.

Gliding Movements

Gliding movements (Figure 8.6a) are the simplest type of joint movements. One flat, or nearly flat, bone surface glides or slips over another similar surface. The bones are merely displaced in relation to one another. Gliding movements occur at the intercarpal and intertarsal joints, and between the flat articular processes of the vertebrae (see Table 8.2).

Angular Movements

Angular movements (Figure 8.6b–g) change—increase or decrease—the angle between two bones. Angular movements may occur along any plane of the body and include flexion, extension, abduction, adduction, and circumduction.

(a) Gliding movement between carpals, shown in posterior view of right hand

Gliding

Hyperextension

Extension

Flexion

(b) Flexion and extension of the head (movement between the skull and atlas [C_1])

Extension

Flexion

Flexion

(c) Flexion and extension of the vertebral column

Flexion

Extension

Flexion

Extension

(d) Flexion and extension of the shoulder and knee

Dorsiflexion

Plantar flexion

(e) Dorsiflexion and plantar flexion of the foot

FIGURE 8.6
Movements allowed by synovial joints. (a) Gliding movements. (b–g) Angular movements. (h,i) Rotation.

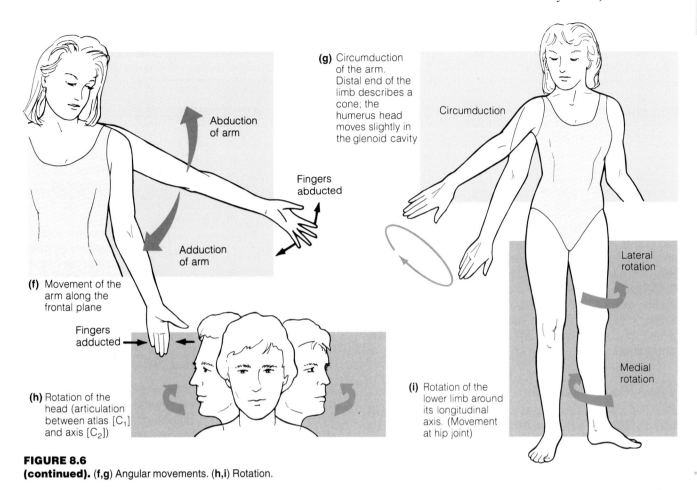

(g) Circumduction of the arm. Distal end of the limb describes a cone; the humerus head moves slightly in the glenoid cavity

Abduction of arm

Fingers abducted

Circumduction

Adduction of arm

(f) Movement of the arm along the frontal plane

Fingers adducted

(h) Rotation of the head (articulation between atlas [C₁] and axis [C₂])

Lateral rotation

Medial rotation

(i) Rotation of the lower limb around its longitudinal axis. (Movement at hip joint)

FIGURE 8.6
(continued). (f,g) Angular movements. **(h,i)** Rotation.

Flexion. Flexion (flek′shun) is a bending movement that *decreases the angle* of the joint and brings the two articulating bones closer together. The movement usually occurs along the sagittal plane. Examples include bending the head forward on the chest (Figure 8.6b) and bending the body trunk or the knee from a straight to an angled position (Figure 8.6c and d). As a less obvious example, the arm is flexed at the shoulder when the arm is lifted in an anterior direction (Figure 8.6d).

Extension. Extension is the reverse of flexion and occurs at the same joints. It involves movement along the sagittal plane that *increases the angle* between the articulating bones, such as straightening a flexed neck, body trunk, elbows, or knees (Figure 8.6b–d). Bending the head backward beyond the upright position is called **hyperextension.** At the shoulder, extension carries the arm to a point behind the shoulder joint.

Dorsiflexion and Plantar Flexion of the Foot.
The terms extension and flexion are not appropriate for describing the up-and-down movements of the foot at the ankle joint (Figure 8.6e). Since the foot joins the leg at a right angle, both upward and downward movements *decrease* this angle and, techni-

cally, both movements are flexion. Therefore, more specific terms are used: lifting the foot so that its superior surface approaches the shin is called **dorsiflexion,** whereas depressing the foot (pointing the toes) is called **plantar flexion.**

Abduction. Abduction ("moving away") is movement of a limb *away* from the midline or median plane of the body, along the frontal plane. Raising the arm (Figure 8.6f) or thigh laterally is an example of abduction. When the term is used to indicate the movement of the fingers or toes, it means spreading them apart. The "midline" reference point in this case is the longest digit: the third finger or second toe. Notice, however, that lateral bending of the trunk away from the body midline in the frontal plane is called *lateral flexion,* not abduction.

Adduction. Adduction ("moving toward") is the opposite of abduction, so it is the movement of a limb *toward* the body midline or, in the case of the digits, toward the midline of the hand or foot (Figure 8.6f).

Circumduction. Circumduction (Figure 8.6g) is moving a limb so that it describes a cone in space (*circum* = around; *duco* = to draw). While the distal end of the limb moves in a circle, the point of the cone (the shoulder or hip joint) is more or less stationary. A pitcher winding up to throw a ball is actually circumducting his or her pitching arm. Because circumduction consists of flexion, abduction, extension, and adduction performed in succession, it is the best (and quickest) way to exercise the muscles that move the hip and shoulder ball-and-socket joints. Circumduction is also a typical movement of the saddle joint of the thumb.

Rotation

Rotation is the turning of a bone around its own long axis. It is the only movement allowed between the first two cervical vertebrae (Figure 8.6h) and is common at the hip and shoulder joints (see Figure 8.6i). Rotation may occur toward the midline or away from it. For example, in *medial rotation* of the thigh, the femur's anterior surface moves toward the median plane of the body; *lateral rotation* is the opposite movement.

Special Movements

Certain movements occur only at specific joints or areas of the body (Figure 8.7). Since these movements involve more than a single joint or cannot be accurately regarded as any of the movements already described, they are classified as special movements.

Supination and Pronation.   The terms **supination** (soo″pĭ-na′shun; "turning backward") and **pronation** (pro-na′shun; "turning forward") typically refer to the movements of the radius around the ulna (Figure 8.7a). Rotating the forearm laterally so that the palm faces anteriorly or superiorly is supination. This is the movement a right-handed person uses to "drive" a screw. In the anatomical position, the hand is supinated and the radius and ulna are parallel. In pronation, the forearm rotates medially and the palm is moved to a posterior- or inferior-facing position. Pronation moves the distal end of the radius across the ulna so that the two bones form an X. This is the forearm's position when we are standing in a relaxed manner. Pronation is used to remove a screw and is a much weaker movement than supination.

A trick to help you keep these terms straight: If you lifted a cup of soup up to your mouth *on your palm,* you would be supinating ("soup"-inating).

Inversion and Eversion.   Inversion and **eversion** are special movements of the foot (Figure 8.7b). In inversion, the sole of the foot turns medially; in eversion, the sole faces laterally.

Protraction and Retraction.   Nonangular anterior and posterior movements in a transverse plane are called **protraction** and **retraction**, respectively (Figure

8.7c). The mandible is protracted when you jut out your jaw and retracted when you move it posteriorly back to its original position. "Squaring" your shoulders in a military stance is another example of retraction.

Elevation and Depression.   **Elevation** means lifting or moving a body part superiorly along a frontal plane (Figure 8.7d). For example, the scapulae are elevated when you shrug your shoulders. Moving the elevated part inferiorly is **depression.** During chewing, the mandible is alternately elevated and depressed.

Opposition.   The saddle joint between metacarpal 1 and the carpals allows a movement called **opposition** of the thumb. Although not illustrated in Figure 8.7, this movement is the action taken when you touch your thumb to the tips of the other fingers on the same hand. It is opposition that makes the human hand such a fine tool for grasping and manipulating objects.

Types of Synovial Joints

Although all synovial joints have common structural features, they do not have a common structural plan. Based on the structure (shape of their articular surfaces) and movements allowed, synovial joints can be classified further into six major categories—plane, hinge, pivot, condyloid, saddle, and ball-and-socket joints (Figure 8.8).

Plane Joints

In **plane joints** (Figure 8.8a) the articular surfaces are essentially flat, and they allow only short slipping or gliding movements. Examples of plane joints are the gliding joints introduced earlier—the intercarpal and intertarsal joints, and the joints between vertebral articular processes. Gliding does not involve rotation around any axis, and gliding joints are the only examples of nonaxial joints.

Hinge Joints

In **hinge joints** (Figure 8.8b), a convex or cylindrical projection of one bone fits into a concave surface or cylindrical groove on another. Motion is along a single plane and is similar to that of a mechanical hinge. The uniaxial hinge joints permit flexion and extension only, typified by bending and straightening the elbow and interphalangeal joints.

Pivot Joints

In a **pivot joint** (Figure 8.8c), the rounded or conical end of one bone protrudes into a "sleeve" or ring composed of bone (and possibly ligaments) of another. The only movement allowed is uniaxial rotation of one bone around its own long axis or against the

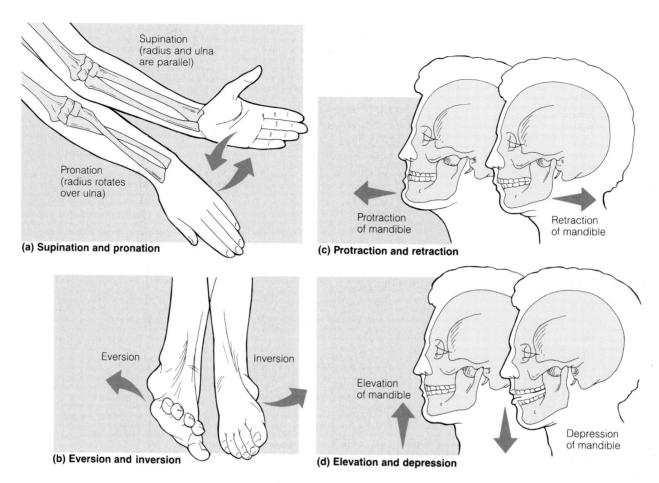

FIGURE 8.7
Special body movements.

other. An example is the joint between the atlas and dens of the axis, which allows you to move your head from side to side to indicate "no." Another is the proximal radioulnar joint, where the head of the radius rotates within a ringlike ligament secured to the ulna.

Condyloid Joints

In **condyloid** (kon'dĭ-loid; "knucklelike"), or **ellipsoidal, joints,** the oval articular surface of one bone fits into a complementary concavity in another (Figure 8.8d). The important characteristic is that both articulating surfaces are oval. The biaxial condyloid joints permit all angular motions, that is, flexion and extension, abduction and adduction, and circumduction. The radiocarpal (wrist) joints and the metacarpophalangeal (knuckle) joints are typical condyloid joints.

Certain joints, specifically the knee and temporomandibular joints, have dual articular surfaces—two convex condyles articulating with two concave surfaces. These joints are classified as **bicondylar joints** and act as *modified hinges.* They have a main move-

ment along a single plane (like a hinge joint), but they also exhibit some rotational movement, which can occur independently or accompany the main movement.

Saddle Joints

Saddle joints (Figure 8.8e) resemble condyloid joints, but they allow greater freedom of movement. Each articular surface has both concave and convex areas; that is, it is shaped like a saddle. The articular surfaces then fit together, concave to convex surfaces. The most clear-cut examples of saddle joints in the body are the carpometacarpal joints of the thumbs.

Ball-and-Socket Joints

In **ball-and-socket joints** (Figure 8.8f), the spherical or hemispherical head of one bone articulates with the concave socket of another. These joints are multiaxial and the most freely moving synovial joints. Universal movement is allowed (that is, in all axes and planes, including rotation). The shoulder and hip joints are ball-and-socket joints.

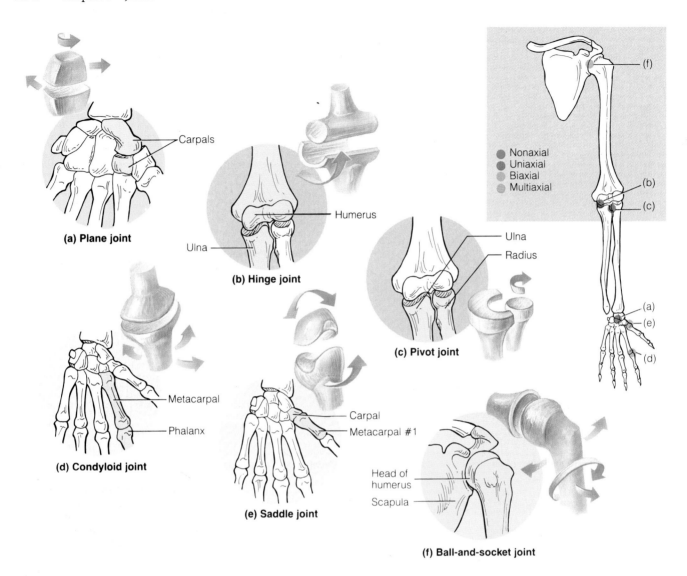

(a) Plane joint

(b) Hinge joint

Carpals

Humerus

Ulna

- ● Nonaxial
- ● Uniaxial
- ● Biaxial
- ● Multiaxial

(f)

(b)

(c)

Ulna

Radius

(c) Pivot joint

(a)

(e)

(d)

Metacarpal

Phalanx

(d) Condyloid joint

Carpal

Metacarpal #1

(e) Saddle joint

Head of humerus

Scapula

(f) Ball-and-socket joint

FIGURE 8.8
Types of synovial joints. Articulating bones being referenced are shown in gold; noninvolved bones are left white. (**a**) Plane joint (e.g., intercarpal and intertarsal joints). (**b**) Hinge joint (e.g., elbow joints and interphalangeal joints). (**c**) Pivot joint (e.g., proximal radioulnar joint). (**d**) Condyloid joint (e.g., metacarpophalangeal joints). (**e**) Saddle joint (e.g., carpometacarpal joint of the thumb). (**f**) Ball-and-socket joint (e.g., shoulder joint).

Selected Synovial Joints

In this section, we examine four joints (shoulder, elbow, hip, and knee) in detail. All of these joints have the five distinguishing characteristics of synovial joints, and we will not discuss these common features again. Rather, we will emphasize the unique structural features, functional abilities, and, in certain cases, functional weaknesses of each of these joints. ⸱

Shoulder (Glenohumeral) Joint

In the shoulder joint, stability has been sacrificed to provide the most freely moving joint of the body. The shoulder joint is a ball-and-socket joint formed by the head of the humerus and the small, shallow, pear-shaped glenoid cavity of the scapula (Figure 8.9). Although the glenoid cavity is slightly deepened by a rim of fibrocartilage, called the **glenoid labrum** (*labrum* = lip), it is only about one-third the size of the humeral head and contributes little to joint stability. The thin articular capsule enclosing the joint cavity (from the margin of the glenoid cavity to the anatomical neck of the humerus) is remarkably loose (a quality that contributes to this joint's freedom of movement rather than its stability).

The ligaments reinforcing the shoulder joint are located primarily on its anterior aspect. These include: (1) the **coracohumeral** (kor′ah-ko-hu′mer-ul) **ligament,** which extends from the coracoid process of the scapula to the greater tubercle of the humerus; this ligament provides the only strong thickening of the capsule and also helps support the weight of the upper limb; (2) the three **glenohumeral** (glě″no-hu′mer-ul) **ligaments,** which strengthen the front of

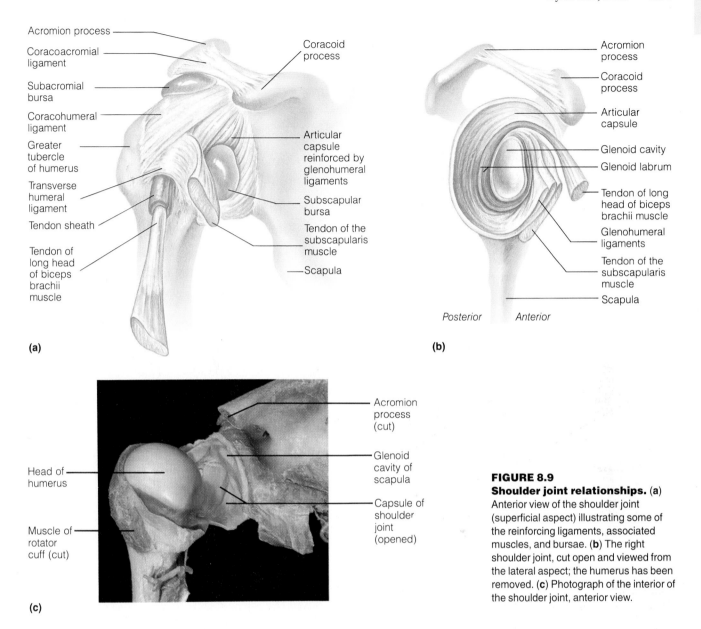

Acromion process
Coracoacromial ligament
Subacromial bursa
Coracohumeral ligament
Greater tubercle of humerus
Transverse humeral ligament
Tendon sheath
Tendon of long head of biceps brachii muscle

Coracoid process
Articular capsule reinforced by glenohumeral ligaments
Subscapular bursa
Tendon of the subscapularis muscle
Scapula

(a)

Acromion process
Coracoid process
Articular capsule
Glenoid cavity
Glenoid labrum
Tendon of long head of biceps brachii muscle
Glenohumeral ligaments
Tendon of the subscapularis muscle
Scapula

Posterior   *Anterior*

(b)

Head of humerus
Muscle of rotator cuff (cut)

Acromion process (cut)
Glenoid cavity of scapula
Capsule of shoulder joint (opened)

(c)

FIGURE 8.9
Shoulder joint relationships. (a) Anterior view of the shoulder joint (superficial aspect) illustrating some of the reinforcing ligaments, associated muscles, and bursae. **(b)** The right shoulder joint, cut open and viewed from the lateral aspect; the humerus has been removed. **(c)** Photograph of the interior of the shoulder joint, anterior view.

the capsule somewhat but are weak and may even be absent; and (3) the **transverse humeral ligament,** which spans the gap between the humeral tubercles. Several bursae are associated with the shoulder joint.

Although the ligaments help reinforce the shoulder joint, the muscle tendons that cross the shoulder joint are far more important. The "superstabilizer" is the tendon of the long head of the biceps brachii muscle of the arm (Figure 8.9a). This tendon runs from the superior margin of the glenoid labrum, travels through the joint cavity, and then exits the cavity and runs within the intertubercular groove of the humerus. It secures the head of the humerus tightly against the glenoid cavity. Four other tendons (and the associated muscles), collectively called the **rotator cuff,** encircle the joint and blend with the articular capsule. These include the tendons of the subscapularis, supraspinatus, infraspinatus, and teres minor

muscles. (The rotator cuff muscles are illustrated in Figure 10.14, p. 316.) Because of this arrangement, the rotator cuff can be severely stretched when the arm is vigorously circumducted; this is a common injury of baseball pitchers. As noted in Chapter 7, shoulder dislocations are fairly common. Since the shoulder's reinforcements are weakest inferiorly, the humerus tends to dislocate downward.

Hip (Coxal) Joint

The hip joint, like the shoulder joint, is a ball-and-socket joint. It has a good range of motion, but not nearly as wide as the shoulder's range. Movements occur in all possible planes but are limited by the joint's ligaments and its deep socket. The hip joint is formed by the articulation of the spherical head of the femur with the deeply cupped acetabulum of the

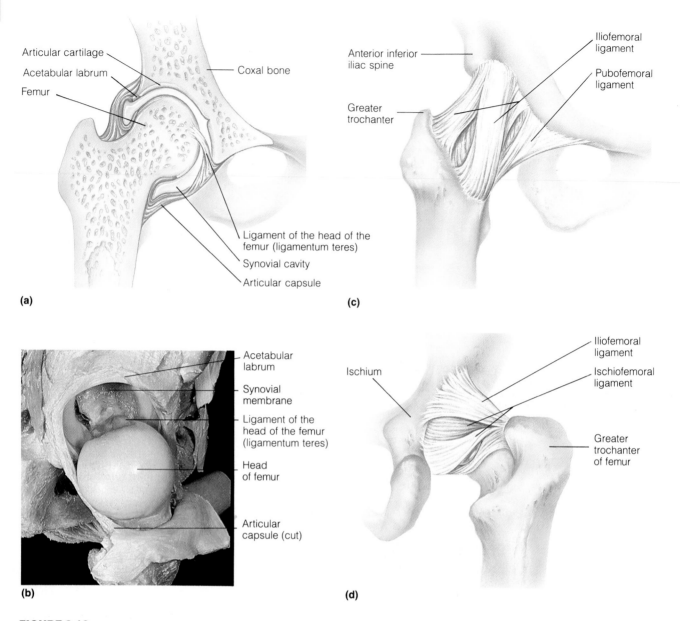

(a)

(b)

(c)

(d)

FIGURE 8.10
Hip joint relationships. (**a**) Frontal section through the right hip joint. (**b**) Photograph of the interior of the hip joint, lateral view. (**c**) Anterior superficial view of the right hip joint. (**d**) Posterior superficial view of the right hip joint.

coxal bone (Figure 8.10). The depth of the acetabulum is enhanced by a circular rim of fibrocartilage called the **acetabular** (as″ĕ-tab′u-lar) **labrum,** which has a diameter less than that of the head of the femur. In contrast to the articulation at the shoulder joint, these articular surfaces fit snugly together, and hip joint dislocations are rare.

The thick articular capsule extends from the rim of the acetabulum to the neck of the femur and completely encloses the joint. Several strong ligaments reinforce the capsule of the hip joint. These include the **iliofemoral** (il″e-o-fem′o-ral) **ligament,** a strong V-shaped ligament anteriorly; the **pubofemoral** (pu″bo-fem′o-ral) **ligament,** a triangular thickening of the

inferior part of the capsule; and the **ischiofemoral** (is″ke-o-fem′o-ral) **ligament,** a spiraling posteriorly located ligament. These ligaments are arranged in such a way that they "screw" the femur head into the acetabulum when a person stands up straight, thereby providing more stability.

The **ligament of the head of the femur,** also called the **ligamentum teres,** is a flat intracapsular ligament that runs from the femur head to the lower lip of the acetabulum. Since this ligament is slack during most hip movements, it is not important in stabilizing the joint. In fact, its mechanical function (if any) is unclear, but it does contain an artery that provides some of the arterial blood supply to the head of the

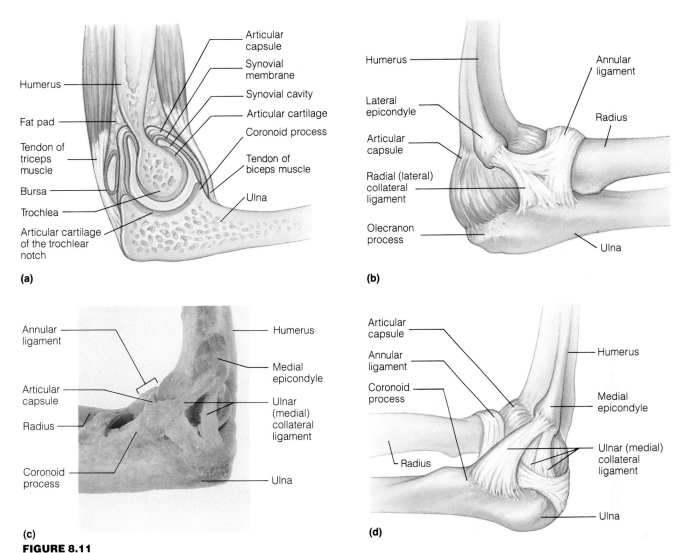

FIGURE 8.11
Elbow joint relationships. (**a**) Midsagittal section of right elbow joint. (**b**) Lateral view of right elbow joint. (**c**) Photograph of right elbow joint showing the important reinforcing ligaments, medial view. (**d**) Medial view of right elbow joint.

femur. Damage to this artery may lead to severe arthritis of the hip joint and degeneration of the femoral head.

Muscle tendons that cross the joint and the bulky hip and thigh muscles that surround it contribute to its stability and strength. However, the deep socket that securely encloses the femoral head and the strong ligaments provide most of the stability of the hip joint.

Elbow Joint

Our upper limbs are flexible extensions that permit us to reach out and manipulate things in our environment. Besides the shoulder joint, the most prominent of the upper limb joints is the elbow. The careful fitting of the humeral and ulnar bone ends forming this joint provides a stable and smoothly operating hinge that allows flexion and extension only (Figure 8.11). (Construction cranes have the same type of flexibility.) Within the joint, both the radius and ulna articu-

late with the condyles (trochlea and capitulum) of the humerus, but it is the close gripping of the trochlea by the ulna's trochlear notch that constitutes the "hinge" and the main stabilizing factor of this joint. A relatively lax articular capsule extends inferiorly from the coronoid and olecranon fossae of the humerus to the same-named processes of the ulna and to the **annular** (an'u-lar) **ligament** surrounding the head of the radius.

The articular capsule, thin anteriorly and posteriorly, allows substantial freedom for elbow flexion and extension. However, side-to-side movements are restricted by two strong ligaments. These are the **ulnar (medial) collateral ligament,** three bands reinforcing the capsule medially, and the **radial (lateral) collateral ligament,** a triangular ligament in the lateral side of the capsule. Additionally, tendons of several muscles (the biceps, triceps, brachialis, and others) cross the elbow joint and provide security.

Flexion at the elbow is limited by the meeting of the soft tissues of the forearm and arm. Extension is

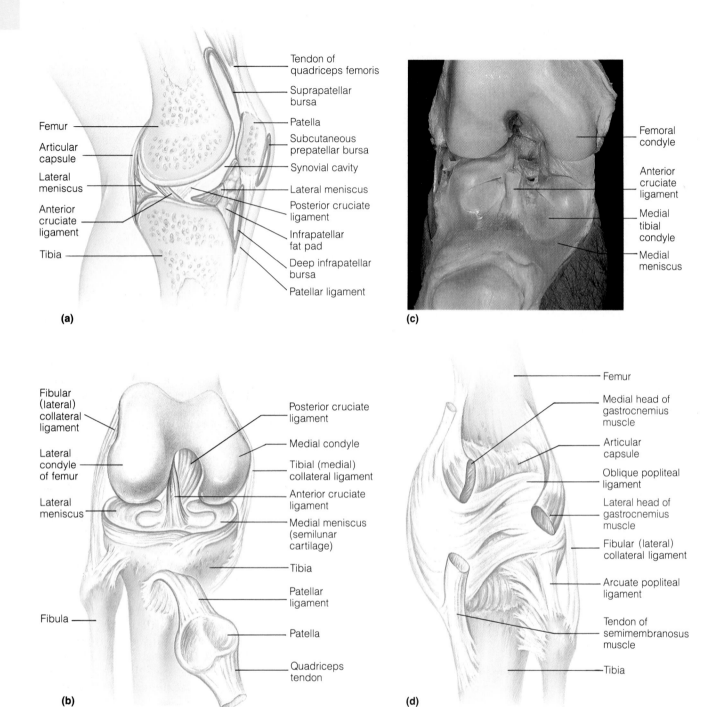

FIGURE 8.12

Knee joint relationships. (a) Midsagittal section of right knee joint. **(b)** Anterior view of slightly flexed right knee joint showing the cruciate ligaments. Articular capsule has been removed; the quadriceps tendon has been cut and reflected distally. **(c)** Photograph of an opened knee joint corresponds to view in (b). **(d)** Posterior superficial view of the ligaments clothing the knee joint.

checked by tension of the medial ligament, by tendons of the forearm flexor muscles, and by the close "fit" of the olecranon process in the olecranon fossa. The radius is a passive "onlooker" in the angular elbow movements, but its head rotates within the annular ligament during supination and pronation of the forearm.

Knee Joint

The knee joint is the largest and most complex joint in the body (Figure 8.12). It allows extension, flexion, and some rotation. Despite its single joint cavity, the knee consists of three joints in one: an intermediate one between the patella and the lower end of the femur (the **femoropatellar joint**), and lateral and medial joints (collectively known as the **tibiofemoral joint**) between the femoral condyles above and the C-shaped **menisci,** or *semilunar cartilages,* of the tibia below. Besides deepening the shallow tibial articular surfaces, the menisci help prevent side-to-side rocking of the femur on the tibia and absorb shock transmitted to the knee joint. (However, the menisci are attached only at their outer margins and are frequently torn free.) The tibiofemoral joint acts primarily as a hinge, permitting flexion and extension. However, it is structurally a bicondylar joint. Some rotation is possible when the knee is partly flexed, but when it is extended, side-to-side movements and rotation are strongly resisted by ligaments and the menisci. The femoropatellar joint is a plane joint, and the patella glides across the distal end of the femur during knee movements.

The knee joint is unique in that its joint cavity is only partially enclosed by a capsule. The relatively thin articular capsule is seen only on the sides and posterior aspects of the knee, where it covers the bulk of the femoral and tibial condyles. Anteriorly, where the capsule is absent, three broad ligaments run from the patella to the tibia below. These are the **patellar ligament** flanked by the **medial** and **lateral patellar retinacula** (ret″ĭ-nak′u-lah; "retainers"), which merge imperceptibly into the articular capsule on each side. The patellar ligament is actually a continuation of the tendon of the bulky quadriceps muscle of the anterior thigh; the retinacula are expansions of the same tendon. Physicians tap the patellar ligament to test the knee-jerk reflex.

The synovial cavity of the knee joint has a complicated shape, with several extensions that lead into "blind alleys." At least a dozen bursae are associated with the knee joint, some of which are shown in Figure 8.12a. For example, notice the *subcutaneous prepatellar bursa,* which is often injured when the knee is bumped, and the *suprapatellar bursa,* which protrudes upward beneath the quadriceps tendon.

Both extra- and intracapsular ligaments are important in stabilizing and strengthening the tenuous knee joint. The **extracapsular ligaments** all act to prevent hyperextension of the knee and are stretched taut when the knee is extended. These include the following:

1. The **fibular (lateral) and tibial (medial) collateral ligaments,** which are critical in preventing lateral or medial rotation when the knee is extended. The pencil-like fibular collateral ligament extends from the lateral epicondyle of the femur to the head of the fibula. The broad tibial collateral ligament runs from the medial epicondyle of the femur to the medial condyle of the tibial shaft below and is fused to the medial meniscus.

2. The **oblique popliteal** (pop″lĭ-te′al) **ligament,** which is actually an expansion of the tendon of the semimembranosus muscle crossing the posterior aspect of the knee joint.

3. The **arcuate popliteal ligament,** which arcs inferiorly from the lateral condyle of the femur to the head of the fibula and reinforces the joint capsule posteriorly.

The **intracapsular ligaments** are called *cruciate* (kroo′she-āt) *ligaments* because they cross each other forming an X (*cruci* = cross) within the notch between the femoral condyles. They help to prevent anterior-posterior displacement of the articular surfaces and to secure the articulating bones when we stand (see Figure 8.12b). Although these ligaments are within the joint capsule, they are *outside* the synovial cavity and synovial membrane nearly covers their surfaces. Note that the two cruciate ligaments are named for their *tibial* attachment site. The **anterior cruciate ligament** passes posteriorly, laterally, and upward from the anterior intercondylar area of the tibia to attach to the femur on the medial surface of its lateral condyle. This ligament prevents backward sliding of the femur on the tibia; it also checks hyperextension of the knee. It is somewhat lax when the knee is flexed and taut when the knee is extended. The stronger **posterior cruciate ligament** is attached to the posterior intercondylar area of the tibia and passes anteriorly, medially, and upward to attach to the lateral side of the medial femoral condyle. This ligament prevents forward sliding of the femur or backward displacement of the tibia; thus, it helps prevent overflexion of the knee joint.

The knee capsule is heavily reinforced by muscle tendons. Most important are the strong tendons of the quadriceps muscles of the anterior thigh and the tendon of the semimembranosus muscle posteriorly. Since the muscles associated with the joint are the major stabilizers of the knee, the greater their strength and tone, the less the chance of knee injury.

Analysis of Knee Movements. During the knee extension that occurs when we rise from a sitting position, the wheel-shaped femoral condyles travel like ball bearings across the flat condyles of the tibia until tension in the anterior cruciate ligament restricts further movement. This forward movement has two components that occur simultaneously (Figure 8.13a). It begins with the femur *sliding* posteriorly on the posterior aspect of its condyles. Then as the femur begins to erect, its condyles *roll* forward, bringing them into full contact with the menisci. Finally, because the lateral femoral condyle stops rolling before the medial condyle stops, the femur *spins* (rotates) medially on the tibia, which effectively "locks" the joint into a rigid structure that can support our body weight. When the knee is extended with a fixed femur (rather than a fixed tibia), the same movements occur (Figure 8.13b). However, in this case (1) the tibia does the moving (slide, roll, and spin), and (2) sliding and rolling occur in the *same* direction.

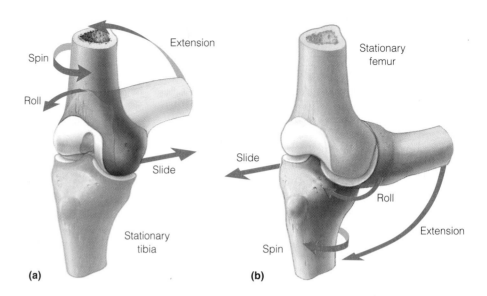

FIGURE 8.13
Knee joint movements. Analysis of articular movements occurring during extension of the right knee joint (viewed from medial aspect; patella, menisci, and other structural features omitted).
(a) With a stationary tibia, i.e., moving femoral condylar surfaces.
(b) With a stationary femur, i.e., moving tibial condylar surfaces. Notice that in each case elements of slide, roll, and spin occur together. In (a) the roll and slide are in opposite directions; in (b) they are in the same direction.

When the joint is fully extended (or slightly hyperextended), all major ligaments of the knee are twisted and taut and the menisci are compressed. For flexion to occur, the ligaments must be untwisted and become slack. This is accomplished by the popliteus muscle, which rotates the femur laterally on the tibia. When the knee is flexed at a right angle, considerable movement is possible—medial and lateral rotation and passive movement of the tibia forward and backward on the femur—because the collateral ligaments are slack in this position. Flexion ends when the thigh and leg make contact.

Of all body joints, the knees are most susceptible to sports injuries because of their high reliance on nonarticular factors for stability and the fact that they carry the body's weight. The knee can absorb a vertical force equal to nearly seven times body weight. However, it is very vulnerable to *horizontal* blows and to the high-pressure twisting movements such as those that occur during football blocking and tackling maneuvers. Most dangerous are lateral blows to the extended knee, which are apt to tear the medial collateral ligament and the medial meniscus attached to it, as well as the relatively weak anterior cruciate ligament (Figure 8.14). It is estimated that 50% of all professional football players have serious knee injuries during their careers. •

HOMEOSTATIC IMBALANCES OF JOINTS

Few of us pay attention to our joints unless something goes wrong with them. Yet considering the stress that our joints endure day in and day out, it is a wonder that joint disorders are so infrequent. Joint pain and malfunction can be caused by a number of factors, but most joint problems result from injuries and inflammatory or degenerative conditions.

Common Joint Injuries

For most of us, sprains and dislocations are the most common trauma-induced joint injuries, but cartilage injuries are equally threatening to athletes.

Sprains

In a **sprain,** the ligaments reinforcing a joint are stretched or torn. The lumbar region of the spine, the ankle, and the knee are common sprain sites. A partially torn ligament will repair itself, but since ligaments are so poorly vascularized, sprains heal slowly and tend to be painful and immobilizing. Completely ruptured ligaments must be repaired surgically and quickly, because inflammation in the joint will break down the neighboring tissues and turn the injured ligament to "mush." Surgical repair can be difficult: A ligament consists of hundreds of fibrous strands, and sewing one back together has been compared to trying to sew two hairbrushes together.

When important ligaments are too severely damaged to be repaired, they must be removed and replaced with substitute ligaments. For example, a piece of tendon from a muscle, or woven collagen bands, can be stapled to the articulating bones. Alternatively, carbon fibers are implanted in the torn ligament to form a supporting mesh, which is then invaded by fibroblasts that reconstruct the ligament.

Cartilage Injuries

Many aerobics devotees, encouraged to "feel the burn" during their workout, may feel the snap and pop of their overstressed cartilage instead. Although most cartilage injuries involve tearing of the knee menisci, growth plate fissures and overuse damage to the articular cartilages of other joints are becoming increasingly common in competitive young athletes such as Olympic hopefuls, particularly gymnasts.

Cartilage is avascular and it rarely can obtain sufficient nourishment to repair itself; thus, it usually stays torn. Because cartilage fragments (called *loose bodies*) can interfere with joint function by causing locking or binding of the joint, most sports physicians recommend that damaged cartilage be removed. Today, this can be done by **arthroscopic** (ar-thro-skop'ik; "looking into joints") **surgery,** a procedure which enables patients to be out of the hospital the same day. The arthroscope, a small instrument bearing a tiny lens and light source, enables the surgeon to view the interior of a joint through a small incision. The ligament is repaired or cartilage fragments are removed through one or more tiny slits, minimizing tissue damage and scarring. Removal of some or all of a meniscus does not severely impair knee joint mobility, but the joint is definitely less stable.

Dislocations

A **dislocation (luxation)** occurs when bones are forced out of their normal positions (alignment) at a joint. It is usually accompanied by sprains, inflammation, and joint immobilization. Dislocations may occur during a serious fall and are common contact sports injuries. Joints of the shoulders, fingers, and thumbs are commonly dislocated. Like fractures, dislocations must be *reduced;* that is, the bone ends must be returned to their proper positions by a physician. **Subluxation** is a partial dislocation of a joint.

Repeat dislocations of the same joint are common. This is because the initial dislocation stretches the joint capsule and ligaments, yielding a loose capsule that provides poor reinforcement for the joint.

Inflammatory and Degenerative Conditions

Inflammatory conditions that affect joints include bursitis, tendonitis, and various forms of arthritis.

Bursitis and Tendonitis

Bursitis is an inflammation of a bursa and is usually caused by excessive stress or friction. Falling on one's knee may result in a painful bursitis of the prepatellar bursa, known as *housemaid's knee* or *water on the knee.* Prolonged leaning on one's elbows may damage the bursa close to the olecranon process, producing *student's elbow,* or *olecranon bursitis.* Bursitis may also result from bacterial infection. Symptoms of bursitis include pain made worse by joint movement, redness, and swelling. Severe cases are treated by injecting anti-inflammatory drugs into the bursa. If excessive fluid accumulates, removing some fluid by needle aspiration may relieve the pressure. **Tendonitis** is inflammation of tendon sheaths. Its causes, symptoms, and treatment mirror those of bursitis.

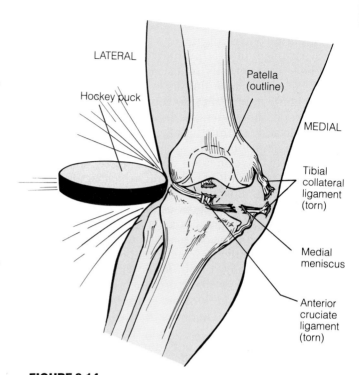

FIGURE 8.14
A common knee injury. Anterior view of a knee being hit by a hockey puck. In sports, most knee injuries result from blows to the lateral side. By separating the femur from the tibia medially, such blows tear both the tibial (medial) collateral ligament and the medial meniscus because the two are attached. The anterior cruciate ligament also tears.

Arthritis

The term **arthritis** describes over 100 different types of inflammatory or degenerative diseases that damage the joints. In all its forms, arthritis is the most widespread crippling disease in the United States. One out of seven Americans suffers its ravages. All forms of arthritis have, to a greater or lesser degree, the same initial symptoms: pain, stiffness, and swelling of the joint. Depending on the specific form, the synovial membrane, articular cartilages, articulating bones, or all of these may suffer damage.

Acute forms of arthritis usually result from bacterial invasion and are treated with antibiotics. The synovial membrane thickens and fluid production decreases, leading to increased friction and pain. Chronic forms of arthritis include osteoarthritis, rheumatoid arthritis, and gouty arthritis.

Osteoarthritis. Osteoarthritis (OA), the most common chronic arthritis, accounts for half of all cases. Although inflammation may occur, OA is generally considered a noninflammatory type of arthritis. It is often referred to as **degenerative joint disease** or "wear-and-tear arthritis." OA is most prevalent in the aged and is probably related to the normal aging process (although it is seen occasionally in younger people and some forms have a genetic basis).

Current theory holds that normal joint use prompts the release of enzymes that break down articular cartilage. In healthy individuals, this damaged cartilage is eventually replaced. In people with OA, however, the balance appears to be tipped toward cartilage destruction; that is, more is destroyed than replaced. Although its specific cause is unknown, OA may reflect the cumulative effects of years of compression and abrasion acting at joint surfaces (accompanied by excessive amounts of the cartilage-destroying enzymes) which ultimately cause the articular cartilages to soften, roughen, fray, and erode.

As the disease progresses, the exposed bone tissue thickens and forms bony spurs that enlarge the bone ends. The spurs encroach on the joint space and may restrict joint movement. Patients complain of stiffness on arising that lessens with activity. The affected joints may make a crunching noise when moving. This sound, called *crepitus* (krep′ĭ-tus), results as the roughened articular surfaces rub together. The joints most often affected are those of the fingers, the cervical and lumbar spine, and large weight-bearing joints of the lower limbs (knees and hips). The course of osteoarthritis is usually slow and irreversible. In most cases, its symptoms can be controlled with aspirin. A new magnetic therapy is reported to provide significant relief to about 70% of the patients treated. Although magnetic therapy seems a bit farfetched, the magnetic fields are assumed to stimulate the growth and repair of articular cartilage and to reverse the effects of OA. Another technique under investigation involves injecting hyaluronic acid into the joint cavity. As described earlier (see p. 227), hyaluronic acid is a natural polysaccharide that lubricates and cushions the joint. Its viscoelastic nature enables it to bounce back to its original shape after being compressed. Hence, it protects the joint surfaces from further erosion. Osteoarthritis is rarely crippling, but it can be, particularly when the hip or knee joints are involved.

Rheumatoid Arthritis.

Rheumatoid (roo′mah-toid) **arthritis (RA)** is a chronic inflammatory disorder with an insidious onset. Though it usually arises between the ages of 30 and 40, it may occur at any age. It affects three times as many women as men. While not as common as osteoarthritis, rheumatoid arthritis affects millions. It occurs in more than 1% of Americans. In the early stages of RA, fatigue and joint tenderness and stiffness are common. Many joints, particularly the small joints of the fingers, wrists, ankles, and feet, are afflicted at the same time and in a symmetrical manner. For example, if the right elbow is affected, most likely the left elbow is also affected. The course of RA is variable and marked by flare-ups (exacerbations) and remissions (*rheumat* = susceptible to change or flux). Other manifestations include anemia, osteoporosis, muscle atrophy, and cardiovascular problems.

FIGURE 8.15
Photograph of a hand deformed by rheumatoid arthritis.

RA is an *autoimmune disease*—a disorder in which the body's immune system attacks its own tissues. The initial trigger for this reaction is unknown, but the streptococcus bacterium and viruses have been suspect. Perhaps these microorganisms bear molecules similar to some naturally present in the joints, and the immune system, once activated, attempts to destroy both.

RA begins with inflammation of the synovial membrane (*synovitis*) of the affected joints, but ultimately all of the joint tissues may become involved. Without treatment, synovial fluid accumulates, causing joint swelling, and inflammatory cells (lymphocytes, neutrophils, and others) migrate into the joint cavity from the blood. In time, the inflamed synovial membrane thickens into a **pannus** ("rag"), an abnormal tissue that clings to the articular cartilages. Eventually, the cartilage (and sometimes the underlying bone) is eroded away by enzymes released by inflammatory cells in the pannus, and scar tissue forms and connects the bone ends. Later this scar tissue ossifies, and the bone ends fuse together. This condition, called *ankylosis* (ang′ki-lo′sis; "stiff condition"), often produces bent, deformed fingers (see Figure 8.15). Not all cases of RA progress to the severely crippling ankylosis stage, but all cases do involve restriction of joint movement and extreme pain.

Sadly, a wonder drug for RA sufferers is still unknown, and all of the drugs in use have some toxic effects, some very severe. Currently the pendulum is swinging from a conservative RA therapy (nonsteroidal anti-inflammatory drugs such as aspirin, and physical therapy) to a more progressive treatment course, particularly for patients with rapidly progressing RA. Powerful drugs (such as methotrexate,

A CLOSER LOOK | Joints: From Knights in Shining Armor to Bionic Man

There is a stark contrast between the time it took to develop joints for armor and the modern development of joint prostheses. The greatest challenge faced by visionary men of the Middle Ages and Renaissance was to design armor joints that allowed mobility while still protecting the human joints beneath. The ball-and-socket joints that they found so difficult to protect were the first to be engineered by modern-day "visionaries" for implantation into the body.

The history of joint prostheses (artificial joints) is less than 50 years old. It dates back to the 1940s and 1950s, when World War II and the Korean War produced large numbers of wounded who needed artificial limbs and joints. Today, about a quarter of a million arthritis patients receive total joint replacements each year, mostly because of the destructive effects of osteoarthritis or rheumatoid arthritis.

The human body attempts to reject or corrode any implanted foreign object. To produce strong, mobile, lasting joints, a substance was needed that was strong, nontoxic to the body, and resistant to the corrosive effects of organic acids present in the blood. In 1963, Sir John Charnley, an English orthopedic surgeon, performed the first total hip replacement and revolutionized the therapy of arthritic hips. His device consisted of a Vitallium metal ball on a stem and a cup-shaped polyethylene plastic socket anchored to the pelvis by methyl methacrylate cement. This cement proved to be exceptionally strong and relatively problem free. It was not until ten years later that total knee joint replacements that operated smoothly and allowed most natural movements of the knee became available. Earlier devices locked abruptly when the knee was extended, causing the patient to fall or the joint to be wrenched free.

Replacement joints employing both metal and plastic, or a bio-ceramic material resembling bone,

are now available for a number of other joints, including the fingers, elbow, and shoulder. Current techniques have produced total hip and knee replacements that last about ten years in elderly patients who do not excessively stress the joint. Most such operations are done to reduce pain and restore about 80% of original joint function.

Replacement joints are not yet strong or durable enough for young, active people and the prosthesis work loose over time. The goal of producing a better fit between implant and bone has encouraged dramatic changes in the way joints are designed, manufactured, and installed. CAD/CAM (computer-aided design and computer-aided manufacturing) techniques are being used to design and create individualized artificial joints (see photo). Fed the patient's X rays and information about the patient's problems, the computer draws from a database of hundreds of normal joints and generates possible designs and modifications for a joint prosthesis that can be reviewed in less than a minute. Once the design is selected, the computer directs the machines that modify the implant or fabricate a totally new joint prosthesis.

The influence of CAD/CAM on

the joint replacement business is enormous. Time and cost have been dramatically reduced. Furthermore, the CAD/CAM technique has paved the way for modular parts that allow only a part of a joint to be replaced (e.g., just the femoral component of the knee if that is the only portion damaged). Thus, the joint surgeon has access to a tremendous variety of modules to customize prostheses.

Joint replacement therapy is coming of age, but perhaps equally exciting is research into the capability of joint tissues to regenerate. We now know that if a joint with localized articular cartilage damage is slowly flexed and extended over a period of weeks, the joint cartilage sometimes regenerates itself. Furthermore, cultured chondrocytes grafted onto joint surfaces can produce enough new cartilage to fill small holes and breaks. This offers hope for younger patients, since it could stave off the need for a joint prosthesis for several years.

And so, through the centuries, the focus has shifted from jointed armor to artificial joints that can be put inside the body to restore lost joint function. Modern technology has in fact accomplished what the armor designers of the Middle Ages never even dreamed of.

azathioprine, cyclosporine, and others) are used from the start to alter the disease course and prevent joint deformity. Joint prostheses, if available, are the last resort for severely crippled RA patients (see *A Closer Look* on p. 243).

Gouty Arthritis. Uric acid, a normal waste product of nucleic acid metabolism, is ordinarily eliminated in urine without any problems. However, when blood levels of uric acid rise excessively, it may be deposited as urate crystals in the soft tissues of joints. This leads to an agonizingly painful attack of **gouty** (gow'te) **arthritis,** or gout. Initial attacks typically affect one joint, often at the base of the great toe.

Gout is far more common in males than in females because males have higher blood levels of uric acid. Some gout sufferers have an excessive rate of uric acid production; others flush uric acid out of the body in urine more slowly than normal. Some patients have both problems. Because gout seems to run in families, genetic factors are definitely implicated.

Untreated gout can be very destructive; the articulating bone ends fuse and immobilize the joint. Fortunately, several drugs (colchicine, allopurinol, and others) that terminate or prevent gout attacks are available. Since some individuals suffer only one attack of gouty arthritis in their lifetime, drug therapy is usually withheld until at least two such attacks have occurred. Patients are advised to avoid foods high in purine-containing nucleic acids, such as liver, kidneys, and sardines.

Lyme Disease

Lyme disease is caused by bacteria (spirochetes) transmitted by bites from ticks that live on deer. Arthritis is a major symptom, especially in the knee joint, along with a rash and flulike symptoms. Although the symptoms eventually decline in most cases, they may persist for years in untreated disease, and occasionally they may proceed to neurological disorders and heartbeat irregularities. Symptoms vary from person to person, but a new blood test has made Lyme disease less difficult to diagnose. It is treatable with antibiotics, but it takes a long time to kill the infecting bacteria. The incidence of Lyme disease seems to be increasing in the United States. •

DEVELOPMENTAL ASPECTS OF JOINTS

As bones form from mesenchyme during the first two months of development, the joints develop in parallel. By eight weeks, the synovial joints resemble adult joints in form and arrangement: Joint cavities are present, synovial membranes are developed, and synovial fluid is being secreted.

Injuries aside, relatively few interferences with joint function occur until late middle age. Eventually, however, advancing years take their toll. The intervertebral discs become more likely to rupture (herniate), and osteoarthritis rears its ugly head. Virtually everyone has osteoarthritis to some degree by the time they are in their 70s. The middle years also see an increased incidence of rheumatoid arthritis.

Just as bones must be stressed to maintain their strength, joints must be exercised prudently to keep the articular cartilages well nourished and to maintain their mobility. The key word is "prudently," because excessive or abusive use of the joints guarantees early onset of osteoarthritis. Although exercise does not prevent arthritis, it strengthens the muscles that help support and stabilize the joints. The buoyancy of water relieves much of the stress on weight-bearing joints, and people who swim or exercise in a pool often retain good joint function as long as they live. As with so many medical problems, it is easier to prevent joint problems than to cure or correct them.

* * *

The importance of joints is obvious: The skeleton's ability to protect other organs and to move smoothly reflects their presence. Now that we have scrutinized joint structure and are familiar with the movements that joints allow, we are ready to consider how the muscles attached to the skeleton cause body movements by acting across its joints.

RELATED CLINICAL TERMS

Ankylosing spondylitis (ang'kĭ-lōz″ing spon″dĭ-li'tis; *ankyl* = crooked, bent; *spondyl* = vertebra) An unusual variant of rheumatoid arthritis that chiefly affects males; it usually begins in the sacroiliac joints and progresses superiorly along the spine; the vertebrae become interconnected by fibrous tissue, causing the spine to become rigid ("poker back").

Arthrology (ar-throl'o-je; *arthros* = joint; *logos* = study) The study of joints.

Rheumatism A term used by laypeople to indicate disease involving muscle or joint pain; consequently may be used to apply to arthritis, bursitis, etc.

Synovitis (sin″o-vi'tis) Inflammation of the synovial membrane of a joint; in healthy joints, only small amounts of synovial fluid are present; but synovitis causes copious amounts to be produced, leading to swelling and limitation of joint movement.

CHAPTER SUMMARY

1. Joints, or articulations, are sites where bones meet. Their functions are to hold bones together and to allow various degrees of skeletal movement.

Classification of Joints (pp. 222–223)

1. Joints are classified structurally as fibrous, cartilaginous, or synovial. They are classed functionally as synarthrotic, amphiarthrotic, or diarthrotic.

Fibrous Joints (pp. 223–225)

1. Fibrous joints occur where bones are connected by fibrous tissue; no joint cavity is present. Nearly all fibrous joints are synarthrotic.

2. Sutures/Syndesmoses/Gomphoses. The major types of fibrous joints are sutures, syndesmoses, and gomphoses.

Cartilaginous Joints (p. 226)

1. In cartilaginous joints, the bones are united by cartilage; no joint cavity is present.

2. Synchondroses/Symphyses. Cartilaginous joints include synchondroses and symphyses. Some synchondroses and all symphyses are amphiarthrotic.

Synovial Joints (pp. 226–240)

1. Most body joints are synovial joints, all of which are diarthrotic.

General Structure (pp. 226–227)

2. All synovial joints have a joint cavity enclosed by a fibrous capsule lined with synovial membrane and reinforced by ligaments, articulating bone ends covered with articular cartilage, and synovial fluid in the joint cavity. Some (e.g., the knee) contain fibrocartilage discs that absorb shock.

Bursae and Tendon Sheaths (p. 228)

3. Bursae are fibrous sacs lined with synovial membrane and containing synovial fluid. Tendon sheaths are similar to bursae but are cylindrical structures that surround muscle tendons. Both allow adjacent structures to move smoothly over one another.

Factors Influencing the Stability of Synovial Joints (pp. 228–229)

4. Articular surfaces providing the most stability have large surfaces and deep sockets and fit snugly together.

5. Ligaments prevent undesirable movements and help to direct joint movement.

6. The tone of muscles whose tendons cross the joint is an important stabilizing factor in many joints.

Movements Allowed by Synovial Joints (pp. 229–232)

7. When a skeletal muscle contracts, the insertion (movable attachment) moves toward the origin (immovable attachment). Three common types of movements can occur when muscles contract across joints: (a) gliding movements, (b) angular movements (which include flexion, extension, abduction, adduction, and circumduction), and (c) rotation.

8. Special movements include supination and pronation, inversion and eversion, protraction and retraction, elevation and depression, and opposition.

Types of Synovial Joints (pp. 232–233)

9. Synovial joints differ in their range of motion. Motion may be nonaxial (gliding), uniaxial (in one plane), biaxial (in two planes), or multiaxial (in all three planes).

10. The six major categories of synovial joints are plane joints (movement nonaxial), hinge joints (movement uniaxial), pivot joints (uniaxial, rotation permitted), condyloid joints (biaxial with angular movements in two planes), saddle joints (biaxial, like condyloid joints, but with freer movement), and ball-and-socket joints (multiaxial and rotational movement).

Selected Synovial Joints (pp. 234–240)

11. The elbow is a hinge joint in which the ulna (and radius) articulates with the humerus, allowing flexion and extension. Its articular surfaces are highly complementary and are the most important factor contributing to joint stability.

12. The shoulder joint is a ball-and-socket joint formed by the glenoid cavity of the scapula and the humeral head. The most freely movable joint of the body, it allows all angular and rotational movements. Its articular surfaces are shallow. Its capsule is lax and poorly reinforced by ligaments. The tendons of the biceps brachii and rotator cuff muscles help to stabilize it.

13. The hip joint is a ball-and-socket joint formed by the acetabulum of the coxal bone and the femoral head. It is highly adapted for weight bearing. Its articular surfaces are deep and secure. Its capsule is heavy and strongly reinforced by ligaments.

14. The knee joint is the largest joint in the body. It is a hinge joint formed by the articulation of the tibial and femoral condyles (and anteriorly by the patella and patellar surface of the femur). Extension, flexion, and (some) rotation are allowed. Its articular surfaces are shallow and condyloid. C-shaped menisci deepen the articular surfaces. The joint cavity is enclosed by a capsule only on the sides and posterior aspects. Several extracapsular ligaments and the intracapsular anterior and posterior cruciate ligaments help prevent displacement of the joint surfaces. Muscle tone of the quadriceps and semimembranosus muscles is important in knee stability.

Homeostatic Imbalances of Joints (pp. 240–244)

Common Joint Injuries (pp. 240–241)

1. Sprains involve stretching or tearing of joint ligaments. Since ligaments are poorly vascularized, healing is slow.

2. Cartilage injuries, particularly of the knee, are common in contact sports and may result from excessive twisting or high pressure. The avascular cartilage is unable to repair itself.

3. Dislocations involve displacement of the articular surfaces of bones. They must be reduced.

Inflammatory and Degenerative Conditions (pp. 241–244)

4. Bursitis and tendonitis are inflammations of a bursa and a tendon sheath, respectively.

5. Arthritis is joint inflammation or degeneration accompanied by stiffness, pain, and swelling. Acute forms generally result from bacterial infection. Chronic forms include osteoarthritis, rheumatoid arthritis, and gouty arthritis.

6. Osteoarthritis is a degenerative condition most common in the aged. Weight-bearing joints are most affected.

7. Rheumatoid arthritis, the most crippling arthritis, is an autoimmune disease involving severe inflammation of the joints.

8. Gouty arthritis, or gout, is joint inflammation caused by the deposit of urate salts in soft joint tissues.

9. Arthritis is a *symptom* of Lyme disease, a condition caused by bacteria transmitted by tick bites.

Developmental Aspects of Joints (p. 244)

1. Joints form from mesenchyme and in tandem with bone development in the embryo.

2. Excluding traumatic injury, joints usually function well until late middle age, at which time symptoms of osteoarthritis begin to appear in most people.

REVIEW QUESTIONS

Multiple Choice/Matching

1. Match the key terms to the appropriate descriptions.

Key: **(a)** fibrous joints   **(b)** cartilaginous joints
      (c) synovial joints

_____ **(1)** exhibit a joint cavity

_____ **(2)** types are sutures and syndesmoses

_____ **(3)** bones connected by collagen fibers

_____ **(4)** types include synchondroses and symphyses

_____ **(5)** all are diarthrotic

_____ **(6)** many are amphiarthrotic

_____ **(7)** bones connected by a disc of hyaline cartilage or fibrocartilage

_____ **(8)** nearly all are synarthrotic

_____ **(9)** shoulder, hip, jaw, and elbow joints

2. Freely movable joints are (a) synarthroses, (b) diarthroses, (c) amphiarthroses.

3. Anatomical characteristics of a synovial joint include (a) articular cartilage, (b) a joint cavity, (c) an articular capsule, (d) all of these.

4. Factors that influence the stability of a synovial joint include (a) shape of articular surfaces, (b) presence of strong reinforcing ligaments, (c) tone of surrounding muscles, (d) all of these.

 5. The following description—"Articular surfaces deep and secure; capsule heavily reinforced by ligaments and muscle tendons; extremely stable joint"—best describes (a) the elbow joint, (b) the hip joint, (c) the knee joint, (d) the shoulder joint.

6. Ankylosis means (a) twisting of the ankle, (b) tearing of ligaments, (c) displacement of a bone, (d) immobility of a joint due to fusion of its articular surfaces.

7. An autoimmune disorder in which joints are affected bilaterally and which involves pannus formation and gradual joint immobilization is (a) bursitis, (b) gout, (c) osteoarthritis, (d) rheumatoid arthritis.

Short Answer Essay Questions

8. Define joint.

9. Discuss the relative value (to body homeostasis) of immovable, slightly movable, and freely movable joints.

10. Compare the structure, function, and common body locations of bursae and tendon sheaths.

11. Joint movements may be nonaxial, uniaxial, biaxial, or multiaxial. Define what each of these terms means.

12. Compare and contrast the paired movements of flexion and extension with adduction and abduction.

13. How does rotation differ from circumduction?

14. Name two types of uniaxial, biaxial, and multiaxial joints.

15. What is the specific role of the menisci of the knee? of the anterior and posterior cruciate ligaments?

16. The knee has been called "a beauty and a beast." Provide several reasons that might explain the negative (beast) part of this description.

17. Why are sprains and cartilage injuries a particular problem?

CRITICAL THINKING AND CLINICAL APPLICATION QUESTIONS

1. Sophie worked as a cleaning woman for 30 years so she could send her two children to college. Several times, she had been forced to call her employers to tell them she could not come in to work because one of her kneecaps was swollen and painful. What is Sophie's condition, and what probably caused it?

2. As Harry was jogging down the road, he tripped and his left ankle twisted violently to the side. When he picked himself up, he was unable to put any weight on that ankle. The diagnosis was severe dislocation and sprains of the left ankle. The orthopedic surgeon stated that she would perform a closed reduction of the dislocation and attempt ligament repair by using arthroscopy. (a) Is the ankle joint normally a stable joint? (b) What does its stability depend on? (c) What is a closed reduction? (d) Why is ligament repair necessary? (e) What does arthroscopy entail? (f) How will the use of this procedure minimize Harry's recuperation time (and suffering)?

3. A 45-year-old woman appeared at her physician's office complaining of unbearable pain in the distal interphalangeal joint of her right great toe. The joint was very reddened and swollen. When asked if she had ever had such an episode in the past, she recalled a similar attack two years earlier that had disappeared as suddenly as it had come. Her diagnosis was arthritis. (a) What type? (b) What is the precipitating cause of this particular type of arthritis?

Muscles and Muscle Tissue

9

Because flexing muscles look like mice scurrying beneath the skin, some scientist long ago dubbed them *muscles,* from the Latin word *mus* meaning "little mouse." Indeed, the rippling muscles of professional boxers or weight lifters are often the first thing that comes to mind when one hears the word muscle. But muscle is also the dominant tissue in the heart and in the walls of other hollow organs of the body. In all its forms, it makes up nearly half the body's mass. Its most distinguishing functional characteristic is its ability to transform chemical energy (in the form of ATP) into directed mechanical energy. In so doing, muscle becomes capable of exerting force.

Muscles can be viewed as the "machines" of the body. Mobility of the body as a whole reflects the activity of skeletal muscles. These are distinct from the muscles of internal organs, most of which force fluid and other substances through internal body channels.

OVERVIEW OF MUSCLE TISSUES

Muscle Types

The three types of muscle tissue are *skeletal, cardiac,* and *smooth.* These muscle tissues differ in the structure of their cells, their body location, their function, and the means by which they are activated to contract. Before exploring their differences, however, let us look at some of their similarities. First, all muscle cells are elongated and, for this reason, are called **muscle fibers.** Second, muscle contraction depends on two kinds of **myofilaments,** muscle equivalents of the actin- or myosin-containing microfilaments described in Chapter 3. As you will recall, these two proteins play roles in motility and shape changes in virtually every cell in the body, but this property reaches its highest development in the contractile muscle fibers. The third and final similarity concerns terminology: Whenever you see the prefixes **myo** or **mys** (both are word roots meaning "muscle") and **sarco** (flesh), the reference is to muscle. For example, the plasma membrane of muscle fibers is called the *sarcolemma* (sar"ko-lem'ah), literally "muscle" (sarco) "husk" (lemma), and muscle fiber cytoplasm is called *sarcoplasm.*

Skeletal muscle tissue is packaged into the *skeletal muscles* that attach to and cover the bony skeleton. Skeletal muscle fibers are the longest of the muscle cell types, have obvious stripes called **striations,** and can be controlled voluntarily. Although it is often activated by reflexes without our willed "command," skeletal muscle is called **voluntary muscle** because it is the only type subject to conscious control. When you think of skeletal muscle tissue, the key words to keep in mind are *skeletal, striated,* and *voluntary.* Skeletal muscle can contract rapidly, but it tires easily and must rest after short periods of activity. These muscles can exert tremendous power, a fact revealed by reports of people lifting cars to save their loved ones. Skeletal muscle is also remarkably adaptable. For example, your hand muscles can exert a force of a fraction of an ounce to pick up a dropped paper clip and the same muscles can exert a force of about 70 pounds to pick up this book!

Cardiac muscle tissue occurs only in the heart, where it constitutes most of the mass of the heart walls. Like skeletal muscle, cardiac muscle is striated, but it is not voluntary. Most of us have no conscious control over how fast our heart beats. Key words to remember for this muscle type are *cardiac, striated,* and *involuntary.* Cardiac muscle usually contracts at a fairly steady rate set by the heart's pacemaker, but neural controls allow the heart to "shift into high gear" for brief periods, as when you race across the tennis court to make that overhead smash, for instance.

Smooth muscle tissue is found in the walls of hollow visceral organs, such as the stomach, urinary bladder, and respiratory passages. It has no striations, and, like cardiac muscle, it is not subject to voluntary control. We can describe smooth muscle tissue most precisely as *visceral, nonstriated,* and *involuntary.* Contractions of smooth muscle fibers are slow and sustained. If skeletal muscle is like a speedy windup

car that quickly runs down, then smooth muscle is like a steady, heavy-duty engine that lumbers along tirelessly.

Skeletal muscle and smooth muscle are discussed in this chapter. Cardiac muscle is discussed in Chapter 19 (The Heart). Table 9.4 on pp. 276–277 summarizes the most important characteristics of each type of muscle tissue.

Muscle Functions

Muscle performs four important functions for the body: It produces movement, maintains posture, stabilizes joints, and generates heat.

Producing Movement

Just about all movements of the human body and its parts are a result of muscle contraction (or, at least, reflect the contractile properties of the actin- and myosin-containing filaments present in other cell types). Skeletal muscles are responsible for all locomotion and manipulation, and they enable you to respond quickly to changes in the external environment. For example, their speed and power enable you to jump out of the way of a runaway car. Vision relies partly on skeletal muscles that direct your eyeballs, and the silent language of contracting facial muscles can express joy or fury.

Coursing of blood through your body reflects the work of the rhythmically beating cardiac muscle of your heart and the smooth muscle in the walls of your blood vessels, which helps maintain blood pressure. Smooth muscle in organs of the digestive, urinary, and reproductive tracts propels, or squeezes, substances (foodstuffs, urine, a baby) through the organs and along the tract.

Maintaining Posture

We are rarely aware of the workings of the skeletal muscles that maintain body posture. Yet, these muscles function almost continuously, making one tiny adjustment after another that enables us to maintain an erect or seated posture despite the never-ending downward pull of gravity.

Stabilizing Joints

Even as muscles pull on bones to cause movements, they stabilize the joints of the skeleton. As described in Chapter 8, skeletal muscles help stabilize those joints with poor reinforcement or noncomplementary articular surfaces, such as the shoulder and the knee.

Generating Heat

Finally, because no "machine" operates with perfect efficiency, muscles generate heat as they contract.

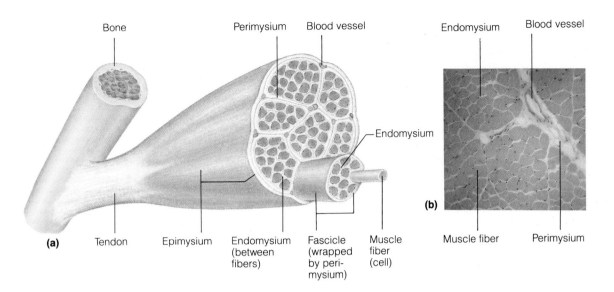

FIGURE 9.1
Connective tissue wrappings of skeletal muscle. (a) In a skeletal muscle, each muscle fiber is wrapped with a delicate connective tissue sheath, the endomysium.

Bundles, or fascicles, of muscle fibers are bound by a collagenic sheath called a perimysium. The entire muscle is strengthened and wrapped by a coarse

epimysium sheath. **(b)** Photomicrograph of a cross section of a skeletal muscle (64 ×).

This heat is vitally important in maintaining normal body temperature. Since skeletal muscle accounts for at least 40% of body mass, it is the muscle type most responsible for generating heat.

Functional Characteristics of Muscle

Muscle tissue is endowed with some distinctive functional properties that enable it to perform its duties. These properties include excitability, contractility, extensibility, and elasticity.

Excitability, or **irritability,** is the ability to receive and respond to a stimulus. (A *stimulus* is an environmental change; it may arise either inside or outside the body.) In the case of muscle, the stimulus is usually a chemical—for example, a neurotransmitter released by a nerve cell, a hormone, or a local change in pH. The response is the generation and transmission of an electrical current (called an action potential) along the sarcolemma that signals the muscle cell to contract.

Contractility is the ability to shorten forcibly when adequately stimulated. This property sets muscle apart from all other tissue types.

Extensibility is the ability to be stretched or extended. Muscle fibers shorten when contracting, but they can be stretched, even beyond their resting length, when relaxed.

Elasticity is the ability of a muscle fiber to resume its resting length after being stretched.

In the following section, we examine the structure and functioning of skeletal muscle in detail. Then we consider smooth muscle more briefly,

largely by comparing it with skeletal muscle. Because cardiac muscle is described in Chapter 19, its further treatment in this chapter is limited to the summary of its characteristics provided in Table 9.4.

SKELETAL MUSCLE

The levels of skeletal muscle organization, gross to microscopic, are summarized in Table 9.1 on p. 250.

Gross Anatomy of a Skeletal Muscle

Each **skeletal muscle** is a discrete organ, made up of hundreds to thousands of muscle fibers. Although muscle fibers predominate, substantial amounts of connective tissue, blood vessels, and nerve fibers are also present. A skeletal muscle's shape and the means of its attachment within the body can be examined easily without the help of a microscope.

Connective Tissue Wrappings

In an intact muscle, the individual muscle fibers are wrapped and held together by several different layers of connective tissue (Figure 9.1). Each muscle fiber is surrounded by a fine sheath of areolar connective tissue called the **endomysium** (en″do-mis′e-um). Several ensheathed muscle fibers are then gathered together side by side into bundles of muscle cells called **fascicles** (fas′ĭ-klz; *fasci* = bundle, band), and each fascicle is bound by a collagenic sheath referred to as a **perimysium** (per″ĭ-mis′e-um). The fascicles are in turn bound together by an even coarser "overcoat"

Table 9.1 Structure and Organizational Levels of Skeletal Muscle

Structure and organizational level		Description	Connective tissue wrappings
Muscle (organ)	Epimysium Fascicle Muscle Tendon	Consists of hundreds to thousands of muscle cells, plus connective tissue wrappings, blood vessels, and nerve fibers	Covered externally by the epimysium
Fascicle (a portion of the muscle)	Part of a fascicle Muscle fiber (cell) Perimysium	Discrete bundle of muscle cells, segregated from the rest of the muscle by a connective tissue sheath	Surrounded by a perimysium
Muscle fiber (cell)	Part of a muscle fiber Nucleus Myofibril	Elongated multinucleate cell; has a banded (striated) appearance	Surrounded by the endomysium
Myofibril or fibril (complex organelle composed of bundles of myofilaments)	Sarcomere Myofibril	Rodlike contractile element; myofibrils occupy most of he muscle cell volume; appear banded, and bands of adjacent myofibrils are aligned; composed of sarcomeres, arranged end to end	
Sarcomere (a segment of a myofibril)	Sarcomere Thin (actin) filament Thick (myosin) filament	The contractile unit, composed of myofilaments made up of contractile proteins	
Myofilament or filament (extended macromolecular structure)	Thin filament Actin molecules Thick filament Head of myosin molecule	Myofilaments are of two types—thick and thin—composed of contractile proteins; the thick filaments contain bundled myosin molecules; the thin filaments contain actin molecules (plus other proteins); the sliding of the thin filaments past the thick filaments produces muscle shortening	

of dense fibrous connective tissue called the **epimysium** (ep″ĭ-mis′e-um). The epimysium surrounds the entire muscle. External to the epimysium is the **deep fascia** (fash′e-ah), a still coarser sheet of fibrous connective tissue that binds muscles into functional groups, and extends to wrap other structures as well.

As shown in Figure 9.1, all of these connective tissue sheaths are continuous with one another as well as with the tendons that join muscles to bones. Therefore, when muscle fibers contract, they pull on these sheaths, which in turn transmit the force to the bone to be moved.

Like all body cells, skeletal muscle fibers are soft and fragile. The connective tissue coverings support each cell, reinforce the muscle as a whole, and provide muscle tissue with its natural elasticity. These sheaths also provide entry and exit routes for the blood vessels and nerve fibers that serve the muscle.

Nerve and Blood Supply

The normal activity of a skeletal muscle is absolutely dependent on its nerve supply and its rich blood supply. Unlike the other muscle tissues, which can contract in the total absence of nerve stimulation, each skeletal muscle fiber is supplied with a nerve ending that controls its activity.

Contracting muscle fibers use huge amounts of energy, which requires a more or less continuous delivery of oxygen and nutrients by way of arteries. Muscle cells also give off large amounts of metabolic wastes that must be removed through veins if contraction is to remain efficient. In general, each muscle is served by an artery and one or more veins.

The blood vessels and nerve fibers supplying each muscle fiber typically enter the central part of the muscle and branch profusely through its connective tissue septa, finally invading the delicate endomysium surrounding each muscle fiber. Muscle capillaries, the smallest of the blood vessels, are long and winding. This feature permits them to accommodate changes in muscle length—by straightening when the muscle is stretched and contorting when the muscle contracts.

Attachments

Recall from Chapter 8 that (1) most muscles span joints and are attached to bones (or other structures) in at least two places and (2) when a muscle contracts, the movable bone, the muscle's **insertion,** moves toward the immovable or less movable bone, the muscle's **origin.** In the muscles of the limbs, the origin typically lies proximal to the insertion.

Muscle attachments, whether origin or insertion, may be direct or indirect. In **direct,** or **fleshy, attachments,** the epimysium of the muscle is fused to the periosteum of a bone or perichondrium of a cartilage. In **indirect attachments,** the muscle's connective tissue wrappings extend beyond the muscle as a ropelike tendon or a flat, broad **aponeurosis** (ap″o-nu-ro′sis). The tendon or aponeurosis anchors the muscle to the connective tissue covering of a skeletal element (bone or cartilage), to the fascia of other muscles, or to a seam of fibrous tissue called a **raphe** (ra′fe).

Of the two, indirect attachments are much more common in the body because of their durability and small size. Since tendons are mostly tough collagenic fibers, they can cross rough bony projections which would tear apart the more delicate muscle tissues. Because of their relatively small size, more tendons than fleshy muscles can pass over a joint—thus, tendons also conserve space.

Microscopic Anatomy of a Skeletal Muscle Fiber

Each skeletal muscle fiber is a long cylindrical cell with multiple oval nuclei arranged just beneath its **sarcolemma** or plasma membrane surface (see Figure 9.2a and Table 9.1). Skeletal muscle fibers are huge cells. Their diameter typically ranges from 10 to 100 µm—up to ten times that of an average body cell—and their length is phenomenal, often many centimeters. Their large size and multinucleate condition are less surprising once you learn that each skeletal muscle fiber is actually a *syncytium* (sin-sish′e-um; "fused cells") produced by the union of hundreds of embryonic cells.

The **sarcoplasm** of a muscle fiber is similar to the cytoplasm of other cells, but it contains unusually large amounts of stored glycogen and a unique oxygen-binding protein called *myoglobin* that is not found in other cell types. **Myoglobin,** a red pigment that stores oxygen within the muscle cells, is similar to hemoglobin, the pigment that transports oxygen in blood. The usual organelles are present, as well as some that are highly modified in muscle fibers. These are the myofibrils and sarcoplasmic reticulum. The T tubules are unique modifications of the muscle fiber's sarcolemma. Let's look at these special structures more closely.

Myofibrils

When viewed at high magnification, each muscle fiber is seen to contain a large number of rodlike **myofibrils** ("superorganelles") that run in parallel fashion and extend the entire length of the cell (see Figure 9.2b). Each 1–2 µm in diameter, the myofibrils are so densely packed that mitochondria and other organelles appear to be squeezed between them. There are hundreds to thousands of myofibrils in a single muscle fiber, depending on its size, and they account for about 80% of cellular volume. The myofibrils are the contractile elements of skeletal muscle cells, and each consists of a chain of even smaller contractile units called *sarcomeres.*

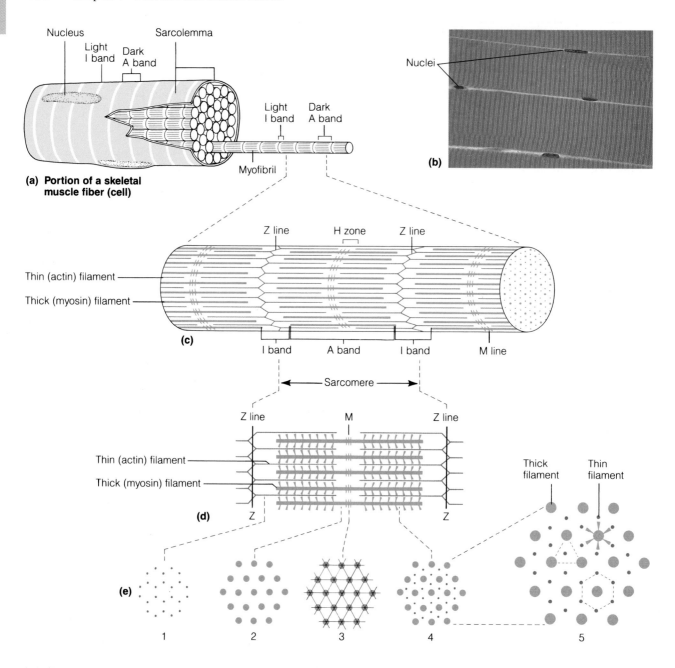

FIGURE 9.2
Microscopic anatomy of a skeletal muscle fiber.

(a) Diagram of part of a muscle fiber (cell) showing the myofibrils it contains. One myofibril is shown extending from the cut end of the muscle fiber. **(b)** Photomicrograph of portions of two isolated muscle fibers (250 ×). Notice the obvious cross striations (alternating light and dark bands). **(c)** A small portion of one myofibril is enlarged to show the myofilaments responsible for the banding pattern. Each sarcomere, or contractile unit, extends from one Z line to the next. **(d)** Enlargement of one sarcomere (sectioned lengthwise). Notice the myosin heads on the thick filaments. **(e)** The latticelike arrangement of the thick and thin filaments becomes obvious when the myofibril is cross-sectioned. (1) In a cut made through the I band, only thin filaments are seen; (2) in a cut made through the H zone, only thick filaments are seen; (3) in a cut made through the M line, thick filaments and connecting fibers are obvious; (4) if a cut is made through a portion of the A band containing both thin and thick filaments and this region is enlarged, we see (5) the hexagonal arrangement of thin filaments around each thick filament and the triangular arrangement of thick filaments around each thin filament.

Striations, Sarcomeres, and Myofilaments.

Striations, a repeating series of dark and light bands, are evident along the length of each myofibril. The dark bands are called **A bands** because they are *anisotropic* (an-i″so-trop′ik); that is, they can polarize visible light. The light bands, called **I bands,** are *isotropic,* or nonpolarizing. In an intact muscle fiber, the myofibril bands are nearly perfectly aligned with one another and are continuous across the width of the cell. This gives the cell as a whole its striped (striated) appearance.

As illustrated in Figure 9.2c, each A band has a

lighter stripe in its midsection called the **H zone** (*H* stands for *helle,* which means "bright"). The H zones are visible only in relaxed muscle fibers for reasons that will soon become obvious. To make things a bit more complicated, each H zone is bisected by a dark line called the **M line.** The I bands also have a midline interruption, a darker area called the **Z line.** A **sarcomere** (sar′ko-mēr; literally, "muscle segment") is the region of a myofibril between two successive Z lines (see Figure 9.2c) and is the smallest contractile unit of a muscle fiber. Thus, the *functional units* of skeletal muscle are actually very minute portions of the myofibrils, and the myofibrils are chains of sarcomeres aligned end-to-end like boxcars in a train.

If we examine the banding pattern of a myofibril at the molecular level, we see that it arises from an orderly arrangement of even smaller structures, called **filaments** or **myofilaments,** within the sarcomeres (Figure 9.2d). The central **thick filaments** extend the entire length of the A band. The more lateral **thin filaments** extend across the I band and partway into the A band. The Z line, also called a *Z disc,* is actually a coin-shaped protein sheet that anchors the thin filaments and also connects each myofibril to the next throughout the width of the muscle cell. The H zone of the A band appears less dense when viewed microscopically because the thin filaments do not overlap the thick ones in this region. The M line in the center of the H zone is slightly darker because of the presence of fine strands that hold adjacent thick filaments together in that area.

A longitudinal view of the myofilaments, such as that in Figure 9.2d, is a bit misleading because it gives the impression that each thick filament interdigitates with only four thin filaments. We can get a more accurate picture of the three-dimensional relationships of the filaments if we examine cross sectional views from different regions of a sarcomere (see Figure 9.2e). In areas where thick and thin filaments overlap, each thick filament is surrounded by a hexagonal arrangement of six thin filaments. Each thin filament, in turn, is bordered by a triangular arrangement of three thick filaments.

Ultrastructure and Molecular Composition of the Myofilaments.

Thick filaments (about 16 nm in diameter) are composed primarily of the protein **myosin** (Figure 9.3a). Each myosin molecule has a distinctive structure. It has a rodlike *tail,* or *axis,* terminating in two globular *heads.* At the molecular level, myosin's tail consists of two interwoven *heavy* polypeptide chains; its heads are the ends of the heavy chains, made "fat" by the attachment of two smaller *light* polypeptide chains. The heads are sometimes called **cross bridges** because they link the thick and thin myofilaments together during contraction. As explained shortly, these cross bridges generate the tension developed by a muscle cell when it contracts. Each thick filament within a sarcomere contains about 200 myosin molecules. As shown in Figure 9.3b and

(a) Myosin molecule

(b) Portion of a thick filament

(c) Portion of a thin filament

(d) Longitudinal section of filaments within one sarcomere of a myofibril

FIGURE 9.3
Myofilament composition in skeletal muscle. (a) An individual myosin molecule has a stalklike tail, from which two "heads" protrude. **(b)** Each thick filament consists of many myosin molecules, whose heads protrude at opposite ends of the filament, as shown in **(d). (c)** A thin filament contains two strands of F actin twisted together. Each strand is made up of G actin subunits. (Though depicted as oval structures, the G actin monomers are actually believed to be kidney-bean shaped.) Tropomyosin molecules coil around the F actin, helping to reinforce the filament. A troponin complex is attached to each tropomyosin molecule. **(d)** Arrangement of the filaments in a sarcomere (longitudinal view). In the center of the sarcomere, the thick elements are devoid of myosin heads, but at points of thick and thin filament overlap, the heads extend toward the actin with which they interact during contraction.

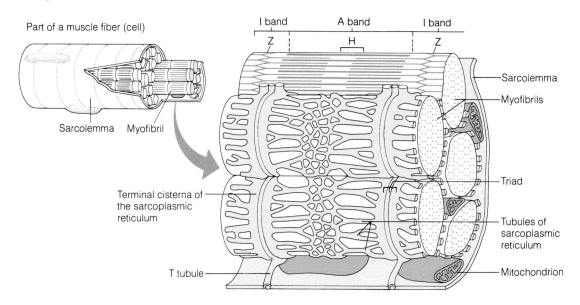

FIGURE 9.4
Relationship of the sarcoplasmic reticulum and T tubules to the myofibrils of skeletal muscle. The tubules of the sarcoplasmic reticulum encircle each myofibril like a "holey" sleeve. At certain points, the tubules fuse to form communicating channels. This occurs primarily at the level of the H zone and in the regions abutting the A-I junctions, where the saclike elements are called terminal cisternae. The T tubules, inward invaginations of the sarcolemma, run deep into the cell between the terminal cisternae at the A-I junctions. Sites of close contact of these three elements (terminal cisterna, T tubule, and terminal cisterna) are called triads.

d, the myosin molecules are bundled together so that their tails form the central part of the filament and their globular heads face outward and in opposite directions at each end. As a result, the central portion of a thick filament is smooth, but its ends are studded with a staggered array of myosin heads. The heads of myosin molecules contain ATP binding sites and ATPase enzymes that split ATP to generate the energy for muscle contraction. **Titin (connectin),** a stretchy protein associated with the thick filaments, attaches the thick filaments to the Z discs and helps to stabilize them. Titin is the largest of the muscle proteins.

The thin filaments (7–8 nm thick) are composed chiefly of **actin** (Figure 9.3c). The polypeptide subunits of actin, called *globular actin* or *G actin,* bear the active sites to which the myosin cross bridges attach during contraction. The generally kidney bean–shaped G actin monomers are polymerized into long strands called *fibrous actin* or *F actin.* The backbone of each thin filament appears to be formed by two strands of F actin that coil around each other, forming a helical structure that looks like a twisted double strand of pearls. Several regulatory proteins are also present in the thin filament. Two strands of **tropomyosin** (tro"po-mi'o-sin), a rod-shaped protein, spiral about the F actin core and help to stiffen it. Successive tropomyosin molecules are arranged end to end along the F actin chains and, in a relaxed muscle fiber, they block actin's active sites so that the myosin heads cannot bind to the thin filaments. The other major protein in the thin filament, **troponin** (tro'ponin), is actually a three-polypeptide complex. One of these polypeptides (TnI) is an inhibitory subunit that binds to actin. Another (TnT) binds to tropomyosin

and helps to position it on actin. The third (TnC) binds calcium ions. Both troponin and tropomyosin help to control the myosin-actin interactions involved in contraction.

Sarcoplasmic Reticulum and T Tubules

Skeletal muscle fibers (cells) contain two sets of intracellular tubules that participate in regulation of muscle contraction: (1) the sarcoplasmic reticulum and (2) the T tubules (Figure 9.4).

Sarcoplasmic Reticulum. The **sarcoplasmic reticulum (SR)** is an elaborate smooth endoplasmic reticulum (p. 79). Its interconnecting tubules surround each myofibril like the sleeve of a loosely crocheted sweater surrounds your arm. Most of these tubules run longitudinally along the myofibril. However, the sarcoplasmic reticulum also forms larger, perpendicular cross channels over the A-I junctions called **terminal cisternae** ("end sacs"). These terminal cisternae occur in pairs.

The major role of the SR is to regulate intracellular levels of ionic calcium: It stores calcium and releases it "on demand" when the muscle fiber is stimulated to contract. As you will see, calcium provides the final "go" signal for contraction.

T Tubules. At each A-I junction, the sarcolemma of the muscle cell penetrates into the cell interior to form a hollow elongated tube called the **transverse tubule** or **T tubule,** the lumen of which is continuous with the extracellular space. As each T tubule pro-

Terminal cisterna of the sarcoplasmic reticulum

T tubule

Tubules of sarcoplasmic reticulum

Triad

(a)

External face of SR membrane

SR "foot" (4 integral proteins)

(b)

Internal (lumen) face of T tubule

Integral trans-membrane proteins

(c)

"Double zipper"

T-SR junction at triad

(d)

FIGURE 9.5
The T tubule–SR (T-SR) junction. (a) Diagrammatic view of the main structures at the T tubule–SR junction at triads. **(b)** The external face of the SR cisterna. Notice that groups of four integral proteins constitute an SR "foot," which protrudes into the intermembrane space. **(c)** Half of the T tubule has been cut away to reveal the location of its transmembrane proteins that face complementary particles on the adjoining SR cisterna. **(d)** The T tubule superimposed on the SR cisterna (the T-SR junction), illustrating the "double zipper"–like alignment of the T tubule and SR junctional proteins.

trudes deep into the cell, it runs between the paired terminal cisternae of the SR so that **triads,** successive groupings of the three membranous structures (terminal cisterna, T tubule, terminal cisterna), are formed. As they pass from one myofibril to the next, the T tubules also encircle each sarcomere. The thousands of T tubules of each muscle cell are collectively called the **T system.**

Muscle contraction is ultimately controlled by nerve-initiated impulses that travel along the sarcolemma of the muscle cell. Since T tubules are continuations of the sarcolemma, they can conduct impulses to the deepest regions of the muscle cell and to every sarcomere. Thus, the T tubules can be thought of as a "rapid telegraphy" system that ensures that every myofibril in the muscle fiber contracts at virtually the same time. Additionally, T tubules provide inlets to bring extracellular fluid (containing glucose, oxygen, and various ions) into close contact with deeper parts of the muscle cell.

Triad Relationships.   The roles of the T tubules and SR in providing signals for contraction are tightly linked. Since structure determines function, we might expect to find some structural evidence of the intimate relationship of these organelles where they come into closest contact—at the triads. And, so we do. Electron microscopic studies of the T-SR junctions reveal that they are like *double zippers* of integral proteins (Figure 9.5). At each triad region, a double row of *foot proteins* (integral proteins of the SR membrane) protrude into the intermembrane space toward the T tubule. Facing the SR feet is a similar, but less dense, array of integral proteins of the T tubule membrane. The SR proteins are known to be calcium channels, and though it remains to be proved, investigators suggest that the T tubule pro-

teins act as voltage sensors. We will return to consider their interaction shortly (see p. 261).

Contraction of a Skeletal Muscle Fiber

Sliding Filament Mechanism of Contraction

When a muscle cell contracts, its individual sarcomeres shorten. As the length of their sarcomeres decreases, the myofibrils also shorten, resulting in shortening of the cell as a whole.

If we examine the contractile event closely, we find that none of the filaments change in length as the sarcomeres shorten. So how can muscle cell shortening be explained? The **sliding filament theory of contraction,** proposed in 1954 by Hugh Huxley, states that during contraction the thin filaments slide past the thick ones so that the actin and myosin filaments overlap to a greater degree (Figure 9.6). In a relaxed muscle fiber, the thick and thin filaments overlap only slightly but, during contraction, the thin filaments penetrate more and more deeply into the central region of the A band. Notice that as the thin filaments slide centrally, the Z lines to which they are attached are pulled *toward* the thick filaments. Overall, the distance between successive Z lines is reduced, the I bands shorten, the H zones disappear, and the A bands move closer together but do not diminish in length.

What causes the filaments to slide? This question brings us back to the cross bridges (myosin heads) that protrude all around the ends of the thick filaments. When muscle fibers are activated by the nervous system, the cross bridges attach to active (myosin-bind-

What zones disappear in a contracted sarcomere?

FIGURE 9.6

Sliding filament model of contraction. At full contraction, the Z lines abut the myosin filaments and the actin filaments overlap each other. The numbers indicate the sequence of events, with 1 being relaxed and 3 being fully contracted. The photomicrographs (top view in each case) show enlargements of 20,000 ×.

ing) sites on actin in the thin filaments, and the sliding begins. Each cross bridge attaches and detaches several times during a contraction, acting much like a tiny ratchet to generate tension and pull the thin filaments toward the center of the sarcomere. As this event occurs simultaneously in sarcomeres throughout the cell, the muscle cell shortens. Attachment of the myosin cross bridges to actin requires calcium ions, and the nerve impulse leading to contraction causes an increase in calcium ions within the muscle cell. We discuss the nerve impulse and the calcium fluxes later; here let us concentrate on the contraction mechanism itself.

When intracellular calcium levels are low, the muscle cell is relaxed, and the myosin binding sites on actin are physically blocked by tropomyosin mole-

cules (Figure 9.7a). However, when calcium ions become available, they bind to regulatory sites on troponin (Figure 9.7b), causing it to change its conformation and detach momentarily from actin. This event physically moves tropomyosin deeper into the groove of the F actin helix and away from the myosin binding sites (Figure 9.7c and d). Thus, the tropomyosin "blockade" is removed when calcium is present.

Once binding sites on actin are exposed, the following events occur in rapid succession (Figure 9.8).

1. **Cross bridge attachment.** The activated myosin heads are strongly attracted to the exposed binding sites on actin and cross bridge binding occurs.

2. **Power stroke.** As a myosin head binds, it pivots, changing from its high-energy configuration to its bent, low-energy shape, which pulls on the thin filament, sliding it toward the center of the sarcomere. At the same time, ADP and inorganic phosphate (P_i) generated during the *prior* contraction cycle are released from the myosin head.

3. **Cross bridge detachment.** As a new ATP molecule binds to the myosin head, myosin's hold on actin loosens and the cross bridge releases from actin.

4. **"Cocking" of the myosin head.** Hydrolysis of ATP to ADP and P_i by ATPase provides the energy needed to return the myosin head to its high-energy, or "cocked," position, which provides the potential energy needed for its next attachment–power stroke sequence. (The ADP and P_i remain attached to the myosin head during this phase.) At this point, the cycle is back where it started. The myosin head is in its high-energy configuration, ready to take another "step" and attach to an actin site farther along the thin filament. This "walking" of the myosin cross bridges along the adjacent thin filaments during muscle shortening is much like a centipede's gait. Some myosin heads ("legs") are always in contact with actin (the "ground"), so that the thin filaments cannot slide backward as this cycle is repeated again and again during contraction.

A single power stroke of all the cross bridges in a muscle results in a shortening of only about 1%. Since contracting muscles routinely shorten 30% to 35% of their total resting length, each myosin cross bridge must attach and detach many times during a single contraction. It is likely that only half of the myosin heads of a thick filament are actively exerting a pulling force at the same instant; the balance are randomly seeking their next binding site. Sliding of thin filaments continues as long as the calcium signal and ATP are present. As the SR reclaims calcium ions from the sarcoplasm and troponin again changes shape, tropomyosin inhibition is restored, contraction ends, and the muscle fiber relaxes.

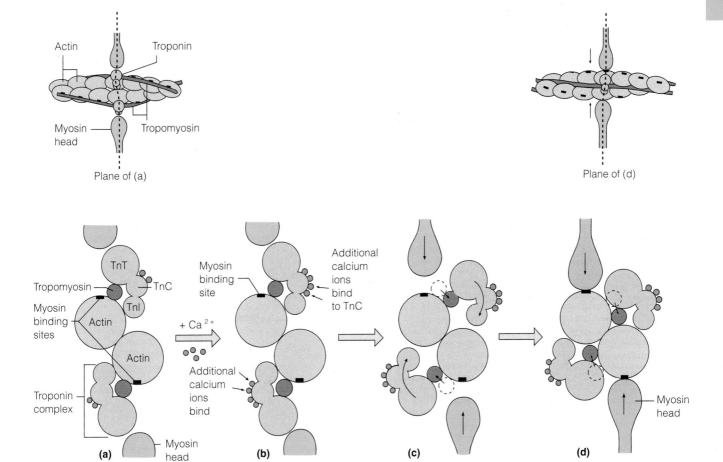

FIGURE 9.7
Role of ionic calcium in the contraction mechanism. Views **(a)**–**(d)** are cross-sectional views of the thin (actin) filament. **(a)** At low intracellular Ca^{2+} concentration, tropomyosin blocks the binding sites on actin preventing myosin cross bridge attachment, which enforces the relaxed muscle state. **(b)** At higher intracellular Ca^{2+} concentrations, additional calcium binds to troponin. (Inactive troponin binds two Ca^{2+}; calcium-activated troponin binds an additional two Ca^{2+} at a separate regulatory site.) **(c)** Calcium-activated troponin undergoes a conformational change that moves the tropomyosin away from the myosin binding sites. **(d)** This allows the myosin heads to bind, permitting contraction (sliding of the thin filaments by the myosin cross bridges) to occur.

Although the sliding filament theory is the most popular and best accepted model of muscle contraction, you should be aware that there is still controversy about several of its aspects. For example, it has been shown that actin has ATPase activity and undergoes conformational changes. This suggests that actin molecules actively contribute to the pulling action instead of just acting as passive cables along which the myosin heads tread. Additionally, the proposed number of ATP molecules used is being challenged. According to the sliding filament theory, it is one ATP per power stroke, but current research indicates that myosin may interact with several actin monomers per ATP molecule hydrolyzed.

Rigor mortis (death rigor) illustrates the fact that cross bridge detachment is ATP driven. Most muscles begin to stiffen 3 to 4 hours after death. Peak rigidity occurs at 12 hours and then gradually dissipates over the next 48 to 60 hours. Because dying cells are unable to exclude calcium (which is in higher concentration in the extracellular fluid), the calcium influx into muscle cells promotes myosin cross bridge binding. However, shortly after breathing stops, ATP synthesis ceases, and cross bridge detachment is impossible. Actin and myosin become irreversibly cross-linked, producing the stiffness of dead muscle. Rigor mortis disappears as biological molecules, including actin and myosin, break down several hours after death. •

Regulation of Contraction

For a skeletal muscle fiber to contract, it must be stimulated by a nerve ending and must propagate an electrical current, or *action potential,* along its sarcolemma. This electrical event causes the transient rise in intracellular calcium ion levels that is the final trigger for contraction. The series of events linking the electrical signal to contraction is called *excitation-contraction coupling.*

? *What would be the result if the muscle fiber suddenly ran out of ATP when the sarcomeres had only partially contracted?*

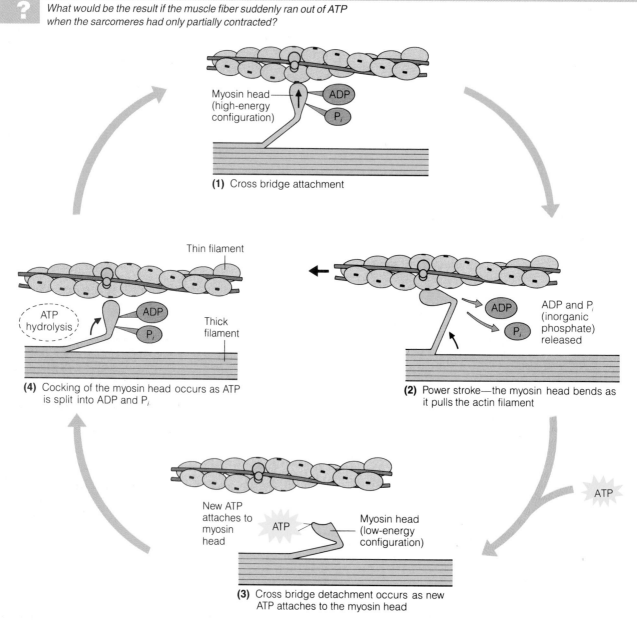

(1) Cross bridge attachment

Myosin head (high-energy configuration)

ADP

P_i

Thin filament

ATP hydrolysis

ADP

P_i

Thick filament

(4) Cocking of the myosin head occurs as ATP is split into ADP and P_i

ADP

P_i

ADP and P_i (inorganic phosphate) released

(2) Power stroke—the myosin head bends as it pulls the actin filament

ATP

New ATP attaches to myosin head

ATP

Myosin head (low-energy configuration)

(3) Cross bridge detachment occurs as new ATP attaches to the myosin head

FIGURE 9.8
Sequence of events involved in the sliding of the actin filaments during contraction. A small section of adjacent thick and thin filaments is used to illustrate the interactions that occur between the two types of myofilaments. These events occur only in the presence of ionic calcium (Ca^{2+}).

The Neuromuscular Junction and the Nerve Stimulus.

Skeletal muscle cells are stimulated by *motor neurons* of the somatic (voluntary) division of the nervous system. Although these motor neurons "reside" in the brain or spinal cord, their long thread-like extensions called *axons* travel, bundled within nerves, to the muscle cells they serve. The axon of each motor neuron divides profusely as it enters the muscle, and each of these axonal endings forms a branching **neuromuscular junction** with a single muscle fiber (Figure 9.9). As a rule, each muscle fiber has only one neuromuscular junction located in its approximate middle. Although the axonal ending and the muscle fiber are exceedingly close, they do not actually touch, but remain separated by a space called the **synaptic cleft.** The synaptic cleft is filled with a *basal lamina* (a gel-like substance rich in glycoproteins). Within the flattened moundlike axonal ending are **synaptic vesicles,** small membranous sacs containing a neurotransmitter called **acetylcholine** (as"ĕ-

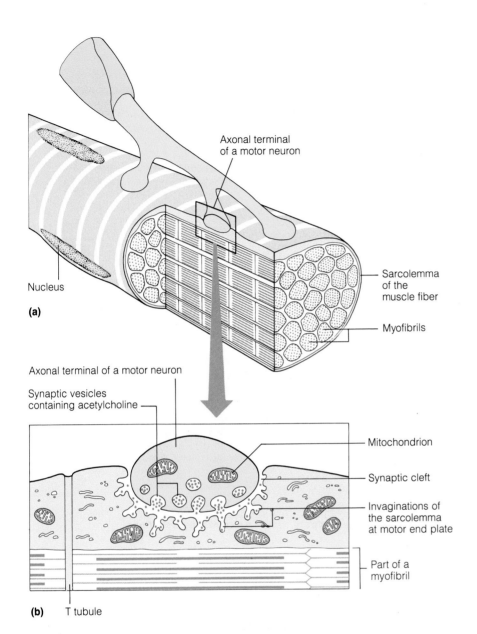

(a)

Nucleus

Axonal terminal
of a motor neuron

Sarcolemma
of the
muscle fiber

Myofibrils

Axonal terminal of a motor neuron

Synaptic vesicles
containing acetylcholine

Mitochondrion

Synaptic cleft

Invaginations of
the sarcolemma
at motor end plate

Part of a
myofibril

(b) T tubule

FIGURE 9.9
The neuromuscular junction.
(a) Axonal ending of a motor neuron forming a neuromuscular junction with a muscle fiber. **(b)** The axonal terminal contains vesicles filled with the neurotransmitter acetylcholine (ACh), which is released when the action potential reaches the axonal terminal. Acetylcholine diffuses across the synaptic cleft and attaches to ACh receptors on the sarcolemma, initiating depolarization of the sarcolemma. The sarcolemma is highly invaginated adjacent to the synaptic cleft, and acetylcholine receptors are present in this region.

til-ko′lēn) or **ACh.** The **motor end plate,** the specific troughlike part of the muscle fiber's sarcolemma that helps form the neuromuscular junction, is highly folded. These *junctional folds* provide a large surface area for the many ACh receptors located there.

When a nerve impulse reaches the end of an axon, voltage-regulated calcium channels in its membrane open, allowing Ca^{2+} to flow in from the extracellular fluid. Once inside the axon terminal, calcium causes some of the synaptic vesicles to fuse with the axonal membrane and release ACh into the synaptic cleft by *exocytosis.* ACh diffuses across the cleft and attaches to ACh receptors on the sarcolemma. The electrical events triggered in a muscle cell membrane when ACh binds are similar to those that take place in excited nerve cell membranes. We outline these events here and then consider them in more detail in Chapter 11.

Generation of an Action Potential Across the Sarcolemma.

Like the plasma membranes of all cells, a resting sarcolemma is *polarized* (Figure 9.10a). That is, there is a voltage across the membrane and the inside is negative. (The resting membrane potential is described in Chapter 3, pp. 73–74.) Binding of ACh molecules to appropriate receptors on the sarcolemma opens *chemically regulated* ion gates and leads to transient permeability changes in the sarcolemma. The result is a change in membrane potential (voltage) such that the muscle cell interior becomes slightly *less negative,* an event called **depolarization.** Initially, depolarization is a local event (occurring only at the receptor site), but if the nerve stimulus is strong enough, an action potential is generated that passes in *all directions* from the neuromuscular junction across the sarcolemma, just as ripples move away from a pebble dropped into a stream.

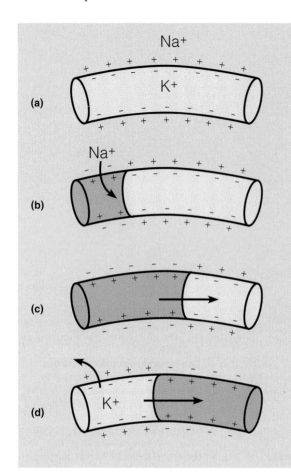

(a) Electrical conditions of a resting (polarized) sarcolemma. The outside face is positive, while the inside face is negative. The predominant extracellular ion is sodium (Na^+); the predominant intracellular ion is potassium (K^+). The sarcolemma is relatively impermeable to both ions.

(b) Step 1: Depolarization and generation of the action potential. Stimulation by a motor nerve fiber (via the release of acetylcholine) causes that patch of sarcolemma to become permeable to sodium (sodium gates open). As sodium ions diffuse rapidly into the cell, the resting potential is decreased (i.e., depolarization occurs). If the stimulus is strong enough, an action potential is initiated.

(c) Step 2: Propagation of the action potential. The positive charge inside the initial patch of sarcolemma changes the permeability of an adjacent patch, opening voltage-regulated Na^+ gates there. Consequently the membrane potential in that region decreases and depolarization occurs there as well. Thus, the action potential propagates itself rapidly over the entire sarcolemma.

(d) Step 3: Repolarization. Immediately after the depolarization wave passes, the sarcolemma permeability changes once again: Na^+ gates close and K^+ gates open, allowing K^+ to diffuse from the cell. This restores the electrical conditions of the resting (polarized) state. Repolarization occurs in the same direction as depolarization, and must occur before the muscle fiber can be stimulated again. The ionic concentrations of the resting state are restored later by the sodium-potassium pump.

FIGURE 9.10
Summary of events in the generation and propagation of an action potential in a skeletal muscle fiber.

The **action potential** is the result of a predictable sequence of electrical changes that occurs along the sarcolemma (Figure 9.10). Essentially, three steps are involved.

1. First, the membrane is depolarized. This is a consequence of sodium (Na^+) channel opening and Na^+ entering the cell (see Figure 9.10b).

2. During step 2, the action potential is propagated as the local depolarization wave spreads to the adjacent areas of the sarcolemma and opens voltage-regulated sodium gates there (see Figure 9.10c). Sodium ions, normally restricted from entering, now diffuse into the cell following their electrochemical gradient.

3. Step 3 is **repolarization,** which restores the sarcolemma to its initial polarized state. The repolarization wave, which quickly follows the depolarization wave, is a consequence of Na^+ gates closing and K^+ gates opening. Since the potassium ion concentration is substantially higher inside the cell than in the extracellular fluid, K^+ diffuses rapidly out of the muscle fiber (Figure 9.10d).

During repolarization, a muscle fiber is said to be in a **refractory period,** because the cell is insensitive to further stimulation until repolarization is complete. Notice that repolarization only restores the *electrical conditions* of the resting (polarized) state. The ATP-dependent Na^+-K^+ pump must be "revved-up" to restore the ionic conditions of the resting state, but several contractions can occur before ionic imbalances interfere with contraction.

Once initiated, the action potential is unstoppable and ultimately results in full contraction of the muscle cell. This phenomenon, referred to as the **all-or-none response,** means that muscle fibers contract to the full extent of their ability or not at all. Although the action potential itself is very brief (1–2 milliseconds [ms]), the contraction phase of a muscle fiber may persist for 100 ms or more and far outlasts the electrical event that triggers it.

Destruction of Acetylcholine. After ACh is released from the motor neuron and binds to the ACh receptors, it is swiftly destroyed by **acetylcholinesterase** (as″ĕ-til-ko″lin-es′ter-ās), or **AChE,** an enzyme located on the sarcolemma at the neuromuscular junction and in the basal lamina of the synaptic cleft. This prevents continued muscle fiber contraction in the absence of additional nervous system stimulation.

Table 9.2 Roles of Ionic Calcium (Ca^{2+}) in Muscle Contraction

Role	Mechanism
Promotes neurotransmitter release	When voltage-regulated calcium gates open as the nerve impulse reaches the axon terminal, Ca^{2+} enters the terminal and triggers fusion of synaptic vesicles with the axonal membrane and exocytosis of the neurotransmitter.
Triggers Ca^{2+} release from the SR (postulated)	When an action potential is transmitted along the T tubules of skeletal and cardiac muscle fibers, voltage-regulated calcium gates (protein tetrameres in T tubules) open, causing a local rise in Ca^{2+} concentration. This rise stimulates the release of Ca^{2+} from the SR, possibly by binding to calsequestrin (a calcium-transport protein that forms part of the SR membrane).
Triggers sliding of myofilaments and ATPase activity	(1) When Ca^{2+} binds to troponin in skeletal and cardiac muscles, structural changes occur in troponin that expose active sites on actin. As a result, myosin cross bridge binding can occur and ATPases on myosin "heads" are activated.
	(2) When Ca^{2+} binds to calmodulin (an intracellular calcium-binding protein) in smooth muscle, a kinase is activated that catalyzes phosphorylation of myosin. As a result, myosin cross bridges are activated and sliding begins.
Promotes glycogen breakdown and ATP synthesis	When Ca^{2+} binds to and activates calmodulin, the activated calmodulin mobilizes a kinase enzyme that initiates the breakdown of glycogen to glucose. The muscle fiber then metabolizes glucose to produce ATP for muscular work.

Many toxins, drugs, and diseases interfere with events occurring at the neuromuscular junction. For example, *myasthenia gravis* (*asthen* = weakness; *gravi* = heavy), a disease characterized by drooping of the upper eyelids, difficulty in swallowing and talking, and generalized muscle weakness, involves a shortage of ACh receptors. The blood contains antibodies to ACh receptors, which suggests that myasthenia gravis is an autoimmune disease. Although the receptors may initially be present in normal numbers, they appear to be destroyed as the disease progresses.

Muscular paralysis and asphyxiation occur when curare and certain other chemicals (e.g., organophosphates found in pesticides) enter the body. *Curare,* the arrowhead poison used by natives of South America, binds to ACh receptors and blocks ACh attachment. Thus, even though the nervous system is still releasing ACh (the "go" signal), the muscles are unable to respond and respiratory arrest occurs. Curare and similar drugs are used clinically in small amounts to allow intubation and prevent muscular movements during surgery. •

Roles of Ionic Calcium in Muscle Contraction.

Except for the brief period following muscle cell excitation, calcium ion concentrations in the sarcoplasm are kept almost undetectably low. There is a reason for this: ATP provides the energy source for cellular processes, and as we have seen, its hydrolysis yields inorganic phosphates (P$_i$). If the intracellular concentration of ionic calcium were always high, calcium and phosphate ions would combine to form hydroxyapatite crystals, the stony-hard salts found in bone matrix. Such calcified cells would die. Also, since calcium's physiological roles are so vital (see Table 9.2), its cytoplasmic concentration is exquisitely regulated by intracellular proteins, such as **calsequestrin** (found within the SR cisternae) and **calmodulin,** which can alternately bind calcium (removing it from solution) and release it to provide a metabolic signal.

Excitation-Contraction Coupling.

Excitation-contraction coupling is the sequence of events by which transmission of an action potential along the sarcolemma leads to the sliding of myofilaments. The action potential is very brief and ends well before any signs of contraction are obvious. The period from action potential initiation to the beginning of mechanical activity (shortening) is called the *latent period* (*laten* = hidden). The events of excitation-contraction coupling occur during this period. As you will see, the electrical signal does not act directly on the myofilaments; rather, it causes the rise in intracellular calcium ion concentration that allows the filaments to slide (Figure 9.11).

Excitation-contraction coupling consists of the following steps:

1. The action potential propagates along the sarcolemma and down the T tubules.

2. Transmission of the action potential past the triad regions causes the terminal cisternae of the SR to release calcium ions into the sarcoplasm, where Ca^{2+} becomes available to the myofilaments. It is not known exactly how an action potential coursing along the T tubules causes the SR to release calcium, but the "double zippers" (Figure 9.5, p. 255) at the T-SR junctions of the triads are involved. One model proposes that the groups of

(1) Why is Ca²⁺ called the final trigger for contraction? (2) What constitutes the initial trigger?

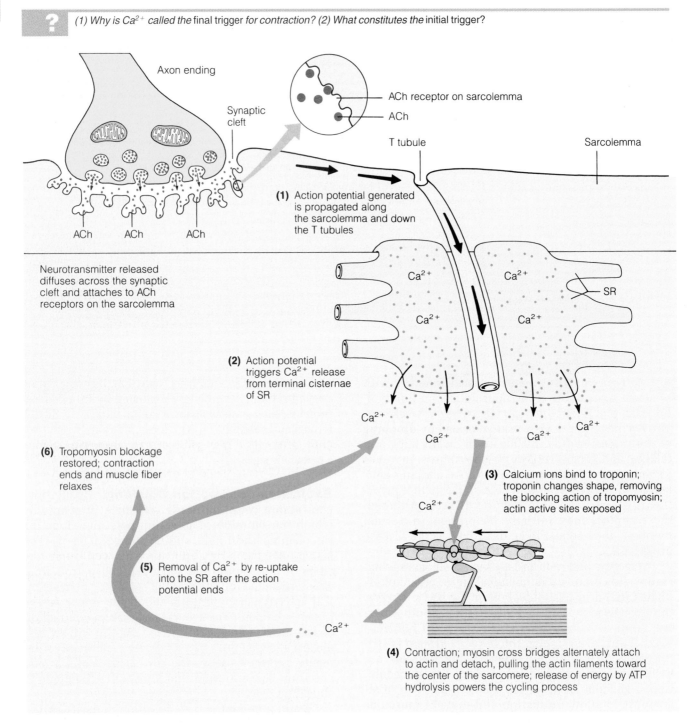

Axon ending

ACh receptor on sarcolemma

ACh

Synaptic cleft

T tubule

Sarcolemma

ACh ACh ACh

(1) Action potential generated is propagated along the sarcolemma and down the T tubules

Neurotransmitter released diffuses across the synaptic cleft and attaches to ACh receptors on the sarcolemma

Ca^{2+} Ca^{2+}

SR

Ca^{2+} Ca^{2+}

(2) Action potential triggers Ca^{2+} release from terminal cisternae of SR

Ca^{2+} Ca^{2+} Ca^{2+}

Ca^{2+}

(6) Tropomyosin blockage restored; contraction ends and muscle fiber relaxes

Ca^{2+}

(3) Calcium ions bind to troponin; troponin changes shape, removing the blocking action of tropomyosin; actin active sites exposed

(5) Removal of Ca^{2+} by re-uptake into the SR after the action potential ends

Ca^{2+}

(4) Contraction; myosin cross bridges alternately attach to actin and detach, pulling the actin filaments toward the center of the sarcomere; release of energy by ATP hydrolysis powers the cycling process

FIGURE 9.11
Sequence of events in excitation-contraction coupling. Events (1) through (5) indicate the sequence of events in the coupling process. As shown in the clockwise flow of events, contraction continues until the calcium signal ends (6).

four protein particles on the T tubule side are sensitive to voltage and change their conformation (3-D shape) in response to the action potential. Their voltage-regulated change is somehow communicated to the underlying SR foot. (Some propose that the T tubule tetramers also function as calcium channels when activated, so that communication is chemical. Others believe the T-SR interaction is mechanical in nature.) The foot, in

turn, undergoes shape changes that open its calcium channel. Since these events occur at every triad in the cell, within 1 ms massive amounts of Ca^{2+} flood into the sarcoplasm from the SR cisternae (see Table 9.2).

3. As already described, some of this calcium binds to troponin, which then changes shape and removes the blocking action of tropomyosin.

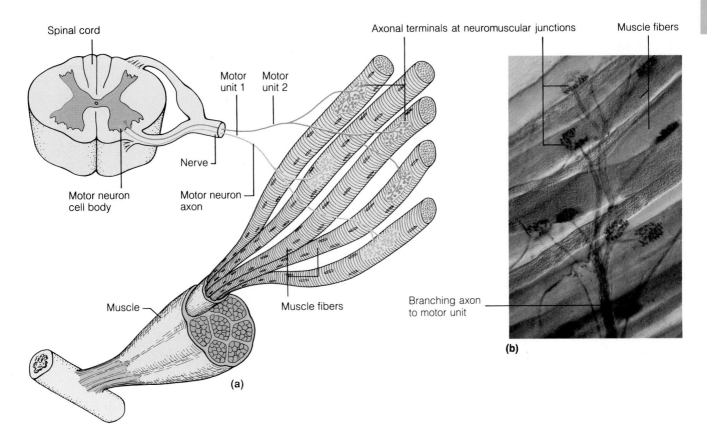

FIGURE 9.12
Motor units. Each motor unit consists of a motor neuron and all of the muscle fibers it innervates. **(a)** Schematic view of portions of two motor units. The nucleus-containing cell bodies of the motor neurons reside in the spinal cord, and their axons extend to the muscle. Within the muscle, each axon divides into a number of axonal terminals, which are distributed to muscle fibers scattered throughout the muscle. **(b)** Photomicrograph of a portion of a motor unit (115 ×). Notice the diverging axonal terminals and the neuromuscular junctions with the muscle fibers.

4. The myosin cross bridges attach and pull the thin filaments toward the center of the sarcomere. This occurs when the intracellular calcium is present at a concentration of about 10^{-5} M.

5. The short-lived calcium signal ends, usually within 30 ms after the action potential is over. The fall in calcium levels reflects the operation of a continuously active, ATP-dependent calcium pump that moves calcium back into the tubular central part of the SR to be stored once again.

6. When intracellular calcium levels drop too low to allow contraction, the tropomyosin blockade is reestablished and myosin ATPases are inhibited. Cross bridge activity ends and relaxation occurs.

This entire sequence of events is repeated when another nerve impulse arrives at the neuromuscular junction. When the impulses are delivered very rapidly, calcium ions continue to be made available and intracellular calcium levels increase greatly due to successive "rounds" of calcium release from the SR. In such cases, the muscle cells do not completely relax between successive stimuli and contraction is stronger and more sustained (within limits) until nervous stimulation ceases.

Contraction of a Skeletal Muscle

In its relaxed state, a muscle is unimpressive. It is soft and not at all what you would expect of a "prime mover" of the body. However, within a few milliseconds, it can become a hard elastic structure with dynamic characteristics that intrigue not only biologists, but engineers and physicists.

Now we are ready to consider muscle contraction on the gross level. Although single muscle cells respond to stimulation in an all-or-none fashion, a skeletal muscle, consisting of huge numbers of cells, contracts with varying force and for different periods of time. To understand how this occurs, we must look at the nerve-muscle functional unit called a *motor unit* and investigate how a muscle responds to stimuli of varying frequencies and intensities.

The Motor Unit

Each muscle is served by at least one motor nerve, which contains hundreds of motor neuron axons (Figure 9.12). As an axon enters a muscle, it branches into a number of axonal terminals, each of which forms a neuromuscular junction with a single muscle fiber. A motor neuron and all the muscle fibers it supplies is called a **motor unit** (Figure 9.12). When a motor neuron fires (transmits an electrical impulse), all the muscle fibers that it innervates respond by contracting. The average number of muscle fibers per motor unit is 150, but it may be as high as several hundred or as few as 4. Muscles that exert very fine control (such as the muscles controlling movements of the fingers and eyes) have small motor units. By contrast, large, weight-bearing muscles, whose movements are less precise (such as the hip muscles), have large motor units. The muscle fibers in a single motor unit are not clustered together, but are spread throughout the muscle. As a result, stimulation of a single motor unit causes a weak contraction of the entire muscle.

The Muscle Twitch and Development of Muscle Tension

Muscle contraction is easily investigated in a laboratory setting. Most such studies are done *in vitro* (outside the body; "in glass") using the calf muscle of a frog. The isolated muscle is attached to an apparatus that produces a **myogram,** a graphic recording of mechanical contractile activity. (The line recording the activity is called a *tracing.*)

The response of a muscle to a single brief threshold stimulus is called a **muscle twitch.** The muscle contracts quickly and then relaxes. A twitch may be strong or weak, depending on the number of motor units activated. In any myogram tracing of a twitch, three distinct phases are obvious (Figure 9.13a).

1. **Latent Period.** The latent period is the few milliseconds following stimulation when excitation-contraction coupling is occurring. During this period no response is seen on the myogram.

2. **Period of Contraction.** The period of contraction is the time from the onset of shortening to the peak of tension development, when cross bridges are active and the myogram tracing rises to a peak. This period lasts 10–100 ms. If the tension (pull) becomes great enough to overcome the resistance of an attached load, the muscle shortens.

3. **Period of Relaxation.** The period of contraction is followed by the period of relaxation. This final phase, lasting 10–100 ms, is initiated by reentry of Ca^{2+} into the SR. Since contractile force is no longer being generated, muscle tension gradually decreases to zero and the tracing returns to the baseline. If the muscle has shortened during contraction, it now returns to its initial length. At least part of the rebound that returns a muscle to its initial shape and length is due to the recoil of its elastic noncontractile elements (organelles, sarcolemma, and associated connective tissues) which are distorted or stretched during the contraction phase. (These so-called *series-elastic elements* are discussed further on p. 271.)

FIGURE 9.13
The muscle twitch. (a) Myogram tracing of a twitch contraction, showing its three phases: the latent period, the period of contraction, and the period of relaxation. **(b)** Comparison of the twitch responses of the extraocular, gastrocnemius, and soleus muscles.

As you can see in Figure 9.13b, twitch contractions of some muscles are rapid and brief, as with the extraocular muscles controlling eye movements. In contrast, the fleshy calf muscles (gastrocnemius and soleus) contract more slowly and usually remain contracted for much longer periods. These differences between muscles reflect the metabolic properties of the myofibrils and enzyme variations.

Graded Muscle Responses

Although *muscle twitches*—the single, jerky contractions observed in the laboratory—sometimes occur as a result of certain neuromuscular problems, this is *not* the way our muscles normally operate *in vivo* (in the body). Instead, our muscle contractions are relatively long and smooth and vary in strength as different demands are placed on them. Variations in the degree of muscle contraction (an obvious requirement for proper control of skeletal movement) are referred to as **graded responses.** In general, muscle contraction can be graded in two ways: (1) by changing the *speed of stimulation* and (2) by changing the *number of motor units activated.*

Muscle Response to Increasingly Rapid Stimulation: Wave Summation and Tetanus.

If two identical stimuli (electrical shocks or nerve impulses) are delivered to a muscle in rapid succession, the second twitch will be stronger than the first. On the myogram it will appear to "ride" on the shoulders of the first contraction (Figure 9.14). This phenomenon, called **wave,** or **temporal, summation,** occurs because the second contraction is induced before the muscle has completely relaxed after the first. Since the muscle is already partially contracted and more calcium is being released to replace that being reclaimed by the SR, tension produced during the second contraction causes more shortening than the first. In other words, the contractions are summed. (However, the refractory period must *always* be honored. Thus, if a second stimulus is delivered before repolarization is complete, no summation occurs.) If the stimulus (voltage) is held constant and the muscle is stimulated at an increasingly faster rate, the relaxation time between the twitches becomes shorter and shorter, the concentration of Ca^{2+} in the sarcoplasm higher and higher, and the degree of summation greater and greater. Finally, all evidence of muscle relaxation disappears and the contractions fuse into a smooth, sustained contraction called **tetanus** (tet'ah-nus; *tetan* = rigid, tense).

Tetanus (not to be confused with the bacterial disease of the same name) reflects the usual manner of muscle contraction in the body. That is, motor neurons usually deliver *volleys* of impulses (impulses in rapid succession) rather than the single impulses that result in twitch contractions.

Vigorous muscle activity cannot continue indefinitely. Prolonged tetanus inevitably leads to a situation in which the muscle is unable to contract and its tension drops to zero, a condition called *muscle fatigue.* A pivotal factor in muscle fatigue is the muscle's inability to generate enough ATP to power the contractile process. This and other factors causing muscle fatigue are discussed later in the chapter.

Muscle Response to Stronger Stimuli: Multiple Motor Unit Summation.

Although wave summation contributes to the force of muscle response, its primary function is to produce smooth, continuous muscle contractions by rapidly stimulating a specific number of muscle cells. The force of muscle contraction is controlled more precisely by **multiple motor unit summation.** In the laboratory, this phenomenon, also called **recruitment,** is achieved by delivering shocks of increasing voltage to the muscle, calling more and more muscle fibers into play. The stimulus at which the first observable muscle contraction occurs is called the **threshold stimulus.** Beyond this point, the muscle contracts more and more vigorously as the stimulus strength is increased. The **maximal stimulus** is the strongest stimulus that produces an increase in contractile force. It represents the point at which all the muscle's motor units have been recruited. Increasing stimulus intensity beyond the maximal stimulus does not produce a stronger contraction. In the body, the same phenomenon is caused by neural activation of an increasingly large number of motor units serving the muscle.

In weak and precise muscle contractions, relatively few motor units are stimulated. Conversely, when the muscle contracts forcibly many motor units are activated. This explains how the same hand that pats your cheek can deliver a stinging slap. In any muscle, the smallest motor units (those with the fewest muscle fibers) are controlled by the most excitable motor neurons. These motor units tend to be activated first. The larger motor units, controlled by

(Stimuli)

(1) Twitch   **(2)** Wave summation   **(3)** Incomplete tetanus (unfused)   **(4)** Complete tetanus (fused)

FIGURE 9.14
Wave summation and tetanus. A whole muscle's response to different stimulus frequencies is illustrated. In (1), a single stimulus is delivered, and the muscle contracts and relaxes (twitch contraction). In (2), stimuli are delivered more frequently, so that the muscle does not have adequate time to relax completely, and contraction force increases (wave summation). In (3), more complete twitch fusion (incomplete tetanus) occurs as stimuli are delivered more rapidly. Complete tetanus, a smooth, continuous contraction without any evidence of relaxation, is shown in (4).

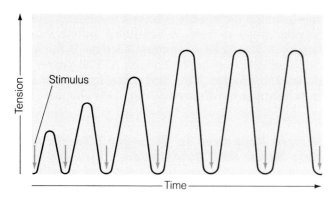

FIGURE 9.15
Myogram of treppe (the staircase effect). Notice that although the stimuli delivered to the muscle are of the same intensity and the muscle is not being stimulated rapidly, the first few contractile responses are increasingly stronger.

less excitable neurons, are activated only when a stronger contraction is necessary.

Although *all* the motor units of a muscle may be recruited simultaneously to produce an exceptionally strong contraction, the more common case is that motor units are activated asynchronously. Some are in tetanus while others are resting and recovering. This phenomenon helps to prolong a tetanic contraction by preventing or delaying fatigue. It also explains how weak contractions promoted by infrequent stimuli can remain smooth.

Treppe: The Staircase Effect

When a muscle begins to contract, its contractions may be only half as strong as those that occur shortly thereafter in response to stimuli of the same strength. Thus, a recording of these contractions shows a staircase pattern called **treppe** (trep'ĕ) (Figure 9.15). Treppe probably reflects the increasing availability of Ca^{2+}. Additionally, as the muscle begins to work and liberates heat, the muscle's enzyme systems become more efficient. Together, these factors produce a slightly stronger contraction with each successive stimulus during the initial phase of muscle activity. This is the basis of the warm-up period required of athletes.

Muscle Tone

Skeletal muscles are described as "voluntary muscles," but even relaxed muscles are almost always in a slightly contracted state, a phenomenon called **muscle tone.** This is due to spinal reflexes that activate first one group of motor units and then another in response to activation of stretch receptors in the muscles and tendons. (These receptors and their activity are described in Chapter 13.) While muscle tone does not produce active movements, it keeps the muscles firm, healthy, and ready to respond to stimulation. Skeletal muscle tone also helps stabilize joints and maintain posture.

Isotonic and Isometric Contractions

Until now, we have been discussing contraction in terms of shortening behavior, but muscles do not always shorten during contraction—sometimes they remain unchanged in length or actually lengthen. The term *contraction* refers to the active process of generating force within a muscle by cross bridge activity. The force exerted by a contracting muscle on some object is referred to as **muscle tension** and the weight, or reciprocal force (resistance to movement), exerted by the object on the muscle is called the **load.** Since muscle tension and load are opposing forces, to move a load the muscle tension must be greater than the load.

There are two main categories of contractions—*isotonic* and *isometric.* In **isotonic** (*iso* = same; *ton* = tension) **contractions,** the muscle changes in length (decreasing the angle at the joint) and moves the load. The tension remains constant through *most* of the contractile period. Isotonic contractions come in two "flavors"—*concentric* and *eccentric.* **Concentric contractions** in which the muscle *shortens* and does work—picking up a book or kicking a ball, for instance—are probably more familiar. The force of concentric contractions often determines the success of our athletic performance. However, **eccentric contractions,** in which the muscle contracts as it *lengthens,* are equally important for coordination and purposeful movements. Eccentric contractions occur in your calf muscle, for example, as you propel yourself up a long, steep hill.

Squats, or deep knee bends, are a simple example of how concentric and eccentric contractions work together in our everyday activities. As the knees flex, the powerful quadriceps muscles of the anterior thigh lengthen (are stretched), but they also contract (eccentrically) at the same time to counteract the force of gravity and control the descent of the torso ("muscle breaking") to prevent joint injury. Raising the body back to its starting position requires that the same muscles (quadriceps) contract concentrically as they shorten to extend the knees again. As you can see, eccentric contractions put the body in position to contract concentrically. All jumping and throwing activities involve both types of contraction to some degree.

Eccentric contractions are about 50% more forceful than concentric ones at the same load, yet they use less oxygen and energy and involve fewer muscle fibers. Moreover, eccentric contractions more often cause delayed-onset muscle soreness 8 to 24 hours after activity. Just why this is so is unclear, but it may be that the muscle stretching or elongation that occurs during eccentric contractions is more likely to cause microtears in the muscles. (Consider how your stretched calf muscles feel the day after hiking up that long, steep hill.)

Effective movement also requires *isometric* (*metric* = measure) *contractions.* In **isometric contractions,** tension continues to increase but the muscle *neither shortens nor lengthens.* Muscles that act primarily to maintain upright posture or to hold joints in

FIGURE 9.16
Methods of regenerating ATP during muscle activity. The fastest mechanism is direct phosphorylation; the slowest is the aerobic mechanism.

stationary positions while movements occur at other joints are contracting isometrically. Isometric contractions also occur when a muscle attempts to move a load that is greater than the force (tension) the muscle is able to develop—such as your arm muscles when you try to lift a piano singlehandedly. In our knee bend example, the anterior thigh muscles contract isometrically at two points: (1) when the squat position is held for a few seconds, both the anterior and posterior thigh muscles contract isometrically to hold the knee in the flexed position; and (2) as one begins to rise to the upright position, the contraction is isometric until the tension in the quadriceps muscle exceeds the load (weight of the upper body) and then muscle shortening (concentric contraction) begins. So the quadriceps contractile sequence for a deep knee bend from start to finish is: (1) knee flex (eccentric), (2) hold squat position (isometric), (3) knee extend (isometric, then concentric). Of course, this does not even begin to consider the isometric contractions of the shoulder girdle and trunk muscles that maintain a relatively vertical trunk posture during the movement.

Purely isotonic or isometric contractions are largely a laboratory phenomenon. In the body, most movements involve both types of contractions. Few muscles operate in isolation. Like squats, most movements require the coordinated activity of several muscles. Also, the load on a particular muscle is likely to change as the muscle shortens. Thus, in complex sports movements, body position continually changes and muscles must respond by moving from one type of contraction response to another.

Electrochemical and mechanical events occurring within a muscle are identical in both isotonic and isometric contractions. However, the result is different. In isotonic contractions, the thin filaments are sliding, whereas in isometric contractions, the cross bridges are generating force but are unsuccessful in moving the thin filaments. (You could say that they are "spinning their wheels" on the same actin binding site.)

Muscle Metabolism

Providing Energy for Contraction

Stored ATP. As a muscle contracts, ATP provides the energy for contractile events (cross bridge movement and detachment) and for operation of the calcium pump. Surprisingly, muscles store very limited reserves of ATP—4 to 6 seconds worth, just enough to get you going. Once contraction begins the reserves are soon exhausted.

Since ATP is the *only* energy source that can be used directly for contractile activities, it must be regenerated continuously if contraction is to continue. ATP is regenerated by three pathways during muscle activity (Figure 9.16): (1) by interaction of ADP with creatine phosphate, (2) by an anaerobic pathway called anaerobic glycolysis, and (3) by aerobic respiration. Anaerobic glycolysis and aerobic respiration are the two metabolic pathways used to produce ATP in all body cells. These pathways, just touched on here, will be described in detail in Chapter 25.

Direct Phosphorylation of ADP by Creatine Phosphate. As we begin to exercise vigorously, ATP stored in working muscles is depleted within 6 seconds. Then **creatine** (kre′ah-tin) **phosphate (CP),** a unique high-energy molecule stored in muscles, is tapped to regenerate ATP rapidly while the metabolic pathways are adjusting to the sudden increased demands for ATP. The reaction that occurs couples CP with ADP (a product of ATP hydrolysis) and is completed in a fraction of a second. The overall result is almost instantaneous transfer of energy and a phos-

phate group from CP to ADP to form ATP:

Creatine phosphate + ADP → creatine + ATP

Muscle cells store substantial amounts of creatine phosphate, and the coupled reaction, catalyzed by the enzyme **creatine kinase,** is so effective that the amount of ATP in muscle cells changes very little during the initial period of contraction. Although approximately five times as much CP is stored as ATP, reserves of CP are also quickly exhausted.

Together, stored ATP and CP provide for maximum muscle power for about 15 to 20 seconds—long enough to energize a 100-meter dash. The coupled reaction is readily reversible, and CP reserves are replenished during periods of inactivity, when the muscle fibers are producing more ATP than they need by other pathways. High levels of ATP favor its reaction with creatine to re-form creatine phosphate (Figure 9.17a).

Aerobic Respiration.

Even as stored ATP and CP are used, more ATP is generated by aerobic (oxygen-requiring) processes. At rest and during light exercise, muscle metabolism is almost entirely aerobic, and free fatty acids are oxidized to produce ATP during such periods. But as the intensity of exercise increases, glucose (obtained from the bloodstream and from the breakdown of stored glycogen) becomes the primary fuel source (see Figure 9.17). (Oxidation of fatty acids alone cannot supply energy fast enough.)

Aerobic respiration occurs in the mitochondria, requires oxygen, and involves a sequence of several chemical reactions in which the bonds of fuel molecules are broken and the energy released is used to make ATP. These reactions are known collectively as **oxidative phosphorylation** (fos″for-ĭ-la′shun). During aerobic respiration, glucose is broken down entirely, yielding water, carbon dioxide, and large amounts of ATP:

Glucose + oxygen → carbon dioxide + water + ATP

The carbon dioxide released diffuses out of the muscle tissue into the blood and is removed from the body by the lungs.

Although the aerobic mechanism provides a high yield of ATP (36 ATP per glucose oxidized), it is relatively slow because of its many steps, and it requires continuous delivery of oxygen and nutrient fuels to keep it going.

Anaerobic Glycolysis and Lactic Acid Formation.

The initial phase of glucose respiration is **glycolysis** (gli-kol′ĭ-sis; "sugar splitting"). During glycolysis, glucose is broken down to two *pyruvic acid* molecules and some of the energy released is captured to form small amounts of ATP (2 per glucose). This pathway occurs in both the presence *and* absence of oxygen, but since it does not *use* oxygen, it is an *anaerobic* (an-a′er-ob-ik) pathway (see Figure 9.16b and 9.17b). Ordinarily, pyruvic acid then enters

the oxygen-requiring aerobic pathways within the mitochondria and reacts with oxygen to produce still more ATP, as previously described. In such cases, since oxygen is ultimately used, the respiration process as a whole is described as *aerobic.* As long as it has enough oxygen and glucose, a muscle cell will form ATP by aerobic reactions. But when muscles contract vigorously for an extended period and contractile activity reaches about 70% of the maximum possible (e.g., running 600 yards with maximal effort), the bulging muscles compress the blood vessels within them, impairing blood and hence oxygen and glucose delivery. Therefore, the sluggish aerobic pathways cannot function fast enough to keep pace with muscle demands for ATP. Under these conditions, most of the pyruvic acid produced during glycolysis is converted into **lactic acid,** and the overall process is referred to as **anaerobic glycolysis.** Thus, during oxygen deficit, lactic acid, rather than carbon dioxide and water, is the end product of cellular metabolism of glucose. Most of the lactic acid diffuses out of the muscles into the bloodstream and is completely washed out of the muscle tissue within 30 minutes after exercise stops. Subsequently, the lactic acid is picked up by liver cells, reconverted to pyruvic acid and released back into the bloodstream for muscle use or oxidized in the liver via the aerobic pathways to carbon dioxide and water (or converted to glycogen).

The anaerobic pathway harvests only about 5% as much ATP from each glucose molecule as the aerobic pathway; however, it produces ATP about 2½ times faster. Thus, when large amounts of ATP are needed for moderate periods (30–40 seconds) of strenuous muscle activity, the anaerobic pathway (glycolysis) can provide most of the ATP needed. Together, stored ATP and CP and the glycolysis–lactic acid system can support strenuous muscle activity for nearly a minute.

Although anaerobic glycolysis is very effective in providing the energy to sustain vigorous exercise when the aerobic pathway cannot do so, it too has shortcomings. Huge amounts of glucose are used to produce relatively small harvests of ATP, and the accumulating lactic acid contributes to muscle fatigue and is at least partially responsible for the muscle soreness resulting from intense exercise.

Energy Systems Used During Sports Activities.

Exercise physiologists have been able to estimate the relative importance of each energy-producing system to athletic performance. Activities that require a surge of power but last only a few seconds, such as weight lifting, diving, and sprinting, rely entirely on ATP and CP stores. (Other energy-producing mechanisms do not have a chance to get going before the activity is over.) The more sustained activities of tennis, soccer, and a 100-meter swim appear to be fueled almost entirely by the

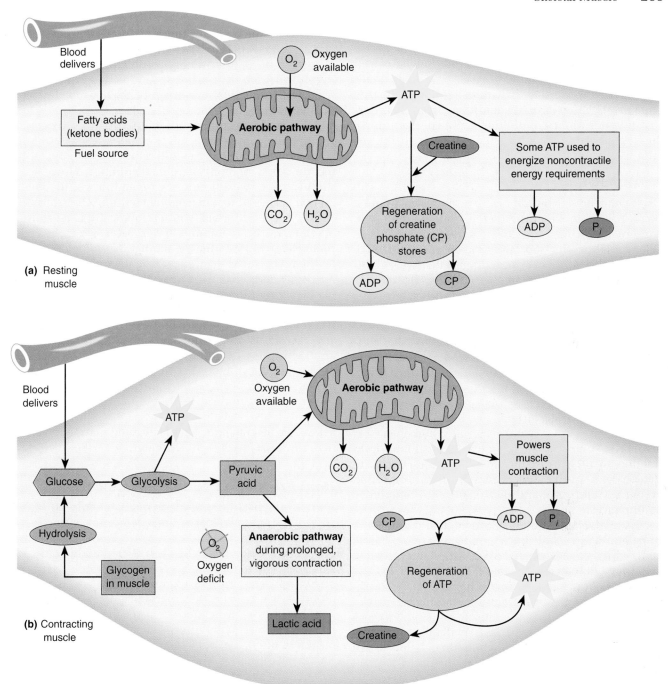

FIGURE 9.17
Skeletal muscle energy metabolism.
(a) In resting muscle, muscle fibers rely heavily on ketone bodies (breakdown products of fatty acids) to fuel the aerobic pathways that lead to ATP production. ATP is used to regenerate the secondary high-energy compound creatine phosphate (CP) and to energize cellular activities other than those involved in contraction. **(b)** As muscle cells begin to contract, ATP is used to power cross bridge activity. As stored ATP is hydrolyzed, CP (and perhaps anaerobic glycolysis) is used to regenerate ATP rapidly during the interval when aerobic pathways are adjusting to the sudden increased demands for ATP. Once this adjustment has been made, the primary source of ATP is provided by the aerobic respiration of glucose obtained from the blood and glycogen stored in muscle. When oxygen delivery and usage fail to keep pace with the requirements of the aerobic pathways, glucose is metabolized only anaerobically, leading to the formation and release of lactic acid. The anaerobic pathway is less efficient; nonetheless, it is capable of producing ATP at a very rapid rate.

anaerobic mechanism producing lactic acid. Prolonged activities, such as marathon runs and jogging, where endurance rather than power is the goal, depend mainly on aerobic mechanisms.

Anaerobic and aerobic pathways are closely intertwined in muscle metabolism. The anaerobic pathways often kick in temporarily early in the exercise session when the aerobic machinery is still attempting to reach full efficiency and CP reserves are exhausted. Then aerobic mechanisms take over *unless* the activity is so strenuous or prolonged that the aerobic mechanism cannot keep pace. The length of time a muscle can continue to contract using aerobic pathways is call **aerobic endurance,** and the point at which muscle metabolism converts to anaerobic glycolysis is called **anaerobic threshold.** As long as ATP demands are kept below the anaerobic threshold, light to moderate muscular activity can continue for several hours in well-conditioned individuals. By contrast, muscles working at peak levels using anaerobic glycolysis fatigue after 1–2 minutes. •

Muscle Fatigue

Glycogen stored in muscle cells provides some independence from blood-delivered glucose, but with continued exertion even those reserves are exhausted. When ATP production fails to keep pace with ATP use, muscles contract less and less effectively. Ultimately muscle fatigue sets in and muscle activity ceases, even though the muscle may still be receiving stimuli. **Muscle fatigue** is a state of *physiological inability to contract.* This is quite different from the phenomenon of psychological fatigue, in which we voluntarily stop exercising when we feel tired. In psychological fatigue, the flesh (muscles) is still willing, but the spirit is not! It is the "will to win" in the face of psychological fatigue that sets athletes apart. Notice that muscle fatigue results from a *relative deficit* of ATP, not its total absence. When no ATP is available, **contractures,** or states of continuous contraction, result because the cross bridges are unable to detach (not unlike the scenario of rigor mortis). Writer's cramp is a familiar example of temporary contractures.

Excessive accumulation of lactic acid and ionic imbalances also contribute to muscle fatigue. Lactic acid, which causes muscle pH to drop (and the muscles to ache), causes extreme fatigue and limits the usefulness of the anaerobic mechanism for ATP production. During transmission of action potentials, potassium is lost from the muscle cells, and excess sodium enters. So long as ATP is available to energize the Na^+- K^+ *pump,* these slight ionic imbalances are corrected. However, without ATP, the pump is inactive and the muscle cells become nonresponsive.

Oxygen Debt

Whether or not fatigue occurs, vigorous exercise causes a muscle's chemistry to change dramatically. For a muscle to return to its resting state, its oxygen reserves must be replenished, the accumulated lactic acid must be reconverted to pyruvic acid, glycogen stores must be replaced, and ATP and creatine phosphate reserves must be resynthesized. Additionally, the liver must convert lactic acid produced during muscle activity and released into the blood to glucose or glycogen. During anaerobic muscle contraction, all of these oxygen-requiring activities occur more slowly and are (at least partially) deferred until oxygen is again available. Thus, we say an *oxygen debt* is incurred, which must be repaid. **Oxygen debt** is defined as the extra amount of oxygen that must be

taken in by the body for these restorative processes, and it represents the difference between the amount of oxygen needed for totally aerobic respiration during muscle activity and the amount that is actually used. All nonaerobic sources of ATP used during muscle activity contribute to this debt.

A simple example will help illustrate oxygen debt. If you were to run the 100-yard dash in 12 seconds, your body would require approximately 6 L of oxygen for totally aerobic respiration. However, the VO_2 max (the amount of oxygen that could actually be delivered to and used by your muscles) during that 12-second interval would be about 1.2 L, far short of the required amount. Thus, you would have incurred an oxygen debt of about 4.8 L, which would be repaid by rapid deep breathing for some time after exertion was ended. This heavy breathing is triggered primarily by high levels of lactic acid in the blood, which indirectly stimulates the respiratory center of the brain. Oxygen use during exertion depends on several factors, including age, size, athletic training, and health. In general, the more exercise to which a person is accustomed, the higher his or her oxygen use (and anaerobic threshold) during exercise and the lower the oxygen debt. For example, the VO_2 max of most athletes is at least 10% greater than that of a sedentary person, and that of a trained marathon runner may be as much as 45% greater. •

Heat Production During Muscle Activity

As with the best human-made engines, only 20% to 25% of the energy released during muscle contraction is actually converted to useful work. The rest is given off as heat, which has to be dealt with if body homeostasis is to be maintained. When you exercise vigorously, you start to feel uncomfortably hot as your blood is warmed by the liberated heat. Ordinarily, heat buildup is prevented from reaching dangerous levels by several homeostatic mechanisms, including radiation of heat from the skin surface and sweating. Shivering represents the opposite end of homeostatic balance, in which muscle contractions are used to produce more heat. Body temperature regulation is described in Chapter 25.

Force, Velocity, and Duration of Muscle Contraction

The main factors affecting the force, velocity, and duration of muscle contraction are described next and summarized in Figure 9.18.

Force of Contraction

The strength, or force, of muscle contraction is affected by (1) the number of muscle fibers contracting, (2) the relative size of the muscle, (3) series-elastic elements, and (4) the degree of muscle stretch. Let's briefly examine the role of each of these factors.

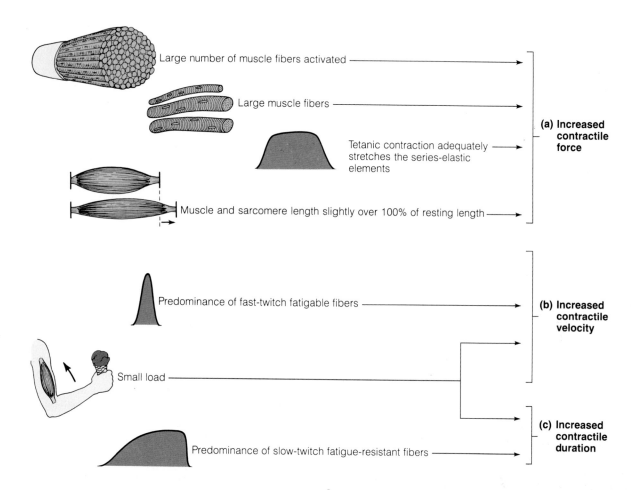

FIGURE 9.18
Factors influencing force, velocity, and duration of skeletal muscle contraction.

Number of Muscle Fibers Stimulated. As already discussed, the more motor units that are recruited, the greater the force of muscle contraction.

Relative Size of the Muscle. The bulkier the muscle (the greater its cross-sectional area), the more tension it can develop and the greater its strength. Regular exercise increases muscle strength by causing muscle cells to *hypertrophy* (hi-per′tro-fe) or increase in size.

Series-Elastic Elements. Muscle shortening in and of itself does not promote movement of body parts. To do useful work, (1) a muscle must be attached to other movable structures and (2) its connective tissue coverings and tendons must be pulled taut. These conditions satisfied, when tension generated by cross bridge activity is transmitted to the muscle cell surfaces (sarcolemmas) and then through the connective tissue wrappings to the load (the muscle insertion), movement occurs. All of the *noncontractile structures* of muscles are collectively called **series-elastic elements,** since they are able to stretch

and recoil. The force, or **internal tension,** generated by the contractile elements (myofibrils), stretches the series-elastic elements. These then transfer their tension, called the **external tension,** to the load.

The point here is that it takes time to take up slack and stretch the series-elastic elements, and while this is happening, the stretching force (internal tension) is already beginning to decline. So, in twitch contractions, the external tension exerted on the load is always less than the internal tension (Figure 9.19a). However, when a muscle is stimulated to tetanus, more time is available to stretch the series-elastic elements, and the external tension approaches that generated by the cross bridges (Figure 9.19b). Thus, the more rapidly a muscle is stimulated, the greater the force it exerts.

Degree of Muscle Stretch. The optimal resting length for muscle fibers is the length at which they can generate maximum force (Figure 9.20). The ideal **length-tension relationship** within a sarcomere occurs when a muscle is slightly stretched and the actin and myosin filaments barely overlap, because

FIGURE 9.19
Relationship of stimulus frequency to external tension exerted on the load.
(a) During a single-twitch contraction, the internal tension developed by the contractile elements peaks and begins to decline well before the series-elastic elements can be stretched to equal tension. As a result, the external tension exerted on the load is always less than the internal tension. **(b)** When the muscle is stimulated rapidly so that tetanus occurs, the internal tension is maintained long enough for the series-elastic components to be stretched to similar tension, so the external tension exerted approaches and finally equals the internal tension.

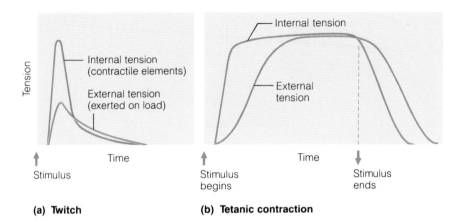

(a) Twitch   **(b) Tetanic contraction**

this permits sliding along nearly the entire length of the actin filaments. If a muscle cell is stretched so that the myofilaments do not overlap at all (Figure 9.20c), the cross bridges have nothing to attach to and tension cannot be generated. At the opposite extreme,

FIGURE 9.20
Length-tension relationships in skeletal muscles. The average length of a sarcomere is 2.0–2.25 μm and maximum force generation is possible when the muscle is a little over 100% of its resting length. Increases and decreases beyond the optimal range result in decreased force and finally an inability to generate tension. Depicted here is the relative sarcomere length in a muscle that is **(a)** strongly contracted, **(b)** at normal resting length, and **(c)** excessively stretched.

the sarcomeres are so compressed and cramped that the Z lines abut the thick myofilaments and the thin filaments touch and interfere with one another (Figure 9.20a). Under these conditions, little further shortening can occur.

Identical relationships exist in a whole muscle. In *in vitro* studies, a severely stretched muscle (say to 175% of its optimal length) cannot develop any tension. Likewise, once a muscle contracts to 60% of its resting length, further shortening is limited. Muscles, like muscle fibers, have an optimal operational length of about 80% to 120% of their normal resting length. In the body, skeletal muscles are maintained very near that optimum length by the way they are attached to bones. Thus, degree of stretch contributes only *slightly* to *in vivo* skeletal muscle strength (but it is very important in determining the force of contraction of heart muscle).

Velocity and Duration of Contraction

Muscles vary in how fast they can contract and how long they can contract before they fatigue. These characteristics are influenced by both load and muscle fiber type.

Load. Because muscles are attached to bones, they are always pitted against some resistance, or load, when they contract. As expected, they contract fastest when there is no added load on them. The greater the load, the longer the latent period, the slower the contraction, and the shorter the duration of contraction (Figure 9.21). If the load exceeds the muscle's ability to move it, the velocity of shortening is zero and the contraction is isometric.

Muscle Fiber Type. Not all muscle fibers are alike. Three discrete types of muscle fibers can be identified on the basis of differences in their size, speed, and endurance (Table 9.3).

Red slow-twitch fibers are typically thin cells that contain *slow-acting myosin ATPases* and contract slowly; hence the name *slow-twitch* fibers. Their red color stems from their plentiful supply of *myoglobin,* which binds oxygen and increases the rate of

Table 9.3 Structural and Functional Characteristics of the Three Types of Skeletal Muscle Fibers

Feature	Red slow-twitch (fatigue-resistant)	White fast-twitch (fatigable)	Intermediate fast-twitch (fatigue-resistant)
Metabolic characteristics:			
Twitch rate	Slow	Fast	Fast
Myosin ATPase activity	Slow	Fast	Fast
Primary pathway for ATP synthesis	Aerobic	Anaerobic	Aerobic
Myoglobin content	High	Low	High
Glycogen stores	Low	High	Intermediate
Rate of fatigue	Slow	Fast	Intermediate
Structural characteristics:			
Color	Red	White (pale)	Red (pink)
Fiber diameter	Small	Large	Intermediate
Mitochondria	Many	Few	Many
Capillaries	Many	Few	Many

oxygen diffusion throughout the muscle cell. Red fibers have abundant mitochondria and a rich capillary supply, and their enzymes catalyze the aerobic pathways for ATP synthesis. These features, along with the abundant myoglobin supply, reveal that these fibers are oxygen dependent, hence they are called *oxidative fibers*. Their primary energy fuel is fat. Because these fibers meet virtually all their energy needs via aerobic pathways (as long as adequate oxygen is available), they are extremely *fatigue resistant* and have high endurance; that is, they can contract for prolonged periods. However, because they are thin fibers, they do not generate much power.

White fast-twitch fibers are generally large pale cells with little myoglobin and a diameter about twice that of the slow-twitch fibers. They contain *fast-acting myosin ATPases* and contract rapidly. They have few mitochondria, but large glycogen reserves. Also called *glycolytic fibers,* they depend on the anaerobic pathway to generate ATP during contraction. Since glycogen reserves are short-lived and lactic acid accumulates quickly in these cells, they tire quickly (hence, are *fatigable* fibers). However, their large diameter reflects their plentiful contractile filaments that allow them to contract powerfully before they "poop out." Thus, the white fast-twitch fibers are best suited for short-term, rapid, intense movements (move furniture across the room, for example).

Intermediate fast-twitch fibers are *red,* or sometimes pink, cells intermediate in size between the two other fiber types. They contain *fast-acting myosin ATPases* like white fibers and contract quickly, but they are more like the red (slow-twitch) fibers in their oxygen dependence, high myoglobin content, and

(a)

(b)

FIGURE 9.21
Influence of load on velocity and duration of contraction. (a) Relationship of load to degree and duration of contraction (shortening). **(b)** Relationship of load to velocity of shortening. As the load increases, the speed of contraction decreases.

rich capillary supply. Since they depend largely on aerobic mechanisms, they are fatigue resistant, but less so than the red slow-twitch fibers.

Although some muscles have a predominance of one fiber type, most body muscles contain a mixture of fiber types, which gives them a range of contractile speeds and fatigue resistance. For example, a muscle in the calf of the leg sometimes propels us in a sprint (using mostly its white fibers), or in long-distance races (making good use of its intermediate fast-twitch fibers), or may simply help maintain our standing posture (using red slow-twitch fibers). As might be expected, all muscle fibers in a particular motor unit are of the same type.

Although everyone's muscles contain mixtures of the three fiber types, some people have relatively more of one variety. These differences are genetically controlled and no doubt determine athletic capabilities to a large extent. For example, muscles of marathon runners have a high percentage of slow-twitch fibers (about 80%), while those of sprinters contain a higher percentage (about 60%) of the fast-twitch fibers. Weight lifters appear to have approximately equal amounts of fast- and slow-twitch fibers. •

Effect of Exercise on Muscles

The amount of work a muscle does is reflected in changes in the muscle itself. When used actively or strenuously, muscles may increase in size or strength or become more efficient and fatigue resistant. On the other hand, muscle inactivity, whatever the cause, *always* leads to muscle weakness and wasting.

Adaptations to Exercise

Aerobic, or **endurance, exercise** such as swimming, jogging, fast walking, and biking results in several recognizable changes in skeletal muscles. Capillaries surrounding the muscle fibers, as well as mitochondria within them, increase in number, and the fibers synthesize more myoglobin. These changes occur in all fiber types, but they are most dramatic in the red slow-twitch fibers that depend primarily on aerobic pathways. The changes result in more efficient muscle metabolism and in greater endurance, strength, and resistance to fatigue.

However, aerobic exercise benefits far more than the skeletal muscles. It makes overall body metabolism and neuromuscular coordination more efficient, improves gastrointestinal mobility (and elimination), and enhances the strength of the skeleton. Aerobic exercise also promotes changes in cardiovascular and respiratory system functioning that improve the delivery of oxygen and nutrients to all body tissues. The heart hypertrophies and develops a greater stroke volume (more blood is pumped out with each beat), fatty deposits are cleared from blood vessel walls, and gas exchange in the lungs becomes more efficient.

The moderately weak, but sustained, type of muscle activity required for endurance exercise does not promote significant skeletal muscle hypertrophy, even though the exercise may go on for hours. Muscle hypertrophy, illustrated by the bulging biceps and chest muscles of a professional weight lifter, results mainly from high-intensity **resistance exercise** (typically under anaerobic conditions) such as weight lifting or isometric exercise, in which the muscles are pitted against high resistance or immovable forces. Here strength, not stamina, is important; a few minutes every other day is sufficient. The increased muscle bulk that results largely reflects increases in the size of individual muscle fibers (particularly the white fast-twitch variety) rather than an increased number of muscle fibers. However, at least some of the increased muscle size results from longitudinal splitting and/or tearing of the enlarged fibers and subsequent growth of these "split" cells. Vigorously stressed muscle fibers contain more mitochondria, form more myofilaments and myofibrils, and store more glycogen. The amount of connective tissue between the cells also increases. Collectively these changes promote significant increases in muscle strength and size.

Resistance training can produce magnificently bulging muscles, but if training is done unwisely, some muscles may be developed more than others. Since muscles work in antagonistic pairs (or groups), opposing muscles must be equally strong to work together smoothly. When muscle training is not balanced, individuals can become *muscle-bound*, i.e., lack flexibility, have a generally awkward stance, and be unable to make full use of their muscles.

Because endurance and resistance exercises produce different patterns of muscular response, it is important to know what your exercise goals are. Lifting weights will not improve your endurance for a triathlon. By the same token, jogging will do little to improve muscle definition for competition in the Mr. or Ms. Muscle contest, nor will it enhance your strength for moving furniture. **Cross training,** which alternates aerobic activities with anaerobic ones provides the best program for optimal health. •

Disuse Atrophy

Muscles must be physically active if they are to remain healthy. Complete immobilization of muscle, resulting from enforced bed rest or loss of neural stimulation, results in muscle *atrophy* (degeneration and loss of mass), which begins almost as soon as the muscles are immobilized. Under such conditions, muscle strength can decrease at the rate of 5% per day!

Even at rest, muscles receive weak intermittent stimuli from the nervous system. When a muscle is totally deprived of neural stimulation, the result is devastating; the paralyzed muscle may ultimately atrophy to about one-quarter of its initial size. Muscle tissue is replaced by fibrous connective tissue, which makes muscle rehabilitation impossible. Atrophy of a denervated muscle may be delayed by electrically stimulating the muscle periodically while waiting to see whether the damaged nerve fibers regenerate. •

Training Smart to Prevent Overuse Injuries

Though most of us lack the time (and perhaps the talent) to train like the pros, we can benefit from their training tips: Don't expect to get in shape by playing a sport; you've got to get in shape *to play* the sport. Regardless of your choice—running, lifting weights, or tennis, for example—exercise stresses muscles. Muscle fibers tear, tendons stretch, and accumulation of lactic acid in the muscle causes pain.

Effective training walks a fine line between working hard enough to improve and preventing exercise burnout or overuse injuries. Whatever the activity, there are certain basic guidelines for training: (1) stretching beforehand to warm up the muscle is an absolute requirement, and (2) exercise gains adhere to the *overload principle.* Forcing a muscle to work hard promotes increased muscle strength and endurance, and as muscles adapt to the increased demands, they must be overloaded even more to produce further gains. To become faster, you must train at an increasingly fast pace. A heavy-workout day should be followed by one of rest or an easy workout to allow the muscles to recover and repair themselves. Doing too much too soon, or ignoring the warning signs of muscle or joint pain, increases the risk of **overuse injuries** that may impair or prevent future sports activities, or even lead to lifetime disability. Children are prone to overuse injuries, particularly when caught in an environment that presses them to "work through the pain" or "tough it out." Changing or restricting activity, using ice packs to prevent or reduce inflammation, and taking nonsteroidal antiinflammatory drugs (Motrin, Advil) to reduce pain are the main treatment modes for virtually all overuse injuries.

SMOOTH MUSCLE

Except for the heart, which is made up of cardiac muscle, the muscle in the walls of hollow organs is almost entirely smooth muscle. Although the chemical and mechanical events of contraction are essentially the same in all muscle tissues, smooth muscle is distinctive in several ways (see Table 9.4 on pp. 276–277).

Arrangement of Smooth Muscle Fibers and Microscopic Structure

Smooth muscle fibers are small, spindle-shaped cells, each with one centrally located nucleus (Figure

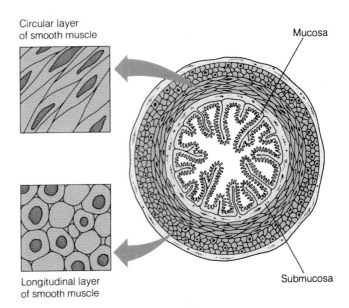

FIGURE 9.22
Arrangement of smooth muscle in the walls of hollow organs. As seen in this simplified cross-sectional view of the intestine, two smooth muscle layers are present (one circular and the other longitudinal) and run at right angles to each other.

9.22). Typically, they have a diameter of 2–10 µm and a length of 100–500 µm. Skeletal muscle fibers are about 20 times wider and thousands of times longer.

Between the smooth muscle fibers is a small amount of fine connective tissue (endomysium) containing blood vessels and nerves. Smooth muscle lacks the coarser connective tissue sheaths seen in skeletal muscle. Smooth muscle fibers are usually organized into sheets of closely apposed fibers. These sheets occur in the walls of all but the smallest blood vessels and in the walls of hollow organs of the respiratory, digestive, urinary, and reproductive tracts. In most cases, at least two sheets of smooth muscle are present, with their fibers oriented at right angles to each other (Figure 9.22). One of these, the *longitudinal layer,* runs parallel to the long axis of the organ. In the other, the *circular layer,* the fibers run around the circumference of the organ. Contraction of the circular layer constricts the lumen (cavity) of the organ and causes the organ to elongate; the longitudinal layer dilates and shortens the organ. The alternating contraction and relaxation of these opposing layers mix substances in the lumen and "squeeze" them through the organ's internal pathway. This phenomenon is called **peristalsis** (per"i-stal'sis; "around contraction"). Contraction of smooth muscle in the rectum, urinary bladder, and uterus helps those organs to expel their contents.

Smooth muscle lacks the highly structured neuromuscular junctions of skeletal muscle. Instead, the innervating nerve fibers, which are part of the autonomic nervous system (described in Chapter 14), have numerous bulbous swellings, called **varicosities.** The

Table 9.4 Comparison of Skeletal, Cardiac, and Smooth Muscle

Characteristic	Skeletal	Cardiac	Smooth
Body location	Attached to bones or (some facial muscles) to skin	Walls of the heart	Single-unit muscle in walls of hollow visceral organs (other than the heart); multiunit muscle in intrinsic eye muscles
Cell shape and appearance	Single, very long, cylindrical, multinucleate cells with very obvious striations	Branching chains of cells; uni- or binucleate; striations	Single, fusiform, uninucleate; no striations
Connective tissue components	Epimysium, perimysium, and endomysium	Endomysium attached to fibrous skeleton of heart	Endomysium
Presence of myofibrils composed of sarcomeres	Yes	Yes, but myofibrils are of irregular thickness	No, but actin and myosin filaments are present throughout
Presence of T tubules and site of invagination	Yes; at A-I junctions	Yes; at Z lines; larger diameter than those of skeletal muscle	No
Elaborate sarcoplasmic reticulum	Yes	Less than skeletal muscle; scant terminal cisternae	No; SR rudimentary

Table 9.4 continued

Characteristic	Skeletal	Cardiac	Smooth
Presence of gap junctions	No	Yes; at intercalated discs	Yes; in single-unit muscle
Fibers exhibit individual neuromuscular junctions	 Yes	No	 Not in single-unit muscle; yes in multiunit muscle
Regulation of contraction	 Voluntary via axonal endings of the somatic nervous system	 Involuntary; intrinsic system regulation; also autonomic nervous system controls; hormones; stretch	 Involuntary; autonomic nerves, hormones, local chemicals, stretch
Source of Ca^{2+} for calcium pulse	Sarcoplasmic reticulum (SR)	SR and from extracellular fluid	SR and from extracellular fluid
Site of calcium regulation	 Troponin on actin-containing thin filaments	 Troponin on actin-containing thin filaments	 Calmodulin on myosin-containing thick filaments
Presence of pacemaker(s)	No	Yes	Yes (in single-unit muscle only)
Effect of nervous system stimulation	Excitation	Excitation or inhibition	Excitation or inhibition
Speed of contraction	 Slow to fast	 Slow	 Very slow
Rhythmic contraction	No	Yes	Yes in single-unit muscle
Response to stretch	Contractile strength increases with degree of stretch (to a point)	Contractile strength increases with degree of stretch	Stress-relaxation response
Respiration	Aerobic and anaerobic	Aerobic	Mainly anaerobic

varicosities release neurotransmitter into a wide synaptic cleft in the general area of the smooth muscle cells. Such junctions are called **diffuse junctions.**

Intracellularly, the sarcoplasmic reticulum of smooth muscle fibers is less developed than that of skeletal muscle and T tubules are notably absent. However, the SR *directly* touches the sarcolemma and smooth muscle cells have a relatively large surface area for their size. Together these anatomical factors allow the SR to receive directly the exciting impulse traveling along the sarcolemma and allow the Ca^{2+} that triggers contraction to enter the cytoplasm from both the SR cisternae and the extracellular space.

No striations are visible, as the name *smooth muscle* indicates. Smooth muscle fibers do contain interdigitating thick and thin filaments, but these differ somewhat from those of skeletal muscle. The proportion and organization of the myofilaments are also different:

1. The ratio of thick to thin actin filaments is much lower in smooth muscle than in skeletal muscle (1:16 compared to 1:2). However, the thick filaments of smooth muscle contain actin-gripping heads along their entire length, a feature which allows this class of muscles to be as powerful as skeletal muscle, size for size.

2. Tropomyosin is associated with the thin filaments, but no troponin complex appears to be present.

3. There are no sarcomeres, but thick and thin filaments are present and generally spiral down the long axis of a smooth muscle cell like the stripes on a barber pole.

4. Like all cells, smooth muscle fibers contain noncontractile *intermediate filaments* that resist tension. These attach to dark-staining **dense bodies** that are scattered throughout the cell and occasionally anchor to the sarcolemma. The dense bodies also anchor groups of thin filaments, and therefore correspond to the Z discs of skeletal muscle. The intermediate filament–dense body network forms a strong, cablelike intracellular cytoskeleton that harnesses the pull generated by the sliding of the myofilaments during contraction (Figure 9.23).

Contraction of Smooth Muscle

Mechanism and Characteristics of Contraction

In most cases, adjacent smooth muscle cells exhibit slow, synchronized contractions; the whole sheet responds to a stimulus in unison. This phenomenon reflects electrical coupling of smooth muscle cells by *gap junctions,* specialized cell connections described in Chapter 3. Skeletal muscle cells are electrically isolated from one another, each stimulated to contract by

Intermediate filament bundles attached to dense bodies

(a) Relaxed smooth muscle cell

(b) Contracted smooth muscle cell

FIGURE 9.23
Intermediate filaments and dense bodies of smooth muscle fibers. Intermediate filaments and dense bodies of smooth muscle fibers harness the pull generated during myosin cross bridge activity. The dense bodies are attached to the sarcolemma, the intermediate filaments, and the actin-containing filaments. **(a)** A relaxed smooth muscle cell. **(b)** A contracted smooth muscle cell.

its own neuromuscular junction; but gap junctions allow smooth muscles to transmit action potentials from cell to cell. Some smooth muscle fibers in organs such as the stomach and small intestine, for example, act as *pacemaker cells,* and once excited, they act as "drummers" to set the contractile pace for the entire muscle sheet. Additionally, some of these pacemakers are self-excitatory, that is, they can depolarize spontaneously in the absence of external stimuli. However, both the rate and intensity of smooth muscle contraction may be modified by neural and chemical stimuli.

The mechanism of contraction in smooth muscle parallels that of skeletal muscle in the following ways: (1) actin and myosin interact by the sliding filament mechanism; (2) the final trigger for contraction is a rise in the intracellular calcium ion level; and (3) the sliding process is energized by ATP.

During excitation-contraction coupling, ionic calcium is released by the tubules of the SR, but it also moves into the cell from the extracellular space. Although ionic calcium serves the same triggering role in all muscle types, the mechanism of activation is different in smooth muscle. Here calcium interacts with regulatory molecules, in this case, calmodulin and a kinase enzyme called *myosin light chain kinase,* that are part of the *thick* filaments in order to activate myosin. The thin filaments lack the troponin complex and so are always ready for contraction. Apparently the sequence of events is: (1) ionic calcium binds to calmodulin, activating it; (2) activated calmodulin activates the kinase enzyme; (3) the activated kinase catalyzes transfer of phosphate from ATP to myosin, which allows it to interact with actin of the thin filaments. As with skeletal muscle, smooth muscle relaxes when intracellular Ca^{2+} levels drop.

Contraction of smooth muscle is slow, sustained, and resistant to fatigue. It takes 30 times longer to contract and relax than does skeletal muscle and can maintain the same tension of contraction for prolonged periods at less than 1% of the energy costs. At least part of the energy economy of smooth muscle reflects the sluggishness of its ATPases (the myosin light chain kinases) compared to those in skeletal muscle. Moreover, smooth muscle myofilaments may "lock together" during prolonged contractions, saving energy in that way as well.

The ATP-efficient contraction of smooth muscle is extremely important to overall body homeostasis. The smooth muscle in small arterioles and other visceral organs routinely maintains a moderate degree of contraction, called *smooth muscle tone,* day in and day out without fatiguing. Since smooth muscle has low energy requirements, its fibers contain relatively few mitochondria, and most ATP is made via anaerobic pathways.

Regulation of Contraction

Activation of smooth muscle by a neural stimulus is identical to that described for skeletal muscle. An action potential is generated as neurotransmitters bind to membrane receptors, and is coupled to the release of calcium ions into the sarcoplasm. However, not all neural signals received by smooth muscle result in its activation, and not all smooth muscle activation results from neural signals.

All somatic nerve endings, i.e., those that serve skeletal muscle, release acetylcholine, which always excites the skeletal muscle. However, nerve fibers of different autonomic nerves serving the smooth muscle of visceral organs release different neurotransmitters, each of which may excite or inhibit a particular group of smooth muscle cells. The effect of a specific neurotransmitter on a given type of smooth muscle depends on whether the receptor molecules on the sarcolemma are stimulatory or inhibitory. For example, when acetylcholine binds to ACh receptors on smooth muscle in the bronchioles (small air passageways of the lungs), the muscle contracts strongly, narrowing the bronchioles. When norepinephrine, released by a different type of autonomic fiber, binds to norepinephrine receptors on the *same* smooth muscle cells, the effect is inhibitory; the muscle relaxes, dilating the air passageways. On the other hand, when norepinephrine binds to smooth muscle in the walls of most blood vessels, it stimulates the smooth muscle cells to contract and constrict the vessel.

Some smooth muscle layers receive no nerve supply at all and instead depolarize spontaneously or in response to chemical stimuli. Others respond to both neural and chemical stimuli. Chemical factors that cause smooth muscle contraction or relaxation without an action potential (by enhancing or inhibiting calcium ion entry into the sarcoplasm) include certain hormones, lack of oxygen, excess carbon dioxide, and low pH. The direct response of smooth muscle to these chemical stimuli can alter smooth muscle activity according to local tissue needs and probably is most responsible for smooth muscle tone. For example, the hormone gastrin stimulates contraction of stomach smooth muscle so that it can churn foodstuffs more efficiently. We will consider how the smooth muscle of specific organs is activated as we discuss each organ in subsequent chapters.

Special Features of Smooth Muscle Contraction

Smooth muscle is intimately involved with the functioning of most hollow organs and has a number of unique characteristics. Some of these—smooth muscle tone; slow, prolonged contractile activity; and low energy requirements—have already been considered. But smooth muscle also responds differently to stretch, can shorten more than other muscle types, and has secretory functions.

Response to Stretch. When cardiac muscle is stretched, it responds with more vigorous contractions; so does skeletal muscle up to a point (about 120% of resting length). Stretching of smooth muscle also provokes a contraction, which automatically moves substances along an internal tract. However, the increased tension persists only briefly, and within a few minutes the tension returns to its original level. This response, called the **stress-relaxation response,** allows a hollow organ to fill or expand slowly (within certain limits) to accommodate a greater volume without promoting expulsive contractions. This is an important attribute, because organs such as the stomach and bladder must be able to store their contents temporarily. If this did not occur, the stretching of your stomach and intestines as you ate would lead to vigorous contractions that would rush the foodstuffs through your digestive tract, providing insufficient time for digestion and absorption of the nutrients. Likewise, your urinary bladder would be unable to store the continuously made urine until it was convenient to empty your bladder.

Length and Tension Changes. Smooth muscle not only stretches much more than skeletal muscle but it generates more tension than skeletal muscles can when stretched to a comparable extent. As you may remember (see Figure 9.20c), precise, highly organized sarcomeres limit the extent a skeletal muscle can be stretched before it is unable to generate force. In contrast, smooth muscle cells appear to contract in a corkscrewlike manner. Their lack of sarcomeres and the irregular, highly overlapping arrangement of their filaments allow them to generate considerable force, even when they are substantially stretched. The total length change that skeletal muscles can undergo and still function efficiently is about 60% (from 30%

shorter to 30% longer than resting length). In contrast, smooth muscle can contract from twice its normal length to half its normal (resting) length—a total length change of 150%. This allows organ cavities to tolerate tremendous changes in volume without becoming flabby when they empty.

Hyperplasia. Certain smooth muscle fibers are able to divide to increase their numbers, that is, to undergo *hyperplasia* (hi"per-pla′ze-ah). Excellent examples are seen in the response of the uterus to estrogen. At puberty, girls' plasma estrogen levels begin to rise. As estrogen binds to uterine smooth muscle receptors, it stimulates the synthesis of more smooth muscle, causing the uterus to grow to adult size. Then, during pregnancy, high blood levels of estrogen stimulate uterine hyperplasia to accommodate the increasing size of the fetus.

Secretory Functions. Smooth muscle fibers synthesize and secrete the proteins collagen and elastin. Thus, the smooth muscle cells themselves, not fibroblasts, secrete the soft connective tissue that surrounds them.

Types of Smooth Muscle

The smooth muscle in different body organs varies substantially in its (1) fiber arrangement and organization, (2) responsiveness to various stimuli, and (3) innervation. However, for simplicity, smooth muscle is usually categorized into two major types: *single-unit* and *multiunit smooth muscle.*

Single-Unit Smooth Muscle

Single-unit smooth muscle, commonly called **visceral muscle,** is by far the more common type. Its cells (1) tend to contract as a unit and rhythmically, (2) are electrically coupled to one another by *gap junctions,* and (3) often exhibit spontaneous action potentials. All the smooth muscle characteristics described so far pertain to single-unit smooth muscle. Thus, the cells of single-unit smooth muscle are arranged in sheets, exhibit the stress-relaxation response, and so on.

Multiunit Smooth Muscle

The smooth muscles in the large airways to the lungs and in large arteries, the arrector pili muscles attached to hair follicles of the skin, and the internal eye muscles that adjust your pupil size and allow you to focus visually are all examples of **multiunit smooth muscle.**

In contrast to the situation in single-unit muscle, gap junctions are rare and spontaneous and synchronous depolarizations infrequent. Multiunit smooth muscle (like skeletal muscle) (1) consists of muscle fibers that are structurally independent of each other;

(2) is richly supplied with nerve endings, each of which forms a motor unit with a number of muscle fibers; and (3) responds to neural stimulation with graded contractions. However, while skeletal muscle is served by the somatic (voluntary) division of the nervous system, multiunit smooth muscle (like single-unit smooth muscle) is innervated by the autonomic (involuntary) division and is also responsive to hormonal controls.

DEVELOPMENTAL ASPECTS OF MUSCLES

With rare exceptions, all muscle tissues develop from embryonic mesoderm cells called **myoblasts.** Myoblasts destined to become smooth or cardiac muscle cells migrate to and surround the rudimentary linings of the visceral organs with which they are associated. Skeletal muscle develops from "blocks" of mesoderm called somites that flank the immature nerve cord and from small clusters of mesodermal cells that form the embryonic limb buds.

The multinucleate skeletal muscle fibers form by the fusion of many myoblasts. Once fusion has occurred, the cells form actin and myosin filaments and become capable of contraction. Ordinarily, skeletal muscles are contracting by week 7 when the embryo is only 2.5 cm (1 inch) long. Initially ACh receptors "sprout" over the entire surface of the developing myoblasts. But, as spinal nerves invade the muscle masses and the nerve endings target individual myoblasts, they release a trophic factor called *agrin.* Agrin binds to the basal lamina of the myoblasts and stimulates the clustering of ACh receptors at the newly forming motor end plates. As the muscle fibers are brought under the control of the somatic nervous system, the relative number of fast-twitch and slow-twitch fiber types is determined as well.

In contrast, myoblasts producing cardiac and smooth muscle fibers do not fuse. The details of development of these muscle tissues are less known, but both develop gap junctions at a very early embryonic stage. Cardiac muscle is functioning as a blood pump by the end of the third week of development (which is often before a woman even realizes that she is pregnant).

Specialized skeletal and cardiac muscle fibers become amitotic but retain the ability to hypertrophy in adults (given appropriate stimulation). By birth, their specialization generally has been completed, and injured muscles (and the heart) are repaired mostly by scar tissue formation after this time. However, myoblastlike cells called *satellite cells* associated with skeletal muscle help to repair injured fibers and allow *very limited* regeneration of dead skeletal muscle fibers. Cardiac muscle totally lacks satellite cells and has no regenerative capability whatsoever. By contrast, smooth muscle has a fair to good ability to regenerate throughout life.

At birth, the skeletal muscles are mostly strap-like, and a baby's movements are uncoordinated and reflexive. As a rule, muscular development reflects the level of neuromuscular coordination, which develops in a head-to-toe and proximal-to-distal direction. A baby can lift its head before it can walk. Gross movements precede fine ones, and infancy sees the rapid progress from random arm waving to such precise movements as the pincer grasp (the movement used to pick up a pin between the index finger and the opposed thumb). All through childhood, our control of our skeletal muscles becomes more and more sophisticated. By midadolescence, we have reached the peak of *natural* neural control of muscles, and can either accept that level of development or improve it by athletic or other types of training.

A frequently asked question is whether the difference in strength between women and men has a biological basis. It does. Individuals vary, but on average, women's skeletal muscles make up approximately 36% of body mass, whereas men's account for about 42%. Men's greater muscular development is due primarily to the effects of testosterone on skeletal muscle, not to the effects of exercise. Since men are usually larger than women, the average difference in strength is even greater than the percent difference in muscle mass would suggest, but body strength per unit muscle mass is the same in both sexes. Strenuous muscle exercise causes more muscle hypertrophy in males than in females, again because of the influence of male hormones. Some athletes take large doses of synthetic male sex hormones ("steroids") to increase their muscle mass. This illegal and dangerous practice is discussed in *A Closer Look* in Chapter 17 (p. 559).

Because of its rich blood supply, skeletal muscle is amazingly resistant to infection throughout life, and given good nutrition and moderate exercise, relatively few problems afflict skeletal muscles. However, muscular dystrophy is a serious condition that deserves more than a passing mention.

The term **muscular dystrophy** refers to a group of inherited muscle-destroying diseases that generally appear during childhood. The affected muscles enlarge due to fat and connective tissue deposit, but the muscle fibers themselves degenerate and atrophy.

The most common and serious form is *Duchenne muscular dystrophy,* which is inherited as a sex-linked recessive disease: Females carry and transmit the abnormal gene, which is expressed almost exclusively in males (1 in every 3500 births). This tragic disease is usually diagnosed when the boy is between two to six years old. Active, normal-appearing children become clumsy and begin to fall frequently as their muscles weaken. The disease progresses relentlessly from the extremities upward, finally affecting the head and chest muscles. Victims rarely live beyond their early 20s due to respiratory failure.

Recent research has pinned down the cause of Duchenne muscular dystrophy: The diseased muscle fibers lack a protein, called *dystrophin,* that is important to maintain the integrity of the sarcolemma. Although there is still no cure for Duchenne, this knowledge has allowed development of some promising new techniques. One, called *myoblast transfer therapy,* involves injecting diseased muscle with healthy myoblast cells that fuse with the unhealthy ones. Once inside the cells, the myoblast nuclei provide the normal gene that allows the fibers to start producing dystrophin and so to grow normally. Clinical trials of this technique on humans have shown limited success. Another approach is to inject *plasmids,* tiny circlets of DNA containing a pared-down version of the dystrophin gene, into affected muscles. About 1% of the muscle cells took up the minigenes and made functional dystrophin protein in initial tests on mice. The large size of human muscles presents a huge challenge to both the cell and gene transfer therapies. Thus far, the only medication that has improved strength and muscle function is the steroid prednisone; however, it is not curative. •

As we age, the amount of connective tissue in our skeletal muscles increases, the number of muscle fibers decreases, and the muscles become stringier, or more sinewy. Since skeletal muscles represent so much of body mass, body weight declines. Loss of muscle mass also leads to decreased muscle strength, usually about a 50% decrease by the age of 80 years. Regular exercise helps offset the effects of aging on the muscular system, and frail elders who begin to "pump iron" (use leg and hand weights) are able to rebuild muscle mass and dramatically increase their strength. Muscles can also suffer indirectly. Aging of the cardiovascular system affects nearly every organ in the body, and muscles are no exception. As atherosclerosis takes its toll and begins to block distal arteries, a circulatory condition called *intermittent claudication* (klaw′dĭ-ka′shun; "limping") occurs in some individuals. This condition restricts blood supply to the legs, leading to excruciating pains in the leg muscles during walking, forcing the person to stop and rest to get relief.

Smooth muscle is remarkably trouble-free. The few problems that impair its functioning result from external irritants. In the gastrointestinal tract, irritation might result from ingestion of excess alcohol, spicy foods, or bacterial infection. Under such conditions, smooth muscle mobility increases in an attempt to rid the body of irritating agents, and diarrhea or vomiting occurs. Specific clinical problems of the heart are considered in Chapter 19.

* * *

The capacity for movement is a property of all cells but, with the exception of muscle, these movements are largely restricted to intracellular events. Skeletal muscles, the major focus of this chapter, permit us to interact with our external environment in an amazing number of ways, but they also contribute to our internal homeostasis as summarized in *Making Connections* (pp. 282–283). We have covered muscle

Making Connections

Endocrine System
- Growth hormone and androgens influence skeletal muscle strength and mass; other hormones help regulate cardiac and smooth muscle activity

Cardiovascular System
- Cardiovascular system delivers oxygen and nutrients to muscles
- Skeletal muscle activity increases efficiency of cardiovascular functioning; helps prevent atherosclerosis and causes cardiac hypertrophy

Lymphatic System/Immunity
- Lymphatic vessels drain leaked tissue fluids; immune system protects muscles from disease
- Physical exercise may enhance or depress immunity depending on its intensity

Respiratory System
- Respiratory system provides oxygen and disposes of carbon dioxide
- Muscular exercise increases respiratory capacity

Digestive System
- Digestive system provides nutrients needed for muscle health; liver metabolizes lactic acid
- Physical activity increases gastrointestinal mobility when at rest

Urinary System
- Urinary system disposes of nitrogenous wastes
- Physical activity promotes normal voiding behavior; skeletal muscle forms the voluntary sphincter of the urethra

Reproductive System
- Testicular androgen promotes increased skeletal muscle size
- Skeletal muscle helps support pelvic organs (e.g., uterus); assists erection of penis and clitoris

Integumentary System
- Skin protects the muscles by external enclosure
- Muscular exercise enhances circulation to skin and improves skin health; exercise also increases body heat, which the skin helps dissipate

Skeletal System
- Bones provide levers for muscle activity
- Skeletal muscle activity maintains bone health and strength

Nervous System
- Nervous system stimulates and regulates muscle activity
- Facial muscle activity allows emotions to be expressed

Closer Connections: The Muscular System and Interrelationships with the Cardiovascular, Endocrine, Lymphatic/Immunity, and Skeletal Systems

Our skeletal muscles are a marvel. In the well-conditioned, they ripple with energy. In those of us who are less athletic, they still allow us to perform the rather remarkable tasks of moving and getting around. No one would argue that the nervous system is indispensable for activating muscles to contract and for keeping them healthy via tone. One functional-clinical example of intrinsically important system interactions is that most premature aging results from inactivity and related diseases. But we don't have to slow up during old age. The flesh is still willing and muscle is responsive to exercise throughout life. Let's look at how skeletal muscle activity affects a few other body systems from the vantage point of overall health and disease prevention.

Cardiovascular System

The single most important barometer of how "well" we age is the health of our cardiovascular system—the vitality of our heart muscle and the absence of fatty deposits in our blood vessels. More than any other factor, exercise helps to maintain that health. Anything that gets you huffing and puffing on a regular basis, be it raquetball or a vigorous walk, helps to keep heart muscle healthy and strong. It also keeps blood vessels clear, delaying atherosclerosis and helping to prevent the most common type of high blood pressure and hypertensive heart disease—ailments that can lead to the deterioration of heart muscle and the kidneys. Uncluttered blood vessels also stave off painful or disabling intermittent claudication in which muscle pain due to ischemia hinders walking. Furthermore, regular exercise boosts blood levels of clot-busting enzymes, helping to ward off heart attacks and strokes, other scourges of old age.

Endocrine System

Muscle has a high rate of metabolism, and even at rest it uses much more energy than does fat. Consequently, exercise that builds moderate muscle mass helps to keep weight down and prevents obesity. Obesity is one of the risk factors for development of age-related diabetes mellitus—the metabolic disorder in which body cells are unresponsive to insulin (secreted by the pancreas) and, hence, unable to utilize glucose normally. Since exercise helps to maintain normal cellular responses to insulin, it helps prevent the cardiovascular consequences (blood vessel problems) of that disease. On the other hand, several hormones, including growth hormone, thyroid hormone, and sex hormones, are essential for normal development and maturation of the skeletal muscles.

Lymphatic System/Immunity

Physical exercise has a marked effect on immunity. Moderate or mild exercise causes a temporary rise in the number of phagocytes, T cells (a particular group of white blood cells), and antibodies, all of which populate lymphatic organs and mount the attack against infectious disease. By contrast, strenuous exercise depresses the immune system. The way in which exercise affects immunity—including these seemingly contradictory observations—is still a mystery, but the so-called stress hormones are probably involved. Like major stressors such as surgery and serious burns, strenuous exercise increases blood levels of stress hormones such as epinephrine and glucocorticoids. These hormones depress the immune system during severe stress. This is thought to be a protective mechanism—the body's way of preventing large numbers of slightly damaged cells from being rejected. Another intriguing possibility is that the mind as well as the muscles influences immunity—an idea fueled by the observation that people under severe psychological stress suffer more viral infections and other symptoms associated with immune suppression.

Skeletal System

Last, but not least, is the fact that weight-bearing exercise of the skeletal muscles promotes skeletal strength, and this helps prevent osteoporosis. Since osteoporosis severely detracts from the quality of life by increasing susceptibility to fractures, this is an extremely important interaction. But, without bones muscles would be ineffective in causing body movement.

Clinical Connections

Muscular System

Case study: Let's continue our tale of Mrs. DeStephano's medical problems, this time looking at the notes made detailing observations of her skeletal musculature.

- Severe lacerations of the muscles of the right leg and knee
- Damage to the blood vessels serving the right leg and knee
- Transection of the sciatic nerve (the large nerve serving most of the lower limb), just above the right knee
- Strains of the right ankle

Her physician orders daily passive range-of-motion (ROM) exercise and electrical stimulation for her right leg and a diet high in protein, carbohydrates, and vitamin C.

1. Describe the step-by-step process of wound healing that will occur in her fleshy (muscle) wounds, and note the consequences of the specific restorative process that occurs.

2. What complications in healing can be anticipated owing to vascular (blood vessel) damage in the right leg?

3. What complications in muscle structure and function result from transection of the sciatic nerve? How will the muscles distal to the point of transection look? What purpose is served by passive ROM and electrical stimulation of her right leg muscles?

4. What has happened to her right ankle? (Explain *strain* and predict its probable treatment.)

5. Explain the reasoning behind the dietary recommendations.

structure from the gross to molecular levels in this chapter and have considered its physiology in some detail. Chapter 10 continues from this point to explain how muscles interact with bones and with each other, and then describes the individual skeletal muscles that contribute to the muscular system of the body.

RELATED CLINICAL TERMS

Calcium channel blockers Drugs that interfere with the movement of Ca^{2+} across the plasma membrane, thus inhibiting muscle contraction. They are most often used to enhance blood flow through the heart by relaxing smooth muscle in the walls of cardiac blood vessels, promoting their dilation.

Cramp Sustained spasm, or tetanic contraction, of an entire muscle, which lasts for just a few seconds or several hours, causing the muscle to become taut and painful; common in calf, thigh, and hip muscles, and usually occurs at night or after exercise; may reflect low blood sugar levels, electrolyte depletion (particularly sodium or calcium), dehydration, or irritability of the spinal cord neurons; simultaneously squeezing and stretching the cramped muscle may help.

Fibromyositis (*fibro* = fiber; *itis* = inflammation) A group of conditions involving inflammation of a muscle, its connective tissue coverings and tendons, and capsules of nearby joints. Symptoms are nonspecific and often involve varying degrees of tenderness associated with specific trigger points.

Hernia Protrusion of an organ through its body cavity wall; may be congenital (owing to failure of muscle fusion during development), but most often is caused by heavy lifting or obesity and subsequent muscle weakening.

Myalgia (mi-al′je-ah; *algia* = pain) Muscle pain resulting from any muscle disorder.

Myopathy (mi-op′ah-the; *path* = disease, suffering) Any disease of muscle.

RICE Acronym for *rest, ice, compression,* and *elevation,* the standard treatment for a pulled muscle, or excessively stretched tendons or ligaments.

Spasm A sudden involuntary muscle twitch ranging in severity from merely irritating to very painful; may be due to chemical imbalances; in spasms of the eyelid or facial muscles, called tics, psychological factors have been implicated; massaging the affected area may help to end the spasm.

Strain Commonly called a "pulled muscle," a strain is excessive stretching and possible tearing of a muscle due to muscle overuse or abuse; the injured muscle becomes painfully inflamed (myositis), and adjacent joints are usually immobilized.

Tetanus (1) A state of sustained contraction of a muscle that is a normal aspect of skeletal muscle functioning. (2) An acute infectious disease caused by the anaerobic bacterium *Clostridium tetani* resulting in persistent painful spasms of some of the skeletal muscles; typically begins gradually with stiffness of jaw and neck muscles and progresses to fixed rigidity of the jaws (lockjaw) and spasms of trunk and limb muscles; usually fatal due to respiratory failure or exhaustion.

CHAPTER SUMMARY

Overview of Muscle Tissues (pp. 247–249)

Muscle Types (pp. 247–248)

1. Skeletal muscle is attached to the skeleton, is striated, and can be controlled voluntarily.

2. Cardiac muscle forms the heart, is striated, and is controlled involuntarily.

3. Smooth muscle, located chiefly in the walls of hollow organs, is controlled involuntarily. Its fibers are not striated.

Functions/Functional Characteristics (pp. 248–249)

4. Muscles move internal and external body parts, maintain posture, stabilize joints, and generate heat.

5. Special functional characteristics of muscle include excitability, contractility, extensibility, and elasticity.

Skeletal Muscle (pp. 249–275)

Gross Anatomy of a Skeletal Muscle (pp. 249–251)

1. Skeletal muscle fibers (cells) are protected and strengthened by connective tissue coverings, including the endomysium, perimysium, and epimysium.

2. Skeletal muscle attachments (origins/insertions) may be direct or indirect via tendons or aponeuroses. Indirect attachments withstand friction better.

3. Common patterns of fascicle arrangement are parallel, pennate (uni-, bi-, and multi-), convergent, and circular.

Microscopic Anatomy of a Skeletal Muscle Fiber (pp. 251–255)

4. Skeletal muscle fibers are long, striated, and multinucleate.

5. Myofibrils are contractile elements that occupy most of the cell volume. Their banded appearance results from a regular alternation of dark (A) and light (I) bands. Myofibrils are chains of sarcomeres; each sarcomere contains thick (myosin) and thin (actin) myofilaments arranged in a regular array. The heads of myosin molecules form cross bridges that interact with the thin filaments.

6. The sarcoplasmic reticulum (SR) is a system of membranous tubules surrounding each myofibril. Its function is to release and then sequester calcium ions.

7. T tubules are invaginations of the sarcolemma that run between the terminal cisternae of the SR. They allow the electrical stimulus and extracellular fluid to come into close contact with deep cell regions.

Contraction of a Skeletal Muscle Fiber (pp. 255–263)

8. According to the sliding filament theory, the thin filaments are pulled toward the sarcomere centers by cross bridge (myosin head) activity of the thick filaments.

9. Sliding of the filaments is triggered by a rise in intracellular calcium ion levels. Troponin binding of calcium moves tropomyosin away from myosin binding sites on actin, allowing cross bridge binding. Myosin ATPases split ATP, which energizes the power strokes and is necessary for cross bridge detachment.

10. Regulation of skeletal muscle cell contraction involves (a) generation and transmission of an action potential along the sarcolemma and (b) excitation-contraction coupling.

11. The action potential is set up when acetylcholine released by a nerve ending binds to ACh receptors on the sarcolemma, causing changes in membrane permeability that allow ion flows that depolarize and then repolarize the membrane. Once initiated, the action potential is self-propagating and unstoppable.

12. In excitation-contraction coupling, the action potential is propagated down the T tubules, causing calcium to be released from the SR into the cell interior. Calcium initiates cross bridge activity and sliding of the filaments. Cross bridge activity ends when calcium is pumped back into the SR.

Contraction of a Skeletal Muscle (pp. 263–267)

13. A motor unit is one motor neuron and all the muscle cells it innervates. The neuron's axon has several branches, each of which forms a neuromuscular junction with one muscle cell.

14. A skeletal muscle's response to a single brief threshold stimulus is a twitch. A twitch has three phases: the latent period, the period of contraction, and the period of relaxation.

15. Graded responses of muscles to rapid stimuli are wave summation and tetanus. A graded response to increasingly strong stimuli is multiple motor unit summation.

16. Isotonic contractions occur when the muscle shortens (concentric contraction) or lengthens (eccentric contraction) as the load is moved. Isometric contractions occur when muscle tension produces neither shortening nor lengthening.

Muscle Metabolism (pp. 267–270)

17. The energy source for muscle contraction is ATP, obtained from a coupled reaction of creatine phosphate with ADP and from aerobic and anaerobic metabolism of glucose. When ATP use exceeds its production, muscle fatigue occurs.

18. When ATP is produced by nonaerobic pathways, lactic acid accumulates and an oxygen debt occurs. To return the muscles to their resting state, ATP must be produced aerobically and used to regenerate creatine phosphate and glycogen reserves and to oxidize accumulated lactic acid.

19. Only 20%–25% of energy released during ATP hydrolysis powers contractile activity. The rest is liberated as heat.

Force, Velocity, and Duration of Muscle Contraction (pp. 270–274)

20. The force of muscle contraction is affected by the number and size of contracting muscle cells (the more and the larger the cells, the greater the force), the series-elastic elements, and the degree of muscle stretch.

21. In twitch contractions, the external tension exerted on the load is always less than the internal tension. When a muscle is tetanized, the external tension equals the internal tension.

22. When the thick and thin filaments are slightly overlapping, the muscle can generate maximum force. With excessive increase or decrease in muscle length, force declines.

23. Factors determining the velocity and duration of muscle contraction include the load (the greater the load, the slower the contraction) and muscle fiber types.

24. There are three types of muscle fibers: (1) white fast-twitch (fatigable) fibers, (2) red slow-twitch (fatigue-resistant) fibers, and (3) intermediate fast-twitch (fatigue-resistant) fibers. Most muscles contain a mixture of fiber types.

Effect of Exercise on Muscles (pp. 274–275)

25. Regular aerobic exercise results in increased efficiency, endurance, strength, and resistance to fatigue of skeletal muscles and more efficient cardiovascular, respiratory, and neuromuscular functioning.

26. Resistance exercises cause skeletal muscle hypertrophy and large gains in skeletal muscle strength.

27. Complete immobilization of muscles leads to muscle weakness and severe atrophy.

28. Improper training and excessive exercise result in overuse injuries, which may be temporarily or permanently disabling.

Smooth Muscle (pp. 275–280)

Microscopic Structure and Arrangement of Smooth Muscle Fibers (pp. 275–278)

1. Smooth muscle fibers are small, spindle shaped, and uninucleate; they display no striations.

2. Smooth muscle cells are most often arranged in sheets. They lack elaborate connective tissue coverings.

3. The SR is poorly developed; T tubules are absent. Actin and myosin filaments are present, but sarcomeres are not. Intermediate filaments and dense bodies form an intracellular network that harnesses the pull generated during cross bridge activity.

Contraction of Smooth Muscle (pp. 278–280)

4. Smooth muscle fibers may be electrically coupled by gap junctions; the pace of contraction may be set by pacemaker cells.

5. Smooth muscle contraction is energized by ATP and is activated by a calcium pulse. However, calcium binds (to calmodulin) on the thick filaments rather than on the thin filaments.

6. Smooth muscle contracts for extended periods at low energy cost and without fatigue.

7. Neurotransmitters of the autonomic nervous system may inhibit smooth muscle fibers or stimulate them. Smooth muscle contraction may also be initiated by pacemaker cells, hormones, or other local chemical factors that influence intracellular calcium levels, and by mechanical stretch.

8. Special features of smooth muscle contraction include the stress-relaxation response, the ability to generate large amounts of force when extensively stretched, hyperplasia under certain conditions, and synthesis and secretion of collagen and elastin.

Types of Smooth Muscle (p. 280)

9. Single-unit smooth muscle has electrically coupled fibers that contract synchronously and often spontaneously.

10. Multiunit smooth muscle has independent, well-innervated fibers that lack gap junctions and pacemaker cells. Stimulation is via autonomic nerves (or hormones). Multiunit muscle contractions are rarely synchronous.

Developmental Aspects of Muscles (pp. 280–284)

1. Muscle tissue develops from embryonic mesoderm cells called myoblasts. Skeletal muscle fibers are formed by the fusion of several myoblasts. Smooth and cardiac fibers develop from single myoblasts and display gap junctions.

2. Specialized skeletal and cardiac muscle cells lose their ability to divide but retain the ability to hypertrophy. Smooth muscle can regenerate and undergo hyperplasia.

3. Skeletal muscle development reflects maturation of the nervous system and occurs in cephalocaudal and proximal-to-distal directions. Peak development of natural neuromuscular control is achieved in midadolescence.

4. Women's muscles account for about 36% of their total body weight and men's for about 42%, a difference due chiefly to the effects of male hormones on skeletal muscle growth.

5. Skeletal muscle is richly vascularized and quite resistant to infection, but in old age, skeletal muscles become fibrous, decline in strength, and atrophy.

REVIEW QUESTIONS

Multiple Choice/Matching

1. The connective tissue covering that encloses the sarcolemma of an individual muscle fiber is called the (a) epimysium, (b) perimysium, (c) endomysium, (d) periosteum.

2. A fascicle is (a) a muscle, (b) a bundle of muscle fibers enclosed by a connective tissue sheath, (c) a bundle of myofibrils, (d) a group of myofilaments.

3. A muscle in which the fibers are arranged at an angle to a central longitudinal tendon has (a) a circular arrangement, (b) a longitudinal arrangement, (c) a pennate arrangement, (d) a parallel arrangement.

4. Thick and thin myofilaments have different compositions. For each descriptive phrase, indicate whether the filament is (a) thick or (b) thin.

_____ **(1)** contains actin
_____ **(2)** contains ATPases
_____ **(3)** attaches to the Z disc
_____ **(4)** contains myosin
_____ **(5)** contains troponin
_____ **(6)** does not lie in the I band

5. The function of the T tubules in muscle contraction is (a) to make and store glycogen, (b) to release Ca^{2+} into the cell interior and then pick it up again, (c) to transmit the action potential deep into the muscle cells, (d) to form proteins.

6. The sites where the motor nerve impulse is transmitted from the nerve endings to the skeletal muscle cell membranes are the (a) neuromuscular junctions, (b) sarcomeres, (c) myofilaments, (d) Z lines.

7. Contraction elicited by a single brief stimulus is called (a) a twitch, (b) wave summation, (c) multiple motor unit summation, (d) tetanus.

8. A smooth, sustained contraction resulting from very rapid stimulation of the muscle, in which no evidence of relaxation is seen, is called (a) a twitch, (b) wave summation, (c) multiple motor unit summation, (d) tetanus.

9. Characteristics of isometric contractions include all but (a) shortening, (b) increased muscle tension throughout, (c) absence of shortening, (d) use in resistance training.

10. During muscle contraction, ATP is provided by (a) a coupled reaction of creatine phosphate with ADP, (b) aerobic respiration of glucose, and (c) anaerobic glycolysis.

_____ **(1)** Which provides ATP fastest?
_____ **(2)** Which does (do) not require that oxygen be available?
_____ **(3)** Which (aerobic or anaerobic pathway) provides the highest yield of ATP per glucose molecule?
_____ **(4)** Which results in the formation of lactic acid?
_____ **(5)** Which has carbon dioxide and water by-products?
_____ **(6)** Which is most important in endurance sports?

11. The neurotransmitter released by somatic motor neurons is (a) acetylcholine, (b) acetylcholinesterase, (c) norepinephrine.

12. The ions that enter the muscle cell during action potential generation are (a) calcium ions, (b) chloride ions, (c) sodium ions, (d) potassium ions.

13. Myoglobin has a special function in muscle tissue. It (a) breaks down glycogen, (b) is a contractile protein, (c) holds a reserve supply of oxygen in the muscle.

14. Aerobic exercise is desirable because it results in all of the following except: (a) increased cardiovascular system efficiency, (b) increase in the number of mitochondria in the muscle cells, (c) increase in the size and strength of existing muscle cells, (d) increased neuromuscular system coordination.

15. The smooth muscle type found in the walls of digestive and urinary system organs and which exhibits gap junctions and pacemaker cells is (a) multiunit, (b) single-unit.

Short Answer Essay Questions

16. Name and describe the four special functional characteristics of muscle that are the basis for muscle response.

17. Distinguish between (a) direct and indirect muscle attachments and (b) a tendon and an aponeurosis.

18. (a) Describe the structure of a sarcomere and indicate the relationship of the sarcomere to the myofilament. (b) Explain the sliding filament theory of contraction using appropriately labeled diagrams of a relaxed and a contracted sarcomere.

19. What is the importance of acetylcholinesterase in muscle cell contraction?

20. Explain how a slight (but smooth) contraction differs from a vigorous contraction of the same muscle using the principal understandings of multiple motor unit summation.

21. Explain what is meant by the term excitation-contraction coupling.

22. Define motor unit.

23. Describe the three distinct types of skeletal muscle fibers.

24. True or False: Most muscles contain a predominance of one skeletal muscle fiber type. Explain the reasoning behind your choice.

25. Describe the cause(s) of muscle fatigue and define this term clearly.

26. Define oxygen debt.

27. Name four factors that influence contractile force and two that influence velocity and duration of contraction.

28. Smooth muscle has some unique properties, e.g., low energy usage, ability to maintain contraction over long periods, and the stress-relaxation response. Tie these properties to the function of smooth muscle in the body.

 CRITICAL THINKING AND CLINICAL APPLICATION QUESTIONS

1. Jim was seriously out of shape the day he joined his friends for a game of touch football. While he was running pell-mell for the ball, his left calf began to hurt. He went to the clinic the next day and was told he had a strain. Jim insisted that this must be wrong, because his joints did not hurt. Clearly, Jim was confusing a *strain* with a *sprain*. Explain the difference.

2. Diego, a 30-year-old male, decided that his physique left much to be desired. In an attempt to rectify this shortcoming, he joined a local health club and began to "pump iron" three times weekly. After three months of training, during which he was able to lift increasingly heavier weights, he noticed that his arm and chest muscles were substantially larger. Explain the structural and functional basis of these changes.

3. When a suicide victim was found, the coroner was unable to remove the drug vial clutched in his hand. Explain the reasons for this. If the victim had been discovered three days later, would the coroner have had the same difficulty? Explain.

The Muscular System

Muscle tissue includes all contractile tissues—skeletal, cardiac, and smooth muscle alike. However, when the **muscular system** is studied, **skeletal muscles,** organs composed of skeletal muscle fibers and their associated connective tissue wrappings and attachments, take center stage. As we have seen, the body activated by its skeletal muscles enjoys an incredibly wide range of movements. The gentle blinking of an eye, standing on tiptoe, and wielding a sledgehammer are just a sampling of the different activities promoted by the muscular system. These activities and the muscular "machines" that bring them about are the focus of this chapter. However, before describing the individual muscles in detail, we will explain the principles of leverage, describe the manner in which muscles "play" with or against each other to promote, restrict, or modify movements, and consider the criteria used for naming muscles.

MUSCLE MECHANICS: IMPORTANCE OF LEVERAGE AND FASCICLE ARRANGEMENT

Most factors contributing to muscle force and speed (load, fiber type, etc.) have already been covered in Chapter 9 with two important exceptions—lever systems (partnerships between the muscular and skeletal systems) and the patterns of fascicle arrangement in muscles. These are attended to next.

Lever Systems: Bone-Muscle Relationships

The operation of most skeletal muscles involves the use of leverage and **lever systems.** A **lever** is a rigid bar that moves on a fixed point, or **fulcrum,** when a force is applied to it. The applied force, or **effort,** is used to move a resistance, or **load.** In your body,

FIGURE 10.1
Lever systems operating at a mechanical advantage and mechanical disadvantage. The equation at the top expresses the relationships among the forces and distances in any lever system. **(a)** 10 kg of force (the effort) is used to lift a 1000 kg car (the load). This lever system, which employs a jack, operates at a mechanical advantage: The load lifted is greater than the applied muscular effort. **(b)** Using a shovel to lift dirt is an example of a lever system that operates at a mechanical disadvantage. A muscular force (effort) of 100 kg is used to lift 50 kg of dirt (the load). Levers operating at a mechanical disadvantage are common in the body because they permit a muscle to be inserted close to the load and provide rapid contractions that have a wide range of motion.

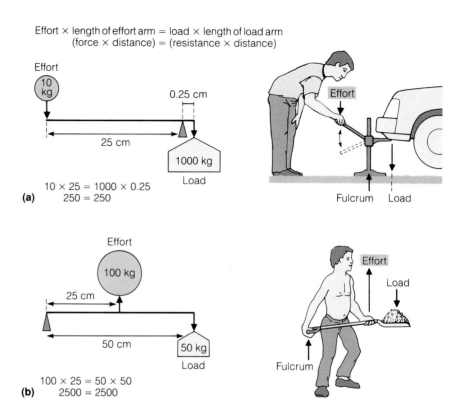

Effort × length of effort arm = load × length of load arm
(force × distance) = (resistance × distance)

Effort
10 kg
0.25 cm
25 cm
1000 kg
Load
10 × 25 = 1000 × 0.25
250 = 250
(a)

Effort
100 kg
25 cm
50 cm
50 kg
Load
100 × 25 = 50 × 50
2500 = 2500
(b)

Effort
Fulcrum Load

Effort
Load
Fulcrum

your joints are the fulcrums, and the bones of your skeleton act as levers. The effort is provided by muscle contraction and is applied at the muscle's insertion point on a bone. The load that is moved is the bone itself, along with overlying tissues and anything else you are trying to move with that particular lever.

A lever allows a given effort to move a heavier load, or to move a load farther or faster, than it otherwise could. If, as shown in Figure 10.1a, the load is close to the fulcrum and the effort is applied far from the fulcrum, a small effort exerted over a relatively large distance can be used to move a large load over a small distance. Such a lever is said to operate at a **mechanical advantage** and is commonly called a *power lever.* For example, as shown to the right in Figure 10.1a, a man can lift a car with such a lever, in this case, a jack. The car moves up only a fraction of an inch with each downward "push" of the jack handle, but relatively little muscle effort is needed. If, on the other hand, the load is far from the fulcrum and the effort is applied near the fulcrum, the force exerted by the muscle must be greater than the load moved or supported (Figure 10.1b). This lever system operates at a **mechanical disadvantage** and is a *speed lever.* Such levers are very useful because they allow the load to move rapidly through a large distance. Wielding a shovel and pitching a baseball are examples. As you can see, small differences in the site of a muscle's insertion (relative to the fulcrum or joint) can translate into large differences in the amount of force a muscle must generate to move a given load or resistance. Regardless of type, all levers follow the

same basic principle: effort farther than load from fulcrum = mechanical advantage; effort nearer than load to fulcrum = mechanical disadvantage.

Depending on the relative position of the three elements—effort, fulcrum, and load—a lever belongs to one of three classes. In **first-class levers,** the effort is applied at one end of the lever and the load is at the other, with the fulcrum somewhere between them (Figure 10.2a). Seesaws, scissors, and the use of a crowbar are familiar examples of first-class levers. First-class leverage also occurs when you lift your head off your chest. Some first-class levers in the body operate at a mechanical advantage (effort is farther from the joint than the load and is less than the load to be moved), but others, such as the operation of the triceps muscle in extending the forearm against resistance, operate at a mechanical disadvantage (effort is closer to the joint and greater than the load to be moved).

In a **second-class lever,** the effort is applied at one end of the lever and the fulcrum is located at the other, with the load at some intermediate point between them (Figure 10.2b). A wheelbarrow demonstrates this type of lever system. Second-class leverage is uncommon in the body; the best example is the act of standing on your toes. Joints forming the ball of the foot act together as the fulcrum, the load is the entire body weight, and the calf muscles inserted into the calcaneus of the heel exert the effort, pulling the heel upward. All second-class levers in the body work at a mechanical advantage because the muscle insertion is always farther from the fulcrum than is

?   *Which of these lever systems as demonstrated at far left in the diagrams would be the fastest lever?*

(a) First-class lever

(b) Second-class lever

(c) Third-class lever

FIGURE 10.2

Lever systems. (a) In a first-class lever, the arrangement of the elements is load-fulcrum-effort. A scissors is in this lever class. In the body, a first-class lever system is activated when you raise your head off your chest. The posterior neck muscles provide the effort, the occipitoatlanto joint is the fulcrum, and the weight to be lifted is the facial skeleton. **(b)** In second-class levers, the arrangement is fulcrum-load-effort, as exemplified by a wheelbarrow. In the body, second-class leverage is exerted when you stand on tiptoe. The joints of the ball of the foot are the fulcrum, the weight of the body is the load, and the effort is exerted by the calf muscles pulling upward on the heel (calcaneus) of the foot. **(c)** In a third-class lever, the arrangement is load-effort-fulcrum. A pair of tweezers or forceps uses this type of leverage. The operation of the biceps brachii muscle in flexing the forearm exemplifies third-class leverage. The load is the hand and distal end of the forearm, the effort is exerted on the proximal radius of the forearm, and the fulcrum is the elbow joint.

the load to be moved. Second-class levers are levers of strength, but speed and range of motion are sacrificed for that strength.

In **third-class levers,** the effort is applied at a point between the load and the fulcrum (Figure 10.2c). These levers operate with great speed and *always* at a mechanical disadvantage. A tweezers or forceps provides this type of leverage. Most skeletal muscles of the body act in third-class lever systems. As illustrated by the activity of the biceps muscle of the arm, the fulcrum is the elbow joint, the force is exerted on the proximal radius, and the load to be lifted is the distal forearm (and anything carried in the hand or over the forearm). Third-class lever systems permit a muscle to be inserted very close to the joint across which movement occurs, allowing rapid, extensive movement with relatively little shortening of the muscle.

In conclusion, differences in the positioning of the three elements modify muscle activity with respect to (1) speed of contraction, (2) range of movement, and (3) the weight of the load that can be lifted. In lever systems that operate at a mechanical disadvantage (speed levers), force is lost but speed is gained, and this can be a distinct advantage. Systems that operate at a mechanical advantage (power levers) are slower, more stable, and used where strength is a priority.

Arrangement of Fascicles

Although all skeletal muscles consist of fascicles, fascicle arrangements vary. This results in muscles with different shapes and functional capabilities. The most common patterns of fascicle arrangement are parallel, pennate, convergent, and circular (Figure 10.3).

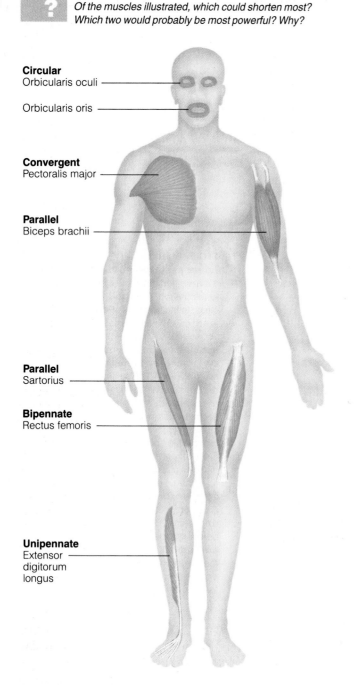

Circular
Orbicularis oculi

Orbicularis oris

Convergent
Pectoralis major

Parallel
Biceps brachii

Parallel
Sartorius

Bipennate
Rectus femoris

Unipennate
Extensor
digitorum
longus

FIGURE 10.3
Relationship of fascicle arrangement to muscle structure.

In a **parallel** arrangement, the long axes of the fascicles run parallel to the long axis of the muscle. Such muscles are either *straplike,* such as the sartorius muscle of the thigh, or *fusiform* (spindle shaped) with an expanded belly (midsection), like the biceps brachii muscle of the arm.

In a **pennate** (pen′āt) pattern, the fascicles are short and they attach obliquely (*penna* = feather) to a central tendon that runs the length of the muscle. If, as seen in the extensor digitorum muscle of the leg, the fascicles insert into only one side of the tendon, the muscle is *unipennate.* If the fascicles insert into the tendon from opposite sides, so that the muscle's "grain" resembles a feather, the arrangement is *bipennate.* The rectus femoris of the thigh is bipennate. There is also a *multipennate* arrangement. This is not shown in Figure 10.3, but it looks like many feathers situated side by side, with all their quills inserted into one large tendon. The deltoid muscle, which forms the roundness of the shoulder, is multipennate.

A **convergent** muscle has a broad origin, and its fascicles *converge* toward a single tendon. Such a muscle is triangular or fan shaped. The pectoralis major muscle of the anterior thorax has a convergent pattern.

The fascicular pattern is **circular** when the fascicles are arranged in concentric rings. Muscles with this arrangement surround external body openings, which they close by contracting. A general term for such muscles is *sphincters* (literally, "squeezers"). Examples are the orbicularis oris muscle around the mouth and the orbicularis oculi muscles surrounding the eyes.

The arrangement of a muscle's fascicles determines its range of motion and power. Since skeletal muscle fibers shorten to about 70% of their resting length when they contract, the longer and the more nearly parallel the muscle fibers are to a muscle's long axis, the more the muscle can shorten. Muscles with parallel fascicle arrangement provide the greatest degree of shortening, but they are not usually very powerful. Muscle power depends more on the total number of muscle cells in the muscle; the greater the number, the greater the power. The stocky bipennate and multipennate muscles "pack in" the most fibers. Such muscles shorten very little, but tend to be very powerful.

INTERACTIONS OF SKELETAL MUSCLES IN THE BODY

The arrangement of body muscles permits them to work either together or in opposition to achieve a wide variety of movements. As you eat, for example, you alternately raise your fork to your lips and lower it to your plate, and both sets of actions are accomplished by your arm and hand muscles. But muscles can only *pull;* they never *push.* Muscle contraction causes shortening, not lengthening, of the muscle and generally as a muscle shortens, its *insertion* (attachment on the movable bone) moves toward its *origin* (its fixed or immovable point of attachment). Thus, whatever one muscle (or muscle group) can do, there is another muscle or group of muscles that can "undo" the action.

Muscles can be classified into four functional groups: prime movers, antagonists, synergists, and fixators. A muscle that provides the major force for producing a specific movement is called a **prime mover,** or **agonist** (ag′o-nist; "leader"), of that movement. The biceps brachii muscle, which fleshes out the anterior arm (and inserts on the radius), is a prime mover of elbow flexion.

Muscles that oppose, or reverse, a particular movement are called **antagonists** (an-tag′o-nists). When a prime mover is active, the antagonist muscles are often stretched and in the relaxed state. Antagonists can also help to regulate the action of a prime mover by contracting to provide some resistance, thus helping to prevent overshoot or slow or stop the action. As you might expect, a prime mover and its antagonist are located on opposite sides of the joint across which they act. Antagonists can also be prime movers in their own right. For example, the biceps brachii muscle of the arm is antagonized by the triceps brachii, the prime mover of elbow extension.

In addition to agonists and antagonists, most movements involve the action of one or more **synergists** (sin′er-jists; *syn* = together, *erg* = work). Synergists aid agonists by (1) promoting the same movement or (2) reducing undesirable or unnecessary movements that might occur as the prime mover contracts. This latter function deserves a bit more explanation. When a muscle crosses two or more joints, its contraction causes movement at all of the spanned joints unless other muscles act as joint stabilizers. For example, the finger flexor muscles cross both the wrist and the phalangeal joints, but you can make a fist without bending your wrist because synergistic muscles stabilize the wrist joint. Additionally, as some flexors act, undesirable rotatory movements may occur; synergists can prevent this movement, allowing all of the prime mover's force to be exerted in the desired direction.

When synergists immobilize a bone, or a muscle's origin, they are more specifically called **fixators** (fik′sa-terz). Recall from Chapter 7 that the scapula is held to the axial skeleton only by muscles and is quite freely movable. Muscles that move the arm originate on the scapula, and if they are to be effective, movements of the scapula must be minimized. The fixator muscles that run from the axial skeleton to the scapula can immobilize the scapula so that only the desired movements occur at the shoulder joint. Additionally, muscles that help to maintain upright posture are fixators.

In summary, although prime movers seem to "get all the credit" for causing certain movements, the actions of antagonistic and synergistic muscles are also important in effecting smooth, coordinated, and precise movements. Furthermore, a muscle may act as a prime mover in one movement, an antagonist for another movement, a synergist for a third movement, and so on.

NAMING SKELETAL MUSCLES

Skeletal muscles are named according to a number of criteria, each of which focuses on particular structural or functional characteristics of a muscle. Paying close attention to these cues can simplify the task of learning muscle names and actions.

1. **Location of the muscle.** Some muscle names indicate the bone or body region with which the muscle is associated. For example, the temporalis (tem″por-ă′lis) muscle overlies the temporal bone, and the intercostal (*costal* = rib) muscles run between the ribs.

2. **Shape of the muscle.** Since muscles often have distinctive shapes, this criterion is sometimes used for naming. For example, the deltoid (del′toid) muscle is roughly triangular (*deltoid* = triangle), and the right and left trapezius (trah-pe′ze-us) muscles together form a trapezoid.

3. **Relative size of the muscle.** Terms such as *maximus* (largest), *minimus* (smallest), *longus* (long), and *brevis* (short) are often used in muscle names—as in gluteus maximus and gluteus minimus (the large and small gluteus muscles, respectively).

4. **Direction of muscle fibers.** The naming of some muscles reveals the direction in which their fibers (and fascicles) run in reference to some imaginary line, usually the midline of the body or the longitudinal axis of a limb bone. In muscles with the term *rectus* (straight) in their names, the fibers run parallel to that imaginary line (axis), whereas the terms *transversus* and *oblique* indicate that the muscle fibers run respectively at right angles and obliquely to that line. Muscles named according to fiber direction include the rectus femoris (straight muscle of the thigh, or femur) and transversus abdominis (transverse muscle of the abdomen).

5. **Number of origins.** When the term *biceps, triceps,* or *quadriceps* forms part of a muscle's name, you can assume that the muscle has two, three, or four origins, respectively. For example, the biceps brachii (bra′-ke-i) muscle of the arm has two origins, or *heads.*

6. **Location of the muscle's origin and/or insertion.** Some muscles are named according to their attachment points. When this criterion is used and both origin and insertion points are noted, the origin is always named first. For instance, the sternocleidomastoid (ster″no-kli″do-mas′toid) muscle of the neck has a dual origin on the sternum (*sterno*) and clavicle (*cleido*), and it inserts on the *mastoid* process of the temporal bone.

7. **Action of the muscle.** When muscles are named for their action, action words such as *flexor, extensor, adductor,* or *abductor* appear in the muscle's name. For example, the adductor longus, located on the medial thigh, brings about thigh adduction; all exten-

? *Which two muscles identified in (a) are
used to do biceps curls (flex the elbow)?
Which would be active during abdominal crunches
(sit-ups)?*

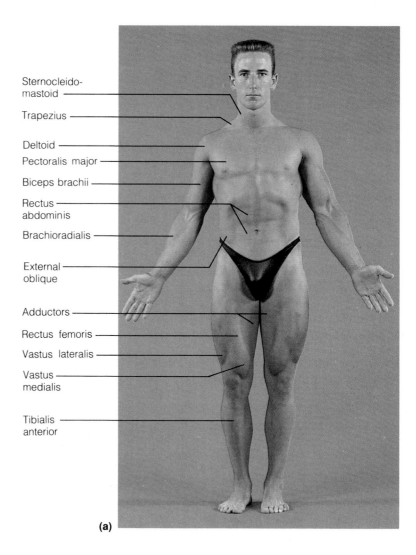

Sternocleido-
mastoid

Trapezius

Deltoid

Pectoralis major

Biceps brachii

Rectus
abdominis

Brachioradialis

External
oblique

Adductors

Rectus femoris

Vastus lateralis

Vastus
medialis

Tibialis
anterior

(a)

FIGURE 10.4
**Anterior view of superficial muscles of the
body. (a)** Photograph of surface anatomy.
(b) Diagrammatic view. The abdominal surface has
been partially dissected on the right side to show
somewhat deeper muscles.

sor muscles of the wrist effect wrist extension; and
the supinator (soo′pĭ-na′tor) muscle supinates the
forearm.

Often, several criteria are combined in the naming of a muscle. For instance, the name *extensor carpi
radialis longus* tells us the muscle's action (extensor),
what joint it acts on (*carpi* = wrist), and that it lies
close to the radius of the forearm (radialis); it also
hints at its size (longus) relative to other wrist extensor muscles. Unfortunately, not all muscle names are
this descriptive.

MAJOR SKELETAL MUSCLES OF THE BODY

The grand plan of the muscular system is all the more
impressive because of the sheer number of skeletal
muscles in the body—there are over 600 of them!
Obviously, trying to remember all the names, locations, and actions of these muscles would be a monumental task. Take heart; only the principal muscles
(approximately 125 pairs of them) will be considered

here. Although this number is far fewer than 600, the
job of learning about all these muscles will still
require a concerted effort on your part to memorize
the necessary information. Yet, memorization will be
useful—and easier—only if you can apply what you
have learned in a practical, or clinical, way. That is,
memorization should be done with a *functional
anatomy focus.* Once you are satisfied that you have
learned the name of a muscle and can identify it on a
cadaver, model, or diagram, you must then flesh out
your learning by asking yourself, "What does it do?"

In the tables that follow, the muscles of the body
have been grouped by function and location, roughly
from head to foot. Each table is keyed to a particular
figure (or group of figures) illustrating the muscles it
describes. The legend at the beginning of each table
provides an orienting overview of the types of movements effected by the muscles listed and gives point-
ers on the way those muscles interact with one another.
The table itself describes each muscle's shape, location relative to other muscles, origin and insertion,
primary actions, and innervation. (Since some instructors want students to defer learning the muscle inner-

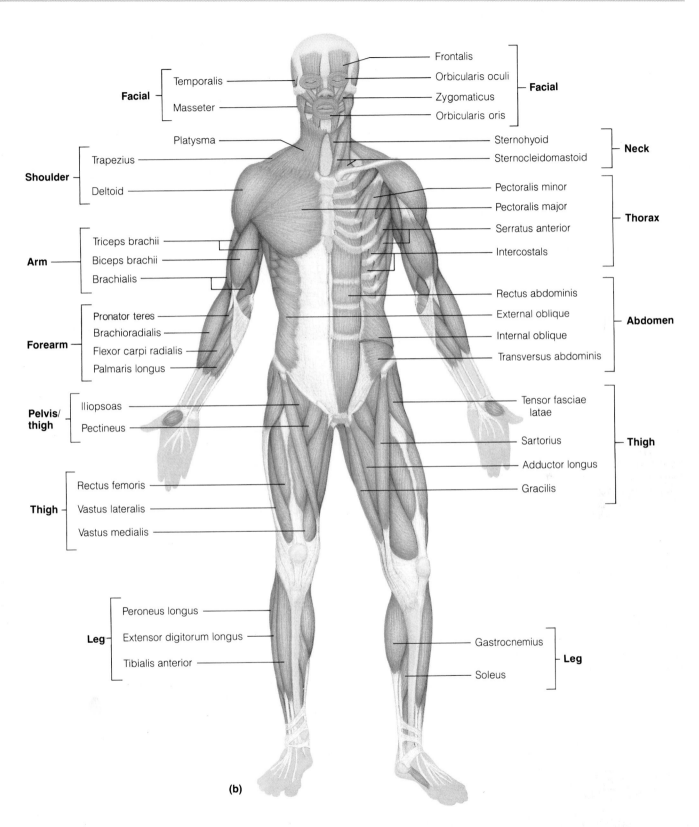

Facial — Temporalis
Masseter

Facial — Frontalis
Orbicularis oculi
Zygomaticus
Orbicularis oris

Platysma

Shoulder — Trapezius
Deltoid

Neck — Sternohyoid
Sternocleidomastoid

Arm — Triceps brachii
Biceps brachii
Brachialis

Thorax — Pectoralis minor
Pectoralis major
Serratus anterior
Intercostals

Forearm — Pronator teres
Brachioradialis
Flexor carpi radialis
Palmaris longus

Abdomen — Rectus abdominis
External oblique
Internal oblique
Transversus abdominis

Pelvis/ thigh — Iliopsoas
Pectineus

Thigh — Tensor fasciae latae
Sartorius
Adductor longus
Gracilis

Thigh — Rectus femoris
Vastus lateralis
Vastus medialis

Leg — Peroneus longus
Extensor digitorum longus
Tibialis anterior

Leg — Gastrocnemius
Soleus

(b)

vations until the nervous system has been studied, you might want to check on what is expected of you in this regard.) Muscle innervations are described in detail in Chapters 12 and 13.

As you consider each individual muscle, be aware of the information its name provides. Then,

after you have read through its entire description, identify the muscle on the figure that corresponds to the table and, in the case of superficial muscles, also on Figure 10.4 or 10.5. This will help you to link the descriptive material in the table to a visual image of the muscle's relative location in a specific body

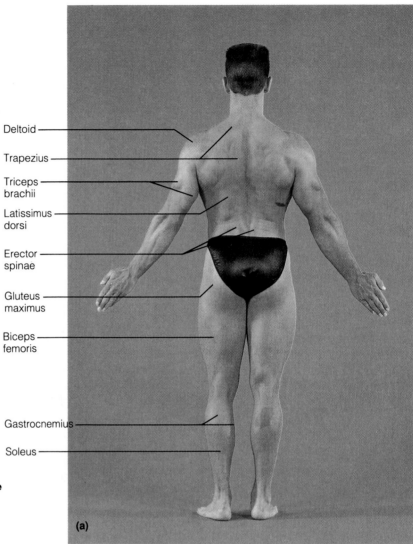

Deltoid

Trapezius

Triceps brachii

Latissimus dorsi

Erector spinae

Gluteus maximus

Biceps femoris

Gastrocnemius

Soleus

Figure 10.5
Posterior view of superficial muscles of the body. (a) Photograph of surface anatomy.
(b) Diagrammatic view.

(a)

region and in the body as a whole. As you scrutinize a muscle's position, try to relate its attachments and location to the actions allowed by the joint(s) it acts across. This will help you to focus in on functional details that often escape student awareness. For example, both the elbow and knee joints are hinge joints that allow flexion and extension. However, the knee flexes to the dorsum of the body (the calf moves toward the posterior thigh), whereas elbow flexion carries the forearm toward the anterior aspect of the arm. Therefore, leg flexors are located on the posterior thigh, while forearm flexors are found on the anterior aspect of the humerus.

Finally, keep in mind that the *best* way to learn muscle actions is to act out their movements yourself while feeling for the muscles contracting (bulging) beneath your skin.

The following list summarizes the organization and sequence of the tables in this chapter:

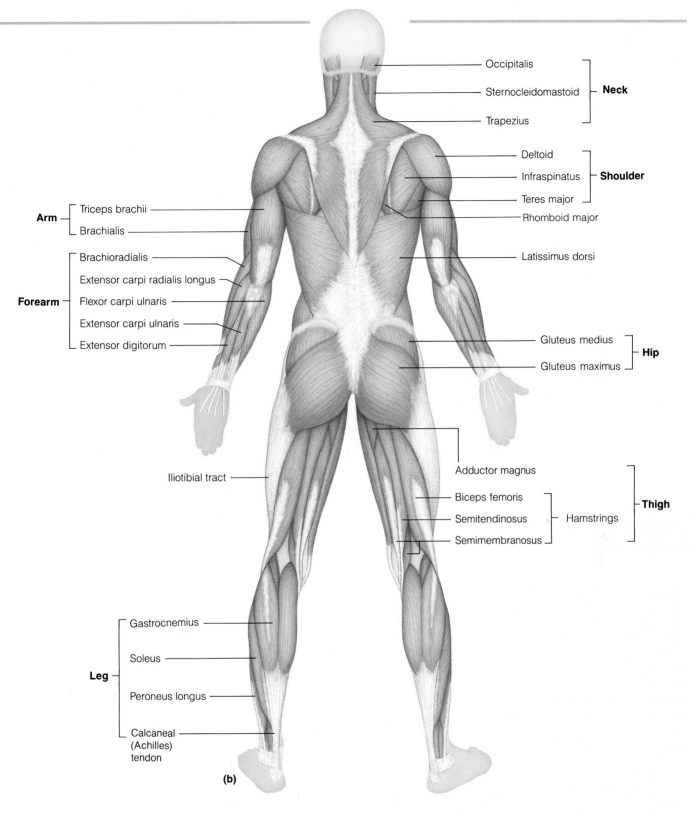

Neck
- Occipitalis
- Sternocleidomastoid
- Trapezius

Shoulder
- Deltoid
- Infraspinatus
- Teres major

Rhomboid major

Latissimus dorsi

Arm
- Triceps brachii
- Brachialis

Forearm
- Brachioradialis
- Extensor carpi radialis longus
- Flexor carpi ulnaris
- Extensor carpi ulnaris
- Extensor digitorum

Hip
- Gluteus medius
- Gluteus maximus

Iliotibial tract

Adductor magnus

Thigh — Hamstrings
- Biceps femoris
- Semitendinosus
- Semimembranosus

Leg
- Gastrocnemius
- Soleus
- Peroneus longus
- Calcaneal (Achilles) tendon

(b)

Table 10.1 Muscles of the Head, Part I: Facial Expression (Figure 10.6)

The superficial muscles of the head involved in promoting facial expression include those of the scalp and face. They are highly variable in shape and strength, and adjacent muscles tend to be fused. They are unusual muscles in that they insert into skin (or other muscles), not bones. In the scalp, the main muscle is the *epicranius,* which has distinct anterior and posterior parts; the lateral scalp muscles are vestigial in humans. Muscles clothing the facial skeleton lift the eyebrows, flare the nostrils, open and close the eyes and mouth, and provide one of the best tools for influencing others—the smile. The tremendous importance of facial muscles in nonverbal communication becomes especially clear when they are paralyzed, as in some stroke victims. All muscles listed in this table are innervated by *cranial nerve VII (the facial nerve).* The external muscles of the eye, which are contained within the orbit and act to direct the eyeball, and the levator palpebrae superioris muscles that raise the eyelids are described in Chapter 16.

Muscle	Description	Origin (O) and insertion (I)	Action	Nerve
MUSCLES OF THE SCALP				
Epicranius (Occipitofrontalis) (ep″ĭ-kra′ne-us; ok-sip″ĭ-to-fron-ta′lis) (*epi* = over; *cran* = skull)	Bipartite muscle consisting of the frontalis and occipitalis muscles connected by a cranial aponeurosis, the galea aponeurotica; the alternate action of these two muscles pulls scalp forward and backward			
• **Frontalis** (fron-ta′lis) (*front* = forehead)	Covers forehead and dome of skull; no bony attachments	O—galea aponeurotica I—skin of eyebrows and root of nose	With aponeurosis fixed, raises the eyebrows (as in surprise); wrinkles forehead skin horizontally	Facial nerve (cranial VII)
• **Occipitalis** (ok-sip″ĭ-tal′is) (*occipito* = base of skull)	Overlies base of occiput; by pulling on the galea, fixes origin of frontalis	O—occipital bone I—galea aponeurotica	Fixes aponeurosis and pulls scalp posteriorly	Facial nerve
MUSCLES OF THE FACE				
Corrugator supercilii (kor′ah-ga-ter soo″per-sĭ′le-i) (*corrugo* = wrinkle; *supercilium* = eyebrow)	Small muscle; activity associated with that of orbicularis oculi	O—arch of frontal bone above nasal bone I—skin of eyebrow	Draws eyebrows together; wrinkles skin of forehead vertically (as in frowning)	Facial nerve
Orbicularis oculi (or-bik′u-lar-is ok′u-li) (*orb* = circular; *ocul* = eye)	Thin, flat sphincter muscle of eyelid; surrounds rim of the orbit; paralysis results in drooping of lower eyelid and spilling of tears	O—frontal and maxillary bones and ligaments around orbit I—tissue of eyelid	Protects eyes from intense light and injury; various parts can be activated individually; produces blinking, squinting, and draws eyebrows downward; strong closure of eyelids causes creasing of skin at lateral aspect of eye (these folds, called "crow's feet," become permanent with aging)	Facial nerve
Zygomaticus (zi-go-mat′ĭ-kus), major and minor (*zygomatic* = cheekbone)	Muscle pair extending diagonally from corner of mouth to cheekbone	O—zygomatic bone I—skin and muscle at corner of mouth	Raises lateral corners of mouth upward (smiling muscle)	Facial nerve
Risorius (ri-zor′e-us) (*risor* = laughter)	Slender muscle running beneath and laterally to zygomaticus	O—lateral fascia associated with masseter muscle I—skin at angle of mouth	Draws corner of lip laterally; tenses lips; synergist of zygomaticus	Facial nerve
Levator labii superioris (lĕ-va′tor la′be-i soo-per″e-or′is) (*leva* = raise; *labi* = lip; *superior* = above, over)	Thin muscle between orbicularis oris and inferior eye margin	O—zygomatic bone and infraorbital margin of maxilla I—skin and muscle of upper lip	Opens lips; raises and furrows the upper lip; flares nostril (as in disgust)	Facial nerve
Depressor labii inferioris (de-pres′or la′be-i in-fer″e-or′is) (*depressor* = depresses; *infer* = below)	Small muscle running from lower lip to mandible	O—body of mandible lateral to its midline I—skin and muscle of lower lip	Draws lower lip downward (as in a pout)	Facial nerve

Muscle	Description	Origin (O) and insertion (I)	Action	Nerve
Depressor anguli oris (ang′gu-li or-is) (*angul* = angle, corner; *or* = mouth)	Small muscle lateral to depressor labii inferioris	O—body of mandible below incisors I—skin and muscle at angle of mouth below insertion of zygomaticus	Zygomaticus antagonist; draws corners of mouth downward and laterally (as in a "tragedy mask" grimace)	Facial nerve
Orbicularis oris	Complicated, multilayered muscle of the lips with fibers that run in many different directions; most run circularly	O—arises indirectly from maxilla and mandible; fibers blended with fibers of other facial muscles associated with the lips I—encircles mouth; inserts into muscle and skin at angles of mouth	Closes lips; purses and protrudes lips (kissing muscle)	Facial nerve
Mentalis (men-ta′lis) (*ment* = chin)	One of the muscle pair forming a V-shaped muscle mass on chin	O—mandible below incisors I—skin of chin	Protrudes lower lip; wrinkles chin	Facial nerve
Buccinator (bu′sĭ-na″ter) (*bucc* = cheek or "trumpeter")	Thin, horizontal cheek muscle; principal muscle of cheek; deep to masseter (see also Figure 10.7)	O—molar region of maxilla and mandible I—orbicularis oris	Draws corner of mouth laterally; compresses cheek (as in whistling, blowing, and sucking); holds food between teeth during chewing; well developed in nursing infants	Facial nerve
Platysma (plah-tiz′mah) (*platy* = broad, flat)	Unpaired, thin, sheetlike superficial neck muscle; not strictly a head muscle, but plays a role in facial expression	O—fascia of chest (over pectoral muscles and deltoid) I—lower margin of mandible, and skin and muscle at corner of mouth	Helps depress mandible; pulls lower lip back and down, i.e., produces downward sag of mouth; tenses skin of neck (e.g., during shaving)	Facial nerve

FIGURE 10.6
Lateral view of muscles of the scalp, face, and neck.

Table 10.2 Muscles of the Head, Part II: Mastication and Tongue Movement (Figure 10.7)

Four pairs of muscles are involved in mastication (chewing and biting) activities, and all are innervated by the mandibular division of *cranial nerve V* (the *trigeminal nerve*). The prime movers of jaw closure (and biting) are the powerful *masseter* and *temporalis* muscles, which can be palpated easily when the teeth are clenched. Grinding movements are provided for by the *pterygoid* muscles. The *buccinator* muscles (see Table 10.1) also play a role in chewing. Normally, gravity is sufficient to depress the mandible, but if there is resistance to jaw opening, neck muscles such as the digastric and mylohyoid muscles (see Table 10.3) are activated.

The tongue is composed of muscle fibers peculiar to itself that curl, squeeze, and fold the tongue during speaking and chewing. These **intrinsic tongue muscles**, arranged in several planes, change the shape of the tongue and contribute to its exceptional nimbleness, but they do not really move the tongue. They are considered in Chapter 24 with the digestive system. Only the **extrinsic tongue muscles,** which serve to anchor and move the tongue, are considered in this table. The extrinsic tongue muscles are all innervated by *cranial nerve XII* (the *hypoglossal nerve*).

Muscle	Description	Origin (O) and insertion (I)	Action	Nerve
MUSCLES OF MASTICATION				
Masseter (mah-se′ter) (*maseter* = chewer)	Powerful muscle that covers lateral aspect of mandibular ramus	O—zygomatic arch I—angle and ramus of mandible	Prime mover of jaw closure; elevates mandible	Trigeminal nerve (cranial V)
Temporalis (tem″por-ah′lis) (*tempora* = time; pertaining to the temporal bone)	Fan-shaped muscle that covers parts of the temporal, frontal, and parietal bones	O—temporal fossa I—coronoid process of mandible via a tendon that passes beneath zygomatic arch	Closes jaw; elevates and retracts mandible; maintains position of the mandible at rest	Trigeminal nerve
Medial pterygoid (me′de-ul ter′ ĭ-goid) (*medial* = toward median plane; *pterygoid* = winglike)	Deep two-headed muscle that runs along internal surface of mandible and is largely concealed by that bone	O—medial surface of lateral pterygoid plate of sphenoid bone, maxilla, and palatine bone I—medial surface of mandible near its angle	Synergist of temporalis and masseter muscles in elevation of the mandible; acts with the lateral pterygoid muscle to promote side-to-side (grinding) movements	Trigeminal nerve
Lateral pterygoid (*lateral* = away from median plane)	Deep two-headed muscle; lies superior to medial pterygoid muscle	O—greater wing and lateral pterygoid plate of sphenoid bone I—condyle of mandible and capsule of temporomandibular joint	Protrudes mandible (pulls it anteriorly); provides forward sliding and side-to-side grinding movements of the lower teeth	Trigeminal nerve
Buccinator	See Table 10.1	See Table 10.1	Trampolinelike action of buccinator muscles helps keep food between grinding surfaces of teeth during chewing	Facial nerve (cranial VII)
MUSCLES PROMOTING TONGUE MOVEMENTS (EXTRINSIC MUSCLES)				
Genioglossus (je″ne-o-glah′sus) (*geni* = chin; *glossus* = tongue)	Fan-shaped muscle; forms bulk of inferior part of tongue; its attachment to mandible prevents tongue from falling backward and obstructing respiration	O—internal surface of mandible near symphysis I—inferior aspect of the tongue and body of hyoid bone	Primarily protrudes tongue, but can depress or act in concert with other extrinsic muscles to retract tongue	Hypoglossal nerve (cranial XII)
Hyoglossus (hi′o-glos″us) (*hyo* = pertaining to hyoid bone)	Flat, quadrilateral muscle	O—body and greater horn of hyoid bone I—inferolateral aspect of tongue	Depresses tongue and draws its sides downward	Hypoglossal nerve
Styloglossus (sti-lo-glah′sus) (*stylo* = pertaining to styloid process)	Slender muscle running superiorly to and at right angles to hyoglossus	O—styloid process of temporal bone I—lateral inferior aspect of tongue	Retracts (and elevates) tongue	Hypoglossal nerve

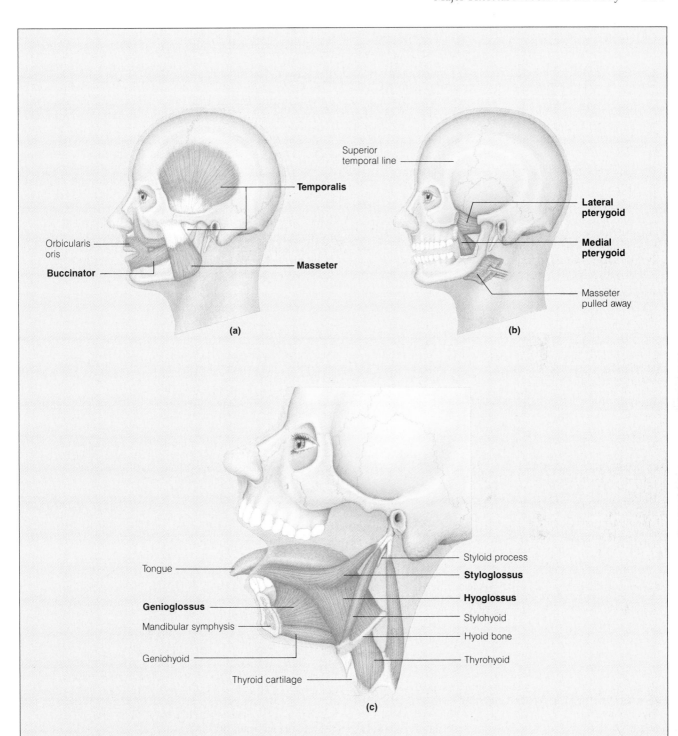

FIGURE 10.7
Muscles promoting mastication and tongue movements. (a) Lateral view of the temporalis, masseter, and buccinator muscles. **(b)** Lateral view of the deep chewing muscles, the medial and lateral pterygoid muscles. **(c)** Extrinsic muscles of the tongue. Some suprahyoid muscles of the throat are also illustrated.

Table 10.3 Muscles of the Anterior Neck and Throat: Swallowing (Figure 10.8)

The neck is divided into two triangles (anterior and posterior) by the sternocleidomastoid muscle (Figure 10.8a). This table considers the muscles of the *anterior* triangle of the neck. These muscles are divided into **suprahyoid** and **infrahyoid muscles,** which lie above and below the hyoid bone respectively. Most of these muscles are deep (throat) muscles involved in the coordinated muscle movements that occur during swallowing.

Swallowing begins when the tongue and buccinator muscles of the cheeks squeeze the food backward along the roof of the mouth toward the pharynx. Then a rapid series of muscular movements in the posterior mouth and pharynx complete the process. These events of swallowing include:
(1) Widening the pharynx to receive the food, and closing the respiratory passageway (larynx) anteriorly to prevent the aspiration of food. These activities are accomplished by the *suprahyoid muscles,* which act to pull the hyoid bone upward and forward toward the mandible. Since the hyoid bone is attached by a strong ligament (thyrohyoid membrane) to the larynx, the larynx is also pulled upward and forward, a maneuver that widens the pharynx and closes the respiratory passageway. (2) Closing off the nasal passages to prevent food from entering the superior nasal cavity. This results from the activation of small muscles that elevate the soft palate. (These muscles, called the *tensor* and *levator veli palatini,* are not described in the table but they are illustrated in Figure 10.8b.) (3) Food is propelled through the pharynx into the esophagus inferiorly by the **pharyngeal constrictor muscles.** (4) Returning the hyoid bone and larynx to their more inferior positions after swallowing, promoted by the *infrahyoid muscles.*

Muscle	Description	Origin (O) and insertion (I)	Action	Nerve supply
SUPRAHYOID MUSCLES (soo"prah-hi'oid)	Muscles that help form floor of oral cavity, anchor tongue, and move larynx superiorly during swallowing; lie superior to hyoid bone			
Digastric (di-gas'trik) (*di* = two; *gaster* = belly)	Consists of two bellies united by an intermediate tendon, forming a V shape under the chin	O—lower margin of mandible (anterior belly) and mastoid process of the temporal bone (posterior belly) I—by a connective tissue loop to hyoid bone	Acting in concert, the digastric muscles elevate hyoid bone and steady it during swallowing and speech; acting from behind, they open mouth (prime mover) and depress mandible	Mandibular branch of trigeminal nerve (cranial V) for anterior belly; facial nerve (cranial VII) for posterior belly
Stylohyoid (sti"lo-hi'oid) (also see Figure 10.7)	Slender muscle below angle of jaw; parallels posterior belly of digastric muscle	O—styloid process of temporal bone I—hyoid bone	Elevates and retracts hyoid, thereby elongating floor of mouth during swallowing	Facial nerve
Mylohyoid (mi"lo-hi'oid) (*myle* = molar)	Flat, triangular muscle just deep to digastric muscle; this muscle pair forms a sling that forms the floor of the anterior mouth	O—medial surface of mandible I—hyoid bone and median raphe	Elevates hyoid bone and floor of mouth, enabling tongue to exert backward and upward pressure that forces food bolus into pharynx	Mandibular branch of trigeminal nerve
Geniohyoid (je'ne-o-hy"oid) (also see Figure 10.7) (*geni* = chin)	Narrow muscle in contact with its partner medially; runs from chin to hyoid bone	O—inner surface of mandibular symphysis I—hyoid bone	Pulls hyoid bone superiorly and anteriorly, shortening floor of mouth and widening pharynx for receiving food during swallowing	First cervical spinal nerve via hypoglossal nerve (cranial XII)
INFRAHYOID MUSCLES	Muscles causing depression of hyoid bone and larynx during swallowing and speaking; because of their ribbonlike appearance, often called *strap muscles* (see also Figure 10.9c)			
Sternohyoid (ster"no-hi'oid) (*sterno* = sternum)	Most medial muscle of the neck; thin; superficial except inferiorly, where covered by sternocleidomastoid	O—manubrium and medial end of clavicle I—lower margin of hyoid bone	Depresses larynx and hyoid bone if mandible is fixed; may also flex skull	C_1–C_3 through ansa cervicalis (slender nerve root in cervical plexus)
Sternothyroid (ster"no-thy'roid) (*thyro* = thyroid cartilage)	Lateral and deep to sternohyoid	O—posterior surface of manubrium of sternum I—thyroid cartilage	Pulls thyroid cartilage (plus larynx and hyoid bone) inferiorly	As for sternohyoid

Muscle	Description	Origin (O) and insertion (I)	Action	Nerve supply
Omohyoid (o"mo-hi'oid) (*omo* = shoulder)	Straplike muscle with two bellies united by an intermediate tendon; lateral to sternohyoid	O—superior surface of scapula I—hyoid bone, lower border	Depresses and retracts hyoid bone	As for sternohyoid
Thyrohyoid (thi"ro-hi'oid) (also see Figure 10.7)	Appears as a superior continuation of sternothyroid muscle	O—thyroid cartilage I—hyoid bone	Depresses hyoid bone and elevates thyroid cartilage	First cervical nerve via hypoglossal
Pharyngeal constrictor muscles—superior, middle, and inferior (far-rin'je-al)	Composite of three paired muscles whose fibers run circularly in pharynx wall; arranged so that the superior muscle is innermost and inferior one is outermost; substantial overlap	O—attached anteriorly to mandible and medial pterygoid plate (superior), hyoid bone (middle), and laryngeal cartilages (inferior), and run around to back of pharynx I—posterior median raphe of pharynx	Working as a group, all constrict pharynx during swallowing, which propels a food bolus to esophagus	Pharyngeal plexus [branches of vagus (X) and glossopharyngeal (IX) nerves]

FIGURE 10.8
Muscles of the anterior neck and throat that promote swallowing.
(a) Anterior view of the suprahyoid and infrahyoid muscles. The sternocleidomastoid muscle (not involved in swallowing) is shown on the left to provide an anatomical landmark.
(b) Lateral view of the constrictor muscles of the pharynx. These muscles are shown in their proper anatomical relationship to the buccinator (a chewing muscle) and the hyoglossus muscle (which promotes tongue movements).

Table 10.4 Muscles of the Neck and Vertebral Column: Head and Trunk Movements (Figure 10.9)

Head Movements. Movements of the head are promoted by muscles originating from the axial skeleton. The major head flexors are the sternocleidomastoid muscles, but the suprahyoid and infrahyoid muscles described in Table 10.3 act as synergists in this action. Lateral head movements are effected by the sternocleidomastoids and a number of deeper neck muscles, including the *scalenes,* and by several straplike muscles of the vertebral column at the back of the neck. Head extension is aided by the superficial trapezius muscles of the back, but the *splenius* muscles deep to the trapezius muscles bear most of the responsibility for head extension.

Trunk movements. Trunk extension is effected by the *deep* or *intrinsic back muscles* associated with the bony vertebral column, muscles that also play an important role in maintaining the normal curvatures of the spine. Muscles of the thorax that connect adjacent ribs (plus the diaphragm) are involved in breathing movements (see Table 10.5), while the superficial back muscles are concerned primarily with movements of the shoulder girdle and upper limbs (see Tables 10.8 and 10.9).

The deep muscles of the back form a broad, thick column extending from the sacrum to the skull. Many muscles of varying length contribute to this mass. It helps to regard each of these individual muscles as a string, which when pulled causes one or several vertebrae to extend or to rotate on the vertebrae below. The largest of the deep

back muscle groups is the *erector spinae* (literally, "spine erectors"). Since the origins and insertions of the different muscle groups overlap extensively, entire regions of the vertebral column can be moved simultaneously and smoothly. Acting in concert, the deep back muscles extend (or hyperextend) the spine, while contraction of the muscles on only one side causes lateral bending of the back, neck or head. Lateral flexion is automatically accompanied by some degree of rotation of the vertebral column. During vertebral movements, the articular facets of the vertebrae glide on each other.

In addition to the long muscles of the back, there are a number of short muscles that extend from one vertebra to the next (Figure 10.9e). These small muscles (the rotatores, multifidus, interspinalis, and intertransversarius muscles) act primarily as synergists in extension and rotation of the spine and as spine stabilizers. They are not described in the table but you can deduce their actions by examining their origins and insertions in the figure.

Trunk muscles also maintain the normal curvatures of the spine, acting as postural muscles. It is these deep trunk *extensors* that are considered in this table. The more superficial muscles, which have other functions, are considered in subsequent tables. For example, the muscles of the abdominal wall also help to effect movements of the vertebral column and body trunk. These muscles, which cause trunk *flexion,* are described in Table 10.6.

Muscle	Description	Origin (O) and insertion (I)	Action	Nerve supply
ANTEROLATERAL NECK MUSCLES (Figure 10.9a and c)				
Sternocleidomastoid (ster"no-kli"do-mas'toid) (*sterno* = breastbone; *cleido* = clavicle; *mastoid* = mastoid process)	Two-headed muscle located deep to platysma on anterolateral surface of neck; fleshy parts on either side of neck delineate limits of anterior and posterior triangles; key muscular landmark in neck; spasms of one of these muscles may cause torticollis (wryneck)	O—manubrium of sternum and medial portion of clavicle I—mastoid process of temporal bone	Prime mover of active head flexion; simultaneous contraction of both muscles causes neck flexion, generally against resistance as when one raises head when lying on back; (head flexion is ordinarily a result of combined effects of gravity and regulated relaxation of head extensors); acting alone, each muscle rotates head toward shoulder on opposite side and tilts or laterally flexes head to its own side	Accessory nerve (cranial nerve XI) and branches of cervical spinal nerves 2–4
Scalenes (ska'lēnz)— anterior, middle, and posterior (*scalene* = uneven)	Located more laterally than anteriorly on neck; deep to platysma and sternocleidomastoid	O—transverse processes of cervical vertebrae I—anterolaterally on first two ribs	Elevate first two ribs (aid in inspiration); may be important in coughing; flex and rotate neck	Cervical spinal nerves

Muscle	Description	Origin (O) and insertion (I)	Action	Nerve supply
INTRINSIC MUSCLES OF THE BACK (Figure 10.9b–e)				
Splenius (sple'ne-us)— capitis and cervicis portions (kah-pit'us; ser-vis'us) (*splenion* = bandage; *caput* = head; *cervi* = neck) (Figures 10.9b and 10.6)	Broad bipartite superficial muscle (capitis and cervicis parts) extending from upper thoracic vertebrae to skull; capitis portion known as "bandage muscle" because it covers and holds down deeper neck muscles	O—ligamentum nuchae,* spinous processes of vertebrae C_7–T_6 I—mastoid process of temporal bone and occipital bone (capitis); transverse processes of C_2–C_4 vertebrae (cervicis)	Act as a group to extend or hyperextend head; when splenius muscles on one side are activated, head is rotated and bent laterally toward same side	Cervical spinal nerves (dorsal rami)

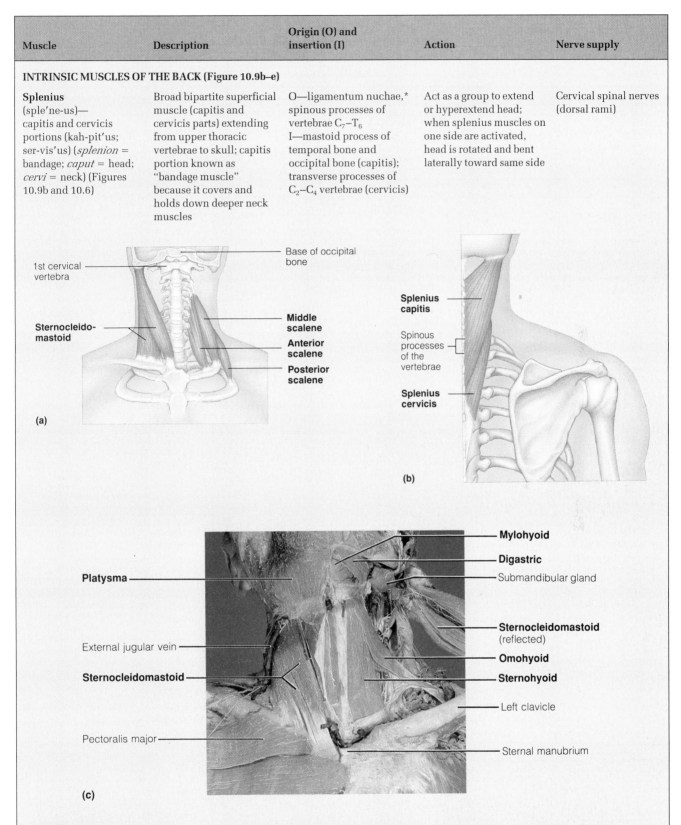

(a)

Base of occipital bone

1st cervical vertebra

Sternocleido-mastoid

Middle scalene

Anterior scalene

Posterior scalene

(b)

Splenius capitis

Spinous processes of the vertebrae

Splenius cervicis

(c)

Mylohyoid

Digastric

Submandibular gland

Sternocleidomastoid (reflected)

Omohyoid

Sternohyoid

Left clavicle

Sternal manubrium

Platysma

External jugular vein

Sternocleidomastoid

Pectoralis major

FIGURE 10.9
Muscles of the neck and vertebral column causing movements of the head and trunk. (a) Muscles of the anterolateral neck. The superficial platysma muscle and the deeper neck muscles have been removed to show clearly the origins and insertions of the sternocleidomastoid and scalene muscles. **(b)** Deep muscles of the posterior neck. **(c)** Photograph of the anterior and lateral regions of the neck. The fascia has been partially removed (left side of photograph) to expose the sternocleidomastoid muscle. On the right side of the photograph, the sternocleidomastoid muscle is reflected to expose the sternohyoid and omohyoid muscles.

(Table continues)

Table 10.4 continued				
Muscle	**Description**	**Origin (O) and insertion (I)**	**Action**	**Nerve supply**
Erector spinae (e-rek′tor spi′ne) Also called **sacrospinalis** (Figure 10.9d, left side)	Prime mover of back extension; erector spinae muscles, each consisting of three columns—the iliocostalis, longissimus, and spinalis muscles—form intermediate layer of intrinsic back muscles; erector spinae provide resistance that helps control action of bending forward at the waist and act as powerful extensors to promote return to erect position; during full flexion (i.e., when touching fingertips to floor), erector spinae are relaxed and strain is borne entirely by ligaments of back; on reversal of the movement, these muscles are initially inactive, and extension is initiated by hamstring muscles of thighs and gluteus maximus muscles of buttocks. As a result of this peculiarity, lifting a load or moving suddenly from a bent-over position is potentially dangerous (in terms of possible injury) to muscles and ligaments of back and intervertebral discs; erector spinae muscles readily go into painful spasms following injury to back structures			
• **Iliocostalis** (il″e-o-kos-tă′lis)— lumborum, thoracis, and cervicis portions (lum′bor-um; tho-ra′sis) (*ilio* = ilium; *cost* = rib)	Most lateral muscle group of erector spinae muscles; extend from pelvis to neck	O—iliac crests (lumborum); inferior 6 ribs (thoracis); ribs 3 to 6 (cervicis) I—angles of ribs (lumborum and thoracis); transverse processes of cervical vertebrae C_6–C_4 (cervicis)	Extend vertebral column, maintain erect posture; acting on one side, bend vertebral column to same side	Spinal nerves (dorsal rami)
• **Longissimus** (lon-jis′ĭ-mus)— thoracis, cervicis, and capitis parts (*longissimus* = longest)	Intermediate tripartite muscle group of erector spinae; extend by many muscle slips from lumbar region to skull; mainly pass between transverse processes of the vertebrae	O—transverse processes of lumbar through cervical vertebrae I—transverse processes of thoracic or cervical vertebrae and to ribs superior to origin as indicated by name; capitis inserts into mastoid process of temporal bone	Thoracis and cervicis act together to extend vertebral column and acting on one side, bend it laterally; capitis extends head and turns the face toward same side	Spinal nerves (dorsal rami)
• **Spinalis** (spi-nă′lis)— thoracis and cervicis parts (*spin* = vertebral column, spine)	Most medial muscle column of erector spinae; cervicis usually rudimentary and poorly defined	O—spines of upper lumbar and lower thoracic vertebrae I—spines of upper thoracic and cervical vertebrae	Extends vertebral column	Spinal nerves (dorsal rami)
Semispinalis (sem′e-spĭ-nă′lis)— thoracis, cervicis, and capitis regions (*semi* = half; *thorac* = thorax) (Figure 10.9d, right side)	Composite muscle forming part of deep layer of intrinsic back muscles; extends from thoracic region to head	O—transverse processes of C_7–T_{12} I—occipital bone (capitis) and spinous processes of cervical (cervicis) and thoracic vertebrae T_1 to T_4 (thoracis)	Extends vertebral column and head and rotates them to opposite side; acts synergistically with sternocleidomastoid muscles of opposite side	Spinal nerves (dorsal rami)
Quadratus lumborum (kwod-ra′tus lum-bor′um) (*quad* = four-sided; *lumb* = lumbar region) (See also Figure 10.18a)	Fleshy muscle forming part of posterior abdominal wall	O—iliac crest and iliolumbar fascia I—transverse processes of upper lumbar vertebrae and lower margin of 12th rib	Flexes vertebral column laterally when acting separately; when pair acts jointly, lumbar spine is extended and 12th rib is fixed; maintains upright posture	T_{12} and upper lumbar spinal nerves (ventral rami)

Mastoid process
of temporal bone

Longissimus capitis

**Semispinalis
capitis**

**Semispinalis
cervicis**

Iliocostalis cervicis

Longissimus cervicis

**Semispinalis
thoracis**

Iliocostalis thoracis

Longissimus thoracis

Spinalis thoracis

Iliocostalis

**Erector
spinae** Longissimus

Spinalis

Multifidis

Iliocostalis lumborum

External oblique

Quadratus lumborum

(d)

FIGURE 10.9 (continued)
(d) Deep muscles of the back. The superficial,
intermediate, and splenius muscles have been
removed. The three muscle columns
(iliocostalis, longissimus, and spinalis)
composing the erector spinae are shown on the
left. The semispinalis muscles are shown on the
right. **(e)** The deepest muscles of the back (the
rotatores, multifidus, interspinales, and
intertransversarius muscles) associated with
the vertebral column.

O = origin
I = insertion

Intertransversarius

Rotatores

Multifidus

Interspinales

(e)

*The ligamentum nuchae (lig"ah-men'tum noo'ke) is a strong, elastic ligament extending from the occipital bone of the skull along the tips of the spinous
processes of the cervical vertebrae. It binds the cervical vertebrae together and inhibits excessive head and neck flexion, thus preventing damage to the spinal
cord in the vertebral canal.

Table 10.5 Muscles of the Thorax: Breathing (Figure 10.10)

The primary function of the deep muscles of the thorax is to promote movements necessary for breathing. Breathing consists of two phases—inspiration, or inhaling, and expiration, or exhaling—brought about by the alternate increase and decrease in the volume of the thoracic cavity.

Three layers of muscles form the anterolateral wall of the thorax, just as three muscle layers form the abdominal wall. However, unlike the extensive abdominal muscles, those of the thorax are very short, extending only from one rib to the next. On contraction, they draw the somewhat flexible ribs closer together. The *external intercostal* muscles form the most superficial layer. They lift the rib cage, an action that increases the anterior to posterior and side-to-side dimensions of the thorax, and are considered inspiratory muscles. The *internal intercostal* muscles form the intermediate layer and aid active expiration by depressing the rib cage. However, quiet expiration is largely a passive phenomenon; i.e., it results from relaxation of the external intercostals and diaphragm and elastic recoil of the lungs. Thus, the internal intercostal muscles act primarily in forced expiratory movements. The deepest muscle layer of the thorax attaches to the internal surfaces of the ribs. It has two discontinuous parts (from posterior to anterior)—the subcostals and the transversus thoracis, each consisting of many muscle slips (fingerlike parts). These muscles are thought to help depress the rib cage (acting as synergists of the internal intercostals), but since their precise function is still controversial, they will not be described further.

The *diaphragm,* the most important muscle of inspiration, forms a muscular partition between the thoracic and abdominopelvic cavities. In the relaxed state, the diaphragm is dome shaped, but when it contracts it moves inferiorly and flattens, increasing the volume of the thoracic cavity. The alternating contraction and relaxation of the diaphragm causes pressure changes in the abdominopelvic cavity below that facilitate the return of venous blood to the heart. In addition to its rhythmic contractions during respiration, one can also contract the diaphragm voluntarily to push down on the abdominal viscera and increase the pressure in the abdominal cavity. This may be done to help evacuate pelvic organ contents (urine, feces, or a baby) or during weight lifting. When one takes a deep breath to fix the diaphragm, the abdomen becomes a firm pillar that will not buckle under the weight being lifted. Needless to say, it is important to have good control of the bladder and anal sphincters during such maneuvers.

With the exception of the diaphragm, which is innervated by the *phrenic nerves,* all muscles described in this table are served by the *intercostal nerves* (anterior rami of the first 11 thoracic spinal nerves) which run between the ribs.

Forced breathing calls into play a number of other muscles that insert into the ribs. For example, during forced inspiration the scalene and sternocleidomastoid muscles of the neck help lift the ribs. Forced expiration is aided by muscles that pull the ribs inferiorly (quadratus lumborum) and those that push the diaphragm superiorly by compressing the abdominal contents (abdominal wall muscles). The mechanics of respiration are considered in greater detail in Chapter 23.

Muscle	Description	Origin (O) and insertion (I)	Action	Nerve supply
External intercostals (in"ter-kos'talz) (*external* = toward the outside; *inter* = between; *cost* = rib)	11 pairs lie between ribs; fibers run obliquely (downward and forward) from each rib to rib below; in lower intercostal spaces, fibers are continuous with external oblique muscle forming part of abdominal wall	O—inferior border of rib above I—superior border of rib below	With first ribs fixed by scalene muscles, pull ribs toward one another to elevate rib cage; aids in inspiration; synergists of diaphragm	Intercostal nerves
Internal intercostals (*internal* = toward the inside, deep)	11 pairs lie between ribs; fibers run deep to and at right angles to those of external intercostals (i.e., run downward and posteriorly); lower internal intercostal muscles are continuous with fibers of internal oblique muscle of abdominal wall	O—superior border of rib below I—inferior border (costal groove) of rib above	With 12th ribs fixed by quadratus lumborum, muscles of posterior abdominal wall and oblique muscles of the abdominal wall, draw ribs together and depress rib cage; aid in expiration; antagonistic to external intercostals	Intercostal nerves
Diaphragm (di'ah-fram) (*dia* = across; *phragm* = partition)	Broad muscle; forms floor of thoracic cavity; in relaxed state is dome shaped; fibers converge from margins of thoracic cage toward a boomerang shaped central tendon	O—inferior border of rib cage and sternum, costal cartilages of last six ribs and lumbar vertebrae I—central tendon	Prime mover of inspiration; flattens on contraction, increasing vertical dimensions of thorax; when strongly contracted, dramatically increases intra-abdominal pressure	Phrenic nerves

(a)

Xyphoid process of sternum

Foramen for inferior
vena cava

Central
tendon of
diaphragm

Foramen
for aorta

12th rib

Foramen for
esophagus

Costal
cartilage

Diaphragm

Lumbar
vertebrae

(b)

FIGURE 10.10
Muscles of respiration. (a) Deep
muscles of the thorax. The external
intercostals (inspiratory muscles) are
shown on the left and the internal
intercostals (expiratory muscles) are
shown on the right. These two muscle
layers run obliquely and at right
angles to each other. **(b)** Inferior view
of the diaphragm, the prime mover of
inspiration. Notice that its muscle
fibers converge toward a central
tendon, an arrangement that causes
the diaphragm to flatten and move
inferiorly as it contracts. The
diaphragm and its tendon are pierced
by the great vessels (aorta and
inferior vena cava) and the
esophagus. **(c)** Photograph of the
diaphragm, superior view.

Aortic arch

Central
tendon of
diaphragm

Pericardium

Diaphragm
(muscular part)

(c)

Table 10.6 Muscles of the Abdominal Wall; Trunk Movements and Compression of Abdominal Viscera (Figure 10.11)

Unlike the thorax, the anterior and lateral abdominal wall has no bony reinforcements (ribs). Instead, it is a composite of four paired muscles, their investing fasciae, and their aponeuroses. Three broad flat muscle pairs, layered one atop the next, form the lateral abdominal walls: The fibers of the *external oblique* muscle run inferomedially and at right angles to those of the *internal oblique,* which immediately underlies it. The fibers of the deep *transversus abdominis* muscle run horizontally across the abdomen at an angle to both. This alternation of fascicle directions is similar to the construction of plywood (which is made of sheets with different grains) and provides great strength. These three muscles blend into broad insertion aponeuroses anteriorly. The aponeuroses, in turn, enclose a fourth muscle pair, the straplike *rectus abdominis* muscles medially, and then fuse forming the **linea alba** ("white line"), a tendinous raphe (seam) that runs from the sternum to the pubic symphysis. The tight enclosure of the rectus abdominis within the aponeuroses prevents these slender vertical muscles from "bowstringing" (protruding anteriorly). The quadratus lumborum muscles forming the *posterior* abdominal wall are considered in Table 10.4.

The abdominal muscles protect and support the viscera most effectively when they are well toned. When not sufficiently exercised or when severely stretched (as during pregnancy), they become weak, allowing the abdomen to become pendulous (i.e., to form a potbelly). Additional functions include lateral flexion and rotation of the trunk and anterior flexion of the trunk against resistance (as in sit-ups). During quiet expiration, the abdominal muscles relax, allowing the abdominal viscera to be pushed inferiorly by the descending diaphragm. When all these abdominal muscles contract in unison, several different activities may be effected, depending on which other muscles are activated simultaneously. For example, when all the abdominal muscles are contracted, the ribs are pulled inferiorly and the abdominal contents compressed. This pushes the visceral organs upward on the diaphragm aiding forced expiration. When the abdominal muscles contract with the diaphragm and the glottis is closed (an action called the Valsalva maneuver), the increased intra-abdominal pressure helps to promote urination, defecation, childbirth, vomiting, coughing, screaming, sneezing, burping, and nose blowing. (Next time you perform one of these activities, feel your abdominal muscles contract under your skin.) These muscles also contract during heavy lifting—sometimes so forcefully that hernias result. Contraction of the abdominal muscles along with contraction of the deep back muscles helps prevent hyperextension of the spine and splints the entire body trunk.

Muscle	Description	Origin (O) and insertion (I)	Action	Nerve supply
MUSCLES OF THE ANTERIOR AND LATERAL ABDOMINAL WALL				
	Four paired flat muscles; very important in supporting and protecting abdominal viscera and play an important role in promoting movement of vertebral column (flexion and lateral bending)			
Rectus abdominis (rek'tus ab-dom'ĭ-nis) (*rectus* = straight; *abdom* = abdomen)	Medial superficial muscle pair; extend from pubis to rib cage; ensheathed by aponeuroses of lateral muscles; segmented by three reinforcing tendinous intersections	O—pubic crest and symphysis I—xiphoid process and costal cartilages of ribs 5–7	Flex and rotate lumbar region of vertebral column; fix and depress ribs, stabilize pelvis during walking, increase intra-abdominal pressure	Intercostal nerves (T_6 or T_7–T_{12})
External oblique (o-blēk') (*external* = toward outside; *oblique* = running at an angle)	Largest and most superficial of the three lateral muscles; fibers run downward and medially (same direction outstretched fingers take when hands put into pants pockets); aponeurosis turns under inferiorly forming inguinal ligament	O—by fleshy strips from outer surfaces of lower eight ribs I—most fibers into linea alba; some into pubic crest and tubercle and iliac crest; majority of fibers insert anteriorly via a broad aponeurosis	When pair contracts simultaneously, aid rectus abdominis muscles in flexing vertebral column and in compressing abdominal wall and increasing intra-abdominal pressure; acting individually, aid muscles of back in trunk rotation and lateral flexion	Intercostal nerves (T_7–T_{12})
Internal oblique (*internal* = toward the inside; deep)	Fibers fan upward and forward and run at right angles to those of external oblique, which it underlies	O—lumbodorsal fascia, iliac crest, and inguinal ligament I—linea alba, pubic crest, last three ribs	As for external oblique	Intercostal nerves (T_7–T_{12}) and L_1
Transversus abdominis (trans-ver'sus) (*transverse* = running straight across or transversely)	Deepest (innermost) muscle of abdominal wall; fibers run horizontally	O—inguinal ligament, lumbodorsal fascia, cartilages of last six ribs; iliac crest I—linea alba, pubic crest	Compresses abdominal contents	Intercostal nerves (T_7–T_{12}) and L_1

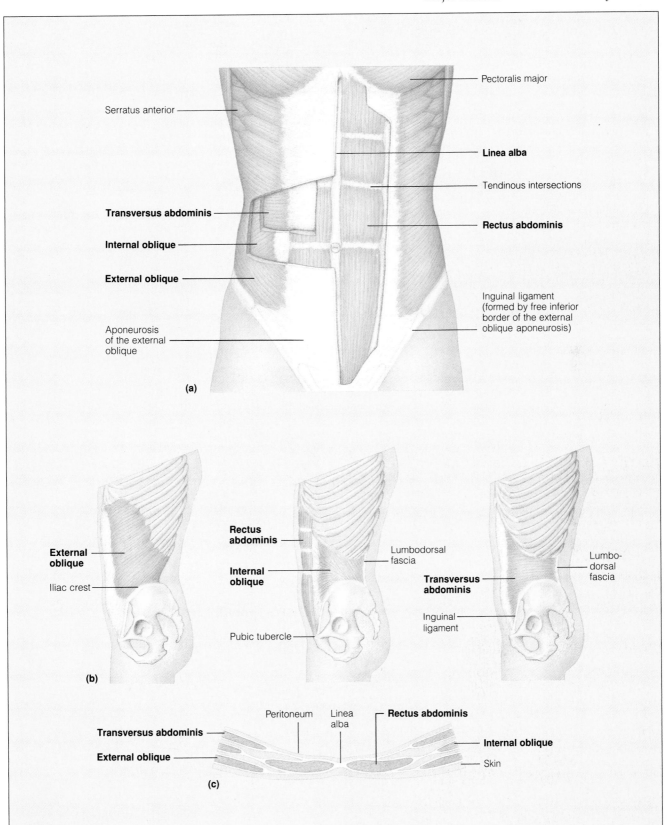

FIGURE 10.11

Muscles of the abdominal wall. (a) Anterior view of the muscles forming the anterolateral abdominal wall. The superficial muscles have been partially cut away on the left side of the diagram to reveal the deeper internal oblique and transversus abdominis muscles. **(b)** Lateral view of the trunk, illustrating the fiber direction and attachments of the external oblique, internal oblique, and transversus abdominis muscles. **(c)** Transverse section through the anterolateral abdominal wall (midregion), showing how the aponeuroses of the lateral abdominal muscles contribute to the rectus abdominis sheath.

Table 10.7 Muscles of the Pelvic Floor and Perineum: Support of Abdominopelvic Organs (Figure 10.12)

Two paired muscles, the *levator ani* and *coccygeus,* form the funnel-shaped pelvic floor, or **pelvic diaphragm.** These muscles (1) close the inferior outlet of the pelvis, (2) support the pelvic floor and elevate it to help release feces, and (3) resist increased intra-abdominal pressure (which would expel contents of the bladder, rectum, and uterus). The pelvic diaphragm is pierced by the rectum and urethra (urinary tube), and by the vagina in females. The body region inferior to the pelvic diaphragm is the *perineum.* The relationships of the perineum are a bit complex and worth explaining. Inferior to the muscles of the pelvic floor, and stretching between the two sides of the pubic arch in the anterior half of the perineum, is the

urogenital diaphragm. This thin triangular sheet of muscle contains the *sphincter urethrae.* This sphincter muscle, which surrounds the urethra, allows one to voluntarily prevent urination when it is inconvenient. Superficial to the urogenital diaphragm, and covered by the skin of the perineum, is the *superficial space,* which contains muscles (*ischiocavernosus* and *bulbospongiosus*) that help maintain erection of the penis and clitoris. In the posterior half of the perineum lies the *external anal sphincter,* a sphincter that encircles the anus and allows voluntary control of defecation. Just anterior to this sphincter is the **central tendon of the perineum,** a strong tendon into which many of the perineal muscles insert.

Muscle	Description	Origin (O) and insertion (I)	Action	Nerve supply
MUSCLES OF THE PELVIC DIAPHRAGM (Figure 10.12a)				
Levator ani (lĕ-va'tor a'ne) (*levator* = raises; *ani* = anus)	Broad, thin, tripartite muscle (pubococcygeus, puborectalis, and iliococcygeus parts); its fibers extend inferomedially, forming a muscular "sling" around male prostate (or female vagina), urethra, and anorectal junction before meeting in the median plane	O—extensive linear origin inside pelvis from pubis to ischial spine I—inner surface of coccyx, levator ani of opposite side, and (in part) into the structures that penetrate it	Supports and maintains position of pelvic viscera; resists downward thrusts that accompany rises in intrapelvic pressure during coughing, vomiting, and expulsive efforts of abdominal muscles; forms sphincters at anorectal junction and vagina	S_3, S_4, and inferior rectal nerve (branch of pudendal nerve)
Coccygeus (kok-sij'e-us) (*coccy* = coccyx)	Small triangular muscle lying posterior to levator ani; forms posterior part of pelvic diaphragm	O—spine of ischium I—sacrum and coccyx	Assists levator ani in supporting pelvic viscera; supports coccyx and pulls it forward after it has been reflected posteriorly by defecation and childbirth	S_4 and S_5
MUSCLES OF THE UROGENITAL DIAPHRAGM (Figure 10.12b)				
Deep transverse perineus (per"ĭ-ne'us) (*deep* = far from surface; *transverse* = across; *perine* = near anus)	Together the pair spans distance between ischial rami; in females, lies posterior to vagina	O—ischial rami I—midline central tendon of perineum; some fibers into vaginal wall in females	Supports pelvic organs; steadies central tendon	Pudendal nerve
Sphincter urethrae (*sphin* = squeeze)	Circular muscle surrounding membranous urethra and vagina (female)	O—ischiopubic rami I—midline raphe	Constricts urethra; helps support pelvic organs	Pudendal nerve
MUSCLES OF THE SUPERFICIAL SPACE (Figure 10.12c)				
Ischiocavernosus (is'ke-o-kav'ern-o'sus) (*ischi* = hip; *caverna* = hollow chamber)	Runs from pelvis to base of penis or clitoris	O—ischial tuberosities I—crus of corpus cavernosa of male penis or female clitoris	Retards venous drainage and maintains erection of penis or clitoris	Pudendal nerve
Bulbospongiosus (bul"bo-spun"je-o'sus) (*bulbon* = bulb; *spongio* = sponge)	Encloses base of penis (bulb) in males and lies deep to labia in females	O—central tendon of perineum and midline raphe of male penis I—anteriorly into corpus cavernosa of penis or clitoris	Empties male urethra; assists in erection of penis in males and of clitoris in females	Pudendal nerve
Superficial transverse perineus (*superficial* = closer to surface)	Paired muscle bands posterior to urethral (and in females, vaginal) opening	O—ischial tuberosity I—central tendon of perineum	Stabilize and strengthen midline tendon of perineum	Pudendal nerve

FIGURE 10.12

FIGURE 10.12
Muscles of the pelvic floor and perineum. (a) Muscles of the pelvic floor (levator ani and coccygeus) seen from above in a female pelvis. (b) Muscles of the urogenital diaphragm (sphincter urethrae and deep transverse perineus) of the perineum, which make up the second (and more superficial) layer of muscles. (c) Muscles of the superficial space of the perineum (ischiocavernosus, bulbospongiosus, and superficial transverse perineus), which lie just deep to the skin of the perineum.

Pelvic diaphragm { **Levator ani** **Coccygeus** }

Piriformis

Coccyx

Obturator internus

Anal canal

Vagina

Urethra

Urogenital diaphragm

Symphysis pubis

Iliococcygeus

Pubococcygeus } **Levator ani**

(a) Muscles of the pelvic diaphragm

Pubic ramus

Sphincter urethrae

Deep transverse perineus

Central tendon

Anus

External anal sphincter

Urethral opening

Vaginal opening

Male

(b) Muscles of the urogenital diaphragm

Female

Penis

Midline raphe

Ischiocavernosus

Bulbospongiosus

Superficial transverse perineus

Levator ani

Clitoris

Urethral opening

Vaginal opening

Anus

(c) Muscles of the superficial space

Table 10.8 Superficial Muscles of the Anterior and Posterior Thorax: Movements of the Scapula (Figure 10.13)

Most superficial thorax muscles are *extrinsic shoulder muscles,* which run from the ribs and vertebral column to the shoulder girdle. They act to fix the scapula to the wall of the thorax or move scapula to effect arm movements. The muscles of the anterior thorax include the *pectoralis major, pectoralis minor, serratus anterior,* and *subclavius.* Except for the pectoralis major, which inserts into the humerus, all muscles of the anterior group insert into the pectoral girdle. Extrinsic muscles of the posterior thorax include the *latissimus dorsi* and *trapezius* muscles superficially and the underlying *levator scapulae* and *rhomboids.* The latissimus dorsi, like the pectoralis major muscles anteriorly, insert into the humerus and are more concerned with movements of the arm than of the scapula. We will defer consideration of these two muscle pairs to Table 10.9 (arm-moving muscles).

The important movements of the pectoral girdle involve displacements of the scapula, i.e., its elevation and depression, rotation, lateral (forward) movements, and medial (backward) movements. The clavicles rotate around their own axes during scapular movements, and provide both stability and precision to scapular movements.

Except for the serratus anterior, the anterior muscles stabilize and depress the shoulder girdle. Thus, most scapular movements are promoted by the serratus anterior muscles anteriorly and by the posterior muscles. The arrangement of muscle attachments to the scapula is such that one muscle cannot bring about a simple (linear) movement on its own. To elevate or depress the scapula or to effect other scapular movements, several muscles must act in combination.

The prime movers of shoulder elevation are the trapezius and levator scapulae. When acting together to shrug the shoulder, their opposite rotational effects counterbalance each other. Scapular depression is largely due to gravity (weight of the arm), but when the scapula is depressed against resistance, the trapezius and serratus anterior (along with the latissimus dorsi discussed in Table 10.9) are active. Forward movements (abduction) of the scapula on the thorax wall, as in pushing or punching movements, are mainly due to serratus anterior activity. Retraction (adduction) of the scapula is effected by the trapezius and rhomboids. Although the serratus anterior and trapezius muscles are antagonists in forward/backward movements of the scapulae, they act in unison to coordinate the *rotational* scapular movements.

Muscle	Description	Origin (O) and insertion (I)	Action	Nerve supply
MUSCLES OF THE ANTERIOR THORAX (Figure 10.13a)				
Pectoralis minor (pek″to-ra′lis mi′nor) (*pectus* = chest, breast; *minor* = lesser)	Flat, thin muscle directly beneath and obscured by pectoralis major	O—anterior surfaces of ribs 3–5 I—coracoid process of scapula	With ribs fixed, draws scapula forward and downward; with scapula fixed, draws rib cage superiorly	Medial pectoral nerve (C_6–C_8)
Serratus anterior (ser-a′tus) (*serratus* = saw)	Lies deep to scapula beneath and inferior to pectoral muscles on lateral rib cage; forms medial wall of axilla; origins have serrated, or sawtooth, appearance; paralysis results in "winging" of vertebral border of scapula away from chest wall, making arm elevation impossible	O—by a series of muscle slips from ribs 1–8 (or 9) I—entire anterior surface of vertebral border of scapula	Prime mover to protract and hold scapula against chest wall; rotates scapula so that its inferior angle moves laterally and upward; raises point of shoulder; important role in abduction and raising of arm and in horizontal arm movements (pushing, punching); called "boxer's muscle"	Long thoracic nerve (C_5–C_7)
Subclavius (sub-kla′ve-us) (*sub* = under, beneath; *clav* = clavicle)	Small cylindrical muscle extending from rib 1 to clavicle	O—costal cartilage of rib 1 I—groove on inferior surface of clavicle	Helps stabilize and depress pectoral girdle; paralysis produces no obvious effects	Nerve to subclavius (C_5 and C_6)
MUSCLES OF THE POSTERIOR THORAX (Figure 10.13b)				
Trapezius (trah-pe′ze-us) (*trapezion* = irregular four-sided figure)	Most superficial muscle of posterior thorax; flat, and triangular in shape; upper fibers run downward to scapula; middle fibers run horizontally to scapula; lower fibers run superiorly to scapula	O—occipital bone, ligamentum nuchae, and spines of C_7 and all thoracic vertebrae I—a continuous insertion along acromion and spine of scapula and lateral third of clavicle	Stabilizes, raises, retracts, and rotates scapula; middle fibers retract (adduct) scapula; superior fibers elevate scapula or can help extend head; inferior fibers depress scapula (and shoulder)	Accessory nerve (cranial nerve XI); C_3 and C_4

Muscle	Description	Origin (O) and insertion (I)	Action	Nerve supply
Levator scapulae (skap'u-le) (*levator* = raises)	Located at back and side of neck, deep to trapezius; thick, straplike muscle	O—transverse processes of C_1–C_4 I—superior vertebral border of scapula	Elevates/adducts scapula in concert with superior fibers of trapezius; tilts glenoid cavity downward; when scapula is fixed, flexes neck to same side	Cervical spinal nerves and dorsal scapular nerve (C_3–C_5)
Rhomboids (rom'boidz)— major and minor (*rhomboid* = diamond shaped)	Two rectangular muscles lying deep to trapezius and inferior to levator scapulae; rhomboid minor is the more superior muscle; both muscles extend from vertebral column to scapula	O—spinous processes of C_7 and T_1 (minor) and spinous processes of T_2–T_5 (major) I—medial border of scapula	Act together (and with middle trapezius fibers) to retract scapula, thus "squaring shoulders"; rotate scapulae so that glenoid cavity rotates downward (as when arm is lowered against resistance; e.g., paddling a canoe); stabilize scapula	Dorsal scapular nerve (C_5)

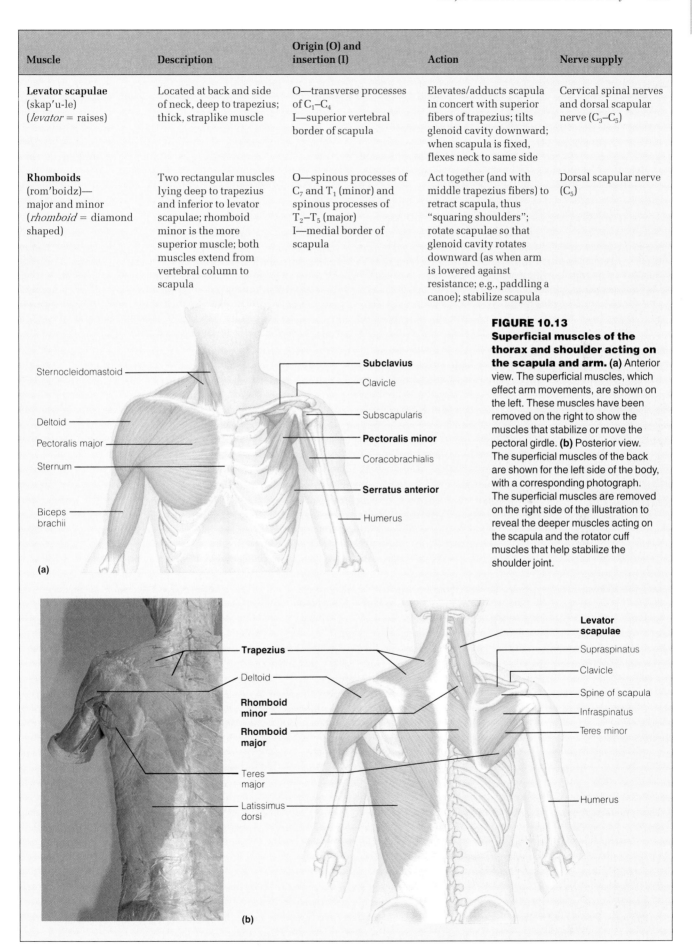

FIGURE 10.13
Superficial muscles of the thorax and shoulder acting on the scapula and arm. (a) Anterior view. The superficial muscles, which effect arm movements, are shown on the left. These muscles have been removed on the right to show the muscles that stabilize or move the pectoral girdle. **(b)** Posterior view. The superficial muscles of the back are shown for the left side of the body, with a corresponding photograph. The superficial muscles are removed on the right side of the illustration to reveal the deeper muscles acting on the scapula and the rotator cuff muscles that help stabilize the shoulder joint.

Table 10.9 Muscles Crossing the Shoulder Joint: Movements of the Arm (Humerus) (Figure 10.14)

Recall that the ball-and-socket shoulder joint is the most flexible joint in the body, but pays the price of instability. A total of nine muscles cross each shoulder joint to insert on the humerus. All muscles acting on the humerus originate from the pectoral girdle; however, the latissimus dorsi and pectoralis major also originate on the axial skeleton.

Of these nine muscles, only the superficial *pectoralis major, latissimus dorsi,* and *deltoid* muscles are prime movers of arm movements. The remaining six are synergists and fixators. Four of these, the *supraspinatus, infraspinatus, teres minor,* and *subscapularis,* are known as **rotator cuff muscles.** They originate on the scapula, and their tendons blend with the fibrous capsule of the shoulder joint en route to the humerus. Although the rotator cuff muscles act as synergists in the angular and rotational movements of the arm, their main function is to reinforce the capsule of the shoulder joint to prevent dislocation of the humerus. The remaining two muscles, the small *teres major* and *coracobrachialis,* cross the shoulder joint, but do not contribute to its reinforcement.

Generally speaking, muscles that originate *anterior* to the shoulder joint (pectoralis major, coracobrachialis, and anterior fibers of the deltoid) *flex* the arm, i.e., lift it anteriorly, usually in the sagittal plane. The prime mover of arm flexion is the pectoralis major. The biceps brachii of the arm (see Table 10.10) also assists in this action. Muscles originating *posterior* to the shoulder joint extend the arm. These include the latissimus dorsi and posterior fibers of the deltoid muscles (both prime movers of arm extension) and the teres major. Thus, the latissimus dorsi and pectoralis muscles are *antagonists* of one another in the flexion–extension movements of the arm.

The middle region of the fleshy deltoid muscle of the shoulder is the prime mover of arm abduction. It is antagonized in this function by the pectoralis major anteriorly and latissimus dorsi posteriorly. Depending on their precise location and insertion points, the various muscles acting on the humerus also promote lateral and medial rotation of the shoulder joint. Since the interactions of these nine muscles are complex and each muscle contributes to more than a single movement, a summary of muscles contributing to the various angular and rotational movements of the humerus is provided in Table 10.12 (Part I).

Muscle	Description	Origin (O) and insertion (I)	Action	Nerve supply
Pectoralis major (pek″to-ra′lis ma′jer) (*pect* = breast, chest; *major* = larger)	Large, fan-shaped muscle covering upper portion of chest; forms anterior axillary fold	O—clavicle, sternum, cartilage of ribs 1–6, and aponeurosis of external oblique muscle I—fibers converge to insert by a short tendon into greater tubercle of humerus	Prime mover of arm flexion; rotates arm medially; adducts arm against resistance; with scapula (and arm) fixed, pulls rib cage upward, thus can help in climbing, throwing, pushing, and in forced inspiration	Lateral and medial pectoral nerves
Latissimus dorsi (lah-tis′ĭ-mus dor′si) (*latissimus* = widest; *dorsi* = back)	Broad, flat, triangular muscle of lower back (lumbar region); extensive superficial origins; covered by trapezius superiorly; contributes to the posterior wall of axilla	O—indirect attachment via lumbodorsal fascia into spines of lower six thoracic vertebrae, lumbar vertebrae, lower 3 to 4 ribs, and iliac crest; also from scapula's inferior angle I—spirals around teres major to insert in floor of intertubercular groove of humerus	Prime mover of arm extension; powerful arm adductor; medially rotates arm at shoulder; depresses scapula; because of its power in these movements, it plays an important role in bringing the arm down in a power stroke, as in striking a blow, hammering, swimming, and rowing	Thoracodorsal nerve

Muscle	Description	Origin (O) and insertion (I)	Action	Nerve supply
Deltoid (del'toid) (*delta* = triangular)	Thick, multipennate muscle forming rounded shoulder muscle mass; responsible for roundness of shoulder; a site commonly used for intramuscular injection, particularly in males, where it tends to be quite fleshy	O—embraces insertion of the trapezius; lateral third of clavicle; acromion and spine of scapula I—deltoid tuberosity of humerus	Prime mover of arm abduction when all its fibers contract simultaneously; antagonist of pectoralis major and latissimus dorsi, which adduct the arm; if only anterior fibers are active, can act powerfully in flexion and medial rotation of humerus, therefore synergist of pectoralis major; if only posterior fibers are active, effects extension and lateral rotation of arm; active during rhythmic arm swinging movements during walking	Axillary nerve (C_5 and C_6)
Subscapularis (sub-scap″u-lar′is) (*sub* = under; *scapular* = scapula)	Forms part of posterior wall of axilla; tendon of insertion passes in front of shoulder joint; a rotator cuff muscle	O—subscapular fossa of scapula I—lesser tubercle of humerus	Chief medial rotator of humerus; assisted by pectoralis major; helps to hold head of humerus in glenoid cavity, thereby stabilizing shoulder joint	Subscapular nerves (C_5–C_7)
Supraspinatus (soo″prah-spi-nah′tus) (*supra* = above, over; *spin* = spine)	Named for its location on posterior aspect of scapula; deep to trapezius; a rotator cuff muscle	O—supraspinous fossa of scapula I—superior part of greater tubercle of humerus	Stabilizes shoulder joint; helps to prevent downward dislocation of humerus, as when carrying a heavy suitcase; assists in abduction	Suprascapular nerve
Infraspinatus (in″frah-spi-nah′tus) (*infra* = below)	Partially covered by deltoid and trapezius; named for its scapular location; a rotator cuff muscle	O—infraspinous fossa of scapula I—greater tubercle of humerus posterior to insertion of supraspinatus	Helps to hold head of humerus in glenoid cavity; rotates humerus laterally	Suprascapular nerve
Teres minor (te′rēz) (*teres* = round; *minor* = lesser)	Small, elongated muscle; lies inferior to infraspinatus and may be inseparable from that muscle; a rotator cuff muscle	O—lateral border of dorsal scapular surface I—greater tubercle of humerus inferior to infraspinatus insertion	Same action(s) as infraspinatus muscle	Axillary nerve
Teres major	Thick, rounded muscle; located inferior to teres minor; helps to form posterior wall of axilla (along with latissimus dorsi and subscapularis)	O—posterior surface of scapula at inferior angle I—crest of lesser tubercle on anterior humerus; insertion tendon fused with that of latissimus dorsi	Extends, medially rotates, and adducts humerus; synergist of latissimus dorsi	Lower subscapular nerve
Coracobrachialis (kor″ah-ko-bra″ke-al′is) (*coraco* = coracoid; *brachi* = arm)	Small, cylindrical muscle	O—coracoid process of scapula I—medial surface of humerus shaft	Flexion and adduction of the humerus; synergist of pectoralis major	Musculocutaneous nerve *(Table continues)*

Table 10.9 (continued)

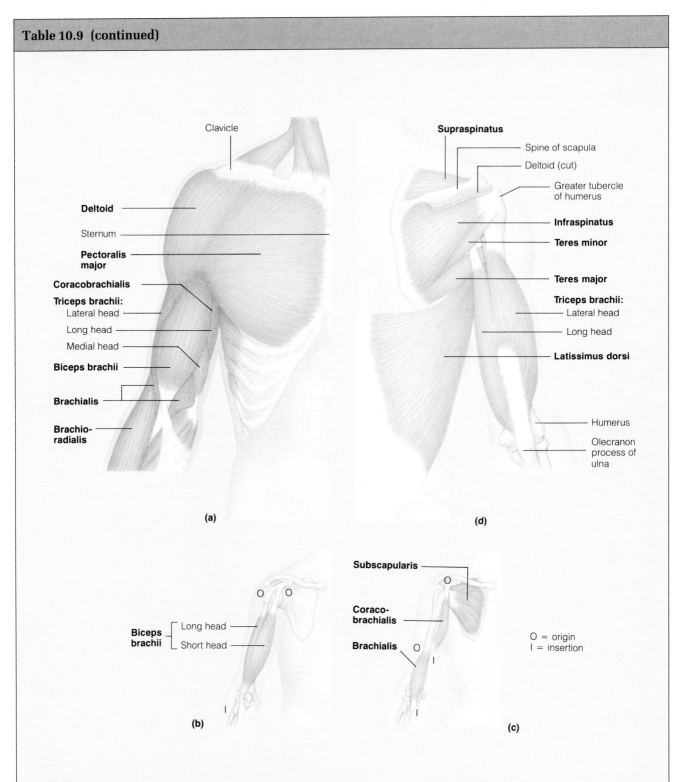

(a)

(d)

(b)

(c)

O = origin
I = insertion

FIGURE 10.14
Muscles crossing the shoulder and elbow joint, respectively causing movements of the arm and forearm. **(a)** Superficial muscles of the anterior thorax, shoulder, and arm, anterior view. **(b)** The biceps brachii muscle of the anterior arm, shown in isolation. **(c)** The brachialis muscle arising from the humerus and the coracobrachialis and subscapularis muscles arising from the scapula, shown in isolation. (Note, however, that the coracobrachialis effects movements of the arm, not the forearm, and the subscapularis stabilizes the shoulder joint.) **(d)** The extent of the triceps brachii muscle of the posterior arm, shown in relation to the deep scapular muscles. The deltoid muscle of the shoulder has been removed.

Muscles fleshing out the arm cross the elbow joint to insert on the forearm bones. Since the elbow is a hinge joint, movements promoted by these muscles are limited almost entirely to flexion and extension of the forearm. Walls of fascia divide the arm into two muscle compartments—the *posterior extensors* and *anterior flexors.* The prime mover of forearm extension is the bulky *triceps brachii* muscle, which forms nearly the entire musculature of the posterior compartment. It is assisted (minimally) by the tiny *anconeus* muscle, which just about spans the elbow joint posteriorly.

All anterior arm muscles cause elbow flexion. In order of decreasing strength, these are the *brachialis, biceps brachii,* and *brachioradialis.* The brachialis and biceps are inserted (respectively) into the ulna and radius and contract simultaneously during flexion; they are the chief forearm flexors. The biceps brachii, a muscle that bulges when the forearm is flexed, is familiar to almost everyone; the brachialis, which lies deep to the biceps, is less known, but is as important in flexing the elbow. The biceps muscle also supinates the forearm and is ineffective in flexing the elbow when the forearm *must* stay pronated. (This is why doing chin-ups with palms facing anteriorly is harder than with palms facing posteriorly.) Since the brachioradialis arises from the distal humerus and inserts on the distal forearm, it resides mainly in the forearm (rather than in the arm as do the rest of this group). Because its force is exerted far from the fulcrum, the brachioradialis is a weak forearm flexor. It becomes active only when the elbow has been partially flexed by the prime movers and is semipronated.

The actions of the muscles described here are summarized in Table 10.12 (Part II).

Muscle	Description	Origin (O) and insertion (I)	Action	Nerve supply
POSTERIOR MUSCLES				
Triceps brachii (tri′seps bra′ke-i) (*triceps* = three heads; *brachi* = arm)	Large fleshy muscle; the only muscle of posterior compartment of arm; three-headed origin; long and lateral heads lie superficial to medial head	O—long head: infraglenoid tubercle of scapula; lateral head: posterior humerus; medial head: posterior humerus distal to radial groove I—by common tendon into olecranon process of ulna	Powerful forearm extensor (prime mover, particularly medial head); antagonist of forearm flexors; long head tendon may help stabilize shoulder joint and assist in arm adduction	Radial nerve
Anconeus (an-ko′ne-us) (*ancon* = elbow) (see Figure 10.16)	Short triangular muscle; closely associated (blended) with distal end of triceps on posterior humerus	O—lateral epicondyle of humerus I—lateral aspect of olecranon process of ulna	Abducts ulna during forearm pronation; synergist of triceps brachii in elbow extension	Radial nerve
ANTERIOR MUSCLES				
Biceps brachii (bi′seps) (*biceps* = two heads)	Two-headed fusiform muscle; bellies unite as insertion point is approached; tendon of long head helps stabilize shoulder joint	O—short head: coracoid process; long head: tubercle above glenoid cavity and lip of glenoid cavity; tendon of long head runs within capsule and descends into intertubercular groove of humerus I—by common tendon into radial tuberosity	Flexes elbow joint and supinates forearm; these actions usually occur at same time (e.g., when you open a bottle of wine, it turns the corkscrew and pulls the cork); weak flexor of arm at shoulder	Musculocutaneous nerve
Brachialis (bra′ke-al-is)	Strong muscle that is immediately deep to biceps brachii on distal humerus	O—front of distal half of humerus; embraces insertion of deltoid muscle I—coronoid process of ulna and capsule of elbow joint	A major forearm flexor (lifts ulna as biceps lifts the radius)	Musculocutaneous nerve
Brachioradialis (bra″ke-o-ra″de-a′lis) (*radi* = radius, ray) (also see Figure 10.15)	Superficial muscle of lateral forearm; forms lateral boundary of antecubital fossa; extends from distal humerus to distal forearm	O—lateral supracondylar ridge at distal end of humerus I—base of styloid process of radius	Synergist in forearm flexion; acts to best advantage when forearm is partially flexed and semipronated; during rapid flexion *and* extension, acts as a shunt muscle to prevent joint separation	Radial nerve (an important exception: the radial nerve typically serves extensor muscles)

Table 10.11 Muscles of the Forearm: Movements of Wrist, Hand, and Fingers (Figures 10.15 and 10.16)

The forearm muscles are functionally divided into two approximately equal groups: those causing wrist movements and those moving the fingers and thumb. In most cases, their fleshy portions contribute to the roundness of the proximal forearm and then they taper to long insertion tendons. Their insertions are securely anchored by strong ligaments called **flexor** and **extensor retinacula** ("retainers"). These "wrist bands" keep the tendons from jumping outward when tensed. Crowded together in the wrist and palm, the muscle tendons are surrounded by slippery tendon sheaths that minimize friction as they slide against one another.

Although many of the forearm muscles actually arise from the humerus (and thus cross both the elbow and wrist joints), their actions on the elbow are slight. Flexion and extension are the movements typically effected at both the wrist and finger joints. In addition, the wrist can be abducted and adducted.

The forearm muscles are subdivided by fascia into two main compartments (the *anterior flexors* and *posterior extensors*), and each compartment has superficial and deep muscle layers. Most flexors in the anterior compartment arise from a common tendon on the humerus and are innervated largely by the median nerve. Though most anterior forearm muscles are wrist or finger *flexors,* two muscles of this group are not flexors but pronators, the *pronator teres* and *pronator quadratus.* Pronation is one of the most important forearm movements.

Muscles of the posterior compartment extend the wrist and fingers. An exception is the *supinator* muscle, which assists the biceps brachii muscle of the arm in supinating the forearm. (Also residing in the posterior compartment is the brachioradialis muscle, the weak elbow flexor considered in Table 10.10.) Like those of the anterior compartment, most muscles of the posterior compartment arise from a common origin tendon on the humerus; however, the location on the humerus differs. All posterior forearm muscles are supplied by the radial nerve.

Although the hand performs many different movements, it contains relatively few of the muscles that control those movements. As described above, most muscles that move the hand are located in the forearm and "operate" the fingers via their long tendons, like operating a puppet by strings. This design makes the hand less bulky and enables it to perform finer movements. The hand movements promoted by the forearm muscles are assisted and made more precise by the small *intrinsic* muscles of the hand. These include four *lumbrical* muscles that lie between the metacarpals on the palmar surface of the hand (Figure 10.15c), and eight *interosseous* muscles that lie deep to the lumbricals (Figure 10.16b). Together, the lumbricals and interossei flex the metacarpophalangeal joints (knuckles) and help extend the fingers. Additionally, four *thenar* muscles act exclusively to circumduct and oppose the thumb (Figure 10.15c).

The locations and actions of the forearm muscles are the focus of the table. Since the forearm muscles are numerous and their interactions varied, a summary of their actions is provided in Table 10.12 (Part III).

Muscle	Description	Origin (O) and insertion (I)	Action	Nerve supply
PART I: ANTERIOR MUSCLES (Figure 10.15)	These eight muscles of the anterior fascial compartment are listed from the lateral to the medial aspect. Most arise from a common flexor tendon attached to the medial epicondyle of the humerus and have additional origins as well. Most of the tendons of these flexors are held in place at the wrist by a thickening of deep fascia called the *flexor retinaculum.*			
SUPERFICIAL MUSCLES				
Pronator teres (pro′na′tor te′rēz) (*pronation* = turning palm posteriorly, or down; *teres* = round)	Two-headed muscle; seen in superficial view between proximal margins of brachioradialis and flexor carpi radialis; forms medial boundary of antecubital fossa	O—medial epicondyle of humerus; coronoid process of ulna I—by common tendon into lateral radius, midshaft	Pronates forearm; weak flexor of elbow	Median nerve
Flexor carpi radialis (flek′sor kar′pe ra″de-a′lis) (*flex* = decrease angle between two bones; *carpi* = wrist; *radi* = radius)	Runs diagonally across forearm; midway, its fleshy belly is replaced by a flat tendon that becomes cordlike at wrist	O—medial epicondyle of humerus I—base of second and third metacarpals; insertion tendon easily seen and provides guide to position of radial artery (used for pulse taking) at wrist	Powerful flexor of wrist; abducts hand; synergist of elbow flexion	Median nerve
Palmaris longus (pahl-ma′ris lon′gus) (*palma* = palm; *longus* = long)	Small fleshy muscle with a long insertion tendon; often absent; may be used as guide to find median nerve that lies lateral to it at wrist	O—medial epicondyle of humerus I—palmar aponeurosis	Weak wrist flexor; may tense fascia of palm (palmar aponeurosis) during hand movements	Median nerve

Muscle	Description	Origin (O) and insertion (I)	Action	Nerve supply
Flexor carpi ulnaris (ul-na′ris) (*ulnar* = ulna)	Most medial muscle of this group; two-headed; ulnar nerve lies lateral to its tendon	O—medial epicondyle of humerus, olecranon process, and posterior surface of ulna I—pisiform bone and base of fifth metacarpal	Powerful flexor of wrist; also adducts hand in concert with extensor carpi ulnaris (posterior muscle); stabilizes wrist during finger extension	Ulnar nerve
Flexor digitorum superficialis (dĭ″ji-tor′um soo″per-fish″e-a′lis) (*digit* = finger, toe; *superficial* = close to surface)	Two-headed muscle; more deeply placed (therefore, actually forms an intermediate layer); overlain by muscles above but visible at distal end of forearm	O—medial epicondyle of humerus, coronoid process of ulna; shaft of radius I—by four tendons into middle phalanges of fingers 2–5	Flexes wrist and middle phalanges of fingers 2–5; the important finger flexor when speed and flexion against resistance are required	Median nerve
DEEP MUSCLES				
Flexor pollicis longus (pah′lĭ-kis) (*pollix* = thumb)	Partly covered by flexor digitorum superficialis; parallels flexor digitorum profundus laterally	O—anterior surface of radius and interosseous membrane I—distal phalanx of thumb	Flexes distal phalanx of thumb; weak flexor of wrist	Median nerve
Flexor digitorum profundus (pro-fun′dus) (*profund* = deep)	Extensive origin; overlain entirely by flexor digitorum superficialis	O—anteromedial surface of ulna and interosseous membrane I—by four tendons into distal phalanges of fingers 2–5	Slow-acting finger flexor; assists in flexing wrist; the only muscle that can flex distal interphalangeal joints	Medial half by ulnar nerve; lateral half by median nerve

FIGURE 10.15
Muscles of the anterior fascial compartment of the forearm acting on the wrist and fingers.
(a) Superficial view of the muscles of the right forearm and hand. (b) The brachioradialis, flexors carpi radialis and ulnaris, and palmaris longus muscles have been removed to reveal the position of the somewhat deeper flexor digitorum superficialis. (c) Deep muscles of the anterior compartment. Superficial muscles have been removed. The lumbricals and thenar muscles of the hand (intrinsic hand muscles) are also illustrated.

Table 10.11 continued

Muscle	Description	Origin (O) and insertion (I)	Action	Nerve supply
Pronator quadratus (kwod-ra′tus) (*quad* = square, four-sided)	Deepest muscle of distal forearm; passes downward and laterally; only muscle that arises solely from ulna and inserts solely into radius	O—distal portion of anterior ulnar shaft I—distal surface of anterior radius	Pronates forearm; acts with pronator teres; also helps hold ulna and radius together	Median nerve
PART II: POSTERIOR MUSCLES (Figure 10.16)	These muscles of the posterior fascial compartment are listed from the lateral to the medial aspect. They are all innervated by the radial nerve or its branches. More than half of the posterior compartment muscles arise from a common extensor origin tendon attached to the posterior surface of the lateral epicondyle of the humerus and adjacent fascia. The extensor tendons are held in place at the posterior aspect of the wrist by the *extensor retinaculum,* which prevents "bowstringing" of these tendons when the wrist is hyperextended. The extensor muscles of the fingers end in a broad hood over the dorsal side of the digits, the extensor expansion.			
SUPERFICIAL MUSCLES				
Extensor carpi radialis longus (ek-sten′sor) (*extend* = increase angle between two bones)	Parallels brachioradialis on lateral forearm, and may blend with it	O—lateral supracondylar ridge of humerus I—base of second metacarpal	Extends and abducts wrist	Radial nerve
Extensor carpi radialis brevis (brĕ′vis) (*brevis* = short)	Somewhat shorter than extensor carpi radialis longus and lies deep to it	O—lateral epicondyle of humerus I—base of third metacarpal	Extends and abducts wrist; acts synergistically with extensor carpi radialis longus to steady wrist during finger flexion	Deep branch of radial nerve
Extensor digitorum	Lies medial to extensor carpi radialis brevis; a detached portion of this muscle, called *extensor digiti minimi,* extends little finger	O—lateral epicondyle of humerus I—by four tendons into extensor expansions and distal phalanges of fingers 2–5	Prime mover of finger extension; extends wrist; can abduct (flare) fingers	Posterior interosseous nerve (branch of radial nerve)
Extensor carpi ulnaris	Most medial of superficial posterior muscles; long, slender muscle	O—lateral epicondyle of humerus and posterior border of ulna I—base of fifth metacarpal	Extends and adducts wrist (in conjunction with flexor carpi ulnaris)	Posterior interosseous nerve
DEEP MUSCLES				
Supinator (soo″pĭ-na′tor) (*supination* = turning palm anteriorly or upward)	Deep muscle at posterior aspect of elbow; largely concealed by superficial muscles	O—lateral epicondyle of humerus; proximal ulna I—proximal end of radius	Assists biceps brachii to supinate forearm; antagonist of pronator muscles	Radial nerve
Abductor pollicis longus (ab-duk′tor) (*abduct* = movement away from median plane)	Lateral and parallel to extensor pollicis longus; just distal to supinator	O—posterior surface of radius and ulna; interosseous membrane I—base of first metacarpal	Abducts and extends thumb	Posterior interosseous nerve (branch of radial nerve)
Extensor pollicis brevis and **longus**	Deep muscle pair with a common origin and action; overlain by extensor carpi ulnaris	O—dorsal shaft of radius and ulna; interosseous membrane I—base of proximal (brevis) and distal (longus) phalanx of thumb	Extends thumb	Posterior interosseous nerve
Extensor indicis (in′dĭ-kis) (*indicis* = index finger)	Tiny muscle arising close to wrist	O—posterior surface of distal ulna; interosseous membrane I—extensor expansion of index finger; joins tendon of extensor digitorum	Extends index finger	Posterior interosseous nerve

Insertion of
triceps brachii

Anconeus

Flexor carpi ulnaris

**Extensor carpi
ulnaris**

Extensor digiti minimi

Extensor indicis

Tendons of extensor
carpi radialis brevis
and longus

Brachioradialis

**Extensor carpi
radialis longus**

**Extensor carpi
radialis brevis**

Extensor digitorum

**Abductor
pollicis longus**

Extensor pollicis brevis

**Extensor pollicis
longus**

Tendons of
extensor
digitorum

Extensor expansion

(a)

Olecranon process
of ulna

Anconeus

Supinator

**Abductor pollicis
longus**

**Extensor pollicis
longus**

**Extensor pollicis
brevis**

Extensor indicis

Interossei

(b)

Brachioradialis

Anconeus

Olecranon process

Ulna

Extensor indicis

Extensor carpi radialis longus

Extensor carpi radialis brevis

Abductor pollicis longus

Extensor pollicis brevis

Extensor pollicis longus

Extensor retinaculum

(c)

FIGURE 10.16
Muscles of the posterior fascial
compartment of the forearm
acting on the wrist and fingers.
The extensor retinaculum that secures

the extensor tendons at the wrist is
illuminated in **(c)**. **(a)** Superficial muscles
of the right forearm, posterior view.
(b) Deep posterior muscles of the right
forearm; superficial muscles have been

removed. The interossei, the deepest
layer of intrinsic hand muscles, are also
illustrated. **(c)** Photograph of the deep
posterior muscles of the right forearm;
superficial muscles have been removed.

Table 10.12 Summary of Actions of Muscles Acting on the Arm, Forearm, and Hand (Figure 10.17)

PART I: MUSCLES ACTING ON THE ARM (HUMERUS) (PM = PRIME MOVER)	ACTIONS AT THE SHOULDER					
	Flexion	Extension	Abduction	Adduction	Medial rotation	Lateral rotation
Pectoralis major	X (PM)			X (PM)	X	
Latissimus dorsi		X (PM)		X (PM)	X	
Deltoid	X (PM) (anterior fibers)	X (PM) (posterior fibers)	X (PM)		X (anterior fibers)	X (posterior fibers)
Subscapularis					X (PM)	
Supraspinatus			X			
Infraspinatus						X (PM)
Teres minor				X (weak)		X (PM)
Teres major		X		X	X	
Coracobrachialis	X			X		
Biceps brachii	X					
Triceps brachii				X		

PART II: MUSCLES ACTING ON THE FOREARM	ACTIONS			
	Elbow flexion	Elbow extension	Pronation	Supination
Biceps brachii	X (PM)			X
Triceps brachii		X (PM)		
Anconeus		X		
Brachialis	X (PM)			
Brachioradialis	X			
Pronator teres			X	
Pronator quadratus			X	
Supinator				X

PART III: MUSCLES ACTING ON THE WRIST AND FINGERS	ACTIONS ON THE WRIST				ACTIONS ON THE FINGERS	
	Flexion	Extension	Abduction	Adduction	Flexion	Extension
Anterior Compartment:						
Flexor carpi radialis	X (PM)		X			
Palmaris longus	X (weak)					
Flexor carpi ulnaris	X (PM)			X		
Flexor digitorum superficialis	X (PM)				X	
Flexor pollicis longus	X (weak)				X (thumb)	
Flexor digitorum profundus	X				X	
Posterior Compartment:						
Extensor carpi radialis longus and brevis		X	X			
Extensor digitorum		X (PM)				X (and abducts)
Extensor carpi ulnaris		X		X		
Abductor pollicis longus			X		(abducts thumb)	
Extensor pollicis longus and brevis						X (thumb)
Extensor indicis						X (index finger)

Flexors

Extensors

Others

Triceps brachii
Lateral
Long
Medial

Posterior compartment of arm
(extends elbow)

Humerus

Brachialis

Short head
Long head
— Biceps brachii

(a)

Posterior compartment
of forearm
(extends wrist and fingers)

Ulna

Extensors

Radius

Pronator teres

Brachioradialis
(elbow flexor)

Abductor
pollicis
longus

Flexors

(b)

Anterior compartment of arm
(flexes elbow)

Anterior compartment of forearm
(flexes wrist and fingers)

FIGURE 10.17
Summary of actions of muscles of the arm and forearm.
(a) Muscles of the arm. **(b)** Muscles of the forearm.

Table 10.13 Muscles Crossing the Hip and Knee Joints: Movements of the Thigh and Leg (Figures 10.18 and 10.19)

The muscles fleshing out the thigh are difficult to segregate into groups on the basis of action. Some thigh muscles act only at the hip joint, others only at the knee, while still others act at both joints. Attempts to classify these muscles solely on the basis of location is equally frustrating because different muscles in a particular location often have very different actions. However, the most *anterior* muscles of the hip and thigh tend to flex the femur at the hip and to extend the leg at the knee—producing the foreswing phase of walking. The *posterior* muscles of the hip and thigh, by contrast, mostly extend the thigh and flex the leg—the backswing phase of walking. The third group of muscles in this region, the *medial,* or *adductor,* muscles, adduct the thigh; they have no effect on the leg. In the thigh, the anterior, posterior, and adductor muscles are separated by walls of fascia into *anterior, posterior* and *medial compartments* (see Figure 10.23a). The deep fascia of the thigh, the **fascia lata,** surrounds and encloses all three groups of muscles like a support stocking.

Movements of the thigh (occurring at the hip joint) are accomplished largely by muscles anchored to the pelvic girdle. Like the shoulder joint, the hip joint is a ball-and-socket joint permitting flexion, extension, abduction, adduction, circumduction, and rotation. Muscles effecting these movements of the thigh are among the most powerful muscles of the body. For the most part, the thigh *flexors* pass in front of the hip joint. The most important of these are the *iliopsoas, tensor fasciae latae,* and *rectus femoris;* they are assisted in this action by the *adductor* muscles of the medial thigh and the straplike *sartorius.* The prime mover of thigh flexion is the iliopsoas.

Thigh *extension* is effected primarily by the massive *hamstring* muscles of the posterior thigh. However, during forceful extension, the *gluteus maximus* of the buttock is activated. Buttock muscles that lie lateral to the hip joint (*gluteus medius* and *minimus*) *abduct* the thigh and rotate it medially. Medial rotation is opposed by six small deep muscles of the gluteal region called the *lateral rotators.* Thigh adduction is the role of the adductor muscles of the medial thigh. Abduction and adduction of the thighs is extremely important during walking to keep the body's weight balanced over the limb that is on the ground.

At the knee joint, flexion and extension are the main movements. The sole knee *extensor* is the *quadriceps femoris* muscle of the anterior thigh, the most powerful muscle in the body. The quadriceps is antagonized by the hamstrings of the posterior compartment, which are prime movers of knee flexion and also act to rotate the leg when the knee is semiflexed.

The actions of the muscles presented here are further summarized in Table 10.15 (Part I).

Muscle	Description	Origin (O) and insertion (I)	Action	Nerve supply
PART I: ANTERIOR AND MEDIAL MUSCLES (Figure 10.18)				
ORIGIN ON THE PELVIS				
Iliopsoas (il″e-o-so′us)	Iliopsoas is a composite of two closely related muscles (iliacus and psoas major) whose fibers pass under the inguinal ligament [see Table 10.6 (external oblique muscle) and Figure 10.11] to insert via a common tendon on the femur.			
• **Iliacus** (il-e-ak′us) (*iliac* = ilium)	Large, fan-shaped, more lateral muscle	O—iliac fossa I—lesser trochanter of femur via iliopsoas tendon	Iliopsoas is the prime mover of hip flexion; flexes thigh on trunk when pelvis is fixed	Femoral nerve
• **Psoas** (so′us) **major** (*psoa* = loin muscle; *major* = larger)	Longer, thicker, more medial muscle of the pair. (Butchers refer to this muscle as the tenderloin)	O—by fleshy slips from transverse processes, bodies, and discs of lumbar vertebrae and T_{12} I—lesser trochanter of femur via iliopsoas tendon	As above; also effects lateral flexion of vertebral column; important postural muscle	Ventral rami L_1–L_3
Sartorius (sar-tor′e-us) (*sartor* = tailor)	Straplike superficial muscle running obliquely across anterior surface of thigh to knee; longest muscle in body; crosses both hip and knee joints	O—anterior superior iliac spine I—winds around medial aspect of knee and inserts into medial aspect of proximal tibia	Flexes and laterally rotates thigh; flexes knee (weak); known as "tailor's muscle" because it helps effect cross-legged position in which tailors are often depicted	Femoral nerve

**FIGURE 10.18
Anterior and medial muscles promoting movements of the thigh and leg. (a)** Anterior view of the deep muscles of the pelvis and superficial muscles of the right thigh. **(b)** Adductor muscles of the medial compartment of the thigh. Other muscles have been removed so that the origins and insertions of the adductor muscles can be seen. **(c)** The vastus muscles of the quadriceps group. The rectus femoris muscle of the quadriceps group and surrounding muscles have been removed to reveal the attachments and extent of the vastus muscles.

(Table continues)

Table 10.13 continued

Muscle	Description	Origin (O) and insertion (I)	Action	Nerve supply
MUSCLES OF THE MEDIAL COMPARTMENT OF THE THIGH				
Adductors (ah-duk′torz)	Large muscle mass consisting of three muscles (magnus, longus, and brevis) forming medial aspect of thigh; arise from inferior part of pelvis and insert at various levels on femur; all used in movements that press thighs together, as when astride a horse; important in pelvic tilting movements that occur during walking and in fixing the hip when the knee is flexed; entire group innervated by obturator nerve. Strain or stretching of this muscle group is called a "pulled groin"			
• **Adductor magnus** (mag′nus) (*adduct* = move toward midline; *magnus* = large)	A triangular muscle with a broad insertion; is a composite muscle that is part adductor and part hamstring in action	O—ischial and pubic rami and ischial tuberosity I—linea aspera and adductor tubercle of femur	Anterior part adducts and laterally rotates and flexes thigh; posterior part is a synergist of hamstrings in thigh extension	Obturator nerve and sciatic nerve
• **Adductor longus** (*longus* = long)	Overlies middle aspect of adductor magnus; most anterior of adductor muscles	O—pubis near pubic symphysis I—linea aspera	Adducts, flexes, and laterally rotates thigh	Obturator nerve
• **Adductor brevis** (*brevis* = short)	In contact with obturator externus muscle; largely concealed by adductor longus and pectineus	O—body and inferior ramus of pubis I—linea aspera above adductor longus	Adducts and laterally rotates thigh	Obturator nerve
Pectineus (pek-tin′e-us) (*pecten* = comb)	Short, flat muscle; over-lies adductor brevis on proximal thigh; abuts adductor longus medially	O—pectineal line of pubis (and superior ramus) I—inferior to lesser trochanter of posterior aspect of femur	Adducts, flexes, and laterally rotates thigh	Femoral and some-times obturator nerve
Gracilis (grah-sĭ′lis) (*gracilis* = slender)	Long, thin, superficial muscle of medial thigh	O—interior ramus and body of pubis I—medial surface of tibia just inferior to its medial condyle	Adducts thigh, flexes, and medially rotates leg, especially during walking	Obturator nerve
MUSCLES OF THE ANTERIOR COMPARTMENT OF THE THIGH				
Quadriceps femoris (kwod′rĭ-seps fem′o-ris)	Quadriceps femoris arises from four separate heads (*quadriceps* = four heads) that form the flesh of front and sides of thigh; these heads (rectus femoris, and lateral, medial, and intermediate vastus muscles) have a common insertion tendon, the quadriceps tendon, which inserts into the patella and then via the patellar ligament into tibial tuberosity. The quadriceps is a powerful knee extensor used in climbing, jumping, running, and rising from seated position; group is innervated by femoral nerve; the tone of quadriceps plays important role in strengthening knee joint			
• **Rectus femoris** (rek′tus) (*rectus* = straight; *femoris* = femur)	Superficial muscle of anterior thigh; runs straight down thigh; long-est head and only muscle of group to cross hip joint	O—anterior inferior iliac spine and superior margin of acetabulum I—patella and tibial tuberosity via patellar ligament	Extends knee and flexes thigh at hip	Femoral nerve
• **Vastus lateralis** (vas′tus lat″er-a′lis) (*vastus* = large; *lateralis* = lateral)	Forms lateral aspect of thigh; a common intra-muscular injection site, particularly in infants (who have poorly devel-oped buttock and arm muscles)	O—greater trochanter, intertrochanteric line, linea aspera I—as for rectus femoris	Extends knee	Femoral nerve
• **Vastus medialis** (me″de-a′lis) (*medialis* = medial)	Forms inferomedial aspect of thigh	O—linea aspera, intertro-chanteric line I—as for rectus femoris	Extends knee; inferior fibers stabilize patella	Femoral nerve
• **Vastus intermedius** (in″ter-me′de-us) (*intermedius* = intermediate)	Obscured by rectus femoris; lies between vastus lateralis and vastus medialis on anterior thigh	O—anterior and lateral surfaces of proximal femur shaft I—as for rectus femoris	Extends knee	Femoral nerve

Muscle	Description	Origin (O) and insertion (I)	Action	Nerve supply
Tensor fasciae latae (ten'sor fă'she-e la'te) (*tensor* = to make tense; *fascia* = band; *lata* = wide)	Enclosed between fascia layers of anterolateral aspect of thigh; functionally associated with medial rotators and flexors of thigh	O—anterior aspect of iliac crest and anterior superior iliac spine I—iliotibial tract*	Flexes and abducts thigh (thus a synergist of the iliopsoas and gluteus medius and minimus muscles); rotates thigh medially; steadies trunk on thigh by making iliotibial tract taut	Superior gluteal nerve

PART II: POSTERIOR MUSCLES (Figure 10.19)

GLUTEAL MUSCLES—ORIGIN ON PELVIS

Gluteus maximus (gloo'te-us mak'sĭ-mus) (*glutos* = buttock; *maximus* = largest)	Largest and most superficial of gluteus muscles; forms bulk of buttock mass; fibers are thick and coarse; important site of intramuscular injection (dorsal gluteal site); overlies large sciatic nerve; covers ischial tuberosity only when standing; when sitting, moves superiorly leaving ischial tuberosity exposed in the subcutaneous position	O—dorsal ilium, sacrum, and coccyx I—gluteal tuberosity of femur; iliotibial tract	Major extensor of thigh; complex, powerful, and most effective when thigh is flexed and force is necessary, as in rising from a forward flexed position and in thrusting the thigh posteriorly in climbing stairs and running; generally inactive during walking; laterally rotates thigh; antagonist of iliopsoas muscle	Inferior gluteal nerve
Gluteus medius (me'de-us) (*medius* = middle)	Thick muscle largely covered by gluteus maximus; important site for intramuscular injections (ventral gluteal site); considered safer than dorsal gluteal site because there is less chance of injuring sciatic nerve	O—between anterior and posterior gluteal lines on lateral surface of ilium I—by short tendon into lateral aspect of greater trochanter of femur	Abducts and medially rotates thigh; steadies pelvis; its action is extremely important in walking; e.g., muscle of limb planted on ground tilts or holds pelvis in abduction so that pelvis on side of swinging limb does not sag; the foot of swinging limb can thus clear the ground	Superior gluteal nerve
Gluteus minimus (mĭ'nĭ-mus) (*minimus* = smallest)	Smallest and deepest of gluteal muscles	O—between anterior and inferior gluteal lines on external surface of ilium I—anterior border of greater trochanter of femur	As for gluteus medius	Superior gluteal nerve

LATERAL ROTATORS

Piriformis (pir'ĭ-form-is) (*piri* = pear; *forma* = shape)	Pyramidal muscle located on posterior aspect of hip joint; inferior to gluteus minimus; issues from pelvis via greater sciatic notch	O—anterolateral surface of sacrum (opposite greater sciatic notch) I—superior border of greater trochanter of femur	Rotates thigh laterally; since inserted above head of femur, can also assist in abduction of thigh when hip is flexed; stabilizes hip joint	S_1 and S_2, L_5
Obturator externus (ob"tu-ra'tor ek-ster'nus) (*obturator* = obturator foramen; *externus* = outside)	Flat, triangular muscle deep in upper medial aspect of thigh	O—outer surface of obturator membrane, external surface of pubis and ischium, and margins of obturator foramen I—by a tendon into trochanteric fossa of posterior femur	Rotates thigh laterally and stabilizes hip joint	Obturator nerve

(Table continues)

*The iliotibial tract is a thickened lateral portion of the *fascia lata* (the fascia that ensheaths all the muscles of the thigh). It extends as a tendinous band from the iliac crest to the knee (see Figure 10.19a).

Table 10.13 (continued)

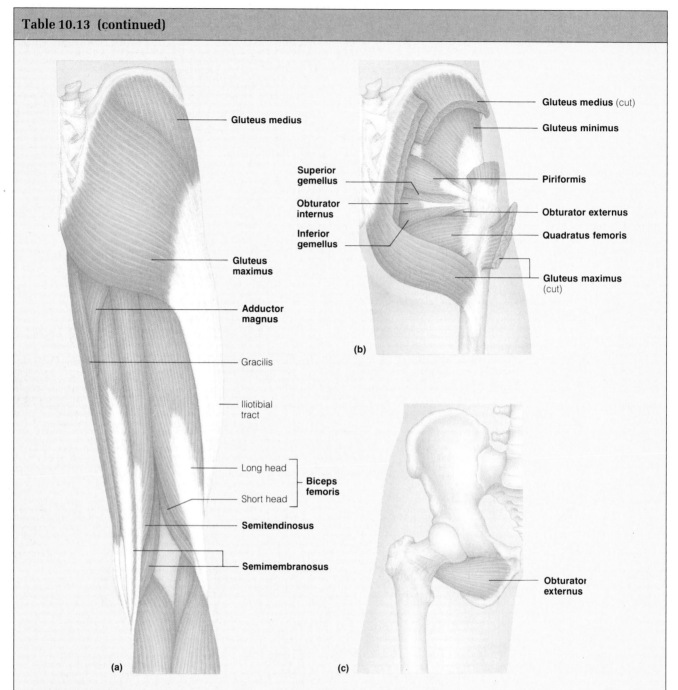

FIGURE 10.19
Posterior muscles of the right hip and thigh. (a) Superficial view showing the gluteus muscles of the buttock and hamstring muscles of the thigh. **(b)** Deep muscles of the gluteal region, which act primarily to rotate the thigh laterally. The superficial gluteus maximus and medius have been removed. **(c)** Anterior view of the isolated obturator externus muscle, showing its course as it travels from its origin on the anterior pelvis to the posterior aspect of the femur.

Muscle	Description	Origin (O) and insertion (I)	Action	Nerve supply
Obturator internus (in-ter′nus) (*internus* = inside)	Surrounds obturator foramen within pelvis; leaves pelvis via lesser sciatic notch and turns acutely forward to insert in femur	O—inner surface of obturator membrane, greater sciatic notch, and margins of obturator foramen I—greater trochanter in front of piriformis	As for obturator externus	L_5 and S_1
Gemellus (jĕ-mĕ′lis)— superior and inferior (*gemin* = twin, double; *superior* = above; *inferior* = below)	Two small muscles with common insertions and actions; considered extrapelvic portions of obturator internus	O—ischial spine (superior); ischial tuberosity (inferior) I—greater trochanter of femur	Rotate thigh laterally and stabilize hip joint	L_4, L_5, and S_1
Quadratus femoris (*quad* = four-sided square)	Short, thick muscle; most inferior of lateral rotator muscles; extends laterally from pelvis	O—ischial tuberosity I—greater trochanter of femur	Rotates thigh laterally and stabilizes hip joint	L_5 and S_1

MUSCLES OF THE POSTERIOR COMPARTMENT OF THE THIGH

Muscle	Description	Origin (O) and insertion (I)	Action	Nerve supply
Hamstrings	The hamstrings are fleshy muscles of the posterior thigh (biceps femoris, semitendinosus, and semimembranosus); they cross both the hip and knee joints and are prime movers of thigh extension and knee flexion; group has a common origin site and is innervated by sciatic nerve; ability of hamstrings to act on one of the two joints spanned depends on which joint is fixed; i.e., if knee is fixed (extended), they promote hip extension; if hip is extended, they promote knee flexion; however, when hamstrings are stretched, they tend to restrict full accomplishment of antagonistic movements; e.g., if knees are fully extended, it is difficult to flex the hip fully (and touch your toes), and when the thigh is fully flexed as in kicking a football, it is almost impossible to extend the knee fully at the same time (without considerable practice); name of this muscle group comes from old butchers' practice of using their tendons to hang hams for smoking; "pulled hamstrings" are common sports injuries in those who run very hard, e.g., football halfbacks			
• **Biceps femoris** (*biceps* = two heads)	Most lateral muscle of the group; arises from two heads	O—ischial tuberosity (long head); linea aspera and distal femur (short head) I—common tendon passes downward and laterally (forming lateral border of popliteal fossa) to insert into head of fibula and lateral condyle of tibia	Extends thigh and flexes knee; laterally rotates leg, especially when knee is flexed	Sciatic nerve
• **Semitendinosus** (sem″e-ten″dĭ-no′sus) (*semi* = half; *tendinosus* = tendon)	Lies medial to biceps femoris; although its name suggests that this muscle is largely tendinous, it is quite fleshy; its slender tendon begins about two-thirds the way down thigh	O—ischial tuberosity in common with long head of biceps femoris I—medial aspect of upper tibial shaft	Extends thigh at hip; flexes knee; with semimembranosus, medially rotates leg	Sciatic nerve
• **Semimembranosus** (sem″e-mem″brah-no′sus) (*membranosus* = membrane)	Deep to semitendinosus	O—ischial tuberosity I—medial condyle of tibia	Extends thigh and flexes knee; medially rotates leg	Sciatic nerve

Table 10.14 Muscles of the Leg: Movements of the Ankle and Toes (Figures 10.20 to 10.22)

The deep fascia of the leg is continuous with the fascia lata that ensheaths the thigh. Like a tight "knee sock" beneath the skin, the leg fascia binds the leg muscles tightly, helping to prevent excessive swelling of muscles during exercise and aiding venous return. Its inward extensions segregate the leg muscles into *anterior, lateral,* and *posterior compartments* (see Figure 10.23b), each with its own nerve and blood supply. Distally the leg fascia thickens to form the **flexor, extensor**, and **peroneal retinaculae**, which secure the muscle tendons in place as they cross the ankle to run to the foot.

Depending on their location and placement, the various muscles of the leg promote movements at the ankle joint (dorsiflexion and plantar flexion), the intertarsal joints (inversion and eversion of the foot), and/or the toes (flexion and extension). Muscles in the *anterior extensor compartment* of the leg (*tibialis anterior, extensor digitorum longus, extensor hallucis longus,* and *peroneus tertius*) are primarily toe extensors and ankle dorsiflexors. Although dorsiflexion is not a powerful movement, it is extremely important in preventing the toes from dragging during walking. Lateral compartment muscles are the per-oneal (*peron* = fibula) muscles that plantar flex and evert the foot. Muscles of the *posterior flexor compartment* (*gastrocnemius, soleus, tibialis posterior, flexor digitorum longus,* and *flexor hallucis longus*) primarily plantar flex the foot and flex the toes. Plantar flexion is the most powerful movement of the ankle (and foot) because it lifts the entire weight of our body. It is necessary for standing on tip-toe and provides the necessary forward thrust when walking and running. The popliteus muscle, which crosses the knee, is important in "unlocking" the extended knee in preparation for flexion.

Intrinsic muscles of the sole of the foot (lumbricals, interossei, and many others) help to flex, extend, abduct, and adduct the toes. Collectively, they are very important (along with the tendons of leg muscles) in supporting the arches of the foot. However, since these muscles are numerous, their arrangement complex, and their individual actions relatively unimportant, we will not consider them further.

The actions of the muscles in this table are summarized in Table 10.15 (Part II).

Muscle	Description	Origin (O) and insertion (I)	Action	Nerve supply
PART I: MUSCLES OF THE ANTERIOR COMPARTMENT (Figures 10.20 and 10.21)				
	All muscles of the anterior compartment are dorsiflexors of the ankle and have a common innervation, the deep peroneal nerve. Paralysis of the anterior muscle group causes *foot drop*, which requires that the leg be lifted unusually high during walking to prevent tripping over one's toes. "Shinsplints" is a painful inflammatory condition of the muscles of the anterior compartment.			
Tibialis anterior (tib″e-a′lis) (*tibial* = tibia; *anterior* = toward the front)	Superficial muscle of anterior leg; laterally parallels sharp anterior margin of tibia	O—lateral condyle and upper $^2/_3$ of tibia: interosseous membrane I—by tendon into inferior surface of medial cuneiform and first metatarsal bone	Prime mover of dorsiflexion; inverts foot; assists in supporting medial longitudinal arch of foot	Deep peroneal nerve
Extensor digitorum longus (*extensor* = increases angle at a joint; *digit* = finger or toe; *longus* = long)	On anterolateral surface of leg; lateral to tibialis anterior muscle	O—lateral condyle of tibia; proximal $^3/_4$ of fibula; interosseous membrane I—second and third phalanges of toes 2–5 via extensor expansion	Dorsiflexes foot; prime mover of toe extension (acts mainly at metatarsophalangeal joints)	Deep peroneal nerve
Peroneus tertius (per″o-ne′us ter′shus) (*perone* = fibula; *tertius* = third)	Small muscle; usually continuous and fused with distal part of extensor digitorum longus; not always present	O—distal anterior surface of fibula and interosseous membrane I—tendon passes anterior to lateral malleolus and inserts on dorsum of fifth metatarsal	Dorsiflexes and everts foot	Deep peroneal nerve
Extensor hallucis (hal′u-sis) **longus** (*hallux* = great toe)	Deep to extensor digitorum longus and tibialis anterior; narrow origin	O—anteromedial fibula shaft and interosseous membrane I—tendon inserts on distal phalanx of great toe	Extends great toe; dorsiflexes foot	Deep peroneal nerve

Peroneus longus

Gastrocnemius

Tibia

Tibialis anterior

Extensor digitorum longus

Soleus

Extensor hallucis longus

Peroneus tertius

Superior and inferior extensor retinacula

(a)

Tibialis anterior

(b)

Extensor hallucis longus

Peroneus tertius

(c)

O = origin
I = insertion

Extensor digitorum longus

(d)

FIGURE 10.20
Muscles of the anterior compartment of the right leg. (a) Superficial view of anterior leg muscles. **(b–d)** Some of the same muscles shown in isolation to allow visualization of their origins and insertions.

(Table continues)

Table 10.14 (continued)

O = origin
I = insertion

- Patella
- Head of fibula
- **Gastrocnemius**
- **Soleus**
- **Peroneus longus**
- **Extensor digitorum longus**
- **Tibialis anterior**
- **Extensor hallucis longus**
- **Peroneus brevis**
- **Flexor hallucis longus**
- Peroneal retinaculum
- Lateral malleolus
- **Peroneus tertius**
- Superior and inferior extensor retinacula

(a)

5th metatarsal

Peroneus longus

(b)

Tendon of peroneus longus

Peroneus brevis

(c)

FIGURE 10.21
Muscles of lateral compartment of the right leg. (a) Superficial view of lateral aspect of the leg, illustrating the positioning of the lateral compartment muscles (peroneus longus and brevis) relative to anterior and posterior leg muscles. **(b)** View of peroneus longus in isolation; inset illustrates the insertion of the peroneus longus on the plantar surface of the foot.
(c) Isolated view of the peroneus brevis muscle.

Muscle	Description	Origin (O) and insertion (I)	Action	Nerve supply
PART II: MUSCLES OF THE LATERAL COMPARTMENT (Figures 10.21 and 10.22)				
	These muscles have a common innervation, the superficial peroneal nerve. Besides plantar flexion and foot eversion, these muscles stabilize the lateral ankle and lateral longitudinal arch of the foot.			
Peroneus longus (See also Figure 10.20)	Superficial lateral muscle; overlies fibula	O—head and upper portion of fibula I—by long tendon that curves under foot to first metatarsal and medial cuneiform	Plantar flexes and everts foot; helps keep foot flat on ground	Superficial peroneal nerve
Peroneus brevis (*brevis* = short)	Smaller muscle; deep to peroneus longus; enclosed in a common sheath	O—distal fibula shaft I—by tendon running behind lateral malleolus to insert on proximal end of fifth metatarsal	Plantar flexes and everts foot	Superficial peroneal nerve
PART III: MUSCLES OF THE POSTERIOR COMPARTMENT (Figure 10.22)				
	The muscles of the posterior compartment have a common innervation, the tibial nerve. They act in concert to plantar flex the ankle.			
SUPERFICIAL MUSCLES				
Triceps surae (tri″seps sur′e) (See also Figure 10.21)	Refers to muscle pair (gastrocnemius and soleus) that shapes the posterior calf and inserts via a common tendon into the calcaneus of the heel; this calcaneal or Achilles tendon is the largest tendon in the body; prime movers of ankle plantar flexion			
• **Gastrocnemius** (gas″truk-ne′me-us) (*gaster* = belly; *kneme* = leg)	Superficial muscle of pair; two prominent bellies that form proximal curve of calf	O—by two heads from medial and lateral condyles of femur I—calcaneus via calcaneal tendon	Plantar flexes foot when knee is extended; since it also crosses knee joint, it can flex knee when foot is dorsiflexed	Tibial nerve
• **Soleus** (so′le-us) (*soleus* = fish)	Deep to gastrocnemius on posterior surface of calf	O—extensive cone-shaped origin from superior tibia, fibula, and interosseous membrane I—calcaneus via calcaneal tendon	Plantar flexes ankle; important locomotor and postural muscle during walking, running, and dancing	Tibial nerve
Plantaris (plan-tar′is) (*planta* = sole of foot)	Generally a small feeble muscle, but varies in size and extent; may be absent	O—posterior femur above lateral condyle I—via a long, thin tendon into calcaneus or calcaneal tendon	Assists in knee flexion and plantar flexion of foot	Tibial nerve
DEEP MUSCLES				
Popliteus (pop-lit′e-us) (*poplit* = back of knee)	Thin, triangular muscle at posterior knee; passes downward and medially to tibial surface	O—lateral condyle of femur I—proximal tibia	Flexes and rotates leg medially to unlock knee from full extension when flexion begins	Tibial nerve
Flexor digitorum longus (*flexor* = decreases angle at a joint)	Long, narrow muscle; runs medial to and partially overlies tibialis posterior	O—posterior tibia I—tendon runs behind medial malleolus and splits into four parts to insert into distal phalanges of toes 2–5	Plantar flexes and inverts foot; flexes toes; helps foot "grip" ground	Tibial nerve
Flexor hallucis longus (See also Figure 10.21)	Bipennate muscle; lies lateral to inferior aspect of tibialis posterior	O—middle part of shaft of fibula; interosseous membrane I—tendon runs under foot to distal phalanx of great toe	Plantar flexes and inverts foot; flexes great toe at all joints; "push off" muscle during walking	Tibial nerve
Tibialis posterior (*posterior* = toward the back)	Thick, flat muscle deep to soleus; placed between posterior flexors	O—extensive origin from superior tibia and fibula and interosseous membrane I—tendon passes behind medial malleolus and under arch of foot; inserts into several tarsals and metatarsals 2–4	Prime mover of foot inversion; plantar flexes ankle; stabilizes medial longitudinal arch of foot (as during ice skating)	Tibial nerve
				(Table continues)

Table 10.14 (continued)

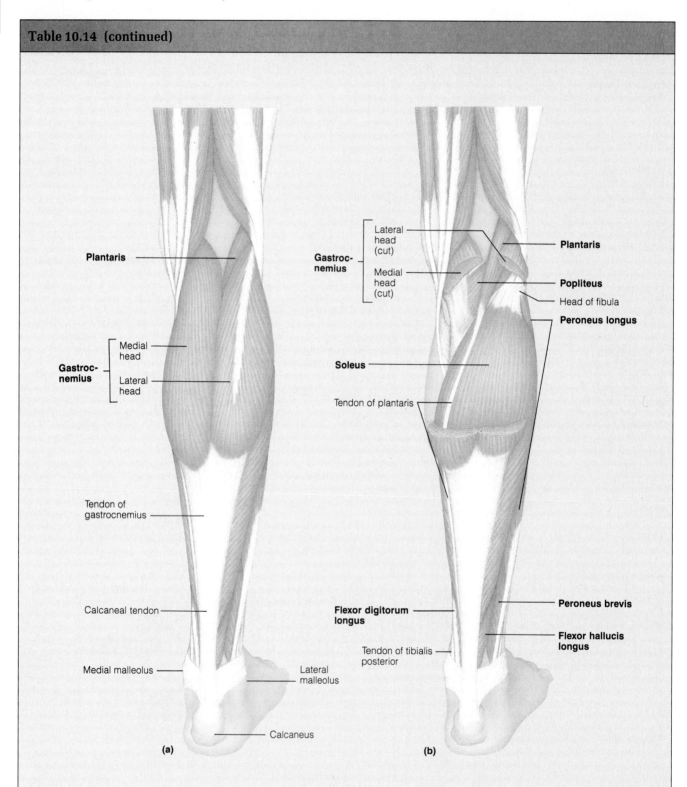

FIGURE 10.22
Muscles of the posterior compartment of the right leg. (a) Superficial view of the posterior leg. (b) The fleshy gastrocnemius has been removed to show the soleus immediately deep to it. (c) The triceps surae has been removed to show the deep muscles of the posterior compartment. (d–f) Individual deep muscles are shown in isolation so that their origins and insertions may be visualized.

O = origin
I = insertion

Plantaris (cut)

Gastrocnemius
lateral head (cut)

Popliteus

Soleus (cut)

Tibialis posterior

Fibula

Peroneus
longus

Flexor hallucis
longus

Peroneus
brevis

Gastroc-
nemius
medial head
(cut)

Flexor
digitorum
longus

Tendon of
tibialis posterior

Medial
malleolus

Calcaneal
tendon (cut)

Calcaneus

(c)

O

I

(d)

O

I

(e)

Flexor
digitorum
longus

Popliteus

I

O

Flexor
hallucis
longus

I

(f)

Table 10.15 Summary of Actions of Muscles Acting on the Thigh, Leg, and Foot (Figure 10.23)

PART I: MUSCLES ACTING ON THE THIGH AND LEG (PM = PRIME MOVER)	ACTIONS AT THE HIP JOINT						ACTIONS AT THE KNEE	
	Flexion	Extension	Abduction	Adduction	Medial rotation	Lateral rotation	Flexion	Extension
Anterior and medial muscles:								
Iliopsoas	X (PM)							
Sartorius	X					X	X	
Adductor magnus		X		X		X		
Adductor longus	X			X		X		
Adductor brevis	X			X		X		
Pectineus	X			X		X		
Gracilis				X			X	
Rectus femoris	X							X (PM)
Vastus muscles								X (PM)
Tensor fasciae latae	X		X		X			
Posterior muscles:								
Gluteus maximus		X (PM)				X		
Gluteus medius			X (PM)		X			
Gluteus minimus			X		X			
Piriformis			X			X		
Obturator internus						X		
Obturator externus						X		
Gemelli						X		
Quadratus femoris						X		
Biceps femoris		X (PM)					X (PM)	
Semitendinosus		X					X (PM)	
Semimembranosus		X					X (PM)	
Gastrocnemius							X	
Plantaris							X	
Popliteus							X (and rotates medially)	

PART II: MUSCLES ACTING ON THE ANKLE AND TOES	ACTIONS AT THE ANKLE JOINT				ACTIONS AT THE TOES	
	Plantar flexion	Dorsiflexion	Inversion	Eversion	Flexion	Extension
Anterior compartment:						
Tibialis anterior		X (PM)	X			
Extensor digitorum longus		X				X (PM)
Peroneus tertius		X		X		
Extensor hallucis longus		X	X (weak)			X (great toe)
Lateral compartment:						
Peroneus longus and brevis	X			X		
Posterior compartment:						
Gastrocnemius	X (PM)					
Soleus	X (PM)					
Plantaris	X					
Flexor digitorum longus	X		X		X (PM)	
Flexor hallucis longus	X		X		X (great toe)	
Tibialis posterior	X		X (PM)			

FIGURE 10.23
Summary of actions of muscles of the thigh and leg.
(a) Muscles of the thigh. (b) Muscles of the leg.

RELATED CLINICAL TERMS

Achilles tendinitis Inflammation of the Achilles (calcaneal) tendon caused by trauma (microtears in the inelastic tendon); accompanied by a leathery, creaking noise with each step. Typically happens in those who participate in running sports (basketball, baseball, track) when the calf muscles contract hard or suddenly. Achilles tendinitis is unique in that the pain is most intense on arising and then diminishes as the tendon is used. If the inflammatory process continues for several weeks, permanent adhesions develop between the tendon sheath and the tendon; these adhesions limit motion and the condition becomes chronic.

Charley horse A muscle contusion, i.e., trauma-induced tearing of muscle followed by bleeding into the tissues (hematoma formation) and severe, prolonged pain; a common occurrence in those involved in contact sports; a charley horse of the quadriceps muscle of the thigh occurs frequently in football players.

Quadriceps and hamstring strains Also called quad and hamstring pulls, these conditions involve tearing of these muscles or their tendons; happen mainly in athletes who do not warm up properly and then fully extend their hip (quad pull) or knee (hamstring pull) quickly or forcefully (e.g., sprinters, tennis players); not painful at first, but pain intensifies within 3 to 6 hours (30 minutes if the tearing is severe). After a week of rest, stretching is the best therapy.

Rupture of the calcaneal tendon Although the calcaneal (Achilles) tendon is the largest, strongest tendon in the body, its rupture is surprisingly common, particularly in older men as a result of stumbling and in young sprinters when the tendon is traumatized during the takeoff; the rupture is followed by abrupt pain; a gap is seen just above the heel, and the calf bulges as the triceps surae are released from their attachment point; plantar flexion is not possible, but dorsiflexion is exaggerated.

Shinsplints Common term for pain in the anterior compartment of the leg caused by irritation of the anterior tibialis muscle as might follow extreme or unusual exercise without adequate prior conditioning; as the inflamed muscle swells, its circulation is impaired by the tight fascial wrappings, leading to pain and tenderness to touch. However, the term is used loosely to indicate a variety of ailments ranging from stress fracture of the tibia, to inflammation of shin fascia, to muscle tears.

Torticollis (tor″tĭ-kol′is; *tort* = twisted) A twisting of the neck in which there is a chronic rotation and tilting of the head to one side, due to injury of the sternocleidomastoid muscle on one side; also called wryneck; sometimes present at birth when the muscle fibers are torn during difficult delivery; exercise that stretches the affected muscle is the usual treatment.

CHAPTER SUMMARY

Muscle Mechanics: Importance of Leverage and Fascicle Arrangement (pp. 287–290)

1. A lever is a bar that moves on a fulcrum. When an effort is applied to the lever, a load is moved. In the body, bones are the levers, joints are the fulcrums, and the effort is exerted by skeletal muscles at their insertions.

2. When the effort is farther from the fulcrum than is the load, the lever operates at a mechanical advantage (is slow and strong). When the effort is exerted closer to the fulcrum than is the load, the lever operates at a mechanical disadvantage (is fast and promotes a large degree of movement).

3. First-class levers (effort-fulcrum-load) may operate at a mechanical advantage or disadvantage. Second-class levers (fulcrum-load-effort) all operate at a mechanical advantage. Third-class levers (fulcrum-effort-load) always operate at a mechanical disadvantage.

Interactions of Skeletal Muscles in the Body (pp. 290–291)

1. Skeletal muscles can only pull (shorten). They are arranged in opposing groups across body joints so that one group can reverse or modify the action of the other.

2. Muscles may be classified on the basis of their interactions as prime movers (agonists), which bear the chief responsibility for producing movement; antagonists, which reverse, or oppose, the action of another muscle; synergists, which aid a prime mover by effecting the same action, stabilizing joints, or preventing undesirable movements; and fixators, which function primarily to immobilize a bone or a muscle's origin.

Naming Skeletal Muscles (pp. 291–292)

1. Criteria used to name muscles include a muscle's location, shape, relative size, fiber (fascicle) direction, number of origins, attachment sites (origin/insertion), and action.

2. Several criteria are combined to name some muscles.

Major Skeletal Muscles of the Body (pp. 292–337)

1. Muscles of the head that produce facial expression tend to be small and to insert into soft tissue (skin and other muscles) rather than into bone. These muscles allow opening and closing of the eyes and mouth, compression of the cheeks, smiling, and other types of facial language (see Table 10.1).

2. Muscles of the head involved in mastication include the masseter and temporalis that elevate the mandible and two deep muscle pairs that promote grinding and sliding jaw movements (see Table 10.2). Extrinsic muscles of the tongue anchor the tongue and control its movements.

3. Deep muscles of the anterior neck promote swallowing movements, including elevation/depression of the hyoid bone, closure of the respiratory passages, and peristalsis of the pharynx (see Table 10.3).

4. Head and trunk movements are promoted by muscles of the neck and by deep muscles of the vertebral column (see Table 10.4). The deep muscles of the posterior trunk can cause extension of large regions of the vertebral column (and head) simultaneously. Head flexion and rotation are effected by the anteriorly located sternocleidomastoid and scalene muscles.

5. Movements of quiet breathing are promoted by the diaphragm and the external intercostal muscles of the thorax (see Table 10.5). Downward movement of the diaphragm increases intra-abdominal pressure.

6. The four muscle pairs forming the abdominal wall are layered like plywood to form a natural muscular girdle that protects, supports, and compresses abdominal contents. These muscles also flex and laterally rotate the trunk (see Table 10.6).

7. Muscles of the pelvic floor (see Table 10.7) support the pelvic viscera and resist increases in intra-abdominal pressure.

8. Except for the pectoralis major and the latissimus dorsi, the superficial muscles of the thorax act to fix or promote movements of the scapula (see Table 10.8). Scapular movements are effected primarily by posterior thoracic muscles.

9. Nine muscles cross the shoulder joint to effect movements of the humerus (see Table 10.9). Of these, seven originate on the scapula and two arise from the axial skeleton. Four muscles contribute to the "rotator cuff" helping to stabilize the multiaxial shoulder joint. Generally speaking, muscles located anteriorly flex, rotate, and adduct the arm. Those located posteriorly extend, rotate, and adduct the arm. The deltoid muscle of the shoulder is the prime mover of shoulder abduction.

10. Muscles causing movements of the forearm form the flesh of the arm (see Table 10.10). Anterior arm muscles are forearm flexors; posterior muscles are forearm extensors.

11. Movements of the wrist, hand, and fingers are effected mainly by muscles originating on the forearm (see Table 10.11). Except for the two pronator muscles, the anterior forearm muscles are wrist and/or finger flexors; those of the posterior compartment are wrist and finger extensors. Intrinsic hand muscles aid in finger (and thumb) movements.

12. Muscles crossing the hip and knee joints effect thigh and leg movements (see Table 10.13). Anteromedial muscles include thigh flexors and/or adductors and knee extensors. Muscles of the posterior gluteal region extend and rotate the thigh. Posterior thigh muscles extend the hip and flex the knee.

13. Muscles of the leg act on the ankle and toes (see Table 10.14). Anterior compartment muscles are largely ankle dorsiflexors. Lateral compartment muscles are plantar flexors and foot everters. Those of the posterior leg are plantar flexors. Intrinsic foot muscles support foot arches and help effect toe movements.

REVIEW QUESTIONS
Multiple Choice/Matching

1. A muscle that assists an agonist by causing a like movement or by stabilizing a joint over which an agonist acts is (a) an antagonist, (b) a prime mover, (c) a synergist, (d) an agonist.

 2. Match the muscle names in column B to the facial muscles described in column A.

Column A	Column B
_____ **(1)** squints the eyes	**(a)** corrugator supercilii
_____ **(2)** raises the eyebrows	**(b)** depressor anguli oris
_____ **(3)** smiling muscle	**(c)** frontalis
_____ **(4)** puckers the lips	**(d)** occipitalis
_____ **(5)** pulls the scalp posteriorly	**(e)** orbicularis oculi
	(f) orbicularis oris
	(g) zygomaticus

3. The prime mover(s) of inspiration is (are) the (a) diaphragm, (b) internal intercostals, (c) external intercostals, (d) abdominal wall muscles.

 4. The arm muscle that both flexes the elbow and supinates the forearm is the (a) brachialis, (b) brachioradialis, (c) biceps brachii, (d) triceps brachii.

5. The chewing muscles that protrude the mandible and produce side-to-side grinding movements are the (a) buccinators, (b) masseters, (c) temporalis, (d) pterygoids.

 6. Muscles that depress the hyoid bone and larynx include all but the (a) sternohyoid, (b) omohyoid, (c) geniohyoid, (d) sternothyroid.

7. Intrinsic muscles of the back that promote extension of the spine (or head) include all but (a) splenius muscles, (b) semispinalis muscles, (c) scalene muscles, (d) erector spinae.

 8. Several muscles act to move and/or stabilize the scapula. Which of the following are small rectangular muscles that square the shoulders as they act together to retract the scapula? (a) levator scapulae, (b) rhomboids, (c) serratus anterior, (d) trapezius.

9. The quadriceps include all but (a) vastus lateralis, (b) vastus intermedius, (c) vastus medialis, (d) biceps femoris, (e) rectus femoris.

10. A prime mover of hip flexion is the (a) rectus femoris, (b) iliopsoas, (c) vasti muscles, (d) gluteus maximus.

11. The prime mover of hip extension *against* resistance is the (a) gluteus maximus, (b) gluteus medius, (c) biceps femoris, (d) semimembranosus.

 12. Muscles that cause plantar flexion include all but the (a) gastrocnemius, (b) soleus, (c) tibialis anterior, (d) tibialis posterior, (e) peroneus muscles.

Short Answer Essay Questions

13. Name four criteria used in naming muscles, and provide an example (other than those used in the text) that illustrates each criterion.

14. Differentiate between the arrangement of elements (load, fulcrum, and effort) in first-, second-, and third-class levers.

15. What does it mean when we say that a lever operates at a mechanical disadvantage, and what benefits does such a lever system provide?

 16. What muscles act to propel a food bolus down the length of the pharynx to the esophagus?

17. Name and describe the action of muscles used to shake your head no. To nod yes.

 18. (a) Name the four muscle pairs that act in unison to compress the abdominal contents. (b) How does their arrangement (fiber direction) contribute to the strength of the abdominal wall? (c) Which of these muscles can effect lateral rotation of the spine? (d) Which can act alone to flex the spine?

19. List all (six) possible movements that can occur at the shoulder joint and name the prime mover(s) of each movement. Then name their antagonists.

20. (a) Name two forearm muscles that are powerful extensors and abductors of the wrist. (b) Name the sole forearm muscle that can flex the distal interphalangeal joints.

21. Name the muscles usually grouped together as the lateral rotators of the hip.

22. Name three thigh muscles that help you keep your seat astride a horse.

23. (a) Name three muscles or muscle groups used as sites for intramuscular injections. (b) Which of these is used most often in infants, and why?

 ## CRITICAL THINKING AND CLINICAL APPLICATION QUESTIONS

1. Assume you have a 10-lb weight in your right hand. Explain why it is easier to flex the right elbow when your forearm is supinated than when it is pronated.

2. When Mrs. O'Brien returned to her doctor for a follow-up visit after childbirth, she complained that she was having problems controlling her urine flow (was incontinent) when she sneezed. The physician asked his nurse to give Mrs. O'Brien instructions on how to perform exercises to strengthen the muscles of the pelvic floor. To what muscles was he referring?

3. Mr. Ahmadi, an out-of-shape 45-year-old man, was advised by his physician to lose weight and to exercise on a regular basis. He followed his diet faithfully and began to jog daily. One day, while on his morning jog, he heard a snapping sound that was immediately followed by a severe pain in his right lower calf. When examined, a gap was seen between his swollen upper calf region and his heel, and he was unable to plantar flex that ankle. What do you think happened? Why was the upper part of his calf swollen?

CHAPTER OUTLINE AND STUDENT OBJECTIVES

1. List the basic functions of the nervous system.

Organization of the Nervous System (pp. 341–342)

2. Explain the structural and functional divisions of the nervous system.

Histology of Nervous Tissue (pp. 342–350)

3. List the types of supporting cells and cite their functions.

4. Describe the important anatomical structures of a neuron and relate each structure to a physiological role.

5. Explain the importance of the myelin sheath and describe how it is formed in the central and peripheral nervous systems.

6. Classify neurons, both structurally and functionally.

7. Differentiate between a nerve and a tract, and between a nucleus and a ganglion.

Neurophysiology (pp. 350–371)

8. Define resting membrane potential and describe its electrochemical basis.

9. Compare and contrast graded and action potentials.

10. Name the two major classes of graded potentials.

11. Explain how action potentials are generated and propagated along neurons.

12. Define absolute and relative refractory periods.

13. Define saltatory conduction and contrast it to conduction along unmyelinated fibers.

14. Define synapse. Distinguish between electrical and chemical synapses structurally and in their mechanisms of information transmission.

15. Distinguish between excitatory and inhibitory post-synaptic potentials.

16. Describe how synaptic events are integrated and modified.

17. Define neurotransmitter and name several classes of neurotransmitters.

Basic Concepts of Neural Integration (pp. 371–375)

18. Describe common patterns of neuron organization and neuronal processing.

19. Distinguish in a general sense between serial and parallel processing.

Developmental Aspects of Neurons (p. 375)

20. Describe the role of astrocytes and nerve cell adhesion molecules (N-CAMs) in neuronal differentiation.

You are driving down the freeway, and a horn blares to your right. You swerve to your left. Charlie leaves a note on the kitchen table: "See you later—have the stuff ready at 6." You know that the "stuff" is chili with taco chips. You are dozing, and your infant son makes a soft cry. Instantly, you awaken. What do all these events have in common? They are all everyday examples of the functioning of your nervous system, which has your body cells humming with activity nearly all of the time.

The **nervous system** is the master controlling and communicating system of the body. Every thought, action, and emotion reflects its activity. Along with the endocrine system, it is responsible for regulating and maintaining body homeostasis. Of the two systems, it is by far the more rapid acting

and complex. Cells of the nervous system communicate by means of electrical signals, which are rapid, specific, and usually cause almost immediate responses. In contrast, the endocrine system typically brings about its effects in a more leisurely way through the activity of hormones released into the blood.

The nervous system has three overlapping functions: (1) It uses its millions of sensory receptors to monitor changes occurring both inside and outside the body. These changes are called *stimuli* and the gathered information is called **sensory input.** (2) It processes and interprets the sensory input and makes decisions about what should be done at each moment—a process called **integration.** (3) It causes a *response* by activating the *effector*

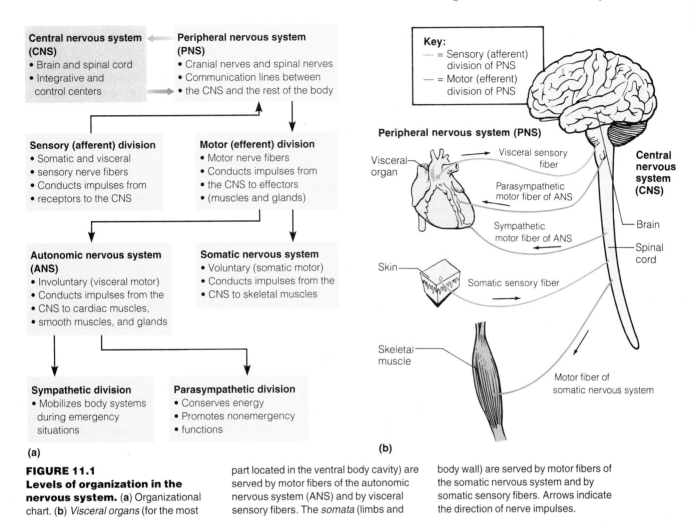

FIGURE 11.1
Levels of organization in the nervous system. (a) Organizational chart. (b) *Visceral organs* (for the most part located in the ventral body cavity) are served by motor fibers of the autonomic nervous system (ANS) and by visceral sensory fibers. The *somata* (limbs and body wall) are served by motor fibers of the somatic nervous system and by somatic sensory fibers. Arrows indicate the direction of nerve impulses.

organs, our muscles or glands; the response is called **motor output.** An example will illustrate how these functions work together. When you are driving and see a red light ahead (sensory input), your nervous system integrates this information (red light means "stop"), and your foot goes for the brake (motor output).

This chapter begins with a brief overview of the organization of the nervous system. It then focuses on the functional anatomy of nervous tissue, especially that of nerve cells, or *neurons,* which are the key to the subtle, efficient system of neural communication.

ORGANIZATION OF THE NERVOUS SYSTEM

We have only a single, highly integrated nervous system; however, for convenience, the nervous system can be divided into two principal parts (Figure 11.1). The **central nervous system (CNS)** consists of the *brain* and *spinal cord,* which occupy the dorsal body cavity. The CNS is the integrating and command center of the nervous system. It interprets incoming sensory information and dictates responses based on past experience, reflexes, and current conditions. The **peripheral nervous system (PNS),** the part of the nervous system *outside* the CNS, consists mainly of the nerves that extend from the brain and spinal cord. *Spinal nerves* carry impulses to and from the spinal cord; *cranial* (kra′ne-al) *nerves* carry impulses to and from the brain. These peripheral nerves serve as communication lines linking all parts of the body to the central nervous system.

The peripheral nervous system has two functional subdivisions (see Figure 11.1). The **sensory,** or **afferent** (af′er-ent; "carrying toward"), **division** consists of nerve fibers that convey impulses *to* the central nervous system from sensory receptors located throughout the body. Sensory fibers conveying impulses from the skin, skeletal muscles, and joints are called *somatic afferents* (*soma* = body), whereas those transmitting impulses from the visceral organs (organs within the ventral body cavity) are called *visceral afferents.* The sensory division keeps the CNS constantly informed of events going on both inside and outside the body.

The **motor,** or **efferent** (ef′er-ent; "carrying

away"), **division** transmits impulses *from* the CNS to effector organs, the muscles and glands. These impulses activate muscles to contract and glands to secrete; that is, they *effect* (bring about) a motor response.

The motor division in turn has two main subdivisions (see Figure 11.1):

1. The **somatic nervous system** is composed of somatic motor nerve fibers that conduct impulses from the CNS to skeletal muscles. It is often referred to as the **voluntary nervous system,** since it allows us to consciously control our skeletal muscles.

2. The **autonomic nervous system (ANS)** consists of visceral motor nerve fibers that regulate the activity of smooth muscles, cardiac muscles, and glands. *Autonomic* literally means "a law unto itself," and because we generally cannot control activities such as the pumping of our hearts or the movement of food through our digestive tracts, the ANS is also referred to as the **involuntary nervous system.** As indicated in Figure 11.1 and described in Chapter 14, the ANS has two functional subdivisions, the **sympathetic** and the **parasympathetic,** which typically bring about opposite effects on the activity of the same visceral organs. What one subdivision stimulates, the other inhibits.

HISTOLOGY OF NERVOUS TISSUE

Nervous tissue is highly cellular. For example, less than 20% of the CNS is extracellular space, which means that the cells there are very densely packed and tightly intertwined. Although exceedingly complex, nervous tissue is made up of just two principal types of cells: (1) *neurons,* the excitable nerve cells that transmit electrical signals, and (2) *supporting cells,* smaller cells that surround and wrap the more delicate neurons. With the possible exception of microglia (a specific group of supporting cells), both types of cells originate from the same ectoderm-derived embryonic tissue, forming neural tube and neural crest (see p. 375). Together they form the structures of both the central and peripheral nervous systems.

Supporting Cells

All neurons associate closely with non-nervous **supporting cells,** of which there are six types. Four of these are in the CNS, and two are in the PNS (Figure 11.2). Each type of supporting cell has a unique function, but in general, these cells provide a supportive scaffolding for the neurons. Selected supporting cells segregate and insulate neurons so that electrical activities of adjacent neurons don't interfere with each other; others produce neurotropic factors that promote neuron health and growth.

The importance of supporting cells in insulating nerve fibers from one another is illustrated in the painful disorder called **tic douloureux** (tik doo″loo-

roo'; "wincing in pain"). In this condition, the supporting cells surrounding the fibers of the trigeminal nerve (the main sensory nerve of the face) degenerate. As a result, impulses in the normally insulated but now exposed nerve fibers that carry *touch* sensations also stimulate the uninsulated *pain* fibers in the same nerve. Because of this abnormal crossover of nerve impulses, the softest touch to the face can produce agonizing pain. •

Supporting Cells in the CNS

The supporting cells in the CNS are collectively called **neuroglia** (nu-rog′le-ah; "nerve glue") or simply **glial** (gle′al) **cells.** (Most authorities restrict the name *neuroglia* to the supporting cells in the CNS, but others consider *all* supporting cells neuroglia.) Like neurons, most glial cells have branching processes and a central cell body (Figure 11.2a–d). Neuroglia can be distinguished, however, by their much smaller size and by their darker-staining nuclei. They outnumber neurons in the CNS by 9 to 1, and make up about half the mass of the brain.

The star-shaped **astrocytes** (as′tro-sītz; "star cells") are the most abundant glial cells. Their numerous radiating projections cling to neurons and capillaries, bracing the neurons and anchoring them to their nutrient supply lines, the blood capillaries (Figure 11.2a). Astrocytes play a role in making exchanges between capillaries and neurons, and like Langerhans' cells of the skin epidermis, they appear to function as antigen-presenting cells in the immune response. Astrocytes control the chemical environment around neurons, most importantly "mopping up" leaked potassium ions (K^+) and recapturing (and recycling) released neurotransmitters. As described later, the electrical charge and ion types outside nerve fibers must be just right for nerve impulses to be conducted. Furthermore, astrocytes (connected together by gap junctions) have been shown to signal each other (and perhaps neurons) via intracellular calcium pulses.

Microglia (mi-krog′le-ah) are small ovoid cells with relatively long "thorny" processes (Figure 11.2b). They are a special type of macrophage that helps protect the CNS by engulfing invading microorganisms and dead neural tissue. The origin of microglia is still controversial, but most authorities believe they derive from blood cells called monocytes, as do other macrophages.

Ependymal (ĕ-pen′dĭ-mul) **cells** range in shape from squamous to columnar and many are ciliated. They line the central cavities of the brain and the spinal cord, where they form a fairly permeable barrier between the cerebrospinal fluid that fills those cavities and the tissue fluid bathing the cells of the CNS. The beating of their cilia helps to circulate the cerebrospinal fluid that cushions the brain and spinal cord (Figure 11.2c).

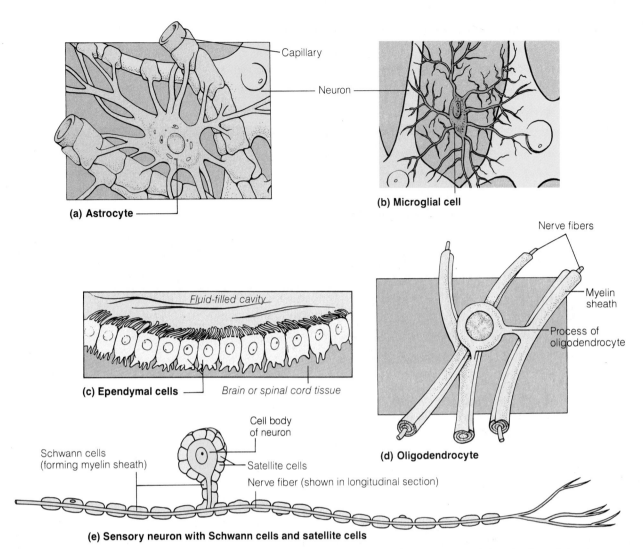

(a) Astrocyte

Capillary

Neuron

(b) Microglial cell

Fluid-filled cavity

(c) Ependymal cells — *Brain or spinal cord tissue*

Nerve fibers

Myelin sheath

Process of oligodendrocyte

(d) Oligodendrocyte

Cell body of neuron

Schwann cells (forming myelin sheath)

Satellite cells

Nerve fiber (shown in longitudinal section)

(e) Sensory neuron with Schwann cells and satellite cells

FIGURE 11.2
Supporting cells of nervous tissue. (a–d) Types of glial cells (supporting cells) found in the central nervous system. Notice in (d) that it is the processes of the oligodendrocytes that form the myelin sheaths around nerve fibers in the CNS. (e) The relationships of Schwann cells (myelinating cells) and satellite cells to a sensory neuron (nerve cell) in the peripheral nervous system.

Though they also branch, the **oligodendrocytes** (ol″ĭ-go-den′dro-sīts) have fewer branches than the astrocytes. Indeed, their name means few *(oligo)* branch *(dendr)* cells. Oligodendrocytes line up along the thicker neuron fibers in the CNS and wrap their cytoplasmic extensions tightly around the fibers, producing insulating coverings called *myelin sheaths* (Figure 11.2d).

Supporting Cells in the PNS

The two kinds of supporting cells in the PNS are *satellite cells* and *Schwann cells.* These very similar cell types differ mainly in location. **Satellite cells** surround neuron cell bodies within ganglia (Figure 11.2e), and are thought to play some role in controlling the chemical environment of neurons with which they are associated. Their name comes from a fancied resemblance to the moons (satellites) around a planet.

Schwann cells (also called *neurolemmocytes*) surround and form myelin sheaths around the larger nerve fibers in the peripheral nervous system (Figure 11.2e). Hence, the Schwann cells are functionally similar to oligodendrocytes. (The formation of myelin sheaths is described later in this chapter.) Schwann cells also act as phagocytes to rid a damaged nerve of deteriorating cell debris and are vital to the process of peripheral nerve fiber regeneration.

Neurons

Neurons, also called **nerve cells,** are the structural units of the nervous system. Neurons are highly specialized cells that conduct messages in the form of nerve impulses from one part of the body to another. Besides their ability to conduct nerve impulses, neurons have some other special characteristics:

1. They have *extreme longevity.* Given good nutri-

Neurons with the longest axons tend to have large cell bodies, while those with short axons usually have small cell bodies. Can you think of an explanation for this relationship?

FIGURE 11.3
Structure of a motor neuron. (a) Scanning electron micrograph showing the neuron cell body and dendrites with obvious dendritic spines (5000 ×). (b) Diagrammatic view.

tion, they can live and function optimally for a lifetime (over 100 years).

2. They are *amitotic.* As neurons assume their roles as communicating links of the nervous system, they lose their ability to divide (undergo mitosis). We pay a high price for this neuron feature because they cannot be replaced if destroyed.

3. They have an exceptionally *high metabolic rate* and require continuous and abundant supplies of oxygen and glucose. Neurons cannot survive for more than a few minutes without oxygen.

Neurons are typically large, complex cells. Although they vary in structure, they all have a *cell body* from which one or more slender *processes* project (Figure 11.3). The plasma membrane of neurons is the site of electrical signaling, and it plays a crucial role in cell-to-cell interactions that occur during development. Most neurons have three functional components in common (Table 11.1, p. 348): (1) a *receptive,* or *input, region;* (2) a *conducting component* that generates and transmits an action potential

(the actual site of action potential generation or initiation is called the *trigger zone*); and (3) a *secretory,* or *output, component* that releases neurotransmitters. As described shortly, each of these functional components is associated with a particular region of a neuron's anatomy.

Neuron Cell Body

The **cell body** consists of a large, spherical nucleus with a conspicuous "owl's eye" nucleolus surrounded by granular cytoplasm. Also called the **perikaryon** (*peri* = around, *kary* = nucleus) or **soma,** it ranges in diameter from 5 to 140 μm. The cell body is the *biosynthetic center* of a neuron. It contains the usual organelles with the exception of centrioles. (Centrioles play an important role in forming the mitotic spindle. Their apparent absence reflects the amitotic nature of most neurons.) Its protein- and membrane-making machinery, consisting of clustered free ribosomes and rough endoplasmic reticulum (ER), is probably the most active and best developed of any cell in the body. This rough ER, referred to as **Nissl** (nis′l) **bodies** or **chromatophilic** (literally, "color loving") **substance,** stains darkly with basic dyes and is obvious microscopically. The Golgi apparatus is also elaborated and forms an arc or complete circle around the nucleus. Mitochondria are scattered everywhere among the other organelles. Microtubules and **neurofibrils,** bundles of intermediate filaments *(neurofilaments),* which are important in intracellular transport and in maintaining cell shape and integrity, are seen throughout the cell body. The cell body of some neurons also contains pigment inclusions. For example, some contain a black melanin, a red iron-containing pigment, or a golden-brown pigment called *lipofuscin* (lip″o-fu′sin). Lipofuscin, a harmless by-product of lysosomal activity, is sometimes called the "aging pigment" because it is particularly abundant in neurons of elderly individuals. The cell body is the focal point for the outgrowth of neuron processes during embryonic development. In most neurons, the plasma membrane of the cell body acts as part of the receptive surface that receives information from other neurons.

Most neuron cell bodies are located within the CNS, where they are protected by the bones of the cranium and vertebral column. Clusters of cell bodies in the CNS are called **nuclei,** whereas the far fewer collections of cell bodies in the PNS are called **ganglia** (gang′gle-ah; *ganglion* = knot on a string, swelling).

Neuron Processes

Cytoplasmic extensions called **processes** extend from the cell body of all neurons. The brain and spinal cord (CNS) contain both neuron cell bodies and their processes. The PNS, for the most part, consists chiefly of neuron processes. Bundles of neuron processes are called **tracts** in the CNS and **nerves** in the PNS.

The two types of neuron processes, *dendrites* and *axons* (ak′sonz), differ from each other in structure and in the functional properties of their plasma membranes. The convention is to describe neuron processes using a motor neuron as an example of a typical neuron. We shall follow this practice, but keep in mind that many CNS neurons and sensory neurons differ considerably from the "typical" pattern presented here.

Dendrites. Dendrites of motor neurons are short, tapering, diffusely branched extensions. Typically, motor neurons have hundreds of dendrites clustering close to the cell body. Virtually all organelles present in the cell body are also found in dendrites. Dendrites correspond to the first of the functional components named earlier, the **receptive** or **input regions;** they provide an enormous surface area for reception of signals from other neurons. In many brain areas, the finer dendrites are highly specialized for information collection. They bristle with thorny appendages called *dendritic spines* (see Figure 11.3a), which rep-

resent points of close contact (synapses) with other neurons. Dendrites conduct electrical signals *toward* the cell body. These electrical signals are *not* nerve impulses (action potentials) but are short-distance signals called *graded potentials* as described shortly.

The Axon. Each neuron has a single **axon** (*axo* = axis, axle). The axon arises from a cone-shaped region of the cell body called the **axon hillock** ("little hill") and then narrows to form a slender process that stays uniform in diameter for the rest of its length (Figure 11.3). In some neurons, the axon is very short or absent, but in others it is long and accounts for nearly the entire length of the neuron. For example, axons of motor neurons controlling the skeletal muscles of your great toe extend from the lumbar region of your spine to your foot, a distance of a meter or more (3–4 feet), making them the longest cells in the body. Any long axon is called a **nerve fiber.** The diameter of different axons varies considerably, and axons with the largest diameters conduct impulses the most rapidly.

Although each neuron has only one axon, axons may give off occasional branches along their length. These rare branches, called **axon collaterals,** extend from the axon at more or less right angles. Whether an axon remains undivided or has collaterals, it usually branches profusely at its end (terminus): 10,000 or more of these **telodendria,** or end-branches (see Figure 11.3), per neuron is not unusual. The bulbous distal endings of the telodendria are variously called **axonal terminals, synaptic knobs,** or **boutons** (boo-tonz; "buttons").

The remaining two functional components discussed earlier are part and parcel of axons. Functionally, axons are the **conducting component** of the neuron. They *generate nerve impulses and transmit them,* typically away from the cell body. In motor neurons, the nerve impulse is generated at the junction of the axon hillock and axon (which is therefore the *trigger zone*) and conducted along the axon to the axonal terminals. These terminals represent the **secretory component** of the neuron. When the impulse reaches the axonal terminals, it causes chemicals (*neurotransmitters*) stored in vesicles there to be released into the extracellular space. Neurotransmitters excite or inhibit neurons (or effector cells) with which the axon is in close contact. Since each neuron both receives signals from and sends signals to scores of other neurons, it carries on "conversations" with many different neurons at the same time.

An axon contains the same organelles found in the dendrites and cell body with one very important exception—it lacks Nissl bodies. Consequently, an axon depends on its cell body to renew the necessary proteins and membrane components and on efficient transport mechanisms to distribute them. Since this is so, axons quickly decay if cut or severely damaged. Because axons are often very long, moving molecules along their length might appear to be a problem. However, through the cooperative effort of several types of cytoskeletal elements (microtubules, actin filaments, etc.), substances are able to travel continuously both away from and toward the cell body along the axon. Substances moved toward the axonal terminals (in the anterograde direction) include mitochondria, cytoskeletal elements, membrane components to be used for renewing the plasma membrane of the axon, or **axolemma** (ak″so-lem′ah), and enzymes that catalyze synthesis of the neurotransmitter chemicals. Substances transported in the opposite (retrograde) direction are mostly organelles being returned to the cell body for degradation or recycling. The reverse transport process is also an important means of intracellular communication for "advising" the cell body of conditions at the axonal terminals. There are two or three different transport mechanisms, the fastest of which is ATP dependent, bidirectional, and uses a "motor" protein (an ATPase) called *kinesin.* This protein propels membranous particles along the microtubules like trains along tracks.

Certain viruses and bacterial toxins that damage neural tissues use retrograde axonal transport as a vehicle to reach the cell body. This transport mechanism has been demonstrated for polio, rabies, and herpes simplex viruses and for tetanus toxin. Its use as a tool to treat genetic diseases by introducing viruses containing "corrected" genes is currently being investigated. •

Myelin Sheath and Neurilemma.   Many nerve fibers, particularly those that are long or large in diameter, are covered with a whitish, fatty (protein-lipoid), segmented sheath called the **myelin** (mi′ĕ-lin) **sheath.** Myelin protects and electrically insulates fibers from one another, and it increases the speed of transmission of nerve impulses. **Myelinated fibers** (axons bearing a myelin sheath) conduct nerve impulses rapidly, whereas **unmyelinated fibers** tend to conduct impulses quite slowly. (The order of difference may be more than 150 times—from 150 m/s to less than 1 m/s.) Note that myelin sheaths are associated only with axons (impulse-conducting fibers). Dendrites are *always* unmyelinated.

Myelin sheaths in the peripheral nervous system are formed by Schwann cells. The Schwann cells first become indented to receive the axon and then wrap themselves around it in a jelly roll fashion (Figure 11.4). Initially, the wrappings are loose, but the Schwann cell cytoplasm is gradually squeezed from between the membrane layers. When the wrapping process is complete, many concentric layers of Schwann cell plasma membrane enclose the axon. This tight coil of wrapped membranes *is* the myelin sheath, and its thickness depends on the number of spirals. Plasma membranes of myelinating cells contain less than 25% protein (as opposed to the typical 50% protein composition seen in the plasma membranes of most body cells). Channel and carrier proteins are notably absent in myelin sheaths, a charac-

teristic that makes myelin sheaths exceptionally good electrical insulators.

The nucleus and most of the cytoplasm of the Schwann cell end up just beneath the outermost part of its plasma membrane, external to the myelin sheath; this portion of the Schwann cell, which surrounds the myelin sheath, is called the **neurilemma** ("neuron husk") or **sheath of Schwann.** Adjacent Schwann cells along an axon do not touch one another, so there are gaps in the sheath. These gaps, called **nodes of Ranvier** (ran′vēr) or **neurofibral nodes,** occur at regular intervals along the myelinated axon. It is at these nodes that axon collaterals can emerge from the axon. Additionally, since the axolemma is exposed only at these nodes, the nerve impulse is forced to jump from node to node along the length of the axon, which greatly increases the speed of conduction (as explained later in this chapter).

Sometimes, Schwann cells surround peripheral nerve fibers, but the coiling process does not occur. In such instances, a single Schwann cell can partially enclose 15 or more axons, each of which occupies a separate tubular recess in the surface of the Schwann cell (see Figure 11.4f). Nerve fibers associated with Schwann cells in this manner are said to be *unmyelinated* and are typically thin fibers.

Both myelinated and unmyelinated axons are also found in the central nervous system. However, it is oligodendrocytes that form CNS myelin sheaths (see Figure 11.2d). In contrast to Schwann cells, each of which can form only one segment (internode) of a myelin sheath, oligodendrocytes have multiple flat processes that can coil around as many as 60 different axons at the same time. Nodes of Ranvier are present, though more widely spaced than in the PNS. However, CNS myelin sheaths lack a neurilemma because cell extensions are doing the coiling rather than entire cells, as is the case when myelin sheaths are formed by Schwann cells. As the oligodendrocyte processes coil around axons, the squeezed-out cytoplasm is forced back toward the centrally located nucleus. When the oligodendrocytes "embrace" but do not wrap CNS axons, the fibers are unmyelinated.

Regions of the brain and spinal cord containing dense collections of myelinated fibers are referred to as **white matter** and are primarily fiber tracts. **Gray matter** contains mostly nerve cell bodies and unmyelinated fibers.

Classification of Neurons

Neurons may be classified structurally or functionally. We will describe both classifications here, but we will use the functional classification in most subsequent discussions.

Structural   Classification.   Neurons   are grouped structurally according to the number of processes extending from their cell body. Three major neuron groups make up this classification: multipolar

FIGURE 11.4
Relationship of Schwann cells to axons in the peripheral nervous system. (a–d) Myelination of a nerve fiber (axon). As illustrated in the three-dimensional views, a Schwann cell envelops an axon in a trough. It then begins to rotate around the axon, enveloping it loosely in successive layers of its plasma membrane. Eventually, the Schwann cell cytoplasm is forced from between the membranes and comes to lie peripherally just beneath the exposed portion of the Schwann cell plasma membrane. The tight membrane wrappings surrounding the axon form the myelin sheath; the area of Schwann cell cytoplasm and its exposed membrane is referred to as the neurilemma, or sheath of Schwann. (e) Three-dimensional "see-through" view of a myelinated axon, showing portions of adjacent Schwann cells and the node of Ranvier (an area of exposed axolemma) between them. (f) Unmyelinated fibers. Schwann cells may associate loosely with several axons (usually of small diameter), which they partially invest. In such cases, Schwann cell coiling around the axons does not occur. (g) Electron micrograph of a myelinated axon, cross-sectional view (20,200 ×).

Table 11.1 Comparison of Structural Classes of Neurons

NEURON TYPE		
Multipolar	**Bipolar**	**Unipolar (pseudounipolar)**

Structural class: Neuron type according to the number of processes extending from the cell body

| Many processes extend from the cell body; all dendrites except for a single axon. | Two processes extend from the cell: one is a fused dendrite, the other is an axon. | One process extends from the cell body and forms central and peripheral processes, which together comprise the axon. Only the distal endings of the peripheral process are dendrites. |

Relationship of anatomy to the three functional regions

☐ = Receptive region (receives stimulus)   ▨ = Conducting region (generates/transmits action potential)   ☐ = Secretory region (releases neurotransmitters)

(Many bipolar neurons do not generate action potentials and, in those that do, the location of the trigger zone is not universal.)

Functional class: Neuron type according to direction of impulse conduction

| 1. Some are **motor neurons** that conduct impulses along the efferent pathways from the CNS to an effector (muscle/gland).

2. Most are **association neurons** (interneurons) that conduct impulses within the CNS; may be one of a chain of CNS neurons, or a single neuron connecting sensory and motor neurons | Essentially all are **sensory neurons** that are located in some special sense organs (in the PNS). For example, bipolar cells of the retina are involved with the transmission of visual inputs from eye to the brain (via intermediate neurons). | Most are **sensory neurons** that conduct impulses along afferent pathways to the CNS for interpretation. |

Relative abundance and location in human body

| Most abundant in body. Major neuron type in the CNS. | Rare. Are found in some special sensory organs (olfactory mucosa, eye). | Found mainly in the PNS. Common only in dorsal root ganglia of the spinal cord and sensory ganglia of cranial nerves. |

Table 11.1 continued

NEURON TYPE		
Multipolar	**Bipolar**	**Unipolar (pseudounipolar)**

Structural variations

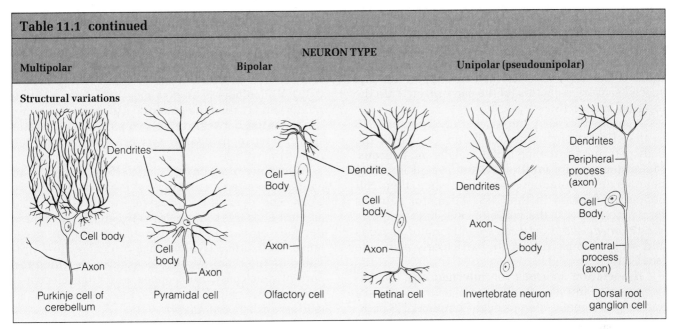

(*polar* = end, pole), bipolar, and unipolar neurons (Table 11.1).

Multipolar neurons have three or more processes. They are the most common neuron type in humans and the major neuron type in the central nervous system. Although the "typical" multipolar neuron exhibits numerous branching dendrites and one axon, some neurons of this class lack an axon entirely and have only dendrites.

Bipolar neurons have two processes—an axon and a dendrite—that extend from opposite sides of the cell body. Bipolar neurons are rare in the adult body. They are found only in some of the special sense organs, where they act as receptor cells. Examples include some neurons in the retina of the eye and in the olfactory mucosa.

Unipolar neurons have a single process that emerges from the cell body. However, it is very short and divides T-like into proximal and distal fibers. The more distal process of the neuron, which is often associated with a sensory receptor, is commonly called the **peripheral process,** whereas that entering the CNS is referred to as the **central process** (see Table 11.1). Unipolar neurons are more accurately called **pseudounipolar neurons** (*pseudo* = false) because they originate as bipolar neurons. Then, during early embryonic development, the two processes converge and partially fuse to form the short single process that issues from the cell body. Unipolar neurons are found chiefly in ganglia in the peripheral nervous system, where they function as sensory neurons.

The fact that the fused peripheral and central processes of unipolar neurons are continuous and function as a single fiber might cause you to wonder whether they are axons or dendrites. The central process is undoubtedly an axon because it conducts impulses away from the cell body (one definition of an axon). However, the peripheral process is perplexing.

Among the facts that favor classifying it as an axon are: (1) It generates and conducts an impulse (the functional definition of an axon); (2) when large, it is heavily myelinated; and (3) it has a uniform diameter and is indistinguishable microscopically from an axon. However, the older definition of a dendrite as a process that transmits the impulse *toward* the cell body keeps interfering with that conclusion. What is it? Although there is still disagreement on this point, we have chosen to emphasize the newer impulse generating and transmitting definition of the axon. Hence, *for unipolar neurons,* we will refer to the collective (combined) length of the peripheral and central process as an axon and will use the term "dendrites" to refer only to the small receptive branches at the end of the peripheral process.

Functional Classification. The functional classification scheme groups neurons according to the direction in which the nerve impulse travels relative to the central nervous system. Based on this criterion, there are sensory neurons, motor neurons, and association neurons (Table 11.1).

Neurons that transmit impulses from sensory receptors in the skin or internal organs *toward* the central nervous system are called **sensory,** or **afferent, neurons.** Except for the bipolar neurons found in some of the special sense organs, virtually all sensory neurons of the body are unipolar, and their cell bodies are located in sensory ganglia outside the CNS. Functionally, only the most distal parts of these unipolar neurons act as impulse receptor sites and the peripheral processes formed by the joining of the dendritic branches are often very long. For example, fibers carrying sensory impulses from the skin of your big toe travel for more than a meter before they reach their cell bodies in a ganglion close to the spinal cord.

Although dendritic endings of some sensory neurons are naked, in which case the dendrites themselves function as sensory receptors, many exhibit receptors that include other cell types. The various types of general sensory receptor end organs, such as those of the skin, are described in Chapter 13. The special sensory receptors (of the ear, eye, etc.) are the topic of Chapter 16.

Neurons that carry impulses *away from* the CNS to the effector organs (muscles and glands) of the body periphery are called **motor, or efferent, neurons.** Motor neurons are multipolar, and except for some neurons of the autonomic nervous system, their cell bodies are located in the CNS. All motor neurons form junctions with their effector cells, but the *neuromuscular junctions* between somatic motor neurons and skeletal muscle cells are particularly elaborate (see Chapter 9).

Association neurons, or **interneurons,** lie between motor and sensory neurons in neural pathways and shuttle signals, often through complex CNS pathways where integration occurs. Association neurons are typically multipolar and most are confined entirely within the CNS. They make up over 99% of the neurons of the body, including most of those in the central nervous system. There is considerable diversity among interneurons both in size and in fiber-branching patterns. The Purkinje and pyramidal cells illustrated in "Structural variations" of Table 11.1 are just two examples of their variety.

NEUROPHYSIOLOGY

Neurons are highly *irritable* (responsive to stimuli). When a neuron is adequately stimulated, an electrical impulse is conducted along the length of its axon. This response is always the same, regardless of the source or type of stimulus. This electrical phenomenon, called the *action potential (nerve impulse),* underlies virtually all functional activities of the nervous system.

In this section, we will consider how neurons become excited or inhibited and how they communicate with other cells in the body. However, we first need to explore some basic principles of electricity and to revisit the understandings of the resting membrane potential.

Basic Principles of Electricity

The human body as a whole is electrically neutral; it has the same number of positive and negative charges. However, there are areas where one type of charge predominates, making such regions positively or negatively charged. Because opposite charges attract each other, energy must be used (work must be done) to separate them. On the other hand, when opposite charges come together, energy is liberated that can be used to do work. The stored energy of a battery, for example, is released when the two points are connected (the circuit is completed), allowing electrons to flow from the negatively charged area to the positively charged area. Thus, separated electrical charges of opposite sign have potential energy. The measure of this potential energy is called **voltage** and is measured in either *volts* or *millivolts* (1 mV = 0.001 V). Voltage is always measured between two points and is called the **potential difference** or simply the **potential** between these two points. The greater the difference in charge between two points, the higher the voltage.

The flow of electrical charge from one point to another is called a **current,** and it can be used to do work—for example, to power a flashlight. The amount of charge that moves between the two points depends on two factors: the voltage and the resistance. **Resistance** is hindrance to charge flow provided by intervening substances through which the current must pass. Substances with high electrical resistance are called *insulators;* those with low resistance are called *conductors.*

The relationship between voltage, current, and resistance is given by **Ohm's law:**

$$\text{Current } (I) = \frac{\text{voltage } (V)}{\text{resistance } (R)}$$

As you can see, the current (I) is directly proportional to the voltage: The greater the voltage (potential difference), the greater the current. And no net current flows between points that have the same potential. Ohm's law also tells us that current is inversely related to the resistance: The greater the resistance, the smaller the current.

In the body, electrical events typically occur in an aqueous medium, and electrical currents reflect the flow of ions (rather than free electrons) across cellular membranes. (There are no free electrons "running around" in living systems.) As described in Chapter 3, there is a slight difference in the numbers of positive and negative ions on the two sides of cellular plasma membranes (there is a charge separation), so there is a voltage across those membranes. The resistance to current flow is provided by the plasma membranes themselves.

Plasma membranes are peppered with a variety of *ion channels* made up of membrane proteins. Some of these membrane channels are *passive,* or *leakage, channels* that are always open. Others are *active,* or *gated, channels* (Figure 11.5). Gated channels have a molecular "gate," usually one or more protein molecules, that can change shape to open or close the channel in response to various signals. **Chemically-gated,** or **transmitter-gated, channels** open when the appropriate neurotransmitter binds. **Voltage-gated,** or **voltage-dependent, channels** open and close in response to changes in the membrane potential, or voltage. We will speak more of this later. Each type of channel is selective as to the type of ion (or ions) it allows to pass. For example, a potassium ion channel generally allows only potassium ions to pass.

When gated ion channels are open, ions diffuse quickly across the membrane following their electrochemical gradients, creating electrical currents and voltage changes across the membrane according to the rearranged equation

$$\text{Voltage } (V) = \text{current } (I) \times \text{resistance } (R)$$

Ions move along *chemical gradients* when they diffuse passively from an area of their higher concentration to an area of lower concentration, and along *electrical gradients* when they move toward an area of opposite electrical charge. Together, electrical and chemical gradients constitute the **electrochemical gradient.** It is these ion flows along electrochemical gradients that underlie all electrical phenomena in neurons.

The Resting Membrane Potential: The Polarized State

The potential difference between two points is measured by using two electrodes connected to a volt-

FIGURE 11.6

Measuring potential difference between two points in neurons. When one electrode of a voltmeter is placed on the external membrane and the other electrode is inserted just inside the membrane, a voltage (membrane potential) of approximately -70 mV (inside negative) is recorded.

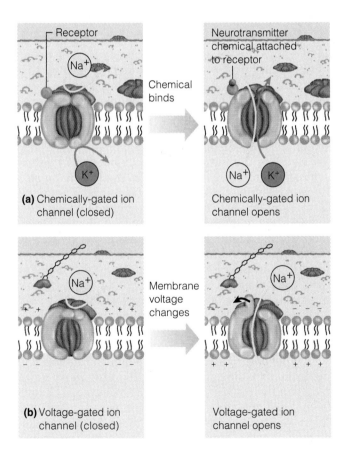

(a) Chemically-gated ion channel (closed)

Chemically-gated ion channel opens

(b) Voltage-gated ion channel (closed)

Voltage-gated ion channel opens

FIGURE 11.5

Operation of gated channels. **(a)** Chemically–(ligand) gated channels (a Na^+-K^+ channel in this example) open when the appropriate neurotransmitter binds to the receptor, allowing simultaneous movement of Na^+ and K^+ through the channel. **(b)** Voltage–gated channels open or close in response to changes in membrane voltage. In this example, a Na^+ channel opens as the membrane interior changes from negative to positive.

meter (Figure 11.6). When one electrode is inserted into the neuron and the other rests on its outside surface, a voltage across the membrane of approximately -70 mV is recorded. The minus sign indicates that the cytoplasmic side (inside) of a neuron's membrane is negatively charged with respect to the outside. This potential difference at rest is called the **resting membrane potential (RMP),** and the membrane is said to be **polarized.** The value of the resting membrane potential varies (from -40 mV to -90 mV) in different types of neurons. (The range is even greater if all cell types are considered.)

The RMP exists only across the membrane; that is, the bulk solutions inside and outside the cell are electrically neutral. As shown in Figure 11.7, the resting membrane potential is generated by differences in the ionic composition of the intracellular and extracellular fluids. The cell cytoplasm contains a lower concentration of sodium (Na^+) and a higher concentration of potassium (K^+) than the extracellular fluid surrounding it. Although there are many other solutes (glucose, urea, and other ions) in both fluids, sodium and potassium play the most important roles in generating the membrane potential. In the extracellular fluid, the positive charges of sodium and other cations are balanced chiefly by chloride ions (Cl^-). Negatively charged (anionic) proteins (A^-) help to balance the positive charges of intracellular cations (primarily K^+).

These ionic differences are the consequence of (1) the differential permeability of the plasma membrane to sodium and potassium ions and (2) the operation of the sodium-potassium pump, which actively transports Na^+ out of the cell and K^+ into the cell (see Figure 11.7). The membrane at rest is impermeable to the large anionic cytoplasmic proteins, slightly per-

FIGURE 11.7
Passive and active forces that establish and maintain the resting membrane potential. Approximate ion concentrations of sodium (Na$^+$), potassium (K$^+$), chloride (Cl$^-$), and protein anions (A$^-$) in the intracellular and extracellular fluids are indicated in millimoles per liter (mM). Although many other ions are present (e.g., Ca^{2+}, PO$_4^{3-}$, and HCO$_3^-$), those shown here are most significant in terms of neural function. Diffusion of K$^+$ to the cell exterior is strongly promoted by its concentration (chemical) gradient. Na$^+$ is strongly attracted to the cell interior by its concentration gradient, but it is less able to cross the cell membrane. The relative differences in the amounts of Na$^+$ and K$^+$ crossing the membranes are indicated by diffusion arrows of different thickness. The resulting net outward diffusion of positive charge leads to a state of relative negativity on the inner membrane face. This membrane potential (-70 mV, inside negative) is maintained by the sodium-potassium pump, which transports 3Na$^+$ out of the cell for each 2K$^+$ transported back into the cell. Notice that the electrical gradient thus maintained resists K$^+$ efflux but enhances the drive for Na$^+$ entry.

meable to sodium, approximately 75 times more permeable to potassium than to sodium, and quite freely permeable to chloride ions. These resting permeabilities reflect the properties of the passive (leakage) ion channels present in the membrane. Consequently, potassium ions diffuse out of the cell along their *concentration gradient* much more easily and quickly than sodium ions can enter the cell along theirs. The net result is that a slightly greater number of positive ions diffuse out than in, leaving the cell interior with a slight excess of negative charge; this chemical event results in an *electrical gradient* that produces the resting membrane potential. Because some K$^+$ is always leaking out of the cell and Na$^+$ is always leaking in, it would appear that the concentration gradients would eventually "run down," resulting in equal concentrations of Na$^+$ and K$^+$ inside and outside the cell. This does not happen because the ATP-driven sodium-potassium pump ejects 3Na$^+$ from the cell while simultaneously transporting 2K$^+$ back into the cell. Thus, the sodium-potassium pump stabilizes the resting membrane potential by maintaining the diffusion gradients for sodium and potassium.

Membrane Potentials That Act as Signals

Cells, particularly neurons and muscle cells, use changes in their membrane potential as communication signals for receiving, integrating, and sending information. A change in membrane potential can be produced by (1) anything that changes membrane permeability to any type of ion or (2) anything that alters ion concentrations on the two sides of the membrane. Two types of signals are produced by a change in the membrane potential: *graded potentials*, which signal over short distances, and *action potentials*, which are long–distance signals.

Because the terms *depolarization* and *hyperpolarization* are used frequently in the following sections to describe the direction of membrane potential changes *relative to the resting membrane potential*, it is important to understand these terms clearly. **Depolarization** is a reduction in membrane potential: The inside of the membrane becomes *less negative* (closer to zero) than the resting potential (Figure 11.8a). For instance, a change from a resting potential of -70 mV to a potential of -50 mV is a depolarization. By convention, depolarization also includes events in which the membrane potential reverses and moves above zero to become positive.

Hyperpolarization occurs when the membrane potential or voltage increases, becoming *more negative* than the resting potential. For example, a change from -70 mV to -90 mV (increased negativity inside) is hyperpolarization (Figure 11.8b). As described shortly, depolarization increases the probability of producing nerve impulses, whereas hyperpolarization decreases this probability.

Graded Potentials

Graded potentials are short-lived, local changes in membrane potential that can be either depolarizations or hyperpolarizations. These changes cause

Hyper *means greater than or more than. When we say the membrane becomes hyperpolarized, what value has increased or become greater?*

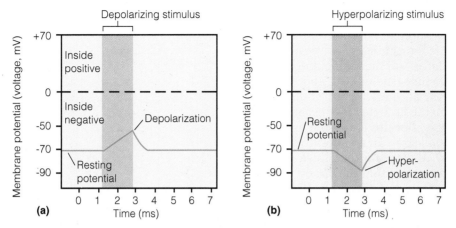

(a)

(b)

FIGURE 11.8
Depolarization and hyperpolarization of the membrane. The resting membrane potential is approximately −70 mV (inside negative) in neurons. Changes in this potential result in depolarization or hyperpolarization of the membrane. **(a)** In depolarization, the membrane potential moves toward 0 mV, the inside becoming less negative (more positive). **(b)** In hyperpolarization, the membrane potential increases, the inside becoming more negative.

local flows of current that decrease with distance traveled. Graded potentials are called "graded" because their magnitude varies directly with the intensity or strength of the stimulus. The more intense the stimulus, the more the voltage changes and the farther the current flows.

Graded potentials are triggered by some change (a stimulus) in the neuron's environment that causes gated ion channels to open. Graded potentials are given different names, depending on where they occur and the functions they perform. For example, when the receptor of a sensory neuron is excited by some form of energy (heat, light, or others), the resulting graded potential is called a *receptor potential.* Receptor potentials are considered in Chapter 13 (p. 429) in conjunction with sensory receptors. When the stimulus is a neurotransmitter released by another neuron, the graded potential is called a *postsynaptic potential,* because the neurotransmitter is released into a fluid-filled gap called a synapse and influences the neuron beyond (post) the synapse. Postsynaptic potentials are examined later in this chapter.

Fluids inside and outside cells are fairly good conductors, and current, carried by ions, flows through them whenever voltage changes occur. Let us assume that a small area of the membrane has been depolarized by a stimulus (Figure 11.9a). Current will flow on both sides of the membrane between the depolarized (active) membrane area and the adjacent polarized (resting) areas. Positive ions migrate toward more negative areas (the direction of cation movement is designated as the direction of current flow), and negative ions simultaneously move in the opposite direction, toward more positive areas (Figure 11.9b). Thus, inside the cell, positive ions (mostly

FIGURE 11.9
The mechanism of a graded potential. **(a)** A small patch of the membrane has become depolarized, resulting in a change in polarity at that point. **(b)** As positive ions flow toward negative areas (and negative ions flow toward adjacent more positive areas), local currents are created that depolarize adjacent membrane areas and allow the wave of depolarization to spread.

K^+) move away from the active area and accumulate on the neighboring membrane areas, where they displace negative ions. Meanwhile, positive ions on the outer membrane face are moving toward the active region of reversed membrane polarity (the depolarized region), which is momentarily less positive. As they move, their "places" on the membrane become occupied by negative ions (such as Cl^- and HCO_3^-), sort of like "ionic musical chairs." Thus, at the neighboring region, the inside becomes less negative and the outside becomes less positive; i.e., the neighboring membrane is depolarized. In an effort to simplify the process, virtually all diagrams that illustrate local currents give the impression that the circuit is completed by ions passing into and out of the cell through the membrane. This is *not* the case. Only the inward current across the membrane is caused by the flow of ions through gated channels. The outward current (the so-called *capacitance current*) reflects changes in the distribution of membrane charges set up as the ions migrate longitudinally *along* the two membrane faces.

As just explained, the flow of current to adjacent membrane areas changes the membrane potential there as well. However, the plasma membrane is permeable like a "leaky" water hose, and most of the charge is quickly lost through the membrane. Consequently, the current flow is *decremental;* that is, it dies out within a few millimeters of its origin (Figure 11.10). Because the current dissipates quickly and dies out with increasing distance, graded potentials can act as signals only over very short distances. Nonetheless, they are essential in initiating action potentials, the long-distance signals.

Action Potentials

The principal way neurons communicate is by generating and propagating **action potentials (APs),** and for the most part, only cells with *excitable membranes*—neurons and muscle cells—can generate action potentials. As illustrated in Figure 11.11a, an action potential is a brief reversal of membrane potential with a total amplitude (change in voltage) of about 100 mV (from -70 mV to $+30$ mV). The whole event is over in a few milliseconds. Unlike graded potentials, action potentials do not decrease in strength with distance. When we considered skeletal muscle physiology in Chapter 9, we indicated briefly that muscle fibers are stimulated to contract when an action potential is transmitted along their sarcolemma. A summary of that discussion is provided in Figure 9.10 (p. 260). Now, let us examine how this happens in more detail.

The events of action potential generation and transmission are identical in skeletal muscle cells and neurons. However, in a neuron, a transmitted action potential is also called a **nerve impulse.** A neuron transmits a nerve impulse only when it is adequately stimulated. The stimulus changes the perme-

? *Since it is obvious from this figure that current flow quickly falls off with distance, which synaptic contacts—those on distal parts of dendrites, those on proximal parts of dendrites, or those on the cell body—would have the greatest potential for producing a threshold stimulus?*

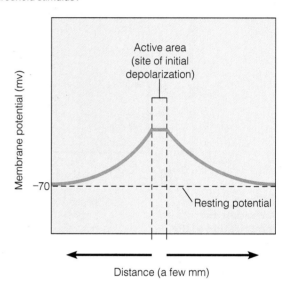

FIGURE 11.10
Changes in membrane voltage produced by a depolarizing graded potential. Such voltage changes are decremental because the current is quickly dissipated by loss of ions through the "leaky" plasma membrane. Consequently, graded potentials are short-distance signals.

ability of the neuron's membrane by opening specific voltage-regulated gated channels that are located on axons. These channels open and close in response to changes in the membrane potential and are activated by local currents (graded potentials) that spread toward the axon along the dendritic and cell body membranes. *Only axons are capable of generating action potentials.* In many neurons, the transition from the local graded potential to the action potential takes place at the axon hillock. In sensory neurons, the action potential is generated by the peripheral (axonal) process just proximal to the receptor region. However, for simplicity, we will just use the term *axon* in our discussion.

Generation of an Action Potential.   The process of action potential generation encompasses three consecutive but overlapping changes in membrane permeability due to opening and closing of active ion gates, all induced by depolarization of the axonal membrane (Figure 11.11). Sequentially, these permeability changes are a transient increase in Na^+ permeability, followed by restoration of Na^+ impermeability, and then a short-lived increase in K^+ permeability. The first two permeability changes occur during the *depolarization phase* of action potential generation, which is indicated by the upward-rising

② Depolarizing phase: Na⁺ channels open.

③ Repolarizing phase: Na⁺ channels closing and K⁺ channels open

(a) Membrane permeability changes and phases of the action potential

① Resting state: All gated Na⁺ and K⁺ channels closed

④ Undershoot: (after potential) K⁺ channels remain open, Na⁺ channels closed

(b) Function of gated ion channels in each phase of the action potential

FIGURE 11.11
The phases of the action potential and the role of gated ion channels in those phases. (a) The action potential can be divided into four phases, during which the voltage-sensitive gates controlling the sodium and potassium channels are in different states and membrane permeability to sodium (P_{Na}) and potassium (P_K) is changing. **(b)** (1) In the resting state, neither channel is open. (2) During the depolarizing phase of the action potential, sodium gates open, but potassium channels remain closed. (3) During the repolarizing phase of the action potential, inactivation gates close the sodium channels, and potassium channels open. (4) During the undershoot (afterpolarization), sodium channels have closed, but potassium channels remain open because the relatively slow gates of those channels have not had time to respond to the repolarization of the membrane. Within another millisecond or two, the resting state (1) is restored, and the system is ready to respond to the next stimulus.

part of the AP curve or spike. The third permeability change is responsible for both the *repolarization* (the downward part of the AP spike) and *undershoot phases* shown in Figure 11.11a. Let's examine each of these phases more carefully to see how something as seemingly simple as the opening and closing of ion channels (shown in Figure 11.11b) can generate a nerve impulse. We will start with a neuron in the resting (polarized) state.

1. Resting state: Active channels closed. In the resting state, virtually all the voltage-gated Na⁺ and K⁺ channels are closed. However, small amounts of K⁺

are passing outward via leakage channels and even smaller amounts of Na⁺ are diffusing in.

These voltage-gated Na⁺ channels actually have two gates that respond to membrane depolarization: *activation gates* that respond rapidly by opening and *inactivation gates* that respond by closing, but do so very slowly. Thus, *depolarization opens and then closes the sodium channels.* Both gates must be open for the channel to allow Na⁺ entry, but the closing of *either* gate effectively closes the channel. Since the information important to our discussion is simply whether the sodium *channels* are open or closed, the activity of the individual Na$^+$ gates will not be described further here.

2a. Depolarizing phase: Increase in sodium permeability and reversal of the membrane potential. As the axonal membrane is depolarized by local currents, voltage-dependent sodium ion channels begin to open and sodium rushes into the cell at the point of depolarization. This influx of positive charge depolarizes that local "patch" of membrane still further, so that the cell interior becomes progressively less negative. When depolarization of the membrane reaches a certain critical level called **threshold** (often between -55 and -50 mV), depolarization becomes self-generating, urged on by the positive feedback. That is, after being initiated by the stimulus, depolarization is driven by the ionic currents created by sodium ion influx. As more sodium enters, the membrane depolarizes further and opens still more voltage-dependent sodium channels until all the sodium channels are open and Na$^+$ permeability is about 1000 times greater than it is in a resting neuron. As a result, the membrane potential becomes less and less negative and then overshoots about $+30$ mV as sodium ions rush inward along their electrochemical gradient. This rapid depolarization and polarity reversal produce the sharply upward, or rising, *spike* of the action potential (see Figure 11.11a).

Earlier, we stated that membrane potential depends on membrane permeability, but here we are saying that membrane permeability depends on membrane potential. Can both statements be true? As a matter of fact, they are, because these two distinct relationships interlock to establish a *positive feedback* cycle (increased Na$^+$ permeability due to increased channel openings leads to greater depolarization which, in turn, leads to increased Na$^+$ permeability, and so on). It is this explosive positive feedback cycle that is responsible for the rising (depolarizing) phase of action potentials and is the property that puts the "action" in the action potential.

2b. Depolarizing phase: Decrease in sodium permeability. The explosively rising phase of the action potential (period of sodium permeability) persists for only about 1 ms and is self-limiting. As the membrane potential passes 0 mV and becomes increasingly positive, the positive intracellular charge resists further sodium entry. In addition, the (inactivation gates of the) sodium channels begin to close after a few milliseconds of depolarization. As a result, the membrane becomes more and more impermeable to sodium, and the net influx of sodium declines and finally stops completely (see Figure 11.11). At this point the AP spike stops rising and reverses direction.

3. Repolarizing phase: Increase in potassium permeability. As sodium entry declines, voltage-regulated potassium gates open and potassium rushes out of the cell, following its electrochemical gradient (see Figure 11.11b). Consequently, the cell interior becomes progressively less positive, and the mem-

brane potential moves back toward the resting level, an event called **repolarization** (see Figure 11.11a). Both the abrupt decline in sodium permeability and the increased permeability to potassium contribute to the repolarization process.

4. Undershoot: Potassium permeability continues. Because the potassium gates are sluggish gates that are slow to respond to the depolarization signal, the period of increased K$^+$ permeability typically lasts a bit longer than is necessary to restore the polarized state. As a result of the excessive K$^+$ efflux, a slight dip—an *after-hyperpolarization* called the **undershoot**—is sometimes seen on the recording following the action potential spike.

Although repolarization restores resting electrical conditions, it does *not* restore the original ionic distributions of the resting state. Following repolarization, this is accomplished by "revving-up" the **sodium-potassium pump.** While it might appear that opening of the voltage-gated channels allows tremendous numbers of sodium and potassium ions to change places during action potential generation, this is not the case. Only small amounts of sodium and potassium are exchanged, and since an axonal membrane has thousands of sodium-potassium pumps, these small ionic changes are quickly corrected.

Propagation of an Action Potential. If the generated action potential is to serve as the neuron's signaling device, it must be **propagated** (sent or transmitted) along the axon's entire length. This process is illustrated in Figure 11.12.

As we have seen, the action potential is generated by the inward movement of sodium ions, and the local patch of depolarized axonal membrane undergoes polarity reversal: The inside becomes positive, and the outside becomes negative. The positive ions in the axoplasm move laterally from the area of polarity reversal toward the membrane area that is still negative (polarized), and those in the extracellular fluid migrate back toward the area of greatest negative charge (the area of polarity reversal) to complete the circuit.

This establishes local current flows that depolarize adjacent membrane areas in the forward direction (away from the origin of the nerve impulse), which opens voltage-dependent channels and triggers an action potential there. Because the area in the opposite direction has just generated an action potential, the sodium gates are closed—no new action potential is generated there. Thus, the impulse always propagates away from its point of origin. (If an *isolated* axon is stimulated by an electrode, the nerve impulse will move away from the point of stimulus in *all* directions along the membrane.) In the body, action potentials are always initiated at one end of the axon and conducted away from that point toward the axon's terminals. Once initiated, an action potential is a *self-propagating* process that continues along the

FIGURE 11.12

Propagation of an action potential. The distance of propagation of the action potential along the axon is shown at time 0 ms, 1 ms, and 2 ms. The condition of the sodium gates is labeled as closed, open, or closing. The small circular arrows indicate the path of movement of sodium ions. The large arrow in each case indicates the direction of action potential propagation. Although not depicted, the current flows created by the opening of potassium channels would be occurring at points where sodium gates are shown as closing. Hence, repolarization would be occurring at such points.

axon at a constant velocity—something like a "domino effect."

Following depolarization, each segment of axonal membrane undergoes repolarization, which restores the resting membrane potential in that region. Since these electrical changes also set up local current flows, the repolarization wave chases the wave of depolarization down the length of the axon. The propagation process just described occurs on unmyelinated axons (and on muscle fiber sarcolemmas). The unique propagation process that occurs in myelinated axons, called *saltatory conduction,* will be described shortly.

Although the phrase *conduction of a nerve impulse* is commonly used, nerve impulses are not really conducted in the same way that an insulated wire conducts current. In fact, neurons are fairly poor conductors of electrical current, and local current flows decline with distance because the charges leak through the membrane. The expression *propagation of a nerve impulse* is more accurate, because the action potential is *regenerated anew* at each membrane patch, and every subsequent action potential is identical to that generated initially.

Threshold and the All-or-None Phenomenon. Not all local depolarization events produce action potentials. The depolarization must reach threshold values if an axon is to "fire." What determines the *threshold point?* One explanation is that threshold is the membrane potential at which the outward current carried by K$^+$ is exactly equal to the inward current created by Na$^+$. Threshold is typically reached when the membrane has been depolarized by 15 to 20 mV from the resting value. It seems to represent an unstable equilibrium state at which one of two things can happen. If an extra sodium ion enters, further depolarization occurs, opening more sodium channels and allowing more sodium ions entry. If, on the other hand, another potassium ion leaves, the membrane potential is driven away from threshold, sodium channels close, and potassium ions continue to diffuse outward until the potential returns to its resting value.

Recall that the local depolarizations are graded potentials and that their magnitude increases with increasing stimulus intensity. Brief weak stimuli (*subthreshold stimuli*) produce subthreshold depolarizations that are not translated into nerve impulses. On the other hand, stronger *threshold stimuli* produce depolarizing currents that push the membrane potential toward and beyond the threshold voltage and increase sodium permeability to such an extent that sodium entry "swamps" (exceeds) the outward movement of potassium ions, allowing the positive feedback cycle to become established and generating an action potential. The critical factor here is the total amount of current that flows through the membrane during a stimulus (electrical charge × time). Strong stimuli depolarize the membrane to threshold quickly. Weaker stimuli must be applied for longer periods to achieve the crucial amount of current flow. Very weak stimuli are unable to trigger an action potential because the local current flows they produce are so slight that they dissipate long before threshold is reached.

The action potential is an **all-or-none phenomenon;** it either happens completely or it doesn't happen at all. It might help to compare the generation of the action potential to lighting a match under a small dry twig. The changes occurring in the part of the twig being heated can be compared to the change in membrane permeability that initially allows more sodium ions to enter the cell. When that part of the twig becomes hot enough (when enough sodium ions have entered the cell), the critical flash point (threshold) is reached and the flame will consume the entire twig, even if you then blow out the match (the action potential will be generated and propagated whether or not the stimulus continues). But if the match is extinguished just before the twig has reached the critical temperature, ignition will not take place. Likewise, if too few sodium ions enter the cell to achieve threshold, no action potential will occur.

Coding for Stimulus Intensity.

Once generated, all action potentials are independent of stimulus strength, and all action potentials are alike. So how can the CNS determine whether a particular stimulus is intense or weak—information it needs to initiate an appropriate response? The answer is really quite simple: Strong stimuli cause nerve impulses to be generated more *often* in a given time interval than do weak stimuli (Figure 11.13). Thus, stimulus intensity is coded for by the number of impulses generated per second—that is, by the *frequency of impulse*

FIGURE 11.14
Recording of an action potential indicating the timing of the absolute and relative refractory periods.

transmission—rather than by increases in the strength (amplitude) of the action potential.

Absolute and Relative Refractory Periods.

When a patch of neuron membrane is generating an action potential and its sodium gates are open, the neuron is incapable of responding to another stimulus, no matter how strong. This period, called the **absolute refractory period** (see Figure 11.14), ensures that each action potential is a separate, all-or-none event and enforces one-way transmission of the action potential. This makes sense if you keep in mind that once an action potential is generated, the sodium gates are kept open by sodium ion currents, not by the stimulus.

The **relative refractory period** is the interval following the absolute refractory period when the sodium gates are closed, the potassium gates are open, and repolarization is occurring (Figure 11.14). During this time, the axon's threshold for impulse generation is substantially elevated. A threshold stimulus is unable to trigger an action potential during the relative refractory period, but an exceptionally strong stimulus can reopen the sodium gates and allow another impulse to be generated. Thus, by intruding into the relative refractory period, strong stimuli cause more frequent generation of action potentials.

FIGURE 11.13
Relationship between stimulus strength, the local potential produced, and action potential frequency. In the tracing, action potentials are shown as vertical lines rather than the typical spike tracings. Upward arrows (↑) indicate points of stimulus application; downward arrows (↓) indicate stimulus cessation; length of arrows indicate strength of stimulus. Notice that a subthreshold stimulus does not generate an action potential at all, but once threshold voltage is reached, the stronger the stimulus, the more frequently action potentials are generated.

Conduction Velocities of Axons.

Conduction velocities of neurons vary widely. Fibers that transmit impulses most rapidly (100 meters per second [m/s] or more) are found in neural pathways where speed is essential, such as those that mediate some postural reflexes. More slowly conducting axons most often serve internal organs (the gut, glands, blood vessels), where slower responses are not usually a handicap. The rate of impulse propagation depends largely on two factors: axon diameter and degree of myelination.

1. **Influence of axon diameter.** As a general rule, the larger the axon's diameter, the faster it conducts impulses. This is because larger axons have a greater cross-sectional area. According to a basic law of physics, resistance to passage of an electrical current declines as the diameter of any "cable" increases.

2. **Influence of a myelin sheath.** On unmyelinated axons, action potentials are generated at sites immediately adjacent to each other and conduction is relatively slow. The presence of a myelin sheath dramatically increases the rate of impulse propagation, because myelin acts as an insulator to prevent almost all leakage of charge from the axon. Current can pass through the membrane of a myelinated axon only at the nodes of Ranvier, where the myelin sheath is interrupted and the axon is bare, and essentially all the voltage-regulated sodium channels are concentrated at the nodes. Thus, when an action potential is generated in a myelinated fiber, the local depolarizing current does not dissipate through the adjacent (nonexcitable) membrane regions but instead is maintained and moves to the next node, a distance of approximately 1 mm, where it triggers another action potential. Consequently, action potentials are triggered only at the nodes. This type of conduction is called **saltatory conduction** (*saltare* = to leap) because the electrical signal jumps from node to node along the axon (Figure 11.15). Saltatory conduction is much faster than the conduction produced by the

continuous spread of local depolarizing currents along unmyelinated membranes.

The importance of myelin to nerve transmission is painfully clear to those with demyelinating diseases such as **multiple sclerosis (MS).** This autoimmune disease affects mostly young adults. Common symptoms are visual disturbances (including blindness), problems controlling muscles (weakness, clumsiness), and urinary incontinence. In this disease, myelin sheaths in the CNS are gradually destroyed, reduced to nonfunctional hardened sheaths called *scleroses.* The loss of myelin (due to immune attack on *myelin basic protein*) results in such substantial shunting and short-circuiting of the current that successive nodes are excited more and more slowly, and eventually impulse conduction ceases. However, the axons themselves are not damaged and growing numbers of sodium channels appear spontaneously in the demyelinated fibers. This may account for the remarkably variable cycles of exacerbation and remission (temporary recovery) that are typical of this disease.

Injections of beta interferon (a hormonelike substance released by cells of the immune system) are providing some relief to certain patients, but even more exciting are results from studies in which patients ingest bovine myelin. Nearly half of the treated patients were free of exacerbations and showed significant improvement in their condition over the year-long study. Researchers suggest that this therapy provokes production of suppressor cells that inhibit the immune attack against myelin basic protein. •

Nerve fibers may be classified as group A, B, or C

How does the location of voltage-gated Na⁺ channels differ in a myelinated axon (as depicted here) and in an unmyelinated axon?

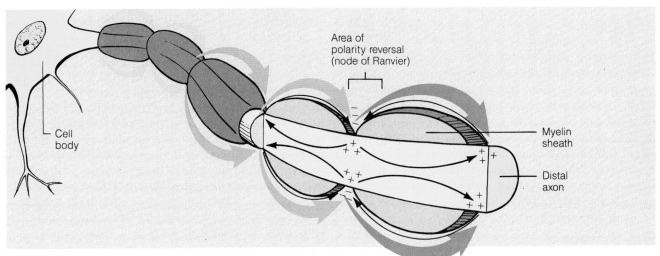

FIGURE 11.15
Saltatory conduction in a myelinated axon. In myelinated fibers, the local current flows (small black arrows in longitudinally sectioned axon and immediately outside the myelin sheath) give rise to a propagated action potential (large light to dark pink arrows) that appears to jump from node to node. Notice that while action potentials are generated only at the nodes, the current flows along the axon from node to node.

FIGURE 11.16
Examples of types of chemical synapses. Axodendritic, axosomatic, and axoaxonic synapses. Axonal terminals of the presynaptic neurons are indicated in different colors at the different synapse types.

fibers based on their diameter, degree of myelination, and speed of conduction. **Group A fibers** are mostly somatic sensory and motor fibers serving the skin, skeletal muscles, and joints. They have the largest diameter and thick myelin sheaths, and conduct impulses at speeds ranging from 15 to 150 m/s. Autonomic nervous system motor fibers serving the visceral organs, visceral sensory fibers, and the smaller somatic sensory fibers transmitting afferent impulses from the skin (such as pain and small touch fibers) belong in the B and C fiber groups. **Group B fibers,** lightly myelinated fibers of intermediate diameter, transmit impulses at the rate of 3–15 m/s. **Group C fibers** have the smallest diameter and are unmyelinated. Hence, these fibers are incapable of saltatory conduction and conduct impulses very slowly, 1 m/s or less.

A number of chemical and physical factors can impair the conduction of impulses. Although their mechanisms of action differ, alcohol, sedatives, and anesthetics all block nerve impulses by reducing membrane permeability to sodium ions. As we have seen, no sodium entry—no action potential.

Cold and continuous pressure interrupt blood circulation (and hence the delivery of oxygen and nutrients) to the neuronal processes, impairing their ability to conduct impulses. For example, your fingers get numb when you hold an ice cube for more than a few seconds. Likewise, when you sit on your foot, it "goes to sleep." When you remove the pressure, the impulses begin to be transmitted once again, leading to an unpleasant prickly feeling. •

The Synapse

The operation of the nervous system depends on the flow of information through elaborate circuits consisting of chains of neurons functionally connected by synapses. A **synapse** (sin'aps), from the Greek *syn,*

meaning "to clasp or join," is a unique junction that mediates the transfer of information from one neuron to the next or from a neuron to an effector cell.

Most synapses occur between the axonal endings of one neuron and the dendrites or the cell bodies (soma) of other neurons and are called **axodendritic** or **axosomatic synapses,** respectively. Less common (and far less understood) are the synapses between axons *(axoaxonic),* between dendrites *(dendrodendritic),* or between dendrites and cell bodies *(dendrosomatic).* Some of these synaptic patterns are illustrated in Figure 11.16.

The neuron conducting impulses toward the synapse is called the **presynaptic neuron.** The neuron that transmits the electrical signal away from the synapse is called the **postsynaptic neuron**. At a *given* synapse, the presynaptic neuron is the information sender, and the postsynaptic neuron is the information recipient. As you might anticipate, most neurons (including all interneurons) function as both presynaptic and postsynaptic neurons, receiving information from some neurons and dispatching it to others. Neurons have anywhere from 1000 to 10,000 axonal terminals making synapses and are stimulated by an equal number of other neurons (Figure 11.17). In the body periphery, the postsynaptic cell may be either another neuron or an effector cell (a muscle cell or gland cell). Synapses between neurons and muscle cells are specifically called *neuromuscular junctions* (described in Chapter 9); those between neurons and gland cells are *neuroglandular junctions.*

There are two varieties of synapses: *electrical* and *chemical.* The major structural and functional properties of these synapses are described next.

Electrical Synapses

Electrical synapses, the less common variety, are *bridged junctions* that correspond to the gap junctions found between certain other body cells (see Fig-parts: (1) a knoblike *axonal terminal* of the presynaptic (transmitting) neuron, which exhibits many tiny, membrane-bounded sacs called **synaptic vesicles,** each containing thousands of neurotransmitter molecules; and (2) a *receptor region* on the membrane of a dendrite or the cell body of the postsynaptic neuron, which bears neurotransmitter receptors, often of several types (Figure 11.18). Although close, the presynaptic and postsynaptic membranes are always separated by the **synaptic cleft,** a fluid-filled space approximately 30 to 50 nm (about one-millionth of an inch) wide. Because the current from the presynaptic membrane dissipates in the fluid-filled cleft, chemical synapses effectively prevent a nerve impulse from being *directly* transmitted from one neuron to another. Instead, transmission of signals across chemical synapses is a *chemical event* that depends on the release, diffusion, and receptor binding of neurotransmitter molecules and results in *unidirectional communication* between neurons. Thus, while transmission of nerve impulses along an axon and across electrical synapses is a purely electrical phenomenon, chemical synapses convert the electrical signals into chemical signals (neurotransmitters) that travel across the synapse to the postsynaptic cells, where they are converted back into electrical signals.

Information Transfer Across Chemical Synapses.

When a nerve impulse reaches the axon terminal, it sets into motion a chain of events that triggers neurotransmitter release. The neurotransmitter crosses the synaptic cleft and, on binding to receptors on the postsynaptic membrane, causes changes in the postsynaptic membrane permeability. The successive events appear to be as follows (Figure 11.18):

1. Calcium gates open in the presynaptic axonal terminal. When the nerve impulse reaches the axon terminal, depolarization of the membrane opens not only Na^+ channels, but voltage-regulated Ca^{2+} channels as well. During the brief time the calcium gates are open, Ca^{2+} floods into the terminal from the extracellular fluid.

2. Neurotransmitter is released by exocytosis. The surge of free calcium into the axonal terminal then acts as an intracellular messenger, causing synaptic vesicles to fuse with the axonal membrane and empty their neurotransmitter contents by exocytosis into the synaptic cleft. The Ca^{2+} is then quickly removed, either taken up into the mitochondria or ejected to the outside by an active calcium membrane pump.

3. Neurotransmitter binds to postsynaptic receptors. The neurotransmitter diffuses across the synaptic cleft and binds reversibly to specific protein receptors that are densely clustered on the postsynaptic membrane.

4. Ion channels open in the postsynaptic membrane. As the receptor proteins bind neurotransmitter

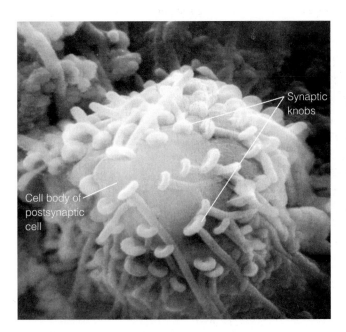

FIGURE 11.17
Scanning electron micrograph showing the abundant synaptic knobs communicating with a single postsynaptic neuron (4,800 ×).

ure 3.4c, p. 65). They contain protein channels that interconnect the cytoplasm of adjacent neurons, and allow the current-carrying ions to flow directly from one neuron to the next. Neurons joined in this way are said to be *electrically coupled,* and transmission across these synapses is very rapid. Depending on the nature of the synapse, communication may be unidirectional or bidirectional.

A key feature of electrical synapses is that they provide a simple means of synchronizing the activity of all interconnected neurons. In adults, electrical synapses are found in regions of the brain responsible for certain stereotyped movements, such as the normal jerky movements of the eyes. They are far more abundant in embryonic nervous tissue, where they permit exchange of guiding clues during early neuronal development so that neurons can connect properly with one another. Most electrical synapses are eventually replaced by chemical synapses as nervous system development continues. However, electrical synapses are abundant in certain nonnervous tissues, such as cardiac and smooth muscle, where they allow sequential and rhythmic excitations.

Chemical Synapses

In contrast to electrical synapses, which are specialized to allow the flow of ions between neurons, **chemical synapses** are specialized for release and reception of chemical **neurotransmitters.** Neurotransmitters (described in detail shortly) function to open or close ion channels that influence membrane permeability and, consequently, membrane potential.

A typical chemical synapse is made up of two

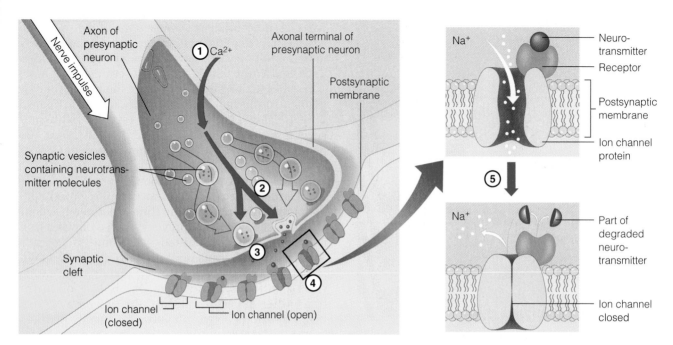

FIGURE 11.18
Events occurring at a chemical synapse in response to depolarization of the axonal terminal. (1) Arrival of the depolarization wave (nerve impulse) results in the opening of calcium gates and influx of calcium (Ca²⁺) into the axonal terminal. (2) Calcium ions promote the fusion of synaptic vesicles with the presynaptic membrane and exocytosis of neurotransmitter. (3) The neurotransmitter diffuses across the synaptic cleft and attaches to receptors on the postsynaptic membrane. (4) Binding of neurotransmitter causes ion channels to open, which results in voltage changes in the postsynaptic membrane. (5) Effects are short-lived because the neurotransmitter is quickly destroyed by enzymes or taken back up into the presynaptic terminal, which closes the ion channels and terminates the synaptic response.

molecules, their three-dimensional shape changes. This causes ion channels to open. The resulting current flows produce local changes in the membrane potential. Depending on the receptor protein to which the neurotransmitter binds and the type of channel the receptor controls, the postsynaptic neuron may be excited or inhibited.

For each nerve impulse reaching the presynaptic terminal, many vesicles (perhaps 300) are emptied into the synaptic cleft. The higher the frequency of impulses reaching the terminals (that is, the more intense the stimulus), the greater the total number of synaptic vesicles that fuse and spill their contents, and the greater the effect on the postsynaptic cell.

Termination of Neurotransmitter Effects.
As long as a neurotransmitter is bound to a postsynaptic receptor, it continues to produce its effects on membrane permeability and blocks reception of additional "messages" from presynaptic neurons. Thus, some means of "wiping the postsynaptic slate clean" is necessary. The effects of neurotransmitters appear to last a few milliseconds before being terminated by one of three mechanisms. Depending on the particular neurotransmitter, the mechanism may be:

1. Degradation by enzymes associated with the postsynaptic membrane or present in the synapse (see Figure 11.18, step 5). This is the case for ACh.

2. Removal from the synapse by reuptake into the presynaptic terminal where it is stored or destroyed by enzymes, as with norepinephrine.

3. Diffusion of the neurotransmitter away from the synapse, ending its effects there.

Synaptic Delay. Although some neurons can transmit impulses at rates that approach 100 m/s (250 mph), neural transmission across a chemical synapse is comparatively slow and reflects the time required for neurotransmitter release, diffusion across the synapse, and binding to receptors. Typically, this **synaptic delay**, which lasts 0.3–5.0 ms, is the *rate-limiting* (slowest) step of neural transmission. Synaptic delay helps explain why transmission along short neural pathways involving only two or three neurons occurs rapidly, while that along the multisynaptic pathways typical of higher mental functioning occurs much more slowly. (However, in practical terms these differences are not noticeable.)

Postsynaptic Potentials and Synaptic Integration

Receptors present on postsynaptic membranes at chemical synapses are specialized to open ion channels, thereby converting chemical signals into electrical signals. However, unlike the voltage-gated ion channels responsible for action potentials, these chemically gated channels are relatively insensitive to changes in membrane potential. Consequently, channel opening at postsynaptic membranes cannot possibly become a self-amplifying or self-generating event. Hence, neurotransmitter receptors mediate local changes in membrane potential (voltage) that are *graded* according to the amount of transmitter released and the time it remains in the area.

Chemical synapses are divided into two types, excitatory and inhibitory, according to how they affect the membrane potential of the postsynaptic neuron (Figure 11.19). *Excitatory postsynaptic potentials (EPSPs)* occur at excitatory synapses and *inhibitory postsynaptic potentials (IPSPs)* are generated at inhibitory synapses. Action potentials are compared with postsynaptic potentials in Table 11.2.

Excitatory Synapses and EPSPs

At excitatory synapses, neurotransmitter binding causes depolarization of the postsynaptic membrane. However, in contrast to what happens on axonal membranes, only a single type of channel opens on postsynaptic membranes (membranes of dendrites and neuronal cell bodies). This channel chiefly allows sodium and potassium ions to diffuse *simultaneously* through the membrane in opposite directions (rather than first opening sodium gates and later potassium gates). Although this may appear to be self-defeating when depolarization is the goal, remember that the electrochemical gradient for sodium is much steeper than that for potassium. Hence, the influx of Na^+ is greater than the efflux of K^+, and net depolarization occurs.

If enough neurotransmitter binds, depolarization of the postsynaptic membrane can successfully reach 0 mV, which is well above an axon's threshold (about −50 mV) for "firing off" an action potential. However, *postsynaptic membranes do not generate or transmit action potentials; only axons* (fibers with voltage-gated channels) *have this capability.* The dramatic polarity reversal seen in axons never occurs in membranes containing *only* chemically gated channels because the opposite movements of K^+ and Na^+ prevent accumulation of excessive positive charge inside the cell. Hence, instead of action potentials, local graded depolarization events called **excitatory postsynaptic potentials (EPSPs)** occur at excitatory postsynaptic membranes (see Figure 11.19a). Each EPSP lasts only a few milliseconds and then the membrane returns to its resting potential. The only function of EPSPs is to help trigger an action potential distally at the axon hillock of the postsynaptic neuron. Although current flows created by individual EPSPs decline with distance, they can and often *do* spread all the way to the axon hillock. If currents reaching the axon hillock are strong enough to depolarize the axon to threshold, axonal voltage-gated channels open and an action potential is generated.

(a) Excitatory postsynaptic potential (EPSP)

(b) Inhibitory postsynaptic potential (IPSP)

FIGURE 11.19

Postsynaptic potentials. (a) An excitatory postsynaptic potential (EPSP) is a local depolarization of the postsynaptic membrane that brings the neuron closer to threshold for action potential generation. It is mediated by neurotransmitter binding which causes the opening of channels that allow simultaneous passage of sodium and potassium through the postsynaptic membrane. **(b)** An inhibitory postsynaptic potential results in hyperpolarization of the postsynaptic neuron and drives the neuron away from the threshold for firing. It is mediated by neurotransmitter binding which opens potassium or chloride gates or both. The blue vertical arrows represent stimulation.

Inhibitory Synapses and IPSPs

Binding of neurotransmitter at inhibitory synapses *reduces* a postsynaptic neuron's ability to generate an action potential. Most inhibitory neurotransmitters induce hyperpolarization of the postsynaptic membrane by making the membrane more permeable to potassium ions, chloride ions, or both. Sodium ion permeability is not affected. If potassium gates are opened, potassium ions move out of the cell; if chloride gates are opened, chloride ions move in. In either case, the charge on the inner face of the membrane becomes relatively more negative. As the membrane potential increases and is driven farther from the axon's threshold, the postsynaptic neuron becomes less likely to "fire" and larger depolarizing currents are required to induce an action potential. Such changes in potential are called **inhibitory postsynaptic potentials (IPSPs)** (see Figure 11.19b).

Table 11.2 Comparison of Action Potentials with Postsynaptic Potentials

Characteristic	Action potential	EPSP	IPSP
Function	Long-distance signaling; constitutes the nerve impulse	Short-distance signaling; depolarization that spreads to axon hillock; moves membrane potential *toward* threshold for generation of action potential	Short-distance signaling; hyperpolarization that spreads to axon hillock; moves potential *away from* threshold for generation of action potential
Stimulus for opening of ionic gates	Voltage (depolarization)	Chemical (neurotransmitter)	Chemical (neurotransmitter)
Initial effect of stimulus	First opens sodium gates, then potassium gates	Opens channels that allow simultaneous sodium and potassium fluxes	Opens potassium and/or chloride channels
Repolarization	Voltage regulated; closing of sodium gates followed by opening of potassium gates	Dissipation of membrane changes with time and distance	
Conduction distance	Not conducted by local current flows; continually regenerated (propagated) along entire axon; intensity does not decline with distance	1–2 mm; local electrical events; intensity declines with distance	
Positive feedback cycle	Present	Absent	Absent
Peak membrane potential	+40 to +50 mV	0 mV	Becomes hyperpolarized; moves toward −90 mV
Summation	None; an all-or-none phenomenon	Present; produces graded depolarization	Present; produces graded hyperpolarization
Refractory period	Present	Absent	Absent

Integration and Modification of Synaptic Events

Summation by the Postsynaptic Neuron.
A single EPSP cannot induce an action potential in the postsynaptic neuron. But if thousands of excitatory axonal terminals are firing on the same postsynaptic membrane, or if a smaller number of terminals are delivering impulses very rapidly, the probability of reaching threshold depolarization increases greatly. Thus, EPSPs can add together, or **summate,** to influence the activity of a postsynaptic neuron. Nerve impulses would never be initiated if this were not so.

Two types of summation occur: temporal and spatial. First we will explain these events in terms of EPSPs. **Temporal summation** occurs when one or more presynaptic neurons transmit impulses in rapid-fire order (Figure 11.20b) and waves of neurotransmitter release occur in quick succession. The first impulse produces a slight EPSP, and before it dissipates, successive impulses trigger more EPSPs. These summate, producing a much greater depolarization of the postsynaptic membrane than would result from a single EPSP.

Spatial summation occurs when the postsynaptic neuron is stimulated by a large number of terminals from the same or (more commonly) different neurons at the same time. As a result, huge numbers of its receptors can bind neurotransmitter and simultaneously initiate EPSPs, which sum up and dramatically enhance the depolarization (Figure 11.20c).

Although we have focused on summation of EPSPs here, IPSPs also summate, both temporally and spatially. In this case, the postsynaptic neuron is inhibited to a greater degree.

Most neurons receive both stimulatory and inhibitory inputs from thousands of other neurons. How is all of this conflicting information sorted out? Each neuron's axon hillock appears to keep a "running account" of all the signals it receives (Figure 11.20d). Not only do EPSPs summate and IPSPs summate, but also EPSPs summate with IPSPs. If the stimulatory effects of EPSPs dominate the membrane potential enough to reach threshold, the neuron will fire. If, on the other hand, the summing process yields only subthreshold depolarization or hyperpolarization, the neuron fails to generate an action potential. However, partially depolarized neurons are **facilitated**—that is, more easily excited by successive depolarization events—because they are already nearer to threshold. Thus, axon hillock membranes function as *neural integrators,* and their potential at any time reflects the sum of all incoming neural information. Since EPSPs and IPSPs are graded potentials that diminish in strength the farther they spread, the most effective synapses are those closest to the axon hillock. Synapses on distal

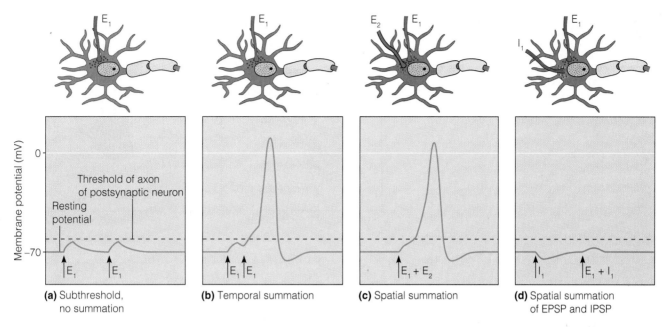

(a) Subthreshold, no summation

(b) Temporal summation

(c) Spatial summation

(d) Spatial summation of EPSP and IPSP

FIGURE 11.20
Neural integration of EPSPs and IPSPs at the axonal membrane of the postsynaptic cell. Synapses E_1 and E_2 are excitatory; synapse I_1 is inhibitory. Each individual impulse is itself subthreshold. **(a)** Synapse E_1 is stimulated and then is stimulated again shortly thereafter. The two EPSPs do not overlap in time, so no interaction (summation) occurs; threshold is not reached in the axon of the postsynaptic neuron. **(b)** Synapse E_1 is stimulated a second time before the initial EPSP has died away; temporal summation occurs, and the axon's threshold is reached, causing an action potential to be generated. **(c)** Synapses E_1 and E_2 are stimulated simultaneously (spatial summation), resulting in a threshold depolarization. **(d)** Synapse I_1 is stimulated, resulting in a short-lived IPSP (hyperpolarization). When E_1 and I_1 are simultaneously stimulated, the changes in potential cancel each other out.

dendrites have far less influence on firing the axon than those on the cell body.

Synaptic Potentiation. Repeated or continuous use of a synapse (even for short periods) considerably enhances the presynaptic neuron's ability to excite the postsynaptic neuron, producing postsynaptic potentials much larger than might be predicted by the stimulus. This phenomenon is called **synaptic potentiation.** The presynaptic terminals at such synapses contain higher concentrations of calcium ions, which (presumably) trigger the release of more neurotransmitter, which, in turn, produces larger EPSPs. Furthermore, synaptic potentiation increases calcium concentrations in the postsynaptic neuron as well. A brief high-frequency pattern of stimulation specifically activates voltage-regulated receptors called *NMDA (N-methyl-D-aspartate) receptors,* located on the postsynaptic membrane, which couple the depolarization to increased calcium entry. Theoretically, as calcium floods into the cell, it activates certain kinase enzymes that promote changes that result in more efficient responses to subsequent stimuli.

When this enhancement occurs *during* repeated (tetanic) stimulation, it is called *tetanic potentiation.* When it is set up and persists for varying periods *after the stimulus ends,* it is called *post-tetanic potentiation.* Functionally, synaptic potentiation can be viewed as a learning process that increases the efficiency of neurotransmission along a particular pathway. Indeed, the hippocampus of the brain, which plays a special role in memory and learning (see pp. 495–496) exhibits especially long post-tetanic potentiations.

Presynaptic Inhibition and Neuromodulation. Postsynaptic activity can also be influenced by events occurring at the presynaptic membrane, such as presynaptic inhibition and neuromodulation. **Presynaptic inhibition** occurs when the release of excitatory neurotransmitter by one neuron is inhibited by the activity of another neuron via an axoaxonic synapse (Figure 11.21). More than one mechanism is involved, but the end result is that less neurotransmitter is released and bound, and smaller EPSPs are formed. (Notice that this is opposite to what we see with synaptic potentiation.) In contrast to postsynaptic inhibition by IPSPs, which decreases the excitability of the postsynaptic neuron, presynaptic inhibition is more like a functional synaptic "pruning"; it reduces excitatory stimulation of the postsynaptic neuron.

Neuromodulation occurs when a neurotransmitter acts via slow changes in target cell metabolism (see p. 570) or chemicals other than neurotransmitters modify neuronal activity. Some *neuromodulators*

FIGURE 11.21

Presynaptic inhibition. Presynaptic inhibition is mediated by inhibitory neurons that form axoaxonal synapses with presynaptic terminals at excitatory synapses. **(a)** When the inhibitory neuron is inactive, it has no effect on the release of neurotransmitter by the presynaptic neuron. **(b)** When the inhibitory axon is firing, less neurotransmitter is released by the presynaptic axonal terminal.

(a) Inhibitory neuron inactive

(b) Inhibitory neuron active

influence the synthesis, release, degradation, or reuptake of neurotransmitter by a presynaptic neuron. Others alter the sensitivity of the postsynaptic membrane to the neurotransmitter. Many neuromodulators are hormones that act at sites relatively far from their release site.

Neurotransmitters and Their Receptors

Neurotransmitters, along with electrical signals, are the "languages" of the nervous system—the means by which each neuron communicates with others to process information and send messages to the rest of the body. These versatile molecules that chemically connect neurons affect body and brain. Sleep, thought, rage, hunger, memory, movement, and even your smile reflect their "doings." Most factors that specifically affect synaptic transmission do so by enhancing or inhibiting neurotransmitter release or destruction, or by blocking their binding to receptors. Just as speech defects may hinder interpersonal communication, interferences with neurotransmitter activity may short-circuit the brain's "conversations" or internal talk (see *A Closer Look* on p. 374).

At present, over 50 different chemicals are either known neurotransmitters or neurotransmitter candidates. As a general rule, to be recognized as a neurotransmitter at a specific type of synapse, a chemical must meet several criteria. The most important of these are:

1. It must be present in the presynaptic terminal and be discharged when the neuron is appropriately stimulated. Some neurotransmitters are synthesized locally in the terminal and enclosed there within vesicles. Others are made in the cell body and dispatched within membranous vesicles to the axonal terminals.

2. When applied experimentally to the postsynaptic membrane, it must mimic natural (endogenous) neurotransmitters by producing ion fluxes and EPSPs or IPSPs.

3. There must be some natural means of removing it from the synaptic junction (see earlier discussion on p. 362).

Although some neurons produce and release only one kind of neurotransmitter, others make two or more and may release any one or all of them. It appears that different neurotransmitters are released at different stimulation frequencies, which avoids producing a jumble of nonsense messages. The coexistence of more than one neurotransmitter in a single neuron makes it possible for that cell to exert several influences rather than a single discrete effect.

Neurotransmitters are classified in two ways: chemically and functionally. Table 11.3 provides a fairly detailed overview of neurotransmitters, some of which are described here. This table will be a handy reference for you to look back to when the neurotransmitters are mentioned in subsequent chapters.

Classification of Neurotransmitters According to Chemical Structure

Neurotransmitters fall into several chemical classes based on molecular structure.

Acetylcholine (ACh). Acetylcholine (as″ĕ-til-ko′lēn) was the first neurotransmitter to be identified. It is still the best understood because it is released at neuromuscular junctions, which are much easier to study than synapses buried within the CNS. ACh is synthesized and enclosed in synaptic vesicles within the axonal terminals in a reaction catalyzed by the enzyme *choline acetyltransferase.* Acetic acid is bound to coenzyme A (CoA) to form acetyl-CoA, which is, in turn, combined with choline. Then the coenzyme is released.

$$\text{Acetyl-CoA} + \text{choline} \xrightarrow{\underset{\text{acetyltransferase}}{\text{choline}}} \text{ACh} + \text{CoA}$$

After ACh is released, it binds to the postsynaptic receptors briefly. Then it is released and degraded to acetic acid and choline by the enzyme **acetylcholinesterase (AChE),** located in the synaptic cleft and on postsynaptic membranes. The released choline is recaptured by the presynaptic terminals and reused to synthesize more ACh.

Acetylcholine is released by all neurons that stimulate skeletal muscles and by some neurons of the autonomic nervous system. ACh-releasing neurons are also prevalent in the central nervous system.

Biogenic Amines. The **biogenic** (bi″o-jen′ik) **amines** include the **catecholamines** (kat″ĕ-kol′ah-mēnz), such as dopamine, norepinephrine, and epinephrine, and the **indolamines,** which include serotonin and histamine. As illustrated in Figure 11.22, **dopamine** and **norepinephrine** (nor″ep-ĭ-nef′rin) **(NE)** are synthesized from the amino acid tyrosine in a common pathway consisting of several steps. Apparently, neurons contain only the enzymes controlling the steps needed to produce their own neurotransmitter. Thus, the sequence stops at dopamine in dopamine-releasing neurons but continues on to NE in NE-releasing neurons. The same pathway is used by the epinephrine-releasing cells of the brain and the adrenal medulla. Since epinephrine produced by the adrenal gland is released to the blood, it is a hormone as well as a neurotransmitter. **Serotonin** (se″ro-to′nin) is synthesized from the amino acid tryptophan. **Histamine** is synthesized from the amino acid histidine.

Biogenic amine neurotransmitters are broadly distributed in the brain, where they play a role in emotional behavior and in the regulation of the biological clock. Additionally, catecholamines (particularly NE) are released by some motor neurons of the autonomic nervous system. Imbalances of these neurotransmitters are associated with mental illness. For example, overproduction of dopamine occurs in schizophrenia, and some researchers believe that the loss of serotonin receptors (and serotonin effects) that occurs in the brains of Alzheimer's patients is responsible for their frequently increased moodiness and aggression. Additionally, certain psychoactive drugs (LSD and mescaline) can bind to biogenic amine receptors and induce hallucinations.

Amino Acids. It has been more difficult to prove a neurotransmitter role when the suspect is an **amino acid.** Whereas ACh and the biogenic amines are found only in neurons, amino acids occur in all cells of the body and are important in many biochemical

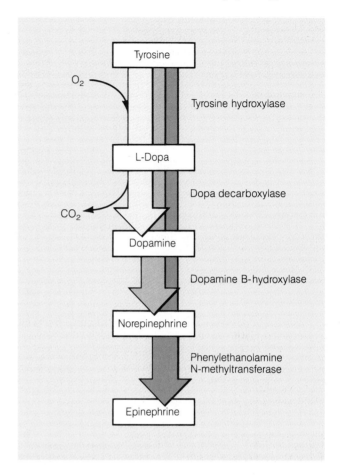

FIGURE 11.22
Common pathway for synthesis of dopamine, norepinephrine, and epinephrine. How far synthesis proceeds along the pathway depends on the enzymes present in the cell. The production of dopamine and norepinephrine takes place in the axonal terminals of neurons releasing these neurotransmitters. Epinephrine, a hormone, is released (along with norepinephrine) by the cells of the adrenal medulla.

reactions. The amino acids for which a neurotransmitter role is certain include **gamma (γ)-aminobutyric acid (GABA), glycine, aspartate,** and **glutamate,** but there are others. Amino acid neurotransmitters have so far been found only in the CNS.

Peptides. The **neuropeptides,** essentially strings of amino acids, include a broad spectrum of molecules with diverse effects. For example, a neuropeptide called **substance P** is an important mediator of pain signals. By contrast, **endorphins** and **enkephalins** (en-kef′ah-linz) act as natural opiates or euphorics, reducing our perception of pain under certain stressful conditions. Enkephalin activity increases dramatically in pregnant women in labor. Endorphin release is enhanced when an athlete gets his or her second wind and is probably responsible

Table 11.3 Neurotransmitters

Neurotransmitter	Functional classes	Sites where secreted	Comments
Acetylcholine $H_3C-\overset{\overset{O}{\|\|}}{C}-O-CH_2-CH_2-\overset{+}{N}-(CH_3)_3$	Excitatory to skeletal muscles; excitatory or inhibitory to visceral effectors, depending on receptors bound Direct action at nicotinic receptors; indirect action via second messengers at muscarinic receptors	CNS: basal nuclei and some neurons of motor cortex of brain PNS: all neuromuscular junctions with skeletal muscle; some autonomic motor endings (all preganglionic and parasympathetic postganglionic fibers)	Effects prolonged (leading to tetanic muscle spasms and neural "frying") by nerve gas and organophosphate insecticides (malathion); release inhibited by botulinus toxin; binding to receptors inhibited by curare (a muscle paralytic agent) and some snake venoms; decreased ACh levels in certain brain areas in Alzheimer's disease; ACh receptors destroyed in myasthenia gravis, an autoimmune disease
Biogenic Amines			
Norepinephrine	Excitatory or inhibitory, depending on receptor type bound Indirect action via second messengers	CNS: brain stem, particularly reticular activating system; limbic system; some areas of cerebral cortex PNS: some autonomic motor neurons (postganglionic sympathetic neuron endings)	A "feeling good" neurotransmitter; release enhanced by amphetamines; removal from synapse blocked by tricyclic antidepressants (Elavil and others) and cocaine; brain levels reduced by reserpine (an antihypertensive drug) leading to depression
Dopamine	Generally excitatory; may be inhibitory in sympathetic ganglia Indirect action via second messengers	CNS: substantia nigra of midbrain; hypothalamus; is the principal neurotransmitter of extrapyramidal system PNS: some sympathetic ganglia	A "feeling good" neurotransmitter; release enhanced by L-dopa and amphetamines; reuptake blocked by cocaine; deficient in Parkinson's disease; may be involved in pathogenesis of schizophrenia
Serotonin	Generally inhibitory Indirect action via second messengers	CNS: brain stem; hypothalamus; limbic system; cerebellum; pineal gland; spinal cord	Activity blocked by LSD; may play a role in sleep, appetite, nausea, migraine headaches, and regulation of mood; drugs that block its uptake (Prozac) relieve anxiety and depression
Histamine	Indirect action via second messengers	CNS: hypothalamus	Also released by mast cells during inflammation and acts as powerful vasodilator

for the "runner's high." Additionally, some claim that the "placebo effect" is due to endorphin release. These pain-killing neurotransmitters remained undiscovered until investigators began to study why morphine and other opiates reduce anxiety and pain. As it turned out, these drugs attach to the same receptors that bind natural opiates, producing similar but stronger effects.

Some neuropeptides, such as somatostatin, vasoactive intestinal peptide (VIP), and cholecystokinin, are also produced by nonneural body tissues and are widespread in the gastrointestinal tract. Such peptides are commonly referred to as **gut-brain peptides**.

Novel Messengers. Just a few years ago, it would have been scientific suicide to suggest that ATP, nitric oxide, and carbon monoxide—all ubiquitous molecules—might be neurotransmitters. Nonetheless, the discovery of these unlikely messengers has opened up a whole new chapter in the story of neurotransmission.

Although it was well known that **adenosine triphosphate (ATP),** the universal form of cellular energy (see p. 55), was stored in synaptic vesicles, its

Neurotransmitter	Functional classes	Sites where secreted	Comments
Amino Acids			
GABA (γ-aminobutyric acid) H₂N−CH₂−CH₂−CH₂−COOH	Generally inhibitory Direct action	CNS: Purkinje cells of cerebellum; spinal cord; granule cells of olfactory bulb; retina	Important in presynaptic inhibition at axoaxonal synapses; inhibitory effects augmented by alcohol (resulting in slowed reflexes and impaired motor coordination) and antianxiety drugs of the benzodiazepine class (e.g., Valium)

Glutamate
 	
H₂N−CH−CH₂−CH₂−COOH
       |
      COOH
	Generally excitatory
	
	Direct action
		CNS: spinal cord; widespread in brain	The "stroke neurotransmitter" (see p. 407)

Glycine H₂N−CH₂−COOH	Generally inhibitory Indirect action via second messengers	CNS: spinal cord; retina	Strychnine blocks glycine receptors, resulting in uncontrolled convulsions and respiratory arrest
Peptides			
Endorphins, dynorphin, enkephalins (illustrated) (Tyr)(Gly)(Gly)(Phe)(Met)	Generally inhibitory Indirect action via second messengers	CNS: widely distributed in brain; hypothalamus; limbic system; pituitary; spinal cord	Natural opiates; inhibit pain by inhibiting substance P; effects mimicked by morphine, heroin, and methadone
Tachykinins: Substance P (illustrated), neurokinin A (NKA) (Arg)(Pro)(Lys)(Pro)(Gln)(Gln)(Phe)(Phe)(Gly)(Leu)(Met)	Excitatory Indirect action via second messengers	CNS: basal nuclei; midbrain; hypothalamus; cerebral cortex PNS: certain sensory neurons of dorsal root ganglia of spinal cord (pain afferents)	Substance P mediates pain transmission in the PNS; in the CNS tachykinins are involved in respiratory and cardiovascular controls and in mood
Somatostatin (Ala)(Gly)(Cys)(Lys)(Asn)(Phe)(Phe) (Trp) (Cys)(Ser)(Thr)(Phe)(Thr) (Lys)	Generally inhibitory Indirect action via second messengers	CNS: hypothalamus; retina and other parts of brain Pancreas	Inhibits release of growth hormone; a gut-brain peptide

Cholecystokinin (CCK)
 	
(Asp)(Tyr)(Met)(Gly)(Trp)(Met)(Asp)(Phe)
        |
       SO₄
	Possible neurotransmitter	Cerebral cortex
		
		Small intestine
			May be related to feeding behaviors; a gut-brain peptide

presence there was thought to promote synthesis and/or reuptake of other neurotransmitters. ATP is now recognized as a major neurotransmitter (perhaps the most primitive one) in both the CNS and PNS. Like glutamate and acetylcholine it produces a fast excitatory response at certain receptors (see below).

Even more preposterous was the idea that **nitric oxide (NO),** a short-lived toxic gas, could be a neurotransmitter. It defies all the official descriptions of neurotransmitters—it is synthesized on demand and diffuses out of the cells making it, rather than being stored in vesicles and released by exocytosis. Instead of attaching to surface receptors, it zooms through the plasma membrane of nearby cells to bind with a peculiar intracellular receptor—iron in *guanylyl cyclase,* the enzyme that makes the second messenger *cyclic GMP.* The precise role of NO in the brain has been elusive, but when the neurotransmitter glutamate binds to NMDA receptors (a specific subset of its receptors), calcium channels open allowing an influx of Ca²⁺ into the cell. The calcium activates calmodulin, a regulatory calcium-binding protein that, in turn, activates *nitric oxide synthase (NOS),* the enzyme needed for NO synthesis. Many believe that

NO is the retrograde messenger involved in long-term potentiation (learning and memory)—i.e., that it travels back from the postsynaptic neuron to the presynaptic neuron where it activates guanylyl cyclase. Excessive release of NO is responsible for much of the brain damage seen in stroke patients (see p. 407). In the myenteric plexus of the intestine, NO causes relaxation of the intestinal smooth muscle.

It may be that NO is just the first of a soon-to-be-discovered class of signaling gases that pass swiftly into cells where they bind briefly to metal-containing enzymes and then vanish. **Carbon monoxide (CO)**, another airy messenger, also stimulates synthesis of cyclic GMP, and some researchers speculate that CO is the main regulator of cyclic GMP levels in the brain. Though NO and CO are found in different brain regions and appear to act in different pathways, their mode of action is very similar. The proposed role of CO in neurotransmission leads to an interesting speculation: heavy smokers who quit bemoan the fact that they can't concentrate for weeks after. Since CO displaces oxygen in the blood, it would seem that they should think better after quitting. Perhaps the higher blood levels of CO they were accustomed to enhanced neurotransmission in certain circuits involved in logic—time will tell.

Classification of Neurotransmitters According to Function

This text cannot begin to describe the incredible diversity of functions that neurotransmitters mediate. Therefore, we limit our discussion to two broad ways of classifying neurotransmitters according to function; more details will be added as appropriate in subsequent chapters.

Effects: Excitatory vs. Inhibitory.
We can summarize this classification scheme by saying that some neurotransmitters are excitatory (cause depolarization), some are inhibitory (cause hyperpolarization), and others exert both effects, depending on the specific receptor types with which they interact. For example, the amino acids GABA and glycine are usually inhibitory, while glutamate is typically excitatory. On the other hand, ACh and NE each bind to at least two receptor types that cause opposite effects. For example, acetylcholine is excitatory at neuromuscular junctions with skeletal muscle and inhibitory when released on cardiac muscle. These effects of ACh and NE will be described more fully in Chapter 14.

Mechanism of Action: Direct vs. Indirect.
Neurotransmitters that open ion channels are said to act directly. These neurotransmitters provoke rapid responses in the postsynaptic cells by promoting changes in membrane potential. ACh and the amino acid neurotransmitters are direct-acting neurotransmitters.

The *indirectly acting* neurotransmitters promote broader, longer-lasting effects by acting through intracellular *second-messenger* molecules. In this way their mechanism of action is similar to that of many hormones. The biogenic amines and the peptides are indirect neurotransmitters.

Neurotransmitter Receptors

In Chapter 3, we introduced the various types of receptors involved in cell signaling. Now we are ready to pick up that "thread" again as we examine the action of receptors that bind neurotransmitters. For the most part, neurotransmitter receptors are either channel-linked receptors that mediate fast synaptic transmission or G protein-linked receptors that oversee slow synaptic responses.

Mechanism of Action of Channel-Linked Receptors.
Channel-linked receptors (equivalent to ligand-gated ion channels) mediate direct transmitter action. These receptors are composed of several protein subunits arranged to form a "rosette" around a central pore (Figure 11.23a). As the ligand binds to one (or more) of the receptor subunits, the proteins promptly change shape. This event opens the central channel and allows ions to pass, altering the membrane potential of the target cell. Channel-linked receptors are always located precisely opposite sites of neurotransmitter release, and their ion channels open instantly upon ligand binding and remain open 1 ms or less while the ligand is bound. At excitatory receptor sites (nicotinic ACh channels and receptors for glutamate, aspartate, and ATP), the channel-linked receptors are *cation* channels that allow small cations (Na^+, K^+, and Ca^{2+}) to pass, but the greatest drive is for Na^+ entry, which contributes to membrane depolarization. Channel-linked receptors that respond to GABA and glycine, and allow K^+ or Cl^- to pass, mediate fast inhibition (hyperpolarization).

Mechanism of Action of G Protein–Linked Receptors.
Unlike responses to neurotransmitter binding at channel-linked receptors, which are immediate, simple, brief, and highly localized to a single postsynaptic cell, the activity mediated by **G protein–linked receptors** is indirect and tends to be slow (100s of ms or more), complex, prolonged, and often diffuse—ideal as a basis for some types of learning. Receptors that fall into this class are transmembrane protein complexes and include muscarinic ACh receptors and those that bind the biogenic amines and peptide neurotransmitters. When a neurotransmitter binds to a G protein–linked receptor, the G protein is activated (Figure 11.23b). Activated G proteins sometimes act directly to open or close ion channels, but more often they bring about their effects by controlling the production of second messengers such as **cyclic AMP, cyclic GMP, or Ca^{2+}**. These, in turn, act as go-betweens to regulate ion channels or to activate kinase enzymes that initiate a cascade of enzymatic

Why is cyclic AMP called a "second messenger"?

FIGURE 11.23
Neurotransmitter receptor mechanisms. (a) Channel-linked receptors (ligand-activated ion channels) open in response to ligand (ACh in this case) binding. When no ligand is bound, the channel is effectively closed and no current passes through the channel. Immediately upon ligand binding, the channel opens and ions begin to flow through the channel. The precise ion current is determined by the structure and charge of the channel proteins. (In ACh channels, cations (Na^+, K^+, and Ca^{2+}) pass, resulting in a depolarizing current. **(b)** Mechanism of a G protein–linked receptor. In the example shown, effects are mediated by cyclic AMP, which acts as a second messenger to relay the signal from the receptor to other cell components. (1) Unbound receptor. (2) Binding of the neurotransmitter (ligand) to the receptor results in receptor–G protein interaction and activation of the G protein. Once GTP replaces GDP in the G protein complex, the G protein is enabled to interact with and activate adenylate cyclase (3). (4) Activated adenylate cyclase catalyzes the formation of cyclic AMP from ATP. (5) Cyclic AMP, acting as an intracellular second messenger, then mediates events leading to the activation of various enzymes that bring about the postsynaptic neuron's response (changes in membrane potential, protein synthesis, etc.).

reactions in the target cells. Some of these modify (activate or inactivate) other proteins (including channel proteins) by attaching phosphate groups to them. Others interact with nuclear proteins that activate genes and induce synthesis of new proteins in the target cell.

BASIC CONCEPTS OF NEURAL INTEGRATION

Until now, we have been concentrating on the activities of individual neurons or, at most, a pair of nerve cells that make synaptic contacts with each other. However, neurons function in groups, and each group contributes to still broader neural functions. Thus, the organization of the nervous system is hierarchical, or ladderlike.

Any time you have a large number of *anything*—people included—there must be *integration;* that is, the parts must be fused into a smoothly operating whole. In this section, we will begin to ascend the ladder of **neural integration,** dealing only with the first rung, *neuronal pools* and their basic patterns of communicating with other parts of the nervous system. Chapter 15 picks up the thread of neural integration once again to examine how sensory inputs interface with motor activity, and looks at the highest levels of neural integration—how we think, remember, and communicate with language.

Organization of Neurons: Neuronal Pools

The millions of neurons in the central nervous system are organized into **neuronal pools,** functional groups of neurons that process and integrate incoming information received from other sources (receptors or different neuronal pools) and then forward, or transmit, the processed information to other destinations.

The composition of a simple type of neuronal pool is shown in Figure 11.24. In this example, one incoming presynaptic fiber branches profusely as it enters the pool and then synapses with several different neurons in the pool. When the incoming fiber is excited, it will excite some postsynaptic neurons and facilitate others. Neurons most likely to generate impulses are those closely associated with the incoming fiber, because they receive the bulk of the synaptic contacts. Those neurons are said to be in the **discharge zone** of the neuronal pool. Neurons farther away from the center are not usually excited to threshold by the incoming fiber, but they are facilitated and can easily be brought to threshold by stimuli from another source. Thus, the periphery of the pool is the **facilitated zone.** Keep in mind, however, that our figure is a gross oversimplification. Most neuronal pools consist of thousands of neurons and include inhibitory as well as excitatory neurons.

Types of Circuits

Individual neurons within a neuronal pool both send and receive information, and synaptic contacts may cause either excitation or inhibition. The patterns of synaptic connections in neuronal pools are called **circuits,** and they determine the functional capabilities

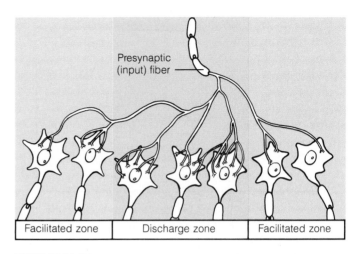

FIGURE 11.24
Simple neuronal pool. This simplified representation of a neuronal pool contains seven neurons and shows the relative position of postsynaptic neurons in the discharge and facilitated zones. Notice that the presynaptic fiber makes more synapses per neuron with neurons in the discharge zone.

of each type of pool. Although some circuits are very complicated, we can gain some understanding of their properties by studying four basic types: diverging, converging, reverberating, and parallel after-discharge circuits. These circuit patterns are shown in simplified form in Figure 11.25.

In **diverging circuits,** one incoming fiber triggers responses in ever-increasing numbers of neurons farther and farther along in the circuit: thus, diverging circuits are often *amplifying* circuits. Divergence can occur along a single pathway or along several (see Figure 11.25a and b, respectively). These circuits are common in both sensory and motor systems. For

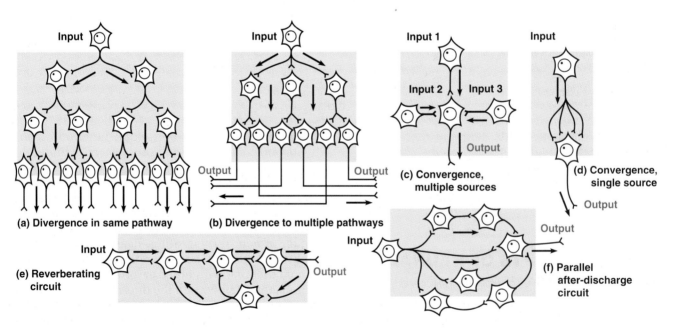

FIGURE 11.25
Types of circuits in neuronal pools.

example, input from a single sensory receptor may be relayed up the spinal cord and on to several different brain regions at the same time. Likewise, impulses traveling downward from a single neuron of the brain can activate a hundred or more motor neurons in the spinal cord and, consequently, thousands of skeletal muscle fibers.

The pattern of **converging circuits** is opposite that of diverging circuits, but they too are common in both sensory and motor pathways. In these circuits, the pool receives inputs from several presynaptic neurons, and the circuit as a whole has a funneling, or *concentrating,* effect. Incoming stimuli may converge from many different areas (see Figure 11.25c) or from the same source (see Figure 11.25d), which results in strong stimulation or inhibition. The former condition helps explain how different types of sensory stimuli can cause the same ultimate effect or reaction. For instance, seeing the smiling face of their infant, smelling the baby's freshly powdered skin, or hearing the baby gurgle can all trigger a flood of loving feelings in parents.

In **reverberating,** or **oscillating, circuits** (see Figure 11.25e), the incoming signal travels through a chain of neurons, each of which makes collateral synapses with neurons in the previous part of the pathway. As a result of the positive feedback, the impulses reverberate (are sent through the circuit again and again), giving a continuous output signal until one neuron in the circuit is inhibited and fails to fire. Reverberating circuits may be involved in control of rhythmic activities, such as the sleep-wake cycle, breathing, and certain motor activities (such as arm swinging when walking). Some researchers believe that such circuits underlie short-term memory. Depending on the arrangement and number of neurons in the circuit, reverberating circuits may continue to oscillate for seconds, hours, or (in the case of the circuit controlling the rhythm of breathing) even a lifetime.

In **parallel after-discharge circuits,** the incoming fiber stimulates several neurons arranged in parallel arrays that eventually stimulate a common output cell (see Figure 11.25f). Impulses reach the output cell at different times, creating a burst of impulses called an *after discharge* that lasts 15 ms or more after the initial input has ended. Unlike the reverberating circuit, this type of circuit has no positive feedback, and once all the neurons have fired, circuit activity ends. Parallel, after-discharge circuits may be involved in complex, exacting types of mental processing, such as performing mathematics or other types of problem solving.

Patterns of Neural Processing

Processing of inputs in the various circuits is both *serial* and *parallel.* In serial processing, the input travels along a single pathway to a specific destination. In parallel processing, the input travels along

FIGURE 11.26
A simple reflex arc. The essential elements in a vertebrate reflex arc—receptor, sensory neuron, integration center, motor neuron, and effector—are illustrated.

several different pathways to be integrated in different CNS regions. Each mode of information handling has unique advantages in the overall scheme of neural functioning.

Serial Processing

In **serial processing,** the whole system works in a predictable all-or-nothing manner. One neuron stimulates the next in sequence, which stimulates the next, and so on, eventually causing a specific, anticipated response. The most clear-cut examples of serial processing are provided by spinal reflexes, but straight-through sensory pathways from the receptors to the brain provide additional examples. Since reflexes are the functional units of the nervous system, it is important that you gain at least some understanding of them early on.

Reflexes are rapid, automatic responses to stimuli, in which a particular stimulus always causes the same motor response. You could say that reflex activity is stereotyped and dependable. For example, touching a hot object makes us withdraw our hand, and an object approaching the eye triggers a blink. Reflexes occur over neural pathways called **reflex arcs** that have five essential components—receptor, sensory neuron, CNS integration center, motor neuron, and effector (Figure 11.26). Reflexes are described in detail in Chapter 13.

Parallel Processing

In **parallel processing,** inputs are segregated into many different pathways, and information delivered by each pathway is dealt with simultaneously by different parts of the neural circuitry. For example, smelling a pickle (the input) may cause you to remember picking cucumbers on a farm; or it may remind you that you don't like pickles or that you must buy some at the market; or perhaps it will call to mind *all* these thoughts. For each person, parallel processing will trigger some pathways that are unique. The same stimulus—pickle smell, in our

A CLOSER LOOK | Pleasure Me, Pleasure Me!

Deep inside the hypothalamus is a small bundle of neural tissue, called the *pleasure center,* that motivates much of human behavior. The pleasure center reinforces our drives to eat, drink, and procreate, but in doing so it also makes us perilously vulnerable. Few would deny that much of what we do and value is driven by the "pleasure principle," and herein lies the genesis of addiction.

Our ability to "feel good" involves brain neurotransmitters. For example, the ecstasy of romantic love has been described as a "brain bath" of norepinephrine, dopamine, and especially phenylethylamine (PEA), which activate the pleasure center. Cole Porter knew what he was talking about when he wrote "I get a kick out of you," because these neurotransmitters are chemical cousins of the amphetamines. People who use "speed" (methamphetamine) artificially stimulate their brains to provide their pleasure flush. However, their pleasure is short lived, because when the brain is flooded with neurotransmitterlike chemicals from the outside, it makes less of its own (why bother?). The wisdom of the body mediates against unnecessary effort.

Cocaine, another pleasure center titillater, has been around for a long time in its prohibitively expensive granular form, which is inhaled, or "snorted." Enter "crack"—the cheaper, much more potent, smokable form of cocaine. For ten dollars or less, a novice user can get "wasted for the night" and flooded with a rush of intense pleasure. But crack is treacherous and intensely addictive. It produces not only a higher high than the inhaled form of cocaine, but also a deeper crash that leaves the user desperate for more.

Researchers are beginning to zero in on how cocaine produces its effects. This drug first helps to stimulate the pleasure center and then "squeezes it dry." Cocaine produces the rush by hooking up to the dopamine reuptake transporter protein, thus blocking the reabsorption of dopamine. As a result, the neurotransmitter remains in the synapse and stimulates the postsynaptic receptor cells again and again,

allowing the body to feel its effects over a prolonged period. This sensation is accompanied by increases in heart rate, blood pressure, and sexual appetite. But over time—and sometimes after just one use—the effect changes. As dopamine reabsorption continues to be blocked, that accumulated in the synapses is washed away and degraded, and the brain's dopamine supply becomes inadequate to maintain normal mood. The sending cells cannot produce neural dopamine fast enough to make up for its loss, and the pleasure circuits go dry. Meanwhile, the postsynaptic cells become hypersensitive, and sprout new receptors in a desperate effort to pick up dopamine signals. The user becomes anxious and, in a very real sense, unable to experience pleasure without cocaine. A vicious cycle of addiction is established. Cocaine is needed to experience pleasure, but using it further depletes the neurotransmitter supply. Heavy, prolonged cocaine use may deplete the supply so totally that pleasure is impossible to achieve and deep depression sets in. Cocaine addicts tend to lose weight, have trouble sleeping, develop cardiac and pulmonary abnormalities ("crack heart and lung"), and have frequent infections.

Cocaine addiction carries with it a desperate craving that is notoriously difficult to manage or treat. Various drugs have been used with mixed success to treat cocaine addicts. Traditional antiaddiction drugs take so long to reduce the overpowering cravings that users commonly drop out of treatment programs. However, three new drugs are generating excitement as likely candidates to help addicts abandon their addiction. Manzindol, an appetite suppressant, binds dopamine receptors more tightly than cocaine. Flupenthixol decanoate, an antidepressant, eases withdrawal cravings within a few days instead of the 2 to 3 weeks typical of similar drugs. Recent reports on buprenorphine, a pain reliever, look even brighter: Researchers found that laboratory monkeys addicted to cocaine rapidly lost interest in the drug after receiving low doses of buprenorphine.

Vials of crack cocaine and pipe.

Crack use in the United States is a national problem. Like heroin, crack has struck our inner cities with swift fury. However, whereas heroin has had a sordid reputation, cocaine use has been seen as more acceptable, and even small-town middle America is getting hooked. Cocaine-related cardiovascular deaths (due to hypertensive crisis) and strokes are increasing daily, and the rising numbers of underweight brain-damaged "crack babies" are threatening a newer horror still.

As if crack itself is not enough to contend with, a mixture of speed and crack called "croak" (funny or prophetic?) and a new smokable form of speed called "ice" have gained a foothold in southern California. Unlike crack, which creates a 20 to 30 minute high, ice produces a high that lasts for 12 to 24 hours, followed by a crash so tyrannical that it seemingly creates psychosis (paranoid schizophrenia). Moreover, a formaldehyde (embalming fluid)-laced marijuana known on the street as "ill face" has become a popular (and probably poisonous) high on the East Coast.

The pleasure center, with its cries of "pleasure me! pleasure me!," is a powerful Pied Piper. We want to feel young and powerful forever, and we want instant solutions to our problems. But drugs are only temporary solutions. The brain, with its complex biochemistry, always circumvents attempts to keep it in a euphoric haze. Perhaps this means that pleasure must be transient and can be experienced only against a background of its absence.

example—promotes many responses beyond simple awareness of the smell. Parallel processing is not repetitious because the circuits do different things with the information, and each "channel" is decoded in relation to all the others to produce a total picture. As will be explained in more detail in Chapters 13 and 15, even simple reflex arcs do not operate in complete isolation. However, a serially processed, predictable spinal reflex arc is completed at the cord level, whereas parallel processing of the same input is going on at the same time at higher brain levels, allowing the sensory event to be consciously perceived and responded to if necessary.

DEVELOPMENTAL ASPECTS OF NEURONS

The nervous system is covered in several chapters, so we limit our attention here to the development of neurons, beginning with the questions, How do nerve cells originate? and How do they mature? The second question involves some crucial understanding of how neurons form the correct connections with each other and with effector organs so that appropriate behavior can occur.

As described in greater detail in Chapter 12, the nervous system originates from a dorsal *neural tube* and the *neural crest* (see Figure 12.2, p. 380), formed from surface ectoderm. By the fourth week after conception, these cells, called *neuroepithelial* cells at this point, are *determined* in their development; that is, they can only become neural tissue. The neuroepithelial cells then begin a three-phase process of differentiation. First, they *proliferate* to produce the appropriate number of cells (both potential neurons and glial cells) needed for nervous system development. Once this phase ends, the potential neurons become amitotic, and enter the second phase as they *migrate* to characteristic positions in the forming nervous system.

The third phase of neuron development is *cellular differentiation* of the amitotic cells, now called **neuroblasts.** Appropriate neuron types must form, appropriate neurotransmitters must be synthesized, and the correct synapses must be made. Little is known about the biochemical specialization of neurons, but we do know that it depends on establishing synaptic contacts and is influenced by the environment through which neurons migrate and by chemical growth factors. Somehow, specific neurotransmitter genes are activated to cause this differentiation.

Synapse formation poses several difficult questions. How does a neuroblast's growing axon "know" where to go—and, once it gets there, where to stop and make the proper connection? The tortuous growth of an axon toward an appropriate target appears to be guided by multiple signals: a scaffold laid down by similar, older "pathfinder" neurons and orienting glial fibers; nerve growth factor released by

astrocytes; inhibitory chemicals that cause the axon to avoid the area, such as RGM (repulsion guiding molecule); and attracting substances released by the target. For example, skeletal muscles release chemicals that attract motor axons to them. Further, a "sticky" molecule called *nerve cell adhesion molecule (N-CAM)* has been identified on skeletal muscle cells and on the surfaces of glial cells. N-CAM seems to provide some sort of nerve glue during the formative period. This molecule is so important in establishing neural patterns that when it is blocked by antibodies, developing neural tissue falls into a tangled, spaghetti-like mass, and neural function is hopelessly impaired.

The growth of an axon and its ability to interact with and sense its environment reside in a special structure at its growing tip called the **growth cone.** The membrane of the growth cone bears N-CAM molecules and has motile extensions that attach to adjacent structures and pull it along. The growth cone also engulfs molecules from its environment that are then transported to the nerve cell body and inform it of the pathway being taken for growth and synapse formation. Once the axon has reached its general target area, it must select the right site on the right target cell to form a synapse. Recognition of one nerve cell by another is quite specific and requires signaling by both presynaptic and postsynaptic cells. Though the exact mechanism of this interchange is far from clear, trial and error occurs, and gap junctions appear and disappear before permanent chemical synapses are formed.

Neurons that fail to make appropriate synaptic contacts or to participate in the flow of impulses from neuron to neuron act as if they have been deprived of some essential nutrient and die. Besides cell death resulting from unsuccessful synapse formation, *programmed cell death* also appears to be a normal part of the developmental process. Of the neurons formed during the embryonic period, perhaps two-thirds die before we are born. Those that remain constitute our total neural endowment for life. With the notable exception of adult cardiac and skeletal muscle cells, nearly all other body cells can divide, and when some die, they are replaced by mitotic divisions of the remaining cells. However, if neurons were to divide, their connections might be hopelessly disrupted.

* * *

In this chapter, we have examined how the amazingly complex neurons, via their electrical and chemical signals, serve the body in a variety of ways: Some serve as "lookouts," others process information for immediate use or for future reference, and others stimulate the body's muscles and glands into activity. With this background, we are ready to study the most sophisticated mass of neural tissue in the entire body—the brain (and its continuation, the spinal cord), the focus of Chapter 12.

RELATED CLINICAL TERMS

Neuroblastoma (nu″ro-blas-to′mah; *blast* = bud; *oma* = tumor) A malignant tumor made up of neuroblasts.

Neurologist (nu-rol′o-jist) A medical specialist in the study of the nervous system, its functions, and its disorders.

Neuropathy (nu-rop′ah-the) Any disease of the nervous tissue, but particularly degenerative disease of nerves.

Neuropharmacology (nu″ro-far″mah-kol′o-je) Scientific study of the effects of drugs on the nervous system.

Neurotoxin Substance that is poisonous or destructive to nervous tissue, e.g., botulism and tetanus toxins.

Rabies (*rabies* = madness) A viral infection of the nervous system transferred to humans by the bites of infected mammals (dogs, bats, skunks, and so on). After entry, the virus is transported via axonal transport in peripheral nerve axons to the CNS, where it causes brain inflammation, delirium, and death.

CHAPTER SUMMARY

1. The nervous system bears a major responsibility for maintaining body homeostasis. Its chief functions are to monitor, integrate, and respond to information in the environment.

Organization of the Nervous System (pp. 341–342)

1. The nervous system is divided anatomically into the central nervous system (brain and spinal cord) and the peripheral nervous system (cranial and spinal nerves and ganglia).

2. The major functional divisions of the nervous system are the sensory (afferent) division, which conveys impulses to the CNS, and the motor (efferent) division, which conveys impulses from the CNS.

3. The efferent division includes the somatic (voluntary) system, which serves skeletal muscles, and the autonomic (involuntary) system, which innervates smooth and cardiac muscle and glands.

Histology of Nervous Tissue (pp. 342–350)

Supporting Cells (pp. 342–343)
1. Supporting cells segregate and insulate neurons and assist neurons in various other ways.

2. Neuroglial cells, CNS supporting cells, include astrocytes, microglia, ependymal cells, and oligodendrocytes. Schwann cells and satellite cells are supporting cells found in the PNS.

Neurons (pp. 343–350)
3. Neurons have a cell body and cytoplasmic processes called axons and dendrites.

4. The cell body is the biosynthetic center of the neuron. Except for those found in ganglia, cell bodies are found in the CNS.

5. Some neurons have many dendrites, receptive sites that conduct signals from other neurons toward the nerve cell body. With few exceptions, all neurons have one axon, which generates and conducts nerve impulses away from the nerve cell body. Terminal endings of axons release neurotransmitter.

6. Transport along axons occurs via different mechanisms. Best understood is the bidirectional, ATP-dependent process that moves particulate material, neurotransmitters, and enzymes toward the axonal terminals and conducts substances destined for degradation back to the cell body. It involves microtubules, microfilaments, and motor proteins.

7. Large nerve fibers (axons) are myelinated. The myelin sheath is formed in the PNS by Schwann cells and in the CNS by oligodendrocytes. The sheath has gaps called nodes of Ranvier. Unmyelinated fibers are surrounded by supporting cells, but the membrane-wrapping process does not occur.

8. Anatomically, neurons are classified according to the number of processes issuing from the cell body as multipolar, bipolar, or unipolar.

9. Functionally, neurons are classified according to the direction of nerve impulse conduction. Sensory neurons conduct impulses toward the CNS, motor neurons conduct away from the CNS, and association neurons lie between sensory and motor neurons in the neural pathways.

Neurophysiology (pp. 350–371)
Basic Principles of Electricity (pp. 350–351)
1. The measure of the potential energy of separated electrical charges is called voltage (V) or potential. Current (I) is the flow of electrical charge from one point to another. Resistance (R) is hindrance to current flow. The relationship among these is given by Ohm's law: $I = V/R$.

2. In the body, electrical charges are provided by ions; cellular plasma membranes provide resistance to ion flow. The membranes contain passive (open) and active (gated) channels.

The Resting Membrane Potential: The Polarized State (pp. 351–352)
3. A resting neuron exhibits a voltage called the resting membrane potential, which is -70 mV (inside negative), owing to differences in sodium and potassium ion concentrations inside and outside the cell.

4. The ionic differences result from greater permeability of the membrane to potassium than to sodium and from the operation of the sodium-potassium pump, which ejects $3Na^+$ from the cell for each $2K^+$ transported in.

Membrane Potentials That Act as Signals (pp. 352–360)
5. Depolarization is a reduction in membrane potential (inside becomes less negative); hyperpolarization is an increase in membrane potential (inside becomes more negative).

6. Graded potentials are small, brief, local changes in membrane potential that act as short-distance signals. The current produced dissipates with distance.

7. An action potential, or nerve impulse, is a large, but brief, depolarization signal (and polarity reversal) that underlies long-distance neural communication. It is an all-or-none phenomenon.

8. Generation of an action potential involves three phases: (1) Increase in sodium permeability and reversal of the membrane potential to approximately $+30$ mV (inside positive). Local depolarization opens voltage-regulated sodium gates; at threshold, depolarization becomes self-generating (driven by sodium ion influx). (2) Decrease in sodium permeability. (3) Increase in potassium permeability and repolarization.

9. In nerve impulse propagation, each action potential provides the depolarizing stimulus for triggering an action potential in the next membrane patch. Regions that have just generated action potentials are refractory; hence, the nerve impulse is propagated in one direction only.

10. If threshold is reached, an action potential is generated; if not, the depolarization remains local.

11. Action potentials are independent of stimulus strength: strong stimuli cause action potentials to be generated more frequently but not with greater amplitude.

12. During the absolute refractory period, a neuron cannot respond to another stimulus because it is already generating an action potential. During the relative refractory period the neuron's threshold is elevated because repolarization is ongoing.

13. In unmyelinated fibers, action potentials are produced in a wave all along the axon; in myelinated fibers, action potentials are generated only at nodes of Ranvier and are propagated more rapidly by saltatory conduction.

14. Nerve fibers are classified according to diameter, degree of myelination, and speed of conduction as A, B, or C fibers.

The Synapse (pp. 360–362)

15. A synapse is a functional junction between neurons. The information-transmitting neuron is the presynaptic neuron; the neuron beyond the synapse is the postsynaptic neuron.

16. Electrical synapses allow ions to flow directly from one neuron to another; the cells are electrically coupled.

17. Chemical synapses are sites of neurotransmitter release and binding. When the impulse reaches the presynaptic axonal terminals, Ca^{2+} enters the cell and mediates neurotransmitter release. Neurotransmitters diffuse across the synaptic cleft and attach to postsynaptic membrane receptors, opening ion channels. After binding, the neurotransmitters are removed from the synapse by enzymatic breakdown or by reuptake into the presynaptic terminal.

Postsynaptic Potentials and Synaptic Integration (pp. 362–366)

18. Binding of neurotransmitter at excitatory chemical synapses results in local graded depolarizations called EPSPs, caused by the opening of channels that allow simultaneous passage of Na^+ and K^+.

19. Neurotransmitter binding at inhibitory chemical synapses results in hyperpolarizations called IPSPs, caused by the opening of K^+ and/or Cl^- gates. IPSPs drive the membrane potential farther from threshold.

20. EPSPs and IPSPs summate temporally and spatially. The membrane of the axon hillock acts as a neuronal integrator.

21. Synaptic potentiation, in which the postsynaptic neuron's response is enhanced, is produced by intense repeated stimulation. Ionic calcium appears to mediate such effects, which may be the basis of learning.

22. Presynaptic inhibition is mediated by axoaxonal synapses that reduce the amount of neurotransmitter released by the inhibited neuron. Neuromodulation occurs when chemicals (often other than neurotransmitters) alter neuronal or neurotransmitter activity.

Neurotransmitters and Their Receptors (pp. 366–371)

23. The major classes of neurotransmitters based on chemical structure are acetylcholine, biogenic amines, amino acids, and peptides.

24. Functionally, neurotransmitters are classified as (1) inhibitory or excitatory (or both) and (2) direct or indirect. Direct-acting neurotransmitters cause channel opening. Indirect-acting neurotransmitters act through second messengers and cause complex changes in target cell metabolism.

25. Neurotransmitter receptors are either channel-linked receptors that open ion channels leading to fast changes in membrane potential, or G protein–linked receptors that oversee slow synaptic responses mediated by G proteins and intracellular second messengers. Most often kinases are activated, which in turn act on ion channels or activate other proteins.

Basic Concepts of Neural Integration (pp. 371–375)

Organization of Neurons: Neuronal Pools (p. 372)

1. CNS neurons are organized into several types of neuronal pools, each with distinguishing patterns of synaptic connections called circuits.

Types of Circuits (pp. 372–373)

2. The four basic circuit types are diverging, converging, reverberating, and parallel after-discharge.

Patterns of Neural Processing (pp. 373–375)

3. In serial processing, one neuron stimulates the next in sequence, producing specific, predictable responses, as in spinal reflexes. A reflex is a rapid, involuntary motor response to a stimulus.

4. Reflexes are mediated over neural pathways called reflex arcs. The minimum number of elements in a reflex arc is five: receptor, sensory neuron, integration center, motor neuron, and effector.

5. In parallel processing, which underlies complex mental functions, impulses are sent along several pathways to different integration centers.

Developmental Aspects of Neurons (p. 375)

1. Neuron development involves proliferation, migration, and cellular differentiation. Cellular differentiation entails neuron specialization, specific neurotransmitter synthesis, and synapse formation.

2. Axonal outgrowth and synapse formation are guided by other neurons, glial fibers, and chemicals (such as N-CAM and nerve growth factor).

3. Neurons that do not make appropriate synapses die, and approximately two-thirds of neurons formed in the embryo undergo programmed cell death before birth.

REVIEW QUESTIONS

Multiple Choice/Matching

1. Which of the following structures is not part of the central nervous system? (a) the brain, (b) a nerve, (c) the spinal cord, (d) a tract.

2. Match the names of the supporting cells found in column B with the appropriate descriptions in column A.

Column A	Column B
_____ **(1)** myelinates nerve fibers in the CNS	**(a)** astrocyte
_____ **(2)** lines brain cavities	**(b)** ependymal cell
_____ **(3)** myelinates nerve fibers in the PNS	**(c)** microglia
_____ **(4)** CNS phagocytes	**(d)** oligodendrocyte
_____ **(5)** may help regulate the ionic composition of the extracellular fluid	**(e)** satellite cell
	(f) Schwann cell

3. What type of current flows through the axolemma during the steep phase of repolarization? (a) chiefly a sodium current, (b) chiefly a potassium current, (c) sodium and potassium currents of approximately the same magnitude.

4. Assume that an EPSP is being generated on the dendritic membrane. Which will occur? (a) specific Na^+ gates will open, (b) specific K^+ gates will open, (c) a single type of channel will open, permitting simultaneous flow of Na^+ and K^+, (d) Na^+ gates will open first and then close as K^+ gates open.

5. The velocity of nerve impulse conduction is greatest in (a) heavily myelinated, large-diameter fibers, (b) myelinated, small-diameter fibers, (c) unmyelinated, small-diameter fibers, (d) unmyelinated, large-diameter fibers.

6. Chemical synapses are characterized by all of the following except (a) the release of neurotransmitter by the presynaptic membranes, (b) postsynaptic membranes bearing receptors that bind neurotransmitter, (c) ions flowing through protein channels from the presynaptic to the postsynaptic neuron, (d) a fluid-filled gap separating the neurons.

7. Biogenic amine neurotransmitters include all but (a) norepinephrine, (b) acetylcholine, (c) dopamine, (d) serotonin.

8. The neuropeptides that act as natural opiates are (a) substance P, (b) somatostatin, (c) cholecystokinin, (d) enkephalins.

9. Inhibition of acetylcholinesterase by poisoning blocks neurotransmission at the neuromuscular junction because (a) ACh is no longer released by the presynaptic terminal, (b) ACh synthesis in the presynaptic terminal is blocked, (c) ACh is not degraded, hence prolonged depolarization is enforced on the postsynaptic neuron, (d) ACh is blocked from attaching to the postsynaptic ACh receptors.

10. The anatomic region of a multipolar neuron that has the lowest threshold for generating an action potential is the (a) soma, (b) dendrites, (c) axon hillock, (d) distal axon.

11. An IPSP is inhibitory because (a) it hyperpolarizes the postsynaptic membrane, (b) it reduces the amount of neurotransmitter released by the presynaptic terminal, (c) it prevents calcium ion entry into the presynaptic terminal, (d) it changes the threshold of the neuron.

12. Identify the neuronal circuits described by choosing the correct response from the key.

Key: (a) converging, **(b)** diverging, **(c)** parallel after-discharge, **(d)** reverberating

_____ **(1)** Impulses continue around and around the circuit until one neuron stops firing.

_____ **(2)** One or a few inputs ultimately influence large numbers of neurons.

_____ **(3)** Many neurons influence a few neurons.

_____ **(4)** May be involved in exacting types of mental activity.

Short Answer Essay Questions

13. Explain both the anatomical and functional divisions of the nervous system. Include the subdivisions of each.

14. (a) Describe the composition and function of the cell body. (b) How are axons and dendrites alike? In what ways (structurally and functionally) do they differ?

15. (a) What is myelin? (b) How does the myelination process differ in the CNS and PNS?

16. (a) Contrast unipolar, bipolar, and multipolar neurons structurally. (b) Indicate where each is most likely to be found.

17. What is the polarized membrane state? How is it maintained? (Note the relative roles of both passive and active mechanisms.)

18. Describe the events that must occur to generate an action potential. Indicate how the ionic gates are controlled, and explain why the action potential is an all-or-none phenomenon.

19. Since all action potentials generated by a given nerve fiber have the same magnitude, how does the CNS "know" whether a stimulus is strong or weak?

20. (a) Explain the difference between an EPSP and an IPSP. (b) What specifically determines whether an EPSP or IPSP will be generated at the postsynaptic membrane?

21. Since at any moment a neuron is likely to have thousands of neurons releasing neurotransmitters at its surface, how is neuronal activity (to fire or not to fire) determined?

22. The effects of neurotransmitter binding are very brief. Explain.

23. During a neurobiology lecture, a professor repeatedly refers to type A and type B fibers, absolute refractory period, and nodes of Ranvier. Define these terms.

24. Distinguish between serial and parallel processing.

25. Briefly describe the three stages of neuron development.

26. What factors appear to guide the outgrowth of an axon and its ability to make the "correct" synaptic contacts?

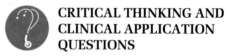

CRITICAL THINKING AND CLINICAL APPLICATION QUESTIONS

1. Mr. Miller is hospitalized for cardiac problems. Somehow, medical orders are mixed up and Mr. Miller is infused with a K^+-enhanced intravenous solution meant for another patient who is taking potassium-wasting diuretics (i.e., drugs that cause excessive loss of potassium from the body in urine). Mr. Miller's potassium levels are normal before the IV is administered. What do you think will happen to Mr. Miller's neuronal resting potentials? To his neurons' ability to generate action potentials?

2. General and local anesthetics block action potential generation, thereby rendering the nervous system quiescent while surgery is performed. What specific process do anesthetics impair, and how does this interfere with nerve transmission?

3. When admitted to the emergency room, John was holding his right hand, which had a deep puncture hole in its palm. He explained that he had fallen on a nail while exploring a barn. John was given an antitetanus shot to prevent neural complications. Tetanus bacteria fester in deep, dark wounds, but how do they travel in neural tissue?

4. Rochelle developed multiple sclerosis when she was 27. After 8 years she had lost a good portion of her ability to control her skeletal muscles. Why did this happen?

CHAPTER OUTLINE AND STUDENT OBJECTIVES

The Brain (pp. 380–408)

1. Describe the process of brain development.

2. Name the major regions of the adult brain.

3. Define the term ventricle and indicate the location of the ventricles of the brain.

4. List the major lobes, fissures, and functional areas of the cerebral cortex.

5. Explain lateralization of hemispheric function.

6. Differentiate between commissures, association fibers, and projection fibers.

7. State the general function of the basal nuclei.

8. Describe the location of the diencephalon, and name its subdivisions.

9. Identify the three major regions of the brain stem, and note the general function of each area.

10. Describe the structure and function of the cerebellum.

11. Localize the limbic system and the reticular formation and explain the role of each functional system.

12. Describe how meninges, cerebrospinal fluid, and the blood-brain barrier protect the central nervous system.

13. Describe the formation of cerebrospinal fluid, and follow its circulatory pathway.

14. Distinguish between a concussion and a contusion.

15. Describe the cause (if known) and major signs and symptoms of cerebrovascular accidents and Alzheimer's disease.

The Spinal Cord (pp. 408–418)

16. Describe the embryonic development of the spinal cord.

17. Describe the gross and microscopic structure of the spinal cord.

18. List the major spinal cord tracts, and describe each in terms of its origin, termination, and function.

19. Distinguish between flaccid and spastic paralysis, and between paralysis and paresthesia.

Diagnostic Procedures for Assessing CNS Dysfunction (pp. 418–419)

20. List and explain several techniques used to diagnose brain disorders.

Developmental Aspects of the Central Nervous System (pp. 419–421)

21. Indicate several maternal factors that can impair development of the nervous system in an embryo.

22. Explain how true senility and reversible senility differ in cause and consequence.

H istorically, the **central nervous system (CNS)**—brain and spinal cord—has been compared to the central switchboard of a telephone system that interconnects and directs a dizzying number of incoming and outgoing calls. Nowadays, many envision the CNS as a kind of computer. These analogies may explain some of the workings of the spinal cord, but neither does justice to the fantastic complexity and flexibility of the human brain. Whether we view it as an evolved biological organ, an impressive computer, or simply a miracle, the human brain is certainly one of the most amazing things known.

During the course of animal evolution, **cephalization** (sĕ"fah-lĭ-za'shun) has occurred. That is, there has been an elaboration of the rostral ("toward the snout"), or anterior, portion of the central nervous system, accompanied by an increased number of neurons in the head. This phenomenon reaches its highest level in the human brain.

This chapter focuses on the structure of the central nervous system and touches on the functions associated with its specific anatomical regions. Its more complex integrative functions, such as sensory and motor integration, sleep-wake cycles, and higher mental functions (consciousness, memory, and language processing) are deferred to Chapter 15.

FIGURE 12.1
Surface anatomy of a human brain, left lateral aspect.

Labels: Left cerebral hemisphere; Brain stem; Cerebellum

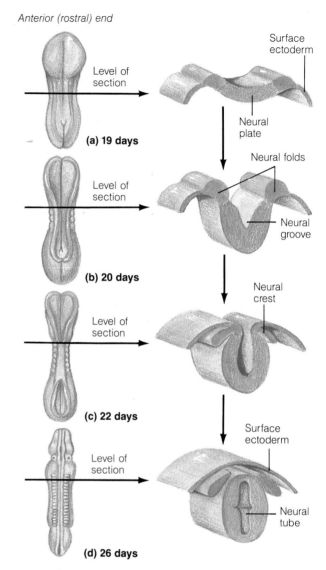

Anterior (rostral) end

(a) 19 days — Level of section; Surface ectoderm; Neural plate

(b) 20 days — Level of section; Neural folds; Neural groove

(c) 22 days — Level of section; Neural crest

(d) 26 days — Level of section; Surface ectoderm; Neural tube

FIGURE 12.2
Development of the neural tube from embryonic ectoderm. Dorsal surface views of the embryo are shown at the left; transverse sections are shown at the right. **(a)** Formation of the neural plate from surface ectoderm. **(b–d)** Progressive development of the neural plate into the neural groove (flanked by neural folds) and then the neural tube. The neural tube forms CNS structures; the neural crest cells form some PNS structures.

THE BRAIN

Well hidden from view within its bony case, the brain was unapproachable by science for centuries. Indeed, Aristotle, who decreed that the heart was the seat of the soul, believed that the brain, composed of water, just cooled it. We now know a good deal more about the brain. Nonetheless, the unimpressive appearance of the human **brain** (Figure 12.1) gives few hints of its remarkable abilities. It is about two good fistfuls of pinkish gray tissue, wrinkled like a walnut, and somewhat the consistency of cold oatmeal. This quivering mass is hardly what one would expect of the keeper of our memories and understandings and the basis of our unique behavior!

The average adult man's brain weighs about 1600 g (3.5 pounds); that of a woman averages 1450 g. In terms of brain weight per body weight, however, males and females have equivalent brain sizes. Brain size does not seem to be the main determinant of brainpower; the complexity of the neural "wiring" appears to be much more important. Albert Einstein's brain was only average in size, and he was an acknowledged genius, while the prehistoric Neanderthal brain (which produced, at best, a limited technology) is estimated to have been 15% larger than that of humans living today.

Embryonic Development of the Brain

We will break from our usual pattern here and discuss embryonic brain development first, because the terminology used for the structural divisions of the adult brain is easier to understand when you comprehend brain embryology. The earliest phase of brain development is shown in Figure 12.2. Starting in the third week of pregnancy, the ectoderm thickens along the dorsal midline axis of the embryo to form the **neural plate,** which eventually gives rise to all neural tissues. The neural plate then invaginates, forming a groove flanked by **neural folds.** As the groove deepens, the superior edges of the neural folds fuse, forming the **neural tube,** which soon detaches from the surface ectoderm and assumes a deeper position. The neural tube is formed by the fourth week of pregnancy and differentiates rapidly into the CNS. The brain forms

(a) Neural tube	(b) Primary brain vesicles	(c) Secondary brain vesicles	(d) Adult brain structures	(e) Adult neural canal regions
Anterior (rostral)	Prosencephalon (forebrain)	Telencephalon	Cerebrum: Cerebral hemispheres (cortex, white matter, basal nuclei)	Lateral ventricles Superior portion of third ventricle
		Diencephalon	Diencephalon (thalamus, hypothalamus, epithalamus)	Most of third ventricle
	Mesencephalon (midbrain)	Mesencephalon	Brain stem: midbrain	Cerebral aqueduct
	Rhombencephalon (hindbrain)	Metencephalon	Brain stem: pons	Fourth ventricle
			Cerebellum	
		Myelencephalon	Brain stem: medulla oblongata	
Posterior (caudal)			Spinal cord	Central canal

FIGURE 12.3
Embryonic development of the human brain. **(a)** The neural tube becomes subdivided into **(b)** the primary brain vesicles, which subsequently form **(c)** the secondary brain vesicles, which differentiate into **(d)** the adult brain structures. **(e)** The adult structures derived from the neural canal.

anteriorly (rostrally) and the spinal cord develops from the caudal ("toward the tail") or posterior portion of the neural tube. Small groups of neural fold cells migrate laterally from between the surface ectoderm and the neural tube to form the tissue called the **neural crest,** which gives rise to sensory neurons and some autonomic neurons destined to reside in ganglia.

As soon as the neural tube is formed, its anterior end begins to expand more rapidly than the remaining portion, and constrictions appear that mark off the three **primary brain vesicles** (Figure 12.3): the **prosencephalon** (pros"en-sef'ah-lon), or **forebrain;** the **mesencephalon** (mes"en-sef'ah-lon), or **midbrain;** and the **rhombencephalon** (romb"en-sef'ah-lon), or **hindbrain.** (Note that the word stem *encephalo* means brain.) The remainder of the neural tube becomes the spinal cord. We will discuss its development later in the chapter.

By the fifth week, five brain regions, the **secondary brain vesicles,** are evident. The forebrain has divided into the **telencephalon** ("endbrain") and **diencephalon** ("interbrain"), and the hindbrain has constricted to form the **metencephalon** ("afterbrain") and **myelencephalon** ("spinal brain"). The midbrain remains undivided. Each of the five secondary brain vesicles then develops rapidly to produce the major structures of the adult brain (Figure 12.3d). The greatest change occurs in the telencephalon, which sprouts two swellings that project anteriorly, looking somewhat like Mickey Mouse's ears. These paired expansions become the *cerebral hemispheres,* re-

ferred to collectively as the **cerebrum** (ser'ĕ-brum). Various areas of the diencephalon, also part of the forebrain, specialize to form the *hypothalamus* (hi"po-thal'ah-mus), *thalamus,* and *epithalamus.* Less dramatic changes occur in the mesencephalon, metencephalon, and myelencephalon as these regions are transformed into the *midbrain, pons* and *cerebellum,* and *medulla oblongata,* respectively. All of these midbrain and hindbrain structures, except for the cerebellum, form the **brain stem.** The central cavity of the neural tube remains continuous and becomes enlarged in four areas to form the fluid-filled *ventricles* (*ventr* = little belly) of the brain. The ventricles are described shortly.

During this period when the brain is growing rapidly, changes also occur in the relative positions of its parts. Because the brain's growth is restricted by a membranous skull, two major flexures develop—the *midbrain* and *cervical flexures*—which bend the forebrain toward the brain stem (Figure 12.4a). A second consequence of restricted space is that the cerebral hemispheres, hindered from continuing their anterior course, are forced to take a horseshoe-shaped course posteriorly and laterally (indicated by the arrows in Figure 12.4b and c). As a result, they grow back over and almost completely envelop the diencephalon and midbrain. Continued growth of the cerebral hemispheres causes their surfaces to crease and fold (Figure 12.4d), producing their typical *convolutions* and increasing their surface area, which allows more neurons to occupy the limited space.

? *Which region of the brain is tremendously elaborated in humans?*

FIGURE 12.4
Effect of space restriction on brain development.
(a) Formation of two major flexures by the fifth week of development causes the telencephalon and diencephalon to be angled toward the brain stem. Development of the cerebral hemispheres at **(b)** 13 weeks, **(c)** 26 weeks, and **(d)** birth. Initially, the cerebral surface is smooth; convolutions become more obvious as development continues. The posterolateral growth of the cerebral hemispheres ultimately completely encloses the diencephalon and superior aspect of the brain stem.

Regions and Organization of the Brain

There are various approaches to describing brain structure. Some neuroanatomists (and textbooks) discuss brain anatomy in terms of the five secondary vesicles (see Figure 12.3c); this is the *embryonic scheme.* In clinical agencies, the names of the adult brain regions are more often heard (see Figure 12.3d). In this text, we will consider the brain in terms of the following subdivisions shown in Figure 12.5: (1) cerebral hemispheres, (2) diencephalon (thalamus, hypothalamus, and epithalamus), (3) brain stem (midbrain, pons, and medulla), and (4) cerebellum. Most anatomists favor this scheme, but some classify the diencephalon as part of the brain stem, while others group it with the cerebral hemispheres as part of the *cerebrum.*

The basic pattern of the CNS is that seen in the spinal cord—a central cavity surrounded by a gray matter core of brain nuclei, external to which is white matter (myelinated fiber tracts). The brain exhibits this basic design but it also contains additional regions of gray matter that are not evident in the spinal cord (Figure 12.6). Both the cerebral hemispheres and the cerebellum have an outer "bark" or cortex of gray matter (neuron cell bodies). This pattern changes with descent through the brain stem— the cortex disappears, but scattered gray matter nuclei are seen within the white matter. At the caudal end of the brain stem, the basic pattern is evident.

To help you picture the spatial relationships among the brain regions, we first consider the fluid-filled ventricles that lie deep within the brain. Then the location and structure of each of the brain regions are described in turn (rostral to caudal) to flesh out the brief summary provided in Table 12.1 on p. 393.

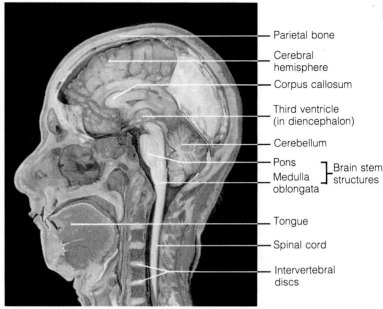

(a)

Cerebral hemisphere

Diencephalon

Brain stem

Cerebellum

(b)

Parietal bone

Cerebral hemisphere

Corpus callosum

Third ventricle (in diencephalon)

Cerebellum

Pons
Medulla oblongata
} Brain stem structures

Tongue

Spinal cord

Intervertebral discs

FIGURE 12.5
Regions of the brain. (a) The brain is a bilateral and essentially symmetrical group of structures that can be considered in terms of four main parts: the cerebral hemispheres, the diencephalon, the brain stem, and the cerebellum. **(b)** Sagittal section of the brain *in situ* (in its normal position in the skull) showing these parts.

Ventricles of the Brain

As noted earlier, the **ventricles** of the brain arise from expansions of the lumen of the embryonic neural tube. They are continuous with each other and with the central canal of the spinal cord (Figure 12.7). The hollow ventricular chambers are filled with cerebrospinal fluid and lined by *ependymal cells,* a type of neuroglia (see Figure 11.2c).

The paired **lateral ventricles,** once called the first and second ventricles, are large C-shaped chambers that reflect the pattern of cerebral growth. One lateral ventricle is located deep within each cerebral hemisphere. Anteriorly, the lateral ventricles lie close together, separated only by a thin median membrane called the **septum pellucidum** (pĕ-lu′sid-um; "transparent wall"). (See Figures 12.7a and 12.14a.) Each lateral ventricle communicates with the narrow **third ventricle** in the diencephalon via a small opening called the **interventricular foramen** *(foramen of Monro).* The third ventricle is continuous with the **fourth ventricle** via the canal-like **cerebral aqueduct** that runs through the midbrain. The fourth ventricle, which lies dorsal to the pons and superior medulla, is continuous with the central canal of the spinal cord inferiorly. Three openings mark the walls of the fourth ventricle: the paired **lateral apertures** in its side walls and the **median aperture** in its roof. These apertures connect the ventricles to the *subarachnoid* (sub″ah-rak′noid) *space,* a fluid-filled space surrounding the brain. The importance of the cerebrospinal (ser″ĕ-bro-spi′nal) fluid, which fills both the internal brain cavities and the subarachnoid space, is discussed later in the chapter.

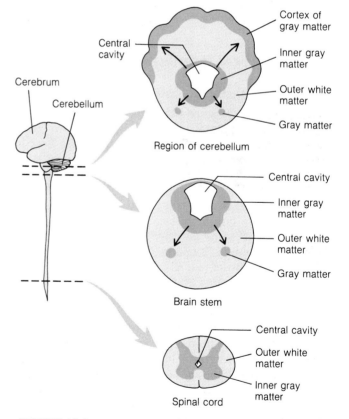

Cerebrum

Cerebellum

Central cavity

Cortex of gray matter

Inner gray matter

Outer white matter

Gray matter

Region of cerebellum

Central cavity

Inner gray matter

Outer white matter

Gray matter

Brain stem

Central cavity

Outer white matter

Inner gray matter

Spinal cord

FIGURE 12.6
Arrangement of gray and white matter in the CNS (highly simplified). From top to bottom, the diagrams represent cross sections at the level of the cerebellum, brain stem, and spinal cord. In each section, the dorsal aspect is above. In general, white matter lies external to gray matter; however, collections of gray matter migrate externally into the white matter in the developing brain (see arrows). The cerebrum resembles the cerebellum in its external cortex of gray matter.

? *Why are the lateral ventricles horn-shaped instead of being vertically erect structures like the third and fourth ventricles?*

FIGURE 12.7

Three-dimensional views of the ventricles of the brain. (a) Anterior view. **(b)** Left lateral view. Note that different regions of the large lateral ventricles are indicated by the terms anterior horn, posterior horn, and inferior horn.

The Cerebral Hemispheres

The **cerebral hemispheres** form the most superior part of the brain (Figure 12.8). Together they account for about 83% of total brain mass and are the most conspicuous parts of an intact brain. Picture how a mushroom cap covers the top of its stalk, and you have a fairly good analogy of how the paired cerebral hemispheres cover and obscure the diencephalon and the top of the brain stem (see Figure 12.5).

Nearly the entire surface of the cerebral hemispheres is marked by elevated ridges of tissue called **gyri** (ji'ri), literally "twisters," separated by shallow grooves called **sulci** (sul'ki), from the Greek meaning "furrows." (Note that the singular form of each of these terms ends in "us," i.e., *gyrus* and *sulcus.*) The deeper grooves, called **fissures,** separate large regions of the brain. The more prominent gyri and sulci are similar in all people and are important anatomical landmarks. The median **longitudinal fissure** separates the cerebral hemispheres from one another (see Figure 12.8c). Another large fissure, the **transverse fissure,** separates the cerebral hemispheres from the cerebellum below (see Figure 12.8a).

Some of the deeper sulci divide each hemisphere into five lobes, most of which are named for the cranial bones that overlie them (see Figure 12.8a). The **central sulcus,** which lies in the frontal plane, separates the **frontal lobe** from the **parietal lobe.** Bordering the central sulcus across each hemisphere are two important gyri, the **precentral gyrus** anteriorly and the

postcentral gyrus posteriorly. The boundary between the parietal lobe and the more posterior **occipital lobe** is established by several landmarks, but perhaps the most conspicuous of these is the **parieto-occipital** (pah-ri″ĕ-to-ok-sip′ĭ-tal) **sulcus,** located on the medial surface of the hemisphere (Figure 12.8b).

The deep **lateral sulcus** outlines the flaplike **temporal lobe** and separates it from the inferior aspects of the parietal and frontal lobes. A fifth lobe of the cerebral hemisphere, the **insula** (in'su-lah; "island"), is buried within the lateral sulcus, forming part of its floor. The insula is covered by portions of the temporal, parietal, and frontal lobes (Figure 12.9).

The cerebral hemispheres fit snugly into the skull. Rostrally, the frontal lobes occupy the anterior cranial fossa; the anterior parts of the temporal lobes fill the middle cranial fossa. The posterior cranial fossa, however, houses the brain stem and cerebellum; the occipital lobes are located well superior to that fossa (see Figure 12.5b).

A frontal section of the brain reveals the three basic regions of each cerebral hemisphere: the outer *cortex* of gray matter, which looks gray in fresh brain tissue; the internal *white matter;* and the *basal nuclei,* islands of gray matter situated deep within the white matter (Figure 12.9).

Cerebral Cortex

The **cerebral cortex** is the "executive suite" of the nervous system. It enables us to perceive, communicate, remember, understand, appreciate, and initiate

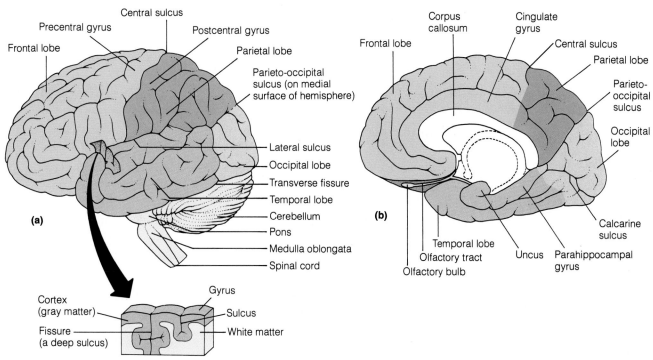

FIGURE 12.8
Lobes and fissures of the cerebral hemispheres. (a) Left lateral view of the brain.
(b) Medial surface of the right hemisphere.

FIGURE 12.9
Major regions of the cerebral hemispheres. The human brain has been sectioned coronally to reveal the relative positions of the cerebral cortex, white matter, and basal nuclei within the cerebral hemispheres. Since the cerebral hemispheres enclose the structures of the diencephalon, that region of the cerebrum is also shown.

? *What anatomical landmark separates motor from sensory areas of the cerebral cortex?*

FIGURE 12.10
Functional areas of the left cerebral cortex. Different colors define functional regions of the cortex. Numbers indicate specific brain regions as plotted by the Brodmann system. The olfactory area, which is deep to the temporal lobe on the medial hemispheric surface, is not identified.

voluntary movements—all qualities associated with *conscious behavior* or **consciousness.** Since it is composed of gray matter, the cerebral cortex consists of neuron cell bodies, dendrites, and unmyelinated axons (plus associated glia and blood vessels), but no fiber tracts. It is only 2–4 mm (about ⅛ inch) thick; however, its many convolutions effectively triple its surface area, and it accounts for roughly 40% of total brain mass.

In the late 1800s, anatomists studying the cerebral cortex were able to map subtle variations in its thickness and in the structure of its contained neurons. Most successful in these efforts was K. Brodmann, who produced an elaborate numbered mosaic of 52 different cortical areas, called **Brodmann areas,** in 1906. With a structural map emerging, early neurologists were anxious to localize *functional* regions of the cortex as well. At that time in history, there were two opposing schools of thought concerning the localization of cerebral functions. The **regional specialization theory** assumed that structurally distinct areas of the cortex carried out distinct functions. The **aggregate field view,** by contrast, proposed that the cortex acted as a whole to produce mental functions. Thus, injury to a specific region would affect all higher mental functions equally. Today, because of modern investigative techniques (PET scans, etc.), we know that both theories have some merit. Specific

motor and sensory functions are indeed localized in discrete cortical areas called *domains.* However, many higher mental functions, such as memory and language, appear to have overlapping domains and are more diffusely located. Although some of the most important Brodmann areas are numbered in Figure 12.10, we will examine the functional regions of the cerebral cortex only in the broadest sense. But first, some generalizations about the cerebral cortex:

1. The cerebral cortex contains three kinds of functional areas: **motor areas** that control voluntary motor functions; **sensory areas** that provide for conscious awareness of sensation; and **association areas** that act mainly to integrate diverse information for purposeful action. (However, remember that there are no sensory or motor "neurons" in the cortex; all neurons confined to the CNS are interneurons.)

2. Each hemisphere is chiefly concerned with the sensory and motor functions of the opposite (contralateral) side of the body.

3. Although they are largely symmetrical in structure, the two hemispheres are not entirely equal in function. Instead, there is a lateralization (specialization) of cortical functions, as discussed later.

4. The final, and perhaps the most important, generalization to keep in mind is that our approach is a gross oversimplification; *no* functional area of the cortex acts alone, and conscious behavior involves the entire cortex in one way or another.

Motor Areas.   Cortical areas controlling motor functions lie in the posterior part of the frontal lobes. These include the primary motor cortex, the premotor cortex, Broca's area, and the frontal eye field.

1.   Primary motor cortex. The **primary,** or **somatic, motor cortex** is located in the precentral gyrus of the frontal lobe of each hemisphere. Large neurons, called **pyramidal cells,** in these gyri allow us to consciously control the movements of our skeletal muscles. Their long axons, which project to the spinal cord, form the massive voluntary motor tracts called the **pyramidal,** or **corticospinal** (kor″tĭ-ko-spi′nal), **tracts.** All other descending motor tracts issue from brain stem nuclei and consist of chains of two, three, or more neurons.

The entire body is represented spatially in the primary motor cortex of each hemisphere. Such an orderly mapping of the body in CNS structures is called **somatotopy** (so″mah-to-to′pe). As illustrated in Figure 12.11, the body is represented upside down—the head at the inferolateral part of the precentral gyrus, and the toes at the medial end. Most of the neurons in these gyri control muscles in body areas having the most precise motor control—that is, the face, tongue, and hands. Consequently, these regions of the (caricature-like) **motor homunculus** (ho-mung′ku-lus; "little man") drawn on the gyrus in Figure 12.11 are shown disproportionally large. The motor innervation of the body is **contralateral** (*contra* = opposite); that is, the left primary motor gyrus controls muscles on the right side of the body, and vice versa.

Damage to localized areas of the primary motor cortex (as from a stroke) paralyzes the body muscles controlled by those areas. If the lesion is in the right hemisphere, the left side of the body will be paralyzed. Only *voluntary* control is lost, however, as the muscles can still contract reflexively. •

2.   Premotor cortex. Just anterior to the precentral gyrus in the frontal lobe is the **premotor cortex** (see Figure 12.10). This region controls learned motor skills of a repetitive or patterned nature, such as playing a musical instrument and typing. The premotor cortex coordinates the movement of several muscle groups simultaneously and/or sequentially, mainly by sending activating impulses to the primary motor cortex. However, the premotor cortex also influences motor activity more directly by supplying about 15% of pyramidal tract fibers. You could think of this region as the memory bank for skilled motor activities.

Destruction of the premotor area, or part of it, results in a loss of the motor skill(s) programmed in that particular region, but muscle strength and the ability to perform the discrete individual movements

are not hindered. For example, if the premotor area controlling the flight of your fingers over the typewriter keyboard were damaged, you would not be able to type with your usual speed, but you could still make the same movements with your fingers. Reprogramming the skill into another set of premotor neurons would require practice, just as the initial learning process did. •

3.   Broca's (bro′kahz) **area. Broca's area** lies anterior to the inferior region of the premotor area and overlaps Brodmann areas 44 and 45. Broca's area has long been considered to be (1) present in one hemisphere only (usually the left) and (2) a special *motor speech area* that directs the muscles of the tongue, throat, and lips involved in articulating words. However, recent studies using PET scans to "light up" active areas of the brain show that this may not be the only or the exclusive function of Broca's area. These indicate that Broca's area (and the corresponding area in the other hemisphere) becomes active as we prepare to speak and even as we think about (plan) many voluntary motor activities other than speech.

4.   Frontal eye field. The **frontal eye field** is located anterior to the premotor cortex and superior to Broca's area. This cortical region controls voluntary movement of the eyes.

Sensory Areas.   Unlike the motor areas, which are confined to the frontal lobe cortex, areas concerned with conscious awareness of sensation occur in the parietal, temporal, and occipital lobes (see Figure 12.10).

1.   Primary somatosensory cortex. The **primary somatosensory cortex** resides in the postcentral gyrus of the parietal lobe, the anteriormost part of the parietal lobe (Brodmann areas 1–3). Neurons in this gyrus receive information, relayed from the general (somatic) sensory receptors located in the skin and from proprioceptors in skeletal muscles, and identify the body region being stimulated. This ability is called **spatial discrimination.** As with the primary motor cortex, the body is represented spatially and in an upside-down fashion according to the site of stimulus input (see Figure 12.11), and the right hemisphere receives input from the left side of the body. The amount of sensory cortex devoted to a particular body region is related to how sensitive that region is (that is, how many receptors it has), not to the size of the body region. In humans, the face (especially the lips) and fingertips are the most sensitive body areas, hence these are the largest parts of the **somatosensory homunculus.**

2.   Somatosensory association area. The **somatosensory association area** lies just posterior to the primary somatosensory cortex (see Figure 12.10) and has many connections with it. The major function of this area is to integrate and analyze different somatic sen-

Why are the motor and sensory homunculi "disformed" anatomically?

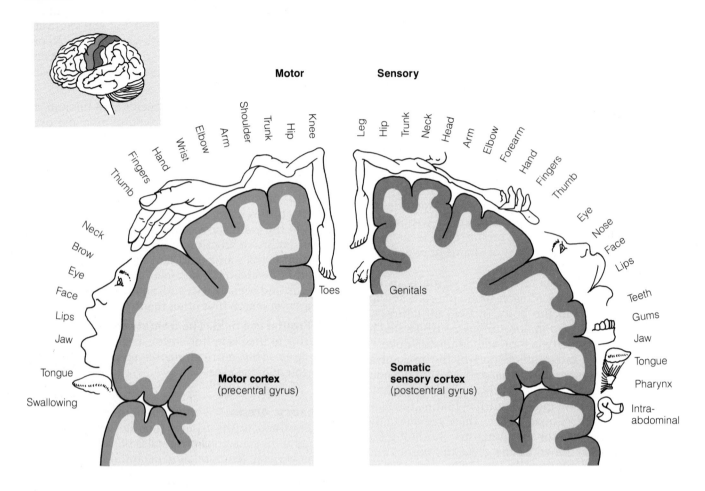

FIGURE 12.11
Motor and sensory areas of the cerebral cortex. The relative amount of cortical tissue devoted to each function is indicated by the amount of the gyrus occupied by the body area diagrams. The primary motor cortex in the precentral gyrus is represented on the left, and the somatic sensory cortex in the postcentral gyrus is represented on the right.

sory inputs (temperature, pressure, etc.) into a comprehensive evaluation of what is being felt relative to its size, texture, and the relationship of its parts. For example, when you reach into your pocket, the somatosensory association area draws upon stored memories of past sensory experiences and perceives the objects you feel as coins or keys. Someone with damage to this area could not recognize these objects without looking at them.

3. Visual areas. The **primary visual cortex** is seen on the extreme posterior tip of the occipital lobe (Figure 12.10). Most of it, however, is located on the medial aspect of the occipital lobe, buried within the deep **calcarine sulcus** (kal'kar-in; "spur-shaped") (Figure 12.8b). The largest of all cortical sensory areas, the primary visual cortex receives visual information that originates on the retinas of the eyes. There is a map of visual space on the primary visual cortex, analogous to the body map on the somatosensory cortex. The right half of visual space is repre-

sented on the left visual cortex, the left half on the right cortex.

The **visual association area** surrounds the primary visual area and covers much of the occipital lobe (Figure 12.10). Communicating with the primary visual area, the visual association area interprets and evaluates visual stimuli in light of past visual experiences, enabling us to recognize a flower or a person's face and to appreciate what we are seeing. We do our "seeing" with these cortical neurons (however, recent experiments on monkeys indicate that complex visual processing extends well beyond the occipital lobe, involving the entire posterior half of the cerebral hemispheres).

Damage to the primary visual cortex results in functional blindness. By contrast, those with damage to the visual association area can see, but they do not comprehend what they are looking at. •

4. Auditory areas. Each **primary auditory cortex** is located in the superior margin of the temporal lobe abutting the lateral sulcus. Sound energy exciting the hearing (cochlear) receptors of the inner ear causes impulses to be transmitted to the primary auditory cortex, where they are related to pitch, rhythm, and loudness. The more posterior **auditory association area** then permits the perception of the sound stimulus, which we "hear" as speech, music, thunder, noise, and so on. Memories of sounds heard in the past appear to be stored here for reference.

5. **Olfactory (smell) cortex.** The olfactory cortices are found in the medial aspects of the temporal lobes in a small region called the *piriform lobe* which is dominated by the hooklike **uncus** (see Figure 12.8b). Afferent fibers from the smell receptors in the superior nasal cavities transmit impulses along the olfactory tracts that are ultimately relayed to the olfactory cortices. The outcome is conscious awareness of different odors.

The olfactory cortex is part of the **rhinencephalon** (ri″nen-sef′ah-lon; "nose brain"), which in more primitive vertebrates is entirely concerned with olfactory reception and perception. The rhinencephalon includes the uncus and associated parts of the cerebral cortex located on or in the medial aspects of the temporal lobes, as well as the protruding olfactory tracts and bulbs that extend to the nose region. During the course of evolution, most of the "old" rhinencephalon has taken on new functions concerned chiefly with emotions and memory. This "newer" emotional brain, called the *limbic system,* is considered on p. 401. The only portions of the rhinencephalon still devoted to smell in humans are the olfactory bulbs and tracts (described in Chapter 16) and the greatly reduced olfactory cortex.

6. **Gustatory (taste) cortex.** The **gustatory** (gus′tah-tor-e) **cortex** (see Figure 12.10), a region involved in the perception of taste stimuli, is located in the parietal lobe deep to the temporal lobe (Brodmann area 43). Logically, it occurs at the tip of the tongue of the somatosensory homunculus.

Association Areas. Association areas include any cortical area that doesn't have the word *primary* in its name. As already described, the primary somatosensory cortex and each of the special sensory areas have nearby association areas with which they communicate. The association areas, in turn, communicate ("associate") with the motor cortex and with other sensory association areas to analyze, recognize, and act on sensory inputs. Each of these areas has multiple inputs and outputs quite independent of the primary sensory and motor areas, indicating that their function is complex indeed. The remaining association areas are described next.

1. **Prefrontal cortex.** The **prefrontal cortex,** which occupies the anterior portions of the frontal lobes (see Figure 12.10), is the most complicated cortical region of all. It is involved with intellect and complex learning abilities (called cognition), and personality. It is

necessary for the production of abstract ideas, judgment, reasoning, persistence, planning, concern for others, and conscience. These qualities all develop slowly in children, so it appears that the prefrontal cortex matures slowly and is heavily dependent on positive and negative feedback from one's social environment. The prefrontal cortex also plays a role in mood and is closely linked to the emotional part of the brain (limbic system). It is the tremendous elaboration of this region that sets human beings apart from other animals.

Tumors or other lesions of the prefrontal cortex may cause mental and personality disorders. Wide mood swings and loss of attentiveness and inhibitions may occur. The affected individual may be oblivious to social restraints, perhaps becoming careless about personal appearance, or rashly attacking a 7-foot opponent rather than running.

A surgical technique called *prefrontal lobotomy,* which severs the connections to the prefrontal cortex, was used from the 1930s to the 1950s to treat severe mental illness. The early results of this procedure were promising because patients became less anxious. However, the cure was later found to be worse than the disease: many patients developed epilepsy and abnormal personality changes, such as lack of judgment or a loss of initiative. Today, psychoactive drugs are the therapy of choice for most mental patients. •

2. **General interpretation area.** The **general interpretation area,** or **gnostic** (nos′tik; "knowing") **area,** is an ill-defined region encompassing parts of the temporal, parietal, and occipital lobes (Figure 12.10). It is found in one hemisphere only, usually the left. This region receives input from all the sensory association areas and appears to be a storage site for complex memory patterns associated with sensation. It integrates all incoming signals into a single thought or understanding of the situation. It sends this assessment to the prefrontal cortex, which adds emotional overtones and decides on an appropriate response. Suppose, for example, you drop a bottle of hydrochloric acid and it splashes on you. You see the bottle shatter; you hear the crash; you feel the burning on your skin; and you smell the acid fumes. However, these individual perceptions do not dominate your consciousness. What *does* is the overall message "danger"—by which time your leg muscles are already activated and are propelling you to the safety shower.

Injury to the gnostic area causes one to become an imbecile—even if all the other sensory association areas are unharmed—because one's ability to interpret the entire situation is lost. •

Research findings suggest that the gnostic area and prefrontal cortex work together to assemble new experiences into logical constructs, or "stories," based on our past experiences. If so, our view of the world is not really objective, but instead is shaped by what we already know and understand. Stories have great appeal in all human cultures. Could this be because storytelling is part of the "hardware" of our mental processing?

3. **Language areas**. Cortical regions involved with language occur in both hemispheres. A specialized integration area called **Wernicke's** (ver′nĭ-kēz) **area** (see Figure 12.10) is found in the posterior temporal lobe of one hemisphere (usually the left). Commonly called the "speech area," Wernicke's area surrounds and encompasses part of the auditory association area. Until recently, Wernicke's area was believed to be *the* area responsible for understanding written and spoken language. However, PET scan brain studies have suggested that this area may be primarily involved in sounding out unfamiliar words, while the more complex process of language *comprehension* actually occurs in the prefrontal areas midway between Brodmann areas 45 and 11. This controversial hypothesis and others concerning language are described in more detail in Chapter 15.

Affective language areas—regions involved in the nonverbal, emotional components of language—appear to be present in the hemisphere opposite Broca's and Wernicke's areas. These "mirror images" allow the lilt or tone of our voice and our gestures to express our emotions when we speak, and permit us to comprehend the emotional content of what we hear. (For example, a soft, melodious response to your question conveys quite a different meaning than a sharp reply.)

Disorders of the affective regions are collectively called *aprosodia* ("lacking expression"). An individual telling you (quite honestly) that he is "so happy to meet you" with a flat voice and stony facial expression would be exhibiting such an impairment. •

4. **Visceral association area.** The cortex of the insula (see Figure 12.9) may be involved in conscious perception of visceral sensations (upset stomach, full bladder, and the like).

Lateralization of Cortical Functioning. Although we use both cerebral hemispheres for almost every activity and the hemispheres share memories and appear nearly identical, there is a division of labor, and each hemisphere has unique abilities not shared by its partner. This phenomenon is called **lateralization.** Although one cerebral hemisphere or the other "dominates" each task, the term **cerebral dominance** designates the hemisphere that is *dominant for language.* In most people (about 90%), the left hemisphere has greater control over language abilities, mathematical abilities and logic. This so-called dominant hemisphere is working when we compose a sentence, balance a checkbook, and memorize a list of names. The other hemisphere (usually the right) is more involved in visual-spatial skills, intuition, emotion, and appreciation of art and

music. It is the poetic, creative, and the "Ah-ha!" (insightful) side of our nature, and it is far better at recognizing faces. Most individuals with left cerebral dominance are right-handed.

In the remaining 10% of people, the roles of the hemispheres are reversed or the hemispheres share their functions equally. Typically, many right cerebral–dominant people are left-handed and more often male. In "lefties" in whom the cerebral cortex functions bilaterally, the mutuality (or duality) of brain control sometimes results in more than the usual dexterity and strength in the nondominant hand and in ambidexterity. In other cases, however, this phenomenon results in cerebral confusion ("Is it your turn, or mine?") and learning disabilities. The reading disorder *dyslexia,* in which otherwise intelligent people may reverse the order of letters or syllables in words (and of words in sentences), has been attributed in some cases to such a lack of cerebral dominance.

Another aspect of cerebral interaction is that each side of the brain exerts controls over the other. The dominant, more intellectual hemisphere prevents rash emotional displays by the nondominant hemisphere. On the other hand, the emotional side of the brain urges us to take time out from routine and to fantasize or do something spontaneous for a change. This lays to rest the common misconception that we have "two brains" and that one dominates the other. The two cerebral hemispheres have perfect and almost instant communication with one another via connecting fiber tracts, as well as complete integration of their functions. Furthermore, although lateralization means that each hemisphere is better than the other at certain functions, neither side is better at everything.

Cerebral White Matter

From what has already been described, it is clear that communication within the brain is extensive. The **cerebral white matter** (see Figure 12.9) deep to the gray matter of the cortex provides for this communication between cerebral areas and between the cerebral cortex and lower CNS centers. It consists largely of myelinated fibers bundled into large tracts. These fibers and the tracts they form are classified according to the direction in which they run as *commissural, association,* or *projection.*

Commissures (kom′ĭ-shūrz), composed of **commissural fibers,** connect corresponding areas of the two hemispheres, enabling them to function as a coordinated whole. The largest commissure is the **corpus callosum** (kah-lo′sum; "thickened body"), which lies superior to the lateral ventricles, deep within the longitudinal fissure (Figure 12.12b). A less important example is the **anterior commissure.**

Association fibers transmit impulses within a single hemisphere. Short association fibers connect adjacent gyri; long association fibers are bundled into tracts and connect different cortical lobes.

FIGURE 12.12
Types of fiber tracts in the white matter of the cerebral medulla.
(a) Midsagittal view of the right cerebral hemisphere. Note the association tracts (tracts connecting different parts of the same hemisphere), and the corpus callosum, a commissure that connects the two cerebral hemispheres.
(b) Frontal section of the brain showing the corpus callosum (commissural fibers) of the cerebrum and projection fibers that run between the cerebrum and lower centers (brain stem and spinal cord). Notice the tight band of projection fibers called the internal capsule that passes between the thalamus and the basal nuclei, and then fans out, as the corona radiata, in the cerebral white matter.

Projection fibers include fibers entering the cerebral hemispheres from lower brain or cord centers, and fibers leaving the cortex to travel to lower areas. Projection fibers tie the cortex to the rest of the nervous system and to the receptors and effectors of the body. Projection fibers run vertically, in contrast to commissural and association fibers, which run horizontally.

At the upper limit of the brain stem, the projection fibers on each side form a compact band called the **internal capsule** (see Figures 12.12b and 12.13a), which passes between the thalamus and some of the basal nuclei. Beyond that point, they radiate fanlike through the cerebral white matter to the cortex. This distinctive arrangement of projection tract fibers is known as the **corona radiata** (radiating crown).

Basal Nuclei

Deep within the cerebral white matter of each hemisphere is a group of subcortical nuclei called the **basal nuclei** or **basal ganglia.*** Although the definition of the precise structures forming the basal

*Since a nucleus is a collection of nerve cell bodies within the CNS, the term *basal nuclei* is correct. The more frequently used historical term *basal ganglia* is a misnomer, because ganglia are PNS structures.

nuclei is controversial, most agree that the **caudate** (kaw′dāt) **nucleus, putamen** (pu-ta′men), and **globus pallidus** (glo′bis pal′ĭ-dus) constitute their main mass (see Figure 12.13b). Together, the putamen ("pod") and globus pallidus ("pale globe") form a lens-shaped mass, commonly called the **lentiform nucleus,** that flanks the internal capsule laterally. The comma-shaped caudate nucleus arches superiorly over the diencephalon and lies medial to the internal capsule. Collectively, the lentiform and caudate nuclei are called the **corpus striatum** (stri-a′tum) because the fibers of the internal capsule that course past these nuclei give them a striped appearance (see Figure 12.13a). The basal nuclei are functionally associated with the *subthalamic nuclei* (located in the lateral "floor" of the diencephalon) and the *substantia nigra* of the midbrain.

The almond-shaped **amygdala** (ah-mig′dah-lah; "almond"), or **amygdaloid nucleus,** sits on the tail of the caudate nucleus. Traditionally, it has been grouped with the basal nuclei, but functionally it belongs to the limbic system (see p. 401).

The basal nuclei receive extensive inputs from the entire cerebral cortex, as well as from other subcortical nuclei and each other. Via relays through the thalamus, the basal nuclei project to the premotor and prefrontal cortices and so influence muscle move-

FIGURE 12.13

Basal nuclei. (a) Three-dimensional view of the basal nuclei, showing their position within the cerebrum. **(b)** A transverse section of the cerebrum and diencephalon showing the relationship of the basal nuclei to the thalamus and the lateral and third ventricles.

ments directed by the primary motor cortex. The basal nuclei have no direct access to motor pathways.

The precise role of the basal nuclei has been elusive because of their inaccessible location and because their functions overlap to some extent with those of the cerebellum. However, their role in motor control appears more complex and there is evidence that the basal nuclei also play some role in cognition. The basal nuclei are thought to be particularly important in starting, stopping, and monitoring movements ordered and executed by the cortex, especially those that are relatively slow and sustained, or stereotyped, such as arm-swinging during walking. They also regulate the *intensity* of these movements, resembling the motor drive that regulates how fast a mechanical motor works. Additionally, they act to inhibit antagonistic or unnecessary movements; thus their input

seems necessary to our ability to perform several activities at once. When the basal nuclei are impaired, the result is disturbances in posture and muscle tone, involuntary movements including tremors, and abnormal slowness of movement. The regulatory activities, role in skills memory, and most common disorders of the basal nuclei are described in more detail in Chapter 15.

The Diencephalon

The **diencephalon** forms the central core of the forebrain and is surrounded by the cerebral hemispheres. It consists largely of three bilaterally symmetric structures—the thalamus, hypothalamus, and epithalamus—which collectively enclose the third ventricle (see Figures 12.9 and 12.14a).

Table 12.1 Functions of Major Brain Regions

Region	Function
Cerebral hemispheres (pp. 384–392)	Cortical gray matter localizes and interprets sensory inputs, controls voluntary and skilled skeletal muscle activity, and functions in intellectual and emotional processing; basal nuclei are subcortical motor centers important in initiation of skeletal muscle movements
Diencephalon (pp. 392–395)	Thalamic nuclei are relay stations in conduction of (1) sensory impulses to cerebral cortex for interpretation, and (2) impulses to and from cerebral motor cortex and lower (subcortical) motor centers, including cerebellum; thalamus is also involved in memory processing
	Hypothalamus is chief integration center of autonomic (involuntary) nervous system; it functions in regulation of body temperature, food intake, water balance, thirst, and biological rhythms and drives; regulates hormonal output of anterior pituitary gland and is an endocrine organ in its own right (produces ADH and oxytocin); part of limbic system
Limbic system (pp. 401–402)	Emotional brain; a functional system involving cerebral and diencephalon structures that mediates emotional response
Brain stem	
Midbrain (pp. 396–397)	Conduction pathway between higher and lower brain centers (e.g., cerebral peduncles contain the fibers of the pyramidal tracts); its superior and inferior colliculi are visual and auditory reflex centers; substantia nigra and red nuclei are subcortical motor centers; contains nuclei for cranial nerves III and IV
Pons (pp. 397–398)	Conduction pathway between higher and lower brain centers; pontine nuclei relay information from the cerebrum to the cerebellum; its respiratory nuclei cooperate with the medullary respiratory centers to control respiratory rate and depth; houses nuclei of cranial nerves V–VII
Medulla oblongata (p. 399)	Conduction pathway between higher brain centers and spinal cord; site of decussation of the pyramidal tracts; houses nuclei of cranial nerves VIII–XII; contains nuclei cuneatus and gracilis (synapse points of ascending sensory pathways transmitting sensory impulses from skin and proprioceptors), and visceral nuclei controlling heart rate, blood vessel diameter, respiratory rate, vomiting, coughing, etc.; its inferior olivary nuclei provide the sensory relay to the cerebellum
Reticular formation (pp. 402–403)	A functional brain stem system that maintains cerebral cortical alertness (reticular activating system) and filters out repetitive stimuli; its motor nuclei help regulate skeletal and visceral muscle activity
Cerebellum (pp. 399–401)	Processes information received from cerebral motor cortex and from proprioceptors and visual and equilibrium pathways, and provides "instructions" to cerebral motor cortex and subcortical motor centers that result in proper balance and posture and smooth, coordinated skeletal muscle movements

The Thalamus

The egg-shaped **thalamus** makes up 80% of the diencephalon and forms the superolateral walls of the third ventricle (see Figure 12.9). It is composed of bilateral masses of gray matter held together by a midline commissure called the **intermediate mass.** *Thalamus* is a Greek word meaning "inner room," which well describes this deep, well-hidden brain region.

The thalamus has many different nuclei, most named according to their relative location (Figure 12.14b). Each of these nuclei has a functional specialty, and both projects fibers to and receives fibers from a specific region of the cerebral cortex. Afferent impulses from all senses and all parts of the body converge on the thalamus and synapse with at least one of its nuclei. For example, the *ventral posterior lateral nucleus* is a major synapse point for fibers carrying impulses from the general somatic sensory receptors (touch, pressure, etc.), and the *lateral* and *medial geniculate* (jĕ-nik′u-lāt; "knee shaped") *bodies* are important visual and auditory relay centers, respectively. Within the thalamus, a sorting-out and information "editing" process occurs. Impulses having to do with similar functions are grouped together and relayed via the internal capsule to the appropriate area of the sensory cortex as well as to specific cortical association centers. As the afferent impulses reach the thalamus, we have a crude recognition of whether the sensation we are about to experience is pleasant or unpleasant. However, specific stimulus localization and discrimination occur in the cerebral cortex.

In addition to sensory inputs, virtually *all* inputs ascending to the cerebral cortex are funneled through the thalamic nuclei. These include impulses participating in the regulation of emotion and visceral function from the hypothalamus (via the anterior nuclei), and some that help to direct the activity of the motor cortices from the cerebellum (via the ventral lateral nucleus), the basal nuclei, and other subcortical

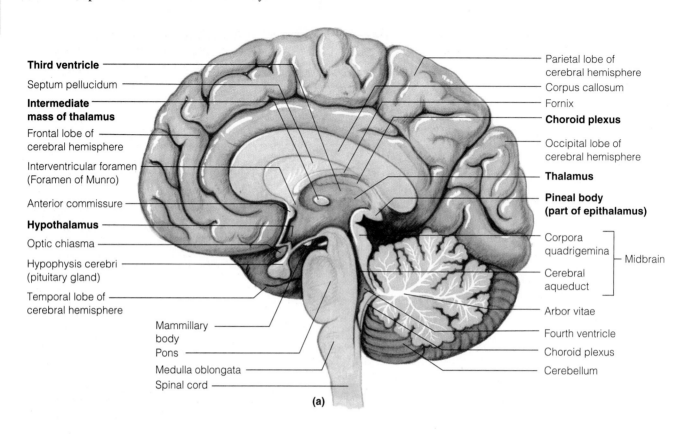

Third ventricle

Septum pellucidum

Intermediate mass of thalamus

Frontal lobe of cerebral hemisphere

Interventricular foramen (Foramen of Munro)

Anterior commissure

Hypothalamus

Optic chiasma

Hypophysis cerebri (pituitary gland)

Temporal lobe of cerebral hemisphere

Mammillary body

Pons

Medulla oblongata

Spinal cord

Parietal lobe of cerebral hemisphere

Corpus callosum

Fornix

Choroid plexus

Occipital lobe of cerebral hemisphere

Thalamus

Pineal body (part of epithalamus)

Corpora quadrigemina — Midbrain

Cerebral aqueduct

Arbor vitae

Fourth ventricle

Choroid plexus

Cerebellum

(a)

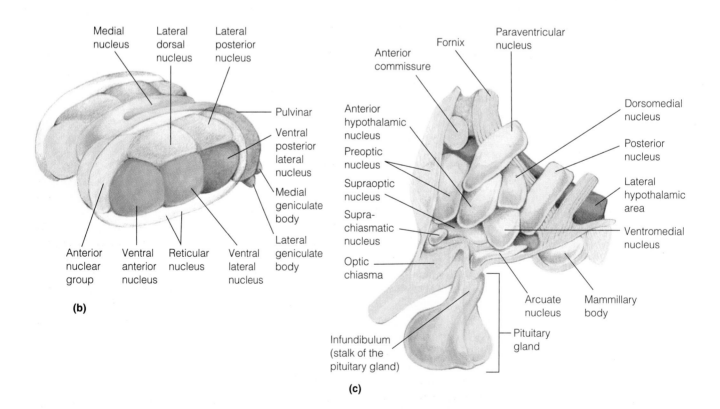

Medial nucleus

Lateral dorsal nucleus

Lateral posterior nucleus

Pulvinar

Ventral posterior lateral nucleus

Medial geniculate body

Lateral geniculate body

Anterior nuclear group

Ventral anterior nucleus

Reticular nucleus

Ventral lateral nucleus

(b)

Anterior commissure

Fornix

Paraventricular nucleus

Anterior hypothalamic nucleus

Preoptic nucleus

Supraoptic nucleus

Supra-chiasmatic nucleus

Optic chiasma

Dorsomedial nucleus

Posterior nucleus

Lateral hypothalamic area

Ventromedial nucleus

Arcuate nucleus

Mammillary body

Infundibulum (stalk of the pituitary gland)

Pituitary gland

(c)

FIGURE 12.14

Diencephalon and brain stem structures. (a) Midsagittal section of the brain.
(b) Thalamus showing the main thalamic nuclei. (The reticular nuclei that "cap" the thalamic nuclei laterally are depicted as curving translucent structures.) **(c)** The main hypothalamic nuclei.

nuclei. Thus the thalamus plays a key role in mediating sensation, motor activities, cortical arousal, and memory. It is truly the gateway to the cerebral cortex.

The Hypothalamus

The **hypothalamus,** named for its position below (*hypo*) the thalamus, caps the top of the brain stem and forms the inferolateral walls of the third ventricle, merging into the midbrain inferiorly (see Figure 12.14a). It extends from the optic chiasma (point of crossover of the optic nerves) to the posterior margin of the mammillary bodies. The **mammillary** (mam′mil-er-e; "little breast") **bodies,** paired pealike nuclei that bulge anteriorly from the hypothalamus, are olfactory relay stations. Between the optic chiasma and mammillary bodies is the **infundibulum** (in″fun-dib′u-lum), a stalk of the hypothalamic tissue that connects the **pituitary gland** to the base of the hypothalamus. Like the thalamus, the hypothalamus contains many functionally important nuclei (Figure 12.14c).

Despite its small size, the hypothalamus is the main visceral control center of the body and is vitally important to overall body homeostasis. Few tissues in the body escape its influence. Its chief homeostatic roles are summarized next.

1. **Autonomic control center.** The hypothalamus regulates involuntary nervous system activity by controlling the activity of autonomic centers in the brain stem and spinal cord. In this role, the hypothalamus can influence blood pressure, rate and force of heart contraction, motility of the digestive tract, respiratory rate and depth, eye pupil size, and many other visceral activities as described in Chapter 14.

2. **Center for emotional response and behavior.** The hypothalamus has numerous connections with cortical association areas and lower brain stem centers, and it lies at the "heart" of the limbic system (the emotional part of the brain). Nuclei involved in the perception of pain, pleasure, fear, and rage, as well as those involved in biological rhythms and drives (such as the sex drive), are found in the hypothalamus.

The hypothalamus acts through autonomic nervous system pathways to initiate most physical expressions of emotion. For example, physical manifestations of fear include a pounding heart, elevated blood pressure, pallor, sweating, and a dry mouth.

3. **Body temperature regulation.** The body's thermostat is in the hypothalamus. The hypothalamus receives input from thermoreceptors located in other parts of the brain as well as in the body periphery, and certain hypothalamic neurons monitor the temperature of blood flowing through the hypothalamus. According to these signals, the hypothalamus initiates cooling (sweating) or heat-retention mechanisms (shivering) as needed to maintain relatively constant body temperature. (See Chapter 25.)

4. **Regulation of food intake.** In response to changing blood levels of certain nutrients (glucose and perhaps amino acids) or hormones (insulin and others), the hypothalamus regulates feelings of hunger and satiety (see Chapter 25).

5. **Regulation of water balance and thirst.** When body fluids become too concentrated, hypothalamic neurons called *osmoreceptors* are activated. They, in turn, excite hypothalamic nuclei that trigger the release of antidiuretic hormone (ADH) from the posterior pituitary. ADH causes the kidneys to retain water. The same conditions also stimulate hypothalamic neurons in the *thirst center*, causing us to drink fluids.

6. **Regulation of sleep-wake cycles.** Acting with other brain regions, the hypothalamus helps regulate the complex phenomenon of sleep. The hypothalamus, through the operation of its suprachiasmatic nucleus (our biological clock) sets the timing of the sleep cycle in response to daylight-darkness cues received from the visual pathways.

7. **Control of endocrine system functioning.** The hypothalamus acts as the helmsman of the endocrine system in two important ways. First, by producing *releasing hormones,* it *controls* the secretion of hormones by the anterior pituitary gland. Second, two of its nuclei, the *supraoptic* and *paraventricular* nuclei, produce hormones called ADH and oxytocin. The endocrine roles of the hypothalamus are described in more detail in Chapter 17.

Hypothalamic disturbances cause a number of disorders in body homeostasis, such as severe body wasting or obesity, sleep disturbances, dehydration, and a broad range of emotional imbalances. For example, infants deprived of a warm, nurturing relationship may develop sleep disorders and fail to thrive. •

The Epithalamus

The **epithalamus** is the most dorsal portion of the diencephalon and forms the roof of the third ventricle. Extending from its posterior border and visible externally is the **pineal** (pin′e-al; "pine cone shaped") **gland** or **body** (see Figures 12.14 and 12.16). The pineal gland secretes the hormone *melatonin* and, along with hypothalamic nuclei, seems to be involved with regulation of the sleep-wake cycle and some aspects of mood (as discussed further in Chapter 17). A cerebrospinal fluid-forming structure called a **choroid plexus** (ko′roid plek′sus) is also part of the epithalamus (see Figure 12.14a).

The Brain Stem

From superior to inferior, the brain stem regions are the midbrain, pons, and medulla oblongata (see Figures 12.14–12.16). Each of these regions is roughly an inch long. Histologically, the organization of the brain stem is similar (but not identical) to that of the spinal cord—deep gray matter surrounded by white matter fiber tracts (see Figure 12.6).

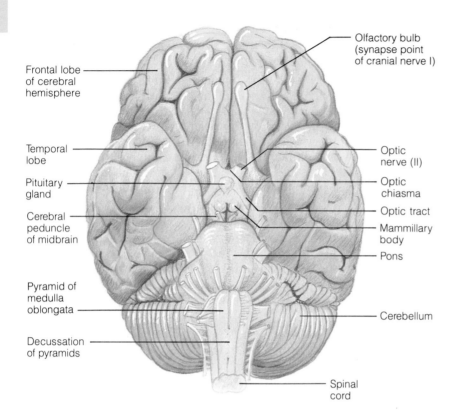

Frontal lobe of cerebral hemisphere

Temporal lobe

Pituitary gland

Cerebral peduncle of midbrain

Pyramid of medulla oblongata

Decussation of pyramids

Olfactory bulb (synapse point of cranial nerve I)

Optic nerve (II)

Optic chiasma

Optic tract

Mammillary body

Pons

Cerebellum

Spinal cord

FIGURE 12.15
Ventral aspect of the human brain, showing the three regions of the brain stem. Only a small portion of the midbrain can be seen; the rest is surrounded by other brain regions.

Brain stem centers produce the rigidly programmed, automatic behaviors necessary for our survival. Positioned between the cerebrum and the spinal cord, the brain stem also provides a pathway for fiber tracts running between higher and lower neural centers. Additionally, brain stem nuclei are associated with 10 of the 12 pairs of cranial nerves (described in Chapter 13), so it is heavily involved with innervation of the head.

The Midbrain

The **midbrain** is located between the diencephalon superiorly and the pons inferiorly (see Figure 12.15). On its ventral aspect the two bulging **cerebral peduncles** (pĕ-dung′klz) form vertical pillars that seem to hold up the cerebrum, hence their name meaning "little feet of the cerebrum." These peduncles contain the large pyramidal (corticospinal) motor tracts descending toward the spinal cord. The *superior cerebellar peduncles,* also fiber tracts, connect the midbrain to the cerebellum dorsally (Figure 12.16).

Running through the midbrain is the hollow **cerebral aqueduct,** which connects the third and fourth ventricles, and delineates the cerebral peduncles ventrally from its dorsal aspect, called the *tectum* ("roof"). Surrounding the aqueduct is gray matter that contains nuclei associated with two cranial nerves, the *oculomotor* (III) and the *trochlear* (trok′le-ar) *nerves* (IV) (see Figures 12.16 and 12.17c). Nuclei are also scattered in the surrounding white matter. The largest of these nuclei are the **corpora quadrigemina** (kor′por-ah kwod″ri-jem′i-nah; "quadruplets"),

which raise four domelike protrusions on the dorsal midbrain surface (see Figures 12.14, 12.16b). The superior pair of nuclei, the **superior colliculi** (kŏ-lik′u-li), are visual reflex centers that coordinate head and eye movements when we visually follow a moving object, and make us turn our heads involuntarily when we detect an object "out of the corner of our eye." The **inferior colliculi,** immediately below, are part of the auditory relay from the hearing receptors of the ear to the sensory cortex. They also act in reflexive responses to sound, as in the *startle reflex,* which causes you to turn your head toward an unexpected sound.

Also embedded in the white matter of the midbrain are two pigmented nuclei, the substantia nigra and red nucleus (Figure 12.17a). The **substantia nigra** (sub-stan′she-ah ni′grah) is a bandlike nucleus located deep to the cerebral peduncle; it is the largest nuclear mass in the midbrain. Its dark (*nigr* = black) color reflects its high content of melanin pigment, a precursor of the neurotransmitter (dopamine) released by these neurons. The substantia nigra is functionally linked to the basal nuclei of the cerebral hemispheres and is considered part of the basal nuclear complex by many authorities. The oval **red nucleus** is found between the substantia nigra and the cerebral aqueduct. Its natural reddish hue is due to its rich vascular supply and the presence of iron pigment in the cell bodies of its neurons. The red nuclei are relay nuclei in some descending motor pathways that effect limb flexion. The midbrain also contains nuclei associated with the *reticular formation* (described on pp. 402–403). The midbrain is the most superior part

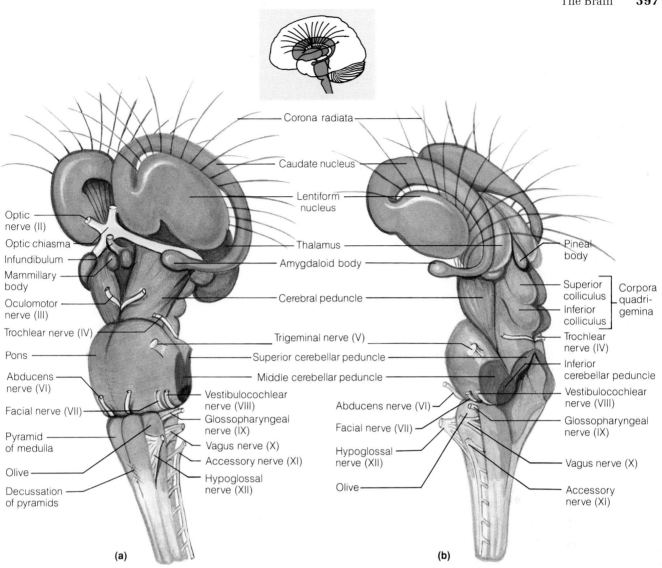

Corona radiata

Caudate nucleus

Lentiform nucleus

Optic nerve (II)

Optic chiasma

Infundibulum

Mammillary body

Oculomotor nerve (III)

Trochlear nerve (IV)

Pons

Abducens nerve (VI)

Facial nerve (VII)

Pyramid of medulla

Olive

Decussation of pyramids

Thalamus

Amygdaloid body

Cerebral peduncle

Trigeminal nerve (V)

Superior cerebellar peduncle

Middle cerebellar peduncle

Vestibulocochlear nerve (VIII)

Glossopharyngeal nerve (IX)

Vagus nerve (X)

Accessory nerve (XI)

Hypoglossal nerve (XII)

Pineal body

Superior colliculus

Inferior colliculus

Corpora quadri-gemina

Trochlear nerve (IV)

Inferior cerebellar peduncle

Vestibulocochlear nerve (VIII)

Glossopharyngeal nerve (IX)

Vagus nerve (X)

Accessory nerve (XI)

Abducens nerve (VI)

Facial nerve (VII)

Hypoglossal nerve (XII)

Olive

(a)   **(b)**

FIGURE 12.16
Relationship of the brain stem to the diencephalon and basal nuclei. Cerebral hemispheres have been removed. **(a)** Anterolateral view. **(b)** Posterolateral view.

of the CNS that contains motor neurons, that is, neurons that extend into the body periphery to innervate muscles and glands.

The Pons

The **pons** is the bulging brain stem region wedged between the midbrain and the medulla oblongata (see Figures 12.14–12.16). Dorsally, it forms part of the anterior wall of the fourth ventricle.

As its name suggests (*pons* = bridge), the pons is chiefly composed of conduction tracts. These fiber pathways course in two directions through the pons. The deep projection fibers run longitudinally and complete the superior-inferior pathway between higher brain centers and the spinal cord. The more superficial ventral fibers issue from numerous *pontine nuclei,* relays for "conversations" between the motor cortex and the cerebellum. These fibers are oriented transversely and dorsally as the *middle cerebellar peduncles* and connect the pons bilaterally with the cerebellum posteriorly.

Several cranial nerve pairs issue from pons nuclei (see Figures 12.16 and 12.17c). These include the *trigeminal* (tri-jem′ĭ-nal) *nerves* (V), the *abducens* (ab-du′senz) *nerves* (VI), and the *facial nerves* (VII). Other important pons nuclei are part of the reticular formation. The *pneumotaxic center,* for example, is a respiratory center. Together with medullary respiratory centers, it helps to maintain the normal rhythm of breathing.

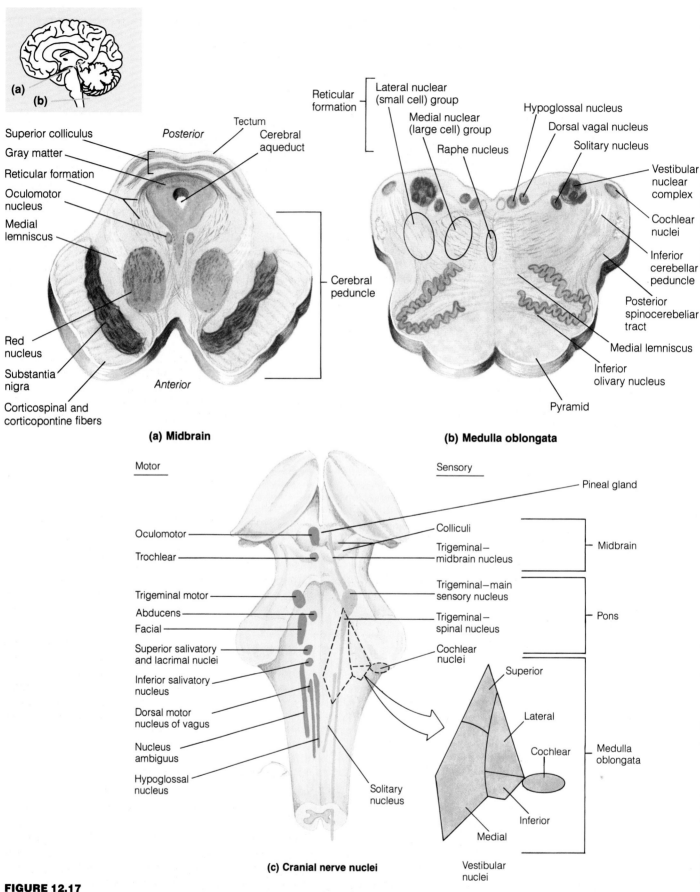

(a) Midbrain

Superior colliculus
Gray matter
Reticular formation
Oculomotor nucleus
Medial lemniscus
Red nucleus
Substantia nigra
Corticospinal and corticopontine fibers
Posterior
Tectum
Cerebral aqueduct
Cerebral peduncle
Anterior

(b) Medulla oblongata

Reticular formation
Lateral nuclear (small cell) group
Medial nuclear (large cell) group
Raphe nucleus
Hypoglossal nucleus
Dorsal vagal nucleus
Solitary nucleus
Vestibular nuclear complex
Cochlear nuclei
Inferior cerebellar peduncle
Posterior spinocerebellar tract
Medial lemniscus
Inferior olivary nucleus
Pyramid

(c) Cranial nerve nuclei

Motor
Sensory
Pineal gland
Oculomotor
Trochlear
Colliculi
Trigeminal—midbrain nucleus
Midbrain
Trigeminal motor
Abducens
Facial
Superior salivatory and lacrimal nuclei
Inferior salivatory nucleus
Dorsal motor nucleus of vagus
Nucleus ambiguus
Hypoglossal nucleus
Trigeminal—main sensory nucleus
Trigeminal—spinal nucleus
Cochlear nuclei
Pons
Solitary nucleus
Superior
Lateral
Cochlear
Inferior
Medial
Vestibular nuclei
Medulla oblongata

FIGURE 12.17
Important brain stem nuclei. Horizontal sections through **(a)** the midbrain and **(b)** the medulla oblongata. **(c)** Posterior view of the brain stem showing the positions of several cranial nerve nuclei in the midbrain, pons, and medulla.

The Medulla Oblongata

The conical **medulla oblongata** (me-dul'ah ob"long-gah'tah), or simply **medulla,** is the most inferior part of the brain stem. It blends imperceptibly into the spinal cord at the level of the foramen magnum of the skull (see Figures 12.14 and 12.15). The central canal of the spinal cord continues upward into the medulla, where it broadens out to form the cavity of the fourth ventricle. Thus, both the medulla and the pons help to form the ventral wall of the fourth ventricle. (The dorsal wall of the ventricle is formed by a thin capillary-rich membrane called a choroid plexus which abuts the more dorsal cerebellum [see Figure 12.14a].)

The medulla has several externally visible landmarks (see Figures 12.15 and 12.16). Particularly obvious on its ventral aspect are two longitudinal ridges called the **pyramids,** formed by the large pyramidal (corticospinal) tracts descending from the motor cortex. Just above the medulla–spinal cord junction, most of these fibers cross over to the opposite side before continuing their descent into the spinal cord. This crossover point is called the **decussation** (de"kus-sa'shun; "a crossing") **of the pyramids.** The consequence of this crossover is that each cerebral hemisphere chiefly controls the voluntary movements of muscles on the opposite, or *contralateral,* side of the body.

Also obvious externally are the inferior cerebellar peduncles, the olives, and the inferiormost five pairs of cranial nerves. The *inferior cerebellar peduncles* are fiber tracts that connect the medulla to the cerebellum dorsally. Situated lateral to the pyramids, the **olives** are oval swellings (which *do* resemble olives) produced mainly by the underlying **inferior olivary nuclei,** wavy folds of gray matter (Figure 12.17b). The olivary nuclei relay sensory information on the state of stretch of our muscles and joints to the cerebellum. The rootlets of the *hypoglossal nerves* (XII) emerge from the groove between the pyramid and olive on each side of the brain stem. Other cranial nerves associated with the medulla are the *glossopharyngeal nerves* (IX), the *vagus nerves* (X), and portions of the *accessory nerves* (XI) (see Figures 12.16 and 12.17c). Additionally, the fibers of the *vestibulocochlear* (ves-tib"u-lo-kok'le-ar) *nerves* (VIII) synapse with the **cochlear nuclei** (which receive information on auditory inputs), and with numerous vestibular nuclei in both the pons and medulla (see Figure 12.17b and c). Collectively, the vestibular nuclei, called the **vestibular nuclear complex,** are involved in mediating responses that maintain equilibrium.

Also housed within the medulla are several nuclei associated with ascending sensory tracts. The most prominent of these are the dorsally located **nucleus gracilis** (grah-sĭ'lis) and **nucleus cuneatus** (ku'ne-āt-us), associated with the medial lemniscal tract (see Figure 12.29). These serve as relay nuclei in a pathway by which general somatic sensory information ascends from the spinal cord to the somatosensory cortex.

The small size of the medulla belies its crucial role as an autonomic reflex center involved in maintaining body homeostasis. Important visceral motor nuclei found in the medulla include the following:

1. **The cardiovascular center.** The cardiovascular center includes cardiac and vasomotor centers. The *cardiac center* adjusts the force and rate of heart contraction to meet the body's needs. *The vasomotor center* regulates blood pressure by acting on smooth muscle in the walls of blood vessels to effect changes in blood vessel diameter. Vessel constriction causes blood pressure to increase; dilation reduces blood pressure.

2. **The respiratory centers.** The medullary respiratory centers control the rate and depth of breathing and (in a negative feedback interaction with centers of the pons) maintain respiratory rhythm.

3. **Various other centers.** Additional centers regulate activities such as vomiting, hiccuping, swallowing, coughing, and sneezing.

Notice that many functions listed above were also attributed to the hypothalamus (p. 395). The overlap is easily explained. The hypothalamus exerts its control over most visceral functions by relaying its instructions through medullary centers, which carry them out.

The Cerebellum

The large, cauliflower-like **cerebellum** (ser"ĕ-bel'um), literally, our "small brain," is exceeded in size only by the cerebrum. It accounts for about 11% of total brain mass. The cerebellum is located dorsal to the pons and medulla (and to the intervening fourth ventricle) and protrudes under the occipital lobes of the cerebral hemispheres, from which it is separated by the transverse fissure (see Figure 12.8a). It rests in the posterior cranial fossa of the skull.

The cerebellum processes inputs received from the cerebral motor cortex, various brain stem nuclei, and sensory receptors to provide the precise timing and appropriate patterns of skeletal muscle contraction needed for smooth, coordinated movements. Cerebellar activity occurs subconsciously; that is, we have no awareness of its functioning.

Anatomy of the Cerebellum

The cerebellum is bilaterally symmetrical; its two **cerebellar hemispheres** are connected medially by the wormlike **vermis** (Figure 12.18). Its surface is heavily convoluted, but since the fissures are all transversely oriented, the cerebellar surface exhibits fine, parallel, pleatlike gyri known as **folia** ("leaves"). Deep fissures subdivide each hemisphere into three lobes: the **anterior, posterior,** and **flocculonodular** (flok"u-lo-nod'u-lar) **lobes.** The small propeller-shaped flocculonodular lobe, which is situated deep

(a)

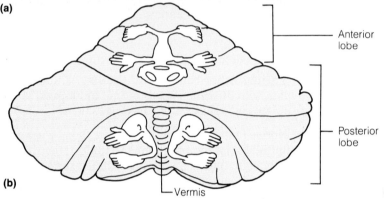

(b)

FIGURE 12.18

Cerebellum. (a) Photograph of the posterior aspect of the cerebellum. The flocculonodular lobe, which lies deep to the vermis, is not visible in this view.
(b) Positioning of congruent motor and sensory maps of the body in the cerebellum. The midline cerebellar region corresponding to the vermis coordinates gross movements of the body girdles and trunk. The intermediate portions of each hemisphere coordinate fine movements of the limbs. The lateral hemisphere regions are involved in the planning of movements.
(c) Photomicrograph of Purkinje cells of the cerebellar cortex. (300×)

(c)

to the vermis and posterior lobe, cannot be seen in a surface view.

Like the cerebrum, the cerebellum has a thin outer cortex of gray matter, internal white matter, and small, deeply situated, paired masses of gray matter, the most familiar of which are the *dentate nuclei.* Several types of neurons populate the cerebellar cortex, including stellate, basket, granule, and Purkinje cells. Of these, the large **Purkinje cells,** with their extensively branched dendrites, are the only cortical neurons that send their axons through the white matter to synapse with the central nuclei of the cerebellum. These nuclei mediate most of the output of the cerebellum. The pattern of white matter in the cerebellum is quite distinctive. Seen in sagittal section (see Figure 12.14a), it resembles a branching tree, a pattern fancifully called the **arbor vitae** (ar'bor vi'te), literally, "tree of life."

The anterior and posterior lobes of the cerebellum, which act to coordinate body movements, have completely overlapping sensory and motor maps of the entire body (see Figure 12.18b). The medial portions (corresponding to the vermis) receive information from the axial (trunk) portion of the body and influence the motor activities of the trunk and girdle muscles by relaying information to the cerebral motor cortex. The intermediate parts of each hemisphere are more concerned with the distal parts of the limbs. The lateral parts of each hemisphere receive inputs from the association areas of the cerebral cortex and appear to play a role in planning rather than execut-

ing movements; hence, these regions are integrative areas. The small flocculonodular lobes, which receive inputs from the equilibrium apparatus of the inner ears, are concerned with maintaining balance and controlling certain eye movements.

As noted earlier, three paired fiber tracts—the cerebellar peduncles—connect the cerebellum to the brain stem (see Figure 12.16). The **superior cerebellar peduncles** connect the cerebellum and midbrain. Fibers in these peduncles originate from neurons in the deep cerebellar nuclei and most communicate with the cerebral motor cortex via thalamic relays. Like the basal nuclei, the cerebellum has no direct connections with the cerebral cortex.

The **middle cerebellar peduncles** connect the pons and cerebellum. They allow one-way communication from the pons to the cerebellar neurons, that enables the cerebellum to be advised of voluntary motor activities initiated by the motor cortex (via relays in the pontine nuclei). The **inferior cerebellar peduncles** connect the cerebellum with the medulla. These peduncles contain afferent tracts conveying sensory information to the cerebellum from (1) muscle proprioceptors throughout the body and (2) the vestibular nuclei of the brain stem, which are concerned with equilibrium and balance. Unlike the contralateral fiber distribution to and from the cerebral cortex, virtually all fibers entering and leaving the cerebellum are **ipsilateral** (*ipsi* = same)—from and to the *same* side of the body.

Cerebellar Processing

The functional scheme of cerebellar processing seems to be as follows:

1. The cerebral motor cortex initiates voluntary muscle contractions and, through collateral fibers of the pyramidal tracts, simultaneously notifies the cerebellum of its activity.

2. At the same time, the cerebellum receives information from proprioceptors throughout the body (regarding the tension in the muscles and tendons, and joint position) and from visual and equilibrium pathways. This information enables the cerebellum to determine where the body is and where it is going, i.e., where the parts of the body are located in space and how they are moving.

3. The cerebellar cortex assesses this information and calculates the best way to coordinate the force, direction, and extent of muscle contraction to prevent overshoot, maintain posture, and ensure smooth, coordinated movements.

4. Then, via the superior peduncles, the cerebellum dispatches its "blueprint" for coordination to the cerebral motor cortex, which makes appropriate adjustments in its motor program. Cerebellar fibers also flow to brain stem nuclei, such as the *red nuclei* of the midbrain, which in turn project to motor neurons of the spinal cord.

The cerebellum can be compared to the control system of an automatic pilot. Just as an automatic pilot compares the plane's instrument settings with its actual course, the cerebellum continually compares the higher brain's intention with the body's performance and sends out messages to initiate the appropriate corrective measures. In this way, it helps promote smooth voluntary movements that are precise and economical in terms of muscular effort. Cerebellar injury results in loss of muscle tone and clumsy, disorganized movements; these disturbances are described in more detail in Chapter 15.

Functional Brain Systems

Functional brain systems are networks of neurons that work together but span relatively large distances within the brain, so they cannot be localized to specific brain regions. The *limbic system,* spread widely throughout the forebrain, and the *reticular formation,* which traverses the brain stem, are excellent examples of functional systems (see Table 12.1).

The Limbic System

The **limbic system** is a complex group of fiber tracts and gray matter areas located on the medial aspect of each cerebral hemisphere and in the diencephalon. Its cerebral structures encircle (*limbus* = ring) the upper part of the brain stem (Figure 12.19), and include parts of the rhinencephalon (the *septal nuclei, cingulate gyrus, parahippocampal gyrus,* and C-shaped *hippocampus*), and part of the *amygdala.* In the diencephalon, the main limbic structures are the *hypothalamus* and the *anterior thalamic nuclei.* The *fornix* ("arch") and other fiber tracts link these limbic system regions together.

The limbic system is our *emotional,* or *affective* (feelings) *brain.* The observation that odors often evoke emotional reactions and memories reflects the origin of much of this system in the primitive "smell

Cingulate gyrus

Septum pellucidum

Septal nuclei

Hypothalamus

Olfactory bulb

Mammillary body

Hippocampus

Corpus callosum

Fornix

Anterior thalamic nuclei (flanking 3rd ventricle)

Amygdaloid nucleus

Parahippocampal gyrus

FIGURE 12.19
The limbic system. Medial view of the brain, showing in gold some of the structures that constitute the limbic system, the emotional-visceral brain. The brain stem is not illustrated.

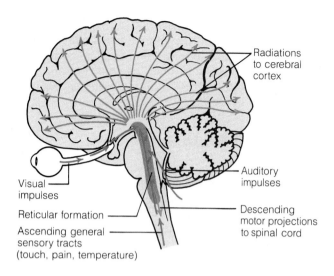

Radiations
to cerebral
cortex

Auditory
impulses

Descending
motor projections
to spinal cord

Visual
impulses

Reticular formation

Ascending general
sensory tracts
(touch, pain, temperature)

FIGURE 12.20
The reticular formation. The reticular formation extends the length of the brain stem. A portion of this formation, the reticular activating system (RAS), maintains alert wakefulness of the cerebral cortex. Ascending arrows on the diagram indicate input of sensory systems to the RAS and then reticular output via thalamic relays to the cerebral cortex. Other reticular nuclei are involved in the coordination of muscle activity. Their output is indicated by the arrow descending the brain stem.

brain" (rhinencephalon). Our reactions to odors are rarely neutral (a skunk smells *bad* and repulses us), and odors are intimately linked to our memory traces of emotionally laden experiences.

Extensive connections between the limbic system and lower and higher brain regions allow the system to integrate and respond to a wide variety of environmental stimuli. Since the hypothalamus is the neural clearinghouse for both autonomic function and emotional response, it is not surprising that some people under acute or unrelenting emotional stress fall prey to visceral illnesses, such as stomach ulcers, high blood pressure, and irritable bowel syndrome. Such emotion-induced illnesses are called **psychosomatic illnesses.** The most extreme consequence of severe emotional upheaval (paralyzing fear, extreme joy, or overwhelming grief, for example) is cardiac arrest.

The limbic system also interacts with higher cerebral cortical areas, such as the prefrontal lobes, so there is an intimate relationship between our feelings (mediated by the affective brain) and our thoughts (mediated by the cognitive brain). As a result, we are consciously aware of the emotional richness of our lives. Communication between the cerebral cortex and the limbic system explains why emotions sometimes override logic and, conversely, why reason can stop us from expressing our emotions in inappropriate situations. As described in Chapter 15, particular limbic system structures—the hippocampus and amygdala—also play an important role in converting new information into long-term memories.

Because the anatomical connections of the limbic system are so complex, it is difficult to pinpoint discrete pathologies of this system. However, specific lesions in the amygdaloid nuclei result in certain personality changes, such as docile behavior, emotional instability, restlessness, and increased interest in fighting, food, or sex. Damage to the anterior part of the cingulate gyrus, on the other hand, destroys the will and the desire to act. •

The Reticular Formation

The **reticular formation** extends through the central core of the medulla oblongata, pons, and midbrain (Figure 12.20). It is an intricate system composed of loosely clustered neurons in what is otherwise white matter. These reticular neurons can be localized into three broad columns along the length of the brain stem (see Figure 12.17b): (1) the midline **raphe** (ra′fe) **nuclei** (*raphe* = seam or crease), which are flanked laterally by (2) the **medial nuclear (large cell) group** and then (3) the **lateral nuclear (small cell) group.** You will be hearing more about some of these nuclei when we discuss sleep in Chapter 15.

The outstanding feature of the reticular neurons is their far-flung axonal connections: Individual reticular neurons project to cells in the hypothalamus, thalamus, cerebellum, and spinal cord. Such widespread connections make reticular neurons ideal for governing the arousal of the brain as a whole. For example, certain reticular neurons, unless inhibited by other brain areas, send a continuous stream of impulses (via thalamic relays) to the cerebral cortex, which maintains the cortex in an alert, conscious state. This particular arm of the reticular formation is known as the **reticular activating system (RAS).** Impulses from all the great ascending sensory tracts synapse with RAS neurons, keeping them active and enhancing their arousing effect on the cerebrum. (This may help explain why many students like to study in a crowded cafeteria.) The RAS also appears to act rather like a filter for this flood of sensory inputs. Repetitive, familiar, or weak signals are damped (filtered out), but unusual, significant, or strong impulses do reach our consciousness. For example, you are probably unaware of the slipping of your watch on your wrist, but if the clasp broke, it would immediately gain your attention.

Between them, the RAS and the cerebral cortex disregard perhaps 99% of all sensory stimuli as unimportant. If this did not occur, the sensory overload would drive us crazy. The drug LSD removes these sensory dampers, promoting a similar type of sensory overload. (Take just a moment to become aware of all the stimuli in your environment. Notice all the colors, shapes, odors, sounds, and so on. How many of these sensory stimuli are you *usually* aware of?) The activity of the RAS is inhibited by sleep centers located in the hypothalamus and other neural regions, and is depressed by alcohol, sleep-inducing drugs, and tranquilizers. Severe injury to this system, as might follow a "knockout punch" that twists the brain stem,

Skin of scalp
Periosteum
Bone of skull
Periosteal — Dura
Meningeal — mater
Arachnoid membrane
Pia mater
Arachnoid villus
Blood vessel
Falx cerebri (in longitudinal fissure only)

Superior sagittal sinus
Subdural space
Subarachnoid space

FIGURE 12.21
Meninges of the brain. Three-dimensional frontal section showing the relationship of the dura mater, arachnoid, and pia mater. The meningeal dura forms the falx cerebri fold, which extends into the longitudinal fissure and attaches the brain to the ethmoid bone of the skull. A dural sinus, the superior sagittal sinus, is enclosed by the dural membranes superiorly. Arachnoid villi, which return cerebrospinal fluid to the dural sinus, are also shown.

results in permanent unconsciousness (irreversible *coma*).

The reticular formation also has a *motor* arm. Some of its motor nuclei project to motor neurons in the spinal cord via the *reticulospinal tracts,* and help control the skeletal muscles during coarse movements of the limbs. Other reticular motor nuclei, such as the vasomotor, cardiac, and respiratory centers of the medulla, are autonomic centers that regulate visceral motor functions.

Protection of the Brain

Nervous tissue is soft and delicate, and the irreplaceable neurons are injured by even slight pressure. However, the brain is protected by a bony enclosure (the skull), membranes (the meninges), and a watery cushion (cerebrospinal fluid). Furthermore, the brain is protected from harmful substances in the blood by the so-called "blood-brain barrier." We described the cranium, the brain's bony encasement, in Chapter 7. Here we will attend to the other protective devices.

Meninges

The **meninges** (mě-nin'jēz; *mening* = membrane) are three connective tissue membranes that lie just external to the central nervous system organs. They (1) cover and protect the CNS, (2) protect blood vessels and enclose venous sinuses, (3) contain cerebrospinal fluid, and (4) form partitions within the skull. From external to internal, the meninges (singular, **meninx**) are the dura mater, arachnoid, and pia mater (Figure 12.21).

The Dura Mater. The leathery **dura mater** (du'rah ma'ter), meaning "tough (or hard) mother," is a double-layered membrane where it surrounds the brain. Its outer layer, the *periosteal layer,* is the inelastic membrane attached to the inner surface of the skull; that is, it is the periosteum. Note that there is no dural periosteal layer surrounding the spinal cord. The deeper *meningeal layer* forms the outermost brain covering and continues caudally in the vertebral canal as the dural sheath of the spinal cord. The brain's dural layers are fused together except in certain areas, where they enclose the **dural sinuses** that collect venous blood from the brain and direct it into the internal jugular veins of the neck.

The Arachnoid Mater. The middle meninx, the **arachnoid mater,** or simply the **arachnoid** (ah-rak'noid), forms a loose brain covering, never dipping into the sulci at the cerebral surface. It is separated from the dura mater by a narrow serous cavity, the **subdural space.** Beneath the arachnoid membrane is the wide **subarachnoid space,** which is spanned by threadlike arachnoid extensions that secure this membrane to the innermost pia mater. (*Arachnida* means "spider," and this membrane was named for its weblike extensions.) The subarachnoid space is filled with cerebrospinal fluid and contains the largest blood vessels serving the brain. Since the arachnoid is fine and elastic, these blood vessels are rather poorly protected.

Knoblike projections of the arachnoid called **arachnoid villi** (vil'i) protrude externally through the dura mater and into the dural sinuses overlying the superior aspect of the brain (Figure 12.21). Cerebrospinal fluid is absorbed into the venous blood of the sinuses through these villi.

The Pia Mater. The **pia** (pi'ah) **mater,** meaning "gentle mother," is composed of delicate connective

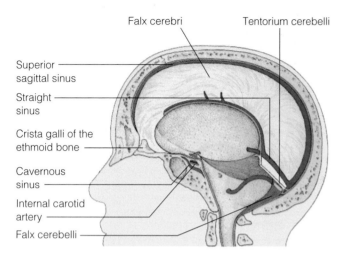

FIGURE 12.22
Partitioning folds of dura mater in the cranial cavity.
Note the falx cerebri, falx cerebelli, and tentorium cerebelli. Some dural sinuses are also shown.

tissue and is richly invested with minute blood vessels. It is the only meninx that clings tightly to the brain, following every convolution. Small arteries entering the brain tissue carry ragged sheaths of pia mater inward with them for short distances.

Dural Septa.   In several places, the meningeal dura mater extends inward to form flat septa that securely anchor the brain to the skull. These septa, which limit excessive movement of the brain within the cranium, include the following (Figure 12.22):

- The **falx cerebri** (falks ser′ĕ-bri), a midsagittal sickle-shaped (*falks* = sickle) fold that dips into the longitudinal fissure between the cerebral hemispheres. It attaches to the crista galli of the ethmoid bone.

- The **falx cerebelli** (ser″ĕ-bel′i), a small vertical sheet in the sagittal plane that forms a midline partition that runs along the vermis of the cerebellum.

- The **tentorium** (ten-to′re-um) **cerebelli**, a nearly horizontal dural fold that extends into the transverse fissure. It forms a partition between the cerebral hemispheres (which it helps to support) and the cerebellum. *Tentorium* means "tent," hence it is a tent over the cerebellum.

Meningitis, an inflammation of the meninges, is a serious threat to the brain because a bacterial or viral meningitis may spread into the nervous tissue of the CNS. This condition of brain inflammation is called *encephalitis* (en′sef-ah-li′tis). Meningitis is usually diagnosed by examining a sample of cerebrospinal fluid taken from the subarachnoid space. •

Cerebrospinal Fluid

Cerebrospinal fluid (CSF), found in and around the brain and spinal cord, forms a liquid cushion that gives buoyancy to the CNS organs. By floating the jellylike brain, the CSF effectively reduces brain weight by 97% and prevents the brain from crushing under its own weight. CSF also protects the brain and spinal cord from blows and other trauma. Additionally, although the brain has a rich blood supply, cerebrospinal fluid helps to nourish the brain.

CSF is a watery "broth" similar in composition to blood plasma, from which it arises. However, it contains less protein and more vitamin C, and its ion concentration is different. For example, CSF contains more sodium, chloride, magnesium, and hydrogen ions than blood plasma, and fewer calcium and potassium ions. CSF composition, particularly its pH, is important in the control of cerebral blood flow and breathing, as described in later chapters. CSF also transports hormones along the ventricular channels.

The **choroid plexuses** that hang from the roof of each ventricle (Figure 12.23a) form CSF. These plexuses are frond-shaped clusters of broad, thin-walled capillaries (*plex* = interwoven) enclosed by a layer of ependymal cells lining the ventricles. Although the capillaries of the choroid plexuses are fairly permeable and tissue fluid filters continuously from the bloodstream, the choroid plexus ependymal cells are joined by tight junctions and have ion pumps that allow them to modify this filtrate by actively transporting only certain ions across their membranes into the CSF pool. This sets up ionic gradients that cause water to diffuse into the ventricles as well. In adults, the total CSF volume of about 150 ml (about half a cup) is replaced every 3 to 4 hours, hence 900–1200 ml of CSF are formed daily. The choroid plexuses also help to cleanse the CSF by removing waste products and other unnecessary solutes.

Once produced, CSF moves freely through the ventricles. Some CSF circulates from the ventricles into the central canal of the spinal cord, but most enters the subarachnoid space via the lateral and medial apertures in the walls of the fourth ventricle (Figure 12.23b). The constant motion of the CSF is aided by the long microvilli of the ependymal cells lining the ventricles. In the subarachnoid space, CSF bathes the outer surfaces of the brain and cord and then returns to the blood in the dural sinuses via the arachnoid villi.

Ordinarily, CSF is produced and drained at a constant rate. However, if something (such as a tumor) obstructs its circulation and/or drainage, it accumulates and exerts pressure on the brain. This condition is called *hydrocephalus* ("water on the brain"). Hydrocephalus in a newborn baby causes its head to enlarge; this is possible because the skull bones have not yet fused. In adults, however, hydrocephalus is more likely to result in brain damage because the skull is rigid and hard, and accumulating

Superior sagittal sinus
Superior cerebral vein
Choroid plexus
Cerebrum covered with pia mater
Septum pellucidum
Corpus callosum
Interventricular foramen
Third ventricle
Pituitary gland

Arachnoid villus
Subarachnoid space
Arachnoid
Meningeal dura mater
Periosteal dura mater
Great cerebral vein
Tentorium cerebelli
Straight sinus
Confluence of sinuses
Cerebellum
Choroid plexus
Cerebral vessels that supply choroid plexus
Central canal of spinal cord
Spinal dura mater (dural sheath)
Inferior end of spinal cord
Filum terminale (inferior end of pia mater)

Cerebral aqueduct
Lateral aperture
Fourth ventricle
Median aperture

(b)

Ependymal cells
Capillary
Connective tissue of pia mater
Section of choroid plexus

Wastes and unnecessary solutes absorbed
Cavity of ventricle
Filtrate containing glucose, oxygen, vitamins, and ions (Na⁺, Cl⁻, Mg²⁺, etc.)

(a)

FIGURE 12.23
Formation, location, and circulation of CSF. (a) Choroid plexus forms CSF. Each choroid plexus consists of a knot of porous capillaries surrounded by a single layer of ependymal cells joined by tight junctions and bearing long microvilli with blunted ends. Although the filtrate moves easily from the capillaries, it must move through and be processed by the ependymal cells before it is allowed to enter the ventricles as cerebrospinal fluid. **(b)** Location and circulatory pattern of CSF. Direction of circulation is indicated by the arrows. (The relative position of the right lateral ventricle is indicated by the pale blue area deep to the corpus callosum and septum pellucidum.)

fluid compresses the blood vessels serving the brain and crushes the soft nervous tissue. Hydrocephalus is treated by inserting a shunt in the ventricles that drains off the excess fluid into a vein in the neck. •

Blood-Brain Barrier

The **blood-brain barrier** is a protective mechanism that helps maintain a stable environment for the brain. No other body tissue is so absolutely dependent on a constant internal milieu as is the brain. In other body regions, the extracellular concentrations of hormones, amino acids, and ions are in constant flux, particularly after eating or exercise. If the brain were exposed to such chemical variations, the neurons would fire uncontrollably, because some hormones and amino acids serve as neurotransmitters and certain ions (particularly potassium) modify the threshold for neuronal firing.

Blood-borne substances within the brain's capillaries are separated from the extracellular space and neurons by (1) the continuous endothelium of the capillary wall; (2) a relatively thick basal lamina surrounding the external face of the capillary; and to a limited extent (3) the bulbous "feet" of the astrocytes that cling to the capillaries. The capillary endothelial cells are almost "seamlessly" joined all around by *tight junctions* (see Chapter 20), making them the least permeable capillaries in the entire body. This relative impermeability of brain capillaries constitutes most (if not all) of the blood-brain barrier. Although it was formerly assumed that the astrocytes contribute to the blood-brain barrier, the electron microscope has revealed that their end feet are too far apart to form any true seal. It now appears that the major role of the astrocyte end feet is to provide the signals that stimulate the endothelial cells of the brain capillaries *to form* the tight junctions characteristic of the blood-brain barrier.

The blood-brain barrier is a selective, rather than an absolute, barrier. Nutrients, such as glucose, essential amino acids, and some electrolytes, move passively by facilitated diffusion through the endothelial cell membranes. Blood-borne metabolic wastes, such as urea and creatinine, as well as proteins, certain toxins, and most drugs, are prevented from entering brain tissue. Small nonessential amino acids and potassium ions not only are prevented from entering the brain, but also are actively pumped from the brain across the capillary endothelium.

The barrier is ineffective against fats, fatty acids, oxygen and carbon dioxide, and other fat-soluble molecules that diffuse easily through all plasma membranes. This explains why blood-borne alcohol, nicotine, and anesthetics can affect the brain.

The structure of the blood-brain barrier is not completely uniform. As noted above, the capillaries of the choroid plexuses are very porous, but the ependymal cells surrounding them have tight junctions. In some brain areas, the blood-brain barrier is entirely absent and, in such areas, the capillary endothelium is quite permeable, allowing blood-borne molecules easy access to the neural tissue. One such region is the vomiting center of the brain stem, which monitors the blood for poisonous substances. Another is in the hypothalamus, which regulates water balance, body temperature, and many metabolic activities; lack of a blood-brain barrier here is essential to allow the hypothalamus to sample the chemical composition of the blood. The blood-brain barrier is incompletely developed in newborn and premature infants, and potentially toxic substances can readily enter the CNS and cause problems not seen in adults.

Injury to the brain, whatever the cause, may cause a localized breakdown of the blood-brain barrier. Most likely, this reflects some change in the capillary endothelial cells or their tight junctions. This supposition is borne out by a procedure that infuses a concentrated solution of mannitol (sugar) prior to infusing chemotherapeutic drugs. The mannitol causes the capillary endothelial cells to shrink, opening up gaps between their tight junctions that allow the drugs to breach the blood-brain barrier and gain access to brain tumors. •

Homeostatic Imbalances of the Brain

Brain dysfunctions are unbelievably varied and extensive. We have mentioned some of them already, and we will discuss developmental problems in the final section of the chapter. Here, we will focus on traumatic brain injuries and degenerative disorders.

Traumatic Brain Injuries

Head injuries are the leading cause of accidental death in the USA. Consider, for example, what happens when you forget to fasten your seat belt and then rear-end another car. Your head is moving and then is suddenly stopped as it hits the windshield. Brain damage is caused not only by localized injury at the site of the blow (the *coup* injury), but also by the ricocheting effect as the brain hits the opposite end of the skull (the *contrecoup* injury).

A **concussion** occurs when brain injury is slight and the symptoms are mild and transient. The victim may be dizzy, "see stars," or lose consciousness briefly, but no permanent neurological damage is sustained. The result of marked tissue destruction is a brain **contusion,** which produces a broad variety of signs and symptoms. In cortical contusions, the individual may remain conscious, but severe brain stem contusions always result in unconsciousness (coma), ranging in duration from hours to a lifetime because of injury to the reticular activating system.

Following head blows, fatal consequences may result from *subdural* or *subarachnoid hemorrhage* (bleeding from ruptured vessels into those spaces). Individuals who are initially lucid following head trauma and then begin to deteriorate neurologically are, in all probability, hemorrhaging intracranially. Accumulating blood within the skull increases intracranial pressure and compresses brain tissue. If the pressure becomes sufficient to force the brain stem inferiorly through the foramen magnum, control of blood pressure, heart rate, and respiration is lost. Intracranial hemorrhages are treated by surgical removal of the hematoma (localized blood mass) and repair of the ruptured blood vessels.

Another consequence of traumatic head injury is **cerebral edema,** or swelling of the brain. This results both from exudate formation during the inflammatory response and from water uptake by brain tissue. Anti-inflammatory drugs such as prednisone and other steroids are routinely administered to head injury patients in an attempt to prevent cerebral edema from aggravating brain injury.

Degenerative Brain Diseases

Two important degenerative diseases of the central nervous system are cerebrovascular accidents and Alzheimer's disease.

Cerebrovascular Accidents. The single most common nervous system disorder and the third leading cause of death in the USA are **cerebrovascular** (ser″ĕ-bro-vas′ku-lar) **accidents (CVAs),** commonly called **strokes.** Strokes occur when blood circulation to a brain area is blocked and vital brain tissue dies. (Deprivation of blood supply to *any* tissue is called **ischemia** (is-ke′me-ah; "to hold back blood") and results in deficient oxygen and nutrient delivery to cells.) The most common cause of CVA is blockage of a cerebral artery by a blood clot. Other causes include compression of brain tissue by hemorrhage or edema and progressive narrowing of brain vessels by atherosclerosis.

Eighty percent of those who suffer massive cerebral hemorrhage die during the initial acute attack; the mortality is far lower in those with nonhemorrhagic strokes. Those who survive a CVA are typically paralyzed on one side of the body and many exhibit sensory deficits. If the language areas are damaged, difficulties in understanding or vocalizing speech develop. Whatever the cause, the nature of the neurological deficits that follow depends on the area and extent of brain damage that occurred. Fewer than 35% of those surviving an initial CVA are alive three years later, because those suffering CVAs from blood clots are likely to have recurrent clotting problems—and more CVAs. Even so, the picture is not hopeless. Some patients recover at least a portion of their lost faculties, because undamaged neurons sprout new branches that spread into the area of injury and take over some lost functions. However, neuronal spread is limited to only about 5 mm (0.2 inch); thus, large lesions always result in less than complete recovery. Physical therapy is usually started as soon as possible to prevent contractures.

Not all strokes are "completed." Temporary episodes of reversible cerebral ischemia, called **transient ischemic attacks (TIAs),** are common. TIAs last from 5 to 50 minutes and are characterized by temporary numbness, paralysis, and impaired speech. While these deficits are not permanent, TIAs do constitute "red flags" that warn of impending, more serious CVAs. If left untreated, about one-third of patients with TIAs eventually suffer a completed stroke. Cumulative trials of aspirin therapy have strongly indicated that 300 mg daily is effective in reducing the risk of both TIAs and CVAs.

Historically, medicine has been able to do little for a stroke patient, but recent findings on the mechanism of cell death following a stroke are particularly exciting. Apparently the main culprit is *glutamate,* an excitatory neurotransmitter that helps shape the processes of learning and memory. Normally, glutamate binding to NMDA (*N*-methyl D-aspartate) receptors (named for the chemical used to identify them) opens specific gates that allow calcium ions (which induce changes essential for learning or potentiation) to enter the stimulated neuron. After brain injury, neurons totally deprived of oxygen begin to disintegrate, unleashing the cellular equivalent of "buckets" of glutamate that acts as an *excitotoxin* to mediate both immediate and delayed changes in ion transport by activating NMDA receptors. The acute change, which occurs within minutes, consists of neuronal uptake of Na^+, Cl^-, and water. The delayed changes, which take place over the next few hours, involve calcium influx and generation of free radicals including NO that kill thousands of surrounding, still-healthy neurons. As more and more newly oxygen-deprived neurons become overexcited and themselves release glutamate, the chain reaction leading to even more cell death is reinforced. These new insights have launched an intense search for drugs, such as NMDA antagonists and calcium channel blockers, that can prevent this neurotoxic domino effect and improve the outlook for future stroke victims. Additional therapies include those that prevent or dissolve blood clots (heparin, tissue plasminogen activator [t-PA], and others).

Alzheimer's Disease. **Alzheimer's** (altz′hi-merz) **disease** is a progressive degenerative disease of the brain that ultimately results in dementia (mental deterioration). CVA patients represent nearly half of nursing home patients; Alzheimer's patients represent most of the remaining half. Although usually seen in elderly people, Alzheimer's disease may begin in middle age. Its victims exhibit widespread cognitive deficits, including memory loss (particularly for recent events), shortened attention span, and disorientation. Formerly good-natured individuals become irritable, moody, and confused. Ultimately, hallucinations occur. These changes develop over a period of several years, during which time the family members watch the person they love "disappear."

Alzheimer's disease is associated with structural changes in the brain, particularly in the cerebral cortex and hippocampus, areas involved with cognitive functions and memory. Alzheimer's runs in families. Individuals with two genes for APO-E4 are eight times as likely to develop Alzheimer's as those who inherit ATP-E3 genes, the more common gene variant for the APO-E protein. APO-E4 directs the synthesis of a protein called apolipoprotein E, which helps process cholesterol, plays a role in atherosclerosis, and is linked to at least one type of heart disease (see p. 624). Microscopic examinations of brain tissue reveal the presence of apolipoprotein E bound to *beta-amyloid protein* deposits in **senile plaques** (aggregations of cells and degenerated fibers around a protein core) and **neurofibrillar tangles** (twisted fibrils within neuron cell bodies).

It has been frustratingly difficult for researchers to uncover how beta amyloid protein acts as a neurotoxin, particularly since it is also present in healthy brain cells (but in lower amounts). Essentially, beta amyloid is a lysosomal breakdown product of a normal cell surface protein called amyloid precursor protein

(APP). All cells break down APP via two pathways: (1) the secretory pathway, which clips off APP where it protrudes from the plasma membrane and yields harmless protein fragments, and (2) the lysosomal pathway, which cleaves beta amyloid from APP. Just what tips the biochemical pathways off balance to favor production of beta amyloid is not understood, but it is known that this tiny protein does its damage by destroying nerve cells' ability to regulate their internal Ca^{2+} levels by enhancing calcium influx mediated by glutamate. Thus, as in stroke patients, the unholy trio of glutamate-NMDA receptors-Ca^{2+} appears to be responsible for at least part of the neural havoc that occurs.

Another line of research has implicated a protein called *tau,* which encourages tubulin proteins to link up to form microtubules. (Recall that microtubules are essential for normal intracellular transport, a crucial function in neurons.) When tau is inappropriately phosphorylated, it tends to abandon its microtubule stabilizing role and to intertwine with other tau molecules to form the neurofibrillary tangles. Not surprisingly, tau harvested from the brains of Alzheimer's victims cannot bind to microtubules. Also, as a transporter of cholesterol, APO-E4 can alter membrane permeability to calcium. Once calcium enters the cell it can trigger the cascade that leads to phosphorylation of tau, breakdown of microtubules, and formation of the neurofibrillary tangles. Presumably, the beta amyloid and tau lines of investigation will eventually merge and point to the treatment for this terrible disorder, but no one has the answer yet. •

THE SPINAL CORD

Gross Anatomy and Protection of the Spinal Cord

The spinal cord, enclosed within the vertebral column, extends from the foramen magnum of the skull (where it merges imperceptibly with the medulla of the brain stem) to the level of the first lumbar vertebra, just inferior to the ribs (Figure 12.24). About 42 cm (17 inches) long and 1.8 cm (¾ of an inch) thick, the glistening-white **spinal cord** provides a two-way conduction pathway to and from the brain. It is a major reflex center: Spinal reflexes are initiated and completed at the spinal cord level. We discuss reflex functions of the cord in Chapter 13. Finally, as described in more detail in Chapter 15, the spinal cord can independently initiate complex patterns of motor activity, such as the alternating flexor-extensor patterns seen in walking. However, these movements, initiated by the so-called spinal *central pattern generators,* are highly stereotyped and must be modulated by brain inputs to be useful. The next section focuses on the anatomy of the cord and on the location and naming of its ascending and descending tracts.

Like the brain, the spinal cord is protected by bone, cerebrospinal fluid, and meninges. The single-layered dura mater of the spinal cord, called the **spinal dural sheath** (see Figures 12.23b and 12.26), is not attached to the bony walls of the vertebral column. Between the bony vertebrae and the dural sheath is a rather large **epidural space** filled with fat and a network of veins. The fat forms a soft padding around the spinal cord. Cerebrospinal fluid fills the subarachnoid space between the *arachnoid* and *pia mater* meninges. Inferiorly, the dural and arachnoid membranes extend well beyond the end of the spinal cord in the vertebral canal, approximately to the second sacral vertebra (S_2). The spinal cord typically ends at L_1 (Figure 12.24a). Thus, the subarachnoid space within the meningeal sac inferior to that point provides a nearly ideal spot for removing cerebrospinal fluid for testing, a procedure called a **lumbar puncture** or **tap.** Since the spinal cord is absent there and the delicate nerve roots drift away from the point of needle insertion, there is little or no danger of damaging the cord (or spinal roots) beyond L_3.

Inferiorly, the spinal cord terminates in a tapering cone-shaped structure called the **conus medullaris** (ko'nus me"dul-ar'is). A fibrous extension of the pia mater, the **filum terminale** (fi'lum ter"mi-nah'le; "terminal filament") extends downward from the conus medullaris to the posterior surface of the coccyx, where it attaches (Figure 12.24c). This attachment anchors the spinal cord in place so it is not jostled by body movements. Furthermore, the spinal cord is anchored to the bony walls of the vertebral canal throughout its length by saw-toothed shelves of pia mater (Figure 12.24d). These lateral shelves are the **denticulate ligaments** (den-tik'u-lāt; "toothed").

In humans, 31 pairs of *spinal nerves* arise from the cord by paired roots and exit from the vertebral column via the intervertebral foramina to travel to the body regions they serve. Just as the vertebral column is segmented, so too is the spinal cord (however, these neural spinal segments are not visible externally). Each segment of the cord is defined by a pair of spinal nerves that lie superior to their corresponding vertebra. The spinal cord is about the width of a thumb for most of its length, but it has obvious enlargements in the cervical and lumbosacral regions, where the nerves serving the upper and lower limbs arise. These enlargements are the **cervical** and **lumbar enlargements,** respectively (see Figure 12.24a). Because the cord does not reach the end of the vertebral column, the lumbar and sacral spinal nerve roots angle sharply downward and travel inferiorly through the vertebral canal for some distance before reaching their intervertebral foramina. The collection of nerve roots at the inferior end of the vertebral canal is named the **cauda equina** (kaw'da e-kwi'nuh) because of its resemblance to a horse's tail. This rather strange arrangement reflects the fact that, during fetal development, the vertebral column grows inferiorly more rapidly than does the spinal cord, forcing the lower spinal nerve roots to "chase" their exit points inferiorly through the vertebral canal.

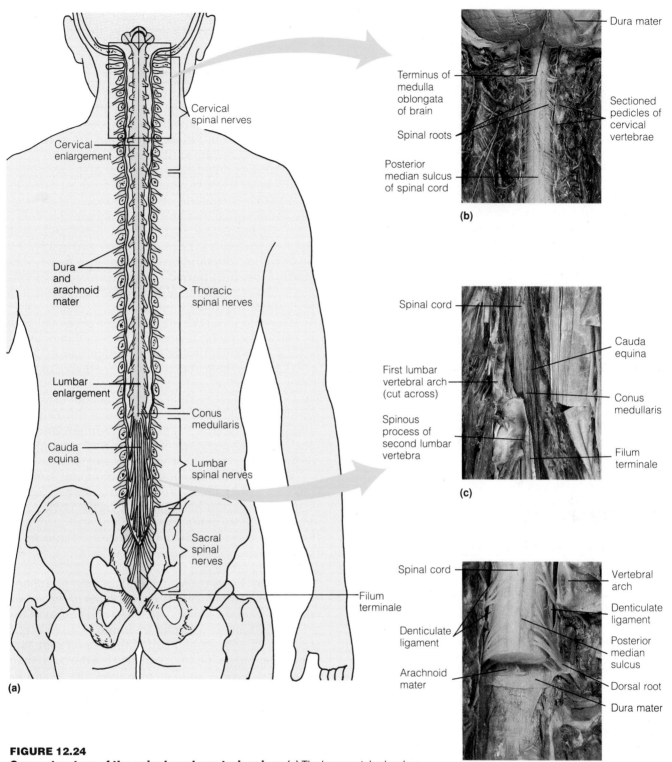

Cervical spinal nerves

Cervical enlargement

Dura and arachnoid mater

Thoracic spinal nerves

Lumbar enlargement

Conus medullaris

Cauda equina

Lumbar spinal nerves

Sacral spinal nerves

Filum terminale

(a)

Dura mater

Terminus of medulla oblongata of brain

Spinal roots

Posterior median sulcus of spinal cord

Sectioned pedicles of cervical vertebrae

(b)

Spinal cord

First lumbar vertebral arch (cut across)

Spinous process of second lumbar vertebra

Cauda equina

Conus medullaris

Filum terminale

(c)

Spinal cord

Denticulate ligament

Arachnoid mater

Vertebral arch

Denticulate ligament

Posterior median sulcus

Dorsal root

Dura mater

(d)

FIGURE 12.24

Gross structure of the spinal cord, posterior view. (a) The bony vertebral arches have been removed to reveal the spinal cord and its nerve roots. The dura and arachnoid mater are cut open and reflected laterally. **(b)** Photograph of the cervical part of the spinal cord. **(c)** Inferior end of the spinal cord, showing the conus medullaris, cauda equina, and filum terminale. **(d)** Enlargement of the spinal cord, showing the denticulate ligament.

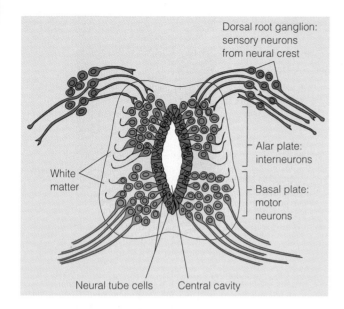

Dorsal root ganglion: sensory neurons from neural crest

Alar plate: interneurons

Basal plate: motor neurons

White matter

Neural tube cells   Central cavity

FIGURE 12.25
Sructure of the embryonic spinal cord. At six weeks of development, aggregations of gray matter called the alar plates (future interneurons) and basal plates (future motor neurons) have formed, and dorsal root ganglia (future sensory neurons) have arisen from neural crest cells.

Embryonic Development of the Spinal Cord

The spinal cord develops from the caudal portion of the embryonic neural tube (see Figures 12.2 and 12.3 on pp. 380 and 381). By the sixth week, each side of the developing cord has two recognizable clusters of neuroblasts that have migrated outward from the original neural tube: a dorsal **alar** (a'lar) **plate** and a ventral **basal plate** (Figure 12.25).

The alar plate neuroblasts become interneurons. The basal plate neuroblasts develop into motor neurons and sprout axons that grow out to the effector organs. Axons that emerge from alar plate cells (and some basal plate cells) form the external white matter of the cord by growing outward along the length of the CNS. As development progresses, the alar plates expand dorsally and the basal plates expand ventrally to produce the H-shaped central mass of gray matter of the adult spinal cord. Neural crest cells that come to lie alongside the cord form the *dorsal root ganglia* containing sensory neuron cell bodies, which send their axons into the dorsal aspect of the cord.

Cross-Sectional Anatomy of the Spinal Cord

The spinal cord is somewhat flattened from front to back, and two grooves mark its surface: the **anterior median fissure** and the more shallow **posterior median sulcus** (see Figure 12.26). These grooves run the length of the cord and partially divide it into right and left halves. As mentioned earlier, the gray matter of the cord is located on the inside, the white matter outside.

Gray Matter and Spinal Roots

As in other regions of the central nervous system, the gray matter of the cord consists of a mixture of neuron cell bodies, their unmyelinated processes, and neuroglia. All neurons whose cell bodies are in the gray matter of the cord are multipolar neurons.

As already noted, the gray matter of the cord looks like the letter H or like a butterfly in cross section (Figure 12.26a). It consists of mirror-image lateral gray masses connected by a cross-bar of gray matter, called the **gray commissure,** that encloses the central canal. The two posterior projections of the gray matter are the **posterior (dorsal) horns;** the anterior pair are the **anterior (ventral) horns.** An additional pair of gray matter columns, the small **lateral horns,** is present in the thoracic and upper lumbar segments of the cord.

The anterior horns mainly house nerve cell bodies of somatic motor neurons. These send their axons out via the **ventral roots** of the spinal cord (Figure 12.26b) to the skeletal muscles (their effector organs). The amount of ventral gray matter present at a given level of the spinal cord reflects the amount of skeletal muscle innervated at that particular level. Thus, the anterior horns are largest in the limb-innervating cervical and lumbar regions of the cord and are responsible for the enlargement seen in those regions.

The lateral horn neurons are autonomic (sympathetic division) motor neurons that serve visceral organs. Their axons leave the cord via the ventral root along with those of the somatic motor neurons. Since the ventral roots contain both somatic and autonomic efferents, they serve both motor divisions of the peripheral nervous system.

Afferent fibers carrying impulses from peripheral sensory receptors form the **dorsal roots** of the spinal cord (see Figure 12.26b). The nerve cell bodies of the associated sensory neurons are found in an enlarged region of the dorsal root called the **dorsal root ganglion** or **spinal ganglion.** After entering the cord, their axons may take a number of routes. For example, some enter the posterior white matter of the cord directly and travel to synapse at higher cord or brain levels, while others synapse with interneurons in the posterior horns of the spinal cord gray matter at the level they enter.

The dorsal and ventral roots are very short and fuse laterally to form the **spinal nerves.** The spinal nerves, which are part of the peripheral nervous system, are considered further in Chapter 13.

The spinal gray matter can be divided further according to its neurons' relative involvement in the innervation of the somatic and visceral regions of the body. The following four zones are evident within this gray matter (Figure 12.27): **somatic sensory (SS), visceral** (autonomic) **sensory (VS), visceral motor (VM), somatic motor (SM).**

(a)

(b)

FIGURE 12.26
Anatomy of the spinal cord. (a) Cross section through the spinal cord illustrating its
relationship to the surrounding vertebal column. **(b)** Three-dimensional view of the adult spinal
cord and its meningeal coverings.

FIGURE 12.27
Organization of the gray matter of the spinal cord. In terms of its neurons' involvement in processing sensory and motor activity, the gray matter of the spinal cord can be divided into a sensory half dorsally and a motor half ventrally. SS: interneurons receiving input from somatic sensory neurons. VS: interneurons receiving input from visceral sensory neurons. VM: visceral motor (autonomic) neurons. SM: somatic motor neurons. Note that the dorsal and ventral roots are part of the PNS, not of the spinal cord.

The symptoms of *poliomyelitis* (po″le-o-mi″ĕ-li′tis; *polio* = gray matter; *myelitis* = inflammation of the spinal cord) result from the destruction of anterior horn motor neurons by the poliovirus. Initial symptoms include fever, headache, muscle pain and weakness, and loss of certain somatic reflexes. As the disease progresses, paralysis develops and the muscles served atrophy. The victim may die from paralysis of the respiratory muscles or from cardiac arrest if neurons in the medulla oblongata are destroyed. In most cases, the poliovirus enters the body in feces-contaminated water (such as might occur in a public swimming pool), and the incidence of the disease has traditionally been highest in children and during the summer months. Fortunately, Salk and Sabin polio vaccines have nearly eliminated this disease.

However, many of the "recovered" survivors of the great polio epidemic of the late 1940s and 1950s have begun to experience extreme lethargy, sharp burning pains in their muscles, and progressive muscle weakness and atrophy. Initially dismissed as the flu or psychosomatic illness, these disturbing symptoms are now referred to as *postpolio syndrome.* Though the cause of postpolio syndrome is not known, a likely explanation is that its victims, like all of us, continue to lose neurons throughout life. While a healthy nervous system can recruit nearby neurons to compensate for the losses, polio survivors have already drawn on that "pool" and have few neurons left to take over. Ironically, those who worked hardest to overcome their disease are its newest victims. •

White Matter

The white matter of the spinal cord is composed of myelinated and unmyelinated nerve fibers. These run in three directions: (1) *ascending*—up to higher centers (sensory inputs), (2) *descending*—down to the cord from the brain or within the cord to lower levels (motor outputs) and (3) *commissural*—across from one side of the cord to the other (commissural fibers). The vertical (ascending and descending) tracts make up most of the white matter.

The white matter on each side of the cord is divided into three **white columns,** or **funiculi** (fu-nik′u-li; "long ropes"). These are named according to their position as the **posterior, lateral,** and **anterior funiculi** (see Figure 12.26b). Each funiculus contains several fiber tracts, and each tract is made up of axons with similar destinations and functions. With a few exceptions, the names of the spinal tracts reveal both their origin and destination. The principal ascending and descending tracts of the spinal cord are illustrated schematically in Figure 12.28.

All major spinal tracts are actually *part of multi-neuron pathways* that connect the brain to the body periphery. These great ascending and descending pathways contain not only spinal neurons but also parts of peripheral neurons and neurons in the brain. So, before getting specific about the individual spinal tracts, we will make some generalizations about them and the pathways to which they contribute:

1. Most pathways cross over from one side of the CNS to the other (decussate) at some point along their journey.

2. Most consist of a chain of two or three neurons that contribute to successive tracts of the pathway.

3. Most exhibit *somatotopy,* a precise spatial relationship among the tract fibers that reflects the orderly mapping of the body. For example, in an ascending sensory tract, somatotopy refers to the fact that fibers transmitting inputs from the superior parts of the body lie lateral to those conveying information from inferior body regions.

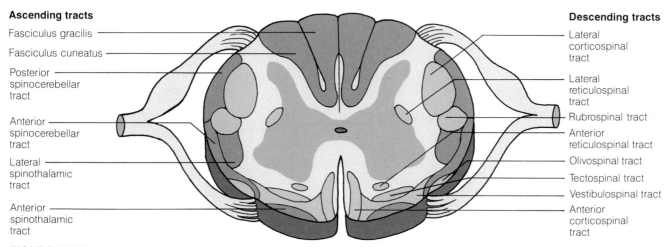

Ascending tracts

Fasciculus gracilis

Fasciculus cuneatus

Posterior spinocerebellar tract

Anterior spinocerebellar tract

Lateral spinothalamic tract

Anterior spinothalamic tract

Descending tracts

Lateral corticospinal tract

Lateral reticulospinal tract

Rubrospinal tract

Anterior reticulospinal tract

Olivospinal tract

Tectospinal tract

Vestibulospinal tract

Anterior corticospinal tract

FIGURE 12.28
Major ascending (sensory) and descending (motor) tracts of the spinal cord, cross-sectional view. Ascending tracts are shown in blue and labeled only on the left side of the figure. Descending tracts are shown in pink and labeled on the right.

4. All pathways and tracts are paired (right and left) with a member of the pair present on each side of the spinal cord or brain.

Ascending (Sensory) Pathways and Tracts.

The ascending pathways conduct sensory impulses upward through chains of two or three successive neurons (*first-, second-,* and *third-order neurons*) to various regions of the brain. Most of the incoming information results from stimulation of general sensory receptors (touch, pressure, temperature, and pain) in the skin and from stimulation of proprioceptors that monitor the degree of stretch in the muscles, tendons, and joints. In general, this information is conveyed along six main pathways on each side of the spinal cord. Four of these pathways transmit impulses to the sensory cortex *for conscious interpretation.* The **fasciculi** (fah-sik′u-li) **cuneatus** and **gracilis** in the posterior funiculus, also called the **dorsal white column,** transmit information from the fine touch and pressure receptors and joint proprioceptors, which can be localized precisely on the body surface. Collectively, the inputs of these sister tracts comprise what is referred to as *discriminative touch* and *conscious proprioception.* The **lateral** and **anterior spinothalamic tracts** (and pathways) convey information on pain, temperature, deep pressure, and coarse touch—sensations that we are aware of, but that we are less able to locate precisely. All four of these pathways cross over (decussate)—the first pair in the medulla and the second pair in the spinal cord. The last pair, the **anterior** and **posterior spinocerebellar tracts,** convey information from proprioceptors (muscle or tendon stretch) to the cerebellum, which uses this information to coordinate skeletal muscle activity. Since the somatosensory cortex is not their terminus, these pathways do *not* contribute to conscious sensation. The fibers of the spinocere-bellar pathways either do not decussate or else cross over twice (thus "undoing" the decussation). These ascending pathways and the spinal cord fiber tracts contributing to them are described in more detail in Table 12.2. Four of these tracts are illustrated in Figure 12.29. Notice that only the fasciculi cuneatus and gracilis are formed by the axons of sensory (first-order) neurons. The other ascending tracts described in Table 12.2 are formed by axons of second-order neurons (interneurons) of the spinal cord with which the transmitting sensory neurons synapse.

Tabes dorsalis (ta′bēz dor-sa′lis) is a slowly progressive condition caused by deterioration of the posterior white matter tracts (gracilis and cuneatus) and associated dorsal roots. It is a late sign of the neurological damage caused by the syphilis bacterium. Because joint proprioceptor tracts are destroyed, affected individuals have poor muscle coordination and an unstable gait. Bacterial invasion of the sensory (dorsal) roots results in pain, which ends when dorsal root destruction is complete. •

Recall that our ability to identify and appreciate the kind of sensation being transmitted depends on the specific location of the target neurons in the cerebral sensory cortex, with which the ascending pathway fibers synapse, and not on the nature of the message, which is *always* action potentials. Each sensory nerve fiber is analogous to a "labeled line" in a telephone system and is identified by the brain as associated with a particular sensory modality. Receiving information via a certain line always tells the brain "who" is calling, whether it is a taste bud or a pressure receptor. Furthermore, when a sensory neuron is excited, the brain interprets its activity as a specific sensory modality, regardless of how the receptor is activated. For example, if we press a pressure receptor in the index fingertip, jolt it with an electrical shock, or electrically stimulate the area of the

FIGURE 12.29
Pathways of selected ascending spinal cord tracts.

(a) Sensory pathways for touch, pressure, and conscious proprioception within the fasciculus gracilis and fasciculus cuneatus tracts (each tract extends only to the medulla oblongata) and the posterior spinocerebellar tract (tract extends only to cerebellum). **(b)** Sensory pathways for pain, temperature, deep pressure, and crude touch within the lateral spinothalamic tract (tract extends only to the thalamus). Notice that the entire ascending pathway is shown in each case.

Table 12.2 Major Ascending (Sensory) Pathways and Spinal Cord Tracts

Spinal cord tract	Location (funiculus)	Origin	Termination	Function
Dorsal column pathways				
Fasciculus cuneatus and fasciculus gracilis	Posterior	Central axons of sensory (first-order) neurons enter dorsal root of the spinal cord and branch; branches enter posterior white column on same side without synapsing	By synapse with second-order neurons in nucleus cuneatus and nucleus gracilis in medulla; fibers of medullary neurons cross over and ascend in medial lemniscal tracts to thalamus, where they synapse with third-order neurons; thalamic neurons then transmit impulses to somatosensory cortex	Both tracts transmit sensory impulses from general sensory receptors of skin and proprioceptors, which are interpreted as discriminative touch, pressure, and "body sense" (limb and joint position) in opposite somatosensory cortex; cuneatus transmits afferent impulses from upper limbs, upper trunk, and neck; it is not present in spinal cord below level of T_6; gracilis carries impulses from lower limbs and inferior body trunk
Spinothalamic pathways				
Lateral spinothalamic	Lateral	Association (second-order) neurons of posterior horn; fibers cross to opposite side before ascending	By synapse with third-order neurons in thalamus; impulses then conveyed to somatosensory cortex by thalamic neurons	Transmits impulses concerned with pain and temperature to opposite side of brain; eventually interpreted in somatosensory cortex
Anterior spinothalamic	Anterior	Association neurons in posterior horns; fibers cross to opposite side before ascending	By synapse with third-order neurons in thalamus; impulses eventually conveyed to somatosensory cortex by thalamic neurons	Transmits impulses concerned with crude touch and pressure to opposite side of brain for interpretation by somatosensory cortex
Spinocerebellar pathways				
Posterior spinocerebellar*	Lateral (posterior part)	Association (second-order) neurons in posterior horn on same side of cord; fibers ascend without crossing	By synapse in cerebellum	Transmits impulses from trunk and lower limb proprioceptors on one side of body to same side of cerebellum; subconscious proprioception
Anterior spinocerebellar*	Lateral (anterior part)	Association (second-order) neurons of posterior horn; contains crossed fibers that cross back to the opposite side in the pons	By synapse in cerebellum	Transmits impulses from the trunk and lower limb on the same side of body to cerebellum; subconscious proprioception

*The posterior and anterior spinocerebellar tracts carry information from the lower limbs and trunk only. The corresponding tracts for the upper limb and neck (rostral spinocerebellar and others) are beyond the scope of this book.

somatosensory cortex that recognizes it, the result will be the same: We will perceive deep touch or pressure and will interpret it as coming from the index fingertip. This phenomenon, by which the brain refers sensations to their usual point of stimulation, is called **projection.**

Descending (Motor) Pathways and Tracts.

The descending tracts that deliver efferent impulses from the brain to the spinal cord are divided into two groups: (1) pyramidal tracts and (2) all others. Motor pathways involve two neurons, referred to as the upper and lower motor neurons. The pyramidal cells of the motor cortex, as well as the neurons in subcortical motor nuclei that give rise to other descending motor pathways, are called **upper motor neurons.** However, remember that all neurons in the brain are interneurons functionally. The anterior horn neurons, which actually *are* motor neurons, are called **lower motor neurons.** These tracts are briefly overviewed here; most of the detailed information is provided in Table 12.3 on p. 418.

The **pyramidal,** or **lateral** and **anterior corticospinal, tracts** are the major motor pathways concerned with voluntary movement, particularly precise or skilled movements such as threading a needle and writing (Figure 12.30a). The pyramidal tracts are also called the **direct pathways** because their axons descend without synapsing from the pyramidal cells of the primary motor cortex all the way to the spinal cord. There they synapse primarily with interneurons, but also directly with anterior horn motor neurons, principally those controlling limb muscles. The anterior horn motor neurons activate the skeletal muscles with which they are associated. The lateral corticospinal tracts, sometimes referred to as the pyramidal tracts proper, decussate in the medulla oblongata (at the pyramids) and their fibers are somatotopically arranged. By contrast, the much smaller anterior corticospinal tracts cross over at the spinal cord level just before synapsing.

Amyotrophic (ah-mi"o-trof'ik) *lateral sclerosis (ALS)*, also called Lou Gehrig's disease, is a devastating neuromuscular condition that involves progressive destruction of anterior horn motor neurons and fibers of the pyramidal tract. As the disease progresses, the sufferer loses the ability to speak, swallow, and breathe; death typically occurs within 5 years. Some cases have been found to be due to a defect in the gene that directs production of superoxide dismutase (SOD), an enzyme that protects cells from the ravages of free radicals (see Chapter 3, p. 81). Antioxidant drugs, which inhibit free radical formation, are being tested for their effectiveness in treating ALS. •

The remaining descending tracts include the **rubrospinal** (roo"bro-spi'nal), **vestibulospinal, reticulospinal**, and **tectospinal tracts**, which originate in different subcortical motor nuclei of the brain stem. These tracts were formerly lumped together as the *extrapyramidal tracts*, or *system*, because their nuclei of origin were presumed to be "independent of" (extra to) the pyramidal tracts. However, pyramidal tract neurons are now known to project to and influence the activity of most "extrapyramidal" nuclei, so modern anatomists prefer to use the term **indirect**, or **multineuronal**, **pathways** or even just the names of the individual motor pathways. (However, clinicians still classify many neurological problems as pyramidal or extrapyramidal in origin.)

Although the cerebellum orchestrates and coordinates voluntary muscle activity, no motor efferents descend directly from the cerebellum to the spinal cord. Rather, as already described, the cerebellum influences motor activity by acting through relays on the motor cortex. It also interacts with subcortical motor centers such as the red nucleus of the midbrain and various reticular nuclei. Motor pathways other than the pyramidal system are very complex and multisynaptic. They are most involved in regulating (1) the axial muscles that maintain balance and posture, (2) the muscles controlling coarse movements of the proximal portions of the limbs, and (3) head, neck, and eye movements that act to follow objects in the visual field. Many of the activities controlled by subcortical motor nuclei are heavily dependent on reflex activity. One of these tracts, the rubrospinal tract, is illustrated in Figure 12.30b.

Our discussion of sensory and motor pathways has focused on body regions below the head (trunk and limbs). In general, the pathways innervating the head are similar except that the axons are located in cranial nerves and the brain stem, not in the spinal cord.

Spinal Cord Trauma

Any localized damage to the spinal cord or spinal roots is associated with some form of functional loss, either **paralysis** (loss of motor function) or **paresthesias** (par"es-the'ze-ahz) (sensory losses). Damage to the ventral root or anterior horn cells results in a **flaccid** (flak'sid) **paralysis** of the skeletal muscles served. Because the lower motor neurons are damaged, nerve impulses do not reach these muscles, which consequently cannot move either voluntarily or involuntarily. When no longer stimulated, the muscles begin to atrophy. However, when only the upper motor neurons of the primary motor cortex are damaged, **spastic paralysis** occurs. Here the spinal motor neurons remain intact and the muscles continue to be stimulated by spinal reflex activity. Thus, the muscles remain healthy, but their movements are no longer subject to voluntary control.

Transection of the spinal cord at any level results in total motor and sensory loss in body regions inferior to the site of damage. If the transection occurs between T_1 and L_1, both lower limbs are affected and the condition is called **paraplegia** (par"ah-ple'je-ah). If the injury occurs in the cervical region, all four

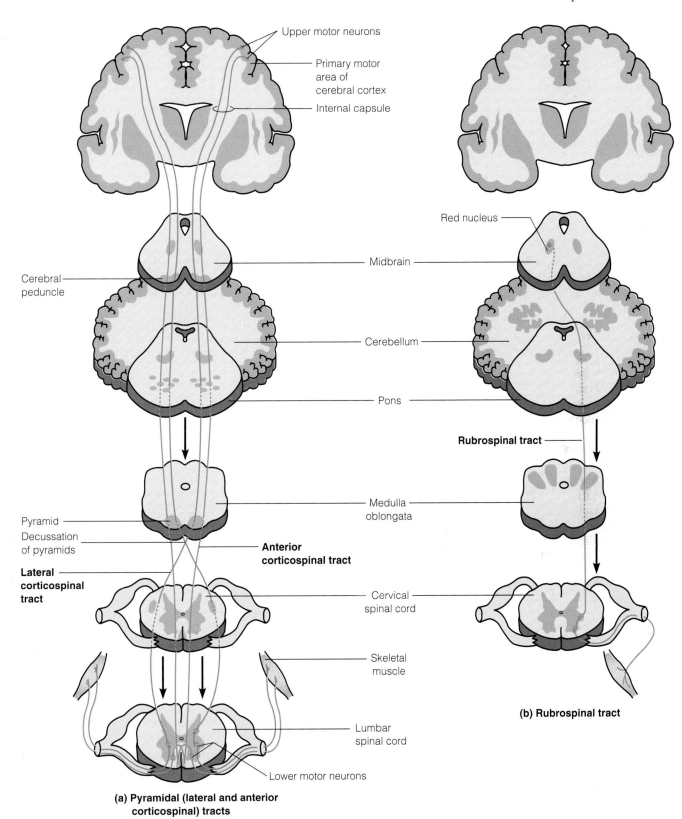

Upper motor neurons

Primary motor area of cerebral cortex

Internal capsule

Red nucleus

Midbrain

Cerebral peduncle

Cerebellum

Pons

Rubrospinal tract

Pyramid

Decussation of pyramids

Medulla oblongata

Anterior corticospinal tract

Lateral corticospinal tract

Cervical spinal cord

Skeletal muscle

(b) Rubrospinal tract

Lumbar spinal cord

Lower motor neurons

(a) Pyramidal (lateral and anterior corticospinal) tracts

FIGURE 12.30
Pathways of selected descending spinal cord tracts. (a) Pathways of the pyramidal tracts (lateral and anterior corticospinal tracts) carrying motor impulses to skeletal muscles.
(b) The rubrospinal tract helps regulate tone of muscles on opposite side of body.

Table 12.3 Major Descending (Motor) Pathways and Spinal Cord Tracts

Spinal cord tract	Location (funiculus)	Origin	Termination	Function
Direct (Pyramidal)				
Lateral corticospinal	Lateral	Pyramidal neurons of motor cortex of the cerebrum; decussate in pyramids of medulla	Anterior horn interneurons that influence motor neurons and occasionally directly with anterior horn motor neurons	Transmits motor impulses from cerebrum to spinal cord motor neurons (which activate skeletal muscles on opposite side of body); voluntary motor tract
Anterior corticospinal	Anterior	Pyramidal neurons of motor cortex; fibers cross over at the spinal cord level	Anterior horn (as above)	Same as lateral corticospinal tract
Indirect Pathways (formerly called extrapyramidal)				
Tectospinal	Anterior	Superior colliculus of midbrain of brain stem (fibers cross to opposite side of cord)	Anterior horn (as above)	Transmits motor impulses from midbrain that are important for coordinated movement of head and eyes toward visual targets
Vestibulospinal	Anterior	Vestibular nuclei in medulla of brain stem (fibers descend without crossing)	Anterior horn (as above)	Transmits motor impulses that maintain muscle tone and activate ipsilateral limb and trunk extensor muscles and muscles that move head; in this way helps maintain balance during standing and moving
Rubrospinal	Lateral	Red nucleus of midbrain of brain stem (fibers cross to opposite side just inferior to the red nucleus)	Anterior horn (as above)	Transmits motor impulses concerned with muscle tone of distal limb muscles (mostly flexors) on opposite side of body
Reticulospinal (anterior, medial, and lateral)	Anterior and lateral	Reticular formation of brain stem (medial nuclear group of pons and medulla); both crossed and uncrossed fibers	Anterior horn (as above)	Transmits impulses concerned with muscle tone and many visceral motor functions; may control most unskilled movements

limbs are affected and **quadraplegia** occurs. *Hemiplegia,* paralysis of one side of the body, usually reflects brain, rather than spinal cord, injury (see p. 387).

Anyone with traumatic spinal cord injury must be watched for symptoms of **spinal shock,** a transient period of functional loss that follows injury to the cord. This phenomenon, commonly seen in *whiplash* (flexion or extension) injuries of the neck, results in immediate depression of all reflex activity caudal to the lesion site. Bowel and bladder reflexes stop, blood pressure falls, and all muscles (somatic and visceral alike) below the injury are paralyzed and insensitive. Since the individual does not perspire in the para-

lyzed body region, a fever may ensue. Neural function usually returns within a few hours following injury; if function does not resume within 48 hours, paralysis is permanent in most cases. Over 10,000 Americans are paralyzed yearly in automotive or sports accidents. •

DIAGNOSTIC PROCEDURES FOR ASSESSING CNS DYSFUNCTION

Anyone who has had a routine physical examination is familiar with the reflex tests done to assess neural function. The doctor taps your patellar tendon with a reflex hammer and your thigh muscles contract, resulting in the knee-jerk response. This response shows that the spinal cord and upper brain centers are functioning normally. However, when reflex tests are abnormal or when brain cancer, intracranial hemorrhage, multiple sclerosis, or hydrocephalus is suspected, other more sophisticated neurological tests are used to identify the problem.

Pneumoencephalography (nu"mo-en-sef"ah-log'-rah-fe) provides a fairly clear X-ray picture of the brain ventricles and has been the procedure of choice for diagnosing hydrocephalus. Cerebrospinal fluid is withdrawn and air injected into the subarachnoid space floats upward into the ventricles, allowing them to be visualized.

A *cerebral angiogram* (an'je-o-gram") is commonly ordered to assess the condition of the cerebral arteries serving the brain (or the carotid arteries of the neck, which feed most of those vessels) in individuals who have suffered a stroke or TIA. A radiopaque dye is injected into an artery and allowed to disperse in the brain. Then an X ray is taken of the arteries of interest; the dye allows visualization of arteries narrowed by arteriosclerosis or blocked by blood clots.

The new imaging techniques described in Chapter 1 (pp. 18–19) have revolutionized the diagnosis of brain lesions. Together *CT* and *MRI scans* allow most tumors, intracranial lesions, multiple sclerosis plaques, and areas of dead brain tissue (infarcts) to be identified quickly. PET scans can localize brain lesions that generate seizures (epileptic tissue) and diagnose Alzheimer's disease.

DEVELOPMENTAL ASPECTS OF THE CENTRAL NERVOUS SYSTEM

Established during the first month of development, the brain and spinal cord continue to grow and mature throughout the prenatal period. Maternal exposure to radiation, various drugs (alcohol, opiates, and others), and infections can harm a developing infant's nervous system, particularly during the initial formative stages. For example, rubella (German measles) often leads to deafness and other types of CNS damage in the newborn. Smoking decreases the amount of oxygen in the blood, and lack of oxygen for even a few minutes causes death of neurons. Hence, a smoking mother may be sentencing her infant to some degree of brain damage.

In difficult deliveries, a temporary lack of oxygen may lead to **cerebral palsy,** but any of the factors listed above may also be a cause. Cerebral palsy is a neuromuscular disability in which the voluntary muscles are poorly controlled or paralyzed as a result of brain damage. In addition to spasticity, speech difficulties, and other motor impairments, about half of cerebral palsy victims have seizures, half are mentally retarded, and about a third have some degree of deafness. Visual impairments are also common. Cerebral palsy does not get worse over time, but its deficits are nonreversible. Cerebral palsy is the largest single cause of crippling in children, affecting six out of every thousand births.

The CNS is plagued by a number of other congenital malformations triggered by genetic or environmental factors during early development. The most serious are congenital hydrocephalus (see p. 404), anencephaly, and spina bifida.

In **anencephaly** (an"en-sef'ah-le; "without brain") the cerebrum and part of the brain stem never develop, presumably because the neural folds fail to fuse rostrally. The child is totally vegetative, unable to see, hear, or process sensory inputs. Muscles are flaccid, and no voluntary movement is possible. Mental life as we know it does not exist. Mercifully, death occurs soon after birth.

Spina bifida (spi'nah bif'i-dah; "forked spine") results from incomplete formation of the vertebral arches and typically involves the lumbosacral region. The technical definition is that laminae and spinous processes are missing on at least one vertebra. If severe, neural deficits occur as well as defects of the spine. *Spina bifida occulta,* the least serious type, involves one or only a few vertebrae and causes no neural problems. Other than a small dimple or tuft of hair over the site of nonfusion, it has no external manifestations. In the more severe form, *spina bifida cystica,* a saclike cyst protrudes dorsally from the child's spine. The cyst may contain meninges and cerebrospinal fluid (a *meningocele* [mě-ning'go-sēl]), or even portions of the spinal cord and spinal nerve roots (a *myelomeningocele*). The larger the cyst and the more neural structures it contains, the greater the degree of neurological impairment. In the worst case, where the inferior spinal cord is rendered functionless, bowel incontinence, bladder muscle paralysis (which predisposes the infant to urinary tract infection and renal failure), and lower limb paralysis occur. Problems with infection are continual because the cyst tends to rupture or leak. Spina bifida cystica is accompanied by hydrocephalus in 90% of all cases. •

One of the last CNS areas to mature is the hypothalamus. Since the hypothalamus contains body temperature regulatory centers, premature babies have problems controlling their loss of body heat and must be kept in temperature-controlled environments. PET scans have revealed that the thalamus and somatosensory cortex are active in a five-day-old baby, but that the visual cortex is not. This explains the observation that infants of this age respond to touch but have poor vision. By 11 weeks, more of the cortex is active, and the baby can reach for a rattle. By eight months, the cortex is very active and the child can think about what he or she sees. Growth and maturation of the nervous system continue throughout childhood and largely reflect progressive myelination. As described in Chapter 9, neuromuscular coordination progresses in a superior-to-inferior direction

A CLOSER LOOK | "He-Brain" Versus "She-Brain"

Women of this generation looking for equal treatment in the marketplace have been buffeted by cultural notions that men are somehow more capable—the superior members of the human race. Yet, when all sexism is finally stripped away and differences in nurture are disregarded, there *is* something different about males and females, and the difference is grounded in their biology.

As boys enter puberty, they tend to exhibit more aggressive behavior, and there is little doubt that the dramatic rise in male sex hormones surging through their blood is responsible for this change. For any hormone to influence behavior, it must first affect the brain. Both male and female sex hormones (testosterone and estrogen, respectively) concentrate selectively in certain brain regions that play an important role in courtship, sex and mating behaviors, and aggression—behaviors in which the sexes differ most. There is also evidence that sexual differences in behavior exist long before the onset of puberty and its raging hormones. Newborn boys show more motor strength and muscle tone, while girls show greater sensitivity to touch, taste, and light and smile more. Comprehensive studies of school-children have demonstrated that girls do better on verbal skills tests, whereas boys are more proficient in spatial-visual tasks. (Interestingly, adult females do better on spatial tasks when their estrogen levels are low, that is, more like the male condition.) Further, although it was once presumed that damage to the left hemisphere would produce greater deficits in verbal tasks and that right hemispheric injury would impair spatial abilities, this has been borne out only for males. As a result of these studies, it has been hypothesized that females have more hemispheric overlap in verbal and spatial functions than do males, who demonstrate earlier lateralization of cortical functioning.

Does greater lateralization for a given function imply superior performance for that function? Apparently not. Females show less lateralization of language functions, yet they tend to be superior to males in language skills. Also, greater lateralization carries a steep price tag, because if a highly lateralized functional area is damaged, the function is terminated. For example, aphasia follows damage to the left hemisphere three times more often in males than in females.

How can these differences in behavior and skills be explained? The accounting may lie deep within the brain. In 1973, it was demonstrated for the first time that male and female brains differ structurally in many ways. The best example concerns a specific region (now called the *sexually dimorphic nucleus*) in the anterior part of the hypothalamus that has a distinctive synaptic pattern in each sex. Castration of male monkeys shortly after birth produced the female hypothalamic pattern, while injection of testosterone into females triggered the development of the male pattern. This discovery rocked the neuroscience community because it was the first evidence that there were structural brain differences in the sexes and that sex hormones circulating before, at, or after birth could *change* the brain. Based on these and later observations, scientists concluded that the basic plan of the mammalian brain is female and stays that way unless "told to do otherwise" by masculinizing (male) hormones. The production of testosterone by male fetuses is the key to anatomical development as a male. It now appears that fetal testosterone is also responsible for development of the male brain pattern. Since these discoveries, a number of other sex-related differences have been found in the central nervous system, including the following:

1. Females tend to have a longer left temporal lobe.

2. In females, the posterior portion of the corpus callosum is bulbous and wide, while in males the corpus callosum is generally cylindrical and fairly uniform in diameter. This may indicate that there are more communicating fibers between the hemispheres in females, which could support the hypothesis that the female brain is less lateralized.

3. Sex differences exist in the spinal cord. Certain clusters of neurons that serve the external genitals are much larger in males than in females and they contain receptors for testosterone, but not estrogen. Testosterone exposure before birth produces the male pattern of these particular spinal cord neurons.

What should we make of these findings? Do these observed differences in the two sexes have little or nothing to do with behavioral subtleties, or do they underlie many (or most) manifestations of maleness or femaleness? It is too soon to know, and studies of sexual dimorphism of the brain are still "in diapers."

and in a proximal-to-distal direction, and we know that myelination also occurs in this sequence.

The brain reaches its maximum weight in the young adult. Over the next 60 years or so, neurons are damaged and die, and brain weight and volume steadily decline. However, the number of neurons lost over the decades is normally only a small percentage of the total, and the remaining neurons can change their synaptic connections, providing for continued learning throughout life.

Although age brings some cognitive declines in spatial ability, speed of perception, decision making, reaction time, and memory, these losses are not significant in the *healthy individual* until after the seventh decade. Then a fairly rapid decline occurs in some, but not all, of these abilities. Ability to build on experience, mathematical skills, and verbal fluency do not decline with age, and many people continue to enjoy intellectual lives and to work at mentally demanding tasks their entire life. Fewer than 5% of people over 65 years old demonstrate true senility. Sadly, there are many cases of "reversible senility" caused by low blood pressure, constipation, poor nutrition, prescription drug effects, depression, dehydration, and hormone imbalances that go undiagnosed. The best way to maintain one's mental abilities in old age may be to seek regular medical checkups throughout life.

Although eventual shrinking of the brain is normal, in some individuals (alcoholics and professional boxers) the process is accelerated. Whether a boxer wins the match or not, the likelihood of brain damage and atrophy increases with every blow. Everyone recognizes that alcohol profoundly affects both the mind and the body. However, these effects may not be temporary. CT scans of alcoholics reveal a reduction in brain size and density appearing at a fairly early age. Both boxers and alcoholics exhibit signs of senility unrelated to the aging process.

* * *

The human cerebral hemispheres—our "thinking caps"—are awesome in their complexity. But no less amazing are the brain regions that oversee all our subconscious, autonomic body functions—the diencephalon and brain stem—particularly when you consider their relatively insignificant size. The spinal cord, which acts as a reflex center and a communication link between the brain and body periphery, is equally important to body homeostasis.

A good deal of new terminology has been introduced in this chapter, and much of it will come up again in one or more of the remaining nervous system chapters. Chapter 13, your next challenge, considers the structures of the peripheral nervous system that work hand in hand with the CNS to keep it informed and to deliver its orders to the effectors of the body.

RELATED CLINICAL TERMS

Cordotomy (kor-dot′o-me) A procedure in which a nerve tract in the spinal cord is severed surgically; usually done to relieve unremitting pain.

Encephalopathy (en-sef″ah-lop′ah-the; *enceph* = brain; *path* = disease) Any disease or disorder of the brain.

Functional brain disorders Psychological disorders for which no structural cause can be found; include neuroses and psychoses (see below).

Microencephaly (mi″kro-en-sef′ah-le; *micro* = small) Congenital condition involving the formation of a small brain, as evidenced by reduced skull size; most microencephalic children are retarded.

Myelitis (mi″ĕ-li′tis; *myel* = spinal cord; *itis* = inflammation) Inflammation of the spinal cord.

Myelogram (*gram* = recording) X ray of the spinal cord after injection of a contrast medium.

Neuroses (nu-ro′sēs) The less debilitating class of functional brain disorders; examples include severe anxiety (panic attacks), phobias (irrational fears), and compulsive-obsessive behaviors (e.g., washing one's hands every few minutes); the affected individual, however, retains contact with reality.

Psychoses (si-ko′sēs) Class of functional brain disorders in which the affected individuals detach themselves from reality and exhibit bizarre behaviors; the *legal* word for psychotic behavior is *insanity;* the psychoses include *schizophrenia* (skit-so-fre′ne-ah), *depression,* and *manic-depressive disease.*

CHAPTER SUMMARY

The Brain (pp. 380–408)

  1. The brain provides for voluntary movements, interpretation and integration of sensation, consciousness, and cognitive function.

Embryonic Development of the Brain (pp. 380–381)

  2. The brain develops from the rostral portion of the embryonic neural tube.

  3. Early brain development yields the three primary brain vesicles: the prosencephalon (cerebral hemispheres and diencephalon), mesencephalon (midbrain), and rhombencephalon (pons, medulla, and cerebellum).

  4. Cephalization results in the envelopment of the diencephalon and superior brain stem by the cerebral hemispheres.

Regions and Organization of the Brain (p. 382)

  5. In a widely used system, the brain is divided into the cerebral hemispheres, diencephalon, brain stem, and cerebellum.

  6. The cerebral hemispheres and cerebellum have gray matter nuclei surrounded by white matter and an outer cortex of gray matter. The brain stem lacks a cortex.

Ventricles of the Brain (p. 383)

  7. The brain contains four ventricles filled with cerebrospinal fluid. The lateral ventricles are in the cerebral hemispheres; the third ventricle is in the diencephalon; the fourth ventricle is in the brain stem and connects with the central canal of the spinal cord.

The Cerebral Hemispheres (pp. 384–392)

8. The two cerebral hemispheres exhibit gyri, sulci, and fissures. The longitudinal fissure partially separates the hemispheres; other fissures or sulci subdivide each hemisphere into lobes.

9. Each cerebral hemisphere consists of the cerebral cortex, the cerebral white matter, and the basal nuclei.

10. Each cerebral hemisphere receives sensory impulses from, and dispatches motor impulses to, the opposite side of the body. The body is represented in an upside-down fashion in the sensory and motor cortices.

11. Functional areas of the cerebral cortex include: (1) motor areas: primary motor and premotor areas of the frontal lobe, the frontal eye field, and Broca's area in the frontal lobe of one hemisphere (usually the left); (2) sensory areas: primary sensory cortex, somatosensory association area, and gustatory area, in the parietal lobe; visual areas in the occipital lobe; and olfactory and auditory areas in the temporal lobe; (3) association areas: prefrontal cortex in the frontal lobe; general interpretation area at junction of temporal, parietal, and occipital lobe on one side (usually the left); Wernicke's area in one hemisphere (temporal lobe) only, usually the left; and affective language areas in one hemisphere (usually the right).

12. The cerebral hemispheres show lateralization of cortical function. In most people, the left hemisphere is dominant (i.e., specialized for language and mathematical skills), and the right hemisphere is more concerned with visual-spatial skills and creative endeavors.

13. Fiber tracts of the cerebral white matter include commissures, association fibers, and projection fibers.

14. The paired basal nuclei include the lentiform nucleus (globus pallidus and putamen) and caudate nucleus. The basal nuclei are subcortical nuclei that help control muscular movements.

The Diencephalon (pp. 392–395)

15. The diencephalon consists of the thalamus, hypothalamus, and epithalamus and encloses the third ventricle.

16. The thalamus is the major relay station for (1) sensory impulses ascending to the sensory cortex and (2) inputs of subcortical motor nuclei and the cerebellum to the cerebral motor cortex.

17. The hypothalamus is an important autonomic nervous system control center and a pivotal part of the limbic system. It maintains water balance and regulates thirst, eating behavior, gastrointestinal activity, body temperature, and the activity of the anterior pituitary gland.

18. The epithalamus consists of the pineal gland and the choroid plexus of the third ventricle.

The Brain Stem (pp. 395–399)

19. The brain stem includes the midbrain, pons, and medulla oblongata.

20. The midbrain contains the corpora quadrigemina (visual and auditory reflex centers), the red nucleus (subcortical motor centers), and nuclei of cranial nerves III and IV. The cerebral peduncles on its ventral face house the pyramidal fiber tracts. The midbrain surrounds the cerebral aqueduct.

21. The pons is mainly a conduction area. Its nuclei contribute to regulation of respiration and cranial nerves V–VII.

22. The pyramids (descending corticospinal tracts) form the ventral face of the medulla oblongata; these fibers cross over (decussation of the pyramids) before entering the spinal cord. Important nuclei in the medulla regulate respiratory rhythm, heart rate, and blood pressure and serve cranial nerves VIII–XII. The olivary nucleus and cough, sneezing, swallowing, and vomiting centers are in the medulla.

The Cerebellum (pp. 399–401)

23. The cerebellum consists of two hemispheres, marked by convolutions and separated by the vermis. It is connected to the brain stem by superior, middle, and inferior peduncles.

24. The cerebellum processes and interprets impulses from the motor cortex and sensory pathways and coordinates motor activity so that smooth, well-timed movements occur.

Functional Brain Systems (pp. 401–403)

25. The limbic system consists of numerous structures that encircle the diencephalon. It is the "emotional-visceral brain."

26. The reticular formation includes nuclei spanning the length of the brain stem. It maintains the alert state of the cerebral cortex (RAS) and its motor nuclei serve both somatic and visceral motor activities.

Protection of the Brain (pp. 403–406)

27. The brain is protected by bone, meninges, cerebrospinal fluid, and the blood-brain barrier.

28. The meninges consist of the outermost dura mater, the arachnoid mater, and the innermost pia mater. They enclose the brain and spinal cord and their blood vessels. Inward folds of the inner layer of the dura mater secure the brain to the skull.

29. Cerebrospinal fluid (CSF), formed by the choroid plexuses from blood plasma, circulates through the ventricles and into the subarachnoid space. It is returned to the dural venous sinuses by the arachnoid villi. CSF supports and cushions the brain and cord and helps to nourish them.

30. The blood-brain barrier reflects the relative impermeability of the epithelium of capillaries of the brain. It allows water, respiratory gases, essential nutrients, and fat-soluble molecules to enter the neural tissue, but prevents entry of other, water-soluble, potentially harmful substances.

Homeostatic Imbalances of the Brain (pp. 406–408)

31. Head trauma may cause brain injuries called concussions (reversible damage) or contusions (nonreversible damage). When the brain stem is affected, unconsciousness (temporary or permanent) occurs. Trauma-induced brain injuries may be aggravated by intracranial hemorrhage or cerebral edema, both of which compress brain tissue.

32. Cerebrovascular accidents (strokes) result when blood circulation to brain neurons is blocked and brain tissue dies. The result may be hemiplegia, sensory deficits, or speech impairment.

33. Alzheimer's disease is a degenerative brain disease in which beta-amyloid protein deposits and neurofibrillar tangles appear. It results in slow, progressive loss of memory and motor control and increasing dementia.

The Spinal Cord (pp. 408–418)

Gross Anatomy and Protection of the Spinal Cord (pp. 408–409)

1. The spinal cord, a two-way impulse conduction pathway and a reflex center, resides within the vertebral column and is protected by meninges and cerebrospinal fluid. It extends from the foramen magnum to the end of the first lumbar vertebra.

2. Thirty-one pairs of spinal nerve roots issue from the cord. The cord is enlarged in the cervical and lumbar regions, where spinal nerves serving the limbs arise.

Embryonic Development of the Spinal Cord (p. 410)

3. The spinal cord develops from the neural tube. Its gray matter forms from the alar and basal plates. Fiber tracts form the outer white matter. The neural crest forms the sensory (dorsal root) ganglia.

Cross-Sectional Anatomy of the Spinal Cord (pp. 410–416)

4. The central gray matter of the cord is H shaped. Anterior horns contain somatic motor neurons. Lateral horns contain visceral (autonomic) motor neurons. Posterior horns contain interneurons.

5. Axons of neurons of the lateral and anterior horns emerge in common from the cord via the ventral roots. Axons of sensory neurons (with cell bodies located in the dorsal root ganglion) enter the posterior aspect of the cord and form the dorsal roots. The ventral and dorsal roots combine to form the spinal nerves.

6. Each side of the white matter of the cord has posterior, lateral, and anterior columns (funiculi), and each funiculus contains a number of ascending and descending tracts. All tracts are paired and most decussate.

7. Ascending (sensory) tracts include the fasciculi gracilis and cuneatus (touch and joint proprioception), spinothalamic tracts (pain, touch, temperature), and spinocerebellar tracts (muscle/tendon proprioception).

8. Descending tracts include the pyramidal tracts (anterior and lateral corticospinal tracts that originate from the primary motor cortex) and the motor tracts originating from subcortical motor nuclei.

Spinal Cord Trauma (pp. 416–418)

9. Injury to the anterior horn neurons or the ventral roots results in flaccid paralysis. (Injury to the upper motor neurons in the brain results in spastic paralysis.) If the dorsal roots or sensory tracts are damaged, paresthesias occur.

Diagnostic Procedures for Assessing CNS Dysfunction (pp. 418–419)

1. Diagnostic procedures used to assess neurological condition and function range from routine reflex testing to sophisticated techniques such as pneumoencephalography, cerebral angiography, CT scans, MRI scans, and PET scans.

Developmental Aspects of the Central Nervous System (pp. 419–421)

1. Maternal and environmental factors may impair embryonic brain development, and oxygen deprivation destroys brain cells. Severe congenital brain diseases include cerebral palsy, anencephaly, hydrocephalus, and spina bifida.

2. Premature babies have trouble regulating body temperature because the hypothalamus is one of the last brain areas to mature prenatally.

3. Development of motor control indicates the progressive myelination and maturation of a child's nervous system.

4. Brain growth ends in young adulthood. Neurons die throughout life and are not replaced; thus, brain weight and volume decline with age.

5. Healthy aged people maintain nearly optimal intellectual function. Disease—particularly cardiovascular disease—is the major cause of declining mental function with age.

REVIEW QUESTIONS

Multiple Choice/Matching

1. The primary motor cortex, Broca's area, and the premotor area are located in (a) the frontal lobe, (b) the parietal lobe, (c) the temporal lobe, (d) the occipital lobe.

2. Choose the proper term from the key to respond to the statements describing various brain areas.

Key:

(a) cerebellum	**(d)** corpus callosum	**(g)** midbrain
(b) corpora quadrigemina	**(e)** hypothalamus	**(h)** pons
(c) corpus striatum	**(f)** medulla	**(i)** thalamus

_____ **(1)** basal nuclei involved in fine control of motor activities

_____ **(2)** region where there is a gross crossover of fibers of descending pyramidal tracts

_____ **(3)** control of temperature, autonomic nervous system reflexes, hunger, and water balance

_____ **(4)** houses the substantia nigra and cerebral aqueduct

_____ **(5)** relay stations for visual and auditory stimuli input; found in midbrain

_____ **(6)** houses vital centers for control of the heart, respiration, and blood pressure

_____ **(7)** brain area through which all the sensory input must travel to get to the cerebral cortex

_____ **(8)** brain area most concerned with equilibrium, body posture, and coordination of motor activity

3. The innermost layer of the meninges, delicate and closely apposed to the brain tissue, is the (a) dura mater, (b) corpus callosum, (c) arachnoid, (d) pia mater.

4. Cerebrospinal fluid is formed by (a) arachnoid villi, (b) the dura mater, (c) choroid plexuses, (d) all of these.

5. A patient has suffered a cerebral hemorrhage that has caused dysfunction of the precentral gyrus of his right cerebral cortex. As a result, (a) he cannot voluntarily move his left arm or leg, (b) he feels no sensation on the left side of his body, (c) he feels no sensation on the right side of his body.

6. Ascending pathways in the spinal cord convey (a) motor impulses, (b) sensory impulses, (c) commissural impulses, (d) all of these.

7. Destruction of the anterior horn cells of the spinal cord results in loss of (a) integrating impulses, (b) sensory impulses, (c) voluntary motor impulses, (d) all of these.

8. Fiber tracts that allow neurons within the same cerebral hemisphere to communicate are (a) association tracts, (b) commissures, (c) projection tracts.

9. A number of brain structures are listed below. If an area is primarily gray matter, write **a** in the answer blank; if mostly white matter, respond with **b**.

_____ **(1)** cerebral cortex

_____ **(2)** corpus callosum and corona radiata

_____ **(3)** red nucleus

_____ **(4)** giant cell and small cell areas

_____ **(5)** medial lemniscal tract

_____ **(6)** cranial nerve nuclei

_____ **(7)** spinothalamic tract

_____ **(8)** fornix

_____ **(9)** cingulate and precentral gyri

10. A professor unexpectedly blew a loud horn in the anatomy and physiology class. The students looked up, startled. The reflexive movements of their eyes were mediated by the (a) cerebral cortex, (b) inferior olives, (c) raphe nuclei, (d) superior colliculi, (e) nucleus gracilis.

Short Answer Essay Questions

11. Make a diagram showing the three primary (embryonic) brain vesicles. Name each and then use clinical terminology to name the resulting adult brain regions.

 12. (a) What is the advantage of having a cerebrum that is highly convoluted? (b) What term is used to indicate its grooves? Its outward folds? (c) What groove divides the cerebrum into two hemispheres? (d) What divides the parietal from the frontal lobe? The parietal from the temporal lobe?

13. (a) Make a rough drawing of the lateral aspect of the left cerebral hemisphere. (b) You may be thinking, "But I just can't draw!" So, name the hemisphere involved with most peoples' ability to draw. (c) On your drawing, locate the following areas and provide the major function of each: primary motor cortex, premotor cortex, somatosensory association area, primary sensory area, visual and auditory areas, prefrontal cortex, Wernicke's and Broca's areas.

14. (a) What does lateralization of cortical functioning mean? (b) Why is the term *cerebral dominance* a misnomer?

15. (a) What is the function of the basal nuclei? (b) Which basal nuclei form the lentiform nucleus? (c) Which arches over the diencephalon?

16. (a) Explain how the cerebellum is physically connected to the brain stem. (b) List ways in which the cerebellum is very similar to the cerebrum.

17. Describe the role of the cerebellum in maintaining smooth, coordinated skeletal muscle activity.

18. (a) Where is the limbic system located? (b) What structures make up this system? (c) How is the limbic system important in behavior?

19. (a) Localize the reticular formation in the brain. (b) What does RAS mean, and what is its function?

20. List four ways in which the CNS is protected.

21. (a) How is cerebrospinal fluid formed and drained? Follow its pathway within and around the brain. (b) What happens if CSF is not drained properly? Why is this consequence more harmful in adults?

22. What constitutes the blood-brain barrier?

23. (a) Differentiate between a concussion and a contusion. (b) Why do severe brain stem contusions result in unconsciousness?

24. Describe the spinal cord, depicting its extent, its composition of gray and white matter, and its spinal roots.

25. Which ascending spinal cord tracts carry sensory impulses concerned with touch and pressure? Concerned with proprioception only? Concerned with pain and temperature?

26. (a) Name the descending pathways that are concerned with voluntary skeletal movements and that form the pyramidal tracts. (b) Name three motor tracts not classed as pyramidal tracts.

27. Differentiate clearly between spastic and flaccid paralysis.

28. How do paraplegia, hemiplegia, and quadraplegia differ?

29. (a) Define cerebrovascular accident or CVA. (b) Describe its possible causes and consequences.

30. (a) What factors account for brain growth after birth? (b) List some structural brain changes observed with aging.

CRITICAL THINKING AND CLINICAL APPLICATION QUESTIONS

1. A 10-month-old infant has an enlarging head circumference and delayed overall development. She has a bulging anterior fontanel and her CSF pressure is elevated. Based on these findings, answer the following questions: (a) What are the possible cause(s) of an enlarged head? (b) What tests might be helpful in obtaining information about this infant's problem? (c) Assuming the tests conducted showed the cerebral aqueduct to be constricted, which ventricles or CSF-containing areas would you expect to be enlarged? Which would likely not be visible? Respond to the same questions based on a finding of obstructed arachnoid villi.

2. Mrs. Jones has had a progressive decline in her mental capabilities in the last five or six years. At first her family attributed her occasional memory lapses, confusion, and agitation to grief over her husband's death six years earlier. When examined, Mrs. Jones was aware of her cognitive problems and was shown to have an IQ score approximately 30 points less than would be predicted by her work history. A CT scan showed diffuse cerebral atrophy. The physician prescribed a mild tranquilizer for Mrs. Jones and told her family that there was little else he could recommend. What is Mrs. Jones's problem?

3. Robert, a brilliant computer analyst, suffered a blow to his anterior skull from a falling rock while mountain climbing. Shortly thereafter, it was obvious to his co-workers that his behavior had undergone a dramatic change. Although previously a smart dresser, he was now unkempt. One morning, he was observed defecating into the wastebasket. His supervisor ordered Robert to report to the company's doctor immediately. What region of Robert's brain was affected by the cranial blow?

4. Mrs. Adams is ready to deliver her first baby. Unhappily, the baby appears to have a myelomeningocele. Would a vaginal or surgical (C-section) delivery be more appropriate and why?

The Peripheral Nervous System and Reflex Activity

13

CHAPTER OUTLINE AND STUDENT OBJECTIVES

Overview of the Peripheral Nervous System (pp. 426–434)

1. Define peripheral nervous system and list its components.

2. Classify sensory receptors according to body location, stimulus detected, and structure.

3. Describe receptor potentials and define adaptation.

4. Define nerve and describe the general structure of a nerve.

5. Distinguish between sensory, motor, and mixed nerves.

6. Define ganglion and indicate the general location of ganglia in the body periphery.

7. Describe the process of nerve fiber regeneration.

8. Compare and contrast the motor endings of somatic and autonomic nerve fibers.

Cranial Nerves (pp. 434–442)

9. Name the 12 pairs of cranial nerves and describe the body region and structures innervated by each.

Spinal Nerves (pp. 436, 442–450)

10. Describe the formation of a spinal nerve, and distinguish between spinal roots and rami. Describe the general distribution of the ventral and dorsal rami.

11. Define plexus. Name the major plexuses, their origin sites, and the major nerves arising from each, and describe the distribution and function of the peripheral nerves.

Reflex Activity (pp. 450–456)

12. Distinguish between autonomic and somatic reflexes.

13. Compare and contrast stretch, flexor, and crossed extensor reflexes.

Developmental Aspects of the Peripheral Nervous System (p. 456)

14. Describe the developmental relationship between the segmented arrangement of peripheral nerves, skeletal muscles, and skin dermatomes.

he human brain, for all its sophistication, would be useless without its links to the outside world. Our very sanity depends on a continual flow of information from the outside. When blindfolded volunteers were suspended in warm water in a sensory deprivation tank (a situation that limited sensory inputs), they began to hallucinate: One saw charging herds of pink and purple elephants, another heard a singing chorus, still others had taste hallucinations. No less important to our well-being are the barrages of orders sent from the CNS to voluntary muscles and other effectors of the body. This almost continual flow of nerve impulses allows us to move and to take care of our own needs. The frustration of paralysis victims (who can no longer dispatch the motor output that controls their muscles) is very real and unrelenting. The **peripheral nervous system (PNS)** provides these links from and to the real world. Its ghostly white nerves thread through virtually every part of the body, enabling the CNS to receive information and to carry out its decisions.

The peripheral nervous system includes all neural structures outside the brain and spinal cord, that is, the *sensory receptors*, peripheral *nerves* and their associated *ganglia*, and efferent *motor endings*. Its basic components are diagrammed in Figure 13.1. We will begin this chapter with an overview of the functional anatomy of each PNS element. Then we will consider the distribution and function of cranial and spinal nerves. Finally, we will examine the components of reflex arcs before looking at the way some important somatic reflexes, played out almost entirely in PNS structures, help to maintain homeostasis.

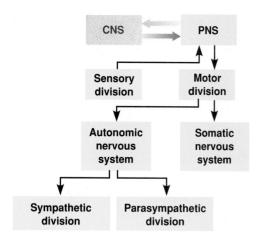

FIGURE 13.1
Place of the PNS in the structural organization of the nervous system.

OVERVIEW OF THE PERIPHERAL NERVOUS SYSTEM

Sensory Receptors

Sensory receptors are structures that are specialized to respond to changes in their environment; such environmental changes are called **stimuli.** Typically, activation of a sensory receptor by an adequate stimulus results in local depolarizations or graded potentials that, in turn, trigger nerve impulses along the afferent fibers coursing to the CNS. (This process is discussed on p. 429.) As described in more detail in Chapter 15, *sensation* (awareness of the stimulus) and *perception* (interpretation of the meaning of the stimulus) occur in the brain. But we are getting ahead of ourselves here. For now, let us just examine how sensory receptors are classified and how they function. Basically, there are three ways to classify sensory receptors: (1) by their location in the body; (2) by the type of stimulus they detect; and (3) by the relative complexity of their structure.

Classification by Location

Three receptor classes are recognized according to their location or the location of the stimulus to which they respond.

1. **Exteroceptors** (ek"ster-o-sep'torz) are sensitive to stimuli arising outside the body (*extero* = outside). As might be expected, most exteroceptors are near or at the body surface. They include touch, pressure, pain, and temperature receptors in the skin and most receptors of the special sense organs.

2. **Interoceptors** (in"ter-o-sep'torz), also called **visceroceptors,** respond to stimuli arising from within the body (*intero* = inside), such as from the internal viscera and blood vessels. The different interoceptors

monitor a variety of stimuli, including chemical changes, stretching of tissues, and temperature. Sometimes, their activation causes us to feel pain, discomfort, hunger, or thirst. However, we are usually unaware of the workings of our visceral receptors.

3. **Proprioceptors** (pro"pre-o-sep'torz), like interoceptors, respond to internal stimuli; however, their location (in the musculoskeletal organs) is much more restricted. Proprioceptors occur in skeletal muscles, tendons, joints, and ligaments and connective tissue coverings of bones and muscles. (Some authorities also include the equilibrium receptors of the inner ear in this class.) Proprioceptors constantly advise the brain of our own movements (*propria* = one's own) by monitoring the degree of stretch of the organs they occupy.

Classification by Stimulus Type Detected

The receptor classes named according to the stimuli that activate them are easy to remember, because the class name usually indicates the stimulus.

1. **Mechanoreceptors** generate nerve impulses when they, or adjacent tissues, are deformed by mechanical forces such as touch, pressure (including blood pressure), vibrations, and stretch.

2. **Thermoreceptors** are sensitive to temperature changes.

3. **Photoreceptors,** such as those of the retina of the eye, respond to light energy.

4. **Chemoreceptors** respond to chemicals in solution (molecules smelled or tasted, or changes in blood chemistry).

5. **Nociceptors** (no"se-sep'torz; *noci* = harm) respond to potentially damaging stimuli that result in pain.

Overstimulation of any receptor is painful and virtually all receptor types function as nociceptors at one time or another. For example, searing heat, extreme cold, excessive pressure, and chemicals released at sites of inflammation are all interpreted as painful.

Classification by Structural Complexity

On the basis of overall receptor structure, there are **simple** and **complex receptors.** The overwhelming majority are simple receptors, which are equivalent structurally to modified dendritic endings of sensory neurons. These simple receptors are found in the skin, mucous membranes, muscles, and connective tissues, and monitor most types of general sensory information. By contrast, the complex receptors are actually **sense organs,** localized collections of cells (usually of many types) working together to accomplish a specific receptive process. Complex receptors are associated with the **special senses** (vision, hearing, smell, and taste). For example, the eye is composed not only of sensory neurons, but also of non-neural cells that form its supporting wall, lens, and other associated structures. Though the complex sense organs (described in detail in Chapter 16) are most familiar to us, the simple sensory receptors associated with the **general senses** are no less important. Here we will concentrate on the structure and function of these tiny sentinels that keep the CNS apprised of what is happening both deep within the body and at its surfaces.

The widely distributed **general sensory receptors** are involved in tactile sensation (a composite mix of touch, pressure, stretch, and vibration), temperature monitoring (heat and cold), and pain, as well as the "muscle sense" provided by proprioceptors. Anatomically, these receptors are either (1) *free dendritic endings* or (2) *encapsulated dendritic endings.* The general sensory receptors are illustrated and classified in Table 13.1 according to both the structural and functional schemes. However, it should be pointed out that the functional classification is still controversial because many of these receptors respond to similar stimuli, and individual receptors may monitor many different kinds of stimuli.

Free Dendritic Endings.   Free, or **naked, dendritic endings** of sensory neurons invade virtually all body tissues, but they are particularly abundant in epithelia and connective tissues. The sensory fibers all have a small diameter, and their distal endings usually have small knoblike swellings. They respond chiefly to pain and temperature, but some respond to tissue movements caused by pressure as well. Thus, although the bare nerve endings are considered "the" pain receptors (nociceptors) that warn of tissue injury, they also function as mechanoreceptors.

Certain free dendritic endings associate with disc-shaped epidermal cells (*Merkel cells*) to form **Merkel discs** that attach to the deeper layers of the skin epidermis and function as light touch receptors. **Root hair plexuses,** free dendritic endings that entwine basketlike in hair follicles, are light touch receptors that detect bending of hairs. The tickle of a mosquito landing on your skin is mediated by root hair plexuses.

Encapsulated Dendritic Endings.   All **encapsulated dendritic endings** consist of one or more terminal fibers of sensory neurons enclosed in a connective tissue capsule. Virtually all the encapsulated receptors are mechanoreceptors; however, they vary greatly in shape, size, and distribution in the body.

Table 13.1 General Sensory Receptors Classified by Structure and Function

Anatomical class (structure)	Illustration	Functional class According to location (L) According to stimulus type (S)	Body location
Unencapsulated Free dendritic nerve endings of sensory neurons		L: Exteroceptors, interoceptors, and proprioceptors S: Nociceptors (pain), thermoreceptors (head and cold), possible mechanoreceptors (pressure)	Most body tissues; most dense in connective tissues (ligaments, tendons, dermis, joint capsules, periostea) and epithelia (epidermis, cornea, mucosae, and glands)
Modified free dendritic endings: Merkel discs		L: Exteroceptors S: Mechanoreceptors (light pressure)	At base of epidermis of skin
Root hair plexuses		L: Exteroceptors S: Mechanoreceptors (hair deflection)	In and surrounding hair follicles

(continued)

Table 13.1 General Sensory Receptors Classified by Structure and Function continued

Anatomical class (structure)	Illustration	Functional class According to location (L) According to stimulus type (S)	Body location
Encapsulated Meissner's corpuscles		L: Exteroceptors S: Mechanoreceptors (light pressure, discriminative touch, vibration of low frequency)	Dermal papillae of hairless skin, particularly lips, nipples, external genitalia, fingertips, eyelids
Krause's end bulbs		L: Exteroceptors S: Mechanoreceptors (probably modified Meissner's corpuscles)	Connective tissue of mucosae (mouth, conjunctiva of eye) and of hairless skin near body openings (lips)
Pacinian corpuscles		L: Exteroceptors, interoceptors and some proprioceptors S: Mechanoreceptors (deep pressure, stretch, vibration of high frequency); rapidly adapting	Subcutaneous tissue of the skin; periostea, mesentery, tendons, ligaments, joint capsules, most abundant on fingers, soles of feet, external genitalia, nipples
Ruffini's corpuscles		L: Exteroceptors and proprioceptors S: Mechanoreceptors (deep pressure and stretch); slowly adapting	Deep in dermis, hypodermis, and joint capsules
Muscle spindles	Intrafusal fibers	L: Proprioceptors S: Mechanoreceptors (muscle stretch)	Skeletal muscles, particularly those of the extremities
Golgi tendon organs		L. Proprioceptors S: Mechanoreceptors (tendon stretch)	Tendons
Joint kinesthetic receptors (Pacinian and Ruffini corpuscles, free dendritic endings, and receptors resembling Golgi tendon organs)		L: Proprioceptors S: Mechanoreceptors	Joint capsules of synovial joints

Meissner's corpuscles (mīs′nerz kor′pus″lz) are small receptors in which a few spiraling dendrites are surrounded by Schwann cells and then by a thin egg-shaped capsule of connective tissue. Meissner's corpuscles are found just beneath the skin epidermis in the dermal papillae and are especially numerous in sensitive and hairless skin areas such as the lips, nipples, and fingertips. Also called **tactile corpuscles,** they are receptors for discriminative touch, and apparently play the same role in light touch reception in hairless skin as do the root hair plexuses in hairy skin.

Krause's end bulbs are considered to be a variation of Meissner's corpuscles. However, while Meissner's corpuscles are found in the skin, Krause's end bulbs are most abundant in mucous membranes. For this reason, they are also called **mucocutaneous corpuscles.**

Pacinian corpuscles, also called **large lamellated corpuscles,** are scattered deep in the dermis, and in subcutaneous tissue underlying the skin. Although they are mechanoreceptors stimulated by deep pressure, they respond only when the pressure is first applied. Thus, Pacinian receptors are best suited to monitor vibration (an "on-off" pressure stimulus). They are the largest of the corpuscular receptors. Some are over 2 mm long and half as wide and are visible to the naked eye. In section, a Pacinian corpuscle resembles a cut onion. Its single dendrite is surrounded by up to 60 layers of flattened Schwann cells, which in turn are enclosed by a connective tissue capsule.

Ruffini's corpuscles, which lie in the dermis, subcutaneous tissue, and joint capsules, contain a spray of dendritic endings enclosed by a flattened capsule. They bear a striking resemblance to Golgi tendon organs (which monitor [tendon] stretch) and they probably play a similar role in other dense connective tissues where they respond to *continuous* pressure.

Muscle spindles (neuromuscular spindles), are fusiform (spindle-shaped) proprioceptors found throughout the skeletal muscles. Each muscle spindle consists of a bundle of modified skeletal muscle fibers, called **intrafusal** (in″trah-fu′zal; *intra* = within, *fusal* = the spindle) **fibers,** enclosed in a connective tissue capsule (see Table 13.1). These intrafusal fibers detect when a muscle is stretched and initiate a reflex that resists the stretch. The details of muscle spindle innervation are considered later in this chapter when the stretch reflex is described (see p. 453).

Golgi tendon organs are proprioceptors that are embedded in tendons, close to the point of skeletal muscle insertion. They consist of small bundles of tendon (collagen) fibers enclosed in a layered capsule, with dendrites coiling between and around the fibers. Golgi tendon organs are stimulated when the associated muscle contracts and stretches the tendon; hence, their activity is functionally associated with that of the muscle spindles. When Golgi tendon organs are activated, the contracting muscle is inhibited, which causes it to relax, ending the stimulation of the Golgi tendon organs.

Joint kinesthetic (kin″es-thet′ik) **receptors** are proprioceptors that monitor stretch in the articular capsules that enclose synovial joints. At least four different receptor types (see Table 13.1) contribute to this receptor category. Together these receptors provide information on joint position and motion (*kines* = movement), a sensation of which we are highly conscious. (Close your eyes and flex and extend your fingers—you can *feel* exactly which joints are moving.)

Sensory Receptor Potentials

Information about our external and internal worlds presents itself in different energy forms—sound, pressure, chemicals, and so on. The sensory receptors associated with sensory neurons are specialized to respond to these energetic stimuli. In order to communicate with other neurons, they must translate the information of their stimulus into nerve impulses, the universal neural language.

As the energy of the stimulus is absorbed by the receptor, it is converted, or **transduced,** into an electrical event. That is, the stimulus causes changes in the membrane permeability of the receptor region that result in a local graded potential, called a **receptor potential,** which is essentially the same as an EPSP (p. 363) generated at a postsynaptic membrane in response to binding of neurotransmitters. In both cases, one type of ion channel is opened that allows ion fluxes (usually of sodium and potassium) across the membrane, and summation of local potentials occurs.

If the receptor potential is of or above threshold strength when it reaches the *voltage-gated* sodium ion channels on the axon (these are usually just proximal to the receptor membrane, often at the first node of Ranvier), those sodium channels will be opened and an action potential will be generated and propagated to the CNS. Hence, a suprathreshold receptor potential becomes a **generator potential.** Action potentials are generated as long as a threshold stimulus is applied, and, as explained earlier, stimulus strength is encoded in the frequency of impulse transmission. For example, a blow to the hand causes faster action potential generation than a soft stroke. Thus, stronger stimuli result in more nerve impulses per second reaching the CNS, which enables the integrative centers to determine the intensity of stimuli acting on the body.

Although receptor potentials are graded potentials that vary with stimulus intensity and can summate, an unusual phenomenon called **adaptation** occurs in certain sensory receptors when they are subjected to an unchanging stimulus. Though the mechanism of adaption is not fully understood, researchers believe that receptor membranes become less responsive with time. As a result, the receptor potentials decline in frequency, or stop completely. Some receptors, such as most of those responding to pressure, touch, and smell, adapt rapidly. This explains why we are not usually aware (after a short period) of the feel of our clothing against our skin. However, some receptors adapt slowly, and others do not adapt at all. Pain receptors and proprioceptors, for example, respond more or less continuously to threshold stimuli. Since pain typically warns of potential or actual tissue damage and proprioceptive sense is essential to balance and coordinated skeletal muscle activity, the nonadaptability of these receptors is important. Slowly adapting receptors include many of the interoceptors that respond to changing levels of chemicals in the blood.

A CLOSER LOOK | Pain: Sound the Alarm, But Pain Me Not!

Pain is a primitive experience that we humans share with nearly all animals. Few of us have not suffered the smarting of a bee sting or the cruel persistence of a headache. Although pain warns of actual or potential tissue damage, its protective value is difficult to appreciate when we are its victims.

Clinically, pain can be measured only by roundabout techniques, such as tapping the painful spot and observing the patient's degree of wincing. This seems a bit strange, given that the other most common sign of disease or injury—fever—is readily measured with a thermometer.

Pain Reception

The principal pain receptors are the several million bare sensory nerve endings that weave through all the tissues and organs of the body (except the brain) and respond to noxious stimuli—a catchall term for anything damaging to tissues. But bradykinin, the most potent pain-producing chemical known, appears to be the universal pain stimulus. Wherever body tissue is injured, enzymes are activated that release bradykinin from larger precursor molecules present in blood and many other tissues. Bradykinin, in turn, unleashes the production of an avalanche of inflammatory chemicals, such as histamine and prostaglandins, that initiate healing. Some scientists think that bradykinin also binds to pain receptor endings, causing them to fire. They are working to create a bradykinin variant to prevent the body's natural bradykinin from binding to the pain receptor endings, extinguishing pain at its source.

Pain Transmission and Perception

Clinically, pain is classified as *somatic* or *visceral*. Somatic pain, arising from the skin, muscles, or joints, can be either superficial or

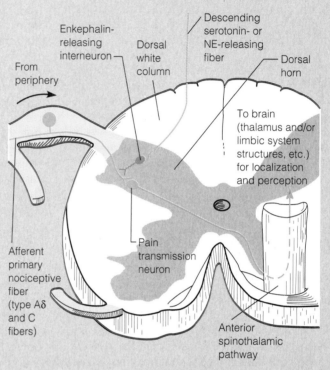

When type A delta and type C pain fibers transmit through to their transmission neurons in the spinothalamic pathway, pain impulses are transmitted to the cerebral cortex. Descending control of pain transmission (analgesia) is mediated by descending central fibers that synapse with small enkephalin-releasing interneurons in the dorsal horn that make inhibitory synapses with the afferent pain fibers. Activation of these interneurons inhibits pain transmission by preventing their release of substance P.

deep. Superficial somatic pain is a sharp, pricking pain that often causes us to cry out. Localizable to the skin epidermis or mucosae, it tends to be brief. This type of pain is transmitted along finely myelinated A delta (δ) fibers at the rate of 12 to 80 m/s (up to 250 ft/s). Deep somatic pain is more likely to be burning, itching, or aching pain; it results from stimulation of pain receptors in the deep skin layers, muscles, or joints. Deep somatic pain is both more diffuse and longer lasting than superficial somatic pain, and it always indicates tissue destruction. Impulses from the deep pain receptors are transmitted slowly (0.4 to over 1 m/s, or up to 3.5 ft/s) along the small, unmyelinated C fibers.

Visceral pain results from noxious stimulation of receptors in the organs of the thorax and abdominal cavity. Like deep somatic pain, it is usually a dull ache, a burning feeling, or a gnawing pain. The most important stimuli for visceral pain are extreme stretching of tissue, ischemia, irritating chemicals, and muscle spasms. Because visceral pain inputs follow the same pathways as somatic pain (convergence), projection by the brain may cause visceral pain to be perceived as somatic in origin. This phenomenon, *referred pain*, is described in Chapter 14 (p. 469).

Both the superficial somatic pain fibers and deep somatic/visceral pain fibers synapse with second-order neurons in the dorsal horns of the spinal cord. Transmission of pain impulses along the first-order neurons causes release of *substance P,* the pain neurotransmitter, into the synaptic cleft. What happens is unclear, but it appears that the axons of most of these second-order neurons cross the cord and enter the anterolateral spinothalamic tracts, which ascend to the thalamus. From the thalamus, impulses are relayed to the somatosensory cortex for interpretation. Some second-order fibers "take the express"—that is, they ascend directly to the thalamus, allowing the sensory cortex to analyze what hurts and how much. Other fibers of the spinothalamic tracts "take the local," making abundant synapses in the brain stem and in the hypothalamus and other limbic system structures (particularly the anterior cingulate gyrus) before reaching the thalamus. This second set of pathways mediates arousal and emotional reactions to pain, and has longer-lasting influences on the CNS.

We all have the same *threshold* for pain; that is, we perceive it at the same stimulus intensity. For example, heat is perceived as painful at 44°–46°C, the range at which it begins to damage tissue. However, reactions to pain, or *pain tolerance,* vary widely and are heavily influenced by cultural and psychological factors. When we say that someone is "very sensitive to pain," we are referring to that person's pain tolerance rather than to their pain threshold. Pain tolerance seems to increase with age, but this may reflect the sociocultural notion that we have to expect pain as we age. Pain is also modified by emotions and mental state. In a disaster, many who feel no pain while struggling to help others may actually be severely injured.

Normally a steady state is maintained that correlates injury and pain. However, long-lasting or very intense pain inputs can disrupt this system, leading to chronic pain. **NMDA receptors,** the same receptors that help

strengthen neural connections during certain kinds of learning, appear to play a similar role in **hyperalgesia,** or pain amplification, in the spinal cord. (Hyperalgesia is familiar to anyone with a bad sunburn who steps into a warm shower.) Normal pain input doesn't turn the spinal cord NMDA receptors on, but repeated pain transmission does. Once turned on, the NMDA receptors sensitize the spinal cord neurons to future signals. NMDA receptor blockers prevent hyperalgesia while leaving the normal pain pathways intact, a phenomenon which suggests a drug therapy for managing chronic and phantom pain.

Pain Modulation and Analgesia

The extraordinary plasticity of human pain suggests that natural neural mechanisms must exist to modulate pain transmission and perception. One of the most dramatic and significant advances in the understanding and management of pain was the publication of Melzack and Wall's *gate control theory of pain* in the 1960s. It suggested that:

1. A pain "gate" exists in the dorsal horn (substantia gelatinosa) where impulses from small unmyelinated pain fibers and large touch (A beta) fibers enter the cord.

2. If impulses along the pain fibers outnumber those transmitted along the touch fibers, the gate opens and pain impulses are transmitted. If the reverse is true, the gate is closed by enkephalin-releasing interneurons in the spinal cord which inhibit transmission of both touch and pain impulses, thus reducing pain perception.

Although several studies have failed to support the gate theory of pain control as originally proposed, it fostered a generation of pain research and some of its clinical predictions are useful. For example, it's been found that (1) threshold stimulation of the large touch fibers (as by massage) results in a burst of firing in the substantia gelatinosa cells, followed

by a brief period of inhibited pain transmission (it *does* close the pain "gate"), and (2) it has been amply proven that direct stimulation, or even transcutaneous electric (TENS), of dorsal column (large-diameter touch) fibers *does* provide extended pain relief (however, the precise mechanisms of these effects are still unknown).

For some time, it has been known that our natural opiates (beta-endorphins and enkephalins) are released in the brain when we are in pain and act to reduce its perception. Hypnosis, natural childbirth techniques, morphine, and stimulus-induced analgesia are all believed to tap into these natural-opiate pathways which originate in certain brain regions. These regions, which include the periventricular gray matter of the hypothalamus and the periaqueductal gray (PAG) matter of the midbrain, oversee descending pain suppressor fibers that synapse in the dorsal horns. When transmitting, these fibers (most importantly some from the medullary nucleus raphe magnus) produce analgesia presumably by synapsing with opiate (enkephalin) releasing interneurons that, in turn, actively inhibit forward transmission of pain inputs (see the diagram). The mechanism of this inhibition appears to be that enkephalin blocks Ca^{2+} influx into the sensory terminals, thereby blocking their release of substance P. However, this is only one mechanism of pain modulation. There is a variety of other neurotransmitter receptor systems in the dorsal horn that regulate pain perception. For example, injectable agents such as clonidine (an antihypertensive drug), baclofen (a GABA receptor agonist), and somatostatin promote analgesia in morphine-tolerant patients. You could say that such pain-reducing techniques—drugs and electrical stimulation and massage—work because the body allows it!

Blood vessels   Perineurium

Fascicle

(a) Endoneurium   Nerve fibers

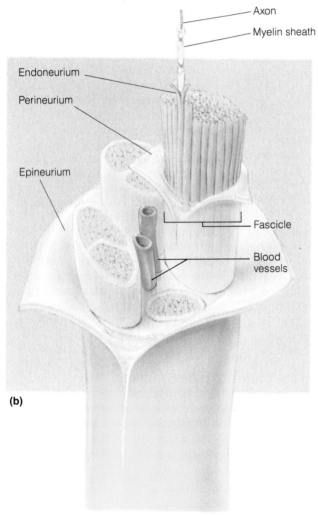

Axon

Myelin sheath

Endoneurium

Perineurium

Epineurium

Fascicle

Blood vessels

(b)

FIGURE 13.2
Structure of a nerve. (a) Scanning electron micrograph of a cross section of a portion of a nerve (400×). (From *Tissues and Organs: A Text-Atlas of Scanning Electron Microscopy* by R. Kessel and R. Kardon. © 1979 W. H. Freeman.) (b) Three-dimensional view of a portion of a nerve, showing connective tissue wrappings.

Nerves and Associated Ganglia

Structure and Classification

A **nerve** is a cordlike organ that is part of the peripheral nervous system. Nerves vary in size, but every nerve consists of parallel bundles of peripheral axons (some myelinated and some not) enclosed by successive wrappings of connective tissue (Figure 13.2).

Within a nerve, each axon is surrounded by a delicate layer of loose connective tissue called **endoneurium** (en"do-nu're-um), which also encloses the fiber's associated myelin and/or neurilemma sheath. Groups of fibers are bound into bundles or **fascicles** by a coarser connective tissue wrapping, the **perineurium.** Finally, all the fascicles are enclosed by a tough fibrous sheath, the **epineurium,** to form the nerve. Neuron processes constitute only a small fraction of a nerve's bulk; the balance consists chiefly of myelin and the protective connective tissue wrappings. Blood vessels and lymphatic vessels are also found within a nerve.

Recall that the PNS is divided into *sensory* (afferent) and *motor* (efferent) divisions. Hence, nerves are classified according to the direction in which they transmit impulses. Nerves containing both sensory and motor fibers and transmitting impulses both to and from the central nervous system are called **mixed nerves.** Nerves that carry impulses toward the CNS only are **sensory (afferent) nerves;** and nerves carrying impulses only away from the CNS are **motor (efferent) nerves.** Most nerves are mixed; purely sensory or motor nerves are extremely rare.

Since mixed nerves often carry both somatic and autonomic (visceral) nervous system fibers, the fibers within them may be classified further according to the region they innervate as *somatic afferent, somatic efferent, visceral afferent,* and *visceral efferent.*

For convenience, the peripheral nerves are classified as *cranial nerves* or *spinal nerves,* depending on whether they arise from the brain or spinal cord, respectively. Although autonomic efferents of cranial nerves are mentioned, this chapter focuses on somatic functions. The discussion of the autonomic nervous system and the visceral functions it serves is deferred to Chapter 14.

Ganglia are collections of neuron cell bodies associated with nerves in the PNS. Ganglia associated with *afferent* nerve fibers contain cell bodies of sensory neurons. (These are the *dorsal root ganglia* studied in Chapter 12.) Ganglia associated with *efferent* nerve fibers contain cell bodies of autonomic motor neurons, as well as a special variety of integrative neurons. These more complicated autonomic ganglia are described in Chapter 14.

Regeneration of Nerve Fibers

Damage to nervous tissue is serious because mature neurons do not divide. If the damage is severe or close to the cell body, the entire neuron may die, and other neurons that are normally stimulated by its axon may die as well. However, in certain cases, cut or compressed axons on peripheral nerves can regenerate successfully.

Almost immediately after a peripheral axon has been severed or crushed, the separated ends seal themselves off and then swell as substances being transported along the axon begin to accumulate in the sealed ends (Figure 13.3a). Within a few hours, the axon and its myelin sheath distal to the site of injury begin to disintegrate because they cannot receive nutrients and other needed materials from the cell body. This process, called **Wallerian degeneration,** spreads distally from the injury site. By the third to fourth day, the distal part of the axon is completely fragmented (Figure 13.3b). Resident Schwann cells, and macrophages that migrate into the trauma zone from neighboring tissues, phagocytize disintegrating myelin and axonal debris. Generally, the entire axon distal to the injury is degraded within a week, but the neurilemma (region containing Schwann cell cytoplasm and nucleus) remains intact within the endoneurium. Once the debris has been disposed of, surviving Schwann cells proliferate in response to mitosis-stimulating chemicals released by the macrophages, and migrate into the injury site. There they form cellular cords that guide the regenerating axon "sprouts" across the gap and to their original contacts (Figure 13.3c and d). The same Schwann cells protect, support, and remyelinate the regenerating axons. They also release growth factors such as nerve growth factor and insulin-like growth factor (NGF and IGF, respectively), and express cell surface adhesion molecules (CAMs) that encourage axonal growth.

Characteristic changes also occur in the neuronal cell body after destruction of the axon. Within two days, the cell body swells (often doubling in size), and its chromatophilic substance breaks apart and disperses to the cell periphery. These events signal that the neuron is preparing to synthesize proteins to support regeneration of its axon.

Axons regenerate at the rate of 1 to 5 mm a day. The greater the distance between the severed nerve endings, the less the chance of recovery because adjacent tissues block growth by protruding into the larger gaps, and axonal sprouts tend to escape into surrounding areas and form a tissue mass called a *neuroma.* Neurosurgeons align cut nerve endings surgically to enhance the chance of successful regeneration, and scaffolding devices—silicon tubes filled with biodegradable collagen—have been successful in guiding axon growth in cases of severe peripheral nerve trauma. Whatever the measures taken, post-trauma axon regrowth is never exactly the same as what existed before the injury, and so pinpoint accuracy in nerve fiber–effector cell realignment is impossible. Indeed, much of the functional recovery after nerve injury involves retraining the nervous system to respond appropriately so that stimulus and response are coordinated.

What is the function of Schwann cells in the regeneration process?

FIGURE 13.3
Events leading to regeneration of nerve fibers in peripheral nerves.

Unlike peripheral nerve fibers, those within the CNS never regenerate distances of more than 1 mm under normal circumstances. Consequently, damage to the brain or spinal cord has been viewed as irreversible. This difference in regenerative capacity seems to have less to do with the neurons themselves than with the "company they keep"—their supporting cells. After CNS injury, microglial cells and astrocytes rid the area of deteriorating cell debris. However, the oligodendrocytes surrounding the injured fibers die, an event called *secondary demyelination,* and fail to oversee and guide fiber regrowth. To make matters worse, the dead oligodendrocytes are eventually replaced by a dense **glial scar** formed by astrocytes, which effectively blocks the progress of sprouting axons, and the myelin sheaths of nearby axons (a product of oligodendrocyte activity) contain growth inhibiting proteins. (Although the presence of growth inhibitors in the brain may appear to be self-defeating when regeneration is the goal, remember that "guardrails" [in this case, chemical ones] must be established during neural development to keep the young axons on their proper pathways.) However, research has shown that CNS axons will grow through (1) segments of cut peripheral nerve containing Schwann cells (whose membranes lack the growth-inhibiting proteins), and (2) *astrocyte bridge implants* (tiny paper "bridges" coated with fetal astrocytes) and establish functional connections. Moreover, neutralization of the myelin-bound growth inhibitors by antibodies can induce substantial fiber regeneration in the rat spinal cord, and dousing CNS neurons with epidermal growth factor (EGF) and the even more potent transforming growth factor (TGF) can prompt mature neurons to divide and form new nervous tissue. The key to CNS regeneration will most likely be found in the molecules that maintain the delicate balance between growth stimulation and inhibition.

Motor Endings

So far we have covered the sensory receptors that detect stimuli, and the structure of nerves containing the afferent and efferent fibers that deliver impulses to and from the CNS. We now turn to motor endings, the PNS elements that activate effectors by releasing neurotransmitters. Since we discussed that topic earlier with the innervation of body muscles, all we need to do here is recap briefly.

Axonal Terminals (Boutons) of Somatic Fibers

As illustrated in Figure 9.9 (p. 259), the terminals of somatic motor fibers that innervate voluntary muscles form elaborate *neuromuscular junctions* with their effector cells. As each axonal ending reaches its target muscle fiber, it splits into a cluster of tiny axonal terminals (boutons) that arborize, or branch treelike, over the motor end plate of the muscle fiber. The axonal terminals contain mitochondria and synaptic vesicles filled with the neurotransmitter acetylcholine (ACh). When a nerve impulse reaches an axonal terminal, the neurotransmitter is released by exocytosis, diffuses across the fluid-filled synaptic cleft (about 50 nm wide), and attaches to ACh receptors on the highly infolded sarcolemma at the junction. ACh binding results in the opening of sodium gates (followed by their closure and opening of potassium gates), which in turn leads to propagation of an action potential across the sarcolemma that stimulates the muscle fiber to contract. The synaptic cleft at somatic neuromuscular junctions is distinctive in that it is filled with a glycoprotein-rich basal lamina (a structure not seen at other synapses).

Varicosities of Autonomic Fibers

The motor endings of autonomic motor neurons form much simpler junctions with smooth and cardiac muscle and visceral glands. The autonomic motor axons branch repeatedly, each branch forming *synapses en passant* with its effector cells. Instead of a cluster of bulblike terminals, an axonal ending serving smooth muscle or glands (but not cardiac muscle) exhibits a series of **varicosities,** knoblike swellings containing mitochondria and synaptic vesicles, that make it look like a string of beads. The autonomic synaptic vesicles typically contain either acetylcholine or norepinephrine. Some varicosities come into close contact with the effector cells. However, the synaptic cleft is always wider than that at somatic neuromuscular junctions, so visceral motor responses tend to be slower than those induced by somatic motor fibers.

CRANIAL NERVES

Twelve pairs of **cranial nerves** are associated with the brain and pass through various foramina of the skull (Figure 13.4). The first two pairs attach to the forebrain; the rest originate from the brain stem. Other than the vagus nerves, which extend well into the ventral body cavity, the cranial nerves serve only head and neck structures.

In most cases, the names of the cranial nerves reveal the most important structures they serve or their primary functions. The cranial nerves are also numbered (traditionally using Roman numerals) from the most rostral to the most caudal. A mini-introduction to the cranial nerves follows:

I. **Olfactory.** These are the tiny sensory nerves of smell, which run from the nasal mucosa to the olfactory bulbs. Be careful not to confuse these with the thick *olfactory* bulbs and *tracts* of the brain (see Figure 13.4a).

II. **Optic.** Since this sensory nerve of vision devel-

Frontal lobe

Temporal lobe

Infundibulum

Facial nerve (VII)

Vestibulo-cochlear nerve (VIII)

Glosso-pharyngeal nerve (IX)

Vagus nerve (X)

Accessory nerve (XI)

Hypoglossal nerve (XII)

Fibers of olfactory nerve (I)

Olfactory bulb

Olfactory tract

Optic nerve (II)

Optic chiasma

Optic tract

Oculomotor nerve (III)

Trochlear nerve (IV)

Trigeminal nerve (V)

Abducens nerve (VI)

Cerebellum

Medulla

(a)

FIGURE 13.4
Summary of location and function of the cranial nerves.
(a) Ventral view of the human brain, showing the cranial nerves. **(b)** Summary of cranial nerves by function. Notice that three cranial nerves (I, II, and VIII) have sensory function only and no motor function. Notice also that four nerves (III, VII, IX, and X) carry parasympathetic fibers that serve visceral muscles and glands. All cranial nerves that have a motor function also carry afferent fibers from proprioceptors in the muscles served; only sensory functions other than proprioception are indicated.

Cranial nerve # and name	Sensory function	Motor function	PS* fibers
I Olfactory	Yes (smell)	No	No
II Optic	Yes (vision)	No	No
III Oculomotor	No	Yes	Yes
IV Trochlear	No	Yes	No
V Trigeminal	Yes (general sensation)	Yes	No
VI Abducens	No	Yes	No

Cranial nerve # and name	Sensory function	Motor function	PS* fibers
VII Facial	Yes (taste)	Yes	Yes
VIII Vestibulocochlear	Yes (hearing and balance)	No	No
IX Glossopharyngeal	Yes (taste)	Yes	Yes
X Vagus	Yes (taste)	Yes	Yes
XI Accessory	No	Yes	No
XII Hypoglossal	No	Yes	No

(b)   * PS - parasympathetic

ops as an outgrowth of the brain, it is really a brain tract.

III. Oculomotor. This nerve has a name meaning "eye mover" because it supplies four of the six extrinsic muscles that move the eyeball in the orbit.

IV. Trochlear. This nerve's name means "pulley" and it innervates an extrinsic eye muscle that loops through a pulley-shaped ligament in the orbit.

V. Trigeminal. Three (*tri*) branches spring from this, the largest of the cranial nerves. It supplies sensory fibers to the face and motor fibers to the chewing muscles.

VI. Abducens. This nerve controls the extrinsic eye muscle that *abducts* the eyeball (turns it laterally).

VII. Facial. A large nerve that innervates muscles of *facial* expression (among other things).

VIII. Vestibulocochlear. This sensory nerve for hearing and balance was formerly called the *auditory nerve.*

IX. Glossopharyngeal. Its name, meaning "tongue and pharynx," reveals the structures it helps to innervate.

X. Vagus. This nerve's name means "wanderer" (as in vagabond), and it is the only cranial nerve to extend beyond the head and neck into the thorax and abdomen.

XI. Accessory. Considered an *accessory* part of the vagus nerve. Formerly called the *spinal accessory.*

XII. Hypoglossal. This nerve runs inferior to the tongue and innervates some tongue-moving muscles, as reflected by its name meaning "under the tongue."

Table 13.2 Cranial Nerves

I The olfactory (ol-fak'to-re) **nerves**

Origin and course: Olfactory nerve fibers arise from olfactory receptor cells located in olfactory epithelium of nasal cavity and pass through cribriform plate of ethmoid bone to synapse in olfactory bulb; fibers of olfactory bulb neurons extend posteriorly as olfactory tract, which runs beneath frontal lobe to enter cerebral hemispheres and terminates in primary olfactory cortex; see also Figure 16.3

Function: Purely sensory; carry afferent impulses for sense of smell

Clinical testing: Person is asked to sniff aromatic substances, such as oil of cloves and vanilla, and to identify each.

Fracture of ethmoid bone or lesions of olfactory fibers may result in partial or total loss of smell, a condition known as *anosmia* (an-oz'me-ah). •

- Frontal lobe of cerebral hemisphere
- Olfactory bulb
- Olfactory tract
- Cribriform plate of ethmoid bone
- **Fibers of olfactory nerve (I)**
- Nasal mucosa

For years, students used the following saying to help them remember the first letters of the former names of the cranial nerves in order: "**O**n **o**ld **O**lympus's **t**owering **t**op, **a** **F**inn **a**nd **G**erman **v**iewed **s**ome **h**ops." However, since two of the cranial nerve names (VIII and XI) have been changed, I suggest you make up your own saying or use the following memory jog sent to me by a student: "**O**n **o**ccasion, **o**ur **t**rusty **t**ruck **a**cts **f**unny—**v**ery **g**ood **v**ehicle **a**ny**h**ow."

In the last chapter, we described how all spinal nerves are formed by the fusion of ventral (motor) and dorsal (sensory) roots. Cranial nerves, on the other hand, vary markedly in their composition. Most cranial nerves are mixed nerves (see Figure 13.4b); however, three pairs (the olfactory, optic, and vestibulocochlear) are associated with special sense organs and are generally considered purely sensory. The cell bodies of the sensory neurons of the olfactory and optic nerves are located *within* the special sense organs with which they are associated. In all other cases, the cell bodies of the sensory neurons contributing to cranial nerves are located in **cranial sensory ganglia** outside the brain. These ganglia are similar to the dorsal root ganglia of the spinal cord; however, some cranial nerves have a single sensory ganglion, others have several, and still others have none.

Several of the mixed cranial nerves contain both somatic and autonomic motor fibers and hence serve both skeletal muscles and visceral organs. Except for some autonomic motor neurons located in ganglia (see Chapter 14), the cell bodies of motor neurons contributing to the cranial nerves are located in gray matter regions (nuclei) of the brain stem.

Having read this overview, you are now ready to tackle the more detailed description of the origin, course, and function of the cranial nerves provided in Table 13.2. Notice that the pathways of the purely sensory nerves (I, II, and VIII) are described from the receptors to the brain, while those of the other nerves are described in the opposite direction (from the brain distally).

SPINAL NERVES

Thirty-one pairs of **spinal nerves,** each containing thousands of nerve fibers, arise from the spinal cord and supply all parts of the body except the head and some areas of the neck. All are mixed nerves. As illustrated in Figure 13.5, the spinal nerves are named according to their point of issue from the spinal cord. There are 8 pairs of cervical spinal nerves (C_1–C_8), 12 pairs of thoracic nerves (T_1–T_{12}), 5 pairs of lumbar nerves (L_1–L_5), 5 pairs of sacral nerves (S_1–S_5), and 1 pair of tiny coccygeal nerves (designated C_0).

Notice that there are eight pairs of cervical nerves but only seven cervical vertebrae. This "discrepancy" is easily explained. The first seven pairs of cervical

Text continues on p. 442

II The optic nerves

Origin and course: Fibers arise from retina of eye to form optic nerve, which passes through optic foramen of orbit; the optic nerves converge to form the optic chiasma (ki-az'mah) where partial crossover of fibers occurs, continue on as optic tracts, enter thalamus, and synapse there; thalamic fibers run (as the optic radiation) to occipital (visual) cortex, where visual interpretation occurs; see also Figure 16.22

Function: Purely sensory; carry afferent impulses for vision

Clinical testing: Vision and visual field are determined with eye chart and by testing the point at which the person first sees an object (finger) moving into the visual field. Fundus of eye viewed with ophthalmoscope to detect papilledema (swelling of optic disc, or site where the optic nerve leaves the eyeball), as well as for routine examination of the optic disc and retinal blood vessels.

Damage to optic nerve results in blindness in eye served by nerve; damage to visual pathway beyond the optic chiasma results in partial visual losses; visual defects are called *anopsias* (ah-nop'se-ahz). •

Eyeball
Retina
Optic nerve (II)
Optic chiasma
Optic tract
Lateral geniculate nucleus of thalamus
Optic radiation
Visual cortex

III The oculomotor (ok"u-lo-mo'tor) nerves

Origin and course: Fibers extend from ventral midbrain (near its junction with pons) and pass through bony orbit, via superior orbital fissure, to eye

Function: Mixed nerves; although oculomotor nerves contain a few proprioceptive afferents, they are chiefly motor nerves (as implied by their name, meaning "motor to the eye"); each nerve includes:

- Somatic motor fibers to four of the six extrinsic eye muscles (inferior oblique and superior, inferior, and medial rectus muscles) that help direct eyeball, and to levator palpebrae superioris muscle, which raises upper eyelid
- Parasympathetic (autonomic) motor fibers to constrictor muscles of iris, which cause pupil to constrict, and to ciliary muscle, controlling lens shape for visual focusing
- Sensory (proprioceptor) afferents, which run from same four extrinsic eye muscles to midbrain

Clinical testing: Pupils are examined for size, shape, and equality. Pupillary reflex is tested with penlight (pupils should constrict when illuminated). Convergence for near vision is tested, as is subject's ability to follow objects up, down, side to side, and diagonally.

In oculomotor nerve paralysis, eye cannot be moved up, down, or inward, and at rest, eye rotates laterally (*external strabismus* [strah-biz'mus]) because the actions of the two extrinsic eye muscles not served by cranial nerve III are unopposed; upper eyelid droops *(ptosis),* and the person has double vision and trouble focusing on close objects. •

Superior orbital fissure
Midbrain
Medial rectus muscle
Superior rectus muscle
Levator palpebrae muscle
Inferior oblique muscle
Ciliary ganglion
Inferior rectus muscle
Parasympathetic motor fibers
Oculomotor nerve (III)
Pons

IV The trochlear (trok'le-ar) nerves

Origin and course: Fibers emerge from dorsal midbrain and course ventrally around midbrain to enter orbits through *superior orbital fissures* along with oculomotor nerves

Function: Mixed nerves, primarily motor; supply somatic motor fibers to, and carry proprioceptor fibers from, one of the extrinsic eye muscles, the superior oblique muscle

Clinical testing: Tested in common with cranial nerve III.

Trauma to, or paralysis of, a trochlear nerve results in double vision and reduced ability to rotate eye inferolaterally. •

Superior oblique muscle
Superior orbital fissure
Pons
Trochlear nerve (IV)

Table 13.2 continued

V The trigeminal nerves

Largest of cranial nerves; fibers extend from pons to face, and form three divisions (*trigemina* = threefold): ophthalmic, maxillary, and mandibular divisions; major general sensory nerves of face; transmit afferent impulses from touch, temperature, and pain receptors; cell bodies of sensory neurons of all three divisions are located in large *trigeminal* (also called *semilunar* or

gasserian) *ganglion;* the mandibular division also contains some motor fibers that innervate chewing muscles

Dentists desensitize upper and lower jaws by injecting local anesthetic (such as Novocain) into alveolar branches of maxillary and mandibular divisions, respectively; since this blocks pain-transmitting fibers of teeth, the surrounding tissues become numb

	Ophthalmic division (V_1)	Maxillary division (V_2)	Mandibular division (V_3)
Origin and course:	Fibers run from face to pons via superior orbital fissure	Fibers run from face to pons via foramen rotundum	Fibers pass through skull via foramen ovale
Function:	Conveys sensory impulses from skin of anterior scalp, upper eyelid, and nose, and from nasal cavity mucosa, cornea, and lacrimal gland	Conveys sensory impulses from nasal cavity mucosa, palate, upper teeth, skin of cheek, upper lip, lower eyelid	Conveys sensory impulses from anterior tongue (except taste buds), lower teeth, skin of chin, temporal region of scalp; supplies motor fibers to, and carries proprioceptor fibers from, muscles of mastication
Clinical testing:	Corneal reflex tested: touching cornea with wisp of cotton should elicit blinking	Sensations of pain, touch, and temperature are tested with safety pin and hot and cold objects	Motor branch assessed by asking person to clench his teeth, open mouth against resistance, and move jaw side to side

Tic douloureux (tik doo"loo-roo'), or *trigeminal neuralgia* (nu-ral'je-ah), caused by inflammation of trigeminal nerve, is widely considered to produce most excruciating pain known; the stabbing pain lasts for a few seconds to a minute, but it can be relentless, occurring a hundred times a day; (the term *tic* refers to victim's wincing during pain); usually triggered by some sensory stimulus, such as brushing teeth or even a puff of air hitting the face, but may reflect pressure on the trigeminal nerve root; analgesics only partially effective; in severe cases, nerve is cut proximal to trigeminal ganglion; this relieves the agony, but also results in loss of sensation on that side of face. •

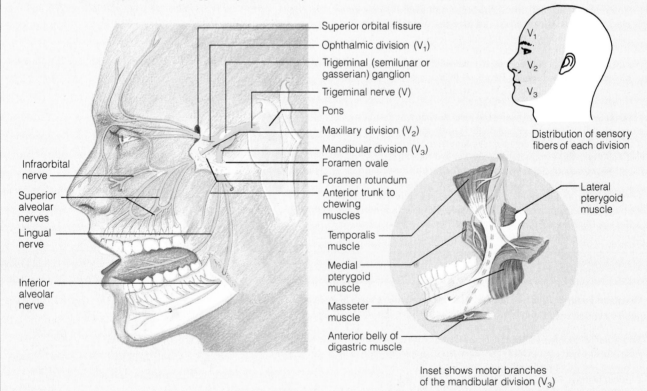

Superior orbital fissure
Ophthalmic division (V_1)
Trigeminal (semilunar or gasserian) ganglion
Trigeminal nerve (V)
Pons
Maxillary division (V_2)
Mandibular division (V_3)
Foramen ovale
Foramen rotundum
Anterior trunk to chewing muscles

Infraorbital nerve
Superior alveolar nerves
Lingual nerve
Inferior alveolar nerve

Distribution of sensory fibers of each division

Temporalis muscle
Medial pterygoid muscle
Masseter muscle
Anterior belly of digastric muscle
Lateral pterygoid muscle

Inset shows motor branches of the mandibular division (V_3)

VI The abducens (ab-du′senz) nerves

Origin and course: Fibers leave inferior pons and enter orbit via superior orbital fissure to run to eye

Function: Mixed nerve, primarily motor; supplies somatic motor fibers to lateral rectus muscle, an extrinsic muscle of the eye; conveys proprioceptor impulses from same muscle to brain.

Clinical testing: Tested in common with cranial nerve III.

In abducens nerve paralysis, eye cannot be moved laterally; at rest, affected eyeball rotates medially *(internal strabismus).* •

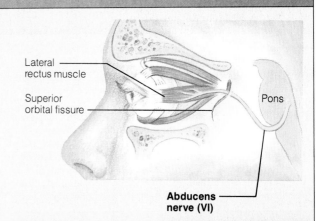

Lateral rectus muscle

Superior orbital fissure

Pons

Abducens nerve (VI)

VII The facial nerves

Origin and course: Fibers issue from pons, just lateral to abducens nerves (see Figure 13.4), enter temporal bone via *internal acoustic meatus,* and run within bone (and through inner ear cavity) before emerging through *stylomastoid foramen;* nerve then courses to lateral aspect of face

Function: Mixed nerves that are the chief motor nerves of face; have five major branches: temporal, zygomatic, buccal, mandibular, and cervical (see **a**)

• Convey motor impulses to skeletal muscles of face (muscles of facial expression), except for chewing muscles served by trigeminal nerves, and transmit proprioceptor impulses from same muscles to pons (see **c**)

• Transmit parasympathetic (autonomic) motor impulses to lacrimal (tear) glands, nasal and palatine glands, and submandibular and sublingual salivary glands. Some of the cell bodies of these parasympathetic motor neurons are in *sphenopalatine* (sfe″no-pal′ah-tīn) and *submandibular ganglia* on the trigeminal nerve (see **b**)

• Convey sensory impulses from taste buds of anterior two-thirds of tongue; cell bodies of these sensory neurons are in *geniculate ganglion* (see **b**)

(a) A simple method of remembering the courses of the five major motor nerves of the face.

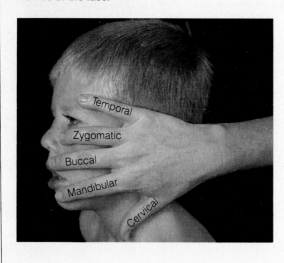

Temporal
Zygomatic
Buccal
Mandibular
Cervical

Geniculate ganglion

Internal acoustic meatus

Sphenopalatine ganglion

Facial nerve (VII)

Lacrimal gland

Parasympathetic nerve fibers

Chorda tympani branch (taste)

Stylomastoid foramen

Submandibular ganglion

Parasympathetic nerve fibers

Sublingual gland

Submandibular gland

Motor branch to muscles of facial expression

(b) Parasympathetic efferents and sensory afferents

Temporal
Zygomatic
Buccal
Mandibular
Cervical

(c) Motor branches to muscles of facial expression and scalp muscles

Table 13.2 continued

VII The facial nerves (continued)

Clinical testing: Anterior two-thirds of tongue is tested for ability to taste sweet (sugar), salty, sour (vinegar), and bitter (quinine) substances. Symmetry of face is checked. Subject is asked to close eyes, smile, whistle, and so on. Tearing is assessed with ammonia fumes.

> *Bell's palsy,* characterized by paralysis of facial muscles on affected side and partial loss of taste sensation, may develop rapidly (often overnight); cause is usually unknown, but inflammation of facial nerve is often suspect; lower eyelid droops, corner of mouth sags (making it difficult to eat or speak normally), tears drip continuously from eye and eye cannot be completely closed; condition may disappear spontaneously without treatment. •

VIII The vestibulocochlear (ves-tib″u-lo-kok′le-ar) nerves

Origin and course: Fibers arise from hearing and equilibrium apparatus located within inner ear of temporal bone and pass through internal acoustic meatus to enter brain stem at pons-medulla border; afferent fibers from hearing receptor in cochlea form the *cochlear division;* those from equilibrium receptors in semicircular canals and vestibule form the *vestibular division* (vestibular nerve); the two divisions merge to form vestibulo-cochlear nerve; see also Figure 16.25

Function: Purely sensory; vestibular branch transmits afferent impulses for sense of equilibrium, and sensory nerve cell bodies are located in *vestibular ganglia;* cochlear branch transmits afferent impulses for sense of hearing, and sensory nerve cell bodies are located in *spiral ganglion* within cochlea

Clinical testing: Hearing is checked by air and bone conduction using tuning fork.

> Lesions of cochlear nerve or cochlear receptors result in *central* or *nerve deafness,* whereas damage to vestibular division produces dizziness, rapid involuntary eye movements, loss of balance, nausea and vomiting. •

IX The glossopharyngeal (glos″o-fah-rin′je-al) nerves

Origin and course: Fibers emerge from medulla and leave skull via *jugular foramen* to run to throat

Function: Mixed nerves that innervate part of tongue and pharynx; provide motor fibers to, and carry proprioceptor fibers from, superior pharyngeal muscles involved in swallowing and gag reflex; provide parasympathetic motor fibers to parotid salivary gland; (some of the nerve cell bodies of these parasympathetic motor neurons are located in *otic ganglion*)

Sensory fibers conduct taste and general sensory (touch, pressure, pain) impulses from pharynx and posterior tongue, from chemoreceptor in the carotid body (which monitor O_2 and CO_2 tension in the blood and help regulate respiratory rate and depth), and from pressure receptors of carotid sinus (which help to regulate blood pressure by providing feedback information); sensory neuron cell bodies are located in *superior* and *inferior ganglia*

Clinical testing: Position of the uvula is checked. Gag and swallowing reflexes are checked. Subject is asked to speak and cough. Posterior third of tongue may be tested for taste.

> Injury or inflammation of glossopharyngeal nerves impairs swallowing and taste, particularly for sour and bitter substances. •

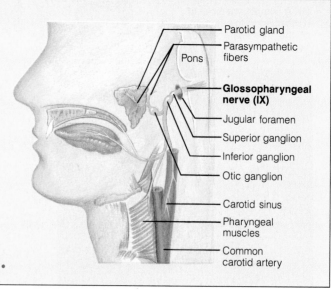

X The vagus (va'gus) nerves

Origin and course: The only cranial nerves to extend beyond head and neck region; fibers emerge from medulla, pass through skull via jugular foramen, and descend through neck region into thorax and abdomen; see also Figure 14.3

Function: Mixed nerves; nearly all motor fibers are parasympathetic efferents, except those serving skeletal muscles of pharynx and larynx (involved in swallowing); parasympathetic motor fibers supply heart, lungs, and abdominal viscera and are involved in regulation of heart rate, breathing, and digestive system activity; transmit sensory impulses from thoracic and abdominal viscera, from the carotid sinus (pressoreceptor for blood pressure) and the carotid and aortic bodies (chemoreceptors for respiration), and taste buds of posterior tongue and pharynx; carry proprioceptor fibers from muscles of larynx and pharynx

Clinical testing: As for cranial nerve IX (IX and X are tested in common, since they both innervate muscles of throat and mouth).

Since nearly all muscles of the larynx ("voice box") are innervated by laryngeal branches of the vagus, vagal nerve paralysis can lead to hoarseness or loss of voice; other symptoms are difficult swallowing and impaired digestive system mobility. Total destruction of both vagus nerves is incompatible with life, because these parasympathetic nerves are crucial in maintaining normal state of visceral organ activity; without their influence, the activity of the sympathetic nerves, which mobilize and accelerate vital body processes (and shut down digestion), would be unopposed. •

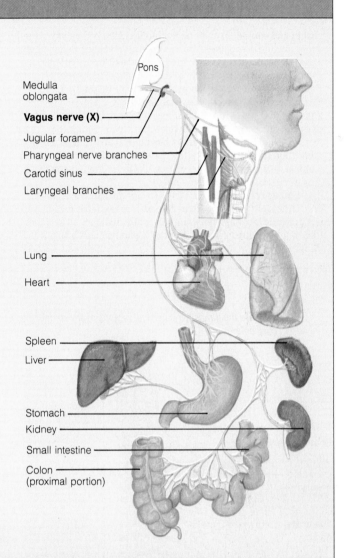

XI The accessory nerves

Origin and course: Unique in that they are formed by union of a *cranial root* and a *spinal root;* cranial root emerges from lateral aspect of medulla of brain stem; spinal root arises from superior region (C_1–C_5) of spinal cord. Spinal portion passes upward along spinal cord, enters skull via foramen magnum, and temporarily joins cranial root; the resulting accessory nerve exits from skull through *jugular foramen;* then cranial and spinal fibers diverge; cranial root fibers join vagus nerve, while spinal root runs to the largest neck muscles

Function: Mixed nerves, but primarily motor in function; cranial division joins with fibers of vagus nerve (X) to supply motor fibers to larynx, pharynx, and soft palate; spinal root supplies motor fibers to trapezius and sternocleidomastoid muscles, which together move head and neck, and conveys proprioceptor impulses from same muscles

Clinical testing: Sternocleidomastoid and trapezius muscles are checked for strength by asking person to rotate head and shrug shoulders against resistance.

Injury to the spinal root of one accessory nerve causes head to turn toward injury side as result of sternocleidomastoid muscle paralysis; shrugging of that shoulder (role of trapezius muscle) becomes difficult. •

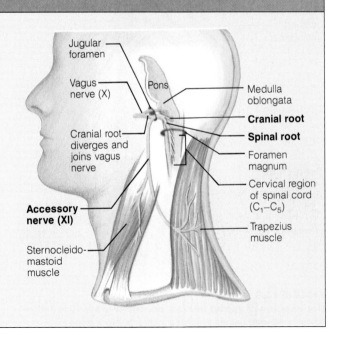

Table 13.2 continued

XII The hypoglossal (hi"po-glos'al) **nerves**

Origin and course: As their name implies (*hypo* = beneath; *glossal* = tongue), hypoglossal nerves mainly serve the tongue; fibers arise by a series of roots from medulla and exit from skull via *hypoglossal canal* to travel to tongue; see also Figure 13.4

Function: Mixed nerves, but primarily motor in function; carry somatic motor fibers to intrinsic and extrinsic muscles of tongue, and proprioceptor fibers from same muscles to brain stem; hypoglossal nerve control allows not only food mixing and manipulation by tongue during chewing, but also tongue movements that contribute to swallowing and speech.

Clinical testing: Person is asked to protrude and retract tongue. Any deviations in position are noted.

> Damage of hypoglossal nerves causes difficulties in speech and swallowing; if both nerves are impaired, the person cannot protrude tongue; if only one side is affected, tongue deviates (leans) toward affected side; eventually paralyzed side begins to atrophy. •

Medulla oblongata

Intrinsic muscles of the tongue

Hypoglossal canal

Hypoglossal nerve (XII)

Extrinsic muscles of the tongue

? *Why are the lumbar and cervical regions of the spinal cord enlarged?*

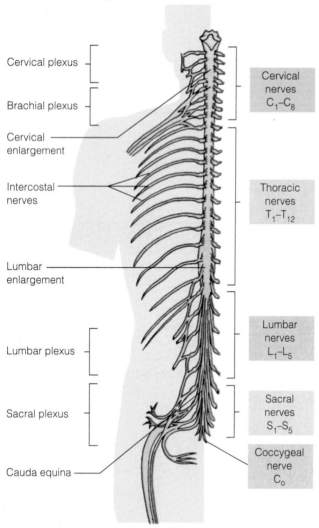

Cervical plexus

Brachial plexus

Cervical enlargement

Intercostal nerves

Lumbar enlargement

Lumbar plexus

Sacral plexus

Cauda equina

Cervical nerves C_1–C_8

Thoracic nerves T_1–T_{12}

Lumbar nerves L_1–L_5

Sacral nerves S_1–S_5

Coccygeal nerve C_o

FIGURE 13.5
Distribution of spinal nerves, posterior view. Note that the spinal nerves are named according to their points of issue.

nerves leave the vertebral canal *superior to* the vertebrae for which they are named. C_8, on the other hand, emerges *inferior to* the seventh cervical vertebra (between C_7 and T_1). Below the cervical level, each spinal nerve leaves the vertebral column *inferior to* the same-numbered vertebra.

Distribution of Spinal Nerves

As mentioned in Chapter 12, each spinal nerve is connected to the spinal cord and formed by two roots, the **dorsal** and **ventral roots.** Each root actually consists of a series of *rootlets* that attach along the whole length of the corresponding spinal cord segment (Figure 13.6). The *ventral roots* contain *motor* (efferent) fibers arising from anterior horn motor neurons that extend to and innervate the skeletal muscles. (The autonomic nervous system efferents also contained in the ventral roots are described in Chapter 14.) *Dorsal roots* contain *sensory* (afferent) fibers, arising from sensory neurons in the dorsal root ganglia, that conduct impulses from peripherally located receptors to the spinal cord.

The spinal roots pass laterally from the cord and unite just distal to the dorsal root ganglion to form a spinal nerve before emerging from the vertebral column via their respective intervertebral foramina. The motor and sensory fibers mingle together in the spinal nerve, so the spinal nerve proper contains both efferent and afferent fibers. The length of the spinal roots increases progressively from the superior to the inferior aspect of the cord. In the cervical region, the roots are short and run horizontally, but the roots of the lumbar and sacral nerves extend inferiorly for some distance through the lower vertebral canal as the *cauda equina* before exiting the vertebral column (see Figure 13.5).

A spinal nerve is quite short (only 1–2 cm)

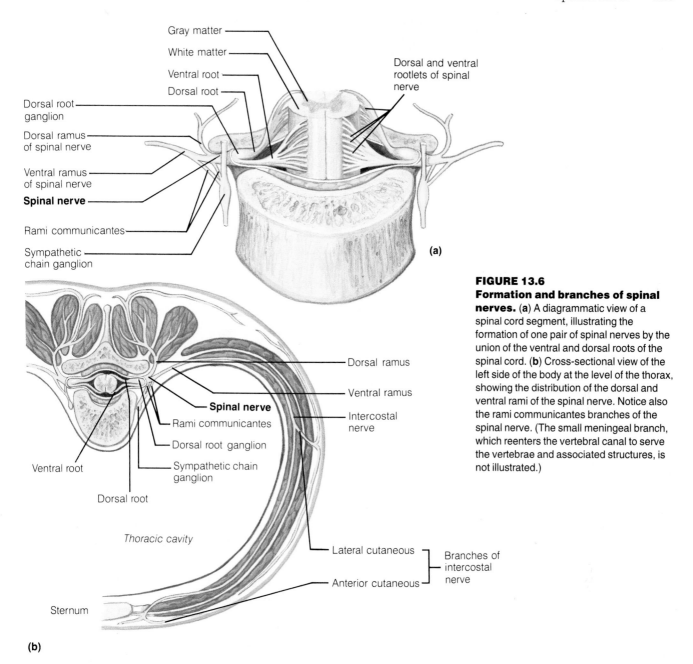

Gray matter

White matter

Ventral root

Dorsal root

Dorsal and ventral rootlets of spinal nerve

Dorsal root ganglion

Dorsal ramus of spinal nerve

Ventral ramus of spinal nerve

Spinal nerve

Rami communicantes

Sympathetic chain ganglion

(a)

Dorsal ramus

Ventral ramus

Spinal nerve

Intercostal nerve

Rami communicantes

Dorsal root ganglion

Ventral root

Sympathetic chain ganglion

Dorsal root

Thoracic cavity

Lateral cutaneous

Branches of intercostal nerve

Anterior cutaneous

Sternum

(b)

FIGURE 13.6
Formation and branches of spinal nerves. (a) A diagrammatic view of a spinal cord segment, illustrating the formation of one pair of spinal nerves by the union of the ventral and dorsal roots of the spinal cord. (b) Cross-sectional view of the left side of the body at the level of the thorax, showing the distribution of the dorsal and ventral rami of the spinal nerve. Notice also the rami communicantes branches of the spinal nerve. (The small meningeal branch, which reenters the vertebral canal to serve the vertebrae and associated structures, is not illustrated.)

because almost immediately after emerging from its foramen, it divides into a large **ventral ramus,** a smaller **dorsal ramus,** and a tiny **meningeal** (mĕ-nin′je-al) **branch** that reenters the vertebral canal to innervate the meninges and blood vessels within. Each ramus, like the spinal nerve itself, is mixed. Finally, joined to the base of ventral rami of spinal nerves in the thoracic region, there are the **rami communicantes.** These rami, which contain autonomic (visceral) nerve fibers, are considered in detail in Chapter 14.

The rest of this section focuses on the spinal nerve rami and their main branches, which supply the entire somatic region of the body (voluntary muscles and skin) from the neck down. The dorsal rami supply the posterior body trunk. The thicker ventral rami supply the rest of the body trunk and the limbs. However, before getting into rami distribution, let's review the difference between roots and rami: roots lie medial to and form the spinal nerves, and each root is strictly sensory *or* motor in function. Rami lie distal to and are lateral branches of the spinal nerves and, like spinal nerves, carry both sensory and motor fibers.

Innervation of the Back

The innervation of the posterior body trunk by the dorsal rami follows a simple, segmental pattern. Via its several branches (Figure 13.6), each dorsal ramus innervates the narrow strip of muscle (and skin) in line with its emergence point from the spinal cord.

Table 13.3 Branches of the Cervical Plexus (See Figure 13.7)

Nerves	Spinal roots (ventral rami)	Structures served
Cutaneous branches (superficial)		
Lesser occipital	C_2 (C_3)	Skin on posterolateral aspect of neck
Greater auricular	C_2, C_3	Skin of ear, skin over parotid gland
Transverse cutaneous	C_2, C_3	Skin on anterior and lateral aspect of neck
Supraclavicular (anterior, middle, and posterior)	C_3, C_4	Skin of shoulder and anterior aspect of chest
Motor branches (deep)		
Ansa cervicalis (superior and inferior roots)	C_1–C_3	Infrahyoid muscles of neck (omohyoid, sternohyoid, and sternothyroid)
Segmental and other muscular branches	C_1–C_5	Deep muscles of neck (geniohyoid and thyrohyoid) and portions of scalenes, levator scapulae, trapezius, and sternocleidomastoid muscles
Phrenic	C_3–C_5	Diaphragm (sole motor nerve supply)

Innervation of the Anterolateral Thorax and Abdominal Wall

The ventral rami of T_1–T_{12} mostly course anteriorly, deep to each rib, as the **intercostal nerves.** The exceptions are the tiny T_1 (most fibers enter the brachial plexus) and T_{12}, which lies inferior to the twelfth rib, making it a **subcostal nerve.** The intercostal nerves supply the intercostal muscles lying between the ribs, the muscle and skin of the anterolateral thorax, and most of the abdominal wall.

The ventral rami are arranged in a simple segmental pattern corresponding to that of the dorsal rami only in the thorax. The ventral rami of nearly all other spinal nerves form networks of nerves called *plexuses,* as described next.

Plexuses Serving the Neck and Limbs

A feature of all spinal nerves except T_2–T_{12} is that their ventral rami branch and join one another lateral to the vertebral column, forming complicated nerve **plexuses** (see Figure 13.5). Such interlacing nerve networks occur in the cervical, brachial, lumbar, and sacral regions and primarily serve the limbs. Only ventral (not dorsal) rami form plexuses. Within the plexuses, fibers of the ventral rami crisscross each other and become redistributed so that (1) each resulting branch of the plexus contains fibers from several different spinal nerves and (2) fibers from each spinal nerve are carried to the body periphery via several different routes or branches. Thus, each muscle in a limb receives its nerve supply from more than one spinal nerve. An advantage of this fiber regrouping is that damage to one spinal segment or root cannot completely paralyze any limb muscle.

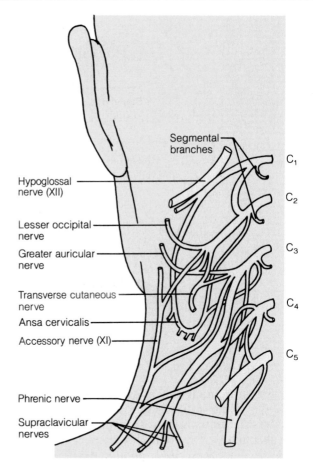

FIGURE 13.7
The cervical plexus. The nerves colored gray connect to the plexus but do not belong to it. (See Table 13.3.)

Cervical Plexus and the Neck

The **cervical plexus** is buried deep in the neck under the sternocleidomastoid muscle. This plexus is formed by the ventral rami of the upper four cervical nerves (Figure 13.7). The branches of the cervical

Table 13.4 Branches of the Brachial Plexus (See Figure 13.8)

Nerves	Cord and spinal roots (ventral rami)	Structures served
Musculocutaneous	Lateral cord (C_5–C_7)	Muscular branches: flexor muscles in anterior arm (biceps brachii, brachialis, coracobrachialis) Cutaneous branches: skin on anterolateral forearm (extremely variable)
Median	By two branches, one from medial cord (C_8, T_1) and one from the lateral cord (C_5–C_7)	Muscular branches to flexor group of anterior forearm (palmaris longus, flexor carpi radialis, flexor digitorum superficialis, flexor pollicis longus, lateral half of flexor digitorum profundus, and pronator muscles); intrinsic muscles of lateral palm and first two fingers Cutaneous branches: skin of lateral two-thirds of hand, palm side and dorsum of fingers 2 and 3
Ulnar	Medial cord (C_8 and T_1)	Muscular branches: flexor muscles in anterior forearm (flexor carpi ulnaris and medial half of flexor digitorum profundus); most intrinsic muscles of hand Cutaneous branches: skin of medial third of hand, both anterior and posterior aspects
Radial	Posterior cord (C_5–C_8, T_1)	Muscular branches: posterior muscles of arm, forearm, and hand (triceps brachii, anconeus, supinator, brachioradialis, extensors carpi radialis longus and brevis, extensor carpi ulnaris, and several muscles that extend the fingers) Cutaneous branches: skin of posterolateral surface of entire limb (except dorsum of fingers 2 and 3)
Axillary	Posterior cord (C_5, C_6)	Muscular branches: deltoid and teres minor muscles Cutaneous branches: some skin of shoulder region
Dorsal scapular	Branches of C_5 rami	Rhomboid muscles and levator scapulae
Long thoracic	Branches of C_5–C_7 rami	Serratus anterior muscle
Subscapular	Posterior cord; branches of C_5 and C_6 rami	Teres major and subscapular muscles
Suprascapular	Upper trunk (C_5, C_6)	Shoulder joint; supraspinatus and infraspinatus muscles
Pectoral (lateral and medial)	Branches of lateral and medial cords (C_5–T_1)	Pectoralis major and minor muscles

plexus are summarized in Table 13.3. Most of its branches are **cutaneous nerves** (nerves that supply only the skin) that transmit sensory impulses from the skin of the neck, the ear area, and the shoulder. Other branches innervate muscles of the anterior neck.

The single most important nerve from this plexus is the **phrenic** (fren′ik) **nerve** (which receives its major input from C_3 and C_4). The phrenic nerve courses inferiorly through the thorax and supplies both motor and sensory fibers to the diaphragm (*phren* = diaphragm). The diaphragm is the chief muscle causing breathing movements (see Chapter 23).

Irritation of the phrenic nerve causes spasms of the diaphragm, or hiccups. If both phrenic nerves are severed, or if the C_3–C_5 region of the spinal cord is crushed or destroyed, the diaphragm is paralyzed and respiratory arrest occurs. Victims are kept alive by mechanical respirators that force air into their lungs and do their breathing for them. •

Brachial Plexus and the Upper Limb

The large important **brachial plexus** is situated partly in the neck and partly in the axilla and provides virtually all the nerves that innervate the upper limb (Table 13.4). It can be palpated (felt) in a living person just superior to the clavicle at the lateral border of the sternocleidomastoid muscle.

This plexus is formed by intermixing of the ventral rami of the inferior four cervical nerves (C_5–C_8) and most of the T_1 ramus. Additionally, it often receives fibers from C_4 or T_2 or both.

The brachial plexus is very complex (some consider it to be the anatomy student's nightmare). Perhaps the simplest approach is to master the terms used for its four major groups of branches: From medial to lateral, these are the (1) ventral rami, misleadingly called *roots,* which form (2) *trunks,* which form (3) *divisions,* which in turn form (4) *cords.* These elements are shown in Figure 13.8a and b. You

FIGURE 13.8

The brachial plexus. (a) Roots, trunks, divisions, and cords of the brachial plexus. (b) Flowchart showing the consecutive branches formed in the brachial plexus from the spinal roots (ventral rami) to the major nerves formed from the cords. (c) Distribution of the major peripheral nerves of the upper limb. (See Table 13.4.)

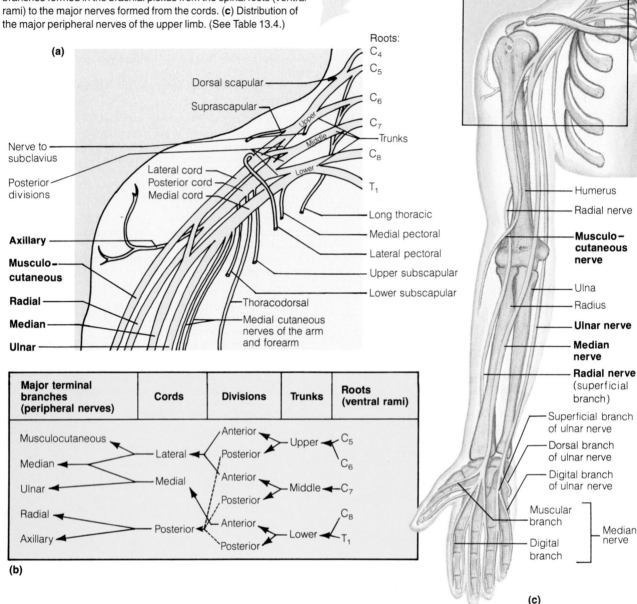

might want to use the saying "**R**eally **t**ired? **D**rink **c**offee" to help you remember this sequence of brachial plexus branching.

The five **roots** (rami C_5–T_1) of the brachial plexus lie deep to the sternocleidomastoid muscle. At the lateral border of that muscle, these roots unite to form **upper, middle,** and **lower trunks,** each of which almost immediately divides into an **anterior** and a **posterior division.** These divisions generally indicate which fibers ultimately serve the front or back of the limb. The divisions pass deep to the clavicle and enter the axilla, where they give rise to three large fiber bundles called the **lateral, medial,** and **posterior cords.** All along the plexus, small nerves branch off. These supply the muscles and skin of the shoulder and superior thorax.

Injuries to the brachial plexus are common; when severe, they cause weakness or paralysis of the entire upper limb. Such injuries occur when the upper limb is pulled hard and the plexus is stretched (as when a football tackler yanks the arm of the halfback), and when the humerus is forced inferiorly (crushing the plexus) by a blow to the top of the shoulder, (as when a cyclist is pitched headfirst off his motorcycle and grinds his shoulder into the pavement). •

The brachial plexus ends within the axilla, where its three cords wind along the axillary artery and then issue the main nerves of the upper limb. Five of these nerves are especially important: the axillary, musculocutaneous, median, ulnar, and radial nerves. These nerves are illustrated in Figure 13.8c. Their distribution and targets are described briefly below, and in more detail in Table 13.4.

The **axillary nerve** branches off the posterior cord. It runs posterior to the neck of the humerus and innervates the deltoid and teres minor muscles and the skin and joint capsule of the shoulder.

The **musculocutaneous nerve,** the major end branch of the lateral cord, courses inferiorly within the anterior arm, supplying motor fibers to the arm muscles that flex the forearm. Beyond the elbow it provides for cutaneous sensation of the lateral forearm.

The **median nerve** descends through the arm without branching. In the anterior forearm, it gives off branches to the skin and to most of the flexor muscles. On reaching the hand, it innervates five intrinsic muscles of the lateral palm. The median nerve activates muscles that pronate the forearm, flex the wrist and fingers, and oppose the thumb.

Median nerve injury makes it difficult to use the pincer grasp (oppose the thumb and index finger) and thus to pick up small objects. Because this nerve runs down the midline of the forearm and wrist, it is a frequent "casualty" of wrist-slashing suicide attempts. •

The **ulnar nerve** descends along the medial aspect of the arm toward the elbow, swings behind the medial epicondyle, and then follows the ulna along the medial forearm. There it supplies the flexor carpi ulnaris and part of the flexor digitorum profundus (the flexors not supplied by the median nerve). It continues into the hand, where it innervates most intrinsic hand muscles and the skin of the medial aspect of the hand. The ulnar nerve produces wrist and finger flexion and adduction and abduction of the medial fingers (with the median nerve).

Where it takes a superficial course, the ulnar nerve is very vulnerable to injury. Striking the "funny bone"—the spot where the ulnar nerve rests against the medial epicondyle or its location at the wrist—causes tingling of the little finger. Severe or chronic damage (caused by perpetually leaning on one's elbows, for example) can lead to sensory loss, paralysis, and atrophy of the muscles served by the ulnar nerve. Affected individuals cannot spread (abduct) their fingers and have trouble making a fist and gripping objects. Because the little and ring fingers become hyperextended at the knuckles and slightly flexed at the distal interphalangeal joints, the hand contorts into a *clawhand.* •

The **radial nerve,** the largest branch of the brachial plexus, is a continuation of the posterior cord. This nerve wraps around the humerus (in the radial groove), runs anteriorly around the lateral epicondyle at the elbow, where it divides into a superficial branch that follows the lateral edge of the radius to the hand and a deep branch (not illustrated) that runs posteriorly. It supplies the posterior skin of the limb along its entire course. Its motor branches innervate essentially all the extensor muscles of the upper limb. The radial nerve produces elbow extension, supination of the forearm, extension of the wrist and fingers, and abduction of the thumb.

Trauma to the radial nerve results in *wristdrop,* an inability to extend the hand at the wrist. Many fractures of the humerus follow the radial groove, causing radial nerve damage. Improper use of a crutch or "Saturday night paralysis," in which an intoxicated person falls asleep with an arm draped over a chair or sofa edge, cause radial nerve compression and ischemia. •

Lumbosacral Plexus and the Lower Limb

The sacral and lumbar plexuses overlap substantially, and since many fibers of the lumbar plexus contribute to the sacral plexus via the **lumbosacral trunk,** the two plexuses are often referred to as the **lumbosacral plexus.** Although the lumbosacral plexus mainly serves the lower limb, it also sends some branches to the abdomen, pelvis, and buttock (as described below).

Lumbar Plexus. The **lumbar plexus** arises from the first four lumbar spinal nerves and lies within the psoas major muscle (Figure 13.9). Its proximal branches innervate parts of the abdominal wall muscles and the iliopsoas, but the major branches of this plexus descend to innervate the anterior and medial thigh. The **femoral nerve,** the largest nerve of the lumbar plexus, runs deep to the inguinal ligament to enter the thigh and then divides into a number of large branches. The motor branches innervate the anterior thigh muscles, which are the principal thigh flexors and knee extensors. The cutaneous branches serve the skin of the anterior thigh and the medial surface of the leg from the knee to the foot. The **obturator** (ob″tu-ra′tor) **nerve** enters the medial thigh via the obturator foramen and innervates the adductor muscles. These and other smaller branches of the lumbar plexus are summarized in Table 13.5.

Compression of the spinal roots of the lumbar plexus, as by a herniated disc, results in major gait problems because the femoral nerve serves the prime movers of both hip flexion and knee extension. Other symptoms are anesthesia of the anterior thigh, and pain in the medial thigh if the obturator nerve is impaired. •

Sacral Plexus. The **sacral plexus** arises from spinal nerves L_4–S_4 and lies immediately caudal to the lumbar plexus (Figure 13.10). The sacral plexus has about a dozen named branches. Around half of these serve the buttock and lower limb; the others innervate pelvic structures and the perineum. The most important branches are described here. Table 13.6 summarizes all but the smallest branches.

The major branch of the sacral plexus is the **sciatic** (si-at′ik) **nerve,** the thickest and longest nerve in the body. Two nerves (the tibial and common peroneal) wrapped in a common sheath, the sciatic nerve leave the pelvis via the greater sciatic notch. It courses deep to the gluteus maximus muscle and enters the posterior thigh just medial to the hip joint (*sciatic* = of the hip). There it gives off motor branches to the hamstring muscles (all thigh extensors and knee flexors) and to part of the adductor magnus. Immediately above the knee, its two divisions diverge.

FIGURE 13.9
The lumbar plexus. (a) Spinal roots (anterior rami) and major branches of the lumbar plexus. (b) Distribution of the major peripheral nerves of the lumbar plexus in the lower limb (anterior view). (See Table 13.5.)

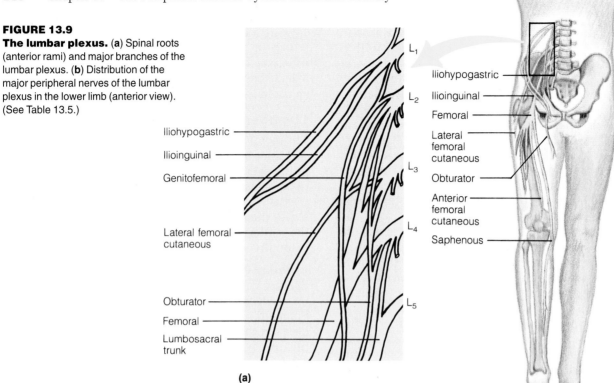

(a)

(b)

Table 13.5 Branches of the Lumbar Plexus (See Figure 13.9)		
Nerves	**Spinal roots (ventral rami)**	**Structures served**
Femoral	L_2–L_4	Skin of anterior and medial thigh via *anterior femoral cutaneous* branch; skin of medial leg and foot, hip; and knee joints via *saphenous* branch; motor to anterior muscles (quadriceps and sartorius) of thigh; pectineus, iliacus
Obturator	L_2–L_4	Motor to adductor magnus (part), longus and brevis muscles, gracilis muscle of medial thigh, obturator externus; sensory for skin of medial thigh and for hip and knee joints
Lateral femoral cutaneous	L_2, L_3	Skin of lateral thigh; some sensory branches to peritoneum
Iliohypogastric	L_1	Skin of lower abdomen, lower back, and hip; muscles of anterolateral abdominal wall (obliques and transversus) and pubic region
Ilioinguinal	L_1	Skin of external genitalia and proximal medial aspect of the thigh; inferior abdominal muscles
Genitofemoral	L_1, L_2	Skin of scrotum in males, of labia majora in females, and of anterior thigh inferior to middle portion of inguinal region; cremaster muscle in males

The **tibial nerve** courses through the popliteal fossa (the region just posterior to the knee joint) and supplies the posterior compartment muscles and the skin of the posterior calf and also the sole of the foot. Important branches of the tibial nerve are the **sural,** which serves the skin of the posterolateral leg, and the **plantar nerves,** which serve most of the foot. The **common peroneal nerve** descends from its point of origin, wraps around the head of the fibula (*perone* = fibula), and then divides into superficial and deep branches. These branches innervate the knee joint,

the skin of the lateral calf and dorsum of the foot, and the muscles of the anterolateral leg (the extensors that dorsiflex the foot).

The next largest branches of the sacral plexus are the **superior** and **inferior gluteal nerves.** Together, they innervate the buttock (gluteal) and tensor fasciae latae muscles. The **pudendal** (pu-den′dal; "shameful") **nerve** innervates the muscles and skin of the perineum, mediates the act of erection, and is involved in voluntary control of urination (see Table 10.7, p. 310). Other branches of the sacral plexus sup-

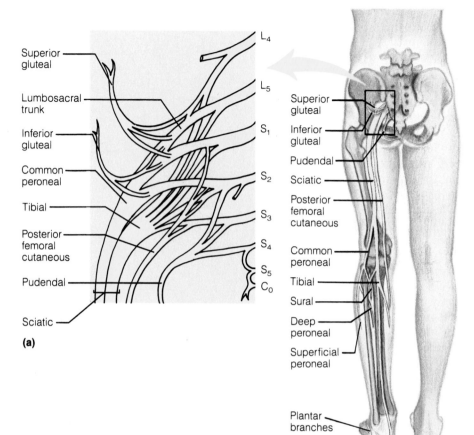

(a)

(b)

FIGURE 13.10
The sacral plexus. (a) The spinal roots (anterior rami) and major branches of the sacral plexus. **(b)** Distribution of the major peripheral nerves of the sacral plexus in the lower limb (posterior view). (See Table 13.6.)

Table 13.6 Branches of the Sacral Plexus (See Figure 13.10)		
Nerves	**Spinal roots (ventral rami)**	**Structures served**
Sciatic nerve	L_4, L_5, S_1–S_3	Composed of two nerves (tibial and common peroneal) in a common sheath that diverge just proximal to the knee
• Tibial (including sural branch and medial and lateral plantar branches)	L_4–S_3	Cutaneous branches: to skin of posterior surface of leg and sole of foot Motor branches: to muscles of back of thigh, leg, and foot (hamstrings [except short head of biceps femoris], posterior part of adductor magnus, triceps surae, tibialis posterior, popliteus, flexor digitorum longus, flexor hallucis longus, and intrinsic muscles of foot)
• Common peroneal (superficial and deep branches)	L_4–S_2	Cutaneous branches: to skin of anterior surface of leg and dorsum of foot Motor branches: to short head of biceps femoris of thigh, peroneal muscles of lateral compartment of leg, tibialis anterior, and extensor muscles of toes (extensor hallucis longus, extensors digitorum longus and brevis)
Superior gluteal	L_4, L_5, S_1	Motor branches: to gluteus medius and minimus and tensor fasciae latae
Inferior gluteal	L_5–S_2	Motor branches: to gluteus maximus
Posterior femoral cutaneous	S_1–S_3	Skin of buttock, posterior thigh, and popliteal region; length variable; may also innervate part of skin of calf and heel
Pudendal	S_2–S_4	Supplies most of skin and muscles of perineum (region encompassing external genitalia and anus and including clitoris, labia, and vaginal mucosa in females, and scrotum and penis in males); external anal sphincter

ply the thigh rotators and muscles of the pelvic floor.

Injury to the proximal sciatic nerve, as might follow a fall, a herniated disc, or improper administration of an injection into the buttock, results in a number of lower limb impairments, depending on the precise nerve roots injured. *Sciatica* (si-at′ĭ-kah), characterized by stabbing pain radiating over the course of the sciatic nerve, is common. When the sciatic nerve is completely transected, the leg becomes nearly useless. The leg cannot be flexed, and all foot and ankle movements are lost. The foot drops into plantar flexion (dangles), a condition called *footdrop.* Recovery from sciatic nerve injury is usually slow and incomplete.

If the lesion occurs below the knee, the thigh muscles are spared. When the tibial nerve is injured, the paralyzed calf muscles cannot plantar flex the foot and a shuffling gait develops. The common peroneal nerve is susceptible to injury largely because of its superficial location at the head and neck of the fibula. Even a tight leg cast, or remaining too long in a side-lying position on a firm mattress, can compress this nerve and cause footdrop. •

Innervation of Joints

The easiest way to remember which nerves serve each synovial joint is to use **Hilton's law,** which says that *any nerve serving a muscle producing movement at a joint also innervates the joint itself and the skin over the joint.* Hence, once you learn which nerves serve the various major muscles and muscle groups, no *new* learning is necessary. For example, the knee is crossed by the quadriceps, gracilis, and hamstring muscles. The nerves to these muscles are the femoral nerve anteriorly and branches of the sciatic and obturator nerves posteriorly. Consequently, these nerves innervate the knee joint as well.

Innervation of Skin: Dermatomes

The area of skin innervated by the cutaneous branches of a single spinal nerve is called a **dermatome** (der′mah-tōm; "skin segment"). All spinal nerves except C_1 participate in dermatomes. Adjacent dermatomes on the body trunk are fairly uniform in width, almost horizontal, and in direct line with their spinal nerves (Figure 13.11). The arrangement of the dermatomes in the limbs is less obvious. The skin of the upper limbs is supplied by the ventral rami of C_5–T_1 (or T_2). The ventral rami of the lumbar nerves supply most of the anterior surfaces of the thighs and legs, while the ventral rami of sacral nerves serve most of the posterior surfaces of the lower limbs.

Dermatome regions are not as cleanly separate as a typical dermatome map indicates. The dermatome regions of the trunk overlap considerably (about 50%); thus, destruction of a single spinal nerve will not result in complete numbness anywhere. In the limbs, the overlap is less complete and some skin regions are innervated by just one spinal nerve.

FIGURE 13.11
Dermatomes (skin segments) of the body are related to the sensory innervation regions of the spinal nerves. All spinal nerves but C_1 participate in the innervation of the dermatomes.

REFLEX ACTIVITY

Many of the body's control systems belong to the general category of stimulus-response sequences known as reflexes. In the most restricted definition of the term, a **reflex** is a rapid, predictable motor response to a stimulus; it is unlearned, unpremeditated, and involuntary. Such basic reflexes may be considered to be built into our neural anatomy.

In many cases, we are aware of the final response of the reflex activity. If you splash a pot of boiling water on your arm, you are likely to drop the pot instantly and involuntarily before you have any sensation of pain. This response is triggered by a spinal reflex without any help from the brain. But the pain signals picked up by the interneurons of the spinal cord are quickly transmitted to the brain, so that within the next few seconds you do become aware of pain, and you also know what happened to cause it.

? *Which neuron in the reflex arc shown is the efferent part of the pathway?*

FIGURE 13.12
The basic components of all human reflex arcs—receptor, sensory neuron, integration center (one or more synapses in the CNS), motor neuron, and effector. (The reflex arc illustrated is polysynaptic.)

In other cases, reflex activities go on without any awareness on our part. This is typical of many reflexively controlled visceral activities, which are regulated by the subconscious lower regions of the central nervous system, specifically, the basal nuclei, brain stem, and spinal cord.

In addition to these basic, inborn types of reflexes, there are many *learned,* or *acquired, reflex responses* that result from practice or repetition. Take, for instance, the complex sequence of reactions that occurs when an experienced driver drives a car. The process is largely automatic, but only because substantial time and conscious effort were expended to acquire the driving skill. However, most reflex actions are subject to modification by learning and conscious effort. If a three-year-old child was standing by your side when you scalded your arm, you most likely would set the pot down (rather than just letting go) because of your conscious recognition of the danger to the child. Thus, there is no clear-cut distinction between basic and learned reflexes.

Components of a Reflex Arc

As you learned in Chapter 11, reflexes occur over highly specific neural paths called **reflex arcs.** However, in order to understand the body reflexes described in this chapter, we have to examine reflex arcs in more detail. Basically, all reflex arcs have five essential components (Figure 13.12):

1. The **receptor,** which is the site of the stimulus action.

2. The **sensory neuron,** which transmits the afferent impulses to the CNS.

3. The **integration center,** which in the simplest reflex arcs may be a single synapse between the sensory neuron and a motor neuron (**monosynaptic reflex**). In more complex reflexes, it involves multiple synapses with chains of interneurons (**polysynaptic reflex**). The integration center is always within the CNS, exemplified by the spinal cord in Figure 13.12.

4. The **motor neuron,** which conducts efferent impulses from the integration center to an effector organ.

5. The **effector,** the muscle fiber or gland cell that responds to the efferent impulses in a characteristic way (by contracting or secreting).

Reflexes are classified functionally as **somatic reflexes** if they activate skeletal muscle, and as **autonomic (visceral) reflexes** when visceral effectors (smooth or cardiac muscle and/or glands) are activated. The next section describes some common types of somatic reflexes mediated by the spinal cord. (Autonomic reflexes are considered in later chapters with the visceral processes they help to regulate.)

Spinal Reflexes

Somatic reflexes mediated by the spinal cord are called **spinal reflexes.** Many spinal reflexes occur without the involvement of higher brain centers. These reflexes work equally well in decerebrate animals (those in which the brain has been destroyed) as long as the spinal cord is functional. Other spinal reflexes require the activity of the brain for their successful completion. Additionally, the brain is "advised" of most types of spinal cord reflex activity and can then facilitate or inhibit them. Moreover, continuous facilitating signals from the brain are required for normal cord activity because, as noted in Chapter 12, if the spinal cord is suddenly transected, *spinal shock* occurs (all functions controlled by the cord are immediately depressed).

Testing of somatic reflexes is important clinically to assess the condition of the nervous system. Exaggerated, distorted, or absent reflexes indicate degeneration or pathology of specific regions of the nervous system, often before other signs are apparent.

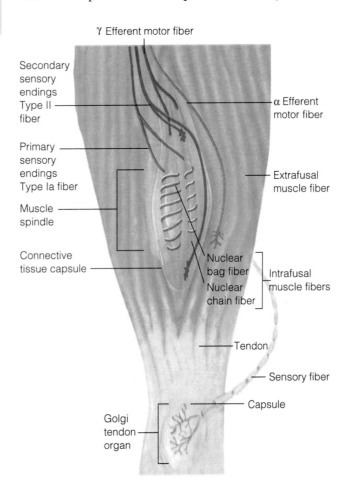

FIGURE 13.13
Anatomy of the muscle spindle and Golgi tendon organ.
Notice the afferent fibers from and efferent fibers to the muscle spindle.

(a) Action potential frequency increases during stretch

(b) Action potential frequency declines during contraction

FIGURE 13.14
Operation of the muscle spindle. (a) Stretching the muscle activates the muscle spindle and causes an increased rate of action potential generation in the associated sensory (Ia) fiber. (b) Contraction of the muscle reduces tension on the muscle spindle and lowers the rate of action potential generation. Arrows indicate the direction of force on the muscle spindles.

Stretch and Deep Tendon Reflexes

If skeletal muscles are to perform normally, the brain must be continually informed of the current state of the muscles, and the muscles must exhibit healthy *tone* (resistance to active or passive stretch at rest). The first requirement depends on transmission of information from *muscle spindles* and *Golgi tendon organs* (proprioceptors located in the skeletal muscles and their associated tendons) to the cerebellum and cerebral cortex. Normal muscle tone, the second requirement, depends on **stretch reflexes** initiated by the muscle spindles, which monitor changes in muscle length. These processes are important to normal skeletal muscle function, posture, and locomotion.

Functional Anatomy of Muscle Spindles.

Before we examine the functional role of muscle spindles, we need to comment briefly on their unique nature. Each muscle spindle consists of 3 to 10 **intrafusal muscle fibers** (modified skeletal muscle fibers less than one-quarter of the size of the effector fibers of the muscle) enclosed in a connective tissue capsule (see Figure 13.13). There are two varieties of these

intrafusal fibers: The larger *nuclear bag fibers* have numerous nuclei clustered in their midregions, whereas the nuclei in the slender *nuclear chain fibers* are distributed evenly along their lengths. Regardless of the fiber type, the central regions of the intrafusal fibers, which lack myofilaments and are noncontractile, serve as the receptive surfaces of the spindle. These regions are wrapped by two types of afferent endings that send sensory inputs to the CNS. The **primary sensory endings** of large **type Ia fibers,** which are stimulated by both the rate and amount of stretch, innervate the center of the spindle. The **secondary sensory endings** of small **type II fibers** are associated with the ends of the spindle and are stimulated only by degree of stretch. The contractile regions of the intrafusal muscle fibers are innervated by **gamma (γ) efferent fibers** that arise from small motor neurons in the ventral horn of the spinal cord. These motor fibers, which maintain the sensitivity of the spindle (as described shortly), are distinct from the **alpha (α) efferent fibers** that stimulate **extrafusal muscle fibers,** the large voluntary muscle fibers of the skeletal muscle, to contract (Figure 13.14).

The Stretch Reflex. Stretching, and consequently exciting, the muscle spindle occurs in one of two ways: (1) by applying an external force that lengthens the entire muscle, such as occurs when carrying a heavy weight or when antagonistic muscles contract *(external stretch),* or (2) by activating the gamma motor neurons that stimulate contraction of the distal ends of the intrafusal fibers, thus stretching the midportion of the spindle *(internal stretch).* Whatever the stimulus, when the spindles are activated their associated sensory neurons transmit impulses at a higher frequency to the spinal cord (Figure 13.14a). There the sensory neurons synapse directly (monosynaptically) with the **alpha (α) motor neurons,** which in turn rapidly excite the extrafusal muscle fibers of the stretched muscle (Figure 13.15a). The reflex muscle contraction that follows resists further stretching

of the muscle. Branches of the afferent fibers also synapse with interneurons that inhibit motor neurons controlling the antagonistic muscles; the resulting inhibition is called **reciprocal inhibition.** Consequently, the stretch stimulus causes the antagonists to relax so that they cannot resist the shortening of the "stretched" muscle caused by the main reflex arc.

While this spinal reflex is occurring, impulses providing information on muscle length and the velocity of muscle shortening are also being relayed mainly via the dorsal white columns to higher brain centers. In this way, muscle tone is maintained and adjusted reflexively to the requirements of posture and movement. If either the afferent or efferent fibers are cut, the muscle immediately loses its tone and becomes flaccid. The stretch reflex is most important in the large extensor muscles which sustain upright

FIGURE 13.15
Events of the stretch reflex.
(a) Events of the stretch reflex by which muscle stretch is damped. The events are shown in circular fashion.
(*1*) Stretching the muscle activates a muscle spindle. (*2*) Impulses transmitted by afferent fibers from muscle spindle to alpha (α) motor neurons in the spinal cord cause the stretched muscle to contract. (*3*) Impulses transmitted by afferent fibers from muscle spindle to interneurons in the spinal cord result in reciprocal inhibition of the antagonist muscle. **(b)** The patellar reflex. Tapping the patellar tendon excites muscle spindles within the quadriceps muscle. Afferent impulses travel to the spinal cord, where synapses occur with motor neurons and interneurons. The motor neurons send activating impulses to the same muscle, resulting in contraction of the quadriceps muscle, which causes extension of the knee and a forward movement of the foot, counteracting the initial stretch. The interneurons make inhibitory synapses with anterior horn neurons that serve the antagonistic muscle group (hamstrings), preventing it from resisting the contraction.

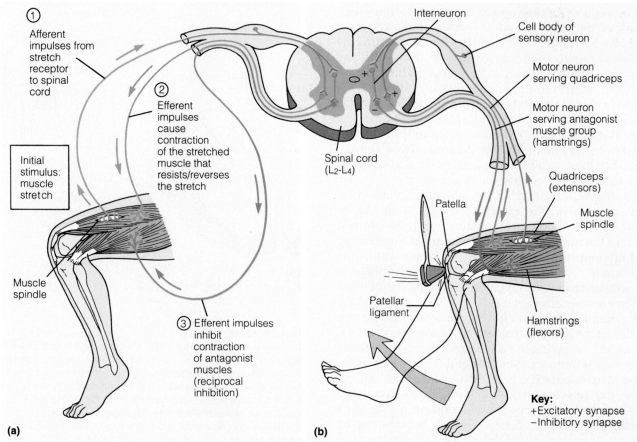

(a)

① Afferent impulses from stretch receptor to spinal cord

Initial stimulus: muscle stretch

② Efferent impulses cause contraction of the stretched muscle that resists/reverses the stretch

Muscle spindle

③ Efferent impulses inhibit contraction of antagonist muscles (reciprocal inhibition)

(b)

Interneuron

Cell body of sensory neuron

Motor neuron serving quadriceps

Motor neuron serving antagonist muscle group (hamstrings)

Spinal cord (L₂-L₄)

Patella

Quadriceps (extensors)

Muscle spindle

Patellar ligament

Hamstrings (flexors)

Key:
+Excitatory synapse
−Inhibitory synapse

posture, such as the quadriceps, and in postural muscles of the trunk. For example, contractions of the postural muscles of the spine are almost continuously regulated by stretch reflexes initiated first on one side of the spine and then on the other.

Although the stretch reflex is essential for normal muscle tone and activity, it essentially never acts alone. It is always accompanied by the **gamma motor neuron reflex arc.** There is a good reason for this: As the muscle shortens, the spindle's rate of firing declines, which in turn reduces impulse generation by the alpha motor neurons (see Figure 13.14b). Thus, the stretch reflex alone would result in crude, jerky muscle contractions. However, this is not what is seen because contractions promoted by stretch reflexes are refined and smoothed out by gamma motor neuron reflex arcs, which regulate the response of the intrafusal muscle fibers of the muscle spindle. Descending fibers of motor pathways synapse with both α and γ motor neurons, and motor impulses are sent simultaneously to the large extrafusal fibers and to intrafusal fibers of the muscle spindles. Stimulation of the intrafusal fibers maintains the muscle spindle's tension (and sensitivity) during muscle contraction, so that the brain continues to be advised of the state of the muscle. Without such a system, information on muscle length and its rate of change would cease to flow from contracting muscles.

The motor supply to the muscle spindle also allows us to voluntarily control the stretch reflex response and the firing rate of alpha motor neurons by manipulating (stimulating or inhibiting) the γ neurons. When the γ neurons are stimulated more rapidly by impulses descending from the brain, the spindle is stretched and highly sensitive, and the force of muscle contraction is maintained or increased. When the γ motor neurons are inhibited, the muscle spindle resembles a loose rubber band and is nonresponsive, and the extrafusal muscles relax.

The ability to modify the stretch reflex is important in many situations. For example, if you want to wind up to pitch a baseball, it is essential to suppress the stretch reflex so that your muscles can produce a large degree of motion. On the other hand, when maximum force is "the ticket," the muscle should be stretched as much and as quickly as possible just before the movement so that a volley of involuntary (γ) efferent impulses reaches the muscle just as the voluntary command is given. This advantage is demonstrated by the crouch that athletes assume just before jumping or running.

The most familiar clinical example of the stretch reflex is the **patellar** (pah-tel'ar), or **knee-jerk, reflex,** elicited by striking the patellar tendon with a reflex hammer (Figure 13.15b). The sudden jolt to the tendon (1) stretches the quadriceps muscle, (2) stimulates the muscle spindles, and (3) results in contraction of the quadriceps muscle and inhibition of its antagonist, the hamstrings. Stretch reflexes can be elicited in any skeletal muscle of the body by suddenly striking its tendon or the muscle itself. All stretch reflexes are monosynaptic and **ipsilateral** (*ipsi* = same; *lateral* = side); that is, they involve a single synapse and motor activity on the same side of the body.

A positive knee jerk (or a positive result for any stretch reflex test) provides two important pieces of information. First, it provides evidence that the sensory and motor connections between that muscle and the spinal cord are intact. Second, the vigor of the motor response indicates the degree of excitability of the spinal cord. When the spinal motor neurons are highly facilitated by impulses descending from higher centers, just touching the muscle tendon will elicit a vigorous reflex response. On the other hand, if the lower motor neurons are besieged by inhibitory signals, even pounding on the tendon may fail to cause the reflex response.

Stretch reflexes tend to be hypoactive or absent in cases of peripheral nerve damage or ventral horn injury involving the tested area. They are absent in those with chronic diabetes mellitus and neurosyphilis and during coma. However, these reflexes are hyperactive when lesions of the corticospinal tract reduce the inhibitory effect of the brain on the spinal cord (as in polio and stroke patients). •

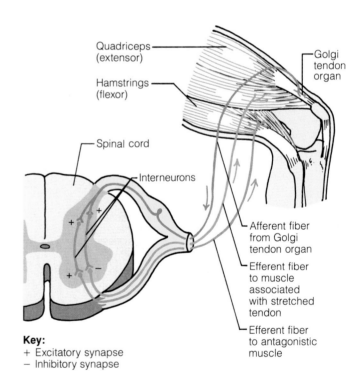

Key:
+ Excitatory synapse
− Inhibitory synapse

FIGURE 13.16

The deep tendon reflex. When the quadriceps muscle of the thigh contracts, the tension in the patellar region increases, activating Golgi tendon organs in the tendon. Afferent neurons associated with the Golgi tendon organs synapse with interneurons in the spinal cord that inhibit motor neurons serving the contracting muscle and stimulate motor neurons activating the antagonistic muscle groups (the hamstrings). As a result, the contracting muscle relaxes and lengthens as the antagonist contracts and shortens.

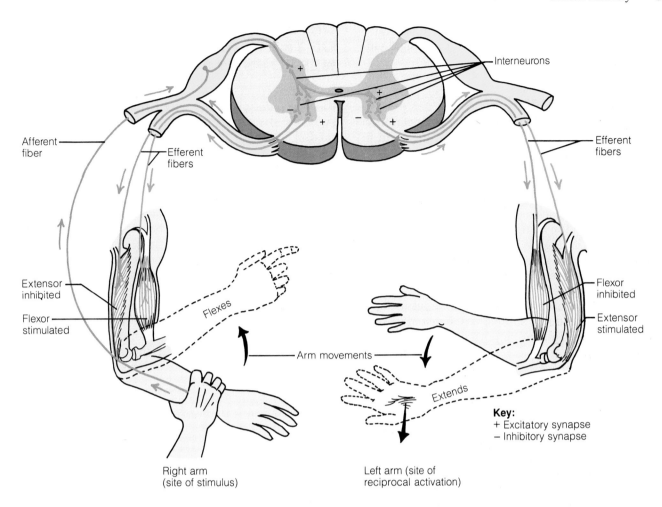

Right arm
(site of stimulus)

Left arm (site of
reciprocal activation)

Key:
+ Excitatory synapse
– Inhibitory synapse

FIGURE 13.17
The crossed extensor reflex. The crossed extensor reflex causes reflex withdrawal of the body part on the stimulated side (flexor reflex) as shown on the left side of the diagram, and extension of the muscles on the opposite side of the body (extensor reflex) as shown on the right side of the diagram. The example illustrated might occur if a stranger suddenly grabbed your arm. The flexor reflex would cause immediate withdrawal of your clutched arm, while the extensor reflex would simultaneously push the intruder away with the other arm by activating extensor muscles on the opposite side of the body.

The Deep Tendon Reflex. While the net effect of stretch reflexes is to cause muscle contraction in response to increased muscle length (stretch), the polysynaptic **deep tendon reflexes** cause exactly the opposite effect: muscle relaxation and lengthening in response to the muscle's contraction (Figure 13.16). When muscle tension increases moderately during muscle contraction or passive stretching, Golgi tendon receptors in the muscle's tendon are activated, and afferent impulses are transmitted to the spinal cord and from there to the cerebellum, where this information is used to help adjust muscle tension appropriately. Simultaneously, motor neurons in spinal cord circuits supplying the contracting muscle are inhibited and antagonist muscles are activated, a phenomenon called **reciprocal activation.** As a result, the contracting muscle relaxes as its antagonist is activated.

Golgi tendon organs help ensure smooth onset and termination of muscle contraction and are partic-ularly important in activities involving rapid switching between flexion and extension, such as running. Notice that the Golgi tendon organs are also stimulated during a clinically induced stretch reflex, such as the flexor reflex, but the brevity of the stimulus and the fact that the stretched muscle is already relaxed prevent it from being inhibited by the deep tendon reflex.

The Flexor Reflex

The **flexor,** or **withdrawal, reflex** is initiated by a painful stimulus (actual or perceived) and causes automatic withdrawal of the threatened body part from the stimulus (see Figure 13.17). The response that occurs when you prick your finger is a good example. So, too, is the trunk flexion that occurs when someone pretends to "throw a punch" at your abdomen. Flexor reflexes are ipsilateral, *polysynaptic reflexes.* Since flexor reflexes are protective reflexes important to our survival, it is not surprising that they are *prepotent.* That is, they override the spinal pathways and prevent any other reflexes from using them at the same time.

The Crossed Extensor Reflex

The **crossed extensor reflex** is a complex spinal reflex consisting of an ipsilateral withdrawal reflex and a contralateral (opposite side) extensor reflex. Incoming afferent fibers synapse with interneurons that control the flexor withdrawal response on the same side of the body and with other interneurons that control the extensor muscles on the opposite side. This reflex is quite obvious when someone unexpectedly grabs for your arm (Figure 13.17). A much more common example occurs when you step barefoot on broken glass. The ipsilateral response causes rapid lifting of the cut foot, while the contralateral response activates the extensor muscles of the opposite leg to support the weight suddenly shifted to it. Crossed extensor reflexes are particularly important in maintaining balance.

Superficial Reflexes

Superficial reflexes are elicited by gentle cutaneous stimulation, such as that produced by stroking the skin with a tongue depressor or a blunt key. The superficial reflexes are clinically important reflexes that depend both on functional upper motor pathways and on cord-level reflex arcs. The best known of these are the plantar and abdominal reflexes.

The **plantar reflex** is a complex response that specifically tests the integrity of the spinal cord from L_4 to S_2 and indirectly determines if the corticospinal tracts are functioning properly. It is elicited by drawing a blunt object downward along the lateral aspect of the plantar surface (sole) of the foot. The normal response is downward flexion (curling) of the toes. However, if the primary motor cortex or corticospinal tract is damaged, the plantar reflex is replaced by an abnormal reflex called **Babinski's sign,** in which the great toe dorsiflexes and the smaller toes fan laterally. Infants exhibit Babinski's sign until they are about a year old because their nervous systems are incompletely myelinated before that age. Despite its clinical significance, the physiological mechanism of Babinski's sign is not understood.

Stroking the skin of the lateral abdomen above, to the side, or below the umbilicus may induce a reflex contraction of the abdominal muscles in which the umbilicus moves toward the stimulated site. These reflexes, called **abdominal reflexes,** check the integrity of the spinal cord and dorsal rami from T_8 to T_{12}. The abdominal reflexes vary in intensity in different people. They are absent when corticospinal tract lesions are present.

DEVELOPMENTAL ASPECTS OF THE PERIPHERAL NERVOUS SYSTEM

As described in Chapter 9, most skeletal muscles of the body derive from paired blocks of mesoderm (somites) distributed segmentally down the posteromedial aspect of the embryonic body. The spinal nerves branch from the developing spinal cord and exit between the forming vertebrae, and each becomes associated with the adjacent muscle mass. The spinal nerves supply both sensory and motor fibers to the developing muscles and also help to direct their maturation. Cranial nerves innervate the muscles of the head in a comparable manner.

The distribution of cutaneous nerves to the skin follows a similar pattern. Most of the scalp and skin of the face is innervated by the trigeminal nerves. Spinal nerves supply cutaneous branches to specific (adjacent) dermatomes that eventually become dermal segments. Thus, the distribution and growth of the spinal nerves correlate with the segmented body plan, which is established by the fourth week of embryonic development.

Growth of the limbs and unequal growth of other body areas result in an adult pattern of dermatomes with unequal sizes and shapes and varying degrees of overlap (see Figure 13.11, p. 450). Since embryonic muscle cells migrate extensively, much of the early segmental pattern is lost. Understanding the pattern of sensory nerve distribution is critical to physicians. For example, in areas of substantial dermatome overlap, two or three spinal nerves must be blocked to perform local surgery.

Sensory receptors atrophy to some degree with age, and there is some lessening of muscle tone in the face and neck. Reflexes occur a bit more slowly during old age. However, this seems to reflect a general loss of neurons and a slowdown in central processing rather than changes in the peripheral nerve fibers. In fact, the peripheral nerves remain viable and normally functional throughout life unless subjected to traumatic injury or ischemia. The most common symptom of ischemia (deprivation of blood supply) is a tingling sensation or numbness in the affected region.

* * *

The peripheral nervous system, composed primarily of nerves, is an essential part of any functional nervous system. Without it, the central nervous system would lack its rich bank of information about events of the external and internal environments. Now that we have connected the CNS to both of these environments, we are ready to consider the autonomic nervous system, a special subdivision of the peripheral nervous system and the topic of Chapter 14.

RELATED CLINICAL TERMS

Nerve conduction studies Diagnostic tests that assess the integrity of nerves as indicated by their conduction velocities; the nerve is stimulated separately at two points, and the time required for the stimulus to reach the muscle it serves is recorded; used to assess suspected peripheral neuropathies.

Neuralgia (nu-ral′je-ah; *neuro* = nerve; *algia* = pain) Sharp spasmlike pain along the course of one or more nerves; usually caused by inflammation or injury to the nerve(s).

Neuritis (nu-ri′tis) Inflammation of a nerve; there are many forms with different effects (e.g., increased or decreased nerve sensitivity, paralysis of structure served, and pain).

Neurofibromatosis (nu″ro-fi″bro-mah-to′sis) A genetic disorder involving developmental changes in the nerves, muscles, bones, and skin. In two-thirds of patients, the only visible signs are patches of tan pigmented skin; in the rest, neurofibromas (connective tissue tumors of nerve fascicles) form. These tumors are grossly disfiguring and can destroy growing bones, causing crippling or defects of the skull; formerly inaccurately known as the Elephant Man's disease.

Paresthesia (par″es-the′ze-ah) An abnormal (burning, tingling) sensation resulting from a disorder of a sensory nerve.

Shingles A viral inflammation caused by *herpes zoster* (the chickenpox virus), which invades the dorsal roots of the spinal nerves. Indicated by blister-like skin lesions along the course of one or more dermatomes. Commonly due to reactivation of the (latent) virus acquired during childhood disease when the immune system is weakened. The reactivated virus migrates along the sensory fibers associated with the infected dorsal root ganglion, causing pain and a characteristic rash.

CHAPTER SUMMARY

Overview of the Peripheral Nervous System (pp. 426–434)

1. The peripheral nervous system consists of sensory receptors, nerves conducting impulses to and from the CNS, their associated ganglia, and motor endings.

Sensory Receptors (pp. 426–431)

2. Sensory receptors are specialized to respond to environmental changes (stimuli).

3. Sensory receptors include the simple (general) receptors for pain, touch, pressure, and temperature found in the skin, as well as those found in skeletal muscles and tendons and in the visceral organs. Complex receptors (sense organs), consisting of sensory receptors and other cells, serve the special senses (vision, hearing, equilibrium, smell, and taste).

4. Receptors are classified according to location as exteroceptors, interoceptors, and proprioceptors and according to stimulus detected as mechanoreceptors, thermoreceptors, photoreceptors, chemoreceptors, and nociceptors.

5. The general sensory receptors are classified structurally as free or encapsulated dendritic endings of sensory neurons. The encapsulated dendritic endings include Meissner's corpuscles, Pacinian corpuscles, Krause's end bulbs, Ruffini's corpuscles, muscle spindles, Golgi tendon organs, and joint kinesthetic receptors.

6. Sensory receptors transduce (convert) stimulus energy into action potentials. As the receptor membrane absorbs energy, a single type of ion channel is opened, which allows ions to move across the membrane and results in a receptor potential that resembles an EPSP. If the stimulus is of threshold strength, an action potential is generated and propagated.

7. Adaptation is the reduced responsiveness of a sensory receptor to unchanging stimulation. Adaptation does not occur in pain receptors or proprioceptors.

Nerves and Associated Ganglia (pp. 432–434)

8. A nerve is a bundle of neuron fibers in the PNS. Each fiber is enclosed by an endoneurium, fascicles of fibers are wrapped by a perineurium, and the whole nerve is bundled by the epineurium.

9. Nerves are classified according to the direction of impulse conduction of their fibers as sensory, motor, or mixed; most nerves are mixed. The efferent fibers may be somatic or autonomic.

10. Injured PNS fibers may regenerate if Schwann cells proliferate, phagocytize the debris, and form a channel to guide axon sprouts to their original contacts. Fibers in the CNS do not normally regenerate because the oligodendrocytes fail to aid the process and growth-inhibiting proteins are present in the myelin of surrounding axons.

11. Ganglia are collections of nerve cell bodies associated with nerves. Examples are the dorsal root (sensory) ganglia and autonomic (motor) ganglia.

Motor Endings (p. 434)

12. Motor endings of somatic nerve fibers (axonal terminals) help to form the synapselike neuromuscular junctions with skeletal muscle cells. Axonal terminals contain synaptic vesicles filled with acetylcholine, which (when released) signals the muscle cell to contract. An elaborate basal lamina fills the synaptic cleft.

13. Autonomic motor endings, called varicosities, are functionally similar, but structurally simpler, beaded terminals that innervate smooth muscle and glands. (Those endings serving cardiac muscle have a uniform diameter.) They do not form specialized neuromuscular junctions and generally a wider synaptic cleft separates them from their effector cells.

Cranial Nerves (pp. 434–442)

1. Twelve pairs of cranial nerves originate from the brain and issue through the skull to innervate the head and neck. Only the vagus nerves extend into the thoracic and abdominal cavities.

2. Cranial nerves are numbered from anterior to posterior in order of emergence from the brain. Their names reflect structures served and/or function.

3. The cranial nerves include:

- The olfactory nerves (I): purely sensory; concerned with the sense of smell.
- The optic nerves (II): purely sensory; transmit visual impulses from the retina to the thalamus.
- The oculomotor nerves (III): mixed nerves, primarily motor; emerge from the midbrain and serve four extrinsic eye muscles, the levator palpebrae superioris of the eyelid, and the intrinsic ciliary muscle and constrictor fibers of the iris; also carry proprioceptive impulses from the skeletal muscles served.
- The trochlear nerves (IV): mixed nerves; emerge from the dorsal midbrain and carry motor and proprioceptor impulses to and from superior oblique muscles of the eyeballs.

- The trigeminal nerves (V): mixed nerves; emerge from the lateral pons; the major sensory nerves of the face; each has three sensory divisions—ophthalmic, maxillary, and mandibular; the mandibular branch also contains motor fibers that innervate the chewing muscles.
- The abducens nerves (VI): mixed nerves; emerge from the pons and serve the motor and proprioceptive functions of the lateral rectus muscles of the eyeballs.
- The facial nerves (VII): mixed nerves; emerge from the pons; major motor nerves of the face; also carry sensory impulses from the taste buds of anterior two-thirds of the tongue.
- The vestibulocochlear nerves (VIII): purely sensory; transmit impulses from the hearing and equilibrium receptors of the inner ears.
- The glossopharyngeal nerves (IX): mixed nerves; issue from the medulla; transmit sensory impulses from the taste buds of the posterior tongue, from the pharynx, and from chemo- and pressoreceptors of the carotid bodies and sinuses; innervate the pharyngeal muscles and parotid glands.
- The vagus nerves (X): mixed nerves; arise from the medulla; almost all motor fibers are autonomic parasympathetic fibers; motor efferents to, and sensory fibers from, the pharynx, larynx, and visceral organs of the thoracic and abdominal cavities.
- The accessory nerves (XI): mixed nerves; consist of a cranial root arising from the medulla and a spinal root arising from the cervical spinal cord; cranial root supplies motor fibers to the pharynx and larynx; spinal root supplies somatic efferents to the trapezius and sternocleidomastoid muscles of the neck and carries proprioceptor afferents from the same muscles.
- The hypoglossal nerves (XII): mixed nerves; issue from the medulla; carry somatic motor efferents to, and proprioceptive fibers from, the tongue muscles.

Spinal Nerves (pp. 436, 442–450)

1. The 31 pairs of spinal nerves (all mixed nerves) are numbered successively according to the region of the spinal cord from which they issue.

Distribution of Spinal Nerves (pp. 442–443)

2. Spinal nerves are formed by the union of dorsal and ventral roots of the spinal cord and are short, confined to the intervertebral foramina.

3. Branches of each spinal nerve include dorsal and ventral rami, a meningeal branch, and rami communicantes (ANS branches).

Innervation of the Back, Anterolateral Thorax, and Abdominal Wall (pp. 443–444)

4. Dorsal rami serve the muscles and skin of the posterior body trunk. Ventral rami, except T_2–T_{12}, form plexuses that serve the limbs. T_2–T_{12} ventral rami give rise to intercostal nerves that serve the thorax wall and abdominal surface.

Plexuses Serving the Neck and Limbs (pp. 444–450)

5. The cervical plexus (C_1–C_4) innervates the muscles and skin of the neck and shoulder. Its phrenic nerve serves the diaphragm.

6. The brachial plexus serves the shoulder, some thorax muscles, and the upper limb. It arises primarily from C_5–T_1. Proximal to distal, the brachial plexus has roots, trunks, divisions, and cords. The main nerves arising from the cords are the axillary, musculocutaneous, median, radial, and ulnar nerves.

7. The lumbar plexus (L_1–L_4) provides the motor supply to the anterior and medial thigh muscles and the cutaneous supply to the anterior thigh and part of the leg. Its chief nerves are the femoral and obturator.

8. The sacral plexus (L_4–S_4) supplies the posterior muscles and skin of the lower limb. Its principal nerve is the large sciatic nerve (composed of the tibial and common peroneal nerves).

Innervation of Joints and Dermatomes (p. 450)

9. Joints are innervated by the same nerves that serve the muscles acting at the joint. All spinal nerves except C_1 innervate specific segments of the skin called dermatomes.

Reflex Activity (pp. 450–456)

Components of a Reflex Arc (p. 451)

1. A reflex is a rapid, involuntary motor response to a stimulus. The reflex arc has five elements: receptor, sensory neuron, integration center, motor neuron, and effector.

Spinal Reflexes (pp. 451–456)

2. Testing of somatic spinal reflexes provides information on the integrity of the reflex pathway and the degree of excitability of the spinal cord.

3. Somatic spinal reflexes include stretch, deep tendon, flexor, crossed extensor, and superficial reflexes.

4. A stretch reflex, initiated by stretching of muscle spindles, causes contraction of the stimulated muscle and inhibits its antagonist. It is monosynaptic and ipsilateral. Stretch reflexes maintain muscle tone, body posture, and movements.

5. Deep tendon reflexes, initiated by stimulation of Golgi tendon organs by increased muscle tension, are polysynaptic reflexes. They cause relaxation of the stimulated muscle and contraction of its antagonist.

6. Flexor reflexes are initiated by painful stimuli. They are polysynaptic, ipsilateral reflexes that are protective in nature.

7. Crossed extensor reflexes consist of an ipsilateral flexor reflex and a contralateral extensor reflex.

8. Superficial reflexes (e.g., the plantar and abdominal reflexes) are elicited by cutaneous stimulation. They require functional cord reflex arcs and corticospinal pathways.

Developmental Aspects of the Peripheral Nervous System (p. 456)

1. Each spinal nerve provides the sensory and motor supply of an adjacent muscle mass (destined to become skeletal muscles) and the cutaneous supply of a dermatome (skin segment).

2. Reflexes decline in speed with age; this probably reflects neuronal loss or sluggish CNS integration circuits.

REVIEW QUESTIONS
Multiple Choice/Matching

1. The large onion-shaped receptors that are found deep in the dermis and in subcutaneous tissue and that respond to deep pressure are (a) Merkel discs, (b) Pacinian receptors, (c) free nerve endings, (d) Krause's end bulbs.

2. Proprioceptors include all of the following except (a) muscle spindles, (b) Golgi tendon organs, (c) Merkel discs, (d) joint kinesthetic receptors.

3. The connective tissue sheath that surrounds a fascicle of nerve fibers is the (a) epineurium, (b) endoneurium, (c) perineurium, (d) neurilemma.

4. Match the names of the cranial nerves in column B to the appropriate description in column A.

Column A		Column B
_____	(1) causes pupillary constriction	(a) abducens
_____	(2) is the major sensory nerve of the face	(b) accessory
_____	(3) serves the sterno-cleidomastoid and trapezius muscles	(c) facial
_____	(4) are purely sensory (three nerves)	(d) glossopharyngeal
_____	(5) serves the tongue muscles	(e) hypoglossal
_____	(6) allows you to chew your food	(f) oculomotor
_____	(7) is impaired in tic douloureux	(g) olfactory
_____	(8) helps to regulate heart activity	(h) optic
_____	(9) serves your ability to hear and to maintain your balance	(i) trigeminal
_____	(10) contain parasympathetic motor fibers (four nerves)	(j) trochlear
		(k) vagus
		(l) vestibulocochlear

5. For each of the following muscles or body regions, identify the plexus and the peripheral nerve (or branch of one) involved. Use choices from keys A and B.

— , — (1) the diaphragm
— , — (2) muscles of the posterior thigh and leg
— , — (3) anterior thigh muscles
— , — (4) medial thigh muscles
— , — (5) anterior arm muscles that flex the forearm
— , — (6) muscles that flex the wrist and digits (two nerves)
— , — (7) muscles that extend the wrist and digits
— , — (8) skin and extensor muscles of the posterior arm
— , — (9) peroneal muscles, tibialis anterior, and toe extensors

Key A: Plexuses
(a) brachial
(b) cervical
(c) lumbar
(d) sacral

Key B: Nerves
(1) common peroneal
(2) femoral
(3) median
(4) musculocutaneous
(5) obturator
(6) phrenic
(7) radial
(8) tibial
(9) ulnar

6. Characterize each receptor activity described below by choosing the appropriate letter and number from keys A and B.

Key A: (a) exteroceptor
(b) interoceptor
(c) proprioceptor

Key B: (1) chemoreceptor
(2) mechanoreceptor
(3) nociceptor
(4) photoreceptor
(5) thermoreceptor

— , — You are enjoying an ice cream cone.
— , — You have just scalded yourself with hot coffee.
— , — The retinas of your eyes are stimulated.
— , — You bump (lightly) into someone.
— , — You have been lifting weights and experience a sensation in your upper limbs.

7. An ipsilateral reflex that causes rapid withdrawal of a body part from a painful stimulus is the (a) crossed extensor, (b) flexor, (c) Golgi tendon, (d) muscle stretch.

Short Answer Essay Questions

8. What is the functional relationship of the peripheral nervous system to the central nervous system?

9. List the structural components of the peripheral nervous system, and describe the function of each component.

10. How is a receptor potential like an EPSP? How is it different?

11. Explain why damage to peripheral nerve fibers is often reversible, whereas damage to CNS fibers rarely is.

12. (a) Describe the formation and composition of a spinal nerve. (b) Name the branches of a spinal nerve (other than the rami communicantes), and indicate their distribution.

13. (a) Define plexus. (b) Indicate the spinal roots of origin of the four major nerve plexuses, and name the general body regions served by each.

14. Differentiate between ipsilateral and contralateral reflexes.

15. What is the homeostatic value of flexor reflexes?

16. Compare and contrast flexor and crossed extensor reflexes.

17. What clinical information can be gained by conducting somatic reflex tests?

18. What is the structural and functional relationship between spinal nerves, skeletal muscles, and dermatomes?

CRITICAL THINKING AND CLINICAL APPLICATION QUESTIONS

1. In 1962 a boy playing in a train yard fell under a train. His right arm was cut off cleanly by the train wheel. Surgeons reattached the arm, sewing nerves and vessels back together. The boy was told he should eventually regain the use of his arm but that it would never be strong enough to pitch a baseball. Explain why full recovery of strength was unlikely.

2. Jefferson, a football back, suffered torn menisci in his right knee joint when tackled from the side. The same injury crushed his common peroneal nerve against the fibula head. What locomotor problems did Jefferson have after this?

3. As Harry fell off a ladder, he grabbed a tree branch with his right hand, but unfortunately lost his grip and fell heavily to the ground. Days later, Harry complained that his upper limb was numb. What was damaged in his fall?

4. Mr. Frank, a former stroke victim who had made a remarkable recovery, suddenly began to have problems reading. He complained of seeing double and also had problems navigating steps. He was unable to move his left eye downward and laterally. What cranial nerve was the site of lesion? (Right or left?)

5. One of a group of rabbit hunters was accidently sprayed with buckshot in both of his gluteal prominences. When his companions saw that he would survive, they laughed and joked about where he had been shot. They were horrified and ashamed a week later when it was announced that their friend would be permanently paralyzed and without sensation in both legs from the knee down, as well as on the back of his thighs. What had happened?

14

The Autonomic
Nervous System

CHAPTER OUTLINE AND STUDENT OBJECTIVES

Overview of the Autonomic Nervous System (pp. 461–463)

1. Compare the somatic and autonomic nervous systems relative to effectors, efferent pathways, and neurotransmitters released.

2. Compare and contrast the general functions of the parasympathetic and sympathetic divisions.

Anatomy of the Autonomic Nervous System (pp. 463–469)

3. Describe the site of CNS origin, locations of ganglia, and general fiber pathways of the parasympathetic and sympathetic divisions.

Physiology of the Autonomic Nervous System (pp. 469–478)

4. Define cholinergic and adrenergic fibers, and list the different types of cholinergic and adrenergic receptors.

5. Briefly describe the clinical importance of drugs that mimic or inhibit adrenergic or cholinergic effects.

6. State the effects of the parasympathetic and sympathetic divisions on the following organs: heart, blood vessels, gastrointestinal tract, lungs, adrenal medulla, and external genitalia.

7. Describe the levels of control of autonomic nervous system functioning.

Homeostatic Imbalances of the Autonomic Nervous System (p. 478)

8. Explain the relationship of some types of hypertension, Raynaud's disease, and the mass reflex reaction to disorders of autonomic functioning.

Developmental Aspects of the Autonomic Nervous System (pp. 478–479)

9. Describe the effects of aging on the autonomic nervous system.

I n its never-ending attempt to maintain balance, the body is far more sensitive to changing events than any human invention or cultural institution. Although all body systems contribute, the relative stability of our internal environment depends largely on the orchestrations of the **autonomic nervous system (ANS),** the system of motor neurons that innervates smooth and cardiac muscle and glands (see Figure 14.1). At every moment, signals flood from the visceral organs into the central nervous system, and autonomic nerves make adjustments as necessary to ensure optimal support for body activities. In response to changing conditions, the ANS shunts blood to more "needy" areas, speeds or slows heart and respiratory rate, adjusts blood pressure and body temperature, and in-creases or decreases stomach secretions. Most of this fine-tuning occurs without our conscious awareness or attention. For instance, few of us realize when our pupils dilate or our arteries constrict. On the other hand, if you've ever been stuck in a grocery store check-out line, and your full bladder was contracting as if it had a "mind of its own," you've been very aware of its activity. Indeed, as the term *autonomic* (*auto* = self; *nom* = govern) implies, this motor subdivision of the peripheral nervous system has a certain amount of functional independence. The autonomic nervous system is also called the **involuntary nervous system,** which reflects its subconscious control, and the **general visceral motor system,** which indicates the location of most of its effectors.

OVERVIEW OF THE AUTONOMIC NERVOUS SYSTEM

Comparison of the Somatic and Autonomic Nervous Systems

Our previous discussions of motor nerves have focused largely on the activity of the somatic nervous system. So, before describing autonomic nervous system anatomy, we will point out the major differences between the somatic and autonomic divisions, as well as some areas of functional overlap. Although both systems have motor fibers, the somatic and autonomic nervous systems differ (1) in their effectors, (2) in their efferent pathways, and (3) to some degree in target organ responses to their neurotransmitters. The differences are summarized in Figure 14.2.

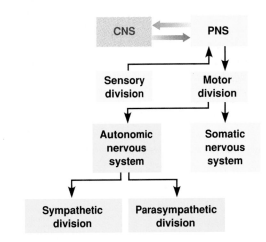

FIGURE 14.1
Place of the ANS in the structural organization of the nervous system.

> Why are the first and second neurons of the two-neuron motor autonomic chain named the preganglionic and postganglionic neurons respectively?

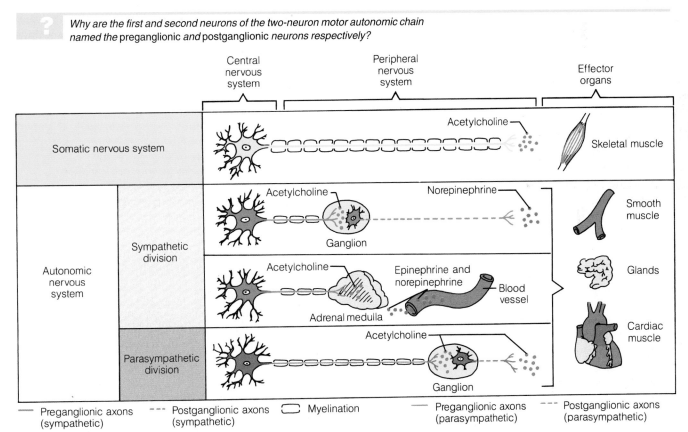

FIGURE 14.2
Comparison of the somatic and autonomic nervous systems.
Somatic Division: Axons of somatic motor neurons extend from the CNS to their effectors (skeletal muscle cells). These axons are typically heavily myelinated. Somatic motor neurons release acetylcholine, and the effect is always stimulatory. *Autonomic Division:* Axons of most preganglionic neurons run from the CNS to synapse in a peripheral autonomic ganglion with a postganglionic neuron. A few sympathetic preganglionic axons synapse with cells of the adrenal medulla. Axons of postganglionic neurons run from the ganglion to the effectors (cardiac and smooth muscle fibers and glands). Preganglionic axons are lightly myelinated; postganglionic axons are unmyelinated. All autonomic preganglionic fibers release acetylcholine; all parasympathetic postganglionic fibers release acetylcholine; most sympathetic postganglionic fibers release norepinephrine. Stimulated adrenal medullary cells release norepinephrine and epinephrine into the blood. Autonomic effects are stimulatory or inhibitory, depending on the postganglionic neurotransmitter released and the receptor types on the effectors.

Effectors

The somatic nervous system stimulates skeletal muscles, whereas the ANS innervates cardiac and smooth muscle and glands. The differing physiology of the effector organs themselves accounts for most of the remaining differences between somatic and autonomic effects on their target organs.

Efferent Pathways and Ganglia

In the somatic nervous system, cell bodies of the motor neurons are in the central nervous system, and their axons extend in spinal nerves all the way to the skeletal muscles they serve. Somatic motor fibers are typically thick, heavily myelinated type A fibers that conduct nerve impulses very rapidly.

In contrast, the motor unit of the ANS is a *two-neuron chain.* The cell body of the first neuron, the **preganglionic neuron,** resides in the brain or spinal cord. Its axon, called the **preganglionic axon,** synapses with the second motor neuron, the **postganglionic neuron,** in an **autonomic ganglion** outside the central nervous system. The **postganglionic axon** then extends to the effector organ. If you take the time to think about the meanings of all these terms while referring to Figure 14.2, understanding the rest of the chapter will be much easier. Notice that the postganglionic neuron is somewhat misnamed, since its cell body is in the ganglion, not beyond ("post") it. Preganglionic axons are lightly myelinated, thin fibers; postganglionic axons are even thinner and are unmyelinated. Consequently, conduction through the autonomic efferent chain is slower than conduction in the somatic motor system. Many pre- and postganglionic fibers are incorporated into spinal or cranial nerves for most of their course.

Autonomic ganglia are *motor* ganglia, containing the cell bodies of motor neurons. Technically, they are synapse sites of pre- and postganglionic neurons. However, the presence of *intrinsic ganglionic cells,* short neurons analogous to interneurons, in some of these ganglia suggests that, in addition to information transmission, certain integrative functions may occur there as well. Also, notice that the somatic motor division *lacks* ganglia entirely. The dorsal root ganglia are part of the sensory, not the motor, division of the peripheral nervous system.

Neurotransmitter Effects

All somatic motor neurons release acetylcholine at their synapses with skeletal muscle fibers. The effect is always excitatory, and if stimulation reaches threshold, the skeletal muscle fiber contracts.

Neurotransmitters released onto visceral effector organs by postganglionic autonomic fibers include **norepinephrine** secreted by most sympathetic fibers, and **acetylcholine** released by parasympathetic fibers. Depending on the receptors present on the target organ, its response to these neurotransmitters may be either excitation or inhibition.

Overlap of Somatic and Autonomic Function

Higher brain centers regulate and coordinate both somatic and visceral motor activities, and nearly all spinal nerves (and many of the cranial nerves) contain both somatic and autonomic fibers. Moreover, most of the body's adaptations to changing internal and external conditions involve both skeletal muscle activity and enhanced responses of certain visceral organs. For example, when skeletal muscles are working hard, they need more oxygen and glucose, and autonomic control mechanisms speed up the heart and breathing to meet these needs and maintain homeostasis. The autonomic nervous system is only one part of our integrated nervous system, but according to convention we will consider it an individual entity and describe its role in isolation in the sections that follow.

The Divisions of the Autonomic Nervous System

The two arms of the autonomic nervous system, the *parasympathetic* and *sympathetic divisions,* generally serve the same visceral organs but cause essentially opposite effects: If one division stimulates certain smooth muscles to contract or a gland to secrete, the other division inhibits that action. Through this process of **dual innervation,** the two divisions counterbalance each other's activities to keep body systems running smoothly. The sympathetic part mobilizes the body during extreme situations (such as fear, exercise, or rage), whereas the parasympathetic arm allows us to unwind as it performs maintenance activities and conserves body energy. Let us now elaborate on these functional differences by focusing briefly on situations in which each division is exerting primary control.

Role of the Parasympathetic Division

The **parasympathetic division** is most active in nonstressful situations. This division, sometimes called the "resting and digesting" system, is chiefly concerned with keeping body energy use as low as possible, even as it directs vital "housekeeping" activities like digestion and elimination of feces and urine. (This explains why it is a good idea to relax after a heavy meal so that digestion is not interfered with by sympathetic activity.) Its activity is best illustrated in a person who relaxes after a meal and reads the newspaper. Blood pressure, heart rate, and respiratory rate are regulated at low normal levels, the gastrointestinal tract is actively digesting food, and the skin is warm (indicating that there is no need to divert blood to skeletal muscles or vital organs). The eye pupils are constricted to protect the retinas from excessive damaging light, and the lenses of the eyes are accommodated for close vision.

Role of the Sympathetic Division

The **sympathetic division** is often referred to as the "fight-or-flight" system. Its activity is evident when we are excited, or find ourselves in emergency or threatening situations, such as being frightened by street toughs late at night. A pounding heart; rapid, deep breathing; cold, sweaty skin; and dilated eye pupils are sure signs of mobilization of the sympathetic nervous system. Not as obvious, but equally characteristic, are changes in brain wave patterns and in the electrical resistance of the skin (galvanic skin resistance)—events that are most frequently recorded during lie detector examinations.

During exercise or any type of vigorous physical activity, the sympathetic division also promotes a number of other adjustments. Visceral (and perhaps cutaneous) blood vessels are constricted, and vessels of the heart and skeletal muscles are dilated. This causes shunting of blood to skeletal muscle and to the vigorously working heart. The bronchioles in the lungs dilate, increasing ventilation (and ultimately increasing oxygen delivery to the body cells), and the liver releases more sugar (glucose) into the blood to provide for the increased energy needs of body cells. At the same time, temporarily nonessential activities, such as gastrointestinal and urinary tract motility, are damped. If you are running from a mugger, digesting lunch can wait! It is far more important that your muscles be provided with everything they need to get you out of danger's way.

The sympathetic division generates a head of steam that enables the body to cope rapidly with situations that threaten homeostasis. Its function is to provide the optimal conditions for an appropriate response to some threat, whether that response is to run, to see better, or to think more clearly.

An easy way to remember the most important roles of the two ANS divisions is to think of the parasympathetic division as the **D** (digesting, defecation, and diuresis [urination]) division and the sympathetic division as the **E** (exercise, excitement, emergency, and embarrassment) division. However, while it is easiest to think of the sympathetic and parasympathetic divisions as working in an all-or-none fashion, this is rarely the case. A dynamic antagonism exists between the two divisions, and fine adjustments are made continuously by both. We will go into more detail on these matters later.

ANATOMY OF THE AUTONOMIC NERVOUS SYSTEM

The sympathetic and parasympathetic divisions are distinguished by:

1. **Their unique origin sites**—the parasympathetic fibers emerge from the brain and sacral spinal cord, whereas sympathetic fibers originate from the thoracolumbar region of the spinal cord.

2. **The different lengths of their fibers**—the parasympathetic division has long preganglionic and short postganglionic fibers, whereas the sympathetic has the opposite condition.

3. **The location of their ganglia**—most parasympathetic ganglia are located in the visceral effector organs, whereas sympathetic ganglia lie close to the spinal cord.

These and other anatomical considerations are summarized in Table 14.1 on p. 465 and illustrated in Figure 14.3.

Parasympathetic (Craniosacral) Division

We will begin our exploration of the autonomic nervous system with the anatomically simpler parasympathetic division. Because its preganglionic fibers spring from opposite ends of the central nervous system—the brain stem and the sacral region of the spinal cord—it is also called the **craniosacral division** (see Figure 14.3, right). The preganglionic axons extend from the CNS nearly all the way to the structures to be innervated. There they synapse with postganglionic neurons located in **terminal** or **intramural** (in"trah-mu'ral) **ganglia** very close to or within the target organs. Very short postganglionic axons issue from the terminal ganglia and run to synapse with effector cells in their immediate area.

Cranial Outflow

Several cranial nerves contain the parasympathetic outflow (Figure 14.3). More specifically, preganglionic fibers run in the oculomotor, facial, glossopharyngeal, and vagus nerves; their cell bodies lie in associated motor cranial-nerve nuclei in the brain stem (see Figure 12.17c). The precise locations of the pre- and postganglionic neurons of the cranial parasympathetics are described next.

1. **Oculomotor nerves (III).** The parasympathetic fibers of the oculomotor nerves innervate smooth muscles within the eyes that cause the pupils to constrict and the lenses of the eyes to bulge—actions that allow focusing on close objects in the field of vision. The preganglionic axons found in the oculomotor nerves issue from the accessory **oculomotor nuclei** in

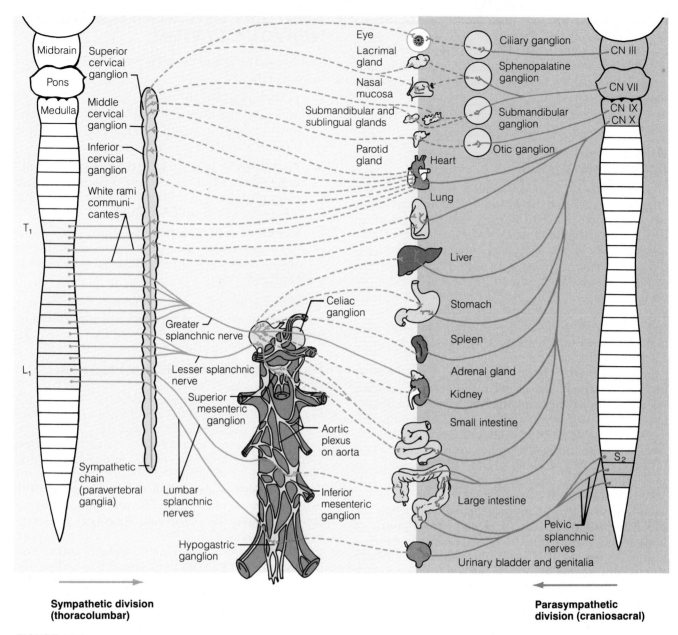

**Sympathetic division
(thoracolumbar)**

**Parasympathetic
division (craniosacral)**

FIGURE 14.3

The autonomic nervous system. Solid lines indicate preganglionic nerve fibers. Terminal ganglia of the vagus nerve fibers are not shown; most of these ganglia are located in or on the target organ. (The least and sacral splanchnic nerves are not shown, and although there are four sympathetic lumbar splanchnic nerves, only two are illustrated for simplicity. Note: CN = cranial nerve.)

the midbrain. The cell bodies of the postganglionic neurons are in the **ciliary ganglia** within the eye orbits (see Table 13.2, p. 437).

2. **Facial nerves (VII).** The parasympathetic fibers of the facial nerves stimulate the secretory activity of many large glands in the head. The pathway that activates the nasal glands and the lacrimal glands of the eyes originates in the **lacrimal nuclei** of the pons. The preganglionic fibers then run to synapse with postganglionic neurons in the **sphenopalatine** (sfe"no-pal'ah-tīn) **ganglia** just posterior to the maxillae. The

preganglionic neurons that stimulate the submandibular and sublingual salivary glands originate in the **superior salivatory nuclei** of the pons and synapse with postganglionic neurons in the **submandibular ganglia,** deep to the mandibular angles.

3. **Glossopharyngeal nerves (IX).** The parasympathetics in the glossopharyngeal nerves originate in the **inferior salivatory nuclei** of the medulla and synapse in the **otic ganglia,** located just inferior to the foramen ovale of the skull. The postganglionic fibers then course to and activate the parotid salivary glands

Table 14.1 Anatomical and Physiological Differences Between the Parasympathetic and Sympathetic Divisions

Characteristic	Parasympathetic	Sympathetic
Origin	Craniosacral outflow: brain stem nuclei of cranial nerves III, VII, IX, and X; spinal cord segments S_2–S_4	Thoracolumbar outflow: lateral horn of gray matter of spinal cord segments T_1–L_2
Location of ganglia	Ganglia in (intramural) or close to visceral organ served	Ganglia within a few cm of CNS: alongside vertebral column (paravertebral ganglia) and anterior to vertebral column (prevertebral ganglia)
Relative length of pre- and postganglionic fibers	Long preganglionic; short postganglionic	Short preganglionic; long postganglionic
Rami communicantes	None	Gray and white rami communicantes. White rami contain myelinated preganglionic fibers; gray contain unmyelinated postganglionic fibers
Degree of branching of preganglionic fibers	Minimal	Extensive
Functional goal	Maintenance functions; conserves and stores energy	Prepares body to cope with emergencies and intense muscular activity
Neurotransmitters	All fibers release ACh (cholinergic fibers)	All preganglionic fibers release ACh; most postganglionic fibers release norepinephrine (adrenergic fibers); postganglionic fibers serving sweat glands and some blood vessels of skeletal muscles release ACh; neurotransmitter activity augmented by release of adrenal medullary hormones (norepinephrine and epinephrine)

which lie anterior to the ears.

These three pairs of cranial nerves (III, VII, and IX) supply the entire parasympathetic innervation of the head. However, only *preganglionic fibers* lie within these respective cranial nerves—postganglionic fibers do not. The distal ends of the preganglionic fibers "jump over" to the trigeminal nerves (V) to synapse; then, the postganglionic fibers travel along with the fibers of the trigeminal nerves to reach the face. This "hitchhiking" takes advantage of the fact that the trigeminal nerves have the broadest facial distribution of all the cranial nerves and, thus, are well suited for this "delivery" role.

4. Vagus nerves (X). The remainder of the parasympathetic cranial outflow consists of vagus (X) nerve fibers. Between them, the two vagus nerves account for about 90% of all preganglionic parasympathetic fibers in the body. They provide fibers to the neck and contribute to nerve plexuses (interweaving networks of nerves) that serve virtually every organ in the thoracic and abdominal cavities. The vagal nerve fibers (preganglionic axons) arise mostly from the **dorsal motor nuclei** of the medulla and terminate by synapsing in terminal ganglia that are usually located within the target organ. Most of these terminal ganglia are not individually named; instead they are collectively called *intramural ganglia,* literally ganglia "within the walls." As the vagus nerves pass into the thorax, they send branches to the following plexuses located within or near the organs served:

- **Cardiac plexuses,** supplying fibers to the heart that slow heart rate.
- **Pulmonary plexuses,** serving the lungs and bronchi.
- **Esophageal** (ĕ-sof″ah-je′al) **plexuses,** supplying the esophagus.

When the main trunks of the vagus nerves reach the esophagus, their fibers intermingle and form the **anterior** and **posterior vagal trunks,** each containing fibers from both vagus nerves. These vagal trunks then "ride" the esophagus down to enter the abdominal cavity. There they send fibers through the large **aortic plexus** (formed by a number of smaller plexuses that run along the aorta) before giving off branches to the abdominal viscera. Sympathetic and parasympathetic fibers intermingle in these abdominal plexuses; the parasympathetic fibers do not synapse there but the sympathetic fibers do. Abdominal organs receiving vagal innervation include the liver, stomach, small intestine, kidneys, pancreas, and the proximal half of the large intestine. The rest of the large intestine and the pelvic organs are served by the sacral outflow.

Sacral Outflow

The sacral outflow arises from neurons located in the lateral gray matter of spinal cord segments S_2–S_4. The axons of these neurons run in the ventral roots of the spinal nerves to the ventral rami and then branch

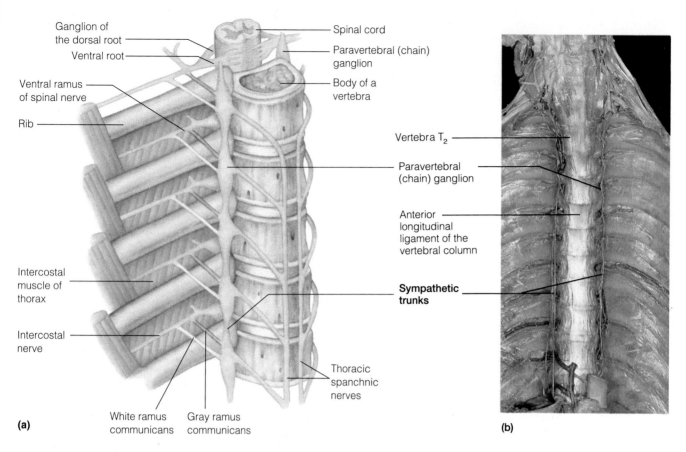

Ganglion of
the dorsal root

Ventral root

Ventral ramus
of spinal nerve

Rib

Intercostal
muscle of
thorax

Intercostal
nerve

Spinal cord

Paravertebral (chain)
ganglion

Body of a
vertebra

Vertebra T$_2$

Paravertebral
(chain) ganglion

Anterior
longitudinal
ligament of the
vertebral column

**Sympathetic
trunks**

Thoracic
spanchnic
nerves

White ramus   Gray ramus
communicans   communicans

(a)

(b)

FIGURE 14.4

The sympathetic trunks. The organs of the anterior thorax have been removed to allow
visualization of the paravertebral ganglia of the sympathetic trunks. **(a)** Diagrammatic view;
(b) photograph.

off to form the **pelvic splanchnic nerves** (see Figure
14.3), which pass through the **inferior hypogastric
(pelvic) plexus.** Some preganglionic fibers synapse
with ganglia in this plexus, but most synapse in intramural ganglia located within the walls of the following organs: distal half of the large intestine, the urinary bladder, ureters, and reproductive organs (e.g.,
uterus and external genitalia).

Sympathetic (Thoracolumbar) Division

The sympathetic division is decidedly more complex
than the parasympathetic division, partly because it
innervates more organs. It supplies not only the internal organs but also visceral structures in the somatic
part of the body. This sounds impossible, but there is
an explanation—some glands and smooth muscle
structures in the soma (sweat glands and the hair-
raising arrector pili muscles of the skin) require autonomic innervation and are served only by sympathetic
fibers. Moreover, all arteries and veins (be they deep
or superficial) have smooth muscle in their walls that
is innervated by sympathetic fibers. But these matters

will be explained in more detail later—let us get on
with the anatomy of the sympathetic division.

All preganglionic fibers of the sympathetic division arise from cell bodies of preganglionic neurons
located in spinal cord segments T$_1$ through L$_2$ (see Figure 14.3, left). For this reason, the sympathetic division is also referred to as the **thoracolumbar** (tho″rah-
ko-lum′bar) **division.** The presence of numerous
preganglionic sympathetic neurons in the gray matter
of the spinal cord produces the **lateral horns** (the so-
called **visceral motor zones** (see Figures 12.26b, p. 411
and 12.27, p. 412). The lateral horns protrude just posterolateral to the ventral horns that house motor neurons of the somatic motor division. (Parasympathetic
preganglionic neurons in the sacral cord are far less
abundant than the comparable sympathetic neurons
in the thoracolumbar regions, and lateral horns are
absent in the sacral region of the spinal cord. This is a
major anatomical difference between the two divisions.) After leaving the cord via the ventral root, the
preganglionic sympathetic fibers pass through a **white
ramus communicans** (plural, **rami communicantes**
[kom-mu′nĭ-kan″tēz]) to enter an adjoining **paravertebral (chain) ganglion** forming part of the **sympathetic**

Posterior column of white matter

Paravertebral (sympathetic chain) ganglion

Dorsal root and dorsal root ganglion

Lateral horn of gray matter (visceral motor zone)

Sympathetic trunk

Ventral ramus of spinal nerve

Gray ramus communicans

White ramus communicans

Ventral root

(b)

Dorsal ramus of spinal nerve

b c

a **(a)**

To effector

Blood vessels

Skin (arrector pili muscles and sweat glands)

Splanchnic nerve

(c)

Prevertebral (collateral) ganglion such as the celiac

Target organ (in abdomen)

FIGURE 14.5

Sympathetic pathways. (a) Synapse in a paravertebral (chain) ganglion at the same level. (b) Synapse in a paravertebral ganglion at a different level. (c) Synapse in a prevertebral (collateral) ganglion anterior to the vertebral column.

trunk or **chain** (Figure 14.4). Looking much like strands of glistening white beads, the sympathetic trunks flank each side of the vertebral column. Thus, these ganglia are named for their location.

Although the sympathetic trunks extend from the neck to the pelvis, sympathetic fibers arise only from the thoracic and lumbar spinal cord segments, as shown in Figure 14.3. The ganglia vary in size, position, and number, but typically there are 23 ganglia in each sympathetic chain: 3 cervical, 11 thoracic, 4 lumbar, 4 sacral, and 1 coccygeal.

Once a preganglionic axon reaches a paravertebral ganglion, one of three things can happen to it:

1. It can synapse with a postganglionic neuron within the same ganglion (see Figure 14.5a).

2. It can ascend or descend the sympathetic chain to synapse in another paravertebral ganglion (see Figure 14.5b). (It is these fibers running from one ganglion to another that connect the ganglia into the sympathetic trunk.)

3. It can pass through the ganglion and emerge from the sympathetic chain without synapsing (see Figure 14.5c).

Preganglionic fibers exhibiting the last pattern help to form the **splanchnic** (splank′nik) **nerves,** which synapse with **prevertebral,** or **collateral, ganglia** located anterior to the vertebral column. Unlike paravertebral (chain) ganglia, the prevertebral ganglia are neither paired nor segmentally arranged.

Notice that regardless of where the synapse occurs, all sympathetic ganglia are close to the spinal cord, and the postganglionic fibers, which run from the ganglion to the organs they supply, are typically much longer than the preganglionic fibers. Recall that the opposite condition occurs in the parasympathetic division. As you will soon see, these anatomical distinctions are functionally important as well.

Pathways with Synapses in a Paravertebral (Sympathetic Chain) Ganglion

When synapses are made in the paravertebral ganglia, the postganglionic axons enter the ventral (or dorsal) ramus of the adjoining spinal nerves by way of communicating branches called **gray rami communicantes** (see Figure 14.5). From there they are distributed via branches of the rami to the sweat glands and arrector pili muscles of the skin. Anywhere along their path, the postganglionic axons may transfer over to nearby blood vessels and then innervate the vascular smooth muscle all the way to their final branches.

Notice that the naming of the rami communicantes as *white* or *gray* (which reflects their appearance) reveals whether or not their fibers are myelinated. Preganglionic fibers composing the white rami are myelinated; postganglionic axons forming the gray rami are not.

The white rami, which carry preganglionic axons to the sympathetic chains, are found only in the T_1–L_2 cord segments, the regions of sympathetic outflow. However, gray rami carrying postganglionic fibers headed for the periphery issue from *every* paravertebral ganglion from the cervical to the sacral region. This allows sympathetic output to reach all parts of the body. Since parasympathetic fibers never run in spinal nerves, rami communicantes are associated *only* with the sympathetic division.

Sympathetic preganglionic fibers serving the head, neck, and thorax emerge from spinal cord segments T_1–T_6 and ascend the sympathetic chain to synapse with postganglionic neurons within cervical ganglia in the neck. Postganglionic fibers issuing from the *cervical ganglia* (see Figure 14.3) furnish the sympathetic outflow to several additional areas of the head and neck. The large **superior cervical ganglion** contributes sympathetic fibers that run with several cranial nerves and with the upper three or four cervical spinal nerves. Besides being distributed to the skin and blood vessels of the head, these fibers stimulate the dilator muscles of the irises of the eyes, inhibit the nasal and salivary glands, and innervate the smooth (tarsal) muscle of the upper eyelid. The superior cervical ganglion also gives off direct branches to the carotid body and sinus, to the larynx and pharynx, and provides several **cardiac nerves** to the heart.

Table 14.2 Segmental Sympathetic Supplies	
Spinal cord segment	**Organs served**
T_1–T_5	Head and neck, heart
T_2–T_4	Bronchi and lungs
T_2–T_5	Upper limb
T_5–T_6	Esophagus
T_6–T_{10}	Stomach, spleen, pancreas
T_7–T_9	Liver
T_9–T_{10}	Small intestine
T_{10}–L_1	Kidney, reproductive organs (uterus, testis, ovary, etc.)
T_{10}–L_2	Lower limb
T_{11}–L_2	Large intestine, ureter, urinary bladder

Postganglionic fibers emerging from the **middle** and **inferior cervical ganglia** enter cervical nerves C_4–C_8. Some of these fibers innervate the heart, but most serve the skin. (The inferior cervical ganglion is also called the *stellate* (stel'āt) *ganglion* because of its starlike shape.) Additionally, some postganglionic fibers emerging from the first five or so thoracic chain ganglia pass directly to the heart, aorta, lungs, and esophagus. Along the way, they contribute to the plexuses associated with those organs. Sympathetic innervation by spinal cord segment is summarized in Table 14.2.

Pathways with Synapses in a Prevertebral (Collateral) Ganglion

The preganglionic fibers of T_5–L_2 synapse in the prevertebral ganglia; thus these fibers enter and leave the sympathetic chains without synapsing. They form several nerves called **splanchnic nerves,** including the **thoracic splanchnic nerves** (greater, lesser, and least) and the **lumbar** and **sacral splanchnics.** The splanchnic nerves contribute to a number of interweaving nerve plexuses known collectively as the **abdominal aortic** (a-or'tik) **plexus,** which clings to the surface of the abdominal aorta (see Figure 14.3). This complex plexus contains several ganglia, some large and some small, that together serve the entire abdominopelvic viscera (*splanchni* = viscera). From the superior to the inferior aspect, the most important of these ganglia (and related subplexuses) are the **celiac, superior mesenteric, inferior mesenteric,** and **hypogastric,** named for the arteries with which they most closely associate. Postganglionic fibers issuing from these ganglia generally travel to their target organs in the company of arteries serving these organs.

The *thoracic splanchnic nerves* synapse mainly at the celiac and superior mesenteric ganglia. Postganglionic fibers issuing from these ganglia are distributed to most of the abdominal viscera: stomach, intestines (except the distal half of the large intestine), liver, spleen, and kidneys. The *lumbar* and *sacral splanchnic nerves* send the bulk of their fibers to the inferior mesenteric and hypogastric ganglia, from which postganglionic fibers serving the distal half of the large intestine, the urinary bladder, and the pelvic reproductive organs issue. For the most part, the sympathetic fibers inhibit the activity of the visceral organs they innervate.

Pathways with Synapses in the Adrenal Medulla

Some fibers traveling in the thoracic splanchnic nerves pass through the celiac ganglion without synapsing and terminate by synapsing with the hormone-producing medullary cells of the adrenal gland (see Figure 14.3). When stimulated by the preganglionic fibers, the medullary cells secrete **norepinephrine** and **epinephrine** (also called *noradrenaline* and *adrenaline,* respectively) into the blood. Embryologically, sympathetic ganglia and the adrenal medulla arise from the same tissue. For this reason, the adrenal medulla is sometimes viewed as a "misplaced" sympathetic ganglion, and its hormone-releasing cells, although lacking nerve processes, are considered equivalent to postganglionic sympathetic neurons.

Visceral Sensory Neurons

Because most anatomists consider the autonomic nervous system to be a visceral motor system, the presence of sensory fibers (mostly visceral pain afferents) in autonomic nerves is often overlooked. However, the **visceral sensory neurons,** which send information concerning chemical changes, stretch, and irritation of the viscera, are the first link in autonomic reflexes. Nearly all the sympathetic and parasympathetic fibers described thus far are accompanied by afferent fibers conducting sensory impulses from glands or muscular structures. Thus, peripheral processes of visceral sensory neurons are found in cranial nerves VII, IX, and X, the splanchnic nerves, and the sympathetic trunk, as well as in spinal nerves. Like sensory neurons serving somatic structures (skeletal muscles and skin), the cell bodies of visceral sensory neurons are located in the sensory ganglia of associated cranial nerves or in the dorsal root ganglia of the spinal cord.

The fact that visceral pain afferents travel along the same pathways as somatic pain fibers helps to explain the phenomenon of **referred pain,** in which pain stimuli arising in the viscera are perceived as

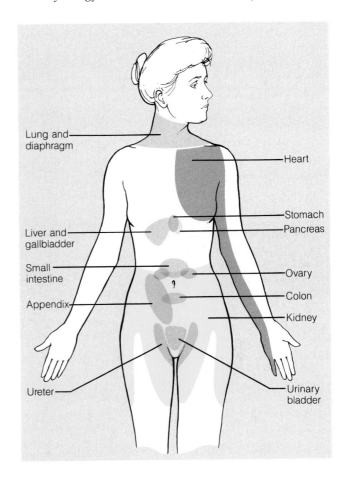

FIGURE 14.6
Referred pain. Anterior cutaneous areas to which pain from certain visceral organs is referred.

somatic in origin. For example, a heart attack may produce a sensation of pain that radiates to the superior thoracic wall and along the medial aspect of the left arm. Since the same spinal segments (T_1–T_5) innervate both the heart and the regions to which pain signals from heart tissue are referred, the brain interprets most such inputs as coming from the more common somatic pathway. Cutaneous areas to which visceral pain is commonly referred are shown in Figure 14.6. (Somatic and visceral pain are described in more detail in *A Closer Look* in Chapter 13.)

PHYSIOLOGY OF THE AUTONOMIC NERVOUS SYSTEM

Neurotransmitters and Receptors

Acetylcholine (ACh) and *norepinephrine (NE)* are the major neurotransmitters released by ANS neurons. Acetylcholine, the same neurotransmitter secreted by somatic motor neurons, is released by (1) all preganglionic axons of the ANS and (2) all parasympathetic

Table 14.3 Cholinergic and Adrenergic Receptors

Neurotransmitter	Receptor type	Major locations	Effect of binding
Acetylcholine	**Cholinergic**		
	Nicotinic	All postganglionic neurons; adrenal medullary cells (also neuromuscular junctions of skeletal muscle)	Excitation
	Muscarinic	All parasympathetic target organs	Excitation in most cases; inhibition of cardiac muscle
		Selected sympathetic targets: • Sweat glands • Blood vessels in skeletal muscles	Activation Inhibition (causes vasodilation)
Norepinephrine (and epinephrine released by adrenal medulla)	**Adrenergic**		
	β₁	Heart predominantly, but also kidneys	Increases heart rate and strength; stimulates renin release by kidneys
	β₂	Lungs and most other sympathetic target organs; abundant on blood vessels serving skeletal muscles and the heart	Stimulates secretion of insulin by pancreas; other effects mostly inhibitory: dilation of blood vessels and bronchioles; relaxes smooth muscle walls of digestive and urinary visceral organs; relaxes pregnant uterus
	β₃	Adipose tissue	Stimulates lipolysis by fat cells
	α₁	Most importantly blood vessels serving the skin, mucosae, abdominal viscera, kidneys, and salivary glands; but virtually all sympathetic target organs except heart	Constricts blood vessels and visceral organ sphincters; dilates pupils of the eyes
	α₂	Membrane of adrenergic axon terminals; blood platelets	Mediates inhibition of NE release from adrenergic terminals; promotes blood clotting

postganglionic axons at synapses with their effectors (see Figure 14.2 and Table 14.1). ACh-releasing fibers are called **cholinergic** (ko″lin-er′jik) **fibers.**

In contrast, most sympathetic postganglionic axons release NE and are classified as **adrenergic** (ad″ren-er′jik) **fibers.** The only exceptions are sympathetic postganglionic fibers innervating the sweat glands of the skin, and some blood vessels within skeletal muscles and the external genitalia, all of which secrete ACh. As mentioned earlier, NE was originally named *noradrenaline,* and the newer term *norepinephrine* has never completely replaced the old. NE-releasing fibers continue to be called adrenergic fibers (perhaps because the term is easier to pronounce than "epinephrinergic fibers").

Unfortunately, the effects of ACh and NE on their effectors are not consistently either excitation or inhibition. The response of visceral effectors to these neurotransmitters depends not only on the neurotransmitters themselves but also on the receptors to which they attach. The two or more kinds of receptors that exist for each of the autonomic neurotransmitters allow them to exert different effects (activation or inhibition) at different body targets (Table 14.3).

Cholinergic Receptors

The two types of receptors that bind ACh are named for certain drugs that bind to them and mimic acetylcholine's effects. The first of these receptors identified were the **nicotinic** (nik″o-tin′ik) **receptors.** A mushroom poison, *muscarine* (mus′kah-rin), activates a different set of ACh receptors, named **muscarinic receptors.** All acetylcholine receptors are either nicotinic or muscarinic.

Nicotinic receptors are found on (1) the motor end plates of skeletal muscle cells (which, however, are somatic and not autonomic targets), (2) all postganglionic neurons, both sympathetic and parasympathetic, and (3) the hormone-producing cells of the adrenal medulla. The effect of ACh binding to nicotinic receptors is *always* stimulatory and results in excitation of the neuron or effector cell.

Muscarinic receptors occur on all effector cells stimulated by postganglionic cholinergic fibers—that is, all parasympathetic target organs and a few sympathetic targets, such as sweat glands and some blood vessels of skeletal muscles. The effect of ACh binding to muscarinic receptors is inhibitory or stimulatory, depending on the target organ. For example, binding of ACh to cardiac muscle receptors slows heart activity, whereas ACh binding to receptors on smooth muscle of the gastrointestinal tract increases its motility.

Adrenergic Receptors

There are also two major classes of adrenergic (NE-binding) receptors: **alpha** (α) and **beta** (β). Organs that respond to NE (or epinephrine) display one or both types of receptor. In general, NE or epinephrine binding to α receptors is stimulatory, while their binding to β receptors is inhibitory. But there are notable exceptions. For example, binding of NE to the β receptors of cardiac muscle prods the heart into more vigorous activity. These differences reflect the fact that both α and β receptors have two or three receptor subclasses (α_1 and α_2; β_1, β_2, and β_3), and each receptor type tends to predominate in certain target organs. An overview of the locations and effects of these receptor subclasses is provided in Table 14.3.

The Effects of Drugs

Knowing the locations of the cholinergic and adrenergic receptor subtypes is important clinically because it allows specific drugs to be prescribed to obtain the desired blocking or stimulatory effects on selected target organs. For example, atropine, an anticholinergic drug that blocks parasympathetic effects, is routinely administered preoperatively to suppress salivation and respiratory system secretions during surgery. It is also used by ophthalmologists to dilate the pupils for eye examination (i.e., as a mydriatic agent). The anticholinesterase drug *neostigmine* inhibits the enzyme acetylcholinesterase, thus preventing enzymatic breakdown of ACh and allowing it to accumulate in the synapses. This drug is used to treat myasthenia gravis, a condition in which skeletal muscle activity is impaired for lack of ACh stimulation. Drugs called *tricyclic antidepressants* (Elavil and Sinequan) help to relieve depression because they prolong the activity of NE on the postsynaptic membrane. As described in Chapter 11 (p. 367), NE is one of our "feeling good" neurotransmitters. Hundreds of over-the-counter drugs used to treat colds, coughs, allergies, and nasal congestion contain drugs that stimulate α-adrenergic receptors. Much of the research going on in pharmaceutical companies is directed toward finding drugs that affect only one subclass of receptor without upsetting the whole adrenergic or cholinergic system. An important breakthrough was finding adrenergic blockers that attach mainly to the β_1 receptors of cardiac muscle. Also called *beta-blockers,* acebutolol (Sectral), metoprolol (Lopressor), and other drugs of their class are used when the goal is to reduce heart rate and prevent arrhythmias (irregular heartbeats) in cardiac patients without interfering with other sympathetic effects.

Interactions of the Autonomic Divisions

As mentioned earlier, most visceral organs are innervated by both sympathetic and parasympathetic fibers—that is, they receive *dual innervation.* Normally, both ANS divisions are partially active, producing a dynamic antagonism that allows visceral activity to be very precisely controlled. However, one division or the other usually exerts the predominant effects in given circumstances. In a few cases, the autonomic divisions actually cooperate with one another to achieve a specific ANS result. The major effects of the two divisions are summarized in Table 14.4.

Antagonistic Interactions

Antagonistic effects, which were described earlier, are most clearly seen on the activity of the heart, respiratory system, and gastrointestinal organs. In a fight-or-flight situation, the sympathetic division increases both your respiratory and heart rates while inhibiting digestion and elimination. When the emergency situation has passed, the parasympathetic division restores heart and breathing rates to resting levels and then attends to processes that refuel the body cells and discard wastes.

Sympathetic and Parasympathetic Tone

Although we have described the parasympathetic division as the "resting and digesting" division, the sympathetic division is the major actor in controlling blood pressure, even at rest. With few exceptions, the vascular system is entirely innervated by sympathetic fibers that keep the blood vessels in a continual state of partial constriction called **sympathetic** or **vasomotor tone.** When faster blood delivery is needed, these fibers deliver impulses more rapidly, causing blood vessels to constrict and blood pressure to rise. Conversely, when blood pressure is to be decreased, the vessels are allowed to dilate. *Alpha-blocker drugs* (such as phentolamine) that interfere with the activity of these **vasomotor fibers** are often used to treat hypertension. During circulatory shock (inadequate blood delivery to body tissues), or when more blood must be provided to meet the increased needs of working skeletal muscles, blood vessels serving the skin and abdominal viscera are strongly constricted. This blood "shunting" helps to maintain circulation to vital organs or enhance blood delivery to skeletal muscles.

On the other hand, parasympathetic effects normally dominate the heart and smooth muscle of digestive and urinary tract organs. Thus, these organs exhibit **parasympathetic tone.** The parasympathetic division prevents unnecessary heart acceleration and also determines the normal activity levels of the digestive and urinary tracts. However, the sympathetic division can override these parasympathetic

Table 14.4 Effects of the Parasympathetic and Sympathetic Divisions on Various Organs

Target organ/system	Parasympathetic effects	Sympathetic effects
Eye (iris)	Stimulates constrictor muscles; constricts eye pupils	Stimulates dilator muscles, dilates eye pupils
Eye (ciliary muscle)	Stimulates muscles, which results in bulging of the lens for accommodation and close vision	No effect
Glands (nasal, lacrimal, salivary, gastric, pancreas)	Stimulates secretory activity	Inhibits secretory activity; causes vasoconstriction of blood vessels supplying the glands
Sweat glands	No effect	Stimulates copious sweating (cholinergic fibers)
Adrenal medulla	No effect	Stimulates medulla cells to secrete epinephrine and norepinephrine
Arrector pili muscles attached to hair follicles	No effect	Stimulates to contract (erects hairs and produces "goosebumps")
Heart muscle	Decreases rate; slows and steadies heart	Increases rate and force of heartbeat
Heart: coronary blood vessels	Constricts coronary vessels	Causes vasodilation
Bladder/urethra	Causes contraction of smooth muscle of bladder wall; relaxes urethral sphincter; promotes voiding	Causes relaxation of smooth muscle of bladder wall; constricts urethral sphincter; inhibits voiding
Lungs	Constricts bronchioles	Dilates bronchioles and mildly constricts blood vessels
Digestive tract organs	Increases motility (peristalsis) and amount of secretion by digestive organs; relaxes sphincters to allow movement of foodstuffs along tract	Decreases activity of glands and muscles of digestive system and constricts sphincters (e.g., anal sphincter)
Liver	No effect	Epinephrine stimulates liver to release glucose to blood
Gallbladder	Excites (gallbladder contracts to expel bile)	Inhibits (gallbladder is relaxed)
Kidney	No effect	Causes vasoconstriction; decreases urine output; promotes renin formation
Penis	Causes erection (vasodilation)	Causes ejaculation
Vagina/clitoris	Causes erection (vasodilation) of clitoris	Causes reverse peristalsis (contraction) of vagina
Blood vessels	Little or no effect	Constricts most vessels and increases blood pressure; constricts vessels of abdominal viscera and skin to divert blood to muscles, brain, and heart when necessary; dilates vessels of the skeletal muscles (via cholinergic fibers and epinephrine) during exercise
Blood coagulation	No effect	Increases coagulation
Cellular metabolism	No effect	Increases metabolic rate
Adipose tissue	No effect	Stimulates lipolysis (fat breakdown)
Mental activity	No effect	Increases alertness

effects during times of stress. Drugs that block parasympathetic responses increase heart rate and cause fecal and urinary retention. Except for the adrenal glands and sweat glands of the skin, most glands are activated by parasympathetic fibers.

Cooperative Effects

The best example of cooperative ANS effects is seen in controls of the external genitalia. Parasympathetic stimulation causes vasodilation of blood vessels in the external genitalia and is responsible for erection of the male penis or female clitoris during sexual excitement. (This may help explain why sexual performance is sometimes impaired when people are anxious or upset and the sympathetic division is dominant.) Sympathetic stimulation then causes ejaculation of semen by the male or reflex peristalsis of a female's vagina.

Unique Roles of the Sympathetic Division

The sympathetic division regulates many functions that are not subject to parasympathetic influence. For example, the adrenal medulla, the sweat glands and arrector pili muscles of the skin, the kidneys, and most blood vessels receive only sympathetic fibers. It is easy to remember that the sympathetic system innervates these structures because most of us sweat under stress, our scalp "prickles" during fear, and our blood pressure skyrockets (from widespread vasoconstriction) when we get excited. We have already described how sympathetic control of blood vessels regulates blood pressure and shunting of blood in the vascular system. We will now mention several other uniquely sympathetic functions.

Thermoregulatory Responses to Heat. The
sympathetic division mediates reflexes that help to regulate body temperature. For example, applying heat to the skin causes reflex dilation of blood vessels in that area. When systemic body temperature is elevated, sympathetic nerves effect widespread dilation of the skin vasculature, allowing the skin to become flushed with warm blood, and activate the sweat glands to help cool the body. Conversely, when body temperature is falling, skin blood vessels are constricted, and blood is restricted to deeper, more vital organs.

Release of Renin from the Kidneys. Sympathetic impulses stimulate the kidneys to release renin, an enzyme that promotes an increase in blood pressure. This renin-angiotensin mechanism is described in Chapter 26.

Metabolic Effects. Through both direct neural stimulation and release of adrenal medullary hormones, the sympathetic division promotes a number of metabolic effects not reversed by parasympathetic activity. These include (1) enhanced metabolic rate of body cells; (2) increases in blood glucose levels; (3) mobilization of fats to be used as fuels; and (4) increased mental alertness via stimulation of the reticular activating system (RAS) of the brain stem. These hormones also change the mechanical properties of skeletal muscle, causing it to contract more strongly and quickly and to become more resistant to fatigue. As a side effect, the muscle spindles are stimulated more often and, consequently, nerve impulses traveling to the muscles occur more synchronously. These neural bursts, which put muscle contractions on a "hair trigger," are great if you have to make a quick jump or run, but they can be embarrassing or even disabling to the nervous musician or surgeon.

Localized Versus Diffuse Effects

In the parasympathetic division, one preganglionic neuron synapses with one (or at most a few) postganglionic neurons. Additionally, all parasympathetic fibers release ACh, which is quickly destroyed by enzymatic (acetylcholinesterase) hydrolysis. Consequently, the parasympathetic division exerts short-lived, localized control over its effectors. In contrast, preganglionic sympathetic axons typically branch profusely on entering the sympathetic trunk and synapse with many postganglionic neurons at several levels. Thus, when the sympathetic division is activated, it responds in a diffuse and highly interconnected way. Indeed, the literal translation of sympathetic (*sym* = together; *pathos* = feeling) relates to the bodywide mobilization it provokes.

Effects produced by sympathetic activation are also much longer-lasting than those of parasympathetic activation. This reflects three phenomena: (1) NE is inactivated more slowly than ACh because it must be taken back up into the presynaptic ending before it is hydrolyzed (or stored); (2) NE, being an indirectly acting neurotransmitter that acts through a second-messenger system (see p. 470), exerts its effects more slowly than ACh, which acts directly; and (3) when the sympathetic division is mobilized, small amounts (15%) of norepinephrine and larger amounts (85%) of epinephrine are secreted into the blood by adrenal medullary cells. Although epinephrine is more potent at increasing heart rate and raising blood sugar levels and metabolic rate, these hormones cause essentially the same effects as NE released by sympathetic neurons. In fact, it is estimated that circulating adrenal medullary hormones produce 25% to 50% of all the sympathetic effects acting on the body at a given time. These effects continue for several minutes until the hormones are destroyed by the liver. Thus, although sympathetic nerve impulses act only briefly, the hormonal effects they provide linger. The widespread and prolonged effect of sympathetic activation helps explain why we need time to "come down" after an extremely stressful experience.

Control of Autonomic Functioning

Although the ANS is not usually considered to be under voluntary control, its activity *is* regulated. Several levels of CNS controls exist—in the spinal cord, brain stem, hypothalamus, and cerebral cortex.

Brain Stem and Spinal Cord Controls

The reticular formation of the brain stem appears to exert the most *direct* influence over autonomic functions. For example, many sympathetic responses can

A CLOSER LOOK | Learned Fear: How Scary Things Get That Way

As you enter your darkened house at night, you hear a faint metallic sound. Your scalp prickles and your ears strain. Half expecting to confront an intruder, you nearly faint when your cat rushes between your feet. We have all lived through such experiences of *learned fear*—predicaments not intrinsically dangerous, yet bristling with signals we associate with a threatening situation.

For the past decade or so, researchers have been probing the brain to uncover the mechanisms of this type of learning to better understand what happens when the fear mechanism gets out of hand. They have found that the key area for learning fear is the *amygdala* (see illustration), a limbic system structure that links our emotions, including fear, to a variety of memories or situations. Fear-charged memories seem to have a lot of clout in the amygdala. For example, a 3-year-old child who plays with matches and gets burned never plays with matches again—so the associations the amygdala makes in response to dangerous situations must be lasting and profound.

The second important brain area regulating fearfulness is the *prefrontal cortex* (superficial lateral areas of the frontal lobe). It seems to assess the

potential for danger and to be crucial for unlearning fear behaviors. The *hypothalamus* rounds out the fear-processing triad of brain areas. In response to stress signals (of any type), it secretes CRH (corticotropin-releasing hormone), which prods the pituitary gland to release ACTH (adrenocorticotropic hormone), which in turn stimulates the adrenal cortex to release cortisol (see right side of illustration). Cortisol, along with sympathetic nervous system activity, prepares the body to defend itself.

The fear response takes time to develop. In humans, activity of the prefrontal cortex increases from the 7th to the 12th month after birth, the period when infants begin to display marked fear of strangers. This is also the time when children become adept at social referencing, that is, they regulate their level of fear based on their interpretation of their parents' facial expressions. It is interesting that extremely fearful children often have parents who are anxiety ridden.

Although the molecular aspects of fear responses are still being worked out, neurons that respond to opiates and to benzodiazepines (both natural neurotransmitters and externally administered drugs) are

involved. When danger is perceived, the opiate-sensing neurons are inhibited, leading to an increased sense of vulnerability. This is followed by suppression of prefrontal cortex neurons that secrete endogenous benzodiazepines. As a result, (1) GABA-releasing neurons are inhibited and (2) behaviors and hormonal responses that prepare the person for fight or flight swing into action.

Over the years, most people develop a set of skills for coping with a range of frightening situations. These include placation (soothing the ruffled feathers of an angry person), shouting and running when confronted with a purse-snatcher, changing the subject, or displacing anxiety by pursuing a different activity. But others become overwhelmed by situations that most would consider non-threatening—they shake uncontrollably when talking to strangers, are afraid to leave their house, or react with terror to cues that bring up memories of danger (such as when a Vietnam veteran hears the drone of a helicopter). Chronic release of cortisol can make us ill in various ways. If glucose is constantly released instead of stored, healthy tissues atrophy and fatigue sets in. In time, cardiovascular changes promote high blood pressure,

---

be elicited by stimulating motor centers in the ventrolateral medulla that reflexively regulate heart rate and blood vessel diameter *(cardiovascular center)* and respiration. Other medullary regions oversee many types of gastrointestinal activities. Most sensory impulses involved in eliciting these autonomic reflexes reach the brain stem via vagus nerve afferents. The pons contains *respiratory centers* that interact with those of the medulla, and there are midbrain centers *(oculomotor nuclei)* concerned with controlling the size of the eye pupils. The defecation and micturition reflexes that promote emptying of the rectum and bladder are integrated at the spinal cord level but are subject to conscious inhibition.

Visceral reflex arcs have essentially the same components as somatic reflex arcs—receptor, sensory neuron, integration center, motor neuron, and effec-

tor—except that a visceral reflex arc has a *two-neuron* motor chain. All of these autonomic reflexes are described in later chapters in relation to the organ systems they serve.

Hypothalamic Controls

The overall integration center of the autonomic nervous system is the hypothalamus. Medial and anterior hypothalamic regions appear to direct parasympathetic functions, whereas lateral and posterior areas direct sympathetic functions. These centers exert their effects via relays through the *reticular formation,* which in turn influences the preganglionic ANS motor neurons in the spinal cord and brain. The hypothalamus contains centers that coordinate heart activity, blood pressure, body temperature, water balwhich can damage the heart, blood vessels, and kidneys. The immune system is depressed, and stress-related illnesses such as ulcers may appear.

Why is there such a difference in the way we humans cope with our fears? It appears that the number of perceived dangers we face is less important than our emotional style of dealing with them. Since most such dangers are socially generated, and

often subjective and ambiguous, those who can anticipate a problem situation and then deflect it or find outlets for their tensions will prevent the harmful effect that chronic fearfulness can have on health. However, at least in some instances, the problem may be physiological—a blunted sensitivity in the CRH-ACTH-cortisol circuit such that the negative feedback signal to the hypothalamus is weak. Thus, the brain receives the signal that corti-

sol levels are low when they are actually high, resulting in chronically high levels of cortisol in the blood. In those with diagnosed anxiety disorders, such as post-traumatic stress syndrome, the problem appears to be inability to rein in the amygdala in the absence of danger. For these people, unlearning of fear behaviors must occur before true control is possible.

The neural pathways and hormonal responses of fear.
(a) Three brain regions that are interconnected by neural pathways (shown schematically by red lines) are critically important in regulating fear-related behaviors. The hypothalamus, in response to signals from the prefrontal cortex and amygdala, directs the release of hormones (b) that support motor responses to perceived threats. (Dashed arrows represent feedback inhibition by cortisol.)

ance, and endocrine activity. It also contains centers that help mediate various emotional states (rage, pleasure) and biological drives (thirst, hunger, sex). (The relationship of certain drug abuse behaviors to hypothalamic pleasure centers is the topic of *A Closer Look* in Chapter 11, p. 374.)

Recall from Chapter 12 (p. 401) that the emotional part of the cerebrum (limbic lobe) has strong links to the hypothalamus. In fact, it is the emotional response of the limbic lobe to danger and stress that signals the hypothalamus to activate the sympathetic system to "fight-or-flight" status. Thus, the hypothalamus serves as the keystone of the emotional/visceral brain, and it is through its centers that emotions influence autonomic nervous system functioning and behavior. The genesis of *learned fear* is examined in *A Closer Look*.

Cortical Controls

It was originally believed that the autonomic nervous system is not subject to voluntary controls. However, studies of meditation and biofeedback have shown that cortical control of visceral activities is possible—a capability that is untapped by most people.

Influence of Meditation on Autonomic Function. Studies of meditating yogis have revealed that they are in a physiological state that is almost the exact opposite of sympathetic-induced hyperactivity. Heart and breathing rates are low, oxygen use and metabolism drop, and EEG recordings indicate a relaxed state. Since this generalized response is so different from the usual local effects of parasympathetic activity, it seems that the meditator is consciously controlling autonomic function.

Making Connections

Systems Connections: Homeostatic Interrelationships Between the Nervous System and Other Body Systems

Endocrine System
• Hormones influence neuronal metabolism

• Sympathetic division of the ANS activates the adrenal medulla; hypothalamus helps regulate the activity of the anterior pituitary gland and produces two hormones

Cardiovascular System
• Cardiovascular system provides blood containing oxygen and nutrients to the nervous system; carries away wastes

• ANS helps regulate heart rate and blood pressure

Lymphatic System/Immunity
• Lymphatic vessels carry away leaked tissue fluids from tissues surrounding nervous system structures; immune elements protect all body organs from pathogens (CNS has additional mechanisms as well)

• Nerves innervate lymphoid organs; the brain plays a role in regulating immune function

Respiratory System
• Respiratory system provides life-sustaining oxygen; disposes of carbon dioxide

• Nervous system regulates respiratory rhythm and depth

Digestive System
• Digestive system provides nutrients needed for neuronal health

• ANS (particularly the parasympathetic division) regulates digestive mobility and glandular activity

Urinary System
• Kidneys help to dispose of metabolic wastes and maintain proper electrolyte composition and pH of blood for neural functioning

• ANS regulates bladder emptying, and renal blood pressure

Reproductive System
• Testosterone causes masculinization of the brain and underlies sex drive and aggressive behavior

• ANS regulates sexual erection and ejaculation in males; erection of the clitoris in females

Integumentary System
• Skin serves as heat loss surface

• Sympathetic division of the ANS regulates sweat glands and blood vessels of skin (therefore heat loss/retention)

Skeletal System
• Bones serve as depot for calcium needed for neural function; protects CNS structures

• Nerves innervate bones

Muscular System
• Skeletal muscles are the effectors of the somatic division

• Somatic division of nervous system activates skeletal muscles; maintains muscle health

Closer Connections: The Nervous System and Interrelationships with the Muscular, Respiratory, and Digestive Systems

The nervous system pokes its figurative nose into the activities of virtually every organ system of the body. Hence, trying to choose the most significant interactions comes pretty close to a lesson in futility. Which is more important: digestion, elimination of wastes, or mobility? Your answer probably depends on whether you are hungry or need to make a "pit stop" at the bathroom when you read this. Since neural interactions with several other systems are thoroughly plumbed in chapters to come, here we will look at the all-important interactions between the nervous system and the muscular, respiratory, and digestive systems.

Muscular System

Most simply said, the muscular system would cease to function without the nervous system. Unlike the visceral muscles or cardiac muscle, both of which have other controlling systems, somatic motor fibers are *it* for skeletal muscle activation and regulation. Somatic nerve fibers "tell" skeletal muscles not only when to contract but also how strongly. Additionally, as the nervous system makes its initial synapses with skeletal muscle fibers, it determines their fate as fast or slow fibers, which forever after affects our potential for muscle speed and endurance. The interactions of the various brain regions (basal nuclei, cerebellum, premotor cortex, etc.) and inputs of stretch receptors also determine our grace—how smooth and coordinated we are. Nonetheless, keep in mind that as long as the skeletal muscle effector cells are healthy, they help determine the viability of the neurons synapsing with them. The relationship is truly synergistic.

Respiratory System

Another system that depends entirely on the nervous system for its function is the respiratory system, which continuously refreshes the blood with oxygen and unloads the carbon dioxide waste to the sea of air that surrounds us. Neural centers in the medulla and pons both initiate and maintain the tidelike rhythm of air flushing into and out of our lungs by activating skeletal muscles that change the volume (thus the gas pressure) within the lungs. If some of those CNS centers are damaged, reflexes set up by stretch receptors in the lungs can still maintain the vital function of breathing.

Digestive System

Although the digestive system responds to many different types of controls—for example, hormones, local pH, and irritating chemicals or bacteria—the parasympathetic nervous system is crucial to its normal functioning. Without the parasympathetic inputs, sympathetic neural activity, which inhibits normal digestion (and hence nourishment of the body), would be unopposed. So important are parasympathetic controls that some of the parasympathetic neurons are actually located in the walls of the digestive organs, in the so-called intrinsic plexuses. Thus, even if all extrinsic controls are severed, the intrinsic mechanisms can still maintain this crucial body function. The role the digestive system plays for the nervous system is the same one it offers to all body systems—it sees that ingested foodstuff gets digested and loaded into the blood for cell use.

Clinical Connections

Nervous System

Case Study: On arrival at Holyoke Hospital, Jimmy Chin, a 10-year-old boy, is immobilized on a rigid stretcher so that he is unable to move his head or trunk. The paramedics report that when they found him some 50 feet from the bus, he was awake and alert, but crying and complaining that he couldn't "get up to find his Mom" and that he had a "wicked headache." He has severe bruises on his lumbar region and head, and lacerations of his back and scalp. His blood pressure is low, body temperature elevated (103°F), and his lower limbs paralyzed and insensitive to painful stimuli. Although still alert on arrival, Jimmy soon becomes drowsy and incoherent and begins to drift in and out of unconsciousness.

Jimmy is immediately scheduled for a CT scan, an operating room is reserved, and an intravenous infusion of dexamethasone, an anti-inflammatory steroid, is started.

Relative to Jimmy's condition:

• Why were his head and torso immobilized for transport to the hospital?

• What do his worsening neurological signs (drowsiness, incoherence, etc.) probably indicate? (Relate this to the type of surgery that will be performed.)

• Why was dexamethasone ordered?

• The CT scan shows no permanent damage to Jimmy's spinal cord, so how can his lower limb paralysis be explained?

Some 24 hours after his brain surgery, Jimmy's lower limb paralysis ends, but then as reflex activity returns, his body begins to go into uncontrolled flexor spasms, and he is incontinent. When examined, he is sweating intensely (diaphoretic) and his blood pressure is way above normal.

• What is this condition called and what precipitates it?

• How does Jimmy's excessively high blood pressure put him at risk?

Influence of Biofeedback on Autonomic Function. The basic premise of **biofeedback training** is that we do not routinely exert voluntary controls over our visceral activities because we have little or no conscious awareness of what is happening within our bodies. During such training, subjects are connected to monitoring devices that provide such awareness, which is called **biofeedback.** The devices detect and amplify changes in physiological processes such as heart rate, blood pressure, and skeletal muscle tone, and these data are then "fed back" to the subject in the form of flashing lights or audible tones. Subjects are asked to try to alter or control some "involuntary" function by concentrating on calming, pleasant thoughts. Since the monitor allows them to identify physiological changes in the desired direction, they gradually develop the ability to recognize the feelings associated with these changes and to produce them at will.

Biofeedback techniques have been quite successful in helping individuals plagued by migraine headaches. They are also being used by cardiac patients to manage stress. By learning to lower their blood pressure and heart rate, many have reduced their risk of heart attack. However, biofeedback training is a time-consuming and often frustrating process, and the training equipment is expensive and difficult to use.

HOMEOSTATIC IMBALANCES OF THE AUTONOMIC NERVOUS SYSTEM

Since the autonomic nervous system is involved in nearly every important process that goes on within the body, it is not surprising that abnormalities of autonomic functioning can have far-reaching effects. Such abnormalities can impair blood delivery and elimination processes and can threaten life itself.

Most autonomic disorders reflect exaggerated or deficient controls of smooth muscle activity. Of these, the most devastating involve blood vessels and include conditions such as hypertension, Raynaud's disease, and the mass reflex reaction.

Hypertension, or high blood pressure, may result from an overactive sympathetic nervous system response promoted by continual high levels of stress. Hypertension, discussed in Chapter 20, is always serious because (1) it increases the work load on the heart, which may precipitate heart disease, and (2) it increases the wear and tear on the artery walls. Stress-induced hypertension is treated with adrenergic receptor blocking drugs.

Raynaud's disease is characterized by intermittent attacks during which the skin of the fingers and toes becomes pale, then cyanotic and painful. Commonly provoked by exposure to cold, it is thought to be an exaggerated vasoconstriction response in the affected body regions. The severity of this disease ranges from merely uncomfortable to such severe constriction of blood vessels that ischemia and gan-

grene (tissue death) may result. In severe cases, preganglionic sympathetic fibers serving the affected regions are severed (a procedure called *sympathectomy*). The involved vessels then dilate, reestablishing adequate blood delivery to the region.

The *mass reflex reaction,* also called *autonomic hyperreflexia,* is a life-threatening condition involving uncontrolled activation of both autonomic and somatic motor neurons. It occurs in a majority of individuals with quadriplegia and in others with spinal cord injuries above the level of T_6. The initial cord injury is followed by *spinal shock* (see p. 418). When reflex activity returns, it is usually exaggerated because inhibitory input from higher centers is lacking. Then episodes of mass reflex, caused by surges of nervous output from large regions of the spinal cord, begin to occur. The usual trigger for the mass reflex is a painful stimulus to the skin or overfilling of a visceral organ, such as the bladder. The body goes into flexor spasms, the colon and bladder empty, and profuse sweating begins. Arterial blood pressure rises to life-threatening levels (200 mm Hg or more), which may rupture a blood vessel in the brain, precipitating a stroke. The precise mechanism of the mass reflex is unknown, but it has been envisioned as a type of epilepsy of the spinal cord. •

DEVELOPMENTAL ASPECTS OF THE AUTONOMIC NERVOUS SYSTEM

Preganglionic neurons of the autonomic nervous system derive from the embryonic *neural tube,* as do somatic motor neurons. ANS structures in the PNS—postganglionic neurons and all autonomic ganglia—derive from the *neural crest* (along with all sensory neurons) (see Figure 12.2). Some neural crest cells form the sympathetic chains. Others migrate ventrally to a site adjacent to the aorta, where they form the prevertebral ganglia. Both types of ganglia receive axons from sympathetic neurons within the cord and in turn send their axons to synapse with their effector cells in the body periphery. This process appears to be guided by **nerve growth factor (NGF),** a protein secreted by the target cells of the postganglionic axons. Some of the neural crest cells take the "long route" and differentiate into the medulla of the adrenal gland. Neural crest cells also contribute to the ciliary and other parasympathetic ganglia of the head and to the terminal parasympathetic ganglia of the viscera. The neural crest cells appear to reach their ultimate destinations by migrating along growing axons.

Congenital abnormalities of the autonomic nervous system are rare, but they do occur. Perhaps the most notable example is *Hirschsprung's disease (congenital megacolon),* in which parasympathetic innervation of the distal part of the large intestine (colon) fails to develop normally. As a result, the distal colon is immobile, and as feces accumulate proximal to the inactive bowel segment, the area becomes enormously distended. The condition is corrected surgically by removing the inactive bowel segment. •

During youth, impairments of autonomic nervous function are usually due to injuries to the spinal cord or autonomic nerves. In old age the efficiency of the autonomic nervous system begins to decline. At least part of the problem appears to be due to structural changes (bloating) of neuropeptide Y–releasing preganglionic axonal terminals, which become congested with neurofilaments with age.

Many elderly people complain of constipation (due to reduced gastrointestinal tract motility), and have dry eyes and frequent eye infections (because of diminished tear formation). Additionally, they may have fainting episodes when they stand up due to **orthostatic hypotension** (*ortho* = straight; *stat* = standing), a form of low blood pressure that occurs because the aging sympathetic vasoconstrictor centers respond more slowly to position changes. These problems are distressing, but they are not usually life threatening, and most can be managed by life-style changes or artificial aids. For example, changing position slowly gives the sympathetic nervous system more time to adjust the blood pressure; drinking ample fluids helps relieve constipation; and eye drops (artificial tears) are available for the dry-eye problem.

* * *

In this chapter, we have described the structure and function of the autonomic nervous system, one arm of the motor division of the peripheral nervous system. Because virtually every organ system still to be considered depends on autonomic controls to function normally, you will be hearing more about the autonomic nervous system in the chapters that follow. Now that we have explored most of the nervous system, this is a good time to examine how it interacts with the rest of the body as summarized in the *Making Connections* feature, p. 476.

RELATED CLINICAL TERMS

Achalasia (ak″ah-la′ze-ah; *a* = not, without; *chalas* = relaxed) A condition in which the esophagus and the sphincter at the esophagus-stomach junction do not relax with swallowing, making it difficult for food to pass along the esophagus and into the stomach; the distal esophagus becomes enormously dilated and vomiting is common. Cause is unknown; may reflect a congenital deficiency of parasympathetic postganglionic neurons in the esophageal wall, or may be a secondary result of fibrosis of the esophagus (as in scleroderma).

Atonic bladder (ah-ton′ik; *a* = without; *ton* = tone, tension) A condition in which the urinary bladder becomes flaccid and overfills, allowing urine to dribble through the sphincters; results from temporary loss of autonomic innervation following spinal cord injury.

Horner's syndrome A condition due to destruction of the superior sympathetic trunk on one side of the body; the affected person exhibits drooping of the upper eyelid (ptosis) and constricted pupil, and does not sweat on the affected side of the head.

Vagotomy (va-got′o-me) Cutting or severing of a vagus nerve; often done to help relieve symptoms of gastrointestinal ulcers because it reduces the secretion of stomach acid and other erosive substances that aggravate ulcers.

CHAPTER SUMMARY

1. The autonomic nervous system is the motor division of the PNS that controls visceral activities, with the goal of maintaining internal homeostasis.

Overview of the Autonomic Nervous System (pp. 461–463)

Comparison of the Somatic and Autonomic Nervous Systems (pp. 461–462)

1. The somatic (voluntary) nervous system provides motor fibers to skeletal muscles. The autonomic (involuntary or visceral motor) nervous system provides motor fibers to smooth and cardiac muscles and glands.

2. In the somatic division, a single motor neuron forms the efferent pathway from the CNS to the effectors. The efferent pathway of the autonomic division consists of a two-neuron chain: the preganglionic neuron in the CNS and the postganglionic neuron in a ganglion.

3. Acetylcholine, the neurotransmitter of somatic motor neurons, is stimulatory to skeletal muscle fibers. Neurotransmitters released by autonomic motor neurons (acetylcholine and norepinephrine) may cause excitation or inhibition.

The Divisions of the Autonomic Nervous System (pp. 462–463)

4. The autonomic nervous system consists of two divisions, the parasympathetic and sympathetic, which normally exert antagonistic effects on many of the same target organs.

5. The parasympathetic division (the resting-digesting system) conserves body energy and maintains body activities at basal levels.

6. Parasympathetic effects include pupillary constriction, glandular secretion, increased digestive tract mobility, and muscle actions leading to elimination of feces and urine.

7. The sympathetic division activates the body under conditions of emergency and is called the fight-or-flight system.

8. Sympathetic responses include dilated pupils, increased heart and respiratory rates, increased blood pressure, dilation of the bronchioles of the lungs, increased blood glucose levels, and sweating. During exercise, sympathetic vasoconstriction shunts blood from the skin and digestive viscera to the heart, brain, and skeletal muscles.

Anatomy of the Autonomic Nervous System (pp. 463–469)

Parasympathetic (Craniosacral) Division (pp. 463–466)

1. Parasympathetic preganglionic neurons arise from the brain stem and from the sacral (S_2–S_4) region of the cord.

2. Preganglionic fibers synapse with postganglionic neurons in terminal ganglia located in or close to their effector organs. Preganglionic fibers are long; postganglionic fibers are short.

3. Cranial fibers arise in the brain stem nuclei of cranial nerves III, VII, IX, and X and synapse in ganglia of the head, thorax, and abdomen. The vagus nerve serves virtually all organs of the thoracic and abdominal cavities.

4. Sacral fibers (S_2–S_4) issue from the lateral region of the cord and form pelvic splanchnic nerves that innervate the pelvic viscera. The preganglionic axons do not travel within rami communicantes or spinal nerves.

Sympathetic (Thoracolumbar) Division (pp. 466–469)

5. Preganglionic sympathetic neurons arise from the lateral horn of the spinal cord from the level of T_1 to L_2.

6. Preganglionic axons leave the cord via white rami communicantes and enter the paravertebral ganglia in the sympathetic trunk. An axon may synapse in a paravertebral ganglion at the same or at a different level, or it may issue from the sympathetic chain without synapsing. Preganglionic fibers are short; postganglionic fibers are long.

7. When the synapse occurs in a paravertebral ganglion, the postganglionic fiber may enter the spinal nerve ramus via the gray ramus communicans to travel to the body periphery. Postganglionic fibers issuing from the cervical paravertebral ganglia also serve visceral organs and blood vessels of the head, neck, and thorax.

8. When synapses do not occur in the paravertebral ganglia, the preganglionic fibers form splanchnic nerves (thoracic, lumbar, and sacral). Most splanchnic nerve fibers synapse in prevertebral ganglia, and the postganglionic fibers serve the abdominal viscera. Some splanchnic nerve fibers synapse with cells of the adrenal medulla.

Visceral Sensory Neurons (p. 469)

9. Virtually all autonomic nerves and ganglia contain visceral sensory fibers.

Physiology of the Autonomic Nervous System (pp. 469–478)

Neurotransmitters and Receptors (pp. 469–471)

1. Two major neurotransmitters, acetylcholine (ACh) and norepinephrine (NE), are released by autonomic motor neurons. On the basis of the neurotransmitter released, the fibers are classified as cholinergic or adrenergic.

2. ACh is released by all preganglionic fibers and all parasympathetic postganglionic fibers. NE is released by all sympathetic postganglionic fibers except those serving the sweat glands of the skin, some blood vessels within skeletal muscles, and the external genitalia (those fibers secrete ACh).

3. Neurotransmitter effects depend on the receptors to which the transmitter binds. Cholinergic (ACh) receptors are classified as nicotinic and muscarinic. Adrenergic (NE) receptors are classified as α_1 and α_2 and β_1, β_2, and β_3.

The Effects of Drugs (p. 471)

4. Drugs that mimic, enhance, or inhibit the action of ANS neurotransmitters are used to treat conditions caused by excessive, inadequate, or inappropriate ANS functioning. Some drugs bind with only one receptor subtype, allowing specific ANS-mediated activities to be enhanced or blocked.

Interactions of the Autonomic Divisions (pp. 471–473)

5. Most visceral organs are innervated by both divisions; they interact in various ways but usually exert a dynamic antagonism. Antagonistic interactions mainly involve the heart, respiratory system, and gastrointestinal organs. Sympathetic activity increases heart and respiratory system activity and depresses gastrointestinal activity. Parasympathetic activity reverses these effects.

6. Most blood vessels are innervated only by sympathetic fibers and exhibit vasomotor tone. Parasympathetic activity dominates the heart and muscles of the gastrointestinal tract (which normally exhibit parasympathetic tone) and glands.

7. The two ANS divisions exert cooperative effects on the external genitalia.

8. Roles unique to the sympathetic division are blood pressure regulation, shunting of blood in the vascular system, thermoregulatory responses, stimulation of renin release by the kidneys, and metabolic effects.

9. Activation of the sympathetic division causes widespread, long-lasting mobilization of the fight-or-flight response. Parasympathetic effects are highly localized and short lived.

Control of Autonomic Functioning (pp. 473–478)

10. Autonomic function is controlled at several levels: (1) Reflex activity is mediated by the spinal cord and brain stem (particularly medullary) centers; (2) hypothalamic integration centers interact with both higher and lower centers to orchestrate autonomic, somatic, and endocrine responses; and (3) cortical centers influence autonomic functioning via connections with the limbic system; conscious controls of autonomic function are possible, as illustrated by meditation and biofeedback training.

Homeostatic Imbalances of the Autonomic Nervous System (p. 478)

1. Most autonomic disorders reflect problems with smooth muscle control. Abnormalities in vascular control, such as occur in hypertension, Raynaud's disease, and the mass reflex reaction, are most devastating.

Developmental Aspects of the Autonomic Nervous System (pp. 478–479)

1. Preganglionic neurons develop from the neural tube; postganglionic neurons develop from the embryonic neural crest.

2. Hirschsprung's disease involves functional blockage of the large intestine due to failure of parasympathetic innervation.

3. The efficiency of the autonomic nervous system declines in old age, as reflected by decreased glandular secretory activity, decreased gastrointestinal motility, and slowed sympathetic vasomotor responses to changes in position.

REVIEW QUESTIONS

Multiple Choice/Matching

1. All of the following characterize the ANS except (a) two-neuron efferent chain, (b) presence of nerve cell bodies in the CNS, (c) presence of nerve cell bodies in the ganglia, (d) innervation of skeletal muscles.

2. Relate each of the following terms or phrases to either the sympathetic (S) or parasympathetic (P) division of the autonomic nervous system:

_____ **(1)** short preganglionic, long postganglionic fibers
_____ **(2)** terminal ganglia

_____ **(3)** craniosacral outflow
_____ **(4)** adrenergic fibers
_____ **(5)** cervical ganglia
_____ **(6)** otic and ciliary ganglia
_____ **(7)** more specific control
_____ **(8)** increases heart rate, respiratory rate, and blood pressure
_____ **(9)** increases gastric motility and secretion of lacrimal, salivary, and digestive juices
_____ **(10)** innervates blood vessels
_____ **(11)** active when you are swinging in a hammock
_____ **(12)** active when you are competing in the Boston Marathon

Short Answer Essay Questions

3. Briefly explain why the following terms are sometimes used to refer to the autonomic nervous system: involuntary nervous system and emotional-visceral system.

4. Describe the anatomical relationship of the white and gray rami to the spinal nerve, and note the kind of fibers found in each ramus type.

5. Indicate the results of sympathetic activation of the following structures: sweat glands, eye pupils, adrenal medulla, heart, lungs, liver, blood vessels of vigorously working skeletal muscles, blood vessels of digestive viscera, salivary glands.

6. Which of the effects listed in response to question 5 would be reversed by parasympathetic activity?

7. Which ANS fibers release acetylcholine? Which release norepinephrine?

8. Describe the meaning and importance of sympathetic tone and parasympathetic tone.

9. List the receptor subtypes for ACh and NE, and indicate the major sites where each type is found.

10. What area of the brain is most directly involved in mediating autonomic reflexes?

11. Describe the importance of the hypothalamus in controlling the autonomic nervous system.

12. Describe the basis and uses of biofeedback training.

13. What manifestations of decreased autonomic nervous system efficiency are seen in elderly individuals?

 ## CRITICAL THINKING AND CLINICAL APPLICATION QUESTIONS

1. Mr. Johnson has been suffering from functional urinary retention and a hypoactive urinary bladder. Bethanechol, a drug that mimics acetylcholine's autonomic effects, is prescribed to manage his problem. First explain the rationale for prescribing bethanechol, and then predict which of the following adverse effects Mr. Johnson might experience while taking this drug (select all that apply). Dizziness, low blood pressure, deficient tear formation, wheezing, increased mucus production in bronchi, deficient salivation, diarrhea, cramping, excessive sweating, undesirable erection of penis.

2. Mr. Jake was admitted to the hospital with excruciating pain in his left shoulder and arm. He was found to have suffered a heart attack. Explain the phenomenon of referred pain as exhibited by Mr. Jake.

3. A 32-year-old woman complains that she has been experiencing aching pains in the medial two fingers of both hands and that, during such episodes, the fingers become blanched and then blue. Her history is taken, and it is noted that she is a heavy smoker. The physician advises her that she must stop smoking and states that he will not prescribe any medication until she has discontinued smoking for a month. What is this woman's problem, and why was she told to stop smoking?

4. Two-year-old Jimmy has a swollen abdomen and is continuously constipated. On examination, a mass was felt over the descending colon, and the X ray showed the colon to be greatly distended in that region. What do you think is wrong with Jimmy, and how does this relate to the innervation of the colon?

15

Neural Integration

CHAPTER OUTLINE AND STUDENT OBJECTIVES

Sensory Integration: From Reception to Perception (pp. 483–485)

1. Describe the role of receptors in sensory processing.

2. Compare and contrast specific and nonspecific ascending somatosensory pathways.

3. Describe the main features of perceptual processing of sensory inputs.

Motor Integration: From Intention to Effect (pp. 486–489)

4. Describe the levels of the motor control hierarchy.

5. Define central pattern generator and command neuron.

6. Compare the roles of the direct and indirect systems in controlling motor activity.

7. Explain the function of the cerebellum and basal nuclei in somatic sensory and motor integration.

8. Describe symptoms of cerebellar and basal nuclear disease.

Higher Mental Functions (pp. 489–498)

9. Define EEG and distinguish between alpha, beta, theta, and delta waves.

10. Explain the importance of slow-wave and REM sleep, and indicate how their patterns change through life.

11. Explain what is meant by the term *holistic processing* in relation to human consciousness.

12. Compare and contrast the stages and categories of memory.

13. Indicate the major brain structures believed to be involved in fact and skill memories and describe their relative roles.

14. List some of the brain areas involved in language understanding and articulation, and indicate the role of each as presently understood.

Although we seldom look at nervous system functioning in its entirety, all of its activities—sensory, integrative, and motor alike—go on simultaneously. Take, for example, a leisurely drive with a friend. Sensory inputs, such as what you see in your visual field and the pressure of the pedals on your feet, keep your CNS constantly apprised of what is going on both inside and outside your body. Your muscles respond to CNS commands to brake or accelerate, and all the while, you carry on an animated conversation with your passenger. This chapter analyzes the neural events that underlie such daily activities.

The immediacy of sensory experiences makes them somehow more understandable than other types of neural functions, so they are good starting points for our studies of neural integration. After considering sensory integration, we will examine how some of the motor activities we take so much for granted (like walking and maintaining our upright posture) are accomplished. Then these topics will be tied together at the highest levels of sensory-motor integration. The final section of this chapter looks at how we think, remember, and relate to others with language—nebulous topics, to be sure, but fertile ground for speculation.

SENSORY INTEGRATION: FROM RECEPTION TO PERCEPTION

Our survival depends not only on **sensation** (awareness of changes in the internal and external environments), but also on **perception** (conscious interpretation of those stimuli). Perception in turn determines how we will respond to the various stimuli. For example, when we hear (sense) the honk of an automobile horn, we might perceive the honk to mean that the car we are driving has strayed across the white line and is dangerously close to causing an accident.

In this section, we will follow sensory inputs from the sensory receptors to the somatosensory cortex and examine the role of the neural structures at each level of the pathway.

General Organization of the Somatosensory System

The **somatosensory system,** or that part of the sensory system dealing with reception in the body wall and limbs, receives inputs from exteroceptors, proprioceptors, and interoceptors. Consequently, it transmits information about several different sensory modalities, each mediated by a specific set of receptors.

As noted in Chapter 12, ascending sensory pathways between receptors and the cerebral cortex typically exhibit a chain of three neurons: the cell body of the *first-order neuron* in the dorsal root ganglion; that of the *second-order neuron* in the dorsal horn of the spinal cord or medulla oblongata; and that of the *third-order neuron* in the thalamus (see Figure 12.29). Although this is the basic scheme for the upward flow of information, collateral synapses occur all along the pathway.

There are three primary levels of neural integration in the somatosensory (or any sensory) system. These are the *receptor level,* the *circuit level,* and the *perceptual level,* corresponding to the sensory receptors, the ascending pathways, and the neuronal circuits in the cerebral cortex (Figure 15.1). Although sensory input is generally relayed in a cephalad direction by these three orders of neurons, it is also processed and used by each order of neuron along the way.

Processing at the Receptor Level

Information about our external and internal worlds presents itself in different energy forms: sound, mechanical, chemical, and so on. The sensory receptors are specialized to respond to these energetic stimuli; the rest of the nervous system responds chiefly to chemicals (neurotransmitters) released as a result of action potential propagation. For sensory neurons to communicate with other neurons, they must translate the information of their stimulus into nerve impulses, the universal neural language. This process—conversion

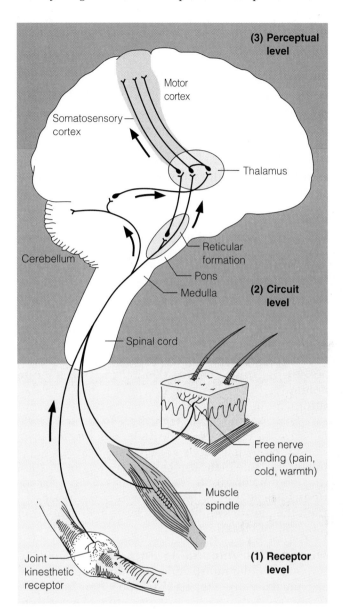

FIGURE 15.1
General organization of the somatosensory system. The three basic levels of neural integration are the receptor level (level 1), the circuit level (level 2), and the perceptual level (level 3). The circuit level involves all CNS centers with the exception of the somatosensory cerebral cortex.

of stimulus energy to electrical energy—is called **transduction.**

As stimulus energy is absorbed by the receptor, changes in the permeability of the receptor membrane occur that result in a graded potential, called a *receptor potential* (see Chapter 13, p. 429). If the receptor potential is of threshold strength, it becomes a *generator potential* that triggers an action potential. Nerve impulse transmission to the CNS will continue as long as a threshold stimulus is applied. Since the strength of the stimulus is encoded in the frequency of impulses sent, stronger stimuli cause more impulses per second to reach the CNS.

Processing at the Circuit Level

Sensory fibers, carrying impulses from cutaneous receptors of the skin and from proprioceptors, branch diffusely as they enter the spinal cord. Some branches become involved in local spinal cord reflexes and directly initiate motor activities. The remaining sensory afferents synapse with second-order neurons in the dorsal horn or continue upward in the white columns to synapse in medullary nuclei. Small-diameter pain fibers synapse with superficially located dorsal horn (substantia gelatinosa) neurons. The large myelinated fibers from pressure and touch receptors make collateral synapses with neurons in the dorsal horns. Interactions between the touch and pain afferents and small dorsal horn interneurons allow pain inputs to be damped at the circuit level.

Somatic sensory information reaches the somatosensory cortex via two major ascending routes: the *nonspecific* and *specific pathways,* found respectively within the anterolateral and dorsal white columns of the spinal cord. These pathways relay information to the brain for three purposes: perception, arousal, and motor control. Also located in the lateral white columns are the *ascending spinocerebellar tracts,* which serve muscle sense. Since these tracts terminate in the cerebellum (see Figure 12.29a), they do not contribute to conscious sensory perception. Instead, the proprioceptor inputs they carry from the muscles and tendons serve motor function rather than sensation per se.

Nonspecific Ascending Pathways.

The evolutionarily older **nonspecific ascending pathways** are so named because they receive inputs from many different types of sensory receptors and make multiple synapses in the brain stem. These pathways, also called the **anterolateral pathways,** are largely formed by the lateral and anterior *spinothalamic tracts* introduced in Chapter 12 (see Table 12.2 and Figure 12.29b). Crossover of fibers occurs in the spinal cord. Most of these fibers transmit pain and temperature impulses, but some convey light touch, pressure, or joint information. The complex sensation of an "itch" also uses this route. The spinothalamic tract fibers synapse with third-order neurons in several thalamic nuclei; but, en route, they give off numerous branches to the reticular formation. The reticular neurons, in turn, form synapses with most parts of the brain—various brain stem motor nuclei, the reticular activating system, and the cerebral cortex.

The nonspecific somatosensory system is heavily involved in emotional aspects of perception (pleasure, aversion) and in pain perception (see *A Closer Look* in Chapter 13, p. 430). It also participates in cortical arousal as well as in certain higher-level motor reflexes and orienting responses (such as turning the head toward a novel stimulus).

Specific Ascending Pathways.

The **specific ascending pathways**, also called the **lemniscal** (lemnis'kul; *lemnisc* = a ribbon) **system,** are chiefly concerned with precise, straight-through transmission of inputs from a single type (or a few related types) of sensory receptor. These pathways are formed by the **dorsal column** (*fasciculus cuneatus* and *fasciculus gracilis*) of the spinal cord and the **medial lemniscal tracts.** The latter arise in the medulla and terminate in the *ventral posterior nuclei* of the thalamus (see Table 12.2 and Figure 12.29a). From the thalamus, impulses are forwarded to specific areas of the somatosensory cortex. The trigeminal nerve (cranial nerve V) also feeds into these pathways. The specific pathways send information about discriminative touch (tactile discrimination), pressure, vibration, and conscious proprioception (limb and joint position) to the cortex. These pathways also send some fibers to the reticular nuclei and so contribute to the arousal mechanism.

The specific and nonspecific divisions of the somatosensory system are *parallel pathways* activated simultaneously, and their interactions with each other and the cerebral cortex are numerous and somewhat redundant. However, parallel pathways are advantageous in that they (1) add richness to our perceptions by allowing the same information to be handled in different ways, and (2) provide insurance—if one pathway is damaged, the other still provides some of the same inputs.

Processing at the Perceptual Level

Perception, the final stage of sensory processing, involves awareness of stimuli and discrimination of their characteristics. As sensory information approaches the thalamus, it begins to enter the level of consciousness. In the thalamus, origins of the sensory input are roughly localized, and their modalities are perceived in a crude sense. But full appreciation of their qualities and sharp localization awaits the arrival of the impulses at the somatosensory cortex.

The entire sensory cortex, primary and association areas alike, is arranged in columns of cortical neurons with each column representing a module, or building block, of sensory perception. The thalamus projects fibers (sorted out by sensation type) to the primary somatosensory cortex and to sensory association areas, allowing parallel processing of the various somatosensory inputs to occur. The result of this processing is an internal, conscious image of the stimulus.

Sensory input generally results in a behavioral response. In human beings, however, a response is not obligatory. When cortical processing produces a conscious image of the stimulus, we can either act or not act on the basis of the image's information and on our conscious prediction of the outcome of each choice. The choice we make depends, of course, on our past experience with similar sensory inputs.

The main aspects of sensory perception are detection, magnitude estimation, spatial discrimination, feature abstraction, quality discrimination, and pattern recognition. We will examine each of these briefly next.

Perceptual Detection.

Detecting that a stimulus has occurred is the simplest level of perception. As a general rule, several receptor impulses must be summated for **perceptual detection** to occur.

Magnitude Estimation.

Magnitude estimation is the ability of the brain to detect how *much* of the stimulus is acting on the body. Because of frequency coding, perception increases as stimulus intensity increases.

Spatial Discrimination.

Spatial discrimination allows us to identify the site or pattern of stimulation. A common tool for studying this quality in the laboratory is the **two-point discrimination test.** The test determines how close together two points on the skin can be and still be perceived as two points when stimulated, rather than one. This test provides a crude map of the density of tactile receptors in the various regions of the skin. As illustrated in Figure 15.2, the distance between perceived points varies from less than 5 mm on highly sensitive body areas to more than 50 mm on less sensitive areas.

Feature Abstraction.

Somatosensory stimulation usually involves an interplay of several stimulus properties. For example, one touch tells us that velvet is warm, compressible, and smooth but not completely continuous. This implies that a unit of perception, or module, is tuned to a coordinated set of several stimulus properties, called a *feature.* The mechanism by which a neuron or circuit is tuned to one feature in preference to others is called **feature abstraction.** When we run our fingers over a slab of marble, we may notice first its coolness, then its hardness, then its smoothness—each a feature that contributes to our perception of the marble surface.

The skin has no texture receptors, only touch, pressure, pain, and temperature receptors. But when their inputs are integrated in parallel fashion, we can appreciate the hardness, coolness, and smoothness of the marble. Feature abstraction enables us to identify a substance or object that has specific texture or shape.

Quality Discrimination.

Each sensory modality has several **qualities**, or submodalities. For example, the submodalities of taste are the qualities sweet, salt, bitter, and sour. **Quality discrimination** is the important ability to differentiate the submodalities of a particular sensation. It is one of the major achievements of our sensory system.

Quality discrimination may be analytic or synthetic. Some senses allow only analytic discrimination, some allow only synthetic discrimination, and others allow both. In **analytic discrimination,** each quality retains its individual nature. If we mix sugar and salt, analytic discrimination allows us to taste

How is the two-point threshold of an area related to its sensitivity?

FIGURE 15.2
Two-point thresholds in the adult. The length of each bar represents the smallest distance (**d**) between the tips of the caliper for which the two points were perceived as separate.

each quality; they do not merge into a new sensation. On the other hand, chocolate is a mixture of qualities (sweet, bitter, and perhaps some salt), but our perception of it is *synthesized* from the primary qualities and is distinct from them. **Synthetic discrimination** is also very important in vision. Our color photoreceptors respond chiefly to red, blue, and green wavelengths of light; yet, through synthetic processes, we are able to see yellow, purple, and orange when different numbers of each type of color receptor are stimulated. Vision and olfaction use only synthetic discrimination.

Pattern Recognition.

Pattern recognition refers to our ability to take in the scene around us and recognize a familiar pattern, an unfamiliar one, or one that has special significance for us. For example, a figure made of dots may be recognized as a familiar face, and when we listen to music, we hear the melody, not just a string of notes. Indeed, most of our sensory experiences consist of complex patterns that we perceive as wholes, but how this is accomplished is teasingly out of reach.

MOTOR INTEGRATION: FROM INTENTION TO EFFECT

In the motor system, we have effectors (muscle fibers) instead of sensory receptors, descending efferent circuits instead of ascending afferent circuits, and motor behavior instead of perception. However, like sensory systems, the basic mechanisms of motor systems operate at three levels. These three levels form a hierarchy of controls of motor activity.

Levels of Motor Control

The idea of multiple and successive levels of motor control, or a **motor hierarchy,** was proposed in 1873 by the English neurologist John Jackson. According to Jackson, the most elementary level of motor control is seen in the reflex activity of the spinal cord and brain stem, the next is in the cerebellum, and the highest level is in the motor cortex of the cerebrum. Each level acts through lower levels, adding to but never replacing them.

Modern research has revealed that the actual pattern of information flow in the motor control hierarchy is somewhat different. The cerebral cortex is the instrument of volition, and is at the highest level of the conscious motor pathways, but it is *not* the ultimate planner and coordinator of complex motor activities. The cerebellum and basal nuclei play this role and are therefore placed at the top of the motor control hierarchy. Further, the present understanding of motor control exerted by lower levels is that some motor activities are mediated by *reflex arcs* (simple stimulus-motor responses that regulate the most automatic and stereotyped responses to stimuli), but complex motor behavior, walking and swimming for example, appears to depend on fixed-action patterns. **Fixed-action patterns** are stereotyped sequential motor actions generated internally or triggered by appropriate environmental stimuli. Once triggered, the entire sequence is released in an all-or-none fashion. Currently, we define three levels of motor control: the *segmental level,* the *projection level,* and the *programs/instructions level.*

These levels, their interactions, and the structures they involve are depicted in Figure 15.3 and described in detail next.

The Segmental Level

The lowest level of the motor hierarchy, the **segmental level,** consists of the **segmental circuits of the spinal cord.** A segmental circuit activates anterior horn neurons of a single cord segment, causing them to stimulate a specific group of muscle fibers. Those circuits that control locomotion are called **central pattern generators (CPGs).**

Most of our information about the control of motor activity by the CNS comes from locomotion studies done over the last century. Early investigators found that isolated portions of nerve cords, freed of all afferent and efferent connections and placed in a physiological solution, generated rhythmic bursts of motor impulses that would excite extensors and flexors rhythmically and in the proper sequence to cause normal patterns of locomotion in an intact animal. This was surprising—a nerve cord, sitting in a dish with no sensory input, was continuing to "regulate locomotion." The revelation that the spinal cord has an intrinsic ability to excite muscles of locomotion in the appropriate pattern led to the concept of the CPG. The mechanism of the CPG is not yet clear, but it probably involves networks of spinal cord neurons arranged in reverberating circuits (see Figure 11.24e). Although all such information has come from animal studies, it is assumed that human locomotion is controlled in pretty much the same way and that the pattern for walking is imprinted in our spinal cords. It is inherited, not learned, and is present even in infants.

What controls a CPG (or other segmental circuit) so that it produces purposeful movements? Clearly, we are not locomoting all the time, and when we are it may be an amble, a jog, or a flat-out sprint. The most accepted theory is that the segmental apparatus is turned on or off by a "switch" located in the higher neural centers. This switch is apparently made up of brain stem interneurons called *command neurons* that form part of the projection level.

The Projection Level

The spinal cord is under the immediate control of the **projection level** of motor control. The projection level consists of cortical motor areas that produce the direct (pyramidal) system, and of brain stem motor areas that oversee the indirect (multineuronal) system. Axons of these neurons *project* to the spinal cord, where they help control reflex and fixed-action pattern activities and produce discrete voluntary movements. As previously noted, the projection level houses the command neurons that control the segmental apparatus.

The Direct (Pyramidal) System. The projection-level neurons of the cerebral cortex are the pyramidal neurons located in the precentral gyri, as well as some premotor area neurons of the frontal lobes. These neurons send impulses through the brain stem via the large **pyramidal (corticospinal) tracts** (see Table 12.3 and Figure 12.30a). Most pyramidal tract fibers synapse in the spinal cord with interneurons or directly with anterior horn motor neurons. Activation of the anterior horn neurons produces voluntary muscle contractions. As the pyramidal tracts descend through the brain stem, they send collaterals to brain stem motor nuclei, basal nuclei, and the cerebellum. Part of the direct pathway called the **corticobulbar tracts** innervates the cranial nerve nuclei of the brain stem.

Although the axons of the cerebrospinal tracts act

? *Which control level is the level of volition?*

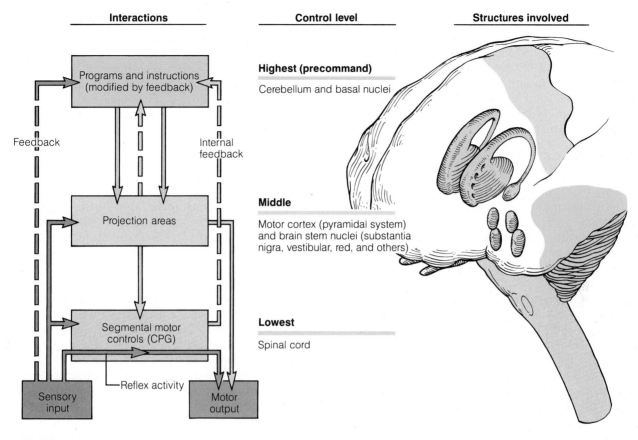

| Interactions | Control level | Structures involved |

FIGURE 15.3
Hierarchy of motor control.

on *all* anterior horn cells (α and γ alike), they influence mainly the lateralmost alpha motor neurons that control skeletal muscles of the distal extremities. Hence the direct pathway primarily regulates fine or skilled voluntary movements.

Lesions of the pyramidal tracts in the cerebral cortex or the medullary pyramids result in *hypotonia,* some degree of weakness or flaccid paralysis of the distal limb muscles and impairment of fine movements. Reflexes, though present, are usually reduced because of loss of input to the gamma motor neurons. Other consequences include loss of the abdominal reflex on one side and appearance of the Babinski reflex (a "fractionated" withdrawal reflex that is suppressed in normal adults). Lesions in other regions of the pyramidal tracts (internal capsule or spinal cord) produce instead increased tone and spasticity because of the intermixing of indirect pathway fibers at those levels. •

The Indirect (Multineuronal) System. The indirect system includes brain stem motor nuclei and *all motor pathways except* the pyramidal pathways.

It is the "home" of the command neurons mentioned earlier. The most important brain stem nuclei of this arm of the projection level are the reticular, vestibular, and red nuclei and the superior colliculi. Collectively, these nuclei set the main patterns of day-by-day motor behavior; i.e., they integrate descending motor commands and process ascending inputs to maintain posture and muscle tone and to perform associated activities needed by the direct system to produce skilled movements.

The **reticular nuclei,** which transmit via the descending **reticulospinal tracts** (see Table 12.3, p. 418), have complex and contrasting functions. Some inhibit flexors, while others activate them; the same situation holds for their innervation of extensor muscles. Their overall effect is to maintain balance by varying the tone of postural muscles. The **vestibular nuclei** receive inputs from the equilibrium apparatus of the ears and from the cerebellum. Impulses conducted downward along the **vestibulospinal tracts** are important in controlling the segmental (spinal cord) apparatus during standing—that is, in supporting the body against gravity. They also modulate the motor activity of eye and neck muscles. The **red** nuclei send facilitating impulses via the **rubrospinal tracts** to motor neurons controlling flexor muscles, whereas the **superior colliculi** and the **tectospinal tracts** mediate head movements in response to visual stimuli. The interactions between these brain stem nuclei presumably control the CPGs of the cord during locomotion and other rhythmic activities, such as arm-swinging and scratching.

The **command neurons,** found in the vestibular nuclear complex and in the red and reticular nuclei of the brain stem, are higher-level interneurons that mediate many of these activities; that is, they function to start, stop, or modify the basic rhythm of CPGs of the spinal cord or of other segmental circuits. In so doing, they help regulate episodic (one-time) movements, repetitive movements, or progressive sequences of movements.

Notice that the cerebral motor cortex can bypass the segmental apparatus of the spinal cord to directly activate the anterior horn motor neurons (see Figure 15.3). Additionally, information is continually fed back from every motor system level. Projection motor pathways not only convey information to lower motor neurons, but also send a copy of that information (*internal feedback*) back to higher command levels, continually informing them of what is happening. The direct and indirect systems provide, to some extent, separate and parallel pathways for controlling the spinal cord, but these systems are interrelated at all levels.

The Programs/Instructions Level

Two other vast systems of brain neurons, located in the cerebellum and basal nuclei, are needed to regulate motor activity—to precisely start or stop movements, to coordinate movements with posture, to block unwanted movements, and to monitor muscle tone. These systems, collectively called **precommand areas,** *control the outputs* of the cortex and brain stem motor centers and stand at the highest level of the motor hierarchy, the **programs/instructions level.** At this level, the sensory and motor systems finally merge and are integrated.

The key center for "on-line" sensorimotor integration and control is the **cerebellum.** Remember from Chapter 12 that the cerebellum is the ultimate target of ascending proprioceptor, tactile, equilibrium, and visual inputs—feedback that it needs for rapid correction of "errors" in motor activity. It also receives information from the motor cortex, via collaterals from descending pyramidal tracts, and from various brain stem nuclei. Since the cerebellum lacks direct connections to the spinal cord, it acts through the projection areas of the brain stem on motor pathways and via the thalamus on the motor cortex. In general, the midline vermis region of the cerebellum exerts control over axial and girdle muscles via the vestibular and reticular nuclei of the brain stem. The intermediate cerebellar regions influence the muscles

controlling the distal parts of the limbs by acting through the cerebral cortex motor areas and the red nuclei of the brain stem.

The **basal nuclei** are also involved in regulating motor activities initiated by cortical neurons, and like the cerebellum, they are at the crossroads of many afferent and efferent pathways. However, they do not receive somatic sensory fibers, nor do they send efferent fibers to the spinal cord. Instead, they receive inputs from *all* cortical areas and send their output back mainly to the premotor and prefrontal areas of the cerebral cortex via thalamic connections. The basal nuclei also have complex interconnections (both inhibitory and excitatory) with each other as well as with the **subthalamic nucleus** of the diencephalon and the **substantia nigra** of the midbrain. Hence, as compared to the cerebellum, the basal ganglia appear to be involved in more complex aspects of motor control (and, perhaps, even cognitive functions). Cells in both the basal nuclei and the cerebellum discharge in advance of willed movements.

Once the frontal motor association areas of your cerebral cortex (Broca's area and others) have indicated their intent to perform a movement such as drumming your fingers, planning the movement (which may involve thousands of synapses in different parts of your brain) occurs in the precommand areas; the primary motor cortex is quiet during this phase. Most involved in this unconscious planning are the most lateral portions of the cerebellar hemispheres (and the dentate nuclei) and the caudate and putamen nuclei of the basal nuclei. When you actually move your fingers, both the precommand areas and the primary motor cortex are active. The precommand area provides the "orders," and then the motor cortex executes those orders by sending activating commands to the appropriate muscle groups.

At the risk of oversimplifying, it appears that the cortex says, "I want to do this," and then lets the precommand areas take over. The basal nuclei appear to function as a liaison between the cerebral cortex and the cerebellum in planning and initiating motor activity. That is, they emphasize the cortical message with their own initiation message to the cerebellum ("prepare for") and then leave the cerebellum to fill in the gaps by providing the proper timing and patterns to execute the movements desired. The programs of the precommand areas control the motor cortex and provide its readiness to initiate a voluntary act. The conscious cortex then chooses to act or not to act, but the groundwork has already been laid.

Homeostatic Imbalances of Motor Integration

The cerebellum is an amazing brain region. Although it contains complete motor and sensory maps, its injury produces neither muscle weakness nor disorders of perception. Damage to the cerebellum affects the same side of the body (produces *ipsi-*

lateral signs and symptoms) and cerebellar disorders fall into three major groups, categorized by the precise location of the lesion: (1) disorders of synergy and muscle tone, (2) disturbances of equilibrium, and (3) speech disorders.

Synergy (sin'er-je; *synerg* = work together) is the coordination of agonist and antagonist muscles by the cerebellum to produce a smooth, well-controlled movement. When synergy is disrupted, **ataxia** (ah-tak'se-ah) always results. Ataxia sufferers exhibit slow, tentative, inaccurate movements. They are unable to touch their finger to their nose with their eyes closed—a feat that healthy individuals accomplish easily. Typically, they have a wide stance and an unsteady "drunken sailor" gait, which predisposes them to falling.

When muscles have healthy tone, manipulated limbs offer some resistance to movement. But when the cerebellum is impaired, muscle tone declines. This leads to **lack of check,** or overshoot (a rapidly moving limb is unable to stop quickly and sharply), and to tremors at the beginning and end of movements.

Cerebellar damage may also produce equilibrium problems and speech difficulties. The so-called **scanning speech** that results is slurred and somewhat slow and singsong in nature.

Diseases involving the basal nuclei reflect some problem in the controls of the basal nuclei, which are either released from inhibitory influences or more strongly stimulated. Characteristic symptoms, collectively called **dyskinesia** (dis-ki-ne'ze-ah; "bad movements"), include disorders of muscle tone and posture, as well as involuntary movements. The abnormal movements range from *tremor,* to slow, writhing movements of the fingers and hands (*athetosis*), to violent, flailing movements of the limbs (*ballism*). The most familiar basal nuclear diseases are Parkinson's disease and Huntington's disease, both involving disturbances of the "motor drive"—the neural circuits that oversee smooth initiation and execution of movement.

Typically striking people in their 50s and 60s, **Parkinson's disease** results from inadequate dopamine release by the substantia nigra, a brain stem nucleus that projects to and innervates the caudate and putamen nuclei. In healthy individuals, dopamine release by the substantia nigra inhibits these cerebral nuclei, preventing them from excessively stimulating their targets in the thalamus. In Parkinson's disease, the dopamine-releasing neurons of the substantia nigra deteriorate, and the dopamine-deprived basal nuclei become overactive, causing the well-known symptoms of the disease. Afflicted individuals have a persistent tremor at rest (exhibited by head nodding and a "pill-rolling" movement of their fingers), a forward-bent walking posture and shuffling gait, lack of facial expression, and they are slow in initiating and executing movement. The drug L-*dopa,* a precursor of dopamine, often helps to alleviate some of these symptoms temporarily. However, L-

dopa is not curative, and some believe that its chronic use ultimately contributes to the degeneration. Much newer to the drug therapy scene are deprenyl and G_{M1} ganglioside. When given in the early stages of the disease, deprenyl slows the neurological deterioration to some extent and, thus, delays severe symptoms and the need to administer L-dopa for as long as 18 months. G_{M1} ganglioside appears to have neurotropic effects on the damaged dopamine system; that is, it may induce sprouting of new dopamine-releasing fibers and synapse formation among remaining healthy neurons of the ventral midbrain.

Even more promising for long-term results are the recent intrabrain transplants of fetal substantia nigra tissue and genetically engineered adult nigral cells, which have produced regression of disease symptoms. However, the use of fetal tissue is highly controversial and riddled with ethical and legal roadblocks, making use of the modified adult nigral cells a more attractive alternative. Though the cause of Parkinson's disease is unknown, the fact that a severe form of the disease has been induced by injecting a synthetic heroin has led to the supposition that environmental chemicals (such as pesticides and herbicides) may increase the risk of developing the disorder.

Huntington's disease is a hereditary disorder that leads to massive degeneration of the basal nuclei and later of the cerebral cortex. Its initial symptoms—abrupt, jerky, and almost continuous "flapping" movements called *chorea* (Greek for "dance")—begin to appear around the age of 35 to 40 years. Although the movements appear to be voluntary, they are not. These manifestations are essentially the opposite of the motor impairments of Parkinson's disease, and Huntington's disease is usually treated with drugs that block, rather than enhance, dopamine's effects. As with Parkinson's disease, fetal tissue implants may provide promise for its treatment in the future.

Huntington's disease is progressive and usually fatal within 15 years of onset of symptoms. The disease—now known to result from a genetic "stutter," an explosive repeat of three bases of DNA near the end of chromosome 4—appears to impair mitochondrial metabolism in affected neurons, resulting in lactic acid buildup in the brain. Late in the disease, marked mental deterioration (dementia) occurs. •

HIGHER MENTAL FUNCTIONS

During the last three decades, an exciting exploration of our "inner space" has been going on that has nearly escaped public notice. Psychology and biology have begun to converge in the investigation of the higher mental functions, or what we commonly call *the mind,* including consciousness, memory, reasoning, and language. The value of these investigations is both theoretical (to determine biological mechanisms of higher mental functioning) and practical (to identify drugs that might cure or ease certain types of mental illness). But researchers in the field of cognition are still struggling to understand how the mind's presently incomprehensible qualities might spring from living tissue and electrical impulses. Souls and synapses are hard to reconcile!

In Chapter 11, we described the simple neuronal pools that provide the basis for neural activity, and in this chapter, we have so far considered the more complex mechanisms of sensorimotor integration. Now we will take another giant step to the highest levels of mental functioning. Since brain waves reflect the electrical activity on which such functioning is based, we will consider them first, along with the related topic of sleep. We will then examine the topics of consciousness, memory, and language. However, be aware that as we ascend the ladder of complexity from a single neuron to the vast constellations of neurons involved in higher mental functions, we move into the realm of uncertainty and are forced to hypothesize or speculate about what must (or should) happen.

Brain Wave Patterns and the EEG

Normal brain function involves continuous electrical activity of the neurons. An **electroencephalogram** (e-lek"tro-en-sef'ah-lo-gram), or **EEG,** is a record of some aspects of this activity, although how much each kind of neuronal activity (action potentials, synaptic potentials, etc.) contributes to it is not known. An EEG is made by placing electrodes at various locations on the scalp and then connecting the electrodes to an apparatus that measures electrical potential differences between various cortical areas (Figure 15.4a). The resulting patterns of neuronal electrical activity are called **brain waves.**

Because people differ genetically, and because everything we have ever experienced has left its imprint in our brain, each of us has a brain wave pattern that is as unique as our fingerprints. However, for simplicity, we can group these complex waves into the four frequency classes illustrated in Figure 15.4b.

Alpha waves are low-amplitude, slow, synchronous waves with an average frequency of 8–13 Hz (hertz, or cycles per second). In most cases, they indicate a brain that is "idling"—a calm, relaxed state of wakefulness.

Given that alpha waves are typically recorded when a person is sitting quietly with eyes closed, the observation that alpha waves are recorded in the left half of an "elite" sprinter's brain just prior to a race is particularly interesting. Alpha waves also appear to be involved in "runner's high" experienced by everyday joggers and competitive runners. Sports physiologists are studying these findings to see if they can be applied (via biofeedback techniques) to maximize the performance of athletes. •

Beta waves are also rhythmic, but they are more irregular than alpha waves and have a higher frequency (14–25 Hz). Beta waves occur when we are awake and mentally alert, as when we concentrate on some problem or visual stimulus.

Theta waves are still more irregular, and they have a frequency of 4–7 Hz. Though common in children and in adults in the early and REM stages of sleep, theta waves are considered abnormal in adults who are awake.

Delta waves are high-amplitude waves with a frequency of 4 Hz or less. They are seen during deep sleep and when the reticular activating system is damped, such as during anesthesia.

Brain waves have a normal frequency range of 1–30 Hz, a dominant rhythm of 10 Hz, and an average amplitude of 20–100 µV. The amplitude reflects the number of neurons firing together in synchrony, not the degree of electrical activity of individual neurons. When the brain is active and neurons are involved in many different activities, complex, low-amplitude brain waves are seen. But when the brain is inactive, as during sleep, large numbers of neurons fire synchronously, producing similar, high-amplitude brain waves.

Brain waves change with age, sensory stimuli, brain disease, and the chemical state of the body. EEG recordings have long been used for diagnosis and localization of many types of brain lesions, such as tumors, infarcts, infections, abscesses, and epileptic lesions. Interference with cerebral cortical functions is suggested by brain waves that are too fast or too slow, and unconsciousness occurs at both extremes. Brain-depressing drugs and coma result in brain wave patterns that are abnormally slow, whereas fright, various types of drug intoxication, and epilepsy are associated with excessively fast brain waves. Since spontaneous brain waves are always present, even during unconsciousness and coma, their absence—called a "flat EEG"—is clinical evidence of brain death.

Abnormal Electrical Activity of the Brain: Epilepsy

Almost without warning, a victim of epilepsy may lose consciousness and fall stiffly to the ground, body wracked by uncontrollable jerking. These seizures, called **epileptic seizures,** reflect abnormal electrical discharges of groups of brain neurons, and while their uncontrolled activity is occurring, no other messages can get through. Epilepsy is not associated with, nor does it cause, intellectual impairments. Some cases of epilepsy are induced by genetic factors, but it can also result from brain injuries caused by blows to the head, stroke, infections, prolonged fever, or tumors. Epilepsy affects about 1% of the population.

There are three recognizable types of epileptic seizures: petit mal, psychomotor, and grand mal. **Petit mal**—literally, "little bad"—is a mild type of epilepsy seen in young children, and it usually disappears by

(a)

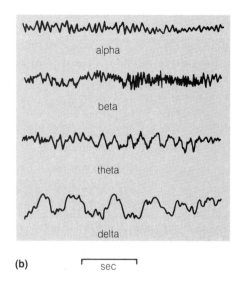

(b)   sec

FIGURE 15.4
Electroencephalography and brain waves. (a) To obtain a recording of brain wave
activity (an EEG), electrodes are positioned on the patient's scalp and attached to a recording
device called an electroencephalograph. **(b)** Typical EEGs. Alpha waves are typical of the
awake but relaxed state; beta waves occur in the awake, alert state; theta waves are common in
children but not in normal awake adults; delta waves occur during deep sleep.

the time they are ten years old. The child's expression
suddenly goes blank, and the child appears to be day-
dreaming for up to 30 seconds. Slight twitching of
facial muscles may occur, but convulsions and
unconsciousness do not. Brain wave patterns in the
hypothalamus and thalamus are depressed (around 3
Hz) during the seizure.

Psychomotor epilepsy (*Jacksonian seizures*) is
accompanied by extremely rapid temporal lobe brain
waves. The victim loses contact with reality and
exhibits uncontrolled motor activity of isolated muscle groups, such as hand clapping or lip smacking.
Sometimes aimless wandering occurs. The strange
manifestations of psychomotor epilepsy have caused
many such cases to be misdiagnosed as mental illness.

Grand mal, the most severe form of epilepsy, is
accompanied by rapid brain waves of 30 Hz or more.
The person loses consciousness and displays intense
convulsions. Bones are often broken during such
seizures, showing the incredible strength of the muscle contractions that occur. Loss of bowel and bladder
control and severe biting of the tongue are common.
The seizure lasts for a few minutes, then the muscles
relax and the person awakens but remains disori-
ented for several minutes thereafter. Many grand mal
sufferers experience a sensory hallucination, such as
a taste, smell, or flashes of light, just before the
seizure begins. This phenomenon, called an **aura,** is
helpful because it gives the person time to lie down
and avoid falling heavily to the floor.

Epilepsy can usually be controlled by anticonvul-
sive drugs. Currently nonsedating drugs (such as val-
proic acid, carbamazepine, and phenytoin) are preferred over the sedating ones (phenobarbital and
benzodiazepines). •

Sleep and Sleep-Awake Cycles

Although most people spend about a third of their
lives asleep, we know little about sleep's biological
basis. But we do know that the alternating cycles of
sleep and wakefulness involve the whole brain and
that they reflect a natural *circadian,* or 24-hour,
rhythm. **Sleep** is defined as a state of changed consciousness, or partial unconsciousness, from which a
person can be aroused by stimulation. This distinguishes sleep from *coma,* a state of unconsciousness
from which a person *cannot* be aroused by even the
most vigorous stimuli. Although cortical activity is
depressed during sleep, brain stem functions, such as
control of respiration, heart rate, and blood pressure,
continue. Even environmental monitoring continues
to some extent, as illustrated by the fact that strong
stimuli ("things that go bump in the night") immediately arouse us. In fact, people who sleepwalk can
avoid objects and navigate stairs perfectly well while
truly asleep.

In the awake state, alertness of the cerebral cortex
(the "conscious brain") is mediated by the *reticular
activating system,* or *RAS* (see Figure 12.20, p. 402).
When RAS activity declines, cerebral cortical activity
declines as well; thus, lesions of the RAS nuclei
result in unconsciousness. However, sleep is much
more than simply turning off the arousal (RAS) mechanism. It is an actively induced process in which the
brain is guided into sleep. RAS centers are involved
not only in maintaining the awake state, but also in
mediating some stages of sleep, especially dreaming
sleep. The hypothalamus is responsible for the timing
of the sleep cycle, i.e., its *suprachiasmatic nucleus*
(our biological clock) regulates its *preoptic nucleus* (a
sleep-inducing center).

Table 15.1 Types and Stages of Sleep

Nonrapid eye movement (NREM) sleep

Stage 1. Eyes are closed and relaxation begins. Thoughts flit in and out and a drifting sensation occurs; vital signs (body temperature, respiration, pulse, and blood pressure) are normal; the EEG pattern shows alpha waves; if stimulated, arousal is immediate.

Stage 2. The EEG pattern becomes more irregular; *sleep spindles*—sudden, short high-voltage wave bursts occurring at 12–14 Hz—appear, and arousal is more difficult.

Stage 3. Sleep deepens, and theta and delta waves appear; vital signs begin to decline, and the skeletal muscles are very relaxed; dreaming is common; usually reached about 20 minutes after the onset of stage 1.

Stage 4. Called slow-wave sleep because the EEG pattern is dominated by delta waves (1–4 Hz); vital signs reach their lowest normal levels, and digestive system motility increases; skeletal muscles are relaxed, but normal sleepers turn approximately every 20 minutes; arousal is difficult; bedwetting and sleepwalking occur during this phase.

Rapid eye movement (REM) sleep

EEG pattern reverts through the NREM stages to the stage 1 pattern. Vital signs increase and digestive system activity declines; skeletal muscles (except for ocular muscles) are inhibited; the stage of most dreaming.

Types of Sleep

The two major types of sleep, which alternate through most of the sleep cycle, are **nonrapid eye movement (NREM) sleep** and **rapid eye movement (REM) sleep.** The types of sleep are defined in terms of their EEG patterns. During the first 30 to 45 minutes of the sleep cycle, we pass through the four stages of NREM sleep, culminating in **slow-wave sleep.** As we pass through these stages and slip into deeper and deeper sleep, the frequency of the EEG pattern declines, but the wave amplitude increases. REM sleep, recognized by an EEG pattern more typical of the awake state, does not appear until after slow-wave sleep has been achieved.

NREM Sleep. All stages of sleep other than REM are collectively referred to as nonrapid eye movement (NREM) sleep. The four stages of NREM sleep, in which both the frequency of brain waves and vital signs decline, are summarized in Table 15.1.

REM Sleep. About 90 minutes after sleep begins, the EEG pattern changes abruptly. It becomes very irregular and appears to backtrack quickly through the stages until alpha waves, small fast waves characteristic of stage 1 and indicating the onset of REM, appear. This brain wave change is coupled with increases in body temperature, heart rate, respiratory rate, and blood pressure and a decrease in gastrointestinal motility. REM sleep is also called **paradoxical sleep** because its EEG pattern is more typical of the awake state. Oxygen use by the brain is tremendous during REM—greater than during the awake state.

Although the eyes move rapidly under the lids during REM, most of the body's muscles are actively inhibited and go limp. This temporary paralysis prevents us from acting out our dreams. Most dreaming occurs during REM sleep, and some suggest that the flitting eye movements are following the visual imagery of our dreams. (Note, however, that most nightmares and night terrors occur during stages 3 and 4 of NREM sleep.) In adolescent and adult males, REM episodes are frequently associated with erections of the penis. The threshold for arousal to consciousness is highest during REM sleep. On the other hand, the sleeper is more likely to awaken spontaneously and to remember his or her dreams during this time.

Sleep Patterns

In young and middle-aged adults, a typical night's sleep alternates between REM and NREM sleep. Following each REM episode, the sleeper descends to stage 4 sleep again. REM occurs (begins anew) about every 90 minutes, with each REM period getting longer. The first REM lasts 5–10 minutes and the final one up to 50 minutes. Hence, our longest dreams are in the "wee hours" of the morning. When the neurons of the dorsal raphe nuclei of the midbrain reticular formation fire at maximal rates, we awaken for the day. According to some researchers, this event is rigidly tied to a rise in core body temperature.

In addition to changes in brain wave patterns during sleep, there are changes in levels of neurotransmitters in certain brain regions. Norepinephrine levels decline and serotonin levels rise during deep sleep. This is not surprising, because norepinephrine helps maintain alertness, and serotonin has long been implicated as the "sleep neurotransmitter," important in slow-wave sleep.

Key generators of REM sleep are reticular cells in the lateral pontine and medial medullary areas. During REM, norepinephrine and acetylcholine levels rise in nuclei active during such periods. For example, the activity of ACh-secreting cells of the giant cell nucleus, part of the pons reticular formation, is believed to cause the arousal pattern of REM sleep, and norepinephrine released by the locus ceruleus of the pons is thought to induce the transient paralysis of REM sleep. NREM sleep areas include the nucleus of the solitary tract, some reticular nuclei, the reticular nucleus of the thalamus, the hypothalamus, and the basal forebrain.

Importance of Sleep

Although we do not really understand the significance of sleep, slow-wave and REM sleep seem to be important in different ways. Shakespeare called sleep "nature's soft nurse," referring to its restorative effects on the body. Slow-wave sleep is presumed to be the restorative stage—the time when most neural mechanisms can wind down to basal levels. When we are deprived of sleep, we spend more time than usual in slow-wave sleep during the next sleep episode.

Volunteers persistently deprived of REM sleep become emotionally unstable and exhibit various personality disorders. REM sleep may give the brain an opportunity to analyze the day's events and to work through emotional problems in dream imagery. Sigmund Freud saw dreams as symbolic expressions of frustrated desires and attempts to fulfill wishes. Another idea is that REM sleep is reverse learning. According to this hypothesis, accidental, repetitious, and meaningless communications continually occur, and they must be eliminated from the neural networks by dreaming if the cortex is to remain a well-behaved and efficient thinking system.

Alcohol and most sleep medications (barbiturates and others) suppress REM sleep but not slow-wave sleep. On the other hand, certain tranquilizers, such as diazepam (Valium) and chlordiazepoxide (Librium), reduce slow-wave sleep much more than REM sleep.

Whatever its importance, the daily sleep requirement declines steadily from 16 hours or so in infants to approximately 7 hours in early adulthood. It then levels off before declining once again in old age. Sleep patterns also change throughout life. REM sleep occupies about half of the total sleeping time in infants and then declines until the age of ten years, when it stabilizes at about 25% (approximately 1.5 to 2 hours per night). In contrast, stage 4 sleep declines steadily from birth and often disappears completely in those over 60. The elderly awaken more frequently during the night because of this perpetually light sleep.

Homeostatic Imbalances of Sleep

Two clinically important disorders of sleep are narcolepsy and insomnia. People with **narcolepsy** lapse involuntarily into sleep during waking hours. These sleep episodes last about 15 minutes, can occur without warning at any time, and often seem to be triggered by a pleasurable event—a good joke, a game of poker, a sports event. This condition can be extremely hazardous when the person must drive, operate machinery, or take a bath. Narcoleptics seem to be unable to control the circuits responsible for REM. In all daytime narcoleptic episodes they

show the typical EEG of REM sleep. During the evening sleep cycle, however, they spend much less time in REM than those with normal sleep patterns.

Insomnia is a chronic inability to obtain the *amount* or *quality* of sleep needed to function adequately during the daytime. Since the sleep requirement varies from 4 to 9 hours a day among healthy people, there is no way to determine the "right" amount. Self-professed insomniacs tend to exaggerate the extent of their sleeplessness, and they have a notorious tendency toward self-medication and barbiturate abuse.

True insomnia often reflects normal age-related changes. In frequent travelers, it may be caused by *jet lag;* but perhaps the most common cause of insomnia is psychological disturbance. We have difficulty falling asleep when we are anxious or upset, and depression is often accompanied by early awakening. •

Consciousness

Consciousness encompasses conscious perception of sensations, voluntary initiation and control of movement, and capabilities associated with higher mental processing (memory, logic, judgment, perseverance, and so on). Clinically, consciousness is defined on a continuum that grades levels of behavior in response to stimuli as (1) *alertness,* (2) *drowsiness* or *lethargy* (which proceeds to sleep), (3) *stupor,* and (4) *coma.* Alertness is the highest state of consciousness and cortical activity, whereas coma is the most depressed state. But when we get away from the clinical definition, consciousness is very difficult to define. A sleeping person obviously lacks something that he or she has when awake, and we call this "something" consciousness. It is equally obvious that human consciousness, with its rich tapestry of perceptions and concepts, is much more than the opposite of sleep; its complexity sets us apart from all other animals.

Scientists have been thinking about thinking for some time. But human consciousness is still a mystery, and most of what you read about it is likely to be speculation—a synthesis provided in an attempt to explain the impressive capabilities of the conscious brain. For example, cognitive scientists have proposed that consciousness is a manifestation of **holistic information processing.** The major suppositions of holistic processing are as follows:

1. *Consciousness involves simultaneous activity of large areas of the cerebral cortex.* Localized damage to any specific region of the cerebral cortex does *not* destroy consciousness.

2. *Consciousness is superimposed on other types of neural activity.* At any time, specific neurons and neuronal pools are involved both in specific localized activities (such as motor control or sensory perception) and in mediating conscious cognitive behaviors.

3. *Consciousness is totally interconnected.* Information for "thought" can be claimed from many locations in the cerebrum simultaneously. For example, retrieval of a specific memory can be triggered by one of several routes—a smell, a place, a particular person, and so on. The cortical cross-file is enormous.

Except for sleep, unconsciousness is always a signal of some impairment of brain function. A transient loss of consciousness is called **fainting** or **syncope** (sing′ko-pe; "cut short"). Most often, it indicates inadequate cerebral blood flow due to low blood pressure, as might follow hemorrhage or sudden emotional stress. Fainting is usually preceded by a feeling of lightheadedness as blood pressure falls to critically low levels.

When a person is totally unresponsive to sensory stimuli for an extended period—eyes closed and no recognizable speech—the condition is called **coma.** Coma is *not* deep sleep. During sleep, the brain is active and oxygen consumption resembles that of the waking state. In contrast, oxygen use is always below resting levels in coma patients.

Blows to the head may induce coma by causing widespread cerebral trauma, due to the damage done by the blow itself or resulting from hemorrhage or edema, or by causing similar trauma to brain stem structures, particularly the reticular formation. Coma may also be produced by tumors or infections that invade the brain stem. Metabolic disturbances such as hypoglycemia (abnormally low blood sugar levels), drug overdose (from opiates, barbiturates, or alcohol), or liver and/or kidney failure depress and interfere with overall brain function and can result in coma. Cerebral infarctions, unless massive and accompanied by extreme swelling of the brain, rarely cause coma.

When the brain has suffered irreparable damage, irreversible coma occurs, even though life-support measures may have restored vitality to other body organs. The result is a dead brain (**brain death**) in an otherwise living body. Physicians must determine whether a patient in an irreversible coma is legally alive or dead, because life support can be removed only after death. •

Memory

Memory is the storage and retrieval of previous experience, or, more simply, the ability to recall our thoughts. Memories are essential for learning and incorporating our experiences into behavior and are part and parcel of our consciousness. Stored somewhere in your 3 pounds of wrinkled brain are ZIP codes, the face of your grandfather, and the taste of yesterday's pizza. In essence, your memory bank reflects your lifetime.

Most of what is known about memory and learning can be summarized in three principles: (1) Memory storage occurs in stages and is continually changing; (2) the hippocampus and surrounding structures play unique roles in memory processing; and (3) memory traces—chemical or structural changes encoding memory—are widely distributed in the brain.

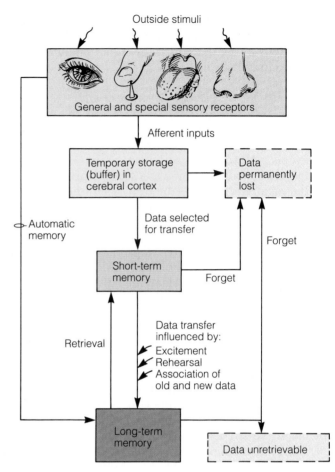

FIGURE 15.5

Memory processing. Sensory inputs are processed by the cerebral cortex (indicated as the temporary storage area), which selects what is to be sent to short-term memory. Rehearsal and other factors help the transfer of information from short-term memory to long-term memory. For long-term memory to become permanent, consolidation must occur. Some information not attended to consciously goes directly into long-term memory (automatic memory).

Stages of Memory

Memory storage, or fixation, involves at least two distinct stages: short-term memory and long-term memory (Figure 15.5). **Short-term memory (STM)** is a fleeting memory of the events that continually parade before you. Lasting for seconds to a few hours, it is the preliminary step to long-term memory, as well as the power that lets you look up a telephone number, dial it, and then never think of it again. The capacity of STM appears to be limited to seven or eight chunks of information, such as the digits of a telephone number or the sequence of words in an elaborate sentence.

In contrast to STM, **long-term memory (LTM)** seems to have a limitless capacity. Although our short-term memory devices cannot recall numbers much longer than a telephone number, we can remember scores of telephone numbers by committing them to LTM. However, our ability to store and to retrieve information declines with aging. Thus, long-term memories too can be forgotten, and our memory bank continually changes with time.

We do not remember or even consciously notice much of what is going on around us. As sensory inputs flood into our cerebral cortex, they are processed, and some of this information is selected for transfer to STM (Figure 15.5). STM serves as a sort of temporary holding bin for data that we may or may not want to retain. The transfer of information from STM to LTM is affected by many factors, including:

1. *Emotional state.* We learn best when we are alert, motivated, and aroused. For example, when we witness shocking events, transferal is almost immediate. Norepinephrine is involved in memory processing, and more NE is released when we are excited or "stressed out," which helps to explain this phenomenon.

2. *Rehearsal.* An opportunity to repeat or rehearse the material enhances memory.

3. *Association of "new" information with "old" information already stored in LTM.* A staunch football fan can tell you who did what in all of the important plays of a particular football game, whereas someone unfamiliar with the sport would find them difficult to understand and therefore to remember.

4. *Automatic memory.* Not all impressions that become part of LTM are consciously formed. For example, when concentrating on a lecturer's speech, automatic memory of the pattern of his tie may also be recorded.

Memories transferred to LTM take time to become permanent. The process of **memory consolidation** apparently involves fitting new facts into the various categories of knowledge already stored in the cerebral cortex.

Categories of Memory

The brain distinguishes between factual knowledge and skills, and we process and store these different kinds of information in different ways. **Fact memory** entails learning explicit information, such as names, faces, words, and dates. It is related to our conscious thoughts and our ability to manipulate symbols and language. Fact memories are learned and are often forgotten quickly, but when committed to LTM, they are usually filed along with the context in which they were learned. For instance, when you think of your new friend Joe, you probably picture him at the basketball game where you met him.

Skill memory is less conscious learning and usually involves motor activities. It is acquired only through practice, as when we learn to ride a bike or play a bass fiddle. Skill memories do not preserve the circumstances of learning; in fact, they are best remembered in the doing. A batter does not consciously recall the moves needed to properly time and swing the bat, nor do you have to think through how to tie your shoes. Once learned, skill memories are hard to unlearn.

Brain Structures Involved in Memory

Much of what we know about learning and memory comes from two sources: experiments with macaque monkeys and studies of amnesia in humans. Such studies have revealed that different brain structures are involved in the two stages of memory (Figure 15.6).

If the human brain uses holistic processing, then fact memory processing must be holistic as well. Specific pieces of each memory must be stored near regions of the brain that need them so that the new inputs can be quickly associated with the old. Accordingly, visual memories would be stored in the occipital cortex, memories of music in the temporal cortex, and so on. Thus, your memory of a dear aunt—the scent of her cologne, the softness of her hands—is found in bits and pieces scattered all over your cortex.

But how are the memory connections made? Extensive research has indicated that the crucial structures for incorporating and storing sensory perceptions in fact memory are the *hippocampus* and the *amygdala* (both part of the limbic system), the *diencephalon* (specific areas of the thalamus and hypothalamus), the *ventromedial prefrontal cortex* (a cortical region tucked beneath the front of the brain), and the *basal forebrain* (a cluster of ACh-secreting neurons anterior to the hypothalamus) (see Figure 15.6a). The proposed scheme of information flow is as follows. When a sensory perception is formed in the cerebral sensory cortex, the cortical neurons dispatch impulses along two parallel circuits to the hippocampus and the amygdala, both of which have connections with the diencephalon, basal forebrain, and prefrontal cortex. The basal forebrain, via its many connections with the sensory cortex, then closes the memory loop by sending impulses back to the sensory cortical areas, initially forming the perception. This feedback presumably causes changes that transform the new perception into a more durable memory. This scheme suggests that the subcortical structures make the initial connections between stored memories and the new perception by accessing cortical regions where the LTM is stored in a kind of "conference call" until the new information can be consolidated. Later recall of the new memory occurs when the same cortical neurons are stimulated.

The prefrontal cortex seems to be necessary for retrieving fact learning from long-term storage depots elsewhere in the brain for use in present tasks. Most likely, it is divided into multiple memory domains, each encoding a different kind of information, such as location of objects, features (color, size, and shape) of objects, and semantic and mathematical knowledge.

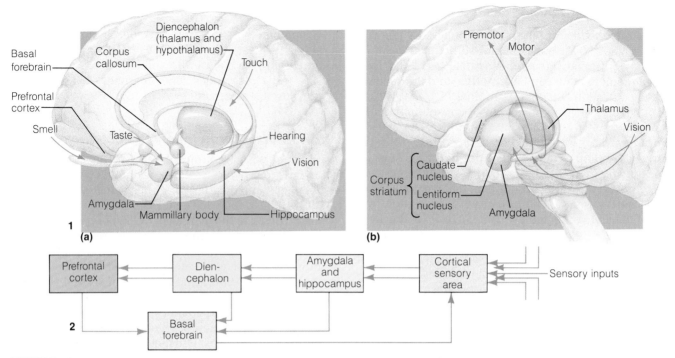

FIGURE 15.6
Proposed memory circuits.
(a) 1 The essential structures of the fact memory circuits. **2** The flowchart indicates how these structures may interact in memory formation. Sensory inputs from the cortex flow through parallel circuits, one involving the hippocampus and the other the amygdala. Both circuits encompass parts of the diencephalon, basal forebrain, and prefrontal cortex. The basal forebrain feeds back to the sensory cortex, closing the memory loop. **(b)** Major structures involved in skills memory. The corpus striatum mediates the automatic connections between a stimulus (visual here) and a motor response.

Its ultimate function appears to be to excite or inhibit other areas of the brain.

Researchers suggest that the hippocampus oversees the circuitry for learning and remembering spatial relationships, while the amygdala is the crossroads or gatekeeper of the memory system. The amygdala has widespread connections with all cortical sensory areas, as well as with the thalamus and the emotional response centers of the hypothalamus. The amygdala seems to be responsible for associating memories formed through different senses and linking them to emotional states generated in the hypothalamus.

Damage to either the hippocampus or amygdala results in only slight memory loss, but bilateral destruction of both structures causes global (widespread) amnesia. Consolidated memories are not lost, but new sensory inputs cannot be associated with old, and the person lives in the here and now from that point on. This phenomenon is called *anterograde* (an′ter-o-grād″) *amnesia,* in contrast to *retrograde amnesia,* which is the loss of memories formed in the distant past. You could carry on an animated conversation with a person with anterograde amnesia, excuse yourself, return 5 minutes later, and that person would not remember you. The same situation occurs when the connections of the hippocampus or amygdala to the diencephalon or prefrontal cortex are cut. Thus, it appears that memory is dependent on the integrity of the entire circuit. •

Individuals suffering from anterograde amnesia can still learn skills. Consequently, a second learning circuit, independent of the pathways used in fact memory, has been suggested (see Figure 15.6b). It appears that the cerebral cortex, activated by sensory inputs, signals the *corpus striatum* (lentiform and caudate nuclei of the basal nuclei) of its intent to mobilize skill memory. The corpus striatum then communicates with one or more of the brain stem nuclei as well as with the cerebral cortex to promote the desired movement. Thus, the corpus striatum forms the link between a perceived stimulus and a motor response. Because conditioning of voluntary muscle contractions is involved in many skills, the cerebellum also plays a role in skill memory. Some authorities prefer to call these pathways the **habit system,** rather than memory in the true sense.

Mechanisms of Memory

In the early 1900s, Karl Lashley, a pioneer neuropsychologist, set out to find the **engram,** the hypothetical unit of memory or permanent memory trace. Now, near the end of the century, the mysterious engram still eludes us. Because STM is so fleeting, it is not believed to involve permanent changes in neural circuits. Nonetheless, biochemical events, such as second-messenger activity and enzyme up-regulation or down-regulation, that occur at postsynaptic sites where short-term memory circuits are being established are similar or identical to the early stages leading to long-term memory.

If an engram exists, it will probably be found in long-term memory depots. Experimental studies reveal that during learning, (1) neuronal ribonucleic acid (RNA) content is altered, (2) dendritic spines change in shape, (3) unique extracellular proteins are deposited at synapses involved in LTM, and (4) presynaptic terminals increase in number and size. Human memory is notoriously difficult to study, and animals, largely limited to skill memories, provide poor models for studying how the human brain reconstructs fact memories. To date, progress has been slow in localizing and determining the specific biochemistry of memory traces in humans.

However, the growing understanding of **NMDA receptors,** named after the chemical *N*-methyl-D-aspartate used to detect them, is changing this picture. As mentioned in Chapter 11, these unique receptors act as calcium channels and mediate long-term potentiation (LTP), the persistent changes in synaptic strength first identified in hippocampal memory pathways that use the amino acid glutamate as their transmitter.

Postsynaptic cells in which LTP can be induced bear two types of glutamate receptors—non-NMDA and NMDA channels. Resting NMDA channels bind magnesium ions (Mg^{2+}) that block calcium passage through the channel. Binding of glutamate to non-NMDA receptors during tetanic (high-intensity) stimulation results in membrane depolarization. The depolarization expels Mg^{2+} from the NMDA receptors and allows glutamate to bind to them, causing calcium channels to open.

Thus, the NMDA receptors are activated by both voltage (a depolarizing current) and a chemical (subsequent binding of glutamate). These signals, which apparently must occur sequentially ("click-click"), lead to the influx of ionic calcium, which provides the transient signal necessary for the induction of LTP and forges and enhances the links that underlie durable memory traces. Details of events from this point on are murky, but Ca^{2+} appears to promote activation of several enzymes in the postsynaptic cells, including proteases and protein kinases. For example, activated protein kinase C (PKC) phosphorylates proteins, causing changes in their shape and activity. It's a good bet that at least some of these "reshaped proteins" bring about changes in the NMDA receptors that limit the extent to which Mg^{2+} can block their calcium channels and increase their sensitivity to glutamate. They may also contribute to changes in the structure of the dendritic spines.

Biochemical changes necessary for LTP are not limited to the postsynaptic neurons. Additional enzymatic cascades must occur simultaneously in the presynaptic terminal that enhance glutamate release and restrict the potentiation events to the involved neurons. The signals for *these* changes appear to be ordered by retrograde transmitters diffusing "back-

ward" from the postsynaptic neuron. The most likely candidates for these retrograde messengers are **nitric oxide (NO)** and **arachidonic acid.** Both are lipid soluble and thus can easily exit the postsynaptic neuron, which lacks synaptic vesicles, and diffuse into the adjacent presynaptic terminal. Presumably the retrograde messenger(s) enhances calcium entry in the presynaptic terminal and activates second-messenger systems that produce the structural changes that sustain the increased glutamate release. Both NO and arachidonic acid have been found in neurons in which LTP is being induced, and certain enzymes activated by the postsynaptic calcium stimulus mobilize nitric oxide synthase, which generates nitric oxide.

Language

Most distinctly human brain functions involve **language,** either directly or indirectly. Conscious thought, memory, and language are inextricably interwoven; one cannot exist without the others.

Spoken language is remarkably complex. To utter a thought, we must choose words that fit the intended meaning, dredge up the grammar to organize the words, and activate the muscles of articulation (larynx, tongue, lips, etc.). All of this occurs in a split second, so it is unlikely that the process is entirely under conscious control. On the other hand, what people say is usually so original (in form, if not in content) that purely reflexive activity cannot explain it either. Human speech has been extremely difficult to investigate. Most such information has come from studies of people with brain lesions that caused specific language deficits.

Until the late 1980s, the medical explanation of how we understand and speak words was that language involved a kind of mental "relay race." The race started in the occipital cortex, which was activated when we read. The cortex then tossed the "baton" to Wernicke's area, the "language comprehension area," where the words were sounded out. Then the baton moved to Broca's area (the motor speech area), which instructed the mouth, tongue, and lip muscles on how to form the words.

However, this simple linear model has been disproved by some recent PET scan studies of the human brain as it sees, hears, speaks, and thinks words. The original language areas are still involved (with modified functions in some cases) but several new language areas have been discovered (Figure 15.7). Furthermore, several parallel pathways are definitely involved. This more flexible scheme allows certain brain regions to be bypassed under certain conditions. Let's look at how this new scheme seems to work.

In adults reading simple material, impulses are sent directly from the visual cortex to the motor areas controlling the articular muscles or to the semantic areas in the frontal lobe. However, Wernicke's area is active in a reading child and in adults reading unfa-

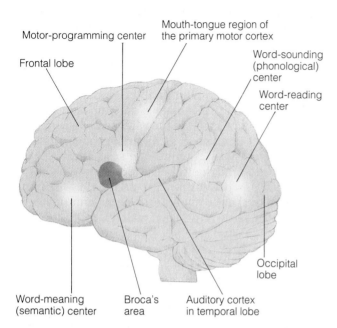

Motor-programming center

Mouth-tongue region of the primary motor cortex

Frontal lobe

Word-sounding (phonological) center

Word-reading center

Occipital lobe

Word-meaning (semantic) center

Broca's area

Auditory cortex in temporal lobe

FIGURE 15.7
Hypothetical language areas. The yellow spots superimposed on this anatomical diagram of the human brain are the cortical regions highly active during language use (as determined by PET scan studies).

miliar words or analyzing visual word input, such as determining which words rhyme. Additionally, Broca's area, the adjacent premotor area, and the appropriate region of the primary motor cortex are *all* active not only when we speak but also when we simply move our tongues or even our hands. The brain area responsible for semantics (analyzing and assigning meaning to words), word association, and symbolic processing is *not* Wernicke's area but clusters of neurons in the left frontal and midfrontal cortex. Furthermore, while the left frontal cortex appears to be essential for enunciating verbs, the left temporal cortex "whips out" nouns. Color concepts and associations appear to reside in the occipital lobe. The basal nuclei and the cerebellum are also involved in language use but their contributions are still poorly understood.

Future studies will probably find that emotional areas of the brain are also involved in language processing when we read aloud passages that depend on vivid imagery and sound as well as on word associations. However, each new discovery inevitably creates new questions—the "mind" within the brain is always just a bit beyond our grasp.

* * *

In this chapter, we have brought together most of the neural machinery studied in earlier chapters and have examined how sensory inputs are integrated with motor activity in the central nervous system. We have also taken a look at the most complex aspects of neural integration, which allow us to think, remember, and converse with others. Now that the nervous system has been viewed as an integrated whole, we are ready to consider the special senses in Chapter 16.

RELATED CLINICAL TERMS

Analgesia (an″al-je′ze-ah; *an* = without; *alge* = pain) Reduced ability to feel pain, not accompanied by loss of consciousness. An analgesic is a pain-relieving drug.

Apraxia (ah-prak′se-ah) Loss of the voluntary ability to perform skilled motor activities, which, however, can still occur automatically. Motor apraxia of speech is sometimes called **motor aphasia**; the individual is unable to speak in grammatical sentences due to lesions of Broca's area and/or the surrounding portions of the more anterior frontal cortex; common in stroke victims who have right-sided paralysis.

Dysarthria (dis-ar′thre-ah) Disorders in the motor pathways resulting in weakness, uncoordinated motion, and characteristic speech disturbances by altering respiration or speech articulation or rhythm. For example, lesions of cranial nerves IX, X, and XII result in nasal, breathy speech, and lesions in upper motor pathways produce a hoarse, strained voice.

Dystonia (dis-to′ne-ah) Impairment of muscle tone.

Hypersomnia (*hyper* = excess; *somnus* = sleep) A condition in which affected individuals sleep as much as 15 hours daily.

Myoclonus (mi″o-klo′nus; *myo* = muscle; *clon* = violent motion, tumult) Sudden contraction of a muscle or muscle part, usually involving muscles of the limbs; myoclonal jerks occurring in normal individuals as they are falling asleep are thought to reflect a fleeting reactivation of the RAS; may also be due to diseases of the reticular formation and/or cerebellum.

Phantom pain A phenomenon in which amputees have chronic pain in their nonexistent (amputated) limb; although not well understood, apparently the cut sensory nerves that previously transmitted inputs from the limb continue to respond to the trauma of amputation, and the brain interprets (projects) these painful stimuli as coming from the missing limb.

CHAPTER SUMMARY

Sensory Integration: From Reception to Perception (pp. 483–485)

1. Sensation is awareness of internal and external stimuli; perception is conscious interpretation of those stimuli.

General Organization of the Somatosensory System (pp. 483–485)

2. The three levels of sensory integration are the receptor, circuit, and perceptual levels. These levels are functions of the sensory receptors, the ascending pathways, and the cerebral cortex, respectively.

3. Sensory receptors transduce (convert) stimulus energy into action potentials. Stimulus strength is frequency coded.

4. Some sensory fibers entering the spinal cord act in local reflex arcs. Some synapse with the dorsal horn neurons (nonspecific ascending pathways), and others continue upward to

synapse in medullary nuclei (specific ascending pathways). Second-order neurons of both specific and nonspecific ascending pathways terminate in the thalamus.

5. The specific sensory pathway consists of the fasciculus cuneatus, the fasciculus gracilis, and the medial lemniscal tracts, which are concerned with straight-through, precise transmission of one or a few related sensory modalities. The nonspecific pathway, consisting of the spinothalamic tracts, is a multimodal pathway that permits brain stem processing of ascending impulses.

6. The origins and modalities of sensory impulses are crudely identified in the thalamus and then projected to the somatosensory cortex and other sensory association areas.

7. Perception—the internal, conscious image of the stimulus that serves as the basis for response—is the result of cortical processing. Regions of the somatosensory cortex devoted to a particular body area reflect the number of receptors in that area.

8. The major aspects of sensory perception are perceptual detection, magnitude estimation, spatial discrimination, feature abstraction, quality discrimination, and pattern recognition.

Motor Integration: From Intention to Effect (pp. 486–489)

1. Motor mechanisms operate at the level of the effectors (muscle fibers), descending circuits, and control levels of motor behavior.

Levels of Motor Control (pp. 486–488)

2. The motor control hierarchy consists of the segmental level, the projection level, and the programs/instructions level.

3. The segmental level is the spinal cord circuitry that activates anterior horn motor neurons to stimulate the muscles. It directly controls reflexes and fixed-action patterns. Segmental circuits controlling locomotion are central pattern generators (CPGs).

4. The projection level consists of descending fibers that project to and control the segmental level. These fibers issue from the brain stem motor areas (indirect system) and cortical motor areas (direct system). Command neurons in the brain stem appear to turn CPGs on and off, or to modulate them.

5. The programs/instructions level consists of the cerebellum and basal nuclei. These constitute the precommand areas that subconsciously integrate mechanisms mediated by the projection level.

Homeostatic Imbalances of Motor Integration (pp. 488–489)

6. Cerebellar deficits cause ipsilateral symptoms, which include disorders in synergy and muscle tone, equilibrium problems, and speech problems. Ataxia is the most common symptom.

7. Basal nuclear deficits result in abnormal muscle tone and involuntary movements (tremors, athetosis, and ballism [chorea]). Parkinson's disease and Huntington's disease are examples.

Higher Mental Functions (pp. 489–498)
Brain Wave Patterns and the EEG (pp. 490–491)

1. Patterns of electrical activity of the brain are called brain waves; a record of this activity is an electroencephalogram (EEG). Brain wave patterns, identified by their frequencies, include alpha, beta, theta, and delta waves.

2. Epilepsy results from abnormal electrical activity of brain neurons. The three types of seizure are petit mal, psychomotor epilepsy, and grand mal.

Sleep and Sleep-Awake Cycles (pp. 491–493)

3. Sleep is a state of altered consciousness from which one can be aroused by stimulation.

4. The two major types of sleep are nonrapid eye movement (NREM) sleep and rapid eye movement (REM) sleep.

5. During stages 1–4 of NREM sleep, brain waves become more irregular and increase in amplitude until delta wave sleep (stage 4) is achieved. REM sleep is indicated by a return to a stage 1 EEG. During REM, the eyes move rapidly under the lids. NREM and REM sleep alternate throughout the night.

6. Slow-wave sleep (stage 4 of NREM) appears to be restorative. REM sleep is important for emotional stability.

7. REM occupies half of an infant's sleep time and then declines to about 25% of sleep time by the age of ten years. Time spent in slow-wave sleep declines steadily throughout life.

8. Narcolepsy is involuntary lapses into sleep that occur without warning during waking periods. Insomnia is a chronic inability to obtain the amount or quality of sleep needed to function adequately.

Consciousness (pp. 493–494)

9. Consciousness includes sensory perception, initiation and control of voluntary movement, and higher mental processing capabilities. It is described clinically on a continuum from alertness to drowsiness to stupor and finally to coma.

10. Human consciousness is thought to involve holistic information processing, which is (1) not localizable, (2) superimposed on other types of neural activity, and (3) totally interconnected.

11. Fainting (syncope) is a temporary loss of consciousness that usually reflects inadequate blood delivery to the brain. Coma is loss of consciousness in which the victim is unresponsive to stimuli.

Memory (pp. 494–497)

12. Memory is the ability to recall one's thoughts. It is essential for learning and is part of consciousness.

13. Memory storage has two stages: short-term memory (STM) and long-term memory (LTM). Transfer of information from STM to LTM takes minutes to hours, but more time is required for LTM consolidation.

14. Fact memory is the ability to learn and consciously remember information. Skill memory is the learning of motor skills, which are then performed without conscious thought.

15. Fact memory appears to involve the hippocampus, amygdala, diencephalon, basal forebrain, and prefrontal cortex. Skill memory pathways are mediated by the corpus striatum.

16. The nature of memory traces in the human brain is not fully known, but NMDA receptors (essentially calcium channels), activated sequentially by depolarization and glutamate binding, play a major role in LTP. The calcium influx that follows their activation mobilizes enzymes that mediate events necessary for memory consolidation. These include (1) structural changes in the receptors and dendritic spines, and (2) generation of NO, which, in turn, acts as a retrograde neurotransmitter to enhance glutamate release from the presynaptic terminal.

Language (pp. 497–498)

17. Language is inseparable from memory and consciousness. We remember and think in words and other symbols.

18. Areas important to language processing include the visual cortex, Wernicke's area, Broca's area and surrounding areas of the premotor area, and a semantic area in the left frontal and midfrontal cortex.

19. Impairments of language areas in the left cerebral hemisphere or conduction pathways between them lead to aphasias.

REVIEW QUESTIONS

Multiple Choice/Matching

1. All of the following descriptions refer to *specific* ascending pathways except (a) include the fasciculus gracilis and fasciculus cuneatus, which terminate in the medulla, (b) include a chain of three neurons, (c) connections are diffuse and polymodal, (d) are concerned with precise transmission of one or a few related sensory modalities.

2. The aspect of sensory perception by which the cerebral cortex identifies the site or pattern of stimulation is (a) perceptual detection, (b) feature abstraction, (c) pattern recognition, (d) spatial discrimination.

3. The neural machinery of the spinal cord is at the (a) programs level, (b) projection level, (c) segmental level.

4. Which of the following is part of the indirect (multineuronal) system? (a) vestibular nuclei, (b) red nucleus, (c) superior colliculi, (d) reticular nuclei, (e) all of these.

5. Brain waves typical of the alert, wide-awake state are (a) alpha, (b) beta, (c) delta, (d) theta.

6. Identify the stage of sleep described by using choices from the key. (Note that responses a–d refer to NREM sleep.)

Key: (a) stage 1, **(b)** stage 2, **(c)** stage 3, **(d)** stage 4, **(e)** REM

_____ **(1)** the stage when vital signs (blood pressure, heart rate, and body temperature) reach their lowest levels

_____ **(2)** indicated by movement of the eyes under the lids; dreaming occurs

_____ **(3)** when sleepwalking is likely to occur

_____ **(4)** when the sleeper is very easily awakened; EEG shows alpha waves

Short Answer Essay Questions

7. Differentiate clearly between sensation and perception.

8. How do synthetic and analytic quality discrimination differ?

9. Central pattern generators (CPGs) are found at the segmental level of motor control. (a) What is the job of the CPGs? (b) What controls them, and where is this control localized?

10. Make a diagram of the hierarchy of motor control. Position the CPGs, the command neurons, and the cerebellum/basal nuclei in this scheme.

11. How do the types of motor activity controlled by the direct (pyramidal) and indirect systems differ?

12. Why are the cerebellum and basal nuclei called *pre* command areas?

13. Define EEG.

14. How do sleep patterns, extent of sleeping time, and amount of time spent in REM and NREM sleep change through life?

15. (a) Define narcolepsy and insomnia. (b) Why is narcolepsy thought to reflect a problem with the sleep control centers? (c) Why is narcolepsy a dangerous condition?

16. (a) Define epilepsy. (b) Which form of this disorder is least distressing? Which is most distressing? Explain.

17. What is an aura?

18. What is holistic information processing, and what are its essential characteristics?

19. Compare and contrast short-term memory (STM) and long-term memory (LTM) relative to storage capacity and duration of the memory.

20. (a) Name several factors that can enhance transfer of information from STM to LTM. (b) Define memory consolidation.

21. Compare and contrast fact and skill memory relative to the types of things remembered and the importance of conscious retrieval.

22. Explain why consciousness, memory, and language are inseparable.

 CRITICAL THINKING AND CLINICAL APPLICATION QUESTIONS

1. Soon after Mr. Acton noted a weakness in his right arm, he was unable to speak or move the arm. During the examination, he seemed to understand what was said to him but could not respond appropriately—he uttered nonsense or garbled his words, and his right cheek and the right side of his mouth drooped. Although lower limb strength and reflexes were normal, reflexes in his right arm were hypoactive. No sensory losses or gait problems were noted. Given this situation, answer the following questions: (a) Specifically, what motor system (direct or indirect) and what brain site(s) are involved? (b) How do the abdominal and plantar reflexes change with lesions in this system? (c) What is Mr. Acton's speech disorder called?

2. Cynthia, a 16-year-old girl, is rushed to the hospital after taking a bad spill off the parallel bars. After a complete neurological workup, her family was told that she would be permanently paralyzed from the waist down. The neurologist then outlined for Cynthia's parents the importance of preventing complications in such cases. The common complications include urinary infection, bed sores and muscular spasms. Using your knowledge of neuroanatomy, explain the underlying reasons for these complications.

3. The medical chart of a 68-year-old man includes the following notes: "Slight tremor of right hand at rest; stony facial expression; difficulty in initiating movements." (a) Based on your present knowledge, what is the diagnosis? (b) What brain areas are most likely involved in this man's disorder, and what is the deficiency? (c) How is this condition currently treated?

The Special Senses

16

CHAPTER OUTLINE AND STUDENT OBJECTIVES

The Chemical Senses: Taste and Smell (pp. 502–506)

1. Describe the location, structure, and afferent pathways of taste and smell receptors, and explain how these receptors are activated.

The Eye and Vision (pp. 506–526)

2. Describe the structure and function of accessory eye structures, eye tunics, lens, and humors of the eye.

3. Trace the pathway of light through the eye to the retina, and explain how light is focused for distant and close vision.

4. Describe the events involved in the stimulation of photoreceptors by light, and compare and contrast the roles of rods and cones in vision.

5. Note the cause and consequences of astigmatism, cataract, glaucoma, hyperopia, myopia, and color blindness.

6. Compare and contrast light and dark adaptation.

7. Trace the visual pathway to the optic cortex, and briefly describe the process of visual processing.

The Ear: Hearing and Balance (pp. 526–539)

8. Describe the structure and general function of the outer, middle, and inner ears.

9. Describe the sound conduction pathway to the fluids of the inner ear, and follow the auditory pathway from the organ of Corti to the temporal cortex.

10. Explain how one is able to differentiate pitch and loudness of sounds and to localize the source of sounds.

11. Explain how the balance organs of the semicircular canals and the vestibule help to maintain dynamic and static equilibrium.

12. List possible causes and symptoms of otitis media, deafness, Ménière's syndrome, and motion sickness.

Developmental Aspects of the Special Senses (pp. 539–542)

13. Describe the embryonic development of the special sense organs and list changes that occur in these organs with aging.

People are responsive creatures. The aroma of freshly baked bread makes our mouths water. A sudden clap of thunder makes us recoil. These irritants and many others are the stimuli that continually greet us and are interpreted by our nervous systems.

We are usually told that we have five senses: touch, taste, smell, sight, and hearing. Actually, touch is made up of a complex of general senses that we considered in Chapter 13. The other four traditional senses—*smell, taste, sight,* and *hearing*—are called special senses. Receptors for a fifth special sense, *equilibrium,* are housed in the ear, along with the organ of hearing. In contrast to the widely distributed general receptors (most of which are modified dendrites of sensory neurons), the **special sensory receptors** are distinct *receptor cells*. These receptor cells are confined to the head region and are highly localized, either housed within complex sensory organs (eyes and ears) or within distinct epithelial structures (taste buds and olfactory epithelium).

This chapter considers the functional anatomy of each of the five special senses. But keep in mind that our perceptions of sensory inputs are overlapping. What we finally experience—our "feel" of the world—is a blending of stimulus effects.

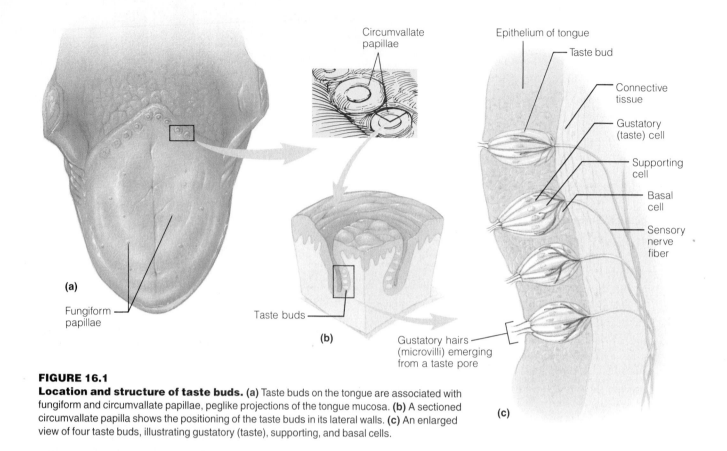

FIGURE 16.1
Location and structure of taste buds. (a) Taste buds on the tongue are associated with fungiform and circumvallate papillae, peglike projections of the tongue mucosa. **(b)** A sectioned circumvallate papilla shows the positioning of the taste buds in its lateral walls. **(c)** An enlarged view of four taste buds, illustrating gustatory (taste), supporting, and basal cells.

THE CHEMICAL SENSES: TASTE AND SMELL

The receptors for taste (gustation) and smell (olfaction) are classified as **chemoreceptors** because they respond to chemicals in an aqueous solution. The taste receptors are excited by food chemicals dissolved in saliva; the smell receptors, by airborne chemicals that dissolve in fluids produced on nasal membranes. The receptors for taste and smell complement each other and respond to many of the same stimuli.

Taste Buds and the Sense of Taste

The word *taste* comes from the Latin *taxare,* meaning "to touch, estimate, or judge." When we taste things, we are in fact intimately testing or judging our environment, and the sense of taste is considered by many to be the most pleasurable of the special senses.

Localization and Structure of Taste Buds

The **taste buds,** the sensory receptor organs for taste, are located primarily in the oral cavity. Of our 10,000 or so taste buds, most are on the tongue. A few are scattered on the soft palate, inner surface of the cheeks, pharynx, and epiglottis of the larynx.

Most taste buds are found in peglike projections of the tongue mucosa called **papillae** (pah-pil'e), which give the tongue surface a slightly abrasive feel. These papillae are of three major types: filiform, fungiform, and circumvallate. In human adults, the latter two types house most of the taste buds. The mushroom-shaped **fungiform** (fun'jĭ-form) **papillae** are scattered over the entire tongue surface, but are most abundant at its tip and along its sides (Figure 16.1a). The round **circumvallate** (ser"kum-val'āt) **papillae** are the largest and least numerous papillae; 7 to 12 of these form an inverted V at the back of the tongue (see Figure 16.1a). Taste buds are located in the epithelium of the side walls of the circumvallate papillae (Figure 16.1b) and on the tops of the fungiform papillae.

Each globular taste bud consists of 40 to 60 *epithelial cells* of three major types: supporting cells, receptor cells, and basal cells (Figure 16.1c). **Supporting cells** form the bulk of the taste bud. They insulate the receptor cells called **gustatory,** or **taste, cells** from each other and from the surrounding tongue epithelium. Long microvilli called **gustatory hairs** project from the tips of both cell types and extend through a **taste pore** to the surface of the epithelium, where they are bathed by saliva. Apparently, the gustatory hairs are the sensitive portions *(receptor membranes)* of the gustatory cells. Coiling intimately around the gustatory cells are sensory dendrites that represent the initial part of the gustatory pathway to the brain. Each afferent fiber receives signals from several receptor cells within the taste bud. Because of their location, taste bud cells are subjected to huge amounts of friction and they are among the most dynamic cells in the body. They are shed every 7 to 10 days. Apparently the **basal cells** act as stem cells, dividing and differentiating into supporting cells, which in turn give rise to new gustatory cells.

Basic Taste Sensations

Normally, our taste sensations are complicated mixtures of qualities. However, when taste is tested with pure chemical compounds, taste sensations can all be grouped into one of four basic qualities: *sweet, sour, salty,* and *bitter.* The sweet taste is elicited by many organic substances including sugars, saccharin, alcohols, some amino acids, and some lead salts (such as those found in lead paint). Sour taste is produced by acids, specifically their hydrogen ions (H^+) in solution, whereas a salty taste is produced by metal ions (inorganic salts). Table salt (sodium chloride) tastes the "saltiest." The bitter taste is elicited by alkaloids (such as quinine, nicotine, caffeine, morphine, and strychnine) as well as a number of nonalkaloid substances, such as aspirin.

Although there are no *structural* differences between the taste buds in different areas of the tongue, the tip of the tongue is most sensitive to sweet and salty substances, the sides to sour, and the back of the tongue (near its root) to bitter (Figure 16.2). However, these differences are not absolute: Most taste buds respond to two, three, or all four taste qualities, and many substances produce a mixture of the basic taste sensations. Furthermore, some substances change in flavor as they move through the mouth. Saccharin is initially tasted as sweet, but acquires a bitter aftertaste at the back of the tongue.

Taste likes and dislikes have homeostatic value. A liking for sugar and salt helps satisfy the body's need for carbohydrates and minerals (as well as some amino acids). Many sour, naturally acidic foods (such as oranges, lemons, and tomatoes) are rich sources of vitamin C, an essential vitamin. Since many natural poisons and spoiled foods are bitter, our dislike for bitterness is protective. (The position of the bitter receptors on the most posterior part of the tongue seems strange, however, because usually by the time we actually taste a bitter substance, we have swallowed some of it.) Although many people learn to enjoy bitter foods such as olives and quinine water, most animals scrupulously avoid bitter substances.

Physiology of Taste

Activation of Taste Receptors.
For a chemical to be tasted, it must dissolve in saliva, diffuse into the taste pore, and contact the gustatory hairs. Bind-

? *Think back to your studies of the cranial nerves as you view Figure 16.2. Which taste sensitivity would be most impaired by injury to the glossopharyngeal nerve?*

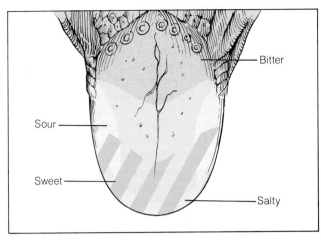

FIGURE 16.2
Relative patterns of taste sensitivity on the tongue dorsum. (Note: since the area most sensitive to sweet overlaps the gray sour and yellow salty areas, the sweet area is indicated by dark pink stripes.)

ing of the food chemical to the gustatory cell membranes induces a depolarizing potential and these cells do contain synaptic vesicles. The current theory is that the generator potentials that elicit action potentials in the associated sensory dendrites are produced by a chemical stimulus via release of the synaptic vesicle (neurotransmitter) contents.

The higher the concentration of a chemical, the more intense its perceived taste. However, the different gustatory cells have different thresholds for activation. The bitter receptors (in line with their protective nature) detect substances present in minute amounts. The sour receptors are less sensitive; the sweet and salty receptors are least sensitive. Taste receptors adapt rapidly, with partial adaptation in 3–5 seconds and complete adaptation in 1–5 minutes.

Mechanism of Taste Transduction.
Transduction, as you may recall, is the sensory mechanism by which stimulus energy is converted into a nerve impulse. The mechanism of taste transduction in the afferent fiber (initiated by a chemical stimulus) is only partly known, but each taste quality appears to have its own special mechanism. Salty taste seems to be due to Na^+ influx through sodium channels; sour is mediated by H^+ blockade of K^+ or Na^+ channels. The bitter and sweet responses are mediated by G protein–dependent mechanisms that act to increase intracellular levels of Ca^{2+} (bitter) or inactivate K^+ channels (sweet). The G protein subunit that mediates transduction of bitter tastes has recently been identified and named *gustducin.*

The Gustatory Pathway

As described in Chapter 13, afferent fibers carrying taste information from the tongue are found primarily in two cranial nerve pairs. A branch of the **facial** nerve (VII), the *chorda tympani,* transmits impulses from taste receptors in the anterior two-thirds of the tongue, whereas the lingual branch of the **glossopharyngeal nerve** (IX) services the posterior third. Taste impulses from the few taste buds in the epiglottis and pharynx are conducted primarily by the **vagus nerve** (X). These afferent fibers synapse in the **solitary nucleus** of the medulla, and from there impulses are transmitted to the thalamus and ultimately to the gustatory cortex in the parietal lobes.

Fibers also project to the hypothalamus and limbic system structures, regions that determine our appreciation of what we are tasting. The gustatory pathway is distinctive because, unlike most other sensory pathways, most of its fibers remain uncrossed. Innervation of the taste buds is essential for their survival—if their afferent fibers are transected, they degenerate.

An important role of taste is to trigger reflexes involved in digestion. As taste impulses pass through the solitary nucleus, they initiate reflexes (via synapses with parasympathetic nuclei) that increase secretion of saliva into the mouth and gastric juice into the stomach. Saliva contains mucus that moistens food and digestive enzymes that begin the digestion of starch. Acidic foods are particularly strong stimulants of the salivary reflex. Additionally, when we eat revolting or foul-tasting substances, gagging or even reflexive vomiting may be initiated.

Influence of Other Sensations on Taste

What we commonly call taste depends heavily on the stimulation of olfactory receptors. Indeed, taste is 80% smell. When the olfactory receptors in the nasal cavity are blocked by nasal congestion (or pinching your nostrils), food is bland. Without smell, our morning coffee would lack its richness and simply taste bitter.

The mouth also contains thermoreceptors, mechanoreceptors, and nociceptors, and the temperature and texture of foods can enhance or detract from their taste. "Hot" foods such as chili peppers actually excite pain receptors in the mouth.

The Olfactory Epithelium and the Sense of Smell

Although our olfactory sense (*olfact* = to smell) is far less acute than that of many other animals, the human nose is still much keener than any machine in picking up small differences in odors. Some people capitalize on this ability by becoming wine tasters.

Localization and Structure of Olfactory Receptors

Olfaction, like taste, detects chemicals in solution. The organ of smell is a yellow-tinged patch of pseudostratified epithelium called the **olfactory epithelium** located in the roof of the nasal cavity (Figure 16.3a). Since air entering the nasal cavity must make a hairpin turn to stimulate olfactory receptors before entering the respiratory passageway below, the human olfactory epithelium is in a poor position for doing its job. (This is why sniffing, which draws more air superiorly across the olfactory epithelium, intensifies the sense of smell.) The olfactory epithelium covers the superior nasal concha on each side of the nasal septum, and contains millions of bowling pin–shaped **olfactory receptor cells.** These are surrounded and cushioned by columnar **supporting cells,** which make up the bulk of the penny-thin epithelial membrane (Figure 16.3b). The supporting cells contain a yellow-brown pigment similar to lipofuscin, which gives the olfactory epithelium its yellow hue. At the base of the epithelium lie the "short" **basal cells.**

The olfactory receptor cells are "unusual" bipolar neurons. Each has a thin apical dendrite that terminates in a knob from which several long cilia called **olfactory hairs** radiate. These olfactory hairs, which substantially increase the receptive surface area, typically lie flat on the nasal epithelium and are covered by a coat of thin mucus produced by the supporting cells and by **olfactory glands** in the underlying connective tissue. This mucus is a solvent that "captures" and dissolves airborne odor molecules. It is renewed continuously, flushing away "old" odor molecules so that new odor chemicals always have access to the receptor cilia. Unlike other cilia in the body, which beat rapidly and in a coordinated manner, olfactory cilia are largely nonmotile. The slender, unmyelinated axons of the olfactory receptor cells are gathered into small fascicles that collectively form the **fiber bundles of the olfactory nerve** (cranial nerve I). They project superiorly through the openings in the cribriform plate of the ethmoid bone, where they synapse in the overlying olfactory bulbs.

Olfactory receptor cells are unique in that they are the only *neurons* that undergo turnover throughout adult life. (Remember, the taste receptors are epithelial cells.) Their typical life span is 60 days, after which they are replaced through the differentiation of the basal cells in the olfactory epithelium.

Specificity of the Olfactory Receptors

Smell is difficult to research because any given odor (say, tobacco smoke) may be made up of hundreds of different chemicals. Taste has been neatly packaged into four taste qualities, but science has yet to discover any similar means for classifying smell. Our keen sense of smell can distinguish 10,000 or so chemicals, but research suggests that our olfactory receptors are stimulated by different combinations of a more limited number of **primary odors,** or olfactory qualities. The actual number of primary odors is still controversial: One camp has it that there are 7 "pri-

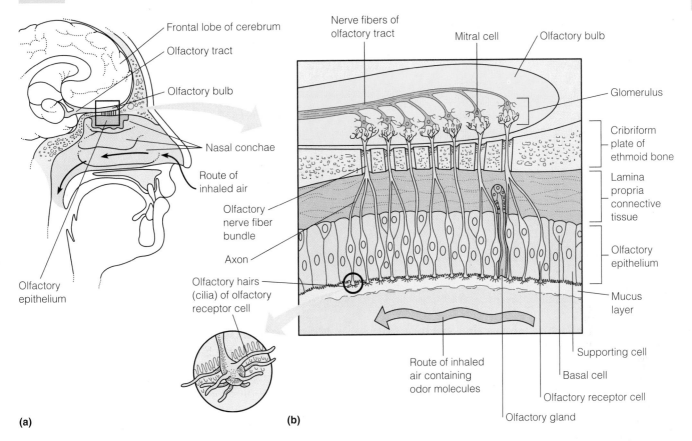

(a)

(b)

FIGURE 16.3
Olfactory receptors. (a) Site of olfactory epithelium in the superior aspect of the nasal cavity. **(b)** Enlarged view illustrating the cellular composition of the olfactory epithelium and the course of the fibers of the olfactory nerve (I) through the ethmoid bone to synapse in the overlying olfactory bulb. The glomeruli and mitral cells (output cells) within the olfactory bulb are also shown.

maries" (floral, musky, camphorous, pepperminty, ethereal, pungent [stinging], and putrid [rotten]); another indicates that we respond to 30 pure odor classes. However, studies done in the early 1990s suggest that there are at least 1000 "smell genes" that are active only in the nose. Each gene encodes a unique receptor protein, and each of the receptor proteins responds to a small group of different odors.

The olfactory neurons are exquisitely sensitive—in some cases, just a few molecules activate them. However, most olfactory receptors appear to have relatively low specificity; that is, they respond to a variety of chemicals. As with taste, some of what we call smell is really pain. The nasal cavities contain pain receptors that respond to irritants such as the sharpness of ammonia, the hotness of chili peppers, and the "chill" of menthol. Impulses from these pain receptors reach the central nervous system via afferent fibers of the trigeminal nerves.

Physiology of Smell

Activation of the Olfactory Receptors. For us to smell a particular chemical, it must be *volatile*—

that is, it must be in the gaseous state as it enters the nasal cavity. Additionally, it must be sufficiently water soluble to dissolve in the fluid coating of the olfactory epithelium. The dissolved chemicals may stimulate the olfactory receptors by binding to protein receptors in the olfactory hair (cilium) membranes and opening specific Na^+ and K^+ channels. This leads to a receptor potential and ultimately (assuming threshold stimulation) to an action potential that is conducted to the first relay station in the olfactory bulb.

Mechanism of Smell Transduction. The details of transduction in olfactory receptor cells are still to be fully worked out. However, there is little doubt that G proteins are involved and that at least in some receptor cells: (1) cyclic AMP is a second messenger and (2) opening of Na^+ channels leads to depolarization and impulse transmission. In addition, some studies indicate that rising intracellular Ca^{2+} may promote receptor cell adaptation by reducing the affinity of the ion channels for cyclic AMP.

The Olfactory Pathway

As noted above, axons of the olfactory receptor cells

Eyebrow

Eyelashes

Site where conjunctiva merges with cornea

Eyelid

Pupil

Palpebral fissure

Caruncle

Lateral canthus

Iris

Medial canthus

Eyelid

Sclera (covered with conjunctiva)

FIGURE 16.4
Surface anatomy of the eye and associated accessory structures. The eyelids are open more widely than normal to show the entire iris.

constitute the olfactory nerves that synapse in the overlying **olfactory bulbs,** the distal ends of the olfactory tracts (see Table 13.2). There, the fibers of the olfactory nerves synapse with **mitral** (mi′tral) **cells** (second-order neurons) in complex structures called **glomeruli** (glo-mer′u-li; "balls of yarn") (see Figure 16.3b). The mitral cells appear to play an important local integration role in olfaction, and depending on local conditions, they may be activated or inhibited. The olfactory bulbs also house *granule cells,* GABA-releasing cells that inhibit mitral cells (via dendro-dendritic synapses), so that only highly excitatory olfactory impulses are transmitted. This inhibition is believed to contribute to the mechanism of *olfactory adaptation* and helps explain how a man working in a paper mill or sewage treatment plant can still enjoy his lunch! The granule cells also receive efferent impulses from the brain, which modify the reaction of the olfactory bulbs to smell under certain conditions. For example, the aromas of food are perceived differently depending on whether we are ravenously hungry or have just finished eating.

When the mitral cells are activated, impulses flow from the olfactory bulbs via the **olfactory tracts** (composed mainly of mitral cell axons) to two main destinations: (1) via the thalamus to the olfactory cortex (piriform lobe and frontal lobe), where smells are consciously interpreted, and (2) via the subcortical route to the hypothalamus, amygdala, and other regions of the limbic system, where the emotional aspects of smells are analyzed and responded to. Smells associated with danger—smoke, cooking gas, or skunk scent—trigger the sympathetic fight-or-flight response. As with tastes, appetizing odors cause increased salivation and stimulation of the digestive tract, and unpleasant odors can trigger protective reflexes such as sneezing and choking. Substances with a sharp smell, like ammonia, cause reflex cessation of breathing.

Homeostatic Imbalances of the Chemical Senses

While dysfunctions of taste or smell do occur, most people seeking medical help for problems of the chemical senses have olfactory disorders, or *anosmias* (an-oz′me-ahz; "without smells"). Although some cases are due to genetic factors, most anosmias result from head injuries that tear the olfactory nerves, the aftereffects of nasal cavity inflammation (due to a cold, an allergy, or smoking), physical obstruction of the nasal cavity (as by polyps), and aging. The culprit in one-third of all cases of chemical sense loss is zinc deficiency, and the cure is rapid once the right form of zinc supplement is prescribed. Zinc is a known growth factor for the receptors of the chemical senses.

Brain disorders can distort the sense of smell. Some people have *uncinate* (uns′ih-nāt) *fits,* olfactory hallucinations during which they experience a particular (usually unpleasant) odor, such as rotting meat. Some such cases are undeniably psychological, but many result from irritation of the olfactory pathway by brain surgery or head trauma. *Olfactory auras* experienced by some epileptics just before they have a seizure are transient uncinate fits. •

THE EYE AND VISION

Of all the sensory receptors in the body, 70% are in the eyes. The photoreceptors sense and encode the patterns made by light in our surroundings. The massive optic tracts that carry the coded information from the eyes to the brain contain over a million nerve fibers. Only the corticospinal tracts controlling all our voluntary muscles are larger! Our brain invests the signals from our eyes with meaning, fashioning images of the world around us.

The adult **eye** is a sphere with a diameter of about

2.5 cm (1 inch). Only the anterior one-sixth of the eye's surface is visible; the rest is enclosed and protected by a cushion of fat and the walls of the bony orbit. The fat pad occupies nearly all of the orbit not occupied by the eye itself. The eye is a complex structure and only a small portion of its tissues are actually involved in photoreception. But before turning our attention to the eye itself, let us consider the accessory structures that protect it or enhance its functioning.

Accessory Structures of the Eye

The **accessory structures** of the eye include the eyebrows, eyelids, conjunctiva, lacrimal apparatus, and extrinsic eye muscles.

Eyebrows

The **eyebrows** are short, coarse hairs that overlie the supraorbital margins of the skull (Figures 16.4 and 16.5a). They help shade the eyes from sunlight and prevent perspiration trickling down the forehead from reaching the eyes. Deep to the skin of the eyebrows are parts of the orbicularis oculi and corrugator muscles. Contraction of the orbicularis muscle depresses the eyebrow, whereas the corrugator moves the eyebrow medially.

Eyelids

Anteriorly, the eyes are protected by the mobile **eyelids** or **palpebrae** (pal′pĕ-bre). The eyelids are separated by the **palpebral fissure** and meet at the medial and lateral angles of the eye—the **medial** and **lateral canthi,** respectively (see Figure 16.4). The medial canthus sports a fleshy elevation called the **caruncle** (kar′ung-kl; "a bit of flesh"). The caruncle contains sebaceous and sweat glands and produces the whitish, oily secretion (fancifully called the Sandman's "eye-sand") that sometimes collects at the medial canthus, especially during sleep. In most Asian peoples, a vertical fold of skin called the *epicanthic fold* commonly appears on both sides of the nose and sometimes covers the inner canthus.

The eyelids are thin, skin-covered folds supported internally by flat connective tissue sheets called **tarsal plates** (see Figure 16.5a). The tarsal plates also anchor the orbicularis oculi and levator palpebrae superioris muscles that run within the eyelid. The orbicularis muscle encircles the eye; when it contracts, the eye closes. Of the two eyelids, the larger upper one is much more mobile, mainly because of the **levator palpebrae superioris** muscle, which raises that eyelid to open the eye. The eyelid muscles are activated reflexively to cause blinking every 3–7 seconds and to protect the eye when it is threatened by foreign objects. Reflex blinking helps prevent desiccation (drying) of the eyes because each time we blink, accessory structure secretions (oil, mucus, and saline solution) are spread across the eyeball surface.

(a)

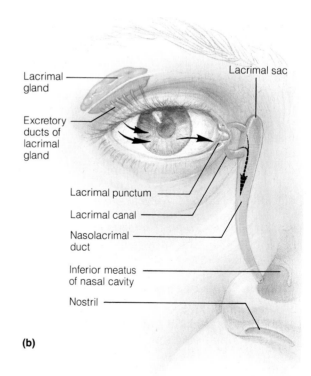

(b)

FIGURE 16.5
Accessory structures of the eye. (a) Sagittal section of the accessory structures associated with the anterior portion of the eye. **(b)** The lacrimal apparatus. Arrows indicate the direction of flow of lacrimal fluid after its release by the lacrimal gland.

Projecting from the free margin of each eyelid are the **eyelashes.** The follicles of the eyelash hairs are richly innervated by nerve endings (root hair plexuses), and when anything touches the eyelashes (even a puff of air), reflex blinking is triggered.

Several types of glands are associated with the eyelids. The **tarsal,** or **Meibomian** (mi-bo′me-an), **glands** are embedded in the tarsal plates (see Figure 16.5a), and their ducts open at the eyelid edge just posterior to the eyelashes. These modified sebaceous glands produce an oily secretion that lubricates the eyelid and the eye and prevents the eyelids from sticking together. Associated with the eyelash follicles are a number of smaller, more typical sebaceous glands. Modified sweat glands called *ciliary glands* lie between the hair follicles (*cilium* = eyelash).

Infection of a tarsal gland results in an unsightly cyst called a *chalazion* (kah-la′ze-on). Inflammation of any of the smaller glands is called a *sty.* •

Conjunctiva

The **conjunctiva** (kon″junk-ti′vah; "joined together") is a delicate mucous membrane that lines the eyelids as the **palpebral conjunctiva** and reflects (folds back) over the anterior surface of the eyeball as the **ocular,** or **bulbar, conjunctiva** (see Figure 16.5a). The latter covers only the white of the eye, not the cornea (the clear "window" over the iris and pupil). The ocular conjunctiva is very thin, and blood vessels are clearly visible beneath it. When the eye is closed, a slitlike space occurs between the conjunctiva-covered eyeball and eyelids. This so-called **conjunctival sac** is where a contact lens lies and eye medications are often administered into its inferior recess. Although the conjunctiva does protect the eye by preventing foreign objects from penetrating beyond the confines of the conjunctival sac, its major function is to produce a lubricating mucus that prevents the eyes from drying out.

Inflammation of the conjunctiva, called *conjunctivitis,* results in reddened, irritated (sometimes "bloodshot") eyes. *Pinkeye,* a conjunctival infection caused by bacteria or viruses, is highly contagious. •

Lacrimal Apparatus

The **lacrimal** (lak′rĭ-mal; "tear") **apparatus** consists of the lacrimal gland and the ducts that drain the excess lacrimal secretions into the nasal cavity (Figure 16.5b). The **lacrimal gland** lies within the orbit above the lateral end of the eye and is visible through the conjunctiva when the lid is everted. It continually releases a dilute saline solution called **lacrimal secretion**—or, more commonly, **tears**—into the superior part of the conjunctival sac through several small excretory ducts. Blinking spreads the tears downward and across the eyeball to the medial canthus, where they enter the paired **lacrimal canals** via two tiny orifices called **lacrimal puncta** (literally, "prick points"),

visible as tiny red dots on the medial margin of each eyelid. From the lacrimal canals, the tears drain into the **lacrimal sac** and then into the **nasolacrimal duct,** which empties into the nasal cavity at the inferior nasal meatus.

Lacrimal fluid contains mucus, antibodies, and **lysozyme,** an enzyme that destroys bacteria. Thus, it cleanses and protects the eye surface as it moistens and lubricates it. Since the activity of the lacrimal glands decreases with age, the eyes tend to become less moist and more vulnerable to infection and irritation during the later years of life. When lacrimal secretion increases substantially, tears spill over the eyelids and fill the nasal cavities, causing congestion. This happens when the eyes are irritated by foreign objects or noxious chemicals and when we are emotionally upset. In the case of eye irritation, enhanced tearing serves to wash away or dilute the irritating substance. The importance of emotionally induced tears is poorly understood. The recent discovery that lacrimal secretion contains enkephalins (natural opiates) and the fact that only humans shed emotional tears suggest that crying is important in reducing stress. Although anyone who has had a good cry would probably agree, this has been difficult to demonstrate scientifically.

Because the nasal cavity mucosa is continuous with that of the lacrimal duct system, a cold or nasal inflammation often causes the lacrimal mucosa to become inflamed and swell. This constricts the ducts and prevents tears from draining from the eye surface, causing "watery" eyes. •

Extrinsic Eye Muscles

The movement of each eyeball is controlled by six straplike **extrinsic eye muscles.** These originate from the bony orbit (*extrins* = from the outside) and insert into the outer surface of the eyeball (Figure 16.6). These muscles allow the eyes to follow a moving object. They also provide external "guy wires" that help to maintain the shape of the eyeball and hold it in the orbit.

Four of the extrinsic muscles, the *rectus muscles,* originate from a common tendinous ring, the **annular ring,** at the back of the orbit and run straight to their insertion on the eyeball. Their locations and the movements that they promote are clearly indicated by their names: **superior, inferior, lateral,** and **medial rectus muscles.** The actions of the two *oblique muscles* are less easily deduced because they take rather strange paths through the orbit. They move the eye in the vertical plane when the eyeball is already turned medially by the rectus muscle. The **superior oblique muscle** originates in common with the rectus muscles, runs along the medial wall of the orbit, and then makes a right-angle turn and passes through a fibrocartilaginous loop, called the **trochlea** (trok′le-ah; "pulley"), before inserting on the superolateral aspect of the eyeball. Its contraction rotates the eye down-

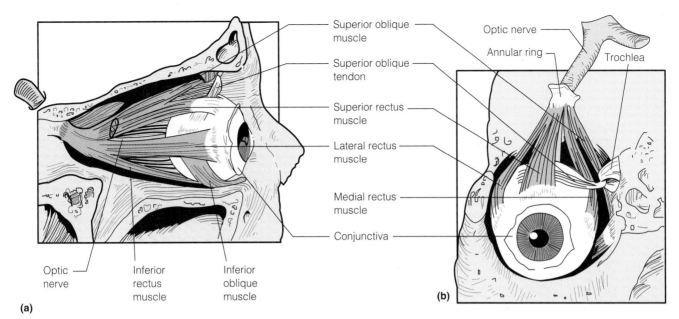

FIGURE 16.6
Extrinsic muscles of the eye.
(a) Lateral view of the right eye.
(b) Anterosuperior view of the right eye.
(c) Summary of cranial nerve
innervations and muscle actions.

Labels in figure:
- Superior oblique muscle
- Superior oblique tendon
- Superior rectus muscle
- Lateral rectus muscle
- Medial rectus muscle
- Conjunctiva
- Optic nerve
- Inferior rectus muscle
- Inferior oblique muscle
- Optic nerve
- Annular ring
- Trochlea

(a)

(b)

(c)

Name	Controlling cranial nerve	Action
Lateral rectus	VI (abducens)	Moves eye laterally
Medial rectus	III (oculomotor)	Moves eye medially
Superior rectus	III (oculomotor)	Elevates eye or rolls it superiorly
Inferior rectus	III (oculomotor)	Depresses eye or rolls it inferiorly
Inferior oblique	III (oculomotor)	Elevates eye and turns it laterally
Superior oblique	IV (trochlear)	Depresses eye and turns it laterally

ward and somewhat laterally. The **inferior oblique muscle** originates from the medial orbit surface and runs laterally and obliquely to insert on the inferolateral eye surface. Hence, it rotates the eye up and laterally.

Students often ask why we have the two oblique muscles, when the four rectus muscles seem to provide all the eye movements we require—medial, lateral, superior, and inferior. The simplest way to answer this question is to point out that the superior and inferior recti cannot elevate or depress the eye *without also turning it medially* because they approach the eye from a posteromedial direction. For an eye to be *directly* elevated or depressed, the lateral pull of the oblique muscles is necessary to cancel the medial pull of the superior and inferior recti.

Except for the lateral rectus and superior oblique muscles, which are innervated respectively by the *abducens* and *trochlear nerves,* all extrinsic eye muscles are served by the *oculomotor nerves.* The actions and nerve supply of these muscles are summarized in Figure 16.6c. The courses of the associated cranial nerves are illustrated in Table 13.2.

The extrinsic eye muscles are among the most precisely and rapidly controlled skeletal muscles in the entire body. This reflects their high axon-to-muscle-fiber ratio: The motor units of these muscles contain 8 to 12 muscle cells and in some cases even fewer. The extrinsic muscles effect two basic types of eye movements:

1. Saccades (sah-kādz'; "jerks on the fibers") are small, jerky movements that quickly move the eye from one point to another, allowing the entire visual field to be seen in a short time. (The **visual field** is the field of view seen when the head is still.)

2. Slow **scanning movements** are *tracking* movements that allow us to follow a particular object moving in our visual fields and to keep our gaze focused on an object as we move our heads. Most eye movements involved in aiming the eyes for visual focusing require the coordinated activity of at least two of these muscles.

When movements of the external muscles of the two eyes are not perfectly coordinated, a person cannot properly focus the images of the same area of the visual field from each eye and so sees two images instead of one. This condition is called **diplopia** (dĭ-plo'pe-ah), or *double vision.* It can result from paralysis or weakness of certain extrinsic muscles, or it may be a temporary consequence of acute alcohol intoxication.

Congenital weakness of the external eye muscles may cause **strabismus** (strah-biz'mus; "cross-eyed"), a condition in which the affected eye rotates medially or laterally. To compensate, the normal and deviant eyes may alternate in focusing on objects. In other cases, only the controllable eye is used and the brain begins to disregard inputs from the deviant eye, which then becomes functionally blind. Strabismus

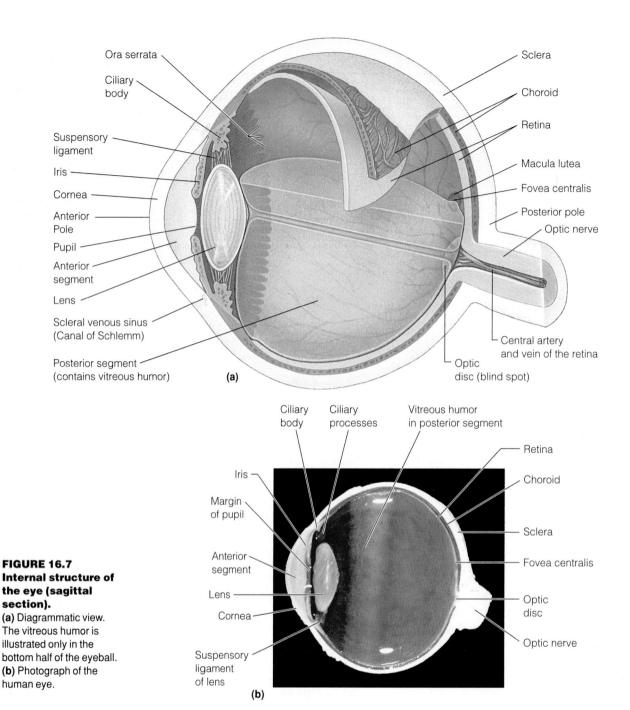

Ora serrata

Ciliary body

Suspensory ligament

Iris

Cornea

Anterior Pole

Pupil

Anterior segment

Lens

Scleral venous sinus (Canal of Schlemm)

Posterior segment (contains vitreous humor)

(a)

Sclera

Choroid

Retina

Macula lutea

Fovea centralis

Posterior pole

Optic nerve

Central artery and vein of the retina

Optic disc (blind spot)

Ciliary body

Ciliary processes

Vitreous humor in posterior segment

Iris

Margin of pupil

Anterior segment

Lens

Cornea

Suspensory ligament of lens

(b)

Retina

Choroid

Sclera

Fovea centralis

Optic disc

Optic nerve

FIGURE 16.7
Internal structure of the eye (sagittal section).
(a) Diagrammatic view. The vitreous humor is illustrated only in the bottom half of the eyeball. **(b)** Photograph of the human eye.

cannot be outgrown. Less severe cases may be treated either with eye exercises to strengthen the weak muscles or by temporarily placing a patch on the stronger eye, which forces the child to use the weaker eye. Surgery on the eye muscles is needed for unyielding conditions. •

Structure of the Eyeball

The eye itself, commonly called the **eyeball**, is a slightly irregular hollow sphere (Figure 16.7). Since the eyeball is shaped roughly like the globe of the earth, it is said to have poles. Its most anterior point is the **anterior pole;** its most posterior point, the **poste-**rior pole. Its wall is composed of three coats, or tunics, the fibrous, vascular, and sensory tunics. Its interior is filled with fluids called *humors* that help to maintain its shape. The lens, the main focusing apparatus of the eye, is supported vertically within the eye, dividing it into *anterior* and *posterior segments.*

Tunics Forming the Wall of the Eyeball

The Fibrous Tunic.   The outermost coat of the eye, the **fibrous tunic,** is composed of dense avascular connective tissue. It has two obviously different regions: the sclera and the cornea. The **sclera** (skle′rah), forming the posterior portion and the bulk of the fibrous tunic, is glistening white and opaque. Seen anteriorly as the "white of the eye," the tough, tendonlike sclera (*sclera* = hard) protects and shapes the eyeball and provides a sturdy anchoring site for the extrinsic eye muscles. Posteriorly, where the sclera is pierced by the optic nerve, it is continuous with the dura mater of the brain. The anterior sixth of the fibrous tunic is modified to form the transparent **cornea,** which bulges anteriorly from its junction with the sclera. The regular arrangement of its collagen fibers makes the cornea crystal clear, allowing it to form a window that lets light enter the eye. As explained shortly, the cornea is also part of the light-bending apparatus of the eye.

The cornea is covered by epithelial sheets on both faces (see Figure 16.12, p. 514). The external sheet, a stratified squamous epithelium, merges with the ocular conjunctiva at the sclera-cornea junction and helps to protect the cornea from abrasion. A simple squamous epithelium, also called the corneal *endothelium,* lines the inner face of the cornea. Its cells have active sodium pumps that maintain the clarity of the cornea by continually ejecting sodium ions from the cornea into the fluids of the eyeball. Water follows (along its osmotic gradients), and so the tightly packed collagen fibers of the cornea remain undisturbed by accumulations of tissue fluid that could force them apart.

The cornea is well supplied with nerve endings, most of which are pain fibers. (For this reason, some people can never adjust to wearing contact lenses.) When the cornea is touched, reflex blinking and increased lacrimal fluid secretion occur. Even so, the cornea is the most exposed part of the eye and is very vulnerable to damage from dust, slivers, etc. Luckily, its capacity for regeneration and repair is extraordinary. Furthermore, it can be replaced surgically. The cornea is the only tissue in the body that can be transplanted from one person to another without the possibility of rejection. Since it has no blood vessels, it is beyond the reach of the immune system.

The Vascular Tunic (Uvea).

The **vascular tunic,** or middle coat of the eyeball, is also called the **uvea** (u′ve-ah; "grape"). The pigmented uvea has three distinct regions: choroid, ciliary body, and iris (see Figure 16.7).

The **choroid** is a highly vascular, dark brown membrane (*choroid* = membranelike) that forms the posterior five-sixths of the uvea. Its blood vessels provide nutrition to all eye tunics. Its brown pigment, produced by melanocytes, helps absorb light, preventing it from scattering and reflecting within the eye (which would cause visual confusion). The choroid is incomplete posteriorly where the optic nerve leaves the eye. Anteriorly, it is continuous with the **ciliary body,** at a sawtoothed junction called the **ora serrata** ("serrated mouth"). The ciliary body, a

Lens

Suspensory ligament

Ciliary processes

FIGURE 16.8
Scanning electron micrograph of the posterior aspect of a portion of the lens, suspensory ligament, and ciliary body. Notice the fineness of the fibers of the suspensory ligament that suspends the lens in the eye (15 ×).

thickened, blood-rich ring of tissue that encircles the lens, consists chiefly of interlacing smooth muscle bundles called **ciliary muscles,** which are important in controlling lens shape. Its surface is thrown into folds called **ciliary processes,** which contain the capillaries that secrete the fluid that fills the cavity of the anterior segment of the eyeball. The **suspensory ligament,** or **zonule,** extends from the ciliary processes to the lens; this halo of fine fibers encircles and helps hold the lens in its upright position in the eye (Figure 16.8).

The **iris,** the visible colored part of the eye, is the most anterior portion of the uvea. Shaped like a flattened doughnut, it lies between the cornea and the lens and is continuous with the ciliary body posteriorly. Its round central opening, the **pupil,** allows light to enter the eye. The iris, made up of circularly and radially arranged smooth muscle fibers, acts as a reflexively activated diaphragm to vary pupil size. In close vision and bright light, the circular muscles contract and the pupil constricts. In distant vision and dim light, the radial muscles contract and the pupil dilates, allowing more light to enter the eye. As described in Chapter 14, pupillary dilation and constriction are controlled by sympathetic and parasympathetic fibers, respectively.

Changes in pupil size may also reflect our interests and emotional reactions to what we are seeing. Pupil dilation often occurs when the subject matter is appealing and during problem solving. (Computing your taxes should make your pupils get bigger and bigger.) On the other hand, boredom or subject matter that is personally repulsive causes pupil constriction.

FIGURE 16.9
Schematic view of the three major neuronal populations (photoreceptors, bipolar cells, and ganglion cells) composing the neural layer of the retina. The axons of the ganglion cells form the optic nerve, which leaves the back of the eyeball at the optic disc. Notice that light passes through the retina to excite the photoreceptor cells (as indicated by the yellow arrows). The flow of electrical signals occurs in the opposite direction: from the photoreceptors to the bipolar cells and finally to the ganglion cells (black arrows).

Although irises come in different colors (*iris =* rainbow), they contain only brown pigment. When they contain a lot of pigment, the eyes appear brown or black. If the amount of pigment is small and restricted to the posterior surface of the iris, the shorter wavelengths of light are scattered from the unpigmented parts of the iris, and the eyes appear blue, green, or gray. This is similar to the scattering of light that makes the sky appear blue. Most newborn babies' eyes are slate gray or blue because their iris pigment is not yet developed.

The Sensory Tunic (Retina). The innermost tunic is the delicate, two-layered **retina** (ret′ĭ-nah). The outer **pigmented layer,** a single-cell-thick lining, abuts the choroid, and extends anteriorly to cover the ciliary body and the posterior face of the iris. Its pigmented epithelial cells, like those of the choroid, absorb light and prevent it from scattering in the eye. They also act as phagocytes and store vitamin A needed by the photoreceptor cells. The transparent inner **neural (nervous) layer** extends anteriorly only to the ora serrata (see Figure 16.7). Actually an out-

pocketing of the brain, the retina contains millions of photoreceptors that transduce light energy as well as other neurons involved in the processing of light stimuli. Although these two layers are very close together, they are not fused. Notice that while the retina is commonly called the **sensory tunic,** only its neural layer plays a direct role in vision.

The neural layer is composed of three main types of neurons: **photoreceptors, bipolar cells,** and **ganglion cells** (Figure 16.9). Local currents produced in response to light spread from the photoreceptors (abutting the pigmented layer) to the bipolar neurons and then to the innermost ganglion cells, where action potentials are generated. The ganglion cell axons make a right-angle turn at the inner face of the retina, then leave the posterior aspect of the eye as the thick optic nerve. The other types of neurons in the retina (horizontal cells and amacrine cells) will be described shortly. The **optic disc,** where the optic nerve exits the eye, is a weak spot in the **fundus** (posterior wall) of the eye because it is not reinforced by the sclera. The optic disc is also called the **blind spot,** because it lacks photoreceptors, and light focused on it cannot be seen.

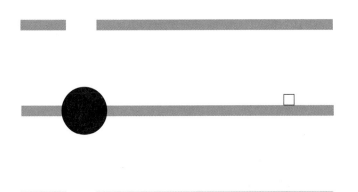

FIGURE 16.10
Demonstration of visual "filling in." Hold the figure about a foot in front of your face. Close your right eye and focus with your left eye on the white square as you slowly move the illustration toward your face. When the black spot falls on your blind spot (optic disc) the spot will disappear and the horizontal line that falls within the blind spot will be filled in. From "Blind Spots," by V. S. Ramachandra, *Scientific American,* May 1992. © Scientific American, Inc.

Nonetheless, we do not routinely notice these gaps in our vision because of the sophisticated visual function called *filling in* that the brain uses to deal with absence of input. This phenomenon can be easily demonstrated by performing the simple test described in Figure 16.10.

The quarter-billion photoreceptors found in the neural retinas are of two types: rods and cones. The more numerous **rods** are our dim-light and peripheral vision receptors. They are more sensitive to light than cones but they do not provide either sharp images or color vision. This is why colors are indistinct and edges of objects appear fuzzy in dim light and at the edges of our visual fields. **Cones,** by contrast, operate in bright light and provide high-acuity color vision. Lateral to the blind spot of each eye is an oval region called the **macula lutea** (mak'u-lah lu'te-ah; "yellow spot") with a minute (0.4 mm) pit in its center called the **fovea centralis** (see Figure 16.7). In this region, the retinal structures abutting the vitreous humor are displaced to the sides. This allows light to pass almost directly to the photoreceptors (mostly cones) rather than through several retinal layers, and it greatly enhances visual acuity. The fovea contains only cones; the macula contains mostly cones; and from the edge of the macula toward the retina periphery, cone density declines gradually. The retina periphery contains only rods, which continuously decrease in density from there to the macula. Only the foveae (plural of fovea) have a sufficient cone density to provide detailed color vision, so anything we wish to view critically is focused on the foveae. Because each fovea is only about the size of the head of a pin, not more than a thousandth of the entire visual field is in *hard focus* (foveal focus) at a given moment. Consequently, for us to visually comprehend a scene that is rapidly changing (as when we drive in traffic), our eyes must flick rapidly back and

forth (in fast saccades movements) to provide the foveae with detailed images of different parts of the visual field.

The neural retina receives its blood supply from two sources. The outer third (containing photoreceptors) is supplied by vessels in the choroid. The inner two-thirds is served by the **central artery** (a branch of the ophthalmic artery) and the **central vein,** which enter and leave the eye through the center of the optic nerve. Radiating outward from the optic disc, these vessels give rise to a rich vascular network that weaves through the retina's inner face (*retin* = net) and is clearly seen when the eyeball interior is examined with an ophthalmoscope (Figure 16.11). The fundus of the eye is the only place in the body where small blood vessels can be observed directly in a living person.

The structure and pattern of vascularization of the retina make it susceptible to *retinal detachment.* This condition, in which the pigmented and nervous layers separate, allowing the jellylike vitreous humor to seep between the two layers, can cause permanent blindness. It usually happens when the retina is torn during a traumatic blow to the head or when the head stops moving suddenly and then is jerked in the opposite direction (as in bungee jumping). The symptom that victims most often describe is "a curtain being drawn across the eye," but some people see sootlike spots or light flashes. If the condition is diagnosed early, it is often possible to reattach the retina with a laser or by cryosurgery (local application of extreme cold) before photoreceptor damage becomes permanent. •

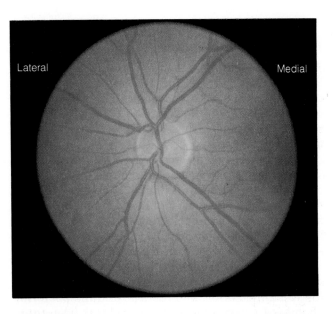

FIGURE 16.11
Part of the posterior wall (fundus) of the retina as seen with an ophthalmoscope. Note the optic disc from which the retinal blood vessels radiate.

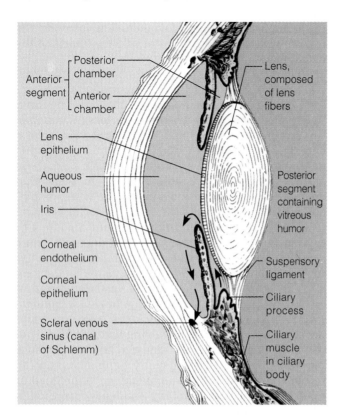

FIGURE 16.12
Structures seen in a transverse section through the anterior portion of the eye. The anterior segment in front of the lens is incompletely divided into the anterior chamber (anterior to the iris) and the posterior chamber (behind the iris), which are continuous through the pupil. Aqueous humor, which fills the chambers, is formed by filtration from capillaries in the ciliary processes and is reabsorbed into the venous blood by the scleral venous sinus. The arrows indicate the circulation pathway.

Internal Chambers and Fluids

As noted earlier, the lens and its halolike suspensory ligament divide the eye into two segments, the anterior segment in front of the lens and the larger posterior segment behind it (Figure 16.12). The **posterior segment** is filled with a clear gel called **vitreous humor** (*vitre* = glassy), consisting of a network of fine collagenic fibrils embedded in a viscous ground substance that binds tremendous amounts of water. Vitreous humor (1) transmits light, (2) supports the posterior surface of the lens and holds the neural retina firmly against the pigmented layer, and (3) contributes to intraocular pressure, helping to counteract the pulling force of the extrinsic eye muscles.

The **anterior segment** (Figure 16.12) is partially subdivided by the iris into the **anterior chamber** (between the cornea and the iris) and the **posterior chamber** (between the iris and the lens). The *entire* anterior segment is filled with **aqueous humor,** a clear fluid similar in composition to blood plasma.

Unlike the vitreous humor, which forms in the embryo and lasts for a lifetime, aqueous humor forms and drains continually and is in constant motion. It filters from the capillaries of the ciliary processes into the posterior chamber, flows through the pupil into the anterior chamber, and drains into the venous blood via the **scleral venous sinus (canal of Schlemm),** an unusual venous channel that encircles the eye in the angle at the sclera-cornea junction. Normally, aqueous humor is produced and drained at the same rate. As a result, a constant intraocular pressure of about 16 mm Hg is maintained, which helps to support the eyeball internally. The aqueous humor supplies nutrients and oxygen to the lens and cornea, and it carries away their metabolic wastes.

If drainage of aqueous humor is blocked, pressure within the eye may increase to dangerous levels and cause compression of the retina and optic nerve—a condition called **glaucoma** (glaw-ko′mah). Destruction of the neural structures eventually causes blindness (*glaucoma* = vision growing gray) unless the condition is detected early. Unfortunately, many forms of glaucoma steal sight so slowly and painlessly that people do not realize they have a problem until the damage is done. Late signs include seeing halos around lights and blurred vision. The glaucoma examination is simple. The sclera is anesthetized, and its deformation is measured as gentle pressure is applied with an instrument called a *tonometer.* This exam should be done yearly after the age of 40. Early glaucoma is treated with eye drops (miotics) that increase the rate of aqueous humor drainage. •

Lens

The **lens** is a biconvex, transparent, flexible structure that can change shape to allow precise focusing of light on the retina. It is enclosed in a thin, elastic capsule and held in place just posterior to the iris by the suspensory ligament (see Figures 16.8 and 16.12). Like the cornea, the lens is avascular; blood vessels interfere with transparency.

The lens has two regions: the lens epithelium and the lens fibers (see Figure 16.12). The **lens epithelium,** confined to the anterior lens surface, consists of cuboidal cells that eventually differentiate into the anucleate **lens fibers** that form the bulk of the lens. The lens fibers, packed tightly together like the layers in an onion, contain little more than precisely folded double-duty proteins called **crystallins.** The structure of the crystallins makes them transparent, and their enzymatic properties allow them to convert sugar into energy for use by the lens. Since new lens fibers are continually added, the lens enlarges throughout life, becoming denser, more convex, and less elastic, all of which eventually impair its ability to focus light properly.

A **cataract** is a clouding of the lens that causes the world to appear distorted, as if seen through frosted glass. Some cataracts are congenital, but most result from age-related hardening and thickening of the lens or are a secondary consequence of diabetes mellitus. Additionally, recent research strongly suggests that heavy smoking and frequent exposure to intense sunlight (particularly ultraviolet B [UVB] radiation, the same part of the sunbeam that causes sunburn and increases skin cancer risk) increases the risk for cataracts. Whatever the promoting factors, the *direct* cause of cataracts is probably inadequate delivery of nutrients to the deeper lens fibers. The metabolic changes that result promote oxidation and clumping of the crystallin proteins. Fortunately, the offending lens can be surgically removed and an artificial lens implanted to save the patient's sight. •

Physiology of Vision

Overview: Light and Optics

To really comprehend the function of the eye as a photoreceptor organ, we need to have some understanding of the properties of light.

Wavelength and Color.

Electromagnetic radiation encompasses all energy wavelengths, from the long radio waves (with wavelengths measured in meters) to the very short gamma (γ) waves and X rays with wavelengths of 0.001 µm and less. The only wavelengths in this spectrum to which our eyes respond are those in the portion designated as **visible light,** which has a wavelength range of approximately 400–700 nm (Figure 16.13a). (1 nm $= 10^{-9}$ m, or one-billionth of a meter.) Visible light travels in the form of waves, and its wavelengths can be measured very accurately. However, light is actually composed of small particles or packets of energy called **photons** or **quanta.** Attempts to reconcile these two findings have led to the present concept of light as packets of energy (photons) traveling in a wavelike fashion at very high speeds (186,000 miles per second or about 300,000 km/s). Thus, light can be thought of as a vibration of pure energy rather than a material substance.

When visible light passes through a prism, each of its component waves bends to a different degree, so that the beam of light is dispersed and a **visible spectrum,** or band of colors, is seen (see Figure 16.13). (In the same manner, the rainbow seen during a summer shower represents the collective prismatic effects of all the tiny water droplets suspended in air.) The visible spectrum progresses from red to violet. Red wavelengths are the longest and have the lowest energy, whereas the violet wavelengths are the shortest and most energetic. Objects have color because they absorb some wavelengths and reflect others. Things that look white reflect all wavelengths of light, whereas black objects absorb them all. A red apple reflects mostly red light; grass reflects more of the green.

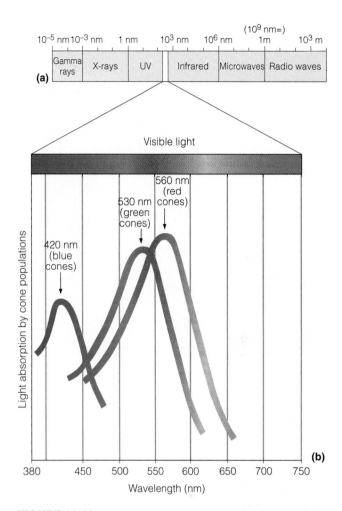

(b)

FIGURE 16.13

The electromagnetic spectrum and cone cell sensitivities. (a) The electromagnetic spectrum extends from the very short gamma waves to the long radio waves. The wavelengths of the electromagnetic spectrum are indicated in nanometers (1 nm $= 10^{-9}$ m). The spectrum of visible light constitutes only a small portion of this energy range. **(b)** Sensitivities of the three cone types to the different wavelengths of the visible spectrum.

Refraction and Lenses.

Light travels in straight lines and is easily blocked by any nontransparent object. Like sound, light can reflect, or bounce, off a surface. **Reflection** of light by objects in our environment accounts for most of the light reaching our eyes.

When light is traveling in a given medium, its speed is constant. But when it passes from one transparent medium into another with a different density, its speed is altered. Light speeds up as it passes into a less dense medium and slows as it passes into a denser medium. Because of these changes in speed, bending or **refraction** of a light ray occurs when it meets the surface of a different medium at an oblique angle rather than at a right angle (perpendicular). The greater the incident angle, the greater the amount of

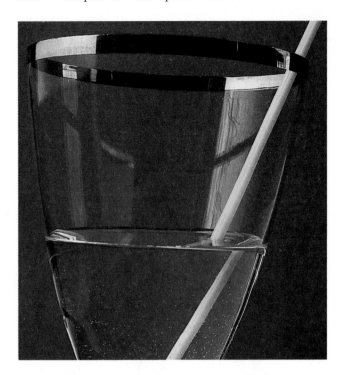

FIGURE 16.14
A pencil standing in a glass of water appears to be broken at the water-air interface. This phenomenon occurs because light is bent toward the perpendicular when it travels from a less dense to a more dense medium (air to water in this example).

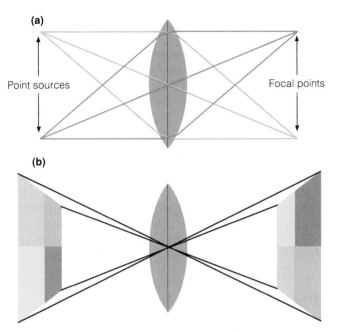

FIGURE 16.15
Bending of light points by a convex lens. (a) How two light points are focused on the opposite side of the lens. **(b)** Formation of an image by a convex lens. Notice that the image is upside down and reversed from right to left.

bending. Figure 16.14 demonstrates the consequence of light refraction when a pencil is placed in a half-full glass of water: The pencil appears to break at the air-water interface.

A lens is a piece of transparent material, curved on one or both surfaces. Since light hits the curve at an angle, it is refracted. If the lens surface is convex, that is, thickest in the center like a camera lens, the light rays are bent so that they converge (come together) or intersect at a single point called the **focal point** (Figure 16.15). In general, the thicker (more convex) the lens, the more the light is bent and the shorter the focal distance (distance between the lens and focal point). The image formed by a convex lens, called a **real image,** is upside down and reversed from left to right. On the other hand, concave lenses, which are thicker at the edges than at the center, like those of magnifying glasses, diverge the light (bend it outward) so that the light rays move away from each other. Consequently, concave lenses prevent light from focusing and extend the focal distance.

Focusing of Light on the Retina

As light passes from air into the eye, it moves successively through the cornea, aqueous humor, lens, and vitreous humor, and then passes *through the entire thickness of the neural layer of the retina* to excite the photoreceptors that abut the pigmented layer (see Fig-

ures 16.7 and 16.9). During its passage, light is bent three times: as it enters the cornea and on entering and leaving the lens. The cornea is responsible for most light refraction in the eye; but its thickness is constant, so its refractory power is unchanging. On the other hand, the lens is highly elastic, and its curvature can be actively changed to allow fine focusing of the image. The humors are of minimal importance in light refraction.

Focusing for Distance Vision.

Our eyes are best adapted ("preset to focus") for distance vision. To look at distant objects, we need only aim our eyeballs so that they are both fixated on the same spot. The **far point of vision** is that distance beyond which no change in lens shape (accommodation) is needed for focusing. For the normal or **emmetropic** (em"ĕ-tro'pik) eye, the far point is 6 m (20 feet).

Any object being viewed can be said to consist of many small points, with light radiating outward in all directions from each point. However, since distant objects appear smaller, light from an object at or beyond the far point of vision approaches the eyes as nearly parallel rays and is focused precisely on the retina by the fixed refractory apparatus (cornea and humors) and the at-rest lens (Figure 16.16a). During distance vision, the ciliary muscles are completely relaxed, and the lens (stretched flat by tension in the suspensory ligaments) is as thin as it gets. Consequently, it is at its lowest refractory power.

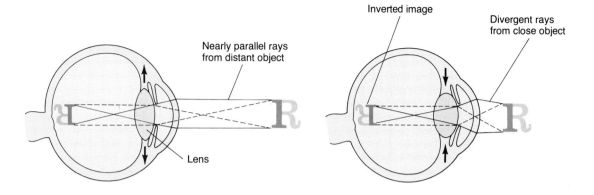

(a) Lens is flattened for distant vision

(b) Lens bulges for close vision

FIGURE 16.16
Focusing for distant and close vision. (a) Light from distant objects (over 6 m away) approaches as parallel rays and, in the normal eye, need not be adjusted for proper focusing on the retina. **(b)** Light from close objects (less than 6 m away) tends to diverge and lens convexity must be increased (accommodation) for proper focusing. Notice in both cases that the image formed on the retina is inverted and reversed from left to right (i.e., it is a real image).

Focusing for Close Vision. Light from objects less than 6 m away diverges as it approaches the eyes and comes to a focal point farther from the lens. Thus, while distance vision is the natural state, close vision demands that the eye make active adjustments. To restore focus, three processes—accommodation of the lenses, constriction of the pupils, and convergence of the eyeballs—must be initiated simultaneously. The signal that induces this trio of reflex responses appears to be a blurring of the retinal image.

1. Accommodation of the lenses. The process by which the refractory power of the lens is increased, and the diverging light rays are bent more sharply, is called **accommodation.** This is accomplished as the ciliary muscles contract; this action pulls the ciliary body anteriorly and inward toward the pupil and releases tension in the suspensory ligament. No longer stretched, the elastic lens recoils and bulges, providing the shorter focal length needed to focus the image of a close object on the retina (Figure 16.16b). Contraction of the ciliary muscles is controlled mainly by the parasympathetic fibers of the oculomotor nerves.

The closest point on which we can focus clearly is called the **near point of vision,** and it represents the maximum bulge the lens can achieve. Although we can see objects closer to us than the near point, they are out of focus and fuzzy. In young adults with emmetropic vision, the near point is 10 cm (4 inches) from the eye. However, it is closer in children and gradually recedes with age, explaining why children can hold their books very close to their faces while many elderly people must hold the newspaper at arm's length. The gradual loss of accommodation

with age reflects the lens's decreasing elasticity. In many people over 50 years of age, the lens is nonaccommodating, a condition known as *presbyopia* (pres″be-o′pe-ah), literally "old person's vision."

2. Constriction of the pupils. The circular (constrictor) muscles of the iris enhance the effect of accommodation by reducing the size of the pupil toward 2 mm. This **accommodation pupillary reflex,** mediated by parasympathetic fibers of the oculomotor nerves, prevents the most divergent light rays from entering the eye and passing through the extreme edge of the lens. Such rays would not be focused properly and would cause blurred vision. Pupillary constriction for close vision makes the eye act like a pinhole camera and increases the clarity and depth of focus.

3. Convergence of the eyeballs. Synchronized movements of the eyeballs (promoted by the extrinsic eye muscles) allow us to fix our gaze on something. The goal is always to keep the object being viewed focused on the retinal fovea of each eye. When we look at distant objects, both eyes are directed either straight ahead or to one side to the same degree, but when we fixate on a close object, our eyes converge. **Convergence,** controlled by somatic motor fibers of the oculomotor nerves, is the medial rotation of the eyeballs by the medial rectus muscles so that each is directed toward the object being viewed. The closer that object, the greater the degree of convergence required; when you focus on the tip of your nose, you "go cross-eyed."

Reading or other close work requires almost continuous accommodation, pupillary constriction, and convergence. This is why prolonged periods of read-

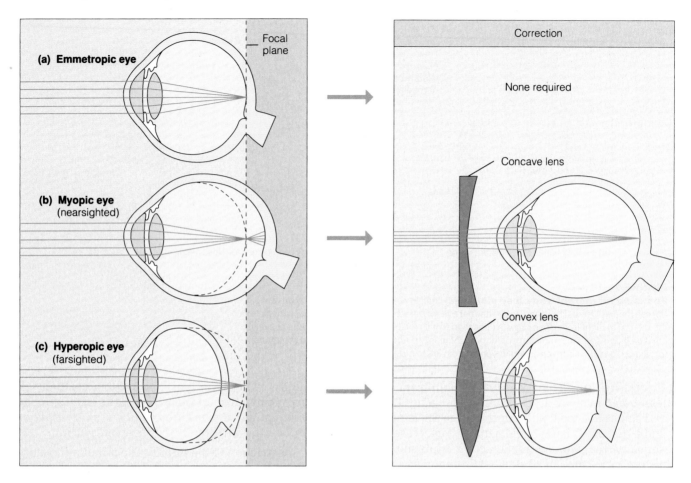

FIGURE 16.17
Problems of refraction. (a) In the emmetropic (normal) eye, light from near and distant objects is focused properly on the retina. **(b)** In a myopic eye, light from a distant object is brought to a focal point before reaching the retina and then diverges again. **(c)** In the hyperopic eye, light from a near object is brought to a focal point behind (past) the retina. (Refractory effect of the cornea is ignored.)

ing tire the eye muscles and can result in *eyestrain*. When you read for an extended time, it is helpful to look up and stare into the distance occasionally. This temporarily relaxes the intrinsic eye muscles.

Homeostatic Imbalances of Refraction.
Visual problems related to refraction can result from a hyperrefractive (overconverging) or hyporefractive (underconverging) lens or from structural abnormalities of the eyeball.

Myopia (mi-o′pe-ah; "short vision") occurs when distant objects are focused not on, but in front of, the retina (Figure 16.17b). Myopic people can see close objects without problems (because of the active ability of their lens to accommodate to the extent necessary), but distant objects are blurred. The common name for myopia is *nearsightedness.* (Notice that this terminology names the aspect of vision that is *unimpaired.*) Myopia results from an eyeball that is too elongated. One of every four American adults is myopic. Correction requires concave lenses that diverge the light before it enters the eye.

Hyperopia (hy′per-o″pe-ah; "far vision"), or *farsightedness,* occurs when the parallel light rays from distant objects are focused *behind* the retina (Figure 16.17c). Hyperopic individuals can see distant objects perfectly well because their ciliary muscles contract almost continuously to increase the light-bending power of the lens, which moves the focal point forward onto the retina. However, diverging light rays from *nearby* objects are focused so far behind the retina that the lens cannot bring the focal point onto the retina even at its full refractory power. Thus, close objects appear blurry, and convex corrective lenses are needed to converge the light more strongly for close vision. Hyperopia usually results from a lazy lens (one with poor refractory power) or an eyeball that is too short.

Unequal curvatures in different parts of the lens (or cornea) lead to blurry images because points of light are focused on the retina as lines (not points). This refractory problem is **astigmatism** (*astigma* = not a point). Special cylindrically ground lenses are used to correct this problem. •

Photoreception

Once light has been focused on the retina, the photoreceptors come into play. We will approach **pho-**

toreception, the process by which the eye detects light energy, by examining several interrelated topics. First we will describe the functional anatomy of photoreceptor cells. Then we will discuss the chemistry of their visual pigments and their response to light. Finally, activation of the photoreceptors and their response to varying levels of light intensity will be covered.

Functional Anatomy of the Photoreceptors.

Although photoreceptors are modified neurons, structurally they resemble tall epithelial cells turned upside down with their "tips" immersed in the pigmented layer of the retina (Figure 16.18a). Going from the pigmented layer into the neural layer, both the rods and cones have an **outer segment** (the receptor region) joined to an **inner segment** by a stalk containing a cilium. The inner segment connects to the *cell body,* which is continuous with an *inner fiber* bearing synaptic endings. The outer segment of the rods is slender and rod shaped (hence their name) and their inner segment connects to the cell body by the *outer fiber.* By contrast, the fatter cones have a short conical outer segment and the inner segment directly joins the cell body.

The outer segments contain an elaborate array of light-absorbing **visual pigments.** These are packaged in membrane-bounded discs that develop as infoldings of the surface (plasma) membrane. This coupling of photoreceptor pigments to cellular membranes magnifies the surface area available for trapping light. In rods, most of these discs pinch off and become discontinuous—stacked like a row of pennies—but in cones the disc membranes are continuous with the plasma membrane. Thus, the interiors of the cone discs are continuous with the extracellular space.

The photoreceptor cells are highly vulnerable to damage; if the retina becomes detached, the photoreceptors immediately begin to degenerate. They are also readily destroyed by intense light, the very energy they are designed to detect. How is it, then, that we do not all gradually go blind? The answer lies in the photoreceptors' unique system for renewal of their light-trapping outer segment. In rods, new discs are assembled at the proximal end of the outer segment from materials synthesized in the cell body. As new discs are made, they push the others peripherally. The discs at the tip of the outer segment continually fragment off and are phagocytized by cells of the pigmented layer. The tips of the outer segments of cones are also removed and renewed, but the precise way the membrane elements migrate into the outer

FIGURE 16.18
Photoreceptors of the retina. (a) Diagrammatic view of the photoreceptors (rods and cones). The relationship of the outer segments of the photoreceptors to the pigmented layer of the retina is also illustrated. Notice that the tip of the outer segment of the rod cell on the right is sloughing off. *(Figure continues on p. 520.)*

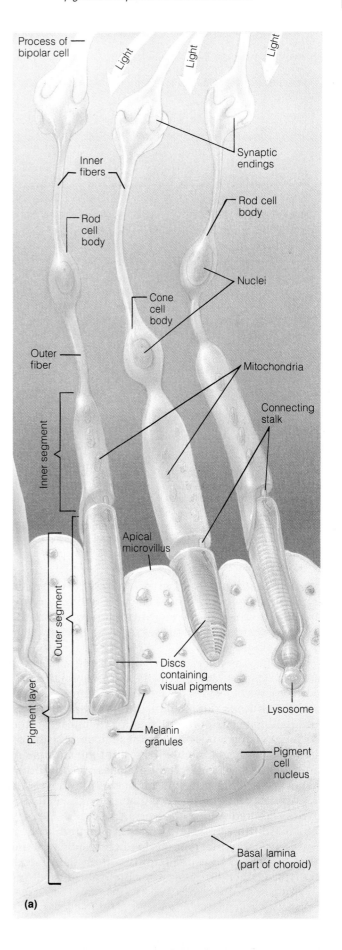

? *What is the advantage of having the photoreceptor pigment form part of the disc membranes?*

Process of bipolar cell

Light

Inner fibers

Synaptic endings

Rod cell body

Rod cell body

Nuclei

Cone cell body

Outer fiber

Mitochondria

Connecting stalk

Inner segment

Apical microvillus

Discs containing visual pigments

Outer segment

Lysosome

Pigment layer

Melanin granules

Pigment cell nucleus

Basal lamina (part of choroid)

(a)

(b)

FIGURE 16.18
Photoreceptors of the retina. *Continued.* **(b)** Diagrammatic
view of a small section of the membrane of a visual
pigment–containing disc of the outer segment of a rod cell. The visual
pigments consist of a light-absorbing molecule called retinal (derived
from vitamin A) bound to an opsin protein. Each type of photoreceptor
has a characteristic kind of opsin protein, which affects the absorption
spectrum of the retinal. In rods, the whole pigment-opsin complex is
called rhodopsin. Notice that the light-absorbing retinal occupies the
core of the rhodopsin molecule.

segment is still unclear. Phagocytic activity occurs in
a circadian (approximately 24-hour) rhythm. Rod tips
are phagocytized in the morning after first exposure
to light. Cone phagocytosis, triggered by darkness,
occurs at night.

Because the rods and each of the three cone types
contain unique visual pigments, they absorb different
wavelengths of light and have different thresholds for
activation. Rods, for example, (1) are very sensitive
(respond to very dim light), making them best suited
for night vision and peripheral vision, and (2) absorb
all wavelengths of visible light, but their inputs are
perceived only in gray tones. Cones, on the other
hand, (1) need bright light for activation (have low
sensitivity), but (2) have pigments that furnish a
vividly colored view of the world.

In addition, rods and cones are "wired" differently to other retinal neurons (and ultimately the ganglion cells that transmit impulses from the retina),
causing further differences in their abilities. Rods

participate in converging pathways, and as many as
100 rods may ultimately feed into each ganglion cell.
As a result, rod effects are summated and considered
collectively, resulting in vision that is fuzzy and
indistinct because of poor resolution. (The visual cortex has no way of knowing exactly *which* rods of the
large number influencing a particular ganglion cell
are actually activated.) In contrast, each cone in the
fovea (or at most a few) has a straight-through pathway to its "own personal ganglion cell." Hence, each
cone essentially has its own "labeled line" to the
higher visual centers. This accounts for the sharp,
detailed, high-resolution views of very small areas of
the visual field provided by cones.

Because rods are absent from the foveae and
cones do not respond to low-intensity light, we see
dimly lit objects best when we do not look at them
directly. However, without foveal focusing, or *hard
focus*, our vision is nondiscriminatory. We see only
vague outlines of objects and recognize them best
when they move. If you doubt this, go out into your
backyard on a moonlit evening and see how much
you can actually discriminate.

The Chemistry of Visual Pigments.   How
does light affect the photoreceptors so that it is ultimately translated into electrical signals? The key is a
light-absorbing molecule called **retinal** that combines
with proteins called **opsins** to form four types of
visual pigments. Depending on the type of opsin to
which it is bound, retinal preferentially absorbs different wavelengths of the visible spectrum. Retinal is
chemically related to vitamin A and is made from it.
The liver stores vitamin A and releases it as needed
by the photoreceptors to make their visual pigments.
The cells of the pigmented layer of the retina absorb
vitamin A from the blood and serve as the "local" vitamin A depot for the rods and cones.

Retinal can assume a variety of distinct three-
dimensional forms, each form called an isomer.
When bound to opsin, retinal has a bent, or kinked,
shape called the **11-*cis* isomer** (Figure 16.19). However, when the pigment is struck by light and absorbs
photons, retinal straightens to its **all-*trans* isomer**
form, causing it to detach from opsin. This is the *only*
light-dependent stage, and this simple photochemi-
cal event initiates a whole chain of chemical and electrical reactions in rods and cones that ultimately
causes electrical impulses to be transmitted along the
optic nerve.

Stimulation of the Photoreceptors

1.   Excitation of Rods The visual pigment of rods is a
deep purple pigment called **rhodopsin** (ro-dop′sin;
rhodo = rose, *opsis* = vision). (Do you suppose the
person who coined the expression "looking at the

FIGURE 16.19
Structure of retinal isomers involved in photoreception. When the visual pigment absorbs light, 11-*cis* retinal is transformed to the all-*trans* isomer.

world through rose-colored glasses" knew the meaning of "rhodopsin"?) Rhodopsin molecules are arranged in a single layer in the membranes of each of the thousands of discs in the rods' outer segments (see Figure 16.18b). Although rhodopsin absorbs light throughout the entire visible spectrum, it maximally absorbs green light.

Rhodopsin is formed and accumulated in the dark in the sequence of reactions shown on the left side of Figure 16.20. As illustrated, vitamin A is oxidized to the 11-*cis* retinal form and then combined with opsin to form rhodopsin. When rhodopsin absorbs light, retinal changes shape from the 11-*cis* to its all-*trans* isomer, and the retinal-opsin combination then breaks down, allowing retinal and opsin to separate. This breakdown is known as the **bleaching of the pigment.** Actually, the story is a good deal more complex than this, and the breakdown of rhodopsin that triggers the transduction process involves a rapid cascade of intermediate steps (right side of Figure 16.20) that takes just a few milliseconds. Once the light-struck all-*trans* retinal actually detaches from opsin, it is shuttled through the gelatinous fluid in the paper-thin subretinal space to the pigmented epithelium by a protein carrier. There, within the pigmented epithelial cells, retinal is slowly reconverted by enzymes to its 11-*cis* isomer in an ATP-requiring process that takes minutes. Then, retinal heads "homeward" again to the photoreceptor cells' outer segments. Rhodopsin is regenerated when 11-*cis* retinal is rejoined to opsin.

2. Excitation of Cones The chemistry of cone function is not completely worked out, but breakdown and regeneration of their visual pigments is essentially the same as for rhodopsin. However, the threshold for cone activation is much higher than that for

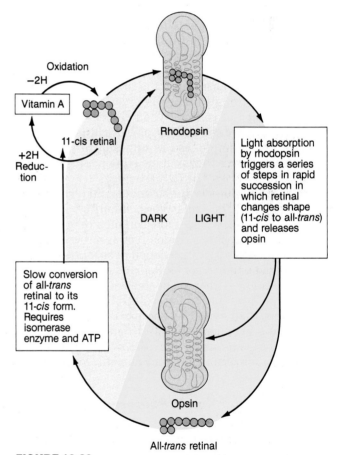

FIGURE 16.20
Sequence of chemical events in the formation and breakdown of rhodopsin. When struck by light, rhodopsin breaks down and is converted to its precursors via a number of intermediate steps. Absorption of light causes rapid conversion of 11-*cis* retinal to all-*trans* retinal, an event that is responsible for transduction of the light stimulus, and subsequently the separation of all-*trans* retinal and opsin. The 11-*cis* retinal is regenerated in energy (ATP)-requiring reactions by enzymatic action from all-*trans* retinal or from vitamin A and recombined with opsin to form rhodopsin.

rods, because cones respond only to high-intensity (bright) light.

Visual pigments of cones, like those of rods, are a combination of retinal and opsins. However, there are three distinct types of cones, and each type is most sensitive to a different wavelength range, which reflects the specific properties of the opsin to which the retinal is bound. The three types of cone opsins differ both from the opsin of the rods and from one another. Each of the different color (cone) opsins provides a unique electrical environment for its retinal that determines retinal's sensitivity to different light wavelengths. The naming of cones reflects the colors (that is, wavelengths) of light that each cone variety absorbs best and that is most efficient at causing the retinal to change shape and detach from its opsin. The blue cones respond maximally to wavelengths around 420 nm, the green cones to wavelengths of 530 nm, and the red cones to wavelengths at or close to 560 nm (see Figure 16.13b). However, as shown in the figure, there is overlap in their absorption spectra, and perception of intermediate hues, such as orange, yellow, and purple, results from differential activation of more than one type of cone at the same time. For example, yellow light stimulates both red and green cone receptors, but if the red cones are stimulated more strongly than the green cones, we see orange instead of yellow. When all cones are stimulated equally, we see white. Color brightness and saturation (for example, red as opposed to pink) also reflects the degree to which the cone populations are stimulated.

Color blindness is due to a congenital lack of one or more of the cone types. Inherited as a sex-linked condition, it is far more common in males than in females. The most common type is red-green color blindness, resulting from a deficit or absolute absence of either red or green cones. Red and green are seen as the same color—either red or green, depending on the cone type present. Many color-blind people are unaware of their condition because they have learned to rely on other cues—such as differences in intensities of the same color—to distinguish something green from something red, such as traffic signals. •

Light Transduction in Photoreceptors

How is the light stimulus transduced into an electrical event, that is, a change in membrane potential? In the dark, **cyclic GMP** (cGMP) binds to sodium channels in the outer segments, holding them open. Consequently, Na⁺ continually enters the outer segment producing a *dark current* that maintains a resting membrane potential (RMP) of about −40 mV. This depolarizing current keeps the Ca^{2+} channels *at their synaptic endings* open and permits more or less continuous neurotransmitter release by the photoreceptors at their synapses with the bipolar cells.

When light triggers pigment breakdown, the net effect is to "turn off" sodium entry. The mechanism involves an enzymatic cascade that ultimately leads to destruction of the cGMP that keeps the sodium gates open in the dark. In this process, described in more detail in Figure 16.21, freed opsin interacts with a G protein subunit called **transducin,** activating it. Transducin, in turn, activates *PPE (phosphodiesterase),* the enzyme that breaks down cGMP, and the sodium gates close. Since the sodium-potassium pump continues to operate, the photoreceptors develop a *hyperpolarizing receptor potential* (− 70 mV) that inhibits their release of neurotransmitter. This is bewildering, to say the least. Here we have receptors built to detect light that are depolarized in the dark and hyperpolarized when exposed to light! Nevertheless, as we will explain in the section called *Visual Processing,* turning off neurotransmitter release by hyperpolarization conveys information just as effectively as depolarization.

The photoreceptors do not generate action potentials. In fact, none of the retinal neurons generate action potentials except the ganglion cells, which is consistent with their function as the output neurons of the retina. In all other cases, only local currents (graded potentials) are produced. This is not surprising if you remember that the primary function of action potentials is to carry information rapidly over long distances. Since the retinal cells are small cells that are very close together, graded potentials can serve quite adequately as signals to regulate neurotransmitter release.

Light and Dark Adaptation

Rhodopsin is amazingly sensitive; even starlight causes some of the molecules to become bleached. As long as the light is low intensity, rods quickly regenerate rhodopsin and the retina continues to respond to light stimuli. However, in high-intensity light, rhodopsin is bleached nearly as rapidly as it is made, and the rods become nonfunctional. At this point, cones begin to take over. Hence, retinal sensitivity automatically adjusts to the amount of light present.

Light adaptation occurs when we move from darkness into bright light, as when leaving a movie matinee. We are momentarily dazzled—all we see is white light—because the sensitivity of the retina is still "set" for dim light. Both rods and cones are strongly stimulated, and large amounts of the photopigments are broken down almost instantaneously, producing a flood of signals that accounts for the glare. Under such conditions, compensations occur. (1) The sensitivity of the retina decreases dramatically (less than a 1% breakdown of rhodopsin results in a huge loss in rod sensitivity), and (2) retinal neurons adapt rapidly, inhibiting rod functioning and switching to the cone system when light conditions favor cone

?   *Assume that everything is proceeding normally in the scheme illustrated, but then a metabolic poison that interferes with the Na$^+$-K$^+$ pump is introduced. What would happen and why?*

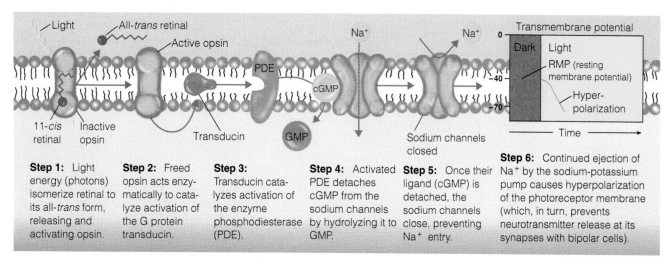

Step 1: Light energy (photons) isomerize retinal to its all-*trans* form, releasing and activating opsin.

Step 2: Freed opsin acts enzymatically to catalyze activation of the G protein transducin.

Step 3: Transducin catalyzes activation of the enzyme phosphodiesterase (PDE).

Step 4: Activated PDE detaches cGMP from the sodium channels by hydrolyzing it to GMP.

Step 5: Once their ligand (cGMP) is detached, the sodium channels close, preventing Na$^+$ entry.

Step 6: Continued ejection of Na$^+$ by the sodium-potassium pump causes hyperpolarization of the photoreceptor membrane (which, in turn, prevents neurotransmitter release at its synapses with bipolar cells).

FIGURE 16.21
Events of phototransduction.

function. These events raise the threshold of the retina, and within about 60 seconds the cones are sufficiently excited by the bright light to take over. Visual acuity and color vision continue to improve over the next 5–10 minutes. Thus, during light adaptation, retinal sensitivity is lost, but visual acuity is gained.

Dark adaptation is essentially the reverse of light adaptation. It occurs when we go from a well-lit area into a dark one. Initially, we see nothing but velvety blackness because (1) our cones stop functioning in low-intensity light, and (2) our rod pigments have been bleached out by the bright light, and the rods are still initially inhibited. But once we are in the dark, rhodopsin accumulates and sensitivity of the retina increases. Dark adaptation is much slower than light adaptation and can go on for hours. However, usually enough rhodopsin is accumulated within 20–30 minutes to allow adequate dim-light vision.

During these adaptations, reflexive changes also occur in pupil size. Bright light shining in one or both eyes causes both pupils to constrict (elicits the *consensual* and *pupillary light reflexes*). These pupillary reflexes are mediated by the pretectal nucleus of the midbrain and by parasympathetic fibers. In dim light, the pupils are dilated, allowing more light to enter the eye interior.

Night blindness, or *nyctalopia* (nic″tă-lo′pe-uh), is a condition in which rod function is seriously hampered, dangerously impairing one's ability to drive safely at night. The most common cause of night blindness is prolonged vitamin A deficiency, which leads to rod degeneration. Vitamin A supplements will restore function if they are administered before degenerative changes occur. Although visual pigment content is reduced in both rods and cones in nyctalopia, the cones usually have sufficient photopigment to respond to their intense stimulus (bright light), except in the most severe cases. On the other hand, even a modest deficiency of rhodopsin in the rods renders them nonfunctional in dim light. •

The Visual Pathway to the Brain

As described earlier, the axons of the retinal ganglion cells issue from the back of the eyeballs in the **optic nerves** (Figure 16.22). At the X-shaped **optic chiasma** (*chiasm* = cross), fibers from the medial aspect of each eye cross over to the opposite side and then continue on via the **optic tracts**. Thus, each optic tract (1) contains fibers from the lateral (temporal) aspect of the eye on the same side and fibers from the medial (nasal) aspect of the opposite eye, and (2) carries all the information from the same half of the visual field. Also notice that, because the lens system of each eye reverses all images, the medial half of each retina receives light rays from the *temporal* (lateralmost) part of the visual field (that is, from the far left or far right rather than from straight ahead), and the lateral half of each retina receives an image of the *nasal* (central) part of the visual field. Consequently, the left optic tract carries (and sends on) a complete representation of the right half of the visual field, and the opposite is true for the right optic tract.

The paired optic tracts sweep posteriorly around the hypothalamus and send most of their axons to

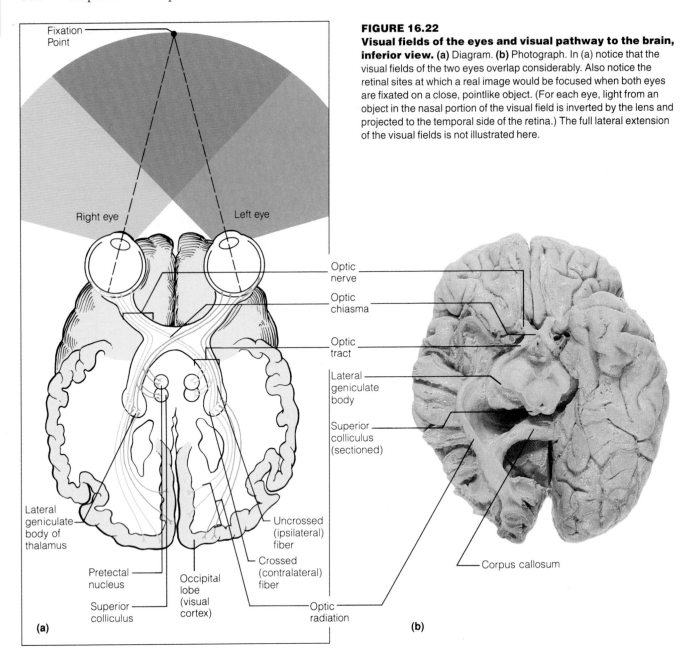

FIGURE 16.22
Visual fields of the eyes and visual pathway to the brain, inferior view. (a) Diagram. **(b)** Photograph. In (a) notice that the visual fields of the two eyes overlap considerably. Also notice the retinal sites at which a real image would be focused when both eyes are fixated on a close, pointlike object. (For each eye, light from an object in the nasal portion of the visual field is inverted by the lens and projected to the temporal side of the retina.) The full lateral extension of the visual fields is not illustrated here.

synapse with neurons in the **lateral geniculate body** of the thalamus, which maintains the fiber separation established at the chiasma. Axons of the thalamic neurons then project through the internal capsule to form the **optic radiation** of fibers in the cerebral white matter. These fibers project to the **primary visual cortex** in the occipital lobes, where conscious perception of visual images (seeing) occurs.

Some nerve fibers in the optic tracts send branches to the midbrain. These fibers end in the **superior colliculi,** visual reflex centers controlling the extrinsic muscles of the eyes, and in the **pretectal nuclei,** which, as already noted, mediate the pupil-

lary light reflexes. Still other fibers of the visual pathway project to the **suprachiasmatic nucleus** of the hypothalamus, which functions as the "timer" to set our daily biorhythms. Visual inputs keep it synchronized with the natural cycles of daylight and darkness.

Stereoscopic Vision and Depth Perception

Stereoscopic vision (literally, "seeing solid") is found in humans and most other primates, as well as in predatory birds and cats. Although both eyes are set anteriorly and look in approximately the same direc-

Light Stimulus Area	On-Center Field	Response of Ganglion Cell During Period of Light Stimulus: On-Center Field	Off-Center Field	Response of Ganglion Cell During Period of Light Stimulus: Off-Center Field
No illumination or diffuse illumination (basal rate)				
Central, all illuminated				
Surround illuminated				

FIGURE 16.23
Responses of on-center and off-center retinal ganglion cells to different types of illumination. (Intermediate amounts of illumination of the central and surround regions lead to intermediate rates of impulse transmission.)

tion, their visual fields, each about 170 degrees, overlap to a considerable extent, and each eye sees a slightly different view (see Figure 16.22). Additionally, the crossing over of about half of the optic nerve fibers at the optic chiasma provides each visual cortex with the same image (or part of the visual field) as viewed by both eyes—but the two eyes behold that image from slightly different angles. In contrast, many animals (pigeons, rabbits, and others) have *panoramic vision.* Their eyes are placed more laterally on the head so that the two visual fields overlap very little, and crossover of the optic nerve fibers is almost complete. Consequently, each visual cortex receives input principally from a single eye and a totally different visual field. Stereoscopic vision provides a smaller total visual field than panoramic vision, but it also provides **depth perception,** an accurate means of locating objects in space. This faculty, also called **three-dimensional vision,** results from cortical "fusion" of the slightly different images delivered by the two eyes.

Depth perception depends on the two eyes working together and accurately focusing on the object. If only one eye is used, depth perception is lost, and the person must learn to judge an object's position based on learned cues (for example, the nearer the object, the larger it appears, and parallel lines converge with distance).

The relationships described above explain patterns of blindness that follow damage to different visual structures. Loss of an eye or destruction of one optic nerve eliminates true depth perception, and peripheral vision is lost on the side of damage. For example, if the "left eye" in Figure 16.22 were lost in a hunting accident, nothing would be seen in the visual field area colored blue in that figure. If neural destruction occurs beyond the optic chiasma—in an optic tract, the thalamus, or visual cortex—then part or all of the opposite half of the visual field is lost. For example, a stroke affecting the left visual cortex leads to blindness in the right half of the visual field, but since the right (undamaged) visual cortex still receives inputs from both eyes, depth perception in the remaining half of the visual field is retained. •

Visual Processing

How does information received by the rods and cones become vision? In the past few years, a tremendous amount of research has been devoted to this question. Some of the basic information that has come out of these studies is presented here.

Retinal Processing.   The retinal ganglion cells generate action potentials at a fairly steady rate (20–30 Hz), even in the dark. Surprisingly, illuminating the entire retina evenly has no effect on that basal rate. However, the activity of individual ganglion cells changes dramatically when a tiny spot of light falls just on certain portions of their receptive field. The receptive field of a ganglion cell consists of the area of the retina that, when stimulated, influences the activity of that ganglion cell (the rods or cones that funnel their impulses to it).

When researchers mapped the receptive fields of ganglion cells receiving inputs only from rods, they found two types of doughnut-shaped (circle-within-a-circle) receptive fields (Figure 16.23). These are called **on-center** and **off-center fields,** based on what happens to the ganglion cell when the central part of its receptive field is illuminated with a spot of light. Ganglion cells with on-center fields are stimulated (depolarized) by light hitting the field center (the "doughnut hole") and are inhibited by light hitting rods in the periphery (the doughnut itself). Ganglion cells with off-center fields are inhibited by light hitting their field center (the "off" region) and stimulated by light hitting the periphery (their "on" region). Equal illumination of "on" and "off" regions causes little change in the basal rate of ganglion cell firing. However, the ganglion cells do respond to differing illumination of parts of their fields, which leads to changes in their rate of impulse generation (see Figure 16.23).

The mechanisms of retinal processing as currently understood can be summarized briefly as follows:

1. The action of light on photoreceptors hyperpolarizes them.

2. Bipolar neurons in the "on" regions are excited (depolarize) when the rods feeding into them are illuminated (and hyperpolarized). Bipolar neurons in the "off" regions are inhibited (hyperpolarize) when the rods feeding into them are stimulated. Notice that the rods release only a single type of neurotransmitter (probably glutamate). The opposite responses of the bipolar neurons in the "on" versus the "off" regions reflect the fact that they have different receptor types for the same neurotransmitter.

3. Bipolar neurons in the center of a receptive field feed straight through to the ganglion cell; this is the *on-line pathway*. Thus, depolarizing bipolar neurons excite the ganglion cell, whereas hyperpolarizing bipolar cells inhibit the ganglion cell.

4. The activity of bipolar neurons in the field periphery, the *off-line pathway*, is modified (reversed) and subjected to *lateral inhibition* by synaptic contacts with the *horizontal cells* of the retina (see Figure 16.9). The horizontal cells, connected to both the photoreceptors and bipolar neurons, are also widely connected to one another by electrical synapses. They are the local integrators that cause the ganglion cells to receive information from the field periphery (surround region) that is *antagonistic* to the information they are receiving from the field center. The horizontal cells also mediate antagonistic reactions between neighboring retinal areas. The "selective destruction" of some of the rod inputs by the horizontal cells allows the retina to convert the pointlike light inputs into perceptually more meaningful contour information by accentuating bright/dark contrasts, or edges, as illustrated very simply in Figure 16.24.

5. The amacrine cells are also local integrator cells that mediate interactions at the bipolar cell-ganglion cell junctions. They exert transient inhibitory effects on the ganglion cells.

Thalamic Processing. The lateral geniculate nuclei (LGN) of the thalamus relay information on movement, segregate the retinal axons in preparation for depth perception, and sharpen the contrast information received from the retina. The inputs from the two eyes project to discrete layers of each lateral geniculate nucleus, and this separation of signals is relayed accurately to the visual cortex. The signals from the two eyes first come together in the thalamus. However, not all parts of the retina are represented equally. Many more synapses are made with axons from the center of the retina than with those from its periphery. Thus, these thalamic nuclei appear to be most concerned with the high-acuity aspects of color vision, and their projections to the visual cortex emphasize visual inputs from the region of high cone density.

Cortical Processing. Two types of areas for processing retinal inputs are found in the visual cortex. The primary visual cortex is also called the **striate cortex** because it is thick with fibers coming in from the LGN. This area contains an accurate topographical map of the retina, and the so-called *simple cortical neurons* that respond to straight edges of dark and light contrast. The receptive field of a simple cortical neuron consists of a group of retinal ganglion cell fields, all with the same orientation and center type. It also houses the "pigeonholes" for form, color, and motion inputs, which it forwards on to visual association areas collectively called the prestriate cortices. The **prestriate cortices,** the home of the *complex cortical neurons,* are centers that process the inputs concerned with form, color, and motion to produce our dynamic visual images.

THE EAR: HEARING AND BALANCE

At first glance, the machinery for hearing and balance appears very crude. Fluids must be stirred to stimulate the mechanoreceptors of the ear: Sound vibra-

FIGURE 16.24
A visual illusion illustrating that the appearance of an object depends on differences in relative brightness, rather than absolute brightness. The gray rings are identical (same size and shade) in both boxes but their brightness appears to vary with the contrast provided by the surrounding background.

tions move fluid to stimulate hearing receptors, whereas gross movements of the head disturb fluids surrounding the balance organs. Nevertheless, our hearing apparatus allows us to hear an extraordinary range of sound, and our highly sensitive equilibrium receptors keep the nervous system continually informed of the position and movements of the head. Although the organs serving these two senses are structurally interconnected within the ear, their receptors respond to different stimuli and are activated independently of one another.

Structure of the Ear

The ear is divided into three major areas: outer ear, middle ear, and inner ear (Figure 16.25). The outer and middle ear structures are involved with hearing only and are rather simply engineered. The inner ear functions in both equilibrium and hearing and is extremely complex.

The Outer (External) Ear

The **outer (external) ear** consists of the auricle and the external auditory canal. The **auricle,** or **pinna,** is what most people call the ear—the shell-shaped projection surrounding the opening of the external auditory canal. The auricle is composed of elastic cartilage covered with thin skin, and an occasional hair. Its rim, the **helix,** is somewhat thicker, and its fleshy, dangling **lobule** ("earlobe") lacks supporting cartilage. The function of the auricle is to direct sound waves into the external auditory canal. Some animals (coyotes, for example) can move their auricles toward a sound source, but in humans the comparable muscles are vestigial and inefficient.

The **external auditory canal (meatus)** is a short, narrow chamber (about 2.5 cm long by 0.6 cm wide) that extends from the auricle to the tympanic membrane. Near the auricle, its framework is elastic cartilage; the remainder of the canal is carved into the temporal bone. The entire canal is lined with skin bearing hairs, sebaceous glands, and modified apocrine sweat glands called **ceruminous** (sĕ-roo′mĭ-nus) **glands.** These glands secrete yellow-brown waxy **cerumen** (sĕ-roo′men; *cere* = wax), or earwax, which provides a sticky trap for foreign bodies and repels insects. In many people, the ear is naturally cleansed as the cerumen dries and then falls out of the external auditory canal. In others, the cerumen tends to build up excessively and become compacted, a condition that can impair hearing.

Sound waves entering the external auditory canal eventually hit the **tympanic membrane,** or **eardrum** (*tympanum* = drum), the boundary between the outer and middle ears. The eardrum is a thin, translucent, connective tissue membrane, covered by skin on its external face and by a mucosa internally. It is shaped like a flattened cone, with its apex protruding

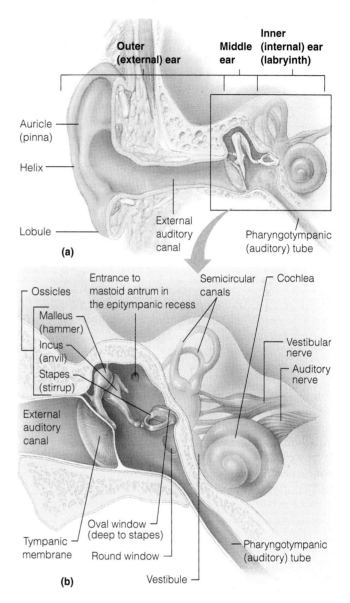

Besides the bony boundaries, what structure(s) separates the outer from the middle ear? The middle and inner ears?

FIGURE 16.25
Structure of the ear. (a) The three regions of the ear.
(b) Enlarged view of the middle and inner ear. Notice that the semicircular canals, vestibule, and cochlea of the inner ear form the bony labyrinth.

medially into the middle ear. Sound waves make the eardrum vibrate; the eardrum, in turn, transfers the sound energy to the tiny bones of the middle ear and sets them into vibration.

The Middle Ear

The **middle ear,** or **tympanic cavity,** is a small, air-filled, mucosa-lined cavity within the petrous portion of the temporal bone. It is flanked laterally by the eardrum and medially by a bony wall with two openings, the superior **oval (vestibular) window** and the inferior **round (cochlear) window.** The round window is closed by the *secondary tympanic membrane.* The superior boundary of the **epitympanic recess** is the "roof" of the middle ear cavity. The **mastoid antrum,** a canal in the posterior wall of the tympanic cavity, allows it to communicate with the *mastoid air cells.* The **pharyngotympanic (auditory) tube** runs obliquely downward to link the middle ear cavity with the nasopharynx (the superiormost part of the throat), and the mucosa of the middle ear is continuous with that lining the pharynx (throat). Normally, the pharyngotympanic tube is flattened and closed, but swallowing or yawning can open it briefly to equalize the pressure in the middle ear cavity with the external air pressure. This is important because the eardrum does not vibrate freely unless the pressure on both of its surfaces is the same. When the pressures are unequal, the eardrum bulges inward or outward, causing hearing difficulty (voices may sound far away) and sometimes earaches. The ear-popping sensation of the pressures equalizing is familiar to anyone who has flown in an airplane.

Inflammation of the middle ear lining, **otitis media** (me'de-ah), is a fairly common result of a sore throat, especially in children, whose auditory tubes are shorter and run more horizontally. In acute forms of otitis media, in which infectious bacteria colonize the middle ear, the eardrum bulges and becomes inflamed and red. Most cases of otitis media are treated with antibiotics. When large amounts of fluid or pus accumulate in the cavity, an emergency *myringotomy* (lancing of the eardrum) may be required to relieve the pressure. During myringotomy a tiny tube is implanted in the eardrum, permitting pus to continue draining into the external ear. The tube falls out by itself within the year. •

The tympanic cavity is spanned by the three smallest bones in the body: the **ossicles** (see Figures 16.25 and 16.26). These bones, named for their shape, are the **malleus** (mal'e-us), or **hammer;** the **incus** (ing'kus), or **anvil;** and the **stapes** (sta'pēz), or **stirrup.** The "handle" of the malleus is secured to the eardrum, and the base of the stapes fits (secured by an *annular ligament*) into the oval window. Tiny ligaments suspend the ossicles, and minisynovial joints link them together into a chain that spans the middle ear cavity. The incus articulates with the malleus laterally and the stapes medially. The ossicles transmit the vibratory motion of the eardrum to the oval window, which in turn sets the fluids of the inner ear into motion, eventually exciting the hearing receptors.

Two tiny skeletal muscles are associated with the ossicles (Figure 16.26). The **tensor tympani** (ten'sor tim'pah-ni) arises from the wall of the auditory tube and inserts into the handle of the malleus. The **stapedius** (stah-pe'de-us) originates from the posterior wall of the middle ear cavity and inserts into the

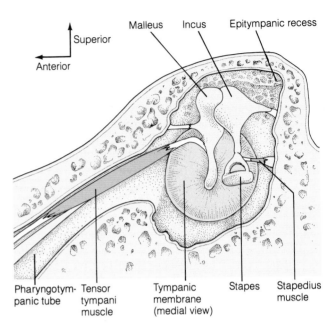

FIGURE 16.26
The three ossicles in the right middle ear, medial view.

stapes. When the ears are assaulted by very loud sounds, these muscles contract reflexively to prevent damage to the hearing receptors. Specifically, the tensor tympani tenses the eardrum by pulling it medially; the stapedius checks vibration of the whole ossicle chain and limits the movement of the stapes in the oval window. This **tympanic,** or **sound attenuation, reflex** reduces the conduction of sound to the inner ear, but its 40-ms lag period prevents it from protecting the receptors from *sudden* loud noises like gunshots.

The Inner (Internal) Ear

The **inner (internal) ear** is also called the **labyrinth** (meaning "maze") because of its complicated shape (see Figure 16.25). It lies deep within the temporal bone behind the eye socket and provides a secure site for all of the delicate receptor machinery housed there. The inner ear consists of two major divisions: the bony labyrinth and the membranous labyrinth. The **bony,** or **osseous, labyrinth** is a system of tortuous channels worming through the bone. Its three structurally and functionally unique regions are the vestibule, the cochlea (kok'le-ah), and the semicircular canals. The views of the bony labyrinth typically seen in most textbooks, including this one, are somewhat misleading because we are talking about a *cavity* here. The representation seen in Figure 16.25 can be compared to a plaster of Paris cast of the cavity or hollow space inside the bony labyrinth. The **membranous labyrinth** is a collection of interconnecting membranous sacs and ducts contained within the

FIGURE 16.27

Membranous labyrinth of the inner ear, shown in relation to the chambers of the bony labyrinth. The locations of the specialized receptors for hearing (organ of Corti) and equilibrium (maculae and cristae ampullares) are also indicated.

bony labyrinth and (more or less) following its contours (Figure 16.27).

The bony labyrinth is filled with **perilymph,** a fluid similar to cerebrospinal fluid. The membranous labyrinth is surrounded by and floats in the perilymph; its interior contains **endolymph,** which is chemically similar to K$^+$-rich intracellular fluid. These two fluids conduct the sound vibrations involved in hearing and respond to the mechanical forces occurring during changes in body position and acceleration. They have no relationship to the lymph circulating in the lymphatic vessels of the body.

The Vestibule.   The **vestibule** is the central egg-shaped cavity of the bony labyrinth. It lies posterior to the cochlea and anterior to the semicircular canals and flanks the middle ear medially. In its lateral wall is the oval window. Suspended within its perilymph and united by a small duct are two membranous labyrinth sacs, the **saccule** and **utricle** (u'tri-kl) (Figure 16.27). The smaller saccule is continuous with the membranous labyrinth extending anteriorly into the cochlea (the *cochlear duct*), whereas the utricle is continuous with the ducts extending into the semicircular canals posteriorly. The saccule and utricle house equilibrium receptors called *maculae* that respond to the pull of gravity and report on changes of head position.

The Semicircular Canals.   The cavities of the bony **semicircular canals** project from the posterior aspect of the vestibule; each is oriented in one of the three planes of space. Accordingly, there is an *ante-*

rior, posterior, and *lateral* semicircular canal in each inner ear. The anterior and posterior canals are oriented at right angles to each other in the vertical plane, whereas the lateral canal lies horizontally (see Figure 16.27). Snaking through each semicircular canal is a corresponding membranous **semicircular duct,** which communicates with the utricle anteriorly. Each of these ducts has an enlarged swelling at one end called an **ampulla,** which houses an equilibrium receptor called a *crista ampullaris* (literally, crest of the ampulla). These receptors respond to angular (rotational) movements of the head.

The Cochlea.   The **cochlea,** from the Latin meaning "snail," is a spiral, conical, bony chamber about half the size of a split pea. It extends from the anterior part of the vestibule and then coils for approximately 2½ turns around a bony pillar called the **modiolus** (mo-di'o-lus) (Figure 16.28a). Running through its center like a wedge-shaped worm is the membranous **cochlear duct,** which ends blindly at the cochlear apex. The cochlear duct houses the **spiral organ of Corti,** the receptor organ for hearing (Figure 16.28b). The cochlear duct and the **spiral lamina,** a thin shelflike extension that spirals up the modiolus like the thread on a screw, together divide the cavity of the bony cochlea into three separate chambers or **scalas** (*scala* = ladder): a superior **scala vestibuli** (ska'lah věs-tǐ'bu-li), which is continuous with the vestibule and abuts the oval window; a middle **scala media** (the cochlear duct itself); and the inferior **scala tympani,** which terminates at the round window. Since the scala media is part of the membranous labyrinth,

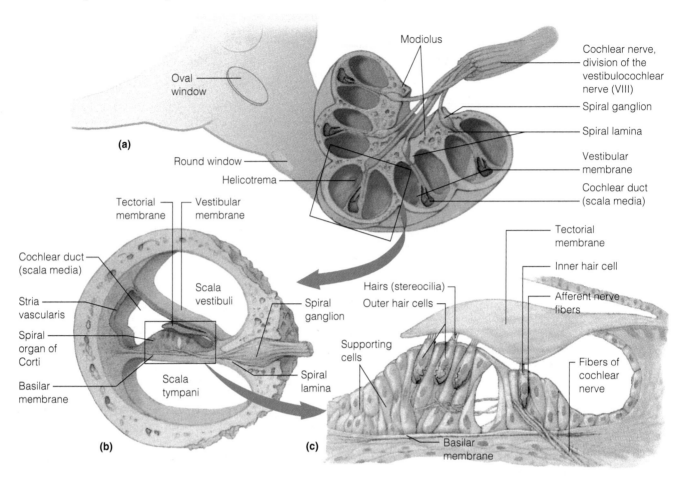

FIGURE 16.28
Anatomy of the cochlea. (a) A section through the coiled cochlea. **(b)** Magnified cross-sectional view of one turn of the cochlea, showing the relationship of the three scalae. The scalae vestibuli and tympani contain perilymph; the cochlear duct (scala media) contains endolymph. **(c)** Detailed structure of the spiral organ of Corti.

it is filled with endolymph. The scala vestibuli and the scala tympani, both part of the bony labyrinth, contain perilymph. The perilymph-containing chambers are continuous with each other at the cochlear apex, a region called the **helicotrema** (hel″ĭ-ko-tre′mah; "the hole in the spiral").

The "roof" of the cochlear duct, separating the scala media from the scala vestibuli, is the **vestibular membrane** (see Figure 16.28b). Its external wall is the **stria vascularis,** composed of an unusual richly vascularized mucosa that secretes the endolymph. The "floor" of the cochlear duct is composed of the bony spiral lamina and the flexible, fibrous **basilar membrane,** which supports the organ of Corti. (We will describe the organ of Corti when we discuss the mechanism of hearing.) The basilar membrane is narrow and thick near the oval window and gradually becomes wider and thinner as it approaches the cochlear apex. As you will see, its structure plays a critical role in sound reception. The *cochlear nerve, a* division of the *vestibulocochlear* (eighth cranial) *nerve,* runs from the organ of Corti through the modiolus on its way to the brain.

Sound and Mechanisms of Hearing

The mechanics of human hearing can be summed up in a single sprawling sentence: Sounds set up vibrations in air that beat against the eardrum that pushes a chain of tiny bones that press fluid in the inner ear against membranes that set up shearing forces that pull on the tiny hair cells that stimulate nearby neurons that give rise to impulses that travel to the brain, which interprets them—and you hear. Before we unravel this intriguing sequence, let us pause to describe sound, the stimulus for hearing.

Properties of Sound

Unlike light, which can be transmitted through a vacuum (for instance, outer space), sound depends on an *elastic* medium for its transmission. Sound also travels much more slowly than light. Its speed in dry air is only about 0.2 miles per second (331 m/s), as opposed to the 186,000 miles per second (about 300,000 km/s) of light. A lightning flash is almost instantly visible, but the sound it creates (thunder) reaches our ears much more slowly. (For each second between the lightning bolt and the roll of thunder, the storm is ⅕ mile farther away.) The speed of sound is constant in a given medium; it is greatest in solids and lowest in gases, including air.

Sound is a pressure disturbance originating from a vibrating object and propagated by the molecules of the medium. Consider a sound arising from a vibrating tuning fork (Figure 16.29a). If the tuning fork is struck on the left, its prongs will move first to the right, creating an area of high pressure by compressing the air molecules there. Then, as the prongs rebound to the left, the air on the left will be compressed, and the region on the right will be a rarefied, or low-pressure, area (since most of its air molecules have been pushed farther to the right). As the fork vibrates alternately from right to left, it produces a series of compressions and rarefactions, collectively called a *sound wave,* which moves outward in all directions (Figure 16.29b). However, the individual air molecules just vibrate back and forth for short distances as they bump other molecules and rebound. Since the outward-moving molecules give up kinetic energy to the molecules they bump, energy is always transferred in the direction in which the sound wave is traveling. Thus, with time and distance, the energy of the wave declines, and the sound dies a "natural death."

We can illustrate a sound wave as an S-shaped curve, or *sine wave,* in which the compressed areas are crests and the rarefied areas are troughs (Figure 16.29c). Sound can be described in terms of two physical properties inferred from this sine wave graph: frequency and amplitude.

Frequency. The sine wave of a pure tone is *periodic;* that is, its crests and troughs repeat at definite distances. The distance between two consecutive crests (or troughs) is called the **wavelength** of the sound and is constant for a particular tone. **Frequency,** expressed in *hertz,* is defined as the number of waves that pass a given point in a given time. The shorter the wavelength, the higher the frequency of the sound (Figure 16.30a).

The frequency range of human hearing is from 20 to 20,000 Hz. Our ears are most sensitive to frequencies between 1500 and 4000 Hz and, in that range, we can distinguish frequencies differing by only 2–3 Hz. We perceive different sound frequencies as differences in **pitch:** The higher the frequency, the higher the pitch. A tuning fork produces a *tone,* a pure (but bland) sound with a single frequency, but most sounds are mixtures of several frequencies. It is this characteristic of sound, called **quality,** that enables us to distinguish between the same musical note—say, high C—sung by a soprano and played on a piano or clarinet. It is the quality of sound that provides the richness and complexity of sounds (and music) that we hear, as well as the sound input we call "noise."

Amplitude. The **intensity** of a sound is related to its energy, or the pressure differences between its compressed and rarefied areas. When we represent a sound wave graphically, as in Figure 16.30b, its intensity corresponds to the **amplitude,** or height, of the sine wave crests.

Intensity is an objective, precisely measurable, physical property of sound, but **loudness** refers to our

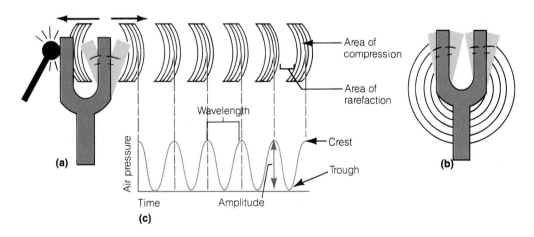

FIGURE 16.29
Sound: source and propagation.
The source of sound is a vibrating object. **(a)** A tuning fork is struck on the left with a mallet. Its tines move to the right, compressing the air molecules in that region. (The tine movement is shown on the right side only and is exaggerated.) Then the tines move in the opposite direction, compressing the air there and leaving a rarefied area to the right side of the tuning fork. **(b)** In this way, sound waves, consisting of alternate areas of compression and rarefaction, are set up and radiate outward in all directions from the sound source. **(c)** The sound wave may be depicted as a sine wave. The peaks of the wave represent areas of high pressure (compressed areas), and the troughs represent areas of low pressure (rarefied areas). For any tone, the distance between two corresponding points on the wave (two crests or two troughs) is called the wavelength. The height (amplitude) of the crests is related to the energy, or intensity, of the sound wave.

FIGURE 16.30
Frequency and amplitude of sound waves. (a) The wave shown in red has a shorter wavelength, and thus a greater frequency, than that shown in blue. The frequency of sound is perceived as pitch. **(b)** The wave shown in red has a greater amplitude (intensity) than that shown in blue and is perceived as being louder.

subjective interpretation of sound intensity. Because we can hear such an enormous range of intensities, from the proverbial pin drop to a steam whistle 100 trillion times as loud, sound intensity (and loudness) is measured in logarithmic units called **decibels** (des′ĭ-belz) **(dB).** On a clinical audiometer, the decibel scale is arbitrarily set to begin at 0 dB, which is the threshold of hearing (barely audible sound) for normal ears. Each 10 dB increase represents a tenfold increase in sound intensity. A sound of 10 dB has ten times more energy than one of 0 dB, and a 20 dB sound has 100 times (10 × 10) more energy than one of 0 dB. However, the same 10 dB increase represents only a twofold increase in loudness. In other words, most people would report that a 20 dB sound seems about twice as loud as a 10 dB sound. The healthy adult ear can pick up differences in sound intensity as small as 0.1 dB, and the normal range of hearing (from barely audible to the loudest sound we can process without excruciating pain) extends over a range of 120 dB. (The threshold of pain is 130 dB.)

Severe hearing loss occurs with frequent or prolonged exposure to sounds with intensities greater than 90 dB, and in the U.S., employees exposed to occupational noise over that range must wear ear (hearing) protection. This figure becomes more meaningful when you realize that a normal conversation is

in the 50 dB range, a noisy restaurant has 70 dB levels, and amplified rock music is, at 120 dB or more, far above the 90 dB danger zone.

Transmission of Sound to the Inner Ear

Hearing occurs when the auditory area of the temporal lobe cortex is stimulated. However, before this can happen, sound waves must be propagated through air, bone, and fluids to reach and stimulate receptor cells in the organ of Corti.

Airborne sound entering the external auditory canal strikes the tympanic membrane and sets it vibrating at the same frequency. The distance the membrane moves in its vibratory motion varies with sound intensity. The greater the intensity, the farther the membrane is displaced. The motion of the tympanic membrane is amplified and transferred to the oval window by the ossicles. If sound hit the oval window directly, most of its energy would be reflected and lost because of the high impedance (resistance to motion) of the cochlear fluid. However, the ossicle lever system acts much like a hydraulic press or piston to transfer the same total force hitting the eardrum to the oval window. Because the tympanic membrane is 17 to 20 times larger than the oval window, the pressure (force per unit area) actually exerted on the oval window is about 20 times that on the tympanic membrane. This increase in pressure overcomes the impedance of cochlear fluid and sets it into wave motion. This situation can be roughly compared to the difference in pressure relayed to the floor by the broad rubber heels of a man's shoes and a woman's tiny spike heels. The man's weight—say, 70 kg (about 150 pounds)—is spread over several square inches, and his heels will not make dents in a pliable vinyl floor. But spike heels will concentrate the same 70 kg force in an area of about 2.5 cm² (1 square inch) and *will* dent the floor.

Resonance of the Basilar Membrane

As the stapes rocks back and forth against the oval window, it sets the perilymph in the scala vestibuli into a similar back-and-forth motion. During these movements, the basilar membrane swings up and down, causing the nearby (basal) part of the cochlear duct to oscillate in time, and a pressure wave travels through the perilymph from the basal end toward the helicotrema, much as a piece of rope held horizontally can be set into wave motion by movements initiated at one end. Sounds of very low frequency (below 20 Hz) create pressure waves that take the complete route through the cochlea—up the scala vestibuli, around the helicotrema, and back toward the round window through the scala tympani (Figure 16.31a). Such sounds do not activate the organ of Corti (are below the threshold of hearing). But sounds of higher frequency (and shorter wavelengths) create pressure teristic of many natural substances is called *resonance.*) The fibers of the basilar membrane span its width like the strings of a guitar. The fibers near the oval window (cochlear base) are short and stiff, and they resonate in response to high-frequency pressure waves (Figure 16.31b). The longer, more floppy basilar membrane fibers near the cochlear apex resonate in time with lower-frequency pressure waves. Thus, sound signals are mechanically processed by the resonance of the basilar membrane, before ever reaching the receptors.

Excitation of Hair Cells in the Organ of Corti

The organ of Corti, which rests atop the basilar membrane, is composed of supporting cells and several long rows of *cochlear hair cells,* specifically one row of **inner hair cells** and three rows of **outer hair cells.** Afferent fibers of the **cochlear nerve** (a division of the vestibulocochlear nerve [VIII]) are coiled about the bases of the hair cells. The "hairs" (stereocilia) of the hair cells are stiffened by actin filaments and protrude into the K+-rich endolymph. The longest of them are enmeshed in the overlying, gel-like **tectorial membrane** (see Figure 16.28c).

Transduction of sound stimuli occurs after the trapped cilia of the hair cells are "tweaked" or bent by localized movements of the basilar membrane. Bending their cilia toward the tallest cilium opens cation channels, which results in an inward K+ current and a graded depolarization. Bending their cilia away from the tallest cilium causes the ion channels to close and produces a graded hyperpolarization. Depolarization increases their neurotransmitter release, which causes the cochlear fibers to transmit a faster stream of impulses to the brain for auditory interpretation. Hyperpolarization produces the exact opposite effect. Although the outer hair cells are much more numerous, they instigate relatively few action potentials. There is some evidence that they act in feedback mechanisms that sharpen the frequency selectivity of the basilar membrane. Hence, the frequency of sound waves directly determines the rhythm of the membrane potential changes that occur in hair cells and the frequency of signaling by cochlear nerve fibers. As you might guess, activation of the hair cells occurs at points of vigorous basilar membrane vibration. Hair cells nearest the oval window are activated by the highest-pitch sounds, and those located at the cochlear apex are stimulated by the lowest-frequency tones.

The Auditory Pathway to the Brain

The ascending auditory pathways to the brain involve several brain stem nuclei, but here we will stress only the major way stations. Impulses generated in the

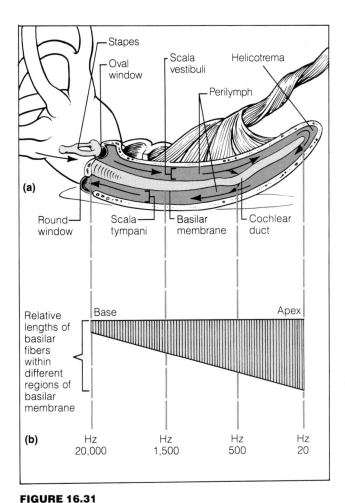

FIGURE 16.31
Resonance of the basilar membrane and activation of the cochlear hair cells. (a) The cochlea is depicted as if it is uncoiled to make the events of sound transmission occurring there easier to follow. Sound waves of low frequency that are below the level of hearing travel around the helicotrema without exciting hair cells. But sounds of higher frequency result in pressure waves that penetrate through the cochlear duct and basilar membrane to reach the scala tympani. This sets up vibrations in the basilar membrane, causing it to vibrate maximally in certain areas in response to certain frequencies of sound. **(b)** Relative lengths of basilar fibers in different regions of the basilar membrane.

waves that fail to reach the helicotrema and instead take a "shortcut" and are transmitted through the cochlear duct into the perilymph of the scala tympani. Fluids are incompressible. Think of what happens when you sit on a water bed—you sit "here" and it bulges over "there." Thus, each time the fluid adjacent to the oval window is forced medially by the stapes, the membrane of the round window bulges laterally into the middle ear cavity and acts as a pressure valve.

As a pressure wave descends through the flexible vestibular membrane, the endolymph of the cochlear duct, and then through the basilar membrane, it sets the entire basilar membrane into vibrations. Maximal displacement of the membrane occurs where the fibers of the basilar membranes are "tuned" to a particular sound frequency (Figure 16.31b). (This characcochlea pass through the **spiral ganglion** (the sensory ganglion of the cochlear nerve) along the afferent fibers of the cochlear nerve to the **cochlear nuclei** of the medulla (Figure 16.32). From there, impulses are sent on to the **superior olivary nucleus** and then via the **lateral lemniscal tract** to the **inferior colliculus** (auditory reflex center in the midbrain). From there impulses are sent on to the **auditory cortex** in the temporal lobe via relays in the **medial geniculate body** of the thalamus. Since some of the fibers from each ear decussate (cross), each auditory cortex receives impulses from both ears.

Auditory Processing

If you are at a Broadway musical, the sound of the instruments, the actors' voices, rustling of clothing, and closing of doors are all intermingled in your sound awareness. Yet, the auditory cortex can distinguish the separate parts of this auditory jumble. Audi-

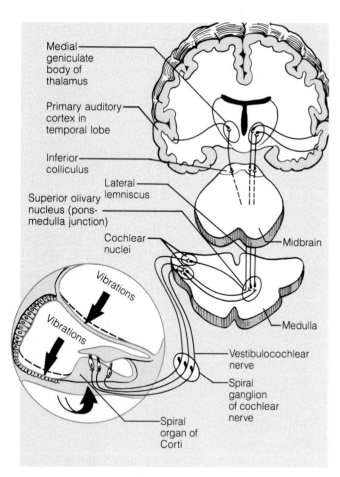

FIGURE 16.32
Simplified diagram of the auditory pathway from the organ of Corti to the auditory cortex in the temporal lobe of the brain. For clarity, only the pathway from the right ear is illustrated.

tory processing is analytic, and whenever the difference between sound wavelengths is sufficient for discrimination, you hear two separate and distinct tones. In fact, the analytic powers of the auditory cortex are so great that we are able to pick single instruments out of a whole orchestra.

Cortical processing of sound stimuli seems to be quite complex. For example, certain cortical cells depolarize at the beginning of a particular tone, others depolarize when the tone ends. However, pure tones seem to be less important as stimuli to the cortical cells than combinations of tones. Some cortical cells depolarize continuously, others appear to have high thresholds (low sensitivity), and so on. Here we will concentrate on the more straightforward aspects of cortical perception of pitch, loudness, and sound location.

Perception of Pitch. As just explained, hair cells in different parts of the organ of Corti are activated by sound waves of different frequencies. When the sound is composed of tones of many frequencies, several populations of cochlear hair cells and cortical cells are activated simultaneously, resulting in the perception of multiple tones.

Early investigators of hearing concluded that impulses from specific hair cells are interpreted as specific pitches. However, the coding mechanism for pitch perception is much more complex and involves local processing in the cochlear nuclei and probably other areas as well. Indeed, both the cochlear nuclei and the primary auditory cortex have *tonotopic maps* that correspond spatially to precise regions of the organ of Corti and to specific frequencies.

Detection of Loudness. Our perception of loudness suggests that certain cochlear cells have higher thresholds than others for responding to a tone of the same frequency. For example, some of the receptors for a tone with a frequency of 540 Hz might be stimulated by a sound wave of very low intensity. As the intensity of the sound increases, more hair cells at the same relative position on the basilar membrane would be recruited by the membrane's more vigorous vibration. As a result, more impulses would reach the auditory cortex and be recognized as a louder sound of the same pitch.

Localization of Sound. As long as both ears are functional, several brain stem nuclei (most importantly the superior olivary nuclei) process signals that help us localize a sound's source in space by means of two cues: the *relative intensity* and the *relative timing* of sound waves reaching the two ears. If the sound source is directly in front, in back, or over the midline of the head, the intensity and timing cues will be the same for both ears. However, when sound is coming from one side, the receptors of the nearer ear will be activated slightly earlier and more vigorously (because of the greater intensity of the sound waves impinging on that ear).

Homeostatic Imbalances of Hearing

Deafness. Any hearing loss, no matter how slight, is **deafness** of some sort. Hearing loss may range from the inability to hear sound of a certain pitch or intensity to a complete inability to detect sound. Deafness is classified as conduction or sensorineural deafness, according to its cause.

Conduction deafness occurs when something interferes with the conduction of sound vibrations to the fluids of the inner ear. The possibilities are almost limitless. For example, impacted earwax blocking the auditory canal interferes with vibration of the eardrum. A *perforated* or *ruptured* eardrum prevents sound conduction from the eardrum to the ossicles. But the most common causes of conduction deafness are middle ear inflammations (otitis media) and **otosclerosis** (o″to-sklĕ-ro′sis) of the ossicles. Otosclerosis ("hardening of the ear"), a common age-related problem, occurs when overgrowth of bony tissue fuses the stapes foot plate to the oval window or fuses the ossicles to one another. With the normal conduction pathway unavailable, sound is instead conducted to the receptors of that ear through vibrations of the skull bones, which is far less satisfactory. Otosclerosis is treated surgically to remove the excess tissue or to replace one or more of the ossicles or the oval window.

Sensorineural deafness results from damage to neural structures at any point from the cochlear hair cells to and including the auditory cortical cells. This type of deafness may be partial or complete and typically results from the gradual loss of the hearing receptor cells throughout life. These cells can also be destroyed at an earlier age by a single explosively loud noise or prolonged exposure to high-intensity sounds, such as rock bands or airport noise, which tears their cilia. Degeneration of the cochlear nerve, cerebral infarcts, and tumors affecting the auditory cortex are other causes. For cases of age- or noise-related cochlear damage, cochlear implants can be inserted into a drilled recess in the temporal bone. These miniature transducer devices convert sound energy into electrical signals that are delivered directly to the cochlear nerve fibers. The cochlear implants provide less than normal hearing; for example, they make human voices sound tinny and robot-like. But the profoundly deaf will agree that partial hearing is better than none.

Tinnitus. Tinnitus (tĭ-ni′tus) is a ringing or clicking sound in the ears in the absence of auditory stimuli. It is more a symptom of pathology than a disease.

For example, tinnitus is one of the first symptoms of cochlear nerve degeneration. It may also result from inflammation of the middle or inner ears and is a side effect of some medications, such as aspirin.

Ménière's Syndrome. Classic **Ménière's** (men″ĕ-ār′z) **syndrome** is a labyrinth disorder that affects both the semicircular canals and the cochlea. The afflicted person has transient but repeated attacks of vertigo, nausea, and vomiting. Balance is so disturbed that standing erect is nearly impossible. A "howling" tinnitus is common, so hearing is impaired (and ultimately lost) as well. The cause of the syndrome is uncertain, but it may result from distortion of the membranous labyrinth by excessive endolymph accumulation. Mild cases can usually be managed by antimotion drugs. For more debilitating attacks, salt restriction and diuretics are used to decrease overall extracellular fluid volumes and, consequently, endolymph fluid volume. In severe cases, surgery may be performed to drain the excess endolymph from the inner ear. A last resort is removal of the entire malfunctioning labyrinth, which is usually deferred until hearing loss is complete. •

Mechanisms of Equilibrium and Orientation

The equilibrium sense is not easy to describe because it does not "see," "hear," or "feel," but responds (frequently without our awareness) to various head movements. Furthermore, this sense depends not only on inputs from the inner ear, but also on vision and on information from stretch receptors of muscles and tendons. Under normal conditions the equilibrium receptors in the semicircular canals and vestibule, collectively called the **vestibular apparatus,** send signals to the brain that initiate reflexes needed to make the simplest changes in position as well as to serve a tennis ball precisely to the right spot (your opponent's backhand). However, if the vestibular apparatus is damaged, the system can adapt and learn to function without it. Thus, it is difficult to credit any one set of receptors with our ability to maintain our orientation and balance in space. Nevertheless, we do know that the equilibrium receptors of the inner ear can be divided into two functional arms, with the receptors in the vestibule and semicircular canals monitoring **static** and **dynamic equilibrium,** respectively.

The Maculae and Static Equilibrium

The sensory receptors for static equilibrium are the **maculae** (mak′u-le; "spots"), one in each saccule wall and one in each utricle wall. These receptors monitor the position of the head in space, and in so doing, they play a key role in control of posture. They

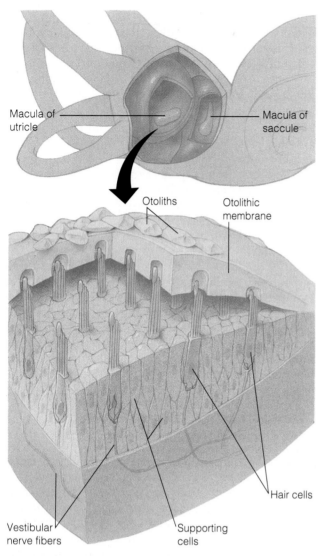

FIGURE 16.33
Structure and function of a macula. The "hairs" of the receptor cells of a macula project into the gelatinous otolithic membrane. Vestibular nerve fibers surround the base of the hair cells.

respond to *linear* acceleration forces, that is, straight-line changes in speed and direction, but not to rotational movement.

Anatomy of the Maculae.   Each macula is a flat epithelial patch containing **supporting cells** and scattered receptor cells called **hair cells** (Figure 16.33). Displacement of the head in any linear direction activates the receptors in either the utricles or the saccules. Named for the hairy look of their free surface, the hair cells have numerous *stereocilia* (long microvilli) and a single *kinocilium* (a true cilium) protruding from their apices. These "hairs" are embedded in the overlying **otolithic** (o'to-lith-ik)

membrane, a flattened jellylike mass studded with tiny stones (calcium carbonate crystals) called **otoliths** ("ear stones"). The otoliths, though small, are dense and so they increase the membrane's weight and its inertia (resistance to change in motion). In the utricle, the macula is horizontal, and the hairs are vertically oriented when the head is upright. Thus, the utricular maculae respond best to acceleration in the horizontal plane and tilting the head to the side, because vertical (up-down) movements do not displace their horizontal otolithic membrane. In the saccule, the macula is nearly vertical, and the hairs protrude horizontally into the otolithic membrane. The saccular maculae respond best to vertical movements, such as the sudden acceleration of an elevator. Although the receptor cells release neurotransmitter continually, movement of their hairs modifies the amount they release, causing an increase or decrease in the rate of impulse generation by the **vestibular nerve** endings coiling around their bases. (Like the cochlear nerve, the vestibular nerve is a subdivision of the vestibulocochlear nerve [VIII].) The cell bodies of the sensory neurons are located in the nearby **superior** and **inferior vestibular ganglia.**

Transducing Gravity and Linear Acceleration Stimuli.   Let's look more closely at the "happenings" in the maculae that lead to sensory transduction. When your head starts or stops moving in a linear direction, inertia causes the otolithic membrane to slide backward or forward like a greased plate over the hair cells, bending the hairs. For example, when you run, the otolithic membranes of the utricle maculae lag behind, bending the hairs backward. When you suddenly stop, the otolithic membrane slides abruptly forward (just as you slide forward in your car when you brake), bending the hair cells forward. Likewise, when you nod your head or fall, the otoliths roll inferiorly, bending the hairs of the maculae in the saccules. When the hairs are bent *toward the kinocilium,* the hair cells are depolarized and step up their pace of neurotransmitter release. As a result, a faster stream of impulses is sent to the brain (Figure 16.34). When the hairs are bent in the opposite direction, the receptors are hyperpolarized, and neurotransmitter release and impulse generation decline. In either case, the brain is informed of the changing position of the head in space. It is important to understand that the maculae respond *only to changes* in acceleration or velocity of head movement. Since the hair cells adapt quickly (resuming their basic level of neurotransmitter release), they do not report on unchanging head positions.

Thus, the maculae help us to maintain normal head position with respect to gravitational pull. They also contribute to dynamic equilibrium (see discussion below) by responding to changes in linear acceleration.

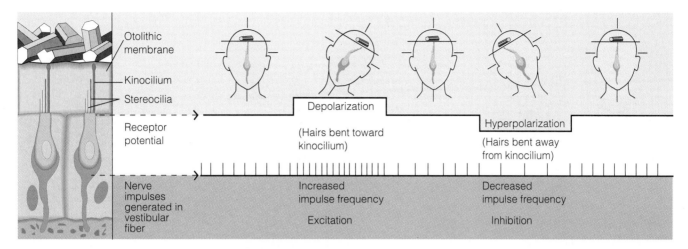

FIGURE 16.34
The effect of gravitational pull on a macula receptor cell in the utricle. When movement of the otolithic membrane (direction indicated by the arrow) bends the hair cells in the direction of the kinocilium, the vestibular nerve fibers depolarize and generate action potentials more rapidly. When the hairs are bent in the direction away from the kinocilium, the hair cells become hyperpolarized, and the nerve fibers send impulses at a reduced rate (i.e., below the resting rate of discharge).

The Crista Ampullaris and Dynamic Equilibrium

The receptor for dynamic equilibrium, called the **crista ampullaris,** or simply *crista,* is a minute elevation in the ampulla of each semicircular canal (see Figure 16.27). Like the maculae, the cristae are excited by head movement (acceleration and deceleration), but in this case the major stimuli are rotatory (angular) movements. When you twirl on the dance floor or suffer through a rough boat ride, these gyroscopelike receptors are working overtime. Since the semicircular canals are located in all three planes of space, all rotatory movements of the head disturb one or another *pair* of cristae (one in each ear).

Anatomy of the Crista Ampullaris. Each crista is composed of supporting cells and hair cells. These hair cells, like those of the maculae, have stereocilia plus one kinocilium that project into the **cupula** (ku'pu-lah), a gel-like mass that resembles a pointed cap (Figure 16.35b and c). The cupula is a delicate, loosely organized network of gelatinous strands that radiate outward to contact the "hairs" of each hair cell. Dendrites of vestibular nerve fibers encircle the base of the hair cells.

Transducing Rotational Stimuli. The cristae respond to *changes* in the velocity of rotatory movements of the head. Because of its inertia, the endolymph in the semicircular ducts moves briefly in the direction *opposite* the body's rotation, deforming the crista in the duct. As the hairs are bent, the hair cells depolarize and impulses reach the brain at a faster rate. Bending the cilia in the opposite direction causes hyperpolarization and reduced impulse gener-

ation. Because the axes of the hair cells in the complementary semicircular ducts are opposite, rotation in a given direction causes depolarization of the receptors in one ampulla of the pair, and hyperpolarization of the receptors in the other (Figure 16.35d).

If the body continues to rotate at a constant rate, the endolymph eventually comes to rest—it moves along at the same speed as the body—and stimulation of the hair cells ends. Consequently, if we are blindfolded, we cannot tell whether we are moving at a constant speed or not moving at all after the first few seconds of continuous rotation. However, when we suddenly stop moving, the endolymph keeps on going, in effect reversing its direction within the canal. This sudden reversal in the direction of hair bending results in membrane voltage changes in the receptor cells and modifies the rate of impulse transmission, which tells the brain that we have slowed or stopped.

The key point to remember when considering both the dynamic and the static equilibrium receptors is that the rigid bony labyrinth moves with the body, while the fluids (and gels) within the membranous labyrinth are free to move at various rates, depending on the forces (gravity, acceleration, etc.) acting on them.

Impulses transmitted from the semicircular canals are particularly important to reflex movements of the eyes. **Vestibular nystagmus** is a complex of rather strange eye movements that occurs during and immediately after rotational motion. As you rotate, your eyes slowly drift in the opposite direction, as though fixed on some object in the environment. This reaction relates to the backflow of endolymph in the semicircular canals. Then, because of compensating mechanisms of the central nervous system, the eyes

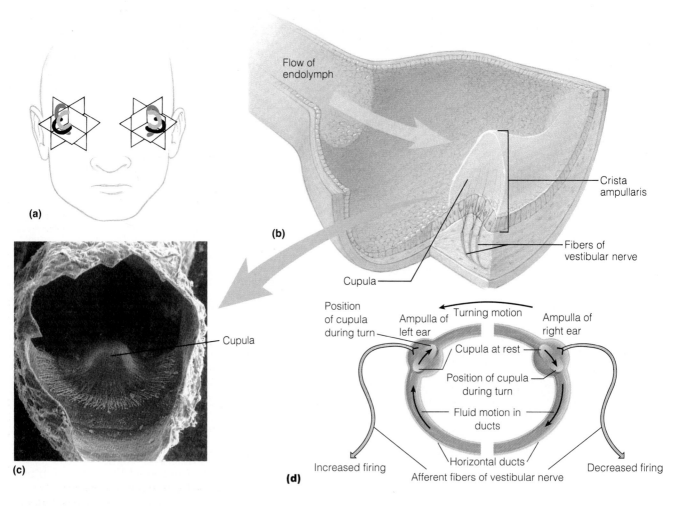

Flow of endolymph

Crista ampullaris

Fibers of vestibular nerve

(b)

Cupula

Cupula

(c)

Position of cupula during turn

Ampulla of left ear

Turning motion

Cupula at rest

Ampulla of right ear

Position of cupula during turn

Fluid motion in ducts

Increased firing

Horizontal ducts

Decreased firing

Afferent fibers of vestibular nerve

(d)

(a)

FIGURE 16.35
Localization and structure of a crista ampullaris. (a) Location of the semicircular canals within the temporal bones of the skull. **(b)** The ampulla of a semicircular duct has been sectioned to show the positioning of a crista ampullaris receptor. **(c)** Scanning EM of a crista ampullaris. (180×) **(d)** View of the horizontal ducts from above shows how paired semicircular canals work together to provide bilateral information on rotatory head movement.

jump rapidly toward the direction of rotation to establish a new fixation point. This alternation of eye movements continues until the endolymph comes to rest. When you stop rotating, at first your eyes continue to move in the direction of the previous spin, and then they jerk rapidly in the opposite direction. This sudden change is caused by the change in the direction in which the cristae are bent after you stop. Nystagmus is often accompanied by vertigo.

The Equilibrium Pathway to the Brain

Our responses to body imbalance, such as stumbling, must be fast and reflexive. If we took time to think about correcting our falls, we would end up on our faces every time! Hence, information from the balance receptors goes directly to reflex centers in the brain stem, rather than to the cerebral cortex as with the other special senses. However, the nerve pathways that connect the vestibular apparatus with the brain are complex and poorly traced. The transmission sequence begins when the hair cells in the vestibular apparatus are activated. As depicted in Figure 16.36, impulses travel initially to one of two destinations: the **vestibular nuclear complex** in the brain stem or the **cerebellum.** The vestibular nuclei, the major integrative center for balance, also receive inputs from the visual and somatic receptors, particularly from proprioceptors in neck muscles that report on the angle or inclination of the head. The vestibular nuclei integrate this information and then send commands to brain stem motor centers that control the extrinsic eye muscles (cranial nerve nuclei III, IV, and VI) and reflex movements of the neck, limb, and trunk muscles (via the vestibulospinal tracts). Reflex movements of the eyes and body produced by their responses allow us to remain focused on the visual field and to quickly adjust our body position to maintain or regain balance. The cerebellum, too, integrates inputs from the eyes and somatic receptors (as well as from the cerebrum). It coordinates the activity of skeletal muscles and regulates muscle tone so that head position, posture, and balance are maintained, often in the face of rapidly changing inputs. Its "specialty" is fine control of delicate postural movements and timing. A few vestibular fibers reach the cerebral cortex, allowing us to become aware of changes in head position, body acceleration, or balance. Inputs from the eyes and somatic receptors are also sent to the reticular nuclei, but their precise function in equilibrium is unclear.

Notice that the vestibular apparatus does not automatically compensate for forces acting on the body. Rather, its job is to send warning signals to the central nervous system, which initiates the appropriate compensations (righting) to keep your body balanced, your weight evenly distributed, and your eyes focused on what you were looking at when the disturbance occurred.

Since responses to equilibrium signals are totally reflexive, we usually become aware of vestibular apparatus activity only when its functioning is less than optimal. Equilibrium problems are usually obvious and unpleasant. Nausea, dizziness, and problems in maintaining balance are common symptoms. Also, there may be nystagmus in the absence of rotational stimuli.

Motion sickness, a common equilibrium disorder, has been difficult to explain, but it appears to be due to sensory input mismatch. For example, if you are inside a ship during a storm, visual inputs indicate that your body is fixed with reference to a stationary environment (your cabin). But as the ship is tossed about by the rough seas, your vestibular apparatus detects movement and sends impulses that "disagree" with the visual information. The brain thus receives conflicting information, and its "confusion" somehow leads to motion sickness. Warning signals, which precede nausea and vomiting, include excessive salivation, pallor, rapid deep breathing, and profuse sweating. Removal of the stimulus usually ends the symptoms. Over-the-counter antimotion drugs, such as meclizine HCl (Bonine) and dimenhydrinate (Dramamine), depress vestibular inputs and help many sufferers. They are most effective when taken "before the fact." Scopolamine-containing timed release skin patches are also used to head off motion sickness. •

DEVELOPMENTAL ASPECTS OF THE SPECIAL SENSES

All the special senses are functional, to a greater or lesser degree, at birth. Smell and taste are sharp at birth, and infants relish food that adults consider bland or tasteless. Some researchers claim that smell is just as important as touch in guiding newborn infants to their mother's breast. However, very young children seem indifferent to odors and can play hap-

FIGURE 16.36
Pathways of the balance and orientation system. The three modes of input—vestibular, visual, and somatic (skin, muscle, and joint) receptors—transmit impulses to two major processing areas: the vestibular nuclei of the brain stem and the cerebellum. (The pathways to and the precise function of the reticular nuclei are unclear.) After vestibular nuclear processing, impulses are sent to one of two major output regions—areas controlling eye movements (oculomotor control) or those controlling the skeletal muscles of the neck (spinal motor control).

pily with their own feces. As they get older, their emotional responses to specific odors and foods increase.

There are few interferences with the chemical senses throughout childhood and young adulthood. Women generally have a more acute sense of smell than men, and nonsmokers have a sharper sense of smell than smokers. Beginning in the fourth decade of life, our ability to taste and smell declines. This reflects the gradual loss of receptors, which are replaced more slowly than in younger people. Over half of people over the age of 65 years have serious problems detecting odors, and their sense of taste is poor, which may explain their loss of appetite and inattention to formerly disagreeable odors.

By the fourth week of development, the beginnings of the eyes are seen in the **optic vesicles** that

FIGURE 16.37
Embryonic development of the eye and the ear. (a)–(e) Development of the eye. **(a)** Section through the diencephalon and optic vesicle at the time of lens placode formation. (The orienting diagram to the right shows the plane of the section.) **(b)** Contact of the optic vesicle with the lens placode causes the lens placode to invaginate. **(c)** The lens placode forms the lens vesicle, which becomes enclosed by the optic cup and then detaches. **(d)** Blood vessels reach the eye interior via the optic fissure and then become enclosed in the optic stalk (which becomes the optic nerve). The optic cup forms the nervous and pigmented layers of the retina, and invading mesoderm forms the other eye tunics and the vitreous humor. **(e)** The lens vesicle differentiates to form the lens; the surrounding accessory structures develop from the surface ectoderm. **(f)–(i)** Development of the ear. (Again, the orienting diagram shows the plane of the section.) **(f)** By about the twenty-first day of development, the otic placodes have formed from thickenings of the surface ectoderm, and the pharynx has been formed from endoderm. **(g)** The otic placodes invaginate, forming the otic pits, and the branchial grooves begin to invaginate from the surface ectoderm. **(h)** At approximately 28 days, the otic vesicles are forming from the otic pits, and the branchial grooves have deepened. **(i)** Between the fifth and eighth weeks of development, the inner ear structures form from the otic vesicles, the endoderm of the pharyngeal pouches gives rise to the pharyngotympanic tubes and the middle ear cavity, and the branchial grooves develop into the external auditory canals. Mesenchyme forms the surrounding bony structures.

protrude from the diencephalon (Figure 16.37a–e). Soon these hollow vesicles indent to form double-layered **optic cups.** The proximal parts of the outgrowths, called the **optic stalks,** form the basis of the optic nerves. Once a growing optic vesicle reaches the overlying surface ectoderm, it induces the ectoderm to thicken and form a **lens placode** (plak'ōd; "plate"), which invaginates to form a **lens vesicle.** Shortly thereafter, the lens vesicle pinches off into the cavity of the optic cup, where it becomes the lens. The lining (internal layer) of the optic cup becomes the neural retina, and the outer layer forms the pigmented layer of the retina. The *optic fissure,* a groove on the underside of each optic cup and stalk, provides a direct pathway for blood vessels to reach the interior of the developing eye. When the fissure closes, the now tubelike optic stalk furnishes a tunnel through which the optic nerve fibers, originating in the neural retina, can pass to the diencephalon, and the blood vessels come to lie in the center of the developing optic nerve. The balance of the eye tissues and the vitreous humor are formed by mesenchymal cells derived from the mesoderm. The interior of the eyeball has a rich blood supply during development, but virtually all of these blood vessels, except those serving the vascular tunic and retina, degenerate before birth.

In the darkness of the uterus, the fetus cannot see. Nonetheless, even before the light-sensitive portions of the photoreceptors develop, the central nervous system connections have been made and are functional. During infancy, many of the synapses made during development disappear as synaptic connections are fine-tuned, and the typical cortical fields that allow binocular vision are established.

Congenital problems of the eyes are relatively uncommon, but their incidence is dramatically increased by certain maternal infections, particularly rubella (German measles), occurring during the critical first three months of pregnancy. Common rubella sequels include blindness and cataracts. •

As a rule, vision is the only special sense not fully functional at birth. Because the eyeballs are foreshortened, most babies are hyperopic. The newborn infant sees only in gray tones, eye movements are uncoordinated, and often only one eye at a time is used. Because the lacrimal glands are not completely developed until about two weeks after birth, babies are tearless for this period, even though they may cry lustily. By five months, infants can follow moving objects with their eyes, but visual acuity is still poor (20/200). By the age of five years, depth perception is present, color vision is well developed, and visual acuity has improved to about 20/30, providing a readiness to begin reading. The initial hyperopia has usually been replaced by emmetropia, which continues until presbyopia begins to set in around age 40 owing to decreasing lens elasticity.

With age, the lens loses its crystal clarity and discolors. The dilator muscles of the iris become less

efficient so the pupils stay partly constricted. These two changes together decrease the amount of light reaching the retina, and visual acuity is dramatically lower in people over 70. In addition, elderly persons are susceptible to certain conditions that cause blindness, such as macular degeneration, glaucoma, cataracts, arteriosclerosis, and diabetes mellitus.

Development of the ear begins in the three-week embryo (Figure 16.37f–i). The inner ear begins developing first, from a thickening of the surface ectoderm, called the **otic** (o'tik) **placode,** which lies lateral to the hindbrain on each side. The otic placode invaginates to form the **otic pit,** and then its edges fuse to form the **otic vesicle,** which detaches from the surface epithelium. The otic vesicle develops into the membranous labyrinth. The surrounding mesenchyme forms the walls of the bony labyrinth of the inner ear.

While the inner ear structures are developing, middle ear structures begin to appear. Lateral out-pocketings, called **pharyngeal pouches,** form from the endoderm lining the pharynx. The middle ear cavity and the pharyngotympanic tube develop from the first pharyngeal pouch. The ossicles, which bridge the cavity, develop from the cartilage of the first and second pouches.

Turning to the outer ear, the external auditory canal and external face of the tympanic membrane differentiate from the **branchial** (brang'ke-al) **groove,** an indentation of the surface ectoderm. The auricle develops from swellings of the surrounding tissue.

Newborn infants can hear, but early responses to sound are mostly reflexive—for example, crying and clenching the eyelids in response to a startling noise. By the fourth month, infants can localize sounds and will turn to the voices of family members. Critical listening begins to occur in toddlers as they increase their vocabulary, and good language skills are very closely tied to the ability to hear well.

Congenital abnormalities of the ears are fairly common. Examples include partly or completely missing pinnae and closed or absent external ear canals. Maternal rubella during the first trimester commonly results in sensorineural deafness. •

Except for ear inflammations resulting from bacterial infections or allergies, few problems affect the ears during childhood and adult life. By the 60s, however, deterioration of the organ of Corti becomes noticeable. We are born with approximately 20,000 hair cells in each ear, but they are not replaced when damaged or destroyed by loud noises, disease, or drugs. It is estimated that if we were to live 140 years, we would have lost all of our hearing receptors.

The ability to hear high-pitched sounds leaves us first. This condition, called **presbycusis** (pres″bĭ-ku'-sis), is a type of sensorineural deafness. Although presbycusis is considered a disability of old age, it is becoming much more common in younger people as our world grows noisier. Since noise is a stressor, one of its physiological consequences is vasoconstriction, and when delivery of blood to the ear is reduced, the ear becomes even more sensitive to the damaging effects of noise.

* * *

Our abilities to see, hear, taste, and smell—and some of our responses to the effects of gravity—are largely the work of our brain. However, as we have discovered in this, the last of the nervous system chapters, the large and often elaborate sensory receptor organs that serve the special senses are works of art in and of themselves.

The final chapter of this unit describes how the body's functions are controlled by chemicals called hormones in a manner quite different from what we have described for neural control.

RELATED CLINICAL TERMS

Blepharitis (blef″ah-ri′tis; *blephar* = eyelash; *itis* = inflammation) Inflammation of the margins of the eyelids.

Enucleation (e-nu″kle-a′shun) Surgical removal of an eyeball.

Exophthalmos (ek″sof-thal′mos; *exo* = out; *phthalmo* = the eye) Anteriorly bulging eyeballs; this condition is seen in some cases of hyperthyroidism.

Ophthalmology (of″thal-mol′o-je) The science that studies the eye and eye diseases. An **ophthalmologist** is a medical doctor who specializes in treating eye disorders.

Optometrist A licensed nonphysician who measures vision and prescribes corrective lenses.

Otitis externa Inflammation and infection of the external auditory canal, caused by bacteria or fungi that enter the canal from outside, especially when the canal is moist (e.g., after swimming).

Otorhinolaryngology (o″to-ri″no-lar″in-gol′o-je) The science that studies the ear, nose, and larynx and the diseases of these body regions.

Papilledema (pap″il-ĕ-de′mah; *papill* = nipple; *edema* = swelling) Nipplelike protrusion of the optic disc into the eyeball, which can be observed by ophthalmoscopic examination; caused by conditions that increase intracranial pressure.

Scotoma (sko-to′mah; *scoto* = darkness) A blind spot other than the normal (optic disc) blind spot; often reflects the presence of a brain tumor pressing on fibers of the visual pathway.

Synesthesia (sin″es-the′ze-ah; *syn* = together; *esthesi* = sensation) Literally, mingling of the senses; a rare condition in which sensory perceptions are mixed up; e.g., some with this condition can "see" sounds as colors or other visual perceptions or can "touch" tastes (feel certain shapes when tasting certain foods); cause is unknown, but the limbic region of the brain appears to be involved.

Trachoma (trah-ko′mah; *trach* = rough) A highly contagious bacterial (chlamydial) infection of the conjunctiva and cornea. Common worldwide, it blinds millions of people in poor countries of Africa and Asia; treated with eye ointments containing antibiotic drugs.

Weber's test Hearing test during which a sounding tuning fork is held to the forehead. In those with normal hearing, the tone is heard equally in both ears. The tone will be heard best in the "good" ear if sensorineural deafness is present, and in the "bad" ear if conduction deafness is present.

CHAPTER SUMMARY

The Chemical Senses: Taste and Smell (pp. 502–506)

Taste Buds and the Sense of Taste (pp. 502–504)

1.   The taste buds are scattered in the oral cavity and pharynx but are most abundant on the papillae of the tongue.

2.   Gustatory cells, the receptor cells of the taste buds, have gustatory hairs (microvilli) that serve as the receptor regions. The gustatory cells are excited by the binding of chemicals to receptors on their microvilli.

3.   The four basic taste qualities—sweet, sour, salty, and bitter—are sensed best at different regions on the tongue.

4.   The taste sense is served by cranial nerves VII, IX, and X, which send impulses to the solitary nucleus of the medulla. From there, impulses are sent to the thalamus and the taste cortex.

The Olfactory Epithelium and the Sense of Smell (pp. 504–506)

5.   The olfactory epithelium is located in the roof of the nasal cavity. The receptor cells are ciliated bipolar neurons. Their axons are the fibers of the olfactory nerve (cranial nerve I).

6.   Individual olfactory neurons show a range of responsiveness to different chemicals.

7.   Olfactory neurons are excited by volatile chemicals that bind to receptors in the olfactory hairs (cilia).

8.   Action potentials of the olfactory nerve fibers are transmitted to the olfactory bulb and then via the olfactory tract to the olfactory cortex. Fibers carrying impulses from the olfactory receptors also project to the limbic system.

Homeostatic Imbalances of the Chemical Senses (p. 506)

9.   Most chemical sense dysfunctions are olfactory disorders. Common causes are nasal damage or obstruction and zinc deficiency.

The Eye and Vision (pp. 506–526)

1.   The eye is enclosed in the bony orbit and cushioned by fat.

Accessory Structures of the Eye (pp. 507–510)

2.   The eyebrows help to shade and protect the eyes.

3.   The eyelids protect and lubricate the eyes by reflex blinking. Within the eyelids are the orbicularis oculi and levator palpebrae muscles, modified sebaceous glands, and sweat glands.

4.   The conjunctiva is a mucosa that lines the eyelids and covers the anterior eyeball surface. Its mucus lubricates the eyeball surface.

5.   The lacrimal apparatus consists of the lacrimal gland (which produces a saline solution containing mucus, lysozyme, and antibodies), the lacrimal canals, the lacrimal sac, and the nasolacrimal duct.

6.   The extrinsic eye muscles (superior, inferior, lateral, and medial rectus and superior and inferior oblique) move the eyeballs.

Structure of the Eyeball (pp. 510–515)

7.   The wall of the eyeball is made up of three layers, or tunics. The outermost fibrous tunic consists of the sclera and

the cornea. The sclera protects the eye and gives it shape; the cornea allows light to enter the eye.

8. The middle pigmented vascular tunic (uvea) consists of the choroid, the ciliary body, and the iris. The choroid provides nutrients to the eye and prevents light scattering within the eye. The ciliary muscles of the ciliary body control lens shape; the iris controls the size of the pupil.

9. The sensory tunic, or retina, consists of an outer pigmented layer and an inner nervous layer. The neural layer contains photoreceptors (rods and cones), bipolar cells, and ganglion cells. Ganglion cell axons form the optic nerve, which exits via the optic disc ("blind spot").

10. The outer segments of the photoreceptors contain the light-absorbing pigment within membrane-bounded discs.

11. The posterior segment, behind the lens, contains vitreous humor, which helps support the eyeball and keep the retina in place. The anterior segment, anterior to the lens, is filled with aqueous humor, formed by capillaries in the ciliary processes and drained into the canal of Schlemm. Aqueous humor is a major factor in maintaining intraocular pressure.

12. The biconvex lens is suspended within the eye by the suspensory ligaments attached to the ciliary body. It is the only dynamic (adjustable) refractory structure of the eye.

Physiology of Vision (pp. 515–526)

13. Light is made up of those wavelengths of the electromagnetic spectrum that excite the photoreceptors.

14. Light is refracted (bent) when passing from one transparent medium to another of different density, or when it strikes a curved surface. Concave lenses disperse light; convex lenses converge light and bring its rays to a focal point.

15. As light passes through the eye, it is bent by the cornea and the lens and focused on the retina. The cornea accounts for most of the refraction, but the lens allows active focusing for different distances.

16. Focusing for distance vision requires no special movements of the eye structures. Focusing for close-up vision requires accommodation (bulging of the lens), pupillary constriction, and convergence of the eyeballs. All three reflexes are controlled by fibers of cranial nerve III.

17. Refractory problems include myopia, hyperopia, and astigmatism.

18. Rods respond to low-intensity light and provide night and peripheral vision. Cones are bright-light, high-discrimination receptors that provide for color vision. Anything that must be viewed precisely is focused on the cone-rich fovea centralis.

19. The light-absorbing molecule retinal is combined with various opsins in the visual pigments. When struck by light, retinal changes shape (11-*cis* to all-*trans*) and releases opsin. Freed opsin activates transducin (a G protein subunit) which in turn activates PPE, an enzyme that breaks down cGMP, allowing the Na^+ gates to close. This results in hyperpolarization of the receptor cells and inhibits their release of neurotransmitter.

20. Rod visual pigment, rhodopsin, is a combination of retinal and opsin. The light-triggered changes in retinal cause hyperpolarization of the rods. Photoreceptors and bipolar cells generate local potentials only; action potentials are generated by the ganglion cells.

21. The three types of cones all contain retinal, but each has a different type of opsin. Each cone type responds maximally to one color of light: red, blue, or green. The chemistry of cone function is similar to that of rods.

22. During light adaptation, photopigments are bleached and rods are inactivated; then, as cones begin to respond to high-intensity light, high-acuity vision ensues. In dark adaptation, cones cease functioning, and visual acuity decreases; rod function begins when sufficient rhodopsin has accumulated.

23. The visual pathway to the brain begins with the optic nerve fibers (ganglion cell axons) from the retina. At the optic chiasma, fibers from the medial half of each retinal field cross over and continue on in the optic tracts to the thalamus. Thalamic neurons project to the optic cortex via the optic radiation. Fibers also project from the retina to the midbrain pretectal nuclei and the superior colliculi, and to the suprachiasmatic nucleus of the hypothalamus.

24. In stereoscopic vision, each eye receives a slightly different view of the visual field. These views are fused by the optic cortices to provide for depth perception.

25. Retinal processing involves the selective destruction of rod inputs that emphasizes bright/dark contrasts and edges. (The horizontal cells of the retina act in lateral inhibition of rod inputs to the ganglion cells.) Thalamic processing subserves high-acuity vision and depth perception. Cortical processing involves simple cortical neurons of the striate (primary) cortex, which receive inputs from the retinal ganglion cells, and complex cortical neurons of the prestriate cortices, which receive inputs from striate cortical cells.

The Ear: Hearing and Balance (pp. 526–539)

Structure of the Ear (pp. 527–530)

1. The auricle and external auditory canal compose the outer ear. The tympanic membrane, the boundary between the outer and middle ears, transmits sound waves to the middle ear.

2. The middle ear is a small chamber within the temporal bone, connected by the pharyngotympanic tube to the nasopharynx. The ossicles span the middle ear cavity and transmit sound vibrations from the eardrum to the oval window.

3. The inner ear consists of the bony labyrinth, within which the membranous labyrinth is suspended. The bony labyrinth chambers contain perilymph; the membranous labyrinth ducts and sacs contain endolymph.

4. The vestibule contains the saccule and utricle. The semicircular canals extend posteriorly from the vestibule in three planes. They contain the semicircular ducts.

5. The cochlea houses the cochlear duct (scala media), which contains the organ of Corti (hearing receptor). Within the cochlear duct, the hair (receptor) cells rest on the basilar membrane, and their hairs project into the gelatinous tectorial membrane.

Sound and Mechanisms of Hearing (pp. 530–535)

6. Sound originates from a vibrating object and travels in waves consisting of alternating areas of compression and rarefaction of the medium.

7. The distance from crest to crest on a sine wave is the sound's wavelength; the shorter the wavelength, the higher the frequency (measured in hertz). Frequency is perceived as pitch.

8. The amplitude of sound is the height of the peaks of the sine wave, which reflect the sound's intensity. Sound intensity is measured in decibels. Intensity is perceived as loudness.

9. Sound passing through the external auditory canal sets the eardrum into vibration at the same frequency. The ossicles amplify and deliver the vibrations to the oval window.

10. Pressure waves in cochlear fluids set specific basilar membrane fibers into resonance. At points of maximal membrane vibration, the hair cells of the organ of Corti are alternately depolarized and hyperpolarized by the vibratory motion. High-frequency sounds stimulate hair cells near the oval window; low-frequency sounds stimulate hair cells near the apex.

11. Impulses generated along the cochlear nerve travel to the cochlear nuclei of the medulla and from there through several brain stem nuclei to the auditory cortex. Each auditory cortex receives impulses from both ears.

12. Auditory processing is analytic; each tone is perceived separately. Perception of pitch is related to the position of the excited hair cells along the basilar membrane. Intensity perception suggests that as sound intensity increases, more hair cells respond. Cues for sound localization include the intensity and timing of sound arriving at each ear.

Homeostatic Imbalances of Hearing (p. 535)

13. Conduction deafness results from interference with conduction of sound vibrations to the fluids of the inner ear. Sensorineural deafness reflects damage to neural structures.

14. Tinnitus is an early sign of sensorineural deafness; it may also result from the use of certain drugs.

15. Ménière's syndrome is a disorder of the membranous labyrinth. Symptoms include tinnitus, deafness, and vertigo. Excessive endolymph accumulation is the suspected cause.

Mechanisms of Equilibrium and Orientation (pp. 535–539)

16. The equilibrium receptors of the inner ear are called the vestibular apparatus.

17. The receptors for static equilibrium are the maculae of the saccule and utricle. A macula consists of hair cells with stereocilia and a kinocilium embedded in an overlying otolithic membrane. Linear movements cause the otolithic membrane to move, pulling on the hair cells. Movements toward the kinocilium depolarize the hair cells and increase the rate of impulse generation in the vestibular nerve fibers. Movements away from the kinocilium have the opposite effect.

18. The dynamic equilibrium receptor, the crista ampullaris within each semicircular duct, responds to angular or rotatory movements in one plane. It consists of a tuft of hair cells whose microvilli are embedded in the gelatinous cupula. Rotatory movements cause the endolymph to flow in the opposite direction, bending the cupula and either exciting or inhibiting the hair cells.

19. Impulses from the vestibular apparatus are sent via vestibular nerve fibers to the vestibular complex of the brain stem and the cerebellum. These centers initiate responses that fix the eyes on objects and activate muscles to maintain balance.

Developmental Aspects of the Special Senses (pp. 539–542)

1. The chemical senses are sharpest at birth and gradually decline with age as replacement of the receptor cells becomes more sluggish.

2. Congenital eye problems are uncommon, but maternal rubella can cause blindness.

3. The eye starts as an optic vesicle, an outpocketing of the diencephalon that invaginates to form the optic cup, which becomes the retina. Overlying ectoderm folds to form the lens vesicle, which comes to lie in the optic cup, where it gives rise to the lens. The remaining eye tissues and the accessory structures are formed by mesenchyme.

4. The eye is foreshortened at birth and reaches adult size at the age of eight or nine years. Depth perception and color vision develop during early childhood.

5. With age, the lens loses its elasticity and clarity, there is a decline in the ability of the iris to dilate, and visual acuity decreases. The elderly are at risk for eye problems resulting from disease.

6. The membranous labyrinth develops from the otic placode, an ectodermal thickening lateral to the hindbrain. Mesenchyme forms the surrounding bony structures. Pharyngeal pouch endoderm, in conjunction with mesenchyme, forms middle ear structures; the outer ear is formed largely by ectoderm.

7. Congenital ear problems are fairly common. Maternal rubella can cause deafness.

8. Response to sound in infants is reflexive. By five months, an infant can locate sound. Critical listening develops in toddlers.

9. Deterioration of the organ of Corti occurs throughout life as noise, disease, and drugs destroy the cochlear hair cells. Age-related loss of hearing (presbycusis) occurs in the 60s and 70s.

REVIEW QUESTIONS

Multiple Choice/Matching

1. Olfactory tract damage would probably affect your ability to (a) see, (b) hear, (c) feel pain, (d) smell.

2. Sensory impulses transmitted over the facial, glossopharyngeal, and vagus nerves are involved in the sensation of (a) taste, (b) touch, (c) equilibrium, (d) smell.

3. Taste buds are found on the (a) anterior part of the tongue, (b) posterior part of the tongue, (c) palate, (d) all of these.

4. Gustatory cells are stimulated by (a) the movement of otoliths, (b) stretch, (c) substances in solution, (d) photons of light.

5. Cells in the olfactory bulb that act as local "integrators" of olfactory inputs are the (a) hair cells, (b) granule cells, (c) basal cells, (d) mitral cells, (e) supporting cells.

6. Olfactory nerve fibers are found (a) in the optic bulbs, (b) passing through the cribriform plate of the ethmoid bone, (c) in the optic tracts, (d) in the olfactory cortex.

7. The accessory glands that produce an oily secretion are the (a) conjunctiva, (b) lacrimal glands, (c) tarsal glands.

8. The portion of the fibrous tunic that is white and opaque is the (a) choroid, (b) cornea, (c) retina, (d) sclera.

9. Which sequence best describes a normal route for the flow of tears from the eyes into the nasal cavity? (a) lacrimal canals, nasolacrimal ducts, nasal cavity, (b) lacrimal ducts, lacrimal canals, nasolacrimal ducts, (c) nasolacrimal ducts, lacrimal canals, lacrimal sacs.

10. Four refractory media of the eye, listed in the sequence in which they refract light, are (a) vitreous humor, lens, aqueous humor, cornea, (b) cornea, aqueous humor, lens, vitreous humor, (c) cornea, vitreous humor, lens, aqueous humor, (d) lens, aqueous humor, cornea, vitreous humor.

11. Damage to the medial recti muscles would probably affect (a) accommodation, (b) refraction, (c) convergence, (d) pupil constriction.

12. The phenomenon of light adaptation is best explained by the fact that (a) rhodopsin does not function in dim light, (b) rhodopsin breakdown occurs slowly, (c) rods exposed to intense light need time to generate rhodopsin, (d) cones are stimulated to function by bright light.

13. Blockage of the canal of Schlemm might result in (a) a sty, (b) glaucoma, (c) conjunctivitis, (d) a cataract.

14. Nearsightedness is more properly called (a) myopia, (b) hyperopia, (c) presbyopia, (d) emmetropia.

15. Of the neurons in the retina, the axons of which of these form the optic nerve? (a) bipolar neurons, (b) ganglion cells, (c) cone cells, (d) horizontal cells.

16. Which sequence of reactions occurs when a person looks at a distant object? (a) pupils constrict, suspensory ligament relaxes, lenses become less convex, (b) pupils dilate, suspensory ligament becomes taut, lenses become less convex, (c) pupils dilate, suspensory ligament becomes taut, lenses become more convex, (d) pupils constrict, suspensory ligament relaxes, lenses become more convex.

17. During embryonic development, the lens of the eye forms (a) as part of the choroid coat, (b) from the surface ectoderm overlying the optic cup, (c) as part of the sclera, (d) from mesodermal tissue.

18. The blind spot of the eye is (a) where more rods than cones are found, (b) where the macula lutea is located, (c) where only cones occur, (d) where the optic nerve leaves the eye.

19. Conduction of sound from the middle ear to the inner ear occurs via vibration of the (a) malleus against the tympanic membrane, (b) stapes in the oval window, (c) incus in the round window, (d) stapes against the tympanic membrane.

20. The transmission of sound vibrations through the inner ear occurs chiefly through (a) nerve fibers, (b) air, (c) fluid, (d) bone.

21. Which of the following statements does not correctly describe the organ of Corti? (a) sounds of high frequency stimulate hair cells at the basal end, (b) the "hairs" of the receptor cells are embedded in the tectorial membrane, (c) the basilar membrane acts as a resonator, (d) sounds of high frequency stimulate cells at the apex of the basilar membrane.

22. Pitch is to frequency of sound as loudness is to (a) quality, (b) intensity, (c) overtones, (d) all of these.

23. The structure that allows pressure in the middle ear to be equalized with atmospheric pressure is the (a) cochlear duct, (b) pharyngotympanic tube, (c) tympanic membrane, (d) pinna.

24. Which of the following is important in maintaining the balance of the body? (a) visual cues, (b) semicircular canals, (c) the saccule, (d) proprioceptors, (e) all of these.

25. Static equilibrium receptors that report the position of the head in space relative to the pull of gravity are (a) organ of Corti, (b) maculae, (c) cristae ampullares.

26. Which of the following is *not* a possible cause of conduction deafness? (a) impacted cerumen, (b) middle ear infection, (c) cochlear nerve degeneration, (d) otosclerosis.

Short Answer Essay Questions

27. Name the four primary taste qualities, and indicate the regions of the tongue that are most sensitive to each quality.

28. Where are the olfactory receptors, and why is that site poorly suited for their job?

29. Why do you often have to blow your nose after crying?

30. How do rods and cones differ functionally?

31. Where is the fovea centralis, and why is it important?

32. Describe the response of rhodopsin to light stimuli. What is the outcome of this cascade of events?

33. Since there are only three types of cones, how can you explain the fact that we see many more colors?

34. Describe the effect of aging on the special sense organs.

CRITICAL THINKING AND CLINICAL APPLICATION QUESTIONS

1. During an ophthalmoscopic examination, Mrs. James was found to have bilateral papilledema. Further investigation indicated that this condition resulted from a rapidly growing intracranial tumor. First, define papilledema. Then, explain its presence in terms of Mrs. James' diagnosis.

2. Sally, a 9-year-old girl, told the clinic physician that her "ear lump hurt" and she kept "getting dizzy and falling down." As she told her story, she pointed to her mastoid process. An otoscopic examination of the external auditory canal revealed a red, swollen eardrum, and her throat was inflamed. Her condition was described as mastoiditis with secondary labyrinthitis (inflammation of the labyrinth). Describe the most likely route of infection and the infected structures in Sally's case. Also explain the cause of her dizziness and falling.

3. Mr. Gaspe appeared at the eye clinic complaining of a chip of wood in his eye. No foreign body was found, but the conjunctiva was obviously inflamed. What name is given to this inflammatory condition, and where would you look for a foreign body that has been floating around on the eye surface for a while?

4. Mrs. Orlando has been noticing flashes of light and tiny specks in her right visual field. When she begins to see a "veil" floating before her right eye, she makes an appointment to see the eye doctor. What is your diagnosis? Is the condition serious? Explain.

5. An engineering student has been working in a disco to earn money to pay for his education. After about eight months, he notices that he is having problems hearing high-pitched tones. What is the cause-and-effect relationship here?

 6. Assume that a tumor in the pituitary gland or hypothalmus is protruding inferiorly and compressing the optic chiasma. What could be the visual outcome?

17

The Endocrine System

CHAPTER OUTLINE AND STUDENT OBJECTIVES

1. Indicate important differences between endocrine and neural controls of body functioning.

The Endocrine System and Hormone Function: An Overview (pp. 547–548)

2. List the major endocrine organs, and describe their locations in the body.

Hormones (pp. 548–553)

3. Describe how hormones are classified chemically.

4. Describe the two major mechanisms by which hormones bring about their effects on their target tissues, and explain how hormone release is regulated.

Major Endocrine Organs of the Body (pp. 553–576)

5. Describe the structural and functional relationships between the hypothalamus and the pituitary gland.

6. List and describe the chief effects of adenohypophyseal hormones.

7. Discuss the structure of the neurohypophysis, and describe the effects of the two hormones it releases.

8. Describe the important effects of the two groups of hormones produced by the thyroid gland. Follow the process of thyroxine formation and release.

9. Note the general functions of parathyroid hormone.

10. List the hormones produced by the cortical and medullary regions of the adrenal gland, and cite their physiological effects.

11. Compare and contrast the effects of the two major pancreatic hormones.

12. Describe the functional roles of the hormone products of the testes and ovaries.

13. Briefly describe the importance of thymic hormones in the operation of the immune system.

Other Endocrine Structures (pp. 576–577)

14. Name a hormone produced by the heart, and localize enteroendocrine cells.

15. Briefly explain the endocrine functions of the placenta, kidney, and skin.

Developmental Aspects of the Endocrine System (pp. 577–580)

16. Describe the effect of aging on endocrine system functioning.

W hen insulin molecules, carried passively along in the blood, attach tenaciously to protein receptors of nearby cells, the response is dramatic: Transported glucose molecules begin to disappear into the cells, and cellular activity accelerates. Such is the power of the second great controlling system of the body, the **endocrine system.** However, the endocrine system does not act alone—it interacts with the nervous system to coordinate and integrate the activity of body cells. The means and speed of control used by these two great regulatory systems are very different. The nervous system regulates the activity of muscles and glands by means of electrochemical impulses delivered by neurons; those organs respond within milliseconds. The endocrine system, on the other hand, influences the metabolic activities of cells by means of **hormones** (*hormon* = to excite), chemical messengers released to the blood to be transported throughout the body. Tissue or organ responses to hormones typically occur after a lag period of seconds or even days. But once initiated, the responses tend to be much more prolonged than those induced by the nervous system. Hormonal targets ultimately include most cells of the body. The scientific study of hormones and the endocrine organs is called **endocrinology.**

THE ENDOCRINE SYSTEM AND HORMONE FUNCTION: AN OVERVIEW

Compared to other organs of the body, the organs of the endocrine system are small and unimpressive. Indeed, to collect 1 kg (2.2 lbs) of hormone-producing tissue, you would need to collect *all* of the endocrine tissue from eight or nine adults! In addition, the anatomical continuity typical of most organ systems does not exist between the endocrine organs. Instead, endocrine organs are widely scattered about the body (Figure 17.1).

As explained in Chapter 4, there are two kinds of glands: endocrine and exocrine. Exocrine glands have ducts through which their nonhormonal products are routed to a membrane surface. In contrast, endocrine glands, also called *ductless glands,* lack ducts. They release hormones into the blood or lymph (*endo* = within; *crine* = to secrete), and they typically have a rich vascular and lymphatic drainage. Most hormone-producing cells are arranged in cords and branching networks in a manner that maximizes the contact between them and the capillaries that receive their secretions. The **endocrine glands** of the body include the pituitary, thyroid, parathyroid, adrenal, pineal, and thymus glands. In addition, several organs of the body contain discrete areas of endocrine tissue and produce hormones as well as exocrine products. Such organs, which include the pancreas and gonads (the ovaries and testes), are also major endocrine glands. The hypothalamus also falls into this latter category. Along with its neural functions, it produces and releases hormones, so we can consider the hypothalamus a **neuroendocrine organ.**

Besides the major endocrine organs, various other tissues and organs produce hormones. For example, pockets of hormone-producing cells are found in the walls of the small intestine, stomach, kidneys, and heart—organs whose chief functions have little to do with hormone production. These other endocrine structures are described on page 576.

Additionally, certain tumor cells, such as those of some cancers of the lung or pancreas, synthesize hormones identical to those made in normal endocrine glands, but in an excessive and uncontrolled fashion. •

Hormones have widespread and diverse effects. The major processes controlled and integrated by these "mighty molecules" are reproduction; growth and development; mobilization of body defenses against stressors; maintenance of electrolyte, water, and nutrient balance of the blood; and regulation of cellular metabolism and energy balance. As you can

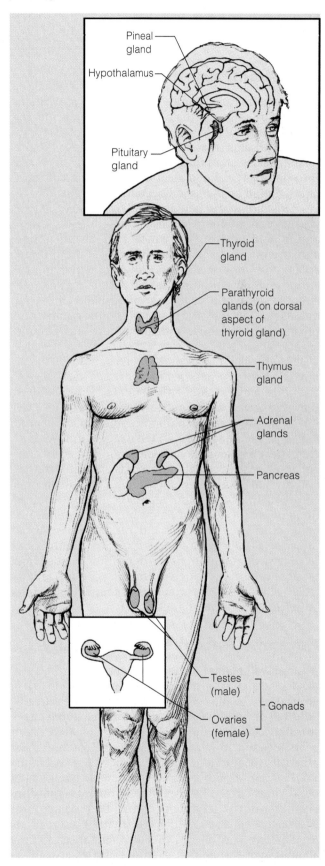

? Besides the major endocrine organs depicted here, what other organs could be drawn in to identify hormone-producing cell clusters?

Pineal gland
Hypothalamus
Pituitary gland
Thyroid gland
Parathyroid glands (on dorsal aspect of thyroid gland)
Thymus gland
Adrenal glands
Pancreas
Testes (male)
Ovaries (female)
Gonads

FIGURE 17.1
Location of the major endocrine organs of the body.

see, the endocrine system orchestrates processes that go on for relatively long periods and, in some instances, continuously.

HORMONES

The Chemistry of Hormones

Hormones may be defined as chemical substances, secreted by cells into the extracellular fluids, that regulate the metabolic function of other cells in the body. Although a large variety of hormones are produced, nearly all of them can be classified chemically into one of two large groups of biochemical molecules: **amino acid–based hormones** and **steroids.**

Most hormones belong to the first group. Molecular size varies widely in this group—from the simple amino acid derivatives, which include the amines and thyroxine, to peptides (short chains of amino acids), to protein macromolecules (long polymers of amino acids). Hormones of the second group, the steroids, are synthesized from cholesterol. Of the hormones produced by the major endocrine organs, only the gonadal hormones and adrenocortical hormones are steroids.

If we also consider the **eicosanoids** (i-ko′sa-noyds), which include *leukotrienes* and *prostaglandins,* we must add a third chemical class. These *paracrines,* or local hormones, are biologically active lipids (made from arachidonic acid) released from nearly all cell membranes. Leukotrienes are signaling chemicals that mediate inflammation and some allergic reactions. Prostaglandins have multiple targets and myriad effects, ranging from raising blood pressure and increasing the expulsive uterine contractions of birth (via stimulation of smooth muscle) to enhancing blood clotting and inflammation. Since the effects of eicosanoids are typically highly localized, they do not quite fit the definition of true circulating hormones, which influence distant targets. Hence, this class of hormonelike chemicals will not be considered further here.

Hormone–Target Cell Specificity

Although all major hormones circulate to virtually all tissues, a given hormone influences the activity of only certain tissue cells, referred to as its **target cells.** For a target cell to respond to a hormone, it must have specific protein **receptors** on its plasma membrane or in its interior, to which that hormone can bind. For example, receptors for adrenocorticotropic hormone (ACTH) are normally found only on certain cells of the adrenal cortex. By contrast, thyroxine is the principal hormonal stimulant of cellular metabolism, and nearly all body cells have thyroxine receptors. An analogy can be drawn between the endocrine gland–target cell response and a radio's transmitter-receiver system. The endocrine gland is the "transmitter," sending signals to the rest of the body, and the receptors on target cells are the "receivers." Like a radio tuned to a single station, the receptors respond only to its particular signal, even though many other signals may be present at the same time. A radio receiver responds to the radio signal by producing sound; a hormone receptor responds to hormone binding by prompting the cell to perform, or "turn on," some genetically determined "preprogrammed" function. Hence, hormones are molecular "triggers" rather than informational molecules.

Although hormone-receptor binding is the crucial first step, the extent of target cell activation by hormone-receptor interaction depends equally on three factors: (1) blood levels of the hormone, (2) the relative numbers of receptors for that hormone on or in the target cells, and (3) the *affinity* (strength) of the union between the hormone and the receptor. Changes in all three factors occur rapidly in response to various stimuli and changes within the body. As a rule, a large number of high-affinity receptors produces a pronounced hormonal effect, whereas a smaller number of low-affinity receptors results in reduced target cell response or outright endocrine dysfunction at the same blood hormone levels. Furthermore, receptors are dynamic structures. In some instances, the target cells form more receptors in response to increasingly higher levels of the specific hormones to which they respond, a phenomenon called **up-regulation.** But in other cases, prolonged exposure to high hormone concentrations desensitizes the target cells, so that they respond less vigorously to hormonal stimulation. This **down-regulation** is thought to involve loss of receptors and effectively prevents the target cells from overreacting to persistently high hormone levels. In addition, hormones may influence the number and affinity not only of their own receptors, but also of receptors responsive to other hormones. For example, progesterone induces a loss of estrogen receptors in the uterus, thus antagonizing estrogen's actions. Conversely, estrogen promotes production of more progesterone receptors in the same cells, enhancing their ability to respond to progesterone.

Mechanisms of Hormone Action

Hormones bring about their characteristic effects on target cells by *altering* cell activity; that is, by increasing or decreasing the rates of normal cellular processes. The precise response is dictated by the target cell type. For example, epinephrine binding to smooth muscle cells in blood vessel walls stimulates them to contract. Epinephrine binding to cells other than muscle cells may have a different effect, but it will *not* cause those noncontractile cells to shorten.

A hormonal stimulus typically produces one or more of the following changes:

1. Changes in plasma membrane permeability and/or electrical state (membrane potential) by opening or closing ion channels.

2. Synthesis of proteins or certain regulatory molecules (such as enzymes) within the cell.

3. Enzyme activation or deactivation.

4. Induction of secretory activity.

5. Stimulation of mitosis.

In general, there are two major mechanisms that harness hormone receptor binding to the specific intracellular machinery needed for hormone action. One involves the services of regulatory molecules called G proteins and one or more intracellular second messengers, which mediate the target cell's response to the hormone. The other involves direct gene (DNA) activation by the hormone itself.

Second-Messenger Systems

Because proteins and peptides cannot penetrate the plasma membranes of tissue cells, virtually all of the amino acid–based hormones exert their effects through intracellular **second messengers** generated by hormone binding to plasma membrane receptors. Of the second messengers, **cyclic AMP,** which also mediates the effects of certain neurotransmitters, is by far the best understood, so it will receive most of our attention.

Intracellular levels of cyclic AMP are determined by interaction of three plasma membrane components of the target cell (Figure 17.2a): (1) the hormone receptor, (2) the signal transducer (a G protein), and (3) the effector enzyme (adenylate cyclase). In this scheme, the hormone, functioning as the **first messenger,** binds to its receptor. The catalytic subunit of the **G protein** then acts as an intermediary to deliver the signal to **adenylate cyclase** to generate cyclic AMP from ATP. The energy for converting the first (hormonal) message into the second (cyclic AMP) is provided by hydrolyzing the high-energy compound **GTP.** (The G protein possesses GTPase activity and cleaves the terminal phosphate group off GTP in much the same way as ATPase enzymes hydrolyze ATP.)

Now that we know how cyclic AMP is generated, we can consider how this "messenger," which is free to diffuse throughout the cell, mediates target cell responses to a hormone. Perhaps its best-known ability is that of initiating a cascade of chemical reactions in which one or more different enzymes, called **protein kinases,** are activated. A given cell may have several types of protein kinases, each of which has distinct substrates. The protein kinases *phosphorylate* (add a phosphate group to) different proteins, many of which are other enzymes. Since phosphorylation activates some of these proteins and inhibits others, a variety of reactions may occur in the same target cell

at the same time. For example, a fat cell responds to epinephrine binding by breaking down glycogen and stored fat, reactions mediated by different enzymes.

This type of intracellular enzymatic cascade has a huge amplification effect because G proteins, once activated, detach from the receptor to "go about their business"; each activated adenylate cyclase generates large numbers of cyclic AMP molecules; and a single kinase enzyme can catalyze literally hundreds of reactions. Hence, as the reaction cascades through one enzyme intermediate after another, the number of product molecules increases dramatically at each step. Theoretically, receptor binding of a single hormone molecule could generate millions of the final product molecules!

? *What process (or system) previously studied used a similar signaling mechanism to activate its target cells?*

(a)

FIGURE 17.2

Second-messenger mechanisms of protein-peptide hormones. (a) Mechanisms that generate cyclic AMP by activation of adenylate cyclase are mediated by G proteins which are activated when the hormone binds to the external membrane receptors. The G proteins exhibit GTPase activity, which catalyzes energy release by hydrolysis of GTP. Cyclic AMP acts intracellularly to activate protein kinase enzymes that mediate the cell's responses to the hormone.

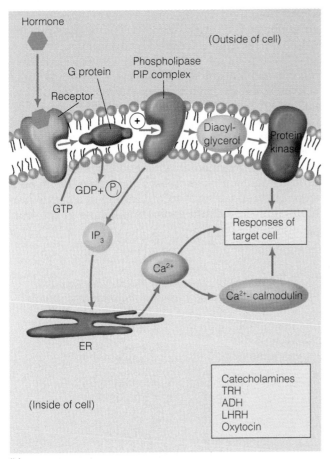

(b)

FIGURE 17.2
Second-messenger mechanisms of protein-peptide hormones *continued.* **(b)** Mechanisms that utilize inositol triphosphate (IP₃) and diacylglycerol as intracellular second messengers are also mediated by G proteins and activate protein kinases, and additionally increase the cytoplasmic concentration of Ca^{2+}. Ionic calcium then acts as a third messenger to modify the activity of cellular proteins. Hormones that act through these mechanisms are listed with the appropriate scheme. (Note: Molecules with similar functions are depicted in the same color.)

The sequence of biochemical reactions set into motion by cyclic AMP depends on the target cell type, the specific protein kinases it contains, and the hormone acting as first messenger. For example, in thyroid cells, cyclic AMP generated in response to the binding of thyroid-stimulating hormone promotes the synthesis of the thyroid hormone thyroxine; in bone and muscle cells, cyclic AMP generated in response to growth hormone binding activates anabolic reactions in which amino acids are built into tissue proteins. Note also that not all G proteins activate adenylate cyclase; some inhibit it (see Figure 17.2a), thus reducing the cytoplasmic concentration of cyclic AMP. Such opposing effects permit a target cell to respond to even slight changes in levels of antagonistic hormones that influence its activity.

Since cyclic AMP is rapidly degraded by the intracellular enzyme **phosphodiesterase,** its action persists only briefly. While at first glance, this may appear to be a problem, it is quite the opposite. Because of the amplification effect just explained, most hormones need to be present for only short periods to promote the desired results. Continued hormone production prompts continued cellular activity; no extracellular controls are necessary to stop the activity.

Although cyclic AMP is the activating second messenger in some tissues for at least 10 of the amino acid–based hormones, some of the same hormones (e.g., epinephrine) act through a different second-messenger system in other tissues. In one such mechanism, hormone docking to the receptor activates a membrane-bound **phospholipase** enzyme that splits **PIP₂** (phosphatidyl inositol biphosphate) into **diacylglycerol** and **IP₃** (inositol triphosphate) (Figure 17.2b), and both of these molecules act as second messengers. Diacylglycerol activates specific protein kinases, whereas IP₃ triggers the release of Ca^{2+} from the endoplasmic reticulum (ER) and other intracellular storage sites. The calcium ions then act as a **third messenger,** either by directly altering the activity of specific enzymes and plasma membrane ion (Ca^{2+}) channels or by binding to the intracellular regulatory protein **calmodulin.**

Hormones known to act on their target cells via cyclic AMP or the PIP mechanism are listed in Figure 17.2. Other hormones act on their target cells through different (and in some cases, unknown) mechanisms or messengers. For example, *cyclic GMP* (cyclic guanosine 3′,5′-monophosphate) is a second messenger for atrial natriuretic factor, a hormone released by heart tissue. Insulin appears to work "solo" without a G protein intermediary or second messengers. Its receptor is a *tyrosine kinase* enzyme that is directly activated by insulin binding. In certain instances, any of the second messengers mentioned—and the hormone receptor itself—can cause changes in intracellular calcium ion levels.

Direct Gene Activation

Being lipid soluble, steroid hormones (and, strangely, thyroid hormone, a small iodinated amine) can diffuse easily into their target cells. Once inside, they bind to an intracellular receptor that is activated by the interaction. The activated hormone-receptor complex then translocates to the nuclear chromatin, where the hormone binds to a DNA-associated *receptor protein* specific for it. This interaction "turns on" a gene, that is, it prompts transcription of DNA to produce a messenger RNA (mRNA). The mRNA is then translated on the cytoplasmic ribosomes, producing specific protein molecules. These protein products include enzymes that promote the metabolic activities induced by that particular hormone and, in some

? *What is the crucial difference between the signaling mechanism depicted here and that shown in Figure 17.2?*

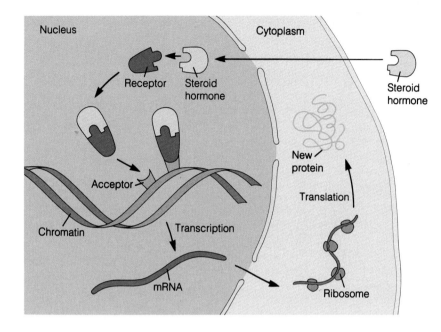

FIGURE 17.3
Direct gene activation mechanism of steroid hormones. Lipid-soluble steroids diffuse through the plasma membrane of the target cell and bind to intracellular receptors, located in the nucleus (as shown) or cytoplasm. Once formed, the hormone-receptor complex binds to specific receptor proteins on the chromatin, initiating transcription of certain genes. The messenger RNA formed migrates into the cytoplasm, where it directs synthesis of specific proteins.

cases, synthesis of structural proteins or proteins that are exported by the target cell. The steroidal gene activation mechanism is depicted in Figure 17.3.

Half-Life, Onset, and Duration of Hormone Activity

Hormones are exceptionally potent chemicals, and they exert profound effects on their target organs at very low concentrations. The concentration of a hormone in blood at any time reflects (1) its rate of release, and (2) the speed of its inactivation and removal from the body. Some hormones are rapidly degraded by enzymes within their target cells, but most are removed from the blood by kidney and liver enzyme systems, and their breakdown products are quickly excreted from the body in urine or, to a lesser extent, in feces. As a result, the persistence of a hormone in the blood, referred to as its **half-life,** is usually brief—from a fraction of a minute to 30 minutes.

The time required for onset of hormone effects varies greatly. Some hormones provoke target organ responses almost immediately. Others, particularly the steroid hormones, may require hours to days before their effects are seen. Additionally, some hormones, such as testosterone secreted by the testes, are secreted in a relatively inactive *(prohormone)* form and must be activated in the target cells.

The duration of hormone action is limited, ranging from 20 minutes to several hours, depending on the hormone. Effects may disappear rapidly as blood levels drop, or they may persist for hours after very low levels have been reached. Because of these many variations, hormonal blood levels must be precisely and individually controlled to meet the continuously changing needs of the body.

Control of Hormone Release

The synthesis and release of most hormones are regulated by some type of **negative feedback system** (see Chapter 1, pp. 10–12). In such a system, hormone secretion is triggered by some internal or external stimulus, after which rising hormone levels (even while causing target organ effects) inhibit further hormone release. As a result, blood levels of many hormones vary only within a very narrow range.

Endocrine Gland Stimuli

The various endocrine glands of the body are stimulated to manufacture and release their hormones by three major types of stimuli: *humoral* (hu'mer-ul), *neural,* and *hormonal.*

Humoral Stimuli.   Some endocrine glands secrete their hormones in direct response to changing blood levels of certain ions and nutrients. These stimuli are called *humoral stimuli* to distinguish them from hor-

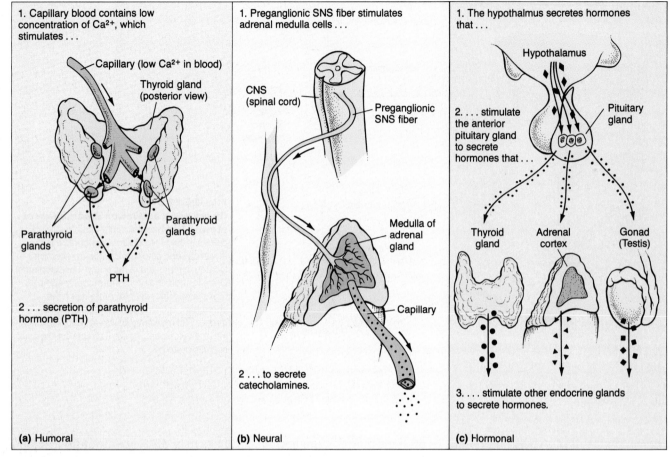

1. Capillary blood contains low concentration of Ca²⁺, which stimulates . . .

Capillary (low Ca²⁺ in blood)

Thyroid gland (posterior view)

Parathyroid glands

Parathyroid glands

PTH

2 . . . secretion of parathyroid hormone (PTH)

(a) Humoral

1. Preganglionic SNS fiber stimulates adrenal medulla cells . . .

CNS (spinal cord)

Preganglionic SNS fiber

Medulla of adrenal gland

Capillary

2 . . . to secrete catecholamines.

(b) Neural

1. The hypothalmus secretes hormones that . . .

Hypothalamus

Pituitary gland

2. . . . stimulate the anterior pituitary gland to secrete hormones that . . .

Thyroid gland

Adrenal cortex

Gonad (Testis)

3. . . . stimulate other endocrine glands to secrete hormones.

(c) Hormonal

FIGURE 17.4
Endocrine gland stimuli: Three different mechanisms.
(a) Humoral stimulus of endocrine gland activity. Low blood calcium levels trigger parathyroid hormone (PTH) release from the parathyroid glands. PTH causes blood calcium levels to rise by stimulating release of Ca²⁺ from bone.

Consequently, the stimulus for PTH secretion ends. **(b)** Neural stimulus of endocrine gland activity. The stimulation of adrenal medullary cells by sympathetic nervous system (SNS) fibers triggers the release of catecholamines (epinephrine and norepinephrine) to the blood. **(c)** Hormonal stimulus of endocrine

gland activity. In the example illustrated, hormones released by the hypothalamus stimulate the anterior pituitary to release hormones that stimulate other endocrine organs to secrete hormones. In this way, the hypothalamus regulates much of endocrine system activity.

monal stimuli, which are also blood-borne chemicals. The term *humoral* harks back to the ancient use of the term *humor* to refer to various body fluids (blood, bile, and others). This is the simplest of the endocrine control systems. For example, cells of the parathyroid glands directly monitor the concentration of calcium ions in blood and, when they detect a decline in the normal Ca²⁺ range, they respond by secreting parathyroid hormone (PTH). Since PTH acts by several routes to reverse that decline, blood Ca²⁺ levels soon rise, ending the initiative for PTH release (Figure 17.4a). Other hormones released in response to humoral stimuli include insulin, produced by the pancreas, and aldosterone, one of the adrenal cortex hormones.

Neural Stimuli. In a few cases, nerve fibers stimulate hormone release. The classic example is sympathetic nervous system stimulation of the adrenal

medulla to release catecholamines (norepinephrine and epinephrine) during periods of stress (Figure 17.4b). In addition, oxytocin and antidiuretic hormone are released from the posterior pituitary in response to nerve impulses from hypothalamic neurons.

Hormonal Stimuli. Finally, many endocrine glands release their hormones in response to hormones produced by other endocrine organs. For example, release of most anterior pituitary hormones is regulated by releasing and inhibiting hormones produced by the hypothalamus, and many anterior pituitary hormones in turn stimulate other endocrine organs to release their hormones into the blood (Figure 17.4c). As the hormones produced by the final target glands increase in the blood, they inhibit the release of anterior pituitary hormones and thus their own release. This hypothalamic–pituitary–target endocrine organ feedback loop lies at the very core of the science of endocrinology, and it will be considered many times in this chapter. Hormone release promoted by the hormonal mechanism tends to be rhythmic, with hormone blood levels rising and falling in a specific pattern.

While these three mechanisms typify most systems that control hormone release, they are by no means all-inclusive or mutually exclusive, and some endocrine organs respond to multiple stimuli.

Nervous System Modulation

Both "turn on" factors (hormonal, humoral, and neural stimuli) and "turn off" factors (feedback inhibition and others) may be modified or modulated by the activity of the nervous system. Without this added safeguard, endocrine system activity would be strictly mechanical, much like a household thermostat. A thermostat can maintain the house temperature at or around its set value, but it cannot sense that your grandmother visiting from Florida feels cold at that temperature and reset itself accordingly. *You* must make that adjustment. Similarly, the nervous system can, in certain cases, override normal endocrine controls as necessary to maintain homeostasis. For example, blood sugar levels are normally kept within a range of 80–120 mg glucose per 100 ml of blood by the action of insulin and several other hormones. However, when the body is under severe stress, blood sugar levels rise much higher because the hypothalamus and sympathetic nervous system centers are strongly activated. This ensures that body cells will have sufficient fuel for the more vigorous activity required of them during such periods.

Remember that the hypothalamus is an autonomic center concerned with homeostatic control of such body functions as water balance and temperature as well as an integrating center for biological rhythms and emotions. This helps explain how a single external stimulus, such as acute blood loss or severe physical trauma, can be followed by bodywide neuroendocrine adjustments.

MAJOR ENDOCRINE ORGANS

The Pituitary Gland (Hypophysis)

Securely seated in the sella turcica of the sphenoid bone, the tiny **pituitary gland,** or **hypophysis** (hi-pof′ĭ-sis; "to grow under"), secretes at least nine major hormones. Usually said to be the size and shape of a pea, the pituitary gland is more accurately described as a pea on a stalk. Its stalk, the funnel-shaped **infundibulum,** connects it to the hypothalamus superiorly (Figure 17.5a). In humans, the pituitary gland has two major lobes, one neural tissue, the other glandular. The **posterior lobe,** or **neurohypophysis** (nu″ro-hi-pof′ĭ-sis), is composed largely of neuroglia and nerve fibers. It releases neurohormones

that it receives ready-made from the hypothalamus. Thus, the neurohypophysis is a hormone-storage area and not a true endocrine gland in the precise sense. The **anterior lobe,** or **adenohypophysis** (ad″ĕ-no-hi-pof′ĭ-sis), is composed of glandular tissue (*adeno = gland*), and it manufactures and releases a number of hormones (Table 17.1 on pp. 556–557).

Arterial blood is delivered to the pituitary via two branches of the internal carotid artery. The *superior hypophyseal artery* supplies the anterior pituitary and the infundibulum; the *inferior hypophyseal artery* supplies the posterior lobe. The veins leaving the pituitary drain into the cavernous sinus (p. 685) and other nearby dural sinuses.

Pituitary-Hypothalamic Relationships

The contrasting histology of the two pituitary lobes reflects the dual origin of this tiny gland. The neurohypophysis is actually part of the brain. It derives from a downgrowth of hypothalamic (nervous) tissue, and maintains its connection with the hypothalamus via a nerve bundle called the **hypothalamic-hypophyseal tract** (Figure 17.5), which runs through the infundibulum. This tract arises from neurons in the **supraoptic** and **paraventricular nuclei** of the hypothalamus (see Figure 12.14c, p. 394). These neurosecretory cells synthesize two **neurohormones,** which are transported along their length to their axon terminals in the neurohypophysis. Oxytocin is made by the paraventricular neurons and antidiuretic hormone (ADH) is synthesized by the supraoptic neurons. When these hypothalamic neurons fire, they release the stored hormones into a capillary bed in the posterior pituitary for distribution throughout the body.

In contrast, the anterior lobe originates from a superior outpocketing of the oral mucosa *(Rathke's pouch)* and is formed from the epithelial tissue. After touching the posterior lobe, the adenohypophysis loses its connection with the oral mucosa and adheres to the neurohypophysis to form the composite organ. There is no direct neural connection between the adenohypophysis and hypothalamus, but there is a vascular connection. Specifically, the **primary capillary plexus** in the infundibulum communicates inferiorly via the small **hypophyseal portal veins** with a **secondary capillary plexus** in the adenohypophysis. The primary and secondary capillary plexuses and the intervening hypophyseal portal veins make up the **hypophyseal portal system*** (Figure 17.5). Via this portal system, **releasing** and **inhibiting hormones** secreted by neurons in the ventral hypothalamus circulate directly to the adenohypophysis, where they regulate the secretory activity of its hormone-

---

*A *portal system* is a somewhat unique arrangement of blood vessels in which a capillary bed feeds into veins which, in turn, feed into another capillary bed.

Neurons in the ventral hypothalamus

Hypothalamic neurons in the paraventricular and supraoptic nuclei

Chromophobes

Infundibulum (connecting stalk)

Hypothalamic hypophyseal tract

Neurohypophysis (storage area for hypothalamic hormones)

Posterior lobe

Venule

Oxytocin ADH

(a)

Arteriole

Hypophyseal portal system

• Primary capillary plexus

• Hypophyseal portal veins

• Secondary capillary plexus

Anterior lobe

(b)

Secretory cells of adenohypophysis

Basophil

Acidophils

Venule

TSH, FSH, LH, ACTH, GH, PRL

FIGURE 17.5
Structural and functional relationships of the pituitary and the hypothalamus. (a) Hypothalamic neurons in the supraoptic and paraventricular nuclei synthesize ADH and oxytocin, which are transported along their axons (hypothalamic-hypophyseal tract) to the neurohypophysis for storage. Tuberoinfundibular neurons in the ventral hypothalamus have very short axons that discharge releasing and inhibiting hormones to the capillaries of the hypophyseal portal system, which runs to the adenohypophysis. These factors influence the adenohypophyseal secretory cells to release (or not release) their hormones. **(b)** Histology of the adenohypophysis (350×). Note the acidophil, basophil, and chromophobe cells.

producing cells. All of these hypothalamic regulatory hormones are amino acid–based, but they vary widely in size from amines to polypeptides.

Adenohypophyseal Hormones

The adenohypophysis has traditionally been called the "master endocrine gland" because of its numerous hormonal products, many of which regulate the activity of other endocrine glands. Although the adenohypophysis has been dethroned by the hypothalamus, which is now known to control anterior pituitary activity, six distinct adenohypophyseal hormones with specific physiological actions in humans are known. All of these are proteins. In addition, a large molecule with the tongue-twisting name **pro-opiomelanocortin** (pro"o"pe-o-mah-lan'o-kor"tin) **(POMC)** has been isolated from the anterior pituitary. POMC is a *prohormone,* that is, a large precursor mol-

ecule from which other active molecules are split by enzymatic cleavage. POMC is the source of adrenocorticotropic hormone, two natural opiates (an enkephalin and beta-endorphin, described in Chapter 11), and *melanocyte-stimulating hormone (MSH).* MSH stimulates melanocytes to increase their synthesis of melanin pigment, but in humans its plasma levels are insignificant and it is probably more important as a CNS neurotransmitter (neuropeptide) than a hormone. Additionally, MSH release is stimulated by dopamine-releasing hypothalamic neurons rather than releasing hormones.

When the adenohypophysis receives an appropriate chemical stimulus from the hypothalamus, one or more of its hormones is released by certain of its cells. Although many different releasing and inhibiting hormones pass from the hypothalamus to the anterior lobe, the individual anterior pituitary target cells distinguish the messages directed to them and respond

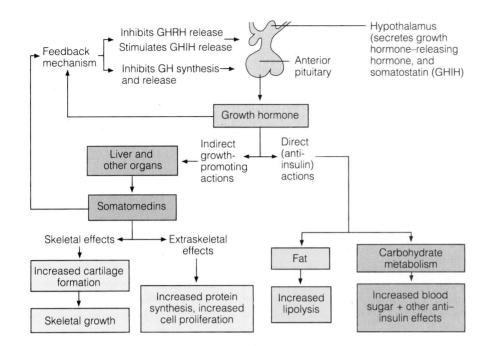

FIGURE 17.6
Proposed scheme for classifying the metabolic actions of growth hormone (GH). The direct actions of GH on target cells stimulate fat breakdown (lipolysis) and release from adipose tissues and hinder glucose uptake from the blood by tissue cells, maintaining blood sugar levels fairly high. (Because these actions antagonize those of the pancreatic hormone insulin, they are referred to as anti-insulin actions.) Indirect, largely anabolic effects of GH are mediated through somatomedins. Elevated levels of GH and somatomedins feed back to promote GHIH release (and depress GHRH release) by the hypothalamus and to inhibit GH release by the anterior pituitary gland.

in kind—synthesizing and secreting the proper hormones in response to specific releasing hormones, and closing down hormone release in response to inhibiting hormones. The releasing hormones are far more important as regulatory factors because little hormone is stored by the secretory cells of the anterior lobe.

Four of the six anterior pituitary lobe hormones—thyroid-stimulating hormone (TSH), adrenocorticotropic hormone (ACTH), follicle-stimulating hormone (FSH), and luteinizing hormone (LH)—are **tropins** or **tropic hormones.** Tropic (*tropi* = turn on, change) hormones regulate the secretory action of other endocrine glands. The three cell types that produce tropic hormones (*thyrotropes, gonadotropes,* and *corticotropes*) are stained blue by basic dyes and thus are collectively classed as *basophil* ("base-loving") *cells* of the anterior pituitary (Figure 17.5b). The remaining two adenohypophyseal hormones—growth hormone (GH) and prolactin (PRL)—exert their major effects on nonendocrine targets. Since these cell types (*somatotropes* and *lactotropes*) stain red with acidic dyes, they constitute the *acidophil* ("acid-loving") *cells* of the anterior pituitary (Figure 17.5b). (The role of the colorless *chromophobes* ["color fearing"] is controversial, but some assume they are still-immature glandular cells.)

With the possible exception of growth hormone and prolactin, for which the mechanism is unknown, all adenohypophyseal hormones affect their target cells via a cyclic AMP second-messenger system. (The adenohypophyseal hormones, their effects, and their relationships to hypothalamic regulatory factors are summarized briefly in Table 17.1.)

Growth Hormone (GH). Growth hormone (GH) is produced by the **somatotropic cells** or **somatotropes.** Although GH stimulates most body cells to increase in size and divide, its major targets are the bones and skeletal muscles. Stimulation of the epiphyseal plate leads to long bone growth; its effects on skeletal muscles promote increased muscle mass.

Essentially an anabolic hormone, GH promotes protein synthesis, and it encourages the use of fats for fuel, thus conserving glucose (Figure 17.6). The second-messenger system through which GH influences its target cells is still controversial, but the growth-promoting effects of GH are known to be mediated indirectly by **somatomedins** (so"mah-to-me'dinz), a family of growth-promoting proteins produced by the liver and perhaps by the kidneys and muscles as well. Somatomedin C, also known as **insulin-like growth factor 1 (IGF-1),** is believed to be the active factor. Specifically, GH (1) stimulates uptake of amino acids from the blood and their incorporation into cellular proteins; (2) stimulates uptake of sulfur (needed for the synthesis of chondroitin sulfate) into cartilage matrix; (3) mobilizes fats from fat depots for transport to cells, increasing blood levels of fatty acids; and (4) deceases the rate of glucose uptake and metabolism. In the liver, it encourages glycogen breakdown and release of glucose to the blood. The elevation in blood sugar levels that subsequently occurs is called the **diabetogenic effect** of GH, because it mimics the high blood sugar levels typical of diabetes mellitus (see p. 573).

Secretion of GH is regulated chiefly by two hypothalamic hormones with antagonistic effects. **Growth hormone–releasing hormone (GHRH)** stimulates GH

Table 17.1 Pituitary Hormones: Regulation and Effects

Hormone/chemical structure	Cell type and staining properties	Regulation of release	Target/effects	Effects of hyposecretion ↓ and hypersecretion ↑
Anterior Pituitary Hormones				
Growth hormone (GH) (Protein)	Somatotrope; acidophil	**Stimulated** by GHRH* release, which is triggered by low blood levels of GH as well as by a number of secondary triggers including estrogens, hypoglycemia, increases in blood levels of amino acids, low levels of fatty acids, exercise and other types of stressors **Inhibited** by feedback inhibition exerted by GH and somatomedin, and by hyperglycemia, hyperlipidemia, obesity, and emotional deprivation, all of which elicit GHIH* release	Body cells, primarily bone and muscle; anabolic hormone; stimulates somatic growth; mobilizes fats; spares glucose	↓ Pituitary dwarfism in children ↑ Gigantism in children; acromegaly in adults
Thyroid-stimulating hormone (TSH) (Glycoprotein)	Thyrotrope; acidophil	**Stimulated** by TRH* and indirectly by pregnancy and cold temperature **Inhibited** by feedback inhibition exerted by thyroid hormones on anterior pituitary and hypothalamus and by GHIH* (somatostatin)	Thyroid gland; stimulates thyroid gland to release thyroid hormone	↓ Cretinism in children; myxedema in adults ↑ Graves's disease; exophthalmos
Adrenocorticotropic hormone (ACTH) (Polypeptide, 39 amino acids)	Corticotrope; basophil	**Stimulated** by CRH*; stimuli that increase CRH release include fever, hypoglycemia, and other stressors **Inhibited** by feedback inhibition exerted by glucocorticoids	Adrenal cortex; promotes release of glucocorticoids and androgens (mineralocorticoids to a lesser extent)	↓ Rare ↑ Cushing's disease
Follicle-stimulating hormone (FSH) (Glycoprotein)	Gonadotrope; basophil	**Stimulated** by GnRH* **Inhibited** by feedback inhibition exerted by estrogen in females and testosterone and inhibin in males	Ovaries and testes; in females, stimulates ovarian follicle maturation and estrogen production; in males, stimulates sperm production	↓ Failure of sexual maturation ↑ No important effects

release, while **growth hormone–inhibiting hormone (GHIH),** also called **somatostatin** (so"mah-to-stat'in) inhibits it. Somatostatin release is [presumably] triggered by the feedback of GH and somatomedins. Rising levels of GH also feed back to inhibit its own release. As indicated in Table 17.1, a number of secondary triggers, such as stress, nutritional factors, and sleep patterns, also influence GH release. Typically, GH secretion has a diurnal cycle, with the highest levels occurring during evening sleep, but the total amount secreted daily peaks during adolescence and then declines with age.

The far-reaching effects of somatostatin deserve special mention. Besides inhibiting growth hormone secretion, it blocks the release of several other adenohypophyseal hormones (see Table 17.1). Additionally, it inhibits the release of virtually all gastrointestinal and pancreatic secretions—both endocrine and exocrine.

Both hypersecretion and hyposecretion of GH may result in structural abnormalities. Hypersecretion in children results in **gigantism,** a condition in which growth is exceptionally rapid. The person becomes abnormally tall (often reaching a height of

Table 17.1 continued

Hormone/ chemical structure	Cell type and staining properties	Regulation of release	Target/effects	Effects of hyposecretion ↓ and hypersecretion ↑
Luteinizing hormone (LH) (Glycoprotein)	Gonadotrope; basophil	**Stimulated** by GnRH* **Inhibited** by feedback inhibition exerted by estrogen and progesterone in females and testosterone in males	Ovaries and testes; in females, triggers ovulation and stimulates ovarian production of estrogen and progesterone; in males, promotes testosterone production	As for FSH
Prolactin (PRL) (Protein)	Lactotrope; acidophil	**Stimulated** by PRH*; PRH release enhanced by estrogens, birth control pills, opiates, and breast-feeding **Inhibited** by PIH*	Breast secretory tissue; promotes lactation	↓ Poor milk production in nursing women ↑ Galactorrhea; cessation of menses in females; impotence in males
Posterior Pituitary Hormones (made by hypothalamic neurons and stored in posterior pituitary)				
Oxytocin (Peptide)	Neurons in paraventricular nucleus of hypothalamus	**Stimulated** by impulses from hypothalamic neurons in response to cervical/uterine stretching and suckling of infant at breast **Inhibited** by lack of appropriate neural stimuli	Uterus; stimulates uterine contractions; initiates labor; breast; initiates milk ejection	Unknown
Antidiuretic hormone (ADH) or vasopressin (Peptide)	Neurons in supraoptic nucleus of hypothalamus	**Stimulated** by impulses from hypothalamic neurons in response to increased osmolarity of blood or decreased blood volume; also stimulated by pain, some drugs, low blood pressure **Inhibited** by adequate hydration of the body and by alcohol	Kidneys; stimulates kidney tubule cells to resorb water	↓ Diabetes insipidus ↑ Syndrome of inappropriate ADH secretion (SIADH)

*Indicates hypothalamic releasing and inhibiting hormones: GHRH = growth hormone–releasing hormone; GHIH = growth hormone–inhibiting hormone; PRH = prolactin-releasing hormone; PIH = prolactin-inhibiting hormone; TRH = thyrotropin-releasing hormone; GnRH = gonadotropin-releasing hormone; CRH = corticotropin-releasing hormone.

2.4 m [8 feet] but has relatively normal body proportions. If excessive amounts of GH are secreted after adult height has been attained and the epiphyseal plates have closed, **acromegaly** (ak″ro-meg′ah-le) results. Acromegaly, literally translated as "enlarged extremities," is characterized by enlargement and thickening of bony areas still responsive to GH, namely bones of the hands, feet, and face (Figure 17.7). Thickening of soft tissues leads to coarse or malformed facial features and an enlarged tongue. Hypersecretion of GH usually results from an adenohypophyseal tumor that churns out excessive amounts of GH. The usual treatment is surgical removal of the tumor; however, anatomical changes that have already occurred are not reversible.

Hyposecretion of GH in adults generally causes no problems, but in rare instances, the deficit is so severe that **progeria** ensues—body tissues begin to atrophy and clinical signs of premature aging appear. Growth hormone deficiency in children results in slowed long bone growth, a condition called **pituitary dwarfism.** Such individuals attain a maximum height of only 1.2 m (4 feet), but usually have fairly normal body proportions. Lack of GH is often accompanied

FIGURE 17.7
An individual with acromegaly. This condition results from hypersecretion of growth hormone in the adult. Notice the enlarged jaw, nose, and hands. Left to right, the same person is shown at age 16, age 33, and age 52.

by deficiencies of other adenohypophyseal hormones, and if thyroid-stimulating hormone and gonadotropins are lacking, the individual will be malproportioned and will fail to mature sexually as well. When pituitary dwarfism is diagnosed before puberty, growth hormone replacement therapy can promote nearly normal somatic growth. Fortunately, human growth hormone is now being produced commercially by genetic engineering techniques. Sadly, the other side of the coin to increased availability of GH is that, like the anabolic steroids (see *A Closer Look* on p. 559), it has become a drug of abuse by some athletes. •

Thyroid-Stimulating Hormone (TSH).
Thyroid-stimulating hormone (TSH), or thyrotropin, is a tropic hormone that stimulates normal development and secretory activity of the thyroid gland. TSH release from the **thyrotropes** of the anterior pituitary is triggered by the hypothalamic peptide **thyrotropin-releasing hormone (TRH).** Rising blood levels of thyroid hormones acting on both the pituitary and the hypothalamus inhibit TSH secretion. The hypothalamus, in response, releases somatostatin, which reinforces the blockade of TSH release. As described later in the discussion of thyroid hormones, certain external factors, acting through the hypothalamic controls, may also influence the release of TSH.

Adrenocorticotropic Hormone (ACTH).
Adrenocorticotropic (ah-dre″no-kor″tĭ-ko-trōp′ik) **hormone (ACTH),** or **corticotropin,** is secreted by the **corticotropes** of the adenohypophysis. ACTH stimulates the adrenal cortex to release corticosteroid hormones, most importantly glucocorticoids that help the body

to resist stressors. ACTH release, elicited by hypothalamic **corticotropin-releasing hormone (CRH),** has a basically diurnal rhythm, with levels peaking in the morning, shortly after one arises. Rising levels of glucocorticoids feed back and block secretion of CRH and consequently ACTH release. Internal and external factors that alter the normal ACTH rhythm by triggering CRH release include fever, hypoglycemia, and stressors of all types. Because CRH is both the ACTH regulator and a neurotransmitter that is active in the central nervous system, some believe it is the stress response integrator.

Gonadotropins.
Follicle-stimulating hormone **(FSH)** and **luteinizing** (lu′te-in-īz″ing) **hormone (LH),** referred to collectively as **gonadotropins,** regulate the function of the gonads (ovaries and testes). In both sexes, FSH stimulates gamete (sperm or egg) production, while LH promotes production of gonadal hormones. In females, LH works with FSH to cause maturation of an egg-containing ovarian follicle. It then independently triggers ovulation (expulsion of the egg from the follicle) and promotes synthesis and release of ovarian hormones (estrogens and progesterone). In males, LH stimulates the interstitial cells of the testes to produce the male hormone testosterone. For this reason, LH is sometimes called **interstitial** (in″ter-stish′al) **cell–stimulating hormone (ICSH)** in males.

Gonadotropins are virtually absent from the blood of prepubertal boys and girls. However, during puberty, the **gonadotropes** are activated and gonadotropin levels begin to rise, causing the gonads to mature to the adult state. In both sexes, gonadotropin release by the adenohypophysis is prompted by

A CLOSER LOOK | Athletes Looking Good and Doing Better With Anabolic Steroids?

American society loves a winner and its top athletes reap large social and monetary rewards. Thus, it is not surprising that some will grasp at anything that will increase their performance—including anabolic steroids. Anabolic steroids, variants of the male sex hormone testosterone engineered by pharmaceutical companies, were introduced in the 1950s to treat victims of certain muscle-wasting diseases and anemia and to prevent muscle atrophy in patients immobilized after surgery. Testosterone is responsible for the increase in muscle and bone mass and other physical changes that occur during puberty and convert boys into men. Convinced that megadoses of the steroids could produce enhanced masculinizing effects in grown men, many athletes and bodybuilders were using the steroids by the early 1960s, and the practice is still going strong today. Indeed, it has been estimated that nearly one in every ten young men has tried steroids, so use is no longer confined to athletes looking for the edge.

It has been difficult to determine the incidence of anabolic steroid use among athletes because the use of drugs has been banned by most international competitions, and users (and prescribing physicians or drug dealers) are naturally reluctant to talk about it. Nonetheless, there is little question that many professional bodybuilders and athletes competing in events that require muscle strength (e.g., shot put, discus throwing, and weight lifting) are heavy users. Sports figures such as football players have also admitted to using steroids as an adjunct to training, diet, and psychological preparation for games. Advantages of anabolic steroids cited by athletes include enhanced muscle mass

and strength, increased oxygen-carrying capability owing to greater red blood cell volume, and an increase in aggressive behavior.

Typically, bodybuilders who use steroids combine high doses (up to 200 mg/day) with heavy resistance training. Intermittent use begins several months before an event, and both oral and injected steroid doses (a method called stacking) are increased gradually as the competition nears.

But do the drugs do all that is claimed for them? Research studies have reported increases in isometric strength and a rise in body weight in steroid users. While these are results weight lifters dream about, there is a hot dispute over whether this also translates into athletic performance requiring the fine muscle coordination and endurance needed by runners, etc. The "jury is still out" on this question, but if you ask users, the answer will most likely be a resounding "yes."

Do the proclaimed advantages conferred by steroid use outweigh the risks? Absolutely not. Physicians say they cause bloated faces (Cushingoid sign of steroid excess); shriveled testes and infertility; damage to the liver that promotes liver cancer; and changes in blood cholesterol levels (which may predispose long-term users to coronary heart disease). The psychiatric hazards of anabolic steroid use may be equally threatening: Recent studies have indicated that one-third of users have serious mental problems. Manic behavior in which the users undergo Jekyll-Hyde personality swings and become extremely violent (termed the *'roid rage*) is common, as are depression and delusions.

The question of why some athletes use these drugs is easy to answer. Some admit to a willingness to do almost anything to win, short of killing themselves. Are they unwittingly doing this as well?

gonadotropin-releasing hormone (GnRH) produced by the hypothalamus. Gonadal hormones, produced in response to the gonadotropins, feed back to suppress FSH and LH release.

Prolactin (PRL). Prolactin (PRL) is a protein hormone structurally similar to growth hormone. Produced by the **lactotropes,** it stimulates the ovaries of some animals and is considered a gonadotropin by

some researchers. However, its only known effect in humans is to stimulate milk production by the breasts (*pro* = for; *lact* = milk). Like GH, prolactin release is controlled by hypothalamic releasing and inhibiting hormones. The exact nature of **prolactin-releasing hormone (PRH)** is unknown, but it is thought to be either vasoactive inhibiting protein (VIP) or TSH. PRH causes prolactin synthesis and release, whereas **prolactin-inhibiting hormone (PIH),** now known to be the neurotransmitter dopamine, prevents prolactin secretion. In males, the influence of PIH predominates, but in women, prolactin levels rise and fall in rhythm with estrogen blood levels. Low estrogen stimulates PIH release, while high estrogen promotes release of PRH and, thus, prolactin. A brief rise in prolactin levels just before the menstrual period partially accounts for the breast swelling and tenderness some women experience at that time, but since this PRL stimulation is so brief, the breasts do not produce milk. In pregnant women, PRL blood levels rise dramatically toward the end of pregnancy, and milk production by the breasts becomes possible. After birth, the infant's suckling stimulates PRH release in the mother, encouraging continued milk production and availability.

Hypersecretion of prolactin is more common than its hyposecretion (which is not a problem in anyone except women who choose to nurse). In fact, hyperprolactinemia is the most frequent abnormality of adenohypophyseal tumors. Clinical signs include inappropriate lactation *(galactorrhea)*, lack of menses, infertility in females, and impotence in males. •

The Neurohypophysis and Hypothalamic Hormones

The neurohypophysis, made largely of neuroglial cells and unmyelinated axons, stores antidiuretic hormone (ADH) and oxytocin, which have been synthesized and forwarded by hypothalamic neurons of the supraoptic and paraventricular nuclei, respectively. These hormones are later released "on demand" in response to nerve impulses from the same hypothalamic neurons.

ADH and oxytocin, each composed of nine amino acids, are almost identical. They differ only in two amino acids, yet they have very different physiological effects on their target organs. ADH influences body water balance, whereas oxytocin stimulates the contraction of smooth muscle, particularly that of the uterus and breasts (see Table 17.1). Both hormones use the PIP second-messenger mechanism to exert their effects on their target cells.

Oxytocin.   Oxytocin (ok″si-to′sin), a strong stimulant of uterine contraction, is released in significantly higher amounts during childbirth (*ocytocia* = childbirth) and in nursing women. The number of oxytocin receptors in the uterus peaks near the end of pregnancy, and uterine smooth muscle becomes more and more sensitive to the stimulatory effects of oxytocin. Stretching of the uterus and cervix as birth nears dispatches afferent impulses to the hypothalamus, and the hypothalamus responds by synthesizing oxytocin and triggering its release from the neurohypophysis. As blood levels of oxytocin rise, the expulsive contractions of labor gain momentum and finally end in

birth. Oxytocin also acts as the hormonal trigger for milk ejection (the "letdown" reflex) in women whose breasts are actively producing milk in response to prolactin. Suckling causes a reflex-initiated release of oxytocin, which targets the specialized myoepithelial cells surrounding the milk-producing glands. As these cells contract, milk is forced from the breast into the mouth of the suckling infant. Both of these mechanisms are *positive feedback mechanisms* and are described in more detail in Chapter 29.

Both natural and synthetic oxytocic drugs (Pitocin and others) are used to induce labor or to hasten normal labor that is progressing slowly. Less frequently, oxytocics are used to stop postpartum bleeding (by compressing ruptured blood vessels at the placental site) and to stimulate the milk ejection reflex.

Until recently, oxytocin's role in males and nonpregnant, nonlactating females was unknown, but new studies reveal that this potent peptide plays a role in sexual arousal and orgasm when the body is already primed for reproduction by sex hormones; then it is responsible for the satisfaction that results from that interaction. In nonsexual relationships, it is thought to promote nurturing and affectionate behavior, i.e., it acts as a "cuddle hormone."

Antidiuretic Hormone (ADH).   *Diuresis* (di″u-re′sis) is urine production. Thus, an *antidiuretic* (an″tĭ-di″u-ret′ik) is a chemical substance that inhibits or prevents urine formation. **Antidiuretic hormone (ADH)** prevents wide swings in water balance, helping to avoid dehydration or excessive fluid volumes. Highly specialized hypothalamic neurons, called *osmoreceptors,* continually monitor the solute concentration (and thus the water concentration) of the blood. When solutes threaten to become too concentrated (as might follow excessive perspiration or inadequate fluid intake), the osmoreceptors transmit excitatory impulses to the hypothalamic neurons in the supraoptic nucleus which synthesize and release ADH. ADH is liberated into the blood by the neurohypophysis, and targets the kidney tubules. The tubule cells respond by reabsorbing more water from the forming urine and returning it to the bloodstream. As a result, less urine is produced and blood volume increases. As solute concentration declines, the osmoreceptors stop depolarizing, effectively ending ADH release. Other stimuli triggering ADH release include pain, low blood pressure, and certain drugs (such as nicotine, morphine, and barbiturates).

Drinking alcoholic beverages inhibits ADH secretion and causes copious urine output. The dry mouth and intense thirst of the "morning after" reflect this dehydrating effect of alcohol. As might be expected, ADH release is also inhibited by drinking excessive amounts of water. *Diuretic drugs* antagonize the effects of ADH and cause water to be flushed from the body. These drugs are used to manage some cases of

FIGURE 17.8
Gross and microscopic anatomy of the thyroid gland.
(a) Location and arterial blood supply of the thyroid gland, anterior view. (b) Photomicrograph of the thyroid gland (150×).

hypertension and the edema (water retention in tissues) typical of congestive heart failure.

At high blood concentrations, ADH has a decided pressor effect; that is, it causes vasoconstriction, primarily of the visceral blood vessels. Under certain conditions, such as severe blood loss, exceptionally large amounts of ADH are released. This, in turn, causes an elevation in systemic blood pressure. The alternative name for this hormone (**vasopressin**) reflects this particular effect.

The only important imbalance of ADH secretion is *diabetes insipidus,* a syndrome marked by the output of large amounts of urine (polyuria) and intense thirst. The name of this condition (*diabetes* = overflow; *insipidus* = tasteless) distinguishes it from diabetes mellitus (*mel* = honey), in which insulin deficiency causes large amounts of blood sugar to be lost in the urine. At one time, urine was tasted to determine the cause of the polyuria.

Diabetes insipidus can be caused by a blow to the head that damages the hypothalamus or the posterior pituitary releasing site. In either case, ADH release is deficient. Though inconvenient, the condition is not serious when the thirst center is operating properly and the person drinks enough water to prevent dehydration. However, it can be life threatening in unconscious or comatose patients, so accident victims with head trauma must be carefully monitored.

Hypersecretion of ADH is rare but may follow hypothalamic injury or be the consequence of ectopic ADH secretion by cancer cells (particularly pulmonary cancers). The syndrome resulting is called *syndrome of inappropriate ADH secretion (SIADH)* and is marked by water retention, weight gain, and hypoosmolarity of the blood. •

The Thyroid Gland

Location and Structure

The butterfly-shaped thyroid gland is located in the anterior neck, on the trachea just inferior to the larynx (Figure 17.8a). Its two lateral **lobes** are connected by a median tissue mass called the **isthmus.** The thyroid gland is the largest pure endocrine gland in the body. Its prodigious blood supply (from the *superior* and *inferior thyroid arteries*), makes thyroid surgery a painstaking endeavor.

Internally, the thyroid gland is composed of hollow, spherical **follicles** (Figure 17.8b). The walls of each follicle are formed largely by cuboidal or squamous epithelial cells called *follicle cells,* which produce the glycoprotein **thyroglobulin** (thi″ro-glob′u-lin). The central cavity, or lumen, of the follicle stores **colloid,** an amber-colored, sticky material consisting of thyroglobulin molecules with attached iodine atoms. *Thyroid hormone* is derived from this iodinated thyroglobulin. The *parafollicular cells,* another population of endocrine cells found in the thyroid gland, produce *calcitonin,* an entirely different hormone (see p. 565). The parafollicular cells lie within the follicular epithelium but protrude into the soft connective tissue that separates and surrounds the thyroid follicles.

Thyroid Hormone (TH)

Thyroid hormone (TH), often referred to as the body's major metabolic hormone, is actually two active iodine-containing hormones, **thyroxine** (thi-rok'sin), or T_4, and **triiodothyronine** (tri"i-o"do-thi'ro-nēn), or T_3. Thyroxine is the major hormone secreted by the thyroid follicles; most triiodothyronine is formed at the target tissues by conversion of T_4 to T_3. These two hormones are very much alike. Each is constructed from two tyrosine amino acids linked together, but thyroxine has four bound iodine atoms, whereas triiodothyronine has three (thus, T_4 and T_3).

Except for the adult brain, spleen, testes, uterus, and the thyroid gland itself, thyroid hormone affects virtually every cell in the body. Generally speaking, it stimulates enzymes concerned with glucose oxidation. In this way, it increases basal metabolic rate (and oxygen consumption) and body heat production; this is known as the hormone's **calorigenic effect** (*calorigenic* = heat producing). Thyroid hormone also provokes an increase in the number of adrenergic receptors in blood vessels, so it plays an important role in maintaining blood pressure (see Chapter 14). Additionally, it is an important regulator of tissue growth and development; it is especially critical for normal skeletal and nervous system development and maturation and reproductive capabilities. A summary of the broad effects of thyroid hormone appears in Table 17.2 on p. 564.

Synthesis. Synthesis of thyroid hormone involves six interrelated processes that begin when thyroid-stimulating hormone (TSH) secreted by the anterior pituitary binds to follicular cell receptors (Figure 17.9):

1. *Formation and storage of thyroglobulin (Figure 17.9, step 1).* Thyroglobulin is synthesized on the ribosomes and then transported to the Golgi apparatus, where sugar residues are attached and the molecules are packed into vesicles. These transport vesicles move to the apex of the follicle cell, where their contents are discharged into the lumen and become part of the stored colloid.

2. *Iodine trapping and oxidation to iodine (Figure 17.9, step 2).* To produce the functional iodinated hormones, the follicle cells must accumulate iodides (anions of iodine) from the blood. Since their intracellular concentration of iodides is over 30 times higher than that in blood, iodide trapping depends on active transport. Upon entry, iodides (I^-) are oxidized (by removal of electrons) and converted to iodine (I_2).

3. *Iodination (Figure 17.9, step 3).* Once formed, iodine is attached to the tyrosine amino acids forming part of the thyroglobulin colloid. This iodination reaction occurs at the apical follicle cell–colloid junction and is mediated by *peroxidase* enzymes.

4. *Coupling of T_2 and T_1 (Figure 17.9, step 4).* Attachment of one iodine to a tyrosine produces **monoiodotyrosine (MIT or T_1);** attachment of two iodines produces **diiodotyrosine (DIT or T_2).** Then, enzymes within the colloid link T_1 and T_2 together. Two linked DITs result in T_4, while coupling of MIT and DIT produce T_3. At this point, however, the hormones are still part of the thyroglobulin colloid.

5. *Colloid endocytosis (Figure 17.9, step 5).* Hormone secretion requires that the follicle cells reclaim iodinated thyroglobulin by endocytosis and combine the vesicles with lysosomes.

6. *Cleavage of the hormones for release (Figure 17.9, step 6).* Within the lysosomes, the hormones are cleaved out of the colloid by lysosomal enzymes. The hormones then diffuse from the follicle cells into the bloodstream. The main hormonal product secreted is T_4. Some T_4 is converted to T_3 before secretion, but most T_3 is generated in the peripheral tissues.

Although we have followed the process of TH synthesis from beginning to end (secretion), the *initial response* to TSH binding is secretion of thyroid hormone. Then more colloid is synthesized to "restock" the follicle lumen. The thyroid gland is unique among the endocrine glands in its ability to store its hormone extracellularly and in large quantities. In the normal thyroid gland, the amount of stored colloid remains relatively constant and is sufficient to provide normal levels of hormone release for several months.

Transport and Regulation. Most released T_4 and T_3 immediately bind to plasma proteins, of which the most important is *thyroxine-binding globulin (TBG)* produced by the liver. Both T_4 and T_3 bind to target tissue receptors, but T_3 binds much more avidly and is about ten times more active. Most peripheral tissues have the enzymes needed to convert T_4 to the more active T_3, a process that entails the enzymatic removal of one iodine group. Several mechanisms of thyroid hormone activity probably exist, and the one used depends on the specific receptor types on or in the various target cells. There is some evidence that cell surface receptors and cyclic AMP are involved in certain target cell responses to thyroid hormone. However, the T_3 form is known to enter some target cells and bind to intracellular receptors within the nucleus initiating transcription of mRNA.

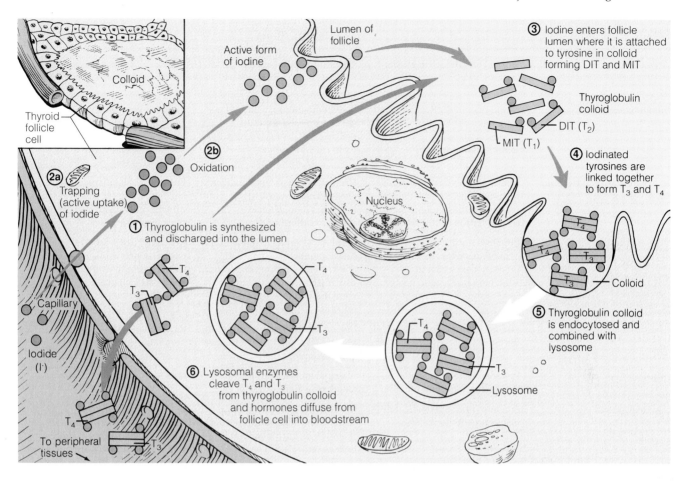

Active form of iodine

Lumen of follicle

③ Iodine enters follicle lumen where it is attached to tyrosine in colloid forming DIT and MIT

Colloid

Thyroid follicle cell

Thyroglobulin colloid

DIT (T₂)

MIT (T₁)

②b Oxidation

④ Iodinated tyrosines are linked together to form T₃ and T₄

②a Trapping (active uptake) of iodide

Nucleus

① Thyroglobulin is synthesized and discharged into the lumen

T₄

T₃

Capillary

T₄

T₃

Colloid

⑤ Thyroglobulin colloid is endocytosed and combined with lysosome

Iodide (I⁻)

T₄

T₃

⑥ Lysosomal enzymes cleave T₄ and T₃ from thyroglobulin colloid and hormones diffuse from follicle cell into bloodstream

Lysosome

T₄

To peripheral tissues

T₃

FIGURE 17.9
Biosynthesis of thyroid hormones. The sequence of steps in thyroxine (T_4) and triiodothyronine (T_3) synthesis. Binding of TSH to the follicle cell receptors (not illustrated) stimulates synthesis of the thyroglobulin colloid, the steps illustrated here, and the subsequent release of T_4 and T_3 from the cell. A complete description of these events appears in the text. (Note: Only iodinated tyrosine amino acids of the thyroglobulin colloid are illustrated. The rest of the colloid is indicated as the unstructured yellow substance.)

Falling thyroxine blood levels trigger TSH, and ultimately thyroxine, release. Rising levels of thyroxine feed back to inhibit the hypothalamic-adenohypophyseal axis, temporarily shutting off the stimulus for releasing TSH. Conditions that increase body energy requirements, such as pregnancy and prolonged cold, stimulate the hypothalamus to secrete *thyrotropin-releasing hormone (TRH)*, which triggers TSH release, and in such instances, TRH overcomes the negative feedback controls. As the thyroid gland releases larger amounts of thyroid hormones, body metabolism and heat generation are enhanced. Factors that inhibit TSH release include somatostatin, rising levels of glucocorticoids and sex hormones (estrogens or testosterone), and excessively high blood iodide concentration.

Both overactivity and underactivity of the thyroid gland can cause severe metabolic disturbances (see Table 17.2.) Hypothyroid disorders may result from some thyroid gland defect or secondarily from deficits of TSH or TRH release. They also occur when the thyroid gland is removed surgically *(thyroidectomy)* and when dietary iodine is inadequate.

In adults, the full-blown hypothyroid syndrome is called **myxedema** (mik″sĕ-de′mah; "mucous swelling"). Symptoms include a low metabolic rate, feeling chilled, constipation, thick, dry skin and puffy eyes, edema, lethargy, and mental sluggishness (but not mental retardation). If myxedema results from lack of iodine, the thyroid gland enlarges, a condition called **endemic** (en-dem′-ik), or *colloidal,* **goiter.** The follicle cells produce colloid but cannot iodinate it or make functional hormones. The pituitary gland secretes increasing amounts of TSH in a futile attempt to stimulate the thyroid to produce TH, but the only result is that the follicles accumulate more and more *unusable* colloid. Untreated, the thyroid cells eventually "burn out" from frantic activity, and the gland atrophies. Before the marketing of iodized salt, parts of the midwestern United States were called the "goiter belt." Because these areas had iodine-poor soil and no access to iodine-rich shell-

Table 17.2 Major Effects of Thyroid Hormone (T_4 and T_3) in the Body

Process or system affected	Normal physiological effects	Effects of hyposecretion	Effects of hypersecretion
Basal metabolic rate (BMR)/ temperature regulation	Promotes normal oxygen consumption and BMR; calorigenesis; enhances effects of catecholamines (and sympathetic nervous system)	BMR below normal; decreased body temperature; cold intolerance; decreased appetite; weight gain; decreased sensitivity to catecholamines	BMR above normal; increased body temperature; heat intolerance; increased appetite; weight loss; increased sensitivity to catecholamines may lead to high blood pressure
Carbohydrate/lipid/protein metabolism	Promotes glucose catabolism; mobilizes fats; essential for protein synthesis; enhances liver secretion of cholesterol	Decreased glucose metabolism; elevated cholesterol/triglyceride levels in blood; decreased protein synthesis; edema	Enhanced catabolism of glucose and fats; weight loss; increased protein catabolism; loss of muscle mass
Nervous system	Promotes normal development of nervous system in fetus and infant; necessary for normal adult nervous system function	In infant, slowed/deficient brain development, retardation; in adult, mental dulling, depression, paresthesias, memory impairment, listlessness, hypoactive reflexes	Irritability, restlessness, insomnia, overresponsiveness to environmental stimuli, exophthalmos, personality changes
Cardiovascular system	Promotes normal functioning of the heart	Decreased efficiency of pumping action of the heart; low heart rate and blood pressure	Rapid heart rate and possible palpitations; high blood pressure; if prolonged, heart failure
Muscular system	Promotes normal muscular development, tone, and function	Sluggish muscle action; muscle cramps; myalgia	Muscle atrophy and weakness
Skeletal system	Promotes normal growth and maturation of the skeleton	In child, growth retardation, skeletal stunting/malproportion, retention of child's body proportions; in adult, joint pain	In child, excessive skeletal growth initially, followed by early epiphyseal closure and short stature; in adult, demineralization of skeleton
Gastrointestinal system	Promotes normal GI motility and tone; increases secretion of digestive juices	Depressed GI motility, tone, and secretory activity; constipation	Excessive GI motility; diarrhea; loss of appetite
Reproductive system	Promotes normal female reproductive ability and normal lactation	Depressed ovarian function; sterility; depressed lactation	In females, depressed ovarian function; in males, impotence
Integumentary system	Promotes normal hydration and secretory activity of skin	Skin pale, thickened, and dry; facial edema; hair coarse and thin; nails hard and thick	Skin flushed, thin, and moist; hair fine and soft; nails soft and thin

fish, goiters were very common there. Depending on the cause, myxedema can be reversed by iodine supplements or hormone replacement therapy.

Severe hypothyroidism in infants is called **cretinism** (kre′tĭ-nizm). The child has a short, disproportionate body, a thick tongue and neck, and is mentally retarded. Cretinism may reflect a genetic deficiency of the fetal thyroid gland or maternal factors, such as lack of dietary iodine. Cretinism is preventable by thyroid hormone replacement therapy, but once developmental abnormalities and mental retardation appear, they are not reversible.

The most common (and puzzling) hyperthyroid pathology is **Graves's disease.** Since patients' serum often contains abnormal antibodies that mimic TSH and continuously stimulate release of thyroid hormone, Graves's disease is believed to be an autoimmune disease. Typical symptoms include an elevated metabolic rate; sweating; rapid, irregular heartbeat; nervousness; and weight loss despite adequate food intake. *Exophthalmos,* protrusion of the eyeballs, may occur if the tissue behind the eyes becomes edematous and then fibrous. Treatments include surgical removal of the thyroid gland or ingestion of radioactive iodine (^{131}I) which selectively destroys the most active thyroid cells. •

Calcitonin

Calcitonin is a polypeptide hormone produced by the **parafollicular,** or **C, cells** of the thyroid gland. Because its most important effect is to lower blood calcium levels, calcitonin is a direct antagonist of parathyroid hormone, produced by the parathyroid glands. Calcitonin targets the skeleton, where it (1) inhibits osteoclast activity and, hence, bone resorption and release of ionic calcium from the bony matrix and (2) stimulates calcium uptake and incorporation into bone matrix. Thus, calcitonin has a bone-sparing effect.

Excessive blood levels of ionic calcium (approximately 20% above normal) act as a humoral stimulus for calcitonin release, whereas declining blood calcium levels inhibit C cell secretory activity. Calcitonin regulation of blood calcium levels is short-lived but extremely rapid.

Calcitonin appears to be important only in childhood, when the skeleton grows quickly and the bones are changing dramatically in mass, size, and shape. In adults, calcitonin is at best a weak hypocalcemic agent.

The Parathyroid Glands

The tiny, yellow-brown **parathyroid glands** are nearly hidden from view in the posterior aspect of the thyroid gland (Figure 17.10a). There are usually two pairs of these glands, but the precise number varies. As many as eight glands have been reported, and some may be located in other regions of the neck or even in the thorax. The parathyroid's glandular cells are arranged in thick, branching cords containing scattered *oxyphil cells* and large numbers of the smaller **chief cells** (Figure 17.10b). The chief cells secrete PTH; the function of the oxyphil cells is unclear.

Discovery of the parathyroid glands was quite accidental. Years ago, surgeons were baffled by the observation that while most patients recovered uneventfully after partial (or even total) thyroid gland removal, others suffered uncontrolled muscle spasms and severe pain, and subsequently died. It was only after several such tragic deaths that the parathyroid glands were discovered and their hormonal function, quite different from that of the thyroid gland hormones, became known.

Parathyroid hormone (PTH), or **parathormone,** the protein hormone of these glands, is the single most important hormone controlling the calcium balance of the blood. Its release is triggered by falling blood calcium levels and inhibited by hypercalcemia. PTH increases ionic calcium levels in blood by stimulating three target organs: the skeleton (which contains considerable amounts of calcium salt in its matrix), the kidneys, and the intestine (Figure 17.11).

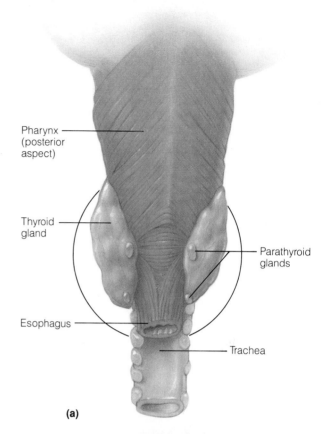

Pharynx (posterior aspect)

Thyroid gland

Parathyroid glands

Esophagus

Trachea

(a)

Capillary

Chief cells

Oxyphil cells

(b)

FIGURE 17.10

The parathyroid glands. (a) Location of the parathyroid glands on the posterior aspect of the thyroid gland. These tiny glands may be more inconspicuous than depicted. **(b)** Micrograph of a section of the parathyroid gland (540×).

PTH release (1) stimulates osteoclasts (bone-resorbing cells) to digest some of the bony matrix and release ionic calcium and phosphates to the blood; (2) enhances reabsorption of calcium (and decreased retention of phosphates) by the kidneys; and (3) increases absorption of calcium by the intestinal mucosal cells. Calcium absorption by the intestine is enhanced indirectly by PTH's effect on vitamin D activation. Vitamin D is required for absorption of calcium from ingested food, but the form in which the vitamin is ingested or produced by the skin is rela-

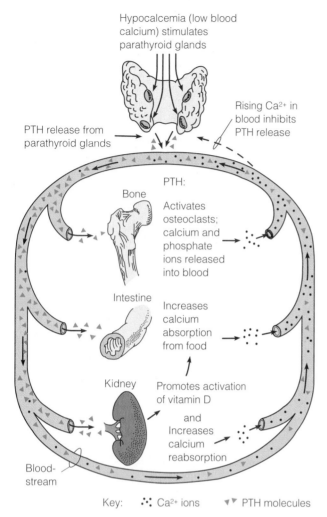

Hypocalcemia (low blood calcium) stimulates parathyroid glands

Rising Ca²⁺ in blood inhibits PTH release

PTH release from parathyroid glands

PTH:

Bone
Activates osteoclasts; calcium and phosphate ions released into blood

Intestine
Increases calcium absorption from food

Kidney
Promotes activation of vitamin D
and
Increases calcium reabsorption

Blood-stream

Key: ∴ Ca²⁺ ions ▼▽ PTH molecules

FIGURE 17.11
Summary of parathyroid hormone's effects on bone, the intestine, and the kidneys. (Note that PTH's effect on the intestine is indirect via activated vitamin D.)

tively inactive. For vitamin D to exert its physiological effects, it must first be converted by the kidneys to its active vitamin D₃ form, *calcitriol* (1,25-dihydroxy-cholecalciferol), a transformation stimulated by PTH.

Since plasma calcium ion homeostasis is essential for so many functions, including transmission of nerve impulses, muscle contraction, and blood clotting, precise control of ionic calcium levels is critical.

Hyperparathyroidism is rare and usually the result of a parathyroid gland tumor. When it occurs, calcium is leached from the bones, and the bones soften and deform as their mineral salts are replaced by fibrous connective tissue. In severe cases of this disorder, called *osteitis cystica fibrosa,* the bones have a moth-eaten appearance on X rays and tend to fracture spontaneously. The resulting abnormally elevated blood calcium level (hypercalcemia) has many outcomes, but the two most notable are (1) depression of the nervous system, which leads to

abnormal reflexes and weakness of the skeletal muscles, and (2) formation of kidney stones as excess calcium salts precipitate in the kidney tubules. Calcium deposits may also form in soft tissues throughout the body and severely impair vital organ functioning.

Hypoparathyroidism, or PTH deficiency, most often follows parathyroid gland trauma or removal during thyroid surgery. The resulting hypocalcemia increases the excitability of neurons and accounts for the classical symptoms of *tetany* such as loss of sensation, muscle twitches, and convulsions. Untreated, the symptoms progress to spasms of the larynx, respiratory paralysis, and death. •

The Adrenal (Suprarenal) Glands

The paired **adrenal** (*ad* = near; *renal* = kidney) **glands** are pyramid-shaped organs perched atop the kidneys, where they are enclosed in a fibrous capsule and a cushion of fat (see Figure 17.1). They are often referred to as the **suprarenal glands** (*supra* = above) as well.

Each adrenal gland is structurally and functionally two endocrine glands in one. The inner **adrenal medulla,** more like a "knot" of nervous tissue than a gland, derives from the neural crest and acts as part of the sympathetic nervous system. The outer **adrenal cortex,** encapsulating the medullary region and forming the bulk of the gland, is derived from embryonic mesoderm. Each of these regions produces its own "set" of hormones (Table 17.3, p. 570), but all adrenal hormones help us cope with "extreme" (stressful) situations.

The Adrenal Cortex

Well over two dozen *steroid* hormones, collectively called **corticosteroids,** are synthesized from cholesterol by the adrenal cortex. The pathway is multistep and involves varying intermediates depending on the hormone being formed. The structures of several corticosteroid hormones are illustrated in Table 17.3.

The large, lipid-laden cortical cells are arranged in three distinct layers or zones (Figure 17.12). The cell clusters forming the superficial **zona glomerulosa** (zo′nah glo-mer″u-lo′sah) mainly produce mineralocorticoids, hormones that help control the balance of minerals and water in the blood. The middle **zona fasciculata** (fah-sik″u-la′tah) cells, arranged in more or less linear cords, secrete the metabolic hormones called glucocorticoids. The cells of the innermost **zona reticularis** (rĕ-tik′u-lar-is), abutting the adrenal medulla, have a netlike arrangement. These cells produce glucocorticoids and small amounts of adrenal sex hormones, or gonadocorticoids. Although, as just described, there is a division of labor in corticosteroid production, the entire spectrum of corticosteroids is produced by all three cortical layers.

Cortex

Medulla

Capsule
Zona glomerulosa
Zona fasciculata
Zona reticularis
Adrenal medulla

(a)   (b)

FIGURE 17.12
Microscopic structure of the adrenal gland. (a) Diagram and (b) photomicrograph of the zona glomerulosa, zona fasciculata, and zona reticularis of the adrenal cortex (50×). (Part of the adrenal medulla is also shown.)

Mineralocorticoids. The essential function of mineralocorticoids is regulation of the electrolyte (mineral salt) concentrations in extracellular fluids, particularly of sodium and potassium ions. The single most abundant positive ion (cation) in the extracellular fluid is sodium, and while sodium is vital to homeostasis, excessive sodium intake and retention may promote high blood pressure (hypertension) in susceptible individuals. Although there are several mineralocorticoids, **aldosterone** (al-dos′ter-ōn) is the most potent and accounts for over 95% of the mineralocorticoids produced (see Table 17.3). As you might guess, maintaining sodium ion balance is aldosterone's primary goal.

Aldosterone decreases excretion of sodium from the body. Its primary target is the distal parts of the kidney tubules, where it stimulates reabsorption of sodium ions from the forming urine and their return into the bloodstream. Aldosterone also enhances sodium ion reabsorption from perspiration, saliva, and gastric juice. The mechanism of aldosterone activity appears to involve the synthesis of an enzyme required for sodium transport.

Regulation of a number of other ions—including potassium, hydrogen, bicarbonate, and chloride—is coupled to that of sodium; and where sodium goes, water follows—an event that leads to changes in blood volume and blood pressure. Hence, sodium ion regulation is crucial to overall body homeostasis. Briefly, aldosterone's effects on the renal tubules cause sodium and water retention accompanied by potassium ion elimination and, in some instances, alterations in the acid-base balance of the blood (by H^+ excretion). Since aldosterone's regulatory effects are brief (lasting approximately 20 minutes), plasma electrolyte balance can be very precisely controlled and modified continuously. These matters are described in greater detail in Chapter 27.

Aldosterone secretion is stimulated by a number of factors: rising blood levels of potassium ions, low blood levels of sodium, and decreasing blood volume and blood pressure. The reverse conditions inhibit aldosterone secretion. Four mechanisms regulate aldosterone secretion: the renin-angiotensin system, plasma concentrations of sodium and potassium ions, controls exerted by ACTH, and plasma concentrations of atrial natriuretic factor (Figure 17.13). These mechanisms are described next.

1. **The renin-angiotensin** (re′nin an″je-o-ten′sin) **system.** The renin-angiotensin system, the major regulator of aldosterone release, influences both the electrolyte-water balance of the blood and blood pressure. Specialized cells of the *juxtaglomerular apparatus* in the kidneys become excited when blood pressure (or blood volume) declines or plasma osmolarity (solute concentration) drops. They respond by releasing **renin** into the blood. Renin cleaves off part of the plasma protein **angiotensinogen** (an″je-o-ten′sin-o-gen), triggering an enzymatic cascade leading to the formation of **angiotensin II,** a potent stimulator of aldosterone release by the glomerulosa cells of the adrenal cortex. However, the renin-angiotensin system does much more than trigger aldosterone release, and all of its widespread effects are ultimately involved in raising the systemic blood pressure. These additional effects are described in detail in Chapters 26 and 27.

2. **Plasma concentration of sodium and potassium ions.** Fluctuating blood levels of sodium and potassium ions can directly influence the zona glomerulosa cells. Increased potassium and decreased sodium are stimulatory; the opposite conditions are inhibitory.

3. **ACTH.** Under normal circumstances, ACTH released by the anterior pituitary has little or no effect on aldosterone release. However, when a person is severely stressed, the hypothalamus secretes more **corticotropin-releasing hormone (CRH).** The rise in ACTH blood levels that follows steps up the rate of aldosterone secretion to a small extent. The increase in blood volume and blood pressure that results helps ensure adequate delivery of nutrients and respiratory gases during the stressful period.

4. **Atrial natriuretic factor (ANF).** Atrial natriuretic factor, a hormone secreted by the heart when blood pressure rises, fine-tunes blood pressure and sodium-water balance of the body mainly by modifying the effects of the renin-angiotensin system. Its major effects on that system are inhibitory: It blocks renin and aldosterone secretion and inhibits other angiotensin-induced mechanisms that enhance water and sodium reabsorption. Consequently, the overall influence of atrial natriuretic factor is to decrease blood pressure by allowing Na$^+$ (and water) to flow out of the body in urine (*natriuretic* = producing salty urine).

Hypersecretion of aldosterone, a condition called *aldosteronism,* typically results from adrenal neoplasms. Two major sets of problems result: (1) hypertension and edema due to excessive sodium and water retention and (2) accelerated excretion of potassium ions. If potassium loss is extreme, neurons become nonresponsive and muscle weakness (and eventually paralysis) occurs. *Addison's disease,* hyposecretory disease of the adrenal cortex, generally involves a deficient output of both mineralocorticoids and glucocorticoids, as described shortly. •

Which of these mechanisms would be triggered by severe blood loss?

FIGURE 17.13
Major mechanisms controlling aldosterone release from the adrenal cortex.

Glucocorticoids. The **glucocorticoids** influence the metabolism of most body cells and help provide resistance to stressors. They are absolutely essential to life. Under normal circumstances, the glucocorticoids help the body adapt to external changes and intermittent food intake by keeping blood sugar levels fairly constant, and maintain blood volume by preventing the shift of water into tissue cells. However, severe stress due to hemorrhage, infections, or physical or emotional trauma evokes a dramatically higher output of glucocorticoids, which helps the body to negotiate the crisis. Glucocorticoid hormones include **cortisol (hydrocortisone)** (see Table 17.3), **cortisone,** and **corticosterone,** but only cortisol is secreted in significant amounts in humans. As for all steroid hormones, the basic mechanism of glucocorticoid activity on target cells is to modify gene activity.

Glucocorticoid secretion is regulated by a typical negative feedback system. Cortisol release is promoted by ACTH, triggered in turn by the hypothalamic releasing hormone CRH. Rising cortisol levels act on both the hypothalamus and the anterior pituitary, preventing CRH release and shutting off ACTH and cortisol secretion. Cortisol secretory bursts, driven by patterns of eating and activity, occur in a definite pattern throughout the day and night. Cortisol blood levels peak shortly after we arise in the morning; lowest levels are seen in the evening just before and shortly after sleep ensues. The normal cortisol rhythm is interrupted by acute stress of any variety as the sympathetic nervous system overrides the (usually) inhibitory effects of elevated cortisol levels and triggers CRH release. The resulting increase in ACTH blood levels causes an outpouring of cortisol from the adrenal cortex.

Stress results in a dramatic rise in blood levels of glucose, fatty acids, and amino acids, all provoked by cortisol. Cortisol's prime metabolic effect is *gluconeo-genesis,* the formation of glucose from noncarbohydrate molecules (fats and proteins). Cortisol also mobilizes fatty acids from adipose tissue, encouraging increased use of fatty acids for the energy needs of most tissue cells and "saving" glucose for the brain. Under cortisol's influence, stored proteins are broken down to provide building blocks for repair or for making enzymes used in metabolic processes. Cortisol enhances epinephrine's vasoconstrictive effects, and the increased blood pressure and circulatory efficiency that result help ensure that these nutrients are quickly distributed to the cells.

Excessive levels of glucocorticoids (1) depress cartilage and bone formation, (2) inhibit inflammation by stabilizing lysosomal membranes and preventing vasodilation, (3) depress the immune system, and (4) promote changes in cardiovascular, neural, and gastrointestinal function. Keep in mind that *ideal amounts of glucocorticoids promote normal function.* Significant anti-inflammatory and anti-immune effects are associated with cortisol excess and are rarely seen when glucocorticoids are present at physiological levels. Recognition of the effects of glucocorticoid hypersecretion has led to widespread use of glucocorticoid drugs to control symptoms of many chronic inflammatory disorders, such as rheumatoid arthritis or allergic responses. However, the use of these potent drugs at higher than normal *(pharmacological)* doses is a double-edged sword. While it relieves some of the symptoms, it also causes the undesirable effects of excessive levels of these hormones.

The pathology of cortisone excess, **Cushing's disease,** or **syndrome,** may be caused by an ACTH-releasing tumor of the pituitary or by a tumor of the adrenal cortex. However, it most often results from the clinical administration of large doses of glucocorticoid drugs. The syndrome is characterized by persistent hyperglycemia *(steroid diabetes),* dramatic

losses in muscle and bone protein, and water and salt retention, leading to hypertension and edema. The so-called cushingoid signs include a swollen "moon" face, redistribution of fat to the abdomen and the posterior neck (causing a "buffalo hump"), a tendency to bruising, and poor wound healing. Because of enhanced anti-inflammatory effects, infections may be masked and become overwhelmingly severe before producing recognizable symptoms. Eventually, muscles weaken and spontaneous fractures force the person to become bedridden. The only treatment is removal of the cause—be it surgical removal of the offending tumor or discontinuation of the drug.

Addison's disease, the major hyposecretory disorder of the adrenal cortex, usually involves deficits in both glucocorticoids and mineralocorticoids. People with Addison's disease tend to lose weight; their plasma glucose and sodium levels drop and potassium levels rise. Severe dehydration and hypotension are common. Corticosteroid replacement therapy at physiological doses is the usual treatment. •

Gonadocorticoids (Sex Hormones). The bulk of the **gonadocorticoids** secreted are **androgens,** or male sex hormones (see Table 17.3). These include *androstenedione* and other steroids that are ineffective themselves as androgens, but which are converted to potent forms, such as *testosterone* and *dihydrotestosterone,* in the peripheral tissues. The adrenal cortex also makes small amounts of female hormones (estrogens). The amount of sex hormones produced by the adrenal cortex is insignificant compared to the amounts made by the gonads during late puberty and adulthood. The exact role of the adrenal sex hormones is still in question, but because adrenal androgen levels rise continuously between the ages of 7 and 13 in both boys and girls, it is assumed that they contribute to the onset of puberty and the appearance of axillary and pubic hair during that time period. In adult women adrenal androgens are thought to be responsible for the sex drive, and they may be converted to estrogens after menopause when ovarian estrogens are no longer produced. Control of gonadocorticoid secretion is not completely understood. Release appears to be stimulated by ACTH, but the gonadocorticoids do not appear to exert feedback inhibition on ACTH release.

Since androgens predominate, hypersecretion of gonadocorticoids usually causes *masculinization,* or *virilization.* In adult males, these effects may be obscured, since virilization by testicular testosterone has already been completed; but in prepubertal males and in females, the results can be dramatic. In the young man, maturation of the reproductive organs and appearance of the secondary sex characteristics occur rapidly, and the sex drive emerges with a vengeance. Females develop a beard and a masculine pattern of body hair distribution, and the clitoris grows to resemble a small penis. •

Table 17.3 Adrenal Gland Hormones: Regulation and Effects

Hormone	Structure	Regulation of Release	Target/effects	Effects of hypersecretion ↑ and hyposecretion ↓
Adrenocortical Hormones				
Mineralocorticoids (chiefly aldosterone)	Aldosterone	Stimulated by renin-angiotensin mechanism (activated by decreasing blood volume or blood pressure), elevated K⁺ or low Na⁺ blood levels, and ACTH (minor influence); inhibited by increased blood volume and pressure, increased Na⁺ and decreased K⁺ blood levels	Kidneys; increased blood levels of Na⁺ and decreased blood levels of K⁺; since water reabsorption accompanies sodium retention, blood volume and blood pressure rise	↑ Aldosteronism ↓ Addison's disease
Glucocorticoids (chiefly cortisol)	Cortisol	Stimulated by ACTH; inhibited by feedback inhibition exerted by cortisol	Body cells; promote gluconeogenesis and hyperglycemia; mobilize fats for energy metabolism; stimulate protein catabolism; assist body to resist stressors; depress inflammatory and immune responses	↑ Cushing's disease ↓ Addison's disease
Gonadocorticoids (chiefly androgens such as testosterone)	Testosterone	Stimulated by ACTH; mechanism of inhibition incompletely understood, but feedback inhibition not seen	Insignificant effects in adults; may be responsible for female libido and source of estrogen after menopause	↑ Virilization of females (androgenital syndrome) ↓ No effects known
Adrenal Medullary Hormones				
Catecholamines (epinephrine and norepinephrine)	Epinephrine	Stimulated by preganglionic fibers of the sympathetic nervous system	Sympathetic nervous system target organs; effects mimic sympathetic nervous system activation; increase heart rate and metabolic rate; increase blood pressure by promoting vasoconstriction	↑ Prolonged flight-or-fight response; hypertension ↓ Unimportant

Note: For the above table, chemical structure diagrams appear in the Structure column — Aldosterone (with CH_2OH, $C=O$, CH, HO), Cortisol (with CH_2OH, $C=O$, OH, HO), Testosterone (with OH), and Epinephrine (with HO, OH, $CH-CH_2-N$, CH_3, H).

The Adrenal Medulla

The centrally located **adrenal medulla** is discussed in Chapter 14 as part of the autonomic nervous system, so it is covered only briefly here. Its spherical **chromaffin** (kro-maf'in) **cells,** which crowd around blood-filled capillaries and sinusoids, are modified postganglionic sympathetic neurons that secrete the *catecholamines* **epinephrine** and **norepinephrine** into the blood.

When the body is activated to its fight-or-flight status by some short-term stressor or emergency, the sympathetic nervous system is mobilized. As a result, blood sugar levels rise, blood vessels constrict and the heart beats faster (together raising the blood pressure), and blood is diverted from temporarily nonessential organs to the brain, heart, and skeletal muscles. At the same time, preganglionic sympathetic nerve endings that weave through the adrenal medulla signal for release of catecholamines, which reinforce and prolong the fight-or-flight response.

Unequal amounts of the two hormones are released; approximately 80% is epinephrine. With a few key exceptions, the two hormones exert the same effects (summarized in Table 14.3, p. 470). Epinephrine is the more potent stimulator of the heart and metabolic activities, while norepinephrine has the

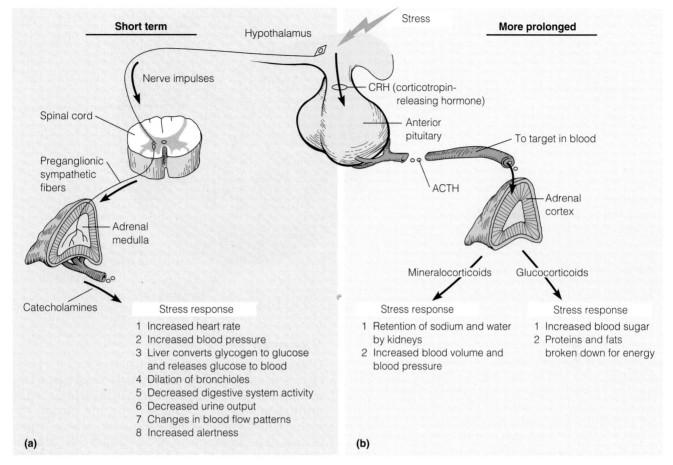

Short term

Hypothalamus

Nerve impulses

Spinal cord

Preganglionic sympathetic fibers

Adrenal medulla

Catecholamines

Stress

CRH (corticotropin-releasing hormone)

Anterior pituitary

ACTH

To target in blood

Adrenal cortex

More prolonged

Stress response
1 Increased heart rate
2 Increased blood pressure
3 Liver converts glycogen to glucose and releases glucose to blood
4 Dilation of bronchioles
5 Decreased digestive system activity
6 Decreased urine output
7 Changes in blood flow patterns
8 Increased alertness

Mineralocorticoids   Glucocorticoids

Stress response
1 Retention of sodium and water by kidneys
2 Increased blood volume and blood pressure

Stress response
1 Increased blood sugar
2 Proteins and fats broken down for energy

(a)

(b)

FIGURE 17.14
Stress and the adrenal gland.
Stressful stimuli cause the hypothalamus to activate the adrenal medulla via sympathetic nerve impulses and the adrenal cortex via hormonal signals. **(a)** The medulla mediates short-term responses to stress by secreting catecholamines (epinephrine and norepinephrine). **(b)** The cortex controls more prolonged responses by secreting its steroid hormones.

greater influence on peripheral vasoconstriction (and blood pressure). Epinephrine is used clinically as a heart stimulant and to cause bronchodilation during acute asthmatic attacks.

Unlike the adrenocortical hormones, which promote long-lasting body responses to stressors, the catecholamines cause fairly brief responses. The interrelationships of the adrenal hormones and the hypothalamus, the "director" of the stress response, are depicted in Figure 17.14.

Since hormones of the adrenal medulla merely intensify the activities set into motion by the sympathetic nervous system neurons, their deficiency is not a problem. Unlike the glucocorticoids, the catecholamines are not essential for life. However, hypersecretion of catecholamines, sometimes arising from a rare chromaffin cell tumor called a *pheochromocytoma* (fe-o-kro"mo-si-to'mah), produces symptoms of massive and uncontrolled sympathetic nervous system activity; hyperglycemia, increased metabolic rate, rapid heart beat and palpitations, hypertension, intense nervousness, and sweating. •

The Pancreas

Located partially behind the stomach in the abdomen, the soft, triangular **pancreas** is a mixed gland composed of both endocrine and exocrine gland cells (Figure 17.15). Like the thyroid and parathyroids, it develops as an outpocketing of the embryonic endoderm, which forms the epithelial lining (and glands) of the gastrointestinal and respiratory tracts. *Acinar cells,* forming the bulk of the gland, produce an enzyme-rich juice that is ducted into the small intestine during food digestion. This exocrine product is discussed in Chapter 24.

Scattered among the acinar cells are approximately a million **pancreatic islets (islets of Langerhans),** minute cell clusters that produce pancreatic hormones. The islets contain two major populations of hormone-producing cells, the glucagon-synthesizing **alpha (α) cells** and the more numerous insulin-producing **beta (β) cells.** Insulin and glucagon are intimately but independently involved in the regulation of blood glucose levels. Their effects are oppo-

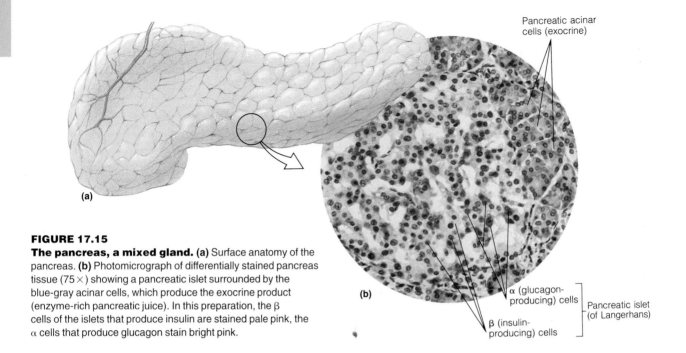

FIGURE 17.15
The pancreas, a mixed gland. (a) Surface anatomy of the pancreas. (b) Photomicrograph of differentially stained pancreas tissue (75×) showing a pancreatic islet surrounded by the blue-gray acinar cells, which produce the exocrine product (enzyme-rich pancreatic juice). In this preparation, the β cells of the islets that produce insulin are stained pale pink, the α cells that produce glucagon stain bright pink.

site: Insulin is a *hypoglycemic* hormone, whereas glucagon is a *hyperglycemic* hormone (Figure 17.16). Islet cells also synthesize other peptides in small amounts. These include *somatostatin* (secreted by the *delta* [δ] *cells*), which inhibits the release of insulin and glucagon; *pancreatic polypeptide (PP)* secreted by the *F cells,* which plays a role in regulating the exocrine (enzyme-secreting) function of the pancreas; and *amylin,* a hormone cosecreted with insulin by the beta cells that appears to antagonize some of insulin's effects.

Glucagon

Glucagon (gloo′kah-gon), a 29-amino-acid polypeptide, is an extremely potent hyperglycemic agent: One molecule of this hormone can cause the release of 100 million molecules of glucose into the blood! The major target of glucagon is the liver, where it promotes (1) breakdown of glycogen to glucose *(glycogenolysis);* (2) synthesis of glucose from lactic acid and from noncarbohydrate molecules such as fatty acids and amino acids *(gluconeogenesis);* and

FIGURE 17.16
Regulation of blood sugar levels by insulin and glucagon. When blood sugar levels are high, the pancreas releases insulin. Insulin stimulates sugar uptake by cells and glycogen formation in the liver, which lowers blood sugar levels; that is, insulin exerts hypoglycemic effects. Glucagon, released when blood sugar levels are low, stimulates glycogen breakdown and thereby raises blood sugar; that is, glucagon is a hyperglycemic hormone.

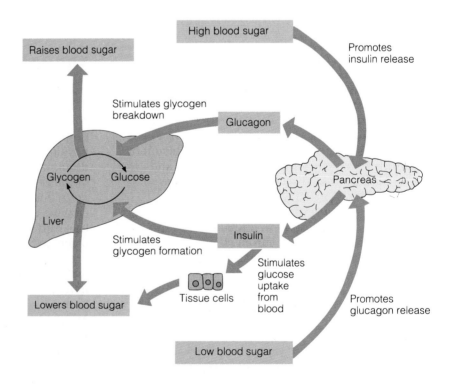

(3) release of glucose to the blood by the liver cells, which causes blood sugar levels to rise. A secondary effect is a fall in the concentration of amino acids in the blood as the liver cells sequester them to make new glucose molecules.

Secretion of glucagon by the α cells is prompted by humoral stimuli, most importantly declining blood sugar levels. However, increasing amino acid levels (as might follow a protein-rich meal) are also stimulatory. Glucagon release is suppressed by rising blood sugar levels and somatostatin. Because glucagon is such an important hyperglycemic agent, it has been speculated that people with persistently low blood sugar levels (hypoglycemics) are deficient in glucagon.

Insulin

Insulin is a small (51-amino-acid) protein consisting of two amino acid chains linked by disulfide bonds. As shown in Figure 17.17, it is initially synthesized as part of a larger polypeptide chain called **proinsulin.** The middle portion of this chain is then excised by enzymes, releasing functional insulin. This "clipping" process occurs in the secretory vesicles just before insulin is released from the beta cell.

Insulin's effects are most obvious when we have just eaten. Insulin's main effect is to lower blood sugar levels, but it also influences protein and fat metabolism. Circulating insulin lowers blood sugar levels by enhancing membrane transport of glucose (and other simple sugars) into body cells, especially muscle cells. (It does *not* accelerate glucose entry into liver, kidney, and brain tissue, all of which have easy access to blood glucose regardless of insulin levels.) Insulin inhibits the breakdown of glycogen to glucose and conversion of amino acids or fatty acids to glucose; thus, it counters any metabolic activity that would increase plasma levels of glucose. Insulin's mechanism of action is still being investigated but, as noted earlier (p. 550), its receptor is a tyrosine kinase enzyme that is activated when insulin binds to it.

After glucose enters the target cells, insulin binding triggers enzymatic activities that (1) catalyze the oxidation of glucose for ATP production, (2) join glucose together to form glycogen, and (3) convert glucose to fat (particularly in adipose tissue). As a rule, energy needs are met first, then glycogen deposit occurs. Finally, if excess glucose is still available, fat deposit occurs. Insulin also induces amino acid uptake and protein synthesis in muscle tissue. In summary, insulin sweeps glucose out of the blood, causing it to be used for energy or converted to other forms (glycogen or fats), and it promotes protein synthesis and fat storage.

The β cells are stimulated to secrete insulin chiefly by elevated blood sugar levels, but rising plasma levels of amino acids and fatty acids also trigger insulin release. As the cells avidly take up sugar

FIGURE 17.17
Structure of insulin. Proinsulin, the initial polypeptide product synthesized by the beta cells of the pancreas is a single polypeptide chain with three disulfide (-S-S-) bonds. This inactive product is converted to insulin by enzymatic cleavage, in which the middle portion of the polypeptide is excised out. Each "bead" in this model is an amino acid.

and other nutrients, and plasma levels of these substances drop, insulin secretion is suppressed. Other hormones also influence insulin release directly or indirectly. For example, any hyperglycemic hormone (such as glucagon, epinephrine, growth hormone, thyroxine, or glucocorticoids) called into action as blood sugar levels drop indirectly stimulates insulin release by promoting glucose entry into the bloodstream. Somatostatin depresses insulin release. Thus, blood sugar levels ultimately reflect a balance of both humoral and hormonal influences. Insulin and (indirectly) somatostatin are the hypoglycemic factors that counter and counterbalance the many hyperglycemic hormones.

Diabetes mellitus (DM) results from hyposecretion or hypoactivity of insulin. When insulin activity is absent or deficient, blood sugar levels remain high after a meal because glucose is unable to enter most tissue cells. Ordinarily, when blood sugar levels rise, hyperglycemic hormones are not released, but when hyperglycemia becomes excessive, the person begins to feel nauseated, which precipitates the fight-or-flight response. This results, inappropriately, in all the reactions that normally occur in the hypoglycemic (fasting) state to make glucose available—that is, glycogenolysis, lipolysis, and gluconeogenesis. Thus, the already high blood sugar levels rise even higher, and excesses of glucose begin to be lost from the body in the urine *(glycosuria).*

When sugars cannot be used as cellular fuel, more fats are mobilized resulting in lipidemia (high fatty acid levels in the blood). In severe cases of diabetes mellitus, blood levels of fatty acids and their metabolites (acetoacetic acid, acetone, and others) rise dramatically. The fatty acid metabolites, collectively called **ketones** (ke′tōnz) or **ketone bodies,** are strong organic acids. When they accumulate faster than they can be used or excreted, the blood pH drops, resulting in **ketoacidosis,** and ketones begin to spill into the urine *(ketonuria).* Severe ketoacidosis is life-threatening. The nervous system responds by initiating rapid deep breathing to blow off carbon dioxide from the blood and increase blood pH. (The physiological basis of this mechanism is explained in Chapter 23.) If untreated, ketoacidosis disrupts virtually all physiological processes, including heart activity and oxygen transport. Severe depression of the nervous system leads to coma and, finally, death.

The three cardinal signs of diabetes mellitus are polyuria, polydipsia, and polyphagia. The excessive glucose in the kidney filtrate acts as an osmotic diuretic, i.e., it inhibits water reabsorption by the kidney tubules, resulting in **polyuria,** a huge urine output that leads to decreased blood volume and dehydration. Serious electrolyte losses also occur because of the need to rid the body of excess ketones. Since ketones are negatively charged, they carry positive ions out with them; as a result, sodium and potassium ions are also lost from the body. Because of the electrolyte imbalance, the person gets abdominal pains and may vomit, and the stress reaction spirals even higher. Dehydration stimulates hypothalamic thirst centers, causing **polydipsia,** or excessive thirst. The final cardinal sign, **polyphagia,** refers to excessive hunger and food consumption, a sign that the person is "starving in the land of plenty." That is, although plenty of glucose is available, it cannot be used, and the body starts to utilize its fat and protein stores for energy metabolism. Figure 17.18 summarizes the consequences of insulin deficiency.

Two major forms of diabetes mellitus have been distinguished: type I and type II. *Type I diabetes mellitus,* or *insulin-dependent diabetes mellitus (IDDM),* was formerly known as *juvenile-onset diabetes.* The symptoms of type I diabetes appear suddenly, usually before the age of 15 years. However, a long asymptomatic period during which the beta cells are systemically destroyed by an autoimmune response precedes these symptoms.

It is likely that type 1 diabetes has several causes. Some investigators believe that *molecular mimicry* is the problem: Some foreign substance that has entered the body and has been recognized as an alien (and provoked an immune response) is so similar to some beta cell proteins that those self (β cell) proteins are also attacked by the immune system. A prime suspect for an environmental trigger is exposure to a specific fragment of albumin in cow's milk during the first few months of life in genetically susceptible infants. This albumin fragment is a look-alike of the *p69* protein that beta cells display on their surface when they are infected by viruses.

Elegant studies on mice have demonstrated that T cells have at least one other target, a specific enzyme called *glutamate decarboxylase (GAD)* present in the beta cells. GAD converts the amino acid glutamate into GABA, a key messenger between neurons and, to a lesser extent, between pancreatic cells. Because most of the body's GAD is in the brain, essentially hidden from the immune system, these researchers suggest that the immune system may not recognize GAD as a self-protein. Like the albumin fragment described above, a piece of GAD closely resembles a virus that has been associated with diabetes. GAD is probably not the whole answer either, but it appears to be an important part of it, because when mice prone to develop diabetes were injected with doses of GAD before the autoimmune attack on the pancreas began, all mice treated escaped developing diabetes.

Type I diabetics totally lack insulin activity, and their disease is difficult to control. Because of the early onset of their disease, type I diabetics typically exhibit long-term vascular and neural problems. The lipidemia and high blood cholesterol levels typical of the disease lead to vascular complications including atherosclerosis, strokes, heart attacks, renal shutdown, gangrene, and blindness. Consequences of neuropathies include loss of sensation, impaired bladder function, and impotence. Previously, the protocol was insulin injections once or twice daily to manage ketoacidosis and, to a lesser extent, hyperglycemia. Currently, the recommendation is for more intense control to reduce vascular and renal complications via more frequent insulin injections (up to four times daily) or insulin infusion delivered continuously by an insulin pump worn externally. Although pancreatic islet cell transplants have been somewhat successful in helping type I diabetics,

Organ response to insulin deficiency		Resulting condition of:		Signs and symptoms
		Blood	Urine	
	Decreased glucose uptake and utilization	Hyperglycemia	Glycosuria	**Polyuria** - dehydration - soft eyeballs
	Glycogenolysis		Osmotic diuresis	**Polydipsia** Fatigue
	Protein catabolism and gluconeogenesis			Weight loss **Polyphagia**
	Lipolysis and ketogenesis	Lipidemia and ketoacidosis	Ketonuria	Acetone breath Hyperpnea
			Loss of Na$^+$, K$^+$; electrolyte and acid-base imbalances	Nausea/vomiting/ abdominal pain Cardiac irregularities Central nervous system depression; coma

= Muscle   = Adipose tissue   = Liver

FIGURE 17.18
Symptomatic results of insulin deficit (diabetes mellitus).

the requirement for immunosuppression is a problem, particularly in young patients. Immune system manipulation to prevent the initial sensitization to the cross-reacting fragment now seems more promising.

Type II diabetes, or *non–insulin-dependent diabetes mellitus (NIDDM)* was formerly called *mature-onset diabetes* because it occurs mostly after the age of 40 years and is increasingly common with age. Heredity or a familial predisposition is particularly striking in this diabetic group. If an identical twin has type II diabetes mellitus, the probability that the other twin will have the disease is 100%. Most type II diabetics produce insulin, but the amount is inadequate or the insulin receptors are unable to respond to insulin, a phenomenon called **insulin resistance.** Type II diabetics are almost always overweight and account for over 90% of the known cases of diabetes mellitus. The link between obesity and DM has been obscure until recently. It now appears that adipose cells of obese people overproduce a hormonelike chemical called *tumor necrosis factor-alpha,* which depresses synthesis of a protein (glut4). Since glut4 enables glucose to pass through insulin-primed plasma membranes, cells cannot take up glucose in its absence. Ketosis is not a major problem for this group, and in many cases the symptoms can be managed solely by exercise and diet (weight loss).

Hyperinsulinism, or excessive insulin secretion, results in low blood sugar levels, or hypoglycemia. Hypoglycemia triggers the release of hyperglycemic hormones, which cause anxiety, nervousness, tremors, and a feeling of weakness. Insufficient glucose delivery to the brain causes disorientation, progressing to convulsions, unconsciousness, and even death. In rare cases, hyperinsulinism results from an islet cell tumor. More commonly, it is caused by an overdose of insulin and is easily treated by ingesting some sugar. •

The Gonads

The male and female **gonads** (see Figure 17.1) produce steroidal sex hormones, identical in every way to those produced by adrenal cortical cells. The major distinction is the source and relative amounts produced. The paired *ovaries* are small, oval organs located in the female's abdominopelvic cavity. Besides producing ova, or eggs, the ovaries produce **estrogens** and **progesterone** (pro-jes′tĕ-rōn). The estrogens are alone responsible for maturation of the reproductive organs and the appearance of the secondary sex characteristics of females at puberty. Acting with progesterone, estrogens promote breast development and cyclic changes in the uterine mucosa (the menstrual cycle).

The *testes,* located in an extra-abdominal skin pouch called the scrotum, produce sperm and male sex hormones, primarily **testosterone** (tes-tos′tĕ-rōn). During puberty, testosterone initiates the maturation of the male reproductive organs and the appearance of secondary sex characteristics and sex drive. In addition, testosterone is necessary for normal sperm production and maintains the reproductive organs in their mature functional state in adult males.

The release of gonadal hormones is regulated by gonadotropins, as described earlier. We will discuss the roles of the gonadal, placental, and gonadotropic hormones in detail in Chapters 28 and 29, where we consider the reproductive system and pregnancy.

The Pineal Gland

The tiny, pine cone–shaped **pineal gland** hangs from the roof of the third ventricle within the diencephalon (see Figure 17.1). Its secretory cells, called **pinealocytes,** are arranged in dense cords and clusters. Lying between clustered pinealocytes in adults are dense particles containing calcium salts ("brainsand" or "pineal sand"). These salts are radiopaque; hence, the pineal gland is a handy landmark for determining the orientation of the brain in X rays.

The endocrine function of the pineal gland is still somewhat of a mystery. Although many peptides and amines (including serotonin, norepinephrine, dopamine, and histamine) have been isolated from this minute gland, its only major secretory product is **melatonin** (mel″ah-to′nin). Melatonin concentrations in the blood wax and wane in a diurnal cycle. Peak levels occur during the night; lowest levels occur during daylight hours around noon.

The pineal gland indirectly receives input from the visual pathways concerning the intensity and duration of daylight. In some animals, mating behavior and gonadal size vary with changes in the relative lengths of light and dark periods, and melatonin mediates these effects. In children, melatonin may have an antigonadotropic effect, that is, it may inhibit precocious (too early) sexual maturation and, thus, affect the timing of puberty.

The *suprachiasmatic (SC) nucleus* of the hypothalamus, an area referred to as our "biological clock," is richly supplied with melatonin receptors, and exposure to bright light (known to suppress melatonin secretion) can reset the clock timing. Hence, changing melatonin levels may also be a means by which the day/night cycles influence physiological processes that show rhythmic variations, such as body temperature, sleep, appetite, and hypothalamic activity in general.

The Thymus

Located deep to the sternum in the thorax is the lobulated **thymus gland.** Large and conspicuous in infants and children, the thymus diminishes in size throughout adulthood. By old age, it is composed largely of adipose and fibrous connective tissues.

The major hormonal product of the thymic epithelial cells is a family of peptide hormones, including **thymopoietins** and **thymosins** (thi′mo-

sinz), which appear to be essential for the normal development of *T lymphocytes (T cells)* and the immune response. The role of thymic hormones is described in Chapter 22 with the discussion of the immune system.

OTHER ENDOCRINE STRUCTURES

Other endocrine cells occur within various organs of the body, including the following (Table 17.4):

1. **The heart.** The atria of the heart contain some specialized cardiac muscle cells that secrete **atrial natriuretic factor (ANF)** (na″tre-u-ret′ik; "producing salty urine"). This peptide hormone decreases blood volume, blood pressure, and blood sodium concentration when these parameters become elevated. ANF accomplishes this task by signaling the kidney to increase its production of salty urine and by inhibiting aldosterone release by the adrenal cortex (see Figure 17.13).

2. **The gastrointestinal tract.** *Enteroendocrine cells* are hormone-secreting cells scattered within the mucosa of organs of the gastrointestinal (GI) tract (e.g., stomach, small intestine). These scattered cells release a huge variety of amine and peptide hormones that help regulate a wide variety of digestive functions including (1) mobility and secretory activity of the GI tract, (2) gallbladder release of stored bile, and (3) regulation of local blood flow. Enteroendocrine cells are sometimes referred to as *paraneurons,* because they are similar in certain ways to neurons. Many of their hormones are chemically identical to neurotransmitters (e.g., serotonin and cholecystokinin) and, in some cases, the hormones simply diffuse to nearby target cells without first entering the bloodstream. A few examples of enteroendocrine cell hormones are provided in Table 17.4; these hormones are described in more detail in Chapter 24.

3. **The placenta.** Besides sustaining the fetus during pregnancy, the placenta secretes several steroid and protein hormones that influence the course of pregnancy (Chapter 29). Placental hormones include estrogens and progesterone (hormones more often associated with the ovary), as well as human chorionic gonadotropin, and others.

4. **The kidney.** As yet unidentified cells in the kidney secrete **erythropoietin** (ĕ-rith″ro-poi′ĕ-tin; "redmaker"). This protein hormone signals the bone marrow to increase its production of red blood cells.

5. **The skin.** The skin produces **cholecalciferol,** an inactive form of vitamin D_3, when modified cholesterol molecules in epidermal cells are exposed to ultraviolet radiation. This compound then enters the blood via the dermal capillaries, is modified in the liver, and becomes fully activated in the kidney. The active form of vitamin D_3, (1,25-dihydroxycholecalcif-

Table 17.4 Some Examples of Hormones Produced by Organs Other Than the Major Endocrine Organs

Source	Hormone	Chemical composition	Trigger	Target organ/effects
GI tract mucosa				
• Stomach	Gastrin	Peptide	Secreted in response to food	Stomach: stimulates glands to release hydrochloric acid (HCl)
• Stomach	Serotonin	Peptide	Secreted in response to food	Stomach: causes contraction of stomach muscle
• Duodenum of small intestine	Intestinal gastrin	Peptide	Secreted in response to food, especially fats	Stomach: inhibits HCl secretion and gastrointestinal tract mobility
• Duodenum	Secretin	Peptide	Secreted in response to food	Pancreas: stimulates release of bicarbonate-rich juice; liver: increases release of bile; stomach: inhibits secretory activity
• Duodenum	Cholecystokinin	Peptide	Secreted in response to food	Pancreas: stimulates release of enzyme-rich juice; gallbladder: stimulates expulsion of stored bile; sphincter of Oddi: causes sphincter to relax, allowing bile and pancreatic juice to enter duodenum
Kidney	Erythropoietin (EPO)	Glycoprotein	Erythropoietin secreted in response to hypoxia	Bone marrow: stimulates production of red blood cells
Skin (epidermal cells)	Cholecalciferol (provitamin D_3)	Steroid	Cholecalciferol activated by the kidneys to active vitamin D_3 (1,25(OH) D_3) and released in response to parathyroid hormone	Intestine: stimulates active transport of dietary calcium across intestinal cell membranes
Heart (atria)	Atrial natriuretic factor	Peptide	Secreted in response to stretching of atria (by rising blood pressure)	Kidney: inhibits sodium ion resorption and renin release; adrenal cortex: inhibits secretion of aldosterone

erol or 1,25 (OH) D_3) is an essential part of the carrier system that enables intestinal cells to absorb Ca^{2+} from the diet. Without this vitamin, the bones become weak and soft.

DEVELOPMENTAL ASPECTS OF THE ENDOCRINE SYSTEM

Hormone-producing glands arise from all three embryonic germ layers. Mesoderm-derived endocrine glands produce steroid hormones. All others produce amines or amino acid and protein hormones.

Barring hypersecretory and hyposecretory disorders, most endocrine organs operate smoothly throughout life until old age. Aging may bring about changes in the rates of hormone secretion, breakdown, and excretion, or in the sensitivity of target cell receptors to their hormones. Research on usual endocrine functioning in the elderly is difficult, however, because functioning is frequently altered by the chronic illnesses common in that age group.

Structural changes in the anterior pituitary occur with age; the amount of connective tissue increases,

vascularization decreases, and the number of hormone-secreting cells declines. This may or may not affect hormone production. For example, blood levels and the release rhythm of ACTH remain constant, whereas levels of TSH and gonadotropins increase with age. GH levels decline, which partially explains muscle atrophy in old age. Recently, endocrinologists have discovered an exciting effect of GH supplementation. When aging clients received injections of genetically engineered GH in clinical tests over a period of 6 months, the injections dramatically spurred muscle growth, reduced body fat, and wiped 20 years off the elders' sagging physiques!

The adrenal gland also shows structural changes with age, but normal controls of cortisol appear to persist as long as a person is healthy. Plasma levels of aldosterone are reduced by half in old age; however, this may reflect a decline in renin release by the kidneys, which become less responsive to renin-evoking stimuli. No age-related differences have been found in the release of catecholamines by the adrenal medulla.

The gonads, particularly the ovaries, undergo significant weight changes with age. In late middle age,

Making Connections

Systems Connections: Homeostatic Interrelationships Between the Endocrine System and Other Body Systems

Nervous System
- Many hormones (growth hormone, thyroxine, sex hormones) influence normal maturation and function of the nervous system
- Hypothalamus controls anterior pituitary function and produces two hormones

Cardiovascular System
- Several hormones influence blood volume, blood pressure, and heart contractility; erythropoietin stimulates red blood cell production
- Blood is the transport medium of hormones; heart produces atrial natriuretic factor

Lymphatic System/immunity
- Lymphocytes "programmed" by thymic hormones seed the lymph nodes; glucocorticoids depress the immune response and inflammation
- Lymph provides a route for transport of hormones

Respiratory System
- Epinephrine influences ventilation (dilates bronchioles)
- Respiratory system provides oxygen; disposes of carbon dioxide; converting enzyme in lungs converts angiotensin I to angiotensin II

Digestive System
- Local GI hormones influence GI function; activated vitamin D necessary for absorption of calcium from diet; catecholamines influence digestive mobility and secretory activity
- Digestive system provides nutrients to endocrine organs

Urinary System
- Aldosterone and ADH influence renal function; erythropoietin released by kidneys influences red blood cell formation
- Kidneys activate vitamin D (considered a hormone)

Reproductive System
- Hypothalamic, anterior pituitary, and gonadal hormones direct reproductive system development and function; oxytocin and prolactin involved in birth and nursing
- Gonadal hormones feed back to influence endocrine system function

Integumentary System
- Androgens cause activation of sebaceous glands; estrogen increases skin hydration
- Skin produces cholecalciferol (provitamin D)

Skeletal System
- PTH and calcitonin regulate calcium blood levels; growth hormone, T_3, T_4, and sex hormones are necessary for normal skeletal development
- The skeleton provides some protection to endocrine organs, especially to those in the brain, chest, and pelvis

Muscular System
- Growth hormone is essential for normal muscular development; other hormones (thyroxine and calecholamines) influence muscle metabolism.
- Muscular system mechanically protects some endocrine glands; muscular activity elicits catecholamine release

Closer Connections: The Endocrine System and Interrelationships with the Nervous and Reproductive Systems

Like most body systems, the endocrine system performs many functions that benefit the body as a whole. For example, without insulin, thyroxine, and various other metabolic hormones, body cells would be unable to get or use glucose, and would die. Likewise, total body growth is beholden to the endocrine system, which coordinates the growth spurts with increases in skeletal and muscular mass so that we don't look out of proportion most of the time. But the interactions that are most noticeable and crucial are those that the endocrine system has with the nervous and the reproductive systems and they begin before birth.

Nervous System

The influence of hormones on behavior is striking. While we are still in the wet darkness of our mother's uterus, testosterone—or lack of it—is determining the "sex" of our brain. If testosterone is produced by the exceedingly tiny male testes, then certain areas of the brain enlarge, develop large numbers of androgen receptors, and thereafter determine the so-called masculine aspects of behavior (aggressiveness, etc.). Conversely, in the absence of testosterone, the brain is feminized. At puberty, Mom and Dad's "little angels," driven by ranging hormonal hills and valleys, turn into strangers. The surge of androgens—produced first by the adrenal cortices, and then by the maturing gonads—produces an often thoughtless aggressiveness and galloping sex drive—typically long before the cognitive abilities of the brain can rein them in.

Neural involvement in hormonal affairs is no less striking. Not only is the hypothalamus an endocrine organ in its own right, it also effectively regulates the bulk of hormonal activity via hormonal controls of the anterior pituitary and neural controls of the posterior pituitary and adrenal medulla. And that's just on a normal day. The effects of trauma on the hypothalamic-pituitary axis can be far-reaching. Lack of loving care to a newborn baby results in failure to thrive; exceptionally vigorous athletic training in the pubertal female can result in bone wasting and infertility; and overwhelming, prolonged emotional stress on almost anyone can lead to Addison's disease (corticosteroid burnout). The shadow the nervous system casts over the endocrine system is long indeed.

Reproductive System

The reproductive system is totally dependent on hormones to "order up the right organs" to match our genetic sex. Testosterone secretion by the testes of male embryos directs formation of the male reproductive tract and external genitalia. Without testosterone, female structures develop—regardless of whether the gonads are testes or ovaries. The next crucial period is puberty, when gonadal sex hormone production rises and steers maturation of the reproductive organs, bringing them to their adult structure and function. Without these hormonal signals, the reproductive organs remain childlike and the person cannot produce offspring. Pregnancy invites more endocrine system interactions with the reproductive system. The placenta, a temporary endocrine organ, churns out estrogen and progesterone, which help maintain the pregnancy and prepare the mother's breasts for lactation, as well as a number of other hormones that influence maternal metabolism. During and after birth, oxytocin and prolactin take center stage to promote labor and delivery, and then milk production and ejection. Other than feedback inhibition exerted by its sex hormones on the hypothalamic-pituitary axis, the influence of reproductive organs on the endocrine system is negligible.

Clinical Connections

Endocrine System

Case study: We have a new patient to consider today. Mr. Gutteman, a 70-year-old male, was brought into the ER in a comatose state and has yet to come out of it. It is obvious that he suffered severe head trauma—his scalp was badly lacerated, and he has an impacted skull fracture. His initial lab tests (blood and urine) were within normal limits. His fracture was repaired and the following orders (and several others) were given:

• Check qh (every hour) and record: spontaneous behavior, level of responsiveness to stimulation, movements, pupil size and reaction to light, speech, and vital signs.

• Turn patient q4h and maintain meticulous skin care and dryness.

Explain the rationale behind these orders.

On the second day of his hospitalization, the aide reports that Mr. Gutteman is breathing irregularly, his skin is dry and flaccid, and that she has emptied his urine reservoir several times during the day. Upon receiving this information, the physician ordered:

• Blood and urine tests for presence of sugar and ketones

• Strict I&O (fluid intake and output recording)

Mr. Gutteman is found to be losing huge amounts of water in urine and the volume lost is being routinely replaced (via IV line). Mr. Gutteman's blood and urine tests are negative for sugar and ketones.

Relative to these findings:

1. What would you say Mr. Gutteman's hormonal problem is and what do you think caused it?

2. Is it life threatening? (Explain your answer.)

the ovaries decrease in size and weight, and they become insensitive to gonadotropins. As female hormone production declines dramatically, the ability to bear children ends, and problems associated with estrogen deficiency, such as arteriosclerosis and osteoporosis, begin to occur. Testosterone production by the testes also wanes with age, but this effect usually is not seen until very old age.

Glucose tolerance (the ability to dispose of a glucose load effectively) begins to deteriorate as early as the fourth decade of life. Blood glucose levels rise higher and return to resting levels slower in the elderly than in young adults. *Glucose tolerance tests* reveal that a high proportion of elderly have *chemical,* or *borderline, diabetes.* Since near-normal amounts of insulin continue to be secreted by the islet cells, it is believed that the decreasing glucose tolerance reflects a declining receptor sensitivity to insulin (pre–type II diabetes).

The synthesis and release of thyroid hormones diminishes somewhat with age. Typically, the follicles are loaded with colloid in the elderly, and fibrosis of the gland occurs. Basal metabolic rate declines with age, but mild hypothyroidism is only one cause of this decline. The increase in body fat relative to muscle is equally important, since muscle tissue is more active metabolically (uses much more oxygen) than fat.

The parathyroid glands change little with age, and PTH levels remain at fairly normal values. While estrogen protects women against the demineralizing effects of PTH, after menopause estrogen production wanes, leaving older women more vulnerable to the bone-demineralizing effects of PTH and osteoporosis (see Chapter 6, p. 172).

*   *   *

In this chapter, we have covered the general mechanisms of hormone action and have provided an overview of the major endocrine organs, their chief targets, and their most important physiological effects, as summarized in *Making Connections* on p. 578. However, every one of the hormones discussed here comes up in at least one other chapter in this text, where its actions are described as part of the functional framework of a particular organ system. For example, the effects of PTH and calcitonin on bone mineralization are described in Chapter 6 along with the discussion of bone remodeling, and gonadal hormones take center stage as the regulators of reproductive system maturation and function in Chapters 28 and 29.

RELATED CLINICAL TERMS

Hirsutism (her′soot-izm; *hirsut* = hairy, rough) Excessive hair growth; usually refers to this phenomenon in women and reflects excessive androgen production.

Hypophysectomy (hi-pof″i-sek′to-me) Surgical removal of the pituitary gland.

Prolactinoma (pro-lak″tĭ-no′mah; *oma* = tumor) The most common type (30% to 40% or more) of pituitary gland tumor; evidenced by hypersecretion of prolactin and menstrual disturbances in women.

Psychosocial dwarfism Dwarfism (and failure to thrive) resulting from stress and emotional disorders that suppress hypothalamic release of growth hormone–releasing hormone and thus anterior pituitary secretion of growth hormone.

Thyroid storm (thyroid crisis) A sudden and dangerous increase in all of the symptoms of hyperthyroidism due to excessive amounts of circulating TH; symptoms of this hypermetabolic state include fever, rapid heart rate, high blood pressure, dehydration, nervousness, and tremors; precipitating factors include stressful situations, excessive intake of TH supplements, and trauma to the thyroid gland.

CHAPTER SUMMARY

1. The nervous and endocrine systems are the major controlling systems of the body. The nervous system exerts rapid controls via nerve impulses; the endocrine system's effects are mediated by hormones and are more prolonged.

The Endocrine System and Hormone Function: An Overview (pp. 547–548)

1. Endocrine organs are ductless, well-vascularized glands that release hormones directly into the blood or lymph. They are small and widely separated in the body.

2. The major endocrine organs are the pituitary, thyroid, parathyroid, adrenal, pineal, and thymus glands, as well as the pancreas and gonads. The hypothalamus is a neuroendocrine organ.

3. Hormonally regulated processes include reproduction; growth and development; mobilization of body defenses to stressors; maintenance of electrolyte, water, and nutrient balance; and regulation of cellular metabolism.

Hormones (pp. 548–553)
The Chemistry of Hormones (p. 548)

1. Most hormones are steroids or amino acid derivatives.

Hormone–Target Cell Specificity (p. 548)

2. The ability of a target cell to respond to a hormone depends on the presence of receptors, within the cell or on its plasma membrane, to which the hormone can bind.

3. Hormone receptors are dynamic structures. Changes in number and sensitivity of hormone receptors may occur in response to high or low levels of stimulating hormones.

Mechanisms of Hormone Action (pp. 548–551)

4. Hormones alter cell activity by stimulating or inhibiting characteristic cellular processes.

5. Cell responses to hormone stimulation may involve changes in membrane permeability, enzyme synthesis, activation or inhibition, secretory activity, gene activation, and others.

6. Second-messenger mechanisms employing intracellular messengers and transduced by G proteins are a common means by which protein, peptide, and amine hormones interact with their target cells. In the cyclic AMP system, the hormone binds to a plasma membrane receptor coupled to adenylate cyclase, which catalyzes the synthesis of cyclic AMP from ATP. Cyclic AMP initiates reactions in which protein kinases and other enzymes are activated, leading to the cellular response. The phosphatidyl inositol mechanism is another important second-messenger system. Other presumed "messengers" are cyclic GMP and calcium.

7. Steroid hormones (and thyroid hormone) enter their target cells and effect responses by activating DNA, initiating messenger RNA formation leading to protein synthesis.

Half-Life, Onset, and Duration of Hormone Activity (p. 551)

8. Blood levels of hormones reflect a balance between secretion and degradation/excretion. The liver and kidneys are the major organs that degrade hormones; breakdown products are excreted in urine and feces.

9. Hormone half-life and duration of activity are limited and vary from hormone to hormone.

Control of Hormone Release (pp. 551–553)

10. Endocrine organs are activated to release their hormones by humoral, neural, or hormonal stimuli. Negative feedback is important in regulating hormone levels in the blood.

11. The nervous system, acting through hypothalamic controls, can in certain cases override or modulate hormonal effects.

Major Endocrine Organs (pp. 553–576)
The Pituitary Gland (Hypophysis) (pp. 553–561)

1. The pituitary gland hangs from the base of the brain by a stalk and is enclosed by bone. It consists of a hormone-producing glandular portion (anterior pituitary) and a neural portion (posterior pituitary), which is an extension of the hypothalamus.

2. The hypothalamus (a) regulates the hormonal output of the anterior pituitary via releasing and inhibiting hormones and (b) synthesizes two hormones that it exports to the posterior pituitary for storage and later release.

3. Four of the six adenohypophyseal hormones are tropic hormones that regulate the function of other endocrine organs. Most anterior pituitary hormones exhibit a diurnal rhythm of release, which is subject to modification by stimuli influencing the hypothalamus.

4. Growth hormone (GH) is an anabolic hormone that stimulates growth of all body tissues but especially skeletal muscle and bone. It may act directly or indirectly via somatomedins. GH mobilizes fats, stimulates protein synthesis, and inhibits glucose uptake and metabolism. Secretion is regulated by growth hormone–releasing hormone (GHRH) and growth hormone–inhibiting hormone (GHIH), or somatostatin. Hypersecretion causes gigantism in children and acromegaly in adults; hyposecretion in children causes pituitary dwarfism.

5. Thyroid-stimulating hormone (TSH) promotes normal development and activity of the thyroid gland. Thyrotropin-releasing hormone (TRH) stimulates its release; negative feedback of thyroid hormone inhibits it.

6. Adrenocorticotropic hormone (ACTH) stimulates the adrenal cortex to release corticosteroids. ACTH release is triggered by corticotropin-releasing hormone (CRH) and inhibited by feedback inhibition of rising glucocorticoid levels.

7. The gonadotropins, follicle-stimulating hormone (FSH) and luteinizing hormone (LH), regulate the functions of the gonads in both sexes. FSH stimulates sex cell production; LH stimulates gonadal hormone production. Gonadotropin levels rise in response to gonadotropin-releasing hormone (GnRH). Negative feedback of gonadal hormones inhibits gonadotropin release.

8. Prolactin (PRL) promotes milk production in humans. Its secretion is prompted by prolactin-releasing hormone (PRH) and inhibited by prolactin-inhibiting hormone (PIH).

9. The neurohypophysis stores and releases two hypothalamic hormones, oxytocin and antidiuretic hormone (ADH).

10. Oxytocin stimulates powerful uterine contractions, which trigger labor and delivery of an infant, and milk ejection in nursing women. It also appears to promote sexual arousal and nurturing. Its release is mediated reflexively by the hypothalamus and represents a positive feedback mechanism.

11. Antidiuretic hormone stimulates the kidney tubules to reabsorb and conserve water; as urine output declines, blood volume and blood pressure rise. ADH is released in response to high solute concentrations in the blood and inhibited by low solute concentrations in the blood. Hyposecretion results in diabetes insipidus.

The Thyroid Gland (pp. 561–565)

12. The thyroid gland is located in the anterior throat. Thyroid follicles store thyroglobulin, a colloid from which thyroid hormone is derived.

13. Thyroid hormone (TH) includes thyroxine (T_4) and triiodothyronine (T_3), which increase the rate of cellular metabolism. Consequently, oxygen use and heat production rise.

14. Secretion of thyroid hormone, prompted by TSH, requires reuptake of the stored colloid by the follicle cells and splitting of the hormones from the colloid for release. Rising levels of thyroid hormone feed back to inhibit the pituitary and hypothalamus.

15. Most T_4 is converted to T_3 (the more active form) in the target tissues. These hormones appear to act via a steroidlike mechanism.

16. Hypersecretion of thyroid hormone results most importantly in Graves's disease; hyposecretion causes cretinism in infants and myxedema in adults.

17. Calcitonin, produced by the parafollicular cells of the thyroid gland in response to rising blood calcium levels, depresses blood calcium levels by inhibiting bone matrix resorption and enhancing calcium deposit in bone.

The Parathyroid Glands (pp. 565–566)

18. The parathyroid glands, located on the dorsal aspect of the thyroid gland, secrete parathyroid hormone (PTH), which causes an increase in blood calcium levels by targeting bone, the intestine, and the kidneys. PTH is the antagonist of calcitonin.

19. PTH release is triggered by falling blood calcium levels and is inhibited by rising blood calcium levels.

20. Hyperparathyroidism results in hypercalcemia and all its effects and in extreme bone wasting. Hypoparathyroidism leads to hypocalcemia, evidenced by tetany and respiratory paralysis.

The Adrenal (Suprarenal) Glands (pp. 566–571)

21. The paired adrenal (suprarenal) glands sit atop the kidneys. Each adrenal gland has two functional portions, the cortex and the medulla.

22. Three groups of steroid hormones are produced by the cortex from cholesterol.

23. Mineralocorticoids (primarily aldosterone) regulate sodium ion resorption by the kidneys and thus indirectly regulate levels of other electrolytes that are coupled to sodium transport. Release of aldosterone is stimulated by the renin-angiotensin mechanism, rising potassium ion or falling sodium levels in the blood, and ACTH. Atrial natriuretic factor inhibits aldosterone release.

24. Glucocorticoids (primarily cortisol) are important metabolic hormones that enable the body to resist stressors by increasing blood glucose, fatty acid, and amino acid levels and enhancing blood pressure. High levels of glucocorticoids depress the immune system and the inflammatory response. ACTH is the major stimulus for glucocorticoid release.

25. Gonadocorticoids (mainly androgens) are produced in small amounts throughout life.

26. Hypoactivity of the adrenal cortex results in Addison's disease. Hypersecretion can result in aldosteronism, Cushing's disease, and/or masculinization.

27. The adrenal medulla produces catecholamines (epinephrine and norepinephrine) in response to sympathetic nervous system stimulation. Its catecholamines enhance and prolong the fight-or-flight response to short-term stressors. Hypersecretion leads to symptoms typical of sympathetic nervous system overactivity.

The Pancreas (pp. 571–575)

28. The pancreas, located in the abdomen close to the stomach, is both an exocrine and an endocrine gland. The endocrine portion (pancreatic islets) releases insulin and glucagon (plus pancreatic polypeptide and amylin) to the blood.

29. Glucagon, released by alpha (α) cells when blood levels of glucose are low, stimulates the liver to release glucose to the blood.

30. Insulin is released by beta (β) cells when blood levels of glucose (and amino acids) are rising. It increases the rate of glucose uptake and metabolism by most body cells. Hyposecretion of insulin results in diabetes mellitus; cardinal signs are polyuria, polydipsia, and polyphagia.

The Gonads (pp. 575–576)

31. The ovaries of the female, located in the pelvic cavity, release two main hormones. Secretion of estrogens by the ovarian follicles begins at puberty under the influence of FSH. Estrogens stimulate maturation of the female reproductive system and development of the secondary sex characteristics. Progesterone is released in response to high blood levels of LH. It works with estrogens in establishing the menstrual cycle.

32. The testes of the male begin to produce testosterone at puberty in response to LH. Testosterone promotes maturation of the male reproductive organs, development of secondary sex characteristics, and production of sperm by the testes.

The Pineal Gland (p. 576)

33. The pineal gland is located in the diencephalon. Its primary hormone is melatonin, which influences daily rhythms and may have an antigonadotropic effect in humans.

The Thymus (p. 576)

34. The thymus gland, located in the upper thorax, declines in size and function with age. Its hormones, thymosins and thymopoietins, are important to the normal development of the immune response.

Other Endocrine Structures (pp. 576–577)

1. Many body organs not normally considered endocrine organs contain isolated cell clusters that secrete hormones. Examples include the heart (atrial natriuretic factor); gastrointestinal tract organs (gastrin, secretin, and others); the placenta (hormones of pregnancy—estrogen, progesterone, and others); the kidneys (erythropoietin); and skin (cholecalciferol).

Developmental Aspects of the Endocrine System (pp. 577–580)

1. Endocrine glands are derived from all three germ layers. Those derived from mesoderm produce steroidal hormones; the others produce the amino acid–based hormones.

2. The natural decrease in function of the female's ovaries during late middle age results in menopause.

3. The efficiency of all endocrine glands seems to decrease gradually as aging occurs. This leads to a generalized increase in the incidence of diabetes mellitus and a lower metabolic rate.

REVIEW QUESTIONS

Multiple Choice/Matching

1. The major stimulus for release of parathyroid hormone is (a) hormonal, (b) humoral, (c) neural.

2. Choose from the following key to identify the hormones described.

Key: (a) aldosterone   **(e)** oxytocin
     (b) antidiuretic hormone   **(f)** prolactin
     (c) growth hormone   **(g)** T_4 and T_3
     (d) luteinizing hormone   **(h)** TSH

———— **(1)** important anabolic hormone; many of its effects mediated by somatomedin

———— **(2)** involved in water balance; causes the kidneys to conserve water

———— **(3)** stimulates milk production

———— **(4)** tropic hormone that stimulates the gonads to secrete sex hormones

———— **(5)** increases uterine contractions during birth

———— **(6)** major metabolic hormone(s) of the body

———— **(7)** causes reabsorption of sodium ions by the kidneys

———— **(8)** tropic hormone that stimulates the thyroid gland to secrete thyroid hormone

———— **(9)** a hormone secreted by the neurohypophysis (two possible choices)

———— **(10)** the only steroid hormone in the list

3. The anterior pituitary secretes all but (a) antidiuretic hormone, (b) growth hormone, (c) gonadotropins, (d) TSH.

4. A hormone *not* involved in sugar metabolism is (a) glucagon, (b) cortisone, (c) aldosterone, (d) insulin.

5. Parathyroid hormone (a) increases bone formation and lowers blood calcium levels, (b) increases calcium excretion from the body, (c) decreases calcium absorption from the gut, (d) demineralizes bone and raises blood calcium levels.

6. A hypodermic injection of epinephrine would (a) increase heart rate, increase blood pressure, dilate the bronchi of the lungs, and increase peristalsis, (b) decrease heart rate, decrease blood pressure, constrict the bronchi, and increase peristalsis, (c) decrease heart rate, increase blood pressure, constrict the bronchi, and decrease peristalsis, (d) increase heart rate, increase blood pressure, dilate the bronchi, and decrease peristalsis.

7. Testosterone is to the male as what hormone is to the female? (a) luteinizing hormone, (b) progesterone, (c) estrogens, (d) prolactin.

8. If anterior pituitary secretion is deficient in a growing child, the child will (a) develop acromegaly, (b) become a dwarf but have fairly normal body proportions, (c) mature sexually at an earlier than normal age, (d) be in constant danger of becoming dehydrated.

9. If there is adequate carbohydrate intake, secretion of insulin results in (a) lower blood sugar levels, (b) increased cell utilization of glucose, (c) storage of glycogen, (d) all of these.

10. Hormones (a) are produced by exocrine glands, (b) are carried to all parts of the body in blood, (c) remain at constant concentration in the blood, (d) affect only non–hormone-producing organs.

11. Some hormones act by (a) increasing the synthesis of enzymes, (b) converting an inactive enzyme into an active enzyme, (c) affecting only specific target organs, (d) all of these.

12. Absence of thyroxine would result in (a) increased heart rate and increased force of heart contraction, (b) depression of the CNS and lethargy, (c) exophthalmos, (d) high metabolic rate.

13. Chromaffin cells are found in the (a) parathyroid gland, (b) anterior pituitary gland, (c) adrenal gland, (d) pineal gland.

14. The hormone secreted by the heart, atrial natriuretic factor, has exactly the opposite function of this hormone secreted by the zona glomerulosa: (a) antidiuretic hormone, (b) epinephrine, (c) calcitonin, (d) aldosterone, (e) androgens.

Short Answer Essay Questions

15. Define hormone.

16. (a) Describe the body location of each of the following endocrine organs: anterior pituitary, pineal gland, pancreas, ovaries, testes, and adrenal glands. (b) List the hormones produced by each organ.

17. Name two endocrine glands (or regions) that are important in the stress response, and explain why they are important.

18. The anterior pituitary is often referred to as the master endocrine organ, but it, too, has a "master." What controls the release of anterior pituitary hormones?

19. The posterior pituitary is not really an endocrine gland. Why not? What is it?

20. A colloidal, or endemic, goiter is not really the result of malfunction of the thyroid gland. What does cause it?

21. List some problems that elderly people might have as a result of decreasing hormone production.

22. Name a hormone secreted by a muscle cell and two hormones secreted by neurons.

CRITICAL THINKING AND CLINICAL APPLICATION QUESTIONS

1. Richard Neis had symptoms of excessive secretion of parathyroid hormone (high blood calcium levels), and his physicians were certain he had a parathyroid gland tumor. Yet when surgery was performed on his neck, the surgeon could not find the parathyroid glands at all. Where should the surgeon look next to find the tumorous parathyroid gland?

2. Mary Morgan has just been brought into the emergency room of City General Hospital. She is perspiring profusely and is breathing rapidly and irregularly. Her breath smells like acetone (sweet and fruity), and her blood sugar tests out at 650 mg/100 ml blood. She is in acidosis. What hormone drug should be administered, and why?

3. Johnny, a five-year-old boy, has been growing by leaps and bounds. His height is 100% above normal for his age group and recently he has been complaining of headaches and vision problems. A CT scan reveals a large pituitary tumor. (a) What hormone is being secreted in excess? (b) What name is given to the condition that Johnny will exhibit if corrective measures are not taken? (c) What is the probable cause of his headaches and visual problems?

4. On the morning of February 27, 1991, as Martina sat lazily scanning the morning newspaper, a headline caught her eye— "Anabolic steroids declared a controlled substance." Hmm, she thought, that's interesting . . . it's about time those drugs got put in the same class with heroin . . . and then continued her browse through the paper. That night, Martina awoke from a dream in a cold sweat. In her dream it seemed that all her male friends and colleagues were being rounded up by government drug agents and charged with illegal possession of a controlled substance. What is the connection, if any, between the morning headline and Martina's bizarre dream?

18

Blood

CHAPTER OUTLINE AND STUDENT OBJECTIVES

Overview: Composition and Functions of Blood (pp. 585–586)

1. Describe the composition and physical characteristics of whole blood. Explain why it is classified as a connective tissue.

2. List six functions of blood.

Blood Plasma (pp. 586–587)

3. Discuss the composition and functions of plasma.

Formed Elements (pp. 587–598)

4. Describe the structural characteristics, function, and production of erythrocytes.

5. List the classes, structural characteristics, and functions of leukocytes. Also describe leukocyte genesis.

6. Describe the structure and function of platelets.

7. Give examples of disorders caused by abnormalities of each of the formed elements. Explain the mechanism of each disorder.

Hemostasis (pp. 598–604)

8. Describe the process of hemostasis. Indicate the factors that limit clot formation and prevent undesirable clotting.

9. Give examples of hemostatic disorders. Note the cause of each condition.

Transfusion and Blood Replacement (pp. 604–607)

10. Describe the ABO and Rh blood groups. Explain the basis of transfusion reactions.

11. List several examples of blood expanders. Describe their function and the circumstances in which they are usually used.

Diagnostic Blood Tests (p. 607)

12. Explain the importance of blood testing as a diagnostic tool.

Developmental Aspects of Blood (p. 607)

13. Describe changes in the sites of blood production and in the type of hemoglobin produced after birth.

14. Name some blood disorders that become more common with age.

Blood is the river of life that surges within us, transporting nearly everything that must be carried from one place to another within the body. Long before modern medicine, blood was viewed as magical, an elixir that held the mystical life force—for when blood drained from the body, life departed as well. Today, centuries later, blood retains enormous importance in the practice of medicine. Clinicians examine this tissue more often than any other to determine the cause of ill health and disease.

In this chapter, we describe the composition and functions of this life-sustaining fluid that serves as a transport "vehicle" for the organs of the cardiovascular system. To get started, we need a brief overview of blood circulation. Blood leaves the *heart* via *arteries,* which branch repeatedly until they become tiny *capillaries.* By moving across the capillary walls, oxygen and nutrients leave the blood and enter the body tissues, and carbon dioxide and wastes move from the tissues to the bloodstream. As oxygen-deficient blood leaves the capillary beds, it flows into *veins,* which return it to the heart. Blood flows from the heart to the lungs, where it picks up oxygen and then returns to the heart to be pumped throughout the body once again. Now let us look more closely at the nature of blood.

OVERVIEW: COMPOSITION AND FUNCTIONS OF BLOOD

Components

Blood is unique in that it is the only fluid tissue in the body. Although blood appears to be a thick, homogeneous liquid, it has both solid and liquid components. Blood is a specialized type of connective tissue in which living blood cells, the **formed elements,** are suspended in a nonliving fluid matrix called **plasma** (plaz'mah). The collagen and elastic fibers typical of other connective tissues are absent from blood, but dissolved fibrous proteins become visible as fibrin strands when blood clotting occurs.

If a sample of blood is spun in a centrifuge, the heavier formed elements are packed down by centrifugal force and the less dense plasma remains at the top (Figure 18.1). Most of the reddish mass at the bottom of the tube consists of *erythrocytes* (ĕ-rith'ro-sīts; *erythro* = red), the red blood cells that transport oxygen. A thin, whitish layer called the **buffy coat** is present at the erythrocyte-plasma junction. This layer contains *leukocytes* (*leuko* = white), the white blood cells that act in various ways to protect the body, and *platelets,* cell fragments that help stop bleeding. Erythrocytes normally constitute about 45% of the total volume of a blood sample, a percentage known as the **hematocrit** (he-mat'o-krit; "blood fraction"). Leukocytes and platelets contribute less than 1% of blood volume. Plasma makes up most of the remaining 55% of whole blood.

Physical Characteristics and Volume

Blood is a sticky, opaque fluid with a characteristic metallic taste. As children, we discover its saltiness the first time we stick a cut finger into our mouth. Depending on the amount of oxygen it is carrying, the color of blood varies from scarlet (oxygen-rich) to a dark red (oxygen-poor). Blood is more dense (heavier) than water and about five times more viscous, largely because of its formed elements. Blood is slightly alkaline, with a pH between 7.35 and 7.45. Its temperature is always slightly higher than body temperature (38°C or 100.4°F).

Blood accounts for approximately 8% of body weight. Its average volume in healthy adult males (5–6 L) is somewhat greater than in healthy adult females (4–5 L).

Functions

Blood performs a number of functions, all concerned in one way or another with substance distribution, regulation of blood levels of particular substances, or body protection. These functions overlap and interact to maintain the constancy of our internal environment.

Distribution

The *distribution functions* of blood include:

- Delivering oxygen from the lungs and nutrients from the digestive tract to all body cells.

Withdraw blood

Place in tube

Centrifuge

Plasma (55% of whole blood)

Buffy coat: leukocytes and platelets (<1% of whole blood)

Erythrocytes (45% of whole blood)

Formed elements

FIGURE 18.1
Major components of whole blood.

- Transporting metabolic waste products from cells to elimination sites (to the lungs for elimination of carbon dioxide, and to the kidneys for disposal of nitrogenous wastes in urine).

- Transporting hormones from the endocrine organs to their target organs.

Regulation

The *regulatory functions* of blood include:

- Maintaining appropriate body temperature by absorbing and distributing heat throughout the body and to the skin surface for dissipation of excess.

- Maintaining normal pH in body tissues. Many blood proteins and other blood-borne solutes act as buffers to prevent excessive or abrupt changes in blood pH, which could jeopardize normal cellular activities. Additionally, blood acts as the reservoir for the body's "alkaline reserve" of bicarbonate atoms.

- Maintaining adequate fluid volume in the circulatory system. Sodium chloride and other salts act with blood proteins, such as albumin, to prevent excessive fluid loss from the bloodstream into the tissue spaces. As a result, the fluid volume in the blood vessels remains ample to provide a source of water for tissue cells and to support efficient blood circulation to all parts of the body.

Protection

The *protective functions* of blood include:

- Preventing blood loss. When a blood vessel is damaged, platelets and plasma proteins initiate clot formation, halting blood loss.

- Preventing infection. Drifting along in blood are antibodies, complement proteins, and white blood cells, all of which help defend the body against foreign invaders such as bacteria and viruses.

BLOOD PLASMA

Blood plasma is a straw-colored, sticky fluid (see Figure 18.1). Although it is about 90% water, plasma contains over 100 different dissolved solutes. These include nutrients, gases, hormones, various wastes and products of cell activity, ions, and proteins (albumin, clotting proteins, and globulins). Table 18.1 summarizes the major plasma components.

Plasma proteins, accounting for about 8% by weight of plasma volume, are the most abundant plasma solutes. Except for blood-borne hormones and gamma globulins, most plasma proteins are produced by the liver. Although plasma proteins serve a variety of functions, note that they are *not* taken up by cells to be used as fuels or metabolic nutrients as are most other plasma solutes, such as glucose, fatty acids, and oxygen. **Albumin** (al-bu'min) accounts for some 60% of plasma protein. It acts as a carrier to shuttle certain molecules through the circulation, is an important blood buffer, and is the major blood protein contributing to the plasma osmotic pressure (the pressure that helps to keep water in the bloodstream). Sodium ions are the other major solute contributing to blood osmotic pressure.

The composition of plasma varies continuously as cells remove or add substances to the blood. However, assuming a healthy diet, plasma composition is kept relatively constant by various homeostatic mechanisms. For example, when blood protein levels

Table 18.1 Composition of Plasma	
Constituent	**Description/importance**
Water	90% of plasma volume; dissolving and suspending medium for solutes of blood; absorbs heat
Solutes *Proteins*	8% (by weight) of plasma volume
• Albumin	60% of plasma proteins; produced by liver; exerts osmotic pressure to maintain water balance between blood and tissues
• Globulins	36% of plasma proteins
alpha, beta	Produced by liver; transport proteins that bind to lipids, metal ions, and fat-soluble vitamins
gamma	Antibodies released primarily by plasma cells during immune response
• Clotting proteins	4% of plasma proteins; include fibrinogen and prothrombin produced by liver; act in blood clotting
• Others	Metabolic enzymes, antibacterial proteins (such as complement), hormones
Nonprotein nitrogenous substances	By-products of cellular metabolism, such as lactic acid, urea, uric acid, creatinine, and ammonium salts
Nutrients (organic)	Materials absorbed from digestive tract and transported for use throughout body; include glucose and other simple carbohydrates, amino acids (digestion products of proteins), fatty acids, glycerol and triglycerides (fat products), cholesterol, and vitamins
Electrolytes	Cations include sodium, potassium, calcium, magnesium; anions include chloride, phosphate, sulfate, and bicarbonate; help to maintain plasma osmotic pressure and normal blood pH
Respiratory gases	Oxygen and carbon dioxide; some dissolved oxygen (most bound to hemoglobin inside RBCs); carbon dioxide transported bound to hemoglobin in RBCs and as bicarbonate ion dissolved in plasma

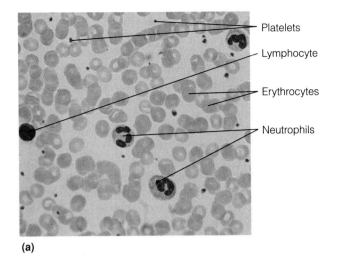

Platelets

Lymphocyte

Erythrocytes

Neutrophils

(a)

FIGURE 18.2
Photomicrographs of human blood stained with Wright's stain. (a) Blood smear (543 ×). (b) Neutrophil (848 ×). (c) Lymphocyte (848 ×). (d) Monocyte (848 ×). (e) Eosinophil (848 ×). (f) Basophil (848 ×).

(b)   **(c)**   **(d)**   **(e)**   **(f)**

become undesirably low, the liver is stimulated to make more proteins; and when the blood starts to become too acidic (acidosis), both the respiratory system and the kidneys are called into action to restore plasma's normal, slightly alkaline pH. Body organs make dozens of adjustments, day in and day out, to maintain the many plasma solutes at life-sustaining levels. In addition to transporting various solutes around the body, plasma distributes heat (a by-product of cellular metabolism) throughout the body.

FORMED ELEMENTS

The **formed elements of blood** are *erythrocytes, leukocytes,* and *platelets.* These elements have some unusual features. (1) Two of the three are not even true cells: Erythrocytes have no nuclei or organelles, and platelets are just cell fragments. Only leukocytes are complete cells. (2) Most of the formed elements survive in the bloodstream for only a few days. (3) Most blood cells do not divide. Instead, they are continuously renewed by division of cells in bone marrow, where they originate. Short-lived and constantly replaced, blood cells may be compared to disposable products in our modern, throwaway society.

If you examine a stained smear of human blood under the light microscope, you will see disc-shaped red blood cells, a variety of gaudily stained spherical white blood cells, and some scattered platelets that look like debris (Figure 18.2). Erythrocytes vastly out-

number the other types of formed elements. Table 18.2 on p. 595 summarizes the important structural and functional characteristics of the various types of formed elements.

Erythrocytes

Structural Characteristics

Erythrocytes or **red blood cells (RBCs),** are small cells, about 7.5 μm in diameter. Shaped like biconcave discs—flattened discs with depressed centers (Figure 18.3)—their thin centers appear lighter in color than their edges. Consequently, erythrocytes look like miniature doughnuts when viewed with a microscope. Mature erythrocytes are bound by a plasma membrane, but lack a nucleus (are *anucleate*) and have essentially no organelles. In fact, they are little more than "bags" of *hemoglobin,* the RBC protein that functions in gas transport. Other proteins are present, but they function mainly to maintain the plasma membrane or promote changes in RBC shape. For example, the biconcave shape of an erythrocyte is maintained by a net of fibrous proteins, especially one called *spectrin,* attached to the cytoplasmic face of its plasma membrane. Furthermore, because the spectrin net is deformable, it gives erythrocytes enough flexibility to change shape as necessary—to twist, turn, and become cup-shaped as they are carried passively along in the bloodstream and through

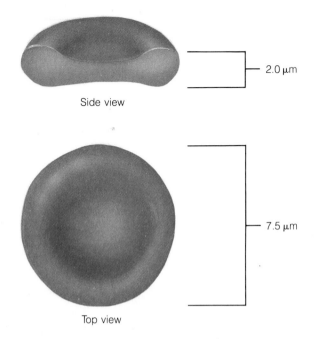

Side view

2.0 μm

7.5 μm

Top view

FIGURE 18.3
Structure of erythrocytes. An erythrocyte is shown in a cut side view and in a superficial surface view. Notice the distinctive biconcave shape.

capillaries with diameters smaller than themselves—and then to resume their biconcave shape.

The erythrocyte is a superb example of complementarity of structure and function. It picks up oxygen in the capillary beds of the lungs and releases it to tissue cells across other capillaries throughout the body. It also transports some 20% of the carbon dioxide released by tissue cells in the opposite direction—back to the lungs. Each of the erythrocyte's structural characteristics contributes to its respiratory functions: (1) Its small size and peculiar shape provide a huge surface area relative to volume (about 30% more surface area than comparable spherical cells). Since no point within its cytoplasm is far from the surface, the biconvex disc shape is ideally suited for gas exchange. (2) Discounting its water content, an erythrocyte is over 97% hemoglobin, the molecule that binds to and transports respiratory gases. (3) Because erythrocytes lack mitochondria and generate ATP by anaerobic mechanisms, they do not consume any of the oxygen they are transporting, making them very efficient oxygen transporters indeed.

Erythrocytes are the major factor contributing to blood viscosity. Women typically have a lower red blood cell count than men (4.3 to 5.2 million cells per cubic millimeter of blood [mm³] vs. 5.1 to 5.8 million cells per cubic millimeter respectively). When the number of red blood cells increases beyond the normal range, blood viscosity increases and blood flows more slowly. Similarly, as the number of red blood cells drops below the lower end of the range, the blood thins and flows more rapidly.

Function

Erythrocytes are completely dedicated to their job of respiratory gas (oxygen and carbon dioxide) transport. Their hemoglobin binds easily and reversibly with oxygen, and most oxygen carried in blood is bound to hemoglobin. Normal values for hemoglobin in grams per 100 milliliters of blood (g/100 ml) are 14 to 20 in infants, 13 to 18 in adult males, and 12 to 16 in adult females.

Hemoglobin is made up of the protein **globin** bound to the red **heme** pigment. Globin is rather complex. It consists of four polypeptide chains—two alpha (α) and two beta (β)—each bound to a ringlike heme group. Each heme group bears an atom of iron set like a jewel in its center (Figure 18.4). Since each iron atom can combine reversibly with one molecule of oxygen, a hemoglobin molecule can transport four molecules of oxygen. A single red blood cell contains about 250 million hemoglobin molecules, so each of these tiny cells can carry about 1 billion molecules of oxygen!

The fact that hemoglobin is contained in erythrocytes, rather than existing free in plasma, prevents it (1) from breaking into fragments that would leak out of the bloodstream (through the rather porous capillary membranes) and (2) from contributing to blood viscosity and osmotic pressure.

Oxygen loading occurs in the lungs and the direction of transport is from lungs to tissue cells. As oxygen-deficient blood moves through the lungs, oxygen diffuses from the air sacs of the lungs into the blood and then into the erythrocytes, where it binds to hemoglobin. When oxygen binds to iron, the hemoglobin, now called **oxyhemoglobin,** assumes a new three-dimensional shape and becomes bright red. In the tissues, the process is reversed. Oxygen detaches from iron, hemoglobin resumes its former shape, and the resulting **deoxyhemoglobin,** or *reduced hemoglobin,* becomes dark red. The released oxygen diffuses from the blood into the tissue fluid and then into the tissue cells.

About 20% of the carbon dioxide transported in the blood combines with hemoglobin, but it binds to amino acids of globin rather than with the heme group. This formation of **carbaminohemoglobin** (kar-bam″ĭ-no-he″mo-glo′bin) occurs more readily when hemoglobin is in the reduced state (dissociated from oxygen). Carbon dioxide loading occurs in the tissues and the direction of transport is from tissues to lungs, where carbon dioxide is eliminated from the body. The mechanisms of loading and unloading these respiratory gases are described in Chapter 23.

Production of Erythrocytes

Blood cell formation is referred to as **hematopoiesis** (hem″ah-to-poi-e′sis), or **hemopoiesis** (*hemo, hemato* = blood; *poiesis* = to make). This process occurs in the **red bone marrow,** which is composed largely of a

β₂   β₁

α₂   α₁

Polypeptide chain

(a) **Hemoglobin**

H₃C   CH₂CH₂COOH

H₂C=CH   CH₂CH₂COOH

H₃C   CH₃

H₂C=CH   CH₃

(b) **Iron-containing heme group**

FIGURE 18.4
Structure of hemoglobin. (a) The intact hemoglobin molecule is composed of the protein globin bound to the iron-containing heme pigments. Each globin molecule has four polypeptide chains: two alpha (α) chains and two beta (β) chains. Each chain is complexed with a heme group, shown as a green-beaded structure. **(b)** Structure of a single heme group.

soft network of reticular connective tissue that borders on wide blood capillaries called *blood sinusoids.* Within this network are immature blood cells, macrophages, fat cells and *reticular cells* (the fibroblasts that secrete the fibers). In adults, red marrow is found chiefly in the bones of the axial skeleton and girdles, and in the proximal epiphyses of the humerus and femur. Each type of blood cell is produced in different numbers in response to changing body needs and different regulatory factors. As they mature, they migrate through the thin walls of the sinusoids to enter the blood.

Although the various formed elements have different functions, there are important similarities in their life histories. All of the formed elements arise

from the same type of *stem cell,* the **hematopoietic stem cell** or **hemocytoblast** (*cyte* = cell, *blast* = bud), which resides in the red bone marrow. However, their maturation pathways differ; and once a cell is *committed* to a specific blood cell pathway, it cannot change. This commitment is signaled by the appearance of membrane surface receptors that respond to specific hormones or growth factors that, in turn, "push" the cell toward further specialization.

Erythrocyte production, or **erythropoiesis** (ĕ-rith″ro-poi-e′sis), involves three distinct phases (Figure 18.5):

1. The immature erythrocyte prepares to synthesize hemoglobin by producing huge numbers of ribosomes.

Stem cell   Committed cell   Developmental pathway

Phase 1
Ribosome synthesis

Phase 2
Hemoglobin accumulation

Phase 3
Ejection of nucleus

Hemocytoblast   Proerythroblast   Early erythroblast   Late erythroblast   Normoblast   Reticulocyte   Erythrocytes

FIGURE 18.5
Erythropoiesis: genesis of red blood cells. Erythropoiesis is a sequence involving proliferation and differentiation of committed red marrow cells through the erythroblast and normoblast stages to the reticulocytes that are released into the bloodstream, and finally become erythrocytes. (The myeloid stem cell, the phase intermediate between the hemocytoblast and the proerythroblast, is not illustrated.)

Normal blood oxygen levels

Stimulus: Hypoxia due to decreased RBC count, decreased availability of O_2 to blood, or increased tissue demands for O_2

Increased O_2-carrying ability of blood

Reduced O_2 levels in blood

More RBCs

Kidney releases erythropoietin

Enhanced erythropoiesis

Erythro-poietin stimulates

Red bone marrow

FIGURE 18.6
Erythropoietin mechanism for regulating the rate of erythropoiesis. Notice that increased erythropoietin release, which stimulates erythropoiesis in bone marrow, occurs when oxygen levels in the blood become inadequate to support normal cellular activity, whatever the cause.

2. Hemoglobin is synthesized and accumulates in the cell's cytoplasm.

3. The erythrocyte ejects its nucleus and most of its organelles.

Erythropoiesis begins when a hemocytoblast descendant called a myeloid stem cell is transformed into a **proerythroblast.** Proerythroblasts, in turn, give rise to the **early (basophilic) erythroblasts** that serve as ribosome-producing factories. During these first two phases, the cells divide many times. Hemoglobin synthesis and accumulation occur as the early erythroblast is transformed into a **late erythroblast** and then a **normoblast.** The "color" of the cell cytoplasm changes as the blue-staining ribosomes become masked by the pink color of hemoglobin. When a normoblast accumulates a hemoglobin concentration of about 34%, its nuclear functions end and its nucleus degenerates and is ejected—causing the cell to collapse inward and assume the biconcave shape. The result is the *reticulocyte.* **Reticulocytes** (essentially young erythrocytes) are so named because they still contain some clumped ribosomes and rough endoplasmic reticulum. The entire process from hemocytoblast to reticulocyte takes three to five days. The reticulocytes enter the bloodstream to begin their task of oxygen transport and usually become fully mature

erythrocytes within two days of release. **Reticulocyte counts** are used clinically as a rough index of the *rate* of RBC formation.

Regulation and Requirements for Erythropoiesis

The number of circulating erythrocytes in a given individual is remarkably constant and reflects a balance between red blood cell production and destruction. This balance is extremely important because having too few erythrocytes leads to tissue hypoxia (oxygen deprivation), whereas too many makes the blood undesirably viscous. To ensure that the number of erythrocytes in the blood remains within the homeostatic range, new cells are produced at the incredibly rapid rate of more than 2 million per second in healthy people. This process is controlled hormonally and depends on adequate supplies of iron and certain B vitamins.

Hormonal Controls. The direct stimulus for erythrocyte formation is provided by **erythropoietin (EPO),** a glycoprotein hormone. Normally, a small amount of erythropoietin circulates in the blood at all times and sustains red blood cell production at a basal rate (Figure 18.6). Although the liver is believed to produce some, the kidneys play the major role in erythropoietin production. When kidney cells become hypoxic (i.e., have inadequate oxygen), they accelerate their release of erythropoietino. The drop in normal blood oxygen levels that triggers erythropoietin formation can result from:

1. Reduced numbers of red blood cells caused by hemorrhage or excess RBC destruction.

2. Reduced availability of oxygen to the blood, as might occur at high altitudes or during pneumonia.

3. Increased tissue demands for oxygen (common in those who engage in aerobic exercise).

Conversely, an overabundance of erythrocytes or an excessive amount of oxygen in the bloodstream depresses erythropoietin production. The easily missed point to keep in mind is that the number of erythrocytes in the blood does *not* control the rate of erythropoiesis. Control is based on their ability to transport enough oxygen to meet tissue demands.

Blood-borne erythropoietin stimulates red marrow cells that *are already committed* to becoming erythrocytes, causing them to mature more rapidly. A marked increase in the rate of reticulocyte release (and, hence, reticulocyte count) occurs one to two days after erythropoietin levels rise in the blood.

Notice that hypoxia (oxygen deficit) does not activate the bone marrow directly. Instead it stimulates the kidneys, which, in turn, provide the hormonal stimulus that activates the bone marrow. Renal dialysis patients whose kidneys have failed produce insufficient erythropoietin to support normal erythropoiesis. Consequently, they routinely have red blood cell counts less than half that of healthy individuals. Recombinant (genetically engineered) erythropoietin has helped such patients immeasurably.

Although created to help those in renal failure, recombinant EPO has also become a substance of abuse in athletes—particularly in professional bike racers and marathon runners seeking increased stamina and performance. However, the consequences in some cases can be deadly. By injecting EPO, healthy athletes increase their normal RBC volume from 45% to as much as 65%. Then, with the dehydration that occurs in a long race, the blood concentrates even further, becoming a thick, sticky "sludge" that can cause clotting, stroke, and even heart failure. •

The male sex hormone *testosterone* also enhances erythropoietin production by the kidneys. Because female sex hormones do not have similar stimulatory effects, testosterone may be at least partially responsible for the higher RBC counts and hemoglobin levels seen in males. Additionally, a wide variety of chemicals released by leukocytes, platelets, and even reticular cells stimulate bursts of RBC production.

Dietary Requirements: Iron and B-Complex Vitamins.   The raw materials required for erythropoiesis include the usual nutrients and structural materials—proteins, lipids, and carbohydrates. Iron and B-complex vitamins are also essential for hemoglobin synthesis (Figure 18.7). Iron is available from the diet, and its absorption into the bloodstream is precisely controlled by intestinal cells in response to changing body stores of iron.

Approximately 65% of the body's iron supply (about 4000 mg) is in hemoglobin. Most of the remainder is stored in the liver, spleen, and (to a much lesser extent) bone marrow. Because free iron is toxic, iron is stored inside cells as protein-iron complexes such as **ferritin** (fer′ĭ-tin) and **hemosiderin** (he″mo-sid′er-in). In blood, iron is loosely bound to a transport protein called **transferrin.** Developing erythrocytes take up iron as needed to form functional hemoglobin molecules.

Small amounts of iron are lost each day in feces, urine, and perspiration. The average daily loss of iron is 1.7 mg in women and 0.9 mg in men. In women, the menstrual flow accounts for additional losses.

Two B-complex vitamins—vitamin B_{12} and folic acid—are essential for DNA synthesis. Thus, even slight deficits jeopardize rapidly dividing cell populations, such as developing erythrocytes.

Fate and Destruction of Erythrocytes

The anucleate condition of erythrocytes carries with it some important limitations. Red blood cells are unable to synthesize proteins, to grow, or to divide. Erythrocytes become "old" as they lose their flexibility and become increasingly rigid and fragile, and their contained hemoglobin begins to degenerate. Red blood cells have a useful life span of 100 to 120 days, after which they become trapped and fragment in smaller circulatory channels, particularly in those of the spleen. For this reason, the spleen is sometimes called the "red blood cell graveyard." Dying erythrocytes are engulfed and destroyed by macrophages. The heme of their hemoglobin is split off from globin. Its core of iron is salvaged, bound to protein (as ferritin or hemosiderin), and stored for reuse. The balance of the heme group is degraded to **bilirubin** (bil′i-roo′bin), a yellow pigment (Figure 18.7). Bilirubin is released to the blood and picked up by liver cells which, in turn, secrete it (in bile) into the intestine, where it is metabolized to *urobilinogen.* Most of this degraded pigment leaves the body in feces, as a brown pigment called *stercobilin.* The protein (globin) part of hemoglobin is metabolized or broken down to amino acids, which are released to the circulation (see Figure 18.7).

? *How would you expect blood levels of bilirubin to change in a person that has severe liver disease?*

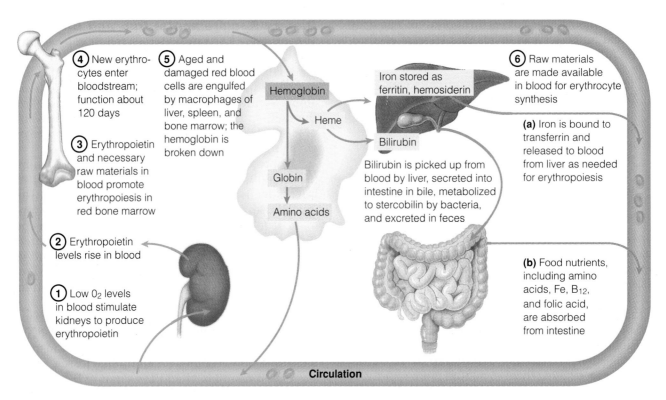

(4) New erythro-cytes enter bloodstream; function about 120 days

(5) Aged and damaged red blood cells are engulfed by macrophages of liver, spleen, and bone marrow; the hemoglobin is broken down

(3) Erythropoietin and necessary raw materials in blood promote erythropoiesis in red bone marrow

(2) Erythropoietin levels rise in blood

(1) Low O_2 levels in blood stimulate kidneys to produce erythropoietin

Hemoglobin

Heme

Globin

Amino acids

Iron stored as ferritin, hemosiderin

Bilirubin

Bilirubin is picked up from blood by liver, secreted into intestine in bile, metabolized to stercobilin by bacteria, and excreted in feces

(6) Raw materials are made available in blood for erythrocyte synthesis

(a) Iron is bound to transferrin and released to blood from liver as needed for erythropoiesis

(b) Food nutrients, including amino acids, Fe, B_{12}, and folic acid, are absorbed from intestine

Circulation

FIGURE 18.7
Life cycle of red blood cells

Erythrocyte Disorders

Most erythrocyte disorders can be classified as anemias or polycythemias. The many varieties and causes of these conditions are described next.

Anemias.   Anemia (ah-ne′me-ah; "lacking blood") is a condition in which the blood has an abnormally low oxygen-carrying capacity. It is a *symptom* of some disorder rather than a disease in and of itself. Its hallmark is blood oxygen levels that are inadequate to support normal metabolism. Anemic individuals are fatigued, often pale, short of breath, and chilly. Common causes of anemia include:

1. Insufficient numbers of red blood cells. Conditions that reduce the red blood cell count include blood loss, destruction of RBCs, and bone marrow failure.

Hemorrhagic (hem″o-raj′ik) *anemias* result from blood loss. In acute hemorrhagic anemia, blood loss is rapid (as might follow a severe stab wound); it is treated by blood replacement. Slight but persistent blood loss (due to hemorrhoids or an undiagnosed bleeding ulcer, for example) causes chronic hemorrhagic anemia. Once the primary problem is resolved,

normal erythropoietic mechanisms replace the deficient blood cells.

In *hemolytic* (he″mo-lit′ik) *anemias,* erythrocytes are ruptured, or lysed, prematurely. Hemoglobin abnormalities, transfusion of mismatched blood, certain bacterial and parasitic infections, and congenital defects of the erythrocyte plasma membrane are all possible causes.

Aplastic anemia results from destruction or inhibition of the hematopoietic components in the red marrow by certain toxins, drugs, and ionizing radiation. Because marrow destruction impairs formation of *all* formed elements, anemia is just one of its signs. Defects in blood clotting and immunity are also present. Blood transfusions provide a stopgap treatment until bone marrow transplants can be done.

2. Decreases in hemoglobin content. When hemoglobin molecules are normal, but erythrocytes contain fewer than the usual number, a nutritional anemia is always suspected.

Iron-deficiency anemia is usually a secondary result of hemorrhagic anemias, but it also results from inadequate intake of iron-containing foods and impaired iron absorption. The erythrocytes produced, called **microcytes,** are small and pale. The obvious treatment is iron supplements, but if chronic hemorrhage is the cause, blood transfusions may also be needed.

When athletes exercise vigorously, their blood volume expands and can increase by as much as 15%. Since this, in effect, dilutes the blood components, a test for the iron content of the blood at such times would indicate iron-deficiency anemia. However, this iron deficiency, an illusion called **athlete's anemia,** is quickly reversed as blood components return to physiologic levels within a day or so of resuming normal activity. •

Pernicious anemia is due to a deficiency of vitamin B_{12}. Because meats, poultry, and fish provide ample amounts of the vitamin, diet is rarely the problem except for strict vegetarians. A substance called **intrinsic factor,** produced by the stomach mucosa, must be present for vitamin B_{12} to be absorbed by intestinal cells. In most cases of pernicious anemia, intrinsic factor is deficient. Consequently, the developing erythrocytes grow but do not divide, and large, pale cells called **macrocytes** result. Treatment involves regular intramuscular injections of vitamin B_{12}.

3. Abnormal hemoglobin. Production of abnormal hemoglobin usually has a genetic basis. Two such examples, thalassemia and sickle-cell anemia, are serious, incurable, and often fatal diseases. In both diseases the globin part of hemoglobin is abnormal and the erythrocytes produced are fragile and rupture prematurely. Standard treatment for these anemias is blood transfusion.

Thalassemias (thal"ah-se'me-ahs; "sea blood") are typically seen in people of Mediterranean ancestry, such as Greeks and Italians. As a result of absent or depressed synthesis of one of the globin chains, the erythrocytes are thin and delicate. The red blood cell count is generally less than 2 million cells per cubic millimeter.

In **sickle-cell anemia,** the abnormal hemoglobin formed, *hemoglobin S (HbS),* becomes spiky and sharp when deprived of oxygen. This causes the red blood cells to become crescent-shaped when they unload oxygen molecules or when the oxygen content of the blood is lower than normal, as during vigorous exercise and other activities that increase metabolic rate. The deformed erythrocytes rupture easily and tend to dam up in small blood vessels. These events interfere with oxygen delivery, leaving the victims gasping for air and in extreme pain. It is amazing that this havoc results from a change in just *one* of the 287 amino acids in a beta chain of the globin molecule! This change causes the beta chains to link together forming stiff rods.

Sickle-cell anemia occurs chiefly in black people who live in the malaria belt of Africa and among their descendants. It strikes nearly 1 of every 400 black newborns in the United States. Apparently the gene that causes sickling of red blood cells also cause ery-

throcytes infected by the malaria-causing parasite to stick to the capillary walls. Then, in the presence of hypoxia, these abnormal erythrocytes lose potassium, an essential ingredient for survival of the parasite. Thus, individuals with the sickle-cell gene have a better chance of surviving in regions where malaria is prevalent. Only those carrying two copies of the defective gene have sickle-cell anemia. Those carrying only one sickling gene have sickle-cell trait; they generally do not display the symptoms, but can transmit the gene to their offspring.

Since fetal hemoglobin (HbF) does not "sickle," even in those destined to make HbS and have sickle-cell anemia, investigators have been looking for ways to switch the fetal hemoglobin gene back on. Hydroxyurea, a drug used to treat chronic leukemia, appears to do just that. This drug reduces the excruciating pain, and complications of sickle cell anemia by 50%—so dramatically that the NIH ended its clinical drug trials (begun in 1992) 4 months early.

Polycythemia. Polycythemia (pol"e-si-the'-me-ah; "many blood cells") is an abnormal excess of erythrocytes that increases the viscosity of the blood, causing it to sludge, or flow sluggishly. *Polycythemia vera,* most often a result of bone marrow cancer, is a serious condition characterized by dizziness and an exceptionally high RBC count (8 to 11 million cells per cubic millimeter). The hematocrit may be as high as 80% and blood volume may double, causing the vascular system to become engorged with blood and severely impairing circulation.

Secondary polycythemias result when less oxygen is available or erythropoietin production increases. The secondary polycythemia that appears in individuals living at high altitudes is a normal physiological response that compensates for the reduced atmospheric pressure and oxygen content of the air in such areas. RBC counts of 6 to 8 million per cubic millimeter are common in such people. •

Blood doping, practiced by some athletes competing in aerobic events, is artificially induced polycythemia. Some of the athlete's red blood cells are drawn off and then reinjected a few days before the event. Because the erythropoietin mechanism is triggered shortly after the blood is removed, the erythrocytes are quickly replaced. Then, when the stored blood is reinfused, a temporary polycythemia results. Since red blood cells carry oxygen, the additional infusion should translate into increased oxygen-carrying capacity due to a higher hematocrit, and hence greater endurance and speed. (Similar results have been produced by injecting recombinant EPO.) Other than problems that might derive from increased blood viscosity, such as temporary high blood pressure or reduced perfusion (blood delivery) to body tissues, blood doping seems to work. However, the practice is considered unethical and has been banned from the Olympic Games. •

Leukocytes

General Structural and Functional Characteristics

Leukocytes (*leuko* = white), or **white blood cells (WBCs),** are the only formed elements that are complete cells, with nuclei and the usual organelles. Leukocytes, which account for less than 1% of total blood volume, are far less numerous than red blood cells. On average, there are 4000 to 11,000 WBCs per cubic millimeter.

Leukocytes are crucial to our defense against disease. They form a mobile army that helps protect the body from damage by bacteria, viruses, parasites, toxins, and tumor cells. As such, they have some very special functional characteristics. Red blood cells are confined to the bloodstream, and they carry out their functions in the blood. But white blood cells are able to slip out of the capillary blood vessels—a process called **diapedesis** (di″ah-pĕ-de′sis; "leaping across") —and the circulatory system is simply their means of transport to areas of the body (largely loose connective tissues or lymphoid tissues) where they are needed to mount inflammatory or immune responses (as described in Chapter 22). Once out of the bloodstream, leukocytes move through the tissue spaces by **amoeboid motion** (by forming flowing cytoplasmic extensions that move them along). By following the "chemical trail" of molecules released by damaged cells or other leukocytes, a phenomenon called **positive chemotaxis,** they can pinpoint and gather in large numbers at areas of tissue damage and infection to destroy foreign substances or dead cells.

Whenever white blood cells are mobilized for action, the body speeds up their production and twice the normal number may appear in the blood within a few hours. A *white blood cell count* of over 11,000 cells per cubic millimeter is called **leukocytosis.** This condition is a normal homeostatic response to bacterial or viral invasion of the body.

Leukocytes are grouped into two major categories on the basis of structural and chemical characteristics: *Granulocytes* contain specialized membrane-bound cytoplasmic granules; *agranulocytes* lack obvious granules. General information about the various leukocytes is provided next. Details of their diameter, concentration in blood, and percentage in the white blood cell population appear in Figure 18.8 and Table 18.2.

Students are often asked to list the leukocytes in order from most abundant to least abundant. The following phrase may help you with this task: **N**ever **l**et **m**onkeys **e**at **b**ananas (neutrophils, lymphocytes, monocytes, eosinophils, basophils).

Granulocytes

The **granulocytes** (gran′u-lo-sīts), which include neutrophils, basophils, and eosinophils, are all spherical

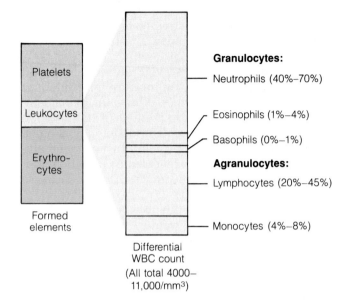

FIGURE 18.8
Types of leukocytes and their relative percentages in the WBC population. (Note that the relationship of the formed elements in the left column is not shown to scale because erythrocytes comprise nearly 98% of the formed elements whereas leukocytes and platelets together account for the remaining 2 + %.)

in shape and larger than erythrocytes. They characteristically have lobed nuclei (rounded nuclear masses connected by thinner strands of nuclear material), and their cytoplasmic granules stain quite specifically with Wright's stain. Functionally, all the granulocytes are phagocytes.

Neutrophils. Neutrophils (nu′tro-filz), the most numerous of the white blood cells, typically account for half or more of the WBC population. Neutrophils are about twice as large as erythrocytes.

The neutrophil cytoplasm stains pale lilac and contains very fine granules (of two varieties) that are difficult to see (see Table 18.2 and Figure 18.2). They are called neutrophils (literally, "neutral-loving") because their granules take up both *basic* (blue) and *acidic* (red) *dyes.* Together, the two types of granules give the cytoplasm an intermediate (lilac) color. Some of these granules contain peroxidases and other hydrolytic enzymes, and are regarded as lysosomes. Others, especially the smaller granules, contain a potent "brew" of antibiotic-like proteins, called **defensins.** Neutrophil nuclei consist of three to six lobes; because of this nuclear variability, they are often called **polymorphonuclear** ("many shapes of the nucleus") **leukocytes (PMNs)** or simply **polys.**

Neutrophils are chemically attracted to sites of inflammation and are active phagocytes. They are especially partial to bacteria and some fungi, which

Table 18.2 Summary of Formed Elements of the Blood

Cell type	Illustration	Description*	Number of cells/ mm³ (μl) of blood	Duration of development (D) and life span (LS)	Function
Erythrocytes (red blood cells; RBCs)		Biconcave, anucleate disc; salmon-colored; diameter 7–8 μm	4–6 million	D: 5–7 days LS: 100–120 days	Transport oxygen and carbon dioxide
Leukocytes (white blood cells, WBCs)		Spherical, nucleated cells	4000–11,000		
Granulocytes • Neutrophil		Nucleus multilobed; inconspicuous cytoplasmic granules; diameter 10–14 μm	3000–7000	D: 6–9 days LS: 6 hours to a few days	Phagocytize bacteria
• Eosinophil		Nucleus bilobed; red cytoplasmic granules; diameter 10–14 μm	100–400	D: 6–9 days LS: 8–12 days	Kill parasitic worms; destroy antigen-antibody complexes; inactivate some inflammatory chemicals of allergy
• Basophil		Nucleus lobed; large blue-purple cytoplasmic granules; diameter 10–12 μm	20–50	D: 3–7 days LS: ? (a few hours to a few days)	Release histamine and other mediators of inflammation; contain heparin, an anticoagulant
Agranulocytes • Lymphocyte		Nucleus spherical or indented; pale blue cytoplasm; diameter 5–17 μm	1500–3000	D: days to weeks LS: hours to years	Mount immune response by direct cell attack or via antibodies
• Monocyte		Nucleus U- or kidney-shaped; gray-blue cytoplasm; diameter 14–24 μm	100–700	D: 2–3 days LS: months	Phagocytosis; develop into macrophages in tissues
Platelets		Discoid cytoplasmic fragments containing granules; stain deep purple; diameter 2–4 μm	250,000–500,000	D: 4–5 days LS: 5–10 days	Seal small tears in blood vessels; instrumental in blood clotting

*Appearance when stained with Wright's stain.

they can ingest and destroy. Bacterial killing is promoted by a process called a **respiratory burst,** in which oxygen is actively metabolized to produce potent germ-killing oxidizing substances such as bleach and hydrogen peroxide, and by defensin-mediated lysis. It appears that when the granules containing defensins are merged with a microbe-containing phagosome, the defensins form long peptide "spears" that pierce holes in the membrane of the ingested "foe." Neutrophil numbers increase explosively during acute bacterial infections such as meningitis and appendicitis.

Eosinophils. Eosinophils (e″o-sin′o-filz) account for 1% to 4% of all leukocytes and are approximately the size of neutrophils. Their blue-red nucleus usually resembles an old-fashioned telephone receiver; that is, it has two lobes connected by a broad band of nuclear material (see Table 18.2). Large, coarse granules that stain from brick red to crimson with acid (eosin) dyes pack the cytoplasm. These granules are lysosome-like and filled with a unique variety of digestive enzymes. However, unlike typical lysosomes, they lack enzymes that specifically digest bacteria.

Eosinophils perform several functions, but perhaps their most important role is to lead the counterattack against parasitic worms, such as flatworms (tapeworms and flukes) and roundworms (pinworms and hookworms) that are too large to be phagocytized. These worms are ingested in food or invade the body via the skin and then typically burrow into the intestinal or respiratory mucosae. Eosinophils tend to reside in the loose connective tissues at the same body sites, and when a parasitic worm "prey" is encountered, they gather around and release the enzymes from their cytoplasmic granules onto the parasite's surface, thus digesting it away. The enzyme most responsible for this digestion is *major basic protein* (MBP). Eosinophils also lessen the severity of allergies by phagocytizing immune (antigen-antibody) complexes involved in allergy attacks and inactivating certain inflammatory chemicals released during allergic reactions.

Basophils.   **Basophils** are the rarest white blood cells, averaging only 0.5% of the leukocyte population (1 in 200). Basophils are the same size as or slightly smaller than neutrophils (see Table 18.2). Their cytoplasm contains large coarse histamine-containing granules that have an affinity for the basic dyes (*basophil* = "base loving") and stain purplish-black. *Histamine* is an inflammatory chemical that acts as a vasodilator (makes blood vessels "leaky") and attracts other white blood cells to the inflamed site. The deep purple nucleus is generally U- or S-shaped with two or three conspicuous constrictions.

Granulated cells similar to basophils, called *mast cells,* are found in connective tissues. Some researchers propose that mast cells are *tissue* basophils, but most believe that each cell type is unique. Although mast cell nuclei tend to be more oval than lobed, the cells are very similar microscopically, and both bind to a particular antibody (immunoglobulin E) that causes the granules to release histamine.

Agranulocytes

The **agranulocytes** include lymphocytes and monocytes, WBCs that lack visible cytoplasmic granules. Although they resemble each other structurally, they are functionally distinct and unrelated cell types. Their nuclei are typically spherical or kidney-shaped.

Lymphocytes.   **Lymphocytes** are the second most numerous leukocytes in the blood. When stained, a typical lymphocyte has a large, dark purple nucleus that occupies most of the cell volume. The nucleus is usually spherical, but may be slightly indented, and is surrounded by a thin rim of pale blue cytoplasm (see Table 18.2 and Figure 18.2). Lymphocyte diameter ranges from 5 to 17 μm, but they are often classified according to size as small (5 to 8 μm), medium (10 to 12 μm), and large (14 to 17 μm).

Although large numbers of lymphocytes exist in the body, only a small proportion of them (mostly the small lymphocytes) is found in the bloodstream. In fact, lymphocytes are so called because most are firmly enmeshed in lymphoid tissues (lymph nodes, spleen, etc.), where they play a crucial role in immunity. **T lymphocytes** (T cells) function in the immune response by acting directly against virus-infected cells and tumor cells. **B lymphocytes** (B cells) give rise to *plasma cells,* which produce **antibodies** (immunoglobulins) that are released to the blood. (The specifics of B and T lymphocyte function are described in Chapter 22.)

Monocytes.   **Monocytes,** with an average diameter of 18 μm, are the largest leukocytes. They have abundant gray-blue cytoplasm and a darkly staining blue-purple nucleus, which is distinctively U- or kidney-shaped (see Table 18.2 and Figure 18.2). Once in the tissues, monocytes differentiate into highly mobile **macrophages** with prodigious appetites. The macrophages increase in number and are actively phagocytic in *chronic* infections such as tuberculosis and they are crucial in the body's defense against viruses and certain intracellular bacterial parasites. As explained in Chapter 22, macrophages are also important in activating lymphocytes to mount the immune response.

Production and Life Span of Leukocytes

Like erythropoiesis, **leukopoiesis** or the production of white blood cells is hormonally stimulated. These hematopoietic hormones, known collectively as **colony-stimulating factors,** or **CSFs,** not only prompt the white blood cell precursors to divide and mature, but also enhance the protective potency of mature leukocytes. Macrophages and T lymphocytes are the most important sources of CSFs, but they are also produced by selected other cell types. Other than the *stem cell growth (steel) factor,* which stimulates the hemocytoblasts, most CSFs are named for the leukocyte population they stimulate: Thus far, *macrophage-monocyte CSF (M-CSF), granulocyte-CSF (G-CSF), granulocyte-macrophage CSF (GM-CSF),* and *multi-CSF* or *interleukin 3 (IL-3),* which stimulates formation of a mixture of white blood cells, have been identified. Additionally, two more interleukins, IL-7 and IL-5, appear to promote the formation of B lymphocytes and eosinophils, respectively.

Apparently the CSFs are released in response to specific chemical signals in the environment. The network of chemicals that marshals an army of leukocytes to fight off some attack on the body is complex and very much tied into the immune response. Many of the hematopoietic hormones (EPO and several of the CSFs) are being used clinically to stimulate the bone marrow of cancer patients who are receiving chemotherapy (which suppresses the marrow) and of those who have received marrow transplants, and to beef up the protective responses of AIDS patients.

Figure 18.9 shows the pathways of leukocyte differentiation. An early branching of the pathway divides the **lymphoid stem cells,** which produce lymphocytes, from the **myeloid stem cells,** which give rise to all other formed elements (other leukocytes, erythrocytes, and platelets). For each granulocyte line, the committed cells, called **myeloblasts** (mi′ĕ-lo-blasts″), accumulate lysosomes and go on to become **promyelocytes.** The distinctive granules of each granulocyte type appear next in the **myelocyte** stage; then cell division stops. In the subsequent **metamyelocyte** stage, the nuclei distort and become arclike, producing the **band cell** stage. Just before granulocytes leave the marrow and enter the circulation, their nuclei constrict, beginning the process of nuclear segmentation. The bone marrow stores mature granulocytes (but not erythrocytes) and usually contains 10 to 20 times more granulocytes than are found in the blood. The normal ratio of granulocytes to erythrocytes produced is about 3:1, which reflects the much shorter life span (0.5 to 9.0 days) of the granulocytes. Most granulocytes are believed to die combating invading microorganisms.

Despite their similar appearances, the two types of agranulocytes have very different lineages. Like granulocytes, monocytes diverge from common multipotent myeloid stem cells. They then progress through **monoblast** and **promonocyte** stages (see Figure 18.9). By contrast, lymphocytes derive from the lymphoid stem cell and progress through the **lymphoblast** and **prolymphocyte** stages. The promonocytes and prolymphocytes leave the bone marrow and travel to the lymphoid tissues, where their further differentiation occurs (as described in Chapter 22). Monocytes may live for several months, whereas the life span of lymphocytes varies from a few days to decades.

Leukocyte Disorders

Excessive production of abnormal leukocytes occurs in leukemia and infectious mononucleosis. At the opposite pole, **leukopenia** (loo″ko-pe′ne-ah) is an abnormally low white blood cell count (*penia* = poverty). It is commonly induced by drugs, particularly glucocorticoids and anticancer agents.

Leukemias. The term *leukemia,* literally "white blood," refers to a group of cancerous conditions of white blood cells. As a rule, the renegade leukocytes are members of a single *clone* (descendants of a single cell) that tend to remain unspecialized and mitotic, and suppress or impair normal bone marrow function. The leukemias are named according to the abnormal cell type primarily involved. For example, *myelocytic leukemia* involves descendants of the myeloblasts, whereas *lymphocytic leukemia* involves the lymphocytes. Leukemia is *acute* (quickly advanc-

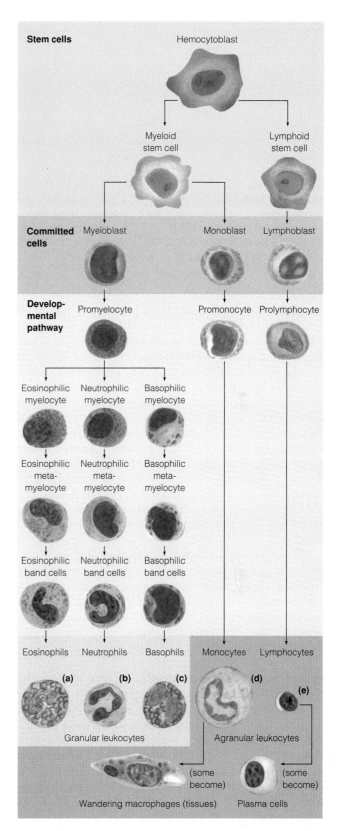

FIGURE 18.9

Formation of leukocytes. Leukocytes arise from ancestral stem cells called hemocytoblasts. **(a–c)** Granular leukocytes develop via a sequence involving myeloblasts. The developmental pathway is common until the granules typical of each granulocyte begin to form. **(d–e)** Agranular leukocytes develop from monoblasts and lymphoblasts. Monocytes, like granular leukocytes, are progeny of the myeloid stem cell. Only lymphocytes arise via the lymphoid stem cell line. Lymphocytes released from the bone marrow are immature; their further differentiation occurs in the lymphoid organs.

FIGURE 18.10

Genesis of platelets. The stem cell (hemocytoblast) gives rise to cells that undergo several mitotic divisions unaccompanied by cytoplasmic division

to produce the megakaryocytes. The cytoplasm of the megakaryocyte becomes compartmentalized by membranes, and the plasma membrane

then fragments, liberating the platelets. (Intermediate stages between the hemocytoblast and megakaryoblast are not illustrated.)

ing) if it derives from blast-type cells like lymphoblasts, and *chronic* (slowly advancing) if it involves proliferation of later cell stages like myelocytes. The more serious acute forms primarily affect children; chronic leukemia is seen more often in elderly people. Without therapy, all leukemias are fatal; only the time course differs.

In acute leukemias, the bone marrow becomes almost totally occupied by the cancerous leukocytes. Because the other blood cell lines are crowded out, severe anemia and bleeding problems result. Other symptoms include fever, weight loss, and bone pain. Although tremendous numbers of leukocytes are produced, they are nonfunctional and cannot defend the body in the usual way. The most common causes of death are internal hemorrhage and overwhelming infections.

Treatments, involving irradiation and administration of antileukemic drugs to destroy the rapidly dividing cells, have been successful in inducing remissions (symptom-free periods) lasting from months to years. Bone marrow transplants are used in selected patients when compatible donors are available.

Infectious Mononucleosis. Once called the kissing disease, *infectious mononucleosis* is a highly contagious viral disease that is most often seen in children and young adults. Caused by the Epstein-Barr virus, its hallmark is excessive numbers of agranulocytes, many of which are atypical. The affected individual complains of being tired and achy, and has a chronic sore throat and a low-grade fever. There is no cure, but with rest the condition typically runs its course to recovery in a few weeks. •

Platelets

Platelets are not cells in the strict sense. They are cytoplasmic fragments of extraordinarily large (up to 60 μm in diameter) cells called **megakaryocytes** (meg"ah-kar′e-o-sītz). In blood smears, each platelet exhibits a blue-staining outer region and an inner area

containing granules that stain purple. The granules contain an impressive array of chemicals that act in the clotting process, including serotonin, Ca^{2+}, a variety of enzymes, ADP, and platelet-derived growth factor (PGDF). Although platelets are sometimes called **thrombocytes** (*thromb* = clot), most anatomists reserve that term for the functionally comparable *nucleated cells* of vertebrates other than mammals.

Platelets are essential for the clotting process that occurs in plasma when blood vessels are ruptured or their lining is injured. By sticking to the damaged site, platelets form a temporary plug that helps seal the break. (This mechanism is explained shortly.) Because platelets are anucleate, they age quickly and degenerate in about ten days if they are not involved in clotting.

Platelet formation is regulated by a hormone called **thrombopoietin.** Their immediate ancestral cells, the megakaryocytes, are progeny of the hemocytoblast and the myeloid stem cell, but their formation is quite unusual (Figure 18.10). In this line, repeated mitoses of the **megakaryoblast** occur, but cytokinesis does not. The final result, the megakaryocyte, is a bizarre cell with a huge, multilobed nucleus and a large cytoplasmic mass. When the megakaryocyte stage is reached, a network of membranes invades the cytoplasm from the plasma membrane and divides the cytoplasm into thousands of compartments. Finally, the cell ruptures, releasing the platelet fragments like stamps being torn from a sheet of postage stamps. The plasma membranes associated with each fragment quickly seal around the cytoplasm to form the grainy, roughly disc-shaped platelets (see Table 18.2), each with a diameter of 2 to 4 μm. Each cubic millimeter of blood contains between 250,000 and 500,000 of the tiny platelets.

HEMOSTASIS

Normally, blood flows smoothly past the intact unperturbed lining (endothelium) of the blood vessel walls. But—if a blood vessel wall breaks, a whole series of reactions is set in motion to accomplish

Table 18.3 Procoagulants (Blood Coagulation Factors)

Factor number	Factor name	Nature/origin	Function or pathway
I	Fibrinogen	Plasma protein; synthesized by liver	Converted to fibrin, weblike substance of clot
II	Prothrombin	Plasma protein; synthesized by liver; formation requires vitamin K	Converted to thrombin, which enzymatically converts fibrinogen to fibrin
III	Thromboplastin or tissue factor (TF)	Lipoprotein complex; released from damaged tissues	Activates extrinsic pathway
IV	Calcium ions	Inorganic ion present in plasma; acquired from diet or released from bone	Needed for essentially all stages of coagulation process
V	Proaccelerin, labile factor, or platelet accelerator	Plasma protein; synthesized in liver; also released by platelets	Both extrinsic and intrinsic mechanisms
VI	Number no longer used; substance now believed to be same as factor V		
VII	Serum prothrombin conversion accelerator (SPCA) or stable factor	Plasma protein; synthesized in liver in process that requires vitamin K	Extrinsic pathway
VIII	Antihemophilic factor (AHF)	Globulin synthesized in liver; deficiency causes hemophilia A	Intrinsic mechanism
IX	Plasma thromboplastin component (PTC) or Christmas factor	Plasma protein; synthesized in liver; deficiency results in hemophilia B; synthesis requires vitamin K	Intrinsic mechanism
X	Stuart factor or Stuart-Prower factor	Plasma protein; synthesized in liver; synthesis requires vitamin K	Both extrinsic and intrinsic pathways
XI	Plasma thromboplastin antecedent (PTA)	Plasma protein; synthesized in liver; deficiency results in hemophilia C	Intrinsic mechanism
XII	Hageman factor	Plasma protein; proteolytic enzyme; source unknown	Intrinsic mechanism; activates plasmin; known to be activated by contact with glass and may initiate clotting in vitro
XIII	Fibrin stabilizing factor (FSF)	Protein present in plasma and platelets; plasma source unknown	Cross-links fibrin and renders it insoluble

hemostasis (he″mo-sta′sis), or stoppage of bleeding (*stasis* = halting). This response, which is fast, localized, and carefully controlled, involves many blood coagulation factors normally present in plasma as well as some substances that are released by platelets and injured tissue cells (Table 18.3).

Hemostasis involves three phases that occur in rapid sequence: (1) vascular spasms, (2) platelet plug formation, and (3) coagulation, or blood clotting. Blood loss at the site is permanently prevented when fibrous tissue grows into the clot and seals the hole in the blood vessel.

Vascular Spasms

The immediate response to blood vessel injury is constriction of the damaged blood vessel (vasoconstriction). Factors that trigger this **vascular spasm** include direct injury to vascular smooth muscle, chemicals released by endothelial cells and platelets, and reflexes initiated by local pain receptors. Generally speaking, the spasm mechanism becomes more and more efficient as the amount of tissue damage increases. The value of the spasm response is obvious: A strongly constricted artery can significantly reduce blood loss for 20–30 minutes, allowing time for platelet plug formation and blood clotting to occur.

Platelet Plug Formation

Platelets play a key role in hemostasis by forming a plug that temporarily seals the break in the vessel wall. They also help to orchestrate subsequent events that lead to blood clot formation. These events are shown in simplified form in Figure 18.11a.

As a rule, platelets do not stick to each other or to the smooth endothelial linings of blood vessels. How-

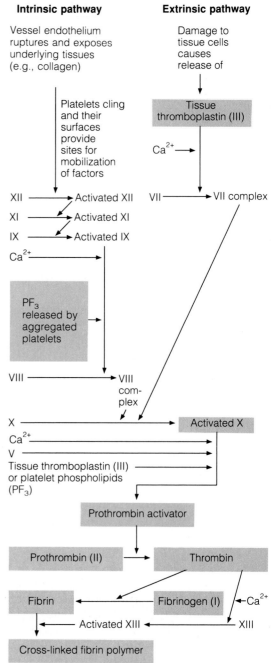

FIGURE 18.11

Events of platelet plug formation and blood clotting.
(a) Simplified schematic of events. Steps numbered 1–3 represent
the major events of coagulation. The color of the arrows indicates
their source or destination: pink from tissue, green from platelets, and
yellow to fibrin. (b) Detailed flowchart indicating the intermediates and
events involved in platelet plug formation and the intrinsic and
extrinsic mechanisms of blood clotting (coagulation). Once the
prothrombin activator is present, the remaining events are common to
both the extrinsic and intrinsic pathways.

ever, when the endothelium is damaged and underlying collagen fibers are exposed, platelets undergo
some remarkable changes. They swell and form
spiked processes. They also become sticky and
adhere tenaciously to the exposed collagen. Once
attached, degranulation occurs; that is, the platelet
granules begin to break down and release several
chemicals. Some, like **serotonin,** enhance the vascu-

lar spasm; others, like **adenosine diphosphate (ADP),**
are potent aggregating agents that attract more
platelets to the area and cause them to release their
contents. **Thromboxane** (throm-boks′ān) **A₂,** a short-
lived prostaglandin derivative that is generated and
released, stimulates both events. Other phospholipids are also released during the degranulation
process. Thus, a positive feedback cycle that activates

and attracts greater and greater numbers of platelets to the area begins and, within one minute, a platelet plug is built up, which further reduces blood loss. The platelet plug is limited to the immediate area where it is needed by the prostaglandin **PGI$_2$** produced by the endothelial cells. Also called **prostacyclin**, PGI$_2$ is a strong inhibitor of platelet aggregation. Platelet plugs are loosely knit, but, when they are reinforced by fibrin threads, they are quite effective in sealing the small tears in a blood vessel that occur with normal activity. Once the platelet plug is formed, the next stage, coagulation, comes into play.

Coagulation

Coagulation or **blood clotting** (Figure 18.11a), during which blood is transformed from a liquid to a gel, is basically a three-phase process.

1. A complex substance called *prothrombin activator* is formed.

2. Prothrombin activator converts a plasma protein called *prothrombin* into *thrombin.*

3. Thrombin catalyzes the joining of *fibrinogen* molecules present in plasma to a *fibrin mesh,* which traps blood cells and effectively seals the hole until the blood vessel can be permanently repaired.

The complete coagulation process is much more complicated, however: Over 30 different substances are involved. Factors that enhance clot formation are called **procoagulants** or **coagulation factors.** Although vitamin K is not directly involved in coagulation, this fat-soluble vitamin is required for the synthesis of four of the procoagulants made by the liver (see Table 18.3). Factors that inhibit clotting are called **anticoagulants.** Whether or not blood clots depends on a delicate balance between these two groups of factors. Normally, anticoagulants dominate and clotting is prevented; but when a vessel is ruptured, procoagulant activity in that area increases dramatically and clot formation begins. The procoagulants are numbered I to XIII (Table 18.3) according to the order of their discovery; hence the numerical order does *not* reflect the reaction sequence. Thromboplastin (III) and Ca^{2+} (IV) are usually indicated by their names, rather than by numerals. Most of these factors are plasma proteins made by the liver that circulate in an inactive form in blood until mobilized.

Phase 1: Two Pathways

Clotting may be initiated by either the **intrinsic** or the **extrinsic pathway,** and in the body both pathways are usually triggered by the same tissue-damaging events. Clotting of blood outside the body (such as in a test tube) is initiated only by the intrinsic mechanism, whereas clotting of blood that has escaped into the

tissues is promoted by the extrinsic pathway. Let's examine the "why" of these differences.

A pivotal molecule in both mechanisms is a phospholipid called **PF$_3$,** which is associated with the external surfaces of aggregated platelets. Apparently, many intermediates of both pathways can be activated only in the presence of PF$_3$. In the slower intrinsic pathway, all factors needed for clotting are present in (intrinsic to) the blood. By contrast, when blood is exposed to an additional factor released by injured cells called **tissue thromboplastin,** or **tissue factor (TF),** the "shortcut" extrinsic mechanism, which completely bypasses several steps of the intrinsic pathway, is triggered. Each pathway requires ionic calcium and involves the activation of a *series* of procoagulants, each functioning as an enzyme to activate the next procoagulant in the sequence. The intermediate steps of each pathway *cascade* toward a common intermediate, factor X (Figure 18.11b). Once factor X has been activated, it complexes with tissue thromboplastin or PF$_3$, factor V, and calcium ions to form **prothrombin activator.** This step is usually the slowest step of the blood clotting process, but once accomplished, the clot forms within 10 to 15 seconds.

Phase 2: Common Pathway

Prothrombin activator catalyzes the transformation of the plasma protein **prothrombin** to the active enzyme **thrombin.**

Phase 3: Common Pathway

Thrombin catalyzes the polymerization of **fibrinogen** (another plasma protein made by the liver). As the fibrinogen molecules become aligned into long, hairlike, insoluble **fibrin** strands, they glue the platelets together and intertwine to make a web that forms the structural basis of the clot. In the presence of fibrin, plasma becomes gel-like and traps formed elements that pass through it (Figure 18.12).

In the presence of calcium ions, thrombin also activates **factor XIII (fibrin stabilizing factor),** a cross-linking enzyme that binds the fibrin strands tightly together and strengthens and stabilizes the clot. Clot formation is normally complete within 3 to 6 minutes after blood vessel damage. Because the extrinsic pathway involves fewer steps, it is more rapid than the intrinsic pathway, and in cases of severe tissue trauma, the extrinsic mechanism can promote clot formation within 15 seconds.

Clot Retraction and Repair

Within 30 to 60 minutes the clot is stabilized further by a platelet-induced process called **clot retraction.** Platelets contain a contractile protein complex called **actomyosin** and they contract in much the same manner as muscle cells. As the platelets contract, they cre-

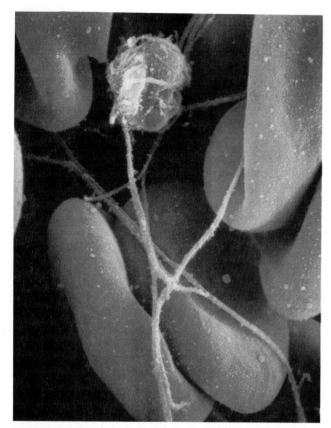

FIGURE 18.12
Scanning electron micrograph of erythrocytes trapped in a fibrin mesh. The more-or-less spherical gray object (top center of photo) is a platelet (15,000 ×).

ate a pull on the surrounding fibrin strands, squeezing **serum** (plasma minus the clotting proteins) from the mass. As a result, the clot is compacted and the ruptured edges of the blood vessel are drawn more closely together. Even as clot retraction is occurring, vessel healing is also taking place. **Platelet-derived growth factor (PDGF)** released by platelet degranulation stimulates smooth muscle and fibroblasts to divide and rebuild the wall. As fibroblasts form a connective tissue patch in the injured area, endothelial cells multiply to restore the endothelial lining.

Fibrinolysis

A clot is not meant to be a permanent solution to blood vessel injury, and a process called **fibrinolysis** removes unneeded clots when healing has occurred. Because small clots are formed continually in vessels throughout the body, this cleanup detail is crucial. Without fibrinolysis, blood vessels would gradually become completely occluded.

The critical natural "clot buster" is a fibrin-digesting enzyme called **plasmin,** produced when the blood protein **plasminogen** is activated. Large

amounts of plasminogen are incorporated into a forming clot, where it remains inactive until appropriate signals reach it. The presence of a clot in and around the blood vessel causes the endothelial cells to secrete **tissue plasminogen activator (t-PA).** Activated factor XII and thrombin released during clotting also serve as plasminogen activators. As a result, most plasmin activity is confined to the clot, and any plasmin that strays into the plasma is quickly destroyed by circulating enzymes. Fibrinolysis begins within two days and continues slowly over several days until the clot is finally dissolved.

Factors Limiting Clot Growth or Formation

Factors Limiting Normal Clot Growth

Once the clotting cascade has begun, it continues until a clot is formed. Normally, two important homeostatic mechanisms prevent clots from becoming unnecessarily large: (1) swift removal of coagulation factors, and (2) inhibition of activated clotting factors. For clotting to occur in the first place, the concentration of activated procoagulants must reach certain critical levels. Any tendency toward clot formation in rapidly moving blood is usually unsuccessful because the activated clotting factors are diluted, washed away, and prevented from accumulating. For the same reasons, further growth of a forming clot is hindered when it contacts normally flowing blood.

Other mechanisms block the final step in which fibrinogen is polymerized into fibrin by restricting thrombin to the clot or inactivating it if it manages to escape into the general circulation. As a clot forms, almost all of the thrombin produced is adsorbed (bound) onto the fibrin threads. This is an important safeguard, because thrombin also exerts positive feedback effects on the coagulation process prior to the common pathway. Not only does it speed up the production of prothrombin activator by acting indirectly through factor V, but it also accelerates the earliest steps of the intrinsic pathway by activating platelets. Thus, fibrin effectively acts as an anticoagulant to prevent enlargement of the clot and prevents thrombin from acting elsewhere. Thrombin not adsorbed to fibrin is quickly inactivated by **antithrombin III,** an alpha-globulin protein present in plasma. Antithrombin III also inhibits the activity of other intrinsic pathway procoagulants, as does **protein C,** another protein produced in the liver.

Heparin, the natural anticoagulant contained in the granules of basophils and mast cells and also produced by endothelial cells, is ordinarily secreted in small amounts into the plasma. It acts as a thrombin inhibitor by enhancing the activity of antithrombin III. Heparin, like most other clotting inhibitors, also inhibits the intrinsic pathway.

Factors Preventing Undesirable Clotting

Factors that normally ward off unnecessary clotting include both structural and molecular characteristics of the endothelial lining of blood vessels. As long as the endothelium is smooth and intact, platelets are prevented from clinging and piling up. Also, the antithrombic substances—heparin and prostacyclin—secreted by the endothelial cells normally prevent platelet adherence. PGI_2 secreted by the endothelial surface actively repels the platelets as they pass by in the bloodstream.

Disorders of Hemostasis

Though blood clotting is one of nature's most elegant creations, it sometimes goes awry, disrupting homeostasis. The two major disorders of hemostasis are at opposite poles. **Thromboembolytic disorders** result from conditions that cause undesirable clot formation. **Bleeding disorders** arise from abnormalities that prevent normal clot formation.

Thromboembolytic Conditions

Despite the body's many safeguards, undesirable intravascular clotting sometimes occurs. A clot that develops and persists in an *unbroken* blood vessel is called a **thrombus.** If the thrombus is large enough, it may block circulation to the cells beyond the occlusion and lead to the death of those tissues. For example, if the blockage occurs in the coronary circulation of the heart (coronary thrombosis), the consequences may be the death of heart muscle and a fatal heart attack. If the thrombus breaks away from the vessel wall and floats freely in the bloodstream, it becomes an **embolus** (plural, *emboli*). An embolus ("wedge") is usually no problem until it encounters a blood vessel that is too narrow for it to pass through. For example, emboli that become trapped in the lungs (pulmonary emboli) can dangerously impair the ability of the body to obtain oxygen, while a cerebral embolus may cause a stroke. Drugs that dissolve blood clots (such as t-PA and streptokinase) and innovative medical techniques for removing clots are described in *A Closer Look* on pp. 648–649 in Chapter 20.

Conditions that roughen the vessel endothelium, such as arteriosclerosis, severe burns, or inflammation, cause thromboembolytic disease by allowing platelets to gain a foothold. Slowly flowing blood or blood stasis is another risk factor, particularly in immobilized patients, and those taking a long flight in economy-class seats. In this case, clotting factors are *not* washed away as usual and accumulate so that clot formation finally becomes possible.

A number of drugs, most importantly aspirin, heparin, and dicumarol, are used clinically to prevent undesirable clotting in patients at risk for heart attack and/or stroke. **Aspirin** is an antiprostaglandin drug that inhibits thromboxane A_2 formation (hence, platelet aggregation and platelet plug formation). Clinical studies of men taking low-dose aspirin (one aspirin every two days) over a period of several years demonstrated a 50% reduction in (anticipated) incidence of heart attack. Heparin (see above) is also prescribed as an anticoagulant drug, as is warfarin, an ingredient in rat poison. **Warfarin** (coumadin) is a mainstay in the treatment of those prone to atrial fibrillation, a condition in which blood pools in the heart, to reduce the risk of stroke. It works via a different mechanism than heparin; it interferes with the action of vitamin K (see Impaired Liver Function below).

Bleeding Disorders

Anything that interferes with the clotting mechanism can result in abnormal bleeding. The most common causes are platelet deficiency (thrombocytopenia) and deficits of some of the procoagulants such as might result from impaired liver function or certain genetic conditions (hemophilias).

Thrombocytopenia. Thrombocytopenia (throm″-bo-si″to-pe′ne-ah), a condition in which the number of circulating platelets is deficient, causes spontaneous bleeding from small blood vessels all over the body. Even normal movement leads to widespread hemorrhage, evidenced by many small purplish blotches, called *petechiae* (pe-te′ke-e), on the skin. Thrombocytopenia can arise from any condition that suppresses or destroys the bone marrow, such as bone marrow malignancy, exposure to ionizing radiation, or certain drugs. A platelet count of under 50,000 platelets per cubic millimeter of blood is usually diagnostic for this condition. Whole blood transfusions provide temporary relief from bleeding.

Impaired Liver Function. When the liver is unable to synthesize its usual supply of procoagulants, abnormal, and often severe, bleeding occurs. The resulting problems can range from an easily resolved vitamin K deficiency (common in newborns and after taking systemic antibiotics) to nearly total impairment of liver function (as in hepatitis or cirrhosis). Vitamin K is required by the liver cells for production of the clotting factors and, because vitamin K is produced by bacteria that reside in the intestines, dietary deficiencies are rarely a problem. However, vitamin K deficiency can occur if fat absorption is impaired, because vitamin K is a fat-soluble vitamin that is absorbed into the blood along with fats. In liver disease the nonfunctional liver cells fail to produce not only the procoagulants but also bile, which is required for fat and vitamin K absorption.

Hemophilias. The term **hemophilia** refers to several different hereditary bleeding disorders that have similar signs and symptoms. *Hemophilia A,* or *classical hemophilia,* results from a deficiency of **factor VIII (antihemophilic factor).** This is the most common type of hemophilia and accounts for 83% of cases. *Hemophilia B* results from a deficiency of factor IX. Both types are sex-linked conditions occurring primarily in males.

Symptoms of hemophilia begin early in life; even minor tissue trauma causes prolonged bleeding into tissues that can be life threatening. Commonly, the person's joints become seriously disabled and painful because of repeated bleeding into the joint cavities after exercise or trauma. Regardless of type, hemophilia is managed clinically by transfusions of fresh plasma or injections of the appropriate purified clotting factor. These therapies provide relief for several days but are expensive and inconvenient. Because hemophiliacs are absolutely dependent on blood transfusions or factor injections, many have become recipients of the hepatitis virus and, since the early 1980s, of HIV, a blood-transmitted virus that severely depresses the immune system causing AIDS. (See Chapter 22.) This dilemma has been resolved because of new testing methods for HIV and the availability of genetically engineered factor VIII. •

TRANSFUSION AND BLOOD REPLACEMENT

Transfusion of Whole Blood

The human cardiovascular system is designed to minimize the effects of blood loss by (1) reducing the volume of the affected blood vessels, which helps to maintain normal circulation, and (2) stepping up the production of red blood cells. However, the body can compensate for only so much blood loss. Losses of 15% to 30% cause pallor and weakness. A loss of more than 30% of blood volume results in severe shock, which can be fatal.

Whole blood transfusions are routine when blood loss is substantial and when treating thrombocytopenia. Infusions of **packed red cells** (whole blood from which most of the plasma has been removed) are preferred to treat anemia. The usual blood bank procedure involves collecting blood from a donor and then mixing it with an anticoagulant, such as certain citrate and oxalate salts, which prevents clotting by binding with calcium ions. The blood can then be stored for several weeks at 4°C until needed. When freshly collected blood is to be transfused, heparin is used as the anticoagulant.

Human Blood Groups

People have different blood types and transfusion of incompatible blood can be fatal. RBC plasma membranes, like those of all body cells, bear highly specific glycoproteins (antigens) at their external surfaces, which identify each of us as unique from all others. One person's erythrocyte proteins may be recognized as foreign if transfused into another person with a different red blood cell type, and the transfused cells may be agglutinated (clumped) and destroyed. Since these RBC antigens promote agglutination, they are more specifically called **agglutinogens** (ag"loo-tin′o-jenz).

There are at least 30 common varieties of naturally occurring red blood cell antigens in humans. Besides these, there are perhaps 100 others that occur in individual families ("private antigens") rather than in the general population. The presence or absence of each antigen allows each person's blood cells to be classified into several different blood groups. The antigens determining the ABO and Rh blood groups cause vigorous transfusion reactions (in which the foreign erythrocytes are destroyed) when they are improperly transfused. Thus, blood typing for these antigens is *always* done before blood is transfused. Other antigens (such as the M, N, Duffy, Kell, and Lewis factors) are mainly of legal or academic importance. Because these factors cause weak or no transfusion reactions, blood is not usually typed for them unless the person is expected to need several transfusions, in which case the many weak transfusion reactions could have cumulative effects. Only the ABO and Rh blood groups are described here.

ABO Blood Groups.

As shown in Table 18.4, the **ABO blood groups** are based on the presence or absence of two agglutinogens, type A and type B. Depending on which of these a person inherits, his or her ABO blood group will be one of the following: A, B, AB, or O. The O blood group, which has neither agglutinogen, is the most common ABO blood group in white, black, and Asian Americans; AB, with both antigens, is the least prevalent. The presence of either the A or the B agglutinogen results in group A or B, respectively.

Unique to the ABO blood groups is the presence in the plasma of *preformed antibodies* called **agglutinins.** The agglutinins act against RBCs carrying ABO antigens that are *not* present on a person's own red blood cells. A newborn has none of these antibodies, but they begin to appear in the plasma within 2 months. They reach peak levels between 8 and 10 years of age and then slowly decline throughout the rest of life. As indicated in Table 18.4, a baby with neither the A nor the B antigen (group O) forms both anti-A and anti-B antibodies, also called *a* and *b*

Table 18.4 ABO Blood Groups

| Blood group | Frequency (% U.S. Population) | | | | RBC antigens (agglutinogens) | Illustration | Plasma antibodies (agglutinins) | Blood that can be received |
	White	Black	Asian	Native American				
AB	4	4	5	<1	A B		None	A, B, AB, O Universal recipient
B	11	20	27	4	B		Anti-A (a)	B, O
A	40	27	28	16	A		Anti-B (b)	A, O
O	45	49	40	79	None		Anti-A (a) Anti-B (b)	O Universal donor

agglutinins respectively. Those with group A blood form anti-B antibodies, while those with group B form anti-A antibodies. Neither antibody is produced by AB infants.

Rh Blood Groups. There are at least eight different types of Rh agglutinogens, each of which is called an **Rh factor.** Only three of these, the C, D, and E antigens, are fairly common. The Rh blood typing system is so named because one Rh antigen (agglutinogen D) was originally identified in *rhesus* monkeys; later the same antigen was discovered in human beings. Most Americans (about 85%) are Rh+ (Rh positive), meaning that their RBCs carry the Rh antigen.

Unlike the ABO system, anti-Rh antibodies are not spontaneously formed in the blood of Rh⁻ (Rh negative) individuals. However, if an Rh⁻ person receives Rh+ blood, the immune system becomes sensitized and, shortly after the transfusion, begins producing anti-Rh antibodies against the foreign antigen. Hemolysis does not occur after the first such transfusion because it takes time for the body to react and start making antibodies. But the second time, and every time thereafter, a typical transfusion reaction occurs in which the recipient's antibodies attack and rupture the donor RBCs.

An important problem related to the Rh factor occurs in pregnant Rh⁻ women who are carrying Rh+ babies. The first such pregnancy usually results in the delivery of a healthy baby. But because the mother is sensitized by her baby's Rh+ antigens that have passed through the placenta into her bloodstream, she will form anti-Rh antibodies unless treated with RhoGAM before or shortly after she has given birth. (The same precautions are taken in women who have miscarried or aborted the fetus.) RhoGAM is a serum containing anti-Rh agglutinins. Because it agglutinates the Rh factor, it blocks the mother's immune response and prevents her sensitization. If the mother is not treated and becomes pregnant again with an Rh+ baby, her antibodies will cross through the placenta and destroy the baby's RBCs, producing a condition known as **hemolytic disease of the newborn,** or **erythroblastosis fetalis.** The baby becomes anemic and hypoxic. Brain damage and even death may result unless transfusions are done *before* birth to provide the fetus with more erythrocytes for oxygen transport. Additionally, one or two *exchange transfusions* (see Related Clinical Terms, p. 609) are done after birth. The baby's Rh+ blood is removed, and Rh⁻ blood is infused. Within 6 weeks, the transfused Rh⁻ erythrocytes have been broken down and replaced with the baby's own Rh+ cells. •

Transfusion Reactions: Agglutination and Hemolysis

When mismatched blood is infused, a **transfusion reaction** occurs in which the donor's red blood cells are avidly attacked by the recipient's plasma agglutinins. (Note that the donor's plasma antibodies are *also* agglutinating the host's RBCs, but they are so diluted in the recipient's circulation that this does not usually present a serious problem.)

The initial event, agglutination of the foreign red blood cells, leads to clogging of small blood vessels throughout the body. During the next few hours, the clumped red blood cells begin to rupture or are destroyed by phagocytes, and their hemoglobin is released into the bloodstream. (When the transfusion reaction is exceptionally severe, the RBCs are lysed almost immediately.) These events lead to two easily recognized problems: (1) The oxygen-carrying capability of the transfused blood cells is disrupted, and (2) the clumping of red blood cells in small vessels hinders blood flow to tissues beyond those points. Less apparent, but more devastating, is the consequence of hemoglobin escaping into the bloodstream. Circulating hemoglobin passes freely into the kidney tubules and, when in high concentration, it precipitates, blocking the kidney tubules and causing renal shutdown. If shutdown is complete (acute renal failure), the person may die.

Transfusion reactions can also cause fever, chills, nausea, vomiting, and general toxicity; but in the absence of renal shutdown, these reactions are rarely lethal. Treatment of transfusion reactions is directed toward preventing kidney damage by infusing alkaline fluids to dilute and dissolve the hemoglobin and wash it out of the body. Diuretics, which increase urine output, are also given. •

As indicated in Table 18.4, group O red blood cells bear neither the A nor the B antigen; thus, theoretically this blood group is the **universal donor.** Indeed, some medical centers are busily involved in enzymatically converting type B blood to type O by clipping off the extra (B-specific) sugar residue. Since group AB plasma is devoid of antibodies to both A and B antigens, group AB people are theoretically **universal recipients** and can receive blood transfusions from any of the ABO groups. However, these classifications are misleading, because they do not take into account the other agglutinogens in blood that can trigger transfusion reactions.

Because homologous (pooled blood) transfusions carry the risk of transfusion reactions and transmission of life-threatening infections (particularly with HIV), public interest in **autologous transfusions** has awakened. Autologous (*auto* = self) transfusions are particularly sought by those considering elective surgery when they are in no immediate danger. The patient *predonates* his or her own blood and it is stored and immediately available if needed during or after the operation. Iron supplements are given, and

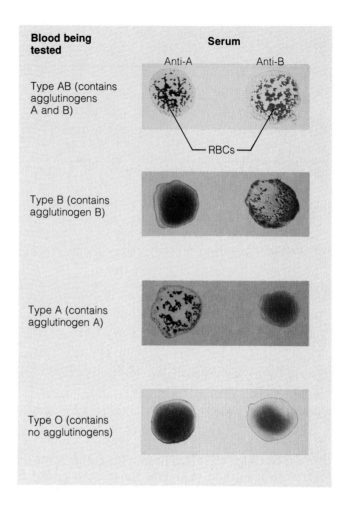

FIGURE 18.13
Blood typing of ABO blood types. When serum containing anti-A or anti-B agglutinins is added to a blood sample diluted with saline, agglutination will occur between the agglutinin and the corresponding agglutinogen (A or B). As illustrated, agglutination occurs with both sera in blood group AB, with anti-B serum in blood group B, with anti-A serum in blood group A, and with neither serum in blood group O.

as long as the patient's preoperative hematocrit is at least 30%, one unit (400 to 500 ml) of blood can be collected every 4 days, with the last unit taken 72 hours prior to surgery.

Blood Typing

The importance of determining the blood group of both the donor and the recipient *before* blood is transfused is glaringly obvious. The general procedure for determining ABO blood type is briefly outlined in Figure 18.13. Because it is critical that blood groups be compatible, cross matching is also done. *Cross matching* tests for agglutination of donor RBCs by the recipient's serum, and of the recipient's RBCs by the donor serum. Typing for the Rh factors is done in the same manner as ABO blood typing.

Plasma and Blood Volume Expanders

When a patient's blood volume is so low that death from shock may be imminent, there may not be time to type blood or appropriate whole blood may be unavailable. Such emergencies demand that blood *volume* be replaced immediately to restore adequate circulation. Although there is not yet a satisfactory whole blood substitute, research is ongoing as described in *A Closer Look* on p. 608.

Plasma can be administered to anyone without concern about a transfusion reaction because the antibodies it contains become harmlessly diluted in the recipient's blood. Except for red blood cells, plasma provides a complete and natural blood replacement. When plasma is not available, various colloidal solutions, or **plasma expanders,** such as *purified human serum albumin, plasminate,* and *dextran* can be infused. All of these have osmotic properties that directly increase the fluid volume of blood. Still another option is to infuse isotonic salt solutions. *Normal saline* or a *multiple electrolyte solution* that mimics the electrolyte composition of plasma (for example, *Ringer's solution*) is a common choice.

DIAGNOSTIC BLOOD TESTS

A laboratory examination of blood yields information that can be used to evaluate a person's current state of health. For example, in some anemias, the blood is pale and yields a low hematocrit. A high fat content *(lipidemia)* gives blood a yellowish hue and forecasts possible problems in those with heart disease. How well a diabetic is controlling diet and blood sugar levels is routinely determined by blood glucose tests. Infections are signaled by leukocytosis and larger than normal buffy coats in the hematocrit. In some types of leukemias, the leukocyte-containing layer may be larger than the erythrocyte layer.

Microscopic studies of blood can reveal variations in the size and shape of erythrocytes that predict iron deficiency or pernicious anemia. Furthermore, a determination of the relative proportion of individual leukocyte types, a **differential white blood cell count,** is a valuable diagnostic tool; for example, a high eosinophil count may indicate a parasitic infection or an allergic response somewhere in the body.

A number of tests provide information on the status of the hemostasis system. For example, the amount of prothrombin present in blood is assessed by determining the **prothrombin time,** and a **platelet count** is done when thrombocytopenia is suspected.

Two batteries of tests—a SMAC, SMA12-60, or similar series, and a **complete blood count (CBC)**—are routinely ordered during physical examinations and before hospital admissions. SMAC is a blood *chemistry* profile. The CBC includes counts of the different types of formed elements, a hematocrit, and tests for clotting factors. Together these tests provide a comprehensive picture of one's general health status in relation to normal blood values.

A listing of the normal values for selected blood tests is provided in Appendix G.

DEVELOPMENTAL ASPECTS OF BLOOD

Before birth, there are many sites of blood cell formation—the fetal yolk sac, liver, and spleen, among others—but by the seventh month of development, the red marrow has become the primary hematopoietic area and remains so (barring serious illness) throughout life. If there is a severe need for blood cell production, however, the liver and the spleen may resume their fetal blood-forming roles. Additionally, inactive yellow bone marrow regions (essentially fatty tissue) may reconvert to active red marrow.

Blood cells develop from collections of mesenchymal cells, called *blood islands,* derived from the mesoderm germ layer. During fetal life, a unique hemoglobin, **hemoglobin F,** is formed that has a higher affinity for oxygen than does adult hemoglobin (hemoglobin A). It contains two alpha and two gamma (γ) polypeptide chains per globin molecule, instead of the paired alpha and beta chains typical of hemoglobin A. After birth, fetal erythrocytes carrying hemoglobin F are rapidly destroyed by the liver, and the baby's erythrocytes begin to produce hemoglobin A.

The most common diseases of the blood that appear during aging are chronic types of leukemias, anemias, and thromboembolytic disease. However, these and most other age-related blood disorders are usually precipitated by disorders of the heart, blood vessels, or immune system. For example, the increased incidence of leukemias in old age is believed to result from the waning efficiency of the immune system, and abnormal thrombus and embolus formation reflects the progress of atherosclerosis, which roughens the blood vessel walls. Anemias that appear in the elderly are often secondary to nutritional deficiencies, drug therapy, or some disorder such as cancer or leukemia. However, the elderly are particularly at risk for pernicious anemia because the stomach mucosa (which produces intrinsic factor) atrophies with age.

* * *

Because blood serves as the vehicle by which the cardiovascular system transports substances throughout the body, it could be considered the servant of the cardiovascular system. On the other hand, without blood, the normal functions of the heart and blood vessels would be impossible. So perhaps the organs of the cardiovascular system, described in Chapters 19 and 20, are subservient to blood. The point of this circular thinking is that blood and the cardiovascular system organs are vitally intertwined in their common functions—to see that nutrients, oxygen, and other vital substances reach all tissue cells of the body and to relieve the cells of their wastes.

The term "blood substitute" is somewhat misleading. Blood has many components that play such a wide variety of roles—from fighting infection to transporting oxygen—that no single artificial substitute yet engineered can fulfill all those functions. However, substitute liquids are available that can transport oxygen from the lungs through the body and can "stretch" a limited blood supply, while sidestepping transfusion reactions. An important benefit of these blood substitutes is that the recipient is not at risk for transmission of blood-borne disease factors. Four of these oxygen-transporting products—Fluosol, chemically altered hemoglobin, artificial red blood cells, and Hemopure—are described briefly.

Fluosol

The main ingredient of *Fluosol,* a milky artificial blood substitute, is a chemical related to the nonstick coating used in cookware. Developed in Japan, the product was first tested in the United States in 1982. Many of the early recipients were people who needed surgery but refused blood transfusions on religious grounds.

Fluosol serves as a dissolving medium for oxygen. In order to "load" sufficient amounts of oxygen into it, patients must breathe pure oxygen by mask or must be in a hyperbaric (high-pressure) chamber. The developers claim that oxygen transported by Fluosol is used more easily by the body tissues because the slippery particles are much smaller than erythrocytes and glide through the capillaries at a faster rate. Although initially promising for therapy of heart attack, carbon monoxide poisoning, and sickle-cell anemia, its use has been clouded by research indicating that Fluosol may depress the patient's immune system. Yet, use of Fluosol to keep donor organs oxygenated while being readied for transplant, and to protect heart muscle from ischemia during a heart attack, still appears promising.

Chemically Altered Hemoglobin

In their search to find a substitute to boost oxygen delivery, scientists have altered the chemistry of hemoglobin

Normal red blood cell and smaller hemoglobin-carrying artificial red cells (neohemocytes) in front of a capillary.

by creating a chemical bridge between two of its four peptide chains and by linking several hemoglobin molecules together. Animal tests have shown that the altered hemoglobin gives up more oxygen to the tissues than normal hemoglobin, even at low temperatures (10°C). Since body temperature is routinely lowered in patients undergoing heart surgery, using the modified hemoglobin during such procedures might boost oxygen delivery to the patient's tissues. An additional plus is that because the cross-linked form of hemoglobin is prevented from fragmenting in the blood (as natural hemoglobin does), the necessity for a RBC plasma membrane "container" is eliminated.

Although test results are promising, there are still important problems to be solved. For example, bacterial endotoxins, potent poisons produced by some bacteria, tend to cling to the modified hemoglobin and there is some evidence that the free hemoglobin provokes a generalized constriction of blood vessels, making oxygen delivery more difficult. Additionally, since the chemically modified hemoglobin is derived from erythrocytes, the risk of transmitting viral and bacterial diseases still exists.

Neohemocytes

Researchers at the University of California at San Francisco have created artificial RBCs, which they call *neohemocytes,* by packaging natural hemoglobin molecules in fat bubbles made from phospholipids and cholesterol. The resulting "red cells" are about one-twelfth the size of human erythrocytes. Although the neohemocytes are destroyed and cleared more rapidly from the bloodstream than are real RBCs, they have a shelf life of 6 months (versus about 35 days for whole blood). This would make neohemocyte infusion a viable choice for trauma patients in immediate need of blood, but clinical trials on humans are still in the distant future.

Hemopure

Hemopure, a natural but nonhuman blood substitute recently approved by the FDA, contains purified hemoglobin extracted from cattle blood. Because there are no plasma membranes to deal with, cross reactions should not be a problem.

Although the FDA has encouraged the development of artificial blood for over 20 years, no marketable product, including those described above, has been approved for anything but experimental use in humans. Blood is still a priceless commodity, and its beautiful complexity has yet to be replaced by modern medical technology.

RELATED CLINICAL TERMS

Blood chemistry tests Chemical analysis of various chemical substances in the blood, e.g., glucose, iron, or calcium determinations, protein tests, bilirubin content, and pH.

Blood fraction Any one of the components of whole blood that has been separated out from the other blood components, such as platelets or clotting factors.

Bone marrow biopsy A sample of red bone marrow is obtained by needle aspiration (typically from the sternum or the iliac crest), and is examined to diagnose disorders of blood-cell formation, leukemia, various marrow infections, and anemias resulting from damage to or failure of the marrow.

Exchange transfusion Direct transfer of blood from a donor to a recipient, as the recipient's blood is being removed; a technique to treat fetal blood incompatibilities and poisoning victims.

Hematology (hem″ah-tol′-o-je) Study of blood.

Hematoma (hem″ah-to′mah) Accumulated, clotted blood in the tissues usually resulting from injury; visible as "black and blue" marks or bruises; eventually absorbed naturally unless infections develop.

Hemochromatosis (he″mo-kro″mah-to′sis) A disorder of iron overload.

Plasmapheresis (plaz″mah-fe-re′sis) Chemical filtering technique used to cleanse plasma of specific blood components such as proteins or toxins. Most important application appears to be for removal of antibodies or immune complexes from the blood of individuals with autoimmune disorders (multiple sclerosis, myasthenia gravis, and others).

Septicemia (sep″ti-se′me-ah; *septos* = rotten) Situation of excessive and harmful levels of bacteria or their toxins in the blood; also called blood poisoning.

CHAPTER SUMMARY

Overview: Composition and Functions of Blood (pp. 585–586)

Components (p. 585)
1. Blood is composed of formed elements and plasma.

Physical Characteristics and Volume (p. 585)
2. Blood is a viscous, slightly alkaline fluid representing about 8% of total body weight. Blood volume of a normal adult is about 5 L.

Functions (pp. 585–586)
3. Distribution functions are delivery of oxygen and nutrients to body tissues, removal of metabolic wastes, and transport of hormones.

4. Regulation functions are maintenance of body temperature, of constant blood pH, and of adequate fluid volume.

5. Protective functions include hemostasis and prevention of infection.

Blood Plasma (pp. 586–587)

1. Plasma is a straw-colored, viscous fluid composed of 90% water. The remaining 10% is solutes, such as nutrients, respiratory gases, salts, hormones, and proteins. Plasma makes up 55% of whole blood.

2. Plasma proteins, most made by the liver, include albumin, globulins, and clotting proteins. Albumin is an important blood buffer and contributes to the osmotic pressure of blood.

Formed Elements (pp. 587–598)

1. Formed elements, accounting for 45% of whole blood, are erythrocytes, leukocytes, and platelets. All formed elements arise from hemocytoblasts in red bone marrow.

Erythrocytes (pp. 587–593)
2. Erythrocytes (red blood cells) are small biconcave cells containing large amounts of hemoglobin. They have no nucleus and few organelles. Spectrin allows the cells to change shape as they pass through tiny capillaries.

3. Oxygen transport is the major function of erythrocytes. In the lungs, oxygen binds to iron atoms in hemoglobin molecules, producing oxyhemoglobin. In body tissues, oxygen dissociates from iron, producing deoxyhemoglobin.

4. Red blood cells begin as hemocytoblasts and, through erythropoiesis, proceed from the proerythroblast (committed cell) stage to the erythroblast (early and late), normoblast, and reticulocyte stages. During this process, hemoglobin accumulates and the organelles and nucleus are extruded. Differentiation of reticulocytes is completed in the bloodstream.

5. Erythropoietin and testosterone enhance erythropoiesis.

6. Iron, vitamin B_{12}, and folic acid are essential for production of hemoglobin.

7. Red blood cells have a life span of approximately 120 days. Old and damaged erythrocytes are removed from the circulation by macrophages of liver and spleen. Released iron from hemoglobin is stored as ferritin or hemosiderin to be reused. The balance of the heme group is degraded to bilirubin and secreted in bile. Amino acids of globin are metabolized or recycled.

8. Erythrocyte disorders include anemias and polycythemia.

Leukocytes (pp. 594–598)
9. Leukocytes are white blood cells. All are nucleated, and all have crucial roles in defending against disease. Two main categories exist: granulocytes and agranulocytes.

10. Granulocytes include neutrophils, basophils, and eosinophils. Basophils contain histamine, which enhances migration of leukocytes to inflammatory sites and promotes vasodilation. Neutrophils are active phagocytes. Eosinophils attack parasitic worms and their numbers increase during allergic reactions.

11. Agranulocytes have crucial roles in immunity. They include lymphocytes, the "immune cells," and monocytes, which differentiate into macrophages.

12. Leukopoiesis is directed by colony-stimulating factors released mainly by lymphocytes.

13. Leukocyte disorders include leukemias and infectious mononucleosis.

Platelets (p. 598)
14. Platelets are fragments of large, multinucleate megakaryocytes formed in red marrow. When a blood vessel is damaged, platelets form a plug to help prevent blood loss and play a central role in the clotting cascade.

Hemostasis (pp. 598–604)

1. Hemostasis is prevention of blood loss. The three major phases of hemostasis are vascular spasms, platelet plug formation, and blood coagulation.

Coagulation (p. 601)

2. Coagulation of blood may be initiated by either the intrinsic or the extrinsic pathway. Platelet phospholipid (PF_3) is crucial to both pathways. Thromboplastin generated by tissue cell injury allows the extrinsic pathway to bypass many steps of the intrinsic pathway. A series of activated procoagulants oversees the intermediate steps of each cascade. The pathways converge as prothrombin is converted to thrombin.

Clot Retraction and Repair (pp. 601–602)

3. After a clot is formed, clot retraction occurs. Serum is squeezed out and the ruptured vessel edges are drawn together. The vessel is repaired by smooth muscle, connective tissue, and endothelial cell proliferation and migration.

Fibrinolysis (p. 602)

4. When healing is complete, clot digestion (fibrinolysis) occurs.

Factors Limiting Clot Growth or Formation (pp. 602–603)

5. Abnormal expansion of clots is prevented by removal of coagulation factors in contact with rapidly flowing blood and by inhibition of activated blood factors. Prostacyclin (PGI_2) secreted by the endothelial cells helps prevent undesirable (unnecessary) clotting.

Disorders of Hemostasis (pp. 603–604)

6. Thromboembolytic disorders involve undesirable clot formation, which can occlude vessels.

7. Thrombocytopenia, a deficit of platelets, causes spontaneous bleeding from small blood vessels. Hemophilia is caused by a genetic deficiency of certain coagulation factors. Liver disease can also cause bleeding disorders because many coagulation proteins are formed by the liver.

Transfusion and Blood Replacement (pp. 604–607)

Transfusion of Whole Blood (pp. 604–606)

1. Whole blood transfusions are given to replace severe blood loss and to treat anemia or thrombocytopenia.

2. Blood group is based on agglutinogens (antigens) present on red blood cell membranes.

3. When mismatched blood is transfused, the recipient's agglutinins (plasma antibodies) clump the foreign RBCs; the clumped cells are then lysed. Blood vessels may be blocked by clumped RBCs; released hemoglobin may precipitate in the kidney tubules, causing renal shutdown.

4. Before whole blood can be transfused, it must be typed and cross matched so that transfusion reactions are avoided. The most important blood groups for which blood must be typed are the ABO and Rh groups.

Plasma and Blood Volume Expanders (p. 607)

5. Transfusions of plasma alone or plasma expanders are given when rapid replacement of blood volume is necessary.

Diagnostic Blood Tests (p. 607)

1. Diagnostic blood tests can provide large amounts of information about the current status of the blood and of the body as a whole.

Developmental Aspects of Blood (p. 607)

1. Fetal hematopoietic sites include the yolk sac, liver, and spleen. By the seventh month of development, the red bone marrow is the primary blood-forming site.

2. Blood cells develop from blood islands derived from mesoderm. Fetal blood contains hemoglobin F. After birth, hemoglobin A is formed.

3. The major blood-related problems associated with aging are leukemia, anemia, and thromboembolytic disease.

REVIEW QUESTIONS

Multiple Choice/Matching

1. The blood volume in an adult averages approximately (a) 1 L, (b) 3 L, (c) 5 L, (d) 7 L.

2. The hormonal stimulus that prompts red blood cell formation is (a) serotonin, (b) heparin, (c) erythropoietin, (d) thrombopoietin.

3. All of the following are true of RBCs except (a) biconcave disc shape, (b) life span of approximately 120 days, (c) contain hemoglobin, (d) contain nuclei.

4. The most numerous WBC is the (a) eosinophil, (b) neutrophil, (c) monocyte, (d) lymphocyte.

5. Blood proteins play an important part in (a) blood clotting, (b) immunity, (c) maintenance of blood volume, (d) all of the above.

6. The white blood cell that releases histamine and other inflammatory chemicals is the (a) basophil, (b) neutrophil, (c) monocyte, (d) eosinophil.

7. The blood cell that is said to be immunologically competent is the (a) lymphocyte, (b) megakaryocyte, (c) neutrophil, (d) basophil.

8. The normal erythrocyte count (per cubic millimeter) for adults is (a) 3 to 4 million, (b) 4.5 to 5 million, (c) 8 million, (d) 500,000.

9. The normal pH of the blood is about (a) 8.4, (b) 7.8, (c) 7.4, (d) 4.7.

10. Suppose your blood was found to be AB positive. This means that (a) agglutinogens A and B are present on your red blood cells, (b) there are no anti-A or anti-B agglutinins in your plasma, (c) your blood is Rh^+, (d) all of the above.

Short Answer Essay Questions

11. (a) Define formed elements and list their three major categories. (b) Which is least numerous? (c) Which comprise(s) the buffy coat in a hematocrit tube?

12. Discuss hemoglobin relative to its chemical structure, its function, and the color changes it undergoes during loading and unloading of oxygen.

13. If you had a high hematocrit, would you expect your hemoglobin determination to be low or high? Why?

14. What nutrients are needed for erythropoiesis?

15. (a) Describe the process of erythropoiesis. (b) What name is given to the immature cell type released to the circulation? (c) How does it differ from a mature erythrocyte?

16. Besides the ability to move by amoeboid action, what other physiological attributes contribute to the function of white blood cells in the body?

17. (a) If you had a severe infection, would you expect your WBC count to be closest to 5000, 10,000, or 15,000 per cubic millimeter? (b) What is this condition called?

18. (a) Describe the appearance of platelets and state their major function. (b) Why should platelets not be called "cells"?

19. (a) Define hemostasis. (b) List the three major steps of coagulation. Explain what initiates each step and what the step accomplishes. (c) In what general way do the intrinsic and extrinsic mechanisms of clotting differ? (d) What ion is essential to virtually all stages of coagulation?

20. (a) Define fibrinolysis. (b) What is the importance of this process?

21. (a) How is clot overgrowth usually prevented? (b) List two conditions that may lead to unnecessary (and undesirable) clot formation.

22. How can liver dysfunction cause bleeding disorders?

23. (a) What is a transfusion reaction and why does it happen? (b) What are its possible consequences?

24. How can poor nutrition lead to anemia?

25. What blood-related problems are most common in the aged?

CRITICAL THINKING AND CLINICAL APPLICATION QUESTIONS

1. Cancer patients being treated with chemotherapeutic drugs designed to destroy rapidly dividing cells are monitored closely for changes in their red and white blood counts. Why so?

2. A young woman with severe vaginal bleeding is admitted to the emergency room. She is 3 months pregnant, and the physician is concerned about the volume of blood she is losing. (a) What type of transfusion will probably be given to this patient? (b) What blood tests will be performed before starting the transfusion?

3. A middle-aged college professor from Boston is in the Swiss Alps studying astronomy during his sabbatical leave. He has been there for 2 days and plans to stay the entire year. However, he notices that he is short of breath when he walks up steps and tires easily with any physical activity. His symptoms gradually disappear, and after 2 months he feels fine. Upon returning to the United States, he has a complete physical exam and is told that his erythrocyte count is higher than normal. (a) Attempt to explain this finding. (b) Will his RBC count remain at this higher-than-normal level? Why or why not?

4. A young child is diagnosed as having acute lymphocytic leukemia. Her parents cannot understand why infection is a major problem for Janie when her WBC count is so high. Can you provide an explanation for Janie's parents?

5. Mrs. Ryan, a middle-aged woman, appears at the clinic complaining of multiple small hemorrhaged spots in her skin and severe nose bleeds. While taking her history, the nurse notes that Mrs. Ryan is taking apronal (a sleeping medication) because she has problems getting to sleep at night. This drug is known to be toxic to red marrow. Using your knowledge of physiology, explain the connection between the bleeding problems and the taking of apronal.

6. A reticulocyte count indicated that 5% of Tyler's red blood cells were reticulocytes. His blood test also indicated he had polycythemia and a hematocrit of 65%. Explain the connection between these three facts.

19 The Cardiovascular System: The Heart

The ceaselessly beating heart within the chest has intrigued people for centuries. The ancient Greeks believed that the heart was the seat of intelligence. Others have thought that it was the source of emotions. While these theories have proven false, we do know that the emotions affect heart rate. When your heart pounds or occasionally skips a beat, you become acutely aware of how much you depend on this dynamic organ for your very life.

Despite its vital importance, the heart does not work alone; it is part of the cardiovascular system, which also includes the blood vessels of the body. Day and night, tissue cells take in nutrients and oxygen and excrete wastes. Because cells can make such exchanges only with their immediate environment, some means of changing and renewing that environment is necessary to ensure a continual supply of nutrients and to prevent pollution from buildup of wastes. The cardiovascular system provides the transport system "hardware" that keeps blood continuously circulating to fulfill this critical homeostatic need.

When stripped of its romantic cloak, the **heart** is no more than the transport system pump; the hollow blood vessels are the delivery routes. Using blood as the transport medium, the heart continually propels oxygen, nutrients, wastes, and many other substances into the interconnecting blood vessels that move to and past the body cells. Blood and blood vessels are considered separately in Chapters 18 and 20, respectively. This chapter focuses on the structure and function of the heart.

(a)

(b) *Anterior*

FIGURE 19.1
Location of the heart in the mediastinum of the thorax.
(a) Relationship of the heart to the sternum, ribs, and diaphragm in a person who is lying down (the heart lies slightly inferior to this position in a standing person). **(b)** Cross-sectional view showing relative position of the heart in the thorax. **(c)** Relationship of the heart and great vessels to the lungs.

HEART ANATOMY

Size, Location, and Orientation

The relative size and weight of the heart belie its incredible strength and endurance. About the size of a fist, the hollow, cone-shaped heart looks enough like the popular valentine image to satisfy the sentimentalists among us (Figure 19.1). Typically, the heart weighs between 250 and 350 grams—less than a pound.

Snugly enclosed within the **mediastinum** (me″de-ah-sti′num), the medial cavity of the thorax, the heart extends for 12 to 14 cm (about 5 inches) from the second rib to the fifth intercostal space (Figure 19.1a). The heart lies anterior to the vertebral column and posterior to the sternum. The lungs flank the heart laterally and partially obscure it. Because the apex of the heart points to the left, it assumes an oblique position in the thorax. Approximately two-thirds of its mass can be seen to the left of the midsternal line; the balance projects to the right. Its broad, flat **base,** or posterosuperior portion, is about 9 cm (3½ in) wide and is directed toward the right shoulder. Its **apex** is directed inferiorly toward the left hip and rests on the diaphragm. If you press your fingers between the fifth and sixth ribs just below the left nipple, you can easily feel the beating of your heart where its apex contacts the chest wall. Hence, this site is referred to as the **point of maximal intensity (PMI).**

Coverings of the Heart

The heart is enclosed in a double-walled fibroserous sac called the **pericardium** (per″ĭ-kar′de-um; *peri* = around, *cardi* = heart) (Figure 19.2). The loosely fitting superficial part of this sac is the **fibrous pericardium.** This tough, dense connective tissue layer (1) protects the heart, (2) anchors it to surrounding structures, such as the diaphragm and the great ves-

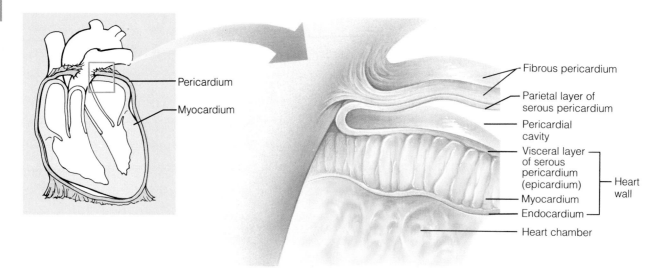

FIGURE 19.2
The pericardial layers and layers of the heart wall.

sels that issue from the heart, and (3) prevents over-filling of the heart with blood.

Deep to the fibrous pericardium is the **serous pericardium,** a thin slippery serous membrane composed of two layers. Its **parietal layer** lines the internal surface of the fibrous pericardium. At the heart base, the parietal layer attaches to the large arteries exiting from the heart, and then turns inferiorly and continues over the external heart surface as the **visceral layer,** also called the **epicardium** ("upon the heart"). The epicardium is an integral part of the heart wall.

Between the two layers of serous pericardium is the slitlike **pericardial cavity,** which contains a film of serous fluid. The serous membranes, lubricated by the fluid, glide smoothly against one another during heart activity, allowing the mobile heart to work in a relatively friction-free environment.

Inflammation of the pericardium, or *pericarditis,* (as might follow bacterial pneumonia), hinders the production of serous fluid and roughens the serous membrane surfaces. Consequently, as the beating heart rubs against its pericardial sac, it creates a rustling sound *(pericardial friction rub)* that can be heard with a stethoscope. Pericarditis may lead to painful adhesions in which the pericardia stick together and impede heart activity. In occasional cases of pericarditis, unusually large amounts of inflammatory fluid seep into the pericardial cavity. This excess fluid compresses the heart, limiting its ability to pump blood. This condition of heart compression by a fluid is called **cardiac tamponade** (tam"po-nād'), literally, "heart plug." Physicians treat cardiac tamponade by inserting a syringe into the pericardial cavity and draining off the excess fluid. •

Layers of the Heart Wall

The heart wall is composed of three layers: a superficial epicardium (described above), a middle myocardium, and a deep endocardium (Figure 19.2). All three layers are richly supplied with blood vessels.

The **myocardium** ("muscle heart"), composed mainly of cardiac muscle, forms the bulk of the heart. It is the layer that actually contracts. Within this layer, the branching cardiac muscle cells are tethered to each other by crisscrossing connective tissue fibers and arranged in spiral or circular *bundles* (Figure 19.3). These interlacing bundles effectively link all parts of the heart together. The connective tissue fibers form a dense network, called the **fibrous skeleton of the heart,** that reinforces the myocardium internally and anchors the cardiac muscle fibers (see also Figure 19.7, p. 619). This network of collagen and elastin fibers is thicker in some areas than others. For example, it constructs ropelike rings that provide additional support where the great vessels issue from the heart and around the heart valves, which otherwise might eventually become overdilated (stretched) because of the continual stress of blood pulsing through them. Additionally, since connective tissue is not electrically excitable, it limits the direct spread of action potentials across the heart to specific pathways. (The importance of this fact is discussed later in this chapter.)

The **endocardium** ("inside the heart") is a glistening white sheet of endothelium (squamous epithelium) resting on a thin connective tissue layer. Located on the inner myocardial surface, it lines the heart chambers and covers the connective tissue skeleton of the valves. The endocardium is continu-

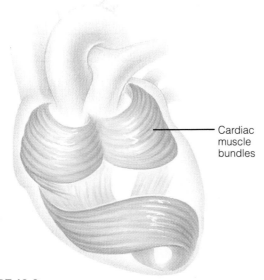

FIGURE 19.3
Packaging of cardiac muscle in the heart. Longitudinal view showing the spiral and circular arrangement of cardiac muscle bundles.

Cardiac muscle bundles

ous with the endothelial linings of the blood vessels leaving and entering the heart.

Chambers and Associated Great Vessels

The heart has four chambers (Figure 19.4, pp. 616–617): two superior **atria** (a'tre-ah) and two inferior **ventricles** (ven'trĭ-kls). The internal partition that divides the heart longitudinally is called either the **interatrial septum** or the **interventricular septum** (Figure 19.4c), depending on which chambers it separates. The right ventricle forms most of the anterior surface of the heart. The left ventricle dominates the inferoposterior aspect of the heart and forms the heart apex. Two grooves visible on the heart surface indicate the boundaries of its four chambers and carry the blood vessels that supply the myocardium. The **atrioventricular groove** (Figure 19.4a, d), or **coronary sulcus,** encircles the junction of the atria and ventricles like a crown (*corona* = crown). The **anterior interventricular sulcus** (Figure 19.4a) marks the anterior position of the interventricular septum separating the right and left ventricles. It continues as the **posterior interventricular sulcus,** which provides a similar landmark on the heart's posterior surface.

Atria: The Receiving Chambers

Except for small, wrinkled, protruding appendages called **auricles** (or'i-kulz; *auricle* = little ear), which increase the atrial volume somewhat, the right and left atria are remarkably free of distinguishing surface

features. Internally, the posterior atrial walls are quite smooth, but the anterior walls are ridged by bundles of muscle tissue. Since the walls look as if they were raked by the tines of a comb, these muscle bundles are called **pectinate** (*pectin* = comb) **muscles.** The interatrial septum bears a shallow depression, the **fossa ovalis** (o-vă'lis) (Figure 19.4c), that marks the spot where an opening, the **foramen ovale,** existed in the fetal heart (see Figure 19.22, p. 638).

Functionally, the atria are receiving chambers for blood returning to the heart from the circulation (*atrium* = entry way). Because they need contract only minimally to push blood "next door" into the ventricles, the atria are relatively small, thin-walled chambers. As a rule, they contribute little to the propulsive pumping activity of the heart.

Blood enters the *right atrium* via three veins: (1) The **superior vena cava** returns blood from body regions superior to the diaphragm; (2) the **inferior vena cava** returns blood from body areas below the diaphragm; and (3) the **coronary sinus** collects blood draining from the myocardium itself. Four **pulmonary veins** enter the *left atrium.* The pulmonary veins transport blood from the lungs back to the heart. These vessels are best seen in a posterior view of the heart (Figure 19.4d).

Ventricles: The Discharging Chambers

Together the ventricles (*ventr* = underside) make up most of the mass of the heart. As already mentioned, the right ventricle forms most of the heart's anterior surface while the left ventricle dominates its inferior surface. Marking the internal walls of the ventricular chambers are irregular ridges of muscle called **trabeculae carneae** (trah-bek'u-le kar'ne-e) (Figure 19.4c), literally, "crossbars of flesh." Still other muscle bundles, the conelike **papillary muscles,** project into the ventricular cavity. As described shortly, the papillary muscles play a role in valve function.

The ventricles are the discharging chambers or actual pumps of the heart (the difference in function between the atria and the ventricles is reflected in the much more massive ventricular walls). When the ventricles contract, blood is propelled out of the heart into the circulation. The right ventricle pumps blood into the **pulmonary trunk,** which routes the blood to the lungs where gas exchange occurs. The left ventricle ejects blood into the **aorta** (a-or'tah), the largest artery in the systemic circulation, indeed, in the body.

Pathway of Blood Through the Heart

Until the sixteenth century, it was believed that blood moved through the heart in a side-to-side fashion by seeping through pores in its midline wall or septum.

?   *Which heart chamber has the thickest walls? What is the significance of this structural difference?*

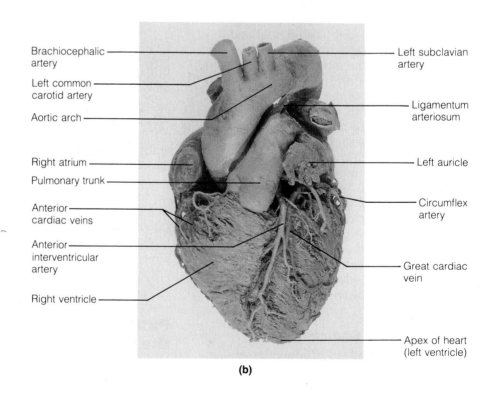

Brachiocephalic artery

Superior vena cava

Right pulmonary artery

Ascending aorta

Pulmonary trunk

Right pulmonary veins

Right atrium

Right coronary artery (in right atrioventricular groove)

Anterior cardiac vein

Right ventricle

Marginal artery

Small cardiac vein

Inferior vena cava

Left common carotid artery

Left subclavian artery

Aortic arch

Ligamentum arteriosum

Left pulmonary ar

Left pulmonary veins

Left atrium

Auricle

Circumflex artery

Left coronary artery (in left atrioventricular gr

Left ventricle

Great cardiac vein

Anterior interventricular ar (in anterior interventricular su

(a)

Apex

Brachiocephalic artery

Left common carotid artery

Aortic arch

Right atrium

Pulmonary trunk

Anterior cardiac veins

Anterior interventricular artery

Right ventricle

Left subclavian artery

Ligamentum arteriosum

Left auricle

Circumflex artery

Great cardiac vein

Apex of heart (left ventricle)

(b)

FIGURE 19.4

Gross anatomy of the heart. (a) Anterior view. **(b)** Photograph of anterior aspect of heart (pericardium removed). **(c)** Frontal section showing interior chambers and valves. **(d)** Posterior view.

Superior vena cava

Right pulmonary artery

Pulmonary trunk

Right atrium

Right pulmonary veins

Fossa ovalis

Pectinate muscles

Tricuspid valve

Right ventricle

Chordae tendineae

Trabeculae carneae

Inferior vena cava

Aorta

Left pulmonary artery

Left atrium

Left pulmonary veins

Pulmonary semilunar valve

Bicuspid (mitral) valve

Aortic semilunar valve

Left ventricle

Papillary muscle

Interventricular septum

Myocardium

Visceral pericardium

(c)

Left pulmonary artery

Left pulmonary veins

Auricle

Left atrium

Great cardiac vein

Posterior vein of left ventricle

Left ventricle

Apex

Aorta

Superior vena cava

Right pulmonary artery

Right pulmonary veins

Base of heart

Right atrium

Inferior vena cava

Right coronary artery (in right atrioventricular groove)

Coronary sinus

Posterior interventricular artery (in posterior interventricular sulcus)

Middle cardiac vein

Right ventricle

(d)

We now know that the heart passages open not from side to side but vertically and that the heart is actually two side-by-side pumps, each serving a separate blood circuit (Figure 19.5). The blood vessels that carry blood to and from the lungs form the **pulmonary circuit** (*pulmonos* = lung). This circuit strictly serves a gas exchange function. The blood vessels that carry blood to and from all body tissues constitute the **systemic circuit.**

The right side of the heart is the *pulmonary circuit pump.* Blood returning from the body, which is oxygen-poor and carbon dioxide-rich (relatively speaking), enters the right atrium and passes into the right ventricle, which pumps it to the lungs via the pulmonary trunk (Figure 19.4a, b). In the lungs, the blood unloads carbon dioxide and picks up oxygen. The freshly oxygenated blood is carried by the pulmonary veins back to the left side of the heart.

The left side of the heart is the *systemic circuit pump.* Freshly oxygenated blood leaving the lungs is returned to the left atrium and passes into the left ventricle, which pumps it into the aorta. From there the blood is transported via smaller systemic arteries to the body tissues, where exchange of gases and nutrients occurs across the capillary walls. The blood, once again laden with carbon dioxide and oxygen-depleted, returns through the systemic veins to the right side of the heart, where it enters the right atrium through the superior and inferior venae cavae. This whole cycle repeats itself continuously.

Although equal volumes of blood are flowing in the pulmonary and systemic circuits at any moment, the two ventricles have very unequal work loads: The pulmonary circuit, served by the right ventricle, is a short, low-pressure circulation, whereas the systemic circuit, associated with the left ventricle, takes a long pathway through the entire body and encounters about five times as much friction, or resistance to blood flow. This functional difference is revealed in the comparative anatomy of the two ventricles (Figure 19.6). The walls of the left ventricle are three

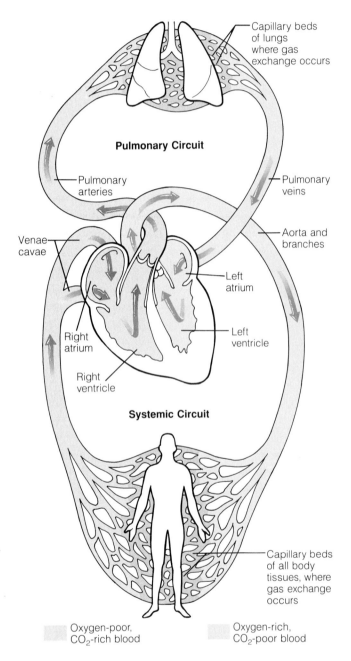

FIGURE 19.5 The systemic and pulmonary circuits. The heart is a double pump that serves two circulations. The right side of the heart pumps blood through the pulmonary circuit* (to the lungs and back to the left heart). The left heart pumps blood via the systemic circuit to all body tissues and back to the right heart. Notice that blood flowing through the pulmonary circuit gains oxygen and loses carbon dioxide as depicted by the color change from blue to pink. Blood flowing through the systemic circuit loses oxygen and picks up carbon dioxide (pink to blue color change). (*For simplicity, the actual number of two pulmonary arteries and four pulmonary veins has been reduced to one each.)

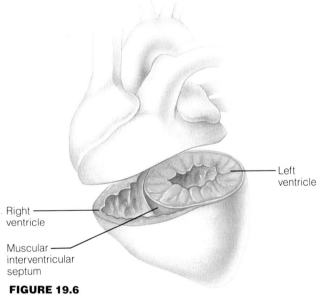

FIGURE 19.6
Anatomical differences in the right and left ventricles.
The left ventricle has a thicker wall and its cavity is basically circular; by contrast, the right ventricle cavity is crescent-shaped and wraps around the left ventricle.

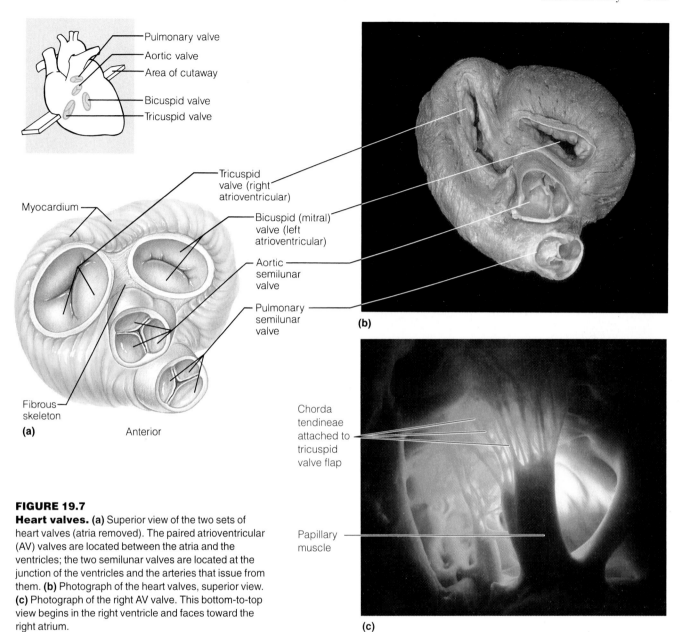

FIGURE 19.7
Heart valves. (a) Superior view of the two sets of heart valves (atria removed). The paired atrioventricular (AV) valves are located between the atria and the ventricles; the two semilunar valves are located at the junction of the ventricles and the arteries that issue from them. **(b)** Photograph of the heart valves, superior view. **(c)** Photograph of the right AV valve. This bottom-to-top view begins in the right ventricle and faces toward the right atrium.

times as thick as those of its counterpart on the right, and its cavity is nearly circular. The right ventricular cavity is flattened into a crescent shape that partially encloses the left ventricle, much the way a hand might loosely grasp a clenched fist. Consequently, the left ventricle can generate much more pressure than the right and is a more powerful pump.

Heart Valves

Blood flows through the heart in one direction: from the atria to the ventricles and out the great arteries leaving the superior aspect of the heart. This one-way traffic is enforced by four heart valves: the paired atrioventricular and semilunar valves (Figures 19.4c and 19.7), which open and close in response to differences in blood pressure on their two sides.

Atrioventricular (AV) Valves

The two **atrioventricular (AV) valves,** located at the junctions of the atria and their respective ventricles, prevent backflow into the atria when the ventricles are contracting. The right AV valve, the **tricuspid** (tri-kus′pid) **valve,** has three flexible cusps (flaps of endo-cardium reinforced by connective tissue cores). The left AV valve, with two flaps, is called the **bicuspid,** or **mitral** (mi′tral), **valve** (because of its resemblance to a bishop's miter or hat). Attached to each of the AV valve flaps are tiny white collagen cords called **chor-dae tendineae** (kor′de ten″dĭ-ne-e; "tendonous cords"), "heart strings," that anchor the cusps to the papillary muscles protruding from the ventricular walls.

When the heart is completely relaxed, the AV valve flaps hang limply into the ventricular chambers

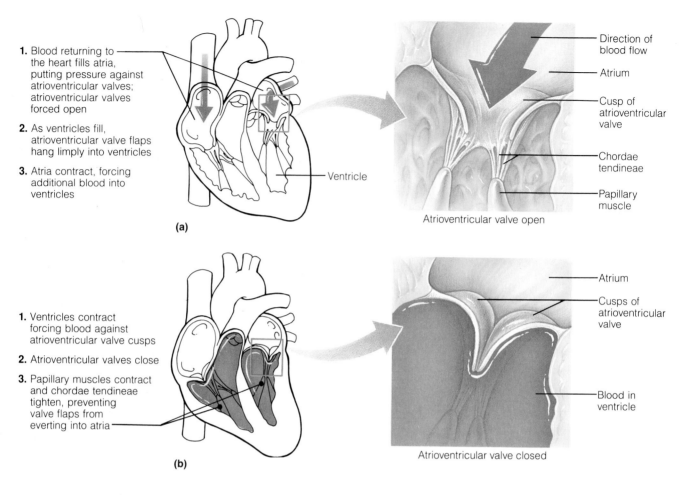

1. Blood returning to the heart fills atria, putting pressure against atrioventricular valves; atrioventricular valves forced open

2. As ventricles fill, atrioventricular valve flaps hang limply into ventricles

3. Atria contract, forcing additional blood into ventricles

Ventricle

(a)

Direction of blood flow

Atrium

Cusp of atrioventricular valve

Chordae tendineae

Papillary muscle

Atrioventricular valve open

1. Ventricles contract forcing blood against atrioventricular valve cusps

2. Atrioventricular valves close

3. Papillary muscles contract and chordae tendineae tighten, preventing valve flaps from everting into atria

(b)

Atrium

Cusps of atrioventricular valve

Blood in ventricle

Atrioventricular valve closed

FIGURE 19.8
Operation of the atrioventricular valves of the heart.
(a) The valves open when the blood pressure exerted on their atrial side is greater than that exerted on their ventricular side. **(b)** The valves are forced closed when the ventricles contract and intraventricular pressure rises, moving their contained blood superiorly. The action of the papillary muscles and chordae tendineae maintains the valve flaps in the closed position.

below; blood flows into the atria and then through the open AV valves into the ventricles. When the ventricles begin to contract, compressing the blood in their chambers, the intraventricular pressure rises, forcing the blood superiorly against the valve flaps. As a result, the valve flap edges meet, closing the valve (Figure 19.8). The chordae tendineae and the papillary muscles serve as guy wires to anchor the valve flaps in their *closed* position. If the cusps were not anchored in this manner, they would be blown upward into the atria, in the same way that an umbrella is blown inside out by a gusty wind.

Semilunar (SL) Valves

The **aortic** and **pulmonary semilunar valves** guard the bases of the large arteries issuing from the ventricles (aorta and pulmonary trunk, respectively) and prevent backflow into the associated ventricles. Each of the semilunar valves is fashioned from three pocketlike cusps; however, their mechanism of action dif-

fers from that of the AV valves. When the ventricles are contracting and intraventricular pressure *exceeds* the blood pressure in the aorta and pulmonary trunk, the semilunar valves are forced open and their cusps flatten against the arterial walls as the blood rushes past them (Figure 19.9). When the ventricles relax, and the blood (no longer propelled forward by the pressure of ventricular contraction) begins to flow backward toward the heart, it fills the cusps and closes the valves.

Let us complete the valve story by mentioning what seems to be an important omission—there are no valves guarding the entrances of the venae cavae and pulmonary veins into the right and left atria, respectively. Small amounts of blood *do* spurt back into these vessels during atrial contraction, but blood backflow is largely prevented because the atrial myocardium compresses (and collapses) these venous entry points as it contracts.

Heart valves are basically simple devices, and the heart—like any mechanical pump—can function

How does the mechanism of action of these valves compare to that of the AV valves illustrated in Figure 19.8?

Aorta

Pulmonary artery

As ventricles contract and intraventricular pressure rises, blood is pushed up against semilunar valves, forcing them open

(a)   Semilunar valve open

As ventricles relax, and intraventricular pressure falls, blood flows back from arteries, filling the cusps of semilunar valves and forcing them to close

(b)   Semilunar valve closed

FIGURE 19.9
Operation of the semilunar valves. (a) During ventricular contraction, the valves are open and their flaps are flattened against the artery walls. **(b)** When the ventricles relax, the backflowing blood fills the valve cusps and closes the valves.

with "leaky" valves as long as the impairment is not too great. However, severe valve deformities can seriously hamper cardiac function. For example, an *incompetent valve* forces the heart to pump and repump the same blood because the valve does not close properly and blood backflows. In valvular *stenosis* ("narrowing"), the valve flaps become stiff (often because of scar tissue formation following endocarditis) and constrict the opening. This stiffness compels the heart to contract more forcibly than normal. In both instances, the work load of the heart increases and, ultimately, the heart may become severely weakened. Under such conditions, the faulty valve (most often the mitral valve) is replaced with a synthetic valve or a pig heart valve. •

BLOOD SUPPLY TO THE HEART: CORONARY CIRCULATION

Although the heart is more or less continuously filled with blood, this contained blood provides very little nourishment to the heart tissues. (The myocardium is too thick to make diffusion a practical means of providing nutrition.) The functional blood supply of the heart is provided by the *right* and *left coronary arteries.* These arteries arise from the base of the aorta and encircle the heart in the atrioventricular groove (Figure 19.10a). The **left coronary artery** runs toward the left side of the heart and then divides into its major branches: the **anterior interventricular artery,** which follows the anterior interventricular sulcus and supplies blood to the interventricular septum and anterior walls of both ventricles; and the **circumflex artery,** which supplies the left atrium and the posterior walls of the left ventricle.

The **right coronary artery** courses to the right side of the heart, where it also divides into two branches: The **marginal artery** serves the myocardium of the lateral part of the right side of the heart. The more important **posterior interventricular artery** runs to the heart apex and supplies the posterior ventricular walls. Near the apex of the heart, it merges (anastomoses) with the anterior interventricular artery. Overall the branches of the right coronary artery supply the right atrium and nearly all of the right ventricle.

The arterial supply of the heart varies considerably. For example, in 15% of people, the left coronary

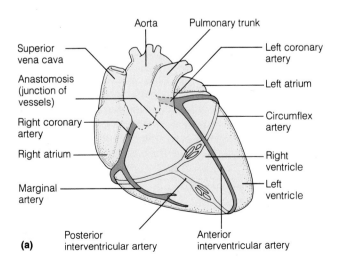

(a)

Superior vena cava

Anastomosis (junction of vessels)

Right coronary artery

Right atrium

Marginal artery

Posterior interventricular artery

Aorta

Pulmonary trunk

Left coronary artery

Left atrium

Circumflex artery

Right ventricle

Left ventricle

Anterior interventricular artery

FIGURE 19.10
Coronary circulation. (a) Arterial supply.

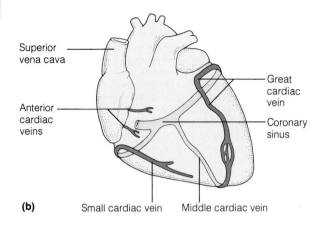

Superior
vena cava

Anterior
cardiac
veins

Great
cardiac
vein

Coronary
sinus

(b) Small cardiac vein Middle cardiac vein

FIGURE 19.10
Coronary circulation *continued.* **(b)** Venous supply. (The lighter-tinted vessels in each case represent those more posterior in the heart.)

artery gives rise to *both* interventricular arteries; in about 4%, a single coronary artery supplies the whole heart. Additionally, there are many anastomoses among the coronary arterial branches. These fusing networks provide additional *(collateral)* routes for blood delivery to the heart muscle, which explains how the heart can receive adequate nutrition even when one of its coronary arteries is almost entirely occluded. Even so, full occlusion of a coronary artery leads to tissue death and heart attack (see below).

The coronary arteries provide an intermittent, pulsating blood flow to the myocardium. These vessels and their main branches lie in the epicardium and send branches inward (deep) to nourish the myocardium. They actively deliver blood when the heart is relaxed, but are largely ineffective when the ventricles are contracting because (1) they are compressed by the contracting myocardium, and (2) the entrances to the coronary arteries are partly blocked by the flaps of the open aortic semilunar valve. Although the heart represents only about 1/200 of body weight, it requires about 1/20 of the body's blood supply. As might be expected, the left ventricle receives the most plentiful blood supply.

After passing through the capillary beds of the myocardium, the venous blood is collected by the **cardiac veins,** whose paths roughly follow those of the coronary arteries. The cardiac veins, in turn, join together to form an enlarged vessel called the **coronary sinus,** which empties the blood into the right atrium. The coronary sinus is obvious on the posterior aspect of the heart (Figure 19.10b). The coronary sinus has three large tributaries: the **great cardiac vein,** found in the anterior interventricular sulcus, the **middle cardiac vein** lying in the posterior interventricular sulcus, and the **small cardiac vein,** which runs along the heart's right inferior margin. Additionally, several **anterior cardiac veins** empty directly into the right atrium anteriorly.

Any blockage of the coronary arterial circulation can be serious; in some cases, it is fatal. **Angina pectoris** (an-ji'nah pek'tor-is), literally, "choked chest," is thoracic pain caused by a fleeting deficiency in blood delivery to the myocardium. It may result from stress-induced spasms of the coronary arteries or increased physical demands on the heart. The myocardial cells are weakened by the temporary lack of oxygen, but they do not die. Far more serious is prolonged coronary blockage, which can lead to a **myocardial infarction** (MI), commonly called a **heart attack** or a **coronary** (see *A Closer Look* on p. 624). Because adult cardiac muscle is amitotic, any areas of cell death are repaired with noncontractile scar tissue. Whether or not a person survives a myocardial infarction depends on the extent and location of the damage. Damage to the left ventricle is most serious. •

PROPERTIES OF CARDIAC MUSCLE FIBERS

Before examining heart operation in detail, we will review the microscopic anatomy of cardiac muscle cells and then consider how they function. Although cardiac muscle is similar to skeletal muscle, it displays some special anatomical features that reflect its unique blood-pumping role. Because skeletal muscle has already been covered in some detail in Chapter 9, it seems appropriate to compare and contrast these two muscle types.

Microscopic Anatomy

Cardiac muscle, like skeletal muscle, is striated, and its contraction is accomplished by the sliding filament mechanism. However, in contrast to the long, cylindrical, multinucleate skeletal muscle fibers, cardiac cells are short, fat, branched, and interconnected. Each fiber contains one or at most two large, pale, centrally located nuclei (Figure 19.11a). The intercellular spaces are filled with a loose connective tissue matrix (the *endomysium*), which contains numerous capillaries. This delicate matrix is connected, in turn, to the previously mentioned fibrous skeleton of the heart that links the cardiac cells together in a coiling array and reinforces the basket-like walls of the heart (see Figures 19.3 and 19.7a). This "skeleton" acts both as a tendon and as an insertion, giving the cardiac cells something to pull or exert their force against.

Skeletal muscle fibers are independent of one another both structurally and functionally. By contrast, the plasma membranes of adjacent cardiac cells interlock via meshing "fingers" at dark-staining junctions called **intercalated** (in-ter'kah-la"ted; *intercala* = insert) **discs** (Figure 19.11b). These discs contain anchoring *desmosomes* and *gap junctions* (specialized cell junctions discussed in Chapter 3). The

FIGURE 19.11
Microscopic anatomy of cardiac muscle. (a) Photomicrograph of cardiac muscle (300×). Notice that the cardiac muscle fibers are short, branched, and striated. Also note the dark-staining intercalated discs or junctions between the adjacent cardiac fibers. **(b)** Three-dimensional diagrammatic view of the relationship of cardiac fibers at the intercalated discs. **(c)** Diagrammatic view of a section of cardiac muscle cells illustrating the banding pattern enforced by the myofilaments. Portions of the sarcoplasmic reticulum and T system are also depicted, as are the positioning of the desmosomes and gap junctions at the intercalated disc connecting two adjoining cardiac muscle cells.

desmosomes prevent adjacent cardiac cells from separating during contraction. Gap junctions allow ions to pass freely from cell to cell, directly transmitting the depolarizing current across the entire heart. Because cardiac fibers are electrically coupled by the gap junctions, the entire myocardium *behaves* as a single unit or **functional syncytium.**

Large mitochondria account for about 25% of the volume of cardiac fibers (compared to only 2% in skeletal muscle), and most of the remaining volume is occupied by myofibrils composed of fairly typical sarcomeres. The sarcomeres exhibit Z lines, A bands, and I bands, which reflect the arrangement of the thick (myosin) and thin (actin) myofilaments composing them (Figure 19.11c). However, in contrast to what is seen in skeletal muscle, the myofibrils of cardiac muscle cells vary in diameter and branch extensively, accommodating the abundant mitochondria. This results in a banding pattern less dramatic than that of skeletal muscle.

The system for delivering Ca^{2+} is less elaborate in cardiac muscle fibers. The T tubules are wider and fewer than those of skeletal muscle and they enter the fibers at the Z lines. (Remember that T tubules are invaginations of the sarcolemma. In skeletal muscle, the T tubules invaginate at the A-I junctions.) The cardiac sarcoplasmic reticulum is less well developed and lacks the large terminal cisternae seen in skeletal muscle. Hence, no *triads* are seen in cardiac muscle fibers.

A CLOSER LOOK | Oh, What a Beautiful Morning—Then, Heart Boosters, Retreads, and Replacements

Getting up can be perilous to your health! Even if you are a morning person, your risk of dropping dead from a heart attack is twice as high the first two hours after you climb out of bed as at any other time of the day or night. For some reason, platelets are stickier, natural t-PA-inhibiting substances are at peak levels in the blood, and plasma levels of stress hormones (norepinephrine and others) increase right after you arise.

When a heart attack hits you, it seems as though a lightning bolt has struck. Few events in life are more frightening. A crushing, breath-robbing pain crashes through your chest. You break into a cold sweat while nausea and a sense of doom overwhelm you. An estimated 1.5 million Americans will suffer a myocardial infarct (MI) this year. Perhaps one-third of them will die almost immediately as a result of it; half will be dead within the year.

But—exactly what is a heart attack? Basically, it is a condition of total interruption of oxygen delivery to part of the myocardium that, if sustained long enough, causes death of heart muscle and its eventual replacement with scar tissue (myocardial infarction). Although it was once presumed that it was the lack of oxygen itself that injured the myocardial cells, this is apparently not so. The trouble starts when the ischemic area is reperfused with blood, and lymphocytes and other inflammatory cells congregate in the area. These "immigrants" release cytokines (signaling chemicals) that prod macrophages and neutrophils (a granulocyte introduced in Chapter 18) to release a deluge of free radicals, including nitric oxide. These toxic substances depress cardiac contractility ("stunned myocardium"), and also appear to cause most of the local tissue damage. If the heart is not "tipped" into fibrillation by the insult, the patient generally survives unless damage to the myocardium is massive. The most common cause of MI is blockage of a coronary artery (particularly those narrowed by ath-

A blood clot in a human coronary artery.

erosclerosis) by a thrombus or embolus (see photo), but irregular and unexplainable spasms of the coronary vessels bedevil some MI victims.

The first signs of heart disease are likely to be different in women than in men. In almost two-thirds of men, the first symptom is a heart attack or sudden death. In 56% of women, the first sign is angina, fleeting sharp squeezing chest pains. Heart attack victims lucky enough to reach the hospital quickly are now routinely treated with t-PA or other clot-dissolving drugs, which stop many heart attacks in progress and help prevent loss of viable heart muscle.

Those who suffer angina or survive a heart attack have been given a painful warning that, if heeded, allows time to make dietary changes, take heart-saving drugs, or have coronary bypass surgery. In coronary bypass surgery blood vessels removed from another body site are used to provide alternate routes for blood circulation in the heart. Not all people with repeated myocardial ischemia are so fortunate. For some, a fatal heart attack is the first and last symptom of heart disease. These victims of *silent ischemia* (periods when the myocardium is starved for oxygen but the person feels no pain) have no

obvious symptoms of heart disease. They are at much greater risk of suffering a heart attack, which, even if not fatal, permanently damages the myocardium. What causes silent heart disease is still a mystery; some suggest that these people have abnormal pain mechanisms. Whatever the cause, a severely damaged heart typically begins its downward spiral toward congestive heart failure and death.

The key to preventing heart attacks and cardiac death is to identify those at risk, early if possible, by using sophisticated medical imaging techniques, such as CT scans and MRI techniques (see pp. 18–19), as well as other diagnostic techniques. Particularly telling is presence of a specific type of low-density lipoprotein (LDL), called *lipoprotein (a)*. (LDLs are the form in which cholesterol is transported in blood to tissue cells.) About one-quarter of all heart attacks in men younger than 60 occur in those with high plasma levels of lipoprotein (a). Unlike levels of other lipoproteins (both HDLs and LDLs), which can vary widely in response to changes in diet, exercise, and drugs, lipoprotein (a) levels remain stable and positively correlated with increased incidence of clotting, vascular spasms, and the

Schematic representation of the autograft heart wrap procedure.

progress of atherosclerosis (see *A Closer Look* in Chapter 20), a major risk factor for heart disease.

Once the possibility of heart attack has been detected, the next step is to reduce its risk. All risk factors that can be eliminated voluntarily—excess weight, high cholesterol and saturated fat in diet, smoking, excess stress—should be attended to first. Vitamins with antioxidant abilities (vitamins E, C, and beta carotene) are being suggested to counter free radical damage in the heart. Drug therapy is the usual next step.

Traditional cardiac drugs, such as nitroglycerine (which dilates the coronary vessels) and digitalis (which slows the heart, enhancing venous return and sparing the heart's energy), are still popular; and "take one aspirin every other day" is suggested for those prone to excessive clotting, particularly those who have already had an MI or stroke. (Aspirin makes platelets less sticky.) A number of

newer, "miracle" drugs, such as beta blockers and calcium channel blockers, are revolutionizing cardiac medicine. When norepinephrine (or epinephrine) attaches to beta receptors, heart rate and force increase. Because beta blockers inhibit this activation by the sympathetic nervous system and successfully prevent increases in blood pressure, they reduce the strain on the heart. Calcium channel blockers such as verapamil help prevent the coronary artery spasms that often trigger heart attacks. Because calcium is necessary for the vascular smooth muscle contraction that produces the spasm in the first place, these drugs prevent vasoconstriction and dilate the arteries, making it easier for the weakened heart to manage its work load.

What are the options for someone whose heart is so devastated by disease that these measures are too little, too late? Until recently, heart transplant surgery has been the only hope for a dying heart. But this procedure is riddled with problems. First, an acceptable tissue match must be found. Then, after complicated and traumatic surgery, the heart recipient is dosed with drugs that suppress the immune system to thwart rejection of the donor heart.

Newer to the scene are artificial hearts and mechanical cardiac assist devices. In December 1982, the first permanent artificial heart, called the Jarvik-7 after its developer, was implanted in Dr. Barney Clark. Barney Clark survived for only ten days with his artificial heart, but since 1982 several more patients have received artificial hearts. Hospitalized and tethered to the huge air compressor that drives the artificial heart, such patients succumbed to strokes, overwhelming infections, and kidney failure. Because of these disappointing results, federal regulations presently allow use of an artificial heart *only* as a lifesaving stopgap measure while the patient awaits a permanent human heart transplant.

More broadly useful for temporary purposes are portable devices that take over part of the work load of an ailing heart. *LVADs* (left ventricular assist devices), the *Heartmate* and others, are mechanical pumps that are

implanted in the abdomen, connected to the left ventricle, and powered by an external battery carried in a backpack or shoulder holster. Intended for only very limited use (1–2 weeks) are the *hemopumps,* pencil-sized pumps that are threaded through an artery into the left ventricle. Their propeller-like blades rotate about 25,000 times per minute to pump blood into the aorta. Slightly different devices, the *intra-aortic balloon pump* or *Cardiovad,* are small balloons inserted into the aorta and inflated by air pressure. Quiet when the left ventricle is contracting, they are activated when the aortic semilunar valve closes. As they inflate, they supplement the ventricle by pushing the ejected blood along the aorta (and into the coronary arteries) with extra force. However, the most exciting technique is *cardiomyoplasty,* an autotransport technique in which the patient's own skeletal muscle is used to form a living patch in the heart wall or to augment its pumping ability. The procedure, first done in February 1985, involves surgically removing the damaged portion of the heart wall, suturing the cut edges together, and reinforcing the wall with borrowed latissimus dorsi muscle from the back (see illustration). The rest of the muscle patch is left attached to the posterior body wall and to its blood and nerve supply. A pacemaker is then attached to the skeletal-muscle patch to stimulate it intermittently, gradually moving the pacemaker rate into synchrony with the heartbeat. Because the muscle tissue is "home grown," there is, obviously, no problem of rejection and the need to find a suitable donor heart for transplant is avoided. The major hurdle in autotransplants has been in coaxing the skeletal muscle, which is built to work in short spurts, to perform in the same manner as cardiac muscle—around the clock. But researchers are working on conditioning skeletal muscle with electrical shocks, thereby increasing the percentage of slow-twitch, fatigue-resistant red fibers. This technique may someday be the most promising option for cardiac patients with debilitated hearts.

Energy Requirements

The greater abundance of mitochondria in cardiac muscle reflects its greater dependence on oxygen for its energy metabolism compared with skeletal muscle. As described in Chapter 9, skeletal muscles can contract for prolonged periods, even during oxygen deficits, by carrying out anaerobic respiration and incurring an oxygen debt. In contrast, the heart relies almost exclusively on aerobic respiration; hence, it cannot incur much of an oxygen debt and still operate effectively.

Both types of muscle tissue use multiple fuel molecules, including glucose, fatty acids, and others. But cardiac muscle is much more adaptable and readily switches metabolic pathways to use whatever nutrient supply is available, including lactic acid generated by skeletal muscle activity. Thus, the danger of an inadequate blood supply to the myocardium is lack of oxygen, not of nutrient fuels.

Mechanism and Events of Contraction

Heart contraction is triggered by action potentials that sweep across the muscle cell membranes. Although about 1% of the cardiac fibers are *autorhythmic* ("self-rhythm") with the special ability to depolarize spontaneously and, thus, to pace the heart, the bulk of the heart muscle is composed of *contractile muscle fibers* responsible for the pumping activity of the heart. The sequence of electrical events in these contractile cells is similar to that of skeletal muscle fibers:

1. Influx of sodium ions from the extracellular fluid into the cardiac cells initiates a positive feedback cycle that causes the rising phase of the action potential (and reversal of the membrane potential from -90 mV to nearly $+30$ mV) by opening **voltage-regulated fast sodium channels** (Figure 19.12). The period of increased sodium permeability is very brief, because the sodium gates are quickly inactivated and the sodium channels close.

2. Transmission of the depolarization wave down the T tubules causes the sarcoplasmic reticulum (SR) to release calcium into the sarcoplasm.

3. Excitation-contraction coupling occurs as Ca^{2+} provides the signal (via troponin binding) for cross bridge activation and couples the depolarization wave to the sliding of the myofilaments.

About 20% of the calcium needed for the calcium pulse that triggers contraction enters from the extracellular space and, once inside, it stimulates the release of much larger amounts of Ca^{2+} (the remaining 80%) from the SR. Ionic calcium is barred from entering nonstimulated cardiac fibers, but when sodium-dependent membrane depolarization occurs,

FIGURE 19.12

Changes in membrane potential and membrane permeability during action potentials of contractile cardiac muscle cells. (a) Relationship between the action potential (membrane potential changes), period of contraction (tension development), and absolute refractory period in a single ventricular cell. (The tracing for an atrial contractile cell is similar but the plateau phase is shorter.) **(b)** Membrane permeability changes during the cardiac contractile cell action potential. (The Na$^+$ permeability rises to a point off the scale during the spike of the action potential.)

the voltage change *also* opens calcium channels that allow Ca^{2+} entry from the extracellular space. These channels are called **slow Ca^{2+} channels** because channel opening is delayed a bit (Figure 19.12b). Although sodium permeability has plummeted to its resting levels and repolarization has already begun by this point, the calcium surge across the membrane prolongs the depolarization potential briefly, producing a **plateau** in the action potential tracing (Figure 19.12a). At the same time, potassium permeability decreases, which also prolongs the plateau and prevents rapid repolarization. Eventually (after a couple hundred milliseconds), the slope of the action potential tracing falls rapidly. This results from closure of the Ca^{2+} channels and opening of K^+ channels, which allows a rapid loss of potassium from the cell that restores the resting membrane potential. During repolarization, calcium ions are pumped back into the SR and the extracellular space.

The following points present some other fundamental differences between skeletal and cardiac muscle:

1. **All-or-none-law.** In skeletal muscle, the *all-or-none law* applies to contractile activity at the cellular level—impulses do not spread from cell to cell. In cardiac muscle, the law applies at the organ level—either the heart contracts as a unit or it doesn't contract at all. This is assured by the transmission of the depolarization wave across the heart from cell to cell through the gap junctions, which tie all cardiac muscle cells together into a single contractile unit.

2. **Means of stimulation.** Each skeletal muscle cell must be independently stimulated to contract by a nerve ending. By contrast, some cardiac muscle cells are self-excitable and can initiate their own depolarization, and that of the rest of the heart, in a spontaneous and rhythmic way. This property, called **automaticity,** or **autorhythmicity,** is described in the next section.

3. **Length of the absolute refractory period.** The absolute refractory period (the inexcitable period when potassium ions are leaving the cells) lasts approximately 250 ms in cardiac muscle cells, nearly as long as the contraction (see Figure 19.12a). Contrast this to the 1–2 ms refractory periods of skeletal muscle fibers, in which contractions last 20 to 100 ms. This long refractory period normally prevents tetanic contractions, which would stop the heart's pumping action.

HEART PHYSIOLOGY

Electrical Events

The ability of cardiac muscle to depolarize and contract is intrinsic; that is, it is a property of the heart muscle itself and does not depend on the nervous system. In fact, even if all nerve connections to the heart are severed, the heart continues to beat rhythmically, as demonstrated by transplanted hearts. Nevertheless, the heart is amply supplied with nerve fibers which can alter the basic rhythm of heart activity set by intrinsic factors. Both sets of controls are examined next.

Setting the Basic Rhythm: The Intrinsic Conduction System

The independent, but coordinated, activity of the heart is a function of (1) the presence of gap junctions (mentioned above), and (2) the activity of the heart's

FIGURE 19.13
Pacemaker and action potentials of autorhythmic cells of the heart.

"in-house" conduction system. The **intrinsic cardiac conduction system** consists of noncontractile cardiac cells specialized to initiate and distribute impulses throughout the heart, so that it depolarizes and contracts in an orderly, sequential manner from atria to ventricles. Thus, the heart beats (nearly) as one cell. Let's look at how this system works.

Action Potential Initiation by Autorhythmic Cells.
Unlike unstimulated contractile cells of the heart (and neurons and skeletal muscle fibers), the **autorhythmic cells** making up the intrinsic conduction system of the heart do *not* maintain a stable resting membrane potential. Instead, they have an **unstable resting potential** that continuously depolarizes, drifting slowly toward threshold for firing. These spontaneously changing membrane potentials are called **pacemaker potentials** and they initiate the action potentials (Figure 19.13) that spread throughout the heart to trigger its rhythmic contractions. The precise mechanism of the pacemaker potential is still in doubt, but it is believed to result from gradually reduced membrane permeability to K^+. Then, because Na^+ permeability is unchanged and it continues to diffuse into the cell at a slow rate, the balance between K^+ loss and Na^+ entry is upset and the membrane interior becomes less and less negative (more positive). Ultimately, when threshold is reached, **fast Ca^{2+} channels** open, allowing explosive entry of Ca^{2+} from the extracellular space. Thus, in these autorhythmic cells, an influx of calcium (rather than sodium) produces the rising phase of the action potential and reverses the membrane potential. As in other excitable cells, the falling phase of the action potential and repolarization reflect increased K^+ permeability and efflux from the cell. Once repolarization is complete, the K^+ channels are inactivated, K^+ permeability declines, and the process of slow depolarization to threshold begins again.

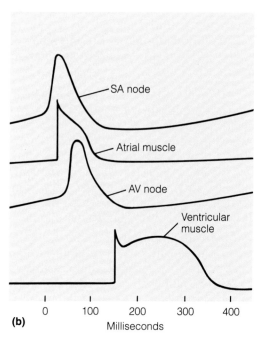

FIGURE 19.14
The intrinsic conduction system of the heart and succession of the action potential through selected areas of the heart during one heartbeat. (a) The depolarization wave is initiated by the SA node and then passes successively through the atrial myocardium to the AV node, the AV bundle, the right and left bundle branches, and the Purkinje fibers in the ventricular myocardium. **(b)** The sequence of potentials generated across the heart is shown from top to bottom beginning with the pacemaker potential generated by the SA node and ending with an action potential (with a broad plateau) typical of the contractile cardiac cells of the ventricles.

Sequence of Excitation.   Autorhythmic cardiac cells are localized in the following areas (Figure 19.14): (1) *sinoatrial (SA) node,* (2) *atrioventricular (AV) node,* (3) *atrioventricular (AV) bundle (bundle of His),* (4) *right and left bundle branches,* and (5) *ventricular walls* as Purkinje fibers. Impulses pass across the heart in the same order.

1.   Sinoatrial (SA) node. The crescent-shaped **sino-atrial** (si″no-a′tre-al) **node** is located in the right atrial wall, just inferior to the entrance of the superior vena cava. A minute cell mass with a mammoth job, the SA node typically generates impulses about 75 times every minute. (However, its inherent rate in the absence of extrinsic neural and hormonal factors is around 100 times per minute.) Because no other region of the conduction system or the myocardium has a faster depolarization rate, the SA sets the pace for the heart as a whole. Hence, it is the heart's **pace-maker** and its characteristic rhythm, the **sinus rhythm,** determines heart rate.

2.   Atrioventricular (AV) node. From the SA node, the depolarization wave spreads via gap junctions throughout the atria and via the *internodal pathway* to the **atrioventricular node,** located in the inferior portion of the interatrial septum immediately above the tricuspid valve. At the AV node, the impulse is delayed momentarily (for about 0.1 s), allowing the atria to respond and complete their contraction before the ventricles contract. (This delay largely reflects the smaller diameter of the fibers here, which conduct impulses more slowly than other parts of the system, just as traffic slows when cars are forced to merge into two lanes from four.) The signaling impulse then passes rapidly through the rest of the system (see 3–5).

3.   Atrioventricular (AV) bundle. From the AV node, the impulse sweeps to the **atrioventricular bundle (bundle of His)** in the inferior part of the interatrial septum. Although the atria and ventricles abut each other, they are not connected by gap junctions. The AV bundle is the *only* electrical connection between them. The balance of the AV junction is insulated by the nonconducting fibrous skeleton of the heart as described earlier.

4.   Bundle branches. The AV bundle persists only briefly before spitting into two pathways—the **right and left bundle branches.** The bundle branches course along the interventricular septum toward the apex of the heart.

5. Purkinje fibers. The **Purkinje** (pur-kin′je) **fibers** complete the pathway through the interventricular septum, penetrate into the heart apex, and then turn superiorly into the ventricular walls. The bundle branches ensure excitation of the septal cells, but the bulk of ventricular depolarization depends on the large, barrel-shaped Purkinje fibers and, ultimately, on cell-to-cell transmission of the impulse by the ventricular muscle cells themselves. Because the left ventricle is much larger than the right, the Purkinje network is more elaborate in that side of the heart.

Interestingly, the Purkinje fibers supply the papillary muscles *before* supplying the lateral walls of the ventricles. This assures that the papillary muscles are contracting to take up the slack on the chordae tendineae before the full force of ventricular contraction hurls the blood against the AV valve flaps. The total time between initiation of the impulse by the SA node and depolarization of the last of the ventricular muscle cells is approximately 0.22 s in a healthy human heart.

Ventricular contraction almost immediately follows the ventricular depolarization wave. A wringing contraction of the ventricles begins at the heart apex and moves toward the atria, following the direction of the excitation wave through the ventricles. This effectively ejects some of the contained blood *superiorly* into the large arteries leaving the ventricles.

Although autorhythmic cardiac cells are found in nearly all parts of the heart, their rates of spontaneous depolarization differ. For example, while the SA node normally "drives" the heart at a rate of 75 beats per minute, the AV node depolarizes at the average rate of about 50/min, the AV bundle and the Purkinje fibers (though they conduct very rapidly) at the rate of only about 30/min. However, these other "pacemakers" cannot dominate the heart unless "everything faster than them" becomes nonfunctional.

The cardiac conduction system not only coordinates and synchronizes heart activity, it also forces the heart as a whole to beat faster. Without it, the impulse would travel much more slowly through the myocardium—at the rate of 0.3 to 0.5 m/s as opposed to several meters per second in most parts of the conduction system. This would allow some muscle fibers to contract well ahead of others, resulting in reduced pumping effectiveness.

Defects in the intrinsic conduction system can cause irregular heart rhythms, or **arrhythmias** (ah-rith′me-ahz), uncoordinated atrial and ventricular contractions, and even fibrillation. **Fibrillation** is a condition of rapid and irregular or out-of-phase contractions (see Figure 19.18d, p. 631) in which the heart has been compared with a squirming bag of worms. Fibrillating ventricles are useless as pumps; and unless the heart can be defibrillated quickly, circulation stops and brain death occurs. Defibrillation is accomplished by electrically shocking the heart, which interrupts its chaotic twitching by depolariz-ing the entire myocardium. The hope is that "with the slate wiped clean" the SA node will again begin to function normally and sinus rhythm will be reestablished.

A defective pacemaking SA node may have several consequences. An **ectopic** (ek-top′ik) **focus** or abnormal pacemaker may appear and assume control of heart rate, or the AV node may become the pacemaker. The pace set by the AV node **(junctional rhythm)** is 40 to 60 beats per minute, slower than sinus rhythm but still adequate to maintain circulation. Occasionally, ectopic pacemakers appear even when the conduction system is operating normally. A small region of the heart becomes hyperexcitable, sometimes as a result of too much caffeine (several cups of coffee) or nicotine (excessive smoking), and generates impulses even more quickly than the SA node. This leads to a *premature contraction* or **extrasystole** (ek″strah-sis′to-le) before the SA node initiates the next contraction.

Because the only route for impulse transmission from the atria to the ventricles is through the AV node, any damage to the AV node, referred to as a **heart block,** interferes with the ability of the ventricles to receive pacing impulses. In total heart block no impulses are conducted from atria to ventricles. The ventricles beat at their intrinsic rate, which is too slow to maintain adequate circulation. In such cases, a *fixed-rate* artificial pacemaker, set to discharge (deliver an impulse) at a constant rate, is usually implanted. Those suffering from partial heart block, in which a fraction of the atrial impulses reach the ventricles, commonly receive *demand-type* pacemakers, which deliver impulses only when the heart is not transmitting on its own. •

Modifying the Basic Rhythm: Extrinsic Innervation of the Heart

Although the basic rate of heartbeat is set by the intrinsic conduction system, fibers of the autonomic nervous system act as "accelerators" and "brakes" of the heart. The sympathetic nervous system increases both the rate and force of heartbeat; conversely, parasympathetic activation slows the heart. Thus, autonomic nervous system controls modify the activity of the intrinsic conduction system. These neural controls are explained in more detail later on p. 636. Here we discuss the anatomy of the nerve supply to the heart.

The cardiac centers are located in the medulla oblongata. The sympathetic **cardioacceleratory center** projects to motor neurons in the T_1–T_5 level of the spinal cord. These, in turn, synapse with postganglionic neurons located in the cervical and upper thoracic chain ganglia (Figure 19.15). From there, postganglionic fibers run through the cardiac plexus to the heart. The parasympathetic center, or **cardioinhibitory center,** projects from the medulla via branches of the vagus nerves (cranial nerves X) to the

FIGURE 19.15
Autonomic innervation of the heart.

FIGURE 19.16
An electrocardiogram tracing (lead I) illustrating the three normally recognizable deflection waves and the important intervals.

heart. Most postganglionic motor neurons lie in ganglia within the heart wall. Although these autonomic nerve fibers project to cardiac musculature throughout the heart, they project most heavily to the SA and AV nodes and the coronary arteries.

Electrocardiography

The electrical currents generated and transmitted through the heart also spread throughout the body and can be monitored with an instrument called an **electrocardiograph.** The graphic recording of electrical changes during heart activity is called an **electrocardiogram (ECG** or **EKG;** *kardio* = German word for heart). Recording electrodes (leads) are positioned at various sites on the body surface; typically 12 standard leads are used to record an ECG. Three of these are bipolar leads that measure the voltage difference between the arms, or an arm and a leg, and nine are unipolar leads. Together the 12 leads provide a fairly comprehensive picture of the electrical activity of the heart.

A typical ECG consists of a series of three distinguishable waves called **deflection waves** (Figure 19.16). The first wave, the small **P wave,** lasting about 0.08 s, results from movement of the depolarization wave from the SA node through the atria. Approximately 0.1 s after the P wave begins, the atria contract.

The large **QRS complex** results from ventricular depolarization and precedes ventricular contraction. Its complicated shape reveals the different size of the two ventricles and the time required for each to depolarize. Average duration of the QRS complex is 0.08 s.

The **T wave** is caused by ventricular repolarization and typically lasts about 0.16 s. Repolarization is slower than depolarization, so the T wave is more spread out and has a lower amplitude (height) than the QRS wave. Because atrial repolarization takes place during the period of ventricular excitation, its occurrence is normally obscured by the large QRS complex being recorded at the same time.

The **P-R (P-Q) interval** is the time (about 0.16 s) from the beginning of atrial excitation to the beginning of ventricular excitation. It includes atrial depolarization (and contraction) as well as the passage of the depolarization wave through the rest of the conduction system. The **Q-T interval,** lasting about 0.36 s, is the period from the beginning of ventricular depolarization through their repolarization and includes the time of ventricular contraction. The relationship of the parts of an ECG tracing to movement of the action potential over the heart is illustrated in Figure 19.17.

In a healthy heart, the size, duration, and timing of the deflection waves tend to be consistent. Thus, changes in the pattern or timing of the ECG may reveal a diseased or damaged heart or problems with the heart's conduction system. For example, an inverted or lost P wave indicates that the AV node has become the pacemaker. A few examples of abnormalities detectable with an ECG appear in Figure 19.18.

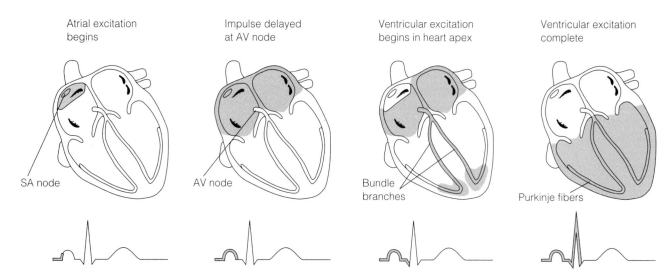

Atrial excitation
begins

SA node

Impulse delayed
at AV node

AV node

Ventricular excitation
begins in heart apex

Bundle
branches

Ventricular excitation
complete

Purkinje fibers

FIGURE 19.17
The sequence of excitation of the heart related to the deflection waves of an ECG tracing.

Mechanical Events: The Cardiac Cycle

The heart undergoes some fairly dramatic writhing movements as it alternately contracts, forcing blood out of its chambers, and then relaxes, allowing its chambers to refill with blood. The terms **systole** (sis′to-le) and **diastole** (di-as′to-le) refer respectively, and literally, to these *contraction* and *relaxation* periods of heart activity. The **cardiac cycle** includes *all* events associated with the flow of blood through the heart during one complete heartbeat, that is, atrial systole and diastole followed by ventricular systole and diastole. However, we use the traditional approach here of describing the cycle in terms of events occuring in the left side of the heart (Figure 19.19).

The cardiac cycle is marked by a succession of pressure and blood volume changes within the heart. Although pressure changes occurring in the right side of the heart are only about one-fifth as great as those occurring in the left, each ventricle pumps the same

(a)

(b)

(c)

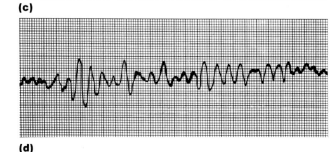

(d)

FIGURE 19.18
Normal and abnormal ECG tracings. (a) Normal sinus rhythm.
(b) Junctional rhythm. SA node nonfunctional, P waves are absent, and heart rate is paced by the AV node at 40–60 beats/min.
(c) Second-degree heart block. Some of the P waves are not conducted through the AV node; hence more P than QRS waves are seen. In cases where P waves are conducted normally, the P:QRS ratio is 1:1. In total heart block, there is no whole number ratio between the P and QRS waves, and the ventricles are no longer paced by the SA node. **(d)** Ventricular fibrillation. Chaotic, grossly irregular, bizarre ECG deflections. Seen in acute heart attack and electrical shock.

volume of blood per beat and the overall relationships are the same for both chambers. Because blood circulates endlessly, we will arbitrarily choose a starting point to follow its route through the heart during a single cardiac cycle. We begin our explanation with the heart in total relaxation: Both the atria and ventricles are quiet, and it is mid-to-late diastole.

1.   Period of ventricular filling: mid-to-late diastole. Pressure in the heart is low, and blood returning from the circulation is flowing passively through the atria and the open AV valves into the ventricles below. The semilunar valves (aortic and pulmonary) are closed. This phase is indicated by interval 1 in Figure 19.19. Approximately 70% of ventricular fill-

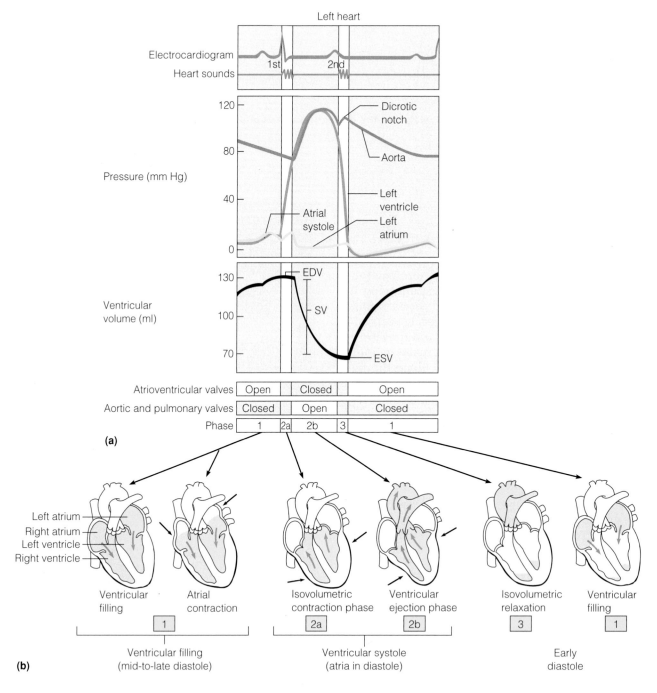

FIGURE 19.19
Summary of events occurring in the heart during the cardiac cycle. (a) Events in the left side of the

heart. An ECG tracing is superimposed on the graph (top) so that pressure and volume changes can be related to electrical events occurring at any point.

Time occurrence of heart sounds is also indicated. **(b)** Events of phases 1 through 3 of the cardiac cycle are depicted in diagrammatic views of the heart.

ing occurs during this period, and the AV valve flaps begin to drift upward toward their closed position. (The remaining 30% is delivered to the ventricles when the atria contract toward the end of this phase.) Now the stage is set for atrial systole. Following depolarization (the P wave in the ECG), the atria contract, compressing the blood in their chambers. This causes a sudden slight rise in atrial pressure, which propels residual blood out of the atrial chambers into the ventricles. Then the atria relax and the ventricles depolarize (QRS complex on the ECG). Atrial diastole persists through the rest of the cycle.

2. Ventricular systole. As the atria relax, the ventricles begin their contraction phase. Their walls close in on the blood in their chambers, and ventricular pressure rises rapidly and sharply, closing the AV valves. For a split second, the ventricles are completely closed chambers and blood volume in the chambers remains constant. This **isovolumetric** (i″so-vol″u-met′rik) **contraction phase** is phase 2a in Figure 19.19. Ventricular pressures continue to rise and when they finally exceed those in the large arteries issuing from them, the semilunar valves are forced open and blood is expelled from the ventricles into the aorta and pulmonary trunk. During this **ventricular ejection phase** (phase 2b in Figure 19.19), the pressure in the aorta normally reaches about 120 mm Hg.

3. Isovolumetric relaxation: early diastole. During this brief phase following the T wave, the ventricles relax. Because blood remaining in their chambers is no longer compressed, ventricular pressure drops rapidly and blood in the aorta and pulmonary trunk starts to backflow toward the heart, closing the semilunar valves. Closure of the aortic semilunar valve causes a brief rise in aortic pressure, indicated in Figure 19.19 as the **dicrotic notch.** Once again the ventricles are totally closed chambers. This **isovolumetric relaxation** phase is indicated by interval 3 in Figure 19.19.

All during ventricular systole, the atria have been in diastole. During that time, they have been filling with blood and the intra-atrial pressure has been rising. When the pressure exerted by blood on the atrial side of the AV valves exceeds that in the ventricles below, the AV valves are forced open and ventricular filling, phase 1, begins again. Atrial pressure drops to its lowest point and ventricular pressure begins to rise, completing the cycle.

Assuming that the average heart beats approximately 75 times each minute, the length of the cardiac cycle is about 0.8 s. Of this time, atrial systole accounts for 0.1 s and ventricular systole takes 0.3 s. The remaining 0.4 s is the period of total heart relaxation, or the **quiescent period.**

Notice two important points: (1) blood flow through the heart is controlled entirely by pressure changes, and (2) blood flows along a pressure gradi-

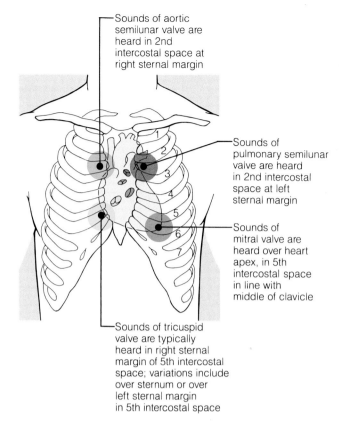

Sounds of aortic semilunar valve are heard in 2nd intercostal space at right sternal margin

Sounds of pulmonary semilunar valve are heard in 2nd intercostal space at left sternal margin

Sounds of mitral valve are heard over heart apex, in 5th intercostal space in line with middle of clavicle

Sounds of tricuspid valve are typically heard in right sternal margin of 5th intercostal space; variations include over sternum or over left sternal margin in 5th intercostal space

FIGURE 19.20
Areas of the thoracic surface where the heart sounds can be best detected.

ent, always from higher to lower pressure through any available opening. The pressure changes, in turn, reflect the alternating contraction and relaxation of the myocardium and cause the opening of the heart valves, which keeps blood flowing in the forward direction.

Heart Sounds

During each cardiac cycle, two distinguishable sounds can be heard when the thorax is auscultated (listened to) with a stethoscope. These **heart sounds,** often described as lub-dup, are associated with closing of heart valves. The timing of heart sounds in the cardiac cycle is shown in Figure 19.19.

The basic rhythm of the heart sounds is lub-dup, pause, lub-dup, pause, and so on. The pause indicates the quiescent period. The first heart sound, which occurs as the AV valves close, signifies the onset of systole when ventricular pressure rises above atrial pressure. It tends to be louder, longer, and more resonant than the second: the short, sharp sound that is heard as the semilunar valves snap shut at the beginning of ventricular diastole. Because the mitral valve closes slightly before the tricuspid valve, and the aortic semilunar valve generally snaps shut just before the pulmonary valve, it is possible to distinguish the individual valve sounds by auscultating four specific regions of the thorax (Figure 19.20). Notice that these four points, while not directly superficial to the valves, do (handily) define the four corners of the normal heart. Knowing normal heart size and location is essential for recognizing an enlarged (and often diseased) heart.

Abnormal or unusual heart sounds are called **murmurs.** Blood flows silently as long as the flow is smooth and uninterrupted. If it strikes obstructions, its flow becomes turbulent and generates sounds, such as heart murmurs, that can be heard with a stethoscope. Heart murmurs are fairly common in young children (and some elderly people) with perfectly healthy hearts, probably because their heart walls are relatively thin and vibrate with rushing blood. However, most often murmurs indicate valve problems. For example, if a valve is *incompetent,* a swishing sound will be heard as the blood backflows or regurgitates through the partially open valve, *after* that valve has (supposedly) closed. A stenotic valve, in which the valvular opening is narrowed, restricts blood flow *through* the valve. In the case of a stenotic aortic valve, for instance, a high-pitched sound can be detected when the valve should be wide open, i.e., during systole just before valve closure. •

Cardiac Output

Cardiac output (CO) is the amount of blood pumped out by *each* ventricle in 1 minute. It is the product of heart rate (HR) and stroke volume (SV). **Stroke volume** is the volume of blood pumped out by a ventricle with each beat. In general, stroke volume is correlated with force of ventricular contraction.

Using the normal resting values for heart rate (75 beats/min) and stroke volume (70 ml/beat), the average adult cardiac output can easily be computed:

$$CO \text{ (ml/min)} = HR \text{ (75 beats/min)} \times SV \text{ (70ml/beat)}$$

$$\text{Thus: } CO = 5250 \text{ ml/min (5.25 L/min)}$$

The normal adult blood volume is about 5 L (a little more than one gallon). Thus, the entire blood supply passes through each side of the heart once each minute. Notice that cardiac output varies directly with SV and HR. Thus CO increases when the stroke volume increases or the heart beats faster or both, and decreases when either or both of these factors decrease.

Cardiac output is highly variable and increases markedly in response to special demands, such as making a dash to catch the bus. The difference between resting and maximal CO is referred to as **cardiac reserve.** In nonathletic people, cardiac reserve is typically four to five times their normal CO (20–25 L/m). But in trained athletes, cardiac output during competition may reach 35 L/m (a seven-times increase). To understand how the heart accomplishes such tremendous increases in output, let's look at how stroke volume and heart rate are regulated.

Regulation of Stroke Volume

At rest, a healthy heart pumps out about 60% of the blood present in its chambers (see Figure 19.19a). Essentially, SV represents the difference between **end diastolic volume (EDV),** the amount of blood that collects in a ventricle during diastole, and **end systolic volume (ESV),** the volume of blood remaining in a ventricle *after* it has contracted. The EDV, determined by the length of ventricular diastole and venous pressure (increases in either *raise* the EDV), is normally about 120 ml. The ESV, determined by arterial blood pressure (the higher the pressure the higher the ESV) and the force of ventricular contraction, is approximately 50 ml. To figure normal stroke volume, these values are simply plugged into the equation:

$$SV \text{ (ml/beat)} = EDV \text{ (120 ml)} - ESV \text{ (50 ml)}$$

$$SV = 70 \text{ ml/beat}$$

Hence, each ventricle pumps out about 70 ml (close to 2 ounces) of blood with each heartbeat.

So what is important here—how do we make sense out of this alphabet soup (SV, ESV, EDV)? Although several factors affect SV by causing changes in EDV or ESV, the three most important are *preload* (the amount the ventricles are stretched by contained blood), *contractility* (cardiac fiber contractile force that is due to factors other than EDV), and *afterload* (back pressure exerted by blood in the large arteries leaving the heart). As described in more detail next, preload affects EDV, whereas contractility and afterload affect the ESV (Figure 19.21).

Preload: Degree of Stretch of Heart Muscle.
According to the **Frank-Starling law of the heart,** the critical factor controlling stroke volume is the **preload** or *degree of stretch of the cardiac muscle cells just before they contract.* Recall that (1) stretching muscle fibers (and sarcomeres) increases the number of active cross bridge attachments that can be made between actin and myosin, and (2) the more muscle fibers are stretched, within physiological limits, the greater the force of contraction will be. Cardiac muscle, like skeletal muscle, exhibits a *length-tension relationship.* However, resting skeletal muscle fibers are kept at or near their optimal length for developing maximal tension, but resting cardiac cells are normally *shorter* than the optimal length. Therefore, increases in their length (stretching) produce dramatic increases in contractile force. The important factor stretching cardiac muscle is the amount of blood returning to the heart (venous return) and distending its ventricles (EDV).

Anything that increases the volume or speed of venous return, such as a slow heart rate or exercise, increases EDV and, consequently, stroke volume and force of contraction. A slow heartbeat allows more time for ventricular filling. Exercise speeds venous return because of an increased heart rate and the

FIGURE 19.21
Factors involved in regulation of cardiac output.

Legend:
- ← Increases, stimulates
- ← Reduces, inhibits

squeezing action of the skeletal muscles on the veins returning blood to the heart. SV may double during vigorous exercise due to these factors. Conversely, low venous return, such as might result from severe blood loss or an extremely rapid heart rate, decreases EDV, causing the heart to beat less forcefully and the SV to drop.

Because the systemic and pulmonary circulations are in series, this intrinsic mechanism ensures equal outputs of the ventricles and proper distribution of blood volume between the two circuits. If one side of the heart suddenly begins to pump more blood than the other, the increased venous return to the opposite ventricle forces it to pump out an equal volume, thus preventing backup or accumulation of blood in the circulation.

Contractility. Although EDV is the major *intrinsic factor* influencing stroke volume, SV can also be enhanced by *extrinsic factors* that increase the *contractility* of heart muscle. **Contractility** is an increase in contractile strength that is independent of muscle stretch and the EDV. Instead, the more vigorous contractions are a direct consequence of enhanced calcium influx into the cytoplasm from the extracellular fluid and the SR. Enhanced contractility results in more complete ejection of blood from the heart, hence a lower ESV and greater SV. This is the result of

increased sympathetic stimulation of the heart. As noted earlier (p. 630), sympathetic fibers serve not only the intrinsic conduction system but the entire heart, and one effect of norepinephrine or epinephrine release is to increase Ca^{2+} entry, which promotes more cross bridge binding and enhances ventricular contractility. Additionally, a whole battery of chemicals influence contractility. For example, contractility is enhanced by certain hormones (glucagon, thyroxine, and epinephrine), some ions (Ca^{2+}), and drugs (digitalis). Factors that increase contractility are called *positive inotropic* (*ino* = muscle, fiber) *agents.* Agents or factors that impair or decrease contractility *(negative inotropic agents)* include acidosis (excess H^+), rising extracellular levels of K^+, and drugs called calcium channel blockers (e.g., verapamil).

Afterload: Back Pressure Exerted by Arterial Blood. **Afterload,** the pressure that has to be exceeded or overcome for the ventricles to eject blood from the heart, is essentially the back pressure exerted on the aortic and pulmonary valves by arterial blood. In healthy individuals, afterload (about 80 mm Hg in the aorta and 20 mm Hg in the pulmonary trunk) is not a major determinant of stroke volume because it is relatively constant. However, in those with hypertension (high blood pressure), it is important indeed because it reduces the ability of the ventricles to eject blood. Consequently, more blood remains in the heart after systole, resulting in increased ESV and reduced stroke volume.

Regulation of Heart Rate

Given a healthy cardiovascular system, stroke volume tends to be relatively constant. However, when blood volume drops sharply or when the heart is seriously weakened, stroke volume declines and cardiac output is maintained by increasing the rate of heartbeat and contractility. Temporary stressors can also influence heart rate—and consequently cardiac output—by acting through neurally, chemically, and physically induced homeostatic mechanisms. These mechanisms are described next.

Autonomic Nervous System Regulation.
By far, the most important extrinsic controls on heart rate are exerted by the autonomic nervous system. When the sympathetic nervous system (SNS) is activated by emotional or physical stressors, such as fright, anxiety, excitement, or exercise (Figure 19.21), sympathetic nerve fibers release norepinephrine at their cardiac synapses. Norepinephrine (and epinephrine as well) bind to β adrenergic receptors in the heart, causing threshold to be reached more quickly; the heart responds by beating faster. Since sympathetic stimulation also enhances contractility, as described above, stroke volume does not decline, as it would if only heart *rate* were increased.

The parasympathetic division opposes sympathetic effects and effectively reduces heart rate when a stressful situation has passed. However, the parasympathetic division may be persistently activated in certain emotional conditions, such as grief and severe depression. Parasympathetic-initiated cardiac responses are mediated by release of acetylcholine, which hyperpolarizes the membranes of its effector cells by *opening* potassium channels.

Under resting conditions, both autonomic divisions continuously send impulses to the SA node of the heart, but the *dominant* influence is inhibitory. Thus, the heart is said to exhibit **vagal tone,** and heart rate is generally slower than it would be if the vagal nerves were not innervating it. Cutting the vagal nerves results in an almost immediate increase in heart rate by about 25 beats/min, reflecting the inherent rate (100 beats/min) of the pacemaking SA node.

When either division of the autonomic nervous system is stimulated more strongly by sensory inputs relayed from various parts of the cardiovascular system, the alternate division is temporarily inhibited. Most such sensory input is generated by *baroreceptors (pressoreceptors)* that respond to changes in systemic blood pressure. For example, the **atrial (Bainbridge) reflex** is a sympathetic reflex initiated by an increase in venous return and blood congestion in the

atria. Stretching of the atrial walls produces an increase in heart rate and force by (1) directly stimulating the SA node, and (2) stimulating baroreceptors in the atria that trigger reflexive adjustments that result in increased sympathetic stimulation of the heart.

Because increased cardiac output results in increased systemic blood pressure and vice versa, blood pressure regulation often involves reflex controls of heart rate. The neural mechanisms that regulate blood pressure are described in more detail in Chapter 20.

Chemical Regulation.
Chemicals normally present in the blood and other body fluids may influence heart rate, particularly if they become excessive or deficient. Some of these chemical factors are described briefly next.

1. **Hormones.** *Epinephrine,* a hormone liberated by the adrenal medulla during periods of sympathetic nervous system activation, produces the same cardiac effects as does norepinephrine released by the sympathetic nerves; that is, it enhances heart rate and contractility. *Thyroxine,* a thyroid gland hormone, causes a slower but more sustained increase in heart rate when it is released in large quantities. Since it also enhances the effect of epinephrine and norepinephrine on the heart, chronically hyperthyroid individuals may develop a weakened heart.

2. **Ions.** Physiologic relationships between intracellular and extracellular ions must be maintained for normal heart function. Plasma electrolyte imbalances pose real dangers to the heart.

Reduced blood levels of ionic calcium *(hypocalcemia)* depress the heart. Conversely, *hypercalcemia* tightly couples the excitation-contraction mechanism and prolongs the plateau phase of the action potential. These events dramatically increase heart irritability, which can lead to spastic heart contractions that permit the heart little rest. Many drugs used to treat heart conditions focus on calcium transport into cardiac cells (see *A Closer Look* on p. 624).

Excesses of ionic sodium and potassium are equally dangerous. Too much sodium *(hypernatremia)* inhibits transport of ionic calcium into the cardiac cells, thus blocking heart contraction. Excessive potassium *(hyperkalemia)* interferes with the depolarization mechanism by lowering the resting potential, and may lead to heart block and cardiac arrest. *Hypokalemia* is also life threatening, in that the heart beats feebly and abnormal rhythms appear. •

Other Factors.
Although they are less important than neural factors, a number of other factors, including age, gender, exercise, and body temperature, also influence heart rate. Resting heart rate is fastest in the fetus (between 140 and 160 beats/min) and gradually

decreases throughout life. Average heart rate is faster in females (72 to 80 beats/min) than in males (64 to 72 beats/min).

Exercise raises heart rate by acting through the sympathetic nervous system, which also increases systemic blood pressure and routes more blood to the working muscles (see Figure 19.21). However, resting heart rate in the physically fit tends to be substantially lower than in people out of condition. In trained athletes, it may be as slow as 40 to 60 beats/min. This apparent paradox is explained below.

Heat increases heart rate by enhancing the metabolic rate of cardiac cells. This explains the rapid, pounding heartbeat you feel when you have a high fever and accounts, in part, for the effect of exercise on heart rate (remember, working muscles generate heat). Cold has the opposite effect: It directly decreases heart rate.

Although heart rate varies with changes in activity, marked and persistent rate changes usually signal cardiovascular disease. **Tachycardia** (tak"e-kar′de-ah; "heart hurry") is an abnormally fast heart rate, over 100 beats per minute, which may result from elevated body temperature, stress, certain drugs, or heart disease. Because tachycardia occasionally promotes fibrillation, persistent tachycardia is considered pathological.

Bradycardia (brad"e-kar′de-ah; *brady* = slow) is a heart rate slower than 60 beats/min. It may result from low body temperature, certain drugs, or parasympathetic nervous activation. It is a known, and desirable, consequence of endurance-type athletic training. As physical and cardiovascular conditioning increases, the heart hypertrophies and its stroke volume increases; thus, resting heart rate can be lower and still provide the same cardiac output. However, persistent bradycardia in poorly conditioned people may result in grossly inadequate blood circulation to body tissues, and bradycardia is a frequent warning of brain edema after head trauma. •

Homeostatic Imbalance of Cardiac Output

The pumping action of the heart ordinarily maintains a balance between cardiac output and venous return. Were this not so, a dangerous damming up of blood (blood congestion) would occur in the veins returning blood to the heart.

When the pumping efficiency (CO) of the heart is so low that blood circulation is inadequate to meet tissue needs, the heart is said to be in **congestive heart failure (CHF)**. Congestive heart failure is usually a progressively worsening condition that reflects weakening of the myocardium by coronary atherosclerosis, persistent high blood pressure, multiple myocardial infarcts, or cardiomyopathy. The manner is which these various conditions damage the myocardium differs, but they are all equally devastating.

1. Coronary atherosclerosis, essentially a clogging of the coronary vessels with fatty buildup, impairs blood and oxygen delivery to the cardiac cells. The heart becomes increasingly hypoxic and begins to contract ineffectively.

2. Normally, pressure in the aorta during diastole is 80 mm Hg, and the left ventricle exerts only slightly over that amount of force to eject blood from its chamber. When aortic blood pressure during diastole rises to 90 mm Hg or more, the myocardium must exert more power to force the aortic valve open to pump out the same amount of blood. If this situation becomes chronic, the ESV rises and the myocardium hypertrophies. Eventually, the stress takes its toll and the myocardium becomes progressively weaker.

3. Successive myocardial infarcts depress pumping efficiency because the dead heart cells are replaced by noncontractile fibrous (scar) tissue.

4. The cause of dilated cardiomyopathy (kar"de-o-my-ah′path-e), or DCM, a condition in which the ventricles stretch and become flabby and the myocardium deteriorates, is often unknown. Drug toxicity (alcohol, cocaine, excess catecholamines, chemotherapeutic agents), hyperthyroidism, and inflammation of the heart are implicated in some cases. Because ventricular contractility is impaired, CO is poor and the condition progressively worsens.

Because the heart is a double pump, each side can initially fail independently of the other. If the left side fails, **pulmonary congestion** occurs. The right side of the heart continues to propel blood to the lungs, but the left side does not adequately eject the returning blood into the systemic circulation. Thus, the blood vessels in the lungs become engorged with blood, the pressure within them increases, and fluid leaks from the circulation into the lung tissue, causing pulmonary edema. If untreated, the person suffocates.

If the right side fails, **peripheral congestion** occurs. Blood stagnates within body organs, and pooled fluids in the tissue spaces impair the ability of body cells to obtain adequate nutrients and oxygen and to rid themselves of wastes. Edema is most noticeable in the extremities (feet, ankles, and fingers).

Failure of one side of the heart puts a greater strain on the opposite side, and ultimately the whole heart fails. A seriously weakened, or *decompensated,* heart is irreparable. Treatment is directed primarily toward (1) conserving heart energy with digitalis derivatives such as digoxin (which makes the heart beat more slowly), (2) removing the excess leaked fluid with *diuretics* (drugs that increase excretion of Na^+ and water by the kidneys), and (3) reducing cardiac afterload by using drugs that drive down blood pressure (e.g., ACE inhibitors). However, heart transplants and the use of skeletal muscle to replace damaged heart muscle have provided additional hope for selected cardiac patients (see *A Closer Look* on p. 624). •

DEVELOPMENTAL ASPECTS OF THE HEART

The human heart, derived from mesoderm, begins its existence as two simple endothelial tubes that quickly fuse to form a single chamber or heart tube that is busily pumping blood by the 22nd day of gestation (Figure 19.22). One or two days later, the heart tube exhibits four slightly bulged areas that represent the earliest heart chambers. From tail to head, following the direction of blood flow, the four chambers are:

1. **Sinus venosus** (ven-o'sus). This chamber initially receives all the venous blood of the embryo. It will become the smooth-walled part of the right atrium and the coronary sinus. The sinus venosus, which eventually gives rise to the sinoatrial node, takes the "podium" and sets heart rate early on in embryonic development.

2. **Atrium.** This embryonic chamber eventually becomes the pectinate muscle-ridged parts of the atria.

3. **Ventricle.** The strongest pumping chamber of the early heart, the ventricle gives rise to the *left* ventricle.

4. **Bulbus cordis.** This chamber, plus its cranial extension, the *truncus arteriosus,* give rise to the pulmonary trunk, first part of the aorta, and most of the *right* ventricle.

During the next three weeks, the heart undergoes dramatic contortions and major structural changes that convert it into a four-chambered organ capable of acting as a double pump—all without missing a beat! The ventricle moves caudally and the atrium cra-nially, assuming their adult positions. The heart divides into its four definitive chambers (the division proceeds in a complex manner through a number of stages), the midline septum forms, and the bulbus cordis splits into the pulmonary trunk and ascending aorta. After the second month, few changes other than growth occur until birth.

The interatrial septum of the fetal heart is incomplete. The *foramen ovale* (literally, "oval door") connects the two atria and allows blood entering the right heart to bypass the pulmonary circuit and the collapsed, nonfunctional fetal lungs. Another lung bypass, the **ductus arteriosus,** exists between the pulmonary trunk and the aorta. (These and other fetal circulatory bypasses are described in more detail in Chapter 29.) At or shortly after birth, these shunts close, completing the separation between the right and left sides of the heart. In the adult heart, the position of the foramen ovale is revealed by the fossa ovalis, and the **ligamentum arteriosum** is the fibrous remnant of the ductus arteriosus (see Figure 19.4a and b).

Congenital heart defects account for nearly half of all infant deaths arising from congenital anomalies. The most common abnormalities produce two basic kinds of disorders in the newborn. They either (1) lead to mixing of oxygen-poor systemic blood with oxygenated pulmonary blood (so that inadequately oxygenated blood reaches the body tissues) or (2) involve narrowed valves or vessels that greatly increase the work load on the heart. Examples of the first type of defect are septal defects (Figure 19.23b) and *patent ductus arteriosus,* in which the connection between the aorta and pulmonary trunk remains open. *Coarctation of the aorta* is an example of the second type of problem, whereas *tetralogy of Fallot*

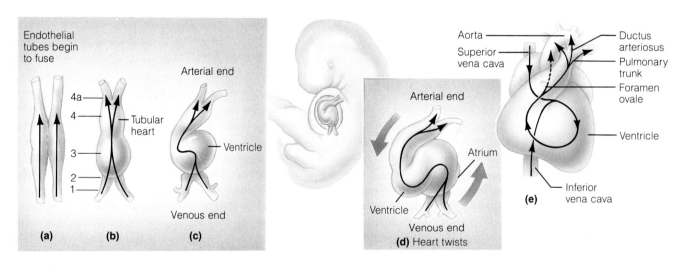

FIGURE 19.22
Development of the human heart during week 4. Ventral view, with the cranial direction toward the top of the figures. **(a)** Around day 21. **(b)** Day 22. **(c)** Day 23. **(d)** Day 24. **(e)** Day 28. In part (b), number 1 is the sinus venosus, 2 is the atrium, 3 is the ventricle, 4 is the bulbus cordis, and 4a is the truncus arteriosus. Arrows show the direction of blood flow.

(a) **Normal heart.** Arrows indicate the path of blood flow through the heart. Red = oxygen-rich blood; blue = oxygen-poor blood.

(b) **Ventricular septal defect.** The superior part of the interventricular septum fails to form; thus, blood mixes between the two ventricles.

Occurs in about 1 in every 500 births

(c) **Transposition of the great vessels.** Aorta comes from right ventricle, pulmonary trunk from left. Results when the bulbus cordis does not divide properly. Unoxygenated blood passes repeatedly around systemic circuit, while oxygenated blood recycles around the pulmonary circuit.

Occurs in about 1 in every 1000 births

Occurs in about 1 in every 1500 births

Narrowed aorta

(d) **Coarctation of the aorta.** A part of the aorta is narrowed, increasing the work load on the left ventricle.

(e) **Tetralogy of Fallot.** Multiple defects (tetra= four): Pulmonary trunk too narrow and pulmonary valve stenosed; ventricular septal defect; aorta opens from both ventricles; wall of right ventricle thickened from overwork.

Occurs in about 1 in every 2000 births

(f) **Pulmonary stenosis.** The pulmonary semilunar valve is narrowed, lessening the flow of blood to the lungs.

Occurs in about 1 in every 2800 births

FIGURE 19.23
Some examples of congenital heart defects. Purple color is used to show the heart areas where the defects are present.

(te-tral′o-je ov fal-o′), a serious condition in which the baby becomes cyanotic within minutes of birth, encompasses both types of disorders (Figure 19. 23d and e). Modern surgical techniques can correct most of these heart defects. Most congenital heart problems are traceable to environmental influences, such as maternal infection or drug intake during month 2 when the major events of heart formation occurred. •

In the absence of congenital heart problems, the heart functions admirably throughout a long lifetime for most people. Homeostatic mechanisms are normally so effective and efficient that people rarely notice when the heart is working harder. In people who exercise regularly and vigorously, the heart gradually adapts to the increased demand by increasing in size and becoming a more efficient and powerful pump. Consequently, stroke volume increases and resting heart rate declines. Aerobic exercise also helps to clear fatty deposits from blood vessel walls throughout the body, thus retarding the process of atherosclerosis and coronary heart disease. Barring

some chronic illnesses, this beneficial cardiac response to exercise persists into ripe old age.

The key word on the benefits of exercise is *regularity;* regular exercise gradually enhances the endurance and strength of the myocardium. Intermittent vigorous exercise, enjoyed by weekend athletes, may push an unconditioned heart beyond its ability to respond to the unexpected demands and bring on a myocardial infarct.

Because of the incredible amount of work the heart does during the course of a lifetime, certain structural changes are inevitable. Age-related changes that affect the heart include:

1. **Sclerosis and thickening of the valve flaps.** This occurs particularly where the stress of blood flow is greatest (mitral valve). Thus, heart murmurs are more common in elderly people.

2. **Decline in cardiac reserve.** Although the passing years seem to cause few changes in resting heart rate,

the aged heart is less able to respond to both sudden and prolonged stressors that demand increased output. Sympathetic control of the heart becomes less efficient (presumably because calcium channels decrease in number in sympathetic nerve endings with age), and heart rate gradually becomes more variable. There is a decline in maximum heart rate, but this is much less of a problem in physically active seniors.

3. Fibrosis of cardiac muscle. Sometimes the nodes of the heart's conduction system become fibrosed (scarred) with age. This increases the incidence of arrhythmias and other conduction problems.

4. Atherosclerosis. Although the insidious progress of atherosclerosis begins in childhood, it is accelerated by inactivity, smoking, and stress. The most serious consequences to the heart are hypertensive heart disease and coronary artery occlusion. These condi-

tions, in turn, increase the risk of heart attack and stroke. Although the aging process itself leads to changes in blood vessel walls that result in atherosclerosis, many investigators feel that diet, not aging, is the single most important contributor to cardiovascular disease. There is some agreement that risk is lowered if people consume less animal fat, cholesterol, and salt.

* * *

The heart is an exquisitely engineered double pump that operates with precision to propel blood into the large arteries leaving its chambers. However, continuous circulation of blood also depends critically on the pressure dynamics existing within the blood vessels. Chapter 20 considers the structure and function of the body's blood vessels and relates this information to the work of the heart to provide a complete picture of cardiovascular functioning.

RELATED CLINICAL TERMS

Asystole (a-sis'to-le) Situation in which the heart fails to contract.

Cardiac catheterization Diagnostic procedure involving passage of a fine catheter (tubing) through a blood vessel into the heart; blood samples are withdrawn, and pressures within the heart can be measured; findings help to detect valve problems, heart deformities, and other heart malfunctions.

Cor pulmonale (kor pul-mun-na'le; *cor* = heart, *pulmo* = lung) A life-threatening condition of right-sided heart failure resulting from elevated blood pressure in the pulmonary circuit (pulmonary hypertension); acute cases may develop suddenly due to a pulmonary embolism; chronic cases are usually associated with chronic lung disorders such as emphysema.

Endocarditis (en"do-kar-di'tis) Inflammation of the endocardium, usually confined to the endocardium of the heart valves. Endocarditis often results from infection by bacteria that have entered the bloodstream but may result from fungal infection or an autoimmune response. Drug addicts may develop endocarditis by injecting themselves with contaminated needles.

Heart palpitation A heartbeat that is unusually strong, fast, or irregular so that the person becomes aware of it; may be caused by certain drugs, emotional pressures ("nervous heart"), or heart disorders.

Mitral valve prolapse Valve disorder affecting up to 5% of the population; most often seen in young women and appears to have a genetic basis; one or more of the flaps of the mitral valve become incompetent and billow into the left atrium during ventricular systole, allowing blood regurgitation; mitral valve prolapse is a common indication for valve replacement surgery.

Myocarditis (mi"o-kar-di'tis; *myo* = muscle, *card* = heart, *itis* = inflammation) Inflammation of the cardiac muscle layer (myocardium) of the heart; sometimes follows an untreated streptococcal infection in children; may weaken the heart and impair its ability to act as an effective pump.

CHAPTER SUMMARY

Heart Anatomy (pp. 613–621)

Size, Location, and Orientation (p. 613)
1.   The human heart, about the size of a clenched fist, is located obliquely within the mediastinum of the thorax.

Coverings of the Heart (pp. 613–614)
2.   The heart is enclosed within a double sac made up of the outer fibrous pericardium and the inner serous pericardium (parietal and visceral layers). The pericardial cavity between the serous layers contains lubricating serous fluid.

Layers of the Heart Wall (pp. 614–615)
3.   Layers of the heart wall, from the interior out, are the endocardium, the myocardium (reinforced by a fibrous skeleton), and the epicardium (visceral layer of the serous pericardium).

Chambers and Associated Great Vessels (p. 615)
4.   The heart has two superior atria and two inferior ventricles. Functionally, the heart is a double pump.

5.   Entering the right atrium are the superior vena cava, the inferior vena cava, and the coronary sinus. Four pulmonary veins enter the left atrium.

6.   The right ventricle discharges blood into the pulmonary trunk; the left ventricle pumps blood into the aorta.

Pathway of Blood Through the Heart (pp. 615–619)
7.   The right heart is the pulmonary circuit pump. Oxygen-poor systemic blood enters the right atrium, passes into the right ventricle, through the pulmonary trunk to the lungs, and back to the left atrium via the pulmonary veins.

8.   The left heart is the systemic circuit pump. Oxygen-laden blood entering the left atrium from the lungs flows into the left ventricle and then into the aorta, which provides the functional supply of all body organs. Systemic veins return the oxygen-depleted blood to the right atrium.

Heart Valves (pp. 619–621)

9. The atrioventricular valves (tricuspid and bicuspid) prevent backflow into the atria when the ventricles are contracting; the pulmonary and aortic semilunar valves prevent backflow into the ventricles when they are relaxing.

Blood Supply to the Heart: Coronary Circulation (pp. 621–622)

1. The right and left coronary arteries branch from the aorta and via their main branches (anterior and posterior interventricular, marginal, and circumflex arteries) supply the heart itself. Venous blood, collected by the cardiac veins (great, middle, and small), is emptied into the coronary sinus.

2. Blood delivery to the myocardium occurs during heart relaxation.

Properties of Cardiac Muscle Fibers (pp. 622–627)

Microscopic Anatomy (pp. 622–626)

1. Cardiac muscle cells are branching, striated, generally uninucleate cells. They contain myofibrils consisting of typical sarcomeres.

2. Adjacent cardiac cells are connected by intercalated discs containing desmosomes and gap junctions. The myocardium behaves as a functional syncytium because of electrical coupling provided by gap junctions.

Energy Requirements (p. 626)

3. Cardiac muscle has abundant mitochondria and depends primarily on aerobic respiration to form ATP.

Mechanism and Events of Contraction (pp. 626–627)

4. The means of action-potential generation in the contractile cardiac muscle mimics that of skeletal muscle. Depolarization of the membrane causes opening of sodium channels and sodium entry, which is responsible for the rising phase of the action potential curve. Depolarization also opens slow calcium channels and entry of Ca^{2+} prolongs the period of depolarization (creates the plateau). The action potential is coupled to sliding of the myofilaments by ionic calcium released by the SR and entering from the extracellular space. Compared to skeletal muscle, cardiac muscle has a prolonged refractory period that prevents tetanization.

Heart Physiology (pp. 627–637)

Electrical Events (pp. 627–630)

1. Certain noncontractile cardiac muscle cells exhibit automaticity and rhythmicity and can independently initiate action potentials. Such cells have an unstable resting potential called a pacemaker potential that gradually depolarizes, drifting toward threshold for firing. These cells comprise the intrinsic conduction system of the heart.

2. The conduction, or nodal, system of the heart consists of the SA and AV nodes, the AV bundle and bundle branches, and the Purkinje fibers. This system coordinates the depolarization of the heart and ensures that the heart beats as a unit. The SA node has the fastest rate of spontaneous depolarization and acts as the heart's pacemaker; it sets the sinus rhythm.

3. Defects in the intrinsic conduction system can cause arrhythmias, fibrillation, and heart block.

4. The heart is innervated by the autonomic nervous system. Autonomic cardiac centers in the medulla include the sympathetic cardioacceleratory center, which projects to the T_1–T_5 region of the spinal cord, which in turn projects to the cervical and upper thoracic chain ganglia. Postganglionic fibers innervate the SA and AV nodes and the cardiac muscle fibers. The parasympathetic cardioinhibitory center exerts its influence via the vagus nerves (X), which project to the heart wall. Most parasympathetic fibers serve the SA and AV nodes.

5. An electrocardiogram is a graphic representation of the cardiac conduction cycle. The P wave reflects atrial depolarization. The QRS complex indicates ventricular depolarization; the T wave represents ventricular repolarization.

Mechanical Events: The Cardiac Cycle (pp. 631–633)

6. Cardiac cycle refers to events occurring during one heartbeat. During mid-to-late diastole, the ventricles fill and the atria contract. Ventricular systole consists of the isovolumetric contraction phase and the ventricular ejection phase. During early diastole, the ventricles are relaxed and are closed chambers until increasing atrial pressure forces the AV valves open and the cycle begins again. At a normal heart rate of 75 beats/min, a cardiac cycle lasts 0.8 s.

7. Pressure changes promote blood flow and valve opening and closing.

Heart Sounds (pp. 633–634)

8. Normal heart sounds arise chiefly from the closing of heart valves. Abnormal heart sounds, called murmurs, usually reflect valve problems.

Cardiac Output (pp. 634–637)

9. Cardiac output, typically 5 L/min, is the amount of blood pumped out by each ventricle in 1 minute. Stroke volume is the amount of blood pumped out by a ventricle with each contraction. Cardiac output = heart rate $\times$ stroke volume.

10. Stroke volume depends to a large extent on the degree of stretch of cardiac muscle by venous return. Approximately 70 ml, it is the difference between end diastolic volume (EDV) and end systolic volume (ESV). Anything that influences heart rate or blood volume influences venous return, hence stroke volume.

11. Activation of the sympathetic nervous system increases heart rate and contractility; parasympathetic activation decreases heart rate and contractility. Ordinarily, the heart exhibits vagal tone.

12. Chemical regulation of the heart is effected by hormones (epinephrine and thyroxine) and ions (sodium, potassium, and calcium). Imbalances in ions severely impair heart activity.

13. Other factors influencing heart rate are age, sex, exercise, and body temperature.

14. Congestive heart failure occurs when the pumping ability of the heart is inadequate to provide normal circulation to meet body needs. Right heart failure leads to systemic edema; left heart failure results in pulmonary edema.

Developmental Aspects of the Heart (pp. 638–640)

1. The heart begins as a simple (mesodermal) tube that is pumping blood by the fourth week of gestation. The fetal heart has two lung bypasses: the foramen ovale and the ductus arteriosus.

2. Congenital heart defects account for more than half of infant deaths. The most common of these disorders lead to inadequate oxygenation of blood or increase the work load on the heart.

3. Age-related changes include sclerosis and thickening of the valve flaps, declines in cardiac reserve, fibrosis of cardiac muscle, and atherosclerosis.

4. Risk factors for cardiac disease include dietary factors, excessive stress, cigarette smoking, and lack of exercise.

REVIEW QUESTIONS
Multiple Choice/Matching

1. When the semilunar valves are open, which of the following are occurring? (a) 2,3, 5,6, (b) 1,2,3,7, (c) 1,3,5,6, (d) 2,4,5,7.
(1) coronary arteries fill
(2) AV valves are closed
(3) ventricles are in systole
(4) ventricles are in diastole
(5) blood enters aorta
(6) blood enters pulmonary arteries
(7) atria contract

2. The portion of the intrinsic conduction system located in the interventricular septum is the (a) AV node, (b) SA node, (c) AV bundle, (d) Purkinje fibers.

3. An ECG provides information about (a) cardiac output, (b) movement of the excitation wave across the heart, (c) coronary circulation, (d) valve impairment.

4. The sequence of contraction of the heart chambers is (a) random, (b) left chambers followed by right chambers, (c) both atria followed by both ventricles, (d) right atrium, right ventricle, left atrium, left ventricle.

5. The fact that the left ventricular wall is thicker than the right reveals that it (a) pumps a greater volume of blood, (b) pumps blood against greater resistance, (c) expands the thoracic cage, (d) pumps blood through a smaller valve.

6. The chordae tendineae (a) close the atrioventricular valves, (b) prevent the AV valve flaps from everting, (c) contract the papillary muscles, (d) open the semilunar valves.

7. In the heart, (1) action potentials are conducted from cell to cell across the myocardium via gap junctions, (2) the SA node sets the pace for the heart as a whole, (3) spontaneous depolarization of cardiac cells can occur in the absence of nerve stimulation, (4) cardiac muscle can continue to contract for long periods of time in the absence of oxygen.
(a) all of the above, (b) 1, 3, 4, (c) 1, 2, 3, (d) 2, 3.

8. The activity of the heart depends on intrinsic properties of cardiac muscle and on neural factors. Thus, (a) vagus nerve stimulation of the heart reduces heart rate, (b) sympathetic nerve stimulation of the heart decreases time available for ventricular filling, (c) sympathetic stimulation of the heart increases its force of contraction, (d) all of the above.

9. Freshly oxygenated blood is first received by the (a) right atrium, (b) left atrium, (c) right ventricle, (d) left ventricle.

Short Answer Essay Questions

 10. Describe the location and position of the heart in the body.

11. Describe the pericardium and distinguish between the fibrous and the serous pericardia relative to histological structure and location.

12. Trace one drop of blood from the time it enters the right atrium until it enters the left atrium. What is this circuit called?

 13. (a) Describe how heart contraction and relaxation influence coronary blood flow. (b) Name the major branches of the coronary arteries, and note the heart regions served by each.

14. The refractory period of cardiac muscle is much longer than that of skeletal muscle. Why is this a desirable functional property?

15. (a) Name the elements of the intrinsic conduction system of the heart in order, beginning with the pacemaker. (b) What is the important function of this conduction system?

16. Draw a normal ECG pattern. Label and explain the significance of its deflection waves.

17. Define cardiac cycle, and follow the events of one cycle.

18. What is cardiac output, and how is it calculated?

19. Discuss how the Frank-Starling law of the heart helps to explain the influence of venous return on stroke volume.

20. (a) Describe the common function of the foramen ovale and the ductus arteriosus in a fetus. (b) What problems result if these shunts remain patent (open) after birth?

CRITICAL THINKING AND CLINICAL APPLICATION QUESTIONS

1. A gang member was stabbed in the chest during a crack-related street fight. He was cyanotic and unconscious from lack of blood delivery to the brain. The diagnosis was cardiac tamponade. What is cardiac tamponade and how does it cause the observed symptoms?

2. You have been called upon to demonstrate the technique for listening to valve sounds. (a) Explain where you would position your stethoscope to auscultate (1) the aortic valve of a patient with severe aortic semilunar valve incompetence and (2) a stenosed mitral valve. (b) During which period(s) would you hear these abnormal valve sounds most clearly? (During atrial diastole, ventricular systole, ventricular diastole, or atrial systole?) (c) What cues would you use to differentiate between an incompetent and a stenosed valve?

3. A middle-aged woman is admitted to the coronary care unit with a diagnosis of left ventricular failure resulting from a myocardial infarction. Her history indicated that she was aroused in the middle of the night by severe chest pain. Her skin is pale and cold, and moist sounds are heard over the lower regions of both lungs. Explain how failure of the left ventricle can cause these signs and symptoms.

The Cardiovascular System: Blood Vessels

20

CHAPTER OUTLINE AND STUDENT OBJECTIVES

Overview of Blood Vessel Structure and Function (pp. 643–650)

1. Describe the three layers that typically form the wall of a blood vessel, and state the function of each.

2. Define vasoconstriction and vasodilation.

3. Compare and contrast the structure and function of the three types of arteries.

4. Describe the structure and function of veins, and explain how veins differ from arteries.

5. Describe the structure and function of a capillary bed.

Physiology of Circulation (pp. 650–667)

6. Define blood flow, blood pressure, and resistance, and explain the relationships between these factors.

7. List and explain the factors that influence blood pressure, and describe how blood pressure is regulated.

8. Define hypertension. Note both its symptoms and consequences.

9. Explain how blood flow is regulated in the body in general and in its specific organs.

10. Define circulatory shock. Note several possible causes.

11. Outline the factors involved in capillary dynamics, and explain the significance of each.

Circulatory Pathways: Blood Vessels of the Body (pp. 667–690)

12. Trace the pathway of blood through the pulmonary circuit, and state the importance of this special circulation.

13. Describe the general functions of the systemic circuit. Name and give the location of the major arteries and veins in the systemic circulation.

14. Describe the structure and special function of the hepatic portal system.

Developmental Aspects of the Blood Vessels (p. 667)

15. Explain how blood vessels develop in the fetus.

16. Provide examples of changes that often occur in blood vessels as a person ages.

The **blood vessels** of the body form a closed delivery system that begins and ends at the heart. The idea that blood circulates in the body dates back to the 1620s to the inspired experiments of William Harvey, an English physician. Prior to that time, it was thought, as proposed by the ancient Greek physician Galen, that blood moved through the body like an ocean tide, first moving out from the heart and then ebbing back into the heart via the same vessels.

Although blood vessels are often compared to a system of plumbing pipes within which blood circulates, this analogy serves only as a starting point. Unlike rigid pipes, blood vessels are dynamic structures that pulsate, constrict and relax, and even proliferate, as demanded by the changing needs of the body. This chapter examines the structure and function of these important circulatory passageways.

OVERVIEW OF BLOOD VESSEL STRUCTURE AND FUNCTION

The three major types of blood vessels are *arteries, capillaries,* and *veins.* As the heart contracts, blood is forced into the large arteries leaving its ventricles. It then moves into successively smaller arteries, finally reaching their smallest branches, the *arterioles* (ar-te're-ōlz; "little arteries"), which feed into the capillary beds of body organs and tissues. Blood draining from the capillaries flows into *venules* (ven'ūlz), and then on into small veins that merge to form larger veins that ultimately empty into the heart. Altogether, the blood vessels in the adult human carry blood on a journey that stretches for about 100,000 km (60,000 miles) through the internal body landscape!

? *What is the functional value of the fact that the capillaries consist of just a single layer of squamous cells underlain by sparse connective tissue?*

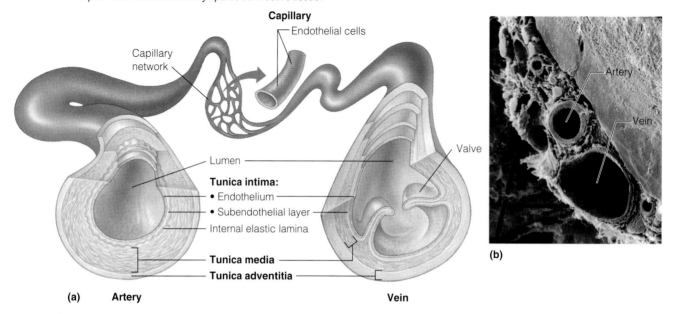

(a) Artery

Vein

(b)

FIGURE 20.1
Structure of arteries, veins, and capillaries. (a) The walls of arteries and veins are composed of three tunics: the tunica intima (endothelium underlain by a subendothelial layer of loose connective tissue), tunica media (smooth muscle cells and elastic fibers), and tunica adventitia (largely collagen fibers). Capillaries, intermediate between arteries and veins in the circulatory pathway, are composed of only the endothelium and a sparse basal lamina. Notice that the tunica media is thick in arteries and thin in veins, while the tunica adventitia is thin in arteries and relatively thicker in veins. **(b)** Scanning electron micrograph of a muscular artery and the corresponding vein in cross section (120×). (From R. G. Kessel and R. H. Kardon, *Tissues and Organs.* ©1979 W. H. Freeman.)

Arteries and veins simply act as conduits for blood. Because arteries carry blood *away from* the heart, they are said to "branch," "diverge," or "fork" as they form smaller and smaller divisions. Veins, by contrast, carry blood *toward* the heart and so are said to "join," "merge," and "converge" into the successively larger vessels approaching the heart. Only the capillaries come into intimate contact with tissue cells and directly serve cellular needs. Exchanges between the blood and tissue cells occur primarily through the gossamer-thin capillary walls.

Structure of Blood Vessel Walls

The walls of all blood vessels, except the very smallest, are composed of three distinct layers, or *tunics* ("cloaks"). These tunics surround a central blood-containing space, or opening, the vessel **lumen** (Figure 20.1).

The innermost tunic is the **tunica intima** (too'nĭ-kah in'tĭ-mah). Its name is easy to remember once you know that this tunic is in *intimate* contact with the blood in the lumen. This tunic contains the *endothelium,* the simple squamous epithelium that lines the lumen of all vessels. The endothelium is a continuation of the endocardial lining of the heart, and its flat cells fit closely together, forming a slick surface that

minimizes friction as blood moves through the vessel lumen. In vessels larger than 1 mm in diameter, a *subendothelial layer* of loose connective tissue supports the endothelium.

The middle tunic, the **tunica media** (me'de-ah), consists mostly of circularly arranged smooth muscle cells and sheets of elastin. The activity of the smooth muscle is regulated by *vasomotor nerve fibers* of the sympathetic division of the autonomic nervous system. Depending on the needs of the body, the vasomotor fibers can cause **vasoconstriction** (reduction in lumen diameter due to smooth muscle contraction) or **vasodilation** (widening of the lumen due to smooth muscle relaxation). Since small changes in blood vessel diameter greatly influence blood flow and blood pressure, the activities of the tunica media are critical in regulating circulatory dynamics. Generally, the tunica media is the bulkiest layer in arteries, which bear the greatest responsibility for maintaining blood pressure and continuous blood circulation (described shortly).

The outermost layer of a blood vessel wall is the **tunica adventitia** (ad"ven-tish'e-ah; "coming from outside"). This tunic is composed largely of loosely woven collagen fibers that protect the blood vessel and anchor it to surrounding structures. The tunica adventitia is infiltrated with nerve fibers and lymphatic vessels and, in larger vessels, a system of tiny blood vessels. These vessels, called the **vasa vasorum** (va′sah va-sor′um)—literally, "vessels of the vessels"—nourish the more external tissues of the blood vessel wall. The deeper portion obtains its nutrients directly from blood in the lumen.

The three vessel types vary in length, diameter, and the relative thickness and tissue makeup of their walls. These differences are described next.

Arterial System

Arteries are vessels that transport blood *away from* the heart. Although systemic arteries always carry oxygenated blood and systemic veins always carry oxygen-poor blood, this is not true for the vessels of the pulmonary circulation (see Figure 20.15, p. 670) or for the special umbilical vessels of a fetus (see Figure 29.13a, p. 1015).

In terms of relative size and function, arteries can be divided into three groups—elastic arteries, muscular arteries, and arterioles.

Elastic Arteries

Elastic arteries are the large, thick-walled arteries near the heart—the aorta and its major branches. These arteries are both the largest in diameter and the most elastic. Their large lumen allows them to serve as low-resistance pathways that conduct blood from the heart to medium-sized arteries. For this reason, they are sometimes referred to as **conducting arteries.** The elastic arteries contain more elastin than any other vessel type. It is present in all three tunics, but the tunica media contains the most. There the elastin constructs concentric "holey" sheets of elastic connective tissue that look like slices of Swiss cheese interspersed between the layers of smooth muscle cells. This abundance of elastin enables these arteries to withstand and smooth out large pressure fluctuations by expanding when the heart forces blood into them, and then recoiling to propel blood onward into the circulation when the heart relaxes. Although elastic arteries also contain substantial amounts of smooth muscle, they are relatively inactive in vasoconstriction. Thus, functionally, the elastic arteries can be visualized as simple elastic tubes.

Because the elastic arteries expand and recoil passively to accommodate changes in blood volume, the blood is kept under continuous pressure. Consequently, blood flows fairly continuously rather than starting and stopping with the pulsatile rhythm of the heartbeat. If the blood vessels become hard and unyielding, as in arteriosclerosis, blood flows more intermittently, similar to the way water flows through a hard rubber garden hose attached to a faucet. When the faucet (the pump) is on, the high pressure makes the water gush out of the hose. But when the faucet is shut off, the water flow abruptly becomes a trickle

and then stops, because the hose walls cannot recoil to keep the water under pressure. Furthermore, without the pressure-smoothing effect of the elastic arteries, the walls of arteries throughout the body experience higher pressures. Battered by high pressures, the arteries eventually weaken and may balloon out or even burst. (These problems are discussed in more detail in *A Closer Look* on pp. 648–649.)

Muscular Arteries

Distally the elastic arteries give way to the **muscular, or distributing, arteries.** The muscular arteries deliver blood to specific body organs and account for most of the named arteries studied in the anatomy laboratory. Their diameter ranges from that of a little finger (1 cm) to that of a pencil lead (about 0.3 mm). Proportionately, they have the thickest media of all vessels. Their tunica media contains relatively more smooth muscle and less elastic tissue than that of elastic arteries; therefore, they are more active in vasoconstriction and are less distensible. [However, there *is* a thickened sheet of elastin (an *elastic lamina*) on each face of the tunica media in the muscular arteries.]

Arterioles

Arterioles have a lumen diameter ranging from 0.3 mm to 10 μm, and are the smallest of the arteries. The larger arterioles exhibit all three tunics, but their tunica media is chiefly smooth muscle with a few scattered elastic fibers. The smaller arterioles, which lead into the capillary beds, are little more than a single layer of smooth muscle cells spiraling around the endothelial lining.

As described shortly, blood flow into the capillary beds from minute to minute is determined by arteriole diameter, which varies in response to changing neural stimuli and local chemical influences. When arterioles constrict, the tissues served are largely bypassed. When arterioles dilate, blood flow into the local capillaries increases dramatically.

Capillaries

The microscopic **capillaries** are the smallest blood vessels. Their exceedingly thin walls consist of just a thin tunica intima (see Figure 20.1a). In some cases, one endothelial cell forms the entire circumference of the capillary wall. Average capillary length is 1 mm and average lumen diameter is 8–10 μm, just large enough for red blood cells to slip through in single file. Most tissues have a rich capillary supply, but there are exceptions. Tendons and ligaments are poorly vascularized. Cartilage and epithelia lack capillaries, but receive nutrients from blood vessels in nearby connective tissues, and the avascular cornea and lens of the eye receive nutrients from the aqueous humor.

If blood vessels are compared to a system of expressways and roads, then the capillaries are the back alleys and driveways that provide direct access to nearly every cell in the body. Given their location and the thinness of their walls, capillaries are ideally suited for their role—exchange of materials (gases, nutrients, hormones, etc.) between the blood and interstitial fluid. The mechanisms of these exchanges are described later in this chapter; here we will focus on capillary structure.

Types of Capillaries

Structurally, there are three types of capillaries—*continuous, fenestrated,* and *sinusoidal.* **Continuous capillaries,** abundant in the skin and muscles, are most common. They are continuous in the sense that their endothelial cells provide an uninterrupted lining. Adjacent cells are joined laterally by *tight junctions.* However, these are usually incomplete, and leave gaps of unjoined membrane called **intercellular clefts** just large enough to allow limited passage of fluids and small solutes. Typically, the endothelial cell cytoplasm contains numerous small pinocytotic vesicles believed to ferry fluids across the capillary wall by bulk transport. However, brain capillaries are unique. There the tight junctions of the continuous capillaries are complete around the entire perimeter of the endothelial cells, and constitute the structural basis of the *blood-brain barrier,* described in Chapter 12.

Fenestrated (fen'es-tra-tid) **capillaries** are similar to the continuous variety except that some of their endothelial cells are riddled with oval *pores* or *fenestrations* (*fenestra* = window). The fenestrations are usually covered by a very delicate membrane, or diaphragm (Figure 20.2), but even so this capillary variety has much greater permeability to fluids and small solutes. Fenestrated capillaries are found where active capillary absorption or filtrate formation occurs. For example, fenestrated capillaries in the small intestine receive the digested food nutrients, and those in endocrine organs allow hormones to gain rapid entry into the blood. Fenestrated capillaries with perpetually open pores occur in the kidneys, where rapid filtration of blood plasma is essential.

Sinusoidal capillaries, or **sinusoids** (si'nŭ-soyds) are highly modified, leaky capillaries found only in certain organs (liver, bone marrow, lymphoid tissues, and some endocrine organs). Sinusoids have large, irregularly shaped lumens, are usually fenestrated, and have fewer tight junctions and larger intercellular clefts than ordinary capillaries. These structural modifications allow large molecules (such as proteins) and even blood cells to pass between the blood and surrounding tissues. In the liver, the endothelium of the sinusoids is discontinuous. They are partially lined by large macrophages called **Kupffer cells,** rather than endothelial cells. In other organs, such as the spleen, phagocytes located just outside the sinu-

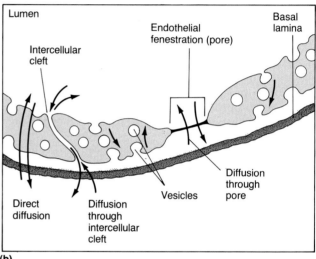

FIGURE 20.2
Capillary structure and transport mechanisms.
(a) Structure of a fenestrated capillary. Continuous capillaries differ only in that they lack the fenestrations. **(b)** The four possible pathways or routes of transport across the wall of an endothelial cell. (The endothelial cell is drawn as if cut in cross section.)

soids stick cytoplasmic extensions through the intercellular clefts into the sinusoidal lumen to get at their "prey." Blood flows sluggishly through the tortuous sinusoid channels, allowing time for it to be modified or processed in various ways. For example, the liver processes nutrient-laden venous blood draining from the digestive organs by absorbing nutrients and removing and destroying any contained bacteria.

Capillary Beds

Capillaries do not function independently. Instead they tend to form interweaving networks called **capillary beds.** In most body regions, a capillary bed consists of two types of vessels: (1) a *vascular shunt* (metarteriole–thoroughfare channel), a short vessel that directly connects the arteriole and venule at opposite ends of the bed, and (2) *true capillaries* (Figure 20.3). The **terminal arteriole** feeding the bed leads into a **metarteriole** (a vessel structurally inter-

(a) Sphincters open

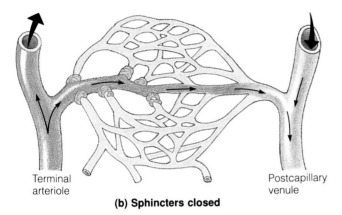

(b) Sphincters closed

FIGURE 20.3
Anatomy of a capillary bed. The composite metarteriole–
thoroughfare channels act as shunts to bypass the true capillaries
when precapillary sphincters controlling blood entry into the true
capillaries are constricted.

mediate between an arteriole and a capillary), which
is directly continuous with the **thoroughfare channel**
(intermediate between a capillary and a venule). The
thoroughfare channel, in turn, joins the **postcapillary
venule** that drains the bed.

The **true capillaries** number 10 to 100 per capillary bed, depending on the organ or tissues served.
They usually branch off the metarteriole (proximal
end of the shunt) and return to the thoroughfare channel (the distal end), but occasionally they spring from
the terminal arteriole and empty directly into the
venule. A cuff of smooth muscle fibers, called a **precapillary sphincter,** surrounds the root of each true
capillary at the metarteriole and acts as a valve to regulate the flow of blood into the capillary. Blood flowing through a terminal arteriole may take one of two
routes: through the true capillaries or through the
shunt. When the precapillary sphincters are relaxed
(open), blood flows through the true capillaries and
takes part in exchanges with tissue cells. When the
sphincters are contracted (closed), blood flows
through the shunts and bypasses the tissue cells.

The relative amount of blood flowing into a capillary bed is regulated by vasomotor nerve fibers and
local chemical conditions. A capillary bed may be
flooded with blood or almost completely bypassed,
depending on conditions in the body or in that specific organ. For example, suppose you have just eaten
and are sitting relaxed, listening to your favorite
musical group. Food digestion is going on, and blood
is circulating freely through the true capillaries of
your gastrointestinal organs to receive the breakdown
products of digestion. However, most of these same
capillary pathways are closed between meals. Further, when you are exercising vigorously, blood is
rerouted from the digestive organs (food or no food) to
the capillary beds of your skeletal muscles where it is
more immediately needed. This helps explain why
vigorous exercise immediately after a meal can cause
indigestion or abdominal cramps.

Venous System

Blood is carried from the capillary beds toward the
heart by veins. En route, the venous vessels increase
in diameter, and their walls gradually thicken as they
progress from venules to the larger and larger veins.

Venules

Venules, ranging from 8 to 100 μm in diameter, are
formed when capillaries unite. The smallest venules,
the **postcapillary venules,** consist entirely of endothelium around which a few fibroblasts congregate.
They are extremely porous (more like capillaries than
veins in this way), and fluid and white blood cells
move easily from the bloodstream through their
walls. In larger venules, both a sparse tunica media
and a thin tunica adventitia are present.

Veins

Venules join to form **veins.** Veins usually have three
distinct tunics, but their walls are always thinner and
their lumens larger than those of corresponding arteries (see Figure 20.1). Consequently, in routine histological preparations, veins are usually collapsed, and
their lumens appear slitlike. There is relatively little
smooth muscle or elastin in the tunica media, which
tends to be thin even in the largest veins. The tunica
adventitia is the heaviest wall layer and is often several times thicker than the tunica media. In the largest
veins—the venae cavae, which return blood directly
to the heart—the tunica adventitia is further thickened by longitudinal bands of smooth muscle.

With their large lumens and thin walls, veins can
accommodate a fairly large blood volume. Since up to
65% of the body's total blood supply is found in the
veins at any time, veins are called **capacitance vessels,** or **blood reservoirs.** Even so, the veins are normally only partially filled with blood.

A CLOSER LOOK | **Arteriosclerosis? Get Out the Cardiovascular Drāno**

When pipes get clogged, it is usually because something gets stuck in them—a greasy mass of bone bits or a "hair ball," But when arteries are narrowed by **atherosclerosis,** their walls thicken and protrude into the vessel lumen, making it easy to close the vessel completely. A roaming blood clot or arterial spasms can do it.

Although all blood vessels are susceptible to this serious condition, the aorta and the coronary arteries are most often affected. The disease progresses through many stages before the arterial walls actually approach the rigid tube system described in the text, but some of the earlier stages are just as lethal.

What triggers this scourge of blood vessels that indirectly causes half of the deaths in the Western world? According to the *response to injury* hypothesis, the initial event is damage to the tunica intima caused by blood-borne chemicals, viruses, or physical factors such as a blow or hypertension. Injured endothelial cells release chemotactic agents and growth (mitosis-inducing) factors, and begin to transport and modify greater amounts of lipids picked up from the blood, particularly low-density lipoproteins (LDLs), the type that deliver cholesterol to tissue cells via the bloodsteam. When the sequestered LDL becomes oxidized (this seems to be a common event), it not only damages neighboring cells but also acts as a chemotactic agent to attract monocytes to the area. Monocytes cling to altered endothelial cells

and then migrate beneath the tunica intima where they become macrophages. The macrophages normally help protect the body by ingesting invading microorganisms and toxic substances including oxidized proteins and lipids. But as they gorge themselves on the oxidized LDLs, they become transformed into lipid-laded *foam cells* and lose their scavenging ability. Soon the macrophages are joined by smooth muscle cells migrating from the tunica media. These also take up lipids and become foam cells. The accumulating foam cells initiate the **fatty streak stage.** The smooth muscle cells also deposit collagen and elastin fibers, thickening the intima and producing lesions called **atheromas** or **atherosclerotic plaques.** When these fatty mounds of muscle and fibrous tissue begin to protrude into the vessel lumen, the person has full-blown atherosclerosis (see photo).

Additionally, impaired endothelial function can account for at least some cases of coronary artery spasms. Under normal conditions, endothelial cells release endothelium-derived relaxing factor (nitric oxide) and prostacyclin—chemicals that promote vasodilation and inhibit platelet aggregation. Atherosclerosis, or even the very early presence of oxidized LDLs, can impair release of these vasodilators and antiaggregating factors. Indeed, this may well be one cause of the increased thrombus formation in those with atherosclerosis.

If you add still another ingredient—a chemical one called *lipopro-*

Yellow atherosclerotic plaques line human blood vessel.

tein (a)—to the picture, the disease course accelerates dramatically. Lipoprotein (a), a special LDL seen only in some people, appears to be most involved in delivering cholesterol to sites where tissue repair is occurring—damaged endothelium for one. Although it is presumed to assist in wound healing, it "backfires" when it is present in excess. Lipoprotein (a) binds to subendothelial tissues more avidly than other LDLs. Because it is similar to a common growth factor, it is thought to promote mitosis of the cells in the vessel wall. Because it resembles plasminogen, it can "stand in" for it at sites where clots have formed. However, it lacks plasminogen's clot-dissolving ability, so by competing successfully with that "clot buster," it may *prevent* disposal of unneeded or undesirable clots.

Because blood pressure within veins is low, they can be much thinner walled than arteries without danger of bursting. However, the low-pressure condition itself demands some special adaptations to help return blood to the heart at the same rate it was pumped into the circulation. The large-diameter lumens of veins (which offer relatively little resistance to blood flow) are one structural adaptation. Another is valves that prevent blood from flowing backward. **Venous valves** are formed from folds of the

tunica intima, and they resemble the semilunar valves of the heart in both structure and function. Venous valves are most abundant in the veins of the limbs, where the upward flow of blood is opposed by gravity. They are absent in veins of the ventral body cavity.

A simple experiment will demonstrate the effectiveness of your venous valves. Hang one hand by your side until the blood vessels on its dorsal aspect become distended with blood. Next place two finger-

Arteriosclerosis is the end stage of the disease. As enlarging plaques hinder diffusion of nutrients from the blood to the deeper tissues of the artery wall, smooth muscle cells in the tunica media die, and the elastic fibers deteriorate. These elements are replaced by nonelastic scar tissue, and calcium salts are deposited in the lesions, now called *complicated plaques*. These events cause the arterial walls to become frayed and often ulcerated, conditions that encourage platelet adhesion and thrombus formation. The increased rigidity of the vessels leads to hypertension. Together, these events increase the risk of myocardial infarcts, strokes, and aneurysms. (However, a diet rich in omega-3 fatty acids, found in the flesh of cold-water fish, may help to lower blood levels of cholesterol.)

So what can be done when the heart is at risk because of atherosclerotic coronary vessels? Traditionally, the choice has been *coronary bypass surgery*, in which veins removed from the legs or small arteries removed from the thoracic cavity are implanted in the heart to restore myocardial circulation. Currently, about 40,000 bypasses are done yearly in the U.S. More recently, intravascular devices have been used as "ammunition" to clear obstructed sites in blood vessels. *Balloon angioplasty*, performed on some 260,000 Americans each year, uses a catheter with a balloon tightly packed into its tip. When the catheter reaches the obstruction, the balloon is inflated, and the fatty mass is compressed against the vessel wall. However, this procedure is only useful to clear a few very localized obstructions. A newer catheter device houses

a fiberscope that allows the surgeon to peer into a lighted vessel, an inflatable cuff to stop the blood flow temporarily, and a power fiber that sends a laser beam to vaporize the arterial clogs. Although angioplasty is faster, cheaper, and much less risky than coronary bypass surgery, it has the same major shortcoming: It does nothing to stop the underlying disease, and in time *restenoses* (new blockages) occur. In fact, new studies have shown that at least part of the reocclusion problem in some angioplasty patients is due to erosion of the endothelium during the procedure and subsequent proliferation of scar tissue to repair the injury. Insertion of *stents*, short metal-mesh tubes that look much like a ziti noodle, into newly dilated vessels has helped solve the restenosis problem. Even more exciting is a gel (currently in animal tests) that is smeared on the area treated by angioplasty and forms a translucent film over the wall. Composed of chemicals called *antisense agents*, the gel blocks the function of a specific gene *(c-myb)* that is essential for smooth muscle proliferation.

Still another technique being tested in those too ill for surgery is *enhanced external counterpulsation*. For one hour daily over a period of about 7 weeks, inflatable belts are wrapped around the patient's lower body. These inflate and deflate in time with the heartbeat, forcing blood from the lower limbs to the chest during diastole. The theory is that the procedure enlarges existing vessels (narrowed by atherosclerosis) and encourages formation of new collateral channels to bypass the diseased vessels.

It was hoped that cholesterol-lowering drugs such as cholestyramine and lovastatin would act as cardiovascular Draño and wash the fatty plaques off the walls. However, their side effects—nausea, bloating, and constipation—are so miserable that many people simply stop taking them. When a clot is trapped by the diseased vessel walls, *thrombolytic (clot-dissolving) agents* are used. These revolutionary drugs include the powerful enzyme *streptokinase* and *tissue plasminogen activator (t-PA)*, a natural substance produced by genetic engineering techniques. Injecting t-PA directly into the heart restores blood flow quickly and puts an early end to many heart attacks in progress. Cardiac patients receiving vessel-opening drugs appear to have a lower incidence of ventricular tachycardia and sudden death following a heart attack.

Beyond these clinical measures, the prudent person will also try to prevent the progress of atherosclerosis—by quitting smoking, losing weight to reduce blood lipid (triglyceride) levels, cutting cholesterol and saturated fats from his or her diet to reduce LDL levels, and taking antioxidant vitamins (E, C, and beta carotene)—and to "undo" some of the damage by exercising to increase blood levels of HDL (the "good" lipoprotein that removes cholesterol from vessel walls and carries it to the liver for elimination). However, getting people to change their life-style is not as easy as it seems. Americans like their burgers and butter. But if heart disease can be reversed by reversing atherosclerosis, many people with diseased arteries may be willing to trade lifelong habits for a healthy old age!

tips against one of the distended veins, and pressing firmly, move the superior finger proximally along the vein and then release that finger. The vein will remain flattened and collapsed, despite the pull of gravity. Finally, remove the distal fingertip and watch the vein refill rapidly with blood.

Varicose veins are veins that have become tortuous and dilated because of incompetent valves. Several factors contribute, including heredity and conditions that hinder venous return, such as pro-

longed standing in one position, obesity, or pregnancy. Both the "potbelly" of an overweight person and the enlarged uterus of a pregnant woman exert downward pressure on vessels of the groin, and restrict return of blood to the heart. Consequently, blood tends to pool in the lower limbs and, with time, the valves weaken and the venous walls stretch and become floppy. Superficial veins, which receive little support from surrounding tissues, are especially susceptible. Another cause of varicose veins is elevated venous pressure. For example, straining to have a baby or a bowel movement raises intra-abdominal pressure, preventing blood from draining from the veins of the anal canal. The resulting varicosities in the anal veins are called *hemorrhoids* (hem″ŏ-roidz). •

Venous sinuses, such as the *coronary sinus* of the heart and the *dural sinuses* of the brain, are highly specialized, flattened veins with extremely thin walls composed only of endothelium. They are supported by the tissues that surround them, rather than by any additional tunics. The dural sinuses, which receive cerebrospinal fluid and blood draining from the brain, are reinforced by the tough dura mater that covers the brain surface.

Vascular Anastomoses

Where vascular channels unite, they form **vascular anastomoses** (ah-nas″to-mo′sēz; "coming together"). Most organs receive blood from more than one arterial branch, and arteries supplying the same territory often merge, forming **arterial anastomoses.** Arterial anastomoses permit free communication between the vessels involved and provide alternate pathways, called **collateral channels,** for blood to reach a given body region. If one branch is blocked by a clot or cut, the collateral channel can often provide the area with an adequate blood supply. Arterial anastomoses are abundant in abdominal organs and around joints, where active movement may hinder blood flow through one channel. Arteries that do not anastomose, or which have a poorly developed collateral circulation, supply the retina, kidneys, and spleen. If their blood flow is interrupted, cells supplied by such vessels die.

The metarteriole–thoroughfare channel shunts of capillary beds that connect arterioles and venules are examples of **arteriovenous anastomoses.** Veins interconnect much more freely than arteries, and **venous anastomoses** are common. (You may be able to see venous anastomoses through the skin on the dorsum of your hand.) Because venous anastomoses are so abundant, occlusion of a vein rarely blocks blood flow or leads to tissue death.

PHYSIOLOGY OF CIRCULATION

Have you ever climbed a mountain? Well, get ready to climb a hypothetical mountain as you learn about circulatory dynamics. Like scaling a mountain, tackling blood pressure regulation and other topics of cardiovascular physiology will be challenging, but then so exhilarating when you succeed. Let's begin the climb.

To sustain life, blood must be kept circulating. It is easy to accept this statement, but to understand how circulation is accomplished takes a bit more effort. By now, you are aware that the heart is the pump, the arteries are conduits, the arterioles are resistance vessels, the capillaries are exchange sites, and the veins are blood reservoirs. Now we need to define three physiologically important terms—blood flow, blood pressure, and resistance—and examine how these factors are related to the physiology of blood circulation.

INTRODUCTION TO BLOOD FLOW, BLOOD PRESSURE, AND RESISTANCE

Definition of Terms

1. **Blood flow** is the actual volume of blood flowing through a vessel, an organ, or the entire circulation in a given period of time (ml/min). If we consider the entire vascular system, blood flow is equivalent to cardiac output (CO), and under resting conditions, it is relatively constant. At a given time, however, blood flow through *individual* body organs may vary widely and is intimately related to their immediate needs.

2. **Blood pressure (BP)** is the force per unit area exerted on the wall of a blood vessel by its contained blood. Blood pressure is expressed in terms of millimeters of mercury (mm Hg). For example, a blood pressure of 120 mm Hg is equal to the pressure exerted by a column of mercury 120 mm high. Unless stated otherwise, the term *blood pressure* means systemic arterial blood pressure in the largest arteries near the heart. It is the pressure gradient—the *differences* in blood pressure within the vascular system—that provides the driving force that keeps blood moving through the body.

3. **Resistance** is opposition to flow and is a measure of the amount of friction blood encounters as it passes through the vessels. Since most friction is encountered in the peripheral circulation, well away from the heart, we generally use the term **peripheral resistance (PR).**

There are three important sources of resistance: blood viscosity, vessel length, and vessel diameter.

• **Blood viscosity.** *Viscosity* (vis-kos′ĭ-te) is the internal resistance to flow and is related to the thickness or "stickiness" of a fluid. The greater the viscosity, the less easily molecules slide past one another and the more difficult it is to get and keep the fluid moving. Blood is much more viscous than water because it contains formed elements and plasma proteins; hence it flows more slowly under the same conditions. Blood viscosity is fairly constant, but infrequent conditions such as polycythemia (excessive numbers of red blood cells) can increase blood viscosity and, hence, blood pressure. On the other hand, if the RBC count is low, as in some anemias, blood becomes less viscous, and peripheral resistance declines.

- **Total blood vessel length.** The relationship between total blood vessel length and resistance is straightforward: the longer the total vessel length, the greater the resistance encountered. An extra pound or two of fat requires that miles of small vessels be added to service it. This significantly increases the peripheral resistance.

- **Blood vessel diameter.** Since both blood viscosity and blood vessel length are normally unchanging, the influence of these factors can be considered constant in healthy people. On the other hand, blood vessel diameter changes often and is a very important factor in altering peripheral resistance. How so? The answer lies in principles of fluid flow. Fluid close to the walls of a tube or channel is slowed by friction as it passes along the wall, whereas fluid in the center of the channel flows more freely and faster. You can verify this by watching the flow of water in a river. Water close to the bank hardly seems to move, while that in the middle of the river flows quite rapidly. Further, the smaller the tube (or blood vessel), the greater the friction, because relatively more of the fluid contacts the tube walls. Resistance varies *inversely* with the *fourth power* of the vessel radius (one-half the diameter). This means, for example, that if the radius of a vessel is doubled, the resistance is one-sixteenth as much ($r^4 = 2 \times 2 \times 2 \times 2 = 16$ and $1/r^4 = \frac{1}{16}$). Thus, the large arteries close to the heart contribute little to peripheral resistance, while the small-diameter arterioles, which can enlarge or constrict in response to neural and chemical controls, are the major determinants of peripheral resistance.

Relationship Between Blood Flow, Blood Pressure, and Resistance

Now that we have defined these terms, let us summarize briefly the relationships between them. Blood flow (F) is directly proportional to the difference in blood pressure (ΔP) between two points in the circulation. That is, if ΔP increases, blood flow speeds up and when ΔP decreases, blood flow also declines. In addition, blood flow is inversely proportional to the peripheral resistance (R); if R increases, blood flow decreases. These relationships are stated by the formula

$$\text{Blood flow } (F) = \frac{\text{difference in blood pressure } (\Delta P)}{\text{peripheral resistance } (R)}$$

Of these two factors influencing blood flow, R is far more important than ΔP. This is because when the arterioles serving a particular tissue dilate (thus decreasing the resistance), blood flow to that tissue increases, even though the systemic pressure is unchanged or may actually be declining.

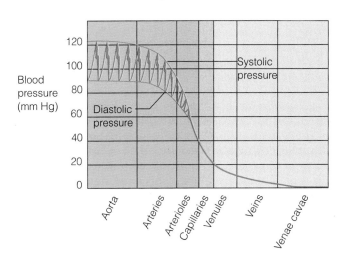

FIGURE 20.4
Blood pressure in various blood vessels of the systemic circulation.

SYSTEMIC BLOOD PRESSURE

Any fluid driven by a pump through a circuit of closed channels operates under pressure, and the nearer the fluid is to the pump, the greater the pressure it is under. The dynamics of blood flow in blood vessels is no exception, and blood flows through the blood vessels along a pressure gradient, always moving from higher- to lower-pressure areas. Fundamentally, *the pumping action of the heart generates blood flow. Pressure results when flow is opposed by resistance.*

As illustrated in Figure 20.4, systemic blood pressure is highest in the aorta and declines throughout the length of the pathway to finally reach 0 mm Hg in the right atrium. The steepest change (drop) in blood pressure occurs in the arterioles, which offer the greatest resistance to blood flow. However, so long as a pressure gradient exists, blood continues to flow from higher- to lower-pressure areas until it completes the circuit back to the heart.

Arterial Blood Pressure

Essentially, arterial blood pressure reflects two factors: (1) how much the elastic arteries close to the heart can be stretched (their *compliance* or *distensibility*) and (2) the volume of blood forced into them at any time. If the amounts of blood entering and leaving them during any given period were equal, arterial pressure would be constant. Instead, as Figure 20.4 reveals, blood pressure changes (rises and falls) in a regular fashion in the elastic arteries near the heart, and blood flow within them is obviously *pulsatile.*

As the left ventricle contracts and expels blood into the aorta, it imparts kinetic energy to the blood, which in turn stretches the elastic aorta, causing aortic pressure to reach its peak. Indeed, if the aorta were opened during this period, blood would spurt upward for 5 or 6 feet! This pressure peak, called the **systolic** (sis-to′lik) **pressure** averages about 120 mm Hg in healthy adults. Blood moves forward into the arterial bed because the pressure in the aorta is higher than the pressure in the more distal vessels. During diastole, the aortic semilunar valve closes, preventing blood from flowing back into the heart, and the walls of the aorta (and other elastic arteries) recoil, maintaining continuous pressure on the reducing blood volume. Consequently, blood continues to flow into the smaller vessels. During this time, aortic pressure drops to its lowest level (approximately 70 to 80 mm Hg in healthy adults), called the **diastolic** (di-as′to-lik) **pressure** (see Figure 20.4). Thus, you can picture the elastic arteries as pressure reservoirs that operate as auxiliary pumps to keep blood circulating throughout diastole, when the heart is relaxing. Essentially, the volume and energy of blood stored within them during systole are given back during diastole.

The difference between the systolic and diastolic pressures is called the **pulse pressure.** Pulse pressure is felt as a throbbing pulsation in an artery (a *pulse*) during systole, as the elastic arteries are expanded by the blood being forced into them by ventricular contraction. Increased stroke volume and faster blood ejection from the heart (due to increased contractility) cause *temporary* increases in the pulse pressure. Pulse pressure is chronically increased by arteriosclerosis because the elastic arteries become less stretchy. Since aortic pressure fluctuates up and down with each heartbeat, the important pressure figure to consider is the **mean (average) arterial pressure (MAP),** because it is this pressure that propels the blood to the tissues throughout the cardiac cycle. Because diastole usually lasts longer than systole, the mean pressure is not simply the value halfway between systolic and diastolic pressures. Instead, the MAP is roughly equal to the diastolic pressure plus one-third of the **pulse pressure.** This can be shown in equation form as:

$$\text{MAP} = \frac{\text{diastolic}}{\text{pressure}} + \frac{\text{pulse pressure}}{3}$$

Thus, the MAP of a person with a systolic blood pressure of 120 mm Hg and a diastolic pressure of 80 mm Hg would be approximately 93 mm Hg (80 + ⅓(40)). Both the MAP and pulse pressure decline with increasing distance from the heart. The MAP loses ground to the never-ending friction between the blood and the vessel walls, and the pulse pressure is gradually phased out in the less elastic muscular arteries. At the end of the arterial tree, blood flow is steady and the pulse pressure has disappeared.

Capillary Blood Pressure

As shown in Figure 20.4, by the time blood reaches the capillaries, blood pressure has dropped to approximately 40 mm Hg and, by the end of the capillary beds, is further reduced to about 20 mm Hg. Such low capillary pressures are desirable for two reasons. (1) Capillaries are fragile and high pressures would rupture them, and (2) most capillaries are extremely permeable and thus even the low capillary pressure forces solute-containing fluids (filtrate) out of the bloodstream into the interstitial space. As described later in this chapter, these fluid flows help to distribute nutrients, gases, and hormones between blood and tissue cells and continuously refresh the interstitial fluid.

Venous Blood Pressure

Unlike arterial pressure, which pulsates with each contraction of the left ventricle, venous blood pressure is steady and changes very little during the cardiac cycle. The entire pressure gradient in the veins, from venules to the termini of the venae cavae, is only about 20 mm Hg as opposed to an average pressure gradient of 60 mm Hg from the aorta to the ends of the arterioles. These pressure differences between arteries and veins become very clear when these vessels are cut. If a vein is cut, the blood flows evenly from the wound; a lacerated artery produces rapid spurts of blood. The very low pressure in the venous system reflects the cumulative effects of peripheral resistance, which dissipates most of the energy of blood pressure (as heat) during each circuit.

Factors Aiding Venous Return

Because venous pressure is normally too low to promote adequate venous return, despite the structural modifications of veins (large lumens and valves), functional adaptations, such as the respiratory and skeletal muscle "pumps," are critically important to venous return.

1. **Respiratory pump.** Pressure changes occurring in the ventral body cavity during breathing create the **respiratory pump** that sucks blood upward toward the heart. As we inhale, abdominal pressure increases squeezing the local veins; since venous valves prevent backflow, blood is forced toward the heart. At the same time, the pressure within the chest decreases, allowing thoracic veins to expand and speeding blood entry into the right atrium of the heart.

2. **Muscular pump.** Skeletal muscle activity, or the so-called **muscular pump,** is even more important: As the skeletal muscles surrounding the deep veins contract and relax, they "milk" blood toward the heart, and once blood passes each successive valve, it cannot flow back (Figure 20.5). People who earn their living in "standing professions," such as hairdressers and dentists, often have swollen ankles, because blood pools in their feet and legs during prolonged periods of skeletal muscle inactivity.

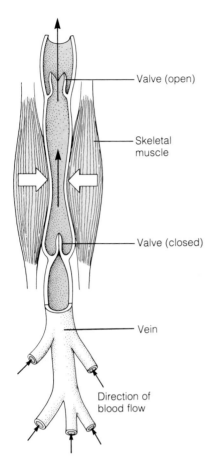

FIGURE 20.5
Operation of the muscular pump. As illustrated, when skeletal muscles contract and press against the flexible veins, the valves proximal to the area of contraction are forced open and blood is propelled toward the heart. The valves distal to the point of contraction are closed by the backflowing blood.

MAINTAINING BLOOD PRESSURE

Maintaining a steady flow of blood from the heart to the toes is vital for proper organ function. But making sure that the energetic person who jumps out of bed in the morning does not keel over from inadequate blood flow to the brain requires the finely tuned cooperation of the heart, blood vessels, and kidneys—all under close supervision of the brain. Central among the homeostatic mechanisms that regulate cardiovascular dynamics are those that maintain blood pressure. So, let's take a quick look back at the variables that affect blood pressure before we examine how they are manipulated to maintain blood pressure within the homeostatic range.

The main factors influencing blood pressure are *cardiac output, peripheral resistance,* and *blood volume.* If we rearrange slightly the formula pertaining to blood flow presented on p. 651, we can see how cardiac output (blood flow of the entire circulation) and peripheral resistance relate to blood pressure.

$$\text{Blood pressure} = \text{cardiac output} \times \text{peripheral resistance}$$

Since CO is, in turn, dependent on blood volume (the heart can't pump out what doesn't enter its chambers), it is clear that blood pressure varies *directly* with CO, PR, and blood volume. Thus, in theory, a change (increase or decrease) in any of these variables causes a corresponding change in blood pressure. However, what really occurs in the body is that changes in one variable that threaten blood pressure homeostasis are quickly compensated for by changes in the other variables.

As described in Chapter 19, CO is equal to *stroke volume* (ml/beat) multiplied by the *heart rate* (beats/min), and normal CO is about 5.5 L/min. Figure 20.6 should help you recall the main factors that determine cardiac output—venous return and the neural and hormonal controls. Although the figure doesn't name the cardiac centers in the medulla, remember that the parasympathetic cardioinhibitory center is "in charge" of heart rate most of the time and, via the vagus nerves, it maintains what is referred to as the *resting heart rate.* During such "resting" periods, stroke volume is controlled mainly by venous return (end-diastolic volume or EDV). Under stressful conditions, the sympathetic cardioaccelera-

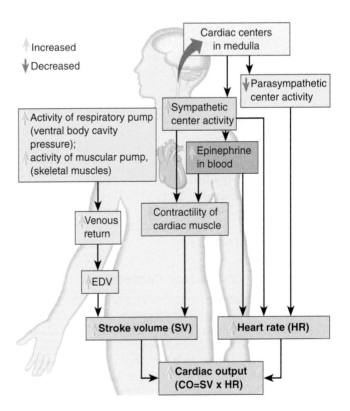

FIGURE 20.6
Summary of major factors enhancing cardiac output.
(Note: Efferent impulses from cardiac centers travel along autonomic nerves; EDV = end-diastolic volume.)

tory center takes over and increases both heart rate (by acting on the SA node and cardiac muscle itself) and stroke volume (by enhancing cardiac muscle contractility). The increase in CO, in turn, results in an increase in the MAP (mean systemic arterial blood pressure).

In the discussion that follows, we will complete the story by focusing on factors that regulate blood pressure by altering peripheral resistance and blood volume, but a flowchart showing the influence of nearly all important factors is provided in Figure 20.9 (p. 658). The *short-term controls* of blood pressure, mediated by the nervous system and blood-borne chemicals, counteract moment-to-moment fluctuations in blood pressure by altering peripheral resistance. By contrast, the slower-acting renal mechanisms which regulate blood volume constitute the *long-term controls* of blood pressure.

Short-Term Mechanisms: Neural Controls

Neural controls of peripheral resistance are directed primarily at two main goals. (1) They alter blood distribution to respond to specific demands. For example, during exercise blood is shunted temporarily from the digestive organs to the skeletal muscles, and heat loss from the body is enhanced when blood vessels in the skin dilate and become flushed with warm blood. (2) They maintain adequate MAP by altering blood vessel diameter. (Remember, very small changes in blood vessel diameter cause substantial changes in systemic blood pressure.) Under conditions of low blood volume, all vessels except those supplying the heart and brain are constricted to allow as much blood as possible to flow to those vital organs.

Most neural controls operate via reflex arcs chiefly involving the following components: baroreceptors and the associated afferent fibers, the vasomotor center of the medulla, vasomotor fibers, and vascular smooth muscle. Occasionally, inputs from chemoreceptors and higher brain centers also influence the neural control mechanism. Each of these factors is described next.

Role of the Vasomotor Center

The neural center that oversees changes in the diameter of blood vessels is the **vasomotor center,** a cluster of sympathetic neurons in the medulla. This center plus the cardiac centers described earlier make up the **cardiovascular center** that integrates blood pressure control by altering cardiac output and blood vessel diameter. The vasomotor center transmits impulses in a fairly steady stream along sympathetic efferents (motor fibers) called **vasomotor fibers,** which exit from the T_1 through L_2 levels of the spinal cord and run to innervate the smooth muscle of blood vessels, most importantly arterioles. As a result, the arterioles

are nearly always in a state of moderate constriction, called **vasomotor tone.** However, the degree of tonic vasoconstriction varies from organ to organ. Generally, arterioles of the skin and digestive viscera receive vasomotor impulses more frequently and tend to be more strongly constricted than those of skeletal muscles. Any increase in sympathetic activity produces generalized vasoconstriction and a rise in blood pressure. Decreased sympathetic activity allows the vascular muscle to relax somewhat and causes blood pressure to decline to basal levels. Most vasomotor fibers release norepinephrine, a potent vasoconstrictor. In skeletal muscle, however, some vasomotor fibers may release acetylcholine, causing vasodilation. Though important to local blood flow, such vasodilator fibers are *not* important to overall regulation of systemic blood pressure.

Vasomotor activity is modified by inputs from: (1) baroreceptors (pressure-sensitive mechanoreceptors that respond to changes in arterial pressure and stretch), (2) chemoreceptors (receptors that respond to changes in blood levels of oxygen, carbon dioxide, and H^+), and (3) higher brain centers (hypothalamus and cerebrum), as well as by certain hormones and other blood-borne chemicals. Let's look at how each of these factors brings about its effect.

Baroreceptor-Initiated Reflexes

Baroreceptors are located not only in the *carotid sinuses* (dilations in the internal carotid arteries which provide the major blood supply to the brain) and *aortic arch* but also in the wall of nearly every large (elastic) artery of the neck and thorax. When arterial blood pressure rises and stretches these receptors, they send off a faster stream of impulses to the vasomotor center. This inhibits the vasomotor center and subsequently results in vasodilation not only of the arterioles but also the veins, and a decline in blood pressure (Figure 20.7). While dilation of the arterioles substantially reduces the peripheral resistance, venodilation shifts blood to the venous reservoirs, causing a decline in venous return and cardiac output. Afferent impulses from the baroreceptors also reach the cardiac centers, where they stimulate parasympathetic activity and inhibit the sympathetic (cardioacceleratory) center, leading to a reduction in heart rate and contractile force. Conversely, a decline in mean arterial pressure initiates reflex vasoconstriction and increases cardiac output, causing blood pressure to rise. Thus, peripheral resistance and cardiac output are regulated in tandem according to baroreceptor inputs so that changes in blood pressure are minimized.

The function of rapidly responding baroreceptors is to protect the circulation against short-term (acute) changes in blood pressure, such as those occurring with changes in posture. For example, blood pressure falls (particularly in the head) when one rises from a reclining to a standing position. The **carotid sinus**

?   *Which part of this feedback loop occurs when you rise from a seated position?*

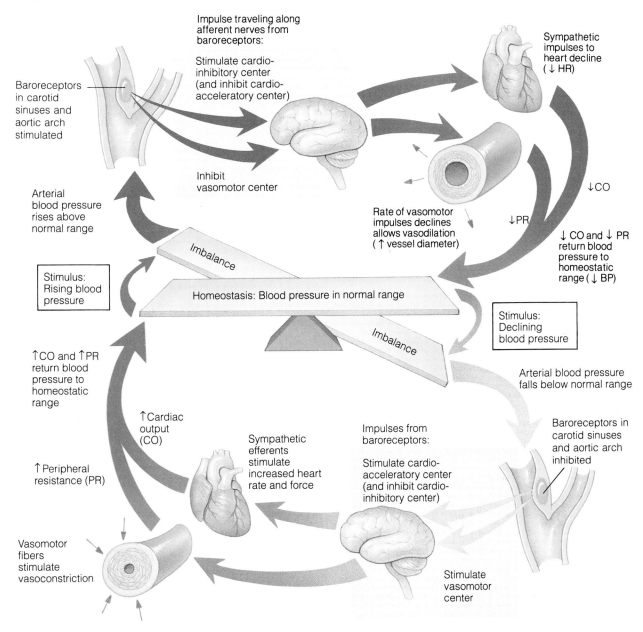

FIGURE 20.7
Baroreceptor reflexes that help to maintain blood pressure homeostasis. (CO = cardiac output; PR = peripheral resistance; HR = heart rate; BP = blood pressure.)

reflex protects the blood supply to the brain, whereas the **aortic reflex** is more concerned with maintaining adequate blood pressure in the systemic circuit as a whole. Baroreceptors are relatively *ineffective* in protecting against sustained pressure changes, as evidenced by the fact that some people have chronic hypertension. In such cases, the baroreceptors are apparently "reset" to monitor pressure changes at a higher set point.

Chemoreceptor-Initiated Reflexes

When the oxygen content or pH of the blood drops sharply or carbon dioxide levels rise, chemoreceptors in the aortic arch and large arteries of the neck transmit impulses to the vasomotor center, and reflex vasoconstriction occurs. The rise in blood pressure that follows helps speed the return of blood to the heart and then to the lungs. The most prominent of these receptors are the *carotid* and *aortic bodies* located close by the baroreceptors in the carotid sinus and aortic arch. Because they are more important in regulating respiratory rate and depth than in blood pressure regulation, their function is considered more fully in Chapter 23.

Influence of Higher Brain Centers

Reflexes that regulate blood pressure are integrated at the brain stem (medulla) level. Although the cerebral cortex and hypothalamus are not involved in routine controls of blood pressure, these higher brain centers can modify arterial blood pressure via relays to the medullary centers. For example, the fight-or-flight response mediated by the hypothalamus has profound effects on blood pressure. (Even the simple act of speaking can make your blood pressure jump if the person you are talking to causes you to become anxious.) The hypothalamus also mediates the redistribution of blood flow and other cardiovascular responses that occur during exercise and changes in body temperature.

Short-Term Mechanisms: Chemical Controls

As we have seen, changing levels of oxygen and carbon dioxide help regulate blood pressure via the chemoreceptor reflexes. But numerous other blood-borne chemicals (described below) influence blood pressure by acting directly on vascular smooth muscle or on the vasomotor center. The most important such agents are hormones (see Table 20.1).

- **Adrenal medulla hormones.** During periods of stress, the adrenal gland releases norepinephrine (NE) and epinephrine to the blood, and both enhance the sympathetic fight-or-flight response (Figure 20.9). As noted earlier, NE has a vasoconstrictive action. Epinephrine increases cardiac output and promotes generalized vasoconstriction (except in skeletal and cardiac muscle, where it generally causes vasodilation). It is interesting to note that *nicotine,* an important chemical in tobacco and one of the strongest toxins known, mimics the effects of the catecholamines. It causes intense vasoconstriction not only by directly stimulating postganglionic sympathetic neurons but also by prompting release of excessive amounts of epinephrine and NE.

- **Atrial natriuretic** (na″tre-u-ret′ik) **factor (ANF).** The atria of the heart produce a peptide hormone, called atrial natriuretic factor, which causes blood volume and blood pressure to decline. As noted in Chapter 17, ANF antagonizes aldosterone and prods the kidneys to excrete more sodium and water from the body, causing blood volume to drop. It also causes a generalized

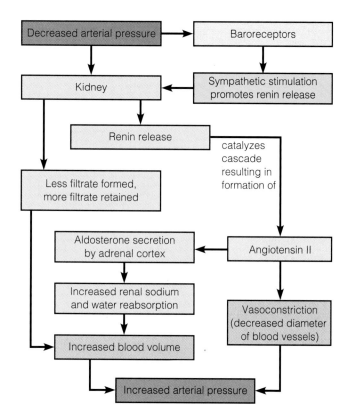

FIGURE 20.8
Slowly acting renal hormonal mechanisms for blood pressure control. Notice that sympathetic nervous system stimulation and action, part of the more rapidly acting short-term control pathway, also participate in this system by triggering renin release.

vasodilation and reduces cerebrospinal fluid formation in the brain.

- **Antidiuretic hormone (ADH).** Antidiuretic hormone is produced by the hypothalamus and stimulates the kidneys to conserve water. ADH is not usually important in short-term blood pressure regulation. However, when blood pressure falls to dangerously low levels (as during severe hemorrhage), ADH is released in greater amounts and helps to restore arterial pressure by causing intense vasoconstriction.

- **Angiotensin II.** Angiotensin (an″je-o-ten′sin) II is generated in response to renin release by the kidneys when renal perfusion is inadequate (Figure 20.8). It causes intense vasoconstriction, promoting a rapid rise in systemic blood pressure. It also stimulates release of aldosterone, which acts in long-term regulation of blood pressure by enhancing blood volume as described shortly.

- **Endothelium-derived factors.** The endothelium is the source of several chemicals that affect vascular smooth muscle (as well as blood clotting). For example, a peptide named **endothelin** is one of the most potent vasoconstrictors known. Released in response to low blood flow, it appears

Table 20.1   Influence of Selected Hormones on Variables Affecting Blood Pressure

Variable affecting BP	Effect on variable	Hormone(s)	Site of action	Result
Cardiac output	↑ (↑ HR and contractility)	Epinephrine and norepinephrine (NE)	Heart (β_1 receptors)	↑ BP
Peripheral resistance	↑ (via vasoconstriction)	Angiotensin II	Arterioles	↑ BP
		Antidiuretic hormone	Arterioles	
		Epinephrine and NE	Arterioles (α receptors)	
	↓ (via vasodilation)	Epinephrine and NE Atrial natriuretic factor	Large veins (β_2 receptors) Arterioles	↓ BP
Blood volume	↓ (salt and water loss)	Atrial natriuretic factor	Kidney tubule cells	↓ BP
	↑ (salt and water retention)	Aldosterone	Kidney tubule cells	↑ BP
	↑ (water retention)	Antidiuretic hormone (ADH)		

to bring about its long-lasting effects by enhancing calcium entry into vascular smooth muscle.

- **Nitric oxide (NO),** originally called *endothelium-derived relaxing factor (EDRF),* is another vasoactive substance secreted by endothelial cells. Released in response to a high blood flow rate and signaling molecules such as acetylcholine and bradykinin (and the vasodilator nitroglycerine), NO, which acts via a cyclic GMP second-messenger system, promotes both reflex (systemic) and highly localized vasodilation. However, NO is quickly destroyed and its potent vasodilator effects are very brief. Until now, it's been accepted that sympathetic nervous system activity "rules" blood vessel diameter. Although there is still much to be learned about NO, it now appears that it plays a *major* role in causing vasodilation—when its synthesis is inhibited, blood pressure skyrockets!

- **Alcohol.** Ingestion of alcohol causes a drop in blood pressure by inhibiting ADH release and by depressing the vasomotor center and promoting vasodilation, especially in the skin. This accounts for the flushed appearance of someone who has drunk a generous amount of an alcoholic beverage.

- **Inflammatory chemicals.** Histamine, kinins, and certain other chemicals released during the inflammatory response and certain allergies are potent vasodilators. They also promote fluid loss from the bloodstream by increasing capillary permeability.

Long-Term Mechanisms: Renal Regulation

Although the baroreceptors respond to short-term changes in blood pressure, they quickly adapt to prolonged or chronic episodes of high or low pressure. This is where the kidneys step in to restore and maintain blood pressure homeostasis by regulating blood volume. Although blood volume varies with age and sex, renal mechanisms usually maintain it at about 5 L.

As noted earlier, blood volume is a major determinant of cardiac output (via its influence on venous pressure, venous return, EDV, and stroke volume). An increase in blood volume is followed by an increase in blood pressure, and anything that increases blood volume, such as excessive salt intake which promotes water retention, raises the MAP because of the greater fluid load in the vascular tree. By the same token, decreased blood volume translates to a fall in blood pressure. Blood loss and the garden-variety dehydration that occurs during vigorous exercise are common causes of reduced blood volume. A sudden drop in BP often signals internal bleeding and a blood volume that is becoming too dangerously low to support normal circulation. However, these assertions (increased blood volume leads to increased BP and decreased blood volume results in declining BP) do not tell the whole story because we are dealing with a dynamic system. The increases in blood volume that cause a rise in blood pressure also stimulate the kidneys to eliminate water, which reduces blood volume and, consequently, blood pressure. Likewise, falling blood

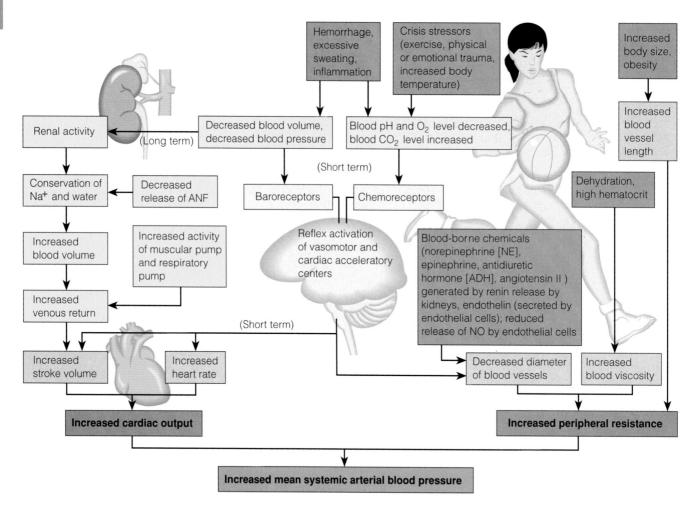

FIGURE 20.9
Summary of factors causing an increase in mean systemic arterial blood pressure.

volume triggers renal mechanisms that increase blood volume and blood pressure. As you can see, blood pressure can be stabilized or maintained within normal limits only when blood volume is stable.

The kidneys act both directly and indirectly to regulate arterial pressure and provide the major long-term mechanism of blood pressure control. The direct mechanism reflects their ability to alter blood volume. When blood volume or blood pressure rises, the rate at which fluid filters from the bloodstream into the kidney tubules is speeded up. In such situations, the kidneys are unable to process the filtrate rapidly enough, and more of this fluid leaves the body in urine. As blood volume goes (drops), so goes the arterial blood pressure. Conversely, when blood pressure or blood volume is low, water is conserved and returned to the bloodstream (see Figures 20.8 and 20.9).

The indirect renal mechanism involves the **renin-angiotensin mechanism.** When arterial blood pressure declines, special cells in the kidneys release the

enzyme *renin* (re'nin) into the blood. Renin triggers a series of enzymatic reactions that produce **angiotensin II,** a potent vasoconstrictor which, by promoting an increase in systemic blood pressure, increases the rate of blood delivery to the kidneys and renal perfusion. Angiotensin II also stimulates the adrenal cortex to release **aldosterone,** a hormone that enhances renal reabsorption of sodium (Figure 20.8). As sodium moves into the bloodstream, water follows; thus, both blood volume and blood pressure rise. The indirect renal mechanism is described in further detail in Chapter 27.

Monitoring Circulatory Efficiency

The efficiency of a person's circulation can be assessed by taking pulse and blood pressure measurements. These measurements, along with those of respiratory rate and body temperature, are referred to collectively as **vital signs** in clinical settings. Let's look at how these vital signs are determined or measured.

Taking a Pulse

The alternating expansion and recoil of elastic arteries during each cardiac cycle create a pressure wave—a **pulse**—that is transmitted through the arterial tree with each heartbeat. You can feel a pulse in any artery that lies close to the body surface by compressing the artery against firm tissue, and this provides an easy way to count heart rate. Because it is so accessible, the point where the radial artery surfaces at the wrist, the *radial pulse,* is routinely used to take a pulse measurement, but there are several other clinically important arterial pulse points (Figure 20.10). Because these same points are compressed to stop blood flow into distal tissues during hemorrhage, they are also called **pressure points.** For example, if you seriously lacerate your hand, you can slow or stop the bleeding by compressing the radial or the brachial artery.

Monitoring the arterial pulse rate is an easy way to access the effects of activity, postural changes, and emotions on heart rate. For example, the pulse of a healthy man may be around 66 beats per minute when he is lying down, rise to 70 when he sits up, and rise to 80 when he suddenly stands. During vigorous exercise or emotional upset, pulse rates between 140 and 180 are not unusual because of sympathetic nervous system effects on the heart.

Measuring Blood Pressure

Most often, systemic arterial blood pressure is measured indirectly by the **auscultatory** (aw-skul′tah-to″re) **method.** This procedure is used to measure blood pressure in the brachial artery of the arm. The *blood pressure cuff,* or *sphygmomanometer* (sfig″mo-mah-nom′ĕ-ter; *sphygmo* = pulse), is wrapped snugly around the arm just superior to the elbow and inflated until the cuff pressure exceeds systolic blood pressure. At this point, blood flow into the arm is stopped and a brachial pulse cannot be felt or heard. As the pressure of the cuff is gradually reduced, the examiner listens (ascultates) carefully for sounds in the brachial artery with a stethoscope. The pressure read as the first soft tapping sounds are heard (the first point at which a small amount of blood is spurting through the constricted artery) is recorded as the systolic pressure. As the cuff pressure is reduced still further, these sounds, called the *sounds of Korotkoff,* become louder and more distinct, but when the artery is no longer constricted and blood flows freely, the sounds can no longer be heard. The pressure at which the sounds disappear is recorded as the diastolic pressure.

In normal adults at rest, systolic blood pressure varies between 110 and 140 mm Hg, and diastolic pressure between 75 and 80 m Hg, but it is important to recognize that blood pressure varies with age, sex, weight, race, and socioeconomic status. What is "normal" for you may not be normal for your grandfather

FIGURE 20.10
Body sites where the pulse is most easily palpated. (The specific arteries indicated are discussed on pp. 672–681.)

or your neighbor. Blood pressure also varies with mood, physical activity, and posture. Nearly all of these variations can be explained in terms of the factors affecting blood pressure that have already been discussed.

Alterations in Blood Pressure

Hypotension

Hypotension, or low blood pressure, is generally considered to be a systolic blood pressure below 100 mm Hg. In many cases, hypotension simply reflects individual variations and is no cause for concern. In fact, low blood pressure is often associated with long life and an old age free of illness.

Elderly people are prone to *orthostatic hypotension*—temporary low blood pressure and dizziness when they rise suddenly from a reclining or sitting position. Because the aging sympathetic nervous system does not respond as quickly as it once did to postural changes, blood pools briefly in the lower limbs, reducing blood pressure and consequently blood delivery to the brain. Making postural changes slowly to give the nervous system time to adjust usually prevents this problem.

Chronic hypotension may hint at poor nutrition, because the poorly nourished are often anemic and have inadequate levels of blood proteins. Because blood viscosity is low, blood pressure is also lower than normal. Chronic hypotension also warns of Addison's disease (inadequate adrenal cortex function), hypothyroidism, or severe tissue wasting. *Acute hypotension* is one of the most important signs of circulatory shock and a threat to patients undergoing surgery and in intensive care units (see p. 665). •

Hypertension

Transient elevations in systolic blood pressure occur as normal adaptations during fever, physical exertion, and emotional upset, such as during anger and fear. Persistent **hypertension,** or high blood pressure, is common in obese people because the total length of their blood vessels is relatively greater than that in thinner individuals.

Chronic hypertension is a common and dangerous disease that warns of increased peripheral resistance. An estimated 30% of people over the age of 50 years are hypertensive. Although hypertension is usually asymptomatic for the first 10 to 20 years, it slowly but surely strains the heart and damages the arteries. For this reason, hypertension is often called the "silent killer." Prolonged hypertension is the major cause of heart failure, vascular disease, renal failure, and stroke. Because the heart is forced to pump against greater resistance, it must work harder, and in time, the myocardium enlarges. When finally strained beyond its capacity to respond, the heart weakens and its walls become flabby. Hypertension also ravages blood vessels, causing small tears in the endothelium that accelerate the progress of atherosclerosis (see *A Closer Look* on pp. 648–649). As the vessels become increasingly blocked, blood flow to the tissues becomes inadequate, and vascular complications of vessels in the brain, heart, kidneys, and retinas of the eyes begin to appear.

Although hypertension and atherosclerosis are often linked, it is difficult to blame hypertension on any distinct anatomical pathology. Hypertension is defined physiologically as a condition of sustained elevated arterial pressure of 140/90 or higher, and the higher the blood pressure, the greater the risk for serious cardiovascular problems. As a rule, elevated diastolic pressures are more significant medically, because they always indicate progressive occlusion and/or hardening of the arterial tree.

About 90% of hypertensive people have **primary,** or **essential, hypertension,** which has no discernible organic cause. However, the following factors are believed to be involved:

1. Diet. Dietary factors that contribute to hypertension include high sodium, saturated fat, and cholesterol intake and deficiencies in certain metal ions (K^+, Ca^{2+}, and Mg^{2+}).

2. Obesity.

3. Age. Clinical signs of the disease usually appear after age 40.

4. Race. More blacks than whites are hypertensive, and the course of the disease also varies in different population groups.

5. Heredity. Hypertension runs in families. Children of hypertensive parents are twice as likely to develop hypertension as are children of normotensive parents.

6. Stress. Particularly at risk are those, called "hot reactors," whose blood pressure zooms upward during every stressful event.

7. Smoking. Nicotine enhances the symphathetic nervous system's vasoconstrictor effects.

Primary hypertension cannot be cured, but most cases can be controlled by restricting salt, fat, and cholesterol intake, losing weight, stopping smoking, stress management, and antihypertensive drugs. Drugs commonly used are diuretics, sympathetic nerve blockers, calcium channel blockers, and ACE inhibitors (drugs that inhibit the renin-angiotensin mechanism by inhibiting angiotensin-converting enzyme).

Secondary hypertension, which accounts for 10% of cases, is due to identifiable disorders, such as excessive renin secretion by the kidneys, arteriosclerosis, and endocrine disorders such as hyperthyroidism and Cushing's disease. Treatment for secondary hypertension is directed toward correcting the causative problem. •

BLOOD FLOW THROUGH BODY TISSUES

Blood flow through body tissues, or **tissue perfusion,** is involved in (1) delivery of oxygen and nutrients to, and removal of wastes from, tissue cells, (2) gas exchange in the lungs, (3) absorption of nutrients from the digestive tract, and (4) urine formation by the kidneys. Furthermore, the rate of blood flow to each tissue and organ is almost exactly the right amount to provide for proper function—no more, no less. When the body is at rest, the brain receives about 13% of total blood flow, the heart 4%, kidneys 20%, and the abdominal organs 24%. The skeletal muscles, which make up almost half of body mass, normally receive about 20%; during exercise, however, nearly all of the increased cardiac output flushes into the skeletal muscles (Figure 20.11).

Velocity of Blood Flow

As shown in Figure 20.12, the speed or velocity (in cm/s) of blood flow changes as blood travels through the systemic circulation. All other factors being constant, it is fastest in the aorta and other large arteries, slowest in the capillaries, and then picks up speed again in the veins leading back to the heart.

Velocity is *inversely* related to the *cross-sectional area* of the blood vessels to be filled. Blood flows fastest where the total cross-sectional area is least. As the arterial system continues to branch, the total cross-sectional area of the vascular bed increases, and the velocity of blood flow declines proportionately. Even though the individual branches have smaller lumens, their combined cross-sectional area and, thus, the volume of blood they can hold is much greater than that of the aorta. For example, the cross-sectional area of the aorta is 2.5 cm^2, and the average velocity of blood flow in the aorta is 40–50 cm/s. However, the total cross-sectional area of the capillaries is 2500 cm^2, so capillary blood flow is very slow (about 0.03 cm/s). Slow capillary blood flow is beneficial because it allows adequate time for exchanges to be made between the blood and tissue cells.

As capillaries combine to form venules and then veins, total cross-sectional area declines and velocity increases. The cross-sectional area of the venae cavae is 8 cm^2, and the velocity of blood flow varies from 10 to 30 cm/s in those vessels, depending on the activity of the skeletal muscle pump.

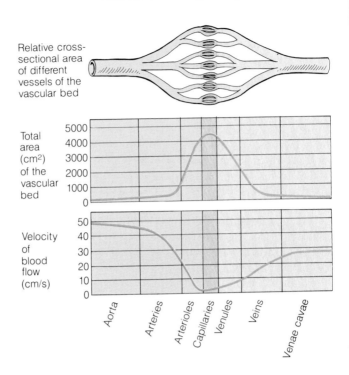

FIGURE 20.12
Relationship between blood flow velocity and total cross-sectional area in various blood vessels of the systemic circulation.

Autoregulation: Local Regulation of Blood Flow

Autoregulation is the automatic adjustment of blood flow to each tissue in proportion to its requirements at any point in time. This process is regulated by local conditions and is largely independent of systemic factors. The mean arterial pressure is identical throughout the body and homeostatic mechanisms adjust cardiac output as needed to maintain that pressure constant. Changes in blood flow through individual organs are controlled *intrinsically* by modifying the diameter of local arterioles feeding the capillaries. You can compare blood flow autoregulation to water use in your home. To get water in a sink, or the garden hose, you have to turn on a faucet. Whether you have several taps open or none, the pressure in the main water pipe in the street remains relatively constant, as it does in the even larger water lines closer to the pumping station. Similarly, the arterioles feeding the capillary beds in an organ have little effect on pressure in the muscular artery feeding the organ, or on the large elastic arteries. The pumping station is, of course, the heart. The beauty of this system is that as long as the water company (circulatory feedback mechanisms) maintains a relatively constant water pressure (MAP), local demand regulates the actual amount of fluid (blood) delivered to various areas.

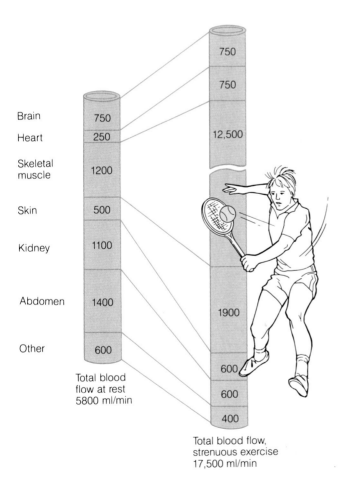

FIGURE 20.11
Distribution of blood flow to selected body organs at rest and during strenuous exercise.

Thus, organs regulate their own blood flows by varying the resistance of their arterioles. As described next, these intrinsic mechanisms may be classed as *metabolic* or *myogenic.*

Metabolic Controls

In most tissues, declining levels of nutrients, particularly oxygen, are the strongest stimuli for autoregulation. Certain substances released by metabolically active tissues (such as potassium and hydrogen ions, adenosine, and lactic acid), prostaglandins, and inflammatory chemicals (histamine and kinins) also serve as autoregulation stimuli. Whatever the precise stimulus, the net result of metabolically controlled autoregulation is immediate vasodilation of the arterioles serving the capillary beds of the "needy" tissues, and so blood flow to the local area temporarily increases. This is accompanied by relaxation of the precapillary sphincters (see Figure 20.3), allowing blood to surge through the true capillaries and become available to the tissue cells.

Myogenic Controls

Inadequate blood perfusion through an organ is quickly followed by a decline in its metabolic rate and, if prolonged, organ death. Likewise, excessively high arterial pressure and tissue perfusion can be dangerous, because it may rupture the more fragile blood vessels. Such changes in local (arteriolar) blood pressure and volume are important in autoregulation because they directly stimulate vascular smooth muscle, provoking **myogenic** (*myo* = muscle; *gen* = origin) **responses.** Vascular smooth muscle responds directly to passive stretch (increased intravascular pressure) with increased tone, which resists the stretch and causes vasoconstriction. Reduced stretch, on the other hand, promotes vasodilation and increases blood flow into the tissue. Hence, the myogenic mechanism keeps tissue perfusion fairly constant in spite of most variations in systemic pressure.

Generally, both chemical (metabolic) and physical factors determine the final autoregulatory response of a tissue. For example, **reactive hyperemia** (hi"per-e′-me-ah) is the dramatic increase in blood flow into a tissue that occurs after the blood supply to the area has been temporarily blocked. It results both from the myogenic response and from an accumulation of metabolic wastes in the area during the time of occlusion.

Long-Term Autoregulation

If the nutrient requirements of a tissue are more than the short-term autoregulatory mechanism can easily supply, a long-term autoregulation mechanism may evolve over a period of weeks or months to enhance the local blood flow still more. The number of blood vessels in the region increases, and existing vessels enlarge. This phenomenon is particularly common in the heart when a coronary vessel is partially occluded. It occurs throughout the body in people who live in high-altitude areas, where the air contains less oxygen.

Blood Flow in Special Areas

Each organ has special requirements and functions that are revealed in its pattern of autoregulation. Autoregulation in the brain, heart, and kidneys is extraordinarily efficient. In those organs, adequate perfusion is maintained even in the face of fluctuating mean arterial pressure.

Skeletal Muscles

Blood flow in skeletal muscle is extremely changeable and varies with muscle activity. When at rest, skeletal muscles receive about 1 L of blood per minute, and only about 25% of their capillaries are open. During such periods, myogenic and general neural mechanisms predominate. As with other vascular smooth muscle, release of norepinephrine causes vasoconstriction of skeletal muscle arterioles. When muscles become active, blood flow increases *(hyperemia)* in direct proportion to their greater *metabolic* activity, a phenomenon called **active** or **exercise hypermia.**

The arterioles in skeletal muscle have cholinergic receptors and both α- and β-adrenergic receptors, which bind epinephrine. When epinephrine is present in low levels, it mediates vasodilation by binding chiefly to the β receptors. Likewise, "occupied" cholinergic receptors are believed to promote vasodilation. Consequently, blood flow can increase tenfold or more during physical activity (see Figure 20.11), and virtually all capillaries in the active muscles open to accommodate the increased flow. By contrast, the high levels of epinephrine typical of massive sympathetic nervous system activation (and extremely vigorous exercise involving large numbers of skeletal muscles) cause intense vasoconstriction mediated by the alpha-adrenergic receptors. This protective response, believed to be initiated by muscle chemoreflexes when muscle oxygen delivery falls below some critical level, ensures that muscle demands for blood flow do not exceed cardiac pumping ability and that vital organs continue to receive an adequate blood supply. Without question, strenuous exercise is one of the most demanding conditions the cardiovascular system faces.

Muscular autoregulation occurs almost entirely in response to the decreased oxygen concentrations (accompanied by local increases in carbon dioxide, lactic acid, and other metabolites) that result from the "revved-up" metabolism of working muscles. However, systemic adjustments, mediated by the vasomotor center, must also occur to ensure that more blood reaches the muscles. Strong vasoconstriction of the vessels of blood reservoirs such as those of the digestive viscera and skin diverts blood away from these regions temporarily, ensuring that more blood reaches the muscles. Ultimately, the major factor determining how long muscles can continue to contract vigorously is the ability of the cardiovascular system to deliver adequate oxygen and nutrients.

The Brain

Total blood flow to the brain averages about 750 ml/min and is maintained at relatively constant levels. The necessity for constant cerebral blood flow becomes crystal clear when one remembers that the brain lies within the rigid cranium and neurons are totally "intolerant" of ischemia.

Cerebral blood flow is regulated by one of the most precise autoregulatory systems in the entire body and is tailored to local neuronal need. Thus, when you make a fist with your right hand, the neurons in the left cerebral motor cortex controlling that movement are receiving a more abundant blood supply than are the adjoining neurons. Brain tissue is exceptionally sensitive to declining pH, and increased blood carbon dioxide levels (resulting in acidic conditions in brain tissue) cause marked vasodilation. Oxygen deficit is a much less potent stimulus for autoregulation. However, greatly excessive carbon dioxide levels abolish autoregulatory mechanisms and severely depress brain activity.

Besides the metabolic controls, the brain also has a myogenic mechanism that protects it from possibly damaging changes in blood pressure. When mean arterial pressure declines, cerebral vessels dilate to ensure adequate brain perfusion. On the other hand, when arterial pressure rises, cerebral vessels constrict, protecting the small, more fragile vessels farther along in the pathway from being ruptured by the excessive pressure. Under certain circumstances, such as brain ischemia caused by rising intracranial pressure (as with a brain tumor), the brain (via the medullary cardiovascular centers) regulates its own blood flow by triggering a rise in systemic blood pressure. However, when systemic pressure changes are extreme, the brain becomes vulnerable. Fainting, or *syncope* (sin'cuh-pe; "cutting short"), occurs when mean arterial pressure falls below 60 mm Hg. Cerebral edema is the usual result of pressures over 160 mm Hg, which dramatically increase brain capillary permeability.

The Skin

Blood flow through the skin (1) supplies nutrients to the cells, (2) aids in body temperature regulation, and (3) provides a blood reservoir. The first function is served by autoregulation in response to the need for oxygen; the second and third require neural intervention. We will concentrate on the skin's temperature-related function here.

Below the skin surface are extensive venous plexuses, in which the blood flow can be changed from 50 ml/min to as much as 2500 ml/min, depending on body temperature. This capability reflects neural adjustments of blood flow through unique coiled arteriovenous anastomoses as well as through arterioles. These tiny shunts are located mainly in the fingertips, palms of the hands, toes, soles of the feet, ears, nose, and lips. They are richly supplied with sympathetic nerve endings (a characteristic that sets them apart from the shunts of most other capillary beds), and are controlled by reflexes initiated by temperature receptors or signals from higher CNS centers. The arterioles, by contrast, are also responsive to local and metabolic autoregulatory stimuli.

When the skin surface is exposed to heat, or body temperature rises for other reasons (such as vigorous exercise), the hypothalamic "thermostat" signals for reduced vasomotor stimulation of the skin vessels. As a result, warm blood flushes into the capillary beds and heat radiates from the skin surface. Vasodilation of the arterioles is enhanced even more when we sweat, because an enzyme in perspiration acts on a protein present in tissue fluid to produce *bradykinin.* Bradykinin, in turn, stimulates the vessel's endothelial cells to release NO, a potent vasodilator.

When the ambient temperature is cold and body temperature drops, superficial skin vessels are strongly constricted. Hence, blood almost entirely bypasses the capillaries associated with the arteriovenous anastomoses, diverting the warm blood to the deeper, more vital organs. Paradoxically, the skin may stay quite rosy because some blood gets "trapped" in the superficial capillary loops as the shunts swing into operation.

The Lungs

Blood flow through the pulmonary circuit to and from the lungs is unusual in many ways. The pathway is short relatively speaking, and pulmonary arteries and arterioles are structurally more like veins and venules. That is, they have thin walls and large lumens. Since resistance to blood flow is low, less pressure is needed to propel blood through the pulmonary arterial system. Consequently, arterial pressure in the pulmonary circulation is much lower than in the systemic circulation (25/10 versus 120/80).

In addition, the autoregulatory mechanism in the pulmonary circulation is exactly opposite that seen in most tissues. Low oxygen levels cause vasoconstriction, and high levels promote vasodilation. While this may seem odd, it is perfectly consistent with the gas exchange role of this circulation. When the air sacs of the lungs are flooded with oxygen-rich air, the pulmonary capillaries become flushed with blood and ready to receive the oxygen load. If the air sacs are collapsed or blocked with mucus, the oxygen content in those areas will be low, and blood will largely bypass those nonfunctional areas.

The Heart

Movement of blood through the smaller vessels of the coronary circulation of the heart is influenced by aortic pressure and the pumping activity of the ventricles. When the ventricles contract, the coronary vessels are compressed, and blood flow through the myocardium stops. As the heart relaxes, the high aortic pressure forces blood through the coronary circulation. Under normal circumstances, the myoglobin in the cardiac cells stores sufficient oxygen to satisfy their oxygen needs during systole. However, an abnormally rapid heartbeat seriously impairs the ability of the myocardium to receive adequate oxygen and nutrients during diastole.

Under resting conditions, blood flow through the heart is about 250 ml/min and is probably controlled by a myogenic mechanism. During strenuous exercise, the coronary vessels dilate in response to local accumulation of carbon dioxide (acidosis), and blood flow may increase three to four times (see Figure 20.11). Consequently, blood flow remains constant despite wide variation (50 to 140 mm Hg) in coronary perfusion pressure. This enhanced blood flow during increased heart activity is important because cardiac cells use as much as 65% of the oxygen carried to them in blood under resting conditions. (Most other tissue cells use about 25% of the oxygen delivered during each circulatory round.) Thus, increased blood flow is the only way to make sufficient additional oxygen available to a more vigorously working heart.

Blood Flow Through Capillaries and Capillary Dynamics

Blood flow through capillary networks is slow and intermittent, rather than steady. This phenomenon, called **vasomotion**, reflects the "on-off" opening and closing of precapillary sphincters in response to local autoregulatory controls.

Capillary Exchanges of Respiratory Gases and Nutrients

Oxygen, carbon dioxide, most nutrients (amino acids, glucose, lipids), and metabolic wastes pass between the blood and interstitial fluid by **diffusion.** Recall that in diffusion, movement always occurs along a concentration gradient—each substance moving from an area of its higher concentration to an area of its lower concentration. Hence, oxygen and nutrients pass from the blood, where their concentration is fairly high, through the interstitial fluid to the tissue cells. Carbon dioxide and metabolic wastes leave the

cells, where their content is higher and diffuse into the capillary blood. In general, small water-soluble solutes, such as amino acids and sugars, pass through fluid-filled capillary clefts (and sometimes through fenestrations), while lipid-soluble molecules, such as respiratory gases, diffuse directly through the lipid bilayer of the endothelial cell plasma membranes (see Figure 20.2). Cytoplasmic vesicles translocate some larger molecules, such as small proteins. As mentioned earlier, capillaries differ in their "leakiness," or permeability. Liver capillaries have large fenestrations that allow even proteins to pass freely, whereas brain capillaries are impermeable to most substances.

Fluid Movements

All the while nutrient and gas exchanges are occurring across the capillary walls by diffusion, bulk fluid flows are also going on. Fluid is forced out of the capillaries through the clefts at the arterial end of the bed, but most of it returns to the bloodstream at the venous end. These fluid flows are relatively unimportant to the capillary exchange process; instead they help determine the relative fluid volumes in the bloodstream and the extracellular space. As we describe next, the *direction and amount* of fluid that flows across the capillary walls reflect the balance (or imbalance) between two dynamic and opposing forces—hydrostatic and osmotic pressures.

Hydrostatic Pressures.   **Hydrostatic pressure** is the force exerted by a fluid pressing against a wall. In capillaries, hydrostatic pressure is the same as *capillary blood pressure*—the pressure of blood against the capillary walls. **Capillary hydrostatic pressure (HP_c)** is also called **filtration pressure** because it forces fluids through the capillary walls. Because blood pressure drops as blood flows through the length of a capillary bed, HP_c is higher at the arterial end of the bed (25–35 mm Hg) than at the venous end (10–15 mm Hg).

In theory, blood pressure—which forces fluid out of the capillaries—is opposed by the **interstitial fluid hydrostatic pressure (HP_{if})** acting outside the capillaries (back pressure) pushing fluid in. Thus, the *net* hydrostatic force acting on the capillaries at any point is the difference between the hydrostatic force that is pushing fluid *out* of the capillary (blood pressure) and the hydrostatic force that is pushing fluid *into* the capillary (interstitial fluid pressure). However, there is usually very little fluid in the interstitial space, because it is constantly withdrawn by the lymphatic vessels (see Chapter 21). Although the hydrostatic pressure in the interstitial space may vary from a slightly negative to slightly positive value, traditionally, it has been assumed to be approximately zero. For simplicity, that is the value we will use here. The *net effective hydrostatic pressures* at the arterial and venous ends of the capillary bed are summarized in Figure 20.13.

Arterial end of capillary
Interstitial fluid
Tissue cells
Venous end of capillary

Net HP 32 mm
Net OP 22 mm
Net HP 15 mm
Net OP 22 mm

Blood flow
Net pressure out 10 mm
Net pressure in 7 mm

Key to terms:

HP_C = 32 mm Hg at arteriole end
HP_C = 15 mm Hg at venule end
HP_{IF} = 0 mm Hg
Net HP = HP_C (32 mm Hg at arteriole end; 15 mm Hg at venule end)

OP_C = 25 mm Hg
OP_{IF} = 3 mm Hg
Net OP = 22 mm Hg

FIGURE 20.13
Forces responsible for fluid flows at capillaries. Direction of fluid movement depends on the difference between two opposing forces, hydrostatic pressure (HP) and osmotic pressure (OP). The net HP is the force that tends to push fluid out of the capillary. The net HP ($HP_c - HP_{if}$) is equal to the hydrostatic pressure of the blood (HP_c), which varies along the length of the capillary. The net OP is the force that draws fluid back into the capillary. The net OP ($OP_c - OP_{if}$) is a constant value, reflecting the fact that blood has a much higher content of nondiffusible solutes (proteins) than interstitial fluid. At the arterial end, net HP forcing fluid outward exceeds OP drawing water inward, resulting in a net loss from the capillary. At the downstream (venule) end, HP is overpowered by OP, and fluid returns to the bloodstream.

Osmotic Pressures.

Osmotic pressure is created by the presence in a fluid of large nondiffusible molecules, such as plasma proteins, that are prevented from moving through the capillary membrane. Such molecules draw water toward them; that is, they encourage osmosis (see Chapter 3) whenever the water concentration in their vicinity is relatively lower than it is on the opposite side of the capillary membrane. Plasma proteins in the capillary blood (primarily albumin molecules) develop a **capillary osmotic pressure (OP_c)** of approximately 25 mm Hg. Since interstitial fluid contains few proteins, its osmotic pressure **(OP_{if})** is substantially lower—ranging from 0.1 to 5 mm Hg. Unlike hydrostatic pressure, osmotic pressure does not vary from one end of the capillary bed to the other. Thus, in our example, the *net osmotic pressure* that pulls fluid back into the capillary blood is given as 22 mm Hg (Figure 20.13).

Hydrostatic-Osmotic Pressure Interactions.

At any point along a capillary, fluids will leave the capillary if net hydrostatic pressure is greater than net osmotic pressure, and fluids will enter the capillary if

net osmotic pressure exceeds net hydrostatic pressure. As shown in Figure 20.13, hydrostatic forces dominate at the arterial end (+ 10 mm Hg), while osmotic forces (− 7 mm Hg) dominate at the venous end. Thus, net fluid flows *out* of the circulation at the arterial ends of capillary beds and *into* the bloodstream at the venous ends. However, more fluid enters the tissue spaces than is returned to the blood, resulting in a net loss of fluid from the circulation of about 1.5 ml/min. This fluid and any leaked proteins are picked up by the lymphatic vessels and returned to the vascular system, which accounts for the relatively low levels of both fluid and proteins in the interstitial space. Were this not so, this "insignificant" fluid loss would empty your blood vessels of plasma in about 24 hours!

Circulatory Shock

Circulatory shock is any condition in which blood vessels are inadequately filled and blood cannot circulate normally. This results in inadequate blood flow to meet tissue needs. If the condition persists, cells die and organ damage ensues.

The most common form of shock, **hypovolemic** (hi″po-vo-le′mik; *hypo* = low, inadequate; *volemia* = blood volume) **shock,** results from large-scale loss of blood volume, as might follow acute hemorrhage, severe vomiting or diarrhea, or extensive burns. If blood volume drops rapidly, heart rate increases in an attempt to correct the problem. Thus, a weak, "thready" pulse is often the first sign of hypovolemic shock. Intense vasoconstriction also occurs, which shifts blood from the various blood reservoirs into the major circulatory channels and enhances venous return. Blood pressure is stable at first, but eventually drops if blood loss continues. A sharp drop in blood pressure is a serious, and late, sign of hypovolemic shock. The key to managing hypovolemic shock is to replace fluid volume as quickly as possible.

Although many body system responses to hypovolemic shock have yet to be explored, acute bleeding is such a threat to life that it seems important to have a comprehensive flowchart of its recognizable signs and symptoms and an accounting of the body's attempt to restore homeostasis. Figure 20.14 provides such a resource. Study it in part now, and then in more detail later when you have completed your studies of the remaining body systems.

In **vascular shock,** blood volume is normal and constant. Poor circulation results from extreme vasodilation that leads to an abnormal expansion of the vascular bed. The huge drop in peripheral resistance that follows is revealed by rapidly falling blood pressure. The most common causes of vascular shock are loss of vasomotor tone due to failure of autonomic nervous system regulation and septicemia. *Septicemia* is a severe systemic bacterial infection; bacterial toxins are notorious vasodilators.

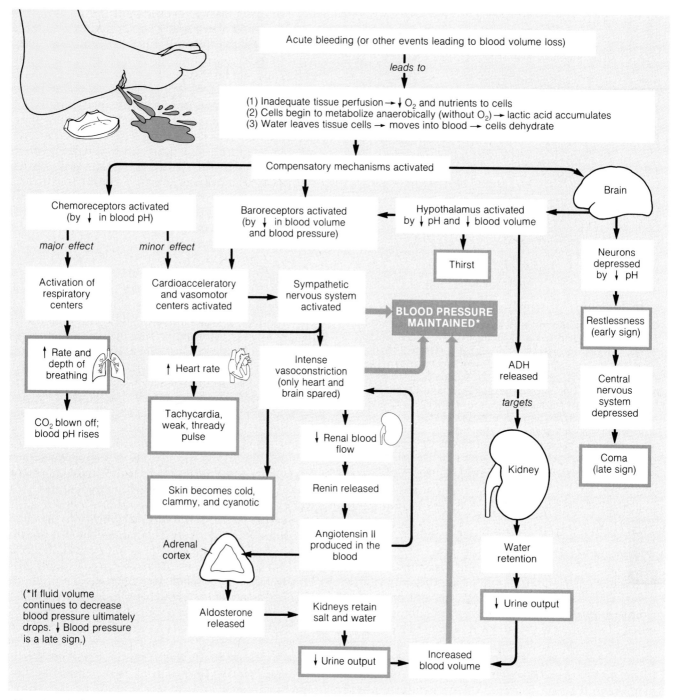

FIGURE 20.14
Events and signs of compensated (nonprogressive) hypovolemic shock.
(Recognizable clinical signs are shown in *red-bordered boxes.*)

A transient type of vascular shock may occur when you sunbathe for a prolonged time. The heat of the sun on your skin causes vasodilation of cutaneous blood vessels. Then, if you stand up abruptly, blood pools briefly (because of gravity) in the dilated vessels of your lower limbs rather than returning promptly to the heart. Consequently, blood pressure falls. The dizziness you feel at this point is a signal that your brain is not receiving enough oxygen.

Cardiogenic shock, or pump failure, occurs when the heart is so inefficient that it cannot sustain adequate circulation. Its usual cause is myocardial damage, as might follow numerous myocardial infarcts.

Orthostatic intolerance, a special case of shock, occurs in astronauts returning to earth. In zero *g* of outer space, body fluids shift upward from the lower limbs where they typically pool. As the fluids distribute more evenly, space travelers tend to get a puffy face and eyes and "chicken legs." The extra fluids in the chest activate baroreceptors which trigger mechanisms that accelerate fluid loss from the blood via urine, and severe dehydration occurs. Blood volume can be as much as 10% lower by the end of the first day. While still weightless, this is not a problem. However, when the astronaut reencounters the tug of gravity, blood pressure plummets as blood rushes to the lower limbs, and dizziness and fainting occur as inadequate blood is sent to the brain. To prevent or ease these symptoms, astronauts infuse saline solution to replace fluid volume before reentry. •

CIRCULATORY PATHWAYS: BLOOD VESSELS OF THE BODY

When referring to the body's complex network of blood vessels, the term **vascular system** is often used. However, the heart is actually a double pump that serves two distinct circulations, each with its own set of arteries, capillaries, and veins. The *pulmonary circulation* is the short loop that runs from the heart to the lungs and back to the heart. The *systemic circulation* routes blood through a long loop to all parts of the body before returning it to the heart. Both circuits are shown schematically in Table 20.2.

Except for special vessels and shunts of the fetal circulation (described in Chapter 29), the principal arteries and veins of the systemic circulation are described and illustrated in Tables 20.3 through 20.12. Notice that by convention, oxygen-rich blood is shown red, while blood that is relatively oxygen-poor is depicted blue, regardless of vessel types.

DEVELOPMENTAL ASPECTS OF THE BLOOD VESSELS

The endothelial lining of blood vessels is formed by mesodermal cells, which collect in little masses called **blood islands** throughout the microscopic embryo. These then form sprouting extensions that reach toward one another and the forming heart to lay down the rudimentary vascular tubes. Meanwhile, adjacent mesenchymal cells surround the endothelial tubes, forming the muscular and fibrous coats of the vessel walls. As noted in Chapter 19, the heart is pumping blood through the rudimentary vascular system by the fourth week of development.

In addition to the fetal shunts that bypass the nonfunctional lungs (the *foramen ovale* and *ductus arteriosus*), other vascular modifications are found in the fetus. A special vessel, the *ductus venosus,* largely bypasses the liver. Also important are the *umbilical vein* and *arteries,* large vessels that circulate blood between the fetal circulation and the placenta where gas and nutrient exchanges occur with the mother's blood (see Chapter 29, Figure 29.13 and pp. 1014–1015). Once the fetal circulatory pattern has been laid down, few vascular changes occur until birth, when the umbilical vessels and shunts are occluded.

In contrast to congenital heart diseases, congenital vascular problems are rare, and blood vessels are remarkably trouble free during youth. But as we age, signs of vascular disease begin to appear, giving a ring of truth to the old saying, "You are only as old as your arteries." In some, the venous valves weaken and purple, snakelike varicose veins appear. In others, more insidious signs of inefficient circulation appear: tingling in the fingers and toes and cramping of muscles.

Although the degenerative process of atherosclerosis begins in youth, its consequences are rarely apparent until middle to old age, when it may precipitate a myocardial infarct or stroke. Until puberty, the blood vessels of boys and girls look alike, but from puberty to about the age of 45 years, women have strikingly less atherosclerosis than men, probably because of the protective effects of estrogen. Between the ages of 45 and 65, this "gap" between the sexes closes and males and females are equally at risk for cardiovascular disease.

Blood pressure changes with age. In a newborn baby, arterial pressure is about 90/55. Blood pressure rises steadily during childhood finally reaching the adult value (120/80). In old age, "normal" blood pressure averages 150/90, which is a hypertensive pressure in younger people. After the age of 40, the incidence of hypertension increases dramatically. Unlike atherosclerosis, which is increasingly important in old age, hypertension claims many youthful victims and is the single most important cause of sudden cardiovascular death in men in their early 40s and 50.

Much of vascular disease is a product of our modern technological culture. "Blessed" with high-protein, lipid-rich diets, empty-calorie snacks, all manner of devices to save energy, and high-stress jobs, many of us are struck down prematurely. Cardiovascular disease can be prevented somewhat by diet modifications, regular aerobic exercise, and the elimination of cigarette smoking. Poor diet and exercise habits and smoking are probably more detrimental to your blood vessels than aging itself could ever be!

*   *   *

Now that we have described the structure and function of blood vessels, our survey of the cardiovascular system is finally complete. The pump, the plumbing, and the circulating fluid form a dynamic organ system that ceaselessly services every other organ system of the body, as summarized by *Making Connections.* However, our study of the so-called *circulatory system* is still unfinished. We have yet to examine the lymphatic system, which acts cooperatively with the cardiovascular system to ensure continuous circulation and to provide sites from which lymphocytes can police the body and provide for immunity. These are the topics of Chapter 21.

Making Connections

Systems Connections: Homeostatic Interrelationships Between the Cardiovascular System and Other Body Systems

Nervous System
• ANS regulates cardiac rate and force; sympathetic division maintains blood pressure and controls blood distribution according to need

• The cardiovascular system delivers oxygen and nutrients; carries away wastes

Endocrine System
• Various hormones influence blood pressure (epinephrine, ANF, thyroxine, ADH); estrogen maintains vascular health in women

• The cardiovascular system delivers oxygen and nutrients; carries away wastes; blood serves as a transport vehicle for hormones

Lymphatic System/Immunity
• The lymphatic system picks up leaked fluid and plasma proteins and returns them to the cardiovascular system; its immune cells protect cardiovascular organs from specific pathogens

• The cardiovascular system delivers oxygen and nutrients to lymphatic organs, which house immune cells; provides transport medium for lymphocytes and antibodies; carries away wastes

Respiratory System
• The respiratory system carries out gas exchange: loads oxygen and unloads carbon dioxide from the blood; respiratory "pump" aids venous return

• The cardiovascular system delivers oxygen and nutrients; carries away wastes

Digestive System
• The digestive system provides nutrients to the blood including iron and B vitamins essential for RBC (& hemoglobin) formation

• The cardiovascular system delivers oxygen and nutrients; carries away wastes

Urinary System
• The urinary system helps regulate blood volume and pressure by altering urine volume and releasing renin

• The cardiovascular system delivers oxygen and nutrients; carries away wastes; blood pressure maintains kidney function

Reproductive System
• Estrogen maintains vascular health in women

• The cardiovascular system delivers oxygen and nutrients; carries away wastes

Integumentary System
• The skin vasculature is an important blood reservoir and provides a site for heat loss from body

• The cardiovascular system delivers oxygen and nutrients; carries away wastes

Skeletal System
• Bones are the sites of hematopoiesis; protect cardiovascular organs by enclosure: and provide a calcium depot

• The cardiovascular system delivers oxygen and nutrients and carries away wastes

Muscular System
• Aerobic exercise enhances cardiovascular efficiency and helps prevent arteriosclerosis; the muscle "pump" aids venous return

• The cardiovascular system delivers oxygen and nutrients; carries away wastes

Closer Connections: The Cardiovascular System and Interrelationships with the Muscular, Nervous, and Urinary Systems

The cardiovascular system is the "king of systems." No body system can live without the blood that surges ceaselessly through cardiovascular channels. Likewise, it is nearly impossible to find a system that does not influence the cardiovascular system in some way. The respiratory and digestive systems enrich blood with oxygen and nutrients, respectively, and, in turn, take a share of the various riches the blood has to offer. By returning leaked plasma fluid to the vascular system, the lymphatic system helps to keep those vessels filled with blood so that circulation is possible. However, the three cardiovascular system partnerships that we will look at more closely here are those it has with the muscular, nervous, and urinary systems.

Muscular System

Talk about "one hand washing the other"—that's a pretty fair analogy for the interaction between the cardiovascular and muscular systems. Muscles cramp and become nonfunctional when deprived of an adequate supply of oxygen-rich blood and their capillary supply expands (or atrophies) along with changes in muscle mass. The arterioles of skeletal muscle even have special beta-adrenergic and ACh receptors, so that they can be dilated by neural reflexes when most other body arterioles are responding to vasoconstrictor "orders." When muscles are active and healthy, so too is the cardiovascular system. Without exercise, the heart weakens and loses mass; but when we exercise aerobically, the heart increases in size and strength. Heart rate goes down as stroke volume rises, and a lower HR means that the heart relaxes more and beats hundreds of thousands times less in a lifetime. Aerobic exercise also enhances HDL blood levels and reduces LDL levels—helping to clear fatty deposits from the vascular walls and deferring atherosclerosis, hypertension, and heart disease. Not a bad trade!

Nervous System

The brain is critically dependent on absolutely continuous oxygen and glucose delivery, thus it should come as no surprise to learn that the brain has the body's most precise autoregulatory circulation mechanism. Acting on acutely sensitive arterioles, this mechanism protects the brain from most deficits. For this, we can be profoundly thankful, for when neurons die, an important part of us dies as well. The cardiovascular system is just as dependent on the nervous system. Although an intrinsic conduction system sets sinus rhythm, it does not even begin to adapt to stimuli that mobilize the cardiovascular system to peak efficiency in maintaining blood pressure during position changes and delivering blood faster during times of stress. This is the job of the autonomic nervous system, which initiates reflexes as necessary to increase or decrease cardiac output and peripheral resistance, and to redirect blood from one organ to others to serve specific needs and protect vital organs.

Urinary System

Like the lymphatic system, the urinary system (primarily the kidneys) helps maintain blood volume and circulatory dynamics, but in a much more complicated way. The kidneys use blood pressure (courtesy of the cardiovascular system) to form the filtrate which the kidney tubule cells then process. Essentially this processing involves reclaiming needed nutrients and water, while allowing metabolic waste and excess ions (including H^+) to leave the body in urine. As a result, blood is continually refreshed and blood composition and volume are carefully regulated. So dedicated are the kidneys to preserving blood volume that urine output stops entirely when blood volume is severely depressed. On the other hand, the kidneys can increase systemic BP by releasing renin when the blood pressure becomes inadequate.

Clinical Connections

Cardiovascular System

Case Study 2: Mr. Hutchinson, another middle-aged victim of the collision on Route 91, has a tourniquet around his thigh when admitted in an unconscious state to Noble Hospital. The emergency technician who brings him in states that his right lower limb was pinned beneath the bus for *at least* 30 minutes. He is immediately scheduled for surgery. Admission notes include the following:

- Multiple contusions of lower limbs
- Compound fracture of the right ulna; bone ends covered with sterile gauze
- Right leg blanched and cold, no pulse
- Blood pressure 90/48; pulse 140/min and thready; patient diaphoretic (sweaty)

1. Relative to what you have learned about tissue requirements for oxygen, what is the condition of the tissues in the right lower limb?

2. Will the fracture be attended to, or will Mr. Hutchinson's other homeostatic needs take precedence? Explain your answer choice and predict his surgical treatment.

3. What do you conclude regarding Mr. Hutchinson's cardiovascular measurements (pulse and BP), and what measures do you expect will be taken to remedy the situation before commencing with surgery?

Table 20.2 Pulmonary and Systemic Circulations

Pulmonary Circulation

The pulmonary circulation (Figure 20.15a) functions only to bring blood into close contact with the alveoli (air sacs) of the lungs so that gaseous exchanges can occur; it does not directly serve the metabolic needs of body tissues.

Oxygen-poor, dark red blood enters the pulmonary circulation as it is pumped from the right ventricle into the large **pulmonary trunk** (Figure 20.15b). The pulmonary trunk runs diagonally upward for about 8 cm and then divides abruptly to form the **right** and **left pulmonary arteries.** In the lungs, the pulmonary arteries subdivide into the **lobar** (lo'bar) **arteries** (three in the right lung and two in the left lung), each of which serves one lung lobe. The lobar arteries accompany the main bronchi into the lungs and then branch profusely, forming arterioles and, finally, the dense networks of **pulmonary capillaries** that surround and cling to the delicate air sacs. It is here that oxygen loading and carbon dioxide unloading between the blood and alveolar air occur. As gas exchanges occur and oxygen content of the blood rises, the blood becomes bright red. The pulmonary capillary beds drain into venules, which in turn join to form the two **pulmonary veins** exiting from each lung. The four pulmonary veins complete the circuit by unloading their precious cargo into the left atrium of the heart. Note that any vessel with the term *pulmonary* or *lobar* in its name is part of the pulmonary circulation. All others are part of the systemic circulation.

Pulmonary arteries carry oxygen-poor, carbon dioxide–rich blood, and pulmonary veins carry oxygen-rich blood.* This is exactly opposite the situation in the systemic circulation, where arteries carry oxygen-rich blood and veins carry carbon dioxide–rich, relatively oxygen-poor blood.

(a)

FIGURE 20.15
Pulmonary circulation. (a) Schematic flowchart. **(b)** Illustration. The arterial system is shown in blue to indicate that the blood carried is oxygen poor; the venous drainage is shown in red to indicate that the blood transported is oxygen rich.

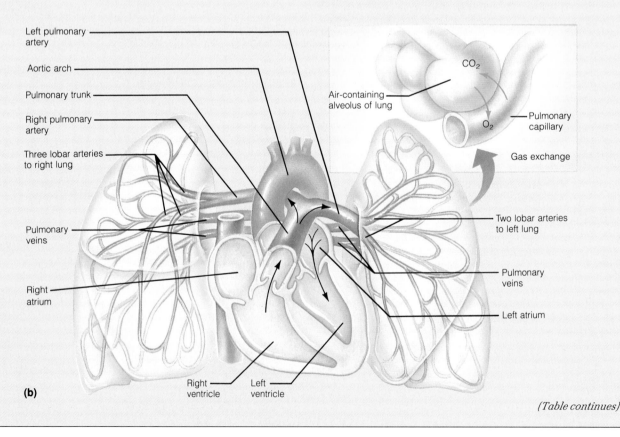

(b)

(Table continues)

Table 20.2   continued

Systemic Circulation

The systemic circulation provides the *functional blood supply* to all body tissues; that is, it delivers oxygen, nutrients, and other needed substances while carrying away carbon dioxide and other metabolic wastes. Freshly oxygenated blood* returning from the pulmonary circuit is pumped out of the left ventricle into the aorta (Figure 20.16). From the aorta, blood can take various routes, since essentially all systemic arteries branch from this single great vessel. The aorta arches upward from the heart and then curves and runs downward along the body midline to its terminus in the pelvis, where it splits to form the two large arteries serving the lower extremities. The branches of the aorta continue to subdivide to produce the arterioles and, finally, the capillaries that ramify through the body organs. Venous blood draining from organs inferior to the diaphragm ultimately enters the inferior vena cava. Except for some thoracic venous drainage (which enters the azygos system of veins), body regions above the diaphragm are drained by the superior vena cava. The venae cavae empty the carbon dioxide-laden blood into the right atrium of the heart.

Two points concerning the two major circulations must be emphasized: (1) Blood passes from systemic veins to systemic arteries only after first moving through the pulmonary circuit (Figure 20.15a), and (2) although the entire cardiac output of the right ventricle passes through the pulmonary circulation, only a small fraction of the output of the left ventricle flows through any single organ (Figure 20.16). The systemic circulation can be viewed as multiple circulatory channels functioning in parallel to distribute blood to all body organs.

As you examine tables that follow and locate the various systemic arteries and veins in the illustrations, be aware of cues that make your memorization task easier. In many cases, the name of a vessel reflects the body region traversed (axillary, brachial, femoral, etc.), the organ served (renal, hepatic, gonadal, etc.), or the bone followed (vertebral, radial, tibial, etc.). Also, notice that arteries and veins tend to run together side by side and, in many places, they also run with nerves. Finally, be alert to the fact that the systemic vessels do not always match on the right and left sides of the body. Some of the large, deep vessels of the trunk region are asymmetrical or unpaired (their initial symmetry is lost during embryonic development), while almost all vessels are bilaterally symmetrical in the head and limbs.

FIGURE 20.16
Schematic flowchart showing an overview of the systemic circulation. The pulmonary circulation is shown in gray for comparison.

*By convention, oxygen-rich blood is shown *red* and oxygen-poor blood is shown *blue*.

Table 20.3   The Aorta and Major Arteries of the Systemic Circulation

The major arteries of the systemic circulation are diagrammed in flowchart form in Figure 20.17a and illustrated in Figure 20.17b. Notice that only the distribution of the aorta is described in detail in this figure. Fine points about the various vessels arising from the aorta are provided in Tables 20.4 through 20.7.

Description and Distribution

Aorta.   This vessel is the largest artery in the body. In adults, the aorta (a-or'tah), is approximately the size of a garden hose where it issues from the left ventricle of the heart. Its internal diameter is 2.5 cm, and its wall is about 2 mm thick; it decreases in size only slightly as it runs to its terminus. The aortic semilunar valve guards the base of the aorta and prevents backflow of blood during diastole. Opposite each of the semilunar valve cusps is an *aortic sinus,* a slight enlargement of the aortic wall containing baroreceptors important in reflex regulation of blood pressure (see p. 654).

Different portions of the aorta are named according to their relative shape or location. The first portion of the aorta, called the **ascending aorta,** runs posteriorly and to

the right of the pulmonary trunk. It persists for only about 5 cm before curving to the left as the aortic arch. The only branches of the ascending aorta are the **right** and **left coronary arteries,** which supply the myocardium (see p. 621). The **aortic arch,** deep to the sternum, begins and ends at the sternal angle (level of T_4). Its three major branches (R to L) are: (1) the **brachiocephalic** (bra″ke-o-sĕ-fal′ik; "armhead") **artery,** which passes superiorly under the right clavicle and branches into the **right common carotid** (kahrot′id) **artery** and the right **subclavian artery,** (2) the **left common carotid artery,** and (3) the **left subclavian artery.** These three vessels provide the arterial supply of the head, neck, upper limbs, and part of the thorax wall. The **thoracic,** or **descending, aorta** runs along the anterior spine from T_5 to T_{12}, sending off numerous small arteries to the thorax wall and viscera before piercing the diaphragm. As it enters the abdominal cavity, it becomes the **abdominal aorta.** This portion of the aorta supplies the abdominal walls and viscera and then ends at the level of L_4 where it splits into the **right** and **left common iliac arteries,** which supply the pelvis and lower limbs.

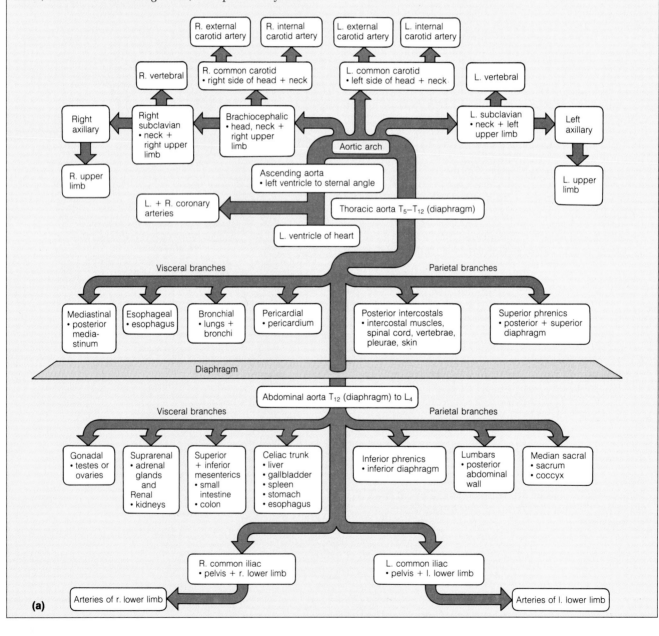

(a)

Table 20.3   continued

FIGURE 20.17
Major arteries of the systemic circulation. **(a)** Schematic flowchart.
(b) Illustration, anterior view.

Internal carotid artery

External carotid artery

Vertebral artery

Brachiocephalic artery

Axillary artery

Ascending aorta

Brachial artery

Abdominal aorta

Superior mesenteric artery

Gonadal artery

Inferior mesenteric artery

Common iliac artery

External iliac artery

Digital arteries

Femoral artery

Popliteal artery

Anterior tibial artery

Posterior tibial artery

Arcuate artery

Common carotid arteries

Subclavian artery

Aortic arch

Coronary artery

Thoracic aorta

Branches of celiac trunk:
• Left gastric artery
• Common hepatic artery
• Splenic artery

Renal artery

Radial artery

Ulnar artery

Internal iliac artery

Deep palmar arch

Superficial palmar arch

(b)

Table 20.4   Arteries of the Head and Neck

Four paired arteries supply the head and neck. These are the common carotid arteries, plus three branches from each subclavian artery: the vertebral arteries, and the thyrocervical and costocervical trunks illustrated in Figure 20.18b. Of these, the common carotid arteries have the broadest distribution. These arteries, and their branches, are diagrammed in Figure 20.18a.

Each common carotid divides into 2 major branches

(the internal and external carotid arteries) and, at the division point, each internal carotid artery has a slight dilation, the **carotid sinus,** that contains baroreceptors that assist in reflex blood pressure control. The **carotid bodies,** chemoreceptors involved in the control of respiratory rate, are located close by. Pressing on the neck in the area of the carotid sinuses can cause unconsciousness (*carot* = stupor) because it mimics high blood pressure, eliciting vasodilation which interferes with blood delivery to the brain.

Description and Distribution
Common carotid arteries.   The origins of these two arteries differ: The right common carotid artery arises from the brachiocephalic artery; the left is the second branch of the aortic arch. The common carotid arteries ascend through the lateral neck, and at the superior border of the larynx (the level of the "Adam's apple"), each divides into its two major branches, the *external* and *internal carotid arteries.*

The **external carotid arteries** supply most tissues of the head except for the brain and orbit. As each artery runs superiorly, it sends branches to the thyroid gland and larynx **(superior thyroid artery),** the tongue **(lingual artery),** the skin and muscles of the anterior face **(facial artery),** and the posterior scalp **(occipital artery).** Each external carotid artery terminates by splitting into a **superficial temporal artery,** which supplies the parotid salivary gland and most of the scalp, and a **maxillary artery,** which supplies the upper and lower jaws and chewing muscles, the teeth, and the nasal cavity. A clinically important branch of the maxillary artery is the *middle meningeal artery* (not illustrated). It enters the skull through the foramen spinosum and supplies the inner surface of the parietal bone, squamous region of the temporal bone, and the underlying dura mater.

The larger **internal carotid arteries** supply the orbits and most (over 80%) of the cerebrum. They assume a deep course and enter the skull through the carotid canals of the temporal bones. Once inside the cranium, each gives off one main branch, the ophthalmic artery, and then divides into the anterior and middle cerebral arteries. The **ophthalmic** (of-thal'mik) **arteries** supply the eyes, orbits, forehead, and nose. Each **anterior cerebral artery** supplies the medial surface of the cerebral hemisphere on its side and also anastomoses with its partner on the opposite side via a short arterial shunt called the **anterior communicating artery** (Figure 20.18d). The **middle cerebral arteries** run in the lateral fissures of their respective cerebral hemispheres and supply the lateral parts of the temporal and parietal lobes.

Vertebral arteries.   These vessels spring from the subclavian arteries at the root of the neck and ascend through foramina in the transverse processes of the cervical vertebrae to enter the skull through the foramen magnum. En route, they send branches to the cervical spinal cord and some deep structures of the neck. Within the cranium, the right and left vertebral arteries join to form the **basilar** (bas'ĭ-lar) **artery,** which ascends along the anterior aspect of the brain stem, giving off branches to the cerebellum, pons, and inner ear (see Figure 20.18b and d). At the pons-midbrain border, the basilar artery divides into a pair of **posterior cerebral arteries,** which supply the occipital lobes and the inferior parts of the temporal lobes of the cerebral hemispheres.

Table 20.4   continued

Superficial temporal artery

Basilar artery

Vertebral artery

Internal carotid artery

External carotid artery

Common carotid artery

Thyrocervical trunk

Costocervical trunk

Subclavian artery

Axillary artery

Ophthalmic artery

Maxillary artery

Occipital artery

Facial artery

Lingual artery

Superior thyroid artery

Larynx

Thyroid gland (overlying trachea)

Clavicle (cut)

Brachiocephalic artery

Internal thoracic artery

(b)

FIGURE 20.18
Arteries of the head, neck, and brain. (a) Schematic flowchart. **(b)** Arteries of the head and neck, right aspect. **(c)** Arteriograph of the arterial supply of the brain. **(d)** Major arteries serving the brain and the circle of Willis. In this inferior view of the brain, the right side of the cerebellum and part of the right temporal lobe have been removed to show the distribution of the middle and posterior cerebral arteries.

(c)

Anterior

Frontal lobe

Optic chiasma

Middle cerebral artery

Internal carotid

Pituitary gland

Temporal lobe

Pons

Occipital lobe

Circle of Willis:

• Anterior cerebral artery

• Anterior communicating artery

• Posterior communicating artery

• Posterior cerebral artery

Basilar artery

Vertebral artery

Cerebellum

(d)

Posterior

Arterial shunts called **posterior communicating arteries** connect the posterior cerebral arteries to the middle cerebral arteries anteriorly. The two posterior and single anterior communicating arteries complete the formation of an arterial anastomosis called the **circle of Willis.** The circle of Willis encircles the pituitary gland and optic chiasma and unites the brain's anterior and posterior blood supplies. It also acts to equalize blood pressure in the two brain areas and provides alternate routes for blood to reach the brain tissue if a carotid or vertebral artery becomes occluded.

Thyrocervical and costocervical trunks.   These short vessels arise from the subclavian artery just lateral to the vertebral arteries on each side (Figure 20.18b and Figure 20.19). The thyrocervical trunk mainly supplies the thyroid gland and some scapular muscles. The costocervical trunk serves the deep neck and superior intercostal muscles.

Table 20.5   Arteries of the Upper Limbs and Thorax

The upper limbs are supplied entirely by arteries arising from the **subclavian arteries** (see Figure 20.19a). After giving off branches to the neck, each subclavian artery courses laterally between the clavicle and first rib to enter the axilla, where its name changes to axillary artery. The thorax wall is supplied by an array of vessels that arise either directly from the thoracic aorta or from branches of the subclavian arteries. Most visceral organs of the thorax receive their functional blood supply from small branches issuing from the thoracic aorta. Because these vessels are so small and tend to vary in number (except for the bronchial arteries), they are not illustrated in Figures 20.19a and b, but several of these are listed on p. 677.

(a)

Description and Distribution

Arteries of the Upper Limb

Axillary artery. As it runs through the axilla accompanied by cords of the brachial plexus, each axillary artery gives off branches to the structures of the axilla, chest wall, and shoulder girdle. These include the **thoracoacromial** (tho″rah-ko-ah-kro′me-al) **trunk,** which supplies the superior shoulder (deltoid) and pectoral region; the **lateral thoracic artery,** which serves the lateral chest wall and breast; the **subscapular artery** to the scapula, dorsal thorax wall, and latissimus dorsi muscle; and the **anterior and posterior circumflex arteries,** which wrap around the humeral neck and help supply the shoulder joint and the deltoid muscle. As the axillary artery emerges from the axilla, it becomes the brachial artery.

Brachial artery. The brachial artery runs down the medial aspect of the humerus and supplies the anterior flexor muscles of the arm. One major branch, the **deep brachial artery,** serves the posterior triceps brachii muscle. As the brachial artery nears the elbow, it gives off several small branches that contribute to an anastomosis serving the elbow joint and connecting it to the arteries of the forearm. As the brachial artery crosses the anterior midline aspect of the elbow, it provides an easily palpated pulse point (brachial pulse) (see Figure 20.10). Immediately beyond the elbow, the brachial artery splits to form the radial and ulnar arteries, which more or less follow the course of similarly named bones down the length of the anterior forearm.

Radial artery. The radial artery, which runs from the median line of the cubital fossa to the styloid process of the radius, supplies the lateral muscles of the forearm, the wrist, and the thumb and index finger. At the root of the thumb, the radial artery provides a convenient site for taking the radial pulse.

Ulnar artery. The ulnar artery supplies the medial aspect of the forearm, fingers 3–5, and the medial aspect of the index finger. Proximally, the ulnar artery gives off a short branch, the **common interosseous** (in″ter-os′e-us) **artery,** which runs between the radius and ulna to serve the deep flexors and extensors of the forearm.

Palmar arches. In the palm, branches of the radial and ulnar arteries anastomose to form two palmar arches, the **superficial** and **deep palmar arches.** The **metacarpal arteries** and the **digital arteries** that supply the fingers arise from these palmar arches.

Arteries of the Thorax Wall

Internal thoracic (mammary) arteries. The internal thoracic (mammary) arteries, which arise from the subclavian arteries, supply blood to most of the anterior thorax wall. Each of these arteries descends lateral to the sternum and gives off **anterior intercostal**

Table 20.5   continued

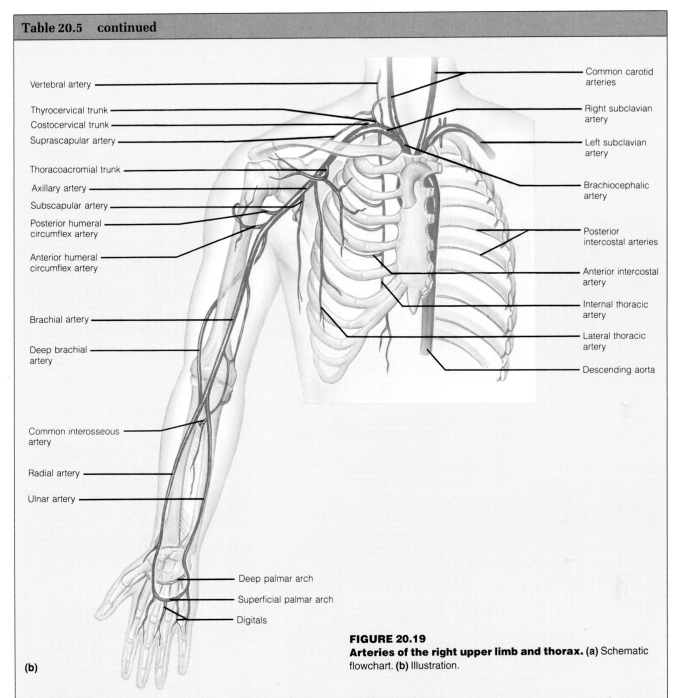

Vertebral artery

Thyrocervical trunk

Costocervical trunk

Suprascapular artery

Thoracoacromial trunk

Axillary artery

Subscapular artery

Posterior humeral circumflex artery

Anterior humeral circumflex artery

Brachial artery

Deep brachial artery

Common interosseous artery

Radial artery

Ulnar artery

Deep palmar arch

Superficial palmar arch

Digitals

Common carotid arteries

Right subclavian artery

Left subclavian artery

Brachiocephalic artery

Posterior intercostal arteries

Anterior intercostal artery

Internal thoracic artery

Lateral thoracic artery

Descending aorta

(b)

FIGURE 20.19
Arteries of the right upper limb and thorax. (a) Schematic flowchart. **(b)** Illustration.

arteries, which supply the structures of the intercostal spaces anteriorly. The internal thoracic artery also sends superficial branches to the mammary glands and terminates in twiglike branches to the anterior abdominal wall and diaphragm.

Posterior intercostal arteries.   The superior two pairs of *posterior intercostal arteries* are derived from the **costocervical trunk.** The next nine pairs issue from the thoracic aorta and course around the rib cage to anastomose anteriorly with the *anterior intercostal arteries.* Inferior to the 12th rib, a pair of **subcostal arteries** emerges from the thoracic aorta (not illustrated). The posterior intercostal arteries supply the posterior intercostal spaces, the deep muscles of the back, the vertebrae, and the spinal cord. Together, the posterior and anterior intercostal arteries supply the intercostal muscles.

Superior phrenic arteries.   One or more paired superior phrenic arteries serve the posterior superior aspect of the diaphragm surface.

Arteries of the Thoracic Viscera
Pericardial arteries.   Several tiny branches supply the posterior pericardium.

Bronchial arteries.   Two left and one right bronchial arteries supply systemic (oxygen-rich) blood to the lungs, bronchi, and pleurae.

Esophageal arteries.   Four to five esophageal arteries supply the esophagus.

Mediastinal arteries.   Many small mediastinal arteries serve the contents of the posterior mediastinum.

Table 20.6   Arteries of the Abdomen

The arterial supply to the abdominal organs arises from the abdominal aorta (Figure 20.20a). Under resting conditions, about half of the entire arterial flow is found in these vessels. Except for the celiac trunk, the superior and inferior mesenteric arteries, and the median sacral artery, all are paired vessels. These arteries supply the abdominal wall, the diaphragm, and visceral organs of the abdominopelvic cavity. The branches are given here in order of their issue.

Description and Distribution

Inferior phrenic arteries.   The inferior phrenics emerge from the aorta at T_{12}, just inferior to the diaphragm. They serve the inferior diaphragm surface.

Celiac trunk.   This very large unpaired branch of the abdominal aorta divides almost immediately into three branches: the common hepatic, splenic, and left gastric arteries (Figure 20.20b). The **common hepatic** (hĕ-pat′ik) **artery** runs superiorly, giving off branches to the stomach, duodenum, and pancreas. Where the **gastroduodenal artery** branches off, it becomes the **hepatic artery proper**, which splits into right and left branches that serve the liver. As the **splenic** (splen′ik) **artery** passes deep to the stomach, it sends branches to the pancreas and stomach and terminates in branches to the spleen. The **left gastric** (*gaster* = stomach) **artery** supplies part of the stomach and the inferior esophagus. The **right** and **left gastroepiploic** (gas″tro-ep″ĭ-plo′ik) **arteries,** branches of the gastroduodenal and splenic arteries, respectively, serve the left (greater) curvature of the stomach. A **right gastric** artery, which supplies the stomach's right (lesser) curvature, commonly arises from the common hepatic artery.

Superior mesenteric (mes-en-ter′ik) **artery.**   This large, unpaired artery arises from the abdominal aorta at the level of L_1 immediately below the celiac trunk (see Figure 20.20d). It runs deep to the pancreas and then enters the mesentery, where its numerous anastomosing branches serve virtually all of the small intestine via the **intestinal arteries**, most of the large intestine—the appendix, cecum, ascending colon (via the **ileocolic artery**), and part of the transverse colon (via the **right** and **middle colic arteries**).

Suprarenal (soo″prah-re′nal) **arteries.**   The suprarenal arteries flank the origin of the superior mesenteric artery as they emerge from the abdominal aorta (Figure 20.20c). They supply blood to the adrenal (suprarenal) glands overlying the kidneys.

Renal arteries.   The short, but wide, right and left renal arteries issue from the lateral surfaces of the aorta slightly below the superior mesenteric artery (between L_1 and L_2). Each serves the kidney on its side.

Gonadal (go-nă′dul) **arteries.**   The paired gonadal arteries are called the **testicular arteries** in males and the **ovarian arteries** in females. In females, these vessels extend into the pelvis to serve the ovaries and part of the uterine tubes. In males the much longer testicular arteries descend through the pelvis and inguinal canal to enter the scrotal sac, where they serve the testes.

Inferior mesenteric artery.   This final major branch of the abdominal aorta is unpaired and arises from the anterior aortic surface at the level of L_3. It serves the distal part of the large intestine—from the midpart of the transverse colon to the midrectum—via its **left colic, sigmoidal,** and **superior rectal branches.** Looping anastomoses between the superior and inferior mesenteric arteries help ensure that blood will continue to reach the various regions of the digestive viscera in cases of trauma to one of these abdominal arteries.

Lumbar arteries.   Four pairs of lumbar arteries arise from the posterolateral surface of the aorta in the lumbar region. These segmental arteries supply the posterior abdominal wall.

Median sacral artery.   The median sacral artery issues from the posterior surface of the abdominal aorta at its terminus. This tiny artery supplies the sacrum and coccyx.

Common iliac arteries.   At the level of L_4, the aorta splits into the right and left common iliac arteries, which supply blood to the lower abdominal wall, pelvic organs, and lower limbs (see Figure 20.21).

(a)

Table 20.6   continued

(b)

Liver (cut)
Inferior vena cava
Celiac trunk
Hepatic artery proper
Common hepatic artery
Right gastric artery
Gallbladder
Gastroduodenal artery
Right gastroepiploic artery
Duodenum
Abdominal aorta

Diaphragm
Esophagus
Left gastric artery
Left gastroepiploic artery
Splenic artery
Spleen
Pancreas (major portion lies posteror to stomach)
Superior mesenteric artery

FIGURE 20.20
Arteries of the abdomen.
(a) Schematic flowchart. **(b)** The celiac trunk and its major branches. **(c)** Major branches of the abdominal aorta. **(d)** Distribution of the superior and inferior mesenteric arteries. (The transverse colon has been reflected superiorly to provide a better view of these arteries.)

(c)

Hiatus (opening) for inferior vena cava
Hiatus (opening) for esophagus
Celiac trunk
Kidney
Abdominal aorta
Lumbar arteries

Diaphragm
Inferior phrenic artery
Suprarenal artery
Renal artery
Superior mesenteric artery
Gonadal (testicular or ovarian) artery
Inferior mesenteric artery
Common iliac artery
Ureter
Median sacral artery

(d)

Celiac artery
Middle colic artery
Right colic artery
Ileocolic artery
Ascending colon
Ileum
Superior rectal artery
Rectum

Transverse colon
Superior mesenteric artery
Intestinal arteries
Left colic artery
Inferior mesenteric artery
Aorta
Sigmoidal arteries
Descending colon
Left common iliac artery
Sigmoid colon

Table 20.7   Arteries of the Pelvis and Lower Limbs

At the level of the sacroiliac joints, the **common iliac arteries** divide into two major branches, the internal and external iliac arteries (Figure 20.21a). The internal iliacs distribute blood mainly to the pelvic region. The external iliacs mainly serve the lower limbs, although they also send some branches to the abdominal wall.

Description and Distribution
Internal iliac arteries.   These paired arteries run into the pelvis and distribute blood to the pelvic walls and viscera (bladder, rectum, uterus and vagina in the female and prostate gland and ductus deferens in the male). Additionally they serve the gluteal muscles via the **superior** and **inferior gluteal arteries,** adductor muscles of the medial thigh via the **obturator artery,** and external genitalia and perineum via the **internal pudendal artery** (not illustrated).

External iliac arteries.   These arteries supply the lower limbs (Figure 20.21b). As they course through the pelvis, they give off branches to the anterior abdominal wall. After passing under the inguinal ligaments to enter the thigh, they become the femoral arteries.

Femoral arteries.   As each of these arteries passes down the anteromedial thigh, it gives off several branches to the muscles of the thigh. The largest of the deep branches is the **deep femoral artery** that serves the posterior (knee flexor) thigh muscles. Proximal branches of the deep femoral artery, the **lateral** and **medial femoral circumflex arteries,** encircle the neck of the femur. The medial femoral circumflex artery supplies most of the blood to the head and neck of the femur. Descending branches of the two circumflex arteries supply the hamstring muscles. As the femoral artery approaches the knee, it passes posteriorly and through a gap in the adductor magnus muscle, the *adductor hiatus*, to enter the popliteal fossa, where its name changes to popliteal artery.

Popliteal artery.   This posterior vessel contributes to an arterial anastomosis that supplies the knee region and then splits into the anterior and posterior tibial arteries of the leg.

Anterior tibial artery.   The anterior tibial artery runs through the anterior compartment of the leg, supplying the extensor muscles along the way. At the ankle, it becomes the **dorsalis pedis artery,** which supplies the ankle and dorsum of the foot, and continues as the **arcuate artery,** which gives off the metatarsal arteries to the metatarsus of the foot. The superficial dorsalis pedis artery provides a clinically important pulse point, the pedal pulse (see Figure 20.10). If the pedal pulse is easily felt, it is fairly certain that the blood supply to the leg is good.

Posterior tibial artery.   This large artery courses through the posteromedial part of the leg and supplies the flexor muscles. Proximally, it gives off a large branch, the **peroneal** (per″o-ne′al) **artery,** which supplies the lateral peroneal muscles of the leg. At the ankle, the posterior tibial artery divides into **lateral** and **medial plantar arteries** that serve the plantar surface of the foot. The **digital arteries** serving the toes arise from the plantar arch formed by the lateral plantar artery.

(a)

Table 20.7 continued

Although there are many similarities between the systemic arteries and veins, there are also important differences:

1. Whereas the heart pumps all of its blood into a single systemic artery—the aorta—blood returning to the heart is delivered largely by two terminal systemic veins, the superior and inferior venae cavae. The single exception to this is the blood draining from the myocardium of the heart, which is collected by the cardiac veins and reenters the right atrium via the coronary sinus (see p. 622).

2. All arteries run deep and are well protected by body tissues along most of their course, but both deep and superficial veins exist. Deep veins parallel the course of the systemic arteries, and with a few exceptions, the naming of these veins is identical to that of their companion arteries. Superficial veins run just beneath the skin and are readily seen, especially in the limbs, face, and neck. Since there are no superficial arteries, the names of the superficial veins do not correspond to the names of any of the arteries.

3. Unlike the fairly clear arterial pathways, venous pathways tend to have numerous interconnections, and many veins are represented by not one but two similarly named vessels. As a result, venous pathways are more difficult to follow.

4. In most body regions, there is a similar and predictable arterial supply and venous drainage. However, the pattern of venous drainage in at least two important body areas is unique. First, venous blood draining from the brain enters large *dural sinuses* rather than typical veins. Second, blood draining from the digestive organs enters a special subcirculation, called the *hepatic portal circulation*, and perfuses through the liver before it reenters the general systemic circulation.

In our survey of the systemic veins, the major tributaries (branches) of the venae cavae will be noted first, followed by a description in Tables 20.9 through 20.12 of the venous pattern of the various body regions. Since veins run toward the heart, the most distal veins will be named first and those closest to the heart last. Deep veins will be named, but since they generally drain the same areas served by their companion arteries, they will not be described in detail. An overview of the systemic veins appears in Figure 20.22.

FIGURE 20.21
Arteries of the right pelvis and lower limb.
(a) Schematic flowchart. **(b)** Illustration.

(Table continues)

Description and Areas Drained

Superior vena cava. This great vein receives blood draining from all areas superior to the diaphragm, except from the pulmonary circuit. The superior vena cava is formed by the union of the **right** and **left brachiocephalic veins** and empties into the superior aspect of the right atrium (see Figure 20.22b). Notice that there are two brachiocephalic veins, but only one brachiocephalic artery. Each brachiocephalic vein is formed in turn by the joining of the **internal jugular** and **subclavian veins** on its side. In most of the flowcharts that follow, only the vessels draining blood from the right side of the body are followed (with the exception of vessels of the azygos circulation of the thorax).

Inferior vena cava. This vein, the widest blood vessel in the body, is substantially longer than the superior vena cava. It returns blood to the heart from all body regions below the diaphragm and corresponds most closely to the abdominal aorta, which lies directly to its left. The distal end of the inferior vena cava is formed by the junction of the paired **common iliac veins** at L_5. From this point, it courses superiorly along the anterior aspect of the spine, receiving venous blood draining from the abdominal walls, gonads, and kidneys. Just before it penetrates the diaphragm, it is joined by the hepatic veins, which transport flood from the liver. Immediately above the diaphragm, the inferior vena cava ends as it enters the inferior aspect of the right atrium of the heart.

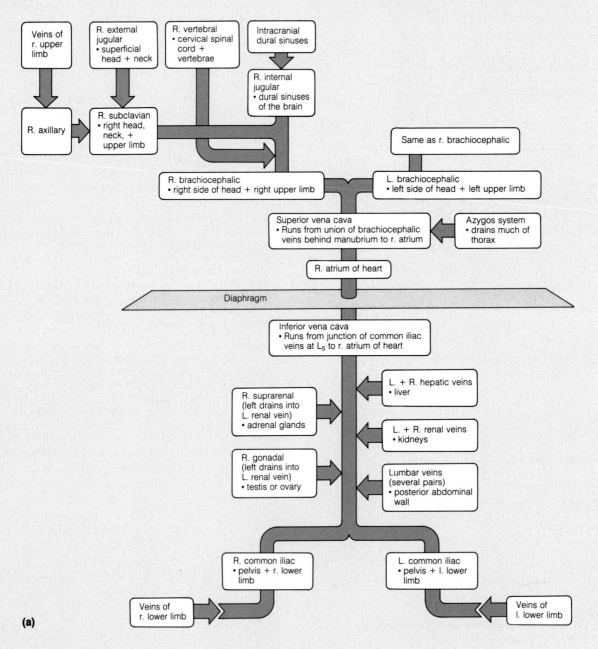

(a)

Table 20.8   continued

Dural sinuses

External jugular vein
Vertebral vein
Internal jugular vein

Superior vena cava

Axillary vein

Great cardiac vein

Hepatic veins

Hepatic portal vein
Superior mesenteric vein

Inferior vena cava

Ulnar vein
Radial vein

Common iliac vein
External iliac vein
Internal iliac vein

Digital veins

Femoral vein

Great saphenous vein

Popliteal vein

Posterior tibial vein

Anterior tibial vein

Peroneal vein

Dorsal venous arch

FIGURE 20.22
Major veins of the systemic circulation. (a) Schematic flowchart. **(b)** Illustration, anterior view. The vessels of the pulmonary circulation are not illustrated, accounting for the incomplete appearance of circulation from the heart.

Subclavian vein

Right and left brachiocephalic veins

Cephalic vein

Brachial vein

Basilic vein

Splenic vein

Median cubital vein

Renal vein

Inferior mesenteric vein

Dorsal digital veins

(b)

Table 20.9 Veins of the Head and Neck

Most blood draining from the head and neck is collected by three pairs of veins: the external jugular veins (which empty into the subclavians), the internal jugular veins, and the vertebral veins which drain into the brachiocephalic vein (see Figure 20.23a). Although most of the extracranial veins have the same names as the extracranial arteries (for example, facial, ophthalmic, occipital, and superficial temporal), their courses and interconnections differ substantially.

Most veins of the brain drain into the **dural sinuses,** an interconnected series of enlarged chambers located between the dura mater layers. The most important of these venous sinuses are the **superior** and **inferior sagittal sinuses** found within the falx cerebri, which dips down between the cerebral hemispheres, and the **cavernous sinuses,** which flank the sphenoid body (see Figure 20.23c). The cavernous sinus receives venous blood from the **ophthalmic vein** of the orbit and the facial vein, which drains the nose and upper lip area. The internal carotid artery and cranial nerves III, IV, VI, and part of V, all run *through* the cavernous sinus on their way to the orbit and face.

Description and Area Drained
External jugular veins. The right and left external jugular veins drain superficial head (scalp and face) structures served by the external carotid arteries. However, their tributaries anastomose frequently, and some of the superficial drainage from these regions enters the internal jugular veins as well. As the external jugular veins descend through the lateral neck, they pass obliquely over the sternocleidomastoid muscles and then empty into the subclavian veins.

Vertebral veins. Unlike the vertebral arteries, the vertebral veins do not serve much of the brain; instead they drain only the cervical vertebrae, the spinal cord, and some small neck muscles. The vertebral veins run inferiorly through the transverse foramina of the cervical vertebrae and join the brachiocephalic veins at the root of the neck.

Internal jugular veins. The paired internal jugular veins, which receive the bulk of blood draining from the brain, are the largest of the paired veins draining the head and neck. They arise from the dural venous sinuses, exit from the skull via the *jugular foramina,* and then descend through the neck alongside the internal carotid arteries. As they move inferiorly, they receive blood from some of the deep veins of the face and neck—branches of the **facial** and **superficial temporal veins** (see Figure 20.23b). At the base of the neck, each internal jugular vein joins the subclavian vein on its own side to form a brachiocephalic vein. As already noted, the two brachiocephalic veins unite to form the superior vena cava.

(a)

Table 20.9   continued

(b)

(c)

FIGURE 20.23

Venous drainage of the head, neck, and brain. (a) Schematic flowchart. **(b)** Veins of the head and neck, right superficial aspect. **(c)** Dural sinuses of the brain, right aspect.

Table 20.10 Veins of the Upper Limbs and Thorax

The deep veins of the upper limbs follow the paths of their companion arteries and have the same names (Figure 20.24a). However, except for the largest, most are paired or double veins that flank their artery on both sides. The superficial veins of the upper limbs are larger than the deep veins and are easily seen just beneath the skin. The median cubital vein, crossing the anterior aspect of the elbow, is commonly used to obtain venous blood samples or administer intravenous medications or blood transfusions.

Blood draining from the mammary glands and the first two to three intercostal spaces enters the **brachiocephalic veins.** However, the vast majority of thoracic tissues and the thorax wall are drained by a rather complex network of veins collectively called the **azygos (az′ĭ-gos) system.** The branching nature of the azygos system provides a collateral circulation for draining the abdominal wall and other areas served by the inferior vena cava, and there are numerous anastomoses between the azygos system and the inferior vena cava.

Description and Areas Drained

Deep veins of the upper limb. The most distal deep veins of the upper limb are the radial and ulnar veins. The deep and superficial **palmar venous arches** of the hand empty into the **radial** and **ulnar veins** of the forearm, which then unite to form the **brachial vein** of the arm. As the brachial vein enters the axilla, it becomes the **axillary vein,** which in turn becomes the **subclavian vein** at the level of the first rib.

Superficial veins of the upper limb. The superficial venous system begins with the **dorsal venous arch** (not illustrated), a plexus of superficial veins in the dorsum of the hand. In the distal forearm, this plexus drains into three major superficial veins— the cephalic and basilic veins and the median vein of the forearm—that anastomose frequently as they course upward (see Figure 20.24b). The **cephalic vein** coils around the radius as it travels superiorly and then continues up the lateral superficial aspect of the arm to the shoulder, where it runs in the groove between the deltoid and pectoralis muscles to join the axillary vein. The **basilic vein** courses along the medial posterior aspect of the forearm, crosses the elbow, and then takes a deep course. In the axilla, it joins the brachial vein, forming the axillary vein. At the anterior aspect of the elbow, the **median cubital vein** connects the basilic and cephalic veins. The **median vein of the forearm** is located between the radial and ulnar veins in the forearm and terminates (variably) at the elbow by entering the basilic or the cephalic vein.

The azygos system: The azygos system consists of the following vessels which flank the vertebral column laterally:

Azygos vein. Found against the right side of the vertebral column; originates in the abdomen from the **right ascending lumbar vein** that drains most of the right abdominal cavity wall and from the **right posterior intercostal veins** (except the first) that drain the chest muscles. At the level of T_4, it arches over the great vessels that run to the right lung and empties into the superior vena cava.

(a)

Table 20.10   continued

FIGURE 20.24
Veins of the right upper limb and shoulder. **(a)** Schematic flowchart. **(b)** Illustration. For clarity, the abundant branching and anastomoses of these vessels are not shown.

(b)

Hemiazygos (hĕ′me-a-zi′gus; "half the azygos") **vein.** Ascends on the left side of the vertebral column. Its origin, from the **left ascending lumbar vein** and the lower (9th–11th) **posterior intercostal veins,** mirrors that of the inferior portion of the azygos vein on the right. About midthorax, the hemiazygos vein passes in front of the vertebral column and empties into the azygos vein.

Accessory hemiazygos vein.   The accessory hemiazygos completes the venous drainage of the left (middle) thorax and can be thought of as a superior continuation of the hemiazygos vein. It receives blood from the 4th to 8th posterior intercostal veins and then crosses to the right to empty into the azygos vein. Like the azygos, it receives venous blood from the lungs (bronchial veins).

Table 20.11	Veins of the Abdomen

Blood draining from the abdominopelvic viscera and abdominal walls is returned to the heart by the **inferior vena cava** (Figure 20.25a). Most of its venous tributaries have names that correspond to the arteries serving the abdominal organs.

Veins draining the digestive viscera empty their blood into a common vessel, the **hepatic portal vein,** which transports this venous blood into the liver before it is allowed to enter the major systemic circulation via the hepatic veins (Figure 20.25b). Such a venous system—veins to capillaries (or sinusoids) to veins—is called a *portal system*. Portal systems always serve very specific regional tissue needs. The hepatic portal system delivers blood laden with nutrients from the digestive organs to the liver. As the blood percolates slowly through the liver sinusoids, the hepatic parenchymal cells remove nutrients required for their various metabolic functions and phagocytic cells lining the sinusoids deftly rid the blood of bacteria and other foreign matter that has penetrated the digestive mucosa. The role of the liver in nutrient processing and metabolism is described in detail in Chapter 25. The veins of the abdomen are listed below in inferior to superior order.

Description and Areas Drained

Lumbar veins. Several pairs of lumbar veins drain the posterior abdominal wall. They empty both directly into the inferior vena cava and into the ascending lumbar veins of the azygos system of the thorax.

Gonadal (testicular or ovarian) veins. The right gonadal vein drains the ovary or testis on the right side of the body and empties into the inferior vena cava. The left member drains into the left renal vein superiorly.

Renal veins. The right and left renal veins drain the kidneys.

Suprarenal veins. The right suprarenal vein drains the adrenal gland on the right and empties into the inferior vena cava. The left suprarenal vein drains into the left renal vein.

Hepatic portal system. The **hepatic portal vein** is a short vessel about 8 cm long; it begins at the level of L_2. Numerous tributaries from the stomach and pancreas contribute to the hepatic portal system (see Figure 20.25c), but the major vessels are as follows:

- **Superior mesenteric vein.** Drains the entire small intestine, part of the large intestine (ascending and transverse regions), and stomach.

- **Splenic vein.** This large vessel collects blood from the spleen, parts of the stomach, and pancreas and then joins the superior mesenteric vein to form the hepatic portal vein.

- **Inferior mesenteric vein.** Drains the distal portions of the large intestine and rectum and joins the splenic vein just before that vessel unites with the superior mesenteric vein.

Hepatic veins. The right and left hepatic veins carry venous blood from the liver to the inferior vena cava.

Cystic veins. The cystic veins drain the gall bladder and join the hepatic veins.

Inferior phrenic veins. The inferior phrenic veins drain the inferior surface of the diaphragm.

(a)

FIGURE 20.25
Veins of the abdomen. (a) Schematic flowchart. **(b)** Tributaries of the inferior vena cava. Venous drainage of abdominal organs not drained by the hepatic portal vein. **(c)** The hepatic portal circulation.

Table 20.11   continued

Hepatic veins

Inferior vena cava

Right
suprarenal vein

Right
gonadal vein

External iliac vein

(b)

Inferior
phrenic vein

Left
suprarenal vein

Renal veins

Left ascending
lumbar vein

Lumbar veins

Left
gonadal vein

Common iliac vein

Internal iliac vein

Hepatic veins

Liver

Hepatic portal vein

Small intestine

Rectum

(c)

Spleen

Inferior vena cava

Splenic vein

Right
gastroepiploic vein

Inferior
mesenteric vein

Superior
mesenteric vein

Large intestine

Table 20.12 Veins of the Pelvis and Lower Limbs

As is the case in the upper limbs, most deep veins of the lower limbs have the same names as the arteries they accompany and many are double. The two superficial saphenous veins (great and small) are poorly supported by surrounding tissues, and are common sites of varicosities. The great saphenous (*saphenous* = obvious) vein is frequently excised and used as a coronary bypass vessel.

Description and Areas Drained
Deep veins. After being formed by the union of the small **medial** and **lateral plantar veins**, the **posterior tibial vein** ascends deep within the calf muscle (Figure 20.26). The **anterior tibial vein** is the superior continuation of the **dorsalis pedis vein** of the foot. At the knee it unites with the posterior tibial vein to form the **popliteal vein,** which crosses the back of the knee. As the popliteal vein emerges from the knee, it becomes the **femoral vein**, which drains the deep structures of the thigh. The femoral vein becomes the **external iliac vein** as it enters the pelvis. In the pelvis, the external iliac vein unites with the **internal iliac vein** to form the **common iliac vein.**

FIGURE 20.26
Veins of the right lower limb. (a) Schematic flowchart of anterior and posterior vessels. **(b)** Anterior view of the lower limb. **(c)** Posterior view of the leg and foot.

The distribution of the internal iliac veins parallels that of the internal iliac arteries.

Superficial veins. The **great** and **small saphenous** (sah-fe′nus) **veins** issue from the **dorsal venous arch** of the foot (Figure 20.26b). These veins anastomose frequently with each other and with the deep veins along their course. The great saphenous vein is the longest vein in the body. It travels superiorly along the medial aspect of the leg to the thigh, where it empties into the femoral vein just distal to the inguinal ligament. The small saphenous vein runs along the lateral aspect of the foot and then through the deep fascia of the calf muscles, which it drains. At the knee, it empties into the popliteal vein.

RELATED CLINICAL TERMS

Aneurysm (an'u-rizm; *aneurysm* = a widening) A balloon-like outpocketing of an artery wall that places the artery at risk for rupture; may reflect a congenital weakness of the artery wall, but more often reflects gradual weakening of the artery by chronic hypertension or arteriosclerosis; the most common sites of aneurysm formation are the abdominal aorta and arteries feeding the brain and kidneys.

Angiogram (an'je-o-gram"; *angio* = a vessel; *gram* = writing) Diagnostic technique involving the infusion of a radiopaque substance into the circulation for X ray examination of specific blood vessels.

Diuretic (*diure* = urinate) A chemical substance that promotes urine formation, thus reducing blood volume; diuretic drugs are frequently prescribed to manage hypertension.

Microangiopathic lesion (*micro* = small) An abnormal thickening of a capillary basement membrane due to the deposit of glycoproteins; the result is thickened—but leaky—capillary walls; a vascular hallmark of long-standing diabetes mellitus.

Phlebitis (flě-bi'tis; *phleb* = vein; *itis* = inflammation) Inflammation of a vein accompanied by painful throbbing and redness of the skin over the inflamed vessel; most often caused by bacterial infection or local physical trauma.

Phlebotomy (flě-bot'o-me; *tomy* = cut) A venous incision made for the purpose of withdrawing blood or bloodletting.

Thrombophlebitis Condition of undesirable intravascular clotting initiated by a roughening of a venous lining; often follows severe episodes of phlebitis; an ever-present danger is that the clot may become detached and form an embolus.

CHAPTER SUMMARY

Overview of Blood Vessel Structure and Function (pp. 643–650)

1. Blood is transported throughout the body via a continuous system of blood vessels. Arteries transport blood away from the heart; veins carry blood back to the heart. Capillaries carry blood to tissue cells and are exchange sites.

Structure of Blood Vessel Walls (pp. 644–645)
2. All blood vessels except capillaries have three layers: the tunica intima, the tunica media, and the tunica adventitia. Capillary walls are composed of the tunica intima only.

Arterial System (p. 645)
3. Elastic (conducting) arteries are the large arteries close to the heart that expand and recoil to accommodate changing blood volume. Muscular (distributing) arteries carry blood to specific organs; they are less stretchy and more active in vasoconstriction. Arterioles regulate blood flow into capillary beds.

4. Arteriosclerosis is a degenerative vascular disease. Initiated by endothelial lesions, it progresses through fatty streak, atherosclerotic, and arteriosclerotic stages.

Capillaries (pp. 645–647)
5. Capillaries are microscopic vessels with very thin walls. Most exhibit clefts, which aid in the exchange between the blood and interstitial fluid. Capillaries at sites of active absorption have fenestrations that enhance their permeability.

6. Vascular shunts (metarterioles–thoroughfare channels) connect the terminal arteriole and venule at opposite ends of a capillary bed. Most true capillaries arise from and rejoin the shunt channels. The amount of blood flowing into the true capillaries is regulated by precapillary sphincters.

Venous System (pp. 647–650)
7. Veins have comparatively larger lumens than arteries, and a system of valves prevents backflow of blood. Respiratory and skeletal muscle pumps aid venous return of blood to the heart.

8. Most veins are normally only partially filled with blood; thus, they can serve as blood reservoirs.

Vascular Anastomoses (p. 650)
9. The joining together of arteries serving a common organ is called an arterial anastomosis. Such vascular patterns provide alternate channels for blood to reach the same organ. Vascular anatomoses also form between veins and between arterioles and venules.

PHYSIOLOGY OF CIRCULATION (pp. 650–667)

Introduction to Blood Flow, Blood Pressure, and Resistance (pp. 650–651)

1. Blood flow is the amount of blood flowing through a vessel, an organ, or the entire circulation in a given period of time. Blood pressure is the force per unit area exerted on a vessel wall by the contained blood. Resistance is opposition to blood flow; blood viscosity and blood vessel length and diameter contribute to resistance.

2. Blood flow is directly proportional to blood pressure and inversely proportional to resistance.

Systemic Blood Pressure (pp. 651–652)

1. Systemic blood pressure is highest in the aorta and lowest in the venae cavae. The steepest drop in BP occurs in the arterioles, where resistance is greatest.

2. Arterial BP depends on compliance of the elastic arteries and on how much blood is forced into them. Arterial blood pressure is pulsatile. Arterial pressure peaks during systole (systolic pressure). During diastole, as blood is forced distally in the circulation by the recoiling elastic arteries, arterial BP drops to its lowest value, called the diastolic pressure.

3. Pulse pressure is systolic pressure minus diastolic pressure. The mean arterial pressure (MAP) = diastolic pressure plus pulse pressure/3, and is the pressure that keeps blood moving throughout the cardiac cycle.

4. Low capillary pressure (40 to 20 mm Hg) protects the delicate capillaries from rupture while still allowing adequate exchange across the capillary walls.

5. Venous pressure is low (declining to zero) because of the cumulative effects of resistance, and nonpulsatile. Both structural (venous valves and large lumens) and functional adaptations (the muscular and respiratory pumps) promote venous return.

Maintaining Blood Pressure (pp. 652–660)

1. Blood pressure varies directly with CO, PR, and blood volume. Vessel diameter is the major factor determining PR, and small changes in vessel (chiefly arteriolar) diameter significantly affect blood pressure.

Short-Term Mechanisms: Neural Controls (pp. 654–656)
2. BP is regulated by autonomic neural reflexes involving baroreceptors or chemoreceptors, the vasomotor center (a sympathetic center that regulates blood vessel diameter), and vasomotor fibers which act on vascular smooth muscle.

3. Activation of the receptors by falling BP (and to a lesser extent by a rise in blood CO_2, or falling blood pH or O_2 levels) stimulates the vasomotor center to increase vasoconstriction and the cardioacceleratory center to increase heart rate and contractility. Rising BP inhibits the vasomotor center (permitting vasodilation) and activates the cardioinhibitory center.

4. Higher brain centers (cerebrum and hypothalamus) may modify neural controls of BP by influencing the medullary control enters.

Short-Term Mechanisms: Chemical Controls (pp. 656–657)

5. Blood-borne chemicals that increase BP by promoting vasoconstriction include epinephrine and NE (these also increase heart rate and contractility), ADH, angiotensin II (generated in response to renin release by kidney cells), and endothelin released by vascular endothelial cells.

6. Chemicals that reduce BP by promoting vasodilation include atrial natriuretic peptide (also causes a decline in blood volume), nitric oxide released by the vascular endothelium, inflammatory chemicals, and alcohol.

Long-Term Mechanisms: Renal Regulation (pp. 657–658)

7. The kidneys regulate blood pressure by regulating blood volume. In the direct mechanism, rising BP enhances filtrate formation and fluid losses in urine; falling BP causes the kidneys to retain more water, increasing blood volume.

8. Indirect renal regulation of blood volume involves the renin-angiotensin mechanism, a hormonal mechanism. When BP falls, the kidneys release renin, which triggers the formation of angiotensin II (a potent vasoconstrictor) and release of aldosterone, which causes salt and water to be retained.

Monitoring Circulatory Efficiency (pp. 658–659)

9. Pulse and blood pressure measurements are used to assess cardiovascular efficiency.

10. The pulse is the alternating expansion and recoil of arterial walls with each heartbeat. Pulse points are also pressure points.

11. Blood pressure is routinely measured by the auscultatory method. Normal blood pressure in adults is 120/80 (systolic/diastolic). Hypotension is rarely a problem. Hypertension is the major cause of myocardial infarct, stroke, and renal disease.

Alterations in Blood Pressure (pp. 659–660)

12. Hypotension, or low blood pressure (systolic pressure below 100 mm Hg), is a sign of health in the well conditioned. In other individuals it warns of poor nutrition, disease, or circulatory shock.

13. Chronic hypertension (high blood pressure) is persistent BP readings of 140/90 or higher. It is dangerous because it indicates increased peripheral resistance which strains the heart and promotes vascular complications of other organs, particularly the eyes and kidneys. Risk factors are high-fat diet, high-salt diet, obesity, advanced age, stress, and being a member of the black race or a family with a history of hypertension.

Blood Flow Through Body Tissues (pp. 660–667)

1. Blood flow is involved in delivering nutrients and wastes to and from cells, gas exchange, absorbing nutrients, and forming urine.

Velocity of Blood Flow (pp. 660–661)

2. Blood flows fastest where the cross-sectional area of the vascular bed is least (aorta), and slowest where the cross-sectional area is greatest (capillaries), The slow flow in capillaries allows time for nutrient-waste exchanges.

Autoregulation: Local Regulation of Blood Flow (pp. 661–662)

3. Autoregulation is the local adjustment of blood flow to individual organs based on their immediate requirements. It is largely controlled by local chemical factors that cause vasodilation of arterioles serving the area and open the precapillary sphincters. Myogenic controls respond to changes in blood pressure.

Blood Flow in Special Areas (pp. 662–664)

4. In most instances, autoregulation is controlled by oxygen deficits and accumulation of local metabolites. However, autoregulation in the brain is controlled primarily by a drop in pH and by myogenic mechanisms; and vasodilation of pulmonary circuit vessels occurs in response to high levels of oxygen.

Blood Flow Through Capillaries and Capillary Dynamics (pp. 664–665)

5. Nutrients, gases, and other solutes smaller than plasma proteins cross the capillary wall by diffusion. Water-soluble substances move through the clefts or fenestrations; fat-soluble substances pass through the lipid portion of the endothelial cell membrane.

6. Fluid flows occurring at capillary beds reflect the relative effect of outward (net hydrostatic pressure) forces minus the effect of inward (net osmotic pressure) forces. In general, fluid flows out of the capillary bed at the arterial end and reenters the capillary blood at the venule end.

7. The small net loss of fluid and protein into the interstitial space is collected by lymphatic vessels and returned to the cardiovascular system.

Circulatory Shock (pp. 665–667)

8. Circulatory shock occurs when blood perfusion of body tissues is inadequate. Most cases of shock reflect low blood volume (hypovolemic shock), abnormal vasodilation (vascular shock), or pump failure (cardiogenic shock).

Circulatory Pathways: Blood Vessels of the Body (pp. 667–690)

1. The pulmonary circulation transports O_2-poor, CO_2–laden blood to the lungs for oxygenation and carbon dioxide unloading. Blood returning to the right atrium of the heart is pumped via the pulmonary trunk, pulmonary arteries, and lobar arteries to the pulmonary capillaries by the right ventricle. Blood issuing from the lungs is returned to the left atrium by the pulmonary veins. (See Table 20.2 and Figure 20.15.)

2. The systemic circulation transports oxygenated blood from the left ventricle to all body tissues via the aorta and its branches. Venous blood returning from the systemic circuit is delivered to the right atrium via the venae cavae.

3. Tables 20.2 to 20.12 and Figures 20.16 to 20.26 illustrate and describe the arteries and veins of the systemic circulation.

Developmental Aspects of the Blood Vessels (p. 667)

1. The fetal vasculature develops from embryonic blood islands and mesenchyme and is functioning in blood delivery by the fourth week.

2. Fetal circulation differs from circulation after birth with respect to pulmonary and hepatic shunts and special umbilical vessels. These are normally occluded shortly after birth.

3. Blood pressure is low in infants and rises to adult values.

4. Age-related vascular problems include varicose veins, hypertension, and arteriosclerosis. Hypertension is the most important cause of sudden cardiovascular death in middle-aged men. Arteriosclerosis is the most important cause of cardiovascular disease in the aged.

REVIEW QUESTIONS
Multiple Choice/Matching

1. Which statement does not accurately describe veins? (a) They have less elastic tissue and smooth muscle than arteries, (b) they contain more fibrous tissue than arteries, (c) most veins in the extremities have valves, (d) they always carry deoxygenated blood.

2. Which of the following tissues is mainly responsible for vasoconstriction? (a) elastic tissue, (b) smooth muscle, (c) collagenic tissue, (d) adipose tissue.

3. Peripheral resistance in the cardiovascular system (a) is inversely related to the diameter of the arterioles, (b) tends to increase if blood viscosity increases, (c) is directly proportional to the length of the vascular bed, (d) all of these.

4. Which of the following can lead to decreased venous return of blood to the heart? (a) an increase in blood volume, (b) an increase in venous pressure, (c) damage to the venous valves, (d) increased muscular activity.

5. Arterial blood pressure increases in response to: (a) increasing stroke volume, (b) increasing heart rate, (c) arteriosclerosis, (d) increasing blood volume, (e) all of these.

6. Exchange of nutrients and wastes in the capillary beds is regulated by local chemical and physical controls. Which of the following would *not* result in the dilation of the feeder arterioles and opening of the precapillary sphincters in any capillary bed? (a) a decrease in O_2 content of the blood, (b) an increase in CO_2 content of the blood, (c) a local increase in histamine, (d) a local increase in pH.

7. The structure of a capillary wall differs from that of a vein or an artery because (a) it has two tunics instead of three, (b) there is less smooth muscle, (c) it is single layered—only the tunica intima, (d) none of these.

8. The baroreceptors in the carotid and aortic bodies are sensitive to (a) a decrease in carbon dioxide, (b) changes in arterial pressure, (c) a decrease in oxygen, (d) all of these.

9. The myocardium receives its blood supply directly from (a) the aorta, (b) the coronary arteries, (c) the coronary sinus, (d) the pulmonary arteries.

10. Blood flow in the capillaries is steady despite the rhythmic pumping of the heart because of (a) elasticity of the large arteries, (b) small diameter of capillaries, (c) thin walls of the veins, (d) venous valves.

 11. Tracing the blood from the heart to the right hand, we find that blood leaves the heart and passes through the ascending aorta, the right subclavian artery, the axillary and brachial arteries, and through either the radial or ulnar artery to arrive at the hand. Which artery is missing from this sequence? (a) coronary, (b) brachiocephalic, (c) cephalic, (d) right common carotid.

 12. Which of the following do not drain directly into the inferior vena cava? (a) lumbar veins, (b) hepatic veins, (c) inferior mesenteric vein, (d) renal veins.

Short Answer Essay Questions

13. How is the anatomy of capillaries and capillary beds well suited to their function?

14. Distinguish between elastic arteries, muscular arteries, and arterioles relative to location, histology, and functional adaptations.

15. Write an equation showing the relationship between peripheral resistance, blood flow, and blood pressure.

16. (a) Define blood pressure. Differentiate between systolic and diastolic blood pressure. (b) What is the normal blood pressure value for a young adult?

17. Describe the neural mechanisms responsible for controlling blood pressure.

18. Explain the reasons for the observed changes in blood flow velocity in the different regions of the circulation.

19. How does the control of blood flow to the skin for the purpose of regulating body temperature differ from the control of nutrient blood flow to skin cells?

20. Describe neural and chemical (both systemic and local) effects exerted on the blood vessels when one is fleeing from a mugger. (Be careful, this is more involved than it appears at first glance.)

21. How are nutrients, wastes, and respiratory gases transported to and from the blood and tissue spaces?

 22. (a) What blood vessels contribute to the formation of the hepatic portal circulation? (b) What is the function of this circulation? (c) Why is a portal circulation a "strange" circulation?

23. Physiologists often consider capillaries and postcapillary venules together as if they were identical. (a) What functions do these vessels share? (b) Structurally, how do they differ?

CRITICAL THINKING AND CLINICAL APPLICATION QUESTIONS

 1. Sidney received a small but deep cut from broken glass in the exact midline of the anterior side of his distal forearm. He worried throughout the two-mile drive to the hospital that he would bleed to death because he had heard stories about people committing suicide by slashing their wrist. Judge if Sid's fear of death is justified and explain your reasoning.

2. Mrs. Johnson is brought to the emergency room after being involved in an auto accident. She is hemorrhaging and has a rapid, thready pulse, but her blood pressure is still within normal limits. Describe the compensatory mechanisms that are acting to maintain her blood pressure in the face of blood loss.

3. A 60-year-old man is unable to walk more than 100 yards without experiencing severe pain in his left leg; the pain is relieved by resting for 5–10 minutes. He is told that the arteries of his leg are becoming occluded with fatty material and is advised to have the sympathetic nerves serving that body region severed. Explain how such surgery might help to relieve this man's problem.

4. Your friend, who knows little about science, is reading a magazine article about a patient who had an "aneurysm at the base of his brain that suddenly grew much larger." The surgeons' first goal was to "keep it from rupturing," and the second goal was to "relieve the pressure on the brain stem and cranial nerves." The surgeons were able to "replace the aneurysm with a section of plastic tubing," so the patient recovered. Your friend asks you what all this means. Explain. (Hint: Start by checking this chapter's Related Clinical Terms.)

21

The Lymphatic System

When we mentally tick off the names of the body's organ systems, the lymphatic (lim-fat'ik) system is probably not the first to come to mind. Yet without this quietly working system, our cardiovascular system would stop working and our immune system would be hopelessly impaired. The **lymphatic system** actually consists of two semi-independent parts: (1) a meandering network of *lymphatic vessels* and (2) various *lymphoid tissues and organs* scattered throughout the body. The lymphatic vessels transport fluids that have escaped from the blood vascular system back to the blood, and the lymphoid organs house phagocytic cells and lymphocytes, which play essential roles in body defense and resistance to disease.

LYMPHATIC VESSELS

As blood circulates through the body, exchanges of nutrients, wastes, and gases occur between the blood and the interstitial fluid. As explained in Chapter 20, the hydrostatic and osmotic pressures operating at capillary beds force fluid out of the blood at the arterial ends of the capillary beds ("upstream") and cause most of it to be reabsorbed at the venous ends ("downstream"). The fluid that remains behind in the tissue spaces, as much as 3 L daily, becomes part of the interstitial fluid. These leaked fluids, as well as any plasma proteins that escape from the bloodstream, must be carried back to the blood if the cardiovascular system is to have sufficient blood volume to operate properly. Recall that plasma proteins generate substantial osmotic forces that are essential for keeping water in the bloodstream. This problem of circulatory dynamics is resolved by the **lymphatic vessels,** or **lymphatics,** an elaborate system of drainage vessels that collects the excess protein-containing interstitial fluid and returns it to the bloodstream. Once interstitial fluid enters the lymphatics, it is called **lymph** (*lymph* = clear water).

Distribution and Structure of Lymphatic Vessels

The lymphatic vessels form a one-way system in which lymph flows only toward the heart. This transport system begins in microscopic blind-ended **lymph capillaries** (Figure 21.1a), which weave between the tissue cells and blood capillaries in the loose connective tissues of the body. Lymph capillaries are widespread, occurring almost

(a)

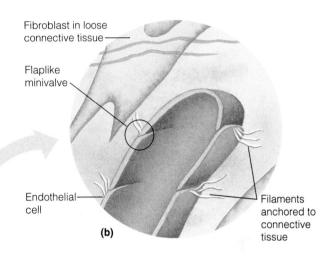

(b)

FIGURE 21.1
Distribution and special structural features of lymphatic capillaries. **(a)** Structural relationship between a capillary bed of the blood vascular system and lymphatic capillaries. Arrows indicate direction of fluid movement. **(b)** Lymphatic capillaries begin as blind-ended tubes. The endothelial cells forming their walls overlap one another, forming flaplike minivalves.

everywhere blood capillaries occur. However, lymph capillaries are absent from bone and teeth, bone marrow, and the entire central nervous system (where the excess tissue fluid drains into the cerebrospinal fluid).

Although similar to blood capillaries, lymphatic capillaries are so remarkably permeable that they were once thought to be open at one end like a straw. We now know that their permeability is due to two unique structural modifications:

1. The endothelial cells forming the walls of lymphatic capillaries are not tightly joined; instead, their edges loosely overlap one another, forming easily opened, flaplike *minivalves* (Figure 21.1b).

2. Bundles of fine filaments anchor the endothelial cells to surrounding structures so that any increase in interstitial fluid volume separates the cell flaps, exposing gaps in the wall, rather than causing the lymphatic capillary to collapse.

These structural specializations create a system analogous to one-way swinging doors in the lymphatic capillary wall. The flaps gape open when the fluid pressure is greater in the interstitial space, allowing fluid to enter the lymphatic capillary. However, when the pressure is greater inside the lymphatic vessels, the endothelial cell flaps are forced together, preventing the lymph from leaking back out and forcing it along the vessel.

Proteins present in the interstitial space are normally prevented from entering the blood capillaries, but they enter lymphatic capillaries easily. In addition, when tissues are inflamed, lymphatic capillaries develop openings that permit the uptake of even larger particles such as cell debris, pathogens (disease-causing microorganisms such as bacteria and viruses), and cancer cells. The pathogenic agents and cancer cells can then use the lymphatics to travel throughout the body. However, this problem is partly resolved by the fact that the lymph takes "detours" through the lymph nodes, where it is cleansed of debris and "examined" by cells of the immune system, as described in more detail shortly.

Highly specialized lymphatic capillaries called **lacteals** (lak′te-alz) are present in the fingerlike villi of the intestinal mucosa. The lymph draining from the digestive viscera is milky white (*lacte* = milk) rather than clear because the lacteals also receive digested fats from the intestine. This creamy lymph, called **chyle** ("juice"), is also delivered to the blood via the lymphatic stream.

From the lymphatic capillaries, lymph flows through successively larger and thicker-walled channels (Figure 21.2)—first collecting vessels, then trunks, and finally the largest of all, the ducts. The **lymphatic collecting vessels** have the same three tunics as veins, but they tend to be thinner-walled, to have more internal valves, and to anastomose more.

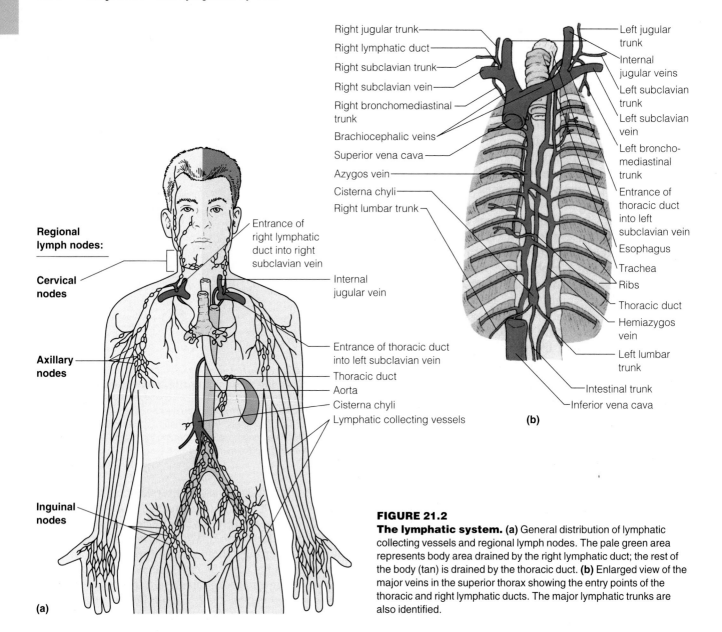

FIGURE 21.2

The lymphatic system. (a) General distribution of lymphatic collecting vessels and regional lymph nodes. The pale green area represents body area drained by the right lymphatic duct; the rest of the body (tan) is drained by the thoracic duct. **(b)** Enlarged view of the major veins in the superior thorax showing the entry points of the thoracic and right lymphatic ducts. The major lymphatic trunks are also identified.

In general the collecting vessels in the skin travel along with superficial *veins,* whereas the deep lymphatic vessels of the trunk and digestive viscera travel with the deep *arteries.* Like the larger veins, the larger lymphatics receive their nutrient blood supply from a branching vasa vasorum.

When the lymphatic vessels are severely inflamed, the related vessels of the vasa vasorum become congested with blood and the pathway of the associated superficial lymphatics becomes visible through the skin as red lines that are tender to the touch. This unpleasant condition is called *lymphangitis* (lim"fan-ji'tis; *angi* = vessel). •

The **lymphatic trunks** are formed by the union of the largest collecting vessels, and drain fairly large areas of the body. The major trunks, named mostly for the regions from which they collect lymph, are the paired **lumbar, bronchomediastinal, subclavian, and jugular trunks,** and the single **intestinal trunk** (Figure 21.2b).

Lymph is eventually delivered to one of two large *ducts* in the thoracic region. The **right lymphatic duct** drains lymph from the right upper arm and the right side of the head and thorax (Figure 21.2a). The much larger **thoracic duct,** which receives lymph from the rest of the body, arises anterior to the first two lumbar vertebrae as an enlarged sac, the **cisterna chyli** (sister'nah ki'li). The cisterna chyli collects lymph from the two large lumbar trunks that drain the lower limbs and from the intestinal trunk that drains the digestive organs. As the thoracic duct runs superiorly, it accepts lymphatic drainage from the left side of the thorax and left upper limb and head region. Each terminal duct empties the lymph into the venous circulation at the junction of the internal jugular vein and subclavian vein on its own side of the body (Figure 21.2b).

Lymph Transport

Unlike the cardiovascular system, the lymphatic system is pumpless. Under normal conditions, lymphatic vessels are very low pressure conduits, and the same mechanisms that promote venous return in blood vessels act here as well—the milking action of active skeletal muscles, pressure changes within the thorax during breathing, and valves to prevent backflow. Lymphatics are usually bundled together in connective tissue sheaths with blood vessels and pulsating of the nearby arteries also promotes lymph flow. In addition to these mechanisms, smooth muscle in the walls of the lymphatic trunks and thoracic duct contracts rhythmically, actually helping to pump the lymph along. Even so, lymph transport is sporadic and much slower than that occurring in veins. About 3 L of lymph enters the bloodstream every 24 hours, a volume almost exactly equal to the amount of fluid lost to the tissue spaces from the bloodstream in the same time period. Movements of adjacent tissues are extremely important in propelling lymph through the lymphatics. When physical activity or passive movement increases, lymph flows much more rapidly (balancing the greater rate of fluid outflow from the bloodstream in such situations). Hence, it is a good idea to immobilize a badly infected body part to hinder flow of inflammatory material from that region.

Anything that prevents the normal return of lymph to the blood, such as blockage of the lymphatics by tumors or removal of lymphatics during cancer surgery (e.g., mastectomy), results in severe localized edema *(lymphedema)*. However, when lymphatics are removed surgically, lymphatic drainage is eventually reestablished by regrowth from the vessels still remaining in the area. •

LYMPHOID CELLS, TISSUES, AND ORGANS: AN OVERVIEW

In order to understand some of the basic aspects of the lymphatic system's role in body protection and immunity, we will investigate the components of lymphoid organs—lymphoid cells and lymphoid tissues—before considering the organs themselves.

Lymphoid Cells

Infectious microorganisms, such as bacteria and viruses, that manage to penetrate the body's epithelial barriers, quickly begin to proliferate in the underlying

FIGURE 21.3
Scanning electron micrograph of reticular tissue in a human lymph node, 850×.

loose connective tissues. These invaders are fought off by the inflammatory response, by phagocytes (macrophages), and by lymphocytes (a variety of white blood cell described in Chapter 18).

Lymphocytes, the main warriors of the immune system, arise in red bone marrow (along with other formed elements). They then mature into one of the two main varieties of immunocompetent cells—**T cells (T lymphocytes)** or **B cells (B lymphocytes)**—which act to protect the body against antigens. Activated T cells manage the immune response and some of them directly attack and destroy foreign cells. B cells protect the body by producing **plasma cells,** daughter cells that secrete antibodies into the blood (or other body fluids). Antibodies immobilize antigens until they can be destroyed by phagocytes or other means. Generally speaking, *antigens* are anything in the body perceived as foreign, such as bacteria and their toxins, viruses, mismatched RBCs, or cancer cells. (The precise roles of the lymphocytes and mechanisms of immunity will be explored in more detail in Chapter 22.)

Lymphoid **macrophages** play a crucial role in body protection and in the immune response by phagocytizing foreign substances and by helping to activate T cells. So, too, do the spiny-looking **dendritic cells** found in lymphoid tissue. Last, but not the least, are the **reticular cells,** fibroblastlike cells that produce the reticular fiber **stroma** (stro'mah) or network that supports the other cell types in the lymphoid organs (see Figure 21.3).

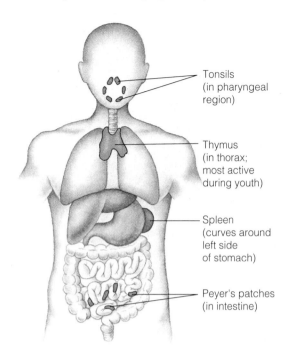

FIGURE 21.4
Lymphoid organs. Location of the tonsils, spleen, thymus, and Peyer's patches.

Lymphoid Tissue

Lymphoid (lymphatic) tissue is an important component of the immune system, mainly because it houses and provides a proliferation site for lymphocytes and an ideal surveillance vantage point for both lymphocytes and macrophages. Lymphoid tissue, a type of loose connective tissue called **reticular connective tissue,** dominates all the lymphoid organs except the thymus. Macrophages live on the fibers of the network, and within the spaces of this network are huge numbers of lymphocytes that squeeze through the walls of capillaries and venules to reside temporarily in the lymphoid tissue (Figure 21.3), and then leave to patrol the body again. The cycling of lymphocytes between the circulatory vessels, lymphoid tissues, and loose connective tissues of the body ensures that lymphocytes reach infected or damaged sites quickly.

Lymphoid tissue comes in various "packages." **Diffuse lymphatic tissue,** consisting of a few scattered reticular tissue elements, is found in virtually every body organ, but larger collections appear in the lamina propria of mucous membranes and within lymphoid organs. Like diffuse lymphatic tissue, **lymphatic follicles (nodules)** lack a capsule, but follicles tend to be solid, spherical bodies consisting of tightly packed reticular elements and cells. Follicles often exhibit lighter-staining centers, called **germinal centers.** B cells predominate in germinal centers, and these centers enlarge dramatically when the B cells are rapidly dividing and producing plasma cells. In many cases, the follicles are found within and forming part of larger lymphoid organs, such as lymph nodes. However, isolated aggregations of lymphatic follicles occur in the intestinal wall as Peyer's patches (Figure 21.4) and in the appendix.

Lymphoid Organs

Lymphoid organs, exemplified by lymph nodes, the spleen, and the thymus (Figure 21.4), are discrete, encapsulated collections of diffuse lymphoid tissue and follicles. The exact pattern of the lymphoid tissues differs in the various lymphoid organs. These are described next.

LYMPH NODES

As lymph is transported back to the bloodstream, it is filtered through the **lymph nodes** that cluster along the lymphatic vessels of the body. There are hundreds of these small organs, but because the lymph nodes are usually embedded in connective tissue, they are not ordinarily seen. Large clusters of lymph nodes occur near the body surface in the inguinal, axillary, and cervical regions of the body—places where the lymphatic vessels converge to form large trunks (see Figure 21.2a).

Lymph nodes have two basic functions, both concerned with body protection. (1) They act as lymph "filters." Phagocytic macrophages in the nodes remove and destroy microorganisms and other debris that has entered the lymph from the loose connective tissues, effectively preventing them from being delivered to the blood and spreading further in the body. (2) They play a role in activating the immune system. Lymphocytes, also strategically located in the lymph nodes, monitor the lymphatic stream for the presence of *antigens* and mount an attack against them. Let's look at how the structure of a lymph node promotes these defensive functions.

Structure of a Lymph Node

Lymph nodes vary in both shape and size, but most of them are bean shaped and less than 2.5 cm (1 inch) in length. Each node is surrounded by a dense fibrous **capsule** from which connective tissue strands called **trabeculae** extend inward to divide the node into a number of compartments (Figure 21.5). Its internal framework or stroma of reticular fibers physically supports the ever-changing population of lymphocytes.

Two histologically distinct regions in a lymph node are the **cortex** and the **medulla.** The outer cortex contains densely packed follicles, many with germinal centers heavy with dividing B cells. Dendritic cells nearly encapsulate the follicles and abut the rest

? *What is the benefit of having fewer efferent than afferent lymphatics in lymph nodes?*

(a)

(b)

FIGURE 21.5
Structure of a lymph node. (a) Longitudinal view of the internal structure of a lymph node and associated lymphatics. Notice that several afferent lymphatics converge on its convex side, whereas fewer efferent lymphatics exit at its hilus. Arrows indicate the direction of lymph flow into and out of the node. **(b)** Photomicrograph of part of a lymph node (15 ×).

of the cortex, which primarily houses T cells in transit. The T cells circulate continuously between the blood, lymph nodes, and lymphatic stream, performing their surveillance role. **Medullary cords,** thin inward extensions of the cortex containing lymphocytes and plasma cells, define the medulla. Throughout the node are **lymph sinuses,** large lymph capillaries spanned by reticular fibers. Numerous macrophages reside on these reticular fibers and phagocytize foreign matter in the lymph as it flows by in the sinuses. Additionally, some of the lymph-borne antigens in the percolating lymph leak into the surrounding reticular tissue, where they activate strategically positioned lymphocytes to mount an immune attack against them.

Circulation in the Lymph Nodes

Lymph enters the convex side of a lymph node through a number of **afferent lymphatic vessels.** It then moves through a large, baglike sinus, the **subcapsular sinus,** into a number of smaller sinuses that cut through the cortex and enter the medulla. The lymph meanders through these sinuses and finally exits the node at its **hilus** (hi'lus), the indented region on the opposite side, via **efferent lymphatic vessels.** Because there are fewer efferent vessels draining the node than afferent vessels feeding it, the flow of

lymph through the node stagnates somewhat, allowing time for the lymphocytes and macrophages to perform their protective functions. In general, lymph passes through several nodes before its cleansing process is completed.

Sometimes lymph nodes are overwhelmed by the very agents they are trying to destroy. For example, when large numbers of bacteria or virus particles are trapped in the nodes, the nodes become inflamed and very tender to the touch. Such an infected lymph node is called a *bubo* (bu'bo). (Buboes are the most obvious symptom of bubonic plague, the "Black Death" that killed over 25% of Europe's population in the late Middle Ages.) Lymph nodes can also become secondary cancer sites, particularly in metastasizing cancers that enter lymphatic vessels and become trapped there. The fact that cancer-infiltrated lymph nodes are swollen but not painful helps to distinguish cancerous lymph nodes from those infected by microorganisms. •

OTHER LYMPHOID ORGANS

Lymph nodes are just one example of many types of **lymphoid organs** or aggregates of lymphatic tissue in the body. Others are the spleen, thymus gland, tonsils, and Peyer's patches of the intestine (see Figure 21.4), as well as bits of lymphatic tissue scattered in

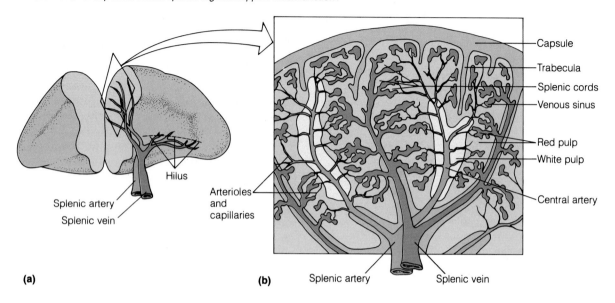

The spleen has two major roles—cleansing blood of debris and aged RBCs and participating in the immune response. Which splenic regions support which function?

(a)

(b)

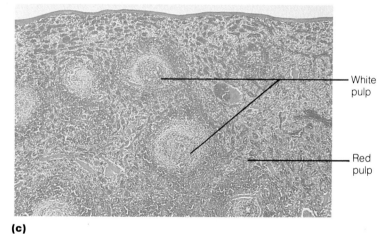

(c)

FIGURE 21.6
Structure of the spleen. (a) Gross structure.
(b) Diagrammatic representation of the histological structure of part of the spleen. **(c)** Photomicrograph of spleen tissue showing white and red pulp regions (60×). The white pulp, consisting mainly of lymphocytes cuffing around branches of the splenic artery, is surrounded by red pulp regions containing abundant erythrocytes and venous sinuses.

the connective tissues. The common feature of all these organs is their tissue makeup: All are composed of *reticular connective tissue.* Although all lymphoid organs help protect the body, only the lymph nodes filter lymph. The other lymphoid organs and tissues typically have efferent lymphatics draining them, but have no associated afferent lymphatic vessels. The distinctive features of these other lymphoid organs and aggregates are described next.

Spleen

The soft, blood-rich **spleen** is the size of a fist and is the largest lymphoid organ. Located in the left side of the abdominal cavity just beneath the diaphragm, it extends to curl around the anterior aspect of the stomach (see Figure 21.4). It is served by the large *splenic artery* and *vein,* which enter and exit the *hilus* on its slightly concave anterior surface (Figure 21.6).

The spleen provides a site for lymphocyte proliferation and immune surveillance and response. But, perhaps even more important are the spleen's main blood-cleansing functions—besides extracting aged and defective blood cells and platelets from the blood, it removes debris, foreign matter, bacteria, viruses, toxins, and so on, from blood flowing through its sinuses. The spleen also performs three additional, and related, functions.

1. It stores some of the breakdown products of red blood cells for later reuse and releases others to the blood for processing by the liver. For example, spleen macrophages salvage and store iron for later use by the bone marrow in making hemoglobin.

2. It is a site of erythrocyte production in the fetus (a capability that normally ceases after birth).

3. It stores blood platelets.

Like lymph nodes, the spleen is surrounded by a fibrous capsule, has trabeculae that extend inward (Figure 21.6), and contains both lymphocytes and macrophages. Consistent with its blood-processing functions, it also contains huge numbers of erythrocytes. Areas composed mostly of lymphocytes suspended on reticular fibers are called **white pulp.** The white pulp clusters or forms "cuffs" around the *central arteries* (small branches of the splenic artery) within the organ and forms what appear to be islands in a sea of red pulp. **Red pulp** is essentially all remaining splenic tissue, i.e., the venous sinuses and the **splenic cords,** regions of reticular connective tissue that contain red blood cells and abundant macrophages. Red pulp is most concerned with the spleen's ability to dispose of worn-out red blood cells and blood-borne pathogens, while white pulp mainly serves the immune functions of the spleen. Notice that the naming of the pulp regions reflects their appearance in fresh spleen tissue rather than their staining properties. Indeed, as can be seen in the photomicrograph in Figure 21.6c, the white pulp takes on a purplish hue and actually appears darker than the red pulp.

Because the spleen's capsule is relatively thin, a direct blow or severe infection may cause it to rupture. Under such conditions the spleen must be removed quickly (a procedure called a *splenectomy*) and the splenic artery tied off to prevent life-threatening hemorrhage. Despite its imposing size and important roles, surgical removal of the spleen seems to create few problems because macrophages in the liver and bone marrow take over most of its functions. •

Thymus

The bilobed **thymus** (thi'mus) has important functions primarily during the early years of life. In infants, it is found in the lower neck region and extends into the mediastinum of the thorax, where it lies deep to the sternum (see Figure 21.4). By secreting hormones (thymosin and thymopoietin), the thymus causes T lymphocytes to become immunocompetent; that is, it enables them to function against specific pathogens in the immune response (see Chapter 22). The thymus varies in size with age. Prominent in newborns, it continues to increase in size during childhood, when it is most active. During adolescence its growth stops, and it starts to atrophy gradually. By old age it has been almost replaced entirely by fibrous and fatty tissue and is difficult to distinguish from surrounding connective tissue.

To understand thymic histology, it helps to compare the thymus to a cauliflower head—then the flowerets represent *thymic lobules,* each containing an outer cortex and an inner medulla (Figure 21.7). The vast majority of thymic cells are lymphocytes. In the cortical regions the rapidly dividing lymphocytes are densely packed, but a few macrophages are scattered

FIGURE 21.7
Histological structure of the thymus. Photomicrograph of a portion of the thymus showing its lobules with cortical and medullary regions (25 ✕).

among them. The lighter-staining medullary areas contain fewer lymphocytes; they also contain some rather bizarre structures called **Hassall's** or **thymic corpuscles.** Hassall's corpuscles appear to be areas of degenerating cells, but their significance is unknown.

The thymus differs from other lymphoid organs in two important ways. (1) It functions strictly in T lymphocyte maturation and, thus, is the only lymphoid organ that does not *directly* fight antigens. In fact, the so-called *blood-thymus barrier* keeps blood-borne antigens from leaking into the cortical regions to prevent premature activation of the immature lymphocytes. (2) The stroma or basic framework of the thymus consists of star-shaped epithelial cells rather than reticular fibers. These *thymocytes* secrete the hormones that stimulate the lymphocytes to become immunocompetent.

Tonsils

The **tonsils** are, perhaps, the simplest lymphoid organs. They form a ring of lymphatic tissue around the entrance to the pharynx (throat), where they appear as "swellings" of the mucosa (Figure 21.4). The tonsils are named according to location. The **palatine tonsils** are located on either side at the posterior end of the oral cavity. These are the largest of the tonsils and the most often infected. The **lingual tonsil** lies at the base of the tongue, and the **pharyngeal tonsils** *(adenoids)* are in the posterior wall of the nasopharynx. The tiny **tubal tonsils** surround the openings of the auditory tubes into the pharynx. The tonsils gather and remove many of the pathogens entering the pharynx in inhaled air or in food.

The lymphoid tissue of the tonsils contains nodules with obvious germinal centers surrounded by diffusely scattered lymphocytes. The tonsil masses are not fully encapsulated, and the epithelium overlying them invaginates deep into their interior, forming

Nervous System

• The nervous system innervates larger lymphatic vessels; opiate neuropeptides influence immune functions; the brain helps regulate immune response; emotional states influence T cell activity

• The lymphatic vessels pick up leaked plasma fluid and proteins in the peripheral nervous system structures; immune cells protect peripheral nervous system structures from specific pathogens

Endocrine System

• The thymus produces hormones that promote development of lymphatic organs and "program" T lymphocytes; hormones released during stress depress immune activity

• Lymphatic vessels pick up leaked fluids and proteins; lymph distributes hormones; immune cells protect endocrine organs from pathogens

Cardiovascular System

• Blood is the source of lymph; lymphatics develop from veins; blood provides the route for circulation of immune elements

• Lymphatic vessels pick up leaked plasma and proteins; spleen destroys aged RBCs, stores iron, and removes debris from blood; immune cells protect cardiovascular organs from specific pathogens

Respiratory System

• The lungs provides oxygen needed by lymphoid/immune cells and eliminates carbon dioxide; the pharynx houses some lymphoid organs (tonsils); the respiratory "pump" aids lymph flow

• Lymphatic vessels pick up leaked fluids and proteins from respiratory organs; immune cells protect respiratory organs from specific pathogens; lymphocytes populate the tonsils; plasma cells in the respiratory mucosa secrete IgA to prevent pathogen invasion of deeper tissues

Digestive System

• The digestive system digests and absorbs nutrients needed by cells of lymphatic organs; gastric acidity inhibits pathogens' entry into blood

• Lymphatic vessels pick up leaked fluids and proteins from digestive organs; lymph transports some products of fat digestion to the blood; lymphoid nodules in the wall of the intestine prevent invasion of pathogens

Urinary System

• Urinary system eliminates wastes and maintains homeostatic water/acid-base/electrolyte balance of the blood for lymphoid/immune cell functioning; urine flushes some pathogens out of the body

• Lymphatic vessels pick up leaked fluid and proteins from urinary organs; immune cells protect urinary organs from specific pathogens

Reproductive System

• Reproductive organs' hormones may influence immune functioning; acidity of vaginal secretions prevents bacterial multiplication

• Lymphatic vessels pick up leaked fluid and proteins from reproductive organs; immune cells protect the organs from specific pathogens

Integumentary System

• The skin's keratinized epithelium provides a mechanical barrier to pathogens; Langerhans' cells and dermal macrophages act as antigen presenters in the immune response; acid pH of skin secretions inhibits growth of bacteria on the skin

• Lymphatic vessels pick up leaked plasma fluid and proteins from the dermis; lymphocytes in lymph enhance the skin's protective role by defending against specific pathogens via the immune response

Skeletal System

• The bones house hematopoietic tissue (red marrow) which produces the lymphocytes (and macrophages) that populate the lymphoid organs and provide body immunity

• Lymphatic vessels pick up leaked plasma fluid and proteins from the periostea; immune cells protect bones from specific pathogens

Muscular System

• The skeletal muscle "pump" aids the flow of lymph; heat produced during muscle activity initiates feverlike effects; muscles protect superficial lymph nodes

• Lymphatic vessels pick up leaked fluids and proteins from skeletal muscle; immune cells protect muscles from specific pathogens

Closer Connections: The Lymphatic System/Immunity and Interrelationship with the Cardiovascular System

All living body cells are bathed by lymph. Nonetheless, the lymphatic system with its ghostly vessels and well-hidden (for the most part) organs and tissues is elusive and hard to pin down. Like a ground mole that tunnels throughout your yard, you know it's there, but you never see it as it quietly goes about its business. Since hormones made by endocrine organs are released into the extracellular space, and lymphatic vessels sequester the fluid containing them, there is little question that lymph is an important medium for delivering hormones throughout the body. Lymph plays a similar delivery role as it delivers fats absorbed by the digestive organs. Our immune system, charged with protecting the body from specific pathogens, is often considered a separate and independent functional system. However, it is impossible to divorce the immune system from the lymphatic system because lymphoid organs are the programming sites and seedbeds for the immune cells and provide crucial vantage points for monitoring blood and lymph for the presence of foreign substances. Less understood are the intimate interactions between the immune cells that populate the lymphoid tissues and the nervous and endocrine systems, but this interesting topic is deferred to Chapter 22 to give you the opportunity to consider the immune system in detail (see *A Closer Look*, p. 716). Although the lymphatic system serves the entire body, its chief "master" is the cardiovascular system. It is this relationship that we will explore further here.

Cardiovascular System

By now you are probably fairly comfortable with the fact that the lymphatic system picks up and returns leaked fluid and proteins to the blood vascular system. So, what's the big deal? We ingest water in virtually everything we eat and drink—lost water is replaceable in a few min-

utes, right? The answer to this question, of course, is "true." But what would still be missing is the leaked proteins, and these plasma proteins (most made by the liver) take time and energy to make. Since plasma proteins play a *major* role in keeping fluid in blood vessels (or encouraging its return), without them our blood vessels would contain too little fluid to support blood circulation. And, without blood circulation, the whole body would die for lack of oxygen and nutrients and drown in its own wastes. Lymphoid organs also help to maintain the health and purity of blood—lymphocytes filter microorganisms and other debris from lymph before it is allowed to reenter the blood, and the spleen performs the same cleansing service for blood. In addition, the spleen disposes of inefficient, deformed, or aged erythrocytes.

However, this relationship is not entirely one-way. Lymphatic vessels spring from veins of the cardiovascular system and blood delivers oxygen and nutrients to all body organs, including lymphoid ones. Blood also provides a means for (1) rapid transport of lymphocytes (immune cells) that continuously patrol the body for foreign substances and (2) broad distribution of antibodies (made by B cells and plasma cells), which bind to foreign substances and immobilize them until they can be disposed of by phagocytosis or other means. Furthermore, the endothelial cells of capillaries express surface protein "signals" (integrins/adhesion molecules) that lymphocytes can recognize when the surrounding area is injured or infected. Hence, capillaries guide immune cells to the sites where their protective services are needed, and the extremely porous walls of the postcapillary venules allow them to slip through the vessel wall to get there.

Clinical Connections

Lymphatic System/Immunity

Case study: Back to following the progress of Mr. Hutchinson, we learn that the routine complete blood count (CBC) performed on admission revealed that his leukocyte count is dangerously low and that follow-up lab tests show that his lymphocytes are deficient. One day post surgery, he complains of pain in his right ring finger (that hand had a crush injury). When examined, it was noted that the affected finger and the dorsum of the right hand were edematous, and red streaks radiated superiorly on his right forearm. Higher than normal doses of antibiotics are prescribed, and a sling is applied to the affected arm. Nurses are instructed to apply gloves and gown when giving Mr. Hutchinson his care.

Relative to these observations:

1. What do the red streaks emanating from the bruised finger indicate? What would you conclude his problem was if there were no red streaks but the right arm was very edematous?

2. Why is it important that Mr. Hutchinson not move the affected arm excessively (i.e., why was the sling ordered)?

3. How might the low lymphocyte count, megadoses of antibiotics, and orders for additional clinical staff protection be related?

4. Do you predict that Mr. Hutchinson's recovery will be uneventful or problematic? Why?

FIGURE 21.8
Histological structure of the palatine tonsil. The exterior surface of the tonsil is covered by squamous epithelium, which invaginates deep into the tonsil. The spherical regions seen are the nodules (10×).

blind-ended structures called **crypts** (Figure 21.8). The crypts trap bacteria and particulate matter, and the bacteria work their way through the mucosal epithelium into the lymphoid tissue, where most are destroyed. It seems a dangerous strategy to "invite" infection this way, but this strategy produces a wide variety of immune cells with a "memory" for the trapped pathogens. Thus, the body takes a calculated risk early on (during childhood) for the benefits of heightened immunity and better health later.

Aggregates of Lymphoid Nodules

Peyer's (pi′erz) **patches,** large isolated clusters of lymph nodules structurally similar to the tonsils, are found in the wall of the distal portion (ileum) of the small intestine (Figures 21.4 and 21.9). Similarly, lymphoid nodules are heavily concentrated in the wall of the **appendix,** a tubular offshoot of the first part (cecum) of the large intestine. Peyer's patches and the appendix are in an ideal position (1) to destroy bacteria (which are present in large numbers in the intestine), thereby preventing these pathogens from breaching the intestinal wall, and (2) to generate many "memory" lymphocytes for long-term immunity. Peyer's patches, the appendix, and the tonsils, all located in the digestive tract, and lymphoid nodules in the walls of the bronchi (organs of the respiratory tract), are part of the collection of small lymphoid tissues referred to as **mucosa-associated**

lymphatic tissue (MALT). Collectively, MALT acts to protect the digestive and respiratory tracts from the never-ending onslaughts of foreign matter that enters those cavities.

DEVELOPMENTAL ASPECTS OF THE LYMPHATIC SYSTEM

By the fifth week of embryonic development, the beginnings of the lymphatic vessels and the main clusters of lymph nodes are apparent in the budding of irregular **lymph sacs** from developing veins. The first of these, the *jugular lymph sacs,* arise at the junctions of the internal jugular and subclavian veins and form a branching system of lymphatic vessels throughout the thorax, upper extremities, and head. The main connections of the jugular lymph sacs to the venous system are retained and become the right lymphatic duct and, on the left, the superior part of the thoracic duct. Caudally the elaborate system of abdominal lymphatics buds largely from the primitive inferior vena cava, and the lymphatics of the pelvic region and lower extremities form from sacs on the iliac veins.

Except for the thymus, which is an endodermal derivative, the lymphoid organs, like the lymphatic vessels, develop from mesoderm. Mesodermal mesenchymal cells migrate to characteristic body sites, where they develop into reticular tissue. The thymus is the first lymphoid organ to appear. It forms as an outgrowth of the lining of the primitive pharynx, detaches, and then migrates caudally into the thorax. It then becomes infiltrated with immature lymphocytes derived from the hematopoietic tissues elsewhere in the embryonic body. Except for the spleen, the other lymphoid organs are poorly developed

FIGURE 21.9
Histological structure of aggregated lymphoid follicles (Peyer's patches) in the wall of the ileum of the small intestine (20×).

before birth. Shortly after birth, they become heavily populated by lymphocytes, and their development parallels the maturation of the immune system (see Chapter 22). There is some evidence that the embryonic thymus produces hormones that control the development of the other lymphoid organs.

*　　*　　*

Although the functions of the lymphatic vessels and lymphoid organs overlap, each helps to maintain body homeostasis in unique ways, as summarized in *Making Connections.* The lymphatic vessels help to maintain blood volume. The macrophages of lymphoid organs remove and destroy foreign matter in the lymphatic stream and blood. Additionally, lymphoid organs and tissues provide sites from which the immune system can be mobilized. In Chapter 22, we continue this story as we examine the inflammatory and immune responses that allow us to resist the constant barrage of pathogens.

RELATED CLINICAL TERMS

Elephantiasis (el″lĕ-fan-ti′ah-sis) Typically a tropical disease in which the lymphatics (particularly those of the male's lower limbs and scrotum) become clogged with parasitic worms; swelling (due to edema) reaches enormous proportions.

Hodgkin's disease A malignancy of the lymph nodes characterized by swollen, nonpainful lymph nodes, fatigue, and often persistent fever and night sweats. Etiology unknown; treated with radiation therapy; high cure rate.

Lymphadenopathy (lim-fad″ĕ-nop′ah-the; *adeno* = a gland; *pathy* = disease) Any disease of the lymph nodes.

Lymphangiography (lim-fan″je-og′rah-fe) Diagnostic procedure in which the lymphatic vessels are injected with radiopaque dye and then visualized with X rays.

Lymphoma Any neoplasm (tumor) of the lymphoid tissue, whether benign or malignant.

Mononucleosis A viral disease common in adolescents and young adults; symptoms include fatigue, fever, sore throat, and swollen lymph nodes. Mononucleosis is caused by the Epstein-Barr virus, which is transmitted in saliva ("kissing disease") and specifically attacks B lymphocytes. This attack leads to a massive activation of T lymphocytes, which in turn attack the virus-infected B cells. Large numbers of oversized T lymphocytes circulate in the bloodstream. (These lymphocytes were originally misidentified as monocytes: *mononucleosis* = a condition of monocytes.) Usually lasts 4 to 6 weeks.

Splenomegaly (sple″no-meg′ah-le; *mega* = big) Enlargement of the spleen due to accumulation of infectious microorganisms; typically caused by septicemia, mononucleosis, and leukemia.

Tonsillitis (ton″sĭ-li′tis; *itis* = inflammation) Congestion of the tonsils, typically with infecting bacteria, which causes them to become red, swollen, and sore.

CHAPTER SUMMARY

1.　Lymphatic vessels, lymph nodes, and other lymphoid organs and tissues make up the lymphatic system. This system returns fluids that have leaked from the blood vascular system back to the blood, protects the body by removing foreign material from the lymph stream, and provides a site for immune surveillance.

Lymphatic Vessels (pp. 694–697)

Distribution and Structure of Lymphatic Vessels (pp. 694–697)
1.　Lymphatic vessels form a one-way network—lymphatic capillaries, collecting vessels, trunks, and ducts—in which fluid flows only toward the heart. The right lymphatic duct drains lymph from the right arm and right side of the upper body; the thoracic duct receives lymph from the rest of the body. These ducts empty into the blood vascular system at the junction of the internal jugular and subclavian veins in the neck.

Lymph Transport (p. 697)
2.　The flow of lymphatic fluid is slow; it is maintained by skeletal muscle contraction, pressure changes in the thorax, and (possibly) contractions of the lymphatic vessels. Backflow is prevented by valves.

3.　Lymphatic capillaries are exceptionally permeable, admitting proteins and particulate matter from the interstitial space.

4.　Pathogens and cancer cells may spread through the body via the lymphatic stream.

Lymphoid Cells, Tissues, and Organs: An Overview (pp. 697–698)

Lymphoid Cells (p. 697)
1.　The cells in lymphoid tissues include lymphocytes (immunocompetent cells called T cells or B cells), plasma cells (antibody-producing offspring of B cells), macrophages (phagocytes that function in the immune response), and reticular cells that form the lymphoid tissue stroma.

Lymphoid Tissue (p. 698)
2.　Lymphoid tissue is reticular connective tissue. It houses macrophages and a continuously changing population of lymphocytes, and is an important element of the immune system.

3.　Lymphoid tissue may be diffusely arranged or densely packaged into follicles (nodules). Follicles often display germinal centers (areas where B cells are proliferating).

Lymphoid Organs (p. 698)
4.　Lymphoid organs are discrete encapsulated structures containing both dense and diffusely arranged reticular tissue. The main lymphoid organs are lymph nodes, the spleen, thymus, tonsils, and nodule aggregates.

Lymph Nodes (pp. 698–699)

Structure of a Lymph Node (pp. 698–699)
1.　Lymph nodes, clustered along lymphatic vessels, filter lymph. Each lymph node has a fibrous capsule, a cortex, and a medulla. The cortex contains mostly lymphocytes, which act in immune responses; the medulla contains macrophages, which engulf and destroy viruses, bacteria, and other foreign debris, as well as lymphocytes and plasma cells.

Circulation in the Lymph Nodes (p. 699)
2.　Lymph enters the lymph nodes via afferent lymphatic ves-

sels and exits via efferent vessels. There are fewer efferent vessels; therefore, lymph flow stagnates within the lymph node, allowing time for its cleansing.

Other Lymphoid Organs (pp. 699–704)

1. Unlike lymph nodes, the spleen, thymus, tonsils, and Peyer's patches do not filter lymph. However, most lymphoid organs contain both macrophages and lymphocytes.

Spleen (pp. 700–701)

2. The spleen provides a site for lymphocyte proliferation and immune function, and destroys aged or defective red blood cells and blood-borne pathogens. It also stores and releases the breakdown products of hemoglobin as necessary, stores platelets, acts as a hematopoietic site in the fetus.

Thymus (p. 701)

3. The thymus is most functional during youth. Its hormones cause T lymphocytes to become immunocompetent.

Tonsils and Aggregates of Lymphoid Nodules (pp. 701–704)

4. Peyer's patches of the intestinal wall, lymphatic nodules of the appendix, tonsils of the pharynx, and nodules in the bronchial walls of the respiratory tract are known as MALT (mucosa-associated lymphatic tissue). They prevent pathogens in the respiratory and digestive tracts from breaching the mucous membrane lining.

Developmental Aspects of the Lymphatic System (pp. 704–705)

1. Lymphatics develop as outpocketings of developing veins. The thymus develops from endoderm; the other lymphoid organs derive from mesenchymal cells of mesoderm.

2. The thymus, the first lymphoid organ to appear, plays a role in the development of other lymphoid organs.

3. Lymphoid organs are populated by lymphocytes, which arise from hematopoietic tissue.

REVIEW QUESTIONS

Multiple Choice/Matching

1. Lymphatic vessels (a) serve as sites for immune surveillance, (b) filter lymph, (c) transport leaked plasma proteins and fluids to the cardiovascular system, (d) are represented by vessels that resemble arteries, capillaries, and veins.

 2. The saclike initial portion of the thoracic duct is the (a) lacteal, (b) right lymphatic duct, (c) cisterna chyli, (d) lymph sac.

3. Entry of lymph into the lymphatic capillaries is promoted by which of the following? (More than one answer may be appropriate.) (a) one-way minivalves formed by overlapping endothelial cells, (b) the respiratory pump, (c) the skeletal muscle pump, (d) greater fluid pressure in the interstitial space.

4. The structural framework of lymphoid organs is (a) areolar connective tissue, (b) hematopoietic tissue, (c) reticular tissue, (d) adipose tissue.

 5. Lymph nodes are densely clustered in all of the following body areas *except* (a) the brain, (b) the axillae, (c) the groin, (d) the cervical region.

6. The germinal centers in lymph nodes are largely sites of (a) macrophages, (b) proliferating B lymphocytes, (c) T lymphocytes, (d) all of these.

7. The red pulp areas of the spleen are sites of (a) venous sinuses, macrophages, and red blood cells, (b) clustered lymphocytes, (c) connective tissue septa.

8. The lymphoid organ that functions primarily during youth and then begins to atrophy is the (a) spleen, (b) thymus, (c) palatine tonsils, (d) bone marrow.

9. Collections of lymphoid tissue (MALT) that guard mucosal surfaces include all of the following *except* (a) appendix nodules, (b) the tonsils, (c) Peyer's patches, (d) the thymus.

Short Answer Essay Questions

10. Compare and contrast blood, interstitial fluid, and lymph.

11. Compare the structure and functions of a lymph node to those of the spleen.

12. (a) What anatomical characteristic ensures that the flow of lymph through a lymph node is slow? (b) Why is this desirable?

 CRITICAL THINKING AND CLINICAL APPLICATION QUESTIONS

1. A 59-year-old woman has undergone a left radical mastectomy (removal of the left breast and left axillary lymph nodes and vessels). Her left arm is severely swollen and painful, and she is unable to raise it more than shoulder height. (a) Explain her signs and symptoms. (b) Can she expect to have relief from these symptoms in time? How so?

 2. A friend tells you that she has tender, swollen "glands" along the left side of the front of her neck. You notice that she has a bandage on her left cheek that is not fully hiding a large infected cut there. Exactly what are her swollen "glands," and how did they become swollen?

22

Nonspecific Body Defenses and Immunity

CHAPTER OUTLINE AND STUDENT OBJECTIVES

NONSPECIFIC BODY DEFENSES (pp. 708–715)

Surface Membrane Barriers (p. 708)

1. Describe the surface membrane barriers and their protective functions.

Nonspecific Cellular and Chemical Defenses (pp. 708–715)

2. Explain the importance of phagocytosis and natural killer cells in nonspecific body defense.

3. Relate the events of the inflammatory process. Identify several inflammatory chemicals and describe their specific roles.

4. Name the body's antimicrobial substances and describe their function.

5. Explain how fever helps protect the body against invading pathogens.

SPECIFIC BODY DEFENSES: IMMUNITY (pp. 715–739)

Antigens (pp. 716–718)

6. Explain what an antigen is and how it affects the immune system.

7. Define complete antigen, hapten, and antigenic determinant.

Cells of the Immune System: An Overview (pp. 718–720)

8. Compare and contrast the origin, maturation process, and general function of B and T lymphocytes. Describe the role of macrophages in immunity.

9. Define immunocompetence and self-tolerance.

Humoral Immune Response (pp. 720–726)

10. Define humoral immunity.

11. Describe the process of clonal selection of a B cell.

12. Recount the roles of plasma cells and memory cells in humoral immunity.

13. Compare and contrast active and passive humoral immunity.

14. Describe the structure of an antibody monomer, and name the five classes of antibodies.

15. Explain the function(s) of antibodies.

16. Describe the development and clinical uses of monoclonal antibodies.

Cell-Mediated Immune Response (pp. 727–734)

17. Define cell-mediated immunity and describe the process of activation and clonal selection of T cells.

18. Describe the functional roles of T cells in the body.

19. Indicate the tests ordered before an organ transplant is done, and note methods used to prevent transplant rejection.

Homeostatic Imbalances of Immunity (pp. 734–737)

20. Give examples of immune deficiency diseases and of hypersensitivity states.

21. Note factors involved in autoimmune disease.

Developmental Aspects of the Immune System (pp. 737–739)

22. Describe changes in immunity that occur with aging.

23. Briefly describe the role of the nervous system in regulating the immune response.

Faced by a perversely hostile army of microorganisms swarming on our skin, and invaded by airborne bacteria and ravaging viruses, we stay amazingly healthy most of the time. The body seems to have evolved a single-minded approach toward such foes—if you're not with us, then you're against us. To implement that stance, it relies heavily on two intrinsic defensive systems that act both independently and cooperatively.

One of these systems, the **nonspecific (or innate) defense system,** is always prepared—that is, it responds immediately to protect the body from all foreign substances. Our nonspecific defenses erect two "barricades." Their *first line of defense* is the external body membranes (intact skin and mucosae) that prevent entry of microorganisms.

The *second line of defense,* called into action by chemical signals when the external defenses are penetrated, uses antimicrobial proteins, as well as phagocytes and other cells to inhibit the invaders' spread throughout the body. The hallmark and most important mechanism of the second line of defense is inflammation.

The second protective arm, the **specific (or adaptive) defense system,** is more commonly called the **immune system.** The immune system mounts the attack against *particular* foreign substances and provides the body's *third line of defense.* Although we consider them separately, the specific and non-specific defenses always work hand in hand to protect the body.

Although certain organs of the body (notably, lymphatic system organs) are intimately involved with the immune response, the immune system is a *functional system* rather than an organ system in an anatomical sense. Its "structures" are trillions of individual immune cells, which inhabit lymphatic tissues and circulate in body fluids, and a diverse array of molecules. The most important of the immune cells are *lymphocytes* and *macrophages.*

When the immune system is operating effectively, it skillfully protects the body from most infectious microorganisms, cancer cells, and transplanted organs or grafts. The immune system does this both directly, by cell attack, and indirectly, by releasing mobilizing chemicals and protective antibody molecules. The resulting highly specific resistance to disease is called **immunity** (*immun* = free). Notice that while this book equates the specific defense system to the immune system, some references include both defensive arms under that heading. In that case, the nonspecific defenses are often referred to as *innate immunity* and the specific defenses as *adaptive immunity.*

NONSPECIFIC BODY DEFENSES

You could say we come "fully equipped" with the nonspecific defenses because they are part and parcel of our body structure. The mechanical barriers that cover body surfaces and the cells and chemicals that act on the initial battlefronts are in place at birth, ready to ward off invading **pathogens** (harmful or disease-causing microorganisms). In many instances, the nonspecific defenses alone are able to destroy pathogens and ward off infection. In others, the immune system must be deployed to reinforce and enhance the nonspecific mechanisms. In either case, the nonspecific defenses effectively reduce the work load of the immune system by preventing entry and spread of microorganisms in the body. Table 22.2 on p. 714 summarizes the most important nonspecific defense mechanisms, which are detailed next.

SURFACE MEMBRANE BARRIERS

The body's first line of defense against the invasion of disease-causing microorganisms—the *skin* and the *mucous membranes,* and the secretions these membranes produce—is highly effective. As long as the epidermis is unbroken, this heavily keratinized epithelial membrane presents a formidable physical barrier to most microorganisms that swarm on the skin. Keratin is also resistant to most weak acids and bases and to bacterial enzymes and toxins. Intact mucosae provide similar mechanical barriers within the body. Recall that mucous membranes line all body cavities that open to the exterior: the digestive, respiratory, urinary, and reproductive tracts. Besides serving as physical barriers, these epithelial membranes produce a variety of protective chemicals:

1. The acidity of skin secretions (pH of 3 to 5) inhibits bacterial growth and sebum contains chemicals that are toxic to bacteria. Vaginal secretions of adult females are also very acidic.

2. The stomach mucosa secretes a concentrated hydrochloric acid solution and protein-digesting enzymes. Both kill pathogens.

3. Saliva, which cleanses the oral cavity and teeth, and lacrimal fluid, which washes the external eye surfaces, contain **lysozyme,** an enzyme that destroys bacteria.

4. Sticky mucous traps many microorganisms that enter the digestive and respiratory passageways.

The respiratory tract mucosae also have structural modifications that counteract potential invaders. The mesh of tiny mucous-coated hairs inside the nose traps inhaled particles, and the mucosa of the upper respiratory tract is ciliated. The cilia sweep dust- and bacteria-laden mucus superiorly toward the mouth, preventing it from entering the lower respiratory passages, where the warm, moist environment provides an ideal site for bacterial growth.

Although the surface barriers are quite effective, they are breached occasionally by small nicks and cuts resulting, for example, from brushing your teeth or shaving. When this happens and microorganisms do invade deeper tissues, the internal nonspecific mechanisms come into play.

NONSPECIFIC CELLULAR AND CHEMICAL DEFENSES

The body uses an enormous number of nonspecific defensive cellular and chemical devices to protect itself. Some of these rely on the destructive powers of phagocytes and natural killer cells, or involve antimicrobial proteins (complement and interferon) that are present in blood or tissue fluid. The inflammatory response enlists the help of macrophages, mast cells, and all types of white blood cells, as well as dozens of chemical substances that kill pathogens and help repair tissue. Fever can also be considered a nonspecific protective response. Although these mechanisms are only a few of the possible protective responses, they are among the most significant.

Phagocytes

Pathogens that get through the skin and mucosae into the underlying connective tissue are confronted by *phagocytes* (*phago* = eat). The chief phagocytes are **macrophages** ("big eaters"), which derive from circulating white blood cells called *monocytes.* Monocytes that leave the bloodstream and enter the tissues enlarge and develop into macrophages. *Free macrophages* wander throughout the body's tissue spaces in search of cellular debris or "foreign invaders." Others, like *Kupffer cells* in the liver and alveolar macrophages of the lungs, are *fixed macrophages* (permanent residents of particular organs). Whatever their mobility, all macrophages are similar structurally and functionally. **Neutrophils,** the most abundant type of white blood cell, also become phagocytic on encountering infectious material in the tissues. Eosinophils, still another type of white blood cell, are only weakly phagocytic. However, they are very important in defending the body against parasitic worms. When they encounter such parasites, they position themselves against them, and then discharge the destructive contents of their large cytoplasmic granules all over their prey.

A phagocyte engulfs particulate matter much the way an amoeba ingests a food particle. Flowing cytoplasmic extensions bind to the particle (Figure 22.1) and then pull it inside, enclosd within a membrane-lined vacuole. The *phagosome* thus formed is then fused with a *lysosome* to form a *phagolysosome* (see Figure 22.7 on p. 720).

Sometimes, the way neutrophils and macrophages kill their ingested prey is much more than simple digestion of the engulfed microorganism by lysosomal enzymes. For example, some pathogens such as the tuberculosis bacillus and some parasites are resistant to lysosomal enzymes and can even multiply within a vacuole inside the macrophage. However, when the macrophage is stimulated by certain chemicals released by cells of the immune system, additional enzymes are activated that produce the **respiratory burst,** an event that liberates a deluge of free radicals (including nitric oxide), which have potent cell-killing ability. Neutrophils also produce antibiotic-like chemicals, called *defensins* (see p. 594), and cause a more widespread and thorough type of cell killing by releasing oxidizing chemicals and a substance identical to household bleach into the extracellular space. Unhappily, the neutrophils

FIGURE 22.1
Phagocytosis by a macrophage. In this scanning electron micrograph (4300×), a macrophage is shown pulling sausage-shaped *E. coli* bacteria toward it with its long cytoplasmic extensions. Several bacteria on the macrophage's surface are being engulfed.

also destroy themselves in the process, whereas macrophages, which rely only on intracellular killing, can go on to kill another day. Too much of a good thing is possible, however. Recent research has indicated that excessively vigorous and prolonged neutrophil activity may cause normal human tissues to become cancerous.

Phagocytic attempts are not always successful. To accomplish ingestion, the phagocytes must first *adhere* or cling to the particle. This is particularly difficult with microorganisms such as *pneumococcus,* which have external capsules made of complex sugars. These pathogens are sometimes able to elude capture because phagocytes cannot bind to their capsule polysaccharides. Adherence is both more probable and more efficient when complement proteins and antibodies coat foreign particles, a process called **opsonization** (literally, "to make tasty"), because they provide sites to which phagocyte receptors can bind.

Natural Killer Cells

Natural killer (NK) cells, which "police" the body in blood and lymph, are a unique group of defensive cells that can lyse and kill cancer cells and virus-infected body cells before the immune system is activated and enlisted in the fight. NK cells are part of a small but distinct group of *large granular* lymphocytes called **null cells** or **third population cells (TPCs).** Unlike lymphocytes of the immune system, which can recognize and react only against *specific* virus-infected or tumor cells, NK cells can act spontaneously against *any* such target, apparently by recognizing cell surface changes that occur on some tumor cells or cells infected with viruses. The name "natural" killer cells reflects the nonspecificity of their killing activity. NK cells are not phagocytic. Their mode of killing involves an attack on the target cell's membrane and release of several cytolytic chemicals. Shortly thereafter, transmembrane channels appear in the target cell's membrane and its nucleus disintegrates rapidly.

Inflammation: Tissue Response to Injury

The **inflammatory response** is triggered whenever body tissues are injured. For example, it occurs in response to physical trauma (a blow), intense heat, and irritating chemicals, as well as to infection by viruses, fungi, and bacteria. The inflammatory response (1) prevents the spread of damaging agents to nearby tissues, (2) disposes of cell debris and pathogens, and (3) sets the stage for repair processes.

The four *cardinal signs* of short-term, or acute, inflammation are *redness, heat* (*inflamm* = set on fire), *swelling,* and *pain.* If the swollen and painful area is a joint, joint movement may be hampered temporarily. This forces the injured part to rest, which aids healing. Some authorities consider *impairment of function* to be the fifth cardinal sign of acute inflammation. We will see how these come about by examining the major events of the inflammatory process, which are depicted in Figure 22.2.

Vasodilation and Increased Vascular Permeability

The inflammatory process begins with a chemical "alarm"—a host of inflammatory chemicals are released into the extracellular fluid. Injured tissue cells, phagocytes, lymphocytes, mast cells, and blood proteins are all sources of these inflammatory mediators, the most important of which are **histamine** (his'tah-mēn), **kinins** (ki'ninz), **prostaglandins (PGs)** (pros"tah-glan'dinz), **complement,** and **lymphokines** (lim'fo-kīnz). Though some of these mediators have individual inflammatory roles as well (see Table 22.1), they all promote dilation of the small blood vessels in the vicinity. As more blood flows into the area, local **hyperemia** (congestion with blood) occurs, accounting for the *redness* and *heat* of an inflamed area.

The liberated chemicals also increase the permeability of local capillaries. Consequently, **exudate**—fluid containing proteins such as clotting factors and antibodies—seeps from the bloodstream into the tissue spaces. This exudate causes the local edema, or *swelling,* that, in turn, presses on adjacent nerve endings, contributing to a sensation of *pain.* Pain also results from the release of bacterial toxins, lack of nutrition to cells in the area, and the sensitizing effects of released prostaglandins and kinins. Aspirin and some other anti-inflammatory drugs produce their analgesic (pain-reducing) effects by inhibiting prostaglandin synthesis.

Although, at first glance, edema may seem to be detrimental, it isn't. The surge of protein-rich fluids into the tissue spaces (1) helps to dilute harmful substances that may be present, (2) brings in large quantities of oxygen and nutrients needed for repair, and (3) allows the entry of clotting proteins (Figure 22.2). The clotting proteins form a gel-like fibrin mesh in the tissue space that effectively isolates the injured area and prevents the spread of bacteria and other harmful agents into surrounding tissues. It also forms a scaffolding for permanent repair.

Table 22.1	Inflammatory Chemicals	
Chemical	**Source**	**Physiological effects**
Histamine	Granules of basophils and mast cells; released in response to mechanical injury, presence of certain microorganisms, and chemicals released by neutrophils	Promotes vasodilation of local arterioles; increases permeability of local capillaries, permitting exudate formation
Kinins (bradykinin and others)	A plasma protein, kininogen, is cleaved by the enzyme kallikrein found in plasma, urine, saliva, and in lysosomes of neutrophils and other types of cells; cleavage releases active kinin peptides	Same as for histamine; also induce chemotaxis of leukocytes and stimulate neutrophils to release lysosomal enzymes, thereby enhancing generation of more kinins; induce pain
Prostaglandins (PGs)	Fatty acid molecules produced from arachidonic acid; found in all cell membranes; generated by lysosomal enzymes of neutrophils and other cell types	Sensitize blood vessels to effects of other inflammatory mediators; one of the intermediate steps of prostaglandin generation produces free radicals, which themselves can cause inflammation; induce pain
Complement	See Table 22.2	
Lymphokines	See Table 22.4	

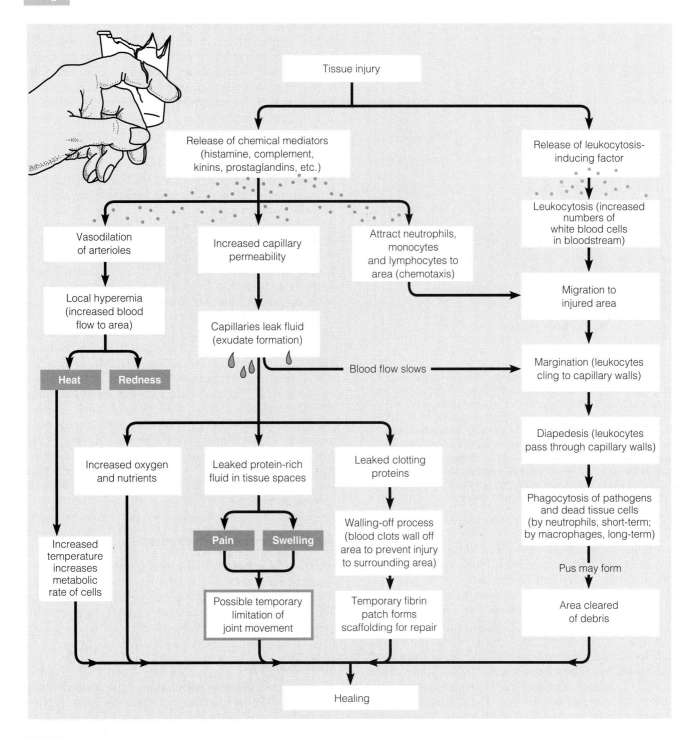

FIGURE 22.2
Flowchart of events in inflammation. The four cardinal signs of acute inflammation are shown in red boxes, as is limitation of joint movement, which constitutes a fifth cardinal sign (impairment of function) in some cases.

Phagocyte Mobilization

Soon after inflammation begins, the damaged area is invaded by more phagocytes—neutrophils and macrophages (Figure 22.3). If the inflammation was provoked by pathogens, a group of plasma proteins known as complement (see p. 712) is activated and immune elements (lymphocytes and antibodies) also invade the injured site and mount an immune response.

Chemicals called **leukocytosis-inducing factors** released by injured cells promote rapid release of neutrophils from red bone marrow, and within a few

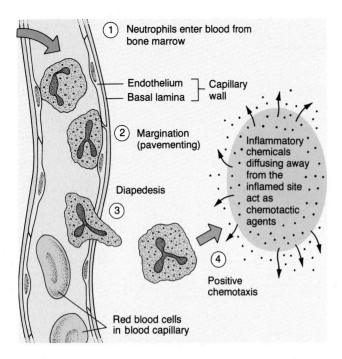

① Neutrophils enter blood from bone marrow

Endothelium
Basal lamina
} Capillary wall

② Margination (pavementing)

Inflammatory chemicals diffusing away from the inflamed site act as chemotactic agents

Diapedesis
③

④

Positive chemotaxis

Red blood cells in blood capillary

FIGURE 22.3
Events of phagocyte mobilization. When leukocytosis-inducing factors are released by injured cells at an inflammatory site, (1) neutrophils are released rapidly from the bone marrow to the blood. Because fluid is lost from the bloodstream at the inflammatory site, blood flow slows locally and (2) margination begins to occur as the neutrophils cling to the capillary walls, and then (3) diapedesis occurs as they squeeze through the capillary walls. Continued migration toward the site of release of the inflammatory chemicals is (4) positive chemotaxis. Once at the inflamed site, the phagocytes help rid the area of pathogens and cellular debris.

hours the number of neutrophils in the bloodstream may increase four- to five-fold. This leukocytosis is a characteristic sign of inflammation. Neutrophils usually migrate randomly, but inflammatory chemicals seem to act as homing devices, or more precisely **chemotactic agents** (Figure 22.3), that attract them and other white blood cells to the site of the injury. Because of the tremendous outpouring of fluid from the blood into the injured area, blood flow in the region slows and the neutrophils begin to cling to the inner walls of the capillaries. This phenomenon is known as **margination** or **pavementing.** The continued chemical signaling prompts the neutrophils to squeeze through the capillary walls, a process called **diapedesis** or **emigration,** and to make their way to the combat zone. Within an hour after the inflammatory response has begun, neutrophils have collected at the injury site and are actively devouring bacteria, toxins, and dead tissue cells.

As the counterattack continues, neutrophils are followed by monocytes that enter the area from the bloodstream. Monocytes are fairly poor phagocytes, but within 8–12 hours after entering the tissues, they swell and develop large numbers of lysosomes, becoming macrophages with insatiable appetites.

These late-arriving macrophages continue to wage the battle, replacing the neutrophils on the battlefield. Macrophages are the central actors in the final disposal of cell debris as an acute inflammation subsides, and they predominate at sites of prolonged, or *chronic,* inflammation. The ultimate goal of an inflammatory response is to clear the injured area of pathogens and dead tissue cells so that tissue can be repaired. Once this is accomplished, healing usually occurs quickly.

In severely infected areas, the battle takes a considerable toll on both sides, and creamy, yellow *pus* may accumulate in the wound. **Pus** is a mixture of dead or dying neutrophils, broken-down tissue cells, and living and dead pathogens. If the inflammatory mechanism fails to fully clear the area of debris, the sac of pus may be walled off by collagen fibers, forming an *abscess.* Surgical drainage of abscesses is often necessary before healing can occur.

Bacteria that are resistant to digestion by macrophages escape the effects of antibiotics by remaining snugly enclosed within their macrophage hosts. In such cases, *infectious granulomas,* tumorlike growths containing a central region of infected macrophages surrounded by uninfected macrophages and an outer fibrous capsule, form. A person may harbor pathogens walled off in granulomas for many years without displaying any symptoms of disease. However, if the person's resistance to infection is compromised or reduced, the encapsulated bacteria may become activated and break out, leading to clinical disease symptoms. •

Antimicrobial Proteins

A variety of **antimicrobial proteins** enhance the body's nonspecific defenses by attacking microorganisms directly or by hindering their ability to reproduce. The most important of these are complement proteins and interferon (Table 22.2).

Complement

The term **complement system,** or simply **complement,** refers to a group of at least 20 plasma proteins that normally circulate in the blood in an inactive state. These proteins include C1 through C9 (C1 is actually three proteins), and factors B, D, and P, plus several regulatory proteins. Complement is a major mechanism for destroying foreign substances in the body. When it is activated, chemical mediators are unleashed that amplify virtually all aspects of the inflammatory process. Another effect is the killing of bacteria and certain other cell types by cell lysis. (Luckily our own cells are equipped with proteins that inactivate complement.) Although complement itself is a nonspecific defensive mechanism, it "complements" or enhances the effectiveness of *both* nonspecific and specific defenses.

FIGURE 22.4
Events and results of complement activation. Complement can be activated by either the classical pathway or the alternative (alternate) pathway. The classical pathway, which is mediated by 11 complement proteins designated C1–C9 (the C1 complex incorporates three of these proteins) requires antigen-antibody interactions. The alternative pathway occurs when plasma proteins called factors B, D, and P interact with the cell wall polysaccharides of certain bacteria and fungi. The two pathways converge to activate C3 (by cleaving it into C3a and C3b), which initiates a common terminal sequence that generates most of the biological activities of complement. Once C3b binds to the target cell's surface, it enzymatically initiates the remaining steps of complement activation. These steps result in the incorporation of MAC, the membrane attack complex (components C5b, and C6 to C9), into the target cell's membrane, creating a funnel-shaped lesion that causes cell lysis. Bound C3b also enhances phagocytosis (a function called opsonization). Released C3a, C5a, and other products of complement activation (C4a) promote the well-known events of inflammation (histamine release, increased vascular permeability, and so on).

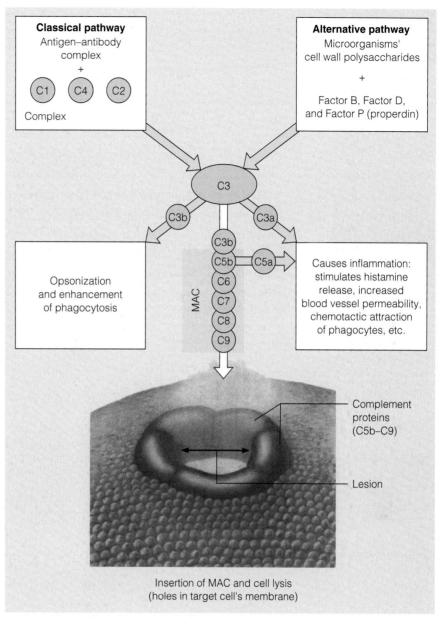

Insertion of MAC and cell lysis
(holes in target cell's membrane)

Complement can be activated by two pathways as outlined in Figure 22.4: the classical pathway or the alternative pathway. The **classical pathway** is linked to the immune system because it depends on binding of antibodies to the invading organisms and the subsequent binding of C1 to the antigen-antibody complexes, a step called **complement fixation** (described in the next section). The **alternative (alternate) pathway** is triggered by an interaction between factors B, D, and P and polysaccharide molecules present on the surface of certain microorganisms.

Each pathway involves a cascade in which complement proteins are activated in an orderly sequence —each causing catalysis of the next step. Both the classical and the alternative pathways ultimately converge on C3, cleaving it into two fragments (C3a and C3b). This event initiates a common terminal pathway that causes cell lysis, promotes phagocytosis,

and enhances inflammation.

This final series of events begins when C3b binds to the target cell's surface, triggering the insertion of a group of complement proteins called **MAC (membrane attack complex)** into the cell's membrane. MAC, in turn, forms and stabilizes an open hole in the target cell's membrane that ensures lysis by interfering with the cell's ability to eject Ca^{2+}. The C3b molecules that coat the microorganism provide "handles" that receptors of macrophages and neutrophils can adhere to, allowing them to engulf the particle more rapidly. As noted earlier, this very important process is called *opsonization*. C3a and other cleavage products produced during complement fixation amplify the inflammatory response by stimulating mast cells and basophils to release histamine and by attracting neutrophils and other inflammatory cells to the area.

Table 22.2   Summary of Nonspecific Body Defenses

Category/associated elements	Protective mechanism
First Line of Defense: Surface membrane barriers	
Intact skin epidermis	Forms mechanical barrier that prevents entry of pathogens and other harmful substances into body
• Acid mantle	Skin secretions (perspiration and sebum) make epidermal surface acidic, which inhibits bacterial growth; sebum also contains bactericidal chemicals
• Keratin	Provides resistance against acids, alkalis, and bacterial enzymes
Intact mucous membranes	Form mechanical barrier that prevents entry of pathogens
• Mucus	Traps microorganisms in respiratory and digestive tracts
• Nasal hairs	Filter and trap microorganisms in nasal passages
• Cilia	Propel debris-laden mucus away from lower respiratory passages
• Gastric juice	Contains concentrated hydrochloric acid and protein-digesting enzymes that destroy pathogens in stomach
• Acid mantle of vagina	Inhibits growth of bacteria and fungi in female reproductive tract
• Lacrimal secretion (tears); saliva	Continuously lubricate and cleanse eyes (tears) and oral cavity (saliva); contains lysozyme, an enzyme that destroys microorganisms
• Urine	Normally acid pH inhibits bacterial growth; cleanses the lower urinary tract as it flushes from the body
Second Line of Defense: Nonspecific cellular and chemical defenses	
Phagocytes	Engulf and destroy pathogens that breach surface membrane barriers; macrophages also contribute to immune response
Natural killer cells	Promote cell lysis by direct cell attack against virus-infected or cancerous body cells; do not depend on specific antigen recognition
Inflammatory response	Prevents spread of injurious agents to adjacent tissues, disposes of pathogens and dead tissue cells, and promotes tissue repair; chemical mediators released attract phagocytes (and immunocompetent cells) to the area
Antimicrobial proteins	
• Interferons	Proteins released by virus-infected cells that protect uninfected tissue cells from viral takeover; mobilize immune system
• Complement	Lyses microorganisms, enhances phagocytosis by opsonization, and intensifies inflammatory and immune responses
Fever	Systemic response initiated by pyrogens; high body temperature inhibits microbial multiplication and enhances body repair processes

Interferon

Viruses—essentially, nucleic acids surrounded by a protein coat—lack the cellular machinery to generate ATP or synthesize proteins. They do their "dirty work" or damage in the body by invading tissue cells and taking over the cellular metabolic machinery needed to reproduce themselves. Although the virus-infected cells can do little to save themselves, they can help protect cells that have not yet been infected by secreting small proteins called **interferons** (in"ter-fēr'onz), or **IFNs.** The interferon molecules diffuse to nearby cells, where they stimulate synthesis of other proteins, which then inhibit, or "interfere" with, viral replication in those cells. Interferon's protection is not *virus-specific,* thus interferon produced against a particular virus protects us against a variety of other viruses.

Interferon is actually a family of related proteins, each with slightly different physiological effects, that is produced by a variety of body cells. Lymphocytes secrete Type II (gamma [γ] or immune) interferon, but most other leukocytes and fibroblasts secrete type I (alpha or beta) interferon. Besides their antiviral effects, interferons activate macrophages, and gamma interferons mobilize natural killer cells. Because both macrophages and natural killer cells can act directly against malignant cells, the interferons are assumed to have some anticancer role.

When interferons were discovered in 1957, researchers hoped that they could be used to cure cancer and treat human viral diseases. Clinical tests of interferon were delayed until the 1980s, when new genetic engineering techniques made it possible to produce large amounts of these proteins. Unfortunately, optimistic predictions that interferon would cure cancer have failed to pan out. Its use has produced routine success only against a rare form of leukemia and Kaposi's sarcoma, a cancer seen infrequently except in AIDS patients (see *A Closer Look* on p. 738). However, interferon has found a niche as an antiviral agent. FDA-approved *alpha IFN* is used to treat genital warts (caused by the herpes virus) and it is the first drug to successfully combat hepatitis C (spread via blood and sexual intercourse), the most common and most dreaded form of hepatitis. Interferon is also being used against devastating viral infections in organ transplant patients, and experimentally in last-ditch attempts to retard the spread of HIV virus in victims of AIDS.

Fever

Inflammation represents a localized response to infection, but sometimes the body's response to the invasion of microorganisms is more widespread. **Fever,** or abnormally high body temperature, represents a systemic response to invading microorganisms. As described further in Chapter 25, body temperature is regulated by a cluster of neurons in the hypothalamus, commonly referred to as the body's thermostat. Normally, the thermostat is set at approximately 36.2°C. (98.2°F). However, the thermostat is reset upward in response to chemicals called **pyrogens** (*pyro* = fire), which are secreted by leukocytes and macrophages exposed to bacteria and other foreign substances in the body.

High fevers are dangerous because excess heat inactivates (denatures) enzymes. On the other hand, mild or moderate fever seems to benefit the body. Bacteria require large amounts of iron and zinc to proliferate, but during a fever the liver and spleen sequester these nutrients, making them less available. Fever also increases the metabolic rate of tissue cells in general, speeding up defensive actions and repair processes.

SPECIFIC BODY DEFENSES: IMMUNITY

Most of us would find it wonderfully convenient if we could walk into a single clothing store and buy a complete wardrobe—hat to shoes—that fit us "to a T" regardless of any special figure problems. We *know* that such a service would be next to impossible to find. And yet we take for granted our **immune system,** the body's built-in *specific defense system,* which stalks and eliminates with nearly equal precision almost any type of pathogen that intrudes into the body.

Essentially, the immune system is a *functional* system that recognizes specific foreign substances and acts to immobilize, neutralize, or destroy them. When it operates effectively, this system protects us from a wide variety of infectious agents, as well as

from abnormal body cells. When it fails, malfunctions, or is disabled, some of the most devastating diseases—such as cancer, rheumatoid arthritis, and AIDS—may result. The activity of the immune system, called the **immune response,** tremendously amplifies the inflammatory response and is responsible for the bulk of complement activation. At first glance, the immune system seems to have a major shortcoming. Unlike the nonspecific defenses which are always ready and able to react, the immune system must "meet" or be primed by an initial exposure to a foreign substance (antigen) before it can protect the body against that substance. However, generation of an immune response is "expensive" metabolically speaking, and specificity of the immune response saves energy.

Although *immunology,* the study of immunity, is a fairly new science, some 2500 years ago the ancient Greeks knew that once someone had a certain infectious disease, that person was unlikely to have the same disease again. The basis of this immunity was revealed in the late 1800s, when researchers demonstrated that animals surviving a serious bacterial infection have protective factors in their blood (now known to be proteins called *antibodies*) that defend them against future attacks by the same pathogen. Furthermore, it was shown that if antibody-containing serum from the surviving animals was injected into animals that had not been exposed to the pathogen, those animals would also be protected. These landmark experiments were exciting because they revealed three important aspects of the immune response:

1. **It is antigen-specific:** It recognizes and is directed against *particular* antigens, that is, against the pathogens or foreign substances that stimulate the immune response.

2. **It is systemic:** Immunity is not restricted to the initial infection site.

3. **It has "memory":** After an initial exposure, it recognizes and mounts even stronger attacks on the previously encountered pathogens.

At first it was assumed that antibodies were the sole artillery of the immune system, but then in the mid-1900s it was discovered that injection of antibody-containing serum did *not* always protect the recipient from diseases the donor had survived. In such cases, however, injection of the donor's lymphocytes did provide immunity. As the pieces began to fall into place, two separate but overlapping arms of immunity were recognized, each of which uses a variety of attack mechanisms that vary with the type of intruder.

Humoral (hu'mor-ul) **immunity,** also called **antibody-mediated immunity,** is provided by the antibodies present in the body's "humors," or fluids (blood, lymph, etc.). Though antibodies are produced by lymphocytes (or their offspring), they circulate freely in the blood and lymph, where they bind pri-

Our immune system's ability to recognize foreign substances is controlled by our genes. However, the power of the mind to affect the body as a whole and its health in particular is amazing, and this intriguing topic deserves more than a passing mention. It is no secret that stress (overwork, grief, depression, etc.) can depress the immune system. More dramatically, scientists have confirmed that a witch doctor can cause death simply by telling those *believing in his powers* that they are going to die. (That's heavy!) On the other hand, some people, including the late magazine publisher Norman Cousins, have maintained that by using humor as therapy, the mind can sometimes cure what the doctor cannot. If we believe the reports coming from Simonton's studies at the Cancer Research Center in Dallas in the late 1970s, we'd have to agree. Cancer patients diagnosed as incurable practiced techniques aimed at squelching negative thoughts. Those patients not only had more active natural killer cells but also had more immunocompetent killer T cells to fight their cancer. Many far outlived their estimated "death date," and more than 25% completely recovered.

Can we really think ourselves sick or well? Since the brain coordinates practically every other system in the body, it seems to be a good bet, but let's take a closer look. It has been known since the early 1900s that important lymphoid organs—the thymus, lymph nodes, and bone marrow— are laced with nerve fibers, but it wasn't until the early 1980s that studies of neuroimmunology began to reveal the true breadth of the links between the brain and the immune system. While the nervous and immune systems have different "languages," they seem to share a few of the same "words," namely some neurotransmitters and neuropeptides (such as the endorphins, or natural opiates). Like neurons, many immune cells have receptors that many (or all?) of the neurotransmitters and neuropeptides can latch onto. Furthermore, once bound, those neurotransmitters affect the immune cells' ability to multiply, migrate, or kill invaders. Then it was discovered that anterior pituitary hormones (subject to hypothalamic controls) can also enhance or inhibit the immune cells' ability to fight disease. Just what these neurotransmitters and hormones were "saying" to the immune cells was and is still unknown. However, since the chemicals being studied are released during times of strong emotional response, depression, or sexual excitement, it follows that emotions can indeed modify our susceptibility to disease. Macrophages, for example, become very sluggish when we are depressed, high levels of endorphins (and heroin) suppress natural killer cell activity, and hormones released in large amounts during stress, such as cortisol and epinephrine, depress T cell activity.

Important as emotions are, our "reasoning" centers also appear to have something to say. The observation that left-handed people are more likely than right-handed people to suffer autoimmune diseases led scientists to study the relative roles of the two cerebral hemispheres in immunity. They concluded that the left hemisphere most directly controls the immune system (through the T cells). The right hemisphere may enhance or depress it, but its inhibitory effect appears stronger and might be more influential in people whose right brain is dominant—that is, left-handed people.

This finding may also provide a few clues to how emotions and positive mental images can promote health (for example, fight cancer). Since imagery is typically a role of the right hemisphere, it may be that such mental exercises somehow "distract" it from suppressing the immune system.

It is well established now that the nervous system communicates with immune cells. The immune system can also "talk back" (send feedback) to the brain and, in so doing, can probably affect one's state of mind. It has been shown that an infection in the body provokes an increase in brain activity in certain areas, which is followed by a temporary decline in neurotransmitter production in those same areas. This apparent ability of the brain to keep track of immune system activity seems to depend on the

---

marily to bacteria and their toxins and to free viruses, inactivating them temporarily and marking them for destruction by phagocytes or complement. When lymphocytes themselves defend the body, the immunity is called **cellular** or **cell-mediated immunity,** because the protective factor is living cells. The cellular arm also has cellular targets—virus- or parasite-infected tissue cells, cancer cells, and cells of foreign grafts. The lymphocytes act against such targets either *directly,* by lysing the foreign cells, or *indirectly,* by releasing chemical mediators that enhance the inflammatory response or activate other lymphocytes or macrophages. Thus, as you can see, although both arms of the immune system respond to virtually the same antigens, they do it in very different ways.

Before we describe the humoral and cell-mediated responses individually, we will consider the antigens that trigger the activity of the remarkable cells involved in these immune responses.

ANTIGENS

Antigens (an'tĭ-jenz), or **Ags,** are substances that can mobilize the immune system and provoke an immune response. As such, they are the ultimate targets of all immune responses. Most antigens are large, complex molecules (both natural and man-made) that are not normally present in the body. Consequently, as far as our immune system is concerned, they are intruders, or **nonself.**

Complete Antigens and Haptens

Complete antigens exhibit two important functional properties: (1) **immunogenicity,** the ability to stimulate proliferation of specific lymphocytes and formation of specific antibodies (the word *antigen* is a contraction of "*anti*body *gen*erating," which refers to lymphokines (interferons and others) and hormones released by immune cells under attack. The immune cells not only can synthesize endorphins and adrenocorticotropic hormone but given the right stimulus, they can also make growth hormone, thyroid-stimulating hormone, and reproductive hormones (almost like tiny floating pituitary glands). Whether these hormones are produced in amounts substantial enough to actually make a difference is still questionable. But, if they are, the possibilities are exciting. For example, during an infection, immune cell endorphins might help to reduce pain and lift one's spirits, and TSH might be responsible for the increased heart and metabolic rates typical of many infectious states. A summary of these "guesstimated" neuroimmune interactions is illustrated in the accompanying diagram.

Just as cooperative behaviors between the nervous and immune systems seem to go on throughout life, their "memory" fades simultaneously. That is, just as a person's short-term memory starts to fade, the immune system's ability to recognize its own body's tissues begins to fail, resulting in increased cancer and autoimmune disease rates in old age.

Much of what has been said here is still met with skepticism in parts of the medical community, but the evidence is strong. Sooner or later, the medical community will have to decide what credit should be given to the mind for maintaining health and promoting recovery from disease.

Chemical signals (neurotransmitters, hormones) **from brain to immune cells** may:

1. modify mobility, ability to multiply, and killing ability of the immune cells (macrophages and lymphocytes)

2. modulate (enhance or inhibit) resistance to and recovery from disease

Chemical signals (lymphokines, endorphins, and hormones) **from immune cells to brain** may:

1. inform brain of type of infection assaulting the body

2. reduce pain; influence heart rate, metabolic rate, sleep patterns, and mood (increase irritability, aggressiveness, etc.)

Hypothalamic releasing factors stimulate anterior pituitary to release hormones

Nerve fibers deliver chemical signals (neurotransmitters, including neuropeptides such as endorphins) to lymphoid organs (sites of immune cells) and to adrenal glands

ACTH and others

Adrenal gland

Epinephrine and norepinephrine

Lymphokines, endorphins, hormones

Activated lymphocytes release lymphokines (interferon and others), endorphins, and certain hormones to the blood

Monokines

Macrophage engulfs microorganism and presents its antigens, releases monokines to signal other immune cells

Microorganisms gain entry into blood and encounter lymphoid organs

LYMPHOID ORGANS OF THE BODY

Postulated scheme for communication and interaction between the nervous system and the immune system.

this particular antigenic property); and (2) **reactivity,** the ability to react with the products of these reactions, that is, with the activated lymphocytes and the antibodies released in response to them.

An almost limitless variety of foreign molecules can act as complete antigens, including virtually all foreign proteins, nucleic acids, some lipids, and many large polysaccharides. Of these, proteins are the strongest antigens. Pollen grains and microorganisms—such as bacteria, fungi, and virus particles—are immunogenic because their surface membranes (or coats in the case of viruses) bear many different foreign macromolecules. Most complete antigens have a molecular mass of 10,000 daltons or more.

As a rule, small molecules—such as peptides, nucleotides, and many hormones—are not immunogenic. But, when they link up with the body's own proteins, the immune system may recognize the combination as foreign and mount an attack that is harmful rather than protective. (Such reactions, called *allergies,* are described later in the chapter.) In such cases, the troublesome small molecule is called a **hapten** (hap'ten; *haptein* = grasp) or **incomplete antigen.** Haptens are reactive but not immunogenic unless they are attached to protein carriers. Besides certain drugs (particularly penicillin), chemicals that act as haptens are found in poison ivy, animal dander, and even some detergents, cosmetics, and other common household and industrial products.

Antigenic Determinants

The ability of a molecule to act as an antigen depends not only on its size but also on the complexity of its structure. Only specific parts of an entire antigen are

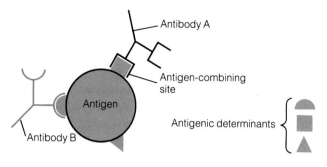

FIGURE 22.5
Antigenic determinants. Antibodies bind to antigenic determinants on the surfaces of antigens. Most antigens express several different antigenic determinants; thus, different antibodies can bind to the same complex antigen. The antigen illustrated has three different antigenic determinants and would be expected to elicit the production of three different types of antibodies. (Note that each antigenic determinant would actually be represented many times.)

immunogenic, and it is these sites, called **antigenic determinants,** to which free antibodies or activated lymphocytes can bind. This binding occurs much in the same manner that an enzyme binds to a substrate.

Most naturally occurring antigens have many different antigenic determinants (Figure 22.5) on their surfaces, some more potent than others in provoking an immune response. Because different antigenic determinants are "recognized" by different lymphocytes, a single antigen may mobilize several lymphocytes and may stimulate formation of many different kinds of antibodies against it. Large proteins have hundreds of chemically different antigenic determinants, which accounts for their high immunogenicity and reactivity. However, large but simple molecules such as plastics, which have many identical, regularly repeating units (and thus are not chemically complex), have little or no immunogenicity. Such substances are used to make artificial implants (hip replacements and others) because they are not rejected by the body.

Self-Antigens

The external surfaces of all our cells are dotted with a large variety of protein molecules. Assuming our immune system has been properly "programmed," these **self-antigens** are not foreign or antigenic to us, but they are strongly antigenic to other individuals. (This is the basis of transfusion reactions and graft rejection.) Among these cell surface proteins is a specific group of glycoproteins that marks a cell as *self.* These proteins, called **MHC proteins,** are coded for by genes of the **major histocompatibility complex (MHC).** Because millions of different combinations of these genes are possible, it is unlikely that any two people except identical twins have the same MHC-encoded proteins. Each MHC molecule has a deep groove that typically displays a peptide, some 8 to 13 amino acids

long. In healthy cells, all of the displayed peptides are derived from the breakdown of cellular proteins during normal protein recycling and tend to be quite diverse. However, in infected cells, the MHC proteins also bind to fragments of (foreign) antigens and, as described shortly, this event plays a crucial role in mobilizing the immune system.

CELLS OF THE IMMUNE SYSTEM: AN OVERVIEW

The three crucial cell types of the immune system are two distinct populations of lymphocytes, and macrophages. **B lymphocytes** or **B cells** oversee humoral immunity; **T lymphocytes** or **T cells** are non–antibody-producing lymphocytes that constitute the cell-mediated arm of immunity. Unlike the two types of lymphocytes, macrophages do not respond to specific antigens but instead play essential auxiliary roles.

Lymphocytes

Like all blood cells, lymphocytes originate in red bone marrow from hemocytoblasts. When immature lymphocytes are released from the bone marrow, they are essentially identical (Figure 22.6). Whether a given lymphocyte matures into a B cell or a T cell depends on where in the body it becomes **immunocompetent,** that is, able (or competent) to recognize a specific antigen by binding to it. T cells arise from immature lymphocytes that migrate from the bone marrow to the thymus, where they undergo a maturation process of two to three days under the direction of thymic hormones. Within the thymus, the immature lymphocytes divide rapidly and their numbers increase enormously, but only the maturing T cells with the sharpest ability to identify *foreign* antigens survive. The vast majority—lymphocytes capable of binding strongly to, and mounting an attack against, *self-antigens* (cell surface proteins of body cells)—are vigorously weeded out and destroyed. Thus, the development of **self-tolerance,** or unresponsiveness to self-antigens, is an essential part of a lymphocyte's "education" during fetal life. This is also true for B cells. B cells develop immunocompetence in bone marrow, but very little is known about the factors that control B cell maturation in humans. However, some self-reactive B cells are inactivated (a phenomenon called *anergy*), while others are killed outright.

When B or T cells become immunocompetent, they display a unique type of receptor on their surfaces. These receptors (some 10^4 to 10^5 per cell) enable the lymphocyte to recognize and bind to a specific antigen. Once these receptors have appeared, a lymphocyte is committed to react to one distinct antigen, and one only, because *all* of the antigen receptors on its external surface are the same. For example, receptors of one lymphocyte can recognize only a single antigenic determinant of the hepatitis A virus, those

? *What is the advantage of having lymphocytes that are mobile (recirculating) rather than fixed in the lymphoid organs?*

Site of lymphocyte origin

Site of development of immunocompetence as T or B cell

Site of antigen challenge and final differentiation to mature B and T cells

Bone marrow

Immature lymphocytes

Circulation in blood

1

1

Thymus

Bone marrow

Immunocompetent T cell migrates via blood

2

Lymph nodes, spleen, other lymphoid tissues, and loose connective tissues

2

Immunocompetent B cell migrates via blood

3

Immunocompetent and mature B and T cells recirculate in blood and lymph

FIGURE 22.6

Lymphocyte traffic. Immature lymphocytes arise in bone marrow. (Note that red marrow, from which the lymphocytes originate, is not found in the medullary cavity of the diaphysis of long bones in adults.) **(1)** Lymphocytes destined to become T cells migrate to the thymus and develop immunocompetence there. B cells develop immunocompetence in the bone marrow. **(2)** After leaving the thymus or bone marrow as immunocompetent cells, lymphocytes "seed" the lymph nodes, spleen, and other lymphoid tissues where the antigen challenge occurs. **(3)** Immunocompetent and mature (antigen-activated) lymphocytes circulate continuously in the bloodstream and lymph and throughout the lymphoid organs of the body.

of another can bind only to a determinant on pneumococcus bacteria, and so forth. Although the antigen receptors of T cells and B cells differ in overall structure, in most cases both T and B lymphocytes are capable of responding to the same antigen variety.

While many of the details of lymphocyte processing are still unknown, we know that lymphocytes become immunocompetent *before* meeting the antigens they may later attack. Thus, *it is our genes, not antigens, that determine what specific foreign substances our immune system will be able to recognize and resist.* (An antigen determines only which of the existing T or B cells will proliferate and mount the attack against it.) Only some of the possible antigens our lymphocytes are programmed to resist will ever invade our bodies. Consequently, only some members of our army of immunocompetent cells will be mobilized in our lifetime. The others will be forever idle.

After becoming immunocompetent, both T cells and B cells disperse to the lymph nodes, spleen, and other lymphoid organs, where their encounters with antigens will occur (Figure 22.6). Then, when the lymphocytes bind with recognized antigens, they complete their differentiation into fully functional T cells and B cells.

Macrophages

Macrophages, which also become widely distributed throughout the lymphoid organs and connective tissues, arise from monocytes formed in the bone marrow. As noted earlier, a major role of macrophages in immunity is to engulf foreign particles and present fragments of these antigens, like signal flags, on their own surfaces where they can be recognized by T cells (Figure 22.7)—that is, they act as *antigen presenters.* (This function is described in more detail shortly.) Macrophages also secrete soluble proteins that activate T cells. Activated T cells, in turn, release chemicals that prod macrophages to become *activated macrophages,* true "killers" that are insatiable phago-

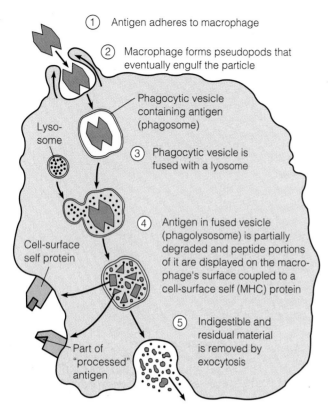

① Antigen adheres to macrophage

② Macrophage forms pseudopods that eventually engulf the particle

Phagocytic vesicle containing antigen (phagosome)

Lyso-some

③ Phagocytic vesicle is fused with a lyosome

Cell-surface self protein

④ Antigen in fused vesicle (phagolysosome) is partially degraded and peptide portions of it are displayed on the macrophage's surface coupled to a cell-surface self (MHC) protein

⑤ Indigestible and residual material is removed by exocytosis

Part of "processed" antigen

FIGURE 22.7
The macrophage's role in immunity: phagocytosis or endocytosis (antigen internalization), antigen processing, and antigen presentation.

cytes and secrete bactericidal chemicals. As you will see, interactions between lymphocytes, and between lymphocytes and macrophages, underlie virtually all phases of the immune response.

Although both macrophages and lymphocytes are found throughout each lymphoid organ, specific cells tend to be more numerous in certain areas. For example, the paracortical areas of lymph nodes house mostly T cells, and B cells tend to populate the *germinal centers* (see Figure 21.5, p. 699), whereas relatively more macrophages are clustered around the medullary sinuses. Macrophages tend to remain fixed in the lymphoid organs, as if waiting for antigens to come to them; but lymphocytes, especially the T cells (which account for 65% to 85% of blood-borne lymphocytes), circulate continuously throughout the body (see Figure 22.6). This greatly increases a lymphocyte's chance of coming into contact with antigens located in different parts of the body, as well as with huge numbers of macrophages and other lymphocytes.

Because lymph capillaries pick up proteins and pathogens from nearly all body tissues, immune cells in lymph nodes are in a strategic position to encounter a large variety of antigens. Lymphocytes and macrophages in the tonsils act primarily against microorganisms that invade the oral and nasal cavi-

ties, whereas the spleen acts as a filter to trap blood-borne antigens.

In summary, the immune system is a two-fisted defensive system that uses lymphocytes, macrophages, and specific molecules to identify and destroy all substances—both living and nonliving—that are in the body, but are not recognized as being part of the body, or self. The immune system's response to such threats depends on the ability of its cells (1) to recognize foreign substances (antigens) in the body by binding to them, and (2) to communicate with one another so that the whole system mounts a response specific to those antigens.

HUMORAL IMMUNE RESPONSE

The **antigen challenge,** the first encounter between an immunocompetent lymphocyte and an invading antigen, usually takes place in the spleen or a lymph node, but may happen in any lymphoid tissue. If the lymphocyte is a B cell, the challenging antigen provokes the *humoral immune response,* in which antibodies are produced against the challenger.

Clonal Selection and Differentiation of B Cells

An immunocompetent but as yet not fully functional B lymphocyte is *activated* (stimulated to complete its differentiation) when antigens bind to its surface receptors and cross-link adjacent receptors together. (As described later, T cells usually collaborate in this process as well.) Antigen binding is quickly followed by receptor-mediated endocytosis of the cross-linked antigen-receptor complexes. These activating events (plus some interactions with T cells described shortly) trigger **clonal** (klo′nul) **selection.** That is, they stimulate the B cell to grow and then to multiply rapidly to form an army of cells all exactly like itself and bearing the same antigen-specific receptors (Figure 22.8). The resulting family of identical cells, all descended from the *same* ancestor cell, is called a **clone.** It is the antigen that does the selecting in clonal selection by "choosing" a lymphocyte with complementary receptors.

Most cells of the clone become **plasma cells,** the antibody-secreting effector cells of the humoral response. Although B cells secrete very limited amounts of antibodies, plasma cells develop the elaborate internal machinery (largely rough endoplasmic reticulum) needed to secrete antibodies at the unbelievable rate of about 2000 molecules per second. Each plasma cell functions at this breakneck pace for 4 to 5 days and then dies. The secreted antibodies, each with the same antigen-binding properties as the receptor molecules on the surface of the parent B cell, circulate in the blood or lymph, where they bind to free antigens and mark them for destruction by other specific or nonspecific mechanisms. The clone cells that do not differentiate into plasma cells become

FIGURE 22.8

Simplified version of clonal selection of a B cell stimulated by antigen binding. The initial meeting stimulates the primary response in which the B cell proliferates rapidly, forming a clone of like cells, most of which differentiate into antibody-producing plasma cells. (Though not indicated in the figure, the production of mature plasma cells takes about five days and eight cell generations.) Cells that do not differentiate into plasma cells become memory cells, which are already primed to respond to subsequent exposures to the same antigen. Should such a meeting occur, the memory cells quickly produce more memory cells and larger numbers of effector plasma cells with the same antigen specificity. Responses generated by memory cells are called secondary responses.

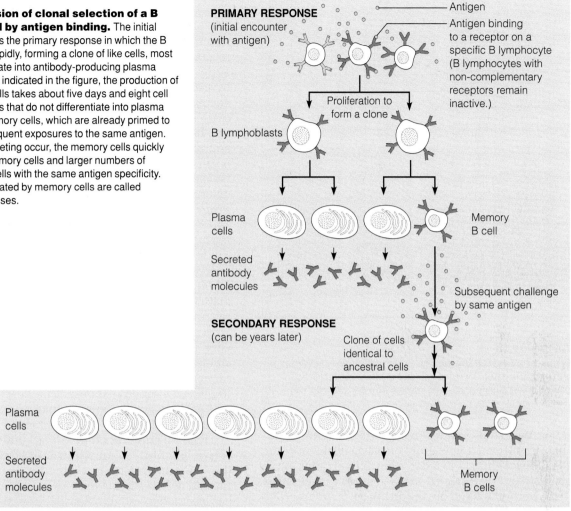

long-lived **memory cells** that can mount an almost immediate humoral response if they encounter the same antigen again (see Figure 22.8).

Immunological Memory

The cellular proliferation and differentiation just described constitute the **primary immune response,** which occurs on the first exposure to a particular antigen. The primary response characteristically has a lag period of several (3 to 6) days after the antigen challenge. This lag period mirrors the time required for the few B cells specific for that antigen to proliferate and for their offspring to differentiate into plasma cells (functional antibody-synthesizing factories). After the mobilization period, plasma antibody levels rise, reaching peak levels in about 10 days, and then begin to decline (Figure 22.9).

If (and when) someone is reexposed to the same antigen, whether it's the second or the twenty-second time, a **secondary immune response** occurs. These secondary immune responses are faster, more prolonged, and more effective, because the immune system has already been primed to the antigen, and sensitized memory cells are already in place and "on alert." These memory cells provide what is commonly called **immunological memory.**

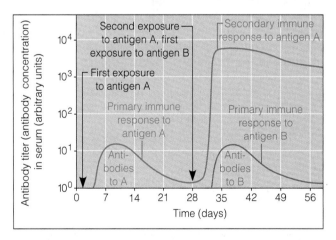

FIGURE 22.9

Primary and secondary humoral responses. The blue graph line shows both a primary response and a secondary response to antigen A. In the primary response, there is a time lag and then a gradual rise and fairly rapid decline in the level of antibodies in the blood. A second exposure to antigen A on day 28 elicits a secondary response that is both more rapid and more intense. Additionally, though not shown on the graph, antibody levels remain high for a much longer time. If a second antigen, antigen B, were also encountered at day 28, the reaction to that antigen would be a primary response, not a secondary one, and its graph line (red) would show a pattern similar to that seen during the primary response to antigen A.

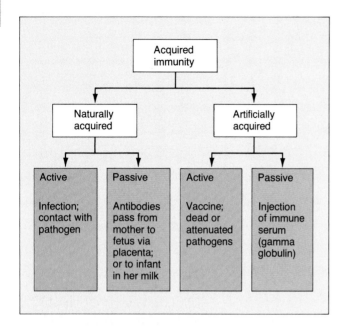

FIGURE 22.10
Types of acquired immunity. Green boxes signify active types of immunity in which the immunological memory is established. Orange boxes signify short-lived passive types of immunity; no immunological memory is established.

Within hours after recognition of the "old-enemy" antigen a new army of plasma cells is being generated. Within 2 to 3 days the antibody titer in the bloodstream rises steeply to reach much higher levels than were achieved in the primary response. The antibodies produced in secondary responses not only bind with greater affinity (more tightly), but their levels in the blood remain high for weeks to months. (Hence, when the appropriate chemical signals are present, plasma cells can keep functioning for much longer than the 4 to 5 days seen in primary responses.) Even in the absence of antigenic stimulation, memory cells persist for long periods in humans and many retain their capacity to produce powerful secondary humoral responses for a lifetime.

The same general phenomena occur in the cellular immune response: A primary response sets up a pool of activated lymphocytes (in this case, T cells) and generates memory cells that can then mount secondary responses.

Active and Passive Humoral Immunity

When your B cells encounter antigens, and produce antibodies against them, you are exhibiting **active humoral immunity** (Figure 22.10). Active immunity is (1) *naturally acquired* during bacterial and viral infections, during which we may develop the symptoms of the disease and suffer a little (or a lot), and (2) *artificially acquired* when we receive **vaccines.** The response of the immune system is much the same whether the antigen invades the body under its own

power, or is deliberately introduced in the form of a vaccine. Indeed, once it was realized that secondary responses are so much more vigorous, the race was on to develop vaccines to "prime" the immune response by providing a first meeting with the antigen. Most vaccines contain dead or *attenuated* (living, but extremely weakened) pathogens. Vaccines provide two benefits: (1) they spare us most of the symptoms and discomfort of the disease that would otherwise occur during the primary response, and (2) their weakened antigens provide functional antigenic determinants that stimulate antibody production and promote immunological memory. So-called *booster shots* that may intensify the immune response at later meetings with the same antigen are also available.

Vaccines have literally wiped out smallpox, have nearly eliminated many childhood killers such as whooping cough, polio, and measles, and have dramatically reduced hepatitis B, tetanus, and pneumonia in adults. Nonetheless, conventional vaccines have some shortcomings. Sometimes they cause the very disease they are trying to prevent when the attenuated antigen isn't weakened enough (a rare consequence of polio vaccine). In other cases, they may trigger an allergic response. The new "naked DNA" antiviral vaccines now undergoing clinical tests appear to circumvent these problems.

Passive humoral immunity is quite different from active immunity, both in the antibody source and in the degree of protection it provides (see Figure 22.10). Instead of being made by your plasma cells, the antibodies are harvested (obtained) from the serum of an immune human or animal donor. As a result, your B cells are *not* challenged by antigens, immunological memory does *not* occur, and the protection provided by the "borrowed" antibodies ends when they naturally degrade in the body. Passive immunity is conferred *naturally* on a fetus when the mother's antibodies cross the placenta and enter the fetal circulation. For several months after birth, the baby is protected from all the antigens to which the mother has been exposed.

Passive immunity is *artificially* conferred when a person receives an infusion of immune serum such as *gamma globulin.* Gamma globulin is commonly administered after exposure to hepatitis. Other immune sera are used to treat poisonous snake bites (an antivenom), botulism, rabies, and tetanus (an antitoxin) because these rapidly fatal diseases would kill a person before active immunity could be established. The donated antibodies provide immediate protection, but their effect is short-lived (two to three weeks).

Antibodies

Antibodies, also called **immunoglobulins** (im″u-no-glob′u-linz), or **Igs,** constitute the **gamma globulin** part of blood proteins. As mentioned, antibodies are soluble proteins secreted by activated B cells or by

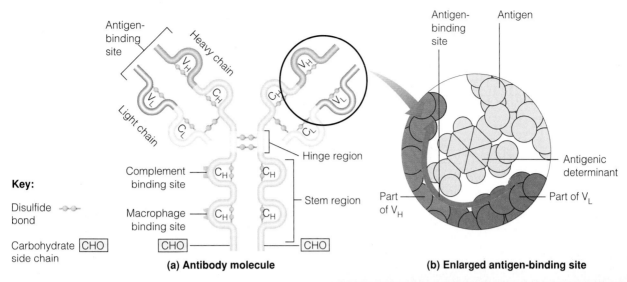

Key:

Disulfide bond

Carbohydrate CHO side chain

(a) Antibody molecule

(b) Enlarged antigen-binding site

FIGURE 22.11

Basic antibody structure. (a) Basic antibody structure consists of four polypeptide chains that are joined together by disulfide bonds (S — S). Two of the chains are short *light chains;* the other two are long *heavy chains.* Each chain has a V (variable) region, which has a markedly different amino acid sequence in different antibodies, and a **C** (constant) region, which is essentially identical in different antibodies of the same class. The variable regions are the antigen-binding sites of the antibody; hence, each antibody monomer has two antigen-binding sites. **(b)** Enlargement of an antigenic determinant bound to an antigen-binding site. **(c)** Computer-generated image of antibody structure. Each tiny colored dot (sphere) represents an individual amino acid of the polypeptide chains.

(c)

plasma cells in response to an antigen, and they are capable of binding specifically with that antigen.

Antibodies are formed in response to an incredible number of different antigens. Despite their variety, all antibodies can be grouped into one of five Ig classes, each slightly different in structure and function. We will see how these Ig classes differ, but first let's take a look at how all antibodies are alike.

Basic Antibody Structure

Regardless of its class, each antibody has a basic structure consisting of four looping polypeptide chains linked together by disulfide (sulfur-to-sulfur) bonds (Figure 22.11). Two of these chains, the **heavy (H) chains,** are identical to each other and contain approximately 400 amino acids each. The other two chains, the **light (L) chains,** are also identical to each other, but are only about half as long. The heavy chains have a flexible *hinge* region at their approximate "middles." Notice that disulfide bonds also bind together amino acids within the same heavy or light chain (see Figure 22.11). Since the amino acids that are bound together are about 110 amino acids apart, the intervening parts of the polypeptide chains loop out. When the four chains are combined, the molecule formed, called an **antibody monomer** (mon'o-

mer), has two identical halves, each consisting of a heavy and a light chain, and the molecule as a whole is **T** or **Y** shaped.

When scientists began investigating antibody structure, they discovered something very peculiar. Each of the four chains forming an antibody has a **variable (V) region** at one end and a much larger **constant (C) region** at the other end. Antibodies responding to different antigens had very different variable regions, but their constant regions were the same (or nearly so) in all antibodies of a given class. This made sense when it was discovered that the variable regions of the heavy and light chains in each arm combine to form an **antigen-binding site** (see Figure 22.11) uniquely shaped to "fit" a specific antigenic determinant or an antigen. Hence, each antibody monomer has two such antigen-binding regions.

The constant regions that form the *stem* of the antibody monomer determine the antibody class and serve common functions in all antibodies: These are the *effector regions* of the antibody that determine the cells and chemicals the antibody can bind to, and how the antibody class will function in antigen elimination. For example, some but not all antibodies can fix complement, some circulate in blood while others are found primarily in body secretions, some cross the placental barrier, and so on.

Table 22.3 Immunoglobulin Classes

IgD
(monomer)

IgD is virtually always attached to the external surface of a B cell, where it functions as the antigen receptor of the B cell; hence IgD is important in B cell activation.

IgM
(pentamer)

IgM exists in monomer and pentamer (five united monomers) forms. The monomer, which is attached to the B cell surface, serves as an antigen receptor. The pentamer (illustrated) circulates in blood plasma and is the first Ig class released by plasma cells during the primary response. (This fact is diagnostically useful because presence of IgM in plasma usually indicates current infection by the pathogen eliciting IgM's formation.) Because of its numerous antigen binding sites, IgM is a potent agglutinating agent and readily fixes and activates complement.

IgG
(monomer)

IgG is the most abundant antibody in plasma, accounting for 75% to 85% of circulating antibodies. It protects against bacteria, viruses, and toxins circulating in blood and lymph, readily fixes complement, and is the main antibody of both primary and secondary responses. It crosses the placenta and confers passive immunity from the mother to the fetus.

IgA
(dimer)

IgA monomer exists in limited amounts in plasma. The dimer (illustrated), referred to as secretory IgA, is found in body secretions such as saliva, sweat, intestinal juice, and milk, and helps prevent attachment of pathogens to epithelial cell surfaces (including mucous membranes and the epidermis).

IgE
(monomer)

IgE is slightly larger than the IgG antibody. It is secreted by plasma cells in skin, mucosae of the gastrointestinal and respiratory tracts, and tonsils. Its stem region becomes bound to mast cells and basophils, and when its receptor ends are triggered by an antigen, it causes the cells to release histamine and other chemicals that mediate inflammation and an allergic reaction. Typically only traces of IgE are found in plasma, but levels rise during severe allergic attacks or chronic parasitic infections of the gastrointestinal tract.

Antibody Classes

The five major immunoglobulin classes are designated IgD, IgM, IgG, IgA, and IgE, on the basis of the C (constant) regions in their heavy chains. As illustrated in Table 22.3, IgD, IgG, and IgE have the same basic Y-shaped structure and thus are *monomers.* IgA occurs in both monomer and *dimer* (two linked monomers) forms. (Only the dimer is shown in the table.) Compared to the other antibodies, IgM is a huge antibody, a *pentamer* (*penta* = five), constructed from five linked monomers.

The antibodies of each class have slightly different biological roles and locations in the body. For example, IgM is the first antibody class that is *released* to the blood by plasma cells. IgG is the most abundant antibody in plasma and is the only Ig class that crosses the placental barrier. Hence, the passive immunity that a mother transfers to her fetus is "with the compliments" of her IgG antibodies. *Only* IgM and IgG can fix complement. The IgA dimer, also called **secretory IgA,** is found primarily in mucus and other secretions that bathe body surfaces. It plays a major role in preventing pathogens from gaining entry into the body. IgD is always bound to the B cell surface; hence it acts as a B cell receptor. IgE antibodies, almost never found in blood, are the "troublemaker" antibodies involved in some allergies. These and other characteristics unique to each of the immunoglobulin classes are summarized in Table 22.3.

Mechanisms of Antibody Diversity

Estimates are that the various plasma cell clones can make over a billion different types of antibodies. Because we probably encounter several thousand different antigens in our lifetime, our immune system allows for a wide margin of error. Since antibodies, like all proteins, are specified by genes, it would seem that an individual must have billions of genes. Not so; each body cell contains perhaps 100,000 genes that code for all the proteins the cells must make.

How can a limited number of genes generate a seemingly limitless number of different antibodies? Recombinant DNA studies have shown that the genes that actually dictate the structure of each antibody are not present as such in embryonic cells. Instead of a complete and active set of "antibody genes," embryonic cells contain a few hundred genetic bits and pieces that can be thought of as an "erector set for antibody genes." These gene segments are shuffled and combined in different ways (a process called **somatic recombination**) by each B cell as it becomes immunocompetent. The information of these newly assembled genes is then expressed in the surface receptors of B cells and in the antibodies later released by their plasma cell "offspring."

In an immature B cell, the gene segments coding for the light and heavy chains (exons) are physically separated by noncoding DNA segments (introns), but are located on the same chromosome. (See p. 93 in Chapter 3 if you need a refresher on this terminology.) The light and heavy chains are manufactured separately and then joined to form the antibody molecule. A simplified version of the somatic-recombination process used to produce one type of light antibody chain is described and illustrated in Figure 22.12. Although the events forming the heavy chains are similar, the process is much more complex because of the larger variety of gene (DNA) segments for the constant regions of the heavy chains (remember, the C regions of the heavy chains determine antibody class). The random mixing of gene segments to make unique antibody genes specifying the H and L chains accounts for only part of the huge variability seen in antibodies. Certain areas of the V gene segments, the so-called *hypervariable regions,* are "hot spots" for somatic mutations that enormously increase antibody variation.

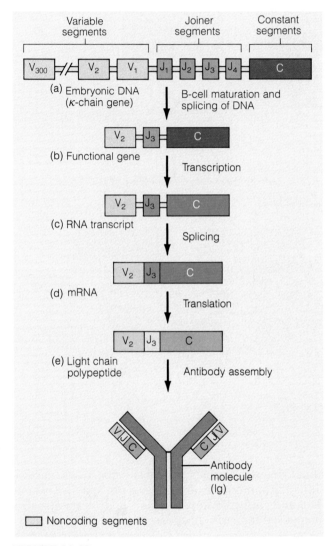

FIGURE 22.12

Somatic recombination and formation of a light antibody chain. (a) In an embryonic cell the gene for kappa light chain has one constant (C) segment, four joiner (J) segments, and 200 to 300 variable (V) segments. These DNA segments are separated by noncoding segments of DNA (gray). **(b)** During B cell maturation, one randomly selected V segment is combined with one of the J segments and the C segment to form the active gene for the light chain. The intervening segments are deleted (spliced out). **(c)** The new gene is transcribed to form the RNA transcript. **(d)** Noncoding segments are spliced out to form the messenger RNA. **(e)** The final mRNA is translated into protein, forming the light chain with variable, joiner, and constant regions. (Note that the J region of the polypeptide is considered part of the variable region (V_L in Figure 22.11).) The V, J, and C regions of the heavy chains are not indicated in the illustrated antibody molecule to simplify the figure.

A single plasma cell can "switch" to make various kinds of heavy chains, producing two or more different antibody classes with the same antigen specificity. For example, the first antibody released in the primary response is IgM; then the plasma cell begins to secrete IgG. During secondary responses, almost all of the Ig protein is IgG.

Antibody Targets and Functions

Though antibodies cannot destroy antigen-bearing "invaders" directly, they can inactivate them and tag them for destruction (Figure 22.13). The common event in all antibody-antigen interactions is the formation of **antigen-antibody** (or **immune**) **complexes.** The defensive mechanisms used by antibodies are neutralization, agglutination, precipitation, and complement fixation. Of these, complement fixation and neutralization are the most important.

Complement fixation and activation is the chief antibody ammunition used against cellular antigens, such as bacteria or mismatched red blood cells. When antibodies bind to cellular targets, they change shape exposing complement-binding sites on their constant regions (see Figure 22.11a). This triggers complement fixation into the antigenic cell's surface and subsequent cell lysis. Additionally, as described earlier, molecules released during complement activation tremendously amplify the inflammatory response and promote phagocytosis via opsonization. Furthermore, since complement-coated antigens are more attractive (stimulating) to B cells, a positive feedback cycle that enlists more and more defensive elements is set into motion.

Neutralization, the simplest effector mechanism, occurs when antibodies block specific sites on viruses or bacterial exotoxins (toxic chemicals secreted by bacteria). As a result, the virus or exotoxin cannot bind to receptor sites on tissue cells to cause injury, and the antigen-antibody complexes are eventually destroyed by phagocytes.

Because antibodies have more than one antigen-binding site, they can bind to the same determinant on more than one antigen at a time; consequently, antigen-antibody complexes can be cross-linked into large lattices. When cell-bound antigens are cross-linked the process causes clumping, or **agglutination,** of the foreign cells. IgM, with ten antigen-binding sites (see Table 22.3), is an especially potent agglutinating agent. Recall that this type of reaction occurs when mismatched blood is transfused (the foreign red blood cells are clumped) and is the basis of tests used for blood typing (see p. 606). A similar mechanism is **precipitation,** in which soluble molecules (instead of cells) are cross-linked into large complexes that settle out of solution. These agglutinated bacteria and immobilized (precipitated) antigen molecules are much more easily captured and engulfed by phagocytes than are freely moving antigens.

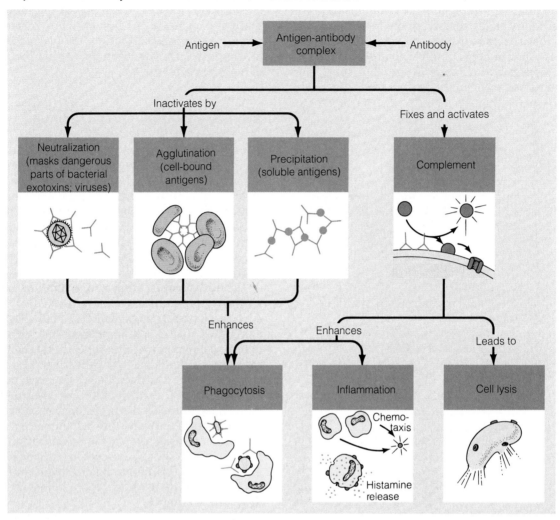

FIGURE 22.13
Mechanisms of antibody action. Antibodies act against free viruses, red blood cell antigens, bacterial toxins, and intact bacteria.

Monoclonal Antibodies

In addition to their use for providing passive immunity, commercially prepared antibodies are used in research, clinical testing, and treating certain cancers. **Monoclonal antibodies,** used for such purposes, are produced by descendants of a single cell, and are pure antibody preparations that exhibit specificity for a single antigenic determinant.

The current technology for making monoclonal antibodies involves fusion of tumor cells and B lymphocytes. The resulting cell hybrids, called **hybridomas** (hi″brĭ-do′mahz), have desirable traits of both parent cells. Like the myeloma (tumor) cells, they proliferate indefinitely in culture; like B cells, they produce a single type of antibody.

Monoclonal antibodies are used for diagnosis of pregnancy, certain sexually transmitted diseases, hepatitis, and rabies. Compared with the conventional diagnostic tests for these conditions, monoclonal antibody tests are much more specific, sensitive, and rapid. Monoclonal antibody tests are also being used for early diagnosis of certain types of cancer, such as colon cancer, and to treat cancers such as leukemia and lymphomas, which are present in the circulation and thus are easily accessible to injected antibodies. Partial remissions have been reported in many cases thought to be hopeless. Even more recently, monoclonal antibodies attached to anticancer drugs have been used as "guided missiles" to deliver the drug only to the cancerous tissue. Such an innovative approach to cancer treatment spares cancer patients the discomfort of traditional chemotherapy treatments, in which the injected toxic drugs circulate freely through the bloodstream, killing not only cancer cells but also rapidly dividing normal tissue cells.

CELL-MEDIATED IMMUNE RESPONSE

Despite their immense versatility, antibodies provide only partial immunity. Their prey is the obvious pathogen. They are fairly ineffective against infectious microorganisms such as the tuberculosis bacillus which quickly slips inside body cells to multiply there. In these cases, the second (cell-mediated) arm of immunity comes into play.

The T cells that mediate cellular immunity are a diverse lot, much more complex than B cells in both classification and function. Based on their general functions, there are three major populations of T cells. **Cytotoxic T cells** are *effector cells* for cell killing. The two varieties of *regulatory cells* are the **helper** and **suppressor T cells.** However, a newer classification of T cells is based on which of a pair of structurally related *cell differentiation glycoproteins* —CD4 or CD8—is diplayed by a mature T cell. These cell surface receptors are distinct from the T cell antigen receptors, but they *do* play a role in interactions that occur between a cell and other structures (other cells or foreign antigens). Because this terminology is now commonly used, it is important to know that **CD4 cells,** also called T4 cells, are primarily helper T cells, whereas **CD8 cells** (T8 cells) include the cytotoxic and suppressor T cell populations. Before going into the details of the cell-mediated immune response, we will recap some introductory information and compare the importance of the humoral and cellular responses in the overall scheme of immunity.

The soluble antibodies, produced by plasma cells (B cell progeny), are in many ways the simplest ammunition of the immune response. Antibodies are specialized to latch onto intact bacteria and soluble foreign molecules in extracellular environments— that is, in body secretions and tissue fluid and circulating in blood and lymph. At the most basic level, antibody production and pathogen multiplication race against each other and the fate of the antibody targets is a case of "the quick or the dead." Remember, however, that forming antibody-antigen complexes does *not* destroy the antigens; instead, they prepare them for disposal by nonspecific defense mechanisms and activated T cells.

In contrast to B cells and antibodies, T cells are unable to "see" free antigens. T cells can recognize and respond only to processed fragments of protein antigens (amino acid sequences rather than 3-D shape) displayed on surfaces of the body's own cells, and then only under specific circumstances. Consequently, T cells are best suited for cell-to-cell interactions, and most of their direct attacks on antigens (mediated by the cytotoxic T cells) are directed against body cells infected by viruses, bacteria, or intracellular parasites; abnormal or cancerous body cells; and cells of infused or transplanted foreign tissues.

Clonal Selection and Differentiation of T Cells

The stimulus for clonal selection and differentiation is the same in B cells and T cells—the binding of antigen. However, as described next, the mechanism by which T cells recognize "their" antigen is very different and has some unique restrictions.

Antigen Recognition and MHC Restriction

Like B cells, immunocompetent T cells are activated when the variable regions of their surface receptors bind to a "recognized" antigen. However, T cells must accomplish *double recognition:* simultaneous recognition of nonself or antiself (the antigen) and self (a MHC protein of a body cell).

Two types of MHC proteins are important to T cell activation. **Class I MHC proteins** are displayed by virtually all body cells except red blood cells. After being synthesized at the endoplasmic reticulum, class I MHC proteins bind with a peptide fragment 8 or 9 amino acids long ferried into the ER from the cytosol by special transport proteins aptly called TAPs (for *T*ransporter associated with *A*ntigen *P*rocessing). The "loaded" class I MHC proteins then migrate to the plasma membrane to exhibit their attached protein fragment. Class I MHC proteins display fragments of proteins synthesized *in the cell*— either bits of cellular (self) proteins or peptides from endogenous antigens. (*Endogenous antigens* are foreign proteins synthesized within a body cell, such as the viral proteins produced by virus-infected cells or alien proteins made by a cancerous cell.

By contrast to the widely distributed class I proteins, class II MHC proteins are found only on the surfaces of mature B cells, some T cells, and *antigen-presenting cells* (see below), and enable the cells of the immune system to recognize one another. Like class I MHC proteins, these are synthesized at the ER and bind to peptide fragments. However, the peptide fragments bound are longer (14–17 amino acids) and come from both cellular proteins and *exogenous antigens* (foreign antigens) that have been phagocytosed and broken down within the phagosome vesicle. Also class II MHC proteins follow a different path to the plasma membrane. They move from the ER through the golgi apparatus and then into the phagosomes where they bind with the degraded protein fragments. Vesicles are recycled to the cell surface where the class II MHC proteins display their booty.

The role of the MHC proteins in the immune response is strikingly important—they provide the means for signaling to immune system cells that infectious microorganisms are hiding within body cells. Without such a mechanism, viruses and certain bacteria that thrive in cells could multiply unbothered and unnoticed. When MHC proteins are com-

Viral antigen

MHC I protein

Processed viral antigen (peptide) presented in combination with MHC I protein

Body cell

CD8 protein

Immunocompetent cytotoxic T cell

Infected tissue cell presenting antigenic peptide recognized by cytotoxic T cell

T cell receptor

Clone formation

Cytotoxic T memory cell

Mature cytotoxic T cells

FIGURE 22.14
Clonal selection of helper and cytotoxic T cells involves simultaneous recognition of self and antiself. Helper and cytotoxic T cells are stimulated to proliferate (clone) and complete their differentiation when they bind to parts of foreign antigens complexed to MHC (major histocompatibility complex) proteins. Immunocompetent cytotoxic T cells are activated when they bind to endogenous antigens (antiself)—part of a virus in this example— complexed to a class I MHC protein. (Class I proteins are displayed on the surfaces of all body cells, enabling cytotoxic T cells to respond to infected or malignant body cells.) The activation of helper T cells is similar, except that the processed antigen is complexed with a class II MHC protein, typically found only on antigen-presenting cells such as macrophages.

plexed with fragments of our own (self) proteins, T cells passing by get the signal "Leave this cell alone, it's ours!" and simply ignore them. But when they are complexed to antigenic peptides (either exogenous or endogenous), they betray the invaders and "sound the alarm" by (1) acting as antigen "holders" and (2) forming the "self" part of the self-antiself complexes that must be recognized for T cells to be activated. MHC proteins can bind huge numbers of different antigenic fragments, but as you will see there are certain exceptions and restrictions that render our T cells unable to respond to specific antigens. For example, there might be a deficit of T cells capable of responding to antigens that are structurally very similar to some of our self proteins.

T Cell Activation

T cell activation is actually a two-step process involving antigen binding and costimulation.

Step 1: Antigen Binding. The first step mostly entails what has already been described: T cell antigen receptors or **TCRs** bind to an antigen–MHC protein complex on the surface of a body cell. Like B cell receptors, a TCR has variable and constant regions, but it consists of two (alpha and beta) rather than four polypeptide chains.

Helper and cytotoxic T cells have different preferences for the class of MHC protein that helps to deliver the activation signal. This constraint, acquired during the "education" process in the thymus, is called **MHC restriction.** Helper T cells can bind only to antigens associated with class II MHC proteins, which are typically displayed on the surfaces of **antigen-presenting cells (APCs).** APCs include macrophages, dendritic cells of lymphoid tissues, Langerhans' cells of the skin epidermis, and antigen-activated B cells. As described earlier (Figure 22.7, p. 720), macrophages (and other APCs) attach very small parts of the antigens to the MHC II proteins for T cell recognition. In addition, mobile APCs like Langerhans cells actually migrate to the lymph nodes and other lymphoid tissues to do their antigen presentation. As a result of this early alert, the body is spared a good deal of tissue damage that might otherwise occur before the antigens finally entered the blood to be carried to the lymph nodes for recognition.

By contrast, cytotoxic T cells are activated by antigen fragments that are presented complexed with MHC I proteins (Figure 22.14). Because virtually all body cells exhibit class I MHC proteins, it is assumed that cytotoxic T cells do not require *special* antigen-presenting cells—any body cell displaying a recognizable self-antiself (MHC I–antigen fragment) complex will do. Nonetheless, antigen-presenting cells produce co-stimulatory molecules that *are* required for T cell activation. Hence, whether a helper or a cytotoxic T cell is involved, the process of antigen presentation is essentially the same—only the presenting cell type and the MHC class recognized differ. The interesting process during which the T cells adhere to and crawl over the surface of other cells examining them for antigens they might recognize is called **immunologic surveillance.** (Note, however, that this term is commonly used to indicate *only* the cytotoxic cells' constant monitoring of body cells for viral or cancer antigens.)

Besides the TCR that acts to recognize the antiself-self complex, other T cell surface proteins appear to be involved in this first step as well. For example, the CD4 and CD8 proteins used to identify the two major T cell groups are adhesion molecules that help maintain the coupling during antigen recognition.

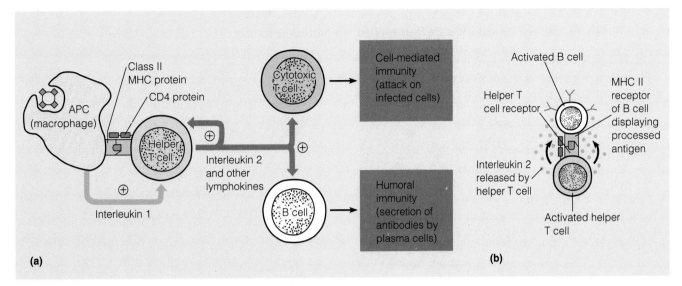

FIGURE 22.15
The central role of helper T cells.
Helper T cells mobilize both arms (cellular and humoral) of the immune response. Once an immunocompetent helper T cell binds to an antigen-presenting cell (APC) such as a macrophage and recognizes the self-antiself complex, it produces a clone of helper T cells (not illustrated), all with identical receptors keyed to MHC II receptors complexed with the same antigen. In addition, the macrophage releases interleukin 1, a costimulator that enhances T cell activation. **(a)** Activated helper T cells release interleukin 2, a costimulator that stimulates proliferation and activity of other helper T cells (specific for the same antigenic determinant). Interleukin 2 also helps activate cytotoxic T cells and B cells. **(b)** T and B cells must sometimes interact directly for full B cell activation to occur. In such cases, helper T cells bind with the self-antiself complexes (processed antigen complexed with MHC proteins) on activated B cell surfaces, and then release interleukin as a costimulatory signal.

Additionally, CD4 and CD8 are associated with kinase enzymes inside the T cell which phosphorylate cell proteins, activating some and inactivating others. When antigen binding occurs, these kinases set events into motion that ultimately signal the T cell to grow and proliferate. Once antigen binding has occurred, the T cell is stimulated but is still "idling," like a car that has been started but not put into gear.

Step 2: Costimulation. Before a T cell can proliferate and form a clone, it must recognize still another or other signals, called **costimulatory signals.** Sometimes the added requirement is T cell binding to still another surface receptor on an APC. For example, macrophages begin to sprout *B7 proteins* on their surfaces when the nonspecific defenses are being mobilized to fend off microorganisms. B7 binding is an important costimulatory signal, particularly to helper T cells. In other cases, the costimulator is a cytokine chemical released by macrophages or T cells; interleukins 1 and 2 are important examples (described below). As you might guess, there are several types of costimulators and different costimulators promote different responses in the activated T cells, but the important understanding is that they nudge the T cells to complete their activation process. Or, to go back to our car analogy, they put the car in gear and step on the gas!

A T cell that binds to antigen without receiving the costimulatory signal is inactivated (becomes tolerant to that antigen). Just why this happens is uncertain, but the current hypothesis is that the two-signal sequence is a safeguard to prevent the immune system from destroying our own healthy cells.

The precise way that suppressor T cells are activated is obscure and controversial. Some appear to bind to *free* antigens (like B cells) without MHC restriction, while others show typical MHC restriction for antigen recognition.

Once activated, a T cell enlarges and proliferates to form a clone of cells that differentiate and perform functions according to their T cell class. This primary response peaks within a week after a single exposure and then gradually wanes. In every case, thousands of clone members become memory T cells. They persist, perhaps for life, providing a reservoir of T cells that can mediate secondary responses to the same antigen.

Cytokines

As in the inflammatory response, chemical mediators enhance the immune response. **Cytokines,** the mediators involved in cellular immunity, include hormone-like **lymphokines,** soluble glycoproteins released by activated T cells, and **monokines,** secreted by macrophages. As mentioned above, some cytokines act as costimulators of T cells. For example, T cell proliferation is enhanced by two *cytokines* that act as costimulators: interleukins 1 and 2 (see Figure 22.15). **Inter-**

leukin 1 (Il-1), released by macrophages, costimulates bound T cells to liberate **interleukin 2 (Il-2)** and to synthesize more Il-2 receptors. Interleukin 2 sets up a positive feedback cycle that encourages activated T cells to divide further or even more rapidly. (Genetically engineered interleukin 2 used in clinical trials has helped to enhance the activity of the body's own cytotoxic T cells against cancer.)

Additionally, all activated T cells secrete one or more other lymphokines that help to amplify and regulate a variety of immune and nonspecific responses. Some cytokines (perforin and lymphotoxin) are cell toxins; others (e.g., gamma interferon) enhance the killing power of macrophages; and still others are inflammatory factors. Lymphokines and their effects on target cells are summarized in Table 22.4 on p. 732.

Specific T Cell Roles

Helper T Cells

Helper T cells are regulatory cells that play a central role in the immune response. Once primed by APC presentation of antigen, their major function is to chemically or directly stimulate proliferation of other T cells and of B cells that have already become bound to antigen (Figure 22.15). In fact, without the "director" helper T cells, there is *no* immune response. Lymphokines furnish the chemical help needed to recruit other immune cells to fight off intruders (Figure 22.15a).

Helper T cells also interact directly with B cells that have mounted antigen fragments on their surfaces bound to MHC II receptors (Figure 22.15b), prodding them into more rapid division and then, like the boss of an assembly line, signaling for antibody formation to begin. Whenever a helper T cell binds to a B cell, the T cell releases interleukin 2 (and other lymphokines), but whether the binding act itself is an activation signal to the B cells is still uncertain. Although B cells may be activated solely by binding to certain antigens **(T-independent antigens)**, most antigens require T cell "help" (costimulation) to activate the B cells to which they bind. This more common variety of antigens is called **T-dependent antigens.** The B cell division process continues as long as it is stimulated by the helper T cell. Thus, the helper T cells function to help unleash the protective potential of the B cells.

Lymphokines released by the helper T cells not only mobilize immune cells and macrophages, they also attract other types of white blood cells, such as neutrophils, into the area and tremendously amplify nonspecific defenses. As the released chemicals summon more and more cells into the battle, the immune response gains momentum, and the antigens are overwhelmed by the sheer numbers of immune elements acting against them.

Cytotoxic T Cells

Cytotoxic T cells, also called **killer T cells,** are the only T cells that can directly attack and kill other cells. Activated cytotoxic T cells roam the body, circulating in and out of the blood and lymph and through lymphatic organs in search of body cells displaying antigens to which they have been sensitized. Although their main targets are virus-infected cells, they also attack tissue cells infected by certain intracellular bacteria (such as the tubercle bacillus) or parasites, cancer cells, and foreign cells introduced into the body by blood transfusions or organ transplants.

Before the onslaught can begin, the cytotoxic cell must "dock" on the target cell by binding to a self-antiself complex. Remember, all body cells display class I antigens, so all infected or abnormal body cells can be destroyed by these T cells as long as the appropriate antigen and costimulatory stimuli (typically Il-2 released by helper T cells) are also present. The attack on foreign human cells, such as those of a graft, is more difficult to explain because *all* of the antigens are nonself. However, the cytotoxic cells apparently "see" the foreign class I MHC antigens as a combination of a class I MHC protein bound to antigen.

The mechanism of the cytotoxic cell's **lethal hit,** which leads to cell lysis, has long been unclear, but the following events occur in at least some cases: (1) The cytotoxic T cell binds tightly to the target cell and, during this period, a cytotoxic chemical, **perforin,** is released from the T cell's granules and inserted into the plasma membrane of the target cell (Figure 22.16). (2) The cytotoxic cell then detaches and continues the search for another prey. Sometime later, the perforin molecules in the target cell membrane polymerize and provoke cell lysis by creating transmembrane pores very much like those produced by complement activation. Other cytotoxic T cells apparently use different or additional signals to induce target cell death. For example, some secrete **lymphotoxin,** which causes fragmentation of the target cell's DNA; some release **tumor necrosis factor (TNF),** which kills slowly over 48 to 72 hours (by some unknown mechanism); and still others secrete **gamma interferon,** which stimulates macrophages to killer status and indirectly enhances the killing process.

Suppressor T Cells

Like the helper cells, mature **suppressor T cells** are regulatory cells. However, their action is inhibitory, because they release lymphokines that suppress the activity of both T and B cells. Suppressor T cells are thought to be vital for winding down and finally stop-

(a)

(b)

FIGURE 22.16
Cytotoxic T cells attack infected and cancerous cells.
(a) A proposed mechanism of target cell lysis by cytotoxic T cells. The initial event is the tight binding of the cytotoxic cell to the target cell. During this binding period, granules within the cytotoxic cell fuse with its plasma membrane and release their perforin contents by exocytosis. The perforin molecules insert into the target cell membrane and, in the presence of ionic calcium, they polymerize, forming cylindrical holes that allow free exchange of ions and water. Target cell lysis occurs long after the cytotoxic cell has detached. **(b)** Scanning electron micrograph of a cancer cell that has been lysed by a cytotoxic T cell. (1250×)

ping the immune response after an antigen has been successfully inactivated or destroyed. This helps prevent uncontrolled or unnecessary immune system activity. Suppressors are also presumed important in preventing autoimmune reactions; however, suppressor T cells are very difficult to study, and most of what is written about them is still hypothetical.

Summary of T Cell Roles

Each type of T cell has unique roles to play in the immune response, yet at the same time is heavily enmeshed in interactions with other immune cells as summarized in Figure 22.17. Cytotoxic T cells prevent infectious microorganisms, hidden from antibody surveillance within cells, from doing their "dirty work" by killing their cellular hosts. Helper T cells costimulate both other T cells and B cells and recruit nonspecific defenses. Suppressor T cells prevent runaway or undesirable immune reactions. Delayed hypersensitivity T cells (not shown in Figure 22.17) enhance the killing activity of macrophages in certain allergic states (see p. 731). But the lesson to

take away with you is that without helper T cells, *there is no immune response* because the helper cells direct and/or help complete the activation of *all* other immune cells. Their crucial role in immunity is painfully evident when they are destroyed as in AIDS (see *A Closer Look* on p. 738).

Organ Transplants and Prevention of Rejection

Organ transplants, a viable treatment option for many patients with end-stage cardiac or renal disease, have been done with mixed success for over 30 years. Immune rejection presents a particular problem when the goal is to provide such patients with functional organs from a living or recently deceased donor. Essentially, there are four major varieties of grafts:

1. **Autografts** are tissue grafts transplanted from one body site to another in the same person.

2. **Isografts** are grafts donated by genetically identical individuals, the only example being identical twins.

Table 22.4   Summary of Functions of Cells and Molecules Involved in the Immune Response

Element	Function in immune response
Cells	
B cell	Lymphocyte that resides in lymph nodes, spleen, or other lymphoid tissues, where it is induced to replicate by antigen binding and helper T cell interactions; its progeny (clone members) form memory cells and plasma cells
Plasma cell	Antibody-producing "machine"; produces huge numbers of antibodies (immunoglobulins) with the same antigen specificity; represents further specialization of B cell clone descendants
Helper T cell	A regulatory T cell that binds with a specific antigen presented by a macrophage; upon circulating into spleen and lymph nodes, it stimulates production of other cells (killer T cells and B cells) to help fight invader; acts both directly and indirectly by releasing lymphokines
Cytotoxic T cell	Also called cytolytic or killer T cells; activated by antigen presented by any body cell; recruited and activity enhanced by helper T cells; its specialty is killing virus-invaded body cells and cancer cells; it is involved in rejection of foreign tissue grafts
Suppressor T cell	Most likely activated by antigen presented by a macrophage; slows or stops activity of B and T cells once infection (or onslaught by foreign cells) has been conquered
Memory cell	Descendant of activated B cell or any class of T cell; generated during initial immune response (primary response); may exist in body for years after, enabling it to respond quickly and efficiently to subsequent infections or meetings with same antigen
Macrophage	Engulfs and digests antigens that it encounters and presents parts of them on its plasma membrane for recognition by T cells bearing receptors for same antigen; this function, antigen presentation, is essential for normal cell-mediated responses; also releases chemicals that activate T cells and prevent viral multiplication
Molecules	
Antibody (immunoglobulin)	Protein produced by B cell or by plasma cell; antibodies produced by plasma cells are released into body fluids (blood, lymph, saliva, mucus, etc.), where they attach to antigens, causing complement fixation, neutralization, precipitation, or agglutination, which "mark" the antigens for destruction by complement or phagocytes
Cytokines	Lymphokines: Chemicals released by sensitized T cells: • *Macrophage migration inhibitory factor* (*MIF*) inhibits macrophage migration and keeps them in the area of antigen deposition • *Interleukin 2* (Il-2) stimulates proliferation of T cells and B cells; activates NK cells • *Interleukin 4* (Il-4) stimulates activated B cells and plasma cell formation; causes plasma cells to secrete IgE antibodies • *Interleukin 5* (Il-5) stimulates B cells; causes plasma cells to secrete IgM and IgA antibodies • *Gamma interferon* (γIFN) renders tissue cells resistant to viral infection; stimulates synthesis and expression of more class I and II MHC proteins; activates NK cells; enhances the activity of B cells and differentiation of cytotoxic T cells; activates macrophages to become killer macrophages (formerly called *macrophage-activating factor* (MAF) which reflects this last activity) • *Transforming growth factor beta* inhibits activation and proliferation of T cells and B cells; a suppressor of the immune response • *Lymphotoxin* (LT), a cell toxin, causes DNA fragmentation • *Perforin*, a cell toxin, causes cell lysis • *Tumor necrosis factor* (TNF) is produced in larger amounts by macrophages; see entry under Monokines Monokines: Chemicals released by activated macrophages: • *Interleukin 1* (Il-1) stimulates T cells and B cells to proliferate and causes fever (believed to be a pyrogen that resets thermostat of hypothalamus) • *Tumor necrosis factor* (TNF), like perforin, causes cell killing but acts more slowly; causes selective damage to blood vessels; enhances granulocyte chemotaxis; helps activate T cells, phagocytes, and eosinophils • *Interleukin 6* (Il-6) induces differentiation of B cells into plasma cells; enhances proliferation and activity of T cells; stimulates liver to secrete mannose-binding protein, which binds to mannose sugar in bacterial capsules and triggers complement binding to the bacteria
Complement	Group of blood-borne proteins activated after binding to antibody-covered antigens; causes lysis of microorganism and enhances inflammatory response
Antigen	Substance capable of provoking an immune response; typically are large complex molecules (e.g., proteins and modified proteins) that are not normally present in the body

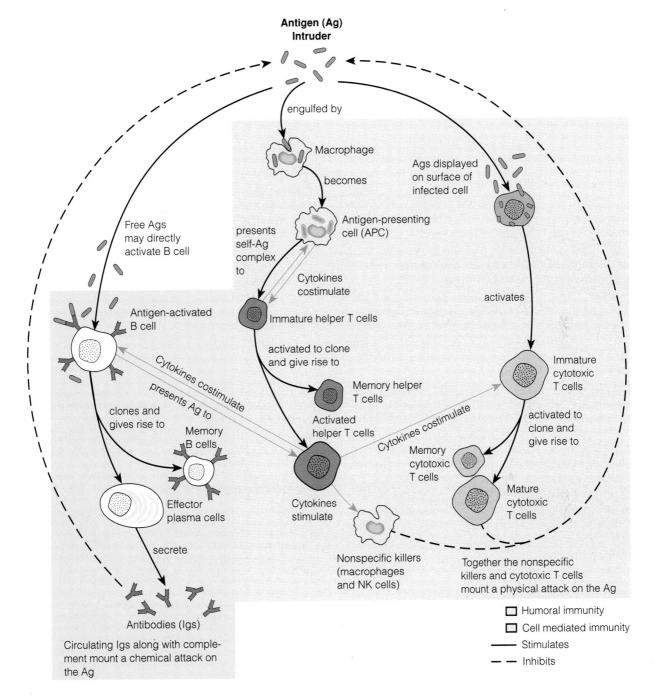

FIGURE 22.17
Summary of the primary immune response. In this simple flowchart, the activities of the humoral and cellular arms of the immune system are indicated by different colored backgrounds. Some events known to be costimulated by cytokines are noted. However, other costimulatory signals are also involved in many of these events. Although complement, NK cells, and phagocytes are nonspecific defenses, they are enlisted in the fight by cytokines released by immune cells.

3. **Allografts** are grafts transplanted from individuals that are not genetically identical but belong to the same species.

4. **Xenografts** are grafts taken from another animal species, such as transplanting a baboon heart into a human being.

Transplant success depends on the similarity of the tissues, because cytotoxic T cells will act vigorously to destroy any foreign tissue in the body. Autografts and isografts are the ideal donor tissues. Given an adequate blood supply and no infection, they are always successful because the MHC-encoded proteins are identical. Xenografts are essentially never successful.* Consequently, the problematic graft type, and the type that is also most frequently used, is the allograft, which is usually obtained from a cadaver.

Before an allograft is even attempted, the ABO and other blood group antigens of the donor and recipient must be determined. They must match to prevent rejection because of attacks on the blood group antigens, which are also present on most body cells. Next, the recipient and donor tissues are typed to determine the extent to which their MHC antigens match. Because MHC variation among human tissues is tremendous, good tissue matches between unrelated individuals are hard to obtain. However, the donor and recipient tissues are matched as closely as possible (at least a 75% match is essential).

Following surgery the patient is treated with *immunosuppressive therapy* involving one or more of the following: (1) corticosteroid drugs, such as prednisone, to suppress inflammation; (2) cytotoxic drugs; (3) radiation (X ray) therapy; (4) antilymphocyte globulins; and (5) an immunosuppressant drug such as cyclosporine. Many of these drugs kill rapidly dividing cells (such as activated lymphocytes), and all of them have severe side effects.

The major problem with immunosuppressive therapy is that the patient's immune system, while suppressed, cannot protect the body against other foreign agents. Although unusual cancer patterns sometimes appear in immunosuppressed patients, the cancers tend to disappear when drug therapy is stopped. Explosive bacterial and viral infection remains the most frequent cause of death in these patients. The key to successful graft survival is to provide enough immunosuppression to prevent graft rejection but not enough to be toxic, and to use antibiotics to keep infection under control.

HOMEOSTATIC IMBALANCES OF IMMUNITY

Under certain circumstances, the immune system is depressed and even fails, or exhibits activities that damage the body itself. Most such problems can be classified as immunodeficiencies, hypersensitivities, or autoimmune diseases.

Immunodeficiencies

The **immunodeficiencies** include both congenital and acquired conditions in which the production or function of immune cells, phagocytes, or complement is abnormal. The most devastating *congenital condition*

is **severe combined immunodeficiency disease (SCID),** in which there is a marked deficit of both B and T cells. Children afflicted with SCID have little or no protection against disease-causing organisms of any type. Minor infections easily shrugged off by most children begin shortly after birth, causing the victims to become deathly ill and wasted. If untreated, this condition is fatal, but successful bone marrow transplants (which provide normal stem cells) improve the chance of survival of SCID victims. One risk of such transplants is that the transplanted cells will identify their new host as foreign and mount a life-threatening attack on the recipient's tissues—a so-called *graft versus host (GVH) response.* (The latter problem has been largely resolved by using monoclonal antibodies to remove the transplanted marrow T cells.) Lacking such a treatment, the only hope for survival is living behind protective barriers (in a plastic "bubble") that keep out all infectious agents.

There are various *acquired immunodeficiencies.* For example, *Hodgkin's disease,* cancer of the lymph nodes, can lead to immunodeficiency by depressing lymph node cells, and immunosuppression is the goal of certain drugs used to treat cancer. Currently, however, the most devastating of the acquired immunodeficiencies is **acquired immune deficiency syndrome (AIDS).** AIDS, which cripples the immune system by interfering with the activity of helper T cells, is highlighted in *A Closer Look* on p. 738.

Hypersensitivities

At first, the immune response was thought to be purely protective. However, it was not long before its dangerous potentials were discovered. **Hypersentivities** or **allergies** (*allo* = altered; *erg* = reaction) are abnormally vigorous immune responses. During such responses, the immune system causes tissue damage as it fights off a perceived "threat" (such as pollen or animal dander) that would otherwise be harmless to the body. The term **allergen** is used to distinguish this type of antigen from those eliciting essentially normal protective immune responses. People rarely die of allergies; they are just miserable with them.

There are different types of hypersensitivity reactions, which are distinguished by (1) their time course, and (2) whether antibodies or T cells are the principal immune elements involved. Allergies mediated by antibodies are the *immediate* and *subacute hypersensitivities.* The most important cell-mediated allergic state is *delayed hypersensitivity.*

Immediate Hypersensitivities

The **immediate hypersensitivities,** also called **acute** or **type I hypersensitivities,** begin within seconds after contact with the allergen and typically subside after about half an hour.

---

*Though still true at publication of this book, this situation is about to change. By microinjecting human genes into fertilized animal (pig) eggs, researchers have been able to neutralize the attack of complement and inhibit the hyperacute rejection response of a xenograft. Genetically altered pigs are now being bred with the hope that human trials using such organs will begin in 1996.

Anaphylaxis.   The most common type of immediate hypersensitivity is **anaphylaxis** (an″ah-fi-lak′sis; "against protection"). The initial meeting with an allergen produces no symptoms but it sensitizes the person. Macrophages digest the allergen and present its fragments to T cells as usual. The steps that follow are obscure, but appear to be mediated by interleukin 4 (Il-4) secreted by T cells. Il-4 stimulates B cells to mature into IgE-secreting plasma cells, which spew out huge amounts of that antibody. When the stem regions of the IgE molecules attach to **mast cells** and **basophils,** sensitization is complete. Anaphylaxis is triggered at later encounters with the same allergen, which promptly binds and cross-links the IgE antibodies on the surfaces of the mast cells and basophils. This event induces an enzymatic cascade involving kinase enzymes and Ca^{2+} influx into the cell, which, in turn, causes the mast cells and basophils to degranulate, releasing a flood of **histamine** and other inflammatory chemicals (chemotactic factors, prostaglandins, and various cytokines). Together, these chemicals induce the inflammatory response typical of anaphylaxis (Figure 22.18).

Anaphylactic reactions may be local or systemic. Since mast cells are particularly abundant in connective tissues of the skin, and beneath the mucosa of respiratory passages and the gastrointestinal tract, these areas are common sites of local allergic reactions. Because histamine causes blood vessels to become leaky, all local reactions are characterized by edema. Other familiar signs and symptoms, such as a runny nose, itching reddened skin (hives), and watery eyes are related to the specific tissues affected. When the allergen is inhaled into the lungs, symptoms of *asthma* appear as smooth muscle in the walls of the bronchioles contracts, constricting the small passages and restricting air flow. When the allergen is ingested (in food or via drugs), gastrointestinal discomfort (cramping, vomiting, or diarrhea) occurs. Over-the-counter (OTC) antiallergy drugs containing antihistamines effectively counteract these histamine-mediated effects.

Fortunately, the bodywide or systemic response, known as **anaphylactic shock,** is fairly rare. It typically occurs when the allergen directly enters the blood and circulates rapidly through the body, as might happen with certain bee stings or spider bites. It may also follow injection of a foreign substance (such as penicillin or other drugs which act as haptens) into susceptible individuals. The mechanism of anaphylactic shock is essentially the same as that of local responses; but when mast cells and basophils are enlisted throughout the entire body, the outcome is life-threatening. The bronchioles constrict (and the tongue may swell), making it difficult to breathe, and the sudden vasodilation and fluid loss from the bloodstream may cause circulatory collapse (hypotensive shock) and death within minutes. Epi-

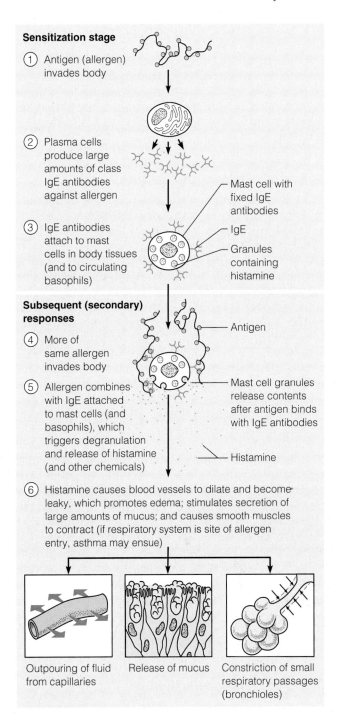

FIGURE 22.18
Mechanism of an acute allergic (immediate hypersensitivity) response.

nephrine is the drug of choice to reverse these histamine-mediated effects.

Atopy.   Though the term "anaphylaxis" covers most immediate hypersensitivities, it does not include the fairly common type called **atopy** (literally, "out of place"). About 10% of people in the USA have inherited a tendency to spontaneously (without prior sensitization) develop immediate-type allergies to certain environmental antigens (such as ragweed or house dust mites). Consequently, when they encounter even very small amounts of the appropriate allergen, they promptly develop hives, hayfever, or asthmatic symptoms.

Subacute Hypersensitivities

The **subacute hypersensitivities,** like the immediate types, are caused by antibodies (in these cases IgG and IgM rather than IgE) and can be transferred via blood plasma or serum. However, their onset is slower (1 to 3 hours after antigen exposure versus a few minutes) and the duration of the reaction is longer (10 to 15 hours versus less than an hour).

Cytotoxic (type II) reactions occur when antibodies bind to antigens on specific body cells, and subsequently stimulate phagocytosis and complement-mediated lysis of the cellular antigens. Type II hypersensitivity may occur in mismatched transfusion reactions during which red blood cells are lysed (by complement).

Immune complex (type III) hypersensitivity results when antigens are widely distributed through the body or blood and the insoluble antigen-antibody complexes formed cannot be cleared from a particular area. (This may reflect a persistent infection or a situation in which huge amounts of antigen-antibody complexes are formed.) An intense inflammatory reaction occurs, complete with complement-mediated cell lysis and neutrophil-mediated extracellular cell killing, that severely damages the local tissues. Examples of type III allergies include pulmonary disorders such as *farmer's lung* (induced by inhaling moldy hay) and *mushroom grower's lung* (caused by inhaling mushroom spores). Additionally, many type III allergic responses are involved in autoimmune disorders, such as glomerulonephritis, as described shortly.

Delayed Hypersensitivities

Delayed hypersensitivity (type IV) reactions mediated by T cells are slower to appear (one to three days) than any of the antibody-mediated hypersensitivity reactions. Their mechanism is basically that of a cell-mediated immune response. The *usual* reaction to most pathogens depends largely on cytotoxic T cells directed against specific antigens. However, delayed hypersensitivity reactions involve both cytotoxic cells and a special subgroup of previously sensitized CD4 cells, sometimes called **delayed hypersensitivity T cells.** Additionally, delayed hypersensitivity reactions depend to a greater extent on lymphokine-activated macrophages and nonspecific killing. Delayed hypersensitivity to antigens can be passively transferred from one person to another by transfu-

sions of whole blood containing the T cells that initiate the response.

Lymphokines released by T cells are the major mediators of these inflammatory responses. Thus, antihistamine drugs are not helpful against delayed hypersensitivity reactions, but corticosteroid drugs are used to provide relief.

The most familiar examples of delayed hypersensitivity reactions are those classed as **allergic contact dermatitis** that follow skin contact with poison ivy, some heavy metals (lead, mercury, and others), and certain cosmetic and deodorant chemicals—all agents that act as haptens. After diffusing through the skin and attaching to self-proteins, they are perceived as foreign and attacked by immune cells. The *Mantoux* and *tine tests,* skin tests for tuberculosis, depend on delayed hypersensitivity reactions. When the tubercle antigens are introduced just under the skin, a small hard (indurated) lesion forms that persists for days if the person has been previously sensitized to the antigen.

Delayed hypersensitivity reactions are responsible for a large number of protective as well as destructive reactions including (1) protection against viruses, bacteria, fungi, and protozoa, (2) resistance against cancer, and (3) rejection of foreign grafts or transplanted organs. They are particularly effective against **facultative intracellular pathogens (FIPs),** which include salmonella bacteria and some yeasts. FIPs are readily phagocytized by macrophages but are not killed and may even multiply within their hosts unless the macrophages are activated to killer status by gamma interferon and certain other lymphokines. Thus, the enhanced release of lymphokines during delayed hypersensitivity reactions plays an important protective role.

Autoimmune Diseases

Occasionally the immune system loses its remarkable ability to distinguish friend (self) from foe (foreign antigens). When this happens, the artillery of the immune system, like friendly fire, can turn against itself; that is, the body produces antibodies *(autoantibodies)* and sensitized cytotoxic T cells that destroy its own tissues. This phenomenon is called **autoimmune disease.**

Some 5% of adults in North America—two-thirds of them women—are afflicted with autoimmune disease. Most common are:

- *Multiple sclerosis* (MS), which destroys the white matter of the brain and spinal cord

- *myasthenia gravis,* which impairs communication between nerves and skeletal muscles

- *Graves disease,* which prompts the thyroid gland to produce excessive amounts of thyroxine

- *Juvenile (type 1) diabetes mellitus,* which destroys pancreatic beta cells, resulting in a deficit of insulin and inability to use carbohydrates

- *Systemic lupus erythematosus (SLE),* a systemic disease that particularly affects the kidneys, lungs, and skin

- *Glomerulonephritis,* a severe impairment of renal function

- *Rheumatoid arthritis (RA),* which systematically destroys joints

Current therapies include approaches that depress certain aspects of the immune response. For example, injections of genetically engineered antibodies to CD4 (a receptor on helper T cells) seem to stabilize the disease of some MS victims.

How does the state of self-tolerance break down? It appears that one or more of the following events may be triggers:

1. **Inefficient/ineffective lymphocyte programming.** Self-reactive T cells or B cells, which should be silenced or eliminated during their programming phase in the thymus and bone marrow, instead escape to the rest of the body. This is believed to occur in multiple sclerosis, in which myelin sheaths are gradually destroyed by autoimmune assaults.

2. **Appearance of self-proteins in the circulation that have not been previously exposed to the immune system.** Not all self-antigens are exposed to immune system scrutiny during fetal development. Consequently, they escape being recognized as self during the programming phase. Such "hidden" antigens are found in sperm cells, the lens of the eye, nervous tissue, and the thyroid gland. For example, developing sperm cells are shielded from the immune system by the blood-testis barrier and, because sperm cells are not formed until puberty, the immune system is not exposed to their antigens. If the testes become inflamed, however, sperm antigens may escape into the circulation; the testes then become a target of the immune response, which causes sterility. In addition, "new self-antigens" can be generated by (1) gene mutations that result in the appearance of new proteins at the external cell surface and (2) changes in the structure of self-antigens by hapten attachment or as a result of infectious damage.

3. **Cross-reaction of antibodies produced against foreign antigens with self-antigens.** Antibodies made against a foreign antigen sometimes cross-react with a self-antigen that has very similar determinants. For instance, antibodies generated during a streptococcal infection are known to cross-react with heart antigens, causing lasting damage to the heart muscle and valves, as well as to joints and kidneys. This autoimmune sequel is called *rheumatic fever.* •

DEVELOPMENTAL ASPECTS OF THE IMMUNE SYSTEM

The development of immunity relies on an orderly development of lymphoid organs and cells. Because the development of lymphatic system organs is described in Chapter 21, we will focus on the cells of the immune system here. Stem cells of the immune system originate in the liver and spleen during very early embryonic development (by the ninth week). Later in fetal development, the bone marrow becomes the predominant source of stem cells (hemocytoblasts), and it persists in this role into adult life. In late fetal life and shortly after birth, the young lymphocytes develop self-tolerance and immunocompetence in their "programming organs" (thymus and bone marrow) and then populate the other lymphoid tissues. Upon antigen challenge, the T and B cells complete their development to fully mature effector and regulatory cells.

The ability of the immune system to recognize foreign substances is controlled by our genes. However, the nervous system also plays an important role in both the control and the activity of the immune response, and studies of neuroimmunomodulation—a term coined to describe links between the brain and the immune system—have begun to reveal some answers. For example, the immune response is definitely impaired in individuals who are depressed or under severe stress—e.g., in those mourning the death of a beloved family member or friend. This intriguing topic is covered in more detail in *A Closer Look* on p. 716.

Our immune system normally serves us very well until late in life. Then, its efficiency begins to wane, and its ability to fight infection declines. Old age is also accompanied by greater susceptibility to both autoimmune and immune deficiency diseases. The greater incidence of cancer in the elderly is assumed to be another example of the progressive failure of the immune system. Just why the immune system begins to fail is not really known, but "genetic aging" and its consequences are probably partly at fault.

* * *

The immune system provides remarkable defenses against disease. These defenses are not only amazingly diverse, but also precisely regulated by both cellular interactions and a flood of chemicals. T cells and antibodies make perfect partners. Antibodies respond swiftly to toxins and molecules on the outer surfaces of microorganisms, while T cells destroy antigens hidden within cells and our own cells that have become mutinous (cancer cells). The nonspecific defensive mechanisms exhibit a different arsenal for body defense, which is simpler perhaps and more easily understood. However, the specific and nonspecific defenses are tightly interlocked, each providing what the other cannot and amplifying each other's effects.

A CLOSER LOOK | AIDS: The Plague of the Twentieth Century

In October 1347, several ships made port in Sicily and within days all of the sailors they carried were dead of bubonic plague. By the end of the fourteenth century, approximately 25% of the population of Europe had been wiped out by this "black death." In January 1987, the U.S. Secretary of Health and Human Services warned that *acquired immune deficiency syndrome (AIDS)* might be the plague of the twentieth century. These are strong words. Are they true?

Although AIDS was first identified in this country in 1981 among homosexual men and intravenous drug users of both sexes, it had begun afflicting the heterosexual population of Africa several years earlier. AIDS-related illness is characterized by severe weight loss, night sweats, and swollen lymph nodes. In full-blown AIDS, these same symptoms are accompanied by increasingly frequent opportunistic infections, including a rare type of pneumonia called *Pneumocystis pneumonia* caused by a fungus, and the bizarre malignancy *Kaposi's sarcoma*, a cancerlike condition of the blood vessels evidenced by purple lesions of the skin. Some AIDS victims develop slurred speech and severe dementia. The course of AIDS is nearly inexorable, finally ending in complete debilitation and death from cancer or overwhelming infection.

AIDS is caused by a virus transmitted solely through blood and bodily body secretions—blood, semen, and vaginal secretions. The virus commonly enters the body via blood transfusions (primarily in other countries where blood is not tested) or blood-contaminated needles and during intimate sexual contact in which microscopic tears in the mucosa (and bleeding) are common or where open lesions induced by sexually transmitted diseases allow the virus access to the blood. Although the virus has also

New AIDS viruses emerge from an infected human cell. (6,000×)

been detected in saliva and tears, it is not believed to be spread via those secretions.

The virus, called HIV (human immunodeficiency virus), destroys helper T cells, resulting in depression of cell-mediated immunity. Although antibody levels rise and cytotoxic T cells initially mount a vigorous response to viral exposure during the acute phase, in time a profound deficit of normal antibodies develops and the cytotoxic cells become nonresponsive to viral cues. The whole immune system is turned topsy-turvy. It is now clear that the long, asymptomatic stage typical of HIV infection is not a time of viral dormancy but a silent war of attrition in which the combatants are closely matched. Most of the viruses are destroyed and helper T cells multiply mightily, but HIV replicates and mutates rapidly producing deadly strains that evade the immune system; these surviving viruses multiply stealthily in the lymphoid tissues of the body. Symptomatic AIDS gradually appears a few months to 10 plus years later as the lymph tissues can no

longer contain the virus. The virus also invades the brain, which accounts for the neurological symptoms (dementia) of some AIDS patients. Although there are exceptions, most AIDS victims die within a few months to eight years after diagnosis.

The infectious specificity of HIV reflects the fact that the CD4 proteins (through which immune cells exchange information) provide the avenue for HIV's attack. A particular HIV coat glycoprotein (gp120) fits into the CD4 receptor like a plug fits into a socket. When the two proteins are docked gp120 exposes one of its regions, known as the V-3 loop, to still another T cell membrane receptor (CD26). V-3 acts as the biochemical key, opening the "locked C26 doorway" so that the contents of the virus flow into the cell's interior. Once inside, HIV "sets up housekeeping," using the enzyme reverse transcriptase to produce DNA from the information encoded in its (viral) RNA. This DNA copy, now called a provirus, then inserts itself into the host cell's DNA and directs the host cell to crank out new copies of viral RNA (and proteins) so that the virus can multiply and infect other immune cells. CD4 also facilitates the spread of the virus from infected to uninfected cells. Although the helper T cells are the main HIV targets, other body cells displaying CD4 proteins, such as macrophages, monocytes, and dendritic cells present at the body's mucosal surfaces, are also at risk for HIV infection. The HIV reverse transcriptase enzyme is not very accurate and produces errors rather frequently, causing HIV's relatively high mutation rate and its changing resistance to drugs.

The years since 1981 have witnessed an AIDS epidemic in the United States. By the end of 1993, over 339,000 cases had been diagnosed nationwide, and over 204,000 (60%) had already died. By mid-1993, estimates of the number of Americans infected with HIV topped one million. The Centers for Disease Control's grim prophecy is that as many as 333,000 Americans will have died from AIDS by the end of 1995. Sometimes anti-HIV antibodies appear in the blood by two weeks after infection, but apparently there is a six-month "window" after infection during which antibodies can develop. Therefore, there are probably many more asymptomatic carriers of the virus for every diagnosed case. Moreover, the disease has a long incubation period (from a few months to over ten years) between exposure and the appearance of clinical symptoms. Not only has the number of identified cases jumped exponentially in the at-risk populations (homosexuals and intravenous drug users), but the "face of AIDS" is changing. Victims now commonly include people who do not belong to the original high-risk groups. Before reliable testing of donated blood was available, some people contracted the virus from blood transfusions. Hemophiliacs have been at particular risk because the blood factors they need were isolated from pooled blood

donations. Although manufacturers began taking measures to kill the virus in 1984, by then an estimated 60% of the hemophiliacs in this country were already infected. The virus can also be transmitted from an infected mother to her fetus. Though homosexual men still account for the bulk of cases transmitted by sexual contact, more and more heterosexuals are contracting this disease. Particularly disturbing is the near-epidemic increase in diagnosed cases among teenagers.

Large city hospitals are seeing more AIDS patients daily, and statistics reporting the number of cases in inner-city ghettos, where intravenous drug use is the chief means of AIDS transmission, are alarming. Currently, the drug community accounts for 25% of all AIDS cases. Furthermore, 75% of AIDS cases in newborns occur where drug abuse abounds. This shocking revelation prompted the National Research Council to recommend that the government provide sterile needles to IV drug users, and needle-dispensing programs have been initiated in many cities.

Though the disease does not appear to be spread by casual contact, concerned parents are demanding that HIV-infected children be kept out of the schools. Because of the high expense of treatment, some employers are demanding AIDS testing before hiring, and insurance companies are denying insurance to those who will not submit to an AIDS test. People have stopped donating blood, afraid that they might become infected (they cannot), so that blood supplies needed for surgical patients are deficient.

Although the diagnostic tests to identify HIV carriers have become increasingly sophisticated, no cure for AIDS has yet been found. However, over 100 drugs are now in the FDA pipeline. AZT (zidovudine), ddI, and ddC, all of which work by interfering with reverse transcriptase (hence, viral replication), are now fully approved for AIDS treatment. In the late 1980s and early 1990s, AZT was

used by some clinicians only for full-blown AIDS; others, however, prescribed it for patients who were still asymptomatic. Federal guidelines now recommend the drug for any infected person with a CD4 cell count below 500 even if they are asymptomatic. (Normal CD4 range is 600 to 1200; those with full-blown AIDS have CD4 counts below 200.) Physicians are urging people to be tested for HIV to enable them to begin treatment as early as is feasible.

Several of the "new" and still experimental drugs may prove to be valuable anti-AIDS agents. An aerosol version of the antibiotic pentamidine, commonly used to treat the deadly *Pneumocystis* pneumonia, is being prescribed to prevent contraction of the pneumonia. Protease blockers that inactivate the enzymes needed for HIV replication, and compound Q (GLQ223), an antitumor drug derived from the root of the Chinese cucumber, also look promising. Clinical testing of vaccines containing genetically engineered gp120 are ongoing. Newest to the scene in the fight against AIDS is a gene therapy in which fake viral genes are "fired" into blood cells of infected volunteers. That researchers would consider tinkering with genes inside healthy blood cells reveals their frustration with controlling HIV.

Besides the drugs undergoing clinical tests, a number of nonapproved therapies and "underground" drugs are being prescribed or independently sought out in other countries by activist groups of AIDS patients. These include Antabuse, a drug used to treat alcoholism, which is similar to the experimental immune-boosting drug DTC. Some will prove useless and others will have unforeseen harmful effects; but when life itself is at stake, this may be a small gamble to take. Perhaps, as urged in the media, the best defense is to practice "safer sex" by using condoms or other barriers and knowing one's sexual partner. The only alternative is abstinence.

RELATED CLINICAL TERMS

Congenital thymic aplasia An immune deficiency disease in which the thymus fails to develop. Affected individuals have no T cells, hence little or no immune protection; fetal thymic and bone marrow transplants have been helpful in some cases.

Eczema (ek′zĕ-mah) A type of immediate hypersensitivity response that results in "weeping" skin lesions and intense itching. Onset is in the first five years of life in 90% of cases. The allergen is uncertain, but familial predisposition is strong.

Hashimoto's thyroiditis An autoimmune disease caused by a cell-mediated attack on the thyroid gland. Normally thyroglobulin (the large colloidal storage form of thyroid hormones) is retained entirely within the thyroid follicles. However, thyroid trauma may cause the release of thyroglobulin into the bloodstream, where it can be identified as foreign and lead to an immune attack on the thyroid gland.

Immunization The process of rendering a subject immune (by vaccination or injection of antiserum).

Immunopathology Disease of the immune system.

Systemic lupus erythematosus (er″ĭ-the′mah-to′sus) (**SLE**) A systemic autoimmune disorder that occurs mainly in young females. Diagnosis is helped by finding antinuclear (anti-DNA) antibodies in the patient's serum. DNA–anti-DNA complexes localize in the kidneys (the capillary filters, or glomeruli), in blood vessels, and in the synovial membranes of joints, resulting in glomerulonephritis, vascular problems, and painful arthritis. Reddened skin lesions, particularly a "butterfly rash" (the sign of the wolf, or *lupus*) on the face are common.

CHAPTER SUMMARY

NONSPECIFIC BODY DEFENSES (pp. 708–715)

Surface Membrane Barriers (p. 708)

1. Skin and mucous membranes constitute the first line of defense. Their role is to prevent pathogens from entering the body. Protective membranes line all body cavities and organs exposed to the exterior.

2. Surface membranes provide mechanical barriers to pathogens. Some have structural modifications and produce secretions that enhance their defensive effects: The skin's acidity, lysozyme, mucus, keratin, and ciliated cells are examples.

Nonspecific Cellular and Chemical Defenses (pp. 708–715)

1. The nonspecific cellular and chemical defenses provide the body's second line of defense.

Phagocytes (p. 709)

2. Phagocytes (macrophages and neutrophils) engulf and destroy pathogens that breach epithelial barriers. This process is enhanced when the pathogen's surface is altered by the attachment of antibodies and/or complement to which the phagocyte's receptors can bind. Cell killing is enhanced by the respiratory burst.

Natural Killer Cells (pp. 709–710)

3. Natural killer cells are large granular lymphocytes that act nonspecifically to kill virus-infected and malignant cells.

Inflammation: Tissue Response to Injury (pp. 710–712)

4. The inflammatory response prevents the spread of injurious agents, disposes of pathogens and dead tissue cells, and promotes healing. Exudate is formed; protective leukocytes enter the area; the area is walled off by fibrin; and tissue repair occurs.

5. The cardinal signs of inflammation are swelling, redness, heat, and pain. These result from vasodilation and increased permeability of blood vessels induced by inflammatory chemicals. If the inflamed area is a joint, impairment of movement may also occur.

Antimicrobial Proteins (pp. 712–715)

6. When complement (a group of plasma proteins) becomes fixed on a foreign cell's membrane, lysis of the target cell occurs. Complement also enhances phagocytosis and the inflammatory and immune responses.

7. Interferons are a group of related proteins synthesized by virus-infected cells and certain immune cells that prevent viruses from multiplying in other body cells.

Fever (p. 705)

8. Fever enhances the body's fight against invading pathogens by increasing metabolism, which speeds up defensive actions and repair processes, and by prompting the liver and spleen to sequester iron and zinc needed for bacterial multiplication.

SPECIFIC BODY DEFENSES: IMMUNITY (pp. 715–739)

1. The immune system recognizes something as foreign and acts to immobilize, neutralize, or remove it. The immune response is antigen-specific and systemic and has memory. It provides the body's third line of defense.

Antigens (pp. 716–718)

1. Antigens are substances capable of generating an immune response.

Complete Antigens and Haptens (pp. 716–717)

2. Complete antigens have both immunogenicity and reactivity. Incomplete antigens or haptens must combine with a body protein before becoming immunogenic.

Antigenic Determinants (pp. 717–718)

3. Antigenic determinants are the portions of antigen molecules that are recognized as foreign. Most antigens have many such sites.

Cells of the Immune System: An Overview (pp. 718–720)

1. Lymphocytes arise from the hemocytoblasts of the bone marrow. T cells develop immunocompetence in the thymus and confer cell-mediated immunity. B cells develop immuno-

competence in the bone marrow and provide humoral immunity. Immunocompetent lymphocytes seed the lymphoid organs, where the antigen challenge occurs, and circulate between the blood, lymph, and lymphoid organs.

2. Immunocompetence is signaled by the appearance of antigen-specific receptors on the surfaces of the lymphocytes.

3. Macrophages arise from monocytes produced in bone marrow. They phogocytize pathogens and present antigenic determinants on their surfaces for recognition by T cells.

Humoral Immune Response (pp. 720–726)

Clonal Selection and Differentiation of B Cells (pp. 720–721)
1. Clonal selection and differentiation of B cells occur when antigens bind to their receptors, causing them to proliferate. Most of the clone members become plasma cells, which secrete antibodies. This is the primary immune response.

Immunological Memory (pp. 721–722)
2. Other clone members become memory B cells, capable of mounting a rapid attack against the same antigen, in subsequent encounters (secondary immune responses). The memory cells provide humoral immunological memory.

Active and Passive Humoral Immunity (p. 722)
3. Active humoral immunity is acquired during an infection or via vaccination. Passive immunity is conferred when a donor's antibodies are injected into the bloodstream, or when the mother's antibodies cross the placenta.

Antibodies (pp. 722–726)
4. The antibody monomer consists of four polypeptide chains, two heavy and two light, connected by disulfide bonds. Each chain has both a constant and a variable region. Constant regions determine antibody function and class. Variable regions enable the antibody to recognize its appropriate antigen.

5. Five classes of antibodies exist: IgA, IgG, IgM, IgD, and IgE. They differ structurally and functionally.

6. Antibody functions include complement fixation and antigen neutralization, precipitation, and agglutination.

7. Monoclonal antibodies are pure preparation of a single antibody type useful in diagnostic tests and cancer treatment. They are prepared by injecting an antigen into a laboratory animal, harvesting its B cells, and fusing them with myeloma cells.

Cell-Mediated Immune Response (pp. 727–734)

Clonal Selection and Differentiation of T Cells (pp. 727–730)
1. Immunocompetent helper and cytotoxic T cells are activated by binding simultaneously to an antigen and a major histocompatibility complex (MHC) protein displayed on the surface of a macrophage and other body cells respectively. Some type of costimulatory signal (physical or chemical) is also essential. Clonal selection occurs and the clone members differentiate into the appropriate regulatory or effector T cells that mount the primary immune response. Certain of the clone members become memory T cells.

Specific T Cell Roles (pp. 730–731)
2. Helper T cells release lymphokines that help activate other immune cells and interact directly with B cells bound to

antigen. Cytotoxic T cells directly attack and lyse infected cells and cancer cells. Suppressor T cells terminate normal immune responses by releasing suppressor factors that dampen the activity of helper T cells and B cells.

3. The immune response is enhanced by interleukin 1, released by macrophages, and by lymphokines (interleukin 2, MIF, γ interferon, etc.), released by activated T cells.

Organ Transplants and Prevention of Rejection (pp. 731–734)
4. Grafts or foreign organ transplants will be rejected by cell-mediated responses unless the patient is immunosuppressed. Infections are major complications in such patients.

Homeostatic Imbalances of Immunity (pp. 734–737)

Immunodeficiencies (p. 734)
1. Immunodeficiency diseases include congenital thymic aplasia, severe combined immunodeficiency disease, and acquired immune deficiency syndrome (AIDS). Overwhelming infections cause death because the immune system is unable to combat them.

Hypersensitivities (pp. 734–736)
2. Hypersensitivity, or allergy, is an abnormally intense reaction to an allergen following the initial immune response. Immediate hypersensitivities mounted by antibodies include anaphylaxis and atopy. Subacute hypersensitivities, involving both antibodies and complement, include antibody-mediated cytotoxic and immune-complex hypersensitivities. Cell-mediated hypersensitivity is called delayed hypersensitivity.

Autoimmune Diseases (pp. 736–737)
3. Autoimmune disease occurs when the body regards its own tissues as foreign and mounts an immune attack against them. Examples include rheumatoid arthritis and multiple sclerosis.

Developmental Aspects of the Immune System (pp. 737–739)

1. Development of the immune response occurs around the time of birth. The ability of the immune system to recognize foreign substances is genetically determined.

2. The nervous system plays an important role in regulating immune responses, possibly through common mediators (neuropeptides). Depression impairs immune function.

3. With aging, the immune system becomes less responsive. The elderly more often suffer from immune deficiency, autoimmune diseases, and cancer.

REVIEW QUESTIONS

Multiple Choice/Matching

1. All of the following are considered nonspecific body defenses *except* (a) complement, (b) phagocytosis, (c) antibodies, (d) lysozyme, (e) inflammation.

2. The process by which neutrophils squeeze through capillary walls in response to inflammatory signals is called (a) diapedesis, (b) chemotaxis, (c) margination, (d) opsonization.

3. Antibodies released by plasma cells are involved in (a) humoral immunity, (b) immediate hypersensitivity reactions, (c) autoimmune disorders, (d) all of the above.

4. Which of the following antibodies can fix complement? (a) IgA, (b) IgD, (c) IgE, (d) IgG, (e) IgM.

5. Which antibody class is abundant in body secretions? (Use the choices from Question 4.)

6. Small molecules that must combine with large proteins to become immunogenic are called (a) complete antigens, (b) reagins, (c) idiotypes, (d) haptens.

7. Lymphocytes that develop immunocompetence in the thymus are (a) B lymphocytes, (b) T lymphocytes, (c) NK cells.

8. Cells that can directly attack target cells include all of the following *except* (a) macrophages, (b) cytotoxic T cells, (c) helper T cells, (d) natural killer cells.

9. Which of the following is involved in the activation of a B cell? (a) antigen, (b) helper T cell, (c) lymphokine, (d) all of the above.

Short Answer Essay Questions

10. Besides acting as mechanical barriers, the skin epidermis and mucosae of the body have other attributes that contribute to their protective roles. Cite the common body locations and the importance of mucus, lysozyme, keratin, acid pH, and cilia.

11. Explain why attempts at phagocytosis are not always successful; note factors that increase the likelihood of success.

12. What is complement? How does it cause bacterial lysis? What are some of the other roles of complement?

13. Interferons are referred to as antiviral proteins. What stimulates their production, and how do they protect uninfected cells? What cells of the body secrete interferons?

14. Differentiate between humoral and cell-mediated immunity.

15. Although the immune system has two arms, it has been said that "no T cells, no immunity." Explain.

16. Define immunocompetence. What event (or observation) signals that a B or a T cell has developed immunocompetence?

17. Describe the process of activation of a helper T cell.

18. Differentiate between a primary and a secondary immune response. Which is more rapid and why?

19. Define antibody. Using an appropriately labeled diagram, describe the structure of an antibody monomer. Indicate and label: variable and constant regions, heavy and light chains.

20. What is the role of the variable regions of an antibody? Of the constant regions?

21. Name the five antibody classes and describe where each is most likely to be found in the body.

22. How do antibodies help defend the body?

23. Do vaccines produce active or passive humoral immunity? Explain your answer. Why is passive immunity less satisfactory?

24. Describe the specific roles of helper, suppressor, and cytotoxic T cells in normal cell-mediated immunity.

25. Name several lymphokines and describe their role in the immune response.

26. Define hypersensitivity. List three types of hypersensitivity reactions. For each, note whether antibodies or T cells are involved and provide two examples.

27. What events can result in autoimmune disease?

28. Declining efficiency of the immune system with age is thought to reflect what event?

 ## CRITICAL THINKING AND CLINICAL APPLICATION QUESTIONS

1. Jenny, a six-year-old child who had been raised in a germ-free environment from birth, has just died after an unsuccessful bone marrow transplant—a victim of one of the most severe examples of an abnormal immune system. An autopsy revealed that Jenny had also suffered from undiagnosed cancer caused by the Epstein-Barr virus. Relative to this case: (a) What is the usual fate of children with Jenny's condition and similar circumstances? (b) Why was the bone marrow transplant attempted (what were the hoped-for results)? (c) Why was Jenny's brother chosen as the bone marrow donor? (d) Attempt to explain Jenny's cancer. (e) What similarities and dissimilarities exist between Jenny's illness and AIDS?

2. Some people with a deficit of IgA exhibit recurrent paranasal sinus and respiratory tract infections. Explain these symptoms.

3. Explain the underlying mechanisms responsible for the cardinal signs of acute inflammation: heat, pain, redness, swelling.

The Respiratory System

23

CHAPTER OUTLINE AND STUDENT OBJECTIVES

Functional Anatomy of the Respiratory System (pp. 744–756)

1. Identify the organs forming the respiratory passageway(s) in descending order until the alveoli are reached. Distinguish between conducting and respiratory zone structures.

2. List and describe several protective mechanisms of the respiratory system.

3. Describe the makeup of the respiratory membrane, and relate its structure to its function.

4. Describe the gross structure of the lungs and pleural coverings.

Mechanics of Breathing (pp. 756–763)

5. Relate Boyle's law to the events of inspiration and expiration.

6. Explain the relative roles of the respiratory muscles and lung elasticity in effecting volume changes that cause air to flow into and out of the lungs.

7. Explain the functional importance of the partial vacuum that exists in the intrapleural space.

8. Describe several physical factors that influence pulmonary ventilation.

9. Explain and compare the various lung volumes and capacities. Indicate types of information that can be gained from pulmonary function tests.

10. Define dead space.

Gas Exchanges in the Body (pp. 763–767)

11. Describe, in general terms, differences in composition of atmospheric and alveolar air, and explain these differences.

12. State Dalton's law of partial pressures and Henry's law. Relate each to events of external and internal respiration.

Transport of Respiratory Gases by Blood (pp. 767–772)

13. Describe how oxygen is transported in the blood, and explain how oxygen loading and unloading is affected by temperature, pH, BPG, and P_{CO_2}.

14. Describe carbon dioxide transport in the blood.

Control of Respiration (pp. 772–777)

15. Describe the neural controls of respiration.

16. Compare and contrast the influences of lung reflexes, volition, emotions, arterial pH, and partial pressures of oxygen and carbon dioxide in arterial blood on respiratory rate and depth.

Respiratory Adjustments During Exercise and at High Altitudes (pp. 777–778)

17. Compare and contrast the hyperpnea of exercise with involuntary hyperventilation.

18. Describe the process and effects of acclimatization to high altitude.

Homeostatic Imbalances of the Respiratory System (pp. 778–780)

19. Compare the causes and consequences of chronic bronchitis, emphysema, and lung cancer.

Developmental Aspects of the Respiratory System (pp. 780–781)

20. Trace the development of the respiratory system in an embryo.

21. Describe normal changes that occur in the respiratory system from infancy to old age.

When John Donne, the seventeenth-century English poet and preacher, wrote "No man is an island, entire of itself," he was referring to the mind and spirit. Nonetheless, this classic statement applies to the workings of the body as well. Far from self-sustaining, the body is critically dependent on the external environment, both as a source for obtaining substances it needs to survive and as a catch basin into which it can cast its wastes.

The trillions of cells making up the body require a continuous supply of oxygen to carry out their vital functions. We cannot do without oxygen for even a little while, as we can without food or water. Further, as cells use oxygen, they give off carbon dioxide, a waste product the body must get rid of. The major function of the **respiratory system** is to supply the body with oxygen and dispose of carbon dioxide. To accomplish this function, at least four distinct processes, collectively called **respiration,** must happen:

1. **Pulmonary ventilation.** Air must be moved in and out of the lungs so that the gases in the air sacs (alveoli) of the lungs are continuously changed and refreshed. This air movement is commonly called **ventilation,** or breathing.

2. **External respiration.** Gas exchange (oxygen loading and carbon dioxide unloading) between the blood and the air of the alveoli must occur.

3. **Transport of respiratory gases.** Oxygen and carbon dioxide must be transported between the lungs and tissue cells of the body. This is accomplished by the cardiovascular system, which uses blood as the transporting fluid.

4. **Internal respiration.** At systemic capillaries, gas exchanges must be made between the blood and tissue cells.*

All four of these processes are highlighted in this chapter. Although only the first two processes are the special responsibility of the respiratory system, it cannot accomplish its primary goal of obtaining oxygen and eliminating carbon dioxide unless the third and fourth processes also occur. Thus, the respiratory and circulatory systems are closely coupled, and if either system fails, the body's cells begin to die from oxygen starvation.

FUNCTIONAL ANATOMY OF THE RESPIRATORY SYSTEM

The organs of the respiratory system include the *nose* and *nasal cavity,* the *pharynx,* the *larynx,* the *trachea,* the *bronchi* and their smaller branches, and the *lungs,* which contain the terminal air sacs, or *alveoli* (Figure 23.1). Functionally, the respiratory system consists of respiratory and conducting zones. The **respiratory zone,** the actual site of gas exchange, is composed of the respiratory bronchioles, alveolar ducts, and alveoli, all microscopic structures. The **conducting zone** includes all other respiratory passageways, which serve as fairly rigid conduits by which air reaches the sites of gas exchange. The conducting zone organs also cleanse, humidify, and warm the incoming air. Thus, the air finally reaching the lungs

---

*The actual use of oxygen and production of carbon dioxide by tissue cells, that is, *cellular respiration,* is the cornerstone of all energy-producing chemical reactions in the body. Cellular respiration, which occurs in all body cells, is discussed more appropriately in the metabolism section of Chapter 25.

Which of the organs shown contains both conducting zone and respiratory zone structures?

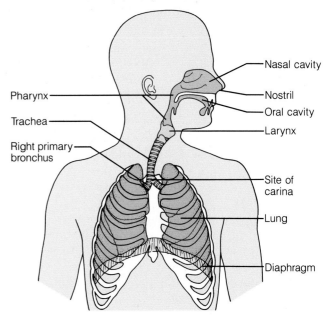

FIGURE 23.1
The major respiratory organs shown in relation to surrounding structures.

has many fewer irritants (duct, bacteria, etc.) than when it entered the system, and it is warm and damp, like the air of the tropics. The functions of the major organs of the respiratory system are summarized briefly in Table 23.1 on p. 756.

The Nose and the Paranasal Sinuses

The Nose

The nose is the only externally visible part of the respiratory system. Unlike the often poetic references to other facial features, such as the eyes or lips, the nose is usually an irreverent target. We are urged to keep our nose to the grindstone and to keep it out of someone else's business. However, considering its important functions, the nose deserves more esteem. The nose (1) provides an airway for respiration, (2) moistens and warms entering air, (3) filters inspired air and cleanses it of foreign matter, (4) serves as a resonating chamber for speech, and (5) houses the olfactory (smell) receptors.

The structures of the nose are divided into the *external nose* and the internal *nasal cavity* for ease of consideration. The named surface features of the *external nose* (Figure 23.2b) include the *root* (area between the eyebrows), *bridge,* and *dorsum nasi* (its anterior margin) which terminates in the *apex* (tip of

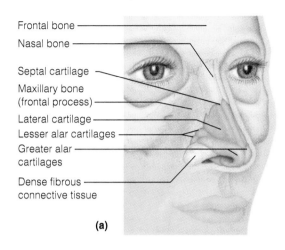

Frontal bone
Nasal bone
Septal cartilage
Maxillary bone
(frontal process)
Lateral cartilage
Lesser alar cartilages
Greater alar
cartilages
Dense fibrous
connective tissue

(a)

Frontalis
muscle
Root and bridge
of nose
Dorsum nasi
Ala of nose
Apex of nose
Philtrum
External
naris (nostril)

(b)

FIGURE 23.2
The external nose. (a) External skeletal framework of the
nose. **(b)** Surface anatomy of the nose.

the nose). Just inferior to the apex is a shallow vertical groove called the *philtrum* (fil'trum; "love"). The external openings of the nose, the *external nares* (na'rez) or *nostrils,* are bounded laterally by the flared *alae.* The skeletal framework of the external nose is fashioned by the nasal and frontal bones superiorly (forming the bridge and root, respectively), the maxillary bones laterally, and flexible plates of hyaline cartilage (the lateral, septal, and alar cartilages) inferiorly (Figure 23.2a). Noses vary a great deal in size and shape, largely because of differences in the nasal cartilages. The skin covering the nose's dorsal and lateral aspects is thin and contains many sebaceous glands.

The **nasal cavity** lies in and posterior to the external nose. During breathing, air enters the nasal cavity by passing through the **external nares,** or **nostrils** (Figure 23.2b and Figure 23.3). The nasal cavity is divided by a midline **nasal septum,** formed anteriorly by hyaline cartilage (the septal cartilage) and posteriorly by the vomer bone and perpendicular plate of the ethmoid bone (see Figure 7.10b, p. 193). The nasal cavity is continuous posteriorly with the nasal portion of the pharynx through the **internal nares,** also called the *posterior nares* or *choanae* (ko-a'ne; "funnels").

The roof of the nasal cavity is formed by the ethmoid and sphenoid bones of the skull. The floor is formed by the *palate* (pal'at), which separates it from the oral cavity below. Anteriorly, where the palate is supported by the maxillary processes and the palatine bones, it is called the **hard palate.** The unsupported posterior portion is the muscular **soft palate.**

The portion of the nasal cavity just superior to the nostrils, called the **vestibule,** is lined with skin containing sebaceous and sweat glands and numerous

hair follicles. The hairs, or **vibrissae** (vi-bris'e; *vibro* = to quiver), filter coarse particles (lint, dust, pollen) from inspired air. The remainder of the nasal cavity is lined with two types of mucous membrane. The **olfactory mucosa,** lining the slitlike superior region of the nasal cavity, contains the receptors for the sense of smell. The balance of the nasal cavity mucosa, the **respiratory mucosa,** is a pseudostratified ciliated columnar epithelium, containing scattered *goblet cells,* that rests on a lamina propria richly supplied with *mucous* and *serous glands.* (By definition, mucous cells secrete mucus, and serous cells secrete a watery fluid containing enzymes.) Each day, these glands secrete about a quart of sticky mucus containing *lysozyme,* an antibacterial enzyme. The mucus traps inspired dust, bacteria, and other debris, while lysozyme attacks and destroys bacteria chemically.

The ciliated cells of the respiratory mucosa create a gentle current that moves the sheet of contaminated mucus posteriorly toward the throat (pharynx), where it is swallowed and digested by stomach juices. We are usually unaware of this important action of our nasal cilia, but when they are exposed to cold environmental temperatures, these cilia become sluggish, allowing mucus to accumulate in the nasal cavity and then dribble out the nostrils. This helps explain why you might have a "runny" nose on a crisp, wintry day.

A rich plexus of thin-walled veins underlies the nasal epithelium and warms the incoming air as it flows across the mucosal surface. When the temperature of inspired air drops, the vascular plexus responds by becoming engorged with blood, thereby intensifying the air-heating process. Because of the abundance and superficial location of these blood vessels, nosebleeds are common and often profuse.

The conchae increase air turbulence in the nasal cavity. Why is this important?

Sphenoidal sinus
Superior meatus
Middle meatus
Pharyngeal tonsil
Opening of auditory (pharyngotympanic) tube
Nasopharynx
Internal nares
Uvula
Palatine tonsil
Fauces
Oropharynx
Laryngopharynx
Vestibular fold
Vocal fold
Esophagus

Frontal sinus
Cribriform plate of ethmoid bone
Superior concha
Middle concha
Vestibule
Inferior concha
Inferior meatus
External nares
Hard palate
Soft palate
Tongue
Lingual tonsil
Epiglottis
Hyoid bone
Thyroid cartilage of larynx
Cricoid cartilage
Thyroid gland
Trachea

(a)

Mucosa of pharynx
Olfactory epithelium
Olfactory bulb
Superior concha and superior meatus
Middle concha and middle meatus
Inferior concha and inferior meatus
Hard palate
Soft palate
Uvula
Tubal tonsil
Pharyngo-tympanic (auditory) tube
Nasopharynx

(b)

FIGURE 23.3
Basic anatomy of the upper respiratory tract. Midsagittal section of the head and neck: **(a)** Illustration. **(b)** Photograph.

Protruding medially from each lateral wall of the nasal cavity are three mucosa-covered projections, the *superior, middle,* and *inferior conchae* (kong'ke). The groove inferior to each concha is a *meatus* (me-a'tus). The curved conchae enhance the air turbulence in the nasal cavity and greatly increase the mucosal surface area exposed to the air. The gases in inhaled air swirl through the twists and turns, but the heavier, nongaseous particles tend to be deflected onto the mucus-coated surfaces, where they become trapped. As a result, few particles larger than 4 μm make it past the nasal cavity.

The nasal mucosa is richly supplied with sensory nerve endings and contact with irritating particles (dust, pollen, and the like) triggers a sneeze reflex. The sneeze forces air outward in a violent burst—a somewhat crude way of expelling irritants from the nose.

The Paranasal Sinuses

The nasal cavity is surrounded by a ring of **paranasal sinuses** located in the frontal, sphenoid, ethmoid, and maxillary bones (see Figure 7.11, p. 193). The sinuses lighten the skull, and together with the nasal cavity they warm and moisten the air. The mucus that they produce ultimately flows into the nasal cavity and the suctioning effect created by nose blowing helps to drain the sinuses.

Cold viruses, streptococcal bacteria, and various allergens can cause *rhinitis* (ri-ni'tis), inflammation of the nasal mucosa accompanied by excessive production of mucus, resulting in nasal congestion and postnasal drip. Because the nasal mucosa is continuous with that of the rest of the respiratory tract and extends tentacle-like into the nasolacrimal (tear) ducts and paranasal sinuses, nasal cavity infections often spread to those regions as well. **Sinusitis,** or inflamed sinuses, is difficult to treat and can result in marked changes in voice quality. When the passageways connecting the sinuses to the nasal cavity are blocked with mucus or infectious material, the air in the sinus cavities is absorbed. The result is a partial vacuum and a *sinus headache* localized over the inflamed areas. •

The Pharynx

The funnel-shaped **pharynx** (far'ingks) connects the nasal cavity and mouth to the larynx and esophagus inferiorly. It serves as a common pathway for food and air. Commonly called the *throat,* the pharynx vaguely resembles a short length of garden hose as it extends for about 13 cm (5 inches) from the base of the skull to the level of the sixth cervical vertebra (see Figures 23.1 and 23.3a).

Based on location, the pharynx has three regions. From superior to inferior, they are the *nasopharynx, oropharynx,* and *laryngopharynx.* The muscular wall of the pharynx is composed of skeletal muscle throughout its length (see Table 10.3, pp. 300–301), but the cellular composition of the mucosal lining varies among the three pharyngeal regions.

The Nasopharynx

The **nasopharynx** is posterior to the nasal cavity, inferior to the sphenoid bone, and superior to the level of the soft palate. Because it lies above the point of food entry into the body, it serves *only* as an air passageway. During swallowing, the soft palate and its pendulous *uvula* (u'vu-lah; "little grape") reflect superiorly, an action that closes off the nasopharynx and prevents food from entering the nasal cavity. (When we giggle, this sealing action fails and fluids being swallowed can end up spraying out the nose.)

The nasopharynx is continuous with the nasal cavity through the internal nares (see Figure 23.3a), and its ciliated pseudostratified epithelium takes over the mucus-propelling job where the nasal mucosa leaves off. The mucosa high on its posterior wall contains masses of lymphatic tissue, the **pharyngeal** (far-rin'je-al) **tonsils,** or **adenoids,** which trap and destroy pathogens entering the nasopharynx in air. (The function of tonsils is described in Chapter 21.)

When the adenoids are infected and swollen, they block air passage in the nasopharynx. This necessitates mouth breathing, so the air is not properly moistened, warmed, or filtered before reaching the lungs. •

The *pharyngotympanic* or *auditory tubes,* which drain the middle ear cavities and allow middle ear pressure to equalize with atmospheric pressure, open into the lateral walls of the nasopharynx (see Figure 23.3b). A ridge of pharyngeal mucosa, referred to as a *tubal tonsil,* arches over each of these openings. Because of their strategic location, the tubal tonsils help protect the middle ear against infections likely to spread from the nasopharynx.

The Oropharynx

The **oropharynx** lies posterior to the oral cavity and is continuous with it through an archway called the **fauces** (faw'sēz) (see Figure 23.3). The oropharynx extends inferiorly from the soft palate to the epiglottis. Given this location, both swallowed food and inhaled air pass through it.

As the nasopharynx blends into the oropharynx, the lining epithelium changes from pseudostratified columnar epithelium to a more protective stratified squamous epithelium. This structural adaptation reflects the increased friction and greater chemical trauma accompanying food passage.

Three tonsils lie embedded in the oropharyngeal mucosa. The paired **palatine tonsils** lie in the lateral walls of the fauces; the **lingual tonsil** covers the base of the tongue.

The Laryngopharynx

Like the oropharynx above, the **laryngopharynx** (lah-ring"go-far'ingks) serves as a common passageway for food and air and is lined with a stratified squamous epithelium. It lies directly posterior to the upright epiglottis and extends to the larynx, where the respiratory and digestive pathways diverge. At that point the laryngopharynx is continuous with the esophagus posteriorly. The esophagus conducts food and fluids to the stomach; air enters the larynx anteriorly. During swallowing, food has the "right of way," and air passage temporarily stops.

The Larynx

Basic Anatomy

The **larynx** (lar'ingks), or voice box, extends for about 5 cm (2 inches) from the level of the fourth to the sixth cervical vertebra. Superiorly it attaches to the hyoid bone and opens into the laryngopharynx. Inferiorly it is continuous with the trachea (see Figure 23.3).

Which structure seals the larynx when we swallow?

(c)   (d)

FIGURE 23.4
Anatomy of the larynx. (a) Anterior superficial view. **(b)** Sagittal view; anterior surface to the right. **(c)** Photograph of the cartilaginous framework of the larynx, posterior view. **(d)** Photograph of the posterior aspect of the larynx.

The larynx has three important functions. Its two main tasks are to provide a *patent* (open) airway and to act as a switching mechanism to route air and food into the proper channels. Since it houses the vocal cords, the third function of the larynx is voice production.

The framework of the larynx is an intricate arrangement of nine cartilages connected by mem-

branes and ligaments (Figure 23.4). Except for the epiglottis, all laryngeal cartilages are hyaline cartilages. The large, shield-shaped **thyroid cartilage** is formed by the anteromedial fusion of two cartilage plates. The ridgelike **laryngeal** (lah-rin′je-al) **prominence,** which marks the fusion point, is obvious externally as the *Adam's apple.* The thyroid cartilage is typically larger in males than in females because male sex hormones stimulate its growth during puberty. Inferior to the thyroid cartilage is the signet ring–shaped **cricoid** (kri′koid) **cartilage,** which is anchored to the trachea inferiorly.

Three pairs of small cartilages, the **arytenoid** (ar″ĭ-te′noid), **cuneiform** (ku-ne′ĭ-form), and **corniculate cartilages** (Figure 23.4b and c), form part of the lateral and posterior walls of the larynx. The most important of these are the pyramid-shaped arytenoid cartilages, which anchor the vocal cords.

The ninth cartilage, the flexible, spoon-shaped **epiglottis** (ep″ĭ-glot′is), is composed of elastic cartilage and is almost entirely covered by a taste bud–containing mucosa. The epiglottis extends from the posterior aspect of the tongue to the anchoring point of its stalk on the anterior rim of the thyroid cartilage (see Figure 23.4b and c). When only air is flowing into the larynx, the inlet to the larynx is open wide and the free edge of the epiglottis projects upward. But during swallowing, the larynx is pulled superiorly and the epiglottis tips to cover the laryngeal inlet. Because this action keeps food out of the lower respiratory passages, the epiglottis has been called the "guardian of the airways." If anything other than air enters the larynx, it initiates the cough reflex, which acts to expel the substance. This protective reflex does not work when we are unconscious, so it is never a good idea to administer fluids when attempting to revive an unconscious person.

Lying under the laryngeal mucosa on each side are the **vocal ligaments,** which attach the arytenoid cartilages to the thyroid cartilage. These ligaments, composed largely of elastic fibers, form the core of mucosal folds called the **vocal folds,** or **true vocal cords,** which appear pearly white because of their avascular nature (Figure 23.4b). The vocal cords vibrate, producing sounds as air rushes up from the lungs. The medial opening between the vocal cords through which air passes is the **glottis.** Superior to the true vocal cords is a similar pair of mucosal folds called the **vestibular folds,** or **false vocal cords.** These play no part in sound production.

The epithelium lining the superior portion of the larynx, an area subject to food contact, is stratified squamous, but below the vocal folds the epithelium is pseudostratified ciliated columnar. The power stroke of its cilia is directed upward toward the pharynx (exactly opposite that of the cilia in the nasopharynx) so that mucus is continually moved *away* from the lungs. We help to move mucus up and out of the larynx when we "clear our throat."

Voice Production

Speech involves the intermittent release of expired air and opening and closing of the glottis. The length of the true vocal folds and the size of the glottis are altered by the action of the intrinsic laryngeal muscles, most of which move the arytenoid cartilages. As the length and tension of the vocal folds change, the pitch of the sound is altered. Generally, the tenser the vocal folds, the faster they vibrate and the higher the pitch. The glottis is wide when we produce deep tones and narrows to a slit for high-pitched sounds. As a young boy's larynx enlarges during puberty, his vocal folds become both longer and thicker. Because this causes them to vibrate more slowly, his voice becomes deeper.

Loudness of the voice depends on the force with which air rushes across the vocal cords. The greater the force, the stronger the vibration and the louder the sound. The vocal cords do not move at all when we whisper, but they vibrate vigorously when we yell.

Although the vocal folds actually produce sounds, the quality of the voice depends on the coordinated activity of many other structures. For example, the pharynx acts as a resonating chamber, or pipe organ, to amplify and enhance the quality of sound. The oral, nasal, and sinus cavities also contribute to vocal resonance. In addition, normal speech and good enunciation depend on the "shaping" of sound into recognizable consonants and vowels by the action of muscles in the pharynx, tongue, soft palate, and lips.

Inflammation of the vocal cords, or **laryngitis,** results in hoarseness or inability to speak above a whisper. Overuse of the voice, very dry air, bacterial infections, and inhalation of irritating chemicals can all cause laryngitis. Whatever the cause, irritation of the laryngeal tissues causes swelling and prevents the vocal folds from moving freely. •

Sphincter Functions of the Larynx

The larynx can be closed by muscle action at two points. As previously described, its inlet is closed by the epiglottis when the larynx moves superiorly during swallowing. In addition to opening and closing the glottis for speech, the vocal folds can perform a sphincter function under certain other conditions, such as when we cough, sneeze, or strain to have a bowel movement. The mechanisms involved in coughs and sneezes are summarized in Table 23.3 (p. 764). In abdominal straining associated with defecation or urination, inhaled air is held temporarily in the lower respiratory tract by closing the glottis. The abdominal muscles then contract, and the intra-abdominal pressure rises. These events, collectively known as **Valsalva's maneuver,** help to empty the rectum or bladder and can also splint (stabilize) the body trunk when one lifts a heavy load.

The Trachea

The **trachea** (tra′ke-ah), or *windpipe,* descends from the larynx through the neck and into the mediastinum. It ends by dividing into the two primary bronchi at midthorax (see Figure 23.1). In humans, the trachea is 10–12 cm (about 4 inches) long and 2.5 cm (1 inch) in diameter. Unlike most other organs in the neck, the trachea is very flexible and mobile.

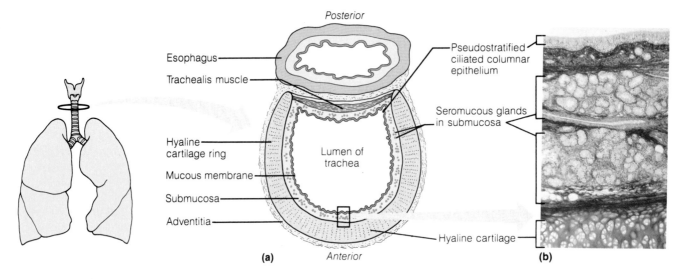

Posterior

Esophagus

Trachealis muscle

Pseudostratified ciliated columnar epithelium

Seromucous glands in submucosa

Hyaline cartilage ring

Lumen of trachea

Mucous membrane

Submucosa

Adventitia

Hyaline cartilage

(a) Anterior   **(b)**

FIGURE 23.5
Tissue composition of the tracheal wall. (a) Cross-sectional view of the trachea, illustrating its relationship to the esophagus, the position of the supporting hyaline cartilage rings in its wall, and the trachealis muscle connecting the free ends of the cartilage rings.
(b) Photomicrograph of a portion of the tracheal wall (cross-sectional view; 50×).

The tracheal wall consists of several layers that are common to many tubular body organs (Figure 23.5). From internal to external, these layers are the *mucosa, submucosa,* and *adventitia.* The epithelium of its **mucosa** is the same goblet cell–containing pseudostratified epithelium that occurs throughout most of the respiratory tract. Its cilia (Figure 23.6) continually propel mucus, loaded with dust particles and other debris, toward the pharynx. The lamina propria has a rich supply of elastic fibers.

Smoking inhibits and ultimately destroys the cilia. When their function is lost, coughing is the only means of preventing mucus from accumulating in the lungs. For this reason, smokers with respiratory congestion should avoid medications that inhibit the cough reflex.

The **submucosa,** a connective tissue layer deep to the mucosa, contains seromucous glands that help produce the mucous "sheets" within the trachea. The outermost **adventitia** layer is a connective tissue layer that is reinforced internally by 16 to 20 C-shaped rings of hyaline cartilage (Figure 23.5). Because of its elastic elements, the trachea is flexible enough to stretch and descend during inspiration and recoil during expiration, but the cartilage rings prevent it from collapsing and keep the airway patent despite the pressure changes that occur during breathing. The open posterior parts of the cartilage rings, which abut the esophagus (see Figure 23.5a), are connected by smooth muscle fibers of the **trachealis muscle** and soft connective tissue. Since this portion of the tracheal wall is not rigid, the esophagus can expand anteriorly as swallowed food passes through it. Contraction of the trachealis muscle decreases the diameter of the trachea, causing expired air to rush upward from the lungs with greater force. This action helps to expel mucus from the trachea when we cough by accelerating the exhaled air to speeds of 100 mph! The last tracheal cartilage is expanded (see Figure 23.1), and a spar of cartilage, called the **carina** (kar-ri'nah; "keel"), projects posteriorly from its inner

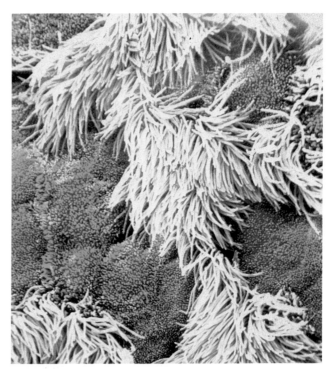

FIGURE 23.6
Cilia. Scanning electron micrograph of cilia in the trachea (221,000×). The cilia appear as yellow, grasslike projections. Mucus-secreting goblet cells (orange) with short microvilli are interspersed between the ciliated cells.

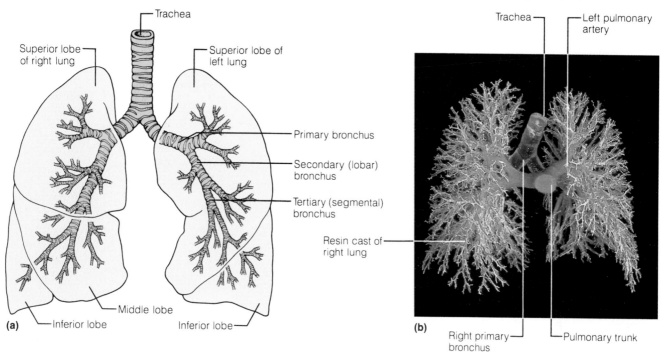

FIGURE 23.7
Conducting respiratory passages. (a) The air pathway inferior to the larynx consists of the trachea and primary, secondary, and tertiary bronchi, which in turn branch into the smaller bronchi and bronchioles until the terminal bronchioles of the lungs are reached. **(b)** Resin cast of the bronchial tree and associated pulmonary arterial supply of the lungs, viewed from the front. Clear resin fills the airways; red resin fills the pulmonary arteries and their branches.

face, marking the point where the trachea ends by splitting into two branches. The mucosa of the carina is highly sensitive and when a foreign object makes contact with it, violent coughing is initiated.

Tracheal obstruction is life threatening. Many people have suffocated after choking on a piece of food that suddenly closed off the trachea (or the glottis of the larynx). The **Heimlich maneuver,** a procedure in which the air in a person's own lungs is used to "pop out," or expel, an obstructing piece of food, has saved many people from becoming victims of such "café coronaries." The Heimlich maneuver is simple to learn and easy to do. However, it is best learned by demonstration because cracked ribs are a distinct possibility when it is done incorrectly. •

The Bronchi and Subdivisions: The Bronchial Tree

The Conducting Zone

The **right** and **left primary (principal) bronchi** (brong′ki) are formed by the division of the trachea approximately at the level of T$_5$ (Figure 23.7a). Each bronchus runs obliquely in the mediastinum before plunging into the medial depression (hilus) of the lung on its own side. The right primary bronchus is wider, shorter, and more vertical than the left and is the more common site for an inhaled foreign object to become lodged. By the time incoming air reaches the bronchi, it is warm, cleansed of most impurities, and saturated with water vapor.

Once inside the lungs, each primary bronchus subdivides into **secondary (lobar) bronchi**—three on the right and two on the left, each of which supplies one lung lobe. The secondary bronchi branch into third-order **tertiary (segmental) bronchi,** which in turn divide repeatedly into smaller and smaller bronchi (fourth-order, fifth-order, etc.) Overall, there are about 23 orders of branching air passageways in the lungs. The air passages under 1 mm in diameter are called **bronchioles** ("little bronchi"), and the tiniest of these, the **terminal bronchioles,** are less than 0.5 mm in diameter. Because of this branching pattern, the conducting network within the lungs is often called the **bronchial** or **respiratory tree.** A resin cast showing the extensive branching of the bronchial tree and its accompanying pulmonary arterial supply is illustrated in Figure 23.7b.

The tissue composition of the walls of the primary bronchi mimics that of the trachea, but as the conducting tubes become smaller, a number of structural changes occur:

1. **The cartilage supports change.** The cartilage rings are replaced by irregular *plates* of cartilage, and by the time the bronchioles are reached, supportive cartilage is no longer present in the tube walls. However, elastic fibers are found in the tube walls throughout the bronchial tree.

(a)

(b)

FIGURE 23.8
Respiratory zone structures. (a) Diagrammatic view of the respiratory unit (respiratory bronchiole, alveolar ducts, alveolar sacs, and alveoli). (b) Scanning electron micrograph of a section of the human lung, showing the network of alveoli that form the final divisions of the bronchial tree (25×). Notice the thinness of the alveolar walls.

2. The epithelium type changes. The mucosal epithelium thins as it changes from pseudostratified columnar epithelium to columnar epithelium and then cuboidal epithelium in the terminal bronchioles. Neither cilia nor mucus-producing cells are present in the bronchioles; thus any airborne debris found at or below the level of the bronchioles is normally removed by macrophages located in the alveoli.

3. The amount of smooth muscle increases. The relative amount of smooth muscle in the tube walls increases as the passageways become smaller. The complete layer of circular smooth muscle in the bronchioles allows them to provide substantial resistance to air passage under certain conditions (as described later).

The Respiratory Zone

The respiratory zone begins as the terminal bronchioles feed into **respiratory bronchioles** within the lung (Figure 23.8). Protruding from these smallest bronchioles are scattered **alveoli** (al-ve′o-li; *alveol* = small cavity). The respiratory bronchioles lead into **alveolar ducts,** straight ducts whose walls consist almost entirely of alveoli. The alveolar ducts then lead into terminal clusters of alveoli called **alveolar sacs.** Many people mistakenly equate alveoli, the actual sites of gas exchange, with alveolar sacs, but they are not the same thing. The alveolar sac is analogous to a bunch of grapes, in which the individual grapes are the alveoli. The opening from an alveolar duct into an alveolar sac is called an **atrium** (meaning an "entrance chamber"). The 300 million or so gas-filled

FIGURE 23.9

Anatomy of the respiratory membrane.
(a) Scanning electron micrograph of casts of alveoli and associated pulmonary capillaries (255×). From *Tissues and Organs* by R. G. Kessel and R. H. Kardon. ©1979 W. H. Freeman. **(b** and **c)** Detailed anatomy of the respiratory membrane composed of the alveolar squamous epithelial cells (type I cells), the capillary endothelium, and the scant basement membranes (fused basal laminas) intervening between. Type II (surfactant-secreting) alveolar cells are also shown, as are the alveolar pores that connect adjacent alveoli. Found within the alveoli, but not forming part of their walls, are the free-roaming alveolar macrophages that phagocytize debris. Diffusion of oxygen occurs from the alveolar air into the pulmonary capillary blood; carbon dioxide diffuses from the pulmonary blood into the alveolus.

(a)

Type II (surfactant-secreting) cell

Type I cell of alveolar wall

Epithelial cell nucleus

Endothelial cell nucleus

Red blood cell

Capillary

O₂   CO₂

Alveolus

(c)

Epithelial cell nucleus

Macrophage

Respiratory membrane

Alveolar epithelium

Fused basal laminas of the alveolar epithelium and the capillary endothelium

Capillary endothelium

(b)

Alveoli (gas filled airspaces)

Red blood cell

Alveolar pores

---

alveoli in the lungs account for most of the lung volume and provide a tremendous surface area for gas exchange.

The Respiratory Membrane.

The walls of the alveoli are composed primarily of a single layer of squamous epithelial cells, called **type I cells,** underlain by a flimsy basal lamina. The thinness of their walls is hard to imagine, but a sheet of tissuepaper is much thicker. The external surfaces of the alveoli are densely covered with a "cobweb" of pulmonary capillaries (Figure 23.9a). Together, the alveolar and capillary walls and their fused basal laminas form the **respiratory membrane (air-blood barrier),** which has

gas on one side and blood flowing past on the other (Figure 23.9c). Gas exchanges occur readily by simple diffusion across the respiratory membrane—the oxygen passing from the alveolus into the blood, and carbon dioxide leaving the blood to enter the gas-filled alveolus.

Scattered amid the type I squamous cells that form the major part of the alveolar walls are cuboidal **type II cells** (Figure 23.9b). The type II cells secrete a fluid containing surfactant that coats the gas-exposed alveolar surfaces. (Surfactant's role in reducing the surface tension of the alveolar fluid is described later in this chapter.)

The lung alveoli have three other significant features: (1) They are surrounded by fine elastic fibers of the same type that surround the entire respiratory tree. (2) Open pores are present between adjacent alveoli (Figure 23.9b). These **alveolar pores** allow equalization of air pressure throughout the lung and provide alternate air routes to any alveoli whose bronchi have collapsed through disease. (3) **Alveolar macrophages** crawl freely along the internal alveolar surfaces. Also called *dust cells*, these free macrophages are remarkably efficient. Although huge numbers of infectious microorganisms are continually carried into the alveoli, alveolar surfaces are usually sterile. Since the alveoli are "dead ends," aged and dead macrophages must be prevented from accumulating within them. Most macrophages simply get swept up by the ciliary current of superior regions and are carried passively to the pharynx. In this manner, we clear and swallow over 2 million dust cells per hour!

The Lungs and Pleural Coverings

Gross Anatomy of the Lungs

The paired **lungs** occupy the entire thoracic cavity except for the *mediastinum,* which houses the heart, great blood vessels, bronchi, esophagus, and other organs (Figure 23.10). Each cone-shaped lung is suspended in its own pleural cavity and connected to the mediastinum by vascular and bronchial attachments, collectively called its **root.** The anterior, lateral, and posterior lung surfaces lie in close contact with the ribs and form a continuously curving surface called a **costal surface.** Just deep to the clavicle is the **apex,** the narrow superior tip of the lung; the concave, inferior surface that rests on the diaphragm is the **base.** On the medial (mediastinal) surface of each lung is an indentation, the **hilus,** through which blood vessels of the pulmonary and systemic circulations enter and leave the lungs. Each primary bronchus also plunges into the hilus on its own side and begins to branch almost immediately. All conducting and respiratory passageways distal to the primary bronchi are found within the lung substance.

Because the apex of the heart is slightly to the left of the median plane, the two lungs differ slightly in shape and size. The left lung is smaller than the right, and the **cardiac notch (impression)**—a concavity in its medial aspect—is molded to and accommodates the heart (see Figure 23.10a). The left lung is subdivided into two (upper and lower) **lobes** by the *oblique fissure,* whereas the right lung is partitioned into three lobes (upper, middle, and lower) by the *oblique* and *horizontal fissures.* Each of the lung lobes, in turn, contains a number of pyramid-shaped **bronchopulmonary segments** separated from one another by connective tissue septa. Each such segment is served by its own artery and vein and receives air from an individual segmental bronchus. Each lung contains 10 bronchopulmonary segments arranged in

similar (but not identical) patterns. The bronchopulmonary segments are clinically important because pulmonary disease is often confined to one (or a few) bronchopulmonary segments. Their connective tissue partitions allow diseased segments to be surgically removed without damaging "neighboring" healthy segments or impairing their blood supply.

The smallest subdivision of the lung that can be seen with the naked eye is the **lobule.** The lobules appear on the lung surface as hexagons ranging from the size of a pencil eraser to the size of a penny (Figure 23.10b). Each lobule is served by a large bronchiole and its branches. In most city dwellers and in smokers, the connective tissue that separates the individual lobules is blackened with carbon.

As mentioned earlier, the lungs consist largely of air spaces. The balance of lung tissue, or its **stroma** (literally "mattress" or "bed"), is mostly elastic connective tissue. As a result, the lungs are soft, spongy, elastic organs that together weigh just over 1 kg (2.5 pounds). The elasticity of healthy lungs helps to reduce the work of breathing, as described shortly.

Blood Supply and Innervation of the Lungs

Blood that is to be oxygenated in the lungs is delivered by the **pulmonary arteries,** which lie posterior to the primary bronchi and accompany them into the lungs (Figures 23.7b and 23.10c). Within the lungs, the pulmonary arteries branch profusely along with the bronchi, and finally feed into the **pulmonary capillary networks** surrounding the alveoli (see Figure 23.9a). Freshly oxygenated blood is delivered from the respiratory zones of the lungs to the heart by the **pulmonary veins,** which course back to the hilus in the connective tissue septa separating the bronchopulmonary segments.

The **bronchial arteries** provide systemic blood to the lung tissues. They arise from the aorta and enter the lungs at the hilus. Within the lung they run along the branching bronchi. Systemic venous blood is drained from the lungs by the bronchial veins.

The lungs are innervated by parasympathetic and (rare) sympathetic motor fibers, and visceral sensory fibers. These nerve fibers enter each lung through the **pulmonary plexus** on the lung root and run along the bronchial tubes and blood vessels within the lungs. Parasympathetic fibers constrict the air tubes, and sympathetic fibers dilate them.

The Pleura

The **pleura** (ploo'rah; "the side") is a thin, double-layered serosa (see Figure 23.10). The **parietal pleura** lines the thoracic wall and superior aspect of the diaphragm. It continues around the heart and between the lungs, forming the lateral walls of the mediastinal enclosure and snugly enclosing the root of the lung. From here, the pleura extends as the **visceral,** or **pulmonary, pleura** to cover the external lung surface, dipping into and lining its fissures.

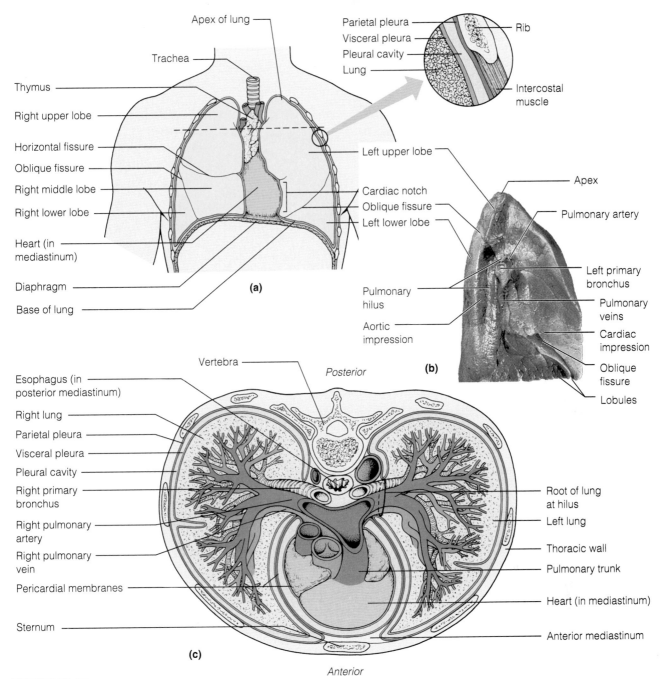

FIGURE 23.10
Anatomical relationships of organs in the thoracic cavity.
(a) Anterior view of the thoracic cavity organs, showing the position of the lungs, which flank mediastinal structures laterally. **(b)** Photograph of medial aspect of left lung. **(c)** Transverse section through the thorax, showing the lungs, the pleural membranes, and the major organs present in the mediastinum. (The plane of the section is shown by the dashed line in **a**; the thymus has been omitted for clarity.)

The pleurae (ploo're) produce **pleural fluid,** a lubricating serous secretion that fills the slitlike **pleural cavity** between them, and allows the lungs to glide easily over the thorax wall during breathing movements. Although the pleurae can slide across one another, their separation is strongly resisted by the surface tension of the pleural fluid between them. Consequently, the lungs cling tightly to the thorax wall and are forced to expand and recoil passively as the volume of the thoracic cavity alternately increases and decreases.

The pleurae also help divide the thoracic cavity into three separate chambers—the central mediastinum and the two lateral pleural compartments, each containing a lung. This compartmentalization helps prevent one mobile functioning organ from interfering with another. It also limits the spread of local infections and the extent of traumatic injury.

Pleurisy (ploo'rĭ-se), inflammation of the pleura, can be caused by decreased secretion of pleural fluid. The pleural surfaces become dry and rough, resulting in friction and stabbing pain with each breath. Conversely, the pleurae may produce excessive fluid, which exerts pressure on the lungs. This type of pleurisy hinders breathing movements, but it is much less painful than the dry rubbing type. •

Table 23.1 Principal Organs of the Respiratory System

Structure	Description, general and distinctive features	Function
Nose	Jutting external portion supported by bone and cartilage; internal nasal cavity divided by midline nasal septum and lined with mucosa	Produces mucus; filters, warms, and moistens incoming air; resonance chamber for speech
	Roof of nasal cavity contains olfactory epithelium	Receptors for sense of smell
	Paranasal sinuses around nasal cavity	Same as for nasal cavity; also lighten skull
Pharynx	Passageway connecting nasal cavity to larynx and oral cavity to esophagus; three subdivisions: nasopharynx, oropharynx, and laryngopharynx	Passageway for air and food
	Houses tonsils	Facilitates exposure of immune system to inhaled antigens
Larynx	Connects pharynx to trachea; framework of cartilage and dense connective tissue; opening (glottis) can be closed by epiglottis or vocal folds	Air passageway; prevents food from entering lower respiratory tract
	Houses true vocal cords	Voice production
Trachea	Flexible tube running from larynx and dividing inferiorly into two primary bronchi; walls contain C-shaped cartilages that are incomplete posteriorly where connected by trachealis muscle	Air passageway; cleans, warms, and moistens incoming air
Bronchial tree	Consists of right and left primary bronchi, which subdivide within the lungs to form secondary and tertiary bronchi and bronchioles; bronchiolar walls contain complete layer of smooth muscle; constriction of this muscle impedes expiration	Air passageways connecting trachea with alveoli; warms and moistens incoming air
Alveoli	Microscopic chambers at termini of bronchial tree; walls of simple squamous epithelium underlain by thin basement membrane; external surfaces intimately associated with pulmonary capillaries	Main sites of gas exchange
	Special alveolar cells produce surfactant	Reduces surface tension; helps prevent lung collapse
Lungs	Paired composite organs located within pleural cavities of thorax; composed primarily of alveoli and respiratory passageways; stroma is fibrous elastic connective tissue, allowing lungs to recoil passively during expiration	House passageways smaller than primary bronchi, alveoli, and respiratory membranes
Pleurae	Serous membranes; parietal pleura lines thoracic cavity; visceral pleura covers external lung surfaces	Produce lubricating fluid and compartmentalize lungs

MECHANICS OF BREATHING

Breathing, or **pulmonary ventilation,** consists of two phases: **inspiration,** the period when air is flowing into the lungs, and **expiration,** the period when gases are leaving the lungs. The mechanical factors that promote these gas flows are the topics of this section.

Pressure Relationships in the Thoracic Cavity

Before we can begin to describe the breathing process, it is important to understand that *respiratory pressures are always described relative to atmospheric pressure.* Atmospheric pressure is the pressure exerted by the air (gases) surrounding the body. At sea level atmospheric pressure is equal to 760 mm Hg (the pressure exerted by a column of mercury 760 mm high). Thus, a negative respiratory pressure such as − 4 mm Hg indicates that the pressure in that area is lower than atmospheric pressure by 4 mm Hg (760 − 4 = 756 mm Hg). By the same token, a positive respiratory pressure is higher than atmospheric pressure and a respiratory pressure of 0 is equal to atmospheric pressure. Now, we are ready to examine the pressure relationships that normally exist in the thoracic cavity.

Intrapulmonary Pressure

The **intrapulmonary** (intra-alveolar) **pressure** is the pressure within the alveoli of the lungs. The intrapulmonary pressure rises and falls with the phases of breathing, but it *always* eventually equalizes itself with the atmospheric pressure outside the body (Figure 23.11).

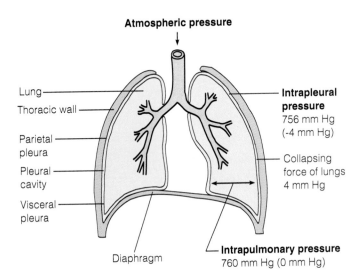

Atmospheric pressure

Lung

Thoracic wall

Parietal pleura

Pleural cavity

Visceral pleura

Diaphragm

Intrapleural pressure
756 mm Hg
(-4 mm Hg)

Collapsing force of lungs
4 mm Hg

Intrapulmonary pressure
760 mm Hg (0 mm Hg)

FIGURE 23.11
Intrapulmonary and intrapleural pressure relationships.
Differences in pressure relative to atmospheric pressure (760 mm Hg) are given in parentheses.

Intrapleural Pressure

The pressure within the pleural cavity, the **intrapleural pressure**, also fluctuates with breathing phases. However, the intrapleural pressure is always about 4 mm Hg less than the pressure in the alveoli. Hence, it is negative relative to both the intrapulmonary and atmospheric pressures.

The negative pressure in the intrapleural space results from the interaction of three factors—two that act to pull the lungs away from the thorax wall, and a third that acts to hold the lungs to the thorax wall. Let's examine these factors more closely. The two principal forces acting to pull the lungs (visceral pleura) away from the thorax wall (parietal pleura) and thus to collapse the lungs are:

- **The natural tendency of the lungs to recoil.** Because of their great elasticity, lungs tend to assume the smallest size possible at any given time.
- **The surface tension of the alveolar fluid.** The fluid film in the alveoli constantly acts to draw the alveoli to their smallest possible dimension.

However, these forces are opposed by:

- **The surface tension created by pleural fluid in the pleural cavity.** Pleural fluid secures the pleurae together in the same way that a drop of water holds two glass slides to one another. They can slide from side to side easily, but separating them requires extreme force.

The net result of the dynamic interplay between these forces is negative intrapleural pressure.

The importance of the negative pressure in the intrapleural space and the tight coupling of the lungs to the thorax wall cannot be overemphasized. *Any condition that equalizes the intrapleural pressure*

with the intrapulmonary (or atmospheric) pressure causes immediate lung collapse. It is the **transpleural pressure** (the difference between the intrapleural and intrapulmonary pressures) that keeps the airspaces of the lungs open or, phrased another way, keeps the lungs from collapsing.

Atelectasis (at″ĕ-lik′tah-sis), or lung collapse, renders the lung useless for ventilation. This phenomenon commonly occurs when air enters the pleural cavity through a chest wound, but may result from a rupture of the visceral pleura, which allows air to enter the pleural cavity from the respiratory tract. The presence of air in the intrapleural space is referred to as a **pneumothorax** (nu″mo-tho′raks). A pneumothorax is reversed by closing the "hole" and drawing air out of the intrapleural space with chest tubes, which allows the lung to reinflate and resume its normal function. Note that since the lungs are in completely separate pleural cavities, one lung can be collapsed without hindering the other. •

Pulmonary Ventilation: Inspiration and Expiration

Pulmonary ventilation, or breathing, is a completely mechanical process that depends on volume changes occurring in the thoracic cavity. A rule to keep in mind throughout the following discussion is that *volume changes lead to pressure changes, which lead to the flow of gases to equalize the pressure.*

$$\Delta V \rightarrow \Delta P \rightarrow F(\text{flow of gases})$$

The relationship between the pressure and volume of gases is given by **Boyle's Law,** an *ideal gas law,* which states that when the temperature is constant, the pressure of a gas varies inversely with its volume. That is, $P_1 V_1 = P_2 V_2$, where P is the pressure of the gas in millimeters of mercury, V is its volume in cubic millimeters, and subscripts 1 and 2 represent the initial and resulting conditions respectively. Gases, like liquids, conform to the shape of their container. However, unlike liquids, gases always *fill* their container. Therefore, in a large volume, the gas molecules will be far apart and the pressure will be low. But, if the volume is reduced, the gas molecules will be compressed and the pressure will rise. Let us see how this relates to the phases of inspiration and expiration.

Inspiration

The process of **inspiration** (inhalation) is easily understood if you visualize the thoracic cavity as a box with a single entrance at the top, the tubelike trachea. The volume of this box is changeable and can be increased by enlarging all of its diameters, thereby decreasing the gas pressure within it. This, in turn, causes air to rush into the box from the atmosphere, since gases always flow down their pressure gradients.

Inspiration ——————————— | ——————————— Expiration ———————————

Inspiratory muscles contract (diaphragm descends; rib cage rises)

↓

Thoracic cavity volume increases

↓

Lungs stretched; intrapulmonary volume increases

↓

Intrapulmonary pressure drops (to −1mm Hg)

↓

Air (gases) flows into lungs down its pressure gradient until intrapulmonary pressure is 0 (equal to atmospheric pressure)

Ribs elevated and sternum flares as external intercostals contract

Diaphragm moves inferiorly during contraction

(a) Changes in anterior-posterior and superior-inferior dimensions

Ribs and sternum depressed as external intercostals relax

Diaphragm moves superiorly as it relaxes

Inspiratory muscles relax (diaphragm rises; rib cage descends due to gravity)

↓

Thoracic cavity volume decreases

↓

Elastic lungs recoil passively; intrapulmonary volume decreases

↓

Intrapulmonary pressure rises (to +1mm Hg)

↓

Air (gases) flows out of lungs down its pressure gradient until intrapulmonary pressure is 0

External intercostals contract

External intercostals relax

(b) Changes in lateral dimensions

FIGURE 23.12
Changes in thoracic volume that lead to the flow of air (gases) during breathing. **(a)** Lateral views of the thorax during inspiration (left) and expiration (right) showing the changes that occur in the superior-inferior dimensions (as the diaphragm alternately contracts and relaxes) and in the anterior-posterior dimensions (as the external intercostal muscles alternately contract and relax). **(b)** Superior view of a transverse thoracic section showing lateral dimension changes resulting from alternate contraction (left) and relaxation (right) of the external intercostal muscles during inspiration and expiration, respectively. Flowcharts of volume changes occurring during inspiration and expiration appear at the sides of the diagrams to which they relate.

Identical relationships exist during normal quiet inspiration, when the **inspiratory muscles**—the diaphragm and external intercostal muscles—are activated. Here's how quiet inspiration works:

1. **Action of the diaphragm.** When the dome-shaped diaphragm contracts, it moves inferiorly and flattens out (Figure 23.12a). As a result, the superior-inferior dimension (height) of the thoracic cavity increases.

2. **Action of the intercostal muscles.** Contraction of the external intercostal muscles lifts the rib cage and pulls the sternum forward (Figure 23.12a and b). Since the ribs curve downward as well as forward around the chest wall, the broadest lateral and antero-posterior dimensions of the rib cage are normally directed obliquely downward. But when the ribs are raised and drawn together, they also swing outward, expanding the diameter of the thorax both laterally and in the anteroposterior plane. This is much like the action that occurs when a curved bucket handle is raised.

Although these actions expand the thoracic dimensions by only a few millimeters along each plane, this is sufficient to increase the volume of the thoracic cavity by almost half a liter (a pint)—the usual volume of air that enters the lungs during a normal quiet inspiration. Of the two types of inspiratory muscles, the diaphragm is far more important in bringing about the volume changes that lead to normal quiet inspiration.

As the thoracic dimensions increase during inspiration, the lungs are stretched and the intrapulmonary volume increases. As a result, intrapulmonary pressure drops about 1 mm Hg relative to atmospheric pressure, and air rushes into the lungs along this pressure gradient. Inspiration ends when intrapulmonary and atmospheric pressures become equal. During the same period, the intrapleural pressure declines to about − 6 mm Hg relative to atmospheric pressure (Figure 23.13).

During the *deep* or *forced inspirations* that occur during vigorous exercise and in some chronic obstructive pulmonary disease victims (see p. 779), the capacity of the thorax is further increased by activation of accessory muscles. Several muscles, including the scalenes and sternocleidomastoid muscles of the neck and the pectoralis minor of the chest, raise the ribs even more than occurs during quiet inspiration. Additionally, the back is extended as the thoracic curvature is straightened by the erector spinae muscles.

Expiration

Quiet **expiration** (exhalation) in healthy individuals is largely a passive process that depends more on the natural elasticity of the lungs than on muscle contraction. As the inspiratory muscles relax and resume their initial resting length, the rib cage descends and the lungs recoil. Thus, both the thoracic and intrapul-

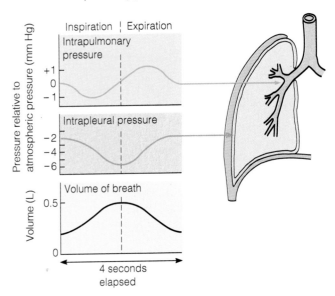

As thoracic volume increases, what happens to the intrapulmonary pressure? To the intrapleural pressure?

FIGURE 23.13
Changes in intrapulmonary and intrapleural pressures during inspiration and expiration. Notice that normal atmospheric pressure (760 mm Hg) is given a value of 0 on the scale.

monary volumes decrease. This compresses the alveoli, and the intrapulmonary pressure rises to about 1 mm Hg above atmospheric pressure (see Figure 23.13), which forces gases to flow out of the lungs.

In contrast, *forced expiration* is an active process produced by contraction of abdominal wall muscles, primarily the oblique and transversus muscles. These contractions (1) increase the intra-abdominal pressure, which forces the abdominal organs superiorly against the diaphragm, and (2) depress the rib cage. The internal intercostal, latissimus dorsi, and quadratus lumborum muscles may also help to depress the rib cage and decrease thoracic volume. It is interesting that the ability of a trained vocalist to hold a particular note depends on the coordinated activity of several muscles normally used in forced expiration. Thus, control of accessory muscles of expiration is very important when precise regulation of airflow from the lungs is desired.

Physical Factors Influencing Pulmonary Ventilation

As we have seen, the lungs are stretched during inspiration and recoil passively during expiration. The inspiratory muscles consume energy to enlarge the thorax. Energy is also used to overcome various factors that hinder air passage and pulmonary ventilation. These factors—respiratory passageway resistance, lung compliance and elasticity, and alveolar surface tension forces—are examined next.

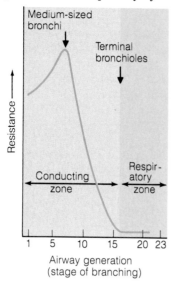

FIGURE 23.14
Resistance of the various segments of the respiratory passageways. The airway resistance peaks in the medium-sized bronchi and then declines sharply as the total cross-sectional area of the airway increases rapidly.

Respiratory Passageway Resistance

The major *nonelastic* source of resistance to gas flow is *friction*, or drag, encountered in the respiratory passageways. The relationship between gas flow, pressure, and resistance is given by the following equation:

$$\text{Gas flow} = \frac{\text{pressure gradient}}{\text{resistance}}$$

Notice that the factors determining gas flow in the respiratory passages and blood flow in the cardiovascular system are equivalent. The amount of gas flowing in and out of the alveoli is directly proportional to the difference in pressure (pressure gradient) between the external atmosphere and the alveoli. Normally, very small differences in pressure are sufficient to produce large changes in the volume of gas flow. The average pressure gradient during normal quiet breathing is 2 mm Hg or less, and yet it moves 500 ml of air in and out of the lungs with each breath.

But, as the equation also indicates, gas flow changes *inversely* with resistance; that is, gas flow decreases as resistance increases. As with resistance in the cardiovascular system, that in the respiratory tree is determined mostly by the diameters of the conducting tubes. As a rule, airway resistance is insignificant because (1) the airway diameters of the initial part of the conducting zone are huge, relatively speaking, and (2) gas flow stops at the terminal bronchioles (where small airway diameters might start to be a problem) and diffusion takes over as the main force driving gas movements. Hence, as shown in Figure 23.14, the greatest resistance to gas flow occurs in the medium-sized bronchi.

However, smooth muscle of the bronchiolar walls is exquisitely sensitive to neural controls and certain chemicals. For example, parasympathetic stimulation reflexly activated by inhaled irritants and inflammatory chemicals such as histamine promote vigorous constriction of the bronchioles and dramatically reduce air passage. Indeed, the strong bronchoconstriction occurring during an *acute asthma attack* can stop pulmonary ventilation almost completely, regardless of the pressure gradient. Conversely, epinephrine released during sympathetic nervous system activation or administered as a drug dilates the bronchioles and reduces airway resistance. Local accumulations of mucus, infectious material, or solid tumors in the passageways are important sources of airway resistance in respiratory disease.

Any factor that amplifies airway resistance demands that breathing movements become more strenuous. However, such compensation is limited. When the bronchioles are severely constricted or obstructed, even the most magnificent respiratory efforts cannot restore ventilation to life-sustaining levels.

Lung Compliance

Healthy lungs are unbelievably stretchy, or distensible. The ease with which the lungs can be expanded—that is, their distensibility—is referred to as **lung compliance**. Specifically, lung compliance (C_L) is a measure of the change in lung volume (ΔV_L) that occurs with a change in the intrapulmonary pressure (ΔP). This is stated as:

$$C_L = \Delta V_L / \Delta P$$

The more the lung expands for a given rise in pressure, the greater its compliance.

Lung compliance depends not only on the elasticity of lung tissue itself, but also on that of the thoracic cage. Compliance is diminished by any factor that (1) reduces the natural resilience of the lungs, such as fibrosis, (2) blocks the bronchi or smaller respiratory passageways, (3) increases the surface tension of the fluid film in the alveoli, or (4) impairs the flexibility of the thoracic cage.

Deformities of the thorax, ossification of the costal cartilages (common during old age), and paralysis of the intercostal muscles all reduce the compliance of the lungs because they hinder thoracic expansion. •

Lung Elasticity

Just as lung distension is required for normal inspiration, lung recoil is essential for normal expiration. These two functional attributes of fibroelastic lung tissue represent opposite sides of the same coin, *lung elasticity.* The importance of lung elasticity becomes glaringly clear when it declines, as in emphysema. Emphysema is described in detail on p. 779.

Alveolar Surface Tension Forces

At any gas-liquid boundary, the molecules of the liquid are more strongly attracted to each other than to the gas. This unequal attraction produces a state of tension at the liquid surface, called **surface tension,** that (1) draws the liquid molecules ever more closely together and reduces their overall contact with the dissimilar gas molecules, and (2) resists any force that tends to increase the area of the surface.

Water is composed of highly polar molecules and has a very high surface tension. Hence, as the major component of the liquid film that coats the alveolar walls, it perpetually acts to reduce the alveoli to their smallest possible size (and also contributes to the lungs' natural recoil during expiration). If the alveolar film was pure water, the alveoli would collapse between breaths. But, the alveolar film contains **surfactant** (ser-fak′tant), a detergent-like lipoprotein produced by the type II alveolar cells. Surfactant interferes with the cohesiveness of water molecules, much the way a laundry detergent reduces the attraction of water for water, allowing water to interact with and pass through fabrics. As a result, the surface tension of alveolar fluid is reduced, and less energy is needed to overcome surface tension forces to expand the lungs and discourage alveolar collapse.

When insufficient amounts of surfactant are present, surface tension forces can collapse the alveoli. This requires that the alveoli be completely reinflated during each inspiration, an effort that uses tremendous amounts of energy. This is the problem faced by newborns with **infant respiratory distress syndrome (IRDS),** a condition peculiar to premature babies. Since little pulmonary surfactant is produced until the last two months of fetal development, babies born prematurely often have too little surfactant to keep the alveoli inflated between breaths. IRDS is treated with positive-pressure respirators that force air into the alveoli, keeping them open between breaths. Spraying natural or synthetic surfactant into the newborn's respiratory passageways is also very helpful. •

Respiratory Volumes and Pulmonary Function Tests

Respiratory Volumes and Capacities

The amount of air that is flushed in and out of the lungs varies substantially depending on the conditions of inspiration and expiration. Consequently, several different respiratory volumes can be described. Specific combinations (sums) of these respiratory volumes, called respiratory capacities, are measured to gain information about a person's respiratory status. The apparatus used to measure respiratory volumes, called a *spirometer,* is described below.

Respiratory Volumes. The **respiratory,** or **lung, volumes** include tidal, inspiratory reserve, expiratory reserve, and residual volumes. The values recorded in Figure 23.15 represent normal values for a healthy 20-year-old-male weighing about 70 kg (155 pounds).

During normal quiet breathing, about 500 ml of air moves into and out of the lungs with each breath. This respiratory volume is referred to as the **tidal volume (TV).** The amount of air that can be inspired forcibly beyond the tidal volume (2100 to 3200 ml) is called the **inspiratory reserve volume (IRV).**

The **expiratory reserve volume (ERV)** is the amount of air—normally 1000 to 1200 ml—that can be evacuated from the lungs after a tidal expiration. Even after the most strenuous expiration, about 1200 ml of air still remains in the lungs; this is the **residual volume (RV).** Residual volume air helps to maintain alveolar patency and prevent lung collapse.

Respiratory Capacities. The **respiratory capacities** include inspiratory capacity, functional residual capacity, vital capacity, and total lung capacity (see Figure 23.15). As noted, the respiratory capacities always consist of two or more lung volumes.

The **inspiratory capacity (IC)** is the total amount of air that can be inspired after a tidal expiration; thus, it is the sum of the tidal and inspiratory reserve volumes. The **functional residual capacity (FRC)** is the combined residual and expiratory reserve volumes and represents the amount of air remaining in the lungs after a tidal expiration.

Vital capacity (VC) is the total amount of exchangeable air. It represents the sum of the tidal, inspiratory reserve, and expiratory reserve volumes. In healthy young males, the VC is approximately 4800 ml. The **total lung capacity (TLC)** is the sum of all lung volumes and is normally around 6000 ml in males. Lung volumes and capacities (with the possible exception of tidal volume) tend to be slightly less in women than in men because of their smaller size.

Dead Space

Some of the inspired air fills the conducting respiratory passageways and never contributes to gas exchange in the alveoli. The volume of these conducting zone conduits, which make up the **anatomical dead space,** typically amounts to about 150 ml. (The rule of thumb is that the anatomical dead space volume in milliliters in a healthy young adult is equal to the person's weight in pounds.) This means that if the tidal volume is 500 ml, only 350 ml of this is involved in alveolar ventilation. The remaining 150 ml of the tidal breath is in the anatomical dead space.

If some of the alveoli cease to act in gas exchange (due to alveolar collapse or obstruction by mucus, for example), the **alveolar dead space** is added to the anatomical dead space, and the sum of the nonuseful volumes is referred to as **total dead space.**

(a) Spirographic record

	Measurement	Adult male average value	Description
Respiratory volumes	Tidal volume (TV)	500 ml	Amount of air inhaled or exhaled with each breath under resting conditions
	Inspiratory reserve volume (IRV)	3100 ml	Amount of air that can be forcefully inhaled after a normal tidal volume inhalation
	Expiratory reserve volume (ERV)	1200 ml	Amount of air that can be forcefully exhaled after a normal tidal volume exhalation
	Residual volume (RV)	1200 ml	Amount of air remaining in the lungs after a forced exhalation
Respiratory capacities	Total lung capacity (TLC)	6000 ml	Maximum amount of air contained in lungs after a maximum inspiratory effort: TLC = TV + IRV + ERV + RV
	Vital capacity (VC)	4800 ml	Maximum amount of air that can be expired after a maximum inspiratory effort: VC = TV + IRV + ERV (should be 80% TLC)
	Inspiratory capacity (IC)	3600 ml	Maximum amount of air that can be inspired after a normal expiration: IC = TV + IRV
	Functional residual capacity (FRC)	2400 ml	Volume of air remaining in the lungs after a normal tidal volume expiration: FRC = ERV + RV

(b) Summary of respiratory volumes and capacities

FIGURE 23.15
Respiratory volumes and capacities. (a) Idealized spirographic record of respiratory
volumes. **(b)** Summary of respiratory volumes and capacities in a healthy young adult male
weighing approximately 70 kg.

Pulmonary Function Tests

Because the various lung volumes and capacities are often abnormal in people with pulmonary disorders, they are routinely measured. A **spirometer** (spi-rom′ĕ-ter) is a simple instrument utilizing a hollow bell inverted over water, that is displaced as the patient breathes into a connecting mouthpiece. As the test is conducted, a graphic recording is made on a rotating drum. Spirometry testing is most useful for evaluating losses in respiratory function and for following the course of certain respiratory diseases. Although it cannot provide a specific diagnosis,

spirometry can distinguish between *obstructive pulmonary disease* involving increased airway resistance (such as chronic bronchitis or asthma) and *restrictive disorders* involving a reduction in total lung capacity due to structural or functional changes in the lungs (such as tuberculosis or polio). For example, increases in TLC, FRC, and RV may occur as a result of hyperinflation of the lungs in obstructive disease, whereas VC, TLC, FRC, and RV are reduced in restrictive diseases, which limit lung expansion.

Much more information can be obtained about a patient's ventilation status by assessing the rate of gas

Table 23.2 Effect of Breathing Rate and Depth on Alveolar Ventilation of Three Hypothetical Patients

Breathing pattern of hypothetical patient	Dead space volume (DSV)	Tidal volume (TV)	Respiratory rate*	Minute ventilation	Alveolar ventilation	% of TV = dead space volume
I—Normal rate and depth	150 ml	500 ml	20/min	10,000 ml/min	7000 ml/min	30%
II—Slow, deep breathing	150 ml	1000 ml	10/min	10,000 ml/min	8500 ml/min	15%
III—Rapid, shallow breathing	150 ml	250 ml	40/min	10,000 ml/min	4000 ml/min	60%

*Respiratory rate values are artificially adjusted to provide equivalent minute respiratory volumes as a baseline for comparison of alveolar ventilation.

movement in and out of the lungs. The **minute** or **total ventilation** is the total amount of gas that flows into and out of the respiratory tract in 1 minute. During normal quiet breathing, the minute ventilation in healthy people is about 6 L/min (500 ml per breath multiplied by 12 breaths per minute). During vigorous exercise, the minute ventilation may reach 200 L/min, as both the depth and rapidity of breathing increase.

Two other useful tests are the FVC and FEV. **FVC,** or **forced vital capacity,** measures the amount of gas expelled when a subject takes a deep breath and then forcefully exhales maximally and as rapidly as possible. **FEV,** or **forced expiratory volume,** determines the amount of air expelled during specific time intervals of the FVC test. For example, the volume exhaled during the first second is FEV_1. Those with healthy lungs can exhale about 80% of the FVC within one second. Those with obstructive pulmonary disease have a low FEV_1, while restrictive disease produces a low FVC.

Alveolar Ventilation

Minute ventilation values provide a rough-and-ready yardstick for assessing respiratory efficiency, but the **alveolar ventilation rate (AVR),** or **alveolar ventilation,** is a better index of effective ventilation. The AVR takes into account the volume of air wasted in dead space areas and measures the flow of fresh gases in and out of the alveoli during a particular time. Alveolar ventilation is computed with the following equation:

$$\begin{array}{ccc} AVR & = & \text{frequency} \times & (TV - \text{dead space}) \\ \text{(ml/min)} & & \text{(breaths/min)} & \text{(ml/breath)} \end{array}$$

In healthy people, alveolar ventilation is usually about 12 breaths per minute multiplied by the difference of 500 – 150 ml per breath, or 4200 ml/min.

Increasing the volume of each inspiration enhances alveolar ventilation and gas exchange more than raising the respiratory rate because anatomical dead space is a constant in a particular individual. Alveolar ventilation drops dramatically during rapid shallow breathing because most of the inspired air

never reaches the exchange sites. Furthermore, as tidal volume approaches the dead space value, effective ventilation approaches zero, regardless of rapidity of breathing. The effects of rate and depth of breathing on effective alveolar ventilation are summarized for three hypothetical patients in Table 23.2.

Nonrespiratory Air Movements

There are many processes other than breathing that move air into or out of the lungs and that may modify the normal respiratory rhythm. Coughs and sneezes clear the air passages of debris or collected mucus. Laughing and crying reflect our emotions. Most of these **nonrespiratory air movements** result from reflex activity, but some are produced voluntarily. Examples of the most common of these movements are given in Table 23.3.

GAS EXCHANGES IN THE BODY

Basic Properties of Gases

Gas exchange in the body occurs by bulk flow of gases (and solutions of gases) and by diffusion of gases through tissues. To fully understand these processes, we must examine some of the physical properties of gases and their behavior in liquids. Two more *ideal gas laws—Dalton's law of partial pressures* and *Henry's law—*provide most of the information we need.

Dalton's Law of Partial Pressures

Dalton's law of partial pressures states that the total pressure exerted by a mixture of gases is the sum of the pressures exerted independently by each gas in the mixture. Further, the pressure exerted by each gas—its **partial pressure**—is directly proportional to its percentage in the total gas mixture.

As noted earlier, atmospheric pressure is approximately 760 mm Hg at sea level. Since air is a mixture of gases, we can examine it more closely in terms of the gases that comprise it. As indicated in Table 23.4, nitrogen makes up about 79% of air, and the partial pressure of nitrogen (written as P_{N_2}) is 78.6% × 760

Table 23.3 Nonrespiratory Air (Gas) Movements	
Movement	**Mechanism and result**
Cough	Taking a deep breath, closing glottis, and forcing air superiorly from lungs against glottis; glottis opens suddenly and a blast of air rushes upward; can dislodge foreign particles or mucus from lower respiratory tract and propel such substances superiorly
Sneeze	Similar to a cough, except that expelled air is directed through nasal cavities as well as through oral cavity; depressed uvula closes oral cavity off from pharynx and routes air upward through nasal cavities; sneezes clear upper respiratory passages
Crying	Inspiration followed by release of air in a number of short expirations; primarily an emotionally induced mechanism
Laughing	Essentially same as crying in terms of air movements produced; also an emotionally induced response
Hiccups	Sudden inspirations resulting from spasms of diaphragm; believed to be initiated by irritation of diaphragm or phrenic nerves, which serve diaphragm; sound occurs when inspired air hits vocal folds of closed glottis
Yawn	Very deep inspiration, taken with jaws wide open; formerly believed to be triggered by need to increase amount of oxygen in blood but this theory is now being questioned; ventilates all alveoli (not the case in normal quiet breathing)

mm Hg, or 597 mm Hg. Oxygen gas (O_2), which accounts for nearly 21% of the atmosphere, has a partial pressure (P_{O_2}) of 159 mm Hg (20.9% × 760 mm Hg). As you can see, nitrogen and oxygen together contribute about 99% of the total atmospheric pressure. Air also contains 0.04% carbon dioxide (CO_2), up to 0.5% water vapor, and insignificant amounts of inert gases such as argon and helium.

At high altitudes, where the atmosphere is less influenced by gravity, all partial pressure values decline in direct proportion to the decline in atmospheric pressure. For example, at 10,000 feet above sea level where the atmospheric pressure is 563 mm Hg, the P_{O_2} is 110 mm Hg. Likewise, atmospheric pressure increases by 1 atmosphere (760 mm HG) for each 33 feet of descent (in water) below sea level. Thus, at 99 feet below sea level, the total pressure on the body is equivalent to 4 atmospheres, or 3040 mm Hg, and the partial pressure exerted by each of the component gases is also quadrupled.

Henry's Law

According to **Henry's law,** when a mixture of gases is in contact with a liquid, each gas will dissolve in the liquid in proportion to its partial pressure. Thus the greater the concentration of a particular gas in the gas phase, the more and the faster gas will go into solution in the liquid. At equilibrium, the gas partial pressures in both phases are the same. If, however, the partial pressure of a gas later becomes greater in the liquid than in the adjacent gas phase, some of the dissolved gas molecules will reenter the gaseous phase. So the direction (and amount) of gas movements is determined by their partial pressures in the two phases. This flexible situation is exactly what occurs when gases are exchanged in the lungs and tissues.

The exact volume of a gas that will dissolve in a liquid at any given partial pressure also depends on the solubility of the gas in the liquid and on the temperature of the liquid. The various gases present in air have very different solubilities in water (or plasma). Carbon dioxide is most soluble. Oxygen is only 1/20 as soluble as CO_2, and nitrogen, which is only half as soluble as oxygen, is nearly insoluble. Thus, at a given partial pressure, much more CO_2 than O_2 will be dissolved, and practically no N_2 will go into solution. Beyond this specific condition, the solubility of *any* gas in water decreases with increasing temperature. Think of club soda, which is produced by forcing CO_2 into water under high pressure. If you take the cap off a refrigerated bottle of club soda, and allow it to stand at room temperature, within just a few minutes you will have plain water—all the carbon dioxide gas will have escaped from solution.

Influence of Hyperbaric Conditions

The effect of *hyperbaric* (hi″per-băr′ik), or high-pressure, conditions on gas exchange in the body is easily explained by the ideal gas laws. *Hyperbaric oxygen chambers* provide clinical applications of Henry's law. These chambers contain oxygen at pressures higher than 1 atmosphere and are used to force greater than normal amounts of oxygen into a patient's blood in cases of carbon monoxide poisoning, circulatory shock, or asphyxiation. The technique is also used to treat individuals with gas gangrene or tetanus poisoning, because the anaerobic bacteria causing these infections cannot live in the presence of high oxygen levels. Other uses of Henry's law are seen in caisson workers (those who build tunnels under water) and scuba divers (see *A Closer Look on* p. 776).

Although breathing oxygen at 2 atmospheres presents no problems for short periods of time, **oxygen toxicity** develops rapidly when the P_{O_2} is greater than 2.5–3 atmospheres. Excessive oxygen concentrations generate large amounts of harmful free radicals. The result is profound central nervous system disturbances, culminating in coma and death. •

Table 23.4 Comparison of Gas Partial Pressures and Approximate Percentages in the Atmosphere and in the Alveoli

Gas	Atmosphere (sea level)		Alveoli	
	Approximate percentage	Partial pressure (mm Hg)	Approximate percentage	Partial pressure (mm Hg)
N_2	78.6	597	74.9	569
O_2	20.9	159	13.7	104
CO_2	0.04	0.3	5.2	40
H_2O	0.46	3.7	6.2	47
	100.0%	760	100.0%	760

Composition of Alveolar Gas

As shown in Table 23.4, the gaseous makeup of the atmosphere is quite different from that in the alveoli. Whereas the atmosphere consists almost entirely of oxygen and nitrogen, alveoli contain more carbon dioxide and water vapor and much less oxygen. These differences reflect the effects of the following: (1) gas exchanges occurring in the lungs (oxygen diffuses from the alveoli into the pulmonary blood and carbon dioxide diffuses in the opposite direction), (2) humidification of air by the conducting passages, and (3) the mixing of alveolar gas that occurs with each breath. Because only 500 ml of air is inspired with each tidal inspiration, alveolar gas is actually a mixture of newly inspired gases and gases remaining in the respiratory passageways between breaths.

The partial pressures of oxygen and carbon dioxide are easily changed by increasing the depth and rate of breathing. High alveolar ventilation flushes more oxygen into the alveoli, increasing the alveolar P_{O_2}, and rapidly eliminates carbon dioxide from the lungs.

Gas Exchanges Between the Blood, Lungs, and Tissues

As described earlier, during *external respiration* oxygen enters and carbon dioxide leaves the blood in the lungs. At the body tissues, where the process is called *internal respiration,* the same gases move in opposite directions by the same mechanism (diffusion). External and internal respiration will be considered consecutively to emphasize their similarities, but keep in mind that gases must be transported by the blood between these two exchange sites.

External Respiration: Pulmonary Gas Exchange

During external respiration, dark red blood flowing through the pulmonary circuit is transformed into the scarlet river that is returned to the heart for distribution by systemic arteries to all body tissues. Although this color change is due to oxygen exchange and its binding to hemoglobin in red blood cells, carbon dioxide exchanges are occurring equally fast.

Several factors influence the movement of oxygen and carbon dioxide across the respiratory membrane. These include (1) partial pressure gradients and gas solubilities, (2) structural characteristics of the respiratory membrane, and (3) functional aspects, such as the matching of alveolar ventilation and pulmonary blood perfusion.

Partial Pressure Gradients and Gas Solubilities. Since the P_{O_2} of deoxygenated blood in the pulmonary arteries is only 40 mm Hg, as opposed to a P_{O_2} of approximately 104 mm Hg in the alveoli, a steep oxygen partial pressure gradient exists, and oxygen diffuses rapidly from the alveoli into the pulmonary capillary blood (Figure 23.16). Equilibrium—that is, a P_{O_2} of 104 mm Hg on both sides of the respiratory membrane—has usually occurred in 0.25 seconds, about one-third the time a red blood cell is in a pulmonary capillary (Figure 23.17). The lesson here is that the time of blood flow through the pulmonary capillaries can be reduced by two-thirds and still provide adequate oxygenation. Carbon dioxide moves in the opposite direction along a much less steep partial pressure gradient of about 5 mm Hg (45 mm Hg to 40 mm Hg) until equilibrium occurs at 40 mm Hg (see Figure 23.16). Carbon dioxide is then expelled gradually from the alveoli during expiration. Even though the pressure gradient for oxygen diffusion is much steeper than that for carbon dioxide, equal amounts of these gases are exchanged because carbon dioxide is 20 times more soluble in plasma and alveolar fluid than oxygen.

Thickness of the Respiratory Membrane. In healthy lungs, the respiratory membrane is only 0.5 to 1 μm thick, and gas exchange is usually very efficient. If the lungs become edematous (as in pneumonia), the exchange membrane thickens dramatically. Under such conditions, even the total time (0.75 sec) that red blood cells are in transit through the pulmonary capillaries may not be enough for adequate gas exchange, and body tissues begin to suffer from oxygen deprivation. •

Surface Area for Gas Exchange. The greater the surface area of the respiratory membrane, the more gas can diffuse across it in a given time period. The alveolar surface area is enormous in healthy lungs. Spread flat, the total gas exchange surface of

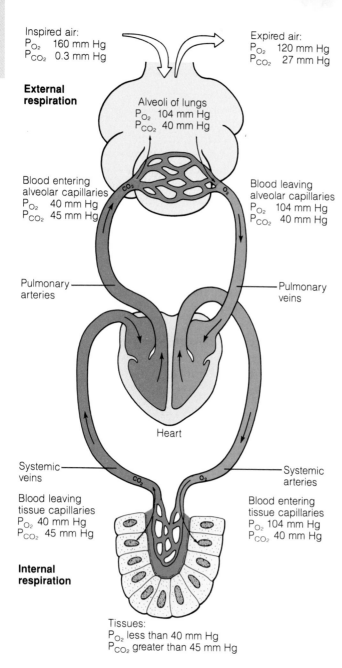

Inspired air:
P_{O_2} 160 mm Hg
P_{CO_2} 0.3 mm Hg

Expired air:
P_{O_2} 120 mm Hg
P_{CO_2} 27 mm Hg

External respiration

Alveoli of lungs
P_{O_2} 104 mm Hg
P_{CO_2} 40 mm Hg

Blood entering
alveolar capillaries
P_{O_2} 40 mm Hg
P_{CO_2} 45 mm Hg

Blood leaving
alveolar capillaries
P_{O_2} 104 mm Hg
P_{CO_2} 40 mm Hg

Pulmonary arteries

Pulmonary veins

Heart

Systemic veins

Systemic arteries

Blood leaving
tissue capillaries
P_{O_2} 40 mm Hg
P_{CO_2} 45 mm Hg

Blood entering
tissue capillaries
P_{O_2} 104 mm Hg
P_{CO_2} 40 mm Hg

Internal respiration

Tissues:
P_{O_2} less than 40 mm Hg
P_{CO_2} greater than 45 mm Hg

FIGURE 23.16
Partial pressure gradients promoting gas movements in the body. Gradients promoting oxygen and carbon dioxide exchanges across the respiratory membrane in the lungs (external respiration) are shown in the top part of the figure. Gradients promoting gas movements across systemic capillary membranes in the body tissues (internal respiration) are indicated at the bottom.

these tiny sacs in a man's lungs is about 140 m², or approximately 40 times greater than the surface area of his skin!

In certain pulmonary diseases, the alveolar surface area actually functioning in gas exchange is drastically reduced. This occurs in emphysema, when the walls of adjacent alveoli break through and the alveolar chambers become larger. It also occurs when tumors, mucus, or inflammatory material blocks gas flow into the alveoli. •

P_{O_2}

P_{O_2} 104 mm Hg

Time in the
pulmonary capillary (s)

Start of capillary

End of capillary

FIGURE 23.17
Oxygenation of blood in the pulmonary capillaries. Note that the time expired from the time blood enters the pulmonary capillaries (indicated by 0) until the P_{O_2} is 104 mm Hg is approximately 0.25 second.

Ventilation-Perfusion Coupling. For gas exchange to be most efficient, there must be a close match, or coupling, between *ventilation* (the amount of gas reaching the alveoli) and *perfusion* (the blood flow in pulmonary capillaries). As explained in Chapter 20 and illustrated in Figure 23.18, local autoregulatory mechanisms continuously respond to alveolar conditions. In alveoli where ventilation is inadequate, the P_{O_2} is low. As a result, the arterioles constrict, and blood is redirected to respiratory areas where oxygen pickup may be more efficient. On the other hand, in alveoli where ventilation is maximal, pulmonary arterioles dilate, increasing blood flow into the associated pulmonary capillaries. Notice that the autoregulatory mechanism controlling pulmonary vascular muscle is exactly opposite that controlling most arterioles in the systemic circulation.

Changes in the P_{CO_2} in the alveoli cause changes in the diameters of the bronchioles. Passageways servicing areas where alveolar CO_2 levels are high dilate, allowing carbon dioxide to be eliminated from the body more rapidly, while those serving areas where the P_{CO_2} is low constrict.

As a result of modifications in these two systems, alveolar ventilation and pulmonary perfusion are synchronized. Poor alveolar ventilation results in low oxygen and high carbon dioxide levels in the alveoli; consequently, the pulmonary capillaries constrict and the airways dilate, bringing airflow and blood flow into closer physiological match. High P_{O_2} and low P_{CO_2} in the alveoli cause respiratory passageways to constrict, and promote flushing of blood into the pulmonary capillaries. Although these homeostatic mechanisms provide the most appropriate conditions for efficient gas exchange, they never completely balance ventilation and perfusion in every alveolus because of the effects of gravity and the occasional

Suppose a patient is receiving oxygen by mask. What will be the condition of the arterioles leading into the oxygen- enriched alveoli? What is the advantage of this response?

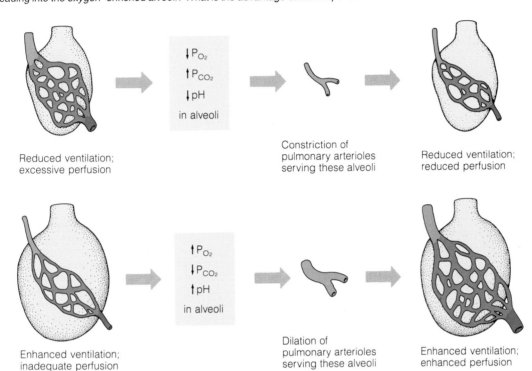

Reduced ventilation; excessive perfusion

↓P_{O_2}
↑P_{CO_2}
↓pH
in alveoli

Constriction of pulmonary arterioles serving these alveoli

Reduced ventilation; reduced perfusion

Enhanced ventilation; inadequate perfusion

↑P_{O_2}
↓P_{CO_2}
↑pH
in alveoli

Dilation of pulmonary arterioles serving these alveoli

Enhanced ventilation; enhanced perfusion

FIGURE 23.18
Ventilation-perfusion coupling. The flowcharts follow the autoregulatory events that result in local matching of alveolar ventilation and blood flow (perfusion) through the pulmonary capillaries.

alveolar duct plugged with mucus. Consequently, blood in the pulmonary veins tends to have a slightly lower P_{O_2} (100 mm Hg) than alveolar air (104 mm Hg) as opposed to the precise equality indicated in Figure 23.16.

Internal Respiration: Capillary Gas Exchange in the Body Tissues

Although the partial pressure and diffusion gradients are reversed, the factors promoting gas exchanges between the systemic capillaries and the tissue cells are essentially identical to those acting in the lungs (see Figure 23.16). As the tissue cells continuously use oxygen for their metabolic activities, they produce equal amounts of carbon dioxide. The P_{O_2} in the tissues is always lower than that in the systemic arterial blood (40 mm Hg versus 104 mm Hg). Consequently, oxygen moves rapidly from the blood into the tissues until equilibrium is reached, and carbon dioxide moves quickly along its partial pressure gradient into the blood. As a result, venous blood draining the capillary beds of the tissues and returning to the heart has a P_{O_2} of 40 mm Hg and a P_{CO_2} of 45 mm Hg.

In summary, the gas exchanges that occur between the blood and the alveoli and between the blood and the tissue cells take place by simple diffusion driven by the partial pressure gradients of O_2 and CO_2 that exist on the opposite sides of the exchange membranes.

TRANSPORT OF RESPIRATORY GASES BY BLOOD

Oxygen Transport

Molecular oxygen is carried in blood in two ways, bound to hemoglobin within red blood cells and dissolved in plasma (see Figure 23.21, p. 771). Oxygen is poorly soluble in water, so only about 1.5% is carried in the dissolved form. Indeed, if this were the *only* means of oxygen transport, a P_{O_2} of 3 atmospheres or a cardiac output of 15 times normal would be required to provide the oxygen levels needed by body tissues! This problem, of course, has been solved by hemoglobin, and 98.5% of the oxygen ferried from the lungs to the tissues is carried in a loose chemical combination with hemoglobin.

Association and Dissociation of Oxygen and Hemoglobin

As described in Chapter 18, hemoglobin (Hb) is composed of four polypeptide chains, each bound to an iron-containing heme group (see Figure 18.4). Since the iron atoms are oxygen-binding sites, each hemoglobin molecule can combine with four molecules of oxygen, and the process of oxygen binding is rapid and reversible.

The hemoglobin-oxygen combination, called **oxyhemoglobin** (ok″sĭ-he″mo-glo′bin), is written as **HbO₂**. Hemoglobin that has released oxygen is called **reduced hemoglobin,** or **deoxyhemoglobin,** and is written as **HHb.** Loading and unloading of O_2 can be indicated by a single reversible equation:

$$HHb + O_2 \underset{Tissues}{\overset{Lungs}{\rightleftharpoons}} HbO_2 + H^+$$

A kind of *cooperation* exists between the four polypeptides of the hemoglobin molecule. After the first O_2 molecule binds to iron, the hemoglobin molecule undergoes a change in shape. As a result, hemoglobin more readily takes up two more oxygen molecules and uptake of the fourth oxygen molecule is even more facilitated. When all four of its heme groups are bound to oxygen, a hemoglobin molecule is said to be *fully saturated.* When one, two, or three oxygen molecules are bound, hemoglobin is *partially saturated.* By the same token, unloading of one oxygen molecule enhances the unloading of the next, and so on. Thus, the *affinity* of hemoglobin for oxygen changes with its state of oxygen saturation, and both loading and unloading of oxygen are very efficient.

The rate at which hemoglobin reversibly binds or releases oxygen is regulated by several factors: P_{O_2}, temperature, blood pH, P_{CO_2}, and the concentration of an organic chemical called BPG in the blood. These factors interact to ensure adequate deliveries of oxygen to tissue cells.

Influence of P₀₂ on Hemoglobin Saturation.
Because of the cooperation just described, the relationship between the amount of O_2 bound to hemoglobin (% of Hb saturation) and the P_{O_2} of the blood is not linear. When hemoglobin saturation is plotted against P_{O_2}, the **oxygen-hemoglobin dissociation curve** is produced. This S-shaped curve has a steep slope between 10 and 50 mm Hg P_{O_2} and then flattens out (plateaus) between 70 and 100 mm Hg (Figure 23.19).

Under normal resting conditions, (P_{O_2} = 104 mm Hg), arterial blood is 98% saturated, and 100 ml of systemic arterial blood contains about 20 ml of oxygen. The *oxygen content* of arterial blood is written as 20 vol % (volumes percent). As arterial blood flows through the systemic capillaries, about 5 ml O_2 per 100 ml of blood is released, yielding a hemoglobin saturation of 75% (and an oxygen content of 15 vol %) in venous blood.

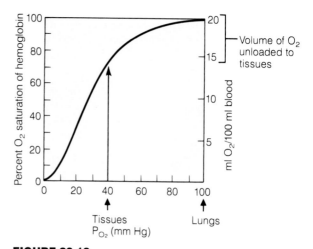

FIGURE 23.19
Oxygen-hemoglobin dissociation curve. Percent O_2 saturation of hemoglobin and blood oxygen content are shown at different oxygen partial pressures (P_{O_2}). Notice that hemoglobin is almost completely saturated with oxygen at a P_{O_2} of 70 mm Hg. Rapid loading and unloading of oxygen to and from hemoglobin occur at the oxygen partial pressures corresponding to the steep portion of the curve. During the systemic circuit, approximately 25% of the hemoglobin-bound oxygen is unloaded to the tissues (that is, approximately 5 ml of the 20 ml of O_2 per 100 ml of blood is released). Thus, hemoglobin of venous blood is still about 75% saturated with oxygen after one round through the body.

The nearly complete saturation of hemoglobin in arterial blood explains why breathing deeply (which increases both the alveolar and arterial blood P_{O_2} above 104 mm Hg) causes *little* increase in the oxygen saturation of hemoglobin. Remember, P_{O_2} measurements indicate only the amount of oxygen dissolved in plasma, not the amount bound to hemoglobin. However, P_{O_2} values are a good index of lung function, and when arterial P_{O_2} is less than alveolar air P_{O_2}, some degree of respiratory impairment exists.

A hemoglobin saturation curve reveals two other important pieces of information. First, hemoglobin is almost completely saturated at a P_{O_2} of 70 mm Hg, and further increases in P_{O_2} cause only small increases in oxygen binding. The adaptive value of this is that adequate oxygen loading and delivery to the tissues can occur when the P_{O_2} of inspired air is well below its usual levels, a situation common at higher altitudes and in those with cardiopulmonary disease. Moreover, because most oxygen *unloading* also occurs on the steep portion of the curve, where the partial pressure changes very little, only 20% to 25% of bound oxygen is unloaded during one systemic circuit (see Figure 23.19), and substantial amounts of oxygen are still available in venous blood (the *"venous reserve"*). Thus, if oxygen tension drops to very low levels in the tissues, as might occur during vigorous muscle activity, much more oxygen can dissociate from hemoglobin to be used by the tissue cells without requiring an increase in respiratory rate or cardiac output.

Influence of Temperature, pH, P*CO₂*, and BPG on Hemoglobin Saturation.

A number of factors—most importantly temperature, H^+ concentration, P_{O_2}, and the amount of BPG in the blood—influence hemoglobin saturation at a given P_{O_2}. (BPG [*2,3-biphosphoglycerate*] is a unique compound that binds reversibly with hemoglobin. It is produced by red blood cells [RBCs] as they break down glucose by the anaerobic process called glycolysis.)

All of these factors influence hemoglobin saturation by modifying hemoglobin's three-dimensional structure, thereby altering its affinity for oxygen. Generally speaking, an *increase* in temperature (Figure 23.20a), P_{CO_2}, H^+ content of the blood (Figure 23.20b), or BPG levels in blood decreases the affinity of Hb for O_2 and causes the oxygen-hemoglobin dissociation curve to shift to the right. This enhances oxygen unloading from the blood. Conversely, a *decrease* in any of these factors increases hemoglobin's affinity for oxygen and shifts the dissociation curve to the left.

If you give a little thought to how these factors might be related, you'll realize that they all tend to be at their highest levels in the systemic capillaries where oxygen unloading is the desired goal. As cells metabolize glucose and use oxygen, they release carbon dioxide, which in turn increases the P_{CO_2} and H^+ content of the capillary blood. Since declining blood pH (acidosis) weakens the hemoglobin-oxygen bond, a phenomenon called the **Bohr effect,** oxygen unloading is accelerated where it is most needed. Additionally, heat is a by-product of metabolic activity, and active tissues are typically warmer than less active ones. The rise in temperature affects hemoglobin's affinity for oxygen both directly and indirectly (via its influence on RBC metabolism and BPG synthesis). Collectively, these factors see to it that much more oxygen is unloaded from oxyhemoglobin in the vicinity of hard-working tissue cells.

Certain hormones, such as thyroxine, testosterone, growth hormones, and catecholamines (epinephrine and norepinephrine), increase RBC metabolic rate and BPG formation. As a result, these hormones enhance oxygen delivery to the tissues.

Impairments of Oxygen Transport

Whatever the cause, inadequate oxygen delivery to body tissues is called **hypoxia** (hi-pok′se-ah). This condition is easy to recognize in fair-skinned people, because their skin and mucosae take on a bluish cast (become cyanotic) when the hemoglobin saturation falls below 75%. In dark-skinned individuals, this color change can be observed only in the mucosae and nailbeds. Based on cause, hypoxia may be classified as follows.

1. *Anemic hypoxia* reflects poor oxygen delivery resulting from too few RBCs or from RBCs that contain abnormal or inadequate amounts of hemoglobin.

*Do increasing temperature and P*CO₂ *affect O₂ unloading in the same or opposite directions?*

FIGURE 23.20

Effects of temperature, P*CO₂*, and blood pH on the oxygen-hemoglobin dissociation curve. Oxygen unloading is accelerated at conditions of **(a)** increased temperature and **(b)** increased P_{CO_2} and/or decreased pH, causing the dissociation curve to shift to the right.

2. *Ischemic (stagnant) hypoxia* results when blood circulation is impaired or blocked. Congestive heart failure may cause body-wide ischemic hypoxia, whereas emboli or thrombi only block oxygen delivery to tissues distal to the obstruction.

3. *Histotoxic hypoxia* occurs when body cells are unable to use oxygen, even though adequate amounts are being delivered. This variety of hypoxia is the consequence of metabolic poisons, such as cyanide.

4. *Hypoxemic (hypoxic) hypoxia* is indicated by reduced arterial P_{O_2}. Possible causes include

imbalances in the ventilation-perfusion coupling mechanism, pulmonary diseases that impair ventilation, and breathing air containing scant amounts of oxygen. **Carbon monoxide poisoning** is a unique type of hypoxemic hypoxia, and is the leading cause of death from fire. As mentioned in Chapter 18, carbon monoxide (CO) is an odorless, colorless gas that competes vigorously with oxygen for heme binding sites. Moreover, because hemoglobin's affinity for carbon monoxide is over 200 times greater than that for oxygen, carbon monoxide is a highly successful competitor—even at minuscule partial pressures, carbon monoxide is able to displace oxygen.

Carbon monoxide poisoning is particularly dangerous because it does not produce the characteristic signs of hypoxia—cyanosis and respiratory distress. Instead the victim is confused and has a throbbing headache. In rare cases, fair skin becomes cherry red (the color of the hemoglobin–carbon monoxide complex), which the eye of the beholder interprets as a healthy "blush." Those with CO poisoning are given hyperbaric therapy (if available) or 100% oxygen until the carbon monoxide has been cleared from the body. •

Carbon Dioxide Transport

Normally active body cells produce about 200 ml of carbon dioxide each minute—exactly the amount excreted by the lungs. Carbon dioxide is transported in the blood from the tissue cells to the lungs in three forms (listed in order from lowest to highest amount transported): as a gas dissolved in plasma, chemically bound to hemoglobin, and in plasma as the bicarbonate ion (Figure 23.21).

1. **Dissolved in plasma.** Some 7% to 10% of the carbon dioxide transported is simply dissolved in plasma. However, most carbon dioxide molecules entering the plasma quickly enter the red blood cells, where most of the chemical reactions that prepare carbon dioxide for transport occur.

2. **Chemically bound to hemoglobin in red blood cells.** Between 20% and 30% of transported carbon dioxide is carried within RBCs as **carbaminohemoglobin** (kar-bam″ĭ-no-he″mo-glo′bin):

$$CO_2 + \text{hemoglobin} \rightleftharpoons HbCO_2 \text{ (carbaminohemoglobin)}$$

This reaction is rapid and does not require a catalyst. Since carbon dioxide binds directly to the amino acids of *globin* (and not to the heme), carbon dioxide transport in RBCs does not compete with the oxyhemoglobin transport mechanism.

The loading and unloading of carbon dioxide to and from hemoglobin are directly influenced by (1) the P_{CO_2} and (2) the degree of oxygenation of hemoglobin. Carbon dioxide rapidly dissociates from hemoglobin in the lungs, where the P_{CO_2} of alveolar

air is lower than that in blood. Carbon dioxide is loaded in the tissues, where the P_{CO_2} is higher than that of the blood. Deoxygenated hemoglobin combines more readily with carbon dioxide than oxygenated hemoglobin (see the discussion of the Haldane effect shortly).

3. **As bicarbonate ion in plasma.** The largest fraction of carbon dioxide (60% to 70%) is converted to **bicarbonate ions (HCO_3^-)** and transported in plasma. As illustrated in Figure 23.21a, when carbon dioxide diffuses into the RBCs, it combines with water, forming carbonic acid (H_2CO_3). H_2CO_3 is unstable and quickly dissociates into hydrogen ions and bicarbonate ions:

$$\underset{\substack{\text{Carbon} \\ \text{dioxide}}}{CO_2} + \underset{\text{Water}}{H_2O} \rightleftharpoons \underset{\substack{\text{Carbonic} \\ \text{acid}}}{H_2CO_3} \rightleftharpoons \underset{\substack{\text{Hydrogen} \\ \text{ion}}}{H^+} + \underset{\substack{\text{Bicarbonate} \\ \text{ion}}}{HCO_3^-}$$

Although this reaction also occurs in plasma, it is thousands of times faster in erythrocytes because they (and not plasma) contain **carbonic anhydrase** (kar-bon′ik an-hi′drās), an enzyme that reversibly catalyzes the conversion of carbon dioxide and water to carbonic acid. Hydrogen ions released during the reaction bind to hemoglobin, triggering the Bohr effect; thus, oxygen release is enhanced by carbon dioxide loading (as HCO_3^-). Because of the buffering effect of hemoglobin, the liberated hydrogen ions cause little change in pH under resting conditions. Hence, blood becomes only slightly more acidic (the pH declines from 7.4 to 7.34) as it passes through the tissues.

Once generated, bicarbonate ions diffuse quickly from the RBCs into the plasma, where they are carried to the lungs. To counterbalance the rapid outrush of negative bicarbonate ions from the RBCs, chloride ions (Cl^-) move from the plasma into the erythrocytes. This ionic exchange process is called the **chloride shift** (see Figure 23.21).

In the lungs, the process is reversed (see Figure 23.21b). As blood moves through the pulmonary capillaries, its P_{CO_2} declines from 45 mm Hg to 40 mm Hg (and respectively from 54 vol % to 49 vol %). For this to occur, carbon dioxide must first be freed from its "bicarbonate housing." Bicarbonate ions reenter the RBCs (and chloride ions move into the plasma) and bind with hydrogen ions to form carbonic acid, which is then split by carbonic anhydrase to release carbon dioxide and water. This carbon dioxide, along with that released from hemoglobin and from solution in plasma, then diffuses along its partial pressure gradient from the blood into the alveoli.

The Haldane Effect

The amount of carbon dioxide transported in blood is markedly affected by the degree of oxygenation of the blood. The lower the P_{O_2} and the hemoglobin saturation with oxygen, the more carbon dioxide that can be

FIGURE 23.21

Transport and exchange of carbon dioxide and oxygen. Gas exchanges occurring **(a)** at the tissues and **(b)** in the lungs. Carbon dioxide is transported primarily as bicarbonate ion (HCO_3^-) in plasma (70%); smaller amounts are transported bound to hemoglobin (indicated as $HbCO_2$) in the red blood cells (22%) or in physical solution in plasma (7%). Nearly all the oxygen transported in blood is bound to hemoglobin as oxyhemoglobin (HbO_2) in red blood cells. Very small amounts (about 1.5%) are carried dissolved in plasma. (Reduced hemoglobin is indicated as HHb). Note that the relative sizes of the transport arrows indicate the proportionate amounts of O_2 and CO_2 being moved by each method.

carried in the blood. This phenomenon, called the **Haldane effect,** reflects the greater ability of reduced hemoglobin to form carbaminohemoglobin and to buffer H^+ by combining with it (see Figure 23.21a). As carbon dioxide enters the systemic bloodstream, it causes more oxygen to dissociate from hemoglobin (the Bohr effect), which in turn allows more carbon dioxide to combine with hemoglobin and more bicar-

bonate ions to be formed (the Haldane effect). In the pulmonary circulation (Figure 23.21b), the situation is reversed. Uptake of oxygen facilitates the release of carbon dioxide. As hemoglobin becomes saturated with oxygen, the hydrogen ions released combine with HCO_3^-, helping to unload CO_2 from the pulmonary blood. The Haldane effect encourages CO_2 exchange in both the tissues and lungs.

Key:
(+) = Positive effect (stimulation)
(−) = Negative effect (inhibition)

Pons
Medulla

Pneumotaxic center
Apneustic center (hypothetical)
Pons
VRG
Medulla
DRG

(−)   (?)

(?)

To inspiratory muscles
To expiratory muscles (internal intercostals and others)

(+)

(+)

External intercostal muscles
Diaphragm

FIGURE 23.22
Postulated neural pathways involved in control of respiratory rhythm. During normal quiet breathing, the self-exciting neurons of the dorsal respiratory group (DRG), or medullary inspiratory center, set the pace by alternately (1) depolarizing and sending impulses to the inspiratory muscles and then (2) becoming quiescent, which allows passive expiration to occur. The neurons of the ventral respiratory group (VRG) appear to be largely inactive during normal quiet breathing. When forced breathing is required, the inspiratory center enlists the activity of accessory respiratory muscles and the expiratory center helps activate the muscles of forced expiration. The pons centers interact with the medullary centers in such a way that the breathing pattern is smooth. The pneumotaxic center normally limits the inspiratory phase and smooths the transitions between inspirations and expirations. The apneustic center of the pons has been postulated, but its presence seems doubtful. Hypothetical interactions of an apneustic center are indicated by dashed arrows.

Influence of Carbon Dioxide on Blood pH

Typically, the H^+ released during carbonic acid dissociation is buffered by hemoglobin or other proteins within the red blood cells or in plasma. The bicarbonate ions generated in the red blood cells diffuse into the plasma, where they act as the *alkaline reserve* part of the carbonic acid–bicarbonate buffer system of the blood. The **carbonic acid–bicarbonate buffer system** is very important in resisting shifts in blood pH (see the equation in point 3 above concerning CO_2 transport). For example, if the hydrogen ion concentration in blood begins to rise, excess H^+ is removed by combining with HCO_3^- to form carbonic acid (a weak acid that does not dissociate at either physiological or acidic pH). If H^+ concentration drops below desirable levels in blood, carbonic acid dissociates, releasing hydrogen ions and lowering the pH again.

Changes in respiratory rate or depth can produce dramatic changes in blood pH by modifying the amount of carbonic acid in the blood. Slow, shallow breathing allows carbon dioxide to accumulate in the blood. As a result, carbonic acid levels increase and blood pH drops. Conversely, rapid, deep breathing quickly flushes carbon dioxide out of the blood and reduces carbonic acid levels, increasing blood pH. Thus, respiratory ventilation can provide a fast-acting system to adjust blood pH (and P_{CO_2}) when it is disturbed by metabolic factors. Respiratory adjustments play a major role in the acid-base balance of the blood, as discussed in detail in Chapter 27.

CONTROL OF RESPIRATION

Neural Mechanisms and Generation of Breathing Rhythm

Although our tidelike breathing seems so beautifully simple, its control is fairly complex. The basic controls of breathing involve the activity of neurons in the reticular formation of the medulla and pons. We will begin this discussion by describing the role of the medulla, which sets the respiratory rhythm, and then move on to the postulated roles of the pons nuclei.

Medullary Respiratory Centers

Clusters of reticular formation neurons in two areas of the medulla oblongata appear to be critically important in respiration. These are (1) the **dorsal respiratory group (DRG)**—a cluster of neurons located dorsally near the root of cranial nerve IX, and (2) the **ventral respiratory group (VRG)**—a network of neurons that extends within the ventral brain stem from the superior end of the spinal cord to the pons–medulla junction. The DRG appears to be the pacesetting respiratory center. For this reason it has been tagged the **inspiratory center.** When its neurons fire, a burst of nerve impulses travels along the phrenic and **intercostal nerves** to excite the diaphragm and external intercostal muscles, respectively (Figure 23.22). As a result, the thorax expands and air rushes into the lungs. The DRG then becomes dormant, and expiration occurs passively as the inspiratory muscles relax and the lungs recoil. This cyclic on-off activity of the inspiratory neurons repeats continuously and produces a respiratory rate of 12–15 breaths per minute, with inspiratory phases lasting for about 2 seconds followed by expiratory phases lasting about 3 seconds. This normal respiratory rate and rhythm is referred to as **eupnea** (ūp-ne′ah; *eu* = good, *pne* = breath). During severe hypoxia, neurons in the DRG generate gasping (perhaps, in a last ditch effort to restore oxygen to the brain). When the medulla inspiratory neurons are completely suppressed, as by an overdose of sleeping pills, morphine, or alcohol, respiration stops completely.

Unlike the DRG, which contains neurons mostly involved in initiating inspiration, the VRG contains a more even mix of neurons involved in inspiration and expiration. Both neuronal networks appear to direct the activity of the respiratory muscles, but the contribution of the VRG is murky. Some presume it is called into play mainly during forced breathing (especially forced expiration) when more strenuous breathing movements are needed.

Pons Respiratory Centers

Although the medullary inspiratory center generates the basic respiratory rhythm, pons centers can influence and modify the activity of medullary neurons. For example, pons centers appear to smooth out the transitions from inspiration to expiration, and vice versa; and when lesions are made in the pneumotaxic center, inspirations become very prolonged.

The **pneumotaxic** (nu″mo-tak′sik) **center** in the superior pons (see Figure 23.22) seems mainly to exert inhibitory effects on the medulla. A second postulated pons respiratory center is the *apneustic center.* Although the existence of the pneumotaxic center has been amply proven, the presence of the apneustic center in the caudal pons has yet to be demonstrated. Long credited as the source of the inspiratory drive (ie, it supposedly stimulates the DRG continuously unless inhibited), the apneustic center is at best a functional concept.

Genesis of the Respiratory Rhythm

There is little question that breathing is rhythmic, but the origin of the oscillatory activity of the inspiratory neurons is still a mystery. One theory is that the inspiratory neurons are *pacemaker neurons,* which have intrinsic automaticity and rhythmicity. Though pacemaker activity has been revealed in neurons of the rostral VRG in newborn infants, no such activity has

been found in adults.

Another hypothesis is that inputs from stretch receptors in the lungs help to establish the respiratory rhythm (see *Hering-Breuer Reflex* below). However, these influences seem relatively unimportant under resting conditions. The most popular theory is that normal respiratory rhythm is a result of reciprocal inhibition of interconnected neuronal networks within the medulla. Whatever the influences acting on the medulla, one thing is sure—the medullary centers are themselves capable of maintaining the normal rhythm of breathing.

Factors Influencing the Rate and Depth of Breathing

Depth and rate of breathing can be modified in response to changing body demands. Inspiratory depth is determined by how actively the respiratory center stimulates the motor neurons serving the respiratory muscles. The greater the frequency, the more motor units are excited and the stronger the contractions of the respiratory muscles. The rate of respiration is determined by how long the inspiratory center is active or, conversely, how quickly it is switched off.

The respiratory centers in the medulla and pons are sensitive to both excitatory and inhibitory stimuli. These stimuli are described next and summarized in Figure 23.23.

Pulmonary Irritant Reflexes

The lungs contain receptors that respond to an enormous variety of irritating factors. When activated, these receptors communicate with the respiratory centers via vagal nerve afferents. Accumulated mucus or inhaled debris such as dust, lint, cigarette smoke, or noxious fumes stimulate receptors in the bronchioles that promote reflex constriction of those air passages. The same irritants stimulate a cough when present in the trachea or bronchi, and a sneeze when they invade the nasal cavity.

The Hering-Breuer Reflex

The visceral pleurae and conducting passages in the lungs contain numerous stretch receptors that are vigorously stimulated when the lungs are inflated. These receptors, in turn, dispatch inhibitory impulses to the medullary respiratory centers that terminate inspiration and allow expiration to occur. As the lungs recoil, the stretch receptors become quiet, and so inspiration is initiated once again. This reflex, called the **inflation** or **Hering-Breuer** (her′ing broy′er) **reflex,** is thought to be more a protective response (to prevent excessive stretching of the lungs) than a normal regulatory mechanism because the threshold of these receptors in humans is very high.

Higher centers of brain (cerebral cortex—voluntary control over breathing)

Other receptors (eg. pain) and emotional stimuli acting through the hypothalamus

±

±

Respiratory centers (medulla and pons)

Peripheral chemoreceptors

$O_2 \downarrow$, $CO_2 \uparrow$, $H^+ \uparrow$

+

Stretch receptors in lungs

−

Central chemoreceptors $CO_2 \uparrow$, $H^+ \uparrow$

+

−

Irritant receptors

+

Receptors in muscles and joints

FIGURE 23.23
Neural and chemical influences on the respiratory centers in the medulla. Excitatory influences (+) increase the frequency of impulses sent to the muscles of respiration and result in deeper, faster breathing. Inhibition of the medullary center (−) has the reverse effect. In some cases, the impulses may be excitatory or inhibitory (indicated by ±), depending on the precise receptors or brain regions activated.

Influence of Higher Brain Centers

Hypothalamic Controls. Strong emotions and pain acting through the limbic system activate sympathetic centers in the hypothalamus, which can modulate respiratory rate and depth by sending signals to the respiratory centers. For example, have you ever touched something cold and clammy and gasped? That response was mediated through the hypothalamus. So too is the breath holding that occurs when we are angry and our increased respiratory rate when we are excited.

Cortical Controls. Although breathing is normally regulated involuntarily by the brain stem respiratory centers, we can also exert conscious control over the rate and depth of our breathing—choosing to hold our breath or voluntarily taking a deep breath, for example. This voluntary control involves direct signals from the cerebral motor cortex to the motor neurons that stimulate the respiratory muscles, bypassing the medullary centers. Our ability to voluntarily hold our breath is limited, however, because the respiratory centers of the brain stem automatically reinitiate breathing when the concentration of carbon dioxide in the blood reaches critical levels. That explains why drowning victims are always found to have inhaled water into their lungs.

Chemical Factors

Although many factors can modify the baseline respiratory rate and depth set by the medullary inspiratory center, the most important factors are changing levels of carbon dioxide, oxygen, and hydrogen ions in arterial blood. Sensors responding to such chemical fluctuations, called **chemoreceptors,** are found in two major body locations. The **central chemoreceptors** are located bilaterally in the medulla; the **peripheral chemoreceptors** (see Figure 23.25) are found within the great vessels of the neck.

Influence of P_{CO_2}. Of all the chemicals influencing respiration, CO_2 is typically the most potent and the most closely controlled. Normally, arterial P_{CO_2} is 40 mm Hg and is maintained within ± 3 mm Hg of this level by homeostatic mechanisms.

How is respiratory compensation in response to changing P_{CO_2} levels accomplished? Actually, since the peripheral chemoreceptors are only weakly responsive to arterial P_{CO_2} levels, this exquisitely sensitive mechanism is mediated mainly through the influence of rising carbon dioxide levels on the central chemoreceptors of the brain stem (Figure 23.24). Carbon dioxide diffuses easily from the blood into the cerebrospinal fluid, where it is hydrated and forms carbonic acid. As the acid then dissociates, hydrogen ions are liberated. (This is the same reaction that occurs when carbon dioxide enters red blood cells, discussed on p. 770.) However, unlike RBCs or plasma, cerebrospinal fluid contains virtually no proteins that can buffer these free hydrogen ions. Thus, as P_{CO_2} levels rise, a condition referred to as **hypercapnia** (hi"per-kap'ne-ah), the pH of cerebrospinal fluid drops, exciting the central chemoreceptors, which make abundant synapses with the respiratory regulatory centers. As a result, the depth and, perhaps, rate of breathing are increased. This breathing pattern, called **hyperventilation,** enhances alveolar ventilation and quickly flushes CO_2 out of the blood, increasing blood pH. An elevation of only 5 mm Hg in arterial P_{CO_2} results in a doubling of alveolar ventilation, even when arterial oxygen content and pH are unchanged. When P_{O_2} and pH are below normal, the response to elevated P_{CO_2} is even greater. Hyperventilation is normally self-limiting, ending when homeostatic blood P_{CO_2} levels are restored.

Notice that while rising carbon dioxide levels act as the initial stimulus, it is the rising hydrogen ion levels that prod the *central* chemoreceptors into activity. In the final analysis, *control of breathing during rest is aimed primarily at regulating the H⁺ concentration in the brain.*

People experiencing anxiety attacks may hyperventilate involuntarily, to the point where they become dizzy and may faint. This reflects the fact that low carbon dioxide levels in the blood **(hypocapnia)** cause cerebral blood vessels to constrict, reducing brain perfusion and producing cerebral ischemia. Such attacks may be averted by breathing into a paper

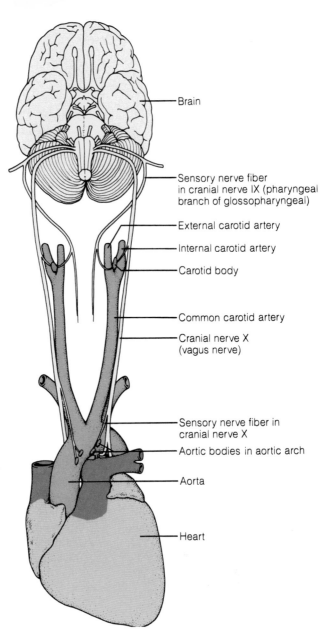

FIGURE 23.25
Location of the peripheral chemoreceptors in the carotid and aortic bodies. Indicated here is the afferent pathway from these receptors via cranial nerves IX and X to the respiratory centers of the medulla. These receptors are most sensitive to the P_{O_2} of the blood; less so to H⁺ and P_{CO_2} levels.

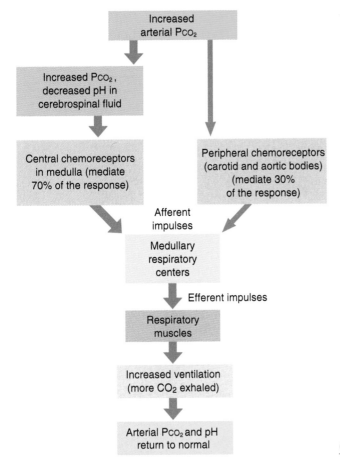

FIGURE 23.24
Negative feedback mechanism by which changes in P_{CO_2} and H⁺ regulate ventilation. The relative influence of the central and peripheral chemoreceptors is indicated by differing arrow thicknesses.

bag. Since the person is rebreathing expired air, which is enriched with carbon dioxide, carbon dioxide is retained in the blood. •

When P_{CO_2} levels are abnormally low, respiration is inhibited and becomes slow and shallow; that is, **hypoventilation** occurs. In fact, periods of **apnea** (breathing cessation) may occur until the arterial P_{CO_2} rises and again stimulates respiration.

Sometimes competing swimmers voluntarily hyperventilate so they can hold their breath longer during swim meets. This is incredibly dangerous for the following reasons. The oxygen content of blood rarely drops much below 60% of normal during regular breath-holding, because as the P_{O_2} drops, carbon dioxide levels rise enough to make breathing unavoidable. However, strenuous hyperventilation

A CLOSER LOOK | Dangerous Raptures of the Deep

Even the nonswimmers among us are beckoned by photos of scuba divers examining brightly colored coral and other ocean creatures as they glide effortlessly through sparkling blue water. "What a life," we think enviously. But hidden beneath that veneer of breathtaking beauty is life-threatening danger for the inexperienced, the careless, and the unlucky. In addition to the significant risk of drowning, scuba divers are exposed to the omnipresent danger of two other medical emergencies—air embolism and decompression sickness.

As a diver descends to greater and greater depths underwater, the pressure on his or her body rises proportionately because of the increasing weight of the water. **Scuba** (self-contained underwater breathing apparatus) **gear** has freed divers from heavy pressurized suits and air lines to the surface, because it permits continual equalization of the air pressure (provided by the mixture of compressed air in the tank) with the water pressure; that is, air enters the lungs at a higher-than-normal pressure. Descent, however, is not usually a problem, unless the diver strives for depths below 100 feet and remains there for an extended time. Although nitrogen ordinarily has very little effect on body functioning, given time and hyperbaric conditions, so much nitrogen is forced into solution in the blood that it provokes a narcotic effect called *nitrogen narcosis*. Since nitrogen is far more soluble in lipids than water, it tends to concentrate in lipid-rich tissues such as the central nervous system, bone marrow, and fat depots. The diver becomes dizzy,

Approximate water depth in meters (feet)

No decompression needed

9 m (30 ft.)
18 m (60 ft.)
27 m (90 ft.)
40 m (130 ft.)

Decompression needed

1   2

Duration in hours

giddy, and appears to be intoxicated; for this reason, the condition is sometimes called "rapture of the deep."

Assuming the diver has taken care to avoid these narcotizing effects, and ascends to the surface gradually (see the graph), dissolved nitrogen gas can be driven out of the tissues and then eliminated by the lungs without any problems. But if the ascent is rapid, the P_{N_2} decreases abruptly and the poorly soluble nitrogen gas appears to "boil" from the tissues and out of solution in the body fluids. Gas bubbles in blood represent potentially lethal emboli, and those formed within joints, bones, and muscles can cause excruciating musculoskeletal pain, commonly called the "bends." Other signs of this *decompression sickness* are mood changes, seizures, itching, and numbness, as well as "migrating" skin rashes and *chokes.* The syndrome

called chokes involves substernal pain, coughing, dyspnea, and, in severe cases, shock. Although these signs and symptoms usually appear within an hour of surfacing, they can be delayed as long as 36 hours.

Air emboli may also occur if the diver ascends suddenly and without exhaling. This situation usually occurs when he or she panics because of laryngospasm after aspiration of seawater, equipment failure, or other hazards, such as extra strong currents or rough waters. Under such conditions, the alveoli are likely to rupture. If connections occur between the alveoli and the pulmonary bloodstream, life-threatening air emboli develop as the diver takes the first breath of air at the surface, and the related problems develop within 2 minutes. Since the ascent is typically made head-up, the emboli usually invade the cerebral circulation, and seizures, localized motor and sensory deficits, and unconsciousness are all possibilities. Indeed, many scuba-related drownings appear to follow loss of consciousness due to air embolism.

The usual and most effective treatment for decompression sickness is hyperbaric therapy, where recompression is reinstituted and then decompression is redone . . . slowly. When an air embolus is suspected, oxygen and antiseizure medications are given until hyperbaric therapy can begin. However, the best therapy is to avoid the need for treatment by making sure that the divers are well instructed in the use of the equipment and acquainted with the possible risks. Assuming that is done, the vacation should be GREAT!

---

can lower the P_{CO_2} so much that a lag period occurs before it rebounds enough to stimulate respiration again. This lag period may allow oxygen levels to fall well below 50 mm Hg, causing the swimmer to black out (and perhaps drown) before he or she has the urge to breathe. •

Influence of P_{O_2}.   Cells sensitive to arterial oxygen levels are found in the peripheral chemoreceptors, that is, in the **aortic bodies** of the aortic arch and in the **carotid bodies** at the bifurcation of the common carotid arteries (Figure 23.25). Those in the carotid bodies are the main oxygen sensors. Under normal conditions, the effect of declining P_{O_2} on ventilation is slight and mostly limited to enhancing the sensitivity of central receptors to increased P_{CO_2}. Arterial P_{O_2} must drop *substantially,* at least to 60 mm Hg, before oxygen levels become a major stimulus for increased ventilation. This is not as strange as it may appear. Remember, there is a huge reservoir of oxygen bound to hemoglobin, and hemoglobin remains almost entirely saturated unless or until the P_{O_2} of alveolar gas and arterial blood falls below 60 mm Hg. The central chemoreceptors then begin to suffer from oxygen starvation, and their activity is depressed. At the same time, the peripheral chemoreceptors become excited and stimulate the respiratory centers to increase ventilation, even if P_{CO_2} is normal. Thus, the peripheral chemoreceptor reflex system can maintain ventilation in those whose alveolar oxygen levels are low even though brain stem centers are depressed by hypoxia.

In people who retain carbon dioxide because of pulmonary disease (e.g., emphysema and chronic bronchitis victims), arterial P_{CO_2} is chronically elevated and chemoreceptors become unresponsive to this chemical stimulus. In such cases, declining P_{O_2} levels acting on the oxygen-sensitive peripheral chemoreceptors provide the principal respiratory stimulus, or the so-called **hypoxic drive.** Gas mixtures administered to such patients during respiratory distress are only slightly enriched with oxygen. Pure oxygen would stop their breathing, because their respiratory stimulus (low P_{O_2} levels) would be removed. •

Influence of Arterial pH.
Changes in arterial pH can modify respiratory rate and rhythm even when carbon dioxide and oxygen levels are normal. Because hydrogen ions diffuse poorly from the blood into the cerebrospinal fluid, the direct effect of arterial H^+ concentration on central chemoreceptors is insignificant compared to the effect of hydrogen ions generated by elevations in P_{CO_2}. The increased ventilation that occurs in response to decreased arterial pH is mediated through the peripheral chemoreceptors.

Although changes in P_{CO_2} and H^+ concentrations are interrelated, they are distinct stimuli. A drop in blood pH (acidosis) may reflect carbon dioxide retention, but it may also result from metabolic causes, such as accumulation of lactic acid during exercise or of fatty (or other organic) acids in patients with poorly controlled diabetes mellitus. Regardless of cause, as arterial pH declines, respiratory system controls attempt to compensate and raise blood pH by eliminating carbon dioxide (and carbonic acid) from the blood; thus, respiratory rate and depth increase.

Summary of Interactions of P_{CO_2}, P_{O_2}, and Arterial pH.
Although every cell in the body must have oxygen to live, the body's need to rid itself of

carbon dioxide is the most important stimulus for breathing in a healthy person. However, as we have seen, carbon dioxide does not act in isolation, and various chemical factors enforce or inhibit one another's effects. These interactions are summarized here:

1. Rising carbon dioxide levels are the most powerful respiratory stimulant. As carbon dioxide is hydrated in cerebrospinal fluid, liberated H^+ acts directly on the central chemoreceptors, causing a reflexive increase in breathing rate and depth. Low P_{CO_2} levels depress respiration.

2. Under normal conditions, blood P_{O_2} affects breathing only indirectly by influencing chemoreceptor sensitivity to changes in P_{CO_2}. Low oxygen tensions augment P_{CO_2} effects; high P_{O_2} levels diminish the effectiveness of carbon dioxide stimulation.

3. When arterial P_{O_2} falls below 60 mm Hg, it becomes the major stimulus for respiration, and ventilation is increased via reflexes initiated by the peripheral chemoreceptors. This may increase oxygen loading into the blood, but it also causes hypocapnia (low P_{CO_2} blood levels) and an increase in blood pH, both of which inhibit respiration.

4. Changes in arterial pH resulting from carbon dioxide retention or metabolic factors act indirectly through the peripheral chemoreceptors to promote changes in ventilation, which in turn modify arterial P_{CO_2} and pH. Arterial pH does not influence the central chemoreceptors directly.

RESPIRATORY ADJUSTMENTS DURING EXERCISE AND AT HIGH ALTITUDES

Effects of Exercise

Respiratory adjustments during exercise are geared to both the intensity and duration of the exercise. Working muscles consume tremendous amounts of oxygen and produce large amounts of carbon dioxide; thus, ventilation can increase 10- to 20-fold during vigorous exercise. Breathing becomes deeper and more vigorous, but the respiratory rate may not be significantly changed. This breathing pattern is called **hyperpnea** (hi″perp-ne′ah) to distinguish it from the deep and often rapid pattern of hyperventilation. Also, the respiratory changes seen in hyperpnea match metabolic demands and so do not lead to significant changes in the O_2 or CO_2 content of the blood. By contrast, hyperventilation may provoke excessive ventilation, resulting in a low P_{CO_2} and alkalosis.

This exercise-enhanced ventilation does *not* appear to be prompted by rising P_{CO_2} and declining

P_{O_2} and pH in the blood for two reasons. First, ventilation increases abruptly at the onset of exercise, followed by a more gradual increase, and finally a steady state of ventilation. Similarly, ventilation declines suddenly when exercise stops, followed by a more gradual decrease to pre-exercise values. Second, while venous levels change, arterial P_{CO_2} and P_{O_2} levels remain surprisingly constant during exercise. In fact, P_{CO_2} levels may decline below normal arterial levels, and P_{O_2} levels may rise very slightly because of the efficiency of the respiratory adjustments. Our present understanding of the mechanisms that produce these observations is sketchy, but the most accepted explanation is as follows.

The abrupt increase in ventilation that occurs as exercise is begun reflects the interaction of the following neural factors: (1) psychic stimuli (that is, our conscious anticipation of exercise), (2) simultaneous cortical motor activation of the skeletal muscles and of the respiratory centers, and (3) proprioceptors in moving muscles, tendons, and joints, which send excitatory impulses to the respiratory centers. The subsequent gradual increase and then plateauing of respiration is probably due to stimulatory effects of rising body temperature on brain stem respiratory centers, and of epinephrine secreted by the adrenal medulla during sympathetic nervous system activation.

The abrupt decrease in ventilation that occurs as exercise ends reflects the "shutting off" of the neural control mechanisms. The subsequent gradual decline in ventilation to baseline levels occurs as the oxygen debt is being repaid and respiration continues to be stimulated by low arterial pH due to lactic acid accumulation during rigorous exercise. This rise in lactic acid levels is *not* a result of inadequate respiratory function, because alveolar ventilation and pulmonary perfusion are as well matched during exercise as during rest. Rather, it reflects cardiac output limitations or inability of the skeletal muscles to further increase their oxygen consumption (see Chapter 9). In light of this fact, the practice of inhaling pure oxygen by mask, commonly used by football players to replenish their "oxygen-starved" bodies as quickly as possible, is useless. The panting athlete *does* have an oxygen deficit. But extra oxygen will not help, because the shortage is in the muscles—not the lungs. •

Effects of High Altitude

Most Americans live between sea level and an altitude of approximately 2400 meters (8000 feet). The differences in barometric pressure within this range are not great enough to cause healthy people any problems when they spend brief periods in the higher-altitude areas. However, when you move (on a long-term basis) from a sea level region to the mountains, where air density and P_{O_2} are lower, your body initially responds with headaches, nausea, and dizziness,

even as it begins to make several respiratory and hemopoietic adjustments. This multistep adaptive response of the body is called **acclimatization.**

As already explained, decreases in arterial P_{O_2} cause the central chemoreceptors to become more responsive to increases in P_{CO_2}, and a substantial decline in P_{O_2} directly stimulates the peripheral chemoreceptors. As a result, increased ventilation occurs as the brain attempts to restore gas exchange to previous levels. Within a few days, the minute respiratory volume stabilizes at a level 2 to 3 L/min higher than that seen at sea level. Since increased ventilation also reduces arterial carbon dioxide levels, the P_{CO_2} of individuals living at high altitudes is typically below 40 mm Hg (its value at sea level).

Because less oxygen is available to be loaded, high-altitude conditions always result in lower than normal hemoglobin saturation levels. For example, at about 6000 m (19,000 feet) above sea level, the oxygen saturation of arterial blood is only 67% (compared to nearly 98% at sea level). But hemoglobin unloads only 20% to 25% of its oxygen at sea level pressures; thus, even at these reduced hemoglobin saturations, oxygen needs of the tissues are still met adequately under resting conditions. Additionally, at high altitudes, hemoglobin's affinity for oxygen is also reduced, and more oxygen is released to the tissues during each circulatory round.

Although the tissues receive adequate oxygen under normal conditions, problems arise when all-out efforts are demanded of the cardiovascular and respiratory systems (as discovered by U.S. athletes competing in Olympic events on the high mesa of Mexico City). Unless one is fully acclimatized, such conditions almost guarantee that body tissues will become severely hypoxic. •

When blood oxygen tension declines, the kidneys intervene by accelerating the production of erythropoietin, which stimulates bone marrow production of red blood cells (see Chapter 18). This phase of acclimatization, which occurs slowly, provides long-term compensation for living at high altitudes.

HOMEOSTATIC IMBALANCES OF THE RESPIRATORY SYSTEM

The respiratory system is particularly vulnerable to infectious diseases because it is open to airborne pathogens. Since many of these inflammatory conditions, such as rhinitis and laryngitis, were considered earlier in the chapter, we will turn our attention to the most disabling respiratory disorders, the group of diseases collectively called *chronic obstructive pulmonary disease (COPD), tuberculosis,* and *lung cancer.* COPD and lung cancer are "living proof" of the devastating effects of cigarette smoking on the body. Long known to promote cardiovascular disease, cigarettes are perhaps even more effective at destroying the lungs.

Chronic Obstructive Pulmonary Disease (COPD)

The **chronic obstructive pulmonary diseases,** exemplified by chronic bronchitis and obstructive emphysema, are a major cause of death and disability in the USA and are becoming increasingly prevalent. These diseases have certain features in common: (1) Patients almost invariably have a history of smoking; (2) **dyspnea** (disp-ne′ah), difficult or labored breathing often referred to as "air hunger," occurs and becomes progressively more severe; (3) coughing and frequent pulmonary infections are common; and (4) most COPD victims ultimately develop respiratory failure (accompanied by hypoxemia, carbon dioxide retention, and respiratory acidosis).

Obstructive emphysema is distinguished by permanent enlargement of the alveoli, accompanied by deterioration of the alveolar walls. Chronic inflammation leads to lung fibrosis, and invariably, the lungs lose their elasticity. Arterial oxygen and carbon dioxide levels remain essentially normal until late in the disease. As the lungs become less elastic, the airways collapse during expiration and obstruct the outflow of air. This has two important consequences: (1) Accessory muscles must be enlisted to breathe, and the victims are perpetually exhausted because they must expend 15% to 20% of their total body energy supply (as opposed to 5% in healthy individuals) just to breathe. (2) For complex reasons, the bronchioles open during inspiration but collapse during expiration, trapping huge volumes of air in the alveoli. This hyperinflation leads to the development of a permanently expanded "barrel chest." Emphysema victims are sometimes called "pink puffers" because their breathing is labored, but they do not become cyanotic (blue) because gas exchange remains surprisingly adequate until late in the disease. In addition to cigarette smoking, hereditary factors may help to cause emphysema in some patients.

In **chronic bronchitis,** inhaled irritants lead to chronic excessive mucus production by the mucosa of the lower respiratory passageways and to inflammation and fibrosis of that mucosa. These responses obstruct the airways and severely impair lung ventilation and gas exchange. Pulmonary infections are frequent because bacteria thrive in the stagnant pools of mucus. Chronic bronchitis patients are sometimes called "blue bloaters" because hypoxia and carbon dioxide retention occur early in the disease and cyanosis is common. However, the degree of dyspnea is usually moderate compared to that of emphysema sufferers. In addition to the major factor of cigarette smoking, environmental pollution may contribute to the development of chronic bronchitis.

Tuberculosis

Tuberculosis (TB), the infectious disease caused by the bacterium *Mycobacterium tuberculosis,* is spread through repeated exposure to the airborne bacteria, usually from an infected person's cough. TB mostly affects the lungs but can spread through the lymphatics to affect other organs as well. Although an estimated one-third of the world's population is infected, most people never develop active TB because a massive inflammatory and immune response usually contains the primary infection by walling it off in fibrous (or calcified) nodules (tubercles) in the lungs. However, the bacteria survive in the nodules and when the person's immunity is low, they may break out and cause symptomatic TB. Its main symptoms are fever, night sweats, weight loss, a racking cough, and spitting up blood.

Until the turn of the century, TB was responsible for one-third of all deaths among 20- to 45-year-old U.S. adults. With the advent of antibiotics in the 1940s, this "killer" was put into retreat and its prevalence declined so dramatically that it was no longer considered a major health threat. However, since 1985, there has been an alarming increase in TB associated with HIV infection, especially among individuals who abuse intravenous drugs and reside in cramped shelters for the homeless. The TB bacterium grows very slowly and drug therapy entails a 12-month course of antibiotics for cure. Most individuals infected with HIV and TB test negative on TB screening tests because of their weakened immune system. Then, when they become symptomatic for TB, many fail to complete the drug course and pass on their microbes to others. Perhaps even more alarming is that deadly drug-resistant TB strains are emerging in the patients who stop taking the drugs (about 20% of the total treated). The threat of TB epidemics is so real that the health centers in some cities have begun detaining such patients in sanitariums against their will for as long as it takes to complete a cure.

Lung Cancer

Lung cancer accounts for fully one-third of cancer deaths in the United States. Its incidence, strongly associated with cigarette smoking (over 90% of lung cancer patients were smokers), is increasing daily. In both sexes, lung cancer is the most prevalent type of malignancy. Its cure rate is notoriously low; overall five-year survival of those with lung cancer is about 7%. Because lung cancer is aggressive and metastasizes rapidly and widely, most cases are not diagnosed until they are well advanced.

Lung cancer appears to follow closely the oncogene-activating steps outlined in *A Closer Look* in Chapter 3 (p. 96). Ordinarily, nasal hairs, sticky mucus, and the action of cilia do a fine job of protecting the lungs from chemical and biological irritants, but when one smokes, these devices are overwhelmed and eventually stop functioning. Continuous irritation prompts the production of more mucus, but smoking paralyzes the cilia that clear this mucus and inhibits lung macrophages. Mucus pooling leads to frequent pulmonary infections, including pneumonia, and COPD. However, it is the irritant effects of the "cocktail" of free radicals and carcinogens in tobacco smoke that eventually translate into lung cancer, causing the mucosal cells to proliferate wildly and lose their characteristic histological structure.

The three most common types of lung cancer are (1) **squamous cell carcinoma** (20–40% of cases), which arises in the epithelium of the bronchi or their larger subdivisions and tends to form masses that cavitate (hollow out) and bleed, (2) **adenocarcinoma** (25–35%) which originates in peripheral lung areas as solitary nodules that develop from bronchial glands and alveolar cells, and (3) **small cell carcinoma** (10–20%), also called **oat cell carcinoma,** which consists of lymphocyte-like cells that originate in the primary bronchi and grow aggressively in cords or small grapelike clusters within the mediastinum. Some small cell carcinomas cause problems beyond their effects on the lungs because they become ectopic sites of hormone production. For example, some secrete ACTH (leading to Cushing's disease) or calcitonin (which results in hypocalcemia).

The most effective treatment for lung cancer is complete removal of the diseased lung, because it has the greatest potential for prolonging life and cure. However, this choice is open to very few lung cancer patients. In most cases, radiation therapy and chemotherapy are the only options. However, this picture may be changing soon. Most non–small cell lung cancers result from absence or mutation of the tumor suppressor gene *p53* or through action of the k-*ras* oncogene. By infusing tumor cells with retroviruses carrying working *p53* genes or k-*ras* gene inhibitors, researchers have achieved an 80% cure rate in mice and are optimistic that similar results might be obtained in gene therapy trials in humans. •

DEVELOPMENTAL ASPECTS OF THE RESPIRATORY SYSTEM

Since embryos develop in a cephalocaudal (head-to-tail) direction, the upper respiratory structures appear first. By the fourth week of development, two thickened plates of ectoderm, the **olfactory placodes** (plak'ōds), have appeared on the anterior aspect of the head (Figure 23.26). These quickly invaginate to form **olfactory pits** that form the nasal cavities. They then extend posteriorly to connect with the developing foregut, which forms at the same time from the endodermal germ layer.

The respiratory epithelium of the lower respiratory organs develops as an outpocketing of the foregut endoderm, which differentiates into the pharyngeal mucosa. This protrusion, called the **laryngotracheal bud,** is present by the fifth week of development. The proximal part of the bud forms the tracheal lining, and its distal end splits and forms the mucosae of the bronchi and all their subdivisions, including (eventually) the lung alveoli. By the eighth week, mesoderm clothes these ectoderm- and endoderm-derived linings and forms the walls of the respiratory passageways and the stroma of the lungs. By 28 weeks, the respiratory system has developed sufficiently to allow a baby born prematurely to breathe on its own. As noted earlier, infants born before this time are likely to exhibit infant respiratory distress syndrome resulting from inadequate surfactant production.

During fetal life, the lungs are filled with fluid, and all respiratory exchanges are made by the placenta. Due to vascular shunts (ductus arteriosus and foramen ovale), circulating blood largely bypasses the lungs (see Chapter 29, p. 1014). At birth, the fluid-filled pathway is drained, and the respiratory passageways fill with air. As the P_{CO_2} in the baby's blood rises, the respiratory centers are excited causing the baby to take its first breath. Consequently, the alveoli inflate and begin to function in gas exchange. However, it is nearly two weeks before the lungs are fully inflated.

Important birth defects of the respiratory system include *cleft palate* and *cystic fibrosis.* **Cystic fibrosis (CF),** the most common lethal genetic disease in the U.S., strikes one out of every 2000 white children and every day two children die of it. CF causes oversecretion of a viscous mucus that clogs the respiratory passages and predisposes the child to eventually fatal respiratory infections. It affects secretory processes in other body systems as well. Most importantly it impairs food digestion by clogging ducts that deliver pancreatic enzymes and bile to the small intestine, and sweat glands produce an extremely salty perspiration. At the heart of CF is a faulty gene that codes for the *CFTR* (cystic fibrosis transmembrane conductance regulator) *protein.* The normal CFTR protein works as a chloride channel to control the flow of Cl^- in and out of cells. In those with the mutated gene, CFTR lacks an essential amino acid and so it gets "stuck" in the ER, unable to reach the membrane to perform its normal role. Consequently, less Cl^- is secreted and less water follows, resulting in the thick mucus typical of CF. Conventional therapy for CF has been mucus-dissolving drugs, "clapping" the chest to loosen the thick mucus, and antibiotics to prevent infection. Presently at least three lines of research are being pursued to try to compensate for the deficient CFTR: (1) using disabled adenoviruses (the cold virus) to carry normal CFTR genes into cells lining the respiratory tract, (2) prodding another channel protein to take over the Cl^- transporting duties, and (3) developing techniques to free the CFTR protein from the ER so that it can assume its normal function at the cell's plasma membrane. •

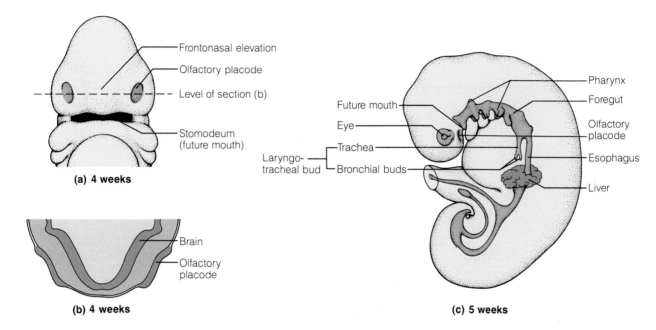

FIGURE 23.26
Embryonic development of the respiratory system. (a) Anterior superficial view of the embryo's head, showing the ectodermal olfactory placodes. **(b)** Transverse section of the embryo's head at four to five weeks, showing the location of olfactory placodes [the level of transection is shown in **(a)**]. **(c)** Development of the lower respiratory passageway mucosae. The laryngotracheal bud is shown outpocketing from the foregut (endodermal) mucosa.

The respiratory rate is highest in newborn infants (40–80 respirations per minute). In infants, it is around 30 per minute; at 5 years it is around 25 per minute; and in adults it is between 12 and 18 per minute. In old age, the rate often increases again. At birth, only about one-sixth of the final number of alveoli are present. The lungs continue to mature throughout childhood, and more alveoli are formed until young adulthood. However, if smoking is begun in the early teens, the lungs never completely mature, and those additional alveoli are lost forever.

In infants, the ribs take a nearly horizontal course. Thus, infants rely almost entirely on descent of the diaphragm to increase thoracic volume for inspiration. By the second year, the ribs are positioned more obliquely, and the adult form of breathing is established.

Most respiratory system problems that occur are the result of external factors—for example, viral or bacterial infections or obstruction of the trachea by a piece of food. However, some unfortunate individuals are plagued with **asthma,** a condition frequently caused by allergy that causes them to wheeze and gasp for air as their respiratory passages swell and their bronchioles constrict. For many years, bacterial pneumonia was one of the worst killers in the United States. Antibiotics have greatly decreased its lethality, but it is still a dangerous disease, particularly in the elderly. By far the most problematic diseases *at present* are those described earlier, COPD, lung can-

cer, and newly diagnosed tuberculosis cases in AIDS patients. •

As we age, the thoracic wall becomes more rigid and the lungs gradually lose their elasticity, resulting in a decreasing ability to ventilate the lungs. Vital capacity declines by about one-third by the age of 70 years. Blood oxygen levels decline slightly and sensitivity to the stimulating effects of carbon dioxide decreases, particularly in a reclining or supine position. As a result, many old people tend to become hypoxic during sleep and exhibit *sleep apnea* (temporary cessation of breathing during sleep).

Additionally, many of the respiratory system's protective mechanisms become less effective with age. Ciliary activity of its mucosa decreases, and the macrophages in the lungs become sluggish. The net result is that the elderly are more at risk for respiratory tract infections, particularly pneumonia and influenza.

*   *   *

Lungs, bronchial tree, heart, and connecting blood vessels—together, these organs fashion a remarkable system that ensures that blood is oxygenated and relieved of carbon dioxide and that all tissue cells of the body have access to these services. Although the cooperation of the respiratory and cardiovascular systems is quite obvious, all organ systems of the body depend on the functioning of the respiratory system, as summarized in *Making Connections* on p. 782.

Making Connections

 Systems Connections: Homeostatic Interrelationships Between the Respiratory System and Other Body Systems

 Nervous System
- Respiratory system provides oxygen needed for normal neuronal activity; disposes of carbon dioxide
- Medullary and pons centers regulate respiratory rate/depth; stretch receptors in lungs provide feedback

 Endocrine System
- Respiratory system provides oxygen; disposes of carbon dioxide
- Epinephrine dilates the bronchioles; testosterone promotes laryngeal enlargement in pubertal males

 Cardiovascular System
- Respiratory system provides oxygen; disposes of carbon dioxide; carbon dioxide present in blood as HCO_3^- and H_2CO_3 contributes to blood buffering
- Blood is the transport medium for respiratory gases

 Lymphatic System/Immunity
- Respiratory system provides oxygen; disposes of carbon dioxide; tonsils in pharynx house immune cells
- Lymphatic system helps to maintain blood volume required for respiratory gas transport; immune system protects respiratory organs from bacteria, bacterial toxins, viruses, and cancer

 Digestive System
- Respiratory system provides oxygen; disposes of carbon dioxide
- Digestive system provides nutrients needed by respiratory system

 Urinary System
- Respiratory system provides oxygen; disposes of carbon dioxide
- Kidneys dispose of metabolic wastes of respiratory system organs (other than carbon dioxide)

 Reproductive System
- Respiratory system provides oxygen; disposes of carbon dioxide

 Integumentary System
- Respiratory system provides oxygen; disposes of carbon dioxide
- Skin protects respiratory system organs by forming surface barriers

 Skeletal System
- Respiratory system provides oxygen; disposes of carbon dioxide
- Bones protect lungs and bronchi by enclosure

Muscular System
- Respiratory system provides oxygen needed for muscle activity; disposes of carbon dioxide
- Activity of the diaphragm and intercostal muscles essential for producing volume changes that lead to pulmonary ventilation; regular exercise increases respiratory efficiency

Closer Connections: The Respiratory System and Interrelationships with the Cardiovascular, Lymphatic/Immune, and Muscular Systems

Every day we inhale and exhale nearly 20,000 liters of air. This activity accomplishes two things—it supplies the body with the oxygen it needs to oxidize food and release energy, and it expels carbon dioxide, the major waste product of that process. As crucial as breathing is, most of us don't think very often about the importance of having fresh air on call. But the phenomenon of gulping for air is familiar to every athlete. Indeed, the respiratory rate of a competitive swimmer may jump to over 40 breaths/min and the amount of air taken in per breath may soar from the usual 500 ml to as much as 6 to 7 liters.

The respiratory system is beautifully engineered for its function. Its alveoli are flushed with new air more than 15,000 times each day and the alveolar walls are so indescribably thin that red blood cells moving single-file through the pulmonary capillaries can make the gaseous "swaps" with the air-filled alveoli within a fraction of a second. Although every cell in the body depends on this system for the oxygen it needs to live, the respiratory system interactions that we will consider here are those it has with the cardiovascular, lymphatic, and muscular systems.

Cardiovascular System

For all intents and purposes, the interaction between the respiratory and cardiovascular systems is so intimate that these two systems are inseparable. Respiratory system organs, as important as they are, can only make the gas exchanges that occur in the lungs. Although all body cells depend on the respiratory system to provide needed oxygen, they pick up that oxygen not from the lungs, but from the blood. Thus, without blood to act as the intermediary and the heart and blood vessels to act as the

hardware to pump the blood around the body, all the efforts of the respiratory system would be useless.

Lymphatic System/Immunity

Of all body systems, only the respiratory system is completely exposed to the external environment (yes, the skin is exposed but its exposed parts are all dead). Because air contains a rich mix of potentially dangerous inhabitants (bacteria, viruses, fungi, asbestos fibers, pollen grains, etc.), the respiratory system is continuously at risk for infection or damage from external agents. Lymphoid outposts help protect the respiratory tract and enhance the defenses (cilia, mucus) that the respiratory system itself erects. Particularly well situated to apprehend intruders at the oral-nasal-pharynx junction are the palatine, pharyngeal, lingual, and tubal tonsils. Their macrophages engulf foreign antigens and they provide sites where lymphocytes are sensitized to mount immune responses. Their effectiveness is revealed by the fact that respiratory tract infections are much more frequent in people who have had their tonsils removed.

Muscular System

Skeletal muscle cells, like other body cells, need oxygen to live. The notable part of this interaction is that most respiratory compensations that occur service increased muscular activity. (It is difficult to think of incidents where this is not the case—the exceptions concern disease conditions.) When we are at rest, the respiratory system operates at basal levels, but any time physical activity becomes more vigorous, the respiratory rhythm picks up the beat to match supply to need and maintain the acid-base balance of the blood.

Clinical Connections

Respiratory System

Case study: Barbara Joley was in the bus that was hit broadside. When she was freed from the wreckage, she was deeply cyanotic and her respiration had stopped. Her heart was still beating, but her pulse was fast and thready. The EMT reported that when Barbara was found, her head was cocked at a peculiar angle and it looked like she had a fracture at the level of the C_2 vertebra. The following questions refer to these observations.

1. How might the "peculiar" head position explain Barbara's cessation of breathing?

2. What procedures (do you think) should have been initiated immediately by the emergency personnel?

3. Why is Barbara cyanotic? Explain cyanosis.

4. Assuming that Barbara survives, how will her accident affect her life-style in the future?

Barbara survived transport to the hospital and notes recorded during the admission process included the following observations.

- Right thorax compressed; ribs 7 to 9 fractured
- Right lung atelectasis

Relative to these notes:
5. What is atelectasis and why is only the right lung affected?

6. How do the recorded injuries relate to the atelectasis?

7. What treatment will be done to reverse the atelectasis? What is the rationale for this treatment?

RELATED CLINICAL TERMS

Aspiration (as″pĭ-ra′shun) (1) The act of breathing or drawing something into the lungs or respiratory passages. Pathological aspiration in which vomit or excessive mucus is drawn into the lungs may occur when a person is unconscious or anesthetized; turning the head to one side helps to prevent this event. (2) Withdrawal of fluid by suction (use of an aspirator); done during surgery to keep an area free of blood or other body fluids; mucus is aspirated from the trachea of tracheotomy patients.

Bronchoscopy (*scopy* = viewing) Use of a viewing tube to examine the internal surface of the main bronchi in the lung. The tube is inserted through the nose or mouth and guided inferiorly through the larynx and trachea. Forceps may be attached to the tip of the tube to remove trapped objects, take biopsy samples, or retrieve samples of mucus for examination.

Cheyne-Stokes (chān′stōks) **breathing** A very abnormal breathing pattern sometimes seen just before death (the "death rattle") and in people with combined neurological and cardiac disorders; consists of bursts of tidal volume breaths (increasing and then decreasing in depth) alternating with periods of apnea; cause is poorly understood, but trauma and hypoxia of the brain stem centers, as well as imbalances between the P_{CO_2} levels of arterial blood and cerebrospinal fluid, may be factors.

Deviated septum Condition in which the nasal septum takes a more lateral course than usual and may obstruct breathing; often manifests in old age, but may also result from nose trauma.

Endotracheal tube A thin plastic tube threaded into the trachea through the nose or mouth; used to deliver oxygen to patients who are breathing inadequately. Used on patients who are in a coma, under anesthesia, or have diseases that make breathing difficult.

Epistaxis (ep″ĭ-stak′sis; *epistazo* = to bleed at the nose) Nosebleed; nasal hemorrhage; commonly follows trauma to the nose or excessive nose blowing; most nasal bleeding is from the highly vascularized anterior septum and can be stopped by pinching the nostrils closed or packing them with cotton.

Hantavirus pulmonary syndrome An acute respiratory distress syndrome caused by inhaling hantavirus. The syndrome is rapidly fatal in most cases, progressing from flulike symptoms to lethal pulmonary edema in which patients literally drown in their own plasma within 24 hours. The virus is carried by rodents (deer mice and others) and shed in their feces and urine; disturbance of rodent burrows causes the virus particles to become airborne. Responsible for a number of unexplained deaths in the southwest part of the U.S. in 1990, the virus was identified as the disease agent in pulmonary edema deaths in 12 states by 1993.

Orthopnea (or″thop-ne′ah; *ortho* = straight, upright) Inability to breathe in the horizontal (lying down) position.

Otorhinolaryngology (o″to-ri″no-lar″in-gol′o-je; *oto* = ear; *rhino* = nose) Branch of medicine that deals with diagnosis and treatment of diseases of the ears, nose, and throat.

Pneumonia Infectious inflammation of the lungs, in which fluid accumulates in the alveoli; the sixth most common cause of death in the United States. Over 50 different varieties of pneumonia: Most are viral or bacterial, but some result from fungi (the type of pneumonia often associated with AIDS, *Pneumocystis carinii* pneumonia).

Pulmonary embolism Obstruction of the pulmonary artery or one of its branches by an embolus; most often the embolus is a blood clot that has been carried from the lower limbs and through the right side of the heart into the pulmonary circulation; symptoms are chest pain, productive bloody cough, tachycardia, and rapid, shallow breathing; can cause sudden death unless treated quickly; usual treatment is administration of oxygen by mask, morphine to relieve pain and anxiety, and anticoagulant drugs to help dissolve the clot.

Stuttering Condition in which the vocal cords of the larynx are out of control and the first syllable of words is repeated in "machine-gun" fashion; cause is undetermined, but problems with neuromuscular control of the larynx and emotional factors are suspect; many stutterers become fluent when whispering or singing, both of which involve a change in the manner of vocalization.

Sudden infant death syndrome (SIDS) Unexpected death of an apparently healthy infant during sleep; commonly called crib death, SIDS is one of the most frequent causes of death in infants under one year old; cause is unknown, but it is believed to be a problem of immaturity of the respiratory control centers.

Tracheotomy (tra″ke-ot′o-me) Surgical opening of the trachea; done to provide an alternate route for air to reach the lungs when more superior respiratory passageways are obstructed (as by food or a crushed larynx).

CHAPTER SUMMARY

1. Respiration involves four processes: ventilation, external respiration, internal respiration, and transport of respiratory gases in the blood. Both the respiratory system and the cardiovascular system are involved in respiration.

Functional Anatomy of the Respiratory System (pp. 744–756)

2. Respiratory system organs are divided functionally into conducting zone structures (nose to bronchioles), which filter, warm, and moisten incoming air; and respiratory zone structures (respiratory bronchioles to alveoli), where gas exchanges occur.

The Nose and the Paranasal Sinuses (pp. 744–747)

3. The nose provides an airway for respiration, warms, moistens, and cleanses incoming air, and houses the olfactory receptors.

4. The external nose is shaped by bone and cartilage plates. The nasal cavity, which opens to the exterior, is divided by the nasal septum. Paranasal sinuses and nasolacrimal ducts drain into the nasal cavities.

The Pharynx (p. 747)

5. The pharynx extends from the base of the skull to the level of C_6. The nasopharynx is an air conduit; the oropharynx and laryngopharynx are common passageways for food and air. Pairs of tonsils are found in the oropharynx and nasopharynx.

The Larynx (pp. 747–749)

6. The larynx, or voice box, contains the vocal cords. It also provides a patent airway and serves as a switching mechanism to route food and air into the proper channels.

7. The epiglottis prevents food or liquids from entering the respiratory channels during swallowing.

The Trachea (pp. 749–751)

8. The trachea extends from the larynx to the primary bronchi. The trachea is reinforced by C-shaped cartilage rings, which keep the trachea patent, and its mucosa is ciliated.

The Bronchi and Subdivisions: The Bronchial Tree (pp. 751–754)

9. The right and left main bronchi run into their respective lungs, within which they continue to subdivide into smaller and smaller passageways.

10. The terminal bronchioles lead into respiratory zone structures: alveolar ducts, alveolar sacs, and finally alveoli. Gas exchange occurs in the alveoli, across the respiratory membrane.

11. As the respiratory conduits become smaller, cartilage is reduced in amount and finally lost; the mucosa thins, and smooth muscle in the walls increases.

The Lungs and Pleural Coverings (pp. 754–756)

12. The lungs, the paired organs of gas exchange, flank the mediastinum in the thoracic cavity. Each is suspended in its own pleural cavity via its root and has a base, an apex, and medial and costal surfaces. The right lung has three lobes; the left has two.

13. The lungs are primarily air passageways/chambers, supported by an elastic connective tissue stroma.

14. The pulmonary arteries carry blood returned from the systemic circulation to the lungs, where gas exchange occurs. The pulmonary veins return newly oxygenated blood back to the heart to be distributed throughout the body. The bronchial arteries provide the nutrient blood supply of the lungs.

15. The parietal pleura lines the thoracic wall and mediastinum; the pulmonary pleura covers external lung surfaces. Pleural fluid reduces friction during breathing movements.

Mechanics of Breathing (pp. 756–763)

Pressure Relationships in the Thoracic Cavity (pp. 756–757)

1. Intrapulmonary pressure is the pressure within the alveoli. Interpleural pressure is the pressure within the pleural cavity; it is always negative relative to intrapulmonary and atmospheric pressures.

Pulmonary Ventilation: Inspiration and Expiration (pp. 757–759)

2. Gases travel from an area of higher pressure to an area of lower pressure.

3. Inspiration occurs when the diaphragm and intercostal muscles contract, increasing the dimensions (and volume) of the thorax. As the intrapulmonary pressure drops, air rushes into the lungs until the intrapulmonary and atmospheric pressures are equalized.

4. Expiration is largely passive, occurring as the inspiratory muscles relax and the lungs recoil. When intrapulmonary pressure exceeds atmospheric pressure, gases flow from the lungs.

Physical Factors Influencing Pulmonary Ventilation (pp. 759–761)

5. Friction in the air passageways causes resistance, which decreases air passage and causes breathing movements to become more strenuous. The greatest resistance to air flow occurs in the midsize bronchi.

6. Lung compliance depends on elasticity of lung tissue and flexibility of the bony thorax. When either is impaired, expiration becomes an active process, requiring energy expenditure.

7. Surface tension of alveolar fluid acts to reduce alveolar size and collapse the alveoli. This tendency is resisted in part by surfactant.

Respiratory Volumes and Pulmonary Function Tests (pp. 761–763)

8. The four respiratory volumes are tidal, inspiratory reserve, expiratory reserve, and residual. The four respiratory capacities are vital, functional residual, inspiratory, and total lung. Respiratory volumes and capacities may be measured by spirometry.

9. Anatomical dead space is the air-filled volume (about 150 ml) of the conducting passageways. If alveoli become nonfunctional in gas exchange, their volume is added to the anatomical dead space, and the sum is the total dead space.

10. Alveolar ventilation is the best index of ventilation efficiency, because it accounts for anatomical dead space.

$$AVR = \left(\begin{array}{c} TV - \text{anatomical dead space} \\ (ml/breath) \end{array} \right) \times \text{respiratory rate}$$

11. The FVC and FEV tests, which determine the rate at which VC air can be expelled, are particularly valuable in distinguishing between obstructive and restrictive disease.

Nonrespiratory Air Movements (p. 763)

12. Nonrespiratory air movements are voluntary or reflex actions that clear the respiratory passageways or express emotions.

Gas Exchanges in the Body (pp. 763–767)

Basic Properties of Gases (pp. 763–764)

1. Gaseous movements in the body occur by bulk flow and by diffusion.

2. Dalton's law states that each gas in a mixture of gases exerts pressure in proportion to its percentage in the total mixture.

3. Henry's law states that the amount of gas that will dissolve in a liquid is proportional to the partial pressure of the gas. Solubility of the gas in the liquid and the temperature are other important factors.

Composition of Alveolar Gas (p. 765)

4. Alveolar gas contains more carbon dioxide and water vapor and considerably less oxygen than atmospheric air.

Gas Exchanges Between the Blood, Lungs, and Tissues (pp. 765–767)

5. External respiration is the process of gas exchange that occurs in the lungs. Oxygen enters the pulmonary capillaries; carbon dioxide leaves the blood and enters the alveoli. Factors influencing this process include the partial pressure gradients, the thickness of the respiratory membrane, surface area available, and the matching of alveolar ventilation and pulmonary perfusion.

6. Internal respiration is the gas exchange that occurs between the systemic capillaries and the tissues. Carbon dioxide enters the blood, and oxygen leaves the blood and enters the tissues.

Transport of Respiratory Gases by Blood (pp. 767–772)

Oxygen Transport (pp. 767–770)

1. Molecular oxygen is carried in blood bound to hemoglobin in the red blood cells. The amount of oxygen bound to hemoglobin depends on the P_{O_2} and P_{CO_2} of blood, blood pH, the presence of BPG, and temperature. A very small amount of oxygen gas is transported dissolved in plasma.

2. Hypoxia occurs when inadequate amounts of oxygen are delivered to body tissues. When this occurs, the skin and mucosae may become cyanotic.

Carbon Dioxide Transport (pp. 770–772)

3. CO_2 is transported in the blood dissolved in plasma, chemically bound to hemoglobin, and (primarily) as bicarbonate ion in plasma. Loading and unloading of O_2 and CO_2 are mutually beneficial.

4. Accumulation of CO_2 leads to acidosis; depletion of CO_2 from blood leads to respiratory alkalosis.

Control of Respiration (pp. 772–777)

Neural Mechanisms and Generation of Breathing Rhythm (pp. 772–773)

1. Medullary respiratory centers are the inspiratory center (dorsal respiratory group) and the expiratory center. The inspiratory center is responsible for the rhythmicity of breathing.

2. The pneumotaxic center (and perhaps other respiratory centers in the pons) influence the activity of the medullary inspiratory center.

Factors Influencing the Rate and Depth of Breathing (pp. 773–777)

3. Pulmonary irritant reflexes are initiated by dust, mucus, fumes, and pollutants.

4. The Hering-Breuer reflex is a protective reflex initiated by extreme overinflation of the lungs; it acts to initiate expiration.

5. Emotions, pain, and other stressors can alter respiration by acting through hypothalamic centers. Respiration can also be controlled voluntarily for short periods of time.

6. Important chemical factors modifying baseline respiratory rate and depth are arterial levels of CO_2, H^+, and O_2.

7. An increasing level of carbon dioxide is the most powerful respiratory stimulant. It acts (via the release of H^+ in cerebrospinal fluid) on the central chemoreceptors to cause a reflexive increase in the rate and depth of breathing. Hypocapnia depresses respiration and results in hypoventilation and, possibly, apnea.

8. Acidosis and a decline in blood P_{O_2} act on peripheral chemoreceptors and enhance the response to carbon dioxide.

9. Arterial P_{O_2} levels below 60 mm Hg constitute the hypoxic drive.

Respiratory Adjustments During Exercise and at High Altitudes (pp. 777–778)

Effects of Exercise (pp. 777–778)

1. As exercise begins, there is an abrupt increase in ventilation (hyperpnea) followed by a more gradual increase in ventilation. When exercise stops, there is an abrupt decrease in ventilation followed by a gradual decline to baseline values. Continued stimulation of respiration is due to lactic acid accumulation.

2. P_{O_2}, P_{CO_2}, and blood pH remain quite constant during exercise and hence do not appear to account for changes in ventilation. Psychological factors and proprioceptor inputs may contribute.

Effects of High Altitude (p. 778)

3. At high altitudes, there is a decrease in arterial P_{O_2} and hemoglobin saturation levels because of the decrease in barometric pressure compared to sea level. Hyperventilation helps restore gas exchange to physiological levels.

4. Long-term acclimatization involves increased erythropoiesis.

Homeostatic Imbalances of the Respiratory System (pp. 778–780)

1. The major respiratory disorders are COPD (emphysema and chronic bronchitis) and lung cancer; a significant cause is cigarette smoking. Tuberculosis is re-emerging as a major health problem.

Chronic Obstructive Pulmonary Disease (COPD) (p. 779)

2. Emphysema is characterized by permanent enlargement and destruction of alveoli. The lungs lose their elasticity, and expiration becomes an active process.

3. Chronic bronchitis is characterized by excessive mucus production in the lower respiratory passageways, which severely impairs ventilation and gas exchange. Patients may become cyanotic as a result of chronic hypoxia.

Tuberculosis (p. 779)

4. Tuberculosis (TB), an infectious disease caused by an airborne bacterium, mainly affects the lungs. Although most infected individuals remain asymptomatic by walling off the bacteria in tubercles, when immunity is depressed disease symptoms ensue. Recent TB increases in AIDS patients and some patients' failure to complete drug therapy have produced multidrug-resistant TB strains.

Lung Cancer (pp. 779–780)

5. Lung cancer, promoted by free radicals and other carcinogens, is extremely aggressive and metastasizes rapidly.

Developmental Aspects of the Respiratory System (pp. 780–783)

1. The superior respiratory system mucosa develops from the invagination of the ectodermal olfactory placode; that of the inferior passageways develops from an outpocketing of the endodermal foregut lining. Mesoderm forms the walls of the respiratory conduits and the lung stroma.

2. Premature infants have problems keeping their lungs inflated owing to the lack of surfactant in their alveoli, resulting in infant respiratory distress syndrome (IRDS). Surfactant is formed late in fetal development.

3. Cystic fibrosis (CF), the most common fatal hereditary disease, results from an abnormal CFTR protein that forms a chloride channel. As a result, thick mucus is produced which clogs respiratory passages and invites infection.

4. With age, the thorax becomes more rigid, the lungs become less elastic, and vital capacity declines. In addition, the stimulatory effect of increased arterial levels of carbon dioxide is less apparent, and respiratory system protective mechanisms are less effective in old age.

REVIEW QUESTIONS

Multiple Choice/Matching

1. Cutting the phrenic nerves will result in (a) air entering the pleural cavity, (b) paralysis of the diaphragm, (c) stimulation of the diaphragmatic reflex, (d) paralysis of the epiglottis.

2. Following the removal of his larynx, an individual would (a) be unable to speak, (b) be unable to cough, (c) have difficulty swallowing, (d) be in respiratory difficulty or arrest.

3. Under ordinary circumstances, the Hering-Breuer reflex is initiated by (a) the inspiratory center, (b) the apneustic center, (c) overinflation of the alveoli and bronchioles, (d) the pneumotaxic center.

4. The detergent-like molecule that keeps the alveoli from collapsing between breaths because it reduces the surface tension of the water film in the alveoli is called (a) lecithin, (b) bile, (c) surfactant, (d) reluctant.

5. Which of the following determines the *direction* of gas movement? (a) solubility in water, (b) partial pressure gradient, (c) the temperature, (d) molecular weight and size of the gas molecule.

6. When the inspiratory muscles contract, (a) the size of the thoracic cavity is increased in diameter, (b) the size of the thoracic cavity is increased in length, (c) the volume of the thoracic cavity is decreased, (d) the size of the thoracic cavity is increased in both length and diameter.

7. The nutrient blood supply of the lungs is provided by (a) the pulmonary arteries, (b) the aorta, (c) the pulmonary veins, (d) the bronchial arteries.

8. Oxygen and carbon dioxide are exchanged in the lungs and through all cell membranes by (a) active transport, (b) diffusion, (c) filtration, (d) osmosis.

9. Which of the following would not normally be treated by 100% oxygen therapy? (Choose all that apply.) (a) anoxia, (b) carbon monoxide poisoning, (c) respiratory crisis in an emphysema patient, (d) eupnea.

10. Most oxygen carried in the blood is (a) in solution in the plasma, (b) combined with plasma proteins, (c) chemically combined with the heme in red blood cells, (d) in solution in the red blood cells.

11. Which of the following has the greatest stimulating effect on the respiratory center in the brain? (a) oxygen, (b) carbon dioxide, (c) calcium, (d) willpower.

12. In mouth-to-mouth artificial respiration, the rescuer blows air from his or her own respiratory system into that of the victim. Which of the following statements are correct?
1. Expansion of the victim's lungs is brought about by blowing air in at higher than atmospheric pressure (positive-pressure breathing).
2. During inflation of the lungs, the intrapleural pressure increases.
3. This technique will not work if the victim has a hole in the chest wall, even if the lungs are intact.
4. Expiration during this procedure depends on the elasticity of the alveolar and thoracic walls.
   (a) all of these, (b) 1, 2, 4, (c) 1, 2, 3, (d) 2, 4.

13. A baby holding its breath will (a) have brain cells damaged because of low blood oxygen levels, (b) automatically start to breathe again when the carbon dioxide levels in the blood reach a high enough value, (c) suffer heart damage because of increased pressure in the carotid sinus and aortic arch areas, (d) be called a "blue baby."

14. Under ordinary circumstances, which of the following blood components is of no physiological significance? (a) bicarbonate ions, (b) carbaminohemoglobin, (c) nitrogen, (d) chloride.

15. Damage to which of the following would result in cessation of breathing? (a) the pneumotaxic center, (b) the medulla, (c) the stretch receptors in the lungs, (d) the apneustic center.

16. The bulk of carbon dioxide is carried (a) chemically combined with the amino acids of hemoglobin as carbaminohemoglobin in the red blood cells, (b) as the ion HCO_3^- in the plasma after first entering the red blood cell, (c) as carbonic acid in the plasma, (d) chemically combined with the heme portion of Hb.

Short Answer Essay Questions

 17. Trace the route of air from the external nares to an alveolus. Name subdivisions of organs where applicable, and differentiate between conducting and respiratory zone structures.

 18. (a) Why is it important that the trachea is reinforced with cartilage rings? (b) Of what advantage is it that the rings are incomplete posteriorly?

19. Briefly explain the anatomical "reason" why most men have deeper voices than boys or women.

20. The lungs are mostly passageways and elastic tissue. (a) What is the role of the elastic tissue? (b) Of the passageways?

21. Describe the functional relationships between volume changes and gas flow into and out of the lungs.

22. What is it about the structure of the respiratory membrane that makes the alveoli ideal sites for gas exchange?

23. Discuss how respiratory passageway resistance, lung compliance and elasticity, and alveolar surface tension influence pulmonary ventilation.

24. (a) Differentiate clearly between minute respiratory volume and alveolar ventilation rate. (b) Which provides a more accurate measure of ventilatory efficiency, and why?

25. State Dalton's law of partial pressures and Henry's law.

26. Define partial pressure of a gas.

27. (a) Define hyperventilation. (b) If you hyperventilate, do you retain or expel more carbon dioxide? (c) What effect does hyperventilation have on blood pH?

28. Describe age-related changes in respiratory function.

 ## CRITICAL THINKING AND CLINICAL APPLICATION QUESTIONS

1. Harry, the swimmer with the fastest time on the Springfield college swim team, routinely hyperventilates before a meet, as he says "to sock some more oxygen into my lungs so I can swim longer without having to breathe." First of all, what very basic fact about the loading of oxygen has Harry forgotten (a lapse of memory leading to false thinking)? Second, how is Harry jeopardizing not only his time but his life?

2. A member of the "Blue's" gang was rushed into an emergency room after receiving a knife wound in the left side of his thorax. The diagnosis was pneumothorax and a collapsed lung. Explain exactly (a) why the lung collapsed, and (b) why only one lung (not both) collapsed.

 3. Consider the following: (a) Two girls in a high school cafeteria were giggling over lunch, and both accidentally sprayed milk out their nostrils at the same time. Explain in anatomical terms why swallowed fluids can sometimes come out the nose. (b) A boy in the same cafeteria then stood on his head and showed he could drink milk upside down without any of it entering his nasal cavity or nose. What prevented the milk from flowing downward into his nose?

4. A surgeon had to remove three adjacent bronchopulmonary segments from the left lung of a patient with tuberculosis. Almost half of the lung was removed, yet there was no severe bleeding, and relatively few blood vessels had to be cauterized (closed off). Why was the surgery so easy to perform?

24

The Digestive System

CHAPTER OUTLINE AND STUDENT OBJECTIVES

Overview of the Digestive System (pp. 789–795)

1. Describe the overall function of the digestive system, and differentiate between organs of the alimentary canal and accessory digestive organs.

2. List and define briefly the major processes occurring during digestive system activity.

3. Describe the location and function of the peritoneum and the peritoneal cavity. Define retroperitoneal and name the retroperitoneal organs.

4. Describe the tissue composition of the four layers of the alimentary tube wall, and note the general function of each layer.

FUNCTIONAL ANATOMY OF THE DIGESTIVE SYSTEM (pp. 795–830)

5. Describe the gross and microscopic anatomy and basic function of each organ and accessory organ of the alimentary canal.

6. Explain the dental formula and differentiate clearly between deciduous and permanent teeth.

7. Describe the composition and functions of saliva, and explain how salivation is regulated.

8. Describe the mechanisms of chewing and swallowing.

9. Describe structural modifications of the wall of the stomach and small intestine that enhance the digestive process in these regions.

10. Describe the composition of gastric juice, name the cell types responsible for secreting its various components, and describe the importance of each component in stomach activity.

11. Explain how gastric secretion and motility in the stomach are regulated.

12. Describe the function of local hormones produced by the small intestine.

13. State the roles of bile and of pancreatic juice in digestion.

14. Describe how entry of pancreatic juice and bile into the small intestine is regulated.

15. List the major functions of the large intestine, and describe the regulation of defecation.

PHYSIOLOGY OF CHEMICAL DIGESTION AND ABSORPTION (pp. 830–837)

16. List the major enzymes or enzyme groups involved in chemical digestion; name the foodstuffs on which they act; and name the end products of protein, fat, carbohydrate, and nucleic acid digestion.

17. Describe the process of absorption of digested foodstuffs that occurs in the small intestine.

Developmental Aspects of the Digestive System (pp. 837–841)

18. Describe the embryonic development of the digestive system.

19. Describe important abnormalities of the gastrointestinal tract at different stages of life.

Children have a special fascination for the workings of the digestive system. They relish crunching a potato chip, delight in making "mustaches" with milk, and giggle when their stomach "growls." As adults, we know that a healthy digestive system is essential to maintaining life, for it converts foods into the raw materials that build and fuel our body's cells. Specifically, the digestive system takes in food, breaks it down into nutrient molecules, absorbs these molecules into the bloodstream, and then rids the body of the indigestible remains.

? *Knowing that the accessory organs do not actually help form the digestive tube (alimentary canal), which of the organs shown are the* accessory digestive organs?

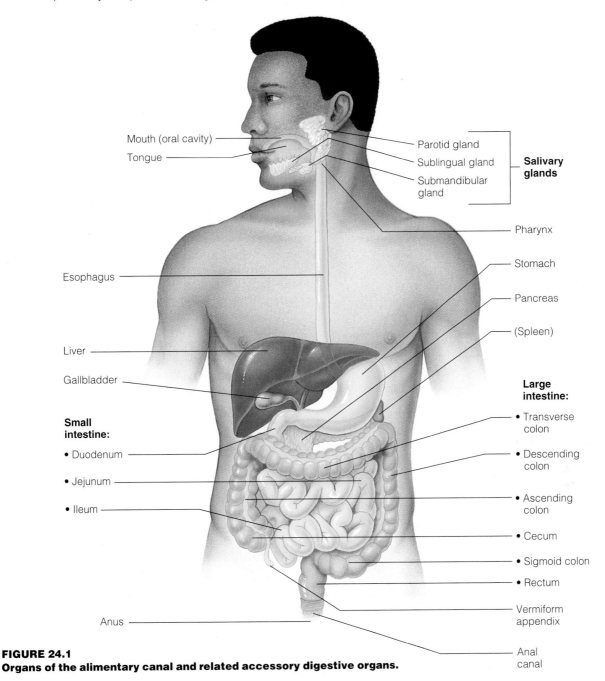

FIGURE 24.1
Organs of the alimentary canal and related accessory digestive organs.

OVERVIEW OF THE DIGESTIVE SYSTEM

The organs of the digestive system (Figure 24.1) can be separated into two main groups: (1) those of the *alimentary* (al″ĭ-men′tar-e; *aliment* = nourish) *canal* and (2) the *accessory digestive organs.*

The **alimentary canal,** also called the **gastrointestinal (GI) tract,** is the continuous, muscular diges- tive tube that winds through the ventral body cavity and is open at both ends. It **digests** food—breaks it down into smaller fragments (*digest* = dissolved)— and **absorbs** the digested fragments through its lining into the blood. The organs of the alimentary canal are the *mouth, pharynx, esophagus, stomach, small intestine,* and *large intestine.* The large intestine leads to the terminal opening, or *anus.* In a cadaver, the alimentary canal is approximately 9 m (about 30

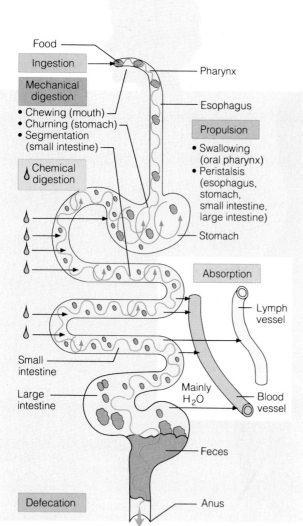

FIGURE 24.2
Schematic summary of gastrointestinal tract activities.
Gastrointestinal tract activities include ingestion, mechanical digestion, chemical (enzymatic) digestion, propulsion, absorption, and defecation. Sites of chemical digestion are also sites that produce enzymes or that receive enzymes or other secretions made by accessory organs outside the alimentary canal. The mucosa of the GI tract secretes mucus, which protects and lubricates.

feet) long, but in a living person, it is considerably shorter because of its relatively constant muscle tone. Food material within this tube is technically outside the body, because the canal is open to the external environment at both ends.

The **accessory digestive** organs are the *teeth, tongue, gallbladder,* and a number of large digestive glands—the *salivary glands, liver,* and *pancreas.* The teeth and tongue are in the mouth, or oral cavity, while the digestive glands and gallbladder lie outside the GI tract and connect to it by ducts. The accessory digestive glands produce saliva, bile, and digestive enzymes—secretions that contribute to the breakdown of foodstuffs.

Digestive Processes

The digestive tract can be viewed as a "disassembly line" in which food becomes less complex at each step of processing and its nutrients become available to the body. Although this processing is often summarized in two words—*digestion* and *absorption*—many activities, such as smooth muscle contraction, secretion, and regulatory events, are not really covered by either term. Thus, to describe digestive system processes more completely, we must consider six essential activities: ingestion, propulsion, mechanical digestion, chemical digestion, absorption, and defecation (Figure 24.2).

1. **Ingestion** is simply the process of taking food into the digestive tract, usually via the mouth.

2. **Propulsion** is the process that moves food through the alimentary canal. It includes *swallowing,* which is initiated voluntarily, and *peristalsis* (per"ĭ-stal'sis), an involuntary process. **Peristalsis** (*peri* = around; *stalsis* = constriction), the major means of propulsion, involves alternate waves of contraction and relaxation of muscles in the organ walls (Figure 24.3a). Its net

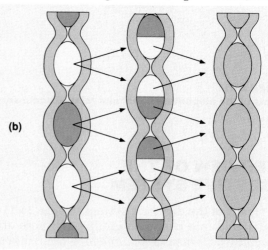

(b)

FIGURE 24.3
Peristalsis and segmentation.
(a) In peristalsis, adjacent segments of the intestine (or other alimentary tract organs) alternately contract and relax, which results in movement of food along the tract distally. **(b)** In segmentation, nonadjacent segments of the intestine alternately contract and relax. Because the active segments are separated by inactive regions, the food is moved forward and then backward. This results in mixing of the food, rather than food propulsion.

effect is to squeeze food along the pathway from one organ to the next, but some mixing occurs as well. From the time food enters the pharynx, its movement is completely reflexive. In fact, the peristaltic waves are so powerful that food and fluids will reach your stomach even if you stand on your head.

3. **Mechanical digestion** physically prepares food for chemical digestion by enzymes. Mechanical processes include chewing, mixing of food with saliva by the tongue, churning food in the stomach, and **segmentation,** or rhythmic local constrictions of the intestine (Figure 24.3b). Segmentation mixes food with digestive juices and increases the rate of absorption by repeatedly moving different parts of the food mass over the intestinal wall.

4. **Chemical digestion** is a series of catabolic steps in which large food molecules are broken down to their monomers (chemical building blocks), which are small enough to be absorbed by the GI tract lining. Chemical digestion is accomplished by enzymes secreted by various glands into the lumen of the alimentary canal. The enzymatic breakdown of food-stuffs begins in the mouth and is essentially complete in the small intestine.

5. **Absorption** is the passage of digested end products (plus vitamins, minerals, and water) from the GI tract lumen to the blood or lymph. For absorption to occur, these substances must first enter the mucosal cells by active or passive transport processes. The small intestine is the major absorptive site.

6. **Defecation** is the elimination of indigestible substances from the body via the anus in the form of feces.

Some of these processes are the job of a single organ. For example, only the mouth ingests and only the large intestine defecates. But most digestive system activities require the cooperation of several organs and occur bit by bit as food moves along the tract. Later, when we discuss the functioning of each GI tract organ, we will consider which of these specific processes it performs (Table 24.2 on p. 812 provides a summary of this information), as well as the neural or hormonal factors that regulate and integrate these processes.

Basic Functional Concepts

A theme stressed throughout this book has been the body's efforts to maintain the constancy of its internal environment, particularly of the blood. Most organ systems respond to changes in that environment either by attempting to restore some plasma variable to its former levels or by changing their own function. The digestive system, however, creates an optimal environment for its functioning in the lumen (cavity) of the GI tract, an area that is actually *outside* the body, and essentially all digestive tract regulatory mechanisms act to control luminal conditions so that digestion and absorption can occur there as effectively as possible.

1. **Digestive activity is provoked by a range of mechanical and chemical stimuli.** Sensors (mechanoreceptors and chemoreceptors of various types) involved in controls of GI tract activity are located in the walls of the tract organs (Figure 24.4). These sensors respond to several stimuli, the most important

FIGURE 24.4
Schematic of the long and short neural reflex pathways initiated by stimuli in the gastrointestinal tract.

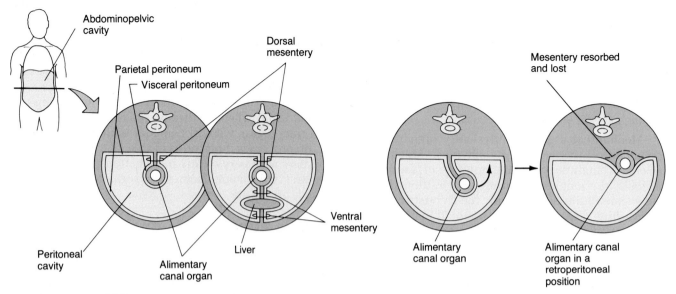

(a) Transverse section of abdominal cavity

(b) Some organs become retroperitoneal

FIGURE 24.5

The peritoneum and the peritoneal cavity. (a) Simplified cross sections through the abdominal cavity showing the relative locations of the visceral and parietal peritoneums, and dorsal (left) and ventral (right) mesenteries. Note that the peritoneal cavity is much smaller than depicted here, as it is nearly filled by the organs within it. **(b)** Some alimentary canal organs lose their mesentery during development and become retroperitoneal.

being stretch of the organ wall by food in the lumen, osmolarity (solute concentration) and pH of the contents, and the presence of substrates and end products of digestion. When activated by appropriate stimuli, these receptors initiate reflexes that activate or inhibit effectors that secrete digestive juices into the lumen or hormones into the blood (glandular cells) or mix lumen contents and move them along the length of the tract (smooth muscle of the GI tract walls).

2. Controls of digestive activity are both extrinsic and intrinsic. Another novel trait of the digestive tract is that many of its controlling systems are themselves intrinsic—a product of "in-house" nerve plexuses or local hormone-producing cells. As described shortly, the wall of the alimentary canal contains two nerve plexuses. These plexuses extend essentially the entire length of the GI tract and influence each other both in the same and in different digestive organs. As a result, two kinds of reflex activity occur, short and long. *Short reflexes* are mediated entirely by the local *(enteric)* plexuses in response to GI tract stimuli. *Long reflexes* are initiated by stimuli arising within or outside the GI tract and involve CNS centers and extrinsic autonomic nerves (Figure 24.4).

The stomach and small intestine also contain hormone-producing cells that, when stimulated by local chemical factors, nerve fibers, or local stretch, release their products to the extracellular space. These hormones circulate in the blood and are distributed to their target cells within the same or different digestive tract organs, which they prod into secretory or contractile activity.

Digestive System Organs: Relationship and Structural Plan

Relationship of the Digestive Organs to the Peritoneum

Most digestive system organs reside in the abdominopelvic cavity, the largest of our ventral body cavities. As described in Chapter 1, all ventral body cavities contain slick, friction-reducing *serous membranes.* The **peritoneum** of the abdominopelvic cavity is the most extensive of these membranes (Figure 24.5a). The **visceral peritoneum** covers the external surfaces of most digestive organs and is continuous with the **parietal peritoneum** that lines the walls of the abdominopelvic cavity. Between the two peritoneums is the **peritoneal cavity,** a slitlike potential space containing fluid secreted by the serous membranes. The serous fluid lubricates the mobile digestive organs, allowing them to glide easily across one another as they carry out their digestive activities.

Connecting the visceral and parietal peritoneums is a fused double layer of parietal peritoneum, called a **mesentery** (mes'en-ter"e). Mesenteries provide routes for blood vessels, lymphatics, and nerves to reach the digestive viscera. They also hold organs in place and store fat. In most places the mesentery is *dorsal* and attaches to the posterior abdominal wall, but there are examples of *ventral* mesenteries as well (Figure 24.5a). Some of the mesenteries, or peritoneal folds, are given specific names (such as the *omenta*). These are described more completely later on.

Most, but not all, alimentary canal organs lie within the peritoneal cavity. For example, some parts of the small intestine originate in the cavity but then adhere to the dorsal abdominal wall (Figure 24.5b). As this occurs, they lose their mesentery and come to lie posterior to the peritoneum. These organs, which also include most of the pancreas and parts of the large intestine, are called **retroperitoneal** (*retro* = behind) **organs.** By contrast, organs that hang suspended by a mesentery in the peritoneal cavity are called **intraperitoneal** or **peritoneal organs.** It is not known why some digestive organs end up in the retroperitoneal position, while others are suspended freely. One explanation is that anchoring various segments of the alimentary canal to the posterior abdominal wall minimizes the chances that this long tube will twist or kink during peristaltic movements. (Kinking and obstruction of the tract lead to tissue necrosis and death.)

Peritonitis, or inflammation of the peritoneum, may occur when one suffers a piercing wound of the abdomen, a perforating ulcer (that leaks stomach juices into the peritoneal cavity), or a burst appendix (that sprays bacteria-containing feces all over the peritoneum). In peritonitis, the peritoneal coverings tend to stick together around the infection site. This localizes the infection and provides time for macrophages to mount the attack to prevent the inflammation from spreading. If peritonitis becomes *generalized* (widespread within the peritoneal cavity), it is dangerous and often lethal. Treatment includes removing as much "infectious debris" as possible from the peritoneal cavity and administering "megadoses" of antibiotics. •

Blood Supply

The **splanchnic circulation** includes those arteries that branch off the abdominal aorta to serve the digestive organs and the *hepatic portal circulation.* The arterial supply—i.e., the hepatic, splenic, and left gastric branches of the celiac trunk that serve the spleen, liver, and stomach, and the mesenteric arteries (superior and inferior) that serve the small and large intestines (see Table 20.6, p. 678)—normally receives one-quarter of the cardiac output. This percentage (blood volume) increases after a meal has been eaten. The hepatic portal circulation (described on pp. 688 to 689) collects nutrient-rich venous blood draining from the digestive viscera and delivers it to the liver. The liver collects the absorbed nutrients for metabolic processing or for storage before releasing them back to the bloodstream for general cellular use.

Histology of the Alimentary Canal

Most digestive organs only have a "share" in the common work of digestion. Consequently, it helps to con-

sider structural characteristics that promote similar functions in virtually all parts of the alimentary canal before we attempt to describe the functional anatomy of the digestive system in a cohesive way.

From the esophagus to the anal canal, the walls of every organ of the alimentary canal are made up of the same four basic layers, or *tunics* (Figure 24.6). From the lumen outward, these layers are the *mucosa, submucosa, muscularis externa,* and *serosa* (or *adventitia*). Each layer contains a predominant tissue type that plays a specific role in food breakdown.

The Mucosa.   The **mucosa,** or **mucous membrane,** is a moist epithelial membrane that lines the lumen of the alimentary canal from the mouth to the anus. Its major functions are (1) *secretion* of mucus, digestive enzymes, and hormones, (2) *absorption* of the end products of digestion into the blood, and (3) *protection* against infectious disease. The mucosa in a particular region of the GI tract may express one or all three of these capabilities.

The mucosa consists of three sub-layers: (1) a surface epithelium, (2) a lamina propria, and (3) a deep muscularis mucosae. Typically, the **epithelium** of the mucosa is a *simple columnar epithelium* that is rich in mucus-secreting *goblet cells.* The slippery mucus it produces protects certain digestive organs from being digested themselves by enzymes working within their cavities and eases food passage along the tract. In some digestive organs, such as the stomach and small intestine, the mucosa contains both enzyme-secreting and hormone-secreting cells. Thus, in such sites, the mucosa is a diffuse kind of endocrine organ as well as part of the digestive organ.

The **lamina propria** (*proprius* = one's own), which underlies the epithelium, is loose areolar connective tissue. Its capillaries nourish the epithelium and absorb digested nutrients. Its isolated lymph nodules, part of MALT, the mucosa-associated lymphatic tissue described on p. 704, are important in the defense against bacteria and other pathogens, which have rather free access to our digestive tract. Particularly large collections of lymph nodules occur at strategic locations, such as within the pharynx (as the tonsils) and in the appendix. External to the lamina propria is the **muscularis mucosae,** a scant layer of smooth muscle cells that produces local movements of the mucosa. In the small intestine, it throws the mucosa into a series of small folds that vastly increase its surface area.

The Submucosa.   The **submucosa,** just external to the mucosa, is a moderately dense connective tissue containing blood and lymphatic vessels, lymph nodules, nerve fibers, and a rich supply of elastic fibers. Its luxuriant vascular network supplies surrounding tissues of the GI tract wall.

Autonomic nerve fiber

Blood vessel

Mesentery

Lumen

Intrinsic gland in submucosa

Lymph nodule

Villi (in small intestine only)

Intrinsic nerve plexuses:
Myenteric nerve plexus
Submucosal nerve plexus

Mucosa:
Epithelium

Lamina propria

Muscularis mucosae

Submucosa

Muscularis externa:
Circular muscle layer

Longitudinal muscle layer

Serosa (visceral peritoneum)

Ducts from accessory glands (liver, pancreas and salivary glands)

Enteric neuron

Location of major blood and lymphatic vessels and submucosal nerve plexus

Myenteric nerve plexus

(a)

(b)

FIGURE 24.6
The basic structure of the wall of alimentary canal consists of four layers: the mucosa, submucosa, **muscularis externa, and serosa.** **(a)** Cross-sectional view with part of the wall removed to show the intrinsic nerve plexuses. **(b)** Schematic view of a portion of a cross section of the wall, indicating its major components and their arrangements.

The Muscularis Externa.

The **muscularis externa**, also simply called the **muscularis**, is responsible for segmentation and peristalsis; that is, it mixes and propels foodstuffs along the digestive tract. This thick muscular tunic typically has an inner *circular layer* and an outer *longitudinal layer* of smooth muscle cells. In several places along the GI tract, the circular layer thickens to form *sphincters* that act as valves to prevent backflow and control food passage from one organ to the next.

The Serosa.

The **serosa**, the protective outermost layer of the intraperitoneal organs, is the *visceral peritoneum.* It is formed of areolar connective tissue covered with *mesothelium,* a single layer of squamous epithelial cells.

In the esophagus, which is located in the thoracic instead of the abdominopelvic cavity, the serosa is replaced by an **adventitia** (ad″ven-tish′e-ah). The adventitia is an ordinary fibrous connective tissue that binds the esophagus to surrounding structures. Retroperitoneal organs have *both* a serosa (on the side facing the peritoneal cavity) and an adventitia (on the side abutting the dorsal body wall).

Enteric Nervous System of the Alimentary Canal

The alimentary canal has its own in-house nerve supply, staffed by the so-called **enteric** (*enter* = gut) **neurons**, which communicate widely with each other to regulate digestive system activity. These enteric neurons constitute the bulk of the two major *intrinsic nerve plexuses* within the walls of the alimentary canal: the submucosal and myenteric nerve plexuses (Figure 24.6).

The **submucosal nerve plexus** occupies the submucosa and chiefly regulates the activity of glands and smooth muscle in the mucosa tunic. The large **myenteric** (mi-en′ter-ik; "intestinal muscle") **nerve plexus** lies between the circular and longitudinal layers of smooth muscle of the muscularis externa. It provides the major nerve supply to the GI tract wall and controls GI tract mobility. Control of the patterns of segmentation and peristalsis is largely automatic, involving local reflex arcs between enteric neurons in the same or different plexuses or (even) organs.

The enteric nervous system is linked to the central nervous system by afferent visceral fibers and by sympathetic and parasympathetic branches (motor fibers) of the autonomic nervous system that enter the intestinal wall and synapse with neurons in both plexuses. Thus, as mentioned earlier, digestive activity is also susceptible to extrinsic controls exerted by autonomic fibers via long reflex arcs. Generally speaking, parasympathetic inputs enhance secretory activity and mobility, whereas sympathetic impulses inhibit digestive activities.

FUNCTIONAL ANATOMY OF THE DIGESTIVE SYSTEM

Now that we have summarized some points that unify functioning digestive system organs and have surveyed their common "anatomical landscape," we are ready to consider the special structural and functional capabilities of each organ of this system. Most of the digestive organs are shown in their normal body positions in Figure 24.1, so you will probably find it helpful to refer back to that illustration as you study the following sections.

THE MOUTH, PHARYNX, AND ESOPHAGUS

The mouth is the only part of the alimentary canal involved in ingestion or food entry in the body. However, most digestive functions associated with the mouth reflect the activity of the related accessory organs, such as the teeth, salivary glands, and tongue, because within the mouth food is chewed, and mixed and moistened with saliva containing enzymes that begin the process of chemical digestion. The mouth also begins the propulsive process of swallowing, during which food is carried through the pharynx and esophagus to the stomach.

The Mouth

The **mouth,** a mucosa-lined cavity, is also called the **oral cavity,** or **buccal** (buk′al) **cavity.** Its boundaries are the lips anteriorly, the cheeks laterally, the palate

superiorly, and the tongue inferiorly (Figure 24.7). Its anterior opening is the *oral orifice.* Posteriorly, the oral cavity is continuous with the *oropharynx.* The walls of the mouth, which have to withstand considerable wear, are lined with a stratified squamous epithelium instead of the more typical simple columnar epithelium. The epithelium on the gums, hard palate, and dorsum of the tongue is slightly keratinized for extra protection against abrasion during eating.

The Lips and Cheeks

The **lips (labia)** and the **cheeks** have a core of skeletal muscle covered externally by skin. The *orbicularis oris muscle* forms the bulk of the fleshy lips. The cheeks are formed largely by the *buccinators.* The lips and the cheeks help keep food between the teeth when we chew and play a small role in speech. The recess bounded externally by the lips and cheeks and internally by the gums and teeth is called the **vestibule** ("porch"). The area that lies within the teeth and gums is the **oral cavity proper.**

The lips are much larger than most people think, because anatomically they extend from the inferior margin of the nose to the superior boundary of the chin. The reddened area where one applies lipstick or lands a kiss is called the **red margin.** This is a transitional zone where the highly keratinized skin meets the oral mucosa. The red margin is poorly keratinized and translucent, allowing the red color of blood in the underlying capillaries to show through. There are no sweat or sebaceous glands in the red margin, so it must be moistened with saliva periodically to prevent it from becoming dry and cracked (chapped lips). The **labial frenulum** (fren′u-lum) is a median fold that joins the internal aspect of each lip to the gum (Figure 24.7b).

The Palate

The **palate,** which forms the roof of the mouth, has two distinct parts: the hard palate anteriorly and the soft palate posteriorly (see Figure 24.7). The **hard palate** is underlain by bone (the palatine bones and the palatine processes of the maxillae), and it forms a rigid surface against which the tongue forces food during chewing. The mucosa on either side of its *raphe* (ra′fe), a midline ridge, is slightly corrugated, which helps to create friction.

The **soft palate** is a mobile fold formed mostly of skeletal muscle and lacks bony reinforcement. Projecting downward from its free edge is the fingerlike **uvula** (u′vu-lah). The soft palate rises reflexly to close off the nasopharynx when we swallow. (To demonstrate this action, try to breathe and swallow at the same time.) Laterally, the soft palate is anchored to the tongue by the **palatoglossal arches** and to the wall of the oropharynx by the more posterior **palatopharyngeal arches.** These two paired folds form the boundaries of the **fauces** (faw′sēz; *fauc* = throat), the arched area of the oropharynx that contains the palatine tonsils.

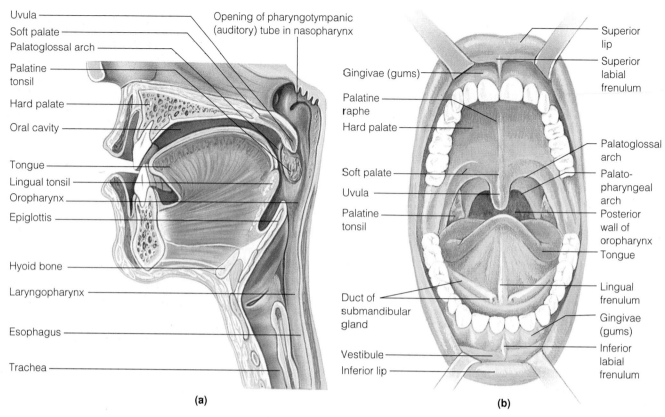

FIGURE 24.7
Anatomy of the oral cavity (mouth). **(a)** Sagittal section of the oral cavity and pharynx.
(b) Anterior view of the oral cavity.

The Tongue

The **tongue** occupies the floor of the mouth and fills most of the oral cavity when the mouth is closed (see Figure 24.7). Though it houses most of our taste buds and contains some mucous and serous glands, the tongue is mostly composed of interlacing masses of skeletal muscle fibers. During chewing, the tongue grips the food and constantly repositions it between the teeth. Tongue movements also mix food with saliva and form it into a compact mass called a **bolus** (bo′lus; "a lump"), and then initiate swallowing. During speech, the versatile tongue helps us form consonants (k, d, t, etc.).

The tongue has both intrinsic and extrinsic skeletal muscle fibers. The **intrinsic muscles** are confined within the tongue and are not attached to bone. Their muscle fibers, which run in all three planes (longitudinal, transverse, and vertical), allow the tongue to change its shape (but not its position), becoming thicker, thinner, longer, or shorter as needed for speech and swallowing. The **extrinsic muscles** extend to the tongue from their points of origin on bones of the skull or the soft palate, as described in Chapter 10 (see Table 10.2 and Figure 10.7). The extrinsic muscles alter the tongue's position. They protrude and retract the tongue, and move it from side to side. The

tongue is divided by a median septum of connective tissue, and each half contains identical groups of muscles.

A fold of mucosa, called the **lingual frenulum,** secures the tongue to the floor of the mouth (see Figure 24.7b). This frenulum also limits posterior movements of the tongue.

Children born with an extremely short lingual frenulum are often referred to as "tongue-tied" because of speech distortions that result when movement of the tongue is restricted. This congenital condition, called *ankyloglossia* ("fused tongue"), is corrected surgically by cutting the frenulum. •

The superior tongue surface bears *papillae,* peglike projections of the underlying mucosa. The three types of papillae—filiform, fungiform, and circumvallate—are shown in Figure 24.8. The **filiform papillae** are conical and give the tongue surface a roughness that aids in licking semisolid foods (such as ice cream) and provide friction for manipulating foods in the mouth. These papillae, the smallest and most numerous type, align in parallel rows on the tongue dorsum. They contain keratin, which stiffens them and gives the tongue its whitish appearance.

The mushroom-shaped **fungiform papillae** are scattered widely over the tongue surface. Each has a vascular core that gives it a reddish hue. Ten to

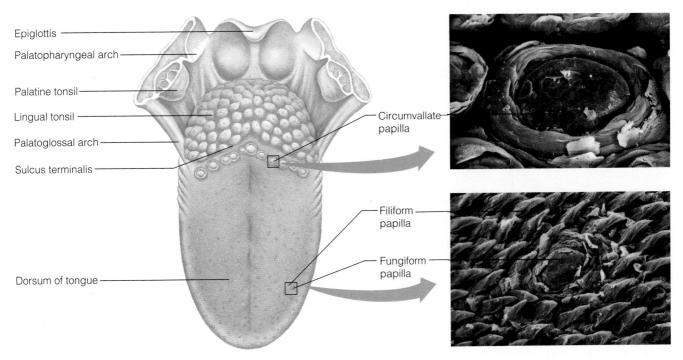

Epiglottis

Palatopharyngeal arch

Palatine tonsil

Lingual tonsil

Palatoglossal arch

Sulcus terminalis

Dorsum of tongue

Circumvallate papilla

Filiform papilla

Fungiform papilla

FIGURE 24.8
Surface view of the dorsal surface of the tongue. Also shown are the locations and detailed structures of the circumvallate, fungiform, and filiform papillae. The tonsils closely associated with the oral cavity are also illustrated. (Top right, 300×; bottom right, 140×.) From *Tissues and Organs* by R. G. Kessel and R. H. Kardon. ©1979 W. H. Freeman.

twelve large **circumvallate,** or **vallate, papillae** are located in a V-shaped row at the back of the tongue. They resemble the fungiform papillae but have an additional surrounding furrow. As described in Chapter 16, both the fungiform and circumvallate papillae house taste buds.

Immediately posterior to the circumvallate papillae is the **sulcus terminalis,** a groove that distinguishes the anterior two-thirds of the tongue that lies in the oral cavity from its posterior third residing in the oropharynx. The mucosa covering the posterior-most aspect and root of the tongue lacks papillae, but it is still bumpy because of the nodular *lingual tonsil,* which lies just deep to its mucosa (see Figure 24.8).

The Salivary Glands

A number of glands both inside and outside the oral cavity produce and secrete **saliva.** Saliva (1) cleanses the mouth, (2) dissolves food chemicals so that they can be tasted, (3) moistens food and aids in compacting it into a bolus, and (4) contains enzymes that begin the chemical breakdown of starchy foods.

Most saliva is produced by three pairs of **extrinsic salivary glands** that lie outside the oral cavity and empty their secretions into it. Their output is augmented slightly by small **intrinsic salivary glands,** also called **buccal glands,** scattered throughout the oral cavity mucosa.

The extrinsic salivary glands include the parotid, submandibular, and sublingual glands (Figure 24.9), paired compound tubuloalveolar glands that develop from the oral mucosa and remain connected to it by ducts. The large **parotid** (pah-rot′id; *par* = near, *otid* = the ear) **gland** lies anterior to the ear between the masseter muscle and the skin. The prominent **parotid duct** pierces the buccinator muscle and opens into the vestibule next to the second molar in the upper jaw. Branches of the facial nerve run through the parotid gland on their way to the muscles of facial expression.

Mumps, a common children's disease, is an inflammation of the parotid glands caused by the mumps virus *(myxovirus),* which spreads from person to person in saliva. If you check the location of the parotid glands in Figure 24.9a, you can readily understand why people with mumps complain that it hurts to open their mouth or chew. Besides the discomfort caused by the obvious enlargement of the parotid glands, other signs and symptoms of mumps are moderate fever, and pain when swallowing acid foods (sour pickles, grapefruit juice, etc.). Mumps viral infections in adult males carry a 25% risk that the testes may become infected as well, leading to sterility. •

The **submandibular gland** lies along the medial aspect of the mandibular body. Its duct runs beneath the mucosa of the oral cavity floor and opens at the

FIGURE 24.9

The major salivary glands. (a) The parotid, submandibular, and sublingual salivary glands associated with the left aspect of the oral cavity. **(b)** Photomicrograph of the sublingual salivary gland (75×), which is a mixed salivary gland consisting predominantly of mucus-producing cells (white) and a few serous-secreting units (purple). The serous cells sometimes form demilunes (caps) around the bases of the mucous cells.

base of the lingual frenulum (see also Figure 24.7). The small **sublingual gland** lies anterior to the submandibular gland under the tongue. It opens via many ducts into the floor of the mouth.

To a greater or lesser degree, the salivary glands are composed of two major types of secretory cells: mucous and serous. The **serous cells** produce a watery secretion containing enzymes and the ions of saliva, whereas the **mucous cells** produce **mucus,** a stringy, viscous solution. The parotid glands contain only serous cells. The submandibular and buccal glands contain approximately equal numbers of serous and mucous cells. The sublingual glands (see Figure 24.9b) contain mostly mucous cells.

Several of the substances found in saliva have important physiological functions. For instance, they may enhance the activity of its enzymes or protect the oral cavity. Hence, it is worthwhile to consider the composition of saliva in more detail.

Composition of Saliva

Saliva is largely water—97% to 99.5%—and therefore is hypo-osmotic. Its osmolarity depends on the precise glands that are active and the nature of the stimulus for salivation. As a rule, saliva is slightly acidic (pH 6.75 to 7.00) but its pH may vary. Its solutes include electrolytes (sodium, potassium, chloride, phosphate, and bicarbonate ions); the digestive enzyme salivary amylase; the proteins mucin (mu'sin), lysozyme, and IgA; and metabolic wastes (urea and uric acid). When dissolved in water, the glycoprotein *mucin* forms thick mucus that lubricates the oral cavity and hydrates foodstuffs. Protection against microorganisms is provided by (1) IgA antibodies, and (2) lysozyme, a bacteriostatic enzyme that inhibits bacterial growth in the mouth and may help to prevent tooth decay. Additionally, *growth factor,* found in the saliva of many animals, may aid in the healing of licked wounds and has recently been identified in human saliva.

Control of Salivation

The intrinsic salivary glands secrete saliva continuously in amounts just sufficient to keep the mouth moist. But when food enters the mouth, the extrinsic glands are activated and copious amounts of saliva pour out. The average output of saliva is 1000–1500 ml per day.

Salivation is controlled primarily by the parasympathetic division of the autonomic nervous system. When we ingest food, chemoreceptors and pressoreceptors in the mouth send signals to the **salivatory nuclei** in the brain stem (pons and medulla). As a result, parasympathetic nervous system activity increases and motor fibers in the *facial (VII)* and *glossopharyngeal (IX) nerves* trigger a dramatically increased output of watery (serous), enzyme-rich saliva. The chemoreceptors are activated most strongly by acidic substances such as vinegar and citrus juice. The pressoreceptors are activated by virtually any mechanical stimulus in the mouth—even rubber bands.

Sometimes just the sight or smell of food is enough to get the juices flowing. The mere thought of hot fudge sauce on peppermint stick ice cream will make many a mouth water! Irritation of the lower regions of the GI tract by bacterial toxins, spicy foods, or hyperacidity—particularly when accompanied by a feeling of nausea—also increases salivation. This response may help wash away or neutralize the irritants.

In contrast to parasympathetic controls, the sympathetic division causes release of a thick mucin-rich saliva. Extremely strong mobilization of the sympathetic division constricts blood vessels serving the salivary glands and almost completely inhibits the saliva release, causing the mouth to become dry. Dehydration also inhibits salivation because low blood volume results in reduced filtration pressure at capillary beds.

Any disease process that inhibits saliva secretion causes difficulty in talking, swallowing, and eating. Because decomposing food particles are allowed to accumulate and bacteria flourish, *halitosis* (hal″i-to′sis; "bad breath") results. •

The Teeth

The **teeth** lie in sockets (alveoli) in the gum-covered margins of the mandible and maxilla. The role of the teeth in food processing needs little introduction. We **masticate,** or chew, by opening and closing our jaws and moving them from side to side while continually using our tongue to move the food between our teeth. In the process, the teeth tear and grind the food, breaking it down into smaller fragments.

Dentition and the Dental Formula

Ordinarily, by age 21, two sets of teeth, the **primary** and **permanent dentitions,** have formed (Figure 24.10). The primary dentition consists of the **deciduous teeth** (*decid* = falling off), also called **milk** or **baby teeth.** The first teeth to appear, at about age six months, are the lower central incisors. Additional pairs of teeth erupt at one- to two-month intervals until about 24 months, when all 20 milk teeth have emerged.

As the deeper **permanent teeth** enlarge and develop, the roots of the milk teeth are resorbed from below, causing them to loosen and fall out between the ages of 6 and 12 years. Generally, all the teeth of the permanent dentition but the third molars have erupted by the end of adolescence. The third molars, also called the *wisdom* teeth, emerge later, between the ages of 17 and 25 years. There are usually 32 permanent teeth in a full set, but sometimes the wisdom teeth fail to erupt or are completely absent.

When a tooth remains embedded in the jawbone, it is said to be *impacted.* Impacted teeth can cause a good deal of pressure and pain and must be removed surgically. Wisdom teeth are most commonly impacted. •

FIGURE 24.10
Human deciduous and permanent teeth. Approximate time of tooth eruption is shown in parentheses. Since the same number and arrangement of teeth exist in both upper and lower jaws, only the lower jaw is shown in each case. The shapes of individual teeth are shown on the right.

Teeth are classified according to their shape and function as incisors, canines, premolars, and molars (see Figure 24.10). The chisel-shaped **incisors** are adapted for cutting. The conical or fanglike **canines** (eyeteeth) tear and pierce. The **premolars** (bicuspids) and **molars** have broad crowns with rounded cusps (tips) and are best suited for grinding or crushing. The molars (literally "millstones"), which have four or five cusps, are the best grinders. During chewing, the upper and lower molars repeatedly lock together, the cusps of the uppers fitting into valleys in the lowers, and vice versa. This action generates tremendous crushing forces.

The **dental formula** is a shorthand way of indicating the numbers and relative positions of the different types of teeth in the mouth. This formula is written as a ratio, uppers over lowers, for *one-half* of the mouth. Since the other side is a mirror image, the total dentition is obtained by multiplying the dental formula by 2. The primary dentition consists of two incisors (I), one canine (C), and two molars (M) on each side of each jaw, and its dental formula is written as

$$\frac{\text{2I, 1C, 2M (upper jaw)}}{\text{2I, 1C, 2M (lower jaw)}} \times 2 \quad \text{(20 teeth)}$$

Similarly, the permanent dentition (two incisors, one canine, two premolars[PM], and three molars) is

$$\frac{\text{2I, 1C, 2PM, 3M}}{\text{2I, 1C, 2PM, 3M}} \times 2 \quad \text{(32 teeth)}$$

Tooth Structure

Each tooth has two major regions: the crown and the root (Figure 24.11). The enamel-covered **crown** is the exposed part of the tooth above the **gingiva** (jin′jĭ-vah), or **gum,** which surrounds the tooth like a tight collar. **Enamel** is an acellular, brittle material that persists throughout (and after) life. It is heavily mineralized with calcium salts, and is the hardest substance in the body. The cells that produce the enamel degenerate at the time of tooth eruption, leaving none for repair purposes. Consequently, any breaches of the enamel caused by decay or cracks will not heal and must be artificially filled.

The portion of the tooth embedded in the jawbone is the **root.** Canine teeth, incisors, and premolars have one root, although the first upper premolars commonly have two. As for molars, the upper molars have three roots, while the lower molars have two. The crown and root are connected by a constricted tooth region called the **neck.** The outer surface of the root is covered by a calcified connective tissue called **cementum,** which attaches the tooth to the thin **periodontal** (per″e-o-don′tal; "around the tooth") **ligament.** This ligament anchors the tooth in place in the bony alveolus of the jaw, forming a fibrous joint called a *gomphosis* (see p. 225). Where the gingiva borders on a tooth, it dips downward to form a shallow groove called the *gingival sulcus.* In youth, the gingival margin adheres tenaciously to the enamel covering the crown. The gums begin to recede with age, and then the gingiva adheres to the more sensitive cementum covering the superior region of the root. As a result, the teeth *appear* to get longer in old age—hence the expression "long in the tooth" sometimes applied to elderly people.

Dentin, a bonelike material, underlies the enamel cap and forms the bulk of a tooth. It surrounds a central **pulp cavity,** which contains a number of soft tissue structures (connective tissue, blood vessels, and nerve fibers) collectively called **pulp.** Pulp supplies nutrients to the tooth tissues and provides for tooth sensation. Where the pulp cavity extends into the root, it becomes the **root canal.** At the proximal end of each root canal is an **apical foramen** that provides a route for blood vessels, nerves, and other structures to enter the pulp cavity of the tooth.

Dentin contains unique radial striations called *dentinal tubules* (Figure 24.11). Each tubule is filled with an elongated cellular process of an **odontoblast**

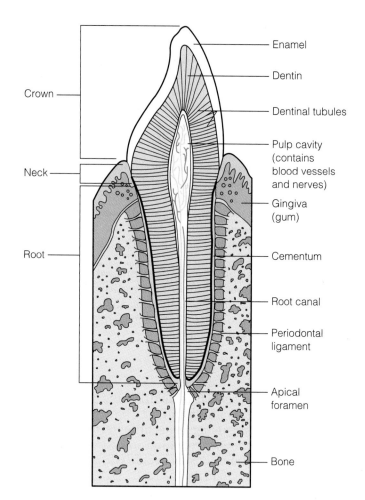

FIGURE 24.11
Longitudinal section of a canine tooth within its bony alveolus.

(o-don′to-blast; "tooth former"), the cell type that secretes and maintains the dentin. The spherical cell bodies of odontoblasts line the underlying pulp cavity just deep to the dentin. Dentin is formed throughout adult life and gradually encroaches on the pulp cavity. New dentin can also be laid down fairly rapidly to compensate for tooth damage or decay.

Death of a tooth's nerve and consequent darkening of the tooth is commonly caused by a blow to the jaw. Swelling in the local area pinches off the blood supply to the tooth and the nerve dies. Typically the pulp becomes infected by bacteria some time later and must be removed by *root canal therapy.* After the cavity is sterilized and filled with an inert material, the tooth is capped. •

Although enamel, dentin, and cementum are all calcified and resemble bone, they differ from bone in that they are avascular. Enamel also differs from cementum and dentin because it lacks collagen as its main organic component.

Tooth and Gum Disease

Dental caries (kār′ez; "rottenness"), or **cavities,** result from a gradual demineralization of enamel and underlying dentin by bacterial action. The decay process begins when **dental plaque** (a film of sugar, bacteria, and other mouth debris) adheres to the teeth. Metabolism of the trapped sugars by the bacteria produces acids (particularly lactic acid), which can dissolve the calcium salts of the teeth. Once the salts are leached out, the remaining organic matrix of the tooth is readily digested by protein-digesting enzymes released by the bacteria. Frequent brushing and flossing daily help prevent damage by removing forming plaque.

Even more serious than tooth decay is the effect of unremoved plaque on the gums. As dental plaque accumulates, it calcifies, forming **calculus** (kal′ku-lus; "stone"), or tartar. When this occurs in the gingival sulci, it can disrupt the seals between the gingivae and the teeth, putting the gums at risk for infection. In the early stages of such an infection, the gums become red, sore, and swollen and may bleed. This inflammatory condition is called *gingivitis* (jin″ji-vi′tis). Gingivitis is reversible if the calculus is removed, but if it is neglected the bacteria eventually invade the bone around the teeth, forming pockets of infection and dissolving the bone away. This more serious condition is called **periodontal disease,** or **periodontitis.** Periodontal disease affects up to 95% of all people over the age of 35 and accounts for 80% to 90% of tooth loss in adults. Still, tooth loss is not inevitable. Even advanced cases of periodontitis can be treated by scaling the teeth, cleaning the infected pockets, then cutting the gums to shrink the pockets, and antibiotic therapy. Together, these treatments alleviate the bacterial infestations and encourage reattachment of the surrounding tissues to the teeth and bone. Clinical treatment is followed up by a home regimen of plaque removal by consistent frequent brushing and flossing and saline or hydrogen peroxide rinses. •

The Pharynx

From the mouth, food passes posteriorly into the **oropharynx** and then the **laryngopharynx** (see Figure 24.7). Both of these are common passageways for food, fluids, and air. (The nasopharynx has no digestive role.)

The histology of the pharyngeal wall resembles that of the oral cavity. The mucosa contains a friction-resistant stratified squamous epithelium amply supplied with mucus-producing glands. The external muscle layer consists of two *skeletal muscle* layers. The cells of the inner layer run longitudinally. Those of the outer layer, the *pharyngeal constrictor muscles,* encircle the wall like three stacked fists (see Figure 10.8, p. 301). Alternating contractions of these muscles propel food into the esophagus below.

The Esophagus

The **esophagus** (ĕ-sof′ah-gus; "carry food"), a muscular tube about 25 cm (10 inches) long, is collapsed when not involved in food propulsion. After food is transported through the laryngopharynx, it is routed into the esophagus posteriorly as the epiglottis closes off the larynx to food entry.

As shown in Figure 24.1, the esophagus takes a fairly straight course through the mediastinum of the thorax and then pierces the diaphragm at the **esophageal hiatus** (hi-a′tus; "gap") to enter the abdomen. It joins the stomach at the **cardiac orifice.** The cardiac orifice (see Figure 24.13) is surrounded by the **cardiac,** or **gastroesophageal** (gas″tro-ĕsof″ah-je′al) **sphincter,** which is a *physiological* sphincter. That is, it acts as a valve, but the only structural evidence of this sphincter is a slight thickening of the circular smooth muscle at that point. The muscular diaphragm, which surrounds this sphincter, helps keep it closed when food is not being swallowed.

Unlike the mouth and pharynx, the esophagus wall has all four of the basic alimentary canal layers described on pp. 793–794. The following features are of interest:

1. The esophageal mucosa contains a nonkeratinized stratified squamous epithelium. At the esophagus-stomach junction, the abrasion-resistant epithelium changes abruptly to the simple columnar epithelium of the stomach, which is specialized for secretion (Figure 24.12b).

2. When the esophagus is empty, its mucosa and submucosa are thrown into longitudinal folds (Figure 24.12a), but when food is in transit, these folds flatten out.

3. The submucosa contains mucus-secreting *esophageal glands.* As a bolus moves through the esophagus, it compresses these glands, causing them to secrete lubricating mucus that "greases" the esophageal walls and aids food passage.

4. The muscularis externa is skeletal muscle in its superior third, a mixture of skeletal and smooth muscle in its middle third, and entirely smooth muscle in its inferior third.

5. Instead of a serosa, the esophagus has a fibrous adventitia composed entirely of connective tissue, which blends with surrounding structures along its route.

Heartburn is the burning, radiating substernal pain that occurs when gastric juice (which is extremely acidic) regurgitates into the esophagus. Symptoms are so similar to those of a heart attack that many first-time sufferers of heartburn are rushed to the hospital emergency room. Heartburn is most likely to happen when one has eaten or drunk to excess, and in conditions that force abdominal contents superiorly, such as extreme obesity and pregnancy. It is also

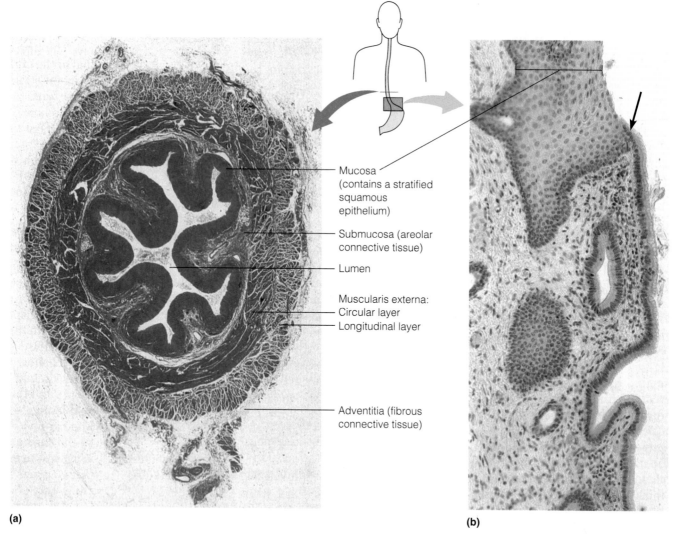

Mucosa (contains a stratified squamous epithelium)

Submucosa (areolar connective tissue)

Lumen

Muscularis externa:
Circular layer
Longitudinal layer

Adventitia (fibrous connective tissue)

(a)

(b)

FIGURE 24.12
Microscopic structure of the wall of the esophagus. (a) Cross-sectional view of the esophagus showing its four tunics (5×). The section shown is taken from the region close to the stomach junction, so the muscularis is composed of smooth muscle. (Superiorly, at the pharyngeal junction, the esophageal muscularis is composed of skeletal muscle.) **(b)** Longitudinal section through the esophagus-stomach junction (132×). Arrow shows the point of abrupt transition from the stratified squamous epithelium of the esophagus (top) to the simple columnar epithelium of the stomach (bottom).

common in those with a **hiatus hernia,** a structural abnormality in which the superior part of the stomach protrudes slightly above the diaphragm. Since the diaphragm no longer reinforces the cardiac sphincter, gastric juice may flow back into the esophagus, particularly when lying down. If the episodes are frequent and prolonged, *esophagitis* (inflammation of the esophagus) and *esophageal ulcers* may result. However, these consequences can usually be prevented or managed by avoiding late-night snacks and by using antacid preparations. •

Digestive Processes Occurring in the Mouth, Pharynx, and Esophagus

The mouth and its accessory digestive organs are involved in most digestive processes. The mouth ingests and, as described below, begins mechanical digestion by chewing and initiates propulsion by swallowing. Salivary amylase, the enzyme in saliva, starts the chemical breakdown of polysaccharides (starch and glycogen) into smaller fragments of linked glucose molecules. (If you chew a piece of bread for a few minutes, it will begin to taste sweet as sugars are released.) Except for a few drugs that are absorbed through the oral mucosa (for example, nitroglycerine), essentially no absorption occurs in the mouth.

In contrast to the multifunctional mouth, the pharynx and esophagus merely serve as conduits to pass food from the mouth to the stomach. Their single digestive function is food propulsion, accomplished by the role they play in swallowing.

Since chemical digestion is covered in a special physiology section later in the chapter, only the mechanical processes of chewing and swallowing need to be discussed here.

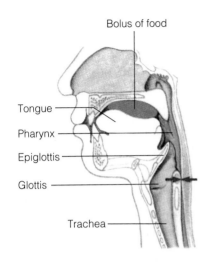

Bolus of food

Tongue

Pharynx

Epiglottis

Glottis

Trachea

Upper esophageal
sphincter contracted
(a)

Soft palate

Uvula

Epiglottis

Esophagus

Upper esophageal
sphincter relaxed
(b)

Upper esophageal
sphincter contracted
(c)

FIGURE 24.13
Deglutition (swallowing). The process
of swallowing consists of a voluntary
(buccal) phase **(a)** and involuntary
(pharyngeal-esophageal) phases **(b–e)**.
(a) During the buccal phase, the tongue
rises and presses against the hard palate; in
so doing, it forces the food bolus into the
oropharynx. Once food enters the pharynx,
the involuntary phase of swallowing begins.
(b) Food passage into respiratory
passageways is prevented by the rising of
the uvula and larynx; relaxation of the upper
esophageal sphincter allows food entry into
the esophagus. **(c)** The constrictor muscles
of the pharynx contract, forcing food into the
esophagus inferiorly, and the upper
esophageal sphincter contracts once food
entry has occurred. **(d)** Food is conducted
along the length of the esophagus to the
stomach by peristaltic waves. **(e)** The
gastroesophageal sphincter opens, and
food enters the stomach.

Relaxed muscles

Bolus of food

Circular muscles contract, constricting passageway and pushing bolus down

Longitudinal muscles contract, shortening passageway ahead of bolus

Gastroesophageal sphincter closed

Stomach

Relaxed muscles

Gastroesophageal sphincter open

(d)

(e)

Mastication (Chewing)

As food enters the mouth, its mechanical breakdown
is begun by **mastication,** or chewing. The cheeks and
closed lips hold the food between the teeth, the
tongue mixes the food with saliva to soften it, and the
teeth cut and grind solid foods into smaller morsels.
Mastication is partly voluntary and partly reflexive.
We initiate it by voluntarily putting food into our
mouths and contracting the muscles that close our
jaws. Continued jaw movements are controlled
mainly by stretch reflexes and in response to pressure
inputs from receptors in the cheeks, gums, and
tongue, but they can be voluntary as desired.

Deglutition (Swallowing)

To send food on its way from the mouth, it is first
compacted by the tongue into a bolus and then swallowed. **Deglutition** (deg″loo-tish′un), or swallowing,
is a complicated process that involves the coordi-

nated activity of the tongue, soft palate, pharynx,
esophagus, and over 22 separate muscle groups. It has
two major phases, the buccal and the pharyngeal-
esophageal (Figure 24.13).

The **buccal phase** occurs in the mouth and is voluntary. In the buccal phase, we place the tip of the
tongue against the hard palate, and then contract the
tongue to force the bolus into the oropharynx (Figure
24.13a). As food enters the pharynx and stimulates
tactile receptors there, it passes out of our control and
into the realm of involuntary reflex activity.

The involuntary **pharyngeal-esophageal phase** of
swallowing is controlled by the swallowing center
located in the medulla and lower pons. Motor
impulses from that center are transmitted via various
cranial nerves, most importantly the vagus nerves, to
the muscles of the pharynx and esophagus. As illustrated in Figure 24.13b, once food enters the pharynx,
all routes except the desired one—into the digestive
tract—are blocked off. The tongue blocks off the

?   *What structural modification of a tunic underlies the stomach's ability to* mechanically digest food?

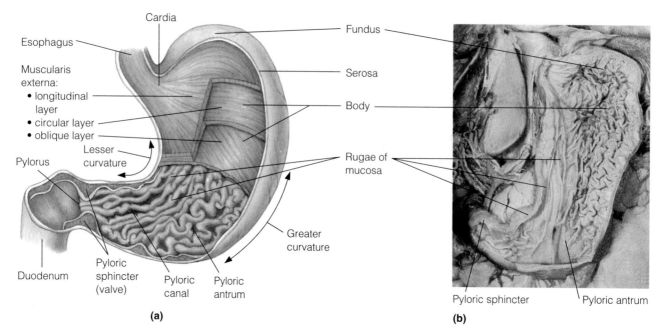

(a)   **(b)**

FIGURE 24.14
Anatomy of the stomach. (a) Gross internal anatomy (frontal section). **(b)** Photograph of internal aspect of stomach; notice the many rugae.

mouth, the soft palate rises to close off the nasopharynx, and the larynx rises so that the epiglottis covers its opening into the respiratory passageways.

Food is squeezed through the pharynx into the esophagus by wavelike peristaltic contractions (Figure 24.13c–e). The entire time for solid food passage from the oropharynx to the stomach is 4 to 8 seconds. Fluids pass within 1 to 2 seconds. Just before the peristaltic wave (and food) reaches the end of the esophagus, the gastroesophageal sphincter relaxes reflexively to allow food to enter the stomach.

If we try to talk or inhale while swallowing, the various protective mechanisms may be short-circuited and food may enter the respiratory passageways. This event typically triggers the coughing reflex in an attempt to expel the food. •

THE STOMACH

Below the esophagus, the GI tract expands to form the **stomach** (see Figure 24.1), a temporary "storage tank" where the chemical breakdown of proteins begins and food is converted to a creamy paste called **chyme** (kīm; "juice"). The stomach lies in the left side of the abdominal cavity, nearly hidden by the liver and diaphragm. Though relatively fixed at both (esophageal and small intestinal) ends, the stomach is quite movable in between. It tends to lie high and run horizontally in short, stout people (a steer-horn stomach) and is often elongated vertically in tall, thin people (a J-shaped stomach).

Gross Anatomy

The adult stomach is approximately 25 cm (10 inches) long, but its diameter and volume depend on how much food it contains. Although an empty stomach has a volume of about 50 ml, when it is really distended it can hold about 4 L (one gallon) of food and may extend nearly all the way to the pelvis! When empty, the stomach collapses inward, throwing its mucosa (and submucosa) into large, longitudinal folds called **rugae** (roo'ge; *ruga* = wrinkle, fold) (Figure 24.14).

The major regions of the stomach are shown in Figure 24.14a. The small **cardiac region,** or **cardia** ("near the heart"), surrounds the cardiac orifice, through which food enters the stomach from the esophagus. The **fundus** is the dome-shaped part of the stomach, tucked beneath the diaphragm, that bulges superolaterally to the cardia. The **body** is the midportion of the stomach. It is continuous inferiorly with the funnel-shaped **pyloric region.** The wider and more superior part of the pyloric region, the **pyloric antrum** (*antrum* = cave) narrows to form the **pyloric canal,** which terminates at the **pylorus.** The pylorus is continuous with the duodenum (the first part of the small intestine) through the **pyloric sphincter,** which controls stomach emptying (*pylorus* = gatekeeper).

The entire extent of the convex lateral surface of the stomach is its **greater curvature,** and its concave medial surface is the **lesser curvature** (Figure 24.14a).

FIGURE 24.15
Microscopic anatomy of the stomach. (a) Layers of stomach wall (longitudinal section).
(b) Enlarged view of gastric pits showing the locations of the HCl-producing parietal cells and the
pepsin-secreting chief cells.

Extending from these curvatures are two mesenteries, called *omenta* (o-men'tah), that help to "tether" the stomach to other digestive organs and the body wall (see Figure 24.23, p. 816). The **lesser omentum** runs from the liver to the lesser curvature of the stomach, where it becomes continuous with the visceral peritoneum covering the stomach. The **greater omentum** drapes inferiorly from the greater curvature of the stomach to cover the coils of the small intestine. It then runs dorsally and superiorly (enclosing the spleen on its way) to wrap the transverse portion of the large intestine before blending with the *mesocolon,* a dorsal mesentery that secures the large intestine to the parietal peritoneum of the posterior abdominal wall. The greater omentum is riddled with fat deposits (*oment* = fatty skin) that give it the appearance of a lacy apron covering and protecting the abdominal contents. It also contains large collections of lymph nodes. The immune cells and macrophages in these nodes "police" the peritoneal cavity and intraperitoneal organs.

The stomach is served by the autonomic nervous system. Sympathetic fibers from thoracic splanchnic nerves are relayed through the celiac plexus. Parasympathetic fibers are provided by the vagus nerve. The arterial supply of the stomach is provided by branches (gastric and splenic) of the celiac trunk (see Figure 20.20, p. 678). The corresponding veins are part of the hepatic portal system (see Figure 20.25, p. 688) and ultimately drain into the hepatic portal vein.

Microscopic Anatomy

The stomach wall exhibits the four tunics typical of most of the alimentary canal, but its muscularis and mucosa are modified for the special roles of the stomach. Besides the usual circular and longitudinal layers of smooth muscle, the muscularis externa has an innermost smooth muscle layer that runs *obliquely* (Figure 24.14a and Figure 24.15). This arrangement allows the stomach not only to move food along the tract, but also to churn, mix, and pummel the food, physically breaking it down into smaller fragments.

The lining (surface) epithelium of the stomach mucosa is a simple columnar epithelium composed entirely of goblet cells, which produce large amounts of protective mucus. This otherwise smooth lining is dotted with millions of deep **gastric pits** (Figure 24.15), which lead into the **gastric glands** that collectively produce the stomach secretion called **gastric juice.** The cells forming the walls of the gastric pits are generally like those of the lining mucosa, but those composing the gastric glands vary in different regions of the stomach. For example, the cells in the glands of the cardia are primarily mucus secreting, whereas cells of the pyloric antrum produce most of the stimulatory hormone called gastrin. The glands of the stomach body, where most chemical digestion occurs, are substantially larger and produce the majority of the stomach secretions. The glands in these regions contain a variety of secretory cells, including the four types described here:

1. **Mucous neck cells,** found in the upper, or "neck," regions of the glands, produce a different type of mucus from that secreted by the mucus-secreting cells of the surface epithelium. It is not yet understood what special function this mucus performs.

2. **Parietal (oxyntic) cells,** scattered among the chief cells (described next), secrete *hydrochloric acid (HCl)* and *intrinsic factor.* HCl makes the stomach contents extremely acidic (pH 1.5–3.5), a condition necessary for the activation and optimal activity of pepsin, and harsh enough to kill many of the bacteria ingested with foods. Intrinsic factor is a glycoprotein required for the absorption of vitamin B_{12} in the small intestine.

3. **Chief,** or **zymogenic** (zi″mo-jeh′nik), **cells** produce *pepsinogen* (pep-sin′o-jen), the inactive form of the protein-digesting enzyme **pepsin.** The chief cells occur mainly in the basal regions of the gastric glands. When the chief cells are stimulated, the first pepsinogen molecules they release are activated by HCl encountered in the apical region of the gland (Figure 24.15b). But, once pepsin is present, it also catalyzes the conversion of pepsinogen to pepsin. This positive feedback process is limited only by the amount of pepsinogen present. The activation process involves removal of a small peptide fragment from the pepsinogen molecule, causing it to change shape and expose its active site.

4. **Enteroendocrine** (en″ter-o-en′do-krin; "gut endocrine") **cells** release a variety of hormones or hormonelike products directly into the lamina propria. These products, including **gastrin, histamine, endorphins** (natural opiates), **serotonin, cholecystokinin,** and **somatostatin,** diffuse into the blood capillaries, and ultimately influence several digestive system target organs (Table 24.1). Gastrin, in particular, plays essential roles in regulating stomach secretion and mobility, as described shortly.

The stomach mucosa is exposed to some of the harshest conditions in the entire digestive tract. Gastric juice is corrosively acidic (the H^+ concentration in the stomach can be 100 thousand times that found in blood), and its protein-digesting enzymes can digest the stomach itself. However, the stomach is not a passive victim of its formidable environment. It mounts an agressive counterattack to protect itself, producing what is called the **mucosal barrier.** Three factors create this barrier: (1) A thick coating of alkaline mucus is built up on the stomach wall; (2) the

epithelial cells of the mucosa are joined together by tight junctions that prevent gastric juice from leaking into the underlying tissue layers; and (3) damaged epithelial mucosal cells are shed and quickly replaced by division of *undifferentiated stem cells* that "reside" where the gastric pits join the gastric glands. The epithelium of the stomach's luminal surface is completely renewed every three to six days.

Anything that breaches the gel-like mucosal barrier produces inflammation of the underlying layers of the stomach wall, a condition called *gastritis.* Persistent damage to the underlying tissues can promote **gastric ulcers,** erosions of the stomach wall. The most distressing symptom of gastric ulcers is gnawing epigastric pain. The pain typically occurs 1–3 hours after eating and is often relieved by eating again. The danger of ulcers whenever they occur is perforation of the organ wall followed by peritonitis and, perhaps, massive hemorrhage.

Common predisposing factors for ulcer formation include hypersecretion of hydrochloric acid and/or hyposecretion of mucus. Aspirin and nonsteroidal anti-inflammatory drugs (ibuprofen), smoking, alcohol, coffee, and stress appear to promote ulcer formation by influencing HCl or mucus production. However, recent studies provide convincing evidence that most recurrent ulcers are the work of acid-resistant corkscrew-shaped *Helicobacter pylori* bacteria, which attach to the epithelium and destroy the protective mucosal layer, leaving denuded areas. This theory has been difficult to prove because the bacterium is ubiquitous, found not only in some 70% to 90% of ulcer and gastritis sufferers, but in a substantial number (about 40%) of healthy people as well. Even more troubling are current studies that link this bacterium to certain types of stomach cancer. The theory is that a cytotoxin produced by the bacteria triggers an immune response, which can lead to cancerous growth in the stomach.

Gastric ulcers are no longer managed with diets rich in milk products, because although dairy products do neutralize stomach acid briefly, their high calcium and protein content actually stimulates HCl secretion. In ulcers found to be colonized by *Helicobacter,* the goal is to kill the embedded bacteria. Triple drug therapy (a combination of antibiotics, traditional antiulcer drugs, and bismuth [the active ingredient in Pepto-Bismol]) effectively promotes healing and prevents recurrence. In other cases, drugs that inhibit HCl secretion—H_2 blockers that block histamine's effects, such as cimetidine (Tagamet) and ranitidine (Zantac)—are the therapy of choice for treating gastric ulcers.

Digestive Processes Occurring in the Stomach

Except for ingestion and defecation, the stomach is involved in the whole spectrum of digestive activities. Besides serving as a "holding area" for ingested food, the stomach continues the demolition job begun

Table 24.1 Hormones and Hormonelike Products That Act in Digestion[*]

Hormone	Site of production	Stimulus for production	Target organ	Activity
Gastrin	Stomach mucosa	Food (particularly partially digested proteins) in stomach (chemical stimulation); acetylcholine released by nerve fibers	Stomach	• Causes gastric glands to increase secretory activity; most pronounced effect is on HCl secretion • Stimulates gastric emptying
			Small intestine	• Stimulates contraction of intestinal muscle
			Ileocecal valve	• Relaxes ileocecal valve
			Large intestine	• Stimulates mass movements
Serotonin	Stomach mucosa	Food in stomach	Stomach	• Causes contraction of stomach muscle
Histamine	Stomach mucosa	Food in stomach	Stomach	• Activates parietal cells to release HCl
Somatostatin	Stomach mucosa; duodenal mucosa	Food in stomach; stimulation by sympathetic nerve fibers	Stomach	• Inhibits gastric secretion of all products; inhibits gastric motility and emptying
			Pancreas	• Inhibits secretion
			Small intestine	• Inhibits GI blood flow; thus inhibits intestinal absorption
			Gallbladder	• Inhibits contraction and bile release
Intestinal gastrin	Duodenal mucosa	Acidic and partially digested foods in duodenum	Stomach	• Stimulates gastric glands and motility
Secretin	Duodenal mucosa	Acidic chyme (also partially digested proteins, fats, hypertonic or hypotonic fluids, or irritants in chyme)	Stomach	• Inhibits gastric gland secretion and gastric motility during gastric phase of secretion
			Pancreas	• Increases output of pancreatic juice rich in bicarbonate ions; potentiates CCK's action
			Liver	• Increases bile output
Cholecystokinin (CCK)	Duodenal mucosa	Fatty chyme, in particular, but also partially digested proteins	Liver/pancreas	• Potentiates secretin's actions on these organs
			Pancreas	• Increases output of enzyme-rich pancreatic juice
			Gallbladder	• Stimulates organ to contract and expel stored bile
			Hepatopancreatic sphincter (of Oddi)	• Relaxes to allow entry of bile and pancreatic juice into duodenum
Gastric inhibitory peptide (GIP)[†]	Duodenal mucosa	Fatty and/or glucose-containing chyme	Stomach	• Inhibits gastric gland secretion and gastric motility during gastric phase
Vasoactive intestinal peptide (VIP)	Duodenal mucosa	Chyme containing partially digested foods	Duodenum	• Stimulates buffer secretion; dilates intestinal capillaries
			Stomach	• Inhibits HCl production

[*]Except for somatostatin, all of these polypeptides also stimulate the growth (particularly of the mucosa) of the organs they affect.
[†]Also called gastric insulinotropic peptide because it stimulates the release of insulin from the pancreatic islets.

in the oral cavity by further degrading food both physically and chemically. It then delivers chyme, the product of its activity, into the small intestine at an appropriate rate.

Protein digestion is initiated in the stomach and is essentially the only type of enzymatic digestion that occurs there. The most important protein-digesting enzyme produced by the gastric mucosa is pepsin. In children, however, the stomach glands also secrete **rennin,** an enzyme that acts on milk protein (casein), converting it to a curdy substance that looks like soured milk. Two common lipid-soluble substances—alcohol and aspirin—pass easily through the stomach mucosa into the blood, but some other lipid-soluble drugs also pass. The movement of aspirin and large quantities of alcohol through the

? *What would be the effect of enhanced* sympathetic *activity on gastric secretory activity?*

FIGURE 24.16
Neural and hormonal mechanisms that regulate release of gastric juice.
Stimulatory factors are shown on the left; inhibitory factors are shown on the right.

gastric mucosa may cause gastric bleeding; thus, these substances should be avoided by those with gastric ulcers.

Depite the obvious benefits of preparing food to enter the intestine, the only stomach function essential to life is secretion of intrinsic factor. **Intrinsic factor** is required for intestinal absorption of vitamin B_{12}, needed to produce mature erythrocytes—in its absence, *pernicious anemia* results. However, if vitamin B_{12} is administered by injection, individuals can survive with minimal digestive problems even after total gastrectomy (stomach removal). (The stomach's activities are summarized in Table 24.2 on p. 812.)

Since chemical digestion and absorption are described later, we will complete our discussion of stomach digestive functions here by focusing on events that (1) control secretory activity of the gastric glands and (2) regulate stomach motility and emptying.

Regulation of Gastric Secretion

Gastric secretion is controlled by both neural and hormonal mechanisms, and under normal conditions the gastric mucosa pours out as much as 2 to 3 L of gastric juice each day. Nervous control is provided by long (vagus nerve–mediated) and short (local enteric) nerve reflexes. When the vagus nerves actively stimulate the stomach, secretory activity of virtually all of its glands increases. (By contrast, activation of sympathetic nerves depresses secretory activity.) Hormonal control of gastric secretion is largely the province of gastrin, which stimulates secretion of both enzymes and HCl, and hormones produced by the small intestine, which are mostly gastrin antagonists.

Stimuli acting at three distinct sites—the head, stomach, and small intestine—provoke or inhibit gastric secretory activity and, accordingly, the three phases of gastric secretion are called the *cephalic, gastric,* and *intestinal phases* (Figure 24.16). However, the effector site is the stomach in each case and, once initiated, one or all three phases may be occurring at the same time.

1. The cephalic (reflex) phase. The cephalic, or reflex, phase of gastric secretion occurs *before* food enters the stomach and is triggered by the aroma, taste, sight, or thought of food. During this phase, the brain gets the stomach ready for its upcoming digestive chore. Inputs from activated olfactory receptors and taste buds are relayed to the hypothalamus, which in turn stimulates the vagal nuclei of the medulla oblongata, causing motor impulses to be transmitted via the vagus nerves to the stomach glands. The enhanced secretory activity that results from the sight or thought of food is considered to be a *conditioned reflex* and occurs only when we like or want the food. If we are depressed or have no appetite, this part of the cephalic reflex is dampened.

2. The gastric phase. Once food reaches the stomach, local neural and hormonal mechanisms initiate the gastric phase. This phase provides about two-thirds of the gastric juice released. The most important stimuli are distension, peptides, and low acidity. Stomach distension activates stretch receptors and initiates both local (myenteric) reflexes and the long vagovagal reflexes. In the latter type of reflex, impulses travel to the medulla and then back to the stomach via vagal fibers. Both types of reflexes lead to acetylcholine (ACh) release, which in turn stimulates the output of more gastric juice by the secretory cells.

Though neural influences initiated by stomach distension are important, the hormone gastrin secreted in response to low acidity and peptides probably plays a greater role in stimulating stomach gland secretion during the gastric phase. Chemical stimuli provided by partially digested proteins, and caffeine (present in colas, coffee, and tea), directly activate gastrin-secreting entoendocrine cells called *G cells.* Gastrin, in turn, stimulates the gastric glands to spew out even more gastric juice. Although gastrin also stimulates the release of enzymes, its main target is the HCl-secreting parietal cells. Gastrin secretion is *inhibited* when the gastric contents become highly acidic (pH below 2).

When protein foods are in the stomach, the pH of the gastric contents generally rises because proteins act as buffers to tie up H^+. The rise in pH stimulates gastrin and subsequently HCl release, which in turn provides the acidic conditions needed for protein digestion. The more protein in the meal, the greater the amount of gastrin and HCl released. As proteins are digested, the gastric contents gradually become more acidic, which again inhibits the gastrin-secreting cells. This negative feedback mechanism helps maintain an optimal pH for the functioning of the gastric enzymes.

G cells are also activated by the neural reflexes already described. Emotional upsets, fear, anxiety, or

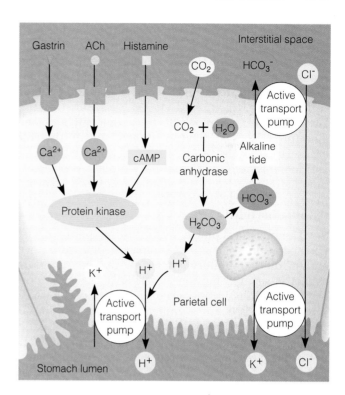

FIGURE 24.17

Regulation and mechanism of HCl secretion. Binding of histamine, gastrin, and acetylcholine (ACh) to parietal cell membrane receptors initiates intracellular events (mediated by second-messenger systems) that lead to HCl secretion into the stomach lumen. H^+ and HCO_3^- (bicarbonate ions) are generated from the dissociation of carbonic acid (H_2CO_3). As H^+ and Cl^- are pumped into the lumen, HCO_3^- is pumped into the interstitial space in exchange for chloride ions (Cl^-).

other states that trigger the fight-or-flight response inhibit gastric secretion, because (during such times) the sympathetic division overrides parasympathetic controls of digestion (Figure 24.16).

The control of the HCl-secreting parietal cells is unique and multifaceted. Basically, HCl secretion is stimulated by three chemicals, all of which work through second-messenger systems (Figure 24.17). ACh released by parasympathetic nerve fibers and *gastrin* secreted by G cells both bring about their effects by increasing intracellular Ca^{2+} levels. *Histamine,* released by mucosal cells called histaminocytes, acts through cyclic AMP (cAMP). When only one of the three chemicals binds to the parietal cells, HCl secretion is scanty, but when all three bind, volumes of HCl pour out. (Antihistamines, such as cimetidine, which bind to the H_2 receptors of parietal cells, are used with great success to treat gastric ulcers due to hyperacidity.) The process of HCl formation within the parietal cells is complicated and as yet poorly understood. Presently, the consensus is that H^+ is actively pumped into the stomach lumen against a tremendous concentration gradient. As hydrogen ions are secreted, chloride ions (Cl^-) are also pumped into the lumen to maintain an electrical balance in the stomach. The Cl$^-$ are obtained from blood plasma, while the H$^+$ appear to come from the breakdown of carbonic acid (formed by the combination of carbon dioxide and water) within the parietal cell, i.e.: $CO_2 + H_2O \rightarrow H_2CO_3 \rightarrow H^+ + HCO_3^-$ (Figure 24.17). As H$^+$ is pumped from the cell and the amount of HCO$_3^-$ (bicarbonate ion) within the cell becomes excessive, HCO$_3^-$ is ejected through the basal cell membrane into the capillary blood. As a result, blood draining from the stomach is more alkaline than the blood serving it; this phenomenon is called the **alkaline tide.**

3.   **The intestinal phase.** The intestinal phase of gastric secretion has two components—one excitatory and the other inhibitory (Figure 24.16). The *excitatory* aspect is set into motion as partially digested food begins to fill the initial part (duodenum) of the small intestine. This event stimulates intestinal mucosal cells to release a hormone that encourages the gastric glands to continue their secretory activity. The effects of this hormone mirror those of gastrin, so it has been named **intestinal (enteric) gastrin.** However, intestinal mechanisms stimulate gastric secretion only briefly. As the intestine distends with chyme containing large amounts of H$^+$, fats, partially digested proteins, and various irritating substances, the *inhibitory* component is triggered in the form of the **enterogastric reflex.**

The enterogastric reflex is actually a trio of reflexes that (1) inhibit the vagal nuclei in the medulla, (2) inhibit local reflexes, and (3) activate sympathetic fibers that cause the pyloric sphincter to tighten and prevent further food entry into the small intestine. As a result, gastric secretory activity declines. As described in more detail in the next section, these "brakes" on gastric activity protect the small intestine from harm due to excessive acidity and match the small intestine's processing abilities to the amount of chyme entering it at a given time.

In addition, the factors just named trigger the release of several intestinal hormones, collectively called **enterogastrones,** and including **secretin** (se-kre'tin), **cholecystokinin** (ko"le-sis"to-ki'nin) **(CCK), vasoactive intestinal peptide (VIP),** and **gastric inhibitory peptide (GIP).** All of these hormones inhibit gastric secretion when the stomach is very active. These hormones also play other roles, which are summarized in Table 24.1 (p. 807).

Gastric Motility and Emptying

Stomach contractions, accomplished by the trilayered muscularis, not only cause its emptying but also compress, knead, twist, and continually mix the food with gastric juice to produce chyme. Since the mixing movements are accomplished by a unique type of peristalsis (for example, in the pylorus it is bidirectional rather than unidirectional), the processes of mechanical digestion and propulsion are inseparable in the stomach.

Response of the Stomach to Filling.   Although the stomach stretches to accommodate incoming food, internal stomach pressure remains constant until about 1 L of food has been ingested. Thereafter, the pressure rises. The relatively unchanging pressure in a filling stomach reflects two phenomena: (1) reflex-mediated relaxation of the stomach musculature and (2) plasticity of visceral smooth muscle.

Reflexive relaxation of stomach smooth muscle in the fundus and body occurs both in anticipation of and in response to food entry into the stomach. While food is traveling through the esophagus after being swallowed, the stomach muscles relax. This **receptive relaxation** is coordinated by the swallowing center of the brain stem and mediated by the vagus nerves. The stomach also actively dilates in response to gastric filling, which activates stretch receptors in the wall. This phenomenon, called **adaptive relaxation,** is independent of extrinsic nerve influences and appears to depend on local reflexes involving *nitric oxide (NO) releasing neurons.*

Plasticity is the intrinsic ability of visceral smooth muscle to exhibit the stress-relaxation response, i.e., to be stretched without greatly increasing its tension and contracting expulsively. As described in Chapter 9 (p. 279), plasticity is very important in hollow organs, like the stomach, that must serve as temporary reservoirs.

Gastric Contractile Activity.   After a meal, peristalsis begins near the cardiac sphincter, where it produces only gentle rippling movements of the stomach wall. But, as the peristaltic contractions approach the pylorus, where the stomach musculature is thicker, they become much more powerful. Consequently, the contents of the fundus remain relatively undisturbed, while foodstuffs close to the pylorus receive a truly lively pummeling and mixing.

The pyloric region of the stomach, which holds about 30 ml of chyme, acts as a "dynamic filter" that allows only liquids and small particles to pass through the barely open pyloric valve during the digestive period. Normally, each peristaltic wave reaching the pyloric muscle "spits" or squirts 3 ml or less of chyme into the small intestine. Because the contraction also *closes* the valve, which is normally partially relaxed, the rest (about 27 ml) is propelled backward into the stomach, where it is mixed further (Figure 24.18). This back-and-forth pumping action effectively breaks up solids in the gastric contents.

Although the intensity of the stomach's peristaltic waves can be modified a good deal, their rate is constant—always around three/min. This contractile rhythm is set by the spontaneous activity of *pacemaker cells* located in the longitudinal smooth muscle layer in the stomach's greater curvature. The pacemaker cells depolarize and repolarize spontaneously three times each minute, establishing the so-called *slow-wave* electrical activity of the stomach, or its **basic electrical rhythm (BER).** Since the pacemakers

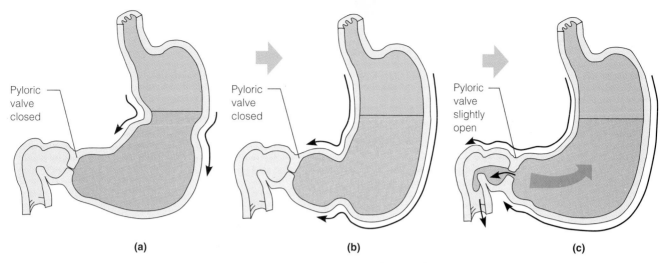

FIGURE 24.18
Peristaltic waves act primarily in the inferior portion of the stomach to mix and move chyme through the pyloric valve. **(a)** Peristaltic waves move toward the pylorus. **(b)** The most vigorous peristalsis and mixing action occurs close to the pylorus. **(c)** The pyloric end of the stomach acts as a pump that delivers small amounts of chyme into the duodenum, while simultaneously forcing most of its contained material backward into the stomach, where it undergoes further mixing.

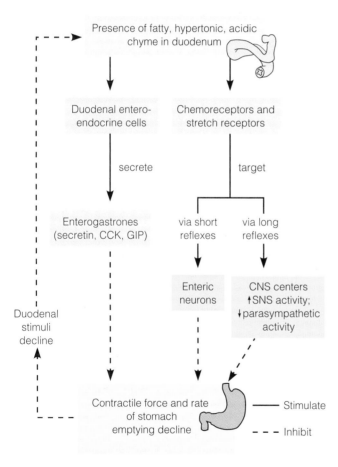

FIGURE 24.19
Neural and hormonal factors inhibiting gastric emptying. These controls ensure that the food will be well liquefied in the stomach and prevent the small intestine from being overwhelmed.

are electrically coupled to the rest of the smooth muscle sheet by gap junctions, their "beat" is transmitted efficiently and quickly to the entire muscularis. Although the pacemakers set the maximum rate of contraction, they do not initiate the contractions or regulate their force. Instead, they generate subthreshold depolarization waves, which are then "ignited" (enhanced by further depolarization and brought to threshold) by neural and hormonal factors.

Factors that increase the strength of stomach contractions are the same factors that enhance gastric secretory activity. Distension of the stomach wall by food activates stretch receptors and gastrin-secreting cells, which both ultimately stimulate gastric smooth muscle and so increase gastric motility. Thus, the more food there is in the stomach, the more vigorous the stomach mixing and emptying movements will be—within certain limits—as described next.

Regulation of Gastric Emptying. The stomach usually empties completely within 4 hours after a meal. However, the larger the meal (the greater its distension) and the more liquefied its contents, the faster the stomach empties. Fluids pass through the stomach very quickly. Solids linger, remaining until they are well mixed with gastric juice and converted to the liquid state.

The rate of gastric emptying depends as much—and perhaps more—on the contents of the duodenum as on what is happening in the stomach. The stomach and duodenum act in tandem like a "coupled meter" that functions at less than full capacity. As chyme enters the duodenum, receptors in its wall respond to chemical signals and to stretch, initiating the enterogastric reflex and the hormone (enterogastrone) mechanisms described earlier. These mechanisms inhibit gastric secretory activity and prevent further duodenal filling by reducing the vigor of pyloric contractions (Figure 24.19).

Table 24.2 Overview of the Functions of the Gastrointestinal Organs

Organ	Major functions	Comments/additional functions
Mouth and associated accessory organs	○ Ingestion: food is voluntarily placed into oral cavity ○ Propulsion: voluntary (buccal) phase of deglutition (swallowing) initiated by tongue; propels food into pharynx ● Mechanical digestion: mastication (chewing) by teeth and mixing movements by tongue ○ Chemical digestion: chemical breakdown of starch is begun by salivary amylase present in saliva produced by salivary glands	Mouth serves as a receptacle; most functions performed by associated accessory organs; mucus present in saliva helps dissolve foods so they can be tasted and moistens food so that tongue can compact it into a bolus that can be swallowed; oral cavity and teeth cleansed and lubricated by saliva
Pharynx and esophagus	○ Propulsion: peristaltic waves move food bolus to stomach, thus accomplishing involuntary (pharyngeal-esophageal) phase of deglutition	Primary food chutes; mucus produced helps to lubricate food passageways
Stomach	● Mechanical digestion and propulsion: peristaltic waves mix food with gastric juice and propel it into the duodenum ○ Chemical digestion: digestion of proteins begun by pepsin ○ Absorption: absorbs a few fat-soluble substances (aspirin, alcohol, some drugs)	Also serves as storage site for food until it can be moved into the duodenum; hydrochloric acid produced is a bacteriostatic agent and activates protein-digesting enzymes; mucus produced helps lubricate and protect stomach from self-digestion; intrinsic factor produced is required for intestinal absorption of vitamin B_{12}
Small intestine and associated accessory organs (liver, gallbladder, pancreas)	● Mechanical digestion and propulsion: segmentation by smooth muscle of the small intestine continually mixes contents with digestive juices and moves food along tract and through ileocecal valve at a slow rate, allowing sufficient time for digestion and absorption ○ Chemical digestion: digestive enzymes conveyed in from pancreas and brush border enzymes attached to villi membranes complete digestion of all classes of foods ○ Absorption: breakdown products of carbohydrate, protein, fat, and nucleic acid digestion; vitamins; electrolytes; and water are absorbed by active and passive mechanisms	Small intestine is highly modified for digestion and absorption (plicae circulares, villi, and microvilli); alkaline mucus produced by intestinal glands and bicarbonate-rich juice ducted in from pancreas help neutralize acidic chyme and provide proper environment for enzymatic activity; bile produced by liver emulsifies fats and enhances (1) fat digestion and (2) absorption of fatty acids, monoglycerides, cholesterol, phospholipids, and fat-soluble vitamins; gallbladder stores and concentrates bile; bile is released to small intestine in response to hormonal signals
Large intestine	○ Chemical digestion: some remaining food residues are digested by enteric bacteria (which also produce vitamin K and some B vitamins) ○ Absorption: absorbs most remaining water, electrolytes (largely NaCl), and vitamins produced by bacteria ● Propulsion: propels feces toward rectum by peristalsis, haustral churning, and mass movements ● Defecation: reflex triggered by rectal distension; eliminates feces from body	Temporarily stores and concentrates residues until defecation can occur; copious mucus produced by goblet cells eases passage of feces through colon

* The colored circles beside the functions correspond to the color coding of digestive functions illustrated in Figure 24.2.

A carbohydrate-rich meal moves through the duodenum rapidly, but fats form an oily layer at the top of the chyme and are digested more slowly by enzymes acting in the intestine. Thus, when chyme entering the duodenum is high in fats, food may remain in the stomach for 6 hours or more.

Vomiting, or **emesis,** is an unpleasant experience that causes stomach emptying by a different route. Many factors signal the stomach to "launch

lunch," but the most common are extreme stretching of the stomach or intestine or the presence of irritants such as bacterial toxins, excessive alcohol, spicy foods, and certain drugs in those organs. Sensory impulses from the irritated sites reach the **emetic** (e-met'ik) **center** of the medulla and initiate a number of motor responses. The skeletal muscles of the abdominal wall and diaphragm contract, increasing intra-abdominal pressure, the cardiac sphincter relaxes,

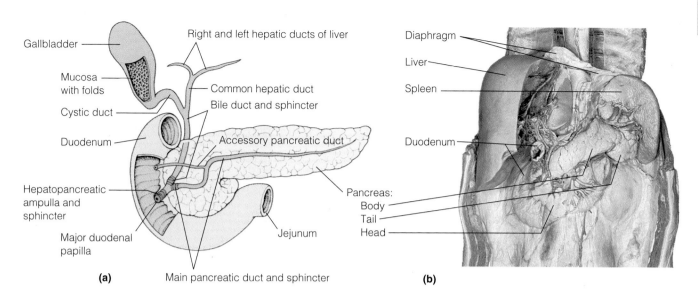

FIGURE 24.20
The duodenum of the small intestine, and related organs.
(a) Converging toward and emptying into the duodenum are various ducts from the pancreas, gallbladder, and liver. Except for the bile-carrying ducts, these structures lie inferior to the stomach.

(b) Photograph of duodenum, pancreas, and some adjacent organs in the posterior abdomen. (The stomach and much of the liver have been removed.)

and the soft palate rises to close off the nasal passages. As a result, the stomach (and perhaps duodenal) contents are forced upward through the esophagus and pharynx and out the mouth. Before vomiting, an individual typically is pale-faced, feels nauseated, and salivates. Excessive vomiting can lead to dehydration because water is lost that would normally be absorbed, and to severe disturbances in the electrolyte and acid-base balance of the body (see *A Closer Look* on p. 817). Since large amounts of hydrochloric acid are lost in vomitus, the blood becomes alkaline as the stomach attempts to replace its lost acid. •

THE SMALL INTESTINE AND ASSOCIATED STRUCTURES

In the small intestine, usable food is finally prepared for its journey into the cells of the body. However, this vital function cannot be accomplished without the aid of secretions from the liver (bile) and pancreas (digestive enzymes). Thus, these necessary organs will also be considered in this section.

The Small Intestine

The **small intestine** is the body's major digestive organ. Within its twisted passageways, digestion is completed and virtually all absorption occurs.

Gross Anatomy

The small intestine is a convoluted tube extending from the pyloric sphincter to the **ileocecal** (il″e-o-se′kal) **valve** where it joins the large intestine (see Figure 24.30, p. 827). It is the longest part of the alimentary tube, but its diameter is only about 2.5 cm (1 inch). Although it is 6 to 7 m (approximately 20 feet) long in a cadaver, the small intestine is only about 2 m (6 feet) long during life (because of muscle tone).

The small intestine has three subdivisions: the duodenum, which is mostly retroperitoneal, and the jejunum and ileum, both intraperitoneal organs. The relatively immovable **duodenum** (du″o-de′num; "twelve finger widths long"), which curves around the head of the pancreas (see Figure 24.20), is about 25 cm (10 inches) long. Although it is the shortest intestinal subdivision, the duodenum has the most features of interest. The ducts delivering bile and pancreatic juice from the liver and pancreas, respectively, unite close to the duodenum at a bulblike point called the **hepatopancreatic ampulla** (hep″ah-to-pan″kre-at′ik am-pul′ah; ampulla = flask). The ampulla opens into the duodenum via the volcano-shaped **major duodenal papilla** (see Figure 24.20). The entry of bile and pancreatic juice is controlled by a muscular valve called the **hepatopancreatic sphincter,** or **sphincter of Oddi.**

FIGURE 24.21
Structural modifications of the small intestine that increase its surface area for digestion and absorption.
(a) Enlargement of a few plicae circulares, showing associated fingerlike villi. (b) Diagrammatic view of the structure of a villus. (c) Two absorptive cells that exhibit microvilli on their free (luminal) surface. (d) Photomicrograph of the small intestinal mucosa, showing villi. A small portion of the submucosa containing duodenal glands is also shown (150×).

The **jejunum** (jĕ-joo'num; "empty") is about 2.5 m (8 feet) long and extends from the duodenum to the ileum. The **ileum** (il'e-um; "twisted") approximately 3.6 m (12 feet) in length, joins the large intestine at the ileocecal valve. The jejunum and ileum hang in sausagelike coils in the central and lower part of the abdominal cavity, suspended from the posterior abdominal wall by the fan-shaped **mesentery** (see Figure 24.23). These more distal parts of the small intestine are encircled and framed by the large intestine.

Nerve fibers serving the small intestine include parasympathetics from the vagus and sympathetics from the thoracic splanchnic nerves, both relayed through the superior mesenteric (and celiac) plexus. The arterial supply is primarily from the superior mesenteric artery (p. 678). The veins run parallel to the arteries and typically drain into the superior mesenteric vein. From there, the nutrient-rich venous blood from the small intestine drains into the hepatic portal vein (p. 688).

Microscopic Anatomy

Modifications for Absorption. The small intestine is highly adapted for nutrient absorption. Its length alone provides a huge surface area, and its wall has three structural modifications—*plicae circulares, villi,* and *microvilli*—that amplify its absorptive surface enormously. One estimate is that the intestinal surface area is about 200 m² (equal to the floor space of an average two-story house)! Most absorption occurs in the proximal part of the small intestine so these modifications decrease in number toward its distal end.

The **plicae circulares** (pli'ke ser"ku-lar'ēs), or **circular folds,** are deep, permanent folds of the mucosa and submucosa (Figure 24.21a). Nearly 1 cm tall, these folds force chyme to spiral through the lumen. This continually mixes the chyme with intestinal juice and slows its movement, allowing time for full nutrient absorption.

(a)

(b)

FIGURE 24.22
Scanning electron micrographs of the villi and microvilli of the small intestine. (a) Villi (VI), 90×. (b) Microvilli (MV) of absorptive cells. The larger globular bodies (above left and lower right) are mucus granules released by adjacent goblet cells (8545×). From *Tissues and Organs* by R. G. Kessel and R. H. Kardon. ©1979 W. H. Freeman.

Villi (vil'i) are fingerlike projections of the mucosa, over 1 mm high, that give it a velvety texture, much like the soft nap of a Turkish towel (Figures 24.21b and 24.22a). The epithelial cells of the villi are chiefly absorptive columnar cells. Within the lamina propria core of each villus are a dense capillary bed and a modified lymphatic capillary called a **lacteal** (lak'te-al). Digested foodstuffs are absorbed through the epithelial cells into both the capillary blood and the lacteal. The villi are large and leaflike in the duodenum (the intestinal site of most active absorption) and gradually become narrower and shorter along the length of the small intestine. Each villus contains a "slip" of smooth muscle in its core, which allows it to alternately shorten and lengthen. Such pulsations (1) increase the amount of contact between the villus surface and the "nutrient soup" contents of the intestinal lumen, making absorption more efficient, and (2) act to "milk" lymph along through the lacteals.

Microvilli, tiny projections of the plasma membrane of the absorptive cells of the mucosa, give the mucosal surface a fuzzy appearance sometimes called the **brush border** (Figures 24.21c and 24.22b). Besides amplifying the absorptive surface, the plasma membranes of the microvilli bear enzymes, referred to collectively as **brush border enzymes.** Brush border enzymes are mostly disaccharidases and peptidases, which complete the digestion of carbohydrates and proteins, respectively, in the small intestine.

Histology of the Wall. Although the external anatomy of the different subdivisions of the small intestine appears to be nearly identical, their internal and microscopic anatomies reveal some important differences. The four tunics typical of the GI tract are also seen here, but the mucosa and submucosa are modified to reflect the relative location of the intestine in the digestive pathway (see Figure 24.21b, d).

The epithelium of the mucosa is largely simple columnar *absorptive cells* bound by tight junctions and richly endowed with microvilli. It also has many mucus-secreting *goblet cells* and scattered *enteroendocrine cells* (the source of the enterogastrones).

Between the villi, the mucosa is studded with *pits* (openings) that lead into tubular intestinal glands called **intestinal crypts,** or **crypts of Lieberkühn** (le'ber-kyoon). The epithelial cells that line these crypts secrete *intestinal juice,* a watery mixture containing mucus that serves as a carrier fluid for absorption of nutrients from the chyme. Located deep in the crypts are specialized secretory cells called *Paneth cells.* These cells help to fortify the small intestine's defenses against certain bacteria by releasing *lysozyme,* an antibacterial enzyme. The crypts decrease in number along the length of the small intestine, but the goblet cells become more abundant.

The various epithelial cells apparently arise from stem cells at the base of the crypts and gradually migrate up the villi, where they are shed from the villus tips. In this way, the villus epithelium is renewed every three to six days. The rapid replacement of intestinal (and gastric) epithelial cells has clinical as well as physiological significance. Treatments for cancer, such as radiation therapy and chemotherapy,

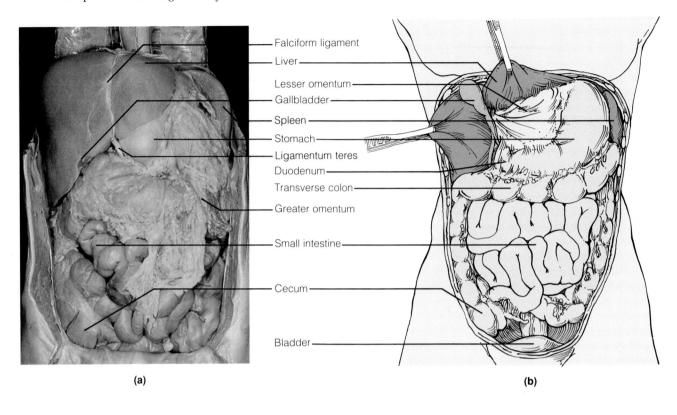

(a)

Falciform ligament
Liver
Lesser omentum
Gallbladder
Spleen
Stomach
Ligamentum teres
Duodenum
Transverse colon
Greater omentum
Small intestine
Cecum
Bladder

(b)

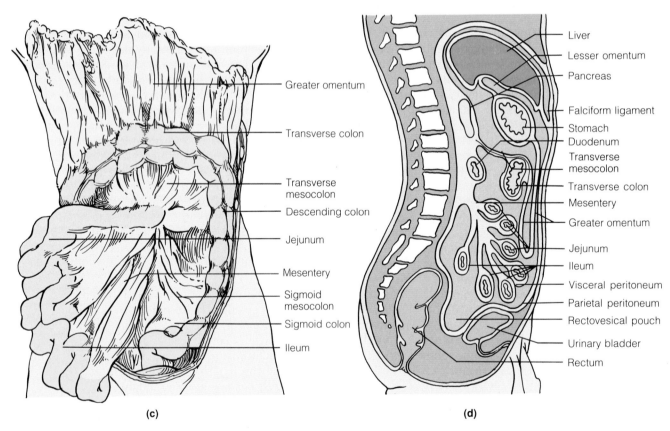

Greater omentum
Transverse colon
Transverse mesocolon
Descending colon
Jejunum
Mesentery
Sigmoid mesocolon
Sigmoid colon
Ileum

(c)

Liver
Lesser omentum
Pancreas
Falciform ligament
Stomach
Duodenum
Transverse mesocolon
Transverse colon
Mesentery
Greater omentum
Jejunum
Ileum
Visceral peritoneum
Parietal peritoneum
Rectovesical pouch
Urinary bladder
Rectum

(d)

FIGURE 24.23
Mesenteries of the abdominal digestive organs. (a) The greater omentum, a dorsal mesentery connecting the greater curvature of the stomach to the dorsal body wall, is shown in its normal position covering the abdominal viscera. **(b)** The lesser omentum, a ventral mesentery attaching the liver to the lesser curvature of the stomach (the liver and gallbladder have been reflected superiorly). **(c)** The greater omentum has been reflected superiorly to reveal the mesentery attachments of the small and large intestine. **(d)** Sagittal section of the abdominopelvic cavity of a male, showing the relationships of the peritoneal attachments.

A LOOK | The Paradox of Ox-Hunger

The more fortunate citizens of ancient Rome enjoyed an occasional orgy—a time of feasting and sexual merriment, interrupted only by purging (vomiting) to make room for still more gorging. *Bulimia* (bu-lim′e-ah), a modern version of binge-purge behavior, has become a daily affair for ever-increasing numbers of young Americans. The American abhorrence of obesity has produced both this eating disorder and another called anorexia nervosa. These disorders have affected primarily young women of high school and college age. Recently, however, high school males on the wrestling team, or frantic to get on it, have joined the ranks of anorexics and bulimics.

The better known of these two conditions, *anorexia nervosa* (an″o-rek′se-ah ner-vo′sa), is a self-induced wasting away in which patients frequently overexercise and refuse to eat anything at all. *Bulimia,* from the Greek meaning "ox-hunger," or insatiable hunger, is the other side of the same coin, although their symptoms are different. Both disorders are rooted in a pathological fear of becoming fat and a passionate need to control eating.

For some bulimics, food costs of $50- to $100-a-day are normal. As if starving, they eat huge amounts of food, often ingesting up to 55,000 calories in a single hour. Then, they induce vomiting. This paradoxical behavior may be repeated three to four times daily. Others take 200 or more laxatives each week to prevent their bodies from retaining the enormous amounts of food consumed. Surprisingly, the vast majority of bulimics have a normal body weight and look healthy. However, most are prone to such ailments as swollen salivary glands, pancreatitis, and liver and kidney problems. The constant vomiting damages both the stomach and the esophagus, and stomach acid flushing upward through the mouth severely erodes tooth enamel. In the

worst cases, bulimia kills. Purging empties the body of potassium and causes severe electrolyte disturbances, which places the heart at risk to fail. Stomach rupture may cause death from massive hemorrhage.

Although the disorder knows no race or class, bulimics are typically single, white women from affluent families who have had some college education. Despite obvious accomplishments, they have little self-regard and are scared of success or feel that they do not deserve it. Bulimics often have problems establishing their independence or personal growth within their families. Some researchers believe that eating helps to relieve the anger and frustration that evolve as these young people strive for perfection. The eating itself is associated with feelings of disgust. But the purging, which is under the complete control of the bulimic, is his or her "victory" over all obstacles and stressors. It provides relief from anxiety and disciplines and cleanses the body—in effect providing a new

beginning. The bonus is a slim figure that brings attention and approval.

Many bulimics exhibit symptoms of depression, and up to one-third have attempted suicide. In 6% of cases, bulimia so fills the person's life that all social contacts are shunned. Some authorities view bulimia as an obsessive-compulsive disorder (like compulsive handwashing); others consider it an addiction. The latter camp believes that bulimics use food, rather than alcohol or drugs, to regulate their tensions because they are "good girls or boys" and food abuse has no apparent moral or legal consequences. Recently, bulimia has been linked to deficient secretion of cholecystokinin, a gut-brain peptide that is secreted during eating and appears to play a role in satiety. Nonetheless, psychological factors still appear to be very important.

Eating disorders evolve slowly and become increasingly entrenched with time. They are not just attention-getting devices. In fact, bulimia victims tend to be secretive about their binges and most wait five years or more before seeking help. The seriousness of bulimia is all too often underestimated, and its treatment is notoriously difficult. Techniques that are often used simultaneously include (1) hospitalization (to control food intake or outgo or to isolate the patient from family), (2) behavior modification (learning to eat three meals daily), (3) education in nutrition, and (4) antidepressant drugs for severely depressed patients. The treatment is usually prolonged and, when hospitalization is involved, always expensive. Moreover, treatment succeeds only in suppressing the symptoms of bulimia rather than in curing it, and bulimics must fight the urge to resume their binge-purge behavior for the rest of their lives. Bulimia is not only a paradox, it is a nightmare of frustration and despair for those who suffer from it.

preferentially destroy the cells in the body that are dividing most quickly. This kills cancer cells, but it also nearly obliterates the GI tract epithelium, causing nausea, vomiting, and diarrhea after each such treatment.

The submucosa is typical areolar connective tissue, and it contains both individual and *aggregated* lymphoid nodules, the latter called **Peyer's** (pi'erz) **patches.** Peyer's patches increase in abundance toward the end of the small intestine, reflecting the fact that the large intestine contains huge numbers of bacteria that must be prevented from entering the bloodstream. A set of elaborated mucus-secreting **duodenal** *(Brunner's)* **glands** is found in the submucosa of the duodenum only. These glands (see Figure 24.21d) produce an alkaline (bicarbonate-rich) mucus that helps neutralize the acidic chyme moving in from the stomach. When this protective mucus barrier is inadequate, the intestinal wall is eroded and *duodenal ulcers* result.

The muscularis is typical and bilayered. Except for the bulk of the duodenum, which is retroperitoneal and has an adventitia, the external intestinal surface is covered by visceral peritoneum (serosa).

Intestinal Juice: Composition and Control

The intestinal glands normally secrete 1 to 2 L of **intestinal juice** daily. The major stimulus for its production is distension or irritation of the intestinal mucosa by hypertonic or acidic chyme. Normally, the pH range of intestinal juice is slightly alkaline (7.4–7.8), and it is isotonic with blood plasma. Intestinal juice is largely water but it also contains a good deal of mucus, which is secreted both by the duodenal glands and by goblet cells of the mucosa. Intestinal juice is relatively enzyme-poor because most intestinal enzymes are bound (brush border) enzymes.

The Liver and Gallbladder

The *liver* and *gallbladder* are accessory organs associated with the small intestine. The liver, one of the body's most important organs, has many metabolic and regulatory roles. However, its *digestive* function is to produce bile for export to the duodenum. Bile is a fat emulsifier; that is, it breaks up fats into tiny particles so that they are more accessible to digestive enzymes. We will describe bile and the emulsification process when we discuss the digestion and absorption of fats later in the chapter. Although the liver also processes nutrient-laden venous blood delivered to it from the digestive organs, this function concerns its metabolic rather than its digestive role. (The metabolic functions of the liver are described in Chapter 25.) The gallbladder is chiefly a storage organ for bile.

Gross Anatomy of the Liver

The ruddy, blood-rich **liver** is the largest gland in the body, weighing about 1.4 kg (3 pounds) in the average adult. It occupies most of the right hypochondriac and epigastric regions, extending farther to the right of the body midline than to the left. Located under the diaphragm, the liver lies almost entirely within the rib cage which provides some protection (see Figures 24.1 and 24.24c).

Typically, the liver is said to have four primary lobes. The largest of these, the *right lobe,* is visible on all liver surfaces and separated from the smaller *left lobe* by a deep fissure (Figure 24.24a). The posterior-most *caudate lobe* and the *quadrate lobe,* which lies inferior to the left lobe, are visible in an inferior view of the liver (Figure 24.24b). A mesentery, the **falciform ligament,** separates the right and left lobes and suspends the liver from the diaphragm and anterior abdominal wall (see also Figure 24.23a and d). Running along the free inferior edge of the falciform ligament is the **round ligament,** or **ligamentum teres** (te'rēz), a fibrous remnant of the fetal umbilical vein (Figures 24.24 and 24.23a). Except for the superior-most liver area (the *bare area*), which is fused to the diaphragm, the entire liver is enclosed by a serosa (the visceral peritoneum). As mentioned earlier, a dorsal mesentery, the lesser omentum (see Figure 24.23b), anchors the liver to the lesser curvature of the stomach. The **hepatic artery** and the **hepatic portal vein,** which enter the liver at the **porta hepatis** ("gateway to the liver") and the common bile duct, which runs inferiorly from the liver, all travel through the lesser omentum to reach their destinations. The gallbladder rests in a recess on the inferior surface of the right liver lobe (Figure 24.24).

The traditional scheme of defining the liver's lobes (outlined above) has been criticized because it is based on superficial features of the liver, such as the ligamentum teres and falciform ligament. Some anatomists emphasize that the primary lobes of the liver should be defined as the territories served by the right and left hepatic ducts. These two territories are delineated by a plane drawn from the indentation (sulcus) of the inferior vena cava to the gallbladder recess (see Figure 24.24b). Those to the right of the plane are the right lobe and those to its left constitute the left lobe. According to this scheme, the small quadrate and caudate lobes are part of the left lobe.

Bile leaves the liver through several bile ducts that ultimately fuse to form the large **common hepatic duct,** which travels downward toward the duodenum. Along its course, that duct fuses with the **cystic duct** draining the gallbladder to form the **bile duct** (Figure 24.20).

Microscopic Anatomy of the Liver

The liver is composed of sesame seed–sized structural and functional units called **liver lobules** (Figure 24.25). Each lobule is a roughly hexagonal (six-sided) structure consisting of plates of liver cells, or **hepato-**

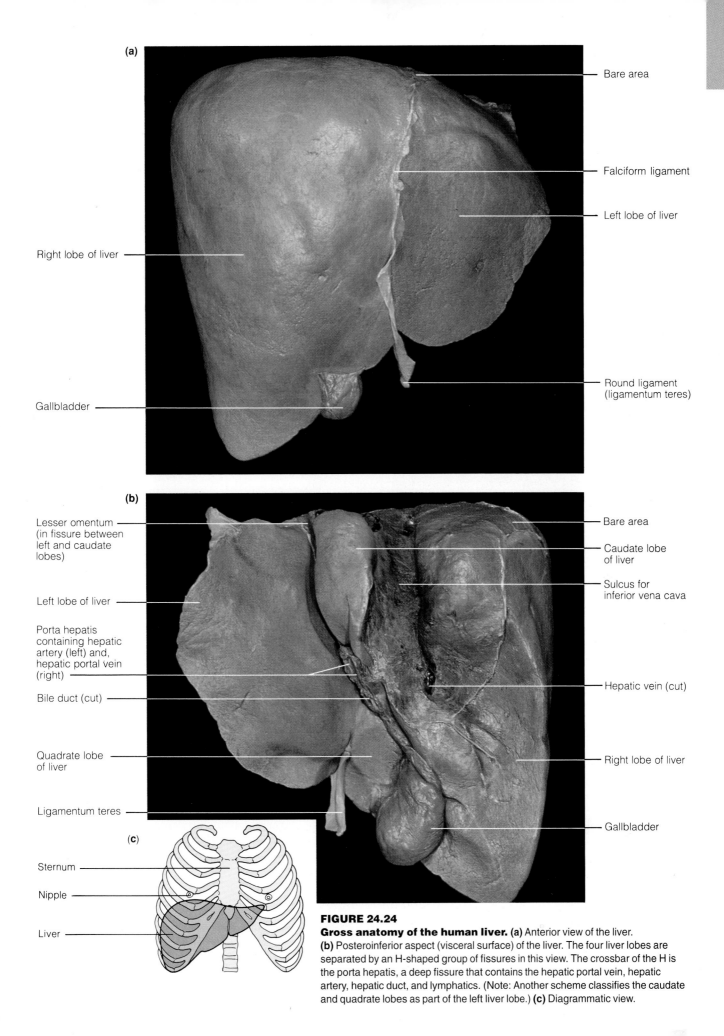

(a)

Bare area

Falciform ligament

Left lobe of liver

Round ligament
(ligamentum teres)

Right lobe of liver

Gallbladder

(b)

Lesser omentum
(in fissure between
left and caudate
lobes)

Left lobe of liver

Porta hepatis
containing hepatic
artery (left) and,
hepatic portal vein
(right)

Bile duct (cut)

Quadrate lobe
of liver

Ligamentum teres

Bare area

Caudate lobe
of liver

Sulcus for
inferior vena cava

Hepatic vein (cut)

Right lobe of liver

Gallbladder

(c)

Sternum

Nipple

Liver

FIGURE 24.24
Gross anatomy of the human liver. (a) Anterior view of the liver.
(b) Posteroinferior aspect (visceral surface) of the liver. The four liver lobes are
separated by an H-shaped group of fissures in this view. The crossbar of the H is
the porta hepatis, a deep fissure that contains the hepatic portal vein, hepatic
artery, hepatic duct, and lymphatics. (Note: Another scheme classifies the caudate
and quadrate lobes as part of the left liver lobe.) **(c)** Diagrammatic view.

FIGURE 24.25
Microscopic anatomy of the liver.
(a) Schematic view of the cut surface of the liver, showing the hexagonal nature of its lobules. **(b)** Photomicrograph of one liver lobule (50×). **(c)** Three-dimensional representation of one liver lobule, showing its blood supply and the platelike arrangement of the hepatocytes. (The arrows indicate the direction of blood flow.) **(d)** Enlarged schematic view of a small portion of one liver lobule, illustrating the components of a portal triad (portal tract) region, the positioning of the bile canaliculi, and the Kupffer cells in the sinusoids. The directions of blood and bile flow are also indicated.

cytes (hep'ah-to-sīts), organized like bricks in a garden wall. The hepatocyte plates radiate outward from a **central vein** running within the longitudinal axis of the lobule. To make a rough "model" of a liver lobule, open a thick paperback book until its two covers meet: The pages represent the plates of hepatocytes and the hollow cylinder formed by the rolled spine represents the central vein.

At each of the six corners of a lobule is a **portal triad** (*portal tract* region), so named because three basic structures are always present there: a branch of the *hepatic artery* (supplying arterial blood to the liver), a branch of the *hepatic portal vein* (carrying nutrient-rich venous blood from the digestive viscera), and a *bile duct.* Between the hepatocyte plates are enlarged, very leaky capillaries, the **liver sinusoids.** Blood from both the hepatic portal vein and the hepatic artery percolates from the triad regions through these sinusoids and empties into the central vein. Inside the sinusoids are star-shaped **hepatic macrophages,** also called **Kupffer** (ko͞op'fer) **cells** (see Figure 24.25d), which remove debris, such as bacteria and worn-out blood cells, from the blood as it flows past. Besides producing bile, the versatile hepatocytes (1) process the blood-borne nutrients in various ways (e.g., they store glucose as glycogen and use amino acids to make plasma proteins); (2) store fat-soluble vitamins; and (3) play important roles in detoxification, such as ridding the blood of ammonia by converting it to urea (Chapter 25). Thanks to the hepatocytes, the blood leaving the liver contains fewer nutrients and waste materials than the blood that entered it.

Secreted bile flows through tiny canals, called **bile canaliculi** (kan"ah-lik'u-li; "little canals"), that run between adjacent hepatocytes toward the bile duct branches in the portal triads (see Figure 24.25d). Notice that blood and bile flow in opposite directions in the liver lobule. Bile entering the bile ducts eventually leaves the liver via the common hepatic duct to travel toward the duodenum.

Hepatitis (hep"ah-ti'tis), or inflammation of the liver, is most often due to infection by hepatitis B virus (HBV) following transmission of the virus in blood (by means of blood transfusions or contaminated needles). Hepatitis B is a serious problem in its own right, but it carries with it a greater menace—an elevated risk of liver cancer. Hepatitis A, a more benign form, is transmitted via sewage-contaminated water and by the feces-mouth route, which explains why it is important for restaurant employees to scrub their hands after using the washroom. Vaccines produced in yeast have been very effective in preventing and/or treating hepatitis A and B. The life-threatening C form of this disease is now being successfully treated by combination drug therapy (the immune-suppressing steroid prednisone and genetically engineered interferon). Nonviral causes of acute hepatitis include drug toxicity and wild mushroom poisoning.

Cirrhosis (sĭ-ro'sis; "orange colored") is a diffuse and progressive chronic inflammation of the liver that typically results from chronic alcoholism or severe chronic hepatitis. The alcohol-poisoned or damaged hepatocytes regenerate, but the liver's connective tissue regenerates faster. As a result, the liver becomes fibrous and its activity is depressed. As the scar tissue eventually shrinks, it obstructs blood flow throughout the hepatic portal system, causing **portal hypertension.** Fortunately, some veins of the portal system anastomose with veins that drain into the venae cavae *(portal-caval anastomoses),* but these connecting veins are small and tend to burst when forced to carry large volumes of blood. Signs of their failure include vomiting blood, and a snakelike network of distended veins surrounding the navel. This network is called *caput medusae* (kap'ut me-du'se; "medusa head") after a monster in Greek mythology whose hair was made of writhing snakes. •

Composition of Bile.   Bile is a yellow-green, alkaline solution containing bile salts, bile pigments, cholesterol, neutral fats, phospholipids (lecithin and others), and a variety of electrolytes. Of these *only* bile salts and phospholipids aid the digestive process.

Bile salts, primarily cholic acid and chenodeoxycholic acids, are cholesterol derivatives. Their role is to *emulsify* fats—that is, to distribute them throughout the watery intestinal contents. (Another example of emulsification is homogenization, which distributes cream throughout the watery phase of milk.) As a result, large fat globules entering the small intestine are physically separated into suspensions of millions of small fatty droplets that provide large surface areas for the fat-digesting enzymes to work on. Bile salts also facilitate fat and cholesterol absorption (discussed later) and help solubilize cholesterol, both that contained in bile and that entering the small intestine via the diet. Although many substances secreted in bile leave the body in feces, bile salts are not among them. Instead, bile salts are conserved by means of a recycling mechanism called the **enterohepatic circulation.** In this process, bile salts are (1) reabsorbed into the blood by the distal part of the small intestine (ileum), (2) returned to the liver via the hepatic portal blood, and then (3) resecreted in newly formed bile.

The chief bile pigment is **bilirubin** (bil"ĭ-roo'bin), a waste product of the heme portion of hemoglobin formed during the breakdown of worn-out erythrocytes. The globin and iron of hemoglobin are saved and recycled, but bilirubin is absorbed from the blood by the liver cells and actively excreted into the bile. Most of the bilirubin in bile is metabolized in the small intestine by resident bacteria, and one of its breakdown products, *urobilinogen* (u"ro-bi-lin'o-jen), gives feces a brown color. In the absence of bile, feces are gray-white in color and have fatty streaks (because essentially no fats are digested or absorbed).

Collectively, the hepatocytes produce 500 to 1000 ml of bile daily, and bile production is stepped up when the GI tract contains fatty chyme. Bile salts

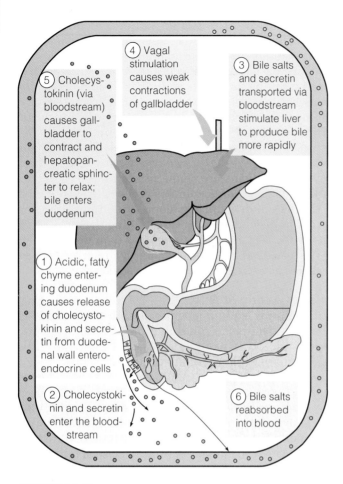

⑤ Cholecys-
tokinin (via
bloodstream)
causes gall-
bladder to
contract and
hepatopan-
creatic sphinc-
ter to relax;
bile enters
duodenum

④ Vagal
stimulation
causes weak
contractions
of gallbladder

③ Bile salts
and secretin
transported via
bloodstream
stimulate liver
to produce bile
more rapidly

① Acidic, fatty
chyme enter-
ing duodenum
causes release
of cholecysto-
kinin and secre-
tin from duode-
nal wall entero-
endocrine cells

② Cholecystoki-
nin and secretin
enter the blood-
stream

⑥ Bile salts
reabsorbed
into blood

FIGURE 24.26
**Mechanisms promoting the secretion of bile and its
entry into the duodenum.** When digestion is not occurring, bile
is stored and concentrated in the gallbladder. However, when acidic
chyme enters the small intestine, a number of mechanisms are
initiated that accelerate the liver's output of bile, cause the gallbladder
to contract, and promote the relaxation of the hepatopancreatic
sphincter, which allows bile (and pancreatic juice) to enter the small
intestine, where it plays a role in fat emulsification. The single most
important stimulus of bile secretion by the hepatocytes is an
increased level of bile salts in the enterohepatic circulation.

themselves are the major stimulus for enhanced bile
secretion (Figure 24.26), and when the enterohepatic
circulation is returning large amounts of bile salts to
the liver, the liver's output of bile rises dramatically.
Secretin, released by intestinal cells exposed to fatty
chyme, stimulates the cells lining the bile ducts in the
liver to secrete a watery, bicarbonate-rich juice that
lacks bile salts.

The Gallbladder

The **gallbladder** is a thin-walled, green muscular sac,
approximately 10 cm (4 inches) long, that snuggles in
a shallow fossa on the ventral surface of the liver (see
Figures 24.1 and 24.24). Its rounded head protrudes
from the inferior margin of the liver. The gallbladder
stores bile that is not immediately needed for diges-

tion and concentrates it by absorbing some of its
water and ions. (In some cases, bile released from the
gallbladder is ten times as concentrated as that entering it.) When empty, or when storing only small
amounts of bile, its mucosa is thrown into honey-
comb-like folds that, like the rugae of the stomach,
allow the mucosa to expand as the organ fills. When
its muscular wall contracts, bile is expelled into its
duct, the **cystic duct,** and then flows into the bile
duct. The gallbladder, like most of the liver, is covered by visceral peritoneum.

Regulation of Bile Release into the Small Intestine

When digestion is not occurring, the hepatopancreatic sphincter (guarding the entry of bile and pancreatic juice into the duodenum) is tightly closed and the
released bile backs up the cystic duct into the gallbladder, where it is stored until needed. Although the
liver makes bile continuously, bile does not usually
enter the small intestine until the gallbladder contracts. The major stimulus for gallbladder contraction
is *cholecystokinin (CCK),* an intestinal hormone (Figure 24.26). CCK is released to the blood when acidic,
fatty chyme enters the duodenum. Besides stimulating gallbladder contraction, CCK has two other
important effects: (1) it stimulates the secretion of
pancreatic juice, and (2) it relaxes the hepatopancreatic sphincter so that bile and pancreatic juice can
enter the duodenum. CCK and the other digestive
hormones are summarized in Table 24.1, p. 807.
Parasympathetic impulses delivered by the vagus
nerves have a minor impact on stimulating gallbladder contraction.

Bile is the major vehicle for cholesterol excretion
from the body. When the amount of bile salts (or
lecithin) in bile is inadequate to solubilize the cholesterol it contains or when cholesterol levels are excessive, cholesterol may crystallize, forming **gallstones,**
or *biliary calculi* (bil'e-a″re kal'ku-li), which obstruct
the flow of bile from the gallbladder or through the
cystic or bile ducts. When the gallbladder or its duct
contracts, the sharp crystals cause agonizing pain
(that radiates to the right thoracic region). Current
treatments for gallstones include drugs that dissolve
the crystals, pulverizing them with ultrasound vibrations (lithotripsy), vaporizing them with lasers, and
the classical treatment, surgical removal of the gallbladder. The gallbladder can be removed without
impairing digestive functions because, in such
instances, the bile duct simply enlarges to assume the
bile-storing role. Gallstones are easy to diagnose
because they show up well on ultrasound imaging (a
technique described on pp. 18–19).

Blockage of the bile duct prevents both bile salts
and bile pigments from entering the intestine. As a
result, the yellow bile pigments accumulate in the
blood and eventually are deposited in the skin, caus-

Intralobular duct

Acinar cells

Basement membrane

Zymogen granules

Rough endoplasmic reticulum

(a)

(b)

Acinus

FIGURE 24.27
Structure of the acinar (enzyme-producing) tissue of the pancreas. (a) One acinus (a secretory unit). The acinar cells have large amounts of rough endoplasmic reticulum (reflecting their high level of protein synthesis) in their basal regions. The cell apices contain abundant zymogen (enzyme-containing) granules.
(b) Photomicrograph of pancreatic acinar tissue (200×).

ing it to become yellowish, or *jaundiced.* Jaundice caused by blocked ducts is called *obstructive jaundice,* but jaundice may also reflect liver disease (in which the liver is unable to carry out its normal metabolic duties). •

The Pancreas

The **pancreas** (pan'kre-as; *pan* = all, *creas* = flesh, meat) is a soft, pink, tadpole-shaped gland that extends across the abdomen from its *tail* (abutting the spleen) to its *head,* which is encircled by the C-shaped duodenum (see Figures 24.1 and 24.20). Most of the pancreas is retroperitoneal and lies deep to the greater curvature of the stomach.

An accessory digestive organ, the pancreas is important to the digestive process because it produces a broad spectrum of enzymes that break down all categories of foodstuffs, which the pancreas then delivers to the duodenum. This exocrine product, called **pancreatic juice,** drains from the pancreas via the centrally located **main pancreatic duct.** The pancreatic duct generally fuses with the bile duct (conveying bile from the liver and gallbladder) just before it enters the duodenum (at the hepatopancreatic ampulla). A smaller *accessory pancreatic duct* empties directly into the duodenum.

Within the pancreas are the **acini** (as'ĭ-ni; singular = acinus), clusters of secretory cells surrounding ducts (Figure 24.27). These cells are "chock full" of rough endoplasmic reticulum and exhibit deeply staining **zymogen** (zi'mo-jen; "fermenting") **granules** containing the digestive enzymes they manufacture.

The pancreas also has an endocrine function. Scattered amidst the acini are the more lightly staining *pancreatic islets (islets of Langerhans),* mini-endocrine glands that release insulin and glucagon, hormones which play an important role in carbohydrate metabolism, as well as several other hormones (see Chapter 17).

Composition of Pancreatic Juice

Approximately 1200 to 1500 ml of clear pancreatic juice is produced daily. It consists mainly of water, and contains enzymes and electrolytes (primarily bicarbonate ions). The acinar cells produce the enzyme-rich component of pancreatic juice. The epithelial cells lining the pancreatic ducts release the bicarbonate irons that make it alkaline (about pH 8). This high pH enables pancreatic fluid to neutralize the acid chyme entering the duodenum and provides the optimal environment for activity of intestinal and pancreatic enzymes. Like pepsin of the stomach, pancreatic proteases (protein-digesting enzymes) are produced and released in inactive (precursor) forms, which are then activated in the duodenum, where they do their work. This prevents the pancreas from self-digestion. For example, within the duodenum, *trypsinogen* is activated to **trypsin** by **enterokinase,** an intestinal brush border enzyme. Trypsin, in turn, activates two other pancreatic proteases (*procarboxypeptidase* and *chymotrypsinogen*) to their active forms, **carboxypeptidase** (kar-bok"se-pep'tĭ-dās) and **chymotrypsin** (ky"mo-trip'sin), respectively (Figure 24.28). Other pancreatic enzymes—**amylase, lipases,** and **nucleases**—are secreted in active form, but require that ions or bile be present in the intestinal lumen for optimal activity.

Regulation of Pancreatic Secretion

Secretion of pancreatic juice is regulated both by local hormones and by the parasympathetic nervous system (Figure 24.29). Hormonal control, the more important regulatory mechanism, is exerted by two intestinal hormones: (1) *secretin,* released in response to the presence of HCl in the intestine and (2) *chole-*

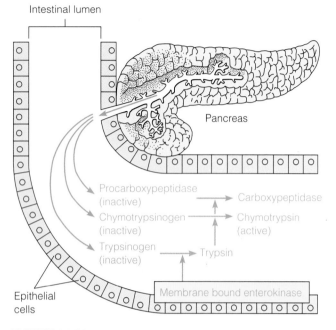

Intestinal lumen

Pancreas

Procarboxypeptidase
(inactive)

Carboxypeptidase

Chymotrypsinogen
(inactive)

Chymotrypsin
(active)

Trypsinogen
(inactive)

Trypsin

Epithelial
cells

Membrane bound enterokinase

FIGURE 24.28
**Activation of pancreatic proteases in the small
intestine.** Pancreatic proteases are secreted in an inactive form
and are activated in the duodenum. Enterokinase, a membrane-
bound (brush border) intestinal enzyme, activates trypsinogen to the
active trypsin form. Trypsin, itself a proteolytic enzyme, then activates
procarboxypeptidase and chymotrypsinogen.

cystokinin, released in response to the entry of proteins and fats. Both hormones act on the pancreas, but
secretin targets the duct cells, prompting their release
of watery *bicarbonate-rich* pancreatic juice, whereas
CCK stimulates the acini to release *enzyme-rich* pancreatic juice. Vagal stimulation causes release of pancreatic juice primarily during the cephalic and gastric
phases of gastric secretion.

Normally, the amount of HCl produced in the
stomach is exactly balanced by the amount of bicarbonate (HCO_3^-) actively secreted by the pancreas,
and as HCO_3^- is secreted into the pancreatic juice,
H^+ enters the blood. Consequently, the pH of venous
blood returning to the heart remains relatively
unchanged because the alkaline blood draining from
the stomach is neutralized by the acidic blood draining the pancreas.

Digestive Processes Occurring
in the Small Intestine

Although food reaching the small intestine is unrecognizable, it is far from digested chemically. Carbohydrates and proteins are partially degraded, but virtually no fat digestion has occurred up to this point. The
process of food digestion is accelerated during the

chyme's tortuous 3- to 6-hour journey through
the small intestine, and it is here that virtually all
absorption of nutrients takes place. Like the stomach,
the small intestine is uninvolved in ingestion and
defecation.

Requirements for Optimal
Intestinal Digestive Activity

Although the small intestine is "where the (digestive
and absorptive) action is," intestinal juice provides
little of what is needed to perform these functions.
Most substances required for its chemical digestive
activity—bile, digestive enzymes (except for the
brush border enzymes), and bicarbonate ions (to neutralize the acidic chyme and provide the proper pH
for enzymatic catalysis)—are *imported* from the liver
and pancreas. Hence, anything that impairs liver or
pancreatic function or the timely delivery of their
juices to the small intestine severely hinders our ability to digest food and absorb its nutrients.

Optimal digestive activity in the small intestine
also depends on a slow, measured delivery of chyme
from the stomach. As indicated earlier, the small
intestine is able to process only small amounts of
chyme at one time. Why is this so? Entering chyme is
usually hypertonic. Thus, if large amounts of chyme
were rushed into the small intestine, the osmotic
water loss from the blood across the intestinal wall
into the lumen would result in dangerously low
blood volume. Additionally, the low pH of entering
chyme must be adjusted upward and the chyme must
be well mixed with bile and pancreatic juice before
digestion can continue. These modifications take
time. Thus, food movement into the small intestine is
carefully controlled by the pumping action of the
stomach pylorus (see p. 810), which prevents the
duodenum from being overwhelmed. Since the actual
chemistry of digestion and absorption is covered in
detail later, next we will examine how the small
intestine mixes and propels food along its length, and
how its motility is regulated.

Motility of the Small Intestine

Intestinal smooth muscle mixes chyme thoroughly
with bile and the pancreatic and intestinal juices, and
moves food residues through the ileocecal valve into
the large intestine. In contrast to the peristaltic waves
of the stomach, which both mix and propel food, *segmentation* is the most common motion of the small
intestine.

If X-ray fluoroscopy is used to examine the small
intestine after it is "loaded" with a meal, it looks like
the intestinal contents are being "massaged"—that is,
the chyme is simply moved backward and forward in
the lumen a few centimeters at a time by alternating
contraction and relaxation of rings of smooth muscle.
These segmenting movements of the intestine (see
Figure 24.3b), like the peristalsis of the stomach, are

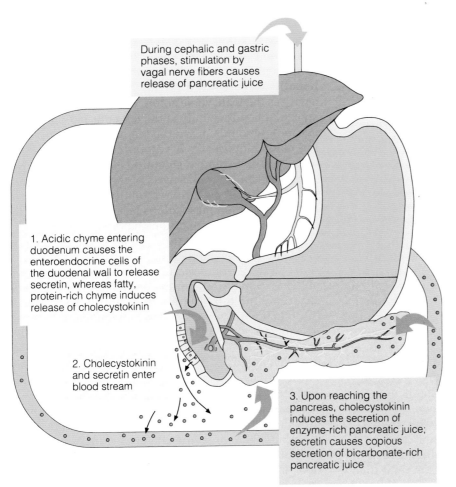

During cephalic and gastric phases, stimulation by vagal nerve fibers causes release of pancreatic juice

1. Acidic chyme entering duodenum causes the enteroendocrine cells of the duodenal wall to release secretin, whereas fatty, protein-rich chyme induces release of cholecystokinin

2. Cholecystokinin and secretin enter blood stream

3. Upon reaching the pancreas, cholecystokinin induces the secretion of enzyme-rich pancreatic juice; secretin causes copious secretion of bicarbonate-rich pancreatic juice

FIGURE 24.29
Regulation of pancreatic juice secretion by hormonal and neural factors. Hormonal controls, exerted by secretin and cholecystokinin (steps 1–3), are the main regulatory factors. Neural control is mediated by parasympathetic fibers of the vagus nerves, primarily during the cephalic and gastric phases of gastric secretory activity.

initiated by intrinsic pacemaker cells in the longitudinal smooth muscle layer. However, unlike the stomach pacemakers, which have only one rhythm, the pacemakers in the duodenum depolarize more frequently (12 contractions per minute) than those in the ileum (8 or 9 contractions per minute). As a result, segmentation also produces a slow steady movement of the intestinal contents toward the ileocecal valve at a rate that allows ample time to complete digestion and absorption. The intensity of segmentation is altered by long and short reflexes (which parasympathetic activity enhances and sympathetic activity decreases) and hormones. The more intense the contractions, the greater the mixing effect; however, the basic contractile rhythms of the various intestinal regions remain unchanged.

True peristalsis occurs only after most of the nutrients have been absorbed. At this point, segmenting movements wane, and peristaltic waves initiated at the duodenal end begin to sweep slowly along the length of the intestine, moving 10–70 cm before dying out. Each successive wave is initiated a bit more distally, and this pattern of peristaltic activity is called the **migrating mobility complex.** A complete "trip"

from duodenum to ileum takes about two hours. The process then repeats itself, sweeping out the last remnants of the meal plus bacteria, sloughed-off mucosal cells, and other debris into the large intestine. This "housekeeping" function is critical for preventing the overgrowth of bacteria that migrate from the large intestine into the small intestine. As food again enters the stomach with the next meal, peristaltic activity ceases and is replaced by segmentation. The local enteric neurons of the GI tract wall coordinate these intestinal mobility patterns.

Most of the time, the ileocecal sphincter is constricted and closed. However, two mechanisms—one neural and the other hormonal—cause it to relax when ileal mobility increases and allow food residues to enter the cecum. Enhanced secretory and contractile activity of the stomach initiates the **gastroileal** (gas″tro-il′e-ul) **reflex,** a long reflex that enhances ileal segmenting contractions. In addition, gastrin released by the stomach increases the motility of the ileum and causes the ileocecal sphincter to relax. Once the chyme has passed through, the backward pressure of the material in the cecum closes the valve's flaps, preventing regurgitation into the ileum.

THE LARGE INTESTINE

The **large intestine** (see Figure 24.1) frames the small intestine on three sides and extends from the ileocecal valve to the anus. Its diameter is greater than that of the small intestine (hence, *large* intestine), but its length is less (1.5 m versus 2 m). Its major function is to absorb water from indigestible food residues (delivered to it in a fluid state) and eliminate them from the body as semisolid **feces** (fe′sēz).

Gross Anatomy

Over most of its length, the large intestine exhibits three features not seen elsewhere—teniae coli, haustra, and epiploic appendages. Except for its terminal end, the longitudinal muscle layer of its muscularis is reduced to three bands of smooth muscle called **teniae coli** (ten′ne-e ko′li; "ribbons of the colon"). Their tone causes the wall of the large intestine to pucker into pocketlike sacs called **haustra** (haw′-strah; "to draw up"). The final, and very obvious, unique feature of the large intestine is its **epiploic** (ep″i-plo′ik) **appendages** (Figure 24.30a), small fat-filled pouches of visceral peritoneum that hang from its surface. Their significance is not known.

The large intestine has the following subdivisions: cecum, appendix, colon, rectum, and anal canal. The saclike **cecum** (se′kum; "blind pouch"), which lies below the ileocecal valve in the right iliac fossa, is the first part of the large intestine (Figure 24.30a). Attached to its posteromedial surface is the blind, wormlike **vermiform appendix.** The appendix contains masses of lymphoid tissue, and as part of MALT (see p. 704), it plays an important role in body immunity. However, it has an important structural shortcoming—its twisted structure provides an ideal location for enteric bacteria to accumulate and multiply.

Inflammation of the appendix, or **appendicitis,** often leads to ischemia and gangrene (death and decay) of the appendix. If the appendix ruptures, feces containing bacteria are sprayed over the abdominal contents, causing *peritonitis.* Although the symptoms of appendicitis are highly variable, the first is usually pain in the umbilical region. Loss of appetite, nausea and vomiting, and relocalization of pain to the lower right abdominal quadrant follow. Immediate surgical removal of the appendix (appendectomy) is the accepted treatment for suspected appendicitis. Appendicitis is most common during adolescence, when the entrance to the appendix is at its widest.

Interestingly, some cases of severe abdominal pain misdiagnosed as appendicitis have proved to be due to perforation of the intestinal lining by living parasitic worms. Though still rare, such incidents are becoming more frequent as growing numbers of Americans seek out raw fish delicacies, such as sushi and sashimi. •

The **colon** has several distinct regions. As the **ascending colon,** it travels up the right side of the abdominal cavity to the level of the right kidney. Here it makes a right-angle turn—the **right colic,** or **hepatic, flexure**—and travels across the abdominal cavity as the **transverse colon.** Directly anterior to the spleen, it bends acutely at the **left colic (splenic) flexure** and descends down the left side as the **descending colon.** Inferiorly, it enters the pelvis, where it becomes the S-shaped **sigmoid colon.** Except for the transverse and sigmoid parts of the colon, which are anchored to the posterior abdominal wall by mesentery sheets called **mesocolons** (see Figure 24.23c and d), the colon is a retroperitoneal organ.

At the level of the third sacral vertebra, the sigmoid colon joins the **rectum,** which runs posteroinferiorly in front of the sacrum. The natural orientation of the rectum allows a number of pelvic organs to be examined digitally (with a finger) through the anterior rectal wall. This is called a **rectal exam.** Despite its name (*rectum* = straight), the rectum has three lateral curves or bends, represented internally as three transverse folds called **rectal valves** (Figure 24.30c). These valves separate feces from flatus, that is, they stop feces from being passed along with gas.

The **anal canal,** the last segment of the large intestine, lies entirely external to the abdominopelvic cavity. About 3 cm long, the anal canal begins where the rectum penetrates the levator ani muscle of the pelvic floor and it opens to the body exterior at the **anus.** The anal canal has two sphincters (Figure 24.30c), an involuntary **internal anal sphincter** composed of smooth muscle (part of the muscularis), and a voluntary **external anal sphincter** composed of skeletal muscle. The sphincters, which act rather like purse strings to open and close the anus, are ordinarily closed except during defecation.

Microscopic Anatomy

The wall of the large intestine (Figure 24.31) differs in several ways from that of the small intestine. The colon *mucosa* is simple columnar epithelium except in the anal canal. Because most food is absorbed before reaching the large intestine, there are no plicae circulares, no villi, and virtually no cells that secrete digestive enzymes. However, its mucosa is thicker, its abundant crypts are deeper, and there are tremendous numbers of goblet cells in the crypts (Figure 24.31a). The lubricating mucus produced by the goblet cells eases the passage of feces to the end of the digestive tract and protects the intestinal wall from irritating acids and gases released by bacteria in residence in the colon.

The mucosa of the anal canal is quite different, reflecting the greater abrasion that this region receives. It hangs in long ridges or folds called **anal columns** and contains stratified squamous epithelium. The **anal sinuses** (Figure 24.30c), recesses

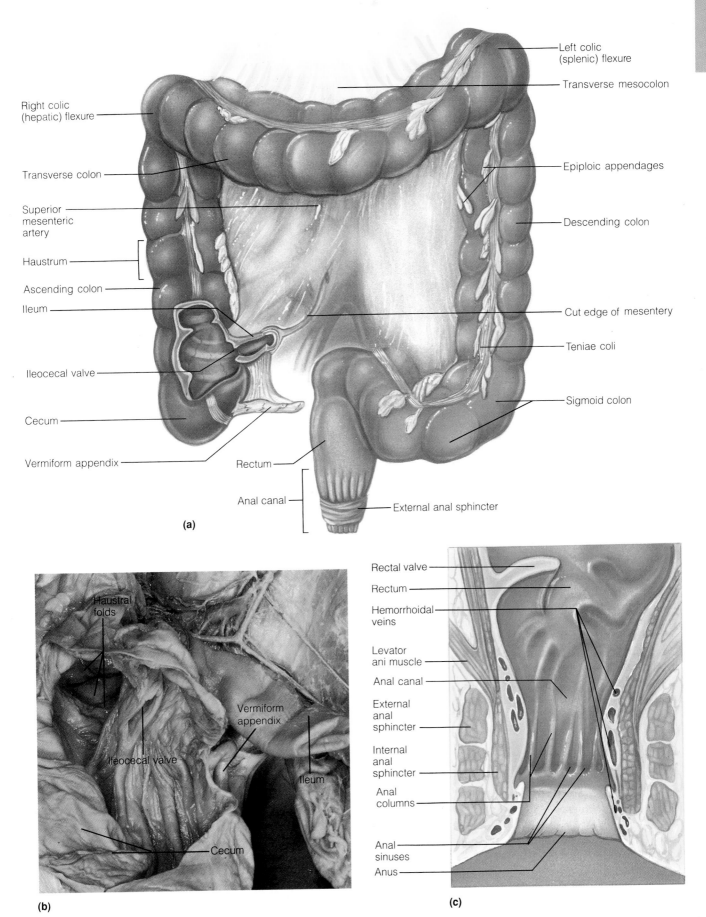

Right colic
(hepatic) flexure

Transverse colon

Superior
mesenteric
artery

Haustrum

Ascending colon

Ileum

Ileocecal valve

Cecum

Vermiform appendix

Rectum

Anal canal

External anal sphincter

Left colic
(splenic) flexure

Transverse mesocolon

Epiploic appendages

Descending colon

Cut edge of mesentery

Teniae coli

Sigmoid colon

(a)

Haustral
folds

Ileocecal valve

Vermiform
appendix

Ileum

Cecum

(b)

Rectal valve

Rectum

Hemorrhoidal
veins

Levator
ani muscle

Anal canal

External
anal
sphincter

Internal
anal
sphincter

Anal
columns

Anal
sinuses

Anus

(c)

FIGURE 24.30
Gross anatomy of the large intestine. (a) Diagrammatic view. **(b)** Photograph of the
interior of the cecum showing the ileocecal valve opening and the haustral folds in the ascending
colon. **(c)** Structure of the anal canal.

Columnar cells with striated border

Lamina propria

Goblet cells

Crypt

Muscularis mucosae

(a)

Lu

(b)

FIGURE 24.31

The mucosa of the large intestine. (a) Light photomicrograph of the mucosa of the large intestine. Notice the abundant mucus-secreting goblet cells (550×). **(b)** Scanning electron micrograph of the mucosal surface of the colon, showing the openings (arrows) of the thousands of crypts (intestinal glands) into the lumen (Lu) From *Tissues and Organs* by R. G. Kessel and R. H. Kardon. ©1979 W. H. Freeman. (20×)

between the anal columns, exude mucus when compressed by feces, which aids in emptying the anal canal. Two superficial venous plexuses are associated with the anal canal, one with the anal columns and the other with the anus itself. Where these (hemorrhoidal) veins are inflamed, itchy varicosities called *hemorrhoids* result.

In contrast to the more proximal regions of the large intestine, haustra are absent in the rectum and anal canal. Consistent with its need to generate strong contractions to perform its expulsive role in defecation, the rectum's muscularis muscle layers are complete and well developed.

Bacterial Flora

Although most bacteria entering the cecum from the small intestine are dead (having been killed by the action of lysozyme, HCl, and protein-digesting enzymes), some are still "alive and kicking." Together with bacteria that enter the GI tract via the anus, these constitute the **bacterial flora** of the large intestine. These bacteria colonize the colon and ferment some of the indigestible carbohydrates (cellulose and others), releasing irritating acids and a mixture of gases (H_2, N_2, and CO_2). Some of these gases (such as methane and hydrogen sulfide) are quite odorous. About 500 ml of gas (flatus) is produced each day, much more when certain carbohydrate-rich foods (such as beans) are eaten. The bacterial flora also syn-

thesize B complex vitamins and most of the vitamin K the liver requires to synthesize some of the clotting proteins.

Digestive Processes Occurring in the Large Intestine

What is finally delivered to the large intestine contains few nutrients, but that residue still has 12 to 24 hours more to spend there. Except for a small amount of digestion of the residue by the enteric bacteria, no further food breakdown occurs in the large intestine.

Although the large intestine harvests vitamins made by the bacterial flora and reclaims most of the remaining water and some of the electrolytes (particularly sodium and chloride), absorption is not the *major* function of this organ. As considered in the next section, the primary concerns of the large intestine are propulsive activities that force the fecal material toward the anus and then eliminate it from the body (defecation).

While the large intestine is undeniably essential for our comfort, it is not essential for life. If the colon is removed, as is often necessitated by colon cancer, the terminal ileum is brought out to the abdominal wall in a procedure called an *ileostomy* (il"e-os'to-me), and food residues are eliminated from there into a sac attached to the abdominal wall. A newer surgical technique, *ileoanal juncture,* links the ileum directly to the anal canal.

Motility of the Large Intestine

The musculature of the large intestine is inactive much of the time, and when it is mobile, its contractions are sluggish or very short lived. The most frequent movements seen in the colon are **haustral contractions,** which are very slow segmenting movements that typically occur every 30 minutes or so. These contractions reflect local controls of smooth muscle within the walls of the individual haustra. As a haustrum fills with food residues, the distension activates its muscle to contract, which propels the luminal contents into the next haustrum. These movements also mix the residue, which aids in the absorption of water.

Mass movements (mass peristalsis) are long, slow-moving, but powerful contractile waves that move over large areas of the colon three or four times daily and force the contents toward the rectum. Typically, they occur during or just after eating, which indicates that the presence of food in the stomach activates the gastroileal reflex in the small intestine and initiates a propulsive colon reflex, the **gastrocolic reflex.** Bulk, or fiber, in the diet increases the strength of colon contractions and softens the stool, allowing the colon to act like a well-oiled machine.

When the diet lacks bulk and the volume of residues in the colon is small, the colon narrows and its contractions become more powerful, increasing the pressure on its walls. This promotes formation of *diverticula* (di″ver-tik′u-lah), small herniations of the mucosa through the colon walls. This condition, called *diverticulosis,* most commonly occurs in the sigmoid colon. *Diverticulitis,* in which the diverticula become inflamed, can be life-threatening if the diverticula rupture. •

The semisolid product delivered to the rectum, feces or the stool, contains undigested food residues, mucus, sloughed-off epithelial cells, millions of bacteria, and just enough water to allow its smooth passage. Of the 500 ml or so of food residue entering the cecum daily, approximately 150 ml becomes feces.

Defecation

The rectum is generally empty, but when feces are forced into it by mass movements, stretching of the rectal wall initiates the **defecation reflex** (Figure 24.32). This is a spinal cord–mediated parasympathetic reflex that causes the walls of the sigmoid colon and the rectum to contract and the anal sphincters to relax. As feces are forced into the anal canal, messages reach the brain allowing us to decide whether the external (voluntary) anal sphincter should remain open or be constricted to stop the passage of feces temporarily. If defecation is delayed, the reflex contractions end within a few seconds, and the rectal walls relax. With the next mass movement, the defecation reflex is initiated again—and so on, until one chooses to defecate or the urge to defecate becomes unavoidable.

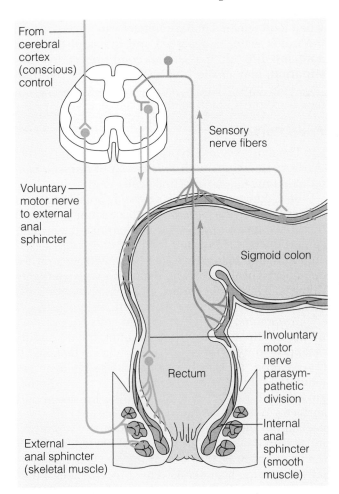

FIGURE 24.32
Defecation reflex. Distension, or stretch, of the rectal walls caused by movement of food residues into the rectum triggers the depolarization of afferent fibers, which synapse with spinal cord neurons. Parasympathetic efferent fibers, in turn, stimulate contraction of the rectal walls and defecation. Defecation may be delayed temporarily by conscious (cortical) controls, which allow voluntary constriction of the external sphincter.

During defecation, the muscles of the rectum contract to expel the feces. We aid this process voluntarily by closing the glottis and contracting our diaphragm and abdominal wall muscles to increase the intra-abdominal pressure (a procedure called *Valsalva's maneuver*). We also contract the levator ani muscle (p. 310), which pulls the anal canal superiorly. This lifting action leaves the feces below the anus—and outside the body. Involuntary or automatic defecation (incontinence of feces) normally occurs in infants because they have not yet gained control of their external anal sphincter. It also occurs in those with spinal cord transections.

Watery stools, or **diarrhea,** result from any condition that rushes food residue through the large intestine before that organ has had sufficient time to absorb the remaining water (as in irritation of the colon by bacteria). Prolonged diarrhea may result in dehydration and electrolyte imbalance. Conversely, when food remains in the colon for extended periods, too much water is absorbed and the stool becomes hard and difficult to pass. This condition, called **constipation,** may ensue from lack of fiber in the diet, improper bowel habits (failing to heed the "call"), lack of exercise, emotional upset, or laxative abuse. •

Food Poisoning

The most common types of **food poisoning** derive from infections with *Salmonella* or *Shigella* bacteria that invade the intestinal wall.

Best known for causing food poisoning and typhoid fever, the *Salmonella* bacterium is spread by three common routes: (1) contaminated eggs and egg products, (2) infected food handlers with feces-contaminated hands (together these two account for one-quarter of all cases, and typically involve patients in nursing homes, hospitals, and mental institutions) and (3) marijuana contaminated with *Salmonella.*

Salmonella invades intestinal cells by pressing up against their microvilli. Soon after, the microvilli disappear and are replaced by tiny blisters that engulf the bacteria. (It is believed that these changes are mediated by binding of the bacterium to epidermal growth factor [EGF] receptors on the intestinal cell surface.) Within two hours, the intestinal cells *look* normal but the *Salmonella* are now busily reproducing within the local lymph nodes. If not contained by the local defenses, they escape into the general circulation, causing bacteremia. This process takes 4 to 7 days, accompanied by symptoms of gastroenteritis (nausea and vomiting followed within a few hours by abdominal cramping often localized to the right lower quadrant) and diarrhea (ranging in severity from 1 to 2 stools/day to a dysentery-like discharge with bloody slimy stools). The condition is diagnosed by stool cultures positive for *Salmonella.* Consequences of bacteremia can be severe, ranging from endocarditis and thrombi, to bone infections and arthritis, to meningitis. The condition is treated symptomatically with antinausea drugs, painkillers, and fluids to replace lost fluids and electrolytes. There is presently no treatment that reduces the symptoms of the gastroenteritis. If severe, antibiotic therapy, though not always successful, may be instituted. Although stool samples usually become negative within a few days, chronic infection of the bile ducts continually reinfects the intestine and symptomatic disease is followed by the carrier state, which may persist for 5 to 6 months or longer. Because their potential for infecting others is so prolonged, names of those infected with *Salmonella* are reported to the state health departments for monitoring.

Shigella infections are typically seen in travelers returning from developing countries. *Shigella* are said to be spread by the four F's: food, feces, fingers, and flies. *Shigella* infections also tend to flare up when public swimming areas become contaminated and whenever natural calamities (such as floods or earth-

quakes) result in overcrowding and poor sanitation. Healthy individuals can usually fend off *Shigella* infections. The most common victims are children under 10, the malnourished, and those with impaired immune systems.

Shigella invades the intestine by producing a toxin that binds to the Gb3 receptor on the intestinal cells. The incubation period of two to three days is followed by nonspecific symptoms: nausea, vomiting, midabdominal cramps, and watery diarrhea. In more severe cases, these symptoms are followed by a shift in focus to the colon. Dysentery occurs, characterized by frequent loose bowel movements containing blood, mucus, and pus, left lower quadrant pain, and rectal urgency. Diagnosis is by stool cultures positive for *Shigella.* As for *Salmonella* infections, treatment is usually symptomatic and antibiotic use is avoided if possible. Unlike *Salmonella* infections, the chronic carrier state rarely develops. •

PHYSIOLOGY OF CHEMICAL DIGESTION AND ABSORPTION

So far in this chapter, we have examined the structure and overall function of the organs that make up the digestive system. Now we will investigate the entire chemical processing (enzymatic breakdown and absorption) of each class of foodstuffs as it moves through the GI tract. These matters, described in detail below, are summarized in Figure 24.33.

CHEMICAL DIGESTION

After foodstuffs have spent even a short time in the stomach, they are unrecognizable. Nonetheless, they are still mostly the starchy foods, meat proteins, butter, etc. that we ingested. Only their appearance has been changed by mechanical digestive activities. By contrast, the products of chemical digestion are the chemical building blocks of the ingested foods and are very different molecules chemically. Let us look more closely at the process of chemical digestion.

Mechanism of Chemical Digestion: Enzymatic Hydrolysis

Chemical digestion is a catabolic process in which large food molecules are broken down to their *monomers* (chemical building blocks), which are small enough to be absorbed by the GI tract lining. Chemical digestion is accomplished by enzymes secreted by both intrinsic and accessory glands into the lumen of the alimentary canal. The enzymatic breakdown of any type of food molecule is called **hydrolysis** (hi-drol'ĭ-sis), since it involves the addition of a water molecule to each molecular bond to be broken (lysed).

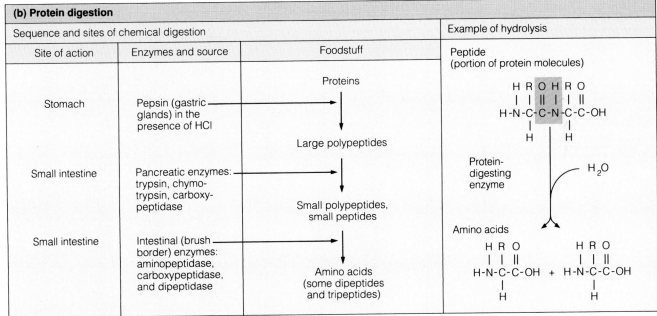

FIGURE 24.33

Chemical digestion of carboydrates, proteins, lipids, and nucleic acids. In most cases, chemical (enzymatic) digestion of food molecules within the gastrointestinal tract involves hydrolysis of the food molecules to their monomers. (Continued on p. 832.)

(c) Lipid digestion

Sequence and sites of chemical digestion			Example of hydrolysis
Site of action	Enzymes and source	Foodstuff	

Unemulsified fats

↓

Monoglycerides and fatty acids   Glycerol and fatty acids

Site of action / Enzymes rows:

- Small intestine — Emulsified by detergent action of bile salts from liver
- Small intestine — Pancreatic lipase

Example of hydrolysis:

Fat

$C_{17}H_{35}$ C=O−O−C−H
$C_{17}H_{35}$ C=O−O−C−H
$C_{17}H_{35}$ C=O−O−C−H

Fat-digesting enzyme $3H_2O$

Fatty acids

$C_{17}H_{35}$ C=O OH
$C_{17}H_{35}$ C=O OH
$C_{17}H_{35}$ C=O OH

+

Glycerol

HO−C−H
HO−C−H
HO−C−H

(d) Nucleic acid digestion

Sequence and sites of chemical digestion			Example of hydrolysis
Site of action	Enzymes and source	Foodstuff	

Nucleic acids

↓

Nucleotides

↓

N - containing bases, ribose, deoxyribose, phosphate

Site of action / Enzymes rows:

- Small intestine — Pancreatic nucleases
- Small intestine — Intestinal (brush border) enzymes: nucleosidases and phosphatases

Example of hydrolysis:

Adenosine monophosphate (AMP)

NH_2

$^-O-P-O-CH_2$

HO   OH

Nucleotide-digesting enzymes $3H_2O$

Adenine

NH_2

Ribose

$HOCH_2$ O   OH

HO   OH

+

Phosphate

$^-O-P-O^-$

Chemical Digestion of Specific Food Groups

Carbohydrates

Depending on our food likes and dislikes, most of us ingest between 200 and 600 grams of carbohydrate foods each day. The monomers of carbohydrates are **monosaccharides** (simple sugars), which are absorbed immediately without further ado. Only three of these are common in our diet: *glucose, fructose,* and *galactose.* The more complex carbohydrates that our digestive system is able to break down to monosaccharides are the disaccharides *sucrose* (table sugar), *lactose* (milk sugar), and *maltose* (grain sugar) and the polysaccharides *glycogen* and *starch.* In an average American diet, most digestible carbohydrates are in the form of starch, with smaller amounts of disaccharides and monosaccharides. Humans do not have enzymes capable of breaking down most other polysaccharides, such as cellulose. Thus, indigestible polysaccharides do not nourish us but, as mentioned earlier, they help move the food along the GI tract by providing bulk, or fiber.

Chemical digestion of starch (and perhaps glycogen) begins in the mouth. **Salivary amylase,** present in saliva, splits starch into *oligosaccharides,* smaller fragments of 2 to 8 linked monosaccharides (in this case glucose molecules). Salivary amylase works best in a slightly acid to neutral environment (pH of 6.75–7.00), which is maintained in the mouth by the buffering effects of bicarbonate and phosphate ions in saliva. Starch digestion continues in the stomach until amylase is inactivated by stomach acid and broken apart by the stomach's protein-digesting enzymes. Generally speaking, the larger the meal, the longer amylase can continue to work in the stomach because foodstuffs in its relatively immobile fundus are poorly mixed with gastric juices.

Starchy foods and other digestible carbohydrates that escape being broken down by salivary amylase are acted on by the highly effective **pancreatic amylase** in the small intestine (see Figure 24.33a). Within about 10 minutes of entering the small intestine, starch is entirely converted to various oligosaccharides, mostly maltose. The intestinal brush border enzymes further digest these products to monosaccharides. The most important of these brush border enzymes are **dextrinase** and **glucoamylase,** which act on oligosaccharides composed of more than three simple sugars, and the disaccharidase enzymes **maltase, sucrase,** and **lactase,** which hydrolyze maltose, sucrose, and lactose respectively into their constituent monosaccharides. Because the colon does not secrete digestive enzymes, chemical digestion *officially ends* in the small intestine. As noted above, however, resident colon bacteria do break down and metabolize the residual complex carbohydrates further, adding much to their nutrition but essentially nothing to ours.

In some people, intestinal lactase is present at birth but then becomes deficient, probably due to genetic factors. In such cases, the person becomes intolerant of milk products (the source of lactose), which has several related consequences. The undigested lactose sugar creates osmotic gradients that not only prevent water from being absorbed in the small and large intestines but also pull water from the interstitial space into the intestines. The result is diarrhea. Bacterial metabolism of the undigested solutes produces large amounts of gas that result in bouts of bloating, flatulence, and cramping pain. The solution to this problem is simple—add lactase enzyme "drops" to your milk or take a lactose tablet before meals containing milk products. •

Proteins

Proteins digested in the GI tract include not only dietary proteins (typically about 125 g per day), but also 15–25 g of enzyme proteins secreted into the GI tract lumen by its various glands and (probably) an equal amount of protein derived from sloughed and disintegrating mucosal cells. In healthy individuals, virtually all of this protein is digested all the way to its **amino acid** monomers.

Protein digestion begins in the stomach as pepsinogen secreted by the chief cells is quickly activated to **pepsin** (actually a group of proteolytic, or protein-digesting, enzymes). Pepsin functions optimally in the highly acid pH range found in the stomach: 1.5–3.5. It preferentially cleaves bonds involving the amino acids tyrosine and phenylalanine, so that proteins are broken into polypeptides and small numbers of free amino acids (see Figure 24.34). Pepsin, which hydrolyzes 10% to 15% of ingested protein, is inactivated by the high pH in the duodenum, so its proteolytic activity is restricted to the stomach. **Rennin** (the enzyme that coagulates milk protein) is apparently not produced in adults.

Protein fragments entering the small intestine from the stomach are greeted by a host of proteolytic enzymes (Figure 24.33b). **Trypsin** and **chymotrypsin** secreted by the pancreas cleave the proteins into smaller peptides. These peptides, in turn, become the grist for the pancreatic and brush border enzyme **carboxypeptidase,** which splits off one amino acid at a time from the end of the polypeptide chain that bears the carboxyl group, and other brush border enzymes such as **aminopeptidase** and **dipeptidase,** which liberate the final amino acid products (Figure 24.34). Aminopeptidase digests a protein, one amino acid at a time, by working from the amine end. Both carboxypeptidase and aminopeptidase can independently dismantle a protein, but the teamwork between these enzymes and between trypsin and chymotrypsin, which attack the more internal parts of the protein, speeds up the process tremendously.

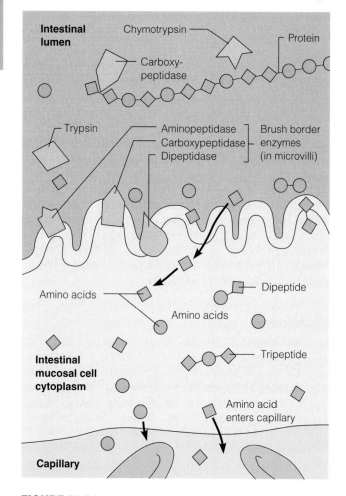

FIGURE 24.34

Protein digestion and absorption in the small intestine.
Proteins and protein fragments are digested to amino acids by the
action of pancreatic proteases (trypsin, chymotrypsin, and
carboxypeptidase), and by brush border enzymes of the intestinal
mucosal cells. The amino acids are then absorbed by active transport
mechanisms into the capillary blood of the villi.

Lipids

Although the American Heart Association recommends a low-fat diet, the amount of lipids (fats) ingested daily varies tremendously among American adults, ranging from 30 g to 150 g or more. The small intestine is the sole site of lipid digestion because the pancreas is essentially the only source of fat-digesting enzymes, or **lipases.** Neutral fats (triglycerides or triacylglycerols) are the most abundant fats in the diet.

Since both triglycerides and their breakdown products are insoluble in water, fats need special "pretreatment" with bile salts to be digested and absorbed in the watery environment of the small intestine. In aqueous solutions, triglycerides aggregate to form large fat globules. Consequently, only the triglyceride molecules at the surfaces of the fatty masses are accessible to the water-soluble lipase enzymes. However, this problem is quickly resolved, because as the fat globules enter the duodenum, they are coated with detergentlike bile salts (Figure 24.35). Bile salts have both nonpolar and polar regions. Their nonpolar (hydrophobic) parts cling to the fat molecules, and their polar (ionized hydrophilic) parts allow them to

repel each other and to interact with water. As a result, fatty droplets are pulled off the large fat globules, and a stable *emulsion*—an aqueous suspension of fatty droplets, each about 1 µm in diameter—is formed. The process of emulsification does *not* break chemical bonds. It just reduces the attraction between fat molecules so that they can be more widely dispersed. This process vastly increases the number of triglyceride molecules exposed to the pancreatic lipases. Without bile, lipids would be incompletely digested in the time food is in the small intestine.

The pancreatic lipases catalyze the breakdown of fats by cleaving off two of the fatty acid chains, thus yielding free **fatty acids** and **monoglycerides** (glycerol with one fatty acid chain attached). Fat-soluble vitamins that ride with fats require no digestion.

Nucleic Acids

Both DNA and RNA, present in small amounts in foods, are hydrolyzed to their **nucleotide** monomers by **pancreatic nucleases** present in pancreatic juice. The nucleotides are then broken apart by intestinal brush border enzymes (**nucleosidases** and **phosphatases**), which release their free bases, pentose sugars, and phosphate ions (see Figure 24.33d).

ABSORPTION

Up to 10 L of food, drink, and GI secretions enter the alimentary canal daily, but only 0.5–1 L reaches the large intestine. Virtually all of the foodstuffs, 80% of the electrolytes, and most of the water are absorbed in the small intestine. Although absorption occurs all along the length of the small intestine, most of it is completed by the time chyme reaches the ileum. Hence, the major absorptive role of the ileum is to reclaim bile salts to be recycled back to the liver for resecretion. At the end of the ileum, all that remains is some water, indigestible food materials (largely plant fibers such as cellulose), and millions of bacteria. This debris is passed on to the large intestine.

Most nutrients are absorbed through the mucosa of the intestinal villi by *active transport* processes driven directly or indirectly (secondarily) by metabolic energy (ATP). They then enter the capillary blood in the villus to be transported in the hepatic portal vein to the liver. The exception is some of the lipid digestion products, which are absorbed passively by diffusion and then enter the lacteal in the villus to be carried to the blood via lymphatic fluid. Because the epithelial cells of the intestinal mucosa are joined at their luminal (apical) surfaces by tight junctions, substances cannot move *between* the cells. Consequently, materials must pass *through* the epithelial cells and into the interstitial fluid abutting their basal membranes if they are to enter the blood capillaries. This reabsorption mechanism is called **transepithelial transport.** The absorption of each nutrient class is described next.

Absorption of Specific Nutrients

Carbohydrates

The monosaccharides glucose and galactose, liberated by the breakdown of starch and disaccharides, are transported into the epithelial cells by common protein carriers and then move into the capillary blood. The carriers, which are located very close to the disaccharidase enzymes on the microvilli, combine with the monosaccharides as soon as the disaccharides are broken down. The transport process for these sugars is secondary active transport coupled to sodium ions. Na$^+$ and the sugars are ferried across the membrane at the same time (cotransported). By contrast, fructose absorption is not ATP dependent. It moves *entirely* by facilitated diffusion.

Proteins

Several types of carriers transport the different classes of amino acids resulting from protein digestion. These carriers, like those for glucose and galactose, are coupled to the active transport of sodium. Short chains of two or three amino acids (dipeptides and tripeptides, respectively) are also actively absorbed, but are digested to their amino acids within the epithelial cells before entering the capillary blood.

Although *whole* proteins are not usually absorbed, in rare cases intact proteins are taken up by endocytosis and released on the opposite side of the epithelial cell by exocytosis. This process is most common in newborn infants, reflecting the immaturity of their intestinal mucosa, and accounts for many early food allergies. The immune system recognizes the intact proteins as antigenic and mounts an attack. These food allergies usually disappear as the mucosa matures. However, this mechanism may also provide a route for IgA antibodies present in breast milk to reach an infant's bloodstream. These antibodies confer some passive immunity on the infant (temporary protection against antigens to which the mother has been sensitized). •

Lipids

Just as bile salts accelerate lipid digestion, they are also essential for the absorption of its end products. As the water-insoluble products of fat digestion—the monoglycerides and free fatty acids—are liberated by lipase activity, they quickly become associated with bile salts and *lecithin* (a phospholipid found in bile) to form micelles. **Micelles** (mi-selz') are collections of fatty elements clustered together with bile salts in such a way that the polar (hydrophilic) ends of the molecules face the water and the nonpolar portions form the micelle core. Also nestled in the hydrophobic core are cholesterol molecules and fat-soluble vitamins. Although micelles are similar to emulsion droplets, they are much smaller "vehicles" and easily diffuse between microvilli to come into close contact with the mucosal cell surface (Figure 24.36). The fatty

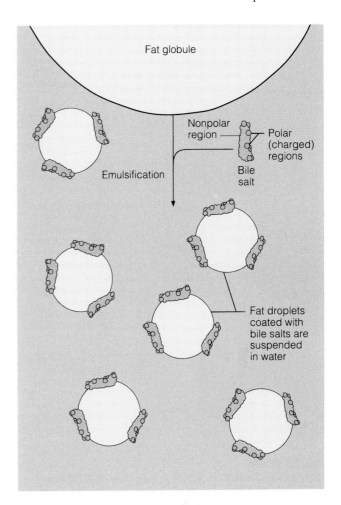

FIGURE 24.35
Role of bile salts in fat emulsification. As large aggregates of fats enter the small intestine, bile salts cling via their nonpolar parts to the fat molecules (triglycerides). Their polar parts, facing the aqueous phase, interact with water and repel each other, causing the fatty globule to be physically broken up into smaller fat droplets and forming a stable emulsion.

substances, cholesterol, and fat-soluble vitamins then leave the micelles and, because of their high lipid solubility, move through the lipid phase of the plasma membrane by simple diffusion. The micelles provide a continuous source of solubilized fat breakdown products that can be released and absorbed as fat digestion continues. Without the micelles, the lipids simply float on the surface of the chyme (like oil on water), inaccessible to the absorptive surfaces of the epithelial cells. Generally, fat absorption is completed in the ileum, but in the absence of bile (as might occur when a gallstone blocks the cystic duct) it happens so slowly that most of the fat passes into the large intestine and is lost in feces.

Once inside the epithelial cells, the free fatty acids and monoglycerides are resynthesized into triglycerides. The triglycerides are then combined with small amounts of phospholipids and cholesterol, and coated with a "skin" of proteins to form water-soluble lipoprotein droplets called **chylomi-**

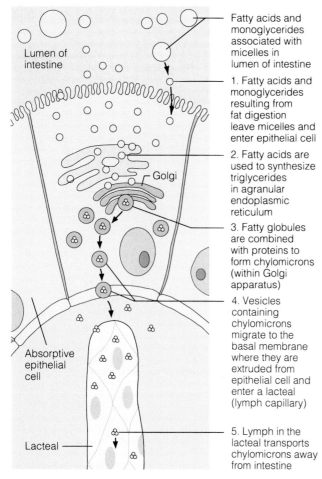

Lumen of intestine

Fatty acids and monoglycerides associated with micelles in lumen of intestine

1. Fatty acids and monoglycerides resulting from fat digestion leave micelles and enter epithelial cell

Golgi

2. Fatty acids are used to synthesize triglycerides in agranular endoplasmic reticulum

3. Fatty globules are combined with proteins to form chylomicrons (within Golgi apparatus)

4. Vesicles containing chylomicrons migrate to the basal membrane where they are extruded from epithelial cell and enter a lacteal (lymph capillary)

Absorptive epithelial cell

5. Lymph in the lacteal transports chylomicrons away from intestine

Lacteal

FIGURE 24.36

Fatty acid absorption. Digestion products of fat breakdown include glycerol, fatty acids, and monoglycerides. The monoglycerides, free fatty acids, phospholipids, and cholesterol associate with bile salt micelles, which serve to "ferry" them to the intestinal mucosa. They then dissociate and enter the mucosal cells by diffusion. Within the mucosal epithelial cells, they are recombined to lipids and packaged with other lipoid substances (phospholipids and cholesterol) and protein to form chylomicrons. The chylomicrons are extruded from the epithelial cells and enter the lacteal for distribution in the lymph. Free fatty acids and monoglycerides enter the capillary bed (not illustrated).

crons (ki″lo-mi′kronz), which are then processed by the Golgi apparatus for extrusion from the cell. This series of events is quite different from the absorption of amino acids and simple sugars, which pass through the epithelial cells unchanged.

While a few free fatty acids enter the capillary blood, the milky-white chylomicrons are too large to pass through the basement membranes of the blood capillaries and instead enter the more permeable lacteals. Thus, most fat enters the lymphatic stream and is eventually emptied into the venous blood in the neck region via the thoracic duct, which drains the digestive viscera. While in the bloodstream, the triglycerides of the chylomicrons are hydrolyzed to free fatty acids and glycerol by **lipoprotein lipase**, an enzyme associated with the capillary endothelium. The fatty acids and glycerol can then pass through the capillary walls to be used by tissue cells for energy or stored as fats in adipose tissue. The residual chylomicron material is combined with proteins by the liver

cells, and these "new" lipoproteins are used to transport cholesterol in the blood.

Nucleic Acids

The pentose sugars, nitrogenous bases, and phosphate ions resulting from nucleic acid digestion are transported across the epithelium by special carriers in the villus epithelium. They then enter the blood.

Vitamins

Although the small intestine absorbs dietary vitamins, the large intestine absorbs some of the K and B vitamins made by its enteric bacterial "guests." As already noted, fat-soluble vitamins (A, D, E, and K) dissolve in dietary fats, become incorporated into the micelles, and move across the villus epithelium by passive diffusion. It follows that gulping pills containing fat-soluble vitamins without simultaneously eating some fat-containing food results in little or no absorption of these vitamins.

Most water-soluble vitamins (B vitamins and vitamin C) are absorbed easily by diffusion. The exception is vitamin B_{12}, which is a very large, charged molecule. Vitamin B_{12} binds to *intrinsic factor,* produced by the stomach. The vitamin B_{12}–intrinsic factor complex then binds to specific mucosal sites in the terminal ileum, which trigger its endocytosis.

Electrolytes

Absorbed electrolytes come from both ingested foods and gastrointestinal secretions. Most ions are actively absorbed along the entire length of the small intestine. However, iron and calcium absorption is largely limited to the duodenum.

As noted, absorption of sodium ions in the small intestine is coupled to active absorption of glucose and amino acids. For the most part, anions passively follow the electrical potential established by sodium transport. Chloride ions are also transported actively, and in the small intestine terminus HCO_3^- is actively secreted into the lumen in exchange for Cl^-.

Potassium ions move across the intestinal mucosa by simple diffusion in response to osmotic gradients. As water is absorbed from the lumen, the resulting rise in potassium levels in chyme creates a concentration gradient for its absorption. Thus, anything that interferes with water absorption (such as diarrhea) not only reduces potassium absorption but also "pulls" K^+ from the interstitial space into the intestinal lumen.

For most nutrients, the amount *reaching* the intestine is the amount absorbed, regardless of the nutritional state of the body. In contrast, the absorption of iron and calcium is intimately related to the body's need for them at the time.

Ionic iron, essential for hemoglobin production, is actively transported into the mucosal cells, where it binds to the protein **ferritin** (fer′ĭ-tin). This phenomenon is called the *mucosal iron barrier.* The intracellular iron-ferritin complexes then serve as local storehouses for iron. When body reserves of iron are adequate, very little is allowed to pass into the portal blood, and most of the stored iron is lost as the epithelial cells later slough off. However, when iron reserves are depleted (as during acute or chronic hemorrhage), iron uptake from the intestine and its release to the blood are accelerated. Menstrual bleeding is a major route of iron loss in females, and the intestinal epithelial cells of women have about four times as many iron transport proteins as do those of men. In the blood, iron binds to **transferrin,** a plasma protein that transports it in the circulation.

Calcium absorption is closely related to blood levels of ionic calcium. It is locally regulated by the active form of **vitamin D,** which acts as a cofactor to facilitate calcium absorption. Decreased blood levels of ionic calcium prompt *parathyroid hormone (PTH)* release from the parathyroid glands. Besides facilitating the release of calcium ions from bone matrix and enhancing the reabsorption of calcium by the kidneys, PTH stimulates renal activation of vitamin D, which in turn accelerates calcium ion absorption in the small intestine.

Water

Approximately 9 L of water, mostly derived from GI tract secretions, enter the small intestine daily. Water is the most abundant substance in chyme, and 95% of it is absorbed in the small intestine by osmosis. The normal rate of water absorption is 300 to 400 ml per hour. Water moves freely in both directions across the intestinal mucosa, but *net osmosis* occurs whenever a concentration gradient is established by the active transport of solutes (particularly Na^+) into the mucosal cells. Thus, water uptake is effectively coupled to solute uptake and, in turn, affects the rate of absorption of substances that normally pass by diffusion. As water moves into the mucosal cells, these substances follow along their concentration gradients.

Malabsorption of Nutrients

Malabsorption, or impaired nutrient absorption, has many and various causes. It can result from anything that interferes with the delivery of bile or pancreatic juice to the small intestine, as well as factors that damage the intestinal mucosa (severe bacterial infections and antibiotic therapy with neomycin) or reduce its absorptive surface area. A common but poorly understood malabsorption syndrome is *gluten enteropathy,* also called *adult celiac disease.* In this condition, gluten, a protein plentiful in some grains (wheat, rye, barley, oats), damages the intestinal villi and reduces the length of the microvilli of the brush border. The resulting diarrhea and malnutrition are usually controlled by eliminating gluten-containing grains (all but rice and corn) from the diet.   •

DEVELOPMENTAL ASPECTS OF THE DIGESTIVE SYSTEM

As described many times before, the very young embryo is flat and consists of three germ layers, which, from top to bottom, are ectoderm, mesoderm, and endoderm. However, this flattened cell mass soon folds to form a cylindrical body, and its internal cavity becomes the cavity of the alimentary tube, which is initially closed at both ends. The epithelial lining of the developing alimentary tube, or **primitive gut,** forms from endoderm (Figure 24.37a). The rest of the wall arises from mesoderm. The anteriormost endoderm (that of the foregut) touches a depressed area of the surface ectoderm called the **stomodeum** (sto"mo-de'um; "on the way to becoming the mouth"). The two membranes fuse, forming the **oral membrane,** which shortly breaks through to form the opening of the mouth. Similarly, the end of the hindgut fuses with an ectodermal depression, called the **proctodeum** (*procto* = anus), to form the **cloacal** (*cloaca* = sewer) **membrane** and then breaks through to form the anus. By eight weeks, the alimentary canal is a continuous "tube" extending from the mouth to the anus and is open to the external environment at each end. Shortly after, the glandular organs (salivary glands, liver with gallbladder, and pancreas) bud out from the mucosa at various points along its length (Figure 24.37b). These glands retain their connections, which become ducts leading into the digestive tract.

The digestive system is susceptible to many congenital defects that interfere with feeding. The most common congenital defects are *cleft palate,* in which the palatine bones or palatine processes of the maxillae (or both) fail to fuse, and *cleft lip,* which often occur together. Of the two, cleft palate is far more serious because the child is unable to suck properly. Another common defect is *tracheoesophageal fistula,* in which there is an opening between the esophagus and the trachea, and the esophagus often lacks a connection to the stomach. The baby chokes and becomes cyanotic during feedings because food enters the respiratory passageways. These defects are usually corrected surgically.

Cystic fibrosis (described in more detail in Chapter 23, p. 780) primarily affects the lungs, but it also significantly impairs the activity of the pancreas. In this genetic disease, the mucous glands produce huge amounts of mucus, which blocks the ducts or passageways of involved organs. Blockage of the pancreatic duct prevents pancreatic juice from reaching the small intestine. As a result, most fats and fat-soluble vitamins are not digested or absorbed, and the stools are bulky and fat-laden. The pancreatic problems can be handled by administering pancreatic enzymes with meals.   •

During fetal life, the developing infant receives all of its nutrients through the placenta; hence,

Text continues on p. 840

Making Connections

Systems Connections: Homeostatic Interrelationships Between the Digestive System and Other Body Systems

Nervous System
• Neural controls of digestive function; in general, parasympathetic fibers accelerate and sympathetic fibers inhibit digestive activity; reflex and voluntary controls of defecation

• Digestive system provides nutrients needed for normal neural functioning; nutrient signals influence neural regulation of satiety

Endocrine System
• Local hormones help regulate digestive function

• Liver removes hormones from blood ending their activity; digestive system provides nutrients needed for energy fuel, growth, and repair; pancreas has hormone-producing cells

Cardiovascular System
• Cardiovascular system transports nutrients absorbed by alimentary canal to all tissues of body; distributes hormones of the digestive tract

• Digestive system provides nutrients to heart and blood vessels; absorbs iron needed for hemoglobin synthesis; absorbs water necessary for normal plasma volume

Lymphatic System/Immunity
• Lacteals drain fatty lymph from digestive tract organs and convey it to blood; Peyer's patches and lymphoid tissue in mesentery houses macrophages and immune cells that protect digestive tract organs against infection

• Digestive system provides nutrients for normal functioning; HCl of stomach provides nonspecific protection against bacteria

Respiratory System
• Respiratory system provides oxygen and carries away carbon dioxide produced by digestive system organs

• Digestive system provides nutrients needed for energy metabolism, growth, and repair

Urinary System
• Kidneys transform vitamin D to its active form, which is needed for calcium absorption

• Digestive system provides nutrients for energy fuel, growth, and repair; excretes some bilirubin produced by the liver

Reproductive System
• Digestive system provides nutrients for energy fuel, growth, and repair and extra nutrition needed to support fetal growth

Integumentary System
• The skin synthesizes vitamin D needed for calcium absorption from the intestine; protects by enclosure

• Digestive system provides nutrients needed for energy fuel, growth, and repair; supplies fats that provide insulation in the dermal and subcutaneous tissues

Skeletal System
• Skeletal system protects some digestive organs by bone; cavities store some nutrients (e.g., calcium, fats)

• Digestive system provides nutrients needed for energy fuel, growth, and repair; absorbs calcium needed for bone salts

Muscular System
• Skeletal muscle activity increases motility of GI tract

• Digestive system provides nutrients needed for energy fuel, growth, and repair; liver removes lactic acid, resulting from muscle activity from the blood

Closer Connections: The Digestive System and Interrelationships with the Cardiovascular, Lymphatic, and Endocrine Systems

As body systems go, the digestive system is very independent. Although the central nervous system can and does influence its activity, that is not a requirement. Indeed, most digestive system activities can be regulated entirely by local controls. Consider, for example, the following: (1) stomach and intestinal muscle is self-pacing, (2) the enteric neurons of the GI tract's intrinsic nerve plexuses carry out reflex activity that can regulate not only the organ they reside in but also adjacent and more distant GI tract organs, and (3) its enteroendocrine cells are probably even more important than neural influences in controlling digestive activity. Also unique is the fact that the digestive system operates in and regulates an environment that is actually outside the body. This is a very difficult chore indeed—consider how quickly that environment can be changed by incoming foods (pizza and beer) or intestinal outflow (diarrhea).

Every cell in the body needs nutrients to stay healthy and grow, so the importance of the digestive system to virtually all body systems is clear-cut. But what systems are essential to the digestive system? If we ignore universal services, like gas exchange and renal regulation of body fluids, then the most crucial interactions are those with the cardiovascular, lymphatic, and endocrine systems. Let's take a look.

Cardiovascular and Lymphatic Systems

The important elements in this interaction are the pickup vessels. Indeed, all digestive activity would be for naught if the digested end products were not absorbed into the blood capillaries and lacteals, where they are accessible to all body cells. Besides its transport function, the lymphatic system also offers protective services via its tonsils, Peyer's patches, and individual lymphoid nodules dispersed all along the length of the alimentary tube. Again, the fact that the alimentary canal is open at both ends makes it easy prey for both pathogenic and opportunistic bacteria and fungi.

Endocrine System

The digestive tract not only has major interactions with the endocrine system, it is itself the largest and most complex endocrine organ in the body. It makes hormones that not only regulate GI tract mobility and secretory activity of the stomach, small intestine, liver, and pancreas (secretin, CCK, GIP, serotonin) but also cause local blood vessels to dilate to receive the digested food products being absorbed (VIP). Furthermore, some digestive organ hormones (CCK and glucagon, for example) help mediate hunger or satiety, and pancreatic hormones (insulin and glucagon) are involved in bodywide regulation of carbohydrate, fat, and amino acid metabolism.

Clinical Connections

Digestive System

Case study: Remember Mr. Gutteman, the gentleman who was dehydrating? It seems that his tremendous output of urine was only one of his current problems. Today, he complains of a headache and feeling bloated, and that he has "the runs" (diarrhea). In order to try to pinpoint the problem, he is asked the following questions.

• Have you had these symptoms previously? (Response: "On rare occasions.")

• Are you allergic to any foods? (Response: "Shellfish doesn't like me and milk gives me the runs.")

As a result of his responses, a lactose-free diet is ordered for Mr. Gutteman instead of the regular diet originally prescribed.

Why is the new diet prescribed? (What is believed to be his problem?)

Mr. Gutteman's problem continues despite the diet change. In fact, the frequency of diarrhea increases and by the end of the

next day, he is complaining of severe lower right abdominal pain, and his stool is largely bloody mucus. Again, he is asked some questions to probe his condition.

• Do you drink alcohol and how much? (Response: "Little or none.")

• Have you traveled outside the country recently? (Response: "No.")

• Have you recently eaten raw eggs or a salad containing mayonnaise at a gathering? (Response: "No.")

• Have you recently eaten at a "new" restaurant? (Response: "Yes, the day of the accident.")

On the basis of these responses, what do you think that Mr. Gutteman's diarrhea stems from? How will it be diagnosed and treated? Why are such patients reported to the Health Department?

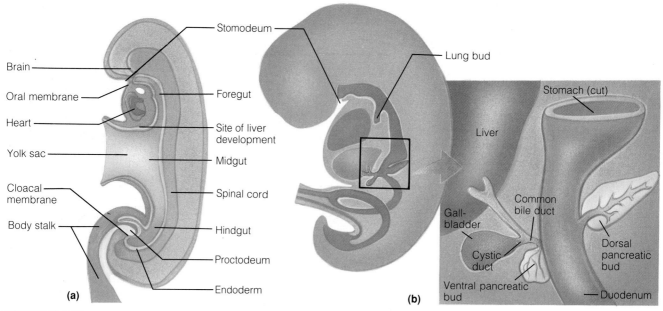

(a)

- Stomodeum
- Brain
- Oral membrane
- Heart
- Yolk sac
- Cloacal membrane
- Body stalk
- Foregut
- Site of liver development
- Midgut
- Spinal cord
- Hindgut
- Proctodeum
- Endoderm

(b)

- Lung bud
- Stomach (cut)
- Liver
- Common bile duct
- Gall-bladder
- Cystic duct
- Ventral pancreatic bud
- Dorsal pancreatic bud
- Duodenum

FIGURE 24.37
Embryonic development of the digestive system. (a) Three-week-old embryo. The endoderm has folded, and the foregut and hindgut have formed. (The midgut is still open and continuous with the yolk sac.) The anterior and posterior points of ectodermal-endodermal fusion (the oral and cloacal membranes, respectively) will shortly break through to form the mouth and anal openings. **(b)** By eight weeks of development, the accessory organs are budding out from the endodermal layer, as shown in the enlargement.

obtaining and processing nutrients is no problem if the mother is adequately nourished. Nonetheless, the fetal GI tract is "trained" in utero for future food digestion as the fetus naturally swallows some of the surrounding amniotic fluid. This fluid contains several chemicals that stimulate GI maturation, including gastrin and epidermal growth factor. By contrast, feeding is a newborn baby's most important activity, and several feeding reflexes enhance the infant's ability to obtain food: The *rooting reflex* helps the infant find the nipple, and the *sucking reflex* helps the baby hold onto the nipple and swallow. Newborn babies tend to double their birth weight within 6 months, and their caloric intake and food processing ability are extraordinary. For example, a six-week-old infant weighing about 4 kg (less than 9 pounds) drinks about 600 ml of milk daily. A 65-kg adult (143 lb) would have to drink 10 L of milk to ingest a corresponding volume of fluid! However, the stomach of a newborn infant is very small, so feeding must be frequent (every 3–4 hours). Peristalsis is inefficient, and vomiting of the feeding is not unusual. As the teeth break through the gums, the infant progresses to solid foods and is usually eating an adult diet by the age of two years.

Unless there are abnormal interferences, the digestive system operates throughout childhood and adulthood with relatively few problems. However, contaminated food or extremely spicy or irritating foods sometimes cause an inflammation of the GI tract, called **gastroenteritis** (gas″tro-en″tĕ-ri′tis). Ulcers and gallbladder problems—inflammation or **cholecystitis** (ko″le-sis-ti′tis), and gallstones—are problems of middle age.

During old age, GI tract activity declines. Fewer digestive juices are produced, absorption is less efficient, and peristalsis slows. The result is less frequent bowel movements and, often, constipation. Taste and smell become less acute, and periodontal disease often develops. Many elderly people live alone or on a reduced income. These factors, along with increasing physical disability, tend to make eating less appealing, and many of our elderly citizens are inadequately nourished.

Diverticulosis and cancer of the GI tract are fairly common problems of the aged. Cancers of the stomach and colon rarely have early signs, and the disease often has metastasized (making it inoperable) before a person seeks medical attention. Should metastasis occur, secondary cancer of the liver is almost guaranteed because of the "detour" the splanchnic venous blood takes through the liver via the hepatic portal circulation. However, when detected early, these cancers are treatable. Perhaps the best advice is to have regular dental and medical checkups. Most oral cancers are detected during routine dental examinations, 50% of all rectal cancers can be felt digitally, and nearly 80% of colon cancers can be seen and removed during a colonoscopy.

Presently, colon cancer is the second largest cause of cancer deaths (behind lung cancer) in the U.S., accounting for over 65,000 deaths per year. Since most colorectal cancers derive from initially benign mucosal tumors called **polyps**, and the incidence of polyp formation increases with age, a yearly colon examination should be a health priority in everyone over the age of 50. As described in *A Closer Look* on pp. 96–97, development of colon cancer is a gradual process that involves mutations in several regulatory genes. Recent studies have identified the mutant gene responsible for the most common hereditary colon cancer (10% of cases). Dubbed *p53* (or *MSH2*) the gene normally acts as a watchdog to make sure that errors in DNA are not passed on before being corrected. When *p53* is damaged or inhibited, its tumor suppressor effect is lost and damaged DNA accumulates, resulting in carcinogenesis.

* * *

As summarized in *Making Connections,* the digestive system keeps the blood well supplied with the nutrients needed by all body tissues to fuel their energy needs and to synthesize new proteins for growth and maintenance of health. Now we are ready to examine how these nutrients are used by body cells, the topic of Chapter 25.

RELATED CLINICAL TERMS

Ascites (ah-si′tēz; *asci* = bag, bladder) Abnormal accumulation of fluid within the peritoneal cavity; if excessive, causes visible bloating of the abdomen; may result from portal hypertension caused by liver cirrhosis, or by heart or kidney disease.

Colitis (ko-li′tis; *itis* = inflammation) Inflammation of the large intestine, or colon.

Dysphagia (dis-fa′je-ah; *dys* = difficult, abnormal; *phag* = eat) Difficult swallowing; usually due to obstruction or physical trauma to the esophagus.

Endoscopy (en-dos′ko-pe; *endo* = within, inside; *scopy* = viewing) Visual examination of a ventral body cavity or the interior of a tubular visceral organ with a flexible tubelike device called an endoscope, which contains a light source and a lens; a general term for a colonoscopy (viewing the colon), sigmoidoscopy (viewing the sigmoid colon), etc.

Enteritis (*enteron* = intestine) Inflammation of the intestine, especially the small intestine.

Gastrectomy (gas-trek′to-me; *gastro* = stomach; *tomy* = cut, excise) Removal of all or part of the stomach; common in severe cases of gastric ulcer.

Hemochromatosis (he″mo-kro″mah-to′sis; *hemo* = blood; *chroma* = color; *osis* = condition of) A syndrome caused by a disorder in iron metabolism, owing to excessive/prolonged iron intake or a breakdown of the mucosal iron barrier; excess iron is deposited in the tissues, resulting in increased skin pigmentation and increased incidence of hepatic cancer and liver cirrhosis; also called *bronze diabetes* and *iron storage disease.*

Ileus (il′e-us) A condition in which all GI tract movement stops and the gut appears to be paralyzed; can result from electrolyte imbalances and blockade of parasympathetic impulses by drugs (such as those commonly used during abdominal surgery); usually reversed when these interferences end; restoration of mobility is indicated by the reappearance of bowel (intestinal) sounds (gurgling, etc.).

Pancreatitis (pan″kre-ah-ti′tis) A rare but extremely serious inflammation of the pancreas; may result from excessively high levels of fat in the blood, but most often results from activation of pancreatic enzymes in the pancreatic duct, causing the pancreatic tissue and duct to be digested; this painful condition can lead to nutritional deficiencies, because pancreatic enzymes are essential to food digestion in the small intestine.

Peptic ulcers Collective term referring to gastric and duodenal ulcers.

Proctology (prok-tol′o-je; *procto* = rectum, anus; *logy* = study of) Branch of medicine dealing with treatment of diseases of the colon, rectum, and anus.

Pyloric stenosis (pi-lor′ik stĕ-no′sis; *stenosis* = narrowing, constriction) Congenital abnormality in which the pyloric sphincter is abnormally constricted; there is usually no problem until the baby begins to take solid food, and then projectile vomiting begins; usually corrected surgically.

Ulcerative colitis Inflammatory disease of the rectum and colon that ranges in severity, progressing from the rectum proximally and involving the mucosa and submucosa tunics; ulceration of the mucosa results in pain, mucus-laden bloody stools, and diarrhea; cause is unknown but genetic factors and autoimmune responses are involved; enhances the risk of colon cancer, so surgical removal of the colon in chronic cases of 10 years or more duration is the accepted treatment.

Xerostomia (ze″ro-sto′me-ah; *zer* = dry, *stom* = mouth) Extreme dryness of the mouth; can be caused by blockage of salivary glands by cysts or autoimmune invasion of the salivary glands or ducts (Sjögren's syndrome).

CHAPTER SUMMARY

Overview of the Digestive System (pp. 789–795)

1. The digestive system includes organs of the alimentary canal (mouth, pharynx, esophagus, stomach, small and large intestines) and accessory digestive system organs (teeth, tongue, salivary glands, liver, gallbladder, and pancreas).

Digestive Processes (pp. 790–791)

2. Digestive system activities include six functional processes: ingestion, or food intake; propulsion, or movement of food through the tract; mechanical digestion, or processes that physically mix or break foods down into smaller fragments; chemical digestion, or food breakdown by enzymatic action; absorption, or transport of products of digestion through the intestinal mucosa into the blood; and defecation, or elimination of the undigested residues (feces) from the body.

Basic Functional Concepts (pp. 791–792)

3. The digestive system controls the environment within its lumen to ensure optimal conditions for digestion and absorption of foodstuffs.

4. Receptors and hormone-secreting cells within the alimentary canal wall respond to stretch and chemical signals that result in stimulation or inhibition of GI secretory activity or motility. The alimentary canal also has a local (intrinsic) nerve supply.

Digestive System Organs: Relationships and Structural Plan (pp. 792–795)

5. The parietal and visceral layers of the peritoneum are continuous with one another via several extensions (mesentery, falciform ligament, lesser and greater omenta), and are separated by a potential space containing serous fluid, which decreases friction during organ activity.

6. The digestive viscera is served by the splanchnic circulation consisting of arterial branches of the celiac trunk and aorta and the hepatic portal circulation.

7. All organs of the GI tract have the same basic pattern of tissue layers in their walls; i.e., all have a mucosa, a submucosa, a muscularis, and a serosa (or adventitia). Intrinsic nerve plexuses (enteric nervous system) are found within the wall.

FUNCTIONAL ANATOMY OF THE DIGESTIVE SYSTEM (pp. 795–830)

The Mouth, Pharynx, and Esophagus (pp. 795–804)

1. Food enters the GI tract via the mouth, which is continuous with the oropharynx posteriorly. The boundaries of the mouth are the lips and cheeks, the palate, and the tongue.

2. The oral mucosa is stratified squamous epithelium, an adaptation seen where abrasion occurs.

3. The tongue is mucosa-covered skeletal muscle. Its intrinsic muscles allow it to change shape; its extrinsic muscles allow it to change position.

4. Saliva is produced by many small buccal glands and three pairs of major salivary glands—parotid, submandibular, and sublingual—that secrete their product into the mouth via ducts. Largely water, saliva also contains ions, proteins, metabolic wastes, lysozyme, IgA, salivary amylase, and mucin.

5. Saliva moistens and cleanses the mouth; moistens foods, aiding their compaction; dissolves food chemicals to allow for taste; and begins chemical digestion of starch (salivary amylase). Saliva output is increased by parasympathetic reflexes initiated by activation of chemical and pressure receptors in the mouth and by conditioned reflexes. The sympathetic nervous system depresses salivation.

6. The 20 deciduous teeth begin to be shed at the age of six and are gradually replaced during childhood and adolescence by the 32 permanent teeth.

7. Teeth are classed as incisors, canines, premolars, and molars. Each tooth has an enamel-covered crown and a cementum-covered root. The bulk of the tooth is dentin, which surrounds the central pulp cavity. A periodontal ligament secures the tooth to the bony alveolus.

8. Food propelled from the mouth passes through the oropharynx and laryngopharynx. The mucosa of the pharynx is stratified squamous epithelium; the skeletal muscles in its wall (constrictor muscles) move food toward the esophagus.

9. The esophagus extends from the laryngopharynx and joins the stomach at the cardiac orifice, which is surrounded by the gastroesophageal sphincter.

10. The esophageal mucosa is stratified squamous epithelium. Its muscularis is skeletal muscle superiorly and changes to smooth muscle inferiorly. It has an adventitia rather than a serosa.

11. The mouth and associated accessory organs accomplish food ingestion and mechanical digestion (chewing and mixing), initiate the chemical digestion of starch (salivary amylase), and propel food into the pharynx (buccal phase of swallowing).

12. Teeth function to masticate food. Chewing is initiated voluntarily and is then controlled reflexively.

13. The tongue mixes food with saliva, compacts it into a bolus, and initiates swallowing (the voluntary phase). The pharynx and esophagus are primarily food conduits that conduct food to the stomach by peristalsis during swallowing. The swallowing center in the medulla and pons controls this phase reflexively. When the peristaltic wave approaches the gastroesophageal sphincter, the sphincter relaxes to allow food entry to the stomach.

The Stomach (pp. 804–813)

14. The C-shaped stomach lies in the upper left quadrant of the abdomen. Its major regions are the cardia, fundus, body, and pyloric region. When empty, its internal surface exhibits rugae.

15. The stomach mucosa is simple columnar epithelium dotted with gastric pits that lead into gastric glands. Secretory cells in the gastric glands include pepsinogen-producing zymogenic cells; parietal cells, which secrete hydrochloric acid and intrinsic factor; mucous neck cells, which produce mucus; and enteroendocrine cells, which secrete a variety of hormones.

16. The mucosal barrier, which protects the stomach from self-digestion and HCl, reflects the fact that the mucosal cells are connected by tight junctions, secrete a thick mucus, and are quickly replaced when damaged.

17. The stomach muscularis contains a third layer of obliquely oriented smooth muscle that allows it to churn and mix food.

18. Protein digestion is initiated in the stomach by activated pepsin and requires acidic conditions (provided by HCl). Few substances are absorbed.

19. Gastric secretory activity is controlled by both nervous and hormonal factors. The three phases of gastric secretion are the cephalic, gastric, and intestinal. For the most part stimuli acting on the head and stomach (cephalic and gastric respectively) stimulate gastric secretion. Most stimuli acting on the small intestine trigger the enterogastric reflex and release of secretin, CCK, and GIP, all of which inhibit gastric secretory activity. Sympathetic activity also inhibits gastric secretion.

20. Mechanical digestion in the stomach is triggered by stomach distension and coupled to food propulsion and stomach emptying. Food movement into the duodenum is controlled by the pylorus and feedback signals from the small intestine. Pacemaker cells in the smooth muscle sheet set the maximal rate of peristaltic waves.

The Small Intestine and Associated Structures (pp. 813–825)

21. The small intestine extends from the pyloric sphincter to the ileocecal valve. Its three subdivisions are the duodenum, jejunum, and ileum. The common bile duct and pancreatic duct join to form the hepatopancreatic ampulla and empty their secretions into the duodenum through the hepatopancreatic sphincter (of Oddi).

22. The duodenal submucosa contains elaborate mucus-secreting duodenal glands (Brunner's glands); that of the ileum contains Peyer's patches (lymph nodules). The duodenum is covered with an adventitia rather than a serosa.

23. Plicae circulares, villi, and microvilli increase the intestinal surface area for digestion and absorption.

24. The small intestine is the major digestive and absorptive organ. Intestinal juice is largely water and is relatively enzyme-poor. The major stimuli for its release are stretch and chemical stimuli.

25. The liver is a lobed organ overlying the stomach. Its digestive role is to produce bile, which it secretes into the common hepatic duct.

26. The structural and functional units of the liver are the hepatic lobules. Blood flowing to the liver via the hepatic artery and hepatic portal vein flows into its sinusoids from which Kupffer cells remove debris and the hepatocytes remove nutrients. The hepatocytes store glucose as glycogen, use amino acids to make plasma proteins, and detoxify metabolic wastes and drugs.

27. Bile is made continuously by the hepatocytes. Bile salts, secretin, and vagal stimulation stimulate bile production.

28. The gallbladder, a muscular sac that lies beneath the right liver lobe, stores and concentrates bile.

29. Bile contains electrolytes, a variety of fatty substances, bile salts, and bile pigments in an aqueous medium. Bile salts are emulsifying agents; they disperse fats and form water-soluble micelles, which solubilize the products of fat digestion.

30. Cholecystokinin released by the small intestine stimulates the gallbladder to contract and the hepatopancreatic sphincter to relax, allowing bile (and pancreatic juice) to enter the duodenum.

31. The pancreas is retroperitoneal between the spleen and small intestine. Its exocrine product, pancreatic juice, is carried to the duodenum via the pancreatic duct.

32. Pancreatic juice is an HCO_3^--rich fluid containing enzymes that digest all categories of foods. Secretion of pancreatic juice is controlled by intestinal hormones and the vagus nerves.

33. Mechanical digestion and propulsion in the small intestine mix chyme with digestive juices and bile and force the residues, largely by segmentation, through the ileocecal valve. Pacemaker cells set the rate of segmentation. Ileocecal valve opening is controlled by the gastroileal reflex and gastrin.

The Large Intestine (pp. 826–830)

34. The subdivisions of the large intestine are the cecum (and appendix), colon (ascending, transverse, descending, and sigmoid portions), rectum, and anal canal. It opens to the body exterior at the anus.

35. The mucosa of most of the large intestine is simple columnar epithelium containing abundant goblet cells. The longitudinal muscle in the muscularis is reduced to three bands (teniae coli), which pucker its wall, producing haustra.

36. The major functions of the large intestine are absorption of water, and some electrolytes (and vitamins made by enteric bacteria), and defecation (evacuation of food residues from the body).

37. The defecation reflex is triggered when feces enters the rectum. It involves parasympathetic reflexes leading to the contraction of the rectal walls and is aided by Valsalva's maneuver.

PHYSIOLOGY OF CHEMICAL DIGESTION AND ABSORPTION (pp. 830–837)

Chemical Digestion (pp. 830–834)

1. Chemical digestion is accomplished by hydrolysis, catalyzed by enzymes.

2. Most chemical digestion is done in the small intestine by intestinal (brush border) enzymes and, more importantly, by pancreatic enzymes. Alkaline pancreatic juice neutralizes the acidic chyme and provides the proper environment for the operation of the enzymes. Both pancreatic juice (the only source of lipases) and bile are necessary for normal fat breakdown.

Absorption (pp. 834–837)

1. Virtually all of the foodstuffs and most of the water and electrolytes are absorbed in the small intestine. Except for fat digestion products, fat-soluble vitamins, and most water-soluble vitamins (which are absorbed by diffusion), most nutrients are absorbed by active transport processes.

2. Fat breakdown products are solubilized by bile salts (in micelles), resynthesized to triglycerides in the intestinal mucosal cells, and combined with other lipids and protein as chylomicrons that enter the lacteals. Other absorbed substances enter the villus blood capillaries and are transported to the liver via the hepatic portal vein.

Developmental Aspects of the Digestive System (pp. 837–841)

1. The mucosa of the alimentary canal develops from the endoderm, which folds to form a tube. The glandular accessory organs (salivary glands, liver, pancreas, and gallbladder) form from outpocketings of the foregut endoderm. The remaining three tunics of the alimentary canal wall are formed by mesoderm.

2. Important congenital abnormalities of the digestive tract include cleft palate/lip, tracheoesophageal fistula, and cystic fibrosis. All interfere with normal nutrition.

3. Various inflammations plague the digestive system throughout life. Appendicitis is common in adolescents, gastroenteritis and food poisoning can occur at any time (given the proper irritating factors), ulcers and gallbladder problems increase in middle age.

4. The efficiency of all digestive system processes declines in the elderly, and periodontal disease is common. Diverticulosis and GI tract cancers such as stomach and colon cancer appear with increasing frequency in an aging population.

REVIEW QUESTIONS

Multiple Choice/Matching

1. Obstruction of the hepatopancreatic sphincter impairs digestion by reducing the availability of (a) bile and HCl, (b) HCl and intestinal juice, (c) pancreatic juice and intestinal juice, (d) pancreatic juice and bile.

2. The action of an enzyme is influenced by (a) its chemical surroundings, (b) its specific substrate, (c) the presence of needed cofactors or coenzymes, (d) all of these.

3. Carbohydrates are acted on by (a) peptidases, trypsin, and chymotrypsin, (b) amylase, maltase, and sucrase, (c) lipases, (d) peptidases, lipases, and galactase.

4. The parasympathetic nervous system influences digestion by (a) relaxing smooth muscle, (b) stimulating peristalsis and secretory activity, (c) constricting sphincters, (d) none of these.

5. The digestive juice product containing enzymes capable of digesting all four major foodstuff categories is (a) pancreatic, (b) gastric, (c) salivary, (d) biliary.

6. The vitamin associated with calcium absorption is (a) A, (b) K, (c) C, (d) D.

7. Someone has eaten a meal of buttered toast, cream, and eggs. Which of the following would you expect to happen? (a) Compared to the period shortly after the meal, gastric motility and secretion of HCl decrease when the food reaches the duodenum; (b) gastric motility increases even while the person is chewing the food (before any swallowing); (c) fat will be emulsified in the duodenum by the action of bile; (d) all of these.

8. The site of production of GIP and cholecystokinin is (a) the stomach, (b) the small intestine, (c) the pancreas, (d) the large intestine.

9. Which of the following is not characteristic of the large intestine? (a) It is divided into ascending, transverse, and descending portions; (b) it contains abundant bacteria, some of which synthesize certain vitamins; (c) is the main absorptive site; (d) it absorbs much of the water and salts remaining in the wastes.

10. The gallbladder (a) produces bile, (b) is attached to the pancreas, (c) stores and concentrates bile, (d) produces secretin.

 11. The sphincter between the stomach and duodenum is (a) the pyloric sphincter, (b) the cardiac sphincter, (c) the hepatopancreatic sphincter, (d) the ileocecal sphincter.

In items 12–16, trace the path of a single protein molecule that has been ingested.

12. The protein molecule will be digested by enzymes secreted by (a) the mouth, stomach, and colon, (b) the stomach, liver, and small intestine, (c) the small intestine, mouth, and liver, (d) the pancreas, small intestine, and stomach.

13. The protein molecule must be digested before it can be transported to and utilized by the cells because (a) protein is only useful directly, (b) protein has a low pH, (c) proteins in the circulating blood produce an adverse osmotic pressure, (d) the protein is too large to be readily absorbed.

14. The products of protein digestion enter the bloodstream largely through cells lining (a) the stomach, (b) the small intestine, (c) the large intestine, (d) the bile duct.

15. Before the blood carrying the products of protein digestion reaches the heart, it first passes through capillary networks in (a) the spleen, (b) the lungs, (c) the liver, (d) the brain.

16. Having passed through the regulatory organ selected above, the products of protein digestion are circulated throughout the body. They will enter individual body cells as a result of (a) active transport, (b) diffusion, (c) osmosis, (d) pinocytosis.

Short Answer Essay Questions

 17. Make a simple line drawing of the organs of the alimentary tube and label each organ. Then add three labels to your drawing—salivary glands, liver, and pancreas—and use arrows to show where each of these organs empties its secretion into the alimentary tube.

18. Name the layers of the alimentary tube wall. Note the tissue composition and major function of each layer.

19. What is a mesentery? Mesocolon? Greater omentum?

20. Name the six functional activities of the digestive system.

21. (a) Describe the boundaries of the oral cavity. (b) Why do you suppose its mucosa is stratified squamous epithelium rather than the more typical simple columnar epithelium?

22. (a) What is the normal number of permanent teeth? Of deciduous teeth? (b) What substance covers the tooth crown? Its root? (c) What substance makes up the bulk of a tooth? (d) What and where is pulp?

23. Describe the two phases of swallowing, noting the organs involved and the activities that occur.

24. Describe the role of these cell types found in the gastric glands: parietal, chief, mucous neck, and enteroendocrine.

25. Describe the regulation of the cephalic, gastric, and intestinal phases of gastric secretion.

 26. (a) What is the relationship between the cystic, hepatic, common bile, and pancreatic ducts? (b) What name is given to the point of fusion of the bile and pancreatic ducts?

27. Explain why fatty stools result from the absence of bile and/or pancreatic juice.

28. Note the function of the Kupffer cells and the hepatocytes of the liver.

29. What are (a) brush border enzymes? (b) chylomicrons?

30. Name one inflammatory condition particularly common to adolescents, two common in middle age, and one common in old age.

31. What are the effects of aging on digestive system activity?

 ## CRITICAL THINKING AND CLINICAL APPLICATION QUESTIONS

1. You are a young research assistant at a pharmaceutical company. Your group has been asked to develop an effective laxative that (1) provides bulk and (2) is nonirritating to the intestinal mucosa. Explain why these requests are important by describing what would happen if the opposite conditions were present.

2. After a heavy meal rich with fried foods, an overweight 45-year-old woman was rushed to the emergency room with severe spasmodic pains in her epigastric region that radiated to the right side of her rib cage. She indicated that the attack came on suddenly, and her abdomen was found to be tender to the touch and somewhat rigid. What do you think is this patient's problem and why is her pain discontinuous (colicky)? What are the treatment options and what might happen if the problem is not resolved?

3. A baby is admitted to the hospital with a history of diarrhea and watery feces occurring over the last three days. The baby has sunken fontanels, indicating extreme dehydration. On examination, the baby is found to have a bacterium-induced colitis, and antibiotics are prescribed. Because of the baby's loss of intestinal juices, do you think that his blood would indicate acidosis or alkalosis? Explain your reasoning.

4. Gary Francis, a middle-aged salesman, complains of a burning pain in the "pit of his stomach," usually beginning about 2 hours after eating and abating after drinking a glass of milk. When asked to indicate the site, he points to his epigastric region. The GI tract is examined by X-ray fluoroscopy. A gastric ulcer is visualized, and a selective vagotomy (cutting the vagal fibers serving the stomach) is recommended. (a) Why is the vagotomy suggested? (b) What are the possible consequences of nontreatment?

Nutrition, Metabolism, and Body Temperature Regulation

25

CHAPTER OUTLINE AND STUDENT OBJECTIVES

Although it seems at times that people can be divided into two camps according to their reactions to food—those who live to eat and those who eat to live—we all recognize the vital importance of food for life. Indeed, it has been said that "you are what you eat," and this is true in that part of the food we eat is converted to our living flesh. In other words, a certain fraction of nutrients is used to build cell structures, replace worn-out parts, and synthesize functional molecules. However, most foods are used as metabolic fuels. That is, they are oxidized and transformed into **ATP**, the chemical energy form needed by cells to drive their many activities. The energy value of foods is measured in units called **kilocalories** (kcal) or "large calories (C)." One kilocalorie is the amount of heat energy needed to raise the temperature of 1 kilogram of water 1°C (1.8°F) and is the unit conscientiously counted by dieters.

In Chapter 24, we considered how foods are digested and absorbed. But what happens to these foods once they have entered the blood? Why do we need bread, meat, and fresh vegetables? Why does everything we eat seem to turn to fat? This chapter will try to answer these questions as it explains both the nature of nutrients and the metabolic roles they play in the body.

NUTRITION

A **nutrient** is a substance in food that is used by the body to promote normal growth, maintenance, and repair. The nutrients needed for health divide neatly into six categories. Three of these—carbohydrates, lipids, and proteins—collectively called the *major nutrients,* make up the bulk of what we eat. Vitamins and minerals, while equally crucial for health, are required in minute amounts. In a strict sense, water, which accounts for about 60% of the volume of the food we eat, is also considered to be a major nutrient. However, since its importance as a dissolving medium (solvent), as a reactant in many chemical reactions, and in many other aspects of body functioning is described in Chapter 2 (pp. 39–40), only the five nutrient classes listed above will be considered in detail here.

Most foods offer a combination of nutrients. For example, a bowl of cream of mushroom soup contains all the major nutrients plus some vitamins and minerals. A diet consisting of foods from each of the five food groups, that is, grains, fruits, vegetables, meats and fish, and milk products, normally guarantees adequate amounts of all of the needed nutrients.

The ability of cells, especially those of the liver, to convert one type of molecule into another is truly remarkable. These interconversions allow the body to use the wide range of chemicals found in different foods and to adjust to varying food intakes. But there are limits to this ability to conjure up new molecules from old. At least 45 and possibly 50 molecules, called **essential nutrients,** cannot be made by such interconversions and must be provided by the diet. As long as all of the essential nutrients are ingested, the body can synthesize the hundreds of additional molecules required for life and good health. The use of the word "essential" to describe the chemicals that must be obtained from outside sources is unfortunate and misleading, to say the least, because both the essential and the nonessential nutrients are equally vital (essential) for normal functioning.

In this initial section, we will review the dietary sources and recommended daily requirements of each of the nutrient categories and note their general importance and uses in the body. Figure 25.1 illustrates the fates of the major nutrient categories in a very brief form.

Carbohydrates

Dietary Sources

Except for milk sugar (lactose) and small amounts of glycogen in meats, all the carbohydrates we ingest are derived from plants. Sugars (monosaccharides and disaccharides) come from fruits, sugar cane, sugar beets, honey, and milk. The polysaccharide starch is found in grains, legumes, and root vegetables. Cellulose, a polysaccharide plentiful in most vegetables, is not digested by humans, but provides roughage, or fiber, which increases the bulk of the stool and facilitates defecation.

Uses in the Body

The monosaccharide **glucose** is the carbohydrate molecule ultimately delivered to and used by body cells. Carbohydrate digestion also yields fructose and galactose, but these monosaccharides are converted to glucose by the liver before they enter the general circulation. Glucose is a major body fuel and is readily used to make ATP (Figure 25.1a). Although many body cells can and do use fats as energy sources, neurons and red blood cells rely almost entirely on glucose to supply their energy needs. Because even a temporary shortage of blood glucose can severely depress brain function and lead to death of neurons, the body carefully monitors and regulates blood sugar (glucose) levels.

Other uses of monosaccharides are meager. Small amounts of pentose sugars are used to synthesize nucleic acids, and a variety of sugars are attached to externally facing plasma membrane proteins and lipids. When blood glucose is present in excess of the body's needs for ATP synthesis, it is converted to glycogen in skeletal muscle, the heart, and the liver, or fat in adipose cells.

Dietary Requirements

The low-carbohydrate diet of Eskimos and the high-carbohydrate diet of peoples in the Far East indicate that humans can be healthy even with wide variations in carbohydrate intake. This, no doubt, reflects the body's ability to use fats and amino acids as fuels. The minimum requirement for carbohydrates is not known, but 100 grams per day is presumed to be the smallest amount needed to maintain adequate blood glucose levels. The current recommendation is 125 to 175 grams of carbohydrate daily with the emphasis

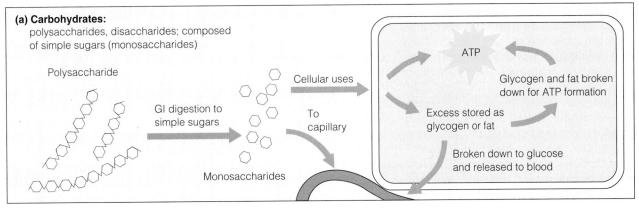

(a) Carbohydrates:
polysaccharides, disaccharides; composed of simple sugars (monosaccharides)

Polysaccharide

GI digestion to simple sugars

Monosaccharides

Cellular uses

To capillary

ATP

Glycogen and fat broken down for ATP formation

Excess stored as glycogen or fat

Broken down to glucose and released to blood

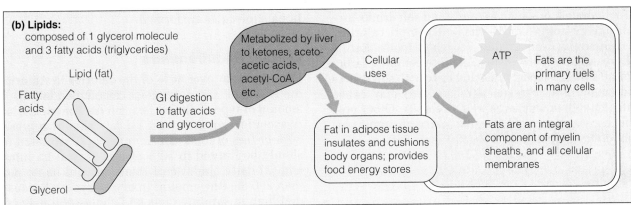

(b) Lipids:
composed of 1 glycerol molecule and 3 fatty acids (triglycerides)

Lipid (fat)

Fatty acids

Glycerol

GI digestion to fatty acids and glycerol

Metabolized by liver to ketones, aceto-acetic acids, acetyl-CoA, etc.

Cellular uses

Fat in adipose tissue insulates and cushions body organs; provides food energy stores

ATP

Fats are the primary fuels in many cells

Fats are an integral component of myelin sheaths, and all cellular membranes

(c) Proteins:
polymers of amino acids

Protein

GI digestion to amino acids

Amino acids

Normally infrequent

Cellular uses

ATP

ATP formation if inadequate glucose and fats or if essential amino acids are lacking

Functional proteins (enzymes, antibodies, hemoblobin, etc.)

Structural proteins (connective tissue fibers, muscle proteins, etc.)

(d) ATP formation (fueling the metabolic furnace):
all categories of food can be oxidized to provide energy molecules (ATP)

Monosaccharides

Acetyl-CoA (from breakdown of fats)

Amino acids (amine first removed and combined with CO_2 by the liver to form urea)

Cellular metabolic "furnace":

Krebs cycle and electron transport chain

Carbon dioxide

Water

ATP

FIGURE 25.1
Overview of nutrient use by body cells. (a) Carbohydrates.
(b) Lipids. **(c)** Proteins. **(d)** ATP formation.

on *complex* carbohydrates. The new battle cry "strive for five" (servings of fruits and vegetables per day) is one of the soundest dietary ideas to come along in a long time. When less than 50 grams per day is consumed, tissue proteins and fats are broken down for energy fuel.

American adults typically consume 200 to 300 grams of carbohydrate each day, accounting for about 46% of dietary food energy. Because starchy foods are less expensive than meat and other high-protein foods, carbohydrates constitute an even greater percentage of the diet in low-income groups. Starchy foods and milk have many valuable nutrients, such as vitamins and minerals. By contrast, highly refined carbohydrate foods such as candy and soft drinks provide energy sources only—the term "empty calories" is commonly used to describe such foods. Eating refined, sugary foods instead of more complex carbohydrates (for instance, replacing milk with soft drinks and whole grain breads with cookies) may cause nutritional deficiencies as well as obesity. Other possible consequences of excessive intake of simple carbohydrates are listed in Table 25.1 on p. 850.

Lipids

Dietary Sources

Although we also ingest cholesterol and phospholipids, the most abundant dietary lipids are neutral fats—triglycerides or triacylglycerols. We eat saturated fats in animal products such as meat and dairy foods and in a few plant products such as coconut. Unsaturated fats are present in seeds, nuts, and most vegetable oils. Major sources of cholesterol are egg yolk, meats (particularly organ meats like liver), and milk products. Fats (but not cholesterol) are digested to fatty acids and monoglycerides and then reconverted to triglycerides for transport in the lymph (see Chapter 24, p. 835).

Although the liver is adept at converting one fatty acid to another, it cannot synthesize *linoleic* (lin″o-le′ik) *acid,* a fatty acid component of *lecithin* (les′ĭ-thin). Thus, linoleic acid is an *essential fatty acid* that must be ingested. Recent research indicates that linolenic acid may also be essential. Fortunately, both of these fatty acids are found in most vegetable oils.

Uses in the Body

The use of triglycerides and cholesterol is controlled mainly by the liver and adipose tissue. Like sugary carbohydrates, fats have fallen into disfavor, particularly in affluent groups where food is plentiful and the "battle of the bulge" is a constant concern. But fats *are* essential for several reasons. Dietary fats help the body absorb fat-soluble vitamins, triglycerides are the major energy fuel of hepatocytes and skeletal muscle, and phospholipids are an integral component of

myelin sheaths and *all* cellular membranes (see Figure 25.1b). Fatty deposits in adipose tissue provide (1) a protective cushion around body organs, such as the kidneys and eyeballs, (2) an insulating layer beneath the skin, and (3) a concentrated source of energy fuel. Regulatory molecules called *prostaglandins* (pros″tah-glan′dinz), formed from linoleic acid via arachidonic (ah″rah-kĭ-don′ik) acid, play a role in smooth muscle contraction, control of blood pressure, and inflammatory responses.

Unlike the neutral fats, cholesterol is not used for energy. It is important as a stabilizing component of plasma membranes and is the precursor from which bile salts, steroid hormones, and other essential functional molecules are formed.

Dietary Requirements

Fats represent over 40% of the calories in American diets. There are no precise recommendations on amount or type of dietary fats, but the American Heart Association suggests that (1) fats should represent 30% or less of total caloric intake, (2) saturated fats should be limited to 10% or less of total fat intake, and (3) daily cholesterol intake should be no more than 250 mg (the amount in one egg yolk). Because a diet high in saturated fats and cholesterol may contribute to cardiovascular disease, these are wise guidelines. Sources of the various lipid classes and consequences of their deficient or excessive intake are summarized in Table 25.1. However, fat requirements for infants and children are higher than those for adults.

Proteins

Dietary Sources

Animal products contain the highest-quality proteins, that is, those with the greatest amount and best ratios of essential amino acids (Figure 25.2). Eggs, milk, and most meat proteins (Table 25.1) are **complete proteins** that meet all of the body's amino acid requirements for tissue maintenance and growth. Legumes (beans and peas), nuts, and cereals are protein-rich but their proteins are nutritionally incomplete because they are low in one or more of the essential amino acids. Cereals are generally low in lysine (li′sēn), while legumes, which are good sources of lysine, are low in methionine (mĕ-thi′o-nin). Leafy green vegetables are well balanced in all essential amino acids except methionine, but contain only small amounts of protein. As you can see, strict vegetarians must carefully plan their diets to obtain all the essential amino acids and prevent protein malnutrition. Cereal grains and legumes when ingested together provide all of the essential amino acids (Figure 25.2b), and some variety of this combination is found in the diets of all cultures (most obviously in

? *John literally "lives" on baked bean sandwiches. Is he getting all the essential amino acids in this rather restricted diet?*

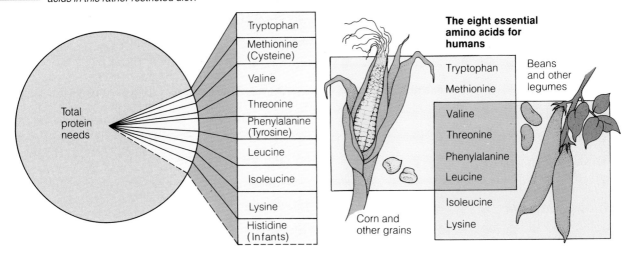

(a) Essential amino acids

(b) Vegetarian diets providing the eight essential amino acids for humans

FIGURE 25.2
Essential amino acids. Eight amino acids must be available simultaneously and in the correct relative amounts for protein synthesis to occur. (The ninth, histidine, is an essential amino acid in infants but not in adults.) **(a)** The relative amounts of the essential amino acids and total proteins needed by adults.

Notice that the essential amino acids represent only a small percentage of the total recommended amino acid (protein) intake. Histidine is graphed with dashed lines because its requirement in adults has not been established. The amino acids shown in parentheses are *not* essential but can substitute in part for methionine and phenylalanine.

(b) Vegetarian diets must be carefully constructed to provide all essential amino acids. As shown, corn has little isoleucine and lysine. Beans have ample isoleucine and lysine but little tryptophan and methionine. All essential amino acids can be obtained by consuming a meal of corn and beans.

the rice and beans seen on nearly every plate in a Mexican restaurant). For nonvegetarians, grains and legumes are useful as partial substitutes for more expensive animal proteins.

Uses in the Body

Proteins are important structural materials of the body, including, for example, keratin of skin, collagen and elastin of connective tissues, and muscle proteins (see Figure 25.1c). In addition, globular functional proteins such as enzymes, hemoglobin, and some hormones regulate an incredible variety of body functions. Even so, whether amino acids are used to synthesize new proteins or are burned for energy depends on a number of factors:

1. The all-or-none rule. *All* amino acids needed to make a particular protein must be present in a cell at the same time and in sufficient amounts. If one is missing, the protein cannot be made. Because essential amino acids cannot be stored, those not used immediately to build proteins are oxidized for energy or converted to carbohydrates or fats.

2. Adequacy of caloric intake. For optimal protein synthesis, the diet must supply sufficient carbohydrate or fat calories for ATP production. When it doesn't, dietary and tissue proteins are used for energy.

3. Nitrogen balance of the body. In healthy adults the rate of protein synthesis equals the rate of protein breakdown and loss. This homeostatic state is reflected in the **nitrogen balance** of the body, which can be determined by chemical analysis based on the fact that the nitrogen content of protein averages 16%. The body is in nitrogen balance when the amount of nitrogen ingested in proteins equals the amount excreted in urine and feces.

The body is in *positive nitrogen balance* when the rate of protein synthesis exceeds the rate of its breakdown and loss—the normal situation in growing children and pregnant women. A positive balance also occurs when tissues are being rebuilt or repaired following illness or injury. Positive nitrogen balance always indicates that the amount of protein being incorporated into tissue is greater than the amount being broken down and used for energy.

In *negative nitrogen balance,* protein breakdown exceeds the use of protein for building structural or functional molecules. This occurs during physical and emotional stress (for example, infection, injury, burns, depression, or anxiety), when the quality of

Table 25.1 Summary of Carbohydrate, Lipid, and Protein Nutrients

Food sources	Recommended daily amounts (RDA) for adults	Problems	
		Excesses	Deficits
Carbohydrates			
• *Complex carbohydrates (starches)*: bread, cereal crackers, flour, pasta, nuts, rice, potatoes	125 to 175 g 55%–60% of total caloric intake	Obesity; nutritional deficits; dental caries; gastrointestinal irritation; elevated triglycerides in plasma	Tissue wasting (in extreme deprivation); metabolic acidosis resulting from accelerated fat use for energy
• *Simple carbohydrates (sugars)*: carbonated drinks, candy, fruit, ice cream, pudding, young (immature) vegetables			
• *Both complex* and *simple carbohydrates*: pastries (pies, cookies, cakes)			
Lipids			
• *Animal sources:* lard, meat, poultry, eggs, milk, milk products	80 to 100 g 30% or less of total caloric intake	Obesity and increased risk of cardiovascular disease (particularly if excesses of saturated fat)	Weight loss; fat stores and tissue proteins catabolized to provide metabolic energy; problems controlling heat loss (due to depletion of subcutaneous fat)
• *Plant sources:* chocolate; corn, soy, cottonseed, olive oils; coconut; corn; peanuts			
• *Essential fatty acids:* corn, cottonseed, soy oils; wheat germ; vegetable shortenings	6000 mg	Not known	Poor growth; skin lesions (eczema–like)
• *Cholesterol:* organ meats (liver, kidneys, brains) egg yolk, fish roe; smaller concentrations in milk products and meat	250 mg or less	Increased levels of plasma cholesterol and LDL lipoproteins; correlated with increased risk of cardiovascular disease	Increased risk of stroke (CVA) in susceptible individuals
Proteins			
• *Complete proteins:* eggs, milk, milk products, meat (fish, poultry, pork, beef, lamb)	0.8 g/kg body weight	Obesity; possible aggravation of chronic disease states	Profound weight loss and tissue wasting; growth retardation in children; anemia; edema (due to deficits of plasma proteins) During pregnancy: miscarriage or premature birth
• *Incomplete proteins:* legumes (soybeans, lima beans, kidney beans, lentils); nuts and seeds; grains and cereals; vegetables			

dietary protein is poor, and during starvation. In such cases, the tissues lose protein faster than it is replaced—an undesirable state of affairs.

4. Hormonal controls. Certain hormones, called **anabolic hormones,** accelerate protein synthesis and growth. The effects of these hormones vary continually throughout life. For example, pituitary *growth hormone* stimulates tissue growth during childhood and conserves protein in adults, and the *sex hormones* trigger the growth spurt of adolescence. Other hormones, such as the adrenal *glucocorticoids* released during stress, enhance protein breakdown and conversion of amino acids to glucose.

Dietary Requirements

Besides supplying essential amino acids, dietary proteins also furnish the raw materials for making nonessential amino acids and various nonprotein nitrogen-containing substances. The amount of protein a person needs reflects his or her age, size, metabolic rate, and current state of nitrogen balance. However, as a rule of thumb, nutritionists recommend a daily protein intake of 0.8 g per kilogram of body weight—approximately 56 g for a 70-kg (154-pound) man and 48 g for a 58-kg (128-pound) woman. About 30 g of protein is supplied by a small serving of fish and a glass of milk. Most Americans eat far more protein than they need.

Vitamins

Vitamins (*vita* = life) are potent organic compounds needed in minute amounts for growth and good health. Unlike other organic nutrients, vitamins are not used for energy and do not serve as building blocks, but they are crucial in helping the body to use those nutrients that do. Without vitamins, all the carbohydrates, proteins, and fats we eat would be useless.

Most vitamins function as **coenzymes** (or parts of coenzymes); that is, they act with an enzyme to accomplish a particular type of catalysis. For example, the B vitamins riboflavin and niacin act as coenzymes (FAD and NAD^+, respectively) in the oxidation of glucose for energy. We will describe the roles of some vitamins in the discussion of metabolism shortly.

Most vitamins are not made in the body and so must be taken in via foods or vitamin supplements. The exceptions to this rule are vitamin D made in the skin, and vitamins B and K synthesized by intestinal bacteria. In addition, the body can convert *carotene* (kar′o-tēn), the orange pigment in carrots and other foods, to vitamin A. (Thus, carotene and substances like it are called *provitamins*.)

Vitamins were discovered only in this century, and initially they were given a convenient letter designation that indicated the order of their discovery. For example, ascorbic (as-kor′bik) acid is called vitamin C. Although chemically descriptive terms have been assigned to the vitamins, this earlier terminology is still commonly used.

Vitamins are classed as either **fat soluble** or **water soluble.** The water-soluble vitamins, which include the B-complex vitamins and vitamin C, are absorbed along with water from the gastrointestinal tract. (The exception is vitamin B_{12}, which must bind to gastric intrinsic factor to be absorbed.) Only insignificant amounts of water-soluble vitamins are stored in the body and, unless used, they are excreted in urine. Consequently, few conditions resulting from excessive levels of these vitamins *(hypervitaminosis)* are known.

Fat-soluble vitamins (vitamins A, D, E, and K) bind to ingested lipids and are absorbed along with their digestion products. Anything that interferes with fat absorption also interferes with the uptake of fat-soluble vitamins. Except for vitamin K, fat-soluble vitamins are stored in the body, and pathologies due to fat-soluble vitamin toxicity, particularly vitamin A hypervitaminosis, are well documented clinically.

Vitamins are found in all major food groups, but no one food contains all required vitamins. Thus, a balanced diet is the best way to ensure a full vitamin complement. Certain vitamins (A, C, and E) are *antioxidants* that disarm tissue-damaging free radicals and, as such, they have anticancer effects. Diets rich in broccoli, cabbage, and Brussels sprouts (all good sources of vitamins A and C) appear to reduce cancer risk. However, controversy abounds concerning the ability of vitamins to work wonders, such as the idea that huge doses (megadoses) of vitamin C will prevent colds. The notion that taking megadoses of vitamin supplements is the road to eternal youth and glowing health is useless at best and, at worst, may cause serious health problems, particularly in the case of fat-soluble vitamins. Table 25.2 lists the vitamins, their sources, their importance to body function, and the consequences of their deficiency or excess. (Note that while most vitamins are quantified in mg or μg, some are still measured in the older International Units [IU].)

Minerals

The body requires moderate amounts of seven **minerals** (calcium, phosphorus, potassium, sulfur, sodium, chloride, and magnesium) and trace amounts of about a dozen others (Table 25.3, p. 855). Minerals make up about 4% of the body by weight, with calcium and phosphorus (as bone salts) accounting for about three-quarters of this amount.

Minerals, like vitamins, are not used for fuel, but work with other nutrients to ensure a smoothly functioning body. Incorporation of minerals into structures gives added strength. For example, calcium, phosphorus, and magnesium salts harden the teeth and strengthen the skeleton. However, most minerals are ionized in body fluids or bound to organic compounds to form molecules such as phospholipids, hormones, enzymes, and other functional proteins. For example, iron is essential to the oxygen-binding heme of hemoglobin. Sodium and chloride ions, the major electrolytes in blood, help to maintain (1) normal osmolarity and water balance of body fluids and (2) responsiveness of neurons and muscle cells to stimuli. The amount of a particular mineral present in the body gives few clues to its importance in body function. For example, a few milligrams of iodine can make a critical difference to health.

A fine balance between uptake and excretion is crucial for retaining needed amounts of minerals while preventing toxic overload. For example, sodium, present in virtually all natural foods (and added in large amounts to processed foods), may contribute to high blood pressure if ingested in excess.

Fats and sugars are practically devoid of minerals, and highly refined cereals and grains are poor sources. The most mineral-rich foods are vegetables, legumes, milk, and some meats. Specific minerals and their roles in the body are summarized in Table 25.3.

Table 25.2 Vitamins

Vitamin	Description/ comments	Sources/ recommended daily amounts (RDA) for adults	Importance in body	Problems	
				Excesses	Deficits
Fat-soluble vitamins					
• A (retinol)	Group of compounds including retinol and retinal; 90% is stored in liver, which can supply body needs for a year; stable to heat, acids, alkalis; easily oxidized; rapidly destroyed by exposure to light	Formed from provitamin carotene in intestine, liver, kidneys; carotene found in deep-yellow and deep-green leafy vegetables; vitamin A found in fish liver oils, egg yolk, liver, fortified foods (milk, margarine) RDA: males 5000 IU, females 4000 IU	Required for synthesis of photoreceptor pigments of rods and cones, integrity of skin and mucosae, normal tooth and bone development; normal reproductive capabilities; important antioxidant (hence, anti-cancer and antiatherosclerosis effects)	Toxic when ingested in excess of 50,000 IU daily for months; symptoms: nausea, vomiting, anorexia, headache, hair loss, bone and joint pain, bone fragility, enlargement of liver and spleen	Night blindness; epithelial changes; dry skin and hair, skin sores; increased respiratory, digestive, urogenital infections; drying of conjunctiva; clouding of cornea; most prevalent vitamin deficiency in world
• D (antirachitic factor)	Group of chemically distinct sterols; concentrated in liver and to lesser extent in skin, kidneys, spleen, other tissues; stable to heat, light, acids, alkalis, oxidation	Vitamin D_3 (cholecalciferol) is chief form in body cells; produced in skin by irradiation of 7-dehydrocholesterol by UV light; active form (1,25-dihydroxyvitamin D_3) produced by chemical modification of vitamin D_3 in liver, then kidneys; major food sources: fish liver oils, egg yolk, fortified milk RDA: 400 IU	Functionally a hormone; increases calcium blood levels by enhancing absorption of calcium; in conjunction with PTH mobilizes calcium from bones; both mechanisms serve calcium homeostasis of blood (essential for normal neuromuscular function, blood clotting, bone and tooth formation)	1800 IU/day may be toxic to children, massive doses induce toxicity in adults; symptoms: vomiting, diarrhea, fatigue, weight loss, calcification of soft tissues, irreversible cardiac and renal damage	Faulty mineralization of bones and teeth; rickets in children, osteomalacia in adults; poor muscle tone, restlessness, irritability
• E (antisterility factor)	Group of related compounds called tocopherols, chemically related to sex hormones; stored primarily in muscle and adipose tissues; resistant to heat, light, acids; unstable in presence of oxygen	Vegetable oils, nuts, whole grains, dark-green leafy vegetables RDA: 30 IU	An antioxidant that disarms free radicals; helps prevent oxidation of unsaturated fatty acids and cholesterol, thus helps prevent atherosclerosis	Thrombophlebitis, hypertension; slow wound healing	Extremely rare, precise effects uncertain: possible hemolysis of RBCs, macrocytic anemia; fragile capillaries
• K (coagulation vitamin)	Number of related compounds known as quinones; small amounts stored in liver; heat resistant; destroyed by acids, alkalis, light, oxidizing agents; activity antagonized by certain anticoagulants and antibiotics that interfere with synthetic activity of enteric bacteria	Most synthesized by bacteria in large intestine; food sources: leafy green vegetables, cabbage, cauliflower, pork liver RDA: males 70 μg, females 55 μg; obtaining adequate amount is not a problem	Essential for formation of clotting proteins and some other proteins made by liver; as intermediate in electron transport chain, participates in oxidative phosphorylation in all body cells	None known, not stored in appreciable amounts	Easy bruising and bleeding (prolonged clotting time)

Table continues

Table 25.2 continued

Vitamin	Description/ comments	Sources/ recommended daily amounts (RDA) for adults	Importance in body	Problems	
				Excesses	Deficits

Water-soluble vitamins:

Vitamin	Description/ comments	Sources/ recommended daily amounts (RDA) for adults	Importance in body	Excesses	Deficits
• C (ascorbic acid)	Simple 6-carbon crystalline compound derived from glucose; rapidly destroyed by heat, light, alkalis; about 1500 mg is stored in body, particularly in adrenal gland, retina, intestine, pituitary; when tissues are saturated, excess excreted by kidneys	Fruits and vegetables, particularly citrus, cantaloupe, strawberries, tomatoes, fresh potatoes, leafy green vegetables RDA: 60 mg; 100 mg for those who smoke	Antioxidant; acts in hydroxylation reactions in formation of nearly all connective tissues; in conversion of tryptophan to serotonin (vasoconstrictor); in conversion of cholesterol to bile salts; enhances iron absorption and use; required for conversion of folacin (a B vitamin) to its active form	Result of megadoses (10 or more times RDA); enhanced mobilization of bone minerals and blood coagulation; exacerbation of gout, kidney stone formation	Defective formation of intercellular cement; fleeting joint pains, poor tooth and bone growth; poor wound healing, increased susceptibility to infection; extreme deficit causes scurvy (bleeding gums, anemia, cutaneous hemorrhage, degeneration of muscle and cartilage, weight loss)
• B_1 (thiamine)	Rapidly destroyed by heat; very limited amount stored in body; excess eliminated in urine	Lean meats, liver, fish, eggs, whole grains, leafy green vegetables, legumes RDA: 1.5 mg	Part of coenzyme cocarboxylase, which acts in carbohydrate metabolism; required for transformation of pyruvic acid to acetyl CoA, for synthesis of pentose sugars and acetylcholine; for oxidation of alcohol	None known	Beriberi; decreased appetite, vision disturbances; unsteadiness when standing or walking, confusion, loss of memory; profound fatigue; heart enlargement, tachycardia
• B_2 (riboflavin)	Named for its similarity to ribose sugar: has green-yellow fluorescence; quickly decomposed by UV, visible light, alkalis; body stores are carefully guarded; excess eliminated in urine	Widely varying sources such as liver, yeast, egg white, whole grains, meat, poultry, fish, legumes; major source is milk RDA: 1.7 mg	Present in body as coenzymes FAD and FMN (flavin mononucleotide), both of which act as hydrogen acceptors in body; also is component of amino acid oxidases	None known	Dermatitis; cracking of lips at corners (cheilosis); lips and tongue become purple-red and shiny; ocular problems: light sensitivity, blurred vision; one of the most common vitamin deficiencies
• Niacin (nicotinamide)	Simple organic compounds stable to acids, alkalis, heat, light, oxidation (even boiling does not decrease potency); very limited amount stored in body, day-to-day supply is desirable; excess secreted in urine	Diets that provide adequate protein usually provide adequate niacin because amino acid tryptophan is easily converted to niacin; preformed niacin provided by poultry, meat, fish; less important sources: liver, yeast, peanuts, potatoes, leafy green vegetables RDA: 20 mg	Constituent of NAD^+ and NADP (nicotinamide adenine dinucleotide phosphate), coenzymes involved in glycolysis, oxidative phosphorylation, fat breakdown; inhibits cholesterol synthesis	Result of megadoses; hyperglycemia; vasodilation leading to flushing of skin, tingling sensations; possible liver damage; gout	Pellagra after months of deprivation (rare in U.S.); early signs are vague: listlessness, headache, weight loss, loss of appetite; progresses to soreness and redness of tongue and lips; nausea, vomiting, diarrhea; photosensitive dermatitis: skin becomes rough, cracked, may ulcerate; neurological symptoms also occur: characterized by the 4 Ds: dermatitis, diarrhea, dementia, and death (in final stage)

Table continues

Table 25.2 continued

Vitamin	Description/comments	Sources/recommended daily amounts (RDA) for adults	Importance in body	Problems	
				Excesses	**Deficits**
• B₆ (pyridoxine)	Group of three pyridines occurring in both free and phosphorylated forms in body; stable to heat, acids; destroyed by alkalis, light; body stores very limited	Meat, poultry, fish; less important sources: potatoes, sweet potatoes, tomatoes, spinach RDA: 2 mg	Active form is coenzyme pyridoxal phosphate, which functions in several enzyme systems involved in amino acid metabolism; also required for conversion of tryptophan to niacin, for glycogenolysis, for formation of antibodies and hemoglobin	Depressed deep tendon reflexes, numbness, loss of sensation in extremities	Infants: nervous irritability, convulsions, anemia, vomiting, weakness, abdominal pain; adults: seborrhea lesions around eyes and mouth
• Pantothenic acid	Quite stable, little loss of activity with cooking except in acidic or alkaline solutions; liver, kidneys, brain, adrenal, heart tissues contain large amounts	Name derived from Greek *panthos* meaning everywhere; widely distributed in animal foods, whole grains, legumes; liver, yeast, egg yolk, meat especially good sources; some produced by enteric bacteria RDA: 10 mg	Functions in form of coenzyme A in reactions that remove or transfer acetyl group, e.g., formation of acetyl CoA from pyruvic acid, oxidation and synthesis of fatty acids; also involved in synthesis of steroids and heme of hemoglobin	None known	Symptoms vague: loss of appetite, abdominal pain, mental depression, pains in arms and legs, muscle spasms neuromuscular degeneration (neuropathy of alcoholics is thought to be related to deficits)
• Biotin	Urea derivative containing sulfur; crystalline in its free form; stable to heat, light, acids; in tissues, is usually combined with protein; stored in minute amounts, particularly in liver, kidneys, brain, adrenal glands	Liver, egg yolk, legumes, nuts; some synthesized by bacteria in gastrointestinal tract RDA: not established, probably about 0.3 mg (because biotin content of feces and urine is greater than dietary intake, it is assumed that formation of the vitamin by enteric bacteria provides far more than is needed)	Functions as coenzyme for a number of enzymes that catalyze carboxylation, decarboxylation, deamination reactions; essential for reactions of Krebs cycle, for formation of purines and nonessential amino acids, for use of amino acids for energy	None known	Scaly skin, muscular pains, pallor, anorexia, nausea, fatigue; elevated blood cholesterol levels
• B₁₂ (cyanocobalamin)	Most complex vitamin; contains cobalt; stable to heat; inactivated by light and strongly acidic or basic solutions; intrinsic factor required for transport across intestinal membrane; stored principally in liver; liver stores of 2000–3000 μg sufficient to provide for body needs for 3–5 years	Liver, meat, poultry, fish, dairy foods except butter, eggs; not found in plant foods RDA: 3–6 μg	Functions as coenzyme in all cells, particularly in gastrointestinal tract, nervous system, and bone marrow; in bone marrow, acts in synthesis of DNA; when absent, erythrocytes do not divide but continue to increase in size; essential for synthesis of methionine and choline	None known	Pernicious anemia, signified by pallor, anorexia, dyspnea, weight loss, neurological disturbances; most cases reflect impaired absorption rather than actual deficit

Table continues

Table 25.2 continued

Vitamin	Description/ comments	Sources/ recommended daily amounts (RDA) for adults	Importance in body	Problems	
				Excesses	Deficits
• Folic acid (folacin)	Pure vitamin is bright-yellow crystalline compound; stable to heat; easily oxidized in acidic solutions and light; stored mainly in liver	Liver, deep-green vegetables, yeast, lean beef, eggs, veal, whole grains; synthesized by enteric bacteria RDA: 0.4 mg	Basis of coenzymes that act in synthesis of methionine and certain other amino acids, choline, DNA; essential for formation of red blood cells and for normal neural tube development in the embryo	None known	Macrocytic or megaloblastic anemia; gastrointestinal disturbances; diarrhea; spina bifida risk in newborn

Notes

1. Each vitamin has specific functions; one vitamin cannot substitute for another. Many reactions in body require several vitamins, and lack of one can interfere with activity of others.

2. Diet that includes recommended amounts of the five food groups will furnish adequate amounts of all vitamins except vitamin D. Each food group makes a special vitamin contribution. For example, fruits and vegetables are principal sources of vitamin C; dark-green leafy vegetables and deep-yellow vegetables and fruits are primary sources of vitamin A (carotene); milk is principal source of riboflavin; meat, poultry, and fish are outstanding sources of niacin, thiamin, and vitamins B_6 and B_{12}. Whole grains are also important sources of niacin and thiamin.

3. Because vitamin D is present in natural foods in only very small amounts, infants, pregnant and lactating women, and people who have little exposure to sunlight should use vitamin D supplements (or supplemented foods, e.g., fortified milk).

4. Vitamins A and D are toxic in excessive amounts and should be used in supplementary form only when prescribed by a physician. Because most water-soluble vitamins are excreted in urine when ingested in excess, the effectiveness of taking supplements is questionable.

5. Many vitamin deficiencies are secondary to disease (including anorexia, vomiting, diarrhea, or malabsorption diseases) or reflect increased metabolic requirements due to fever or stress factors. Specific vitamin deficiencies require therapy with the vitamins that are lacking.

Table 25.3 Minerals

Mineral	Distribution in body/comments	Sources/ recommended daily amounts (RDA) for adults	Importance in body	Problems	
				Excesses	Deficits
Calcium (Ca)	Most stored in salt form in bones; the most abundant cation in body; absorbed from intestine in presence of vitamin D; excess excreted in feces; blood levels regulated by PTH and calcitonin	Milk, milk products, leafy green vegetables, egg yolk, shellfish RDA: 1200 mg, dropping to 800 mg after age 25	In salt form, required for hardness of bones, teeth; ionic calcium in blood and cells essential for normal membrane permeability, transmission of nerve impulses, muscle contraction, normal heart rhythm, blood clotting; activates certain enzymes; helps prevent hypertension	Depressed neural function; calcium salt deposit in soft tissues; kidney stones	Muscle tetany; osteomalacia, osteoporosis; retarded growth and rickets in children
Phosphorus (P)	About 80% found in inorganic salts of bones, teeth; remainder in muscle, nervous tissue, blood; absorption aided by Vitamin D; about 1/3 dietary intake excreted in feces; metabolic by-products excreted in urine	Diets rich in proteins are usually rich in phosphorus; plentiful in milk, eggs, meat, fish, poultry, legumes, nuts, whole grains RDA: 800 mg	Component of bones and teeth, nucleic acids, proteins, phospholipids, ATP, phosphates (buffers) of body fluids; thus, important for energy storage and transfer, muscle and nerve activity, cell permeability	Not known, but excess in diet may depress absorption of iron and manganese	Rickets, poor growth

Table continues

Table 25.3 continued

Mineral	Distribution in body/comments	Sources/ recommended daily amounts (RDA) for adults	Importance in body	Problems	
				Excesses	Deficits
Magnesium (Mg)	In all cells, particularly abundant in bones; absorption parallels that of calcium; excreted chiefly in urine	Milk, dairy products, whole-grain cereals, nuts, legumes, leafy green vegetables RDA: 300–350 mg	Constituent of many coenzymes that play a role in conversion of ATP to ADP; required for normal muscle and nerve irritability	Diarrhea	Neuromuscular problems, tremors, muscle weakness, irregular heart beat; seen in alcoholism, severe renal disease, prolonged diarrhea, and those taking diuretic drugs
Potassium (K)	Principal intracellular cation, 97% within cells; fixed proportion of K is bound to proteins, and measurements of body K are used to determine lean body mass; K^+ leaves cells during protein catabolism, dehydration, glycogenolysis; most excreted in urine	Widely distributed in foods; normal diet provides 2–6 g/day; avocados, dried apricots, meat, fish, fowl, cereals RDA: not established; diet adequate in calories provides ample amount, i.e., 2500 mg	Helps maintain intracellular osmotic pressure; needed for normal nerve impulse conduction, muscle contraction, glycogenesis, protein synthesis	Usually a complication of renal failure or severe dehydration, but may result from severe alcoholism; paresthesias, muscular weakness, cardiac abnormalities	Rare but may result from severe diarrhea or vomiting; muscular weakness, paralysis, nausea, vomiting, tachycardia, heart failure
Sulfur (S)	Widely distributed: particularly abundant in hair, skin, nails; excreted in urine	Meat, milk, eggs, legumes (all rich in sulfur-containing amino acids) RDA: not established; diet adequate in proteins meets body's needs	Essential constituent of many proteins (insulin), some vitamins (thiamin and biotin); found in mucopolysaccharides present in cartilage, tendons, bone	Not known	Not known
Sodium (Na)	Widely distributed: 50% found in extracellular fluid, 40% in bone salts, 10% within cells; absorption is rapid and almost complete; excretion, chiefly in urine, controlled by aldosterone	Table salt (1 tsp = 2000 mg); cured meats (ham, etc.), sauerkraut, cheese; diet supplies substantial excess RDA: not established; probably about 2500 mg	Most abundant cation in extracellular fluid: principal electrolyte maintaining osmotic pressure of extracellular fluids and water balance; as part of bicarbonate buffer system, aids in acid-base balance of blood; needed for normal neuromuscular function; part of pump for transport of glucose and other nutrients	Hypertension; edema	Rare but can occur with excessive vomiting, diarrhea, sweating, or poor dietary intake; nausea, abdominal and muscle cramping, convulsions
Chlorine (Cl)	Exists in body almost entirely as chloride ion; principal anion of extracellular fluid; highest concentrations in cerebrospinal fluid and gastric juice; excreted in urine	Table salts (as for sodium); usually ingested in excess RDA: not established; normal diet contains 3–9 g	With sodium, helps maintain osmotic pressure and pH of extracellular fluid; required for HCl formation by stomach glands; activates salivary amylase; aids in transport of CO_2 by blood (chloride shift)	Vomiting	Severe vomiting or diarrhea leads to Cl loss and alkalosis; muscle cramps; apathy

Table continues

Table 25.3 continued

Mineral	Distribution in body/comments	Sources/ recommended daily amounts (RDA) for adults	Importance in body	Problems — Excesses	Problems — Deficits
Trace minerals*					
Iron (Fe)	60% to 70% in hemoglobin; remainder in skeletal muscle, liver, spleen, bone marrow bound to ferritin; only 2% to 10% of dietary iron is absorbed because of mucosal barrier; lost from body in urine, perspiration, menstrual flow, shed hair; sloughed skin and mucosal cells	Best sources: meat, liver; also in shellfish, egg yolk, dried fruit, nuts, legumes, molasses RDA: males 10 mg females 15 mg	Part of heme of hemoglobin, which binds bulk of oxygen transported in blood; component of cytochromes, which function in oxidative phosphorylation	Hemochromatosis (inherited condition of iron excess); damage to liver (cirrhosis and liver cancer), heart, pancreas (causing diabetes)	Iron-deficiency anemia; pallor, lethargy, flatulence, anorexia, paresthesias, impaired cognitive performance in children; inability to maintain body temperature; depressed killing by phagocytes (due to inability to produce the respiratory burst)
Iodine (I)	Found in all tissues, but in high concentrations only in thyroid gland; absorption controlled by blood levels of protein-bound iodine; excreted in urine	Cod liver oil, iodized salt, shellfish, vegetables grown in iodine-rich soil RDA: 0.15 mg	Required to form thyroid hormones (T_3 and T_4), which are important in regulating cellular metabolic rate	Depressed synthesis of thyroid hormones	Hypothyroidism: cretinism in infants, myxedema in adults (if less severe, simple goiter)
Manganese (Mn)	Most concentrated in liver, kidneys, spleen; excreted largely in feces	Nuts, legumes, whole grains, leafy green vegetables, fruit RDA: 2.5–5 mg	Acts with enzymes catalyzing synthesis of fatty acids, cholesterol, urea, hemoglobin; needed for normal neural function, lactation, oxidation of carbohydrates, protein hydrolysis	Appears to contribute to obsessive behavior and hallucinations	Not known
Copper (Cu)	Concentrated in liver, heart, brain, spleen; excreted in feces	Liver, shellfish, whole grains, legumes, meat; typical diet provides 2–5 mg daily RDA: 2–3 mg	Required for synthesis of hemoglobin; essential for manufacture of melanin, myelin, some intermediates of electron transport chain	Rare; abnormal storage results in Wilson's disease	Rare
Zinc (Zn)	Concentrated in liver, kidneys, brain; excreted in feces	Seafood, meat, cereals, legumes, nuts, wheat germ, yeast RDA: 15 mg	Constituent of several enzymes; as component of carbonic anhydrase, important in CO_2 metabolism; required for normal growth, wound healing, taste, smell, sperm production	Difficulty in walking; slurred speech; masklike facial expression; tremors	Loss of taste and smell; growth retardation; learning impairment; depressed immunity
Cobalt (Co)	Found in all cells; larger amounts in bone marrow	Liver, lean meat, poultry, fish, milk RDA: not established	A constituent of vitamin B_{12}, which is needed for normal maturation of red blood cells	Goiter, polycythemia; heart disease	See deficit of vitamin B_{12} (Table 25.2)
Fluorine (F)	Component of bones, teeth, other body tissues; excreted in urine	Fluoridated water RDA: 1.5–4 mg	Important for tooth structure; may help prevent dental caries (particularly in children) and osteoporosis in adults	Mottling of teeth	Not known

Table continues

Table 25.3 continued

Mineral	Distribution in body/comments	Sources/ recommended daily amounts (RDA) for adults	Importance in body	Problems	
				Excesses	Deficits
Selenium (Se)	Stored in liver, kidneys	Meat, seafood, cereals RDA: 0.05–2 mg	Antioxidant; constituent of certain enzymes; spares vitamin E	Nausea, vomiting, irritability, fatigue, weight loss, loss of hair	Not known
Chromium (Cr)	Widely distributed	Liver, meat, cheese, whole grains, brewer's yeast, wine RDA: 0.05–2 mg	Required for synthesis of glucose tolerance factor (GTF) without which glucose cannot be properly metabolized; enhances effectiveness of insulin on carbohydrate metabolism; may increase blood levels of HDLs while decreasing levels of LDLs	Not known	Impairs ability of insulin to work, hence increases insulin secretion and risk of adult onset diabetes mellitus

*Trace minerals together account for less than 0.005% of body weight.

METABOLISM

Overview of Metabolic Processes

Once inside body cells, nutrients become involved in an incredible variety of biochemical reactions. These reactions are known collectively as **metabolism** (*metabol* = change), a broad term referring to all chemical reactions necessary to maintain life. During metabolism, substances are constantly being built up and torn down. Cells use energy to extract more energy from foods, and then use some of this energy to drive their activities. Even at rest, the body uses energy on a grand scale.

Anabolism and Catabolism

Metabolic processes are either *anabolic* (synthetic) or *catabolic* (degradative). **Anabolism** (ah-nab'o-lizm) includes reactions in which larger molecules or structures are built from smaller ones; for example, the bonding of amino acids to make proteins and of proteins and lipids to form cell membranes. **Catabolism** (kah-tab'o-lizm) involves processes that break down complex structures to simpler ones. Hydrolysis of foods in the digestive tract is catabolic. So too is the group of reactions collectively called **cellular respiration,** during which food fuels (particularly glucose) are broken down within cells and some of the energy released is captured to form ATP, the cells' energy currency. ATP then serves as the "chemical drive

shaft" that links energy-releasing catabolic reactions to cellular work. Recall from Chapter 2 that reactions driven by ATP are coupled reactions. ATP is never hydrolyzed directly. Instead enzymes shift its high-energy phosphate groups to other molecules, which are then said to be **phosphorylated** (fos"for-ĭ-la'ted). Phosphorylation energizes, or primes, the molecule to change in a way that increases its activity, produces motion, or does work. For example, many regulatory enzymes that catalyze key steps in metabolic pathways are activated by phosphorylation.

Figure 25.3 is a flowchart of the processing of energy-containing nutrients in the body. As you can see, three major stages are involved.

- Stage 1 is digestion, which occurs in the gastrointestinal tract, as described in Chapter 24. The absorbed nutrients are then transported in blood to the tissue cells.

- In stage 2, which occurs in the cytoplasm of body cells, the newly delivered nutrients are (1) built into cellular molecules (lipids, proteins, and glycogen) by anabolic pathways or (2) broken down by catabolic pathways to *pyruvic* (pi-roo'vik) *acid* and *acetyl CoA* (as'ĕ-til ko-a').

- Stage 3, which is almost entirely catabolic, occurs in the mitochondria of cells, requires oxygen, and completes the breakdown of newly digested or stored foodstuffs, producing carbon dioxide and water and harvesting large amounts of ATP.

FIGURE 25.3
The three stages of metabolism of energy-containing nutrients in the body. In stage 1, foods are degraded to their absorbable forms by digestive enzymes in the gastrointestinal (GI) tract. In stage 2, the absorbed nutrients are transported in blood to the body cells, where they may be incorporated into cellular molecules (anabolism) or broken down via glycolysis and other reactions to pyruvic acid and/or acetyl CoA, and then funneled into the catabolic pathways of stage 3. Stage 3 consists of the pathways of the Krebs cycle and oxidative phosphorylation, which go on within the mitochondria. During the Krebs cycle, acetyl CoA is broken apart: Its carbon atoms are liberated as carbon dioxide (CO_2), and the hydrogen atoms removed are delivered to a chain of receptors (the electron transport chain), which ultimately delivers them (as protons and free electrons) to molecular oxygen so that water is formed. Some of the energy released during the electron transport chain reactions is used to form the bonds of high-energy ATP molecules. Once generated, ATP provides the energy needed by cells to power their many activities. The reactions of glycolysis (stage 2) and the Krebs cycle and oxidative phosphorylation (stage 3) collectively constitute cellular respiration.

The primary function of cellular respiration, consisting of glycolysis of stage 2 and all events of stage 3, is to generate ATP, which traps some of the chemical energy of the original food molecules in its own high-energy bonds. Thus, food fuels, such as glycogen and fats, *store* energy in the body, and these stores are later *mobilized to produce ATP for cellular use.* You do not need to memorize this schematic now, but as you will soon see, it provides a cohesive summary of nutrient processing and metabolism in the body.

Oxidation-Reduction Reactions and the Role of Coenzymes

The energy-yielding (ATP-yielding) reactions within cells are **oxidation reactions.** *Oxidation* was originally defined as the combination of oxygen with other elements. Examples are the rusting of iron (the slow formation of iron oxide) and the burning of wood and other fuels. In burning, oxygen combines rapidly with carbon, producing (in addition to carbon dioxide and water) an enormous amount of energy, which is liberated as heat and light. But then it was discovered that oxidation *also* occurs when hydrogen atoms are *removed* from compounds, so the definition was expanded to its current form: Oxidation occurs via the gain of oxygen or the loss of hydrogen. As explained in Chapter 2, whichever way oxidation occurs, the oxidized substance always *loses* (or nearly loses) electrons as they move to (or toward) a substance that more strongly attracts them.

This process can be explained by reviewing the consequences of different electron-attracting abilities of atoms (see p. 34). Because hydrogen is very electropositive, its lone electron usually spends more time orbiting the other atoms of molecules that hydrogen helps to form. But, when a hydrogen *atom* is removed, its electron goes with it, and the molecule as a whole loses that electron. Conversely, oxygen is very electron-hungry (electronegative), so when oxygen binds with other atoms the shared electrons spend a disproportionate amount of time in oxygen's vicinity. Again, the molecule as a whole loses electrons. As you will soon see, essentially all oxidation of food fuels involves the step-by-step removal of pairs of hydrogen atoms (and, thus, pairs of electrons) from the substrate molecules, eventually leaving only carbon dioxide (CO_2). Molecular oxygen (O_2) is the *final* electron acceptor. It combines with the removed hydrogen atoms at the very end of the process, to form water (H_2O).

Whenever one substance loses electrons (is oxidized), another substance gains them (is reduced). Thus, oxidation and reduction are coupled reactions and we speak of **oxidation-reduction (O-R),** or **redox, reactions** in the same breath. The key understanding about redox reactions is that "oxidized" substances *lose* energy and "reduced" substances *gain* energy as energy-rich electrons are transferred from the first to the second. Consequently, as food fuels are oxidized, their energy is transferred to a "bucket brigade" of other molecules and ultimately to ADP to form energy-rich ATP molecules.

Like all other chemical reactions in the body, oxidation-reduction reactions are catalyzed by enzymes. Enzymes are discussed in detail in Chapter 2, pp. 51–53. The enzymes that catalyze oxidation-reduction reactions by removing hydrogen are specifically called **dehydrogenases** (de-hi′dro-jen-ās″ez), while those catalyzing the transfer of oxygen are **oxidases.** Most of these enzymes require the help of a specific coenzyme typically derived from one of the B

vitamins. Although the enzymes catalyze the removal of hydrogen atoms to oxidize a substance, they cannot *accept* the hydrogen (hold on to it). Their *coenzymes,* however, act as reversible hydrogen (or electron) acceptors, becoming reduced each time a substrate is oxidized. Two very important coenzymes of the oxidative pathways are **nicotinamide** (nik″o-tin′ah-mīd) **adenine dinucleotide (NAD⁺),** based on *niacin,* and **flavin adenine dinucleotide (FAD),** derived from *riboflavin.* The oxidation of succinic acid to fumaric acid and the simultaneous reduction of FAD to $FADH_2$, an example of a coupled oxidation-reduction reaction, is shown below.

Mechanisms of ATP Synthesis

How do our cells capture some of the energy liberated during cellular respiration to make ATP molecules? There appear to be two mechanisms—substrate-level phosphorylation and oxidative phosphorylation.

Substrate-level phosphorylation occurs when high-energy phosphate groups are transferred directly from phosphorylated substrates (metabolic intermediates) to ADP (Figure 25.4a). Essentially, it occurs because the high-energy bonds attaching the phosphate groups to the substrates are even more unstable than those of ATP. ATP is synthesized by this route during one of the steps of glycolysis, and once during each turn of the Krebs cycle (Figure 25.5). The enzymes catalyzing substrate-level phosphorylations are located in both the cytoplasm and the aqueous mitochondrial matrix.

Oxidative phosphorylation is much more complicated, but it also releases most of the energy that is eventually captured in ATP bonds during cellular respiration. This process, which is carried out by electron transport proteins forming part of the cristae membranes in the mitochondria, is an example of a **chemiosmotic process.** Chemiosmotic processes couple the movement of substances across membranes to chemical reactions. In this case, some of the energy released during the oxidation of food fuels (the "chemi" part of the term) is used to pump (*osmo* = push) hydrogen ions or protons (H^+) across the inner (cristae) mitochondrial membrane into the intermembrane space (Figure 25.4b). This creates a steep diffusion gradient for protons across the membrane. Then, when protons do flow back across the membrane (through a membrane channel protein called *ATP synthase*), some of this gradient energy is captured and used to attach phosphate groups to ADP.

Carbohydrate Metabolism

Because all food carbohydrates are eventually transformed to glucose, the story of carbohydrate metabolism is really a tale of glucose metabolism. Glucose enters the tissue cells by facilitated diffusion, a process that is greatly enhanced by insulin. Immediately upon entry into the cell, glucose is phosphorylated to form glucose-6-phosphate by transfer of a phosphate group (PO_4^{3-}) to its sixth carbon during a coupled reaction with ATP:

$$Glucose + ATP \rightarrow glucose\text{-}6\text{-}PO_4 + ADP$$

Because most body cells lack the enzymes needed to reverse this reaction, it effectively traps glucose within the cells. Since glucose-6-phosphate is a *different* molecule from simple glucose, the reaction also keeps intracellular glucose levels low, maintaining a diffusion gradient for glucose entry. Only intestinal mucosa cells, kidney tubule cells, and liver cells have the enzymes needed to reverse this phosphorylation reaction, which reflects their unique roles in glucose uptake *and* release. The catabolic and anabolic pathways for carbohydrates all begin with glucose-6-phosphate.

Oxidation of Glucose

Glucose is the pivotal fuel molecule in the oxidative (ATP-producing) pathways. The complete catabolism of glucose is shown by the overall equation:

$$C_6H_{12}O_6 + 6O_2 \rightarrow 6H_2O + 6CO_2 + 38\ ATP + heat$$
(glucose) (oxygen)(water) (carbon
                                     dioxide)

This equation gives few hints that glucose breakdown is a very complex process or that it involves three of the pathways included in Figure 25.3 and diagrammed in Figure 25.5:

1. Glycolysis (color-coded pink throughout the chapter);

2. The Krebs cycle (color-coded green); and

3. The electron transport chain and oxidative phosphorylation (color-coded violet).

Since these metabolic pathways occur in a definite order, we will consider them sequentially.

Glycolysis. Glycolysis (gli-kol'ĭ-sis; "sugar splitting") is a series of ten chemical steps by which glucose is converted into two *pyruvic acid* molecules, yielding small amounts of ATP (2 ATP per glucose molecule). Glycolysis occurs in the cytosol of cells, where its steps are catalyzed by specific soluble enzymes. Except for the first step during which glucose entering the cell is phosphorylated to glucose-6-phosphate, all of its steps are fully *reversible.* Glycolysis is an *anaerobic* (an-a'er-ōb-ik; *an* = without, *aero* = air) *process.* Although this is sometimes (mistakenly) interpreted to mean that the pathway occurs only in the *absence* of oxygen, this is *not* the case. The correct interpretation is that glycolysis *does not use oxygen and occurs whether or not oxygen is present.* Figure 25.6 shows the glycolytic pathway in an abbreviated form that considers its three major phases. The total glycolytic pathway, complete with the names and structural formulas of all intermediates and a description of the events of each step, appears in Appendix E.

(a)

(b)

FIGURE 25.4
Mechanisms of phosphorylation. (a) Substrate-level phosphorylation occurs when a high-energy phosphate group is transferred enzymatically directly from a substrate to ADP to form ATP. Substrate phosphorylation occurs both in the cytoplasm and in the mitochondrial matrix. **(b)** Oxidative phosphorylation, which occurs in mitochondria, reflects the activity of electron transport proteins that act as proton "pumps" to create a proton gradient across the cristae membranes. The source of energy for this pumping is energy released during oxidation of food fuels. As the protons flow passively back into the mitochondrial fluid matrix (through ATP synthases), energy of their diffusion gradient is used to bind phosphate groups to ADP.

FIGURE 25.5
An overview of sites of ATP formation during cellular respiration. Glycolysis occurs outside the mitochondria in the cytosol. The Krebs cycle and the electron transport chain reactions occur within the mitochondria. During glycolysis, each glucose molecule is broken down to two molecules of pyruvic acid. The pyruvic acid enters the mitochondrial matrix, where the Krebs cycle decomposes it to carbon dioxide. During glycolysis and the Krebs cycle, small amounts of ATP are formed by substrate-level phosphorylation. Chemical energy from glycolysis and the Krebs cycle, in the form of energy-rich electrons, is then transferred to the electron transport chain, which is built into the membrane of the cristae. The electron transport chain carries out oxidative phosphorylation, which accounts for most of the ATP generated by cellular respiration.

1. **Sugar activation.** In phase 1, glucose is phosphorylated and converted to fructose-6-phosphate, which is then phosphorylated again. These three steps yield fructose-1,6-diphosphate and use two ATP molecules. The two separate reactions of the sugar with ATP provide the *activation energy* needed to prime the later stages of the pathway—hence this phase is sometimes referred to as the *energy investment phase*. (The importance of activation energy is described in Chapter 2.)

2. **Sugar cleavage.** During phase 2, fructose-1,6-diphosphate is split into two 3-carbon fragments that exist (reversibly) as one of two isomers: glyceraldehyde (glis″er-al′dĕ-hīd) 3-phosphate or dihydroxyacetone (di″hi-drok″se-as′ĕ-tōn) phosphate.

3. **Oxidation and ATP formation.** In phase 3, consisting of six steps, two major events happen. First, the two 3-carbon fragments are oxidized by the removal of hydrogen, which is picked up by NAD⁺. Hence, some of glucose's energy is transferred to NAD⁺. Second, inorganic phosphate groups (P_i) are attached to each oxidized fragment by high-energy bonds. Then, as these terminal phosphates are cleaved off later, enough energy is captured to form a total of four ATP molecules. As noted earlier, formation of ATP by this method is called *substrate-level phosphorylation*.

The final products of glycolysis are two molecules of **pyruvic acid** and two molecules of reduced NAD^+ (NADH + H⁺),* with a net gain of two ATP molecules per glucose molecule. Four ATPs are produced, but remember that two are used in phase 1 to "prime the pump." Each pyruvic acid molecule has the formula $C_3H_4O_3$, and glucose is $C_6H_{12}O_6$. Thus, between them the two pyruvic acid molecules have lost 4 hydrogen atoms, which are now bound to two molecules of NAD^+. Although a small amount of ATP has been harvested, the other two end products (H_2O and CO_2) of glucose oxidation have yet to appear.

The fate of pyruvic acid, which still contains most of glucose's chemical energy, depends on the availability of oxygen at the time it is produced. If glycolysis is to continue and pyruvic acid is to enter the next processing phase, the Krebs cycle, the reduced coenzymes (NADH + H⁺) formed during glycolysis must be relieved of the accepted hydrogen so that they can continue to act as hydrogen acceptors. When oxygen is readily available, this is no problem. NADH + H⁺ simply delivers its burden of hydrogen atoms to the enzymes of the electron transport chain in the

* NAD carries a positive charge (NAD^+); thus, when it accepts the hydrogen pair, NADH + H⁺ is the resulting reduced product.

FIGURE 25.6

The three major phases of glycolysis. During phase 1, glucose is activated by phosphorylation and converted to fructose-1,6-diphosphate. In phase 2, fructose-1,6-diphosphate is cleaved into two 3-carbon fragments (reversible isomers). In phase 3, the 3-carbon fragments are oxidized (by removal of hydrogen) and 4 ATP molecules are formed. The fate of pyruvic acid depends on whether or not molecular O_2 is available.

mitochondria, which in turn deliver them to molecular oxygen, forming water. However, when oxygen is not present in sufficient amounts, as might occur during strenuous exercise, the NADH + H⁺ produced during glycolysis unloads its hydrogen baggage *back onto pyruvic acid,* thus reducing it. This addition of two hydrogen atoms to pyruvic acid yields **lactic acid**

(see bottom right of Figure 25.6). Some of the lactic acid produced diffuses out of the cells and is transported to the liver. When oxygen is again available, lactic acid is oxidized back to pyruvic acid and enters the **aerobic pathways** (the oxygen-requiring Krebs cycle and electron transport chain within the mitochondria). There it is completely oxidized to water and carbon dioxide. The liver may also convert lactic acid all the way back to glucose-6-phosphate (reverse glycolysis) and then store it as glycogen or free it of its phosphate and release it to the blood.

Although glycolysis generates ATP very rapidly, glycolysis alone produces only 2 ATP/glucose molecule, as compared to the 36 ATP/glucose harvested when glucose is completely oxidized. Except for red blood cells (which typically carry out *only* glycolysis), prolonged anaerobic metabolism ultimately results in acid-base problems. Consequently, *totally* anaerobic conditions resulting in lactic acid formation provide only a temporary (or emergency) means of rapid ATP production when oxygen is in low supply. It can go on without tissue damage for the longest periods in skeletal muscle, for much shorter periods in cardiac muscle, and almost not at all in the brain.

Krebs Cycle. The **Krebs cycle,** named after its discoverer Hans Krebs, is the next stage of glucose oxidation. The Krebs cycle occurs in the aqueous mitochondrial matrix and is fueled largely by pyruvic acid produced during glycolysis and by fatty acids resulting from fat breakdown.

After pyruvic acid enters the mitochondria, the "first order of business" is to convert it to *acetyl CoA.* This multistep process, which links glycolysis to the Krebs cycle, involves three events:

1. **Decarboxylation,** in which one of pyruvic acid's carbons is removed and released as carbon dioxide gas (a waste product of metabolism). CO_2 diffuses out of the cells into the blood to be expelled by the lungs.

2. **Oxidation** by the removal of hydrogen atoms. The removed hydrogens are picked up by NAD⁺.

3. Combining the resulting acetic acid with *coenzyme A* to produce the final product, **acetyl coenzyme A,** or simply **acetyl CoA.** Coenzyme A (CoA-SH) is a sulfur-containing coenzyme derived from pantothenic acid, a B vitamin.

Acetyl CoA is now ready to enter the Krebs cycle and be broken down completely by the mitochondrial enzymes. Coenzyme A shuttles the 2-carbon acetic acid to the enzyme that can condense it with a 4-carbon acid called **oxaloacetic** (ok″sah-lo″ah-sēt′ik) **acid** to produce the 6-carbon **citric acid.** Citric acid is the first substrate of the cycle, and biochemists (in particular) prefer to call the Krebs cycle the **citric acid cycle.** Figure 25.7 summarizes the basic events of the Krebs cycle.

? *What two major kinds of chemical reactions are occurring in this cycle, and how are these reactions indicated symbolically?*

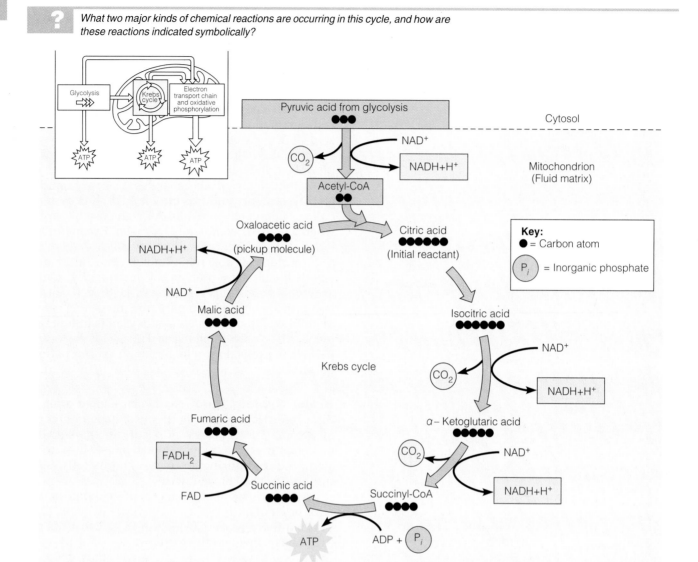

FIGURE 25.7
Simplified version of the Krebs cycle. During each turn of the cycle, two carbon atoms are removed from the substrates as CO_2 (decarboxylation reactions); four oxidations by removal of hydrogen atoms occur, producing four molecules of reduced coenzymes (3 NADH + H⁺ and 1 $FADH_2$); and one ATP is synthesized by substrate-level phosphorylation. An additional decarboxylation reaction and an oxidation reaction occur to convert pyruvic acid, the product of glycolysis, to acetyl CoA, the molecule that actually enters the Krebs cycle pathway.

As the cycle moves along through its eight successive steps, the atoms of citric acid are rearranged to produce different intermediate molecules, most called **keto acids.** The acetic acid which enters the cycle is broken apart carbon by carbon (decarboxylated) and is oxidized, simultaneously generating NADH + H⁺ and $FADH_2$. At the end of the cycle, acetic acid has been totally disposed of and oxaloacetic acid, the *pickup molecule,* is regenerated. Because two *decarboxylation* and four *oxidation* events occur, the products of the Krebs cycle are two molecules of carbon dioxide and four molecules of reduced coenzymes (3 NADH + H⁺ and 1 $FADH_2$). The addition of water at certain steps accounts for some of the released hydrogen. One molecule of ATP is formed (via substrate-level phosphorylation) during each turn of the cycle. The detailed events of each of the eight steps of the Krebs cycle are described in Appendix E.

Now let's account for the pyruvic acid molecules entering the mitochondrion. A total of three carbon dioxides and five molecules of reduced coenzymes—1 $FADH_2$ and 4 NADH + H⁺ (equal to the removal of 10 hydrogen atoms)—are formed for each pyruvic acid. Thus, the products of glucose oxidation in the Krebs cycle are twice that (remember 1 glucose = 2 pyruvic acids): six CO_2, ten molecules of reduced coenzymes, and two ATP molecules. Notice that it is these Krebs cycle reactions that produce the CO_2 evolved during glucose oxidation. The reduced coenzymes, which carry their "extra electrons" in high-energy linkages, must now be oxidized if the Krebs cycle (and glycolysis) is to continue.

Although the glycolytic pathway is exclusive to carbohydrate oxidation, breakdown products of carbohydrates, fats, and proteins can feed into the Krebs cycle to be oxidized for energy. Likewise, some Krebs cycle intermediates can be siphoned off to make fatty acids and nonessential amino acids, as described shortly. Thus, the Krebs cycle, besides serving as the final common pathway for the oxidation of food fuels, is a source of building materials for anabolic (biosynthetic) reactions.

Electron Transport Chain and Oxidative Phosphorylation.
Like glycolysis, none of the reactions of the Krebs cycle directly use oxygen. This is the exclusive function of the **electron transport chain,** which oversees the final catabolic reactions that occur on the inner mitochondrial membranes. However, because the reduced coenzymes produced during the Krebs cycle are the "grist" (substrates) of the electron transport chain "mill," these pathways are coupled, and both phases are considered to be oxygen requiring (aerobic).

In the electron transport chain, the hydrogens removed during the oxidation of food fuels are finally combined with molecular oxygen, and the energy released during those reactions is harnessed to attach inorganic phosphate groups (P_i) to ADP. As noted above, this type of phosphorylation process is called *oxidative phosphorylation.* Let us look more closely at this rather complicated process.

Most components of the electron transport chain are proteins bound to metal atoms *(cofactors).* These proteins, which form part of the structure of the inner mitochondrial membrane (cristae), are quite varied in composition. For example, some of the proteins, the **flavins,** contain flavin mononucleotide (FMN) derived from the vitamin riboflavin. Others contain both sulfur (S) and iron (Fe), but most are brightly colored iron-containing pigments called **cytochromes** (si'to-krōmz; *cyto* = cell, *chrom* = color). Neighboring carriers are clustered together to form three major **respiratory enzyme complexes** that are alternately reduced and oxidized by picking up electrons and then passing them on to the next complex in the sequence. As shown in Figure 25.8, the first such complex accepts hydrogen atoms from NADH + H^+, oxidizing it to NAD^+. $FADH_2$ transfers its hydrogen "baggage" slightly further along into the chain. The hydrogens delivered to the electron transport chain by the reduced coenzymes are quickly split into pro-

tons (H^+) and electrons. The protons escape into the watery matrix and the electrons are shuttled along the membrane from one acceptor to the next. Ultimately hydrogen is delivered to molecular oxygen to form water as indicated by the reaction

$$2H\,(2H^+ + 2e^-) + \tfrac{1}{2}\,O_2 \rightarrow H_2O$$

Virtually all the water resulting from glucose oxidation is formed during oxidative phosphorylation. Because NADH + H^+ and $FADH_2$ are oxidized as they release their burden of picked-up hydrogen atoms, the net reaction for the electron transport chain is

$$\underset{\substack{\text{(reduced} \\ \text{coenzyme)}}}{\text{Coenzyme-2H}} + \tfrac{1}{2}\,O_2 \rightarrow \underset{\substack{\text{(oxidized} \\ \text{coenzyme)}}}{\text{coenzyme}} + H_2O$$

The transfer of electrons from NADH + H^+ to oxygen releases large amounts of energy (is exergonic). If hydrogen combined directly with molecular oxygen, the energy would be released in one big burst and most of it would be lost to the environment as heat. Instead energy is released in many small steps as the electrons stream from one electron acceptor to the next. Each successive carrier has a greater affinity for electrons than those preceding it. Therefore, the electrons cascade "downhill" from NADH + H^+ to progressively lower energy levels until they are finally delivered to oxygen, which has the greatest affinity of all for electrons (Figure 25.9). You could say that oxygen "pulls" the electrons down the chain.

The electron transport chain functions as an energy conversion machine, using the stepwise release of electronic energy to pump protons from the fluid matrix into the intermembrane space. Because the crista membrane is nearly impermeable to H^+, this chemiosmotic process creates an **electrochemical proton (H^+) gradient** across the inner membrane that temporarily stores potential energy (gradient energy) that will be used to synthesize ATP (Figure 25.8).

The proton gradient has two major aspects: (1) It creates a pH gradient, with the hydrogen ion concentration in the matrix much lower than that in the intermembrane space; and (2) it generates a voltage across the membrane that is negative ($-$) on the matrix side and positive ($+$) between the mitochondrial membranes. Both conditions strongly attract the protons back into the matrix. However, the only areas of the membrane that are freely permeable to H^+ are large enzyme-protein complexes called **ATP synthases.** As the protons take this "route," they create an electrical current, and ATP synthase harnesses this electrical energy to catalyze attachment of a phosphate group to ADP to form ATP (Figure 25.8), thus completing the process of oxidative phosphorylation.

The proton gradient also supplies energy to actively pump needed metabolites (ADP, pyruvic acid, inorganic phosphate) and calcium ions across the relatively impermeable inner mitochondrial

How does this process of ATP synthesis differ from substrate-level phosphorylation?

FIGURE 25.8
One hypothetical mechanism of oxidative phosphorylation.
Schematic diagram showing the flow of electrons through the three major respiratory enzyme complexes—(1) NADH dehydrogenase complex (FMN, Fe-S), (2) cytochrome b–c_1 complex, and (3) cytochrome oxidase complex (a–a_3)—of the electron transport chain during the transfer of two electrons from reduced NAD^+ to oxygen. Coenzyme Q

and cytochrome c are mobile and act as carriers between the major complexes.

The electron transport chain is an energy converter; it transforms chemical energy into a gradient of H^+. As the high-energy electrons flow along their energy gradient, some of the energy is used by each complex to pump protons from the mitochondrial matrix into the intermembrane space. These protons create an electrochemical proton gradient that drives them back across

the inner membrane through the ATP synthase complex. ATP synthase uses the energy of proton flow (electrical energy) to synthesize ATP from ADP and P_i present in the matrix. Oxidation of each $NADH + H^+$ to NAD^+ yields 3 ATP. Because $FADH_2$ unloads its hydrogen atoms beyond the first respiratory complex, less energy (2 ATP) is captured as a result of its oxidation.

membrane. (The outer membrane is quite freely permeable to these substances, so no "help" is needed there.) Indeed, calcium pickup and storage by mitochondria is an important emergency backup mechanism for eliminating a Ca^{2+} overload in the cytosol. However, the supply of energy from oxidation is not limitless; so when more of the proton gradient energy is used to drive these transport processes, less is available to make ATP.

Studies of metabolic poisons, some quite deadly, support this chemiosmotic model of oxidative phosphorylation. For example, cyanide disrupts the process by blocking the flow of electrons from cytochrome a_3 to oxygen. Poisons commonly called "uncouplers" abolish the proton gradient by making

the crista membrane permeable to H^+. Consequently, although the electron transport chain continues to deliver electrons to oxygen at a furious pace, and oxygen consumption rises, no ATP is made.

The stimulus for ATP production is entry of *ADP* into the mitochondrial fluid matrix. As ADP is transported in, ATP is moved out in a coupled transport process.

Summary of ATP Production. When oxygen is present, cellular respiration is remarkably efficient. Of the total of 686 kilocalories (kcal) of energy present in 1 mole of glucose, as much as 278 kcal can be captured in the bonds of ATP molecules. The rest is liberated as heat. (The mole is explained on p. 30.)

FIGURE 25.9

Electronic energy gradient in the electron transport chain. Each member of the chain oscillates between a reduced state and an oxidized state. A component of the chain becomes reduced when it accepts electrons from its "uphill" neighbor (which has a lower affinity for the electrons). Each member of the chain reverts to its oxidized form as it passes electrons to its "downhill" neighbor (which has a greater affinity for the electrons). At the "bottom" of the chain is oxygen, which is *very* electronegative. The overall energy drop for electrons traveling from NADH to oxygen is 53 kcal/mol, but this fall is broken up into a series of smaller steps by the electron transport chain.

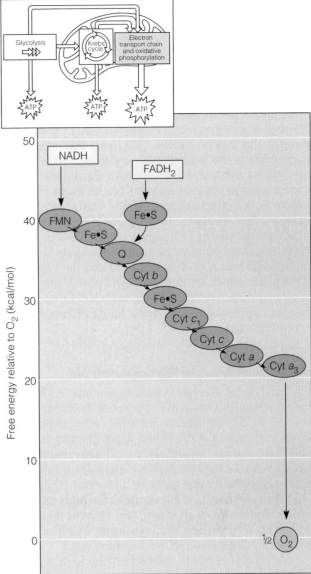

This corresponds to an energy capture of about 40%. This is far more efficient than any man-made machines, which use only 10% to 30% of the energy actually available to them.

Once we have tallied the net gain of 4 ATP molecules per glucose produced directly by substrate-level phosphorylations (2 during glycolysis and 2 during the Krebs cycle), all that remains to be calculated is the number of ATP molecules produced by oxidative phosphorylation (Figure 25.10).

Each NADH + H$^+$ that transfers a pair of high-energy electrons to the electron transport chain contributes enough energy to the proton gradient to generate about three ATP molecules. The oxidation of FADH$_2$ is somewhat less efficient because it doesn't donate electrons to the "top" of the electron transport chain. For each 2 hydrogen atoms delivered by

FIGURE 25.10

The aerobic oxidation of one molecule of glucose yields a net gain of 36 to 38 ATP molecules. A net gain of four ATP molecules is produced by substrate-level phosphorylation events occurring during glycolysis and the citric acid cycle. The balance is produced by oxidative phosphorylation events occurring in the electron transport chain.

FADH$_2$, *two* ATPs are produced. Thus, the 8 NADH + H$^+$ and the 2 FADH$_2$ produced during the Krebs cycle are "worth" 24 and 4 ATPs respectively. The 2 NADH + H$^+$ generated during glycolysis yields 4 (or 6) ATP molecules. Overall, complete oxidation of one glucose molecule to carbon dioxide and water yields 38 or 36 molecules of ATP (Figure 25.10). The alternative figures given represent the present uncertainty about the energy yield of reduced NAD$^+$ generated *outside* the mitochondria. The inner mitochondrial membrane is *not* permeable to reduced NAD$^+$ generated in the cytosol, so that formed during glycolysis uses a *shuttle molecule* to deliver its extra electron pair to the electron transport chain. One shuttle molecule, *malate,* unloads the electrons at the very beginning of the electron transport chain, yielding three ATP. Another, *glycerol phosphate,* unloads later and yields only two ATP. Heart muscle and liver cells use the malate system, while the glycerol phosphate system is especially active in the brain. Which of these shuttle systems predominates in other kinds of human cells is not known.

Glycogenesis and Glycogenolysis

Although most glucose is used to generate ATP molecules, unlimited amounts of glucose do *not* result in unlimited ATP synthesis, because cells cannot store large amounts of ATP. When more glucose is available than can be immediately oxidized, rising intracellular ATP concentrations eventually inhibit glucose catabolism and initiate processes that store glucose as glycogen or fat. Because the body can store much more fat than glycogen, fats account for 80% to 85% of stored energy. (Fat synthesis will be considered in the discussion of lipid metabolism.)

When glycolysis is "turned off" by high ATP levels, glucose molecules are combined in long chains to form glycogen, the animal carbohydrate storage product. This process, called **glycogenesis** (*glyco* = sugar; *genesis* = origin), begins when glucose entering cells is phosphorylated to glucose-6-phosphate and then converted into its isomer, *glucose-1-phosphate.* The terminal phosphate group is cleaved off as the enzyme *glycogen synthase* catalyzes the attachment of glucose to the growing glycogen chain (Figure 25.11). Liver and skeletal muscle cells are most active in glycogen synthesis and storage.

When blood levels of glucose drop, glycogen lysis or splitting, occurs. This process is known as **glycogenolysis** (gli″ko-jĕ-nol′ĭ-sis). The enzyme *glycogen phosphorylase* oversees phosphorylation and cleavage of glycogen to release glucose-1-phosphate, which is then converted to glucose-6-phosphate, a form that can enter the glycolytic pathway to be oxidized for energy.

In muscle cells and most other cells, glucose-6-phosphate resulting from glycogenolysis is trapped because it cannot cross the cell membrane. However, hepatocytes (and some kidney and intestinal cells)

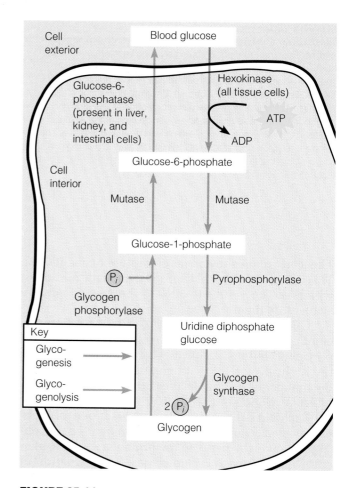

FIGURE 25.11
Glycogenesis and glycogenolysis. When glucose supplies exceed cellular need for ATP synthesis, glycogenesis, the conversion of glucose into glycogen for storage, occurs. Glycogenolysis, the breakdown of glycogen to release glucose, is stimulated by falling blood sugar levels. Notice that glycogen is synthesized and degraded by different enzymatic pathways.

contain *glucose-6-phosphatase,* a unique enzyme which removes the terminal phosphate, producing free glucose. Because glucose readily diffuses from the cell into the blood, the liver can use its glycogen stores to provide blood sugar for the benefit of other organs when blood glucose levels drop. Liver glycogen is also an important energy source for skeletal muscles that have depleted their own glycogen reserves.

A common misconception is that athletes need to eat more protein to improve their athletic performance and maintain their greater muscle mass. Actually, a diet rich in *complex* carbohydrates, which lays in muscle glycogen, is much more effective in sustaining intense muscle activity than are high-protein meals. Notice that the emphasis is on *complex* carbohydrates. Eating a candy bar before an athletic event to provide "quick" energy does more harm than good because it stimulates insulin secretion, which favors glucose use and retards fat use at a time when fat use should be maximal. Building muscle protein or avoiding its loss requires not only extra protein, but also extra (protein-sparing) calories to meet the greater energy needs of the increasingly massive muscles.

Long-distance runners in particular are well aware of the practice called glycogen loading, popularly called "carbo loading," for endurance events. Glycogen loading, which "tricks" the muscles into storing more glycogen than they normally have the capacity for, involves (1) eating meals high in protein and fat while exercising heavily over a period of several days (this depletes muscle glycogen stores) and then (2) two to three days before the event decreasing exercise intensity (to about 40% of the norm) and switching abruptly to a high-carbohydrate diet. This causes a rebound in muscle glycogen stores of two to four times the normal amount. However, glycogen retains water, and the resulting weight increase and fluid retention may hamper the ability of muscle cells to obtain adequate oxygen. Some athletes using the procedure have complained of cardiac and skeletal muscle pain. Consequently, its use should be cautioned against. •

Gluconeogenesis

When too little glucose is available to stoke the "metabolic furnace," glycerol and amino acids are converted to glucose. This process of forming new *(neo)* sugar from *noncarbohydrate* molecules, called **gluconeogenesis,** occurs in the liver. It takes place when dietary sources and glucose reserves have been depleted and blood glucose levels are beginning to decline. Gluconeogenesis protects the body, the nervous system in particular, from the damaging effects of low blood sugar *(hypoglycemia)* by ensuring that ATP synthesis can continue. The hormones triggering this process and the way fats and proteins are siphoned into these pathways are considered in the discussions of fat and protein metabolism.

Lipid Metabolism

Fats are the body's most concentrated source of energy. They contain very little water, and the energy yield from the catabolism of fats is approximately twice that gained from either glucose or protein breakdown; that is, 9 kcal per g fat in contrast to 4 kcal per g from carbohydrate or protein. Most products of fat digestion are transported in lymph in the form of fatty-protein droplets called *chylomicrons* (see Chapter 24). Eventually, the lipids in the chylomicrons are hydrolyzed by plasma enzymes, and the resulting fatty acids and glycerol are taken up by body cells where they are processed in various ways. In this section we focus on the oxidation of fats for energy and on some of their anabolic uses.

Oxidation of Glycerol and Fatty Acids

Of the various lipids, only neutral fats are routinely oxidized for energy. Catabolism of neutral fats involves

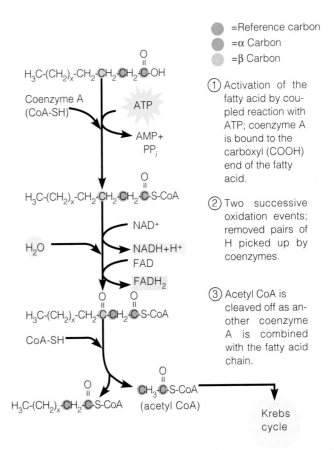

FIGURE 25.12
Events of beta oxidation. The process begins as the fatty acid is activated in a coupled reaction with ATP and coenzyme A is attached to the first carbon (the reference carbon) of the fatty acid chain. Each successive 2-carbon (acetyl) segment is oxidized twice and then cleaved off as another coenzyme A is added to the remaining portion of the fatty acid. Cleavage occurs between the α (second) and β (third) carbons of the fatty acid chain. Acetyl CoA released during each round enters the Krebs cycle. The reduced coenzymes resulting from beta oxidation (like those resulting from the oxidation of acetyl CoA in the Krebs cycle) are oxidized via the electron transport chain. (PP$_i$ = pyrophosphate [two linked phosphate groups].)

the separate oxidation of their two different building blocks: glycerol and fatty acid chains. Most body cells easily convert glycerol to glyceraldehyde phosphate, a glycolysis intermediate which then flows into the Krebs cycle. Glyceraldehyde is equal to half a glucose molecule, and ATP energy harvest from its complete oxidation is approximately half that of glucose (18–19 ATP/glycerol).

Beta oxidation, the initial phase of fatty acid oxidation, occurs in the mitochondria. Although many different types of reactions (oxidation, dehydration, and others) are involved, the *net result* of beta oxidation is that the fatty acid chains are broken apart into two-carbon *acetic acid* fragments, and reduced coenzymes are produced (Figure 25.12). Each acetic acid molecule is fused to coenzyme A, forming acetyl CoA. The term "beta oxidation" reflects the fact that the carbon in the beta (third) position is oxidized during the process. The splitting step (cleavage) occurs

? *What is the central molecule in lipid metabolism?*

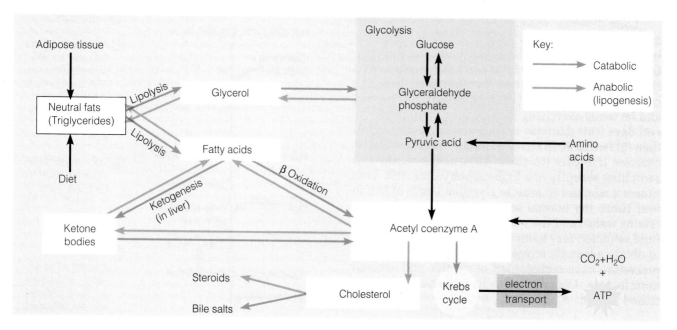

FIGURE 25.13
Metabolism of triglycerides.
When needed for energy, dietary or stored fats enter the catabolic pathways. Glycerol enters the glycolytic pathway (as glyceraldehyde phosphate) and the fatty acids are broken down by beta oxidation to acetyl CoA, which enters the Krebs cycle. When fats are to be synthesized (lipogenesis) and stored in fat depots, the intermediates are drawn from glycolysis and the Krebs cycle in a reversal of the processes noted above. Likewise, excess dietary fats are stored in adipose tissues. When triglycerides are in excess or are the primary energy source, the liver releases their breakdown products (fatty acids → acetyl CoA) in the form of ketone bodies. Excessive amounts of carbohydrates and amino acids are also converted to triglycerides (lipogenesis).

between the second (alpha) and third (beta) carbon atoms in each case; that is, between the first and second carbon atoms beyond the terminal (reference) carbon. Acetyl CoA is then picked up by oxaloacetic acid and enters the aerobic pathways to be completely oxidized to carbon dioxide and water.

Notice that unlike glycerol, which enters the glycolytic pathway, acetyl CoA resulting from fatty acid breakdown *cannot* be used for gluconeogenesis because the metabolic pathway is irreversible past pyruvic acid.

Lipogenesis and Lipolysis

There is a continual turnover of neutral fats in adipose tissue: New fats are "put in the larder" for later use, while stored fats are broken down and released to the blood. That bulge of fatty tissue you see today does *not* contain the same fat molecules it did a month ago.

When glycerol and fatty acids from dietary fats are not immediately needed for energy, they are recombined into triglycerides and stored. About 50% ends up in subcutaneous tissue, the balance is stockpiled in other fat depots of the body. Triglyceride synthesis, or **lipogenesis** (see Figure 25.13), occurs when cellular ATP and glucose levels are high. Excess ATP leads also to an accumulation of the intermediates of glucose metabolism, including acetyl CoA and glyceraldehyde-PO_4, which would

otherwise feed into the Krebs cycle. But, when present in excess, these two metabolites are channeled into pathways leading to triglyceride synthesis. Acetyl CoA molecules are condensed together, forming fatty acid chains that grow 2 carbons at a time. (This accounts for the fact that almost all fatty acids in the body contain an even number of carbon atoms.) Because acetyl CoA, an intermediate in glucose catabolism, is also the *starting point* for synthesis of fatty acids (see Figure 25.13), glucose is easily converted into fat. Glyceraldehyde phosphate is converted to glycerol, which is condensed with the fatty acids to form triglycerides. Thus, even if the diet is fat-poor, excessive carbohydrate intake provides *all the raw materials* needed to form neutral fats. When blood sugar is high, lipogenesis is the major activity in adipose tissues and is also an important liver function.

Lipolysis (lĭ-pol'ĭ-sis; "fat splitting"), the breakdown of stored fats into glycerol and fatty acids, is essentially lipogenesis in reverse. The fatty acids and glycerol products are released to the blood, helping to ensure that body organs have continuous access to fat fuels for aerobic respiration. (The liver, cardiac muscle, and resting skeletal muscles actually prefer fatty acids as an energy fuel.) The meaning of the adage "fats burn in the flame of carbohydrates" becomes clear when carbohydrate intake is inadequate. Under such conditions, lipolysis is accelerated as the body attempts to fill the fuel gap with fats. However, the entry of acetyl CoA into the Krebs cycle depends on the availability of oxaloacetic acid to act as a pickup molecule to form citric acid. When carbohydrates are deficient, oxaloacetic acid is converted to glucose (to fuel the brain). Under such conditions, fat oxidation is incomplete, acetyl CoA accumulates, and the liver converts acetyl CoA molecules to **ketones,** or **ketone bodies,** which are released into the blood. This conversion process is called **ketogenesis** (Figure 25.13). Ketones include acetoacetic acid, β-hydroxybutyric acid, and acetone, all formed from acetic acid. (The *keto acids* cycling through the Krebs cycle and the *ketone bodies* resulting from fat metabolism are quite different and should not be confused.)

When ketones accumulate in the blood faster than they can be used by tissue cells for fuel, *ketosis* results and large amounts of ketones are excreted from the body in urine. Ketosis is a common consequence of starvation, unwise dieting (in which inadequate carbohydrates are eaten), and diabetes mellitus. Because most ketone bodies (like fatty acids) are organic acids, the outcome of ketosis is *metabolic acidosis.* The body's buffer systems cannot tie up the acids fast enough, and blood pH drops to dangerously low levels. The person's breath smells fruity as acetone vaporizes from the lungs, and breathing becomes more rapid as the respiratory system tries to blow off blood carbonic acid as carbon dioxide to force the blood pH upward. In severe cases of untreated metabolic acidosis, the person may become comatose or even die as the acid pH depresses the nervous system. •

Synthesis of Structural Materials

All body cells use phospholipids and cholesterol to build their membranes. Phospholipids are also important components of myelin sheaths of neurons. In addition, the liver (1) synthesizes lipoproteins for transport of cholesterol, fats, and other substances in the blood, (2) makes thromboplastin, a clotting factor, (3) synthesizes cholesterol from acetyl CoA, and (4) uses cholesterol for forming bile salts. Certain endocrine organs (ovaries, testes, and adrenal cortex) use cholesterol as the basis for synthesizing their steroid hormones.

Protein Metabolism

Like all biological molecules, proteins have a limited life span and must be broken down to their amino acids and replaced before they begin to deteriorate. Newly ingested amino acids transported in the blood are taken up by cells by active transport processes and used to *replace* tissue proteins at the rate of about 100 grams each day. When more protein is ingested than is needed for these constructive (or anabolic) purposes, amino acids are oxidized for energy or converted to fat.

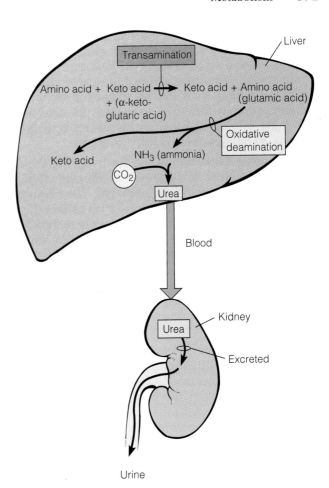

FIGURE 25.14
Simplified version of the transamination and oxidative processes that occur when amino acids are oxidized for energy. As shown at the top of the figure, transamination involves the switching of an amine group from an amino acid to a keto acid (an intermediate of the Krebs cycle, usually α ketoglutaric acid). As a result the amino acid becomes a keto acid (it now has an O atom replacing its amine group, NH_2) and the keto acid becomes an amino acid, typically glutamic acid. Oxidative deamination is the process in which the amine group forming part of glutamic acid is released as ammonia, and then combined with CO_2 by the liver cells to form urea. (The urea is then released to the blood and excreted in urine by the kidneys.)

Oxidation of Amino Acids

Before amino acids can be oxidized for energy, they must be *deaminated* (i.e., their amine group [NH_2] must be removed). The resulting molecule is then converted to pyruvic acid or one of the keto acid intermediates in the Krebs cycle. The key molecule in these interconversions is *glutamic* (gloo-tam'ik) *acid,* a common nonessential amino acid. The events that occur, shown in simplified form in Figure 25.14 (and in detail in Appendix E), appear to be as follows:

1. **Transamination** (trans″am-ĭ-na′shun). A number of amino acids can transfer their amine group to α-ketoglutaric acid (a Krebs cycle keto acid) to form glutamic acid. The transferring amino acid becomes a keto acid (that is, it has an oxygen atom where the amine group formerly was), and the keto acid (α-ketoglutaric acid) becomes an amino acid (glutamic acid). This reaction is fully reversible.

2. **Oxidative deamination.** In the liver, the amine group of glutamic acid is removed as **ammonia (NH₃)**, and α-ketoglutaric acid is regenerated. The liberated ammonia molecules are combined with carbon dioxide, yielding **urea** and water. The urea is released to the blood and removed from the body in urine. Because ammonia is toxic to body cells, particularly brain cells, the ease with which glutamic acid funnels amine groups into the **urea cycle** is extremely important. This mechanism rids the body not only of the ammonia produced during oxidative deamination of amino acids, but also of blood-borne ammonia produced by intestinal bacteria.

3. **Keto acid modification.** The goal of amino acid degradation is to produce molecules that can be oxidized in the Krebs cycle or converted to glucose. Hence, keto acids resulting from transamination are altered as necessary to produce metabolites that can enter the Krebs cycle. The most important of these metabolites are pyruvic acid (actually an intermediate before Krebs cycle pathways), acetyl CoA, α-ketoglutaric acid, and oxaloacetic acid (see Figure 25.7). Since the reactions of glycolysis are reversible, deaminated amino acids that are converted to pyruvic acid can also be reconverted to glucose and contribute to gluconeogenesis.

Synthesis of Proteins

Amino acids are the most important anabolic nutrients. Not only do they form all protein structures, but they form the bulk of the body's functional molecules as well. As described in Chapter 3, protein synthesis (directed by messenger RNA molecules) occurs on ribosomes, where cytoplasmic enzymes oversee the formation of peptide bonds linking amino acids into protein polymers. The amount and type of protein synthesized are precisely controlled by hormones (growth hormone, thyroxine, sex hormones, insulin, and others), so protein anabolism reflects the hormonal balance at each stage in the life cycle.

During the course of your lifetime, your cells synthesize 225–450 kg (about 500–1000 pounds) of proteins, depending on your size. However, you need not consume anywhere near that amount because nonessential amino acids are easily formed by siphoning keto acids from the Krebs cycle and transferring amine groups to them by transamination. Most of these transformations occur in the liver, which also provides nearly all the nonessential amino acids

needed to produce the relatively small amount of protein that the body synthesizes each day. However, a complete set of amino acids must be present for protein synthesis to take place, so all of the essential amino acids must be provided by the diet. If some are not, the rest are oxidized for energy even though they may be needed for anabolism. In such cases, negative nitrogen balance always results because body protein is broken down to supply the essential amino acids needed.

Catabolic-Anabolic Steady State of the Body

The body exists in a *dynamic catabolic-anabolic state.* With few exceptions (notably DNA), organic molecules are continuously broken down and rebuilt—frequently at a head-spinning rate.

The blood is the common transport pool for all body cells, and it contains many kinds of nutrients—glucose, ketone bodies, fatty acids, glycerol, and lactic acid. Some organs routinely use blood energy sources other than glucose, thus sparing (saving) glucose for tissues with stricter glucose requirements.

The body's total supply of nutrients constitutes its **nutrient pools**—amino acid, carbohydrate, and fat stores—which can be drawn on to meet its varying needs (Figure 25.15a). These pools are interconvertible, because their pathways are linked by key intermediates (see Figure 25.15b). The liver, adipose tissue, and skeletal muscles are the primary effector organs determining the amounts and direction of the molecular conversions shown in the figure.

The *amino acid pool* (Figure 25.15a) consists of the body's total supply of free amino acids. A small amount of amino acids and proteins is lost daily in urine and in sloughed hairs or skin cells. Typically, these are replaced via the diet; otherwise, amino acids arising from tissue breakdown return to the pool. This pool is the source of amino acids for resynthesizing body proteins and for forming several amino acid derivatives. In addition, as described above, deaminated amino acids can participate in gluconeogenesis. Not all events of amino acid metabolism occur in all cells. For example, *only* the liver forms urea, and excreting urea from the body is a major role of the kidneys (and to a small extent the skin). Nonetheless, the concept of a common amino acid pool is valid because all cells are connected by the blood.

Because carbohydrates are easily and frequently converted to fats, the *carbohydrate* and *fat pools* are usually considered together (Figure 25.15). There are two major differences between this pool and the amino acid pool: (1) Fats and carbohydrates are oxidized directly to produce cellular energy, whereas amino acids can be used to supply energy *only after*

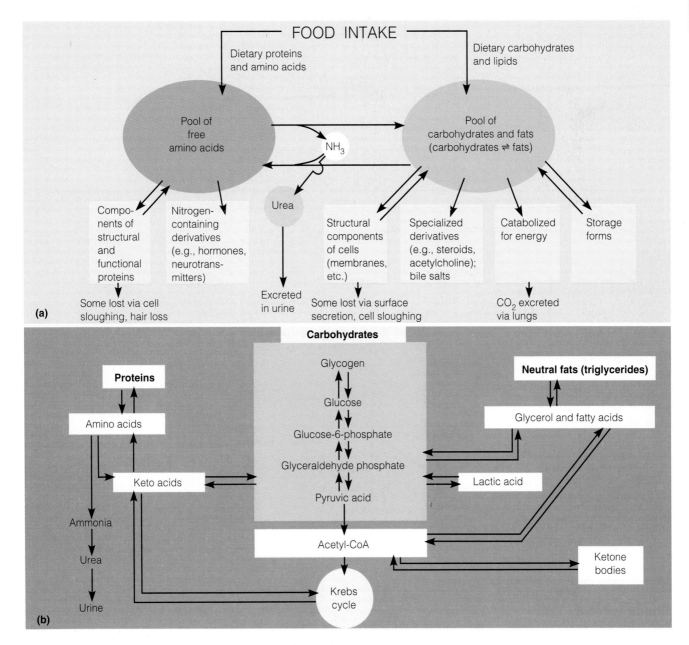

FIGURE 25.15
Carbohydrate, fat, and amino acid pools and pathways of interconversion.
(a) Carbohydrate-fat and amino acid pools. Sources contributing to the pools and fates of intermediates drawn from the pools are indicated. **(b)** Simplified flowchart showing the intermediates through which carbohydrates, fats, and proteins can be interconverted.

being converted to a carbohydrate intermediate.
(2) Excess carbohydrate and fat can be stored as such, whereas excess amino acids are *not* stored as protein. Instead, they are oxidized for energy or converted to fat or glycogen for storage.

Eating large amounts of protein does not significantly increase body tissue protein or add to the diameter of that biceps muscle! The only way muscle mass is increased is by placing extra demands on the skeletal muscles by resistance exercise, as described in Chapter 9 (p. 274). •

Absorptive and Postabsorptive States: Events and Controls

Metabolic controls act to equalize blood concentrations of nutrients between two nutritional states. Sometimes referred to as the *fed state,* the **absorptive state** is the time during and shortly after eating, when nutrients are flushing into the bloodstream from the gastrointestinal tract. The **postabsorptive** *(fasting)* **state** is the period when the GI tract is empty and energy sources are supplied by the breakdown of

FIGURE 25.16

Summary of the major events and principal metabolic pathways of the absorptive state. (Although not indicated in part **(b)**, amino acids are also taken up by tissue cells and used for protein synthesis, and fats are the primary energy fuel of muscle, liver cells, and adipose tissue.)

body reserves. Those who eat "three squares" a day are in the absorptive state for the 4 hours during and after each meal and in the postabsorptive state in the late morning, late afternoon, and all night. However, postabsorptive mechanisms can sustain the body for much longer intervals if necessary—even to accommodate weeks of fasting—as long as water is taken in.

Absorptive State

During the absorptive state (Figure 25.16) anabolic processes exceed catabolic ones. Glucose is the major energy fuel. Dietary amino acids and fats are used to remake degraded body protein or fat, and small amounts are oxidized to provide ATP. Excess metabolites, regardless of source, are transformed to fat if not used for anabolism. We will consider the fate of each nutrient group during this phase and the hormonal control of its pathways.

Carbohydrates. Absorbed monosaccharides are delivered directly to the liver, where fructose and galactose are converted to glucose. Glucose, in turn, is released to the blood or converted to glycogen and fat. Glycogen formed in the liver is stored there, but most of the fat synthesized by the hepatocytes is released to the blood and picked up for storage by adipose tissues. Blood-borne glucose not sequestered by the liver enters body cells to be metabolized for energy; any excess is stored in skeletal muscle cells as glycogen or in adipose cells as fat.

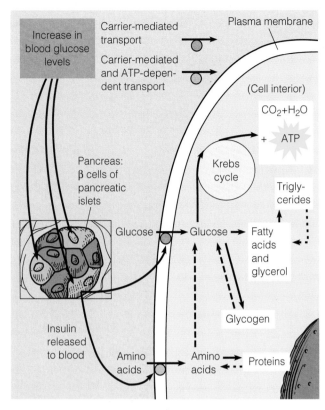

FIGURE 25.17
Effects of insulin on metabolism. Solid arrows indicate processes enhanced by insulin; dashed arrows indicate reactions inhibited by insulin. When insulin concentrations are low (i.e., during the postabsorptive period), the activity of the dashed-arrow pathways is enhanced and normal effects of insulin are inhibited. (Note that not all the effects indicated occur in all tissue cells.)

Triglycerides. Nearly all products of fat digestion enter the lymph in the form of chylomicrons (see p. 835), which are hydrolyzed to fatty acids and glycerol before they can pass through the capillary walls. *Lipoprotein lipase,* the enzyme that catalyzes this fat hydrolysis, is particularly active in the capillaries of muscle and fat tissues. Adipose cells, skeletal muscle cells, and liver cells use triglycerides (triacylglycerols) as their primary energy source, and, when dietary carbohydrates are limited, other cells begin to oxidize more fat for energy. Although some fatty acids and glycerol are used for anabolic purposes by the general population of tissue cells, most enter adipose tissue where they are reconverted to triglycerides and stored.

Amino Acids. Absorbed amino acids are delivered to the liver, which deaminates some of them to keto acids. The keto acids may flow into the Krebs cycle pathway to be used for ATP synthesis, or they may be converted to liver fat stores. The liver also uses some of the amino acids to synthesize plasma proteins, including albumin, clotting proteins, and transport proteins. However, most amino acids flushing through the liver sinusoids remain in the blood for uptake by other body cells, where they are used for protein synthesis.

Hormonal Control. **Insulin** directs essentially all the events of the absorptive state (Figure 25.17). Rising blood glucose levels (above 100 mg glucose/100 ml blood) after a carbohydrate-containing meal act as a humoral stimulus that prods the beta cells of the pancreatic islets to secrete more insulin. (This glucose-induced stimulation of insulin release is enhanced by several GI tract hormones including gastrin, CCK, and secretin.) A second important stimulus is elevated amino acid levels in the blood. As insulin binds to membrane receptors of its target cells, it activates carrier-mediated facilitated diffusion of glucose into the cells. Within seconds to minutes, the rate of glucose entry into tissue cells is increased 15 to 20 times. (The exception is brain cells, which actively take up glucose whether or not insulin is present.) Once glucose has entered the tissue cells, insulin enhances its oxidation for energy and stimulates its conversion to glycogen and, in adipose tissue, to triglycerides. Insulin also "revs up" the active transport of amino acids into cells, promotes protein synthesis, and inhibits virtually all liver enzymes that promote gluconeogenesis.

As you can see, insulin is a **hypoglycemic** (hi″po-gli-se′mik) **hormone.** It sweeps glucose out of the blood into the tissue cells, thereby lowering blood sugar levels. Additionally, it enhances glucose oxidation or storage while simultaneously inhibiting any process that might increase blood sugar levels.

Diabetes mellitus, a consequence of inadequate insulin production or abnormal insulin receptors, is a metabolic disorder with far-reaching consequences. Without insulin (or receptors that "recognize" it), glucose becomes unavailable to most body cells. Thus, blood glucose levels remain high, and large amounts of glucose are excreted in urine. Metabolic acidosis, protein wasting, and weight loss occur as large amounts of fats and tissue proteins are used for energy. (Diabetes mellitus is described in more detail in Chapter 17.) •

Postabsorptive State

The primary goal during the postabsorptive state, that is, between meals when blood sugar levels are drop-

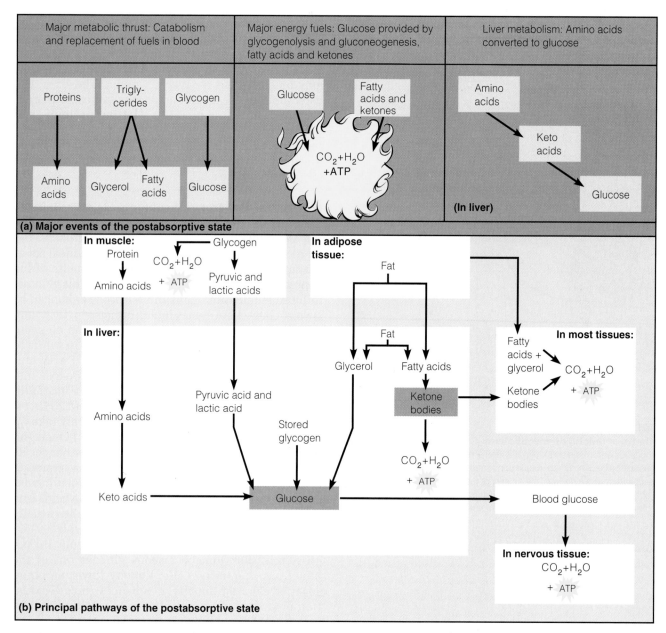

FIGURE 25.18
Summary of the major events and principal metabolic pathways of the postabsorptive state.

ping, is to maintain blood glucose levels within the homeostatic range (90–100 mg glucose/100 ml). The importance of constant blood glucose has already been explained. The brain *must* use glucose as its energy source. Most events of the postabsorptive state either make glucose available to the blood or spare glucose for the organs that most need it (Figure 25.18).

Sources of Blood Glucose. Glucose can be obtained from stored glycogen, from tissue proteins, and in limited amounts from fats, by several routes:

1. **Glycogenolysis in the liver.** The liver's stores of glycogen (about 100 g) are the first line of glucose

reserves. They are mobilized quickly and efficiently and can maintain blood sugar levels for about 4 hours during the postabsorptive period.

2. **Glycogenolysis in skeletal muscle.** Glycogen stores in skeletal muscle are approximately equal to liver reserves. Before liver glycogen is exhausted, glycogenolysis begins in skeletal muscle and to a lesser extent in other tissues. However, the glucose produced is not released to the blood because, unlike the liver, skeletal muscle does not have the enzymes needed to dephosphorylate glucose. Instead, glucose is partly oxidized to pyruvic acid (or, during anaerobic conditions, lactic acid), which enters the blood, is reconverted to glucose by the liver, and is

released to the blood again. Thus, skeletal muscle contributes to blood sugar homeostasis indirectly, via liver mechanisms.

3. **Lipolysis in adipose tissues and the liver.** Adipose and liver cells produce glycerol by lipolysis, and the liver converts it to glucose (gluconeogenesis), which is released to the blood. Because acetyl CoA, the beta oxidation product of fatty acids, is produced beyond the *reversible* steps of glycolysis, fatty acids cannot be used to bolster blood sugar levels.

4. **Catabolism of cellular protein.** Tissue proteins become the major source of blood glucose when fasting is prolonged and glycogen and fat stores are nearly exhausted (and during stress accompanied by enhanced glucocorticoid secretion). Cellular amino acids (mostly from muscle) are deaminated and converted to glucose in the liver. During extremely long fasts (several weeks), the kidneys also carry out gluconeogenesis and contribute fully as much glucose to the blood as does the liver.

Even when threatened by prolonged fasting, the body sets priorities. Muscle proteins are the first to go (to be catabolized). Movement is not nearly as important as maintaining wound healing and the immune response. But as long as life continues, so does the body's production of ATP needed to drive life processes. Obviously, there are limits to the amount of tissue protein breakdown that can occur before the body stops functioning. The heart is almost entirely muscle protein, and when it is severely cannibalized, the result is death.

Glucose Sparing. Even collectively, all of the manipulations to increase blood glucose are inadequate to provide energy supplies for prolonged fasting periods. Luckily, the body can adapt to burn more fats and proteins, which enter the Krebs cycle along with glucose breakdown products. The increased use of noncarbohydrate fuel molecules (especially triacylglycerols) to conserve glucose is called **glucose sparing.**

As the body progresses from the absorptive to the postabsorptive state, the brain continues to take its share of blood glucose; but virtually every other organ in the body switches to fatty acids as its major energy source, thus sparing glucose for the brain. During this transition phase, lipolysis begins in adipose tissues and released fatty acids are picked up by tissue cells and oxidized for energy. In addition, the liver oxidizes fats to ketone bodies and releases them into the blood for use by tissue cells. If fasting continues for longer than four or five days, the brain too begins to use large quantities of ketone bodies as well as glucose as its energy fuel. The survival value of the brain's ability to use an alternative fuel source is obvious. Much less tissue protein has to be ravaged to form glucose.

Hormonal and Neural Controls. The sympathetic nervous system and several hormones interact to control events of the postabsorptive state. Consequently, regulation of this phase is much more complex than that of the absorptive state when a single hormone, insulin, holds sway.

An important trigger for initiating postabsorptive events is damping of insulin release, which occurs as glucose blood levels begin to drop. As insulin levels decline, all insulin-induced cellular responses are inhibited as well.

Declining glucose levels also stimulate release of the insulin antagonist **glucagon** by the alpha cells of the pancreatic islets. Like other hormones acting during the postabsorptive state, glucagon is a *hyperglycemic hormone,* that is, it promotes a rise in blood glucose. Glucagon targets the liver and adipose tissue (Figure 25.19). The hepatocytes respond by accelerating glycogenolysis and gluconeogenesis, whereas adi-

? *What hormone is glucagon's main antagonist?*

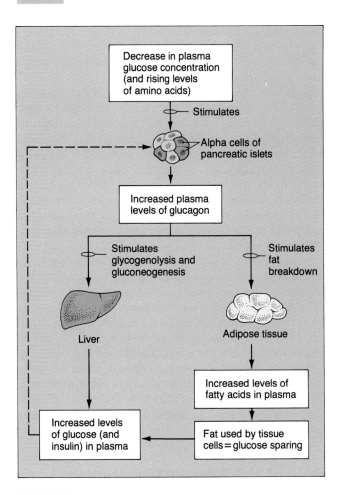

FIGURE 25.19

Influence of glucagon on plasma glucose concentrations. The negative-feedback control exerted by rising plasma glucose levels on glucagon secretion is also indicated (by the dashed arrow).

pose cells mobilize their fatty stores (lipolysis) and release fatty acids and glycerol to the blood. Thus, glucagon acts to "refurbish" blood energy fuels by enhancing both glucose and fatty acid levels. Glucagon release is inhibited after the next meal or whenever blood sugar levels rise and insulin secretion is turned on once again.

Thus far, the picture is pretty straightforward. Increasing blood sugar levels trigger insulin release, which "pushes" glucose into the cells, and blood sugar levels decline. This stimulates secretion of glucagon, which "pulls" glucose from the cells into the blood. However, there is more than a push-pull mechanism here, because *both* insulin and glucagon release are strongly stimulated by rising levels of amino acids in the blood. This effect is insignificant when we eat a normally balanced meal, but it has an important adaptive role when we eat a high-protein, low-carbohydrate meal. In this instance, the stimulus for insulin release is strong; and if it were not counterbalanced, the brain might be damaged by the resulting abrupt onset of hypoglycemia as glucose is rushed out of the blood. Simultaneous release of glucagon modulates the effects of insulin and helps stabilize blood glucose levels.

The sympathetic nervous system plays a crucial role in supplying fuel quickly when blood sugar levels drop suddenly (Figure 25.20). Adipose tissue is well supplied with sympathetic fibers, and epinephrine released by the adrenal medulla in response to sympathetic activation acts on the liver, skeletal muscle, and adipose tissues. Together, these stimuli mobilize fat and promote glycogenolysis—essentially the same effects prompted by glucagon. Bodily injury, anxiety, anger, or any other stressor that mobilizes the fight-or-flight response, including declining blood glucose levels that act on central glucose receptors in the hypothalamus, will trigger this control pathway.

In addition to glucagon and epinephrine, a number of other hormones—including growth hormone, thyroxine, sex hormones, and corticosteroids—influence metabolism and nutrient flow. Growth hormone secretion is enhanced by prolonged fasting or rapid declines in plasma glucose levels, and it exerts important anti-insulin effects (see Chapter 17, p. 555). However, the release and activity of most of these hormones are not specifically related to absorptive or postabsorptive events of metabolism. A checklist of the typical metabolic effects of various hormones is provided in Table 25.4.

Role of the Liver in Metabolism

The anatomy of the liver and its role in bile formation and digestive activities were described in Chapter 24. Here, we will focus on the liver's metabolic functions.

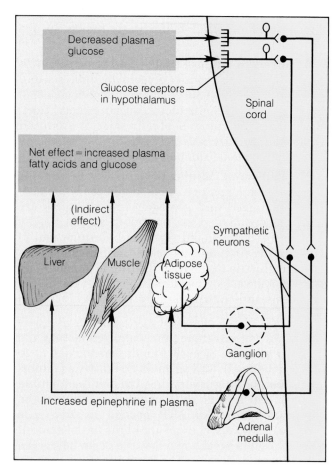

FIGURE 25.20
Sympathetic nervous system–epinephrine mechanism for providing glucose to the blood during the postabsorptive state. A decrease in blood glucose levels stimulates hypothalamic glucose receptors and, via a reflex mechanism (assumed to be as illustrated), blood levels of glucose and fatty acids are increased.

The liver is one of the most biochemically complex organs in the body. Essentially, it processes nearly every class of nutrients and plays a major role in regulating plasma cholesterol levels. While mechanical contraptions can, in a pinch, stand in for a failed heart, lungs, or kidney, the only thing that can do liver's work is a hepatocyte.

General Metabolic Functions

The hepatocytes carry out some 500 or more intricate metabolic functions. The detailed credits that the liver deserves are well beyond the scope of this text, but a brief summary is provided next.

The liver (1) packages fatty acids into forms that can be stored or transported, (2) synthesizes plasma proteins, (3) forms nonessential amino acids and con-

Table 25.4 Summary of Normal Hormonal Influences on Metabolism

Hormone's effects	Insulin	Glucagon	Epinephrine	Growth hormone	Thyroxine	Cortisol	Testosterone
Stimulates glucose uptake by cells	✔				✔		
Stimulates amino acid uptake by cells	✔			✔			
Stimulates glucose catabolism for energy	✔				✔		
Stimulates glycogenesis	✔						
Stimulates lipogenesis and fat storage	✔						
Inhibits gluconeogenesis	✔						
Stimulates protein synthesis (anabolic)	✔			✔	✔		✔
Stimulates glycogenolysis		✔	✔				
Stimulates lipolysis and fat mobilization		✔	✔	✔	✔	✔	
Stimulates gluconeogenesis		✔	✔	✔		✔	
Stimulates protein breakdown (catabolic)						✔	

verts the ammonia resulting from their deamination to urea, a less toxic excretory product, (4) stores glucose as glycogen and regulates blood sugar homeostasis. In addition to these roles in fat, protein, and glucose metabolism, liver cells (5) store certain vitamins, (6) conserve iron salvaged from worn-out red blood cells, (7) degrade hormones, and (8) detoxify substances such as alcohol and drugs. These major metabolic functions are detailed in Table 25.5.

Cholesterol Metabolism and Regulation of Plasma Cholesterol Levels

Cholesterol, though a very important dietary lipid, has received little attention thus far, primarily because it is not used as an energy fuel. It serves instead as the structural basis of bile salts, steroid hormones, and vitamin D and as a major component of plasma membranes. About 15% of blood cholesterol comes from the diet. The other 85% is made from acetyl CoA by the liver and to a lesser extent by other body cells, particularly intestinal cells. Choles-

terol is lost from the body when it is catabolized and secreted in bile salts, which are eventually excreted in feces.

Lipoproteins and Cholesterol Transport. Because triglycerides and cholesterol are completely insoluble in water, they do not circulate free in the bloodstream. Instead, they are transported to and from tissue cells in body fluids bound to small lipid-protein complexes called **lipoproteins.** These complexes solubilize the hydrophobic lipids, and their protein parts contain signals that regulate the entry and exit of particular lipids at specific target cells.

Lipoproteins vary considerably in their relative fat-protein compositions, but they all contain triglycerides, phospholipids, and cholesterol in addition to protein (Figure 25.21). In general, the higher the percentage of lipid in the lipoprotein, the lower its density; and the greater the proportion of protein, the higher its density. On this basis, there are **high-density lipoproteins (HDLs), low-density lipoproteins (LDLs),** and **very low-density lipoproteins (VLDLs).** *Chylomicrons,* which transport absorbed lipids from the gas-

Table 25.5 Summary of Metabolic Functions of the Liver

Metabolic processes targeted	Functions
Carbohydrate metabolism Particularly important in maintaining blood glucose homeostasis	1. Converts galactose and fructose to glucose 2. Glucose buffer function: stores glucose as glycogen when blood glucose levels are high; in response to hormonal controls, performs glycogenolysis and releases glucose to blood 3. Gluconeogenesis: converts amino acids and glycerol to glucose when glycogen stores are exhausted and blood glucose levels are falling 4. Converts glucose to fats for storage
Fat metabolism Although most cells are capable of some fat metabolism, liver bears the major responsibility	1. Primary body site of beta oxidation (breakdown of fatty acids to acetyl CoA) 2. Converts excess acetyl CoA to ketone bodies for release to tissue cells 3. Stores fats 4. Forms lipoproteins for transport of fatty acids, fats, and cholesterol to and from tissues 5. Synthesizes cholesterol from acetyl CoA; catabolizes cholesterol to bile salts, which are secreted in bile
Protein metabolism Other metabolic functions of the liver could be dispensed with and body could still survive; however, without liver metabolism of proteins, severe survival problems ensue: many essential clotting proteins would not be made, and ammonia would not be disposed of, for example	1. Deaminates amino acids (required for their conversion to glucose or use for ATP synthesis); amount of deamination that occurs outside the liver is unimportant 2. Forms urea for removal of ammonia from body; inability to perform this function (e.g., in cirrhosis or hepatitis) results in accumulation of ammonia in blood and depression of brain, a condition called *hepatic coma* 3. Forms most plasma proteins (exceptions are gamma globulins and some hormones and enzymes); plasma protein depletion causes rapid mitosis of the hepatocytes and actual growth of liver, which is coupled with increase in synthesis of plasma proteins until blood values are again normal 4. Transamination: intraconversion of nonessential amino acids; amount that occurs outside liver is inconsequential
Vitamin/mineral storage	1. Stores a 1–2-year supply of vitamin A 2. Stores sizable amounts of vitamins D and B_{12} (1–4-month supply) 3. Stores iron; other than iron bound to hemoglobin, most of body's supply is stored in liver as ferritin until needed; releases iron to blood as blood levels drop
Biotransformation functions	1. Relative to drug metabolism, performs synthetic reactions which yield inactive products that can be secreted by the kidneys and nonsynthetic reactions which may result in products that are more active, changed in activity, or less active 2. Processes bilirubin resulting from RBC breakdown and excretes bile pigments in bile 3. Metabolizes blood-borne hormones to forms that can be excreted in urine

trointestinal tract, are considered to be a separate class and have the lowest density of all.

The liver is the primary source of VLDLs, which transport triglycerides made or processed in the liver to the peripheral tissues, but mostly *to adipose tissues.* Once all the triglycerides are unloaded, the residues of these VLDLs are converted into LDLs, which are cholesterol-rich. The role of the LDLs is to transport cholesterol *to the peripheral tissues,* making it available to the tissue cells for membrane or hormone synthesis and for storage for later use. The LDLs also regulate cholesterol synthesis in the tissue cells.

The major function of HDLs, which are particularly rich in phospholipids and cholesterol, is to transport cholesterol from the peripheral tissues *to the liver,* where it is broken down and becomes part of bile. The liver makes the protein envelopes of the HDL particles and then ejects them into the bloodstream in collapsed form, rather like deflated beach balls. Once in the circulation, these still-incomplete

HDL particles fill with cholesterol picked up from the tissue cells and "pulled" from the artery walls.

High plasma levels of cholesterol (above 200 mg cholesterol/100 ml blood) have been linked to risk of atherosclerosis, which clogs the arteries and causes strokes and heart attacks. However, it is not enough to simply measure total cholesterol. The form in which cholesterol is transported in the blood is more important clinically. As a rule, high levels of HDLs are considered *good* because the transported cholesterol is destined for degradation. High LDL levels are considered *bad,* because when LDLs are excessive, potentially lethal cholesterol deposits are laid down in the artery walls.

Factors Regulating Plasma Cholesterol Levels. A negative feedback loop partially adjusts the amount of cholesterol produced by the liver according to cholesterol in the diet. In other words, a high cholesterol intake inhibits its synthesis by the liver, but it is not a one-to-one relationship because

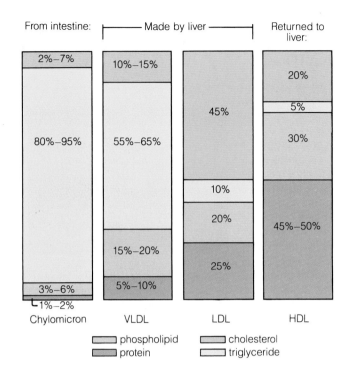

From intestine: Made by liver   Returned to liver:

phospholipid   cholesterol
protein   triglyceride

FIGURE 25.21
Approximate composition of lipoproteins that transport lipids in body fluids. VLDL = very low-density lipoprotein; LDL = low-density lipoprotein; HDL = high-density lipoprotein.

the liver produces a certain basal amount of cholesterol even when dietary intake is excessive. For this reason, severe restriction of dietary cholesterol, although helpful, does not lead to a steep reduction in plasma cholesterol levels.

The relative amounts of saturated and unsaturated fatty acids in the diet have an important effect on plasma cholesterol levels. Saturated fatty acids *stimulate hepatic synthesis* of cholesterol and *inhibit its excretion* from the body. Thus, moderate decreases in intake of saturated fats (found chiefly in animal fats and coconut oil) can reduce plasma cholesterol levels as much as 15% to 20%. In contrast, unsaturated fatty acids (found in most vegetable oils) *enhance excretion* of cholesterol and its catabolism to bile salts, thereby reducing total plasma cholesterol levels. In addition, certain unsaturated fatty acids (omega-3 fatty acids) found in especially large amounts in some cold-water fish lower the proportions of both saturated fats and cholesterol. The omega-3 fatty acids also make blood platelets less sticky, thus helping to prevent spontaneous clotting that can block blood vessels and lower blood pressure (even in nonhypertensive people).

Factors other than diet also influence plasma cholesterol levels. For example, cigarette smoking, coffee drinking, and stress have been implicated in increased

LDL levels, whereas regular aerobic exercise lowers LDL levels and increases levels of HDLs. Interestingly, body shape, i.e., the distribution of body fat, provides clues to risky blood levels of cholesterol and fats. "Apples" (upper body and abdominal fat distribution seen more often in men) tend to have higher levels of cholesterol in general and LDLs in particular than "pears" (fat localized in the hips and thighs, a pattern more common in women).

Most cells other than liver and intestinal cells obtain the bulk of the cholesterol they need for membrane synthesis from the bloodstream. When a cell needs cholesterol, it makes receptor proteins for LDL and inserts them in its plasma membrane. LDL binds to the receptors and is engulfed in coated pits by endocytosis. Within 10 to 15 minutes the endocytotic vesicles fuse with lysosomes, where the cholesterol is freed for use. When excessive cholesterol accumulates within a cell, it inhibits both the cell's own cholesterol synthesis and its synthesis of LDL receptors.

High cholesterol levels undoubtedly put us at risk for cardiovascular disease and heart attack. Now, however, one or more studies have indicated that cholesterol levels below 190 for males and 178 for females may be equally devastating because they may enhance the risk of "bleeding" strokes and death from cerebral hemorrhage. Although most Americans would probably benefit from reducing their intake of saturated fats and cholesterol-rich foods, at least for now, the moderate approach to cholesterol control may be the wisest. •

BODY ENERGY BALANCE

When any fuel is burned, it consumes oxygen and liberates heat. The "burning" of food fuels by our cells is no exception. As described in Chapter 2, energy can be neither created nor destroyed—only converted from one form to another. If we apply this principle (actually the *first law of thermodynamics*) to cell metabolism, it means that bond energy released as foods are catabolized must be precisely balanced by the total energy output of the body. Thus, a dynamic balance exists between the body's energy intake and its energy output:

Energy intake = total energy output
(heat + work + energy storage)

Energy intake is considered equal to the energy liberated during food oxidation. Undigested foods are not part of the equation because they contribute no energy. **Energy output** includes the energy (1) immediately lost as heat (about 60% of the total), (2) used to do work (driven by ATP), and (3) stored in the form of fat or glycogen. (Because losses of organic molecules in urine, feces, and perspiration are very small in healthy people, they are usually ignored.) A close

A CLOSER LOOK | Obesity: Magical Solution Wanted

How fat is too fat? What distinguishes an obese person from one who is merely overweight? The bathroom scale is an inaccurate guide because body weight tells nothing of body composition. A skilled dancer with dense bones and well-developed muscles may weigh several pounds more than an inactive person of the same relative size. Most experts agree that a person is obese when he or she is 20% heavier than the "ideal weight" published in insurance company tables (which, by the way, are artificially low). What is really needed is a measure of body fat, because the most common view of obesity is that it is a condition of excessive triglyceride storage. Although we bewail our inability to rid ourselves of fat, the real problem is that we keep refilling the storehouses by consuming too many calories. A body fat content of 18% to 22% of body weight (males and females, respectively) is considered normal for adults. Anything over that is defined as obesity.

However it's defined, obesity is a perplexing and poorly understood disease. The term "disease" is appropriate because all forms of obesity involve some imbalance in food intake control mechanisms. Despite its well-known adverse effects on health (the obese have a higher incidence of arteriosclerosis, hypertension, coronary artery disease, and diabetes mellitus), it is the most common health problem in the United States. About 50% of

adults and 20% of teenagers are obese. U.S. kids are not only getting fatter but, because they are opting for home video games and nachos instead of touch football, their general cardiovascular fitness is declining as well. In addition to the health problems mentioned, the obese may store excessive levels of fat-soluble toxic chemicals, such as marijuana, the insecticide DDT, and PCB (a cancer-causing chemical) in their bodies. Because DDT interferes with the liver's ability to rid the body of other toxins, these effects may be very far-reaching.

As if this were not enough, the social stigma and economic disadvantages of obesity are legendary. A fat person pays higher insurance premiums, is discriminated against in the job market, has fewer clothing choices, and is frequently humiliated during both childhood and adulthood.

With all its attendant problems, it's a pretty fair bet that few people choose to become obese. So what causes obesity? Let's look at three of the more recent theories.

(1) Large numbers of fat cells deliver signals that tend to stimulate overeating. Some believe that overeating behaviors develop early in life (the "clean your plate" syndrome) and set the stage for adult obesity by increasing the number of fat cells formed during childhood. During early adulthood and thereafter, increases in adipose tissue mass occur by depositing more fat in the existing cells. Thus, the

more cells there are, the more fat can be stored. Further, when there are armies of incompletely filled fat cells, basal plasma levels of fatty acids and glycerol are lower, leading to abnormal hunger.

Besides the signals delivered by blood-borne nutrients or so-called satiety chemicals (hormones and others), researchers have found hints that the fat cells themselves may stimulate overeating. Supporting this idea is the observation that when yo-yo dieters lose weight, their metabolic rate falls sharply. But when they subsequently gain weight, their metabolic rate increases like a furnace being stoked. Each successive weight loss occurs more slowly, and regaining lost weight occurs three times as fast. Thus, it appears that people, like laboratory animals subjected to alternating "feasts and fasts," become increasingly food efficient, and their metabolic rates adjust to counteract any deviation from their weight "set point." The instrument used to solve the problem—dieting (again and again)—becomes self-defeating.

---

look at this situation reveals that *nearly all the energy derived from foodstuffs is eventually converted to heat.* Heat is lost during every cellular activity—when ATP bonds are formed and when they are cleaved to do work, as muscles contract, and through friction as blood flows through blood vessels. Though the cells cannot use this energy to do work, the heat warms the tissues and blood and helps maintain the homeostatic body temperature that allows metabolic reactions to occur at efficient levels. Energy storage becomes an important part of the equation only during periods of growth and net fat deposit.

Regulation of Food Intake

When energy intake and energy outflow are balanced, body weight remains stable. When they are not, weight is either gained or lost. The fact that body weight in most people is surprisingly stable indicates the existence of physiological mechanisms that control food intake (and hence, the amount of food oxidized) or heat production or both.

The control of food intake poses difficult questions to researchers. For example, what type of receptor could sense the body's total content of calories

(2) Obese people are more fuel efficient and more effective "fat storers." Although it is often assumed that obese people eat more than other people, this is not necessarily true—many actually eat less than people of normal weight.

Fat, the nutrient, is the obese person's worst enemy. Fats pack more wallop per calorie (are more fattening) than proteins or carbohydrates because of the way they are processed in the body. For example, when someone ingests 100 excess carbohydrate calories, the body uses 23 of them in metabolic processing and stores 77. However, if the 100 excess calories come from fat, only 3 calories are "burned" and the rest (97) are stored. Furthermore, since carbohydrates are the preferred energy fuel for most body cells, fat stores aren't tapped until carbohydrate reserves are nearly depleted.

These facts apply to everyone, but when you are obese the picture is even bleaker. For example, fat cells of overweight people "sprout" more alpha receptors (the kind that favors fat accumulation). Furthermore, the enzyme lipoprotein lipase, which unloads fat from the blood (usually to fat cells), is exceptionally efficient and more of it is formed in the obese. In fact, obesity research done at Harvard Medical School found no correlation between caloric intake and body weight, but did find that those whose diets were highest in fat (especially saturated fats) were most overweight regardless of the number of calories consumed.

(3) Morbid obesity is the destiny of those inheriting two obesity genes. However, a true genetic predisposition for "fatness"—distributed "without compassion or fairness" by recently discovered recessive obesity genes—appears to account for only about 5% of the U.S. obese. These people, given excess calories, will always deposit them as fat, as opposed to those who lay down more muscle with some of the excess calories.

Rumors and poor choices for dealing with obesity abound. Some of the most unfortunate strategies used for coping with obesity are listed here.

1. **"Water pills."** Diuretics, which prompt the kidneys to excrete more water, are sought as a means of losing weight. At best, these may cause a few pounds of weight loss for a few hours; they can also cause serious electrolyte imbalance and dehydration.

2. **Diet pills.** Some obese use amphetamines (best known are Dexedrine and Benzedrine) to reduce appetite. These work, but only temporarily (until tolerance develops) and can cause a dangerous dependency. Then the user has the problem of trying to dispense with the drug habit. Furthermore, none of the other "pill-type" diet aids cause fat to melt away either. Those that provide fiber to prevent absorption of nutrients can cause serious malnutrition.

3. **Fad diets.** Many magazines print at least one new diet regimen yearly, and diet products sell well. However, many of these diets are nutritionally unhealthy, particularly if they limit certain groups of nutrients. Some of the liquid high-protein diets popular now contain such poor-quality (incomplete) protein that they are actually dangerous. (The worst are those that contain collagen protein instead of a milk or soybean protein source.)

4. **Surgery.** Sometimes sheer desperation prompts surgical solutions, all of which must be carefully considered. Surgical options include having the jaws wired shut, stomach stapling, intestinal bypass surgery, biliopancreatic diversion (BPD), and lipectomy (removal of fat by suction). BPD "rearranges" the digestive tract: Two-thirds of the stomach is removed; the small intestine is cut in half and one 8-foot long portion is sutured into the stomach opening. Since pancreatic juice and bile are diverted away from this "new intestine," far fewer nutrients (and no fats) are digested and absorbed. Although the patients can eat anything they want without gaining weight, BPD is major surgery and carries all of its risks.

Unfortunately, there is no magical solution for obesity. The only way to lose weight is to take in fewer fat calories and increase physical activity to increase muscle mass (muscle consumes more energy at rest than does fat). This prescription stresses the often-forgotten fact that there are two sides to the energy balance equation—caloric intake and energy output (see p. 881)—and recognizes the unique nature of fat handling in the body. Furthermore, low activity levels actually stimulate eating, while physical exercise depresses food intake and increases metabolic rate not only during activity but also for some time after. The only way to keep the weight off is to make these dietary and exercise changes lifelong habits.

and alert one to start or stop eating? Despite heroic research efforts, no such signal or single receptor type has been found. Current theories of how feeding behavior and hunger is regulated focus on one or more of four factors: nutrient signals related to body energy stores, hormones, body temperature, and psychological factors. All these factors appear to operate through feedback signals to the feeding centers of the brain. Brain receptors include thermoreceptors and a variety of chemoreceptors (for glucose, insulin, and others). For years, it was believed that only hypothalamic nuclei regulated hunger and satiety. However, recent evidence indicates that brain stem areas are also involved. Sensors in peripheral locations have also been suggested, with the liver the prime candidate.

Nutrient Signals Related to Energy Stores

At any time, plasma levels of glucose, amino acids, fatty acids, and glycerol provide information to the brain that may help adjust energy intake to energy output. For example:

1. During eating, plasma glucose levels rise and cellular metabolism of glucose increases. Subsequent activation of glucose receptors in the brain alerts appropriate brain areas and ultimately depresses eating. During fasting, this signal would be absent, resulting in hunger and a "turning on" of food-seeking behaviors.

2. Elevated plasma levels of amino acids depress eating, whereas low amino acid levels in blood stimulate it. Neither the precise mechanism nor the receptor type mediating these effects is known.

3. Blood concentrations of fatty acids and glycerol may serve as indicators of the body's total energy stores (in adipose tissue) and act as a long-term mechanism for controlling hunger. According to this theory, the greater the fat reserves, the greater the basal amount of fatty acids and glycerol released to the blood and the more eating behavior is inhibited.

Hormones

Blood levels of hormones that regulate plasma nutrient levels during the absorptive and postabsorptive states may also serve as negative feedback signals to the brain. Insulin, which is released during food absorption, is known to depress hunger and is presumed to be an important satiety signal. In contrast, glucagon levels rise during fasting and stimulate hunger. Other hormonal controls include epinephrine (released during fasting) and cholecystokinin, an intestinal hormone secreted during food digestion. Epinephrine triggers hunger while cholecystokinin depresses it. Though not a hormone, serotonin (a brain neurotransmitter) also appears to be involved in delivering satiety signals.

Body Temperature

Increased body temperature, related to food ingestion and processing, may inhibit eating behavior. Operation of such a thermal signal would help to explain why people in cold climates normally eat more than those in more temperate or warm regions.

Psychological Factors

Although the mechanisms described thus far are totally reflexive, their final outcome may be enhanced or inhibited by psychological factors that have little to do with caloric balance, such as just the thought of food. Psychological factors are thought to be very important in the obese. However, even when psychological factors are the underlying cause of obesity, individuals do *not* continue to gain weight endlessly. Their feeding controls still operate, but have a higher "set point," which maintains total energy content at higher-than-normal levels.

Metabolic Rate and Body Heat Production

The body's rate of energy expenditure (usually expressed per hour) is called the **metabolic rate.** Metabolic rate, which is the total heat produced by all the chemical reactions and mechanical work of the body, can be measured directly or indirectly. In the *direct method,* the person enters a chamber called a **calorimeter** and heat liberated by the body is absorbed by water circulating around the chamber. The rise in the water's temperature is directly related to the heat produced by the person's body. The *indirect method* uses a **respirometer** (Figure 25.22) to measure oxygen consumption, which is directly proportional to heat production. For each liter of oxygen used, the body produces about 4.8 kcal of heat.

Because many factors influence metabolic rate, it is usually measured under standardized conditions. The person is in a postabsorptive state (has not eaten for at least 12 hours), is reclining, and is mentally and physically relaxed. The temperature of the room is maintained at a comfortable 20°–25°C. The measurement obtained under these circumstances, called the **basal metabolic rate (BMR),** reflects the energy the body needs to perform only its most essential activities, such as breathing and maintaining resting levels of neural, cardiac, liver, and kidney function. The BMR, often referred to as the "energy cost of living," is reported in kilocalories per square meter of body surface per hour (kcal/m²/h).

An average 70-kg (154-pound) adult has a BMR of approximately 60–72 kcal/h. A quick approximation of one's BMR can be calculated by multiplying weight in kilograms (note that 2.2 pounds = 1 kg) times the factor 1 for males or the factor 0.9 for females. Although named the *basal* metabolic rate, this measurement is not the lowest metabolic state of the body. That situation occurs during sleep, when the muscles are completely relaxed.

The factors which influence BMR include surface area, age, gender, stress, and hormones. Although BMR is related to overall body weight and size, the critical factor is surface area rather than weight itself. This reflects the fact that as the ratio of body surface area to body volume increases, heat loss to the environment increases and the metabolic rate must be higher to replace the lost heat. Hence, if two people weigh the same, the taller or thinner person will have a higher BMR than the shorter or fatter person.

In general, the younger a person, the higher the BMR. Children and adolescents require large amounts of energy for growth. In old age, BMR declines dramatically as skeletal muscles begin to atrophy. (This helps explain why those elderly who fail to decrease their caloric intake become obese.) Gender also plays a role. Metabolic rate is disproportionately higher in males than in females. Males typically have more muscle tissue, which is very active metabolically even during rest. Fatty tissue, present in greater relative amounts in females, is metabolically sluggish compared to muscle tissue.

Body temperature and metabolic rate tend to rise and fall together. Fever (hyperthermia), resulting from infections and other factors, results in a markedly higher metabolic rate. Stress, whether physical or emotional, increases metabolic rate by mobilizing the sympathetic nervous system. Blood-borne norepinephrine and epinephrine (released by adrenal medullary cells) provoke a rise in metabolic rate primarily by stimulating fat catabolism.

The amount of **thyroxine** produced by the thyroid gland is probably the most important hormonal factor in determining BMR; hence, thyroxine has been dubbed the "metabolic hormone." Its direct effect on most body cells (except for brain cells) is to increase oxygen consumption, presumably by accelerating the use of cellular ATP for operation of the sodium-potassium pump. As ATP reserves decline, cellular respiration accelerates. Thus, the more thyroxine produced, the higher the BMR. In the past, most BMR testing was done to investigate whether sufficient thyroxine was being made. Today, thyroid activity is more easily assessed by blood tests.

Hyperthyroidism causes a host of problems resulting from the excessive metabolic rate it produces. The body catabolizes stored fats and tissue proteins, and, despite increased hunger and food intake, the person often loses weight. Bones weaken and body muscles, including the heart, begin to atrophy. In contrast, *hypothyroidism* results in slowed metabolism, obesity, and diminished thought processes. •

The term **total metabolic rate (TMR)** refers to the total rate of kilocalorie consumption to fuel *all* ongoing activities—involuntary and voluntary. The BMR accounts for a surprisingly large part of the TMR. For example, a woman whose total energy needs per day are about 2000 kcal may spend well over half of these calories (1400 kcal or so) supporting vital body activities. Skeletal muscle activity causes the most dramatic short-term changes in TMR, reflecting the fact that skeletal muscles make up nearly half of body mass. Even slight increases in muscular work can cause remarkable leaps in TMR and heat production. When a well-trained athlete exercises vigorously for several minutes, the metabolic rate may increase to 15 to 20 times normal, and it remains elevated for several hours afterward. Surprisingly, physical training has little effect on BMR. Although it would appear that athletes, especially those with greatly enhanced muscle mass, should have substantially higher BMRs than nonathletes, there is little difference between those of the same sex and surface area. Food ingestion also induces a rapid increase in the total metabolic rate. This effect, called **dietary,** or **food-induced, thermogenesis,** is greatest when proteins are eaten. The heightened metabolic activity of the liver during such periods probably accounts for the bulk of additional

FIGURE 25.22

Indirect measurement of metabolic rate by respirometry. The indirect method for measuring metabolic rate is based on the fact that oxygen use and heat liberation during food oxidation are directly proportional. The person breathes into a respirometer, and the total amount of oxygen consumed during testing (in this case, during walking on a treadmill) is measured. The average amount of oxygen consumed per hour (L/h) is multiplied by 4.8 (the amount of energy liberated when 1 L of oxygen is consumed in the oxidation of protein, carbohydrate, or fat) to calculate the metabolic rate. If, for example, oxygen use is 16 L/h, the metabolic rate is 77.28 kcal/h (16 L/h × 4.83 kcal/L).

energy use. In contrast, fasting or very low caloric intake depresses metabolic rate and results in a slower breakdown of body reserves.

Regulation of Body Temperature

As shown in Figure 25.23, body temperature reflects the balance between heat production and heat loss. Although all body tissues produce heat, those that are most active metabolically produce the greatest amounts. When the body is at rest, most heat is generated by the liver, heart, brain, and endocrine organs. Inactive skeletal muscles account for 20% to 30% of

FIGURE 25.23

As long as heat production and heat loss are properly balanced, body temperature remains constant. Factors contributing to heat production (and temperature rise) are shown on the left side of the scale; those contributing to heat loss (and temperature fall) are shown on the right side of the scale.

body heat. This situation is changed dramatically by even slight alterations in muscle tone and, during vigorous exercise, heat production by the skeletal muscles can be 30 to 40 times that of the rest of the body. For this reason, a change in muscle activity is one of the most important means of modifying body temperature.

Body temperature of human beings averages 36.2°C (98.2°F) and is usually maintained within a narrow range of 35.6°–37.8°C (96°–100°F), despite considerable change in the external (air) temperature. A healthy individual's body temperature fluctuates approximately 1°C (1.8°F) in 24 hours, with a low occurring in the early morning and a high in the late afternoon or early evening.

The adaptive value of this precise temperature homeostasis becomes obvious when we consider the effect of temperature on the rate of biochemical reactions, specifically enzyme activity. At normal body temperature, conditions are optimal for enzymatic activity. As body temperature rises, catalysis is accelerated: With each rise of 1°C, the rate of chemical reactions becomes approximately 10% faster. As the temperature spikes upward beyond the homeostatic range, neurons are depressed and proteins begin to denature (degrade). Most adults go into convulsions when their temperature reaches 41°C (106°F), and 43°C (about 110°F) appears to be the absolute limit for life. In contrast, most body tissues can withstand marked reductions in temperature as long as other conditions are carefully controlled. This fact underlies the use of body cooling during open heart surgery when the heart must be stopped. The low body temperature induced reduces metabolic rate (and consequently nutrient requirements of body tissues and the heart), allowing more time for surgery without incurring tissue damage.

Core and Shell Temperatures

Different regions of the body have different temperatures at rest. The body's **core** (that is, organs within the skull and the thoracic and abdominal cavities) has the highest temperature. Its **shell**, or heat loss surface, essentially the skin, has the lowest temperature in most circumstances. Of the two body sites used routinely to obtain body temperature clinically, the rectum typically has a temperature about 0.4°C (0.7°F) higher than the mouth and is the better indicator of core temperature.

It is core temperature that is precisely regulated. Blood serves as the major *heat transfer* or *exchange agent* between the body core and shell. Whenever the shell is warmer than the external environment, heat is lost from the body. Thus, when heat must be dissipated, warm blood is allowed to flush into the skin capillaries. On the other hand, when it is necessary to conserve heat, blood largely bypasses the skin. This reduces heat loss and allows the shell temperature to fall toward that of the environment. Thus, while the core temperature stays relatively constant, the temperature of the shell may fluctuate substantially (between 20°C [68°F] and 40°C [104°F] for instance) as its "thickness" is adapted to changes in body activity and external temperature. (You really *can* have cold hands and a warm heart.)

Mechanisms of Heat Exchange

The physical mechanisms that govern heat exchange between our skin and the external environment are identical to those controlling heat transfer between inanimate objects. It helps to think of the temperature of an object—whether that object is the skin or a radiator—as a guide to its heat content (*think* heat "concentration"). Then just remember that heat always flows down its concentration gradient from warmer to cooler regions. The body uses four mechanisms of heat transfer—radiation, conduction, convection, and evaporation (Figure 25.24).

Radiation. **Radiation** is the loss of heat in the form of infrared waves (thermal energy). Any dense object that is warmer than objects in its environment—for example, a radiator and (usually) the body—will transfer heat to those objects. Under normal conditions, close to half of body heat loss occurs by radiation.

Because the direction of radiant energy flow is always from warmer to cooler, radiation explains why an initially cold room warms up shortly after it is filled with people (the "body heat furnace," so to speak). The body can also gain heat by radiation, as demonstrated by the warming of the skin during sunbathing.

Conduction/Convection. **Conduction** is the transfer of heat between objects that are in direct contact with each other. For example, when we step into a

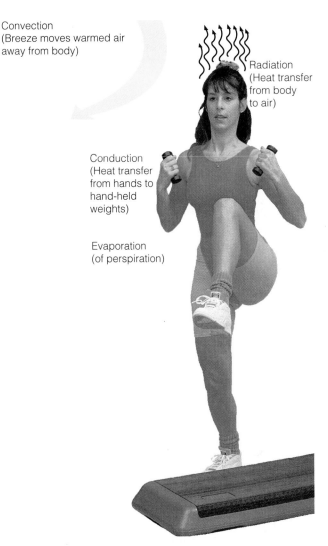

Convection
(Breeze moves warmed air
away from body)

Radiation
(Heat transfer
from body
to air)

Conduction
(Heat transfer
from hands to
hand-held
weights)

Evaporation
(of perspiration)

FIGURE 25.24
**Mechanisms of heat exchange between the body and
the external environment.**

Evaporation. Water evaporates because its molecules absorb heat from the environment and become energetic enough (that is, vibrate fast enough) to escape as gas (water vapor). The heat absorbed by water during evaporation is called **heat of vaporization.** Because water absorbs a great deal of heat before vaporizing, its evaporation from body surfaces removes large amounts of body heat. For every gram of water evaporated, about one-half kilocalorie (0.58 kcal) of heat is removed from the body.

There is a basal level of body heat loss due to the continuous evaporation of water from the lungs, from the mucosa of the mouth, and through the skin. The unnoticeable water loss occurring via these routes is called **insensible water loss** and the accompanying heat loss is called **insensible heat loss.** Insensible heat loss dissipates about 10% of the basal heat production of the body and is a constant; that is, it is not subject to body temperature controls. However, the regulatory mechanisms do initiate heat-promoting activities to counterbalance this heat loss when necessary.

Evaporative heat loss becomes an active (sensible) process when body temperature rises and sweating provides increased amounts of water for vaporization. Extreme emotional states activate the sympathetic nervous system, causing body temperature to rise one degree or so, and vigorous exercise can thrust body temperature upward as much as 2°–3°C (5°–6°F). During vigorous muscular activity, 1–2 L/h of perspiration can be produced and evaporated, removing 600–1200 kcal of heat from the body each hour. This is over 30 times the amount of heat lost via insensible heat loss!

When sweating is profuse and prolonged, especially in untrained individuals, losses of water and salt (NaCl) may cause painful spasms of the skeletal muscles called *heat cramps.* This situation is easily rectified by ingesting fluids. •

Role of the Hypothalamus

Although other brain regions contribute, the hypothalamus, particularly its *preoptic* region, is the major integrating center for thermoregulation. Together the **heat-loss center** (located more anteriorly) and the **heat-promoting center** comprise the **thermoregulatory centers.**

The hypothalamus receives afferent input from (1) **peripheral thermoreceptors,** which are located in the shell (the skin), and (2) **central thermoreceptors** (receptors sensitive to the temperature of blood), located in the body core including the anterior portion of the hypothalamus itself. Much like a thermostat, the hypothalamus responds to this input by initiating appropriate heat-promoting or heat-loss reflex mechanisms via autonomic effector pathways. Although the central thermoreceptors are more critically located than the peripheral ones, changing inputs from the shell probably alert the hypothala-

"hot tub," some of the heat of the water is transferred to our skin, and warm buttocks transfer heat to the seat of a chair by conduction. Unlike radiation, conduction requires molecule-to-molecule *contact* of objects; that is, the thermal energy must move through a material medium.

When the body shell transfers heat to the surrounding air, convection also comes into play. Because warm air tends to expand and rise and cool air (being denser) falls, the warmed air enveloping the body is continually replaced by cooler air molecules. This process, called **convection,** substantially enhances heat exchange from the body surface to the air, because the cooler air absorbs heat by conduction more rapidly than the already-warmed air. Together, conduction and convection account for 15% to 20% of heat loss to the environment. These processes are enhanced by anything that moves air more rapidly across the body surface such as wind or a fan, that is, by *forced convection.*

mus to the need for action to prevent temperature changes in the core, i.e., they allow the hypothalamus to anticipate possible changes to be made.

Heat-Promoting Mechanisms

When the external temperature is cold (or the temperature of circulating blood falls), the hypothalamic heat-promoting center is activated. It, in turn, triggers one or more of the following mechanisms to maintain or increase core body temperature (Figure 25.25).

1. **Vasoconstriction of cutaneous blood vessels.** Activation of the sympathetic vasoconstrictor fibers serving the blood vessels of the skin causes them to be strongly constricted. As a result, blood is restricted to deep body areas and largely bypasses the skin. Because the skin is separated from deeper organs by a layer of insulating subcutaneous (fatty) tissue, heat loss from the shell is dramatically reduced and shell temperature drops toward that of the external environment.

Restricting blood flow to the skin is not a problem for a brief period, but if it is extended (as during prolonged exposure to very cold weather), the skin cells, deprived of oxygen and nutrients, begin to die. This extremely serious condition is called *frostbite.*

2. **Increase in metabolic rate.** Cold stimulates the release of norepinephrine (NE) by sympathetic nerve fibers. NE elevates the metabolic rate, which enhances heat production. This mechanism is called **chemical, or nonshivering, thermogenesis.**

3. **Shivering.** If the mechanisms described above are not enough to handle the situation, shivering is triggered. Brain centers controlling muscle tone become more active and when muscle tone has reached sufficient levels to alternately stimulate stretch receptors in antagonistic muscles, involuntary shuddering contractions of the skeletal muscles begin. Shivering is very effective in increasing body temperature, because muscle activity produces large amounts of heat.

4. **Enhanced thyroxine release.** When environmental temperature decreases gradually, as in the transition from a hot to a cold season, the hypothalamus releases *thyrotropin releasing hormone.* This activates the anterior pituitary to release *thyroid stimulating hormone,* which, in turn, induces the thyroid gland to liberate larger amounts of thyroid hormone (T_3 and T_4) to the blood. Because thyroid hormone increases metabolic rate, body heat production increases, improving the ability to maintain a constant body temperature in cold environmental conditions.

Beside these involuntary adjustments, we humans commonly make a number of *behavioral modifications* to prevent over cooling of our body core. These include:

- Putting on more or warmer clothing to restrict heat loss (a hat, gloves, and "insulated" outer garments).
- Ingesting hot fluids.
- Changing posture to reduce exposed body surface area (hunching over or clasping the arms across the chest).
- Increasing physical activity to generate more heat (jumping up and down, clapping the hands).

Heat-Loss Mechanisms

Heat-loss mechanisms protect the body from excessively high temperatures, which can be particularly damaging to the body. Most heat loss occurs through the skin via the physical mechanisms of heat exchange described on pp. 886 and 887—radiation, conduction/convection, and evaporation. How do the heat-exchange mechanisms fit into the heat-loss temperature regulation scheme? The answer is quite simple. Whenever core body temperature rises above normal, the hypothalamic heat-promoting center is inhibited. At the same time, the heat-loss center is activated and so triggers one or both of the following (Figure 25.25):

1. **Vasodilation of cutaneous blood vessels.** Inhibiting the vasomotor fibers serving blood vessels of the skin allows the vessels to dilate. As the skin vasculature swells with warm blood, heat is lost from the shell by radiation, conduction, and convection.

2. **Enhanced sweating.** If the body is extremely overheated or if the environment is so hot (over 61°C [about 92°F]) that heat cannot be lost by other means, increased heat loss by evaporation becomes necessary. The sweat glands are strongly activated by sympathetic fibers and spew out large amounts of perspiration. Evaporation of perspiration is an efficient means of ridding the body of surplus heat as long as the air is dry. However, when the relative humidity is high, evaporation occurs much more slowly. In such cases, the heat-liberating mechanisms cannot work well, and we feel miserable and irritable.

Behavioral or voluntary measures commonly taken to reduce body heat include:

- Reducing activity.
- Seeking a cooler environment (a shady spot) or using a device to increase convection (a fan) or cooling (an air conditioner).
- Wearing light-colored, loosely fitting clothing that reflects radiant energy and reduces heat gain (this is actually cooler than being nude because bare skin absorbs most radiant energy that strikes it).

When normal heat loss processes become ineffective, the **hyperthermia,** or elevated body temper-

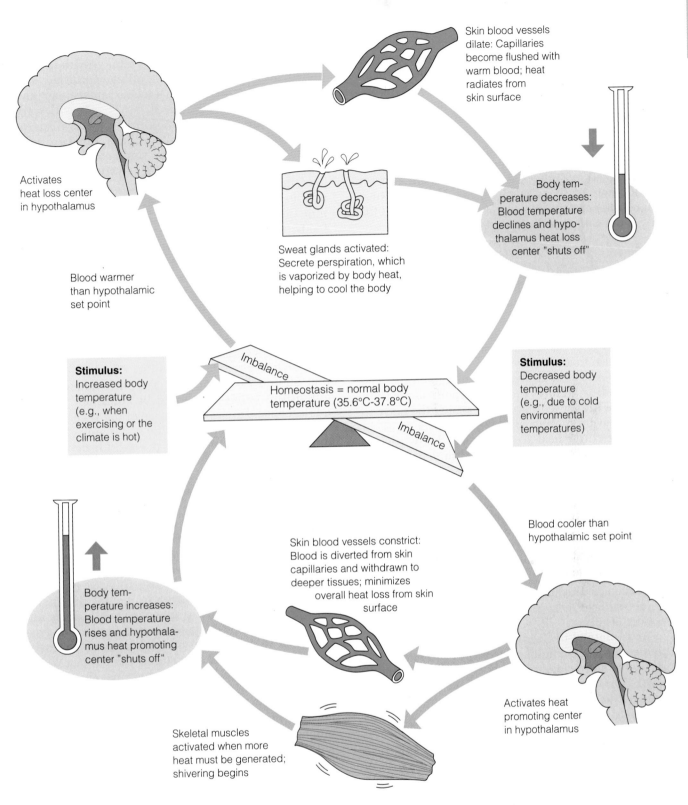

Skin blood vessels dilate: Capillaries become flushed with warm blood; heat radiates from skin surface

Activates heat loss center in hypothalamus

Sweat glands activated: Secrete perspiration, which is vaporized by body heat, helping to cool the body

Body temperature decreases: Blood temperature declines and hypothalamus heat loss center "shuts off"

Blood warmer than hypothalamic set point

Imbalance

Homeostasis = normal body temperature (35.6°C-37.8°C)

Imbalance

Stimulus: Increased body temperature (e.g., when exercising or the climate is hot)

Stimulus: Decreased body temperature (e.g., due to cold environmental temperatures)

Blood cooler than hypothalamic set point

Skin blood vessels constrict: Blood is diverted from skin capillaries and withdrawn to deeper tissues; minimizes overall heat loss from skin surface

Body temperature increases: Blood temperature rises and hypothalamus heat promoting center "shuts off"

Activates heat promoting center in hypothalamus

Skeletal muscles activated when more heat must be generated; shivering begins

FIGURE 25.25
Mechanisms of body temperature regulation.

ature, that ensues depresses the hypothalamus. As a result, heat-control mechanisms are suspended, creating a vicious positive-feedback cycle. Sharply increasing temperatures increase the metabolic rate, which, in turn, increases heat production. The skin becomes hot and dry and, as the temperature contin-ues to spiral upward, multiple organ (including brain) damage becomes a distinct possibility. This condition, called **heat stroke,** can be fatal unless corrective measures are initiated immediately (e.g., effective body cooling by immersion in cool water and administration of fluids).

The terms *heat exhaustion* and *exertion-induced heat exhaustion* are often used to describe the heat-associated collapse of an individual during or following vigorous physical activity. This condition, evidenced by elevated body temperature and mental confusion and/or fainting, is due to dehydration and consequent low blood pressure. In contrast to heat stroke, heat-loss mechanisms are still functional in heat exhaustion; indeed, the symptoms are a direct consequence of those mechanisms. However, heat exhaustion can rapidly progress to heat stroke if the body is not cooled and rehydrated promptly. •

Fever

Fever is *controlled hyperthermia.* Most often, it results from infection somewhere in the body, but it may be caused by other conditions (cancer, allergic reactions, central nervous system injuries). White blood cells, injured tissue cells, and macrophages release *pyrogens,* chemical substances now known to be cytokines, that act directly on the hypothalamus, causing its neurons to release prostaglandins. The prostaglandins, in turn, reset the hypothalamic thermostat to a higher temperature, causing the body to initiate heat-promoting mechanisms. As a result of vasoconstriction, heat loss from the body surface declines, the skin becomes cool, and shivering begins to generate heat. This situation, called "the chills," is a sure sign that body temperature is rising. The temperature rises until it reaches the new setting, and body temperature is maintained at the "fever setting" until natural body defenses or antibiotics reverse the disease process. The thermostat is then reset to a lower (or normal) level, which causes heat-loss mechanisms to swing into action. Sweating begins and the skin becomes flushed and warm. Physicians have long recognized these signs as signals that body temperature is falling.

As explained in Chapter 22, fever, by increasing the metabolic rate, helps speed the various healing processes, and it also appears to inhibit bacterial growth. The danger of fever is that if the body thermostat is set too high, proteins may be denatured and permanent brain damage may occur.

DEVELOPMENTAL ASPECTS OF NUTRITION AND METABOLISM

Good nutrition is essential *in utero,* as well as throughout life. If the mother is ill nourished, the development of her infant is affected. Most serious is the lack of proteins needed for fetal tissue growth, especially brain growth. Additionally, because brain growth continues for the first three years after birth, inadequate calories and proteins during this time will lead to mental deficits or learning disorders. Proteins are needed for muscle and bone growth, and calcium is required for strong bones. Although ana-bolic processes are less critical after growth is completed, sufficient nutrients of all categories are still essential to maintain normal tissue replacement and metabolism.

There are many inborn errors of metabolism (or genetic disorders), but perhaps the two most common are *cystic fibrosis* and *phenylketonuria* (fen"il-ke"to-nu're-ah) *(PKU).* Cystic fibrosis is described in Chapter 24. In PKU, the tissue cells are unable to use one particular amino acid, phenylalanine (fen"il-al'ah-nīn), which is present in all protein foods. The defect involves a deficiency of the enzyme that converts phenylalanine to tyrosine. Because phenylalanine cannot be metabolized, it and its deaminated products accumulate in the blood and act as neurotoxins, leading to brain damage and retardation within a few months. These consequences are uncommon today because most states have mandated a simple urine or blood screening test to identify affected newborns, and these children are put on a special low-phenylalanine diet. When this special diet should be terminated is controversial. Some authorities believe it should be continued through adolescence. However, because of the severe limitations of the low-phenylalanine diet, many clinicians order it discontinued when the child is 6 years old. Because tyrosine is the basis of melanin, all of these children are very blond and fair-skinned.

There are a number of other enzyme defects, classified according to the impaired process as carbohydrate, lipid, or mineral metabolic disorders. For example, two carbohydrate deficits are galactosemia and glycogen storage disease. *Galactosemia* results from an abnormality or lack of liver enzymes needed to transform galactose to glucose. Galactose accumulates in the blood and leads to mental deficits. In *glycogen storage disease,* glycogen synthesis is normal, but one of the enzymes needed to convert glycogen back to glucose is missing. Because excessive amounts of glycogen are stored, its storage organs (liver and skeletal muscles) become glutted with glycogen and enlarge tremendously.

Metabolic and endocrine disorders are often closely intertwined, reflecting the influence of hormones on metabolism. Occasionally, infants are born with hypothyroidism. If not detected and treated with hormone replacement therapy, the child develops *cretinism.* This disorder is evidenced by a low BMR, dwarfism accompanied by skeletal deformities, a thick tongue, intolerance to cold, and mental retardation. •

With the exception of *insulin-dependent diabetes mellitus,* children free of genetic disorders rarely exhibit metabolic problems. However, by middle age and particularly old age, *non–insulin-dependent diabetes mellitus* becomes a major problem, particularly in the obese. (These two manifestations of diabetes are described in Chapter 17.)

Metabolic rate progressively declines throughout the life span. In old age, muscle and bone wasting and declining efficiency of hormonal systems take their toll. Because many elderly are also less active, the metabolic rate sometimes becomes so low that it becomes nearly impossible to obtain adequate nutrition without gaining weight. The elderly also use more medications than any other group, at a time of life when the liver has become less efficient in its detoxifying duties. Consequently, many of the agents prescribed for age-related medical problems influence nutrition. For example:

- Some diuretics prescribed for congestive heart failure or hypertension (to flush fluids out of the body) can cause severe hypokalemia by promoting the excessive loss of potassium.

- Some antibiotics affect absorption of nutrients. For example, sulfa drugs, tetracycline, and penicillin interfere with systems responsible for digestion and absorption. They may also cause diarrhea, thereby decreasing nutrient absorption.

- Mineral oil, a popular laxative with the elderly, interferes with the absorption of fat-soluble vitamins, and high-fiber diets which encourage elimination inhibit calcium absorption.

- Alcohol is used by about half the elderly population in this country. When alcohol is substituted for food, nutrient stores can be depleted. Excessive alcohol intake leads to malabsorption problems, certain vitamin and mineral deficiencies, deranged metabolism, and damage to the liver and pancreas.

In short, the elderly are at risk not only from the declining efficiency of the metabolic processes themselves, but also from a huge variety of life-style and medication factors that affect their nutrition.

Although malnutrition and a waning metabolic rate present problems to some elderly, certain nutrients—notably glucose—appear to contribute to the aging process in people of all ages. Nonenzymatic reactions (the so-called *browning reactions*) between glucose and proteins, long known to discolor and toughen foods, may have the same effects on body proteins. When enzymes attach sugars to proteins, they do so at specific sites and the glycosylated protein molecules produced play well-defined roles in the body. By contrast, nonenzymatic binding of glucose to proteins (a process that increases with age) is haphazard and eventually causes cross-links to form between proteins. The increase in this type of binding probably contributes to lens clouding, atherosclerotic plaque formation, and the general tissue stiffening and loss of elasticity so common in the aged.

*   *   *

Nutrition is one of the most overlooked areas in clinical medicine. Yet, what we eat influences nearly every phase of metabolism and plays a major role in our overall health. Now that we have examined the fates of nutrients within body cells, we are ready to study the urinary system, the organ system that works tirelessly to rid the body of nitrogen wastes resulting from metabolism and to maintain the purity of our internal fluids.

RELATED CLINICAL TERMS

Appetite A desire for food. A psychological phenomenon dependent on memory and associations, as opposed to hunger, which is a physiological need to eat.

Familial hypercholesterolemia (hi″per-ko-les″ter-ol-e′me-ah) An inherited condition in which the LDL receptors are absent or abnormal, the uptake of cholesterol by tissue cells is blocked, and the total concentration of cholesterol (and LDLs) in the blood is enormously elevated (e.g., 680 mg cholesterol/100 ml blood). Affected individuals develop atherosclerosis at an early age, and most die during childhood or adolescence from coronary artery disease. At present the only moderately successful treatment is liver transplantation.

Hypothermia (hi″po-ther′me-ah) Low body temperature resulting from prolonged uncontrolled exposure to cold. Vital signs (respiratory rate, blood pressure, and heart rate) decrease as cellular enzymes become sluggish. Drowsiness sets in and, oddly, the person becomes comfortable even though previously he or she felt extremely cold. Shivering stops at a core temperature of 30°–32°C (87°–90°F) when the body has exhausted its heat-generating capabilities. Uncorrected, the situation progresses to coma and finally death (by cardiac arrest), when body temperatures approach 21°C (70°F).

Ideal weight Actually a misnomer. The average (but not necessarily the most desirable) weight given in insurance tables for persons of a given height and sex.

Kwashiorkor (kwash″e-or′kor) Severe protein deficiency in children, resulting in mental retardation and failure to grow. A consequence of malnutrition or starvation, it is characterized by a bloated abdomen because the level of plasma proteins is inadequate to keep fluid in the bloodstream.

Marasmus (mah-raz′mus) Protein-calorie malnutrition, accompanied by progressive wasting.

Pica (pi′kah) Craving and eating substances not normally considered nutrients, such as clay.

Skin-fold test Clinical test of body fatness. A skin fold in the back of the arm or below the scapula is measured with a caliper. A fold over 1 inch in thickness indicates excess fat. Also called the fat-fold test.

CHAPTER SUMMARY

Nutrition (pp. 846–858)

1. Nutrients include water, carbohydrates, lipids, proteins, vitamins, and minerals. The bulk of the organic nutrients is used as fuel to produce cellular energy (ATP). The energy value of foods is measured in kilocalories (kcal).

2. Essential nutrients are those that cannot be synthesized by body cells and must be ingested in the diet.

Carbohydrates (pp. 846–848)

3. Carbohydrates are obtained primarily from plant products. Absorbed monosaccharides other than glucose are converted to glucose by the liver.

4. Monosaccharides are used primarily for cellular fuel. Small amounts are used for nucleic acid synthesis and to glycosylate plasma membranes.

5. Minimum carbohydrate requirement for adults is 100 g/day.

Lipids (p. 848)

6. Most dietary lipids are triglycerides. The primary sources of saturated fats are animal products; unsaturated fats are present in plant products. The major source of cholesterol is egg yolk.

7. Linoleic and linolenic acids are essential fatty acids.

8. Neutral fats provide reserve energy, cushion body organs, and insulate the body. Phospholipids are used to synthesize plasma membranes and myelin. Cholesterol is used in plasma membranes and is the structural basis of vitamin D, steroid hormones, and bile salts.

9. Fats should represent 30% or less of caloric intake, and saturated fats should be replaced by unsaturated fats if possible. Cholesterol intake should be restricted to 250 mg or less daily.

Proteins (pp. 848–851)

10. Animal products provide high-quality protein containing all (8) of the essential amino acids. Most plant products lack one or more of the essential amino acids.

11. Amino acids are the structural building blocks of the body and of important regulatory molecules.

12. Protein synthesis can and will occur if all essential amino acids are present and sufficient carbohydrate (or fat) calories are available for ATP production. Otherwise, amino acids will be burned for energy.

13. Nitrogen balance occurs when protein synthesis equals protein loss.

14. A dietary intake of 0.8 g of protein/kg body weight is recommended for adults.

Vitamins (pp. 851–855)

15. Vitamins are organic compounds needed in minute amounts. Most act as coenzymes.

16. Except for vitamin D and the K and B vitamins made by enteric bacteria, vitamins are not made in the body.

17. Water-soluble vitamins (B and C) are not stored to excess in the body. Fat-soluble vitamins include vitamins A, D, E, and K; all but vitamin K are stored and can accumulate to toxic amounts.

Minerals (pp. 851, 855–858)

18. Besides calcium, phosphorus, potassium, sulfur, sodium, chloride, and magnesium, the body requires trace amounts of at least a dozen other minerals.

19. Minerals are not used for energy. Some are used to mineralize bone; others are bound to organic compounds or exist as ions in body fluids, where they play various roles in cell processes and metabolism.

20. Mineral uptake and excretion are carefully balanced and regulated to prevent mineral toxicity. The richest sources of minerals are animal products, vegetables, and legumes.

Metabolism (pp. 858–881)

Overview of Metabolic Processes (pp. 858–860)

1. Metabolism encompasses all chemical reactions necessary to maintain life. Metabolic processes are either anabolic or catabolic.

2. Cellular respiration refers to catabolic processes during which energy is released and some is captured in ATP bonds.

3. Energy is released when organic compounds are oxidized. Cellular oxidation is accomplished primarily by the removal of hydrogen (electrons). When molecules are oxidized, others are simultaneously reduced by accepting hydrogen (or electrons).

4. Most enzymes catalyzing oxidation-reduction reactions require coenzymes as hydrogen acceptors. Two important coenzymes in these reactions are NAD^+ and FAD.

5. In animal cells, the two mechanisms of ATP synthesis are substrate-level phosphorylation and oxidative phosphorylation.

Carbohydrate Metabolism (pp. 861–869)

6. Carbohydrate metabolism is essentially glucose metabolism.

7. Phosphorylation of glucose on entry into cells effectively traps it in most tissue cells.

8. Glucose is oxidized completely to carbon dioxide and water via three successive pathways: glycolysis, Krebs cycle, and electron transport chain. Some ATP is harvested in each pathway, but the bulk is captured in the electron transport chain.

9. Glycolysis is a reversible pathway in which glucose is converted into two pyruvic acid molecules; two molecules of reduced NAD^+ are formed, and there is a net gain of two ATPs. Under aerobic conditions, pyruvic acid enters the Krebs cycle; under anaerobic conditions, it is reduced to lactic acid.

10. The Krebs cycle is fueled by pyruvic acid (and fatty acids). To enter the cycle, pyruvic acid is converted to acetyl CoA. The acetyl CoA is then oxidized and decarboxylated. Complete oxidation of two pyruvic acid molecules yields 6 CO_2, 8 NADH + H^+, 2 $FADH_2$, and a net gain of 2 ATP. Much of the energy originally present in the bonds of pyruvic acid is now present in the reduced coenzymes.

11. In the electron transport chain, (a) reduced coenzymes are oxidized by delivering hydrogen to a series of oxidation-reduction acceptors; (b) hydrogen is split into hydrogen ions and electrons (as electrons run downhill from acceptor to acceptor, the energy released is used to pump H^+ into the mitochondrial intramembrane space, which creates an electrochemical proton gradient); (c) the energy stored in the electrochemical proton gradient drives H^+ back through ATP synthase, which uses the energy to form ATP; (d) H^+ and electrons are combined with oxygen to form water.

12. For each glucose molecule oxidized to carbon dioxide and water, 36 or 38 ATP are formed: 4 ATP from substrate-level phosphorylation and 32 or 34 ATP from oxidative phosphorylation.

13. When cellular ATP reserves are high, glucose catabolism is inhibited and glucose is converted to glycogen (glycogenesis) or to fat (lipogenesis). Much more fat than glycogen is stored.

14. Gluconeogenesis is the formation of glucose from noncarbohydrate (fat or protein) molecules. It occurs in the liver when blood glucose levels begin to fall.

Lipid Metabolism (pp. 869–871)

15. End products of lipid digestion (and cholesterol) are transported in blood in the form of chylomicrons.

16. Glycerol is converted to glyceraldehyde-PO_4 and enters the Krebs cycle or is converted to glucose.

17. Fatty acids are oxidized by beta oxidation into acetic acid fragments. These are bound to coenzyme A and enter the Krebs cycle as acetyl CoA. Dietary fats not needed for energy or structural materials are stored in adipose tissue.

18. There is a continual turnover of fats in fatty depots. Breakdown of fats to fatty acids and glycerol is called lipolysis.

19. When excessive amounts of fats are used, the liver converts acetyl CoA to ketone bodies and releases them to the blood. Excessive levels of ketone bodies (ketosis) lead to metabolic acidosis.

20. All cells use phospholipids and cholesterol to build their plasma membranes. The liver forms many functional molecules (lipoproteins, thromboplastin, etc.) from lipids.

Protein Metabolism (pp. 871–872)

21. To be oxidized for energy, amino acids are converted to keto acids that can enter the Krebs cycle. This involves transamination, oxidative deamination, and keto acid modification.

22. Amine groups removed during deamination (as ammonia) are combined with carbon dioxide by the liver to form urea. Urea is excreted in urine.

23. Deaminated amino acids may also be converted to fatty acids and glucose.

24. Amino acids are the body's most important building blocks. Nonessential amino acids are made in the liver by transamination.

25. In adults, most protein synthesis serves to replace tissue proteins and to maintain nitrogen balance.

26. Protein synthesis requires the presence of the essential amino acids. If any are lacking, amino acids are used as energy fuels.

Catabolic-Anabolic Steady State of the Body (pp. 872–873)

27. The amino acid pool provides amino acids for synthesis of proteins and amino acid derivatives, ATP synthesis, and energy storage. To be stored, amino acids are first converted to fats or glycogen.

28. The carbohydrate-fat pool primarily provides fuels for ATP synthesis and other molecules that can be stored as energy reserves.

29. The nutrient pools are connected by the bloodstream; fats, carbohydrates, and proteins may be interconverted via common intermediates.

Absorptive and Postabsorptive States: Events and Controls (pp. 873–879)

30. During the absorptive state (during and shortly after a meal), glucose is the major energy source; needed structural and functional molecules are made; excesses of carbohydrates, fats, and amino acids are stored as glycogen and fat.

31. Events of the absorptive state are controlled by insulin, which enhances the entry of glucose (and amino acids) into cells and accelerates its use for ATP synthesis or storage as glycogen or fat.

32. The postabsorptive (fasting) state is the period when blood-borne fuels are provided by breakdown of energy reserves. Glucose is made available to the blood by glycogenolysis, lipolysis, and gluconeogenesis. Glucose sparing begins and, if fasting is prolonged (4–5 days), the brain also begins to metabolize ketone bodies.

33. Events of the postabsorptive state are controlled largely by glucagon and the sympathetic nervous system, which mobilize glycogen and fat reserves and trigger gluconeogenesis.

Role of the Liver in Metabolism (pp. 878–881)

34. The liver is the body's main metabolic organ and it plays a crucial role in processing (or storing) virtually every nutrient group. It helps maintain blood energy sources, metabolizes hormones, and detoxifies drugs and other substances.

35. The liver synthesizes cholesterol, catabolizes cholesterol and secretes it in the form of bile salts, and makes lipoproteins.

36. LDLs transport triglycerides and cholesterol from the liver to the tissues, whereas HDLs transport cholesterol from the tissues to the liver (for catabolism and elimination).

37. Excessively high LDL levels are implicated in atherosclerosis, cardiovascular disease, and strokes.

Body Energy Balance (pp. 881–890)

1. Body energy intake (derived from food oxidation) is precisely balanced by energy output (heat, work, and energy storage). Eventually, all of the energy intake is converted to heat.

2. When energy balance is maintained, weight remains stable. When excess amounts of energy are stored, obesity results (condition of excessive fat storage, 20% or more above the norm).

Regulation of Food Intake (pp. 882–884)

3. The hypothalamus and other brain centers are involved in the regulation of eating behavior.

4. Factors thought to be involved in regulating food intake include (a) nutrient signals related to total energy storage (e.g., large fatty reserves and increased plasma levels of glucose and amino acids depress hunger and eating); (b) plasma concentrations of hormones that control events of the absorptive and postabsorptive states, and provide feedback signals to brain feeding centers; (c) body temperature; and (d) psychological factors. Psychological factors are thought to underlie some forms of obesity.

Metabolic Rate and Body Heat Production (pp. 884–885)

5. Energy used by the body per hour is the metabolic rate.

6. Basal metabolic rate (BMR), reported in kcal/m²/h, is the measurement obtained under basal conditions; i.e., the person is at comfortable room temperature, supine, relaxed, and in the postabsorptive state. BMR indicates energy needed to drive only the resting body processes.

7. Factors influencing metabolic rate include age, sex, size, body surface area, thyroxine levels, specific dynamic action of foods, and muscular activity.

Regulation of Body Temperature (pp. 885–890)

8. Body temperature reflects the balance between heat production and heat loss and is normally 35.6°–37.8°C, which is optimal for physiological activities.

9. At rest, most body heat is produced by the liver, heart, brain, kidneys, and endocrine organs. Activation of skeletal muscles causes dramatic increases in body heat production.

10. The body core (organs within the skull and the thoracic and abdominal cavities) generally has the highest temperature; its shell (the skin) is usually coolest. The shell is the heat-exchange surface.

11. Blood serves as the major heat-exchange agent between the core and the shell. When skin capillaries are flushed with blood and the skin is warmer than the environment, heat is lost from the body. When blood is withdrawn to deep organs, heat loss from the shell is inhibited.

12. Heat-exchange mechanisms include radiation, conduction/convection, and evaporation. Evaporation, the conversion of water to water vapor, requires the absorption of heat. For each gram of water vaporized, about 0.5 kcal of heat is absorbed.

13. The hypothalamus acts as the body's thermostat. Its heat-promotion and heat-loss centers receive inputs from peripheral and central thermoreceptors, integrate these inputs, and initiate responses leading to heat loss or heat promotion.

14. Heat-promoting mechanisms include vasoconstriction of skin vasculature, increase in metabolic rate (via release of norepinephrine), and shivering. If environmental cold is prolonged, the thyroid gland is stimulated to release more thyroxine.

15. When heat must be removed from the body, dermal blood vessels are dilated, allowing heat loss through radiation, conduction, and convection. When greater heat loss is mandated (or the environmental temperature is so high that radiation and condition are ineffective), sweating is initiated. Evaporation of perspiration is an efficient means of heat loss as long as the humidity is low.

16. Profuse sweating can lead to heat exhaustion, indicated by a rise in temperature, a drop in blood pressure, and collapse. When the body cannot rid itself of surplus heat, body temperature rises to the point where all thermoregulatory mechanisms become ineffective—a potentially lethal condition called heat stroke.

17. Fever is controlled hyperthermia, which follows thermostat resetting to higher levels by prostaglandins and initiation of heat-promotion mechanisms, evidenced by the chills. When the disease process is reversed, heat-loss mechanisms are initiated.

Developmental Aspects of Nutrition and Metabolism (pp. 890–891)

1. Good nutrition is essential for normal fetal development and normal growth during childhood.

2. Inborn errors of metabolism include cystic fibrosis, PKU, glycogen storage disease, galactosemia, and many others. Hor-

monal disorders, e.g., lack of insulin or thyroid hormone, may also lead to metabolic abnormalities. Diabetes mellitus is the most significant metabolic disorder in the young and the old.

3. In old age, metabolic rate declines as enzyme and endocrine systems become less efficient and skeletal muscles atrophy. Reduced caloric needs make it difficult to obtain adequate nutrition without becoming obese.

4. Elderly individuals ingest more medications than any other age group, and many of these drugs negatively affect their nutrition.

REVIEW QUESTIONS

Multiple Choice/Matching

1. Which of the following reactions would liberate the greatest amount of energy? (a) complete breakdown and oxidation of a molecule of sucrose to CO_2 and water, (b) conversion of a molecule of ADP to ATP, (c) respiration of a molecule of glucose to lactic acid, (d) conversion of a molecule of glucose to carbon dioxide and water.

2. The formation of glucose from glycogen is (a) gluconeogenesis, (b) glycogenesis, (c) glycogenolysis, (d) glycolysis.

3. The net gain of ATP from the complete metabolism (aerobic) of glucose is closest to (a) 2, (b) 30, (c) 38, (d) 4.

4. Which of the following *best* defines cellular respiration? (a) intake of carbon dioxide and output of oxygen by cells, (b) excretion of waste products, (c) inhalation of oxygen and exhalation of carbon dioxide, (d) oxidation of substances by which energy is released in usable form to the cells.

5. During aerobic respiration, electrons are passed down the electron transport chain and _____ is formed. (a) oxygen, (b) water, (c) glucose, (d) NADH + H$^+$.

6. Metabolic rate is relatively low in (a) youth, (b) physical exercise, (c) old age, (d) fever.

7. In a temperate climate under ordinary conditions, the greatest loss of body heat occurs through (a) radiation, (b) conduction, (c) evaporation, (d) none of the above.

8. Which of the following is *not* a function of the liver? (a) glycogenolysis and gluconeogenesis, (b) synthesis of cholesterol, (c) detoxification of alcohol and drugs, (d) synthesis of glucagon (e) deamination of amino acids.

9. Amino acids are essential (and important) to the body for all the following *except* (a) production of some hormones, (b) production of antibodies, (c) formation of most structural materials, (d) as a source of quick energy.

10. A person has been on a hunger strike for seven days. Compared to normal, he has (a) increased release of fatty acids from adipose tissue, ketosis, and ketonuria, (b) elevated glucose concentration in the blood, (c) increased plasma insulin concentration, (d) increased glycogen synthetase (enzyme) activity in the liver.

11. Transamination is a chemical process by which (a) protein is synthesized, (b) an amine group is transferred from an amino acid to a keto acid, (c) an amine group is cleaved from the amino acid, (d) amino acids are broken down for energy.

12. Three days after removal of the pancreas from an animal, the researcher finds a persistent increase in (a) acetoacetic acid concentration in the blood, (b) urine volume, (c) blood glucose, (d) all of the above.

13. Hunger, appetite, obesity, and physical activity are interrelated. Thus, (a) hunger sensations arise *primarily* from the stimulation of receptors in the stomach and intestinal tract in response to the absence of food in these organs; (b) obesity, in most cases, is a result of the abnormally high enzymatic activity of the fat-synthesizing enzymes in adipose tissue; (c) in all cases of obesity, the energy content of the ingested food has exceeded the energy expenditure of the body; (d) in a normal individual, increasing blood glucose concentration increases hunger sensations.

14. Body temperature regulation is (a) influenced by temperature receptors in the skin, (b) influenced by the temperature of the blood perfusing the heat regulation centers of the brain, (c) subject to both neural and hormonal control, (d) all of the above.

15. Which of the following yields the greatest caloric value per gram? (a) fats, (b) proteins, (c) carbohydrates, (d) all are equal in caloric value.

Short Answer Essay Questions

16. What is cellular respiration? What is the common role of FAD and NAD$^+$ in cellular respiration?

17. Describe the site, major events, and outcomes of glycolysis.

18. Pyruvic acid is a product of glycolysis, but it is not the substance that enters the Krebs cycle. What is the substance, and what must occur if pyruvic acid is to be transformed into this molecule?

19. Define glycogenesis, glycogenolysis, gluconeogenesis, and lipogenesis. Which is (are) likely to be occurring (a) shortly after a carbohydrate-rich meal, (b) just before waking up in the morning?

20. What is the harmful result when excessive amounts of fats are burned for energy? Name two conditions that might lead to this result.

21. Make a flowchart that indicates the pivotal intermediates through which glucose can be converted to fat.

22. Distinguish between the role of HDLs and that of LDLs.

23. List some factors that influence plasma cholesterol levels. Also list the sources and fates of cholesterol in the body.

24. What is meant by "body energy balance," and what happens if the balance is not precise?

25. Explain the effect of the following on metabolic rate: thyroxine levels, eating, body surface area, muscular exercise, emotional stress, starvation.

26. Explain the terms "core" and "shell" relative to body temperature balance. What serves as the heat-transfer agent from one to the other?

27. Compare and contrast mechanisms of heat loss with mechanisms of heat promotion, and explain how these mechanisms determine body temperature.

CRITICAL THINKING AND CLINICAL APPLICATION QUESTIONS

1. Calculate the number of ATP molecules that can be harvested during the complete oxidation of an 18-carbon fatty acid. (Take a deep breath and think about it—you *can* do it.)

2. Every year dozens of elderly people are found dead in their unheated apartments and listed as victims of hypothermia. What is hypothermia, and how does it kill? Why are the elderly more susceptible to hypothermia than the young?

3. Frank has been diagnosed as having severe atherosclerosis and high blood cholesterol levels. He is told that he is at risk for a stroke or a heart attack. First, what foods would you suggest that he avoid like the plague? What foods would you suggest he add or substitute? What activities would you recommend?

4. In the 1940s, some physicians prescribed low doses of a chemical called dinitrophenol (DNP) to help patients lose weight. This drug therapy was abandoned after a few patients died. DNP uncouples the chemiosmotic machinery. Explain how this causes weight loss.

26

The Urinary System

The kidneys, which maintain the constancy of fluids in our internal environment, are perfect examples of homeostatic organs. Much like a water purification plant that keeps a city's water drinkable and disposes of its wastes, the kidneys are usually unappreciated until they malfunction and body fluids become contaminated with internal "garbage." Every day the kidneys filter several liters of fluid from the bloodstream, allowing toxins, metabolic wastes, and excess ions to leave the body in urine, while returning needed substances to the blood. Although the lungs and skin also participate in excretion, the kidneys are the major excretory organs.

As the kidneys perform these excretory functions, they simultaneously regulate the volume and chemical makeup of the blood, maintaining the proper balance between water and salts and between acids and bases. Frankly, this would be tricky work for a chemical engineer, but the kidneys do it efficiently most of the time.

The kidneys have other regulatory functions as well. They produce the enzyme *renin* (re′nin), which helps regulate blood pressure and kidney function, and the hormone *erythropoietin* (ĕ-rith″ro-poi′ĕ-tin), which stimulates red blood cell production in bone marrow (see Chapter 18). The kidneys also metabolize vitamin D to its active form (see Chapter 17).

Besides the urine-forming kidneys, the organs of the **urinary system** are the paired *ureters* (u-re′terz), the *urinary bladder,* and the *urethra* (u-re′thrah) (Figure 26.1), which provide temporary storage reservoirs and transportation channels for urine.

Esophagus (cut)
Hepatic veins (cut)
Inferior vena cava
Adrenal gland
Renal artery
Renal hilus
Renal vein
Aorta
Kidney
Ureter
Iliac crest

Rectum (cut)

Uterus (part of female reproductive system)

Urinary bladder

Urethra

(a)

T$_{12}$
Kidney
L$_5$
Ureter
Bladder
Urethra

(b)

FIGURE 26.1
Organs of the urinary system. (a) Anterior view of the female urinary organs. (Most unrelated abdominal organs have been omitted.) **(b)** Relationship of the kidneys to the vertebrae and lower ribs.

KIDNEY ANATOMY

Location and External Anatomy

The bean-shaped kidneys lie in a retroperitoneal position (between the dorsal body wall and the parietal peritoneum) in the *superior* lumbar region (Figure 26.2). They extend approximately from the level of the twelfth thoracic vertebra to the third lumbar vertebra, thus the kidneys receive some protection from the lower part of the rib cage (see Figure 26.1b). The right kidney is crowded by the liver and lies slightly lower than the left. An adult's kidney weighs about 150 g (5 ounces) and its average dimensions are 12 cm long, 6 cm wide, and 3 cm thick, about the size of a large bar of soap. The lateral surface of the kidney is convex. Its medial surface is concave and has a vertical cleft called the **renal hilus** that leads into a space within the kidney called the *renal sinus.* Several structures, including the ureters, the renal blood vessels, lymphatics, and nerves, enter or exit the kidney at the hilus and occupy the sinus. Atop each kidney is an *adrenal* (or *suprarenal*) *gland,* which is a distinctly separate organ functionally (see Figure 26.1a).

Three layers of supportive tissue surround each kidney (Figure 26.2). The fibrous **renal capsule** adheres directly to the kidney surface. This transparent capsule provides a strong barrier that prevents infections in surrounding regions from spreading to the kidneys. The middle layer is a fatty mass called the **adipose capsule,** which helps to hold the kidney in place against the posterior trunk muscles and cushions it against blows. The outermost layer, the **renal fascia,** is dense fibrous connective tissue. It surrounds not only the kidney and its attendant membranes, but also the adrenal gland, and anchors these organs to surrounding structures.

The fatty encasement of the kidneys is extremely important in holding the kidneys in their normal body position. If the amount of fatty tissue dwindles (as with extreme emaciation or rapid weight loss), the kidneys may drop to a lower position, an event called *ptosis* (to′sis; "a fall"). Ptosis creates problems when a ureter becomes kinked because the urine, prevented from draining, backs up into the kidney and exerts pressure on its tissue. This condition, called *hydronephrosis* (hi″dro-ně-fro′sis; "water in the kidney"), can severely damage the kidney, leading to necrosis (tissue death) and renal failure. •

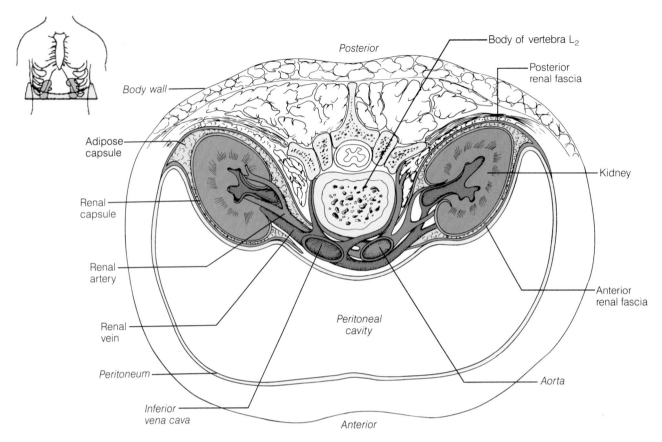

FIGURE 26.2
Position of the kidneys against the posterior body wall. The kidneys are
retroperitoneal and surrounded by three membranes: the renal capsule, the adipose capsule,
and the renal fascia.

Internal Anatomy

A frontal section through a kidney reveals three distinct regions (Figure 26.3): the cortex, the medulla, and the pelvis. The most superficial region, the **renal cortex,** is light in color and has a granular appearance. Deep to the cortex is the darker, reddish-brown **renal medulla,** which exhibits cone-shaped tissue masses called **medullary** or **renal pyramids.** The broad *base* of each pyramid faces toward the cortex; whereas its apex, or *papilla* ("nipple"), points toward the inner region of the kidney. The pyramids appear striped because they are formed almost entirely of roughly parallel bundles of microscopic urine-collecting tubules. The **renal columns,** inward extensions of cortical tissue, separate the pyramids. Each medullary pyramid and its adjacent "cap" of cortical tissue constitutes a **lobe** (one of approximately eight) of the kidney.

Medial to the hilus within the renal sinus is the **renal pelvis,** a flat, funnel-shaped tube which is continuous with the ureter leaving the hilus. Branching extensions of the pelvis form two or three **major calyces** (ka'lih-sēz; singular, *calyx*), each of which

subdivides further to form several **minor calyces,** cup-shaped areas that enclose the papillae of the pyramids. The calyces collect urine, which drains continuously from the papillae, and empty it into the renal pelvis. Urine then flows through the renal pelvis and into the ureter, which transports it to the bladder to be stored. The walls of the calyces, pelvis, and ureter contain smooth muscle, which contracts rhythmically and propels urine along its course by peristalsis.

Infection of the renal pelvis and calyces produces the condition called *pyelitis* (pi″ĕ-li′tis). Infections or inflammatory conditions that affect the entire kidney are called *pyelonephritis* (pi″ĕ-lo-nĕ-fri′tis). Kidney infections are usually caused by fecal bacteria *(E. coli)* that spread from the anal region to the urinary tract. Less often they result from blood-borne bacteria (traveling from other infected sites) that lodge and multiply in the kidneys. In severe cases of pyelonephritis, the kidney becomes swollen, abscesses form, and the pelvis fills with pus. Untreated, the kidneys may be severely damaged, but antibiotic therapy usually achieves total remission. •

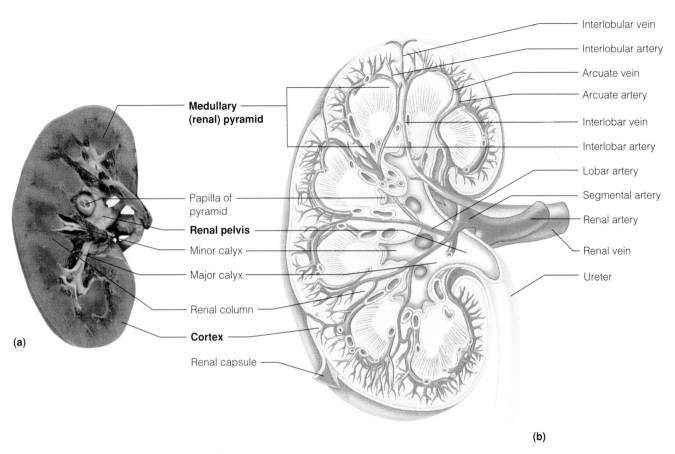

FIGURE 26.3
Internal anatomy of the kidney. (a) Photograph of a frontal section of a kidney.
(b) Diagrammatic view of a coronally sectioned kidney, illustrating major blood vessels.

Blood and Nerve Supply

The kidneys continuously cleanse the blood and adjust its composition, so it is not surprising that they have a very rich blood supply (Figure 26.3). Under normal resting conditions, the large **renal arteries** deliver approximately one-fourth of the total systemic cardiac output (about 1200 ml) to the kidneys each minute. The renal arteries issue at right angles from the abdominal aorta between the first and second lumbar vertebrae. Because the aorta lies to the left of the midline, the right renal artery is longer than the left. As each renal artery approaches a kidney, it divides into five **segmental arteries** that enter the hilus. Within the renal sinus, each segmental artery branches into several **lobar arteries.** Each lobar artery divides to form several **interlobar arteries,** which pass between the medullary pyramids to the cortex.

At the medulla-cortex junction, the interlobar arteries give off branches, called **arcuate** (ar′ku-āt) **arteries,** that arch over the bases of the medullary pyramids. Small **interlobular arteries** radiate from the arcuate arteries to supply the cortical tissue (see Figure 26.5a). More than 90% of the blood entering the kidney perfuses the cortex, which contains the bulk of the *nephrons* (nef′ronz), the structural and functional units of the kidneys.

Veins of the kidney pretty much trace the pathway of the arterial supply in reverse. Blood leaving the renal cortex drains sequentially into the **interlobular, arcuate, interlobar,** and, finally, the **renal veins.** (There are no lobar or segmental veins.) The renal veins issue from the kidneys and empty into the inferior vena cava. Since the inferior vena cava lies to the right of the vertebral column, the left renal vein is about twice as long as the right.

The nerve supply of the kidney and its ureter is provided by the **renal plexus,** a variable network of autonomic nerve fibers and ganglia. The renal plexus is largely supplied by sympathetic fibers from the least thoracic and first lumbar splanchnic nerves, which course along with the renal artery to reach the kidney. These sympathetic fibers are vasomotor fibers that regulate renal blood flow by adjusting the diameter of renal arterioles.

Nephrons

Each kidney contains over 1 million tiny blood-processing units called *nephrons,* which carry out the processes that form urine (Figure 26.4). In addition, there are thousands of *collecting ducts,* each of which collects urine from several nephrons and conveys it to the renal pelvis.

Each **nephron** consists of a **glomerulus** (glo-mer′u-lus; *glom* = ball of yarn), a tuft of capillaries, associated with a **renal tubule.** The end of the renal tubule, called the **glomerular (Bowman's) capsule,** is blind, enlarged, and cup-shaped and completely surrounds the glomerulus (much as a well-worn baseball glove encloses a ball). Collectively, the glomerular capsule and the enclosed glomerulus are called the **renal corpuscle.** The glomerular endothelium is *fenestrated* (penetrated by many small pores), which makes these capillaries exceptionally porous: They allow large amounts of solute-rich fluid to pass from the blood into the glomerular capsule. This plasma-derived fluid or **filtrate** is the raw material that is processed by the renal tubules to form urine.

The external *parietal layer* of the glomerular capsule consists of simple squamous epithelium. This layer has a purely structural role and plays no part in forming filtrate. The *visceral layer,* which clings to the glomerulus (Figure 26.4b), consists of highly modified, branching epithelial cells called **podocytes** (pod′o-sīts; "foot cells"). The branches of the octopus-like podocytes terminate in **foot processes** or **pedicels** ("little feet"), which intertwine with one another as they cling to the basement membrane of the glomerulus. The clefts or openings between the foot processes are called **filtration slits** or **slit pores** (see Figure 26.8 on p. 905).

The remainder of the renal tubule (Figure 26.4b) is about 3 cm (approximately 1.25 inches) long and has three named parts. It leaves the glomerular capsule as the elaborately coiled **proximal convoluted tubule (PCT),** makes a hairpin loop called the **loop of Henle,** and then winds and twists again as the **distal convoluted tubule (DCT)** before it empties its product into a collecting duct. The meandering nature of the renal tubule increases its length and enhances its filtrate processing capabilities. (Designating the convoluted parts of the nephron as proximal or distal indicates their relative closeness to the glomerulus—the PCT being closer.)

The **collecting ducts,** each of which receives urine from many nephrons, run through the medullary pyramids and give them their striped appearance. As the collecting ducts approach the renal pelvis, they fuse to form larger **papillary ducts,** which deliver urine into the minor calyces via the papillae of the pyramids.

Each region of the renal tubule has a unique cellular anatomy, which reflects its specific role in processing filtrate. The walls of the *proximal convoluted tubule* are formed by cuboidal epithelial cells, which actively reabsorb substances from the filtrate and also play a role in secreting substances into it. These cells have large mitochondria and their luminal (exposed) surfaces bear dense microvilli (Figure 26.4b and c) that tremendously increase their surface area and, thereby, their capacity for reabsorbing water and solutes from the filtrate. The U-shaped *loop of Henle* has *descending* and *ascending limbs.* The proximal part of the descending limb is continuous with the proximal tubule and its cells are similar. The rest of the descending limb, called the **thin segment,** is a simple squamous epithelium that is freely permeable to water. The epithelium becomes cuboidal or even low columnar in the ascending part of the loop of Henle, which therefore becomes the **thick segment.** In some nephrons, the thin segment is found only in the descending limb of the loop of Henle. In others, it extends into the ascending limb as well. The epithelial cells of the *distal convoluted tubule,* like those of the proximal tubule, are confined to the cortex and are cuboidal, but they are somewhat thinner and almost entirely lack microvilli. These structural features reveal that the distal tubules play a greater role in secreting solutes into the filtrate than in reabsorbing substances from it. Beginning late in the DCT, the tubule cells become heterogeneous. The two most important cell types seen here, and in the collecting ducts beyond, are *intercalated cells* and the more numerous *principal cells.*

Cortical nephrons represent 85% of the nephrons in the kidneys. Except for small portions of their loops of Henle that dip into the outer medulla, they are located entirely in the cortex. The remaining nephrons are somewhat different in structure. These **juxtamedullary** (juks″tah-me′dul-ah-re) **nephrons** are located close to (*juxta* = near to) the cortex-medulla junction. Their loops of Henle deeply invade the medulla, and their thin segments are much more extensive than those of cortical nephrons (Figure 26.5). The juxtamedullary nephrons play an important role in the kidney's ability to produce concentrated urine.

Capillary Beds (Microvasculature) of the Nephron

Every nephron is closely associated with two capillary beds: the *glomerulus* and the *peritubular capillaries* (Figure 26.5). The glomerulus, specialized for filtration, is unlike any other capillary bed in the body in that it is both fed and drained by arterioles—the **afferent arteriole** and the **efferent arteriole,** respectively. The afferent arterioles arise from the *interlobular arteries* that run through the renal cortex (see also Figure 26.3b). Because (1) arterioles are high-resistance vessels and (2) the afferent arteriole has a larger diameter than the efferent, the blood pressure in the glomerulus is extraordinarily high for a capillary bed and easily forces fluid and solutes out of the blood into the glomerular capsule along nearly its entire length. Most

What would be the path taken by a urea molecule in the glomerular blood to the renal pelvis?

FIGURE 26.4
Location and structure of nephrons. (a) Orientation diagram indicating the location of nephrons in the kidney. **(b)** Schematic view of a nephron depicting the structural characteristics of epithelial cells forming its various regions. **(c)** Photomicrograph of renal cortical tissue. Notice the renal corpuscles and the sections through the various tubules. In the proximal convoluted tubules, the lumens appear "fuzzy" because they are filled with the long microvilli of the epithelial cells that form the tubule walls. In the distal tubules, by contrast, the lumens are clear (magnification: 400×).

FIGURE 26.5
Detailed anatomy of nephrons and their vasculature. (a) Comparison of the tubular
and vascular anatomy of cortical and juxtamedullary nephrons drawn to the same scale.
(b) Detail of the juxtaglomerular apparatus of a nephron. **(c)** Scanning electron micrograph of a
cast of blood vessels associated with nephrons (65×). From R. Kessel and R. Kardon, *Tissues
and Organs,* © 1979 W. H. Freeman.

of this filtrate (99%) is reabsorbed by the renal tubule cells and returned to the blood in the peritubular capillary beds.

The **peritubular capillaries** arise from the efferent arterioles draining the glomeruli. These capillaries cling closely to the renal tubules and empty into nearby venules of the renal venous system. The peritubular capillaries are adapted for absorption rather than filtrate formation. They are low-pressure, porous capillaries that readily absorb solutes and water from the tubule cells as these substances are reclaimed from the filtrate. Furthermore, all substances that are secreted by the nephrons are derived from the blood of the peritubular capillaries.

In the deepest part of the renal cortex, the efferent arterioles serving the juxtamedullary nephrons also continue into long, thin-walled looping vessels called the **vasa recta** (va'sah rek'tah; "straight vessels"). These hairpin vessels extend into the medulla, paralleling the course of their long loops of Henle (see Figure 26.5). In summary, the microvasculature of the nephrons consists of two capillary beds separated by intervening efferent arterioles. The first capillary bed (glomerulus) produces the filtrate. The second (peritubular capillaries) reclaims most of that filtrate.

Vascular Resistance in the Microcirculation.

As blood flows through the renal circulation, it encounters high resistance, first in the afferent and then in the efferent arterioles. As a result, renal blood pressure declines from approximately 95 mm Hg in the renal arteries to 8 mm Hg or less in the renal veins (Figure 26.6). The resistance of the afferent arterioles protects the glomeruli from large fluctuations in systemic blood pressure. Resistance encountered in the efferent arterioles reinforces the high glomerular pressure and reduces the hydrostatic pressure in the peritubular capillaries.

Juxtaglomerular Apparatus

Each nephron has a region called the **juxtaglomerular** (juks"tah-glo-mer'u-lar) **apparatus (JGA),** where the initial portion of its coiling distal tubule lies against the afferent and efferent arterioles, respectively feeding and draining the glomerulus (Figure 26.5b). At the point of contact, all structures are modified.

The arteriole walls have **granular juxtaglomerular (JG) cells**—enlarged, smooth muscle cells with prominent granules containing renin. These cells appear to be mechanoreceptors that directly sense the blood pressure in the afferent arteriole. The **macula densa** (mak'u-lah den'sah; "dense spot") is a group of tall, closely packed tubule cells that lie adjacent to the granular JG cells. The macula densa cells are chemoreceptors or osmoreceptors that respond to changes in the solute content of the filtrate in the tubule lumen. These two distinct cell populations

FIGURE 26.6
Relative blood pressures in the renal circulation. The two areas of highest resistance (thus, points of greatest decline in blood pressure) are the afferent and efferent arterioles, respectively feeding and draining the glomeruli.

play important roles in regulating the rate of filtrate formation and systemic blood pressure as described shortly. The function of the closely associated *lacis cells* is incompletely understood.

KIDNEY PHYSIOLOGY: MECHANISMS OF URINE FORMATION

Of the approximately 1000–1200 ml of blood that passes through the glomeruli each minute, about 650 ml is plasma, and about one-fifth of this (120–125 ml) is forced into the renal tubules. This is equivalent to filtering out your entire plasma volume more than 60 times each day! Considering the magnitude of their task, it is not surprising that the kidneys (which account for only about 1% of body weight) consume 20% to 25% of all the oxygen used by the body at rest.

Filtrate and urine are quite different. Filtrate contains everything that blood plasma does except proteins; but by the time filtrate has percolated into the collecting ducts, it has lost most of its water, nutrients, and essential ions. What remains, now called **urine,** contains mostly metabolic wastes and unneeded substances. The kidneys process about 180 L (47 gallons) of blood-derived fluid daily. Of this amount, only about 1% (1.5 L) actually leaves the body as urine; the rest is returned to the circulation. Essentially, urine formation and the simultaneous adjustment of blood composition involve three processes (Figure 26.7). *Glomerular filtration* is mainly the job of the glomeruli. The renal tubules carry out *tubular reabsorption* and *secretion,* both carefully regulated by renal and hormonal controls. In addition, the collecting ducts work in concert with the nephrons to concentrate or dilute urine.

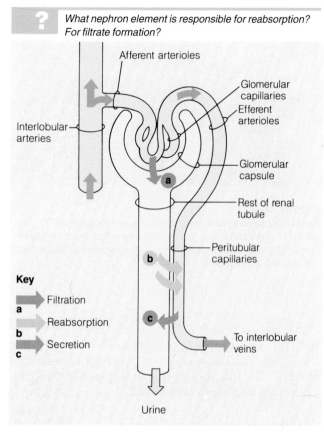

Key

➡ **Filtration**
a

➡ **Reabsorption**
b

➡ **Secretion**
c

FIGURE 26.7
**The kidney depicted schematically as a single, large,
uncoiled nephron.** A kidney actually has millions of nephrons
acting in parallel. The three major mechanisms by which the kidneys
adjust the composition of plasma are **(a)** glomerular filtration,
(b) tubular reabsorption, and **(c)** tubular secretion.

Glomerular Filtration

Urine formation begins with **glomerular filtration.**
Filtration is largely a passive, nonselective process in
which fluids and solutes are forced through a membrane by hydrostatic pressure (see Chapter 3). Since
filtrate formation does not require the use of metabolic energy, the glomeruli can be viewed as simple
mechanical filters. The principles of fluid dynamics
that account for the formation of tissue fluid at all
capillary beds (see Chapter 20) apply to the formation
of filtrate at the glomerulus as well. However, the
glomerulus is a much more efficient filter than are
other capillary beds because (1) its *filtration membrane* is thousands of times more permeable to water
and solutes than are other capillary membranes, and
(2) glomerular blood pressure is much higher than
that of other capillary beds (approximately 60 mm Hg
as opposed to 15 mm Hg or less), resulting in a much
higher *net filtration pressure.* As a result of these differences, the kidneys produce about 180 L of filtrate
daily, in contrast to the 3 to 4 L formed daily by all
other capillary beds of the body combined.

The Filtration Membrane

The **filtration membrane** is the actual filter that lies
between the blood and the interior of the glomerular
capsule. It is a porous membrane that allows free passage of water and solutes smaller than plasma proteins. Its three layers are

1. The fenestrated capillary (glomerular) endothelium

2. The visceral membrane of the glomerular capsule
    made of podocytes

3. The intervening basement membrane composed
    of the fused basal laminas of the other two layers
    (Figure 26.8)

The capillary pores prevent passage of blood
cells. The basement membrane restricts passage of all
but the smallest proteins while permitting most other
solutes to pass. The structural makeup of the basement membrane also seems to confer some electrical
selectivity on the filtration process. Most of its proteins are anionic (negatively charged) glycoproteins
that repel other anions and hinder their passage into
the tubule. Because most plasma proteins are also
polyanions, this electrical repulsion reinforces the
plasma protein blockage imposed by molecular size.
Although there is some uncertainty about what happens to macromolecules that get "hung up" in the filtration membrane, the assumption is that they are
engulfed by the podocytes and degraded.

In general, the filtration membrane allows molecules smaller than 3 nm in diameter—such as water,
glucose, amino acids, and nitrogenous wastes—to
pass freely from the blood into the renal tubule.
Hence, these substances are usually present in the
same concentration in the blood and the glomerular
filtrate. Molecules larger than 3 nm pass with greater
difficulty, and those larger than 7–9 nm are usually
completely barred from entering the tubule. Keeping
the plasma proteins *in* the capillaries maintains the
colloid osmotic pressure of the glomerular blood, preventing the loss of all of its water to the renal tubules.
The presence of proteins or blood cells in the urine
usually indicates some problem with the filtration
membrane.

Net Filtration Pressure

To determine the **net filtration pressure (NFP)** responsible for filtrate formation, we must examine the
forces acting at the glomerular bed (Figure 26.9).
Glomerular hydrostatic pressure (HP$_g$), which is
essentially glomerular blood pressure, is the chief
force pushing water and solutes out of the blood
across the filtration membrane. Although theoretically colloid osmotic pressure in the intracapsular
space of the glomerular capsule "pulls" the filtrate
into the tubule, this pressure is essentially zero because
virtually no proteins enter the capsule. Glomerular
hydrostatic pressure (60 mm Hg) is opposed by forces
that drive fluids back into the glomerular capillaries.

(a)

Afferent arteriole

Efferent arteriole

Glomerular capillary covered by podocyte-containing visceral layer of glomerular capsule

Parietal layer of glomerular capsule

Proximal convoluted tubule

Cytoplasmic extensions of podocytes

Filtration slits

Pedicels (foot processes of podocyte)

Podocyte cell body

Glomerular capillary endothelium (podocyte covering removed)

Fenestrations

Filtration slits

(b)

Podocyte cell body

Pedicels

Capillary endothelium

Basement membrane

Foot processes of podocytes of glomerular capsule

Plasma

Fenestration

Filtration slit

Filtrate in capsular space

(c)

FIGURE 26.8
The filtration membrane. The filtration membrane is composed of three layers: the fenestrated glomerular endothelium, the podocyte-containing visceral layer of the glomerular capsule, and the intervening basement membrane. **(a)** Diagrammatic three-dimensional view of the relationship of the visceral layer of the glomerular capsule to the glomerular capillaries. The visceral epithelium is drawn incompletely to show the fenestrations in the underlying capillary wall. **(b)** Scanning electron micrograph of the visceral layer. Filtration slits between the podocyte foot processes are evident (39,000×). **(c)** Diagrammatic view of a section through the filtration membrane showing all three structural elements.

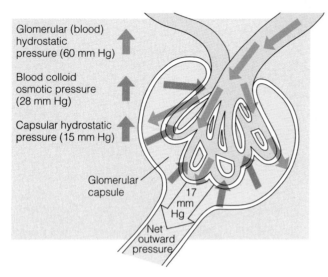

? *What would be the consequence of liver disease for the process shown below?*

Glomerular (blood) hydrostatic pressure (60 mm Hg)

Blood colloid osmotic pressure (28 mm Hg)

Capsular hydrostatic pressure (15 mm Hg)

Glomerular capsule

17 mm Hg

Net outward pressure

FIGURE 26.9
Forces that determine glomerular filtration and the effective filtration pressure. The glomerular hydrostatic (blood) pressure is the major factor forcing fluids and solutes out of the blood. This is opposed by the colloid osmotic pressure of the blood and the hydrostatic pressure that exists within the glomerular capsule. The pressure values cited in the diagram are approximate.

These filtration-opposing forces are (1) **glomerular osmotic pressure (OP$_g$),** or colloid osmotic pressure of plasma proteins in the glomerular blood (about 28 mm Hg), and (2) **capsular hydrostatic pressure (HP$_c$)** exerted by fluids in the glomerular capsule (about 15 mm Hg). Thus, the NFP responsible for forming renal filtrate from plasma is 17 mm Hg:

$$NFP = HP_g - (OP_g + HP_c)$$

$$NFP = 60 \text{ mm Hg} - (28 \text{ mm Hg} + 15 \text{ mm Hg})$$

$$NFP = 60 \text{ mm Hg} - (43 \text{ mm Hg})$$

$$NFP = 17 \text{ mm Hg}$$

Glomerular Filtration Rate (GFR)

The **glomerular filtration rate** or **GFR** is the total amount of filtrate formed per minute by the kidneys. Factors governing filtration rate at capillary beds are (1) total surface area available for filtration, (2) filtration membrane permeability, and (3) net filtration pressure. The normal GFR in both kidneys in adults is 120–125 ml/min (7.5 L/hour, or 180 L/day). Because glomerular capillaries are exceptionally permeable and have a huge surface area (collectively equal to the surface area of the skin), remarkably large amounts of filtrate can be produced even with the usual modest net filtration pressure of 17 mm Hg. The opposite side of this "coin" is that a drop in glomerular pressure of only about 15% stops filtration altogether.

The GFR is *directly proportional* to the net filtration pressure. Hence, a change in any of the pressures

acting at the filtration membrane (see Figure 26.9) changes the NFP and thus the GFR. An increase in arterial (and glomerular) blood pressure in the kidneys increases the GFR, whereas dehydration (which causes an increase in glomerular osmotic pressure) inhibits filtrate formation. Although certain disease states may modify any of these pressures, changes in the GFR *normally* result from changes in glomerular blood pressure, which is subject to both intrinsic and extrinsic controls.

Regulation of Glomerular Filtration

The importance of maintaining a fairly constant GFR becomes clear when one realizes that reabsorption of water and other substances from the filtrate depends to some extent on the *rate* at which filtrate flows through the renal tubules. Although the GFR can increase by 30% without upsetting the balance between glomerular filtration and tubular reabsorption, when massive amounts of filtrate are formed and flow is very rapid, needed substances cannot be adequately reabsorbed and are lost to the body in urine. On the other hand, when filtrate is scanty and flows slowly, nearly all of it is reabsorbed, including most of the wastes that are normally disposed of. Thus, for optimal filtrate processing, the GFR must be precisely regulated.

At least three important mechanisms regulate renal blood flow and the GFR—renal autoregulation (the intrinsic system), neural controls, and the renin-angiotensin system (basically a hormonal mechanism). These plus some less well defined factors are examined next.

Intrinsic Controls: Renal Autoregulation.

Under ordinary conditions, glomerular blood pressure is regulated by the kidneys' autoregulatory, system. By determining its own rate of blood flow, a process called **renal autoregulation,** the kidney can maintain a nearly constant glomerular filtration rate despite fluctuations in systemic arterial blood pressure. It does this by directly regulating the diameter of the afferent and to a lesser extent the efferent arterioles. Although the mechanism of renal autoregulation is still something of a mystery, the two "suspects" are (1) a *myogenic mechanism* that responds to changes in pressure in the renal blood vessels, and (2) a *tubuloglomerular feedback mechanism* that senses changes in the juxtaglomerular apparatus (Figure 26.10). Of the two, the myogenic mechanism is less supported by research. (Additionally, the *renin-angiotensin mechanism,* which mainly functions to maintain homeostasis of systemic blood pressure, acts indirectly to maintain the GFR of the kidneys as discussed later.)

The **myogenic** (mi"o-jen'ik) **mechanism** reflects the general tendency of vascular smooth muscle to contract when it is stretched. Increasing systemic blood pressure causes the afferent arterioles to constrict, which restricts blood flow into the glomerulus (and lowers the downstream glomerular pressure)

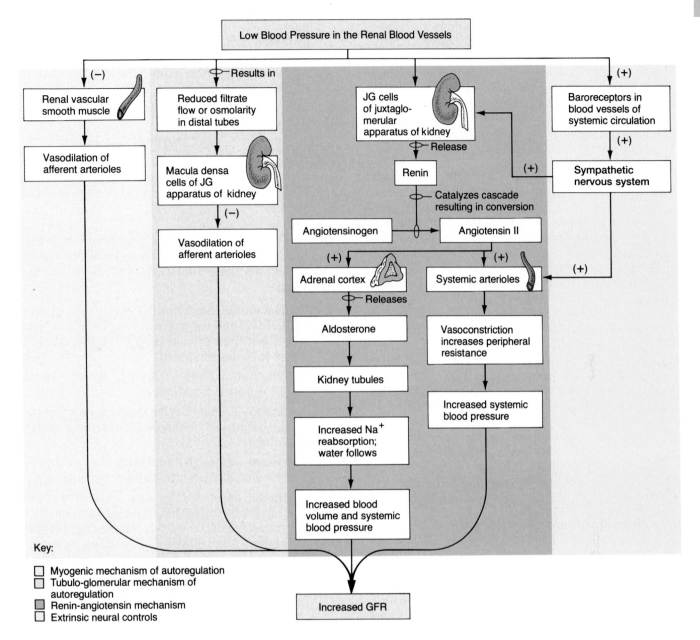

FIGURE 26.10
Flowchart indicating the mechanisms regulating the glomerular filtration rate (GFR) in the kidneys. (Note that (+) indicates a stimulatory effect and (−) indicates an inhibitory effect.)

and prevents glomerular blood pressure from rising to damaging levels. On the other hand, a decline in systemic blood pressure causes dilation of afferent arterioles and an increase in glomerular hydrostatic pressure. Both responses help maintain a normal GFR.

Autoregulation by the **tubuloglomerular feedback mechanism** is "directed" by the *macula densa cells* of the **juxtaglomerular apparatus.** These cells, located in the walls at the junctions of the ascending limbs of the loops of Henle and the distal tubules, respond to rapidly flowing filtrate and/or osmotic signals (filtrate with high sodium and chloride content, or high osmolarity in general) by promoting release of a

chemical that causes intense vasoconstriction of the afferent arterioles. This hinders blood flow into the glomerulus, decreasing the GFR and allowing more time for filtrate processing. On the other hand, when the macula densa cells are exposed to slowly flowing filtrate or filtrate with low osmolarity, they promote vasodilation. This mechanism is believed to be very important in balancing filtration and tubular reabsorption, but neither the vasoconstrictor nor its source is known as yet.

By altering the resistance of the *afferent arterioles* when systemic blood pressure rises and falls, renal autoregulatory mechanisms maintain a relatively constant blood flow through the kidneys over an arterial pressure range from about 80 to 180 mm Hg. Consequently, large changes in water and solute excretion are prevented. However, this intrinsic control system cannot handle extremely low systemic blood pressure, such as might result from serious hemorrhage *(hypovolemic shock)*. Once systemic blood pressure has dropped below 45 mm Hg (the point at which glomerular filtration pressure nearly balances the opposing forces), filtration stops.

Sympathetic Nervous System Controls. Neural controls serve the needs of the body as a whole, and renal autoregulatory mechanisms may be overcome during periods of extreme stress or emergency when it is necessary to shunt blood to the heart, brain, and skeletal muscles at the expense of the kidneys. At such times, stimulation by sympathetic nerve fibers and release of epinephrine by the adrenal medulla interact with alpha-adrenergic receptors on vascular smooth muscle, causing strong constriction of the afferent arterioles, inhibiting filtrate formation. The sympathetic nervous system also stimulates the JG cells (via the binding of norepinephrine to beta-adrenergic receptors) to release renin, bringing about an increase in systemic blood pressure via the renin-angiotensin mechanism. Indeed, direct sympathetic input to the JG cells is the single most important regulator of renin secretion. When the sympathetic nervous system is less intensely activated, the efferent and afferent arterioles are constricted to about the same extent. Because blood flow into and out of the glomerulus is hindered to the same degree, the GFR declines only slightly.

Renin-Angiotensin Mechanism. The **renin-angiotensin mechanism** is triggered when the *juxtaglomerular cells* of the juxtaglomerular apparatus release renin in response to various stimuli. Renin acts enzymatically on **angiotensinogen,** a plasma globulin made by the liver, to release **angiotensin I,** which is in turn converted to **angiotensin II** by converting enzymes associated with the capillary endothelium in various body tissues, particularly the lungs. Angiotensin II, a potent vasoconstrictor, activates vascular smooth muscle throughout the body, causing systemic blood pressure to rise. It also stimulates the adrenal cortex to release aldosterone, which causes the renal tubules to reclaim more sodium ions from the filtrate. Because water follows sodium osmotically, blood volume and blood pressure rise (see Figure 26.10). However, like epinephrine, angiotensin II also causes vasoconstriction of the afferent and efferent arterioles, thereby decreasing the GFR.

Renin release is triggered by several factors acting independently or collectively. These include:

1. Reduced stretch of the granular juxtaglomerular (JG) cells, caused by a drop in systemic blood pressure below 80 mm Hg, directly stimulates them to release more renin.

2. Stimulation of the JG cells by activated macula densa cells. Under conditions in which they prompt a *reduced* release of the vasoconstrictor chemical (promoting vasodilation of the afferent arteriole), they also stimulate the JG cells to release renin.

3. Direct stimulation of the JG cells by the renal sympathetic nerves.

Although the renin-angiotensin mechanism contributes to renal autoregulation, its *main thrust* is to stabilize systemic blood pressure and extracellular fluid volume—processes considered in more detail in Chapter 27.

Other Factors. Renal cells produce a whole battery of chemicals, many of which act locally as signaling molecules (paracrines). Among these are the following.

1. Prostaglandins (eicosanoids)—both vasodilators (PGE_2, PGI_2) and vasoconstrictors (TXA_2) are produced, but their precise roles in regulating GFR are yet to be demonstrated.

2. Endothelium-derived relaxing factor (nitric oxide)—a potent vasodilator.

3. Kallikrein—a renal enzyme that acts on a plasma protein (kininogen) to release bradykinin, a potent vasodilator.

4. Adenosine—although it functions as a vasodilator systemically, it constricts the renal vasculature.

5. Endothelin—probably the most interesting of the local signaling molecules, it causes vasoconstriction of the renal blood vessels (decreasing the GFR) and inhibits renin release. Hence, it is a good candidate for the local vasoconstrictor chemical involved in autoregulation and may be the signal by which increased NaCl at the macula densa inhibits renin release. Its secretion is enhanced by rising blood pressure and epinephrine.

An abnormally low urinary output (less than 50 ml/day) is called *anuria* (ah-nu′re-ah). It usually indicates that glomerular blood pressure is too low to cause filtration, but anuria may also result from acute nephritis, transfusion reactions, or crush injuries. •

Tubular Reabsorption

Because the total blood volume filters into the renal tubules every 45 minutes or so, all of the plasma would be drained away as urine within an hour were it not for the fact that most of the tubule contents are quickly reclaimed and returned to the blood. This reclamation process, called **tubular reabsorption,** is a *transepithelial process* that begins as soon as the filtrate enters the proximal tubules. Because the tubule cells are connected by tight junctions, movement of substances between the cells is extremely limited. Transported

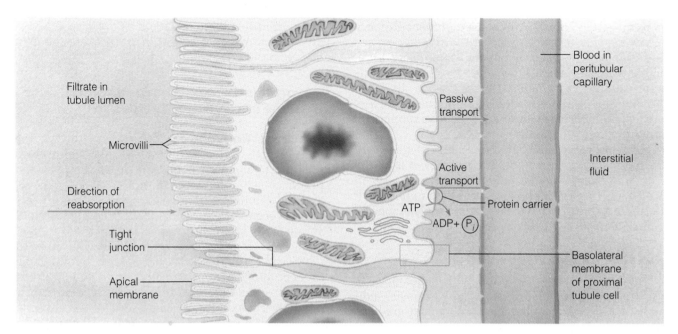

FIGURE 26.11
Directional movement of reabsorbed substances. Most substances reabsorbed by renal tubule cells pass by diffusion from the filtrate through the tubule cell's apical membrane and then through the tubule cell to its basolateral membrane facing the peritubular capillaries. From there the substances move through the basolateral membrane into the interstitial fluid and then into the peritubular capillary blood. The ATP-dependent carriers that transport Na^+ and other substances that must be transported actively are thought to be located in the basolateral membranes of the tubule cells. Most such carriers cotransport another solute along with Na^+. Tight junctions connecting the tubule cells near their apical surfaces prevent movement of substances between the tubule cells, enforcing transepithelial transport.

substances must move through *three* membrane barriers—the *luminal* and *basolateral membranes* of the tubule cells (which abut the filtrate and interstitial fluid respectively) and the *endothelium* of the peritubular capillaries—to reach the blood.

Given healthy kidneys, virtually all organic nutrients such as glucose and amino acids are completely reabsorbed. The kidneys simply maintain or restore the normal plasma concentrations. On the other hand, the rate and degree of reabsorption of water and many ions are continuously regulated and adjusted in response to hormonal signals. Depending on the substances transported, the reabsorption process may be *passive* (none of its steps require ATP) or *active* (at least one of its steps is driven by ATP).

Active Tubular Reabsorption

Substances reclaimed by **active tubular reabsorption** are usually moving against electrical and/or chemical gradients. In most cases, the substance moves easily from the filtrate into the tubule cells by diffusion, but requires the services of an ATP-dependent carrier to eject it across the basolateral membrane of the tubule cell into the interstitial space (Figure 26.11). From there, it moves passively into the adjacent peritubular capillaries. Movement of absorbed substances into the peritubular capillary blood is rapid because of its low hydrostatic pressure and high osmotic pressure (remember, most proteins are not filtered out of the blood into the tubule).

Substances actively reabsorbed include glucose, amino acids, lactate, vitamins, and most ions. In nearly all these cases, transport is linked to that of Na^+, and movement through the tubule cell depends on the ejection of sodium ions (via a Na^+-K^+ pump) across the basolateral membrane into the extracellular space. Sodium ions are the single most abundant cations in the filtrate, and the bulk of energy (about 80%) used for active transport is devoted to Na^+ reabsorption.

There is some overlap of carriers; for example, fructose and galactose compete with glucose for the same Na^+-associated carrier. Even so, the transport systems for the various solutes are quite specific *and limited*.

Excluding Na^+, a **transport maximum (T_m)** is reported in mg/min for nearly every substance that is actively reabsorbed. The T_m reflects the number of carriers in the renal tubules available to "ferry" each particular substance. In general, there are plentiful carriers and high transport maximums for substances such as glucose that need to be retained and few or no carriers for substances of no use to the body. When the carriers are saturated—that is, all bound to the substance they transport—excesses of that substance are excreted in urine. This is exactly what happens in individuals who become hyperglycemic because of uncontrolled diabetes mellitus. As glucose levels approach 400 mg glucose/100 ml plasma, its T_m of 375 mg/min is exceeded and large amounts of glucose are lost in the urine even though the renal tubules are still functioning normally.

Any plasma proteins that squeeze through the filtration membrane are completely removed from the filtrate in the proximal tubule by pinocytosis, also an ATP-requiring process. Once inside the tubule cells, the proteins are digested to their amino acid monomers, which then move into the peritubular blood.

Passive Tubular Reabsorption

In **passive tubular reabsorption,** which encompasses diffusion, facilitated diffusion, and osmosis, substances move along their electrochemical gradient without the use of ATP (see Chapter 3). In the renal tubules, the electrochemical gradient that drives most passive transport is established by active reabsorption of sodium ions from the filtrate. As positively charged sodium ions move through the tubule cells into the peritubular capillary blood, they establish an electrical gradient that favors the passive diffusion of anions (Cl^-, for example) into the peritubular capillaries to restore electrical neutrality in the filtrate and plasma. Just which anion is absorbed depends on the pH of the blood at the time. Sodium movement also establishes a strong osmotic gradient, and water moves by osmosis into peritubular capillaries. Because water is "obliged" to follow salt, this sodium-linked water flow is referred to as **obligatory water reabsorption.**

As water leaves the tubules, the relative concentrations of substances still present in the filtrate increase dramatically, and they too begin to follow their concentration gradients into the tubule cells. This phenomenon of solutes following the movement of the solvent is called **solvent drag.** Solvent drag explains the passive reabsorption of some urea, as well as that of a number of other lipid-soluble substances present in the filtrate, such as fatty acids. Although the gradient provides the driving force, remember that solute size and lipid solubility may be limiting factors. Solvent drag also explains in part why lipid-soluble drugs and environmental toxins are difficult to excrete.

Nonreabsorbed Substances

Some substances are not reabsorbed or are reabsorbed incompletely because they (1) lack carriers, (2) are not lipid soluble, or (3) are too large to pass through plasma membrane pores of the tubular cells. The most important of these substances are the nitrogenous end products of protein and nucleic acid metabolism: **urea, creatinine,** and **uric acid.** Urea is small enough to diffuse through the membrane pores, and 40% to 50% of the urea present in filtrate is reclaimed. Creatinine, a large, lipid-insoluble molecule, is not reabsorbed at all—which makes it useful for measuring the GFR and glomerular function (see p. 916).

Absorptive Capabilities of Different Regions of the Renal Tubules

Proximal Convoluted Tubule. Although the entire length of the renal tubule is involved in reabsorption to some degree (Table 26.1), the proximal tubule cells are by far the most active "reabsorbers" and the events just described occur mainly in this tubular segment. Normally, all of the glucose and amino acids are reabsorbed in the proximal tubule. Some 65% of the Na^+ present in filtrate is absorbed in the proximal tubule; and because water follows in the same proportion, approximately 65% of the water is also reabsorbed there. Additionally, 90% of the filtered bicarbonate (HCO^-_3) and 50% of the chloride (Cl^-) and potassium (K^+) are reclaimed in the PCT. Likewise, the bulk of the *selective* or active transport–dependent reabsorption of electrolytes is accomplished by the time the filtrate reaches the loop of Henle. For the most part, the reabsorption of electrolytes such as calcium, phosphate, and magnesium is hormonally controlled and intimately related to the need to regulate their plasma levels. (These controls are described in Chapter 27.) Nearly all of the uric acid is reabsorbed in the proximal tubule, but it is later secreted back into the filtrate.

Loop of Henle. Beyond the proximal convoluted tubule, the permeability characteristics of the tubule epithelium change dramatically (see Figure 26.13, p. 915). Here, for the first time, water reabsorption is not coupled to solute reabsorption. Water can leave the descending limb of the loop of Henle but not the ascending limb, which, however, is quite permeable to sodium chloride. For reasons that will be explained shortly, these permeability differences play a vital role in the kidneys' ability to form dilute and concentrated urine. Another 25% of the filtered Na^+, 15% of the water, and 40% of the K^+ is reabsorbed in the loop of Henle.

Distal Convoluted Tubule and Collecting Duct. By the time the DCT is reached, only about 10% of the originally filtered NaCl and 20% of the water remain in the tubule. Reabsorption from this point on depends largely on the needs of the body at the time and is regulated by hormones. If necessary, nearly all of the water and Na^+ reaching these regions can be reclaimed. In the absence of regulatory hormones, the distal tubule and collecting duct are relatively impermeable to both water and Na^+. The reabsorption of more water depends on the presence of antidiuretic hormone (ADH), which makes the collecting ducts more permeable to water. This mechanism is described shortly.

Table 26.1 Reabsorption Capabilities of Different Segments of the Renal Tubules and Collecting Tubules

Tubule segment	Substance reabsorbed	Mechanism
Proximal convoluted tubule	Sodium ions (Na^+)	Active transport via ATP-dependent carrier; sets up electrochemical gradient for passive solute diffusion and osmosis
	Virtually all nutrients (glucose, amino acids, vitamins)	Active transport; cotransport with Na^+
	Cations (K^+, Mg^{2+}, Ca^{2+}, and others)	Active transport; cotransport with Na^+
	Anions (Cl^-, HCO_3^-)	Passive transport; driven by electrochemical gradient
	Water	Osmosis; driven by solute reabsorption (obligatory)
	Urea and lipid-soluble solutes	Passive diffusion via solvent drag created by osmotic movement of water
	Small proteins	Pinocytosed by tubule cells and digested to amino acids within tubule cells
Loop of Henle		
Descending loop	Water	Osmosis
Ascending loop	Na^+ and Cl^-	Active transport of Cl^-, Na^+ (and K^+); believed to be a cotransport process
Distal convoluted tubule	Na^+	Active transport; requires aldosterone
	Anions	Diffusion; follow electrochemical gradient created by active reabsorption of Na^+
	Water	Osmosis; facultative water reabsorption; depends on ADH to increase porosity of tubule epithelium in the most distal portion
Collecting duct	Na^+, H^+, K^+, HCO_3^-, and Cl^-	Active transport of cations (typically H^+ or aldosterone-mediated Na^+ transport) creates the electrochemical gradient for passive transport of anions (HCO_3^-, Cl^-)
	Water	Osmosis; facultative water reabsorption; depends on ADH to increase porosity of tubule epithelium
	Urea	Diffusion in response to concentration gradient in the deep medulla region; most remains in medullary interstitial space

Reabsorption of the remaining Na^+ is "fine tuned" under the control of the hormone aldosterone. Several conditions—for example, decreased blood volume or blood pressure, low Na^+ concentration (hyponatremia) or increased K^+ concentration (hyperkalemia) in the extracellular fluid—cause the adrenal cortex to release aldosterone to the blood. Except for hyperkalemia, just about all of these conditions promote the renin-angiotensin mechanism, which, in turn, stimulates the release of aldosterone (see Figure 26.10). Aldosterone targets the principal cells of the DCT and collecting ducts (prodding them to open Na^+ channels and to synthesize more sodium transporters). As a result, very little Na^+ leaves the body in urine. In the absence of aldosterone, essentially no sodium is reabsorbed by these segments, resulting in catastrophic Na^+ losses that are incompatible with life.

A second effect of aldosterone is to increase water absorption because, as sodium is reabsorbed, water follows it back into the blood (if it can). Aldosterone also regulates (reduces) potassium ion concentrations in the blood because aldosterone-induced reabsorp-

tion of sodium is coupled to potassium ion secretion via the Na^+-K^+ pump in the principal cells.

In contrast to aldosterone, which acts to conserve Na^+, *atrial natriuretic factor (ANF),* a hormone released by the atrial cardiac cells when blood volume and/or blood pressure is elevated, inhibits Na^+ reabsorption. Consequently, ANF reduces water reabsorption and blood volume.

Tubular Secretion

The failure of tubule cells to reabsorb some or all of certain filtered solutes is an important means of clearing plasma of unwanted substances. A second such mechanism is **tubular secretion**—essentially, reabsorption in reverse. Substances such as hydrogen and potassium ions, creatinine, ammonium ion, and certain organic acids move from the blood of the peritubular capillaries through the tubule cells or from the tubule cells themselves into the filtrate. Thus, the urine that is eventually excreted is composed of *both filtered and secreted substances.* Some secretion occurs in the proximal tubule, but the cortical parts of the collecting ducts and the late regions of the distal tubules are also very active in secretion (see Figure 26.13, p. 915).

Tubular secretion is important for:

1. Disposing of substances not already in the filtrate, such as certain drugs (penicillin and phenobarbital, for example)

2. Eliminating undesirable substances that have been reabsorbed by passive processes, such as urea and uric acid

3. Ridding the body of excessive potassium ions

4. Controlling blood pH

Nearly all of the potassium ions in urine are derived from active tubular secretion into the collecting ducts under the influence of aldosterone because virtually all of the K^+ present in the filtrate is reabsorbed in the PCT and ascending loop of Henle. When blood pH begins to drop toward the acid end of its homeostatic range, the renal tubule cells actively secrete hydrogen ions into the filtrate and retain more bicarbonate and potassium ions. As a result, the blood pH rises and the urine drains off the excess acid. Conversely, when blood pH approaches the alkaline end of its range, Cl^- rather than HCO_3^- is reabsorbed and more bicarbonate is allowed to leave the body in urine. Renal mechanisms for controlling the acid-base balance of the blood are described in more detail in Chapter 27, pp. 944–946.

Regulation of Urine Concentration and Volume

Because we will make frequent use of the term *osmolarity* (oz"mo-lar′ĭ-te) in this discussion, it is important that this concept be clearly understood. A solution's **osmolarity** is the number of solute particles dissolved in one liter (1000 g) of water and is reflected in the solution's ability to cause osmosis. This capability, called *osmotic activity,* is determined only by the number of nonpenetrating solute particles and is independent of their type and nature. Ten sodium ions have the same osmotic activity as ten glucose molecules or ten amino acids in the same volume of solution. Since the *osmol* (equivalent to 1 mole of a nonionizing substance in 1 L of water) is a fairly large concentration unit, the **milliosmol** (mil″e-oz′mōl) **(mosm),** equal to 0.001 osmol, is used to describe the solute concentration of body fluids.

One of the crucial functions of the kidneys is to keep the solute load of body fluids constant at about 300 mosm by regulating urine concentration and volume. Just how the kidneys accomplish this feat is still a matter of controversy, but the most current hypothesis describes this aspect of renal function in terms of the **countercurrent mechanism.** The term *countercurrent* indicates that something is flowing in opposite directions through adjacent channels. In the kid-

neys the countercurrent mechanism involves the interaction between the flow of filtrate through the loop of Henle and the flow of blood through the limbs of its adjacent blood vessels, the vasa recta. This relationship establishes and maintains an osmotic gradient extending from the cortex through the depths of the medulla that allows the kidneys to vary urine concentration quite dramatically. Let's look at how this mechanism works.

The Countercurrent Mechanism and the Medullary Osmotic Gradient

The osmolarity of the filtrate entering the proximal convoluted tubule is identical to that of plasma, about 300 mosm. As described earlier, large amounts of water *and* salt are reabsorbed by the proximal tubule cells; and though the amount and flow of filtrate are reduced by about 65% by the time the loop of Henle is reached, the filtrate is still isosmotic.

The "stage is set" for conserving most of this remaining filtrate as the osmolarity of the interstitial fluid increases from the cortex to the depths of the medulla. The solute concentration increases from 300 mosm in the cortex to about 1200 mosm in the deepest part of the medulla (Figure 26.12). How can this tremendous concentration of the medullary fluids be explained? The answer lies in the unique workings of the loops of Henle of the juxtamedullary nephrons, which penetrate deep into the renal medulla, and their closely associated vasa recta. Notice that in each case the fluids involved—filtrate and blood respectively—first descend and then ascend through parallel limbs. First, we will follow filtrate processing through the loop of Henle, as portrayed in Figure 26.12a, to see how it functions as a **countercurrent multiplier** to establish the osmotic gradient.

1. **The descending limb of the loop of Henle is relatively impermeable to solutes and freely permeable to water.** Because the osmolarity of the medullary interstitial fluid gradually increases along the course of the descending limb (the mechanism of this increase is explained shortly), water passes out of the filtrate osmotically all along its course. Thus, the osmolarity of the filtrate (particularly as concerns its salt content) reaches its highest point (1200 mosm) at the "elbow" of the loop of Henle.

2. **The ascending limb of the loop of Henle is impermeable to water and actively transports sodium chloride into the surrounding interstitial fluid.** As the filtrate rounds the corner into the ascending limb, the tubule permeability changes, becoming impermeable to water and quite freely permeable to salt. The concentration of sodium and chloride ions in the filtrate entering the ascending limb is very high (and interstitial fluid concentrations are lower). The thick segment of the ascending limb, in particular, actively reabsorbs salt (NaCl) via its Na^+-K^+-$2Cl^-$ cotransporter, and as Na^+ and Cl^- are extruded from the fil-

?   *What portion of the nephron acts as the countercurrent multiplier? As the countercurrent exchanger?*

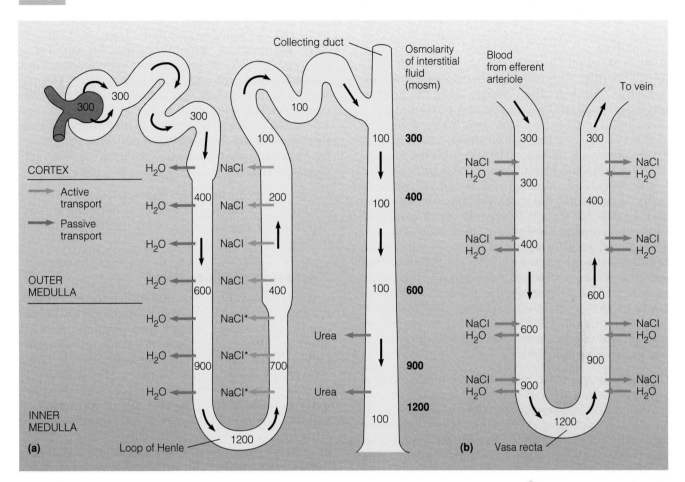

FIGURE 26.12
Hypothetical countercurrent mechanism for establishing and maintaining the medullary osmotic gradient. (a) Filtrate entering the descending limb of the loop of Henle is isosmotic (isotonic) to both blood plasma and the surrounding (cortical) interstitial fluid. As the filtrate flows from the cortex to the medulla in the descending limb, water leaves the tubule by osmosis and the relative solute content (osmolarity) of the filtrate increases from 300 to 1200 mosm. As the filtrate rounds the "bend" and flows into the ascending limb of the loop of Henle, the permeability of the tubule epithelium changes from water permeable, largely solute (salt) impermeable to the opposite condition, water impermeable, salt permeable. Consequently, salt leaves the ascending limb, diluting the filtrate as it approaches the cortex. Thus the different permeabilities of the two limbs of the loop of Henle cooperate to establish the osmotic gradient in the medullary interstitial fluid: The descending limb produces increasingly salty filtrate, while the ascending limb uses this high salt concentration to maintain the high osmolarity of the interstitial fluid in the medulla. Diffusion of urea from the lower portion of the collecting duct also contributes to the high osmolarity in the medulla. **(b)** Dissipation of the medullary osmotic gradient is prevented because the blood in the vasa recta continuously equilibrates with (becomes isosmotic to) the interstitial fluid—becoming more concentrated as it follows the descending limb of the loop of Henle and less concentrated as it approaches the cortical region. This occurs because of the high porosity and sluggish blood flow in these specialized vessels.
*The transport mechanism for NaCl in the thin segment of the loop, though shown as active transport here, is still undetermined.

trate into the medullary interstitial fluid, they contribute to the high osmolarity there. Although Na^+ and Cl^- are also reabsorbed from the filtrate in the thin portion of the ascending limb, the exact nature of that transport mechanism is still controversial.

Whatever the case, the movement of Na^+ and Cl^- out of the filtrate in the ascending limb establishes a strong osmotic gradient for water reabsorption. However, the ascending limb of the loop of Henle is nearly impermeable to water, which, therefore, remains in the filtrate. Because the filtrate loses salt but not water, it becomes increasingly dilute until it is hypo-osmotic, or hypotonic, to blood plasma and cortical fluids. As you can see in Figure 26.12, there is a rather constant difference in filtrate concentration between the two limbs of the loop of Henle. Because the ascending limb is relatively permeable to Na^+ and Cl^-, salt tends to diffuse back into the filtrate in that portion of the tubule, even as it is being actively reabsorbed. Consequently, the filtrate of the ascending limb always has a solute content that is about 200 mosm lower than that in the descending limb and that of the surrounding medullary interstitial fluid. However, because of countercurrent flow, the loop of Henle is able to "multiply" these small changes in solute concentration into a gradient change along the vertical length of the loop (both inside and outside) that is closer to 900 mosm. While the two limbs of the loop of Henle are not in direct contact, they are close enough to influence each other's exchanges with the interstitial fluid they both share. Hence, water diffusing out of the descending limb produces the increasingly "salty" filtrate that the ascending limb uses to raise the osmolarity of the medullary interstitial fluid. Furthermore, the more salt the ascending limb extrudes, the more water diffuses out of the descending limb and the saltier the filtrate in the descending limb becomes. Thus, a positive feedback mechanism is established that produces the high osmolarity of the fluids in the descending limb and the interstitial fluid. The energy that is used to establish the medullary gradient ultimately comes from active sodium transport in the ascending limb.

3. The collecting ducts in the deep medullary regions are permeable to urea. In a normally hydrated person, the dilute urine passes through the distal convoluted tubule and the superior portions of the collecting ducts without modification. The filtrate's content of urea remains high because the tubules in the cortex are impermeable to it. However, as urine passes through the deep medullary regions where the collecting ducts are highly permeable to urea, urea diffuses out of the ducts into the medullary interstitial fluid, where it contributes to the high osmolarity in that region. Urea continues to move passively until its concentrations inside and outside the duct are equal. Even though the ascending limb of the loop of Henle is poorly permeable to urea, when urea concentrations in the medullary interstitial space are very high, some urea does enter the limb. However, it simply gets recycled back to the collecting duct, where it diffuses out again.

4. The vasa recta acts as a countercurrent exchanger maintaining the osmotic gradient while delivering the nutrient blood supply to cells in the area. If ordinary capillaries paralleled the deep loops of Henle, the medullary gradient would quickly be destroyed, because as massive amounts of Na^+ were absorbed from the medulla, equally large amounts of water would be lost into the medullary interstitial fluid. By contrast, the vasa recta play an important role in maintaining the osmotic gradient established by the cycling of salt. Because these capillaries receive only about 10% of the renal blood supply, blood flow through the vasa recta is very sluggish. Moreover, the vasa recta are freely permeable to water and salt, and blood in the vasa recta makes passive exchanges with the surrounding interstitial fluid, achieving equilibrium all along its path. Consequently, as the blood flows into the medullary depths, it loses water and gains salt (becomes hypertonic). Then, as it emerges from the medulla into the cortex, the process is reversed. The blood picks up water and loses salt (see Figure 26.12b). Since blood leaving and then reentering the cortex via the vasa recta has the same solute concentration, the vasa recta acts as a *countercurrent exchanger.* It does not create the medullary gradient (that is set up by the loops of Henle), but it protects it by preventing rapid removal of salt from the medullary interstitial space.

Now that the basic mechanisms establishing the medullary gradient have been explained, we can explore how the kidneys excrete dilute and concentrated urine.

Formation of Dilute Urine

Because tubular filtrate is diluted as it travels through the ascending limb of the loop of Henle, all the kidney needs to do to secrete dilute (hypo-osmotic) urine is allow the filtrate to continue on its way into the renal pelvis. When antidiuretic hormone is not being released by the posterior pituitary, that is basically what happens. The collecting ducts remain essentially impermeable to water, and no further water reabsorption occurs. Moreover, sodium and selected other ions can be removed from the filtrate by active or passive mechanisms by distal and collecting tubule cells so that the urine becomes even more dilute. The osmolarity of urine can reach as low as 65 mosm, about one-fifth the concentration of glomerular filtrate or blood plasma.

Formation of Concentrated Urine

As its name reveals, **antidiuretic hormone (ADH)** inhibits *diuresis* (di"u-re'sis), or urine output. It accomplishes this by increasing the number of water-filled channels in the principal cells of the collecting ducts so that water passes easily into the interstitial space. As a result, the osmolarity of the filtrate becomes equal to that of the interstitial fluid. In the initial parts of the distal tubules in the cortex, the osmolarity of the filtrate is approximately 100 mosm, but as the filtrate flows through the collecting ducts and is subjected to the hyperosmolar conditions in the medulla, water rapidly leaves the filtrate (Figure 26.13e). Depending on the amount of ADH released (which is keyed to the level of body hydration), urine concentration may rise as high as 1200 mosm, the concentration of the interstitial fluid in the deepest part of the medulla. In the presence of such active ADH secretion, 99% of the water in filtrate is reabsorbed and returned to the blood, and only a very small amount of highly concentrated urine is excreted. The ability of our kidneys to produce such concentrated urine is critically tied to our ability to survive without water. Water reab-

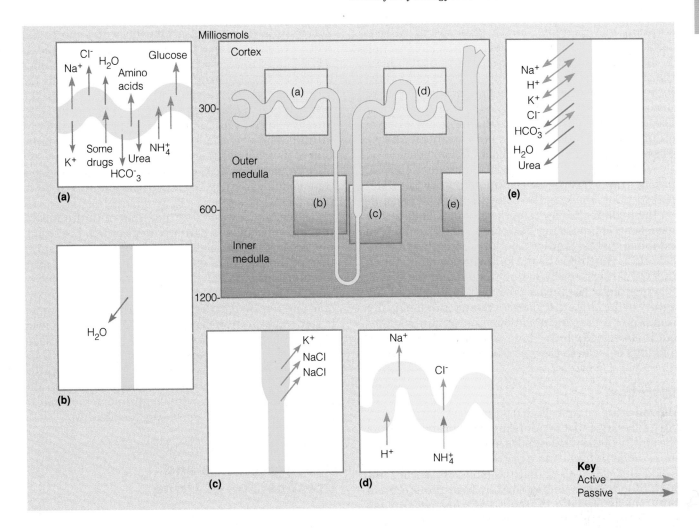

FIGURE 26.13

Summary of nephron functions. The glomerulus provides the filtrate that is processed by the renal tubule. The different regions of the renal tubule carry out reabsorption, secretion, and maintain a gradient of osmolarity within the medullary interstitial fluid. Varying osmolarity at different points in the tubule and interstitial fluid is symbolized in the figure by gradients of color. The inserts that accompany the central figure describe the main transport functions of the four regions of the nephron tubule and of the collecting duct. Blue arrows indicate passive transport processes, red arrows represent primary or secondary active transport. Blood vessels are not shown. **(a) Proximal tubule.** Filtrate that enters the proximal tubule from the glomerular capsule has about the same osmolarity as blood plasma. The main activity of the transport epithelium of the proximal tubule is reabsorption of certain solutes from the filtrate back into the blood. Nearly all nutrients, such as glucose and amino acids, and about 65% of Na^+ are actively transported out of the tubule and enter the peritubular capillaries; Cl^- and water follow passively. The proximal tubule cells also secrete specific substances, such as the ammonium ion and other nitrogenous wastes, into the filtrate and help maintain a constant pH in blood and interstitial fluid by the controlled secretion of H^+ and reabsorption of HCO_3^-. By the end of the proximal tubule, the filtrate volume has been reduced by 65%. **(b) Descending limb.** The descending limb of the loop of Henle is freely permeable to water, but not to salt. As filtrate in the limb descends into the medulla, it loses water by osmosis to the interstitial fluid, which is increasingly hypertonic in that direction. Consequently, salt and other solutes become more concentrated in the filtrate. **(c) Ascending limb.** The filtrate enters the ascending limb of the loop of Henle, which is impermeable to water but is permeable to Na^+ and Cl^-. These ions, which have become concentrated within the descending limb, are actively pumped out of the ascending limb and contribute to the high osmolarity of interstitial fluid in the inner medulla. K^+ is cotransported with Na^+ and Cl^-. Because the tubule epithelium here is not permeable to water, the filtrate becomes more and more dilute as the exodus of salt from the filtrate continues. **(d) Distal tubule.** The distal tubule, like the proximal tubule, is specialized for selective secretion and reabsorption. NH_4^+ and H^+ are secreted, HCO_3^- is absorbed, and, in the presence of aldosterone, more Na^+ is reabsorbed. The water permeability of the distal tubule is extremely low and almost no further H_2O absorption occurs there. **(e) Collecting duct.** The urine, normally quite dilute at this point, begins its journey via the collecting duct back into the medulla, with its increasing osmolarity gradient. In the cortical collecting duct, K^+, H^+, and/or HCO_3^- ions may be reabsorbed or secreted depending on what is required to maintain blood pH homeostasis. The wall of the medullary region of the collecting duct is permeable to urea, and a certain amount of this nitrogenous waste diffuses out of the duct and contributes to the high osmolarity of the inner medulla. In the absence of antidiuretic hormone, the collecting tubules are nearly impermeable to water, and the dilute urine passes out of the kidney. In the presence of ADH, the pores of the collecting tubule enlarge, and the filtrate loses water by osmosis as it passes through medullary regions of increasing osmolarity. Consequently, water is conserved, and concentrated urine is excreted.

sorption that depends on the presence of ADH is called **facultative water reabsorption.**

ADH is released more or less continuously unless the solute concentration of the blood drops too low. Its release is enhanced by any event that increases plasma osmolarity to above 300 mosm/L, such as excessive water loss through sweating or diarrhea, or reduced blood volume or blood pressure (hemorrhage). These mechanisms are considered in Chapter 27.

Although ADH is the "signal" to produce concentrated urine that opens the door (pores) for water reabsorption, the kidneys' ability to respond depends on the high medullary osmotic gradient. Thus far we have been emphasizing the role of salt movements in establishing that gradient, but urea also plays a critical role as illustrated by the following example. When individuals are sorely malnourished and the diet is low in protein, less urea is produced. In such cases, the ability of the kidneys to conserve water is dramatically impaired because the medullary concentration gradient is abnormally low. These people must drink large amounts of water to prevent debilitating dehydration.

Diuretics

Diuretics are chemicals that enhance urinary output. Any substance that is not reabsorbed or that exceeds the ability of the renal tubules to reabsorb it will act as an *osmotic diuretic* and carry water out with it. High blood glucose levels of diabetes mellitus patients and high blood urea levels created by high-protein diets both act as osmotic diuretics. Alcohol encourages diuresis by inhibiting release of ADH. Caffeine (found in coffee, tea, and colas) increases diuresis by promoting renal vasodilation and increasing the GFR. Diuretic drugs commonly prescribed for hypertension or the edema of congestive heart failure increase urine flow by inhibiting sodium ion reabsorption and, thereby, the obligatory water reabsorption that normally follows.

Renal Clearance

The term **renal clearance** refers to the volume of plasma from which a particular substance is completely cleared by the kidneys in a given time, usually 1 minute. Renal clearance tests are used to determine the GFR, which provides information about the amount of functioning renal tissue. Renal clearance tests are also used to detect glomerular damage and to follow the progress of diagnosed renal disease.

The renal clearance rate (RC) of any substance, in ml/min, is calculated from the equation:

$$RC = UV/P$$

where: U is the concentration (mg/ml) of the substance in urine,

V is the flow rate of urine formation (ml/min), and

P is the concentration of the same substance in plasma

Inulin (in'u-lin), a polysaccharide with a molecular weight of approximately 5000, is frequently used as the standard to determine the GFR by renal clearance because it is not reabsorbed, stored, or secreted by the kidneys. Because infused inulin is eliminated in the urine, its renal clearance value is equal to the GFR. Measured values for inulin are $U = 125$ mg/ml, $V = 1$ ml/min, and $P = 1$ mg/ml. Therefore, the computation of its renal clearance is RC = $(125 \times 1)/1 = 125$ ml/min, meaning that, in 1 minute, the kidneys have removed (cleared) all the inulin present in 125 ml of plasma.

A clearance value less than that of inulin means that the substance is partially reabsorbed. For example, urea has a clearance value of 70 ml/min, meaning that, of the 125 ml of glomerular filtrate formed each minute, approximately 70 ml is completely cleared of urea, while the urea in the remaining 55 ml is recovered and returned to the plasma. If the renal clearance is zero, reabsorption is complete. Glucose has a clearance value of zero in healthy individuals, and HCO_3^-, Na^+, Cl^-, and Ca^{2+} are all close to 0 (less than 2 ml/min). If clearance is greater than that of inulin, the tubule cells are secreting the substance into the filtrate. This is the case with creatinine, which has an RC of 140 ml/min, and most drug metabolites.

Characteristics and Composition of Urine

Physical Characteristics

Color and Transparency. Freshly voided urine is generally clear and pale to deep yellow in color. The yellow color is due to the presence of **urochrome** (u'ro-krōm), a pigment that results from the body's destruction of hemoglobin (via bilirubin or bile pigments). The more concentrated the urine, the deeper the yellow color. An abnormal color such as pink or brown, or a smoky tinge, may result from certain foods (beets, rhubarb) or may reflect the presence of bile pigments or blood in the urine. Additionally, some commonly prescribed drugs and vitamin supplements alter the color of urine. Cloudy urine may indicate an infection in some part of the urinary tract.

Odor. Fresh urine is slightly aromatic. But, if it is allowed to stand, it develops an ammonia odor due to bacterial metabolism of its urea solutes. Some drugs and vegetables (asparagus) alter the usual odor of urine, as do some diseases. For example, in diabetes mellitus the urine smells fruity because of its acetone content.

pH. Urine is usually slightly acidic (around pH 6), but changes in body metabolism or diet may cause it to vary from about 4.5 to 8.0. An *acid-ash* diet that contains large amounts of protein and whole wheat

Table 26.2 Abnormal Urinary Constituents

Substance	Name of condition	Possible causes
Glucose	Glycosuria	Nonpathological: excessive intake of sugary foods Pathological: diabetes mellitus
Proteins	Proteinuria, or albuminuria	Nonpathological: excessive physical exertion; pregnancy; high-protein diet Pathological (over 250 mg/day): heart failure, severe hypertension; glomerulonephritis; often initial sign of asymptomatic renal disease
Ketone bodies	Ketonuria	Excessive formation and accumulation of ketone bodies, as in starvation and untreated diabetes mellitus
Hemoglobin	Hemoglobinuria	Various: transfusion reaction, hemolytic anemia, severe burns, etc.
Bile pigments	Bilirubinuria	Liver disease (hepatitis, cirrhosis) or obstruction of bile ducts from liver or gallbladder
Erythrocytes	Hematuria	Bleeding in urinary tract (due to trauma, kidney stones, infection, or neoplasm)
Leukocytes (pus)	Pyuria	Urinary tract infection

products produces acidic urine. A vegetarian *(alkaline-ash)* diet, prolonged vomiting, and bacterial infection of the urinary tract all cause the urine to become alkaline.

Specific Gravity. Because urine is water plus solutes, it weighs more (is more dense) than distilled water. The term used to compare the weight of a substance to the weight of an equal volume of distilled water is **specific gravity.** The specific gravity of distilled water is 1.0. The specific gravity of urine can range from 1.001 to 1.035, depending on its solute concentration. When urine is extremely concentrated, solutes begin to precipitate out of solution.

Chemical Composition

Water accounts for about 95% of urine volume; the remaining 5% consists of solutes. The largest component of urine by weight, apart from water, is *urea,* which is derived from the breakdown of amino acids. Other **nitrogenous wastes** found in urine include *uric acid* (a metabolite of nucleic acid metabolism) and *creatinine* (an end product of creatine phosphate, found in large amounts in skeletal muscle tissue). Normal solute constituents of urine, in order of decreasing concentration, include urea, sodium, potassium, phosphate, and sulfate ions, creatinine, and uric acid. Much smaller but highly variable amounts of calcium, magnesium, and bicarbonate ions are also found in urine. Abnormally high concentrations of any of these urinary constituents may indicate pathology. (Normal urine values are listed in Appendix G.)

With certain diseases urine composition changes dramatically and may include, for example, glucose, blood proteins, red blood cells, hemoglobin, white blood cells (pus), or bile pigments. The presence of such abnormal substances in urine is an important warning of illness and may be helpful in diagnosis (Table 26.2).

URETERS

The **ureters** are slender tubes that convey urine from the kidneys to the bladder (see Figure 26.1). Each ureter begins at the level of L_2 as a continuation of the renal pelvis. From there it descends behind the peritoneum to the base of the bladder, turns medially and runs obliquely through the posterior bladder wall. This arrangement prevents backflow of urine into the ureters during bladder filling because any increase in pressure within the bladder compresses and closes the distal ends of the ureters.

Histologically, the ureter wall is trilayered. The transitional epithelium of its lining *mucosa* is continuous with that of the kidney pelvis superiorly and the bladder medially. Its middle *muscularis* is composed chiefly of two smooth muscle sheets: the inner longitudinal and the outer circular. The *adventitia* covering its external surface is typical fibrous connective tissue (Figure 26.14).

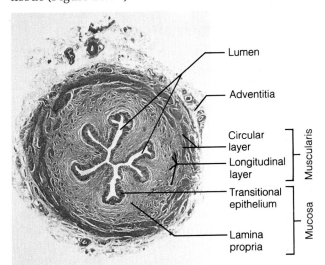

FIGURE 26.14
Structure of the ureter wall (cross-sectional view, 10×).
The muscularis of the ureter contains two smooth muscle layers: an outer, circular layer and an inner, longitudinal layer. Its lumen is lined by a mucosa containing transitional epithelium. The external surface of the ureter is covered by a loose, connective tissue adventitia.

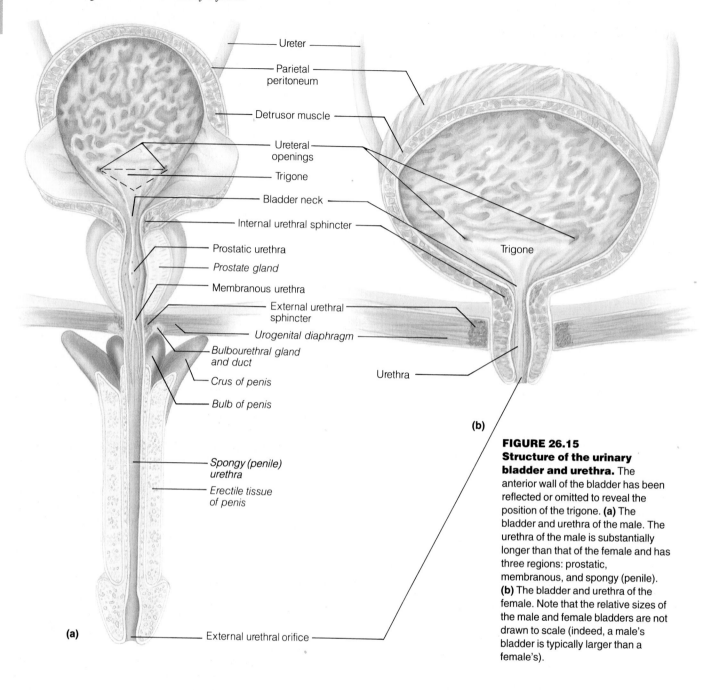

(a)

(b)

FIGURE 26.15
Structure of the urinary bladder and urethra. The anterior wall of the bladder has been reflected or omitted to reveal the position of the trigone. **(a)** The bladder and urethra of the male. The urethra of the male is substantially longer than that of the female and has three regions: prostatic, membranous, and spongy (penile). **(b)** The bladder and urethra of the female. Note that the relative sizes of the male and female bladders are not drawn to scale (indeed, a male's bladder is typically larger than a female's).

The ureters play an active role in transporting urine. Distension of the ureter by incoming urine stimulates its muscularis to contract, which propels urine into the bladder. The vigor and frequency of the peristaltic waves are adjusted to the rate of urine formation. Although the ureters are innervated by both sympathetic and parasympathetic fibers, neural control of their peristalsis appears to be insignificant compared to the local response of ureteral smooth muscle to stretch.

On occasion, calcium, magnesium, or uric acid salts in urine may crystallize and precipitate in the renal pelvis, forming **renal calculi** (kal'ku-li; *calculus* = little stone), or kidney stones. Most calculi are under 5 mm in diameter and can pass through the urinary tract without causing problems. However,

larger calculi can obstruct a ureter and block urine drainage. Increasing pressure within the kidney causes excruciating pain, which radiates to the posterior abdominal wall on the same side. Pain also occurs when the contracting ureter walls close in on the sharp calculi as they are being eased through the ureter by peristalsis.

Predisposing conditions are frequent bacterial infections of the urinary tract, urinary retention, and alkaline urine. Surgery has been the treatment of choice but *lithotripsy,* a newer, noninvasive procedure that uses ultrasound waves to shatter the calculi, is becoming more popular. The pulverized, sandlike remnants of the calculi are then painlessly eliminated in the urine. •

URINARY BLADDER

The **urinary bladder** is a smooth, collapsible, muscular sac that stores urine temporarily. It is located retroperitoneally on the pelvic floor just posterior to the pubic symphysis. In males, the bladder lies immediately anterior to the rectum. The prostate gland (part of the male reproductive system) surrounds its neck inferiorly where it empties into the urethra. In females, the bladder is anterior to the vagina and uterus.

The interior of the bladder has openings for both ureters and the urethra (Figure 26.15). The smooth, triangular region of the bladder base outlined by these three openings is the **trigone** (tri'gōn; *trigon* = triangle). The trigone is important clinically because infections tend to persist in this region.

The bladder wall has three layers: a mucosa containing transitional epithelium, a thick muscular layer, and a fibrous adventitia (except on its superior surface, where it is covered by the parietal peritoneum). The muscular layer, called the **detrusor** (de-tru'sor; "to thrust out") **muscle,** consists of intermingled smooth muscle fibers arranged in inner and outer longitudinal layers and a middle circular layer.

The bladder is very distensible and uniquely suited for its function of urine storage. When it contains little or no urine, the bladder collapses into its basic pyramidal shape. Its walls are thick and thrown into folds *(rugae).* But as urine accumulates, the bladder expands and becomes pear-shaped as it rises superiorly in the abdominal cavity (Figure 26.16). The muscular wall stretches and thins, and the rugae disappear. These changes allow the bladder to store larger amounts of urine without a significant rise in internal pressure (at least until 300 ml has accumulated). A moderately full bladder is about 12.5 cm (5 inches) long and holds approximately 500 ml (1 pint) of urine. However, the bladder can hold more than double that amount if necessary. When it is tense with urine, it can be palpated well above the pubic symphysis; when it is overdistended, it may burst. Although urine is formed continuously by the kidneys, it is usually stored in the bladder until its release is convenient.

URETHRA

The **urethra** is a thin-walled muscular tube that drains urine from the bladder and conveys it out of the body. The epithelium of its mucosal lining is mostly pseudostratified columnar epithelium. However, near the bladder it becomes transitional epithelium, and near its external opening it changes to a protective stratified squamous epithelium.

At the bladder-urethra junction a thickening of the detrusor smooth muscle forms the **internal urethral sphincter.** This involuntary sphincter keeps the urethra closed when urine is not being passed and prevents leaking of urine between voidings. A second

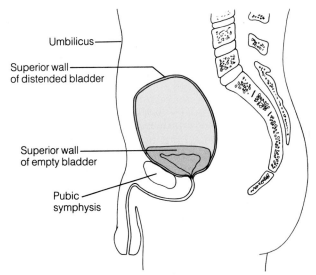

FIGURE 26.16
Relative positioning and shape of a distended and an empty urinary bladder in an adult male.

Umbilicus

Superior wall of distended bladder

Superior wall of empty bladder

Pubic symphysis

sphincter, the **external urethral sphincter (sphincter urethrae),** surrounds the urethra as it passes through the pelvic floor. This sphincter is formed of skeletal muscle and is voluntarily controlled. The *levator ani* muscle of the pelvic floor also serves as a voluntary constrictor of the urethra (see Table 10.7, p. 310).

The length and functions of the urethra differ in the two sexes (see Figure 26.15). In females the urethra is 3–4 cm (1.5 inches) long and is tightly bound to the anterior vaginal wall by fibrous connective tissue. Its external opening, the **external urethral orifice (meatus),** lies anterior to the vaginal opening and posterior to the clitoris (see Figure 28.16, p. 975).

Because the female's urethra is very short and its external orifice is close to the anal opening, improper toilet habits (wiping back to front after defecation) can easily carry fecal bacteria into the urethra. The mucosa of the urethra is continuous with that of the rest of the urinary tract, and an inflammation of the urethra *(urethritis)* can ascend the tract to cause bladder inflammation *(cystitis)* or even renal inflammations (*pyelitis* or *pyelonephritis*). Symptoms of urinary tract infection include *dysuria* (painful urination), urinary *urgency* and *frequency,* fever, and sometimes cloudy or blood-tinged urine. When the kidneys are involved, back pain and a severe headache often occur as well. •

In males the urethra is approximately 20 cm (8 inches) long and has three named regions. The **prostatic urethra,** about 2.5 cm (1 inch) long, runs within the prostate gland. The **membranous urethra,** which runs through the *urogenital diaphragm,* extends for about 2 cm from the prostate gland to the beginning of the penis. The **spongy,** or **penile, urethra,** about 15 cm long, passes through the penis and opens at its tip via the **external urethral orifice.** The male urethra has a double function: It carries semen as well as urine out of the body. The reproductive function of the male urethra is discussed in Chapter 28.

MICTURITION

Micturition (mik″tu-rish′un; *mictur* = urinate), also called **voiding** or **urination,** is the act of emptying the bladder. Ordinarily, when about 200 ml of urine has accumulated, distension of the bladder walls activates stretch receptors, triggering a visceral reflex arc. Afferent (sensory) impulses are transmitted to the sacral region of the spinal cord, and efferent impulses return to the bladder via the parasympathetic **pelvic splanchnic nerves,** causing the detrusor muscle to contract and the internal sphincter to relax (Figure 26.17). As the contractions increase in intensity, they force stored urine through the internal sphincter into the upper part of the urethra. Afferent impulses are also transmitted to the brain, so one feels the urge to void at this point. Because the external sphincter (and the levator ani) is voluntarily controlled, we can choose to keep it closed and postpone bladder emptying temporarily. On the other hand, if the time is convenient, the voluntary sphincter can be relaxed, allowing urine to be expelled from the bladder.

When one chooses not to void, reflex bladder contractions subside within a minute or so and urine continues to accumulate. After 200–300 ml more has collected, the micturition reflex occurs again and, if urination is delayed again, is damped once more. The urge to void eventually becomes irresistible and micturition occurs, whether one wills it or not.

FIGURE 26.17
Micturition reflex arc pathway. Stretching of the bladder wall by urine causes afferent impulses to be transmitted to the sacral region of the spinal cord. Efferent impulses are delivered to the bladder detrusor muscle and the internal sphincter via parasympathetic fibers of the pelvic nerves. The pelvic splanchnic nerve serves the skeletal muscle fibers of the voluntary external sphincter (largely in the pelvic diaphragm). The role of sympathetic efferents is controversial. (Afferent [sensory] fibers are blue; efferent [motor] fibers are red.)

Incontinence, the inability to control micturition voluntarily, is normal in infants. Reflex voiding occurs each time a baby's bladder fills enough to activate the stretch receptors, but the internal sphincter prevents dribbling of urine between voidings just as it does in adults. After the toddler years (and toilet training), incontinence is usually a result of emotional problems, physical pressure during pregnancy, or nervous system problems (stroke or spinal cord lesions). In *stress incontinence,* a sudden increase in intra-abdominal pressure (as during laughing and coughing) forces urine through the external sphincter. This condition is a common consequence of pregnancy when the uncommonly "heavy" uterus stretches the muscles of the pelvic floor and the urogenital diaphragm that support the external sphincter.

In **urinary retention,** the bladder is unable to expel its contained urine. Urinary retention is common after general anesthesia has been given (it seems that it takes a little time for the detrusor muscle to regain its activity). Urinary retention in men often reflects hypertrophy of the prostate gland, which narrows the urethra, making it difficult to void. When urinary retention is prolonged, a slender rubber drainage tube called a **catheter** (kath′ĕ-ter) must be inserted through the urethra to drain the urine and prevent bladder trauma from excessive stretching. •

DEVELOPMENTAL ASPECTS OF THE URINARY SYSTEM

As the kidneys develop in a young embryo, it almost seems as if they are unable to "make up their mind" how to go about it. As illustrated in Figure 26.18, three different sets of kidneys develop from the *urogenital ridges,* paired elevations of the intermediate mesoderm that give rise to both the urinary and reproductive organs. Only the last set persists to become the adult kidneys. During the fourth week of development, the first tubule system, the **pronephros** (pro-nef′ros; "prekidney"), forms and then begins to degenerate as a second, lower set appears. Although the pronephros is never functional and is entirely gone by the sixth week, the **pronephric duct** that connects it to the cloaca persists and is used by the later-developing kidneys. (The cloaca is the terminal part of the gut that opens to the body exterior.) As the second renal system, the **mesonephros** (mez″o-nef′ros; "middle kidney"), claims the pronephric duct, it comes to be called the **mesonephric duct.** The mesonephric kidneys, in turn, degenerate once the third set, the **metanephros** (met″ah-nef′ros; "after kidney"), makes its appearance.

The metanephros starts to develop at about five weeks as hollow **ureteric buds** that push superiorly from the mesonephric duct. The distal ends of the ureteric buds form the renal pelves and collecting tubules; their unexpanded proximal parts, now called the **metanephric ducts,** become the ureters. Nephrons

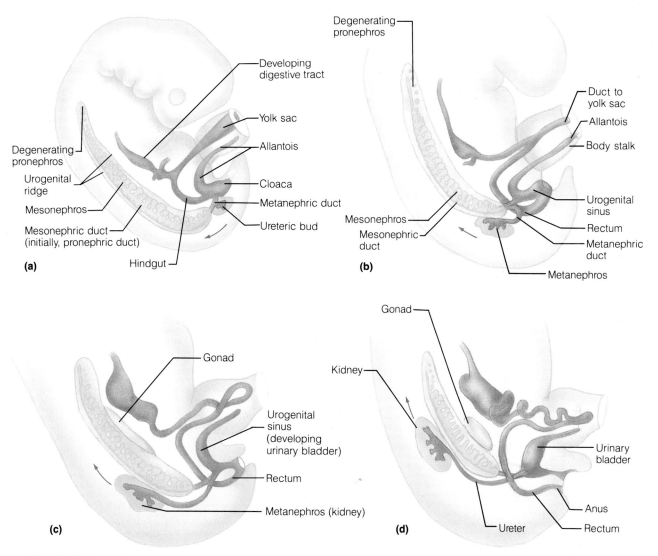

FIGURE 26.18
Development of the urinary system in the embryo. (a) Fifth week. **(b)** Sixth week.
(c) Seventh week. **(d)** Eighth week. (Direction of metanephros migration as it develops is indicated by red arrows.)

develop from a mass of intermediate mesoderm that clusters around the top of each ureteric bud. Because the kidneys develop in the pelvis and then ascend to their final position in the abdomen, they receive their blood supply from successively higher sources. Although the lower blood vessels usually degenerate as the upper ones appear, they sometimes persist and multiple renal arteries are common. The metanephric kidneys are excreting urine by the third month of fetal life, and most of the amniotic fluid that surrounds a developing fetus is actually fetal urine. Nonetheless, the fetal kidneys do not work nearly as hard as they will after birth because exchange through the placenta allows the mother's urinary system to clear most of the undesirable substances from the fetal blood.

As the metanephros is developing, the cloacal chamber subdivides to form the **urogenital sinus,** into which the urinary and genital ducts empty, and the future rectum and anal canal. The urinary bladder

and the urethra then develop from the urogenital sinus.

There are many congenital abnormalities of the urinary system, but three of the most common are horseshoe kidney, hypospadias, and polycystic kidney.

When ascending from the pelvis the kidneys are very close together, and in 1 out of 600 people, they become fused across the midline, forming a single, U-shaped *horseshoe kidney.* This condition is usually asymptomatic, but it may be associated with kidney abnormalities, such as obstructed drainage, which place a person at risk for frequent kidney infections.

Hypospadias (hi"po-spa′de-as), found in male infants only, is the most common congenital abnormality of the urethra. It occurs when the urethral orifice is located on the ventral surface of the penis. This problem is corrected surgically when the child is around 12 months old.

Congenital polycystic kidney is an inherited condition in which the baby's kidneys have many urine-

Although renal failure is not common, it occurs when functioning nephrons become too few to carry out normal kidney functions. Possible causes of renal failure are:

1. Repeated damaging infections of the kidneys.
2. Physical injury to the kidneys or major physical trauma (crushing injury) to other parts of the body.
3. Prolonged pressure on skeletal muscles (causes release of myoglobin, which can clog the renal tubules).
4. Chemical poisoning of the tubule cells by heavy metals (mercury or lead) or organic solvents (dry-cleaning fluid, paint thinner, acetone, and others).
5. Inadequate blood delivery to the tubule cells (as may happen with arteriosclerosis).

In renal failure, filtrate formation decreases or stops completely. Nitrogenous wastes accumulate quickly in the blood when the tubule cells are not working, a condition called *azotemia* (az″o-te′me-ah), and blood pH tumbles to the acidic range. *Uremia* (u-re′me-ah), the bodywide (or systemic) response to azotemia, and electrolyte imbalance set in shortly and totally disrupt life processes. Signs and symptoms of uncontrolled uremia include diarrhea, vomiting, edema (due to Na^+ retention), labored breathing, cardiac irregularities (due to excess K^+), convulsions, coma, and death.

To prevent these consequences of azotemia, the blood must be cleansed of metabolic wastes and its ionic composition must be adjusted to a normal level by *dialysis* (*dialys* = separate) while the kidneys are shut down. In *hemodialysis,* which uses an "artificial kidney" apparatus, the patient's blood is passed through a membrane tubing (see the diagram) that is permeable only to selected substances, and the tubing is immersed in a bathing solution that differs slightly from normal cleansed plasma. As blood circulates through the tubing, substances such as nitrogenous wastes and K^+ present in the blood (but not in the bath) diffuse out of the blood into the surrounding solution and substances

Apparatus for renal dialysis.

Labels: Blood pump; Arterial blood line (to apparatus); Dialyzing (bathing) solution; Cellophane membrane (tubing containing blood); Bubble trap; Venous blood line (from apparatus); Compressed air; Fresh dialyzing solution; Constant-temperature bath; Used dialyzing solution

to be added to the blood, mainly buffers for H^+ (and glucose for malnourished patients), move from the bathing solution into the blood. In this way, needed substances are retained in the blood or added to it, while wastes and ion excesses are removed. Hemodialysis is routinely done three times weekly and each session takes 4 to 8 hours. Serious problems occasionally encountered by hemodialysis patients are thrombosis, infection, and/or ischemia in the extremity containing the A-V shunt. Additionally, because the patient's blood must be heparinized to prevent clotting as it travels through the artificial kidney, there is some risk of hemorrhage.

A less efficient but more convenient procedure for patients is *continuous ambulatory peritoneal dialysis (CAPD).* CAPD uses the patient's own peritoneal membrane as the dialyzing membrane. Isosmotic fluid that is also equal in chemical content to normal plasma and interstitial fluid is introduced into the patient's peritoneal cavity with a catheter and left to equilibrate there for 15 to 60 minutes. Then the dialysate is retrieved from the peri-

toneal cavity and replaced with fresh dialysis fluid. The procedure is repeated until the patient's blood chemistry reaches normal. Because some ambulatory patients may be inattentive to cloudy or bloody dialysis fluid, infection is more common in CAPD than in hemodialysis.

When renal damage is irreversible the kidneys become totally incapable of processing plasma or concentrating urine, and a kidney transplant is the only answer. Unhappily, the signs and symptoms of this life-threatening kidney problem become obvious only after about 75% of renal function has been lost. (This large margin of safety reflects the fact that individual nephrons hypertrophy and begin to function even more effectively as others are progressively lost.) At this point, the signs of *renal insufficiency* become obvious. Glomerular filtration declines. Azotemia occurs as the kidneys lose their ability to form both concentrated and dilute urine, and the urine becomes isotonic with blood plasma. The end stage of renal failure, uremia, occurs when about 90% of the nephrons have been lost.

filled cysts (sacs). It appears to result from abnormal development of the collecting ducts such that they obstruct urine drainage from some of the nephrons, forcing urine to accumulate within the cysts in the kidney. This disease almost invariably causes renal failure during childhood, but kidney transplants have improved chances of survival for some of these children.

Adult polycystic kidney disease, another inherited condition, is distinct from congenital polycystic kidney. The cysts, which represent dilations along the nephrons, develop so gradually that they produce no symptoms until about 40 years of age. Then, both kidneys begin to enlarge as blisterlike cysts containing blood, mucus, or urine accumulate. The damage caused by these cysts progresses slowly, and many victims live without problems until their 60s. Ultimately, however, the kidneys become "knobby" and grossly enlarged, reaching weights of up to 14 kg (30 pounds) each. Most victims die from kidney failure or hypertension. Adult polycystic disease is relatively common, affecting 1 in 500 people. •

Because an infant's bladder is very small and the kidneys are unable to concentrate urine for the first two months, a newborn baby voids 5 to 40 times daily, depending on fluid intake. By 2 months of age, the infant is voiding approximately 400 ml/day, and the amount steadily increases until about adolescence, when adult urine output (about 1500 ml/day) is achieved.

Control of the voluntary urethral sphincter goes hand in hand with nervous system development. By 15 months, most toddlers are aware when they have voided. By 18 months, they can usually hold urine in the bladder for about two hours. This is the first sign that toilet training for micturition can begin. Daytime control usually occurs well before nighttime control is achieved. As a rule, it is unrealistic to expect that complete nighttime control will occur before the child is 4 years old.

From childhood through late middle age, most urinary system problems are infectious conditions. *Escherichia coli* (esh″ĕ-rik′e-ah ko′li) are normal residents of the digestive tract and generally cause no problems there, but these bacteria account for 80% of all urinary tract infections. *Sexually transmitted diseases,* which are chiefly reproductive tract infections (discussed in Chapter 28), may also cause inflammation of the urinary tract, leading to the clogging of some of its ducts. Childhood streptococcal infections such as strep throat and scarlet fever, if not treated promptly, may cause long-term inflammatory damage to the kidneys.

Only about 3% of the aged have histologically normal kidneys, and kidney function declines with age. The kidneys atrophy, the nephrons decrease in size and number, and the tubule cells become less efficient. By age 70, the GFR is only half that of middle-aged adults. This slowing is believed to result from impaired renal circulation due to atherosclerosis. Diabetics are particularly at risk for renal disease, and over 50% of those who have had diabetes mellitus for 20 years (regardless of age) are in renal failure owing to the vascular ravages of this disease.

The bladder of an aged person is shrunken, with less than half the capacity of a young adult (250 ml versus 600 ml). Loss of bladder tone causes an annoying frequency. *Nocturia* (nok-tu′re-ah), the need to get up during the night to urinate, plagues almost two-thirds of this population. Many people eventually experience incontinence, and with it a tremendous blow to their self-esteem.

*   *   *

The ureters, urinary bladder, and urethra have important roles to play in transporting, storing, and eliminating urine from the body. But, when the term "urinary system" is used, it is the kidneys, which produce the urine, that capture center stage. As summarized in *Making Connections* in Chapter 27 (p. 948), the other organ systems of the body contribute to the well-being of the urinary system in many ways. But without continuous kidney function, internal body fluids quickly become contaminated with nitrogenous wastes, and the electrolyte and fluid balance of the blood is dangerously disturbed. No body cell can escape the harmful effects of such imbalances.

Now that renal mechanisms have been described, we are ready to integrate kidney function into the larger topic of fluid and electrolyte balance of the body as a whole—the focus of Chapter 27.

RELATED CLINICAL TERMS

Acute glomerulonephritis (glo-mer″u-lo-nef-ri′tis) **(GN)** Inflammation of the glomeruli, often arising from an immune response. In some cases, circulating immune complexes (antibodies bound to foreign substances, such as streptococcal bacteria) become trapped in the glomerular basement membranes. In other cases, immune responses are mounted against one's own kidney tissue, leading to glomerular damage. In either case, the inflammatory response that follows damages the filtration membrane, increasing its permeability. Blood proteins and even blood cells begin to pass into the renal tubules and are lost in urine. As the osmotic pressure of blood drops, fluid seeps from the bloodstream into the tissue spaces, causing bodywide edema. Renal shutdown requiring dialysis (see *A Closer Look* on page 922) may occur temporarily, but normal renal function usually returns within a few months. If permanent glomerular damage occurs, chronic GN and, ultimately, renal failure result.

Bladder cancer Bladder cancer accounts for about 3% of all cancer deaths. It usually involves neoplasms of the bladder's lining epithelium and may be induced by carcinogens from the environment or the work place that end up in urine. Smoking and artificial sweeteners also have been linked to bladder cancer. Blood in the urine is a common warning sign.

Cystocele (sis′to-sēl; *cyst* = a sac, the bladder; *cele* = hernia, rupture) Herniation of the urinary bladder into the vagina; a common result of tearing of the muscles of the pelvic floor during childbirth.

Cystoscopy (si-tos′ko-pe; *cyst* = bladder; *scopy* = observation) Procedure in which a thin viewing tube is threaded into the bladder through the urethra. Used to examine the bladder's mucosal surface.

Diabetes insipidus (in-si′pi-dus; *insipid* = tasteless, bland) Condition in which large amounts (up to 40 L/day) of dilute urine flush from the body. Results from little or no ADH release due to injury to, or a tumor in, the hypothalamus or posterior pituitary. Can lead to severe dehydration and electrolyte imbalances unless the individual drinks large volumes of liquids to maintain normal fluid balance.

Intravenous pyelogram (IVP) (pi′ĕ-lo-gram; *pyelo* = kidney pelvis; *gram* = written) An X-ray of the kidney and ureter obtained after intravenous injection of a contrast medium. Allows assessment of renal blood vessels for obstructions, viewing of renal anatomy (pelvis and calyces), and determination of rate of excretion of the contrast medium.

Nephrotoxin A substance (heavy metal, organic solvent, or bacterial toxin) that is toxic to the kidney.

Nocturnal enuresis (en″u-re′sis) An inability to control urination at night during sleep; bedwetting. Occurs most often in children who are sound sleepers and in those with a small bladder capacity (children and the aged), but may be due to emotional rather than physical causes.

Renal infarct Area of dead, or necrotic, renal tissue. May result from inflammation, hydronephrosis, or blockage of the vascular supply to the kidney. A common cause of localized renal infarct is obstruction of an interlobar artery. Because interlobar arteries are end arteries (do not anastomose), their obstruction leads to ischemic necrosis of the portions of the kidney they supply.

Urinalysis Analysis of urine as an aid to diagnosing health or disease. The most significant indicators of disease in urine are proteins, glucose, acetone, blood, and pus.

Urologist (u-rol′o-jist) Physician who specializes in diseases of urinary structures in both sexes and in diseases of the reproductive tract of males.

CHAPTER SUMMARY

Kidney Anatomy (pp. 897–903)

Location and External Anatomy (p. 897)

1. The paired kidneys are retroperitoneal in the superior lumbar region.

2. A renal capsule, an adipose capsule, and renal fascia surround each kidney. The fatty adipose capsule helps hold the kidneys in position.

Internal Anatomy (p. 898)

3. A kidney has a superficial cortex, a deeper medulla consisting mainly of medullary pyramids, and a medial pelvis. Extensions of the pelvis (calyces) surround and collect urine draining from the apices of the medullary pyramids.

Blood and Nerve Supply (pp. 899–900)

4. The kidneys receive 25% of the total cardiac output/minute.

5. The vascular pathway through a kidney is as follows: renal artery → segmental arteries → lobar arteries → interlobar arter-

ies → arcuate arteries → interlobular arteries → afferent arterioles → glomeruli → efferent arterioles → peritubular capillary beds → interlobular veins → arcuate veins → interlobar veins → renal vein.

6. The nerve supply of the kidneys is derived from the renal plexus.

Nephrons (pp. 900–903)

7. Nephrons are the structural and functional units of the kidneys.

8. Each nephron consists of a glomerulus (a high-pressure capillary bed) and a renal tubule. Subdivisions of the renal tubule (from the glomerulus) are the glomerular capsule, proximal tubule, loop of Henle, and distal tubule. A second capillary bed, the low-pressure peritubular capillary bed, is closely associated with the renal tubule of each nephron.

9. The more numerous cortical nephrons are located almost entirely in the cortex; only parts of their loops of Henle penetrate into the medulla. Juxtamedullary nephrons are located at the cortex-medulla junction, and their loops of Henle dip deeply into the medulla. Juxtamedullary nephrons play an important role in establishing the medullary osmotic gradient.

10. Collecting ducts receive urine from many nephrons and help concentrate urine. They form the medullary pyramids.

11. The juxtaglomerular apparatus is at the point of contact between the afferent and efferent arterioles and the first part of the distal convoluted tubule. It consists of the granular juxtaglomerular cells and the macula densa.

Kidney Physiology: Mechanisms of Urine Formation (pp. 903–917)

1. Functions of the nephrons include filtration, tubular reabsorption, and tubular secretion. Via these functional processes, the kidneys eliminate nitrogenous metabolic wastes, and regulate the volume, composition, and pH of the blood.

Glomerular Filtration (pp. 904–908)

2. The glomeruli function as filters. High glomerular blood pressure (60 mm Hg) occurs because the glomeruli are fed and drained by arterioles, and the afferent arterioles are larger in diameter than the efferent arterioles.

3. About one-fifth of the plasma flowing through the kidneys is filtered from the glomeruli into the renal tubules.

4. The filtration membrane consists of the fenestrated glomerular endothelium, the intervening basement membrane, and the podocyte-containing visceral membrane of the glomerular capsule. It permits free passage of substances smaller than (most) plasma proteins.

5. Net filtration pressure (usually about 17 mm Hg) is determined by the relationship between forces favoring filtration (glomerular hydrostatic pressure) and forces that oppose it (capsular hydrostatic pressure and blood colloid osmotic pressure).

6. The glomerular filtration rate is directly proportional to the net filtration pressure and is about 125 ml/min (180 L/day).

7. Renal autoregulation, which enables the kidneys to maintain a relatively constant renal blood pressure and glomerular filtration rate, is believed to involve a myogenic mechanism and a tubuloglomerular feedback mechanism mediated by the macula densa.

8. Sympathetic nervous system activation causes constriction of the afferent arterioles, which decreases filtrate formation and stimulates renin release by the JG cells.

9. The renin-angiotensin mechanism mediated by the juxtaglomerular (JG) cells raises systemic blood pressure via generation of angiotensin II, which promotes aldosterone secretion.

Tubular Reabsorption (pp. 908–911)

10. During tubular reabsorption, needed substances are removed from the filtrate by the tubule cells and returned to the peritubular capillary blood.

11. Active tubular reabsorption requires protein carriers and ATP. Transport of many substances is coupled to the active transport of sodium ions and is limited by the number of carriers available. Substances reabsorbed actively include nutrients and most ions.

12. Passive tubular reabsorption is driven by electrochemical gradients established by active reabsorption of sodium ions. Water, many anions, and various other substances (for example, urea) are reabsorbed passively.

13. Certain substances (creatinine, drug metabolites, etc.) are not reabsorbed or are reabsorbed incompletely because of the lack of carriers, their size, or nonlipid solubility.

14. The proximal tubule cells are most active in reabsorption. Most of the nutrients, 65% of the water and sodium ions, and the bulk of actively transported ions are reabsorbed in the proximal convoluted tubules.

15. Reabsorption of additional sodium ions and water occurs in the distal tubules and collecting ducts and is hormonally controlled. Aldosterone increases the reabsorption of sodium (and obligatory water reabsorption); antidiuretic hormone enhances water reabsorption by the collecting ducts.

Tubular Secretion (pp. 911–912)

16. Tubular secretion is a means of adding substances to the filtrate (from the blood or tubule cells). It is important in eliminating drugs, urea, and excess ions and in maintaining the acid-base balance of the blood.

Regulation of Urine Concentration and Volume (pp. 912–916)

17. The graduated hyperosmolarity of the medullary fluids (largely due to the cycling of salt, NaCl) ensures that the filtrate reaching the distal convoluted tubule is dilute (hypo-osmolar). This allows urine with osmolarities ranging from 65 to 1200 mosm to be formed.
    a. The descending limb of the loop of Henle is permeable to water, which leaves the filtrate and enters the medullary interstitium. The filtrate and medullary fluid at the tip of the loop of Henle are hyperosmolar.
    b. The ascending limb is impermeable to water, but Na^+ and Cl^- are actively transported out of the filtrate into the interstitial space. The filtrate becomes more dilute as it continues to lose salt.
    c. As filtrate flows through the collecting ducts in the inner medulla, urea diffuses into the interstitial space. Some urea enters the ascending limb and is recycled.
    d. The blood flow in the vasa recta is sluggish, and the contained blood equilibrates with the medullary interstitial fluid. Hence, blood entering and exiting the medulla in the vasa recta is isotonic to blood plasma. Thus, the high solute concentration of the medulla is maintained.

18. In the absence of antidiuretic hormone, dilute urine is formed because the dilute filtrate reaching the distal tubule is simply allowed to pass from the kidneys.

19. As blood levels of antidiuretic hormone rise, the collecting ducts become more permeable to water, and water moves out of the filtrate as it flows through the hyperosmotic medullary areas. Consequently, smaller amounts of more concentrated urine are produced.

Renal Clearance (p. 916)

20. Renal clearance is the rate (mg/min) at which the kidneys clear the plasma of a particular solute. Studies of renal clearance provide information about renal function or the course of renal disease.

Characteristics and Composition of Urine (pp. 916–917)

21. Urine is typically clear, yellow, aromatic, and slightly acidic. Its specific gravity ranges from 1.001 to 1.035.

22. Urine is 95% water; solutes include nitrogenous wastes (urea, uric acid, and creatinine) and various ions (always sodium, potassium, sulfate, and phosphate).

23. Substances not normally found in urine include glucose, proteins, erythrocytes, pus, hemoglobin, and bile pigments.

24. Daily urinary volume is typically 1.5–1.8 L, but this depends on the state of hydration of the body.

Ureters (pp. 917–918)

1. The ureters are slender tubes running retroperitoneally from each kidney to the bladder. They conduct urine by peristalsis from the renal pelvis to the urinary bladder.

Urinary Bladder (p. 919)

1. The urinary bladder, which functions to store urine, is a distensible muscular sac that lies posterior to the pubic symphysis. It has two inlets (ureters) and one outlet (urethra) that outline the trigone. In males, the prostate gland surrounds its outlet.

2. The bladder wall consists of a transitional epithelium-containing mucosa, a three-layered detrusor muscle, and an adventitia.

Urethra (p. 919)

1. The urethra is a muscular tube that conveys urine from the bladder to the body exterior.

2. Where the urethra leaves the bladder, it is surrounded by an internal urethral sphincter, an involuntary smooth muscle sphincter. Where it passes through the urogenital diaphragm, the voluntary external urethral sphincter is formed by skeletal muscle.

3. In females the urethra is 3–4 cm long and conducts only urine. In males it is 20 cm long and conducts both urine and semen.

Micturition (p. 920)

1. Micturition is emptying of the bladder.

2. Stretching of the bladder wall by accumulating urine initiates the micturition reflex, which causes the detrusor muscle to contract and the internal urethral sphincter to relax (open).

3. Because the external sphincter is voluntarily controlled, micturition can usually be delayed temporarily.

Developmental Aspects of the Urinary System (pp. 920–923)

1. Three sets of kidneys (pronephric, mesonephric, and metanephric) develop from the intermediate mesoderm. The metanephros is excreting urine by the third month of development.

2. Common congenital abnormalities are horseshoe kidney, polycystic kidney, and hypospadias.

3. The kidneys of newborns cannot concentrate urine; their bladder is small and voiding is frequent. Neuromuscular maturation generally allows toilet training for micturition to begin by 18 months of age.

4. The most common urinary system problems in children and young to middle-aged adults are bacterial infections.

5. Renal failure is uncommon but very serious. The kidneys are unable to concentrate urine, nitrogenous wastes accumulate in the blood, and acid-base and electrolyte imbalances occur.

6. With age, nephrons are lost, the filtration rate decreases, and tubule cells become less efficient at concentrating urine.

7. Bladder capacity and tone decrease with age, leading to frequent micturition and (often) incontinence. Urinary retention is a common problem of elderly men.

REVIEW QUESTIONS

Multiple Choice/Matching

1. The lowest blood concentration of nitrogenous waste occurs in the (a) hepatic vein, (b) inferior vena cava, (c) renal artery, (d) renal vein.

2. The glomerular capillaries differ from other capillary networks in the body because they (a) have a larger area of anastomosis, (b) are derived from and drain into arterioles, (c) are not made of endothelium, (d) are sites of filtrate formation.

3. Damage to the renal medulla would interfere *first* with the functioning of the (a) glomerular capsules, (b) distal convoluted tubules, (c) collecting ducts, (d) proximal convoluted tubules.

4. Which is reabsorbed by the proximal convoluted tubule? (a) $Na+$, (b) $K+$, (c) amino acids, (d) all of the above.

5. Glucose is not normally found in the urine because it (a) does not pass through the walls of the glomerulus, (b) is kept in the blood by colloid osmotic pressure, (c) is reabsorbed by the tubule cells, (d) is removed by the body cells before the blood reaches the kidney.

6. Filtration at the glomerulus is directly related to (a) water reabsorption, (b) arterial blood pressure, (c) capsular hydrostatic pressure, (d) acidity of the urine.

7. Renal reabsorption (a) of glucose and many other substances is a T_m-limited active transport process, (b) of chloride is always linked to the passive transport of $Na+$, (c) is the movement of substances from the blood into the nephron, (d) of sodium occurs only in the proximal tubule.

8. If a freshly voided urine sample contains excessive amounts of urochrome, it has (a) an ammonialike odor, (b) a pH below normal, (c) a dark yellow color, (d) a pH above normal.

9. Conditions such as diabetes mellitus, starvation, and low-carbohydrate diets are closely linked to (a) ketosis, (b) pyuria, (c) albuminuria, (d) hematuria.

Short Answer Essay Questions

10. What is the importance of the adipose capsule that surrounds the kidney?

 11. Trace the pathway a creatinine molecule takes from a glomerulus to the urethra. Name every microscopic or gross structure it passes through on its journey.

12. Explain the important differences between blood plasma and renal filtrate, and relate the differences to the structure of the filtration membrane.

13. Describe the mechanisms that contribute to renal autoregulation.

14. Describe what is involved in active and passive tubular reabsorption.

15. Explain how the peritubular capillaries are adapted for receiving reabsorbed substances.

16. Explain the process and purpose of tubular secretion.

17. How does aldosterone modify the chemical composition of urine?

18. Explain why the filtrate becomes hypotonic as it flows through the ascending limb of the loop of Henle. Also explain why the filtrate at the tip of the loop of Henle (and the interstitial fluid of the deep portions of the medulla) is hypertonic.

19. How does the bladder anatomy support its storage function?

20. Define micturition and describe the micturition reflex.

21. Describe the changes that occur in kidney and bladder anatomy and physiology in old age.

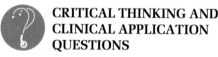 ## CRITICAL THINKING AND CLINICAL APPLICATION QUESTIONS

1. Mrs. Bigda, a 60-year-old woman, was brought to the hospital by the police after falling to the pavement. She is found to have alcoholic hepatitis. She is put on a salt- and protein-restricted diet and diuretics are prescribed to manage her ascites (accumulated fluid in the peritoneal cavity). How will diuretics reduce this excess fluid? Name and describe the mechanism of action of three types of diuretics. Why is her diet salt-restricted?

2. While repairing a frayed utility wire, Herbert, an experienced lineman, slips and falls to the ground. Medical examination reveals a fracture of his lower spine and transection of the lumbar region of the spinal cord. How will Herbert's micturition be controlled from this point on? Will he ever again feel the need to void? Will there be dribbling of urine between voidings? Explain the reasoning behind all your responses.

3. What is cystitis? Why are women more frequent cystitis sufferers than men?

4. Hattie, aged 55, is awakened by excruciating pain that radiates from her right abdomen to the loin and groin regions on the same side. The pain is not continuous but recurs at intervals of 3 to 4 minutes. Diagnose her problem, and cite factors that might favor its occurrence. Also, explain why Hattie's pain comes in "waves."

Fluid, Electrolyte, and Acid-Base Balance

27

CHAPTER OUTLINE AND STUDENT OBJECTIVES

Body Fluids (pp. 928–930)

1. List the factors that determine body water content and describe the effect of each factor.

2. Indicate the relative fluid volume and solute composition of the fluid compartments of the body.

3. Contrast the overall osmotic effects of electrolytes and nonelectrolytes.

4. Describe factors that determine fluid shifts in the body.

Water Balance (pp. 930–934)

5. List the routes by which water enters and leaves the body.

6. Describe the feedback mechanisms that regulate water intake and hormonal controls of water output in urine.

7. Explain the importance of obligatory water losses.

8. Describe possible causes and consequences of dehydration, hypotonic hydration, and edema.

Electrolyte Balance (pp. 934–940)

9. Indicate the routes of electrolyte entry and loss from the body.

10. Describe the importance of ionic sodium in fluid and electrolyte balance of the body, and note its relationship to normal cardiovascular system functioning.

11. Briefly describe mechanisms involved in regulating sodium and water balance.

12. Explain how potassium, calcium, magnesium, and anion balance of plasma is regulated.

Acid-Base Balance (pp. 940–950)

13. List important sources of acids in the body.

14. Name the three major chemical buffer systems of the body and describe how they operate to resist pH changes.

15. Describe the influence of the respiratory system on acid-base balance.

16. Describe how the kidneys regulate hydrogen and bicarbonate ion concentrations in the blood.

17. Distinguish between acidosis and alkalosis resulting from respiratory and metabolic factors. Describe the importance of respiratory and renal compensations to acid-base balance.

Developmental Aspects of Fluid, Electrolyte, and Acid-Base Balance (p. 950)

18. Explain why infants and the aged are at greater risk for fluid and electrolyte imbalances than are young adults.

Have you ever wondered why on certain days you don't urinate for hours at a time, while on others you void large amounts of urine, seemingly every few minutes? Or why on occasion you cannot seem to quench your thirst? These situations and many others reflect one of the body's most important functions: that of maintaining fluid, electrolyte, and acid-base balance.

Cell function depends not only on a continuous supply of nutrients and removal of metabolic wastes, but also on the physical and chemical homeostasis of the surrounding fluids. This was recognized with great style in 1857 by the French physiologist Claude Bernard, who said, "It is the fixity of the internal environment which is the condition of free and independent life." In this chapter, we will examine the composition and distribution of fluids in the internal environment and then "look backward" to consider the roles of various body organs and functions in establishing, regulating, or altering this balance.

Total body water volume = 40 L, 60% body weight

Extracellular fluid volume = 15 L, 20% body weight

| Intracellular fluid volume = 25 L, 40% body weight | Interstitial fluid volume = 12 L, 80% of ECF | Plasma volume = 3 L, 20% of ECF |

FIGURE 27.1
The major fluid compartments of the body. Approximate volume and percentage of body weight values are noted for a 70-kg (154-pound) male.

BODY FLUIDS

Body Water Content

If you are a healthy young adult, water probably accounts for about half your body weight (mass). However, not all bodies contain the same amount of water, and total body water is a function not only of weight, age, and sex but also of the relative amount of body fat. Because of their low body fat and low bone mass, infants are 73% or more water; this high level of hydration accounts for their "dewy" skin, like that of a freshly picked peach. But total water content declines throughout life, accounting for only about 45% of body weight in old age. A healthy young man is about 60% water; a healthy young woman about 50%. This significant difference between the sexes reflects the relatively larger amount of body fat and smaller amount of skeletal muscle in females. Of all body tissues, adipose tissue is *least* hydrated (containing up to 20% water); even bone contains more water than does fat. By contrast, skeletal muscle is about 65% water. Thus, people with greater muscle mass have proportionately more body water.

Fluid Compartments

Water occupies two main **fluid compartments** within the body (Figure 27.1). A little less than two-thirds by volume is in the **intracellular fluid (ICF) compartment,** which actually consists of trillions of tiny individual compartments: the cells. In an adult male of average size (70 kg, or 154 pounds), the ICF accounts for about 25 L of the 40 L of body water. The remaining one-third or so of body water is outside cells, in the **extracellular fluid (ECF) compartment.** The ECF constitutes the body's "internal environment" referred to by Claude Bernard and the external environment of each body cell. The ECF compartment is, in turn, divisible into two important *subcompart-*

ments: (1) **plasma,** the fluid portion of blood within the blood vessels, and (2) **interstitial fluid (IF),** the fluid in the microscopic spaces between tissue cells. Additionally, there are numerous other examples of ECF that are distinct from both plasma and interstitial fluid, such as lymph, cerebrospinal fluid, humors of the eye, synovial fluid, serous fluid, and secretions of the gastrointestinal tract. However, most are similar to interstitial fluid and they are usually considered part of it. In the 70-kg adult male, interstitial fluid accounts for approximately 12 L and plasma about 3 L of the total (15 L) ECF volume (Figure 27.1).

Composition of Body Fluids

Solutes: Electrolytes and Nonelectrolytes

Water serves as the *universal solvent* in which a variety of solutes are dissolved. Solutes may be classified broadly as *electrolytes* and *nonelectrolytes.* The **nonelectrolytes** have bonds (usually covalent bonds) that prevent them from dissociating in solution; therefore, they have no electrical charge. Most nonelectrolytes are organic molecules—glucose, lipids, creatinine, and urea, for example. In contrast, electrolytes are chemical compounds that *do* dissociate into ions (ionize) in water. (See Chapter 2, if necessary, to review these concepts of chemistry.) Because ions are charged particles, they can conduct an electrical current—hence the name **electrolyte.** Typically, electrolytes include inorganic salts, both inorganic and organic acids and bases, and some proteins.

Although all dissolved solutes contribute to the osmotic activity of a fluid, electrolytes have much greater osmotic power than nonelectrolytes because each electrolyte molecule dissociates into at least two ions. For example, a molecule of sodium chloride (NaCl) contributes twice as many solute particles as glucose (which remains undissociated), and a molecule of magnesium chloride ($MgCl_2$) contributes three times as many:

$$NaCl \rightarrow Na^+ + Cl^- \qquad \text{(two particles)}$$

$$MgCl_2 \rightarrow Mg^{2+} + Cl^- + Cl^- \qquad \text{(three particles)}$$

$$glucose \rightarrow glucose \qquad \text{(one particle)}$$

Regardless of the type of solute particle, water moves according to osmotic gradients (from areas of lesser osmolarity to those of greater osmolarity). Thus, electrolytes have the greatest ability to cause fluid shifts.

Electrolyte concentrations of body fluids are usually expressed in **milliequivalents per liter (mEq/L),** a measure of the number of electrical charges in 1 liter of solution. Because the total number of negative charges (anions) in a solution is always equal to the number of positive charges (cations), the milliequivalent system of reporting electrolyte concentrations makes it easier to follow electrolyte shifts.

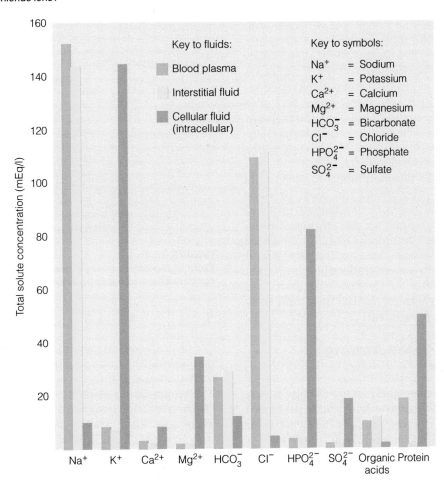

FIGURE 27.2
Comparison of the electrolyte composition of blood plasma, interstitial fluid, and intracellular fluid.

The concentration of any ion in solution in mEq/L can be computed using the equation

$$mEq/L = \frac{\text{concentration of ion (mg/L)}}{\text{atomic weight of ion}} \times \begin{array}{l}\text{\# of}\\\text{electrical}\\\text{charges on}\\\text{one ion}\end{array}$$

Thus, to compute the mEq/L of sodium or calcium ions in solution in plasma, we would determine the normal concentration of these ions in plasma, look up their atomic weights in the periodic table (see Appendix F), and plug these values into the equation:

$$Na^+: \frac{3300 \text{ mg/L}}{23} \times 1 = 143 \text{ mEq/L}$$

$$Ca^{2+}: \frac{100 \text{ mg/L}}{40} \times 2 = 5 \text{ mEq/L}$$

Notice that for ions with a single charge, 1 mEq is equal to 1 mosm, whereas 1 mEq of bivalent ions (those, like calcium, with a double charge) is equal to ½ mosm. In either case, 1 mEq provides the same degree of reactivity.

Comparison of Extracellular and Intracellular Fluids

Even a quick glance at the bar graphs in Figure 27.2 reveals that each fluid compartment has a distinctive pattern of electrolytes. But, except for the relatively high protein content in plasma, the extracellular fluids are very similar. Their chief cation is sodium, and their major anion is chloride. However, plasma contains somewhat fewer chloride ions than interstitial fluid, because the nonpenetrating plasma proteins are normally anions and plasma is electrically neutral.

In contrast to extracellular fluids, intracellular fluid contains only small amounts of Na^+ and Cl^-. Its most abundant cation is potassium, and its major anion is phosphate (HPO_4^{2-}). Cells also contain moderate amounts of magnesium ions and substantial quantities of soluble proteins (about three times the amount found in plasma).

Notice that sodium and potassium ion concentrations in extracellular and intracellular fluids are nearly opposite (Figure 27.2). The characteristic distribution of these ions on the two sides of cellular membranes reflects the activity of cellular ATP-dependent sodium-potassium pumps, which keep intracellular Na^+ concentrations low while maintaining high intracellular K^+ concentrations (see Chapter 2). Renal mechanisms can reinforce these ion distributions by secreting potassium as sodium is reabsorbed from the filtrate.

Electrolytes are the most abundant solutes in the various body fluids and determine most of their chemical and physical reactions, but they do not constitute the *bulk* of dissolved solutes in these fluids. Proteins and some of the nonelectrolyte molecules (phospholipids, cholesterol, and neutral fats) found in the ECF are much larger molecules, and they account for about 90% of the mass of dissolved solutes in plasma, 60% in interstitial fluid, and 97% in the intracellular compartment.

Movement of Fluids Among Compartments

The continuous exchange and mixing of body fluids are regulated by osmotic and/or hydrostatic pressures (Figure 27.3). Although water moves freely between the compartments along osmotic gradients, solutes are unequally distributed because of their molecular size, electrical charge, or dependence on active transport. Anything that changes the solute concentration in any compartment will lead to net water flows.

Exchanges between plasma and interstitial fluid occur across capillary membranes. The pressures driving these fluid movements are described in detail in Chapter 20 on pp. 664–665, and the major points are recapped in the discussion of glomerular filtration on pp. 904–906. Here we will simply note the outcome of these mechanisms. Nearly protein-free plasma is forced out of the bloodstream into the interstitial space by the hydrostatic pressure of blood. This filtered fluid is almost completely reabsorbed into the bloodstream in response to the colloid osmotic pressure of plasma proteins. Under normal circumstances, the small net leakage that occurs is picked up by lymphatic vessels and returned to the bloodstream.

Exchanges between the interstitial and intracellular fluids are more complex because of the selective permeability of cellular membranes. As a general rule, two-way osmotic flows of water are substantial, but ion fluxes are restricted and, in most cases, ions move selectively by active transport. Movements of nutrients, respiratory gases, and wastes are typically unidirectional. For example, glucose and oxygen move into the cells and metabolic wastes move out of the cells and into the blood.

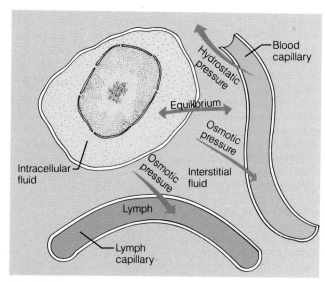

FIGURE 27.3
Fluid movement among compartments follows hydrostatic and osmotic pressure gradients.

Of the various body fluids, only plasma circulates throughout the body and serves as the link between the external and internal environments (Figure 27.4). Exchanges occur almost continuously in the lungs, gastrointestinal tract, and kidneys. Although these exchanges alter plasma composition and volume, they are quickly followed by compensating adjustments in the other two fluid compartments so that balance is restored.

Many factors can cause marked changes in ECF and ICF volumes. However, water moves freely between compartments, so the osmolarities of all body fluids are equal, except for the first few minutes after a change in one of the fluids occurs. Increasing the solute content of the ECF (most importantly, the NaCl concentration) can be expected to cause osmolarity changes in the ICF—namely, a shift of water out of the cells. Conversely, decreasing the osmolarity of the ECF causes water to move into the cells. Thus, the volume of the ICF is determined by the solute concentration of the ECF. These concepts underlie all events that control fluid balance in the body and should be understood thoroughly.

WATER BALANCE

To remain properly hydrated, water intake must equal water output. *Water intake* varies widely from person to person and is strongly influenced by habit, but it is typically about 2500 ml a day in adults (Figure 27.5). Most water enters the body through ingested liquids (about 60%) and solid foods (about 30%). About 10% of body water is produced by cellular metabolism; this is called **metabolic water** or **water of oxidation.**

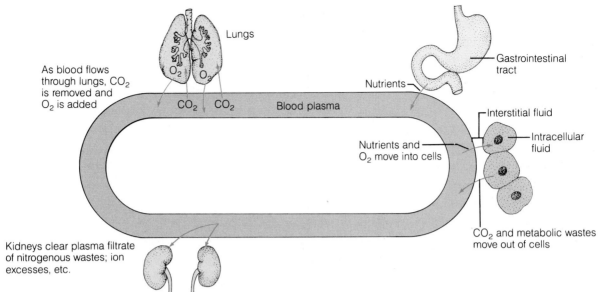

FIGURE 27.4
The continuous mixing of body fluids. Blood plasma serves as the communicating medium between the external and internal environments. Exchanges are made between the plasma and tissue cells (intracellular fluid) through the interstitial space.

Water output occurs by several routes. Some water (28%) vaporizes out of the lungs in expired air or diffuses directly through the skin; this is called *insensible water loss.* Some is lost in obvious perspiration (8%) and in feces (4%). The balance (60%) is excreted by the kidneys in urine.

Healthy people have a remarkable ability to maintain the tonicity of their body fluids within very narrow limits (285–300 mosm/L). A rise in plasma osmolarity triggers (1) thirst, which provokes water intake, and (2) release of antidiuretic hormone (ADH), which causes the kidneys to conserve water and excrete concentrated urine. On the other hand, a decline in osmolarity inhibits both thirst and ADH release, the latter followed by output of large volumes of dilute urine.

Regulation of Water Intake: The Thirst Mechanism

Thirst is the driving force for water intake, but the **thirst mechanism** is poorly understood. It appears that a decrease in plasma volume of 10% (or more, as from hemorrhage) and/or an increase in plasma osmolarity of 1% to 2% results in a dry mouth and excites the hypothalamic *thirst center.* A dry mouth occurs because the rise in plasma osmotic pressure causes less fluid to leave the bloodstream. Because the salivary glands obtain the water they require from the blood, less saliva is produced. The hypothalamic thirst center is stimulated when its osmoreceptors lose water by osmosis to the hypertonic ECF, an event that causes them to become irritable and depolarize. Collectively, these events cause a subjective sensa-

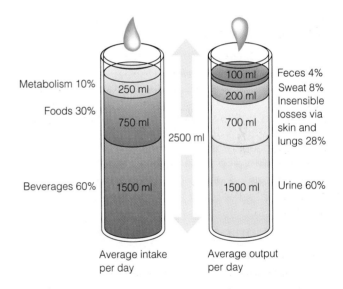

FIGURE 27.5
Major sources of body water (water intake) and routes of water loss from the body (water output). When intake and output are in balance, the body is adequately hydrated.

tion of thirst, which motivates us to get a drink (Figure 27.6). This mechanism helps explain the nagging thirst of a hemorrhaging patient who has lost 800 ml or more of blood and, on a lighter note, why it is that some cocktail lounges and bars provide free *salty* snacks to their patrons.

Curiously, thirst is quenched almost as soon as we begin drinking water, even though the water has yet to be absorbed into the blood. The damping of thirst begins as the mucosa of the mouth and throat is moistened and continues as stretch receptors in the

What effect would eating pretzels have on this mechanism?

FIGURE 27.6
The thirst mechanism for regulating water intake.

stomach and intestine are activated, providing feedback signals that inhibit the thirst center. This premature slaking of thirst prevents us from drinking far more than we need and overdiluting our body fluids, thus allowing time for the osmotic changes to come into play as regulatory factors.

As effective as thirst is, it is not always a reliable indicator of need. This is particularly true during athletic events, when thirst can be satisfied long before sufficient liquids have been consumed to maintain the body in top form. Additionally, the elderly or confused may not recognize or heed thirst signals, and fluid-overloaded renal or cardiac patients may feel thirsty despite their condition.

Regulation of Water Output

Certain amounts of water output are unavoidable. Such **obligatory water losses** help to explain why we cannot survive for long without drinking. Even the most heroic conservation efforts on the part of the kidneys cannot compensate for zero water intake. Obligatory water losses include *insensible water losses* from the lungs and through the skin, water that accompanies undigested food residues in feces, and a minimum daily *sensible water loss* of 500 ml in urine. Obligatory water loss in urine reflects the facts that (1) when we eat an adequate diet, our kidneys must excrete about 900–1200 mosm of solutes to maintain blood homeostasis, and (2) human kidneys must remove urine solutes from the body in water.

Beyond obligatory water loss, the concentration and volume of urine excreted depend on fluid intake, diet, and water loss via other avenues. For example, if you jog on a hot day and perspire profusely, much less urine than usual has to be excreted to maintain

water balance. Normally, the kidneys begin to eliminate excess water about 30 minutes after it is ingested. This delay mainly reflects the time required for ADH release to be inhibited. Diuresis reaches a peak in 1 hour and then declines to its lowest level after 3 hours.

The body's water volume is closely tied to a powerful water "magnet," ionic sodium. Moreover, our ability to maintain water balance through urinary output is really a problem of sodium *and* water balance because the two are always regulated in tandem by mechanisms that serve cardiovascular function and blood pressure.

Disorders of Water Balance

Few people really appreciate the importance of water in keeping the body's "machinery" working at peak efficiency. The principal abnormalities of water balance are dehydration, hypotonic hydration, and edema, and each of these conditions offers a special set of problems to its victims.

Dehydration

Dehydration occurs when water loss exceeds water intake over a period of time and the body is in negative fluid balance. Dehydration is a common sequel to hemorrhage, severe burns, prolonged bouts of vomiting or diarrhea, profuse sweating, water deprivation, and diuretic abuse. Dehydration may also be caused by endocrine disturbances, such as diabetes mellitus or diabetes insipidus (see Chapter 17). Early signs and symptoms of dehydration include a "cottony" or sticky oral mucosa, thirst, dry flushed skin, and decreased urine output *(oliguria).* If prolonged, dehy-

① Excessive loss of water from the extracellular fluid compartment

② Osmotic pressure in extracellular fluid compartment increases

③ Water leaves intracellular fluid compartment by osmosis

Tissue cells

(a)

① Excessive water enters the extracellular fluid compartment

② Osmotic pressure in extracellular fluid compartment decreases

③ Water moves into intracellular fluid compartment by osmosis

Tissue cells

(b)

FIGURE 27.7
Disturbances in water balance. (a) Mechanism of dehydration. **(b)** Mechanism of hypotonic hydration (water intoxication).

dration may lead to weight loss, fever, and mental confusion. In all these situations, water is lost from the ECF (Figure 27.7a). This is followed by the osmotic movement of water from the cells into the ECF, which equalizes the osmolarity of the extracellular and intracellular fluids even though the total fluid volume has been reduced. Though the overall effect is called dehydration, it rarely involves only a deficit of water. Most often, as water is lost electrolytes are lost as well.

Hypotonic Hydration

Hypotonic hydration, a type of cellular *overhydration* also called **water intoxication,** may result from renal insufficiency or from drinking extraordinary amounts of water very quickly. In either case, the ECF is diluted—its sodium content is normal, but water is present in excess. Thus, the hallmark of this condition is **hyponatremia** (low ECF Na^+ level). This, in turn, promotes net osmosis into the tissue cells, causing them to swell as they become abnormally hydrated (Figure 27.7b). These events must be reversed quickly—for example, by intravenous administration of a hypertonic infusion (saline or mannitol), which reverses the osmotic gradient and "pulls" water out of the cells. Otherwise, the resulting electrolyte dilution leads to severe metabolic disturbances evidenced by nausea, vomiting, muscular cramping, and cerebral edema. Water intoxication is particularly damaging to neurons. Uncorrected cerebral edema quickly leads to disorientation, convulsions, coma, and death.

Edema

Edema (ĕ-de'mah; "a swelling") is an atypical accumulation of fluid in the interstitial space, leading to tissue swelling. Edema may be caused by any event

that steps up fluid flow out of the bloodstream or hinders its return.

Factors that accelerate fluid loss from the bloodstream include increased blood pressure and/or capillary permeability. Increased blood (capillary hydrostatic) pressure can result from incompetent venous valves, localized blood vessel blockage, congestive heart failure, hypertension, or high blood volume resulting, for instance, during pregnancy or from abnormal retention of sodium (which promotes water retention). Whatever the cause, the abnormally high blood pressure intensifies filtration at the capillary beds. Increased capillary permeability usually reflects an ongoing inflammatory response. Recall that inflammatory chemicals cause local capillaries to become very porous, allowing large amounts of exudate (containing clotting proteins, nutrients, and immune elements) to form.

Edema caused by hindered fluid return to the bloodstream usually reflects an imbalance in the colloid osmotic pressures on the two sides of the capillary membranes. For example, **hypoproteinemia** (hi"po-pro"te-ĭ-ne'me-ah), a condition of unusually low levels of plasma proteins, results in tissue edema because protein-deficient plasma has an abnormally low colloid osmotic pressure. Fluids are forced out of the capillary beds at the arterial ends by blood pressure as usual, but fail to return to the blood at the venous ends. Thus, the interstitial spaces become congested with fluid. Hypoproteinemia may result from protein malnutrition, liver disease (in which the liver fails to make its normal supply of plasma proteins), or *glomerulonephritis* (in which plasma proteins pass through "leaky" renal filtration membranes and are lost in urine). Although the cause differs, the result is the same when lymphatic vessels are blocked or have been surgically removed. The small amounts of plasma proteins that seep out of the bloodstream are not returned to the blood as usual. As the leaked proteins accumulate, they exert an ever-increasing colloid osmotic pressure, which draws fluid from the blood and holds it in the interstitial space.

Because excess fluid in the interstitial space increases the distance nutrients and oxygen must diffuse between the blood and the cells, edema can impair tissue function. However, the most serious problems resulting from edema concern the operation of the cardiovascular system. As described in Chapter 20, when fluid leaves the bloodstream and accumulates in the interstitial space, both blood volume and blood pressure decline and efficiency of circulatory delivery is severely impaired. •

ELECTROLYTE BALANCE

Electrolytes include salts, acids, and bases, but the term **electrolyte balance** usually refers to the salt balance in the body. Salts provide minerals essential for neuromuscular excitability, secretory activity, membrane permeability, and many other cellular functions. Additionally, salts are important in controlling fluid movements. Although many electrolytes are crucial for cellular activity, we will specifically examine the regulation of sodium, potassium, calcium, and magnesium only. Acids and bases, which are more intimately involved in determining the pH of body fluids, are considered in the next section.

Salts enter the body in foods and fluids, and small amounts are generated during metabolic activity. For example, phosphates are liberated during catabolism of nucleic acids and bone matrix. Obtaining enough electrolytes is usually not a problem. Indeed, most of us have a far greater taste than need for salt (NaCl). We shake table salt on our food despite the fact that natural foods contain ample amounts and processed foods contain exorbitant quantities. The taste for very salty foods is learned. Some liking for salt may be innate, assuring adequate intake of these vital ions.

Salts are lost from the body in perspiration, feces, and urine. When we are salt-depleted, our perspiration is more dilute. Even so, on a hot day significantly more salt than usual can be lost in sweat, and gastrointestinal disorders can lead to large losses in feces or vomitus. Thus, the flexibility of renal mechanisms that regulate the electrolyte balance of the blood is a critical asset. Some causes and consequences of electrolyte excesses and deficiencies are summarized in Table 27.1, p. 935.

In rare instances, severe electrolyte deficiencies prompt a craving for salty foods and an increased willingness to try new substances, such as exotic smoked meats or pickled eggs, in the search for salt. This is common in those with *Addison's disease,* a disorder entailing deficient mineralocorticoid hormone production by the adrenal cortex. When electrolytes other than NaCl are deficient, substances not usually considered to be nutrients, like chalk, clay, starch, and burnt match tips, may be eaten. Such an appetite for abnormal substances is called *pica.* •

The Central Role of Sodium in Fluid and Electrolyte Balance

There is no question that sodium holds a pivotal position in fluid and electrolyte balance and overall body homeostasis. Regulating the balance between sodium input and output is one of the most important functions of the kidneys. Sodium salts ($NaHCO_3$ and NaCl) account for 90% to 95% of all solutes in the ECF, and they contribute about 280 mosm of the total (300 mosm) ECF solute concentration. At its normal plasma concentration of about 142 mEq, sodium is the single most abundant cation in the ECF and is the only one exerting *significant* osmotic pressure. Additionally, cellular plasma membranes are relatively impermeable to Na^+—but some does manage to diffuse in and must be pumped out against its electrochemical gradient. These two qualities give sodium the primary role in controlling ECF volume and water distribution in the body.

It is important to understand that *while the sodium content of the body may change, its concentration in the ECF remains stable because of immediate adjustments in water volume.* Remember, *water follows salt.* Furthermore, because all body fluids are in osmotic equilibrium, a change in plasma sodium levels affects not only plasma volume and blood pressure, but also the ICF and interstitial fluid volumes. In addition, sodium ions continually move back and forth between the ECF and body secretions. For example, large volumes (about 8 L) of sodium-containing secretions (gastric, intestinal, and pancreatic juice, saliva, bile) are "spewed" into the digestive tract daily, only to be almost completely reabsorbed. Finally, renal acid-base control mechanisms (discussed shortly) are coupled to sodium ion transport and engineered to balance sodium ion concentrations.

Regulation of Sodium Balance

Despite the crucial importance of sodium, sodium receptors that specifically monitor Na^+ levels in body fluids have yet to be found. Regulation of sodium-water balance is inseparably linked to blood pressure and blood volume, and entails a variety of neural and hormonal controls. Na^+ reabsorption does *not* exhibit a transport maximum. We will begin our coverage of sodium balance by reviewing the regulatory effect of aldosterone. Then we will examine the various feedback loops that interact to regulate sodium and water balance and blood pressure.

Influence and Regulation of Aldosterone

The hormone **aldosterone** "has the most to say" about renal regulation of sodium ion concentrations in the ECF. But, whether aldosterone is present or not, 65% of the sodium in the renal filtrate is reabsorbed in the proximal tubules of the kidneys and another 25% is reclaimed in the loops of Henle (see Chapter 26).

Table 27.1 Causes and Consequences of Electrolyte Imbalances

Ion	Abnormality/serum value	Possible causes	Consequences
Sodium	Hypernatremia (Na^+ excess in ECF: > 145 mEq/L)	Dehydration; uncommon in healthy individuals; may occur in infants or the confused aged (individuals unable to indicate thirst) or may be a result of excessive intravenous NaCl administration	Thirst; CNS dehydration leads to confusion and lethargy progressing to coma; may cause rupture of cerebral blood vessels; increased neuromuscular irritability evidenced by twitching and convulsions
	Hyponatremia (Na^+ deficit in ECF: < 130 mEq/L)	Solute loss, water retention, or both, (e.g., excessive Na^+ loss through burned skin, excessive sweating, vomiting, diarrhea, tubal drainage of stomach, and as a result of excessive use of diuretics); deficiency of aldosterone (Addison's disease); renal disease; excess ADH release	Most common signs are those of neurologic dysfunction due to brain swelling. If sodium amounts are actually normal but water is excessive, the symptoms are the same as those of water excess: mental confusion; giddiness; coma if development occurs slowly; muscular twitching, irritability, and convulsions if the condition develops rapidly; systemic edema; congestive heart failure in cardiac patients. In hyponatremia accompanied by water loss, the main signs are decreased blood volume and blood pressure (circulatory shock)
Potassium	Hyperkalemia (K^+ excess in ECF: > 5.5 mEq/L)	Renal failure; deficit of aldosterone; rapid intravenous infusion of KCl; burns or severe tissue injuries which cause K^+ to leave cells	Bradycardia; cardiac arrhythmias, depression, and arrest; skeletal muscle weakness; flaccid paralysis
	Hypokalemia (K^+ deficit in ECF: < 3.5 mEq/L)	Gastrointestinal tract disturbances (vomiting, diarrhea), gastrointestinal suction; chronic stress; Cushing's disease; inadequate dietary intake (starvation); hyperaldosteronism; diuretic therapy	Cardiac arrhythmias, possible cardiac arrest; muscular weakness; alkalosis; hypoventilation
Magnesium	Hypermagnesemia (Mg^{2+} excess in ECF: > 6 mEq/L)	Rare (occurs when Mg is not excreted normally); deficiency of aldosterone; excessive ingestion of Mg^{2+}-containing antacids	Lethargy; impaired CNS functioning, coma, respiratory depression
	Hypomagnesemia (Mg^{2+} deficit in ECF: < 1.4 mEq/L)	Alcoholism; loss of intestinal contents, severe malnutrition; diuretic therapy	Tremors, increased neuromuscular excitability, convulsions
Chloride	Hyperchloremia (Cl^- excess in ECF: > 105 mEq/L)	Increased retention or intake; hyperkalemia	Metabolic acidosis due to enhanced loss of bicarbonate; stupor; rapid, deep breathing; unconsciousness
	Hypochloremia Cl^- deficit in ECF: < 95 mEq/L)	Vomiting; hypokalemia; excessive ingestion of alkaline substances	Metabolic alkalosis due to bicarbonate retention
Calcium	Hypercalcemia (Ca^{2+} excess in ECF: > 5.8 mEq/L or 11 mg%)	Hyperparathyroidism; excessive vitamin D; prolonged immobilization; renal disease (decreased excretion); malignancy; Paget's disease; Cushing's disease accompanied by osteoporosis	Bone wasting, pathological fractures; flank and deep thigh pain; kidney stones, nausea and vomiting, cardiac arrhythmias and arrest; depressed respiration, coma
	Hypocalcemia (Ca^{2+} deficit in ECF: < 4.5 mEq/L or 9 mg%)	Burns (calcium trapped in damaged tissues); increased renal excretion in response to stress and increased protein intake; diarrhea; vitamin D deficiency; alkalosis	Tingling of fingers, tremors, tetany, convulsions; depressed excitability of the heart, bleeder's disease

When aldosterone concentrations are high, virtually all the remaining Na^+ (actually NaCl, because Cl^- is cotransported) is actively reabsorbed in the distal convoluted and collecting tubules. Water follows if it can, that is, if the tubule permeability has been increased by ADH. Thus, targeting of the kidneys by aldosterone usually promotes both sodium and water retention. However, when aldosterone release is inhibited, virtually no Na^+ reabsorption occurs beyond the loops of Henle. So, while urinary excretion of large amounts of sodium *always* results in the excretion of large amounts of water as well, the reverse is *not* true.

Substantial amounts of nearly sodium-free urine can be eliminated as needed to achieve water balance.

Recall that aldosterone is produced by adrenal cortical cells. The most important trigger for aldosterone release is the renin-angiotensin mechanism mediated by the juxtaglomerular apparatus of the renal tubules (see Figure 27.10, p. 938). When the juxtaglomerular (JG) apparatus responds to (1) sympathetic nervous system stimulation, (2) decreased filtrate osmolarity, or (3) decreased stretch (due to decreased blood pressure), the JG cells release renin. Renin catalyzes the series of reactions that produce angiotensin II, which, in turn, prompts aldosterone release. Conversely, high renal blood pressure and high filtrate osmolarity depress renin-angiotensin-aldosterone release. The adrenal cortical cells are also directly stimulated to release aldosterone by elevated K^+ levels or low Na^+ levels in the ECF (Figure 27.8).

People with Addison's disease (hypoaldosteronism) lose tremendous amounts of salt and water to urine. As long as they ingest adequate amounts of salt and fluids, people with this condition can avoid problems, but they are perpetually teetering on the brink of hypovolemia and dehydration. •

Aldosterone brings about its effects slowly, over a period of hours to days, and although it has a dramatic effect on tubular reabsorption of sodium, it has a relatively small impact on blood volume. The principal effects of aldosterone are to diminish urinary output and increase blood volume, but before these can change more than a few percent, basic feedback mechanisms for blood volume control come into play. Even people with Cushing's disease (hyperaldosteronism) rarely have ECF and blood volumes more than 5% to 10% above normal.

Cardiovascular System Baroreceptors

Blood volume is carefully monitored and regulated to maintain blood pressure and cardiovascular function. As blood volume (hence pressure) rises, baroreceptors in the heart and in the large vessels of the neck and thorax (carotid arteries and aorta) alert the hypothalamus. Shortly after, sympathetic nervous system impulses to the kidneys decline, allowing the afferent arterioles to dilate. As the glomerular filtration rate rises, sodium and water output increases dramatically. This phenomenon, called *pressure diuresis,* reduces blood volume and, consequently, blood pressure. In contrast, drops in systemic blood pressure lead to constriction of the afferent arterioles, which reduces filtrate formation and urinary output and increases systemic blood pressure (see Figure 27.10). Thus, the baroreceptors provide information on the "fullness" or volume of the circulation that is critical for maintaining cardiovascular homeostasis. Because sodium ion concentration determines fluid volume, the baroreceptors might be regarded as "sodium receptors."

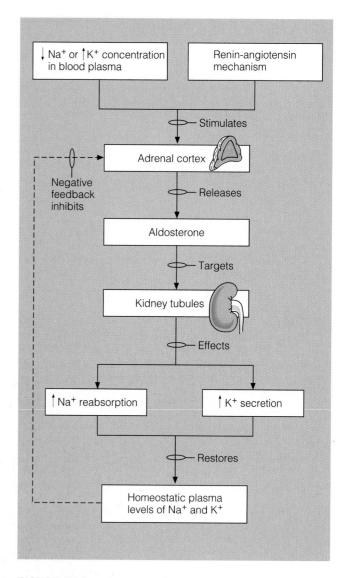

FIGURE 27.8
Mechanisms and consequences of aldosterone release.

Influence and Regulation of ADH

The amount of water reabsorbed in the collecting ducts of the kidneys is proportional to ADH release. When ADH levels are low, most of the water reaching the collecting ducts is simply allowed to pass through. The result is dilute urine and a reduced volume of body fluids. When ADH levels are high, nearly all of the filtered water is reabsorbed and a small volume of highly concentrated urine is excreted.

Osmoreceptors of the hypothalamus sense the ECF solute concentration and trigger or inhibit ADH release from the posterior pituitary accordingly (Figure 27.9). A decrease in sodium ion concentration (for instance, due to the increased blood volume that results from drinking a lot of beer or punch at the weekend "keg" party) inhibits ADH release and allows more water to be excreted in urine, restoring

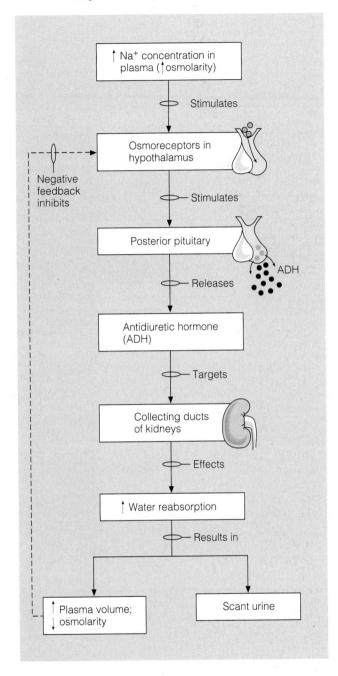

? At what point in this flowchart would plasma osmolarity change dramatically?

FIGURE 27.9
Mechanisms and consequences of ADH release.

normal Na^+ levels in the blood. An increase in sodium levels (which may be due to decreased blood volume) stimulates ADH release both directly by stimulating the hypothalamic osmoreceptors and indirectly via the renin-angiotensin mechanism. (The latter stimulus is not illustrated in Figure 27.9 but is indicated in Figure 27.10.) Factors that specifically

trigger ADH release by reducing blood volume include prolonged fever; excessive sweating, vomiting, or diarrhea; severe blood loss; and traumatic burns. Figure 27.10 summarizes how renal mechanisms involving aldosterone, angiotensin II, and ADH are interrelated and tied into overall controls of blood volume and blood pressure.

Influence and Regulation of Atrial Natriuretic Factor

The influence of **atrial natriuretic factor (ANF)** (also called *atrial natriuretic peptide [ANP]*) can be summarized in one sentence. It reduces blood pressure and blood volume by inhibiting nearly all events that promote vasoconstriction and Na^+ and water retention. Atrial natriuretic factor is a hormone that is released by certain cells of the heart atria when they are stretched by the effects of elevated blood pressure. ANF has potent diuretic and natriuretic (literally, salt-excreting) effects. It promotes excretion of sodium and water by the kidneys, presumably by directly inhibiting the ability of the distal tubule and collecting duct cells to reabsorb Na^+ and by suppressing the release of ADH, renin, and aldosterone. Additionally, ANF acts both directly and indirectly (by inhibiting renin-induced generation of angiotensin II) to relax vascular smooth muscle; thus it causes vasodilation. Collectively, these effects reduce blood pressure.

Influence of Other Hormones

Female Sex Hormones.   The **estrogens** are chemically similar to aldosterone and, like aldosterone, they enhance NaCl reabsorption by the renal tubules. Because water follows, many women "retain fluid" as their estrogen levels rise during the menstrual cycle. The edema experienced by many pregnant women is also largely due to the effect of estrogens. In contrast, **progesterone** seems to decrease sodium reabsorption by blocking the effect of aldosterone on the renal tubules. Thus, progesterone has a diureticlike effect and promotes sodium and water loss.

Glucocorticoids.   The usual effect of **glucocorticoids,** such as cortisol and hydrocortisol, is to enhance tubular reabsorption of sodium, but they also promote an increased glomerular filtration rate which may mask the tubular effects. However, when their plasma levels are high, the glucocorticoids exhibit potent aldosteronelike effects, and promote edema (see Chapter 17, p. 569).

Regulation of Potassium Balance

Potassium, the chief intracellular cation, is required for normal neuromuscular functioning, as well as for several essential metabolic activities, including protein synthesis. Nevertheless, it can be extremely

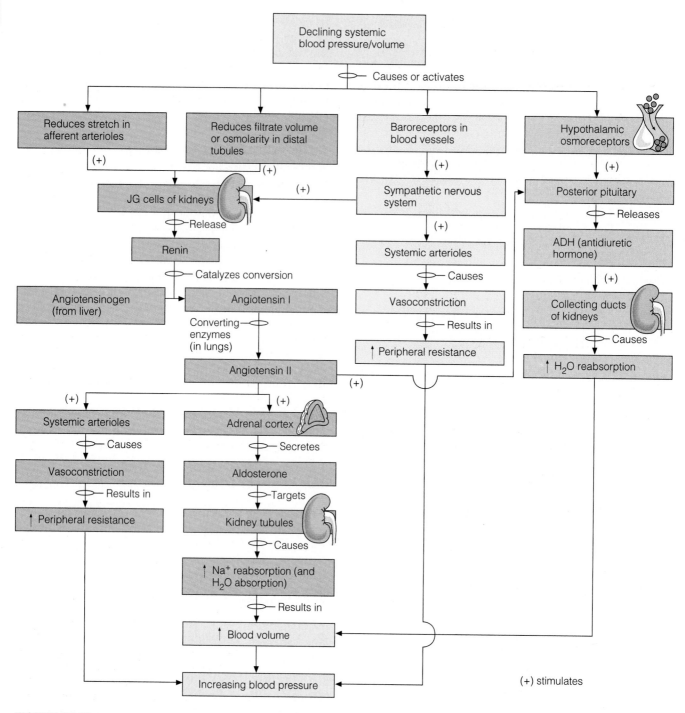

FIGURE 27.10
**Flowchart illustrating how mechanisms regulating sodium and water balance
help maintain blood pressure homeostasis.**

toxic. Because the relative ICF-ECF potassium ion (K⁺) concentration directly affects a cell's resting membrane potential, even a slight change in K⁺ concentration on either side of the membrane has profound effects on neurons and muscle fibers. Potassium excesses in the ECF decrease their membrane potential, causing depolarization, which is often followed by reduced excitability. A deficit of K⁺ in the ECF causes hyperpolarization and nonresponsiveness. The heart is particularly sensitive to K⁺ levels: Both too much and too little K⁺ (hyperkalemia and hypokalemia respectively) can disrupt electrical conduction in the heart, leading to sudden death (see Table 27.1).

Potassium is also part of the body's buffer system, which resists changes in the pH of body fluids. Shifts of hydrogen ions (H^+) into and out of cells induce corresponding shifts of potassium in the opposite direction to maintain cation balance. Thus, ECF potassium levels rise with acidosis, as K^+ leaves and H^+ enters the cells, and fall with alkalosis, as K^+ moves into the cells and H^+ leaves them to enter the ECF. Although these pH-driven shifts do not change the total amount of K^+ in the body, they can seriously interfere with the activity of excitable cells.

Regulatory Site: The Cortical Collecting Duct

Like sodium balance, potassium balance is maintained chiefly by renal mechanisms. However, there are important differences in the way this balance is achieved. The amount of sodium reabsorbed in the tubules is precisely tailored to need, and sodium ions are never secreted into the filtrate.

In contrast, the renal tubules predictably reabsorb 90% of the filtered K^+, leaving 10% to be lost in urine regardless of need. K^+ balance is accomplished chiefly by changing the amount of potassium *secreted* into the filtrate, mainly by the cortical collecting ducts; hence, the responsibility for maintaining K^+ balance falls entirely on tubular segments beyond the nephrons.

As a rule, the relative potassium levels in the ECF are excessive, and K^+ secretion by the principal cells of the cortical collecting ducts is accelerated over basal levels. At times, the amount of potassium excreted may actually exceed the amount filtered. However, when ECF potassium concentrations are abnormally low, K^+ moves from the tissue cells into the ECF and the renal principal cells conserve K^+ by reducing its secretion and excretion to the minimal levels possible. Additionally, a unique population of collecting duct cells, called *intercalated cells,* that are scattered the length of the collecting tubules, can reabsorb some of the K^+ still left in the filtrate, thus helping to reestablish K^+ balance. However, keep in mind that the main thrust of renal regulation of potassium is to *excrete* it and, because the kidneys have a very limited ability to retain potassium, it may be lost in urine even in the face of a deficiency. Consequently, failure to ingest potassium-rich substances eventually results in severe potassium deficiency.

Essentially, two factors determine the rate and extent of potassium secretion—the plasma potassium ion concentration and aldosterone levels.

Influence of Plasma Potassium Concentration

The single most important factor influencing potassium secretion is the K^+ concentration in blood plasma. A high-potassium diet increases the K^+ con-tent of the ECF. This favors entry of K^+ into the principal cells of the collecting duct and prompts them to secrete K^+ into the filtrate so that more potassium is excreted. Conversely, a low-potassium diet or accelerated K^+ loss depresses its secretion (and promotes its limited reabsorption) by the collecting ducts.

Influence of Aldosterone

As aldosterone stimulates the principal cells to reabsorb sodium, it simultaneously enhances potassium ion secretion (see Figure 27.8). To maintain electrolyte balance there is a one-for-one exchange of Na^+ and K^+ in the cortical collecting ducts. For each Na^+ reabsorbed, a K^+ is secreted. Thus, as plasma Na^+ levels rise, K^+ levels fall proportionately.

The adrenal cortical cells are *directly* sensitive to the K^+ content of the ECF bathing them. When it increases even slightly, the adrenal cortex is strongly stimulated to release aldosterone, which increases potassium secretion by the exchange process just described. Thus, potassium controls its own concentrations in the ECF via feedback regulation of aldosterone release. Aldosterone is also secreted in response to the renin-angiotensin mechanism previously described (see p. 936).

In an attempt to reduce NaCl intake, many people have turned to salt substitutes which are high in potassium. However, heavy consumption of these substitutes is safe only when aldosterone release by the adrenal cortex is normal. In the absence of aldosterone, hyperkalemia is swift and lethal regardless of K^+ intake (see Table 27.1). Conversely, when a person has an adrenocortical tumor that pumps out tremendous amounts of aldosterone, ECF potassium levels become so depressed that neurons all over the body hyperpolarize and paralysis occurs. •

Regulation of Calcium Balance

About 99% of the body's calcium is found in bones in the form of calcium phosphate salts, which provide strength and rigidity to the skeleton. Ionic calcium in the ECF is important for normal blood clotting, cell membrane permeability, and secretory behavior. Like sodium and potassium, ionic calcium has potent effects on neuromuscular excitability. Hypocalcemia increases excitability and causes muscle tetany. Hypercalcemia is equally dangerous because it inhibits neurons and muscle cells and may cause life-threatening cardiac arrhythmias (see Table 27.1).

Calcium is closely regulated, rarely deviating from normal limits. Calcium balance is regulated primarily by the interaction of two hormones—parathyroid hormone and calcitonin—and under normal circumstances about 98% of the filtered Ca^{2+} is reabsorbed. The bony skeleton provides a dynamic reservoir from which calcium and phosphorus can be withdrawn or deposited to maintain the balance of these electrolytes.

Influence of Parathyroid Hormone

The most important controls of Ca^{2+} homeostasis are exerted by **parathyroid hormone (PTH),** released by the tiny parathyroid glands located on the posterior aspect of the thyroid gland in the pharynx. Declining plasma levels of Ca^{2+} directly stimulate the parathyroid glands to release PTH, which promotes an increase in calcium levels by targeting the following organs (see Figure 17.11, p. 566):

1. **Bones.** PTH activates osteoclasts (bone-digesting cells), which break down the bone matrix, resulting in the release of Ca^{2+} and PO_4^{2-} to the blood.

2. **Small intestine.** PTH enhances intestinal absorption of Ca^{2+} indirectly by stimulating the kidneys to transform vitamin D to its active form (1,25-dihydroxycholecalciferol, also called 1,25-dihydroxyvitamin D_3), which is a necessary cofactor for calcium absorption by the small intestine.

3. **Kidneys.** PTH increases calcium reabsorption by the renal tubules while simultaneously decreasing phosphate ion (PO_4^{2-}) reabsorption. Thus, calcium conservation and phosphate excretion go hand in hand. The adaptive value of this effect is that the *product* of calcium and phosphate in the ECF remains constant, preventing calcium-salt deposit in bones or soft body tissues (see Chapter 6, p. 168).

As a rule, most (75%) filtered phosphate (including $H_2PO_4^-$, HPO_4^{2-}, and PO_4^{3-}) is reabsorbed in the proximal tubules by active transport. In the absence of PTH, phosphate reabsorption is regulated by its transport maximum. Amounts present in excess of that maximum simply flow out in urine. But when the PTH level rises, active transport of phosphate is inhibited.

When calcium levels in the ECF are within normal limits (9–11 mg/100 ml blood) or are high, PTH secretion is inhibited. Consequently, release of calcium from bone is inhibited, larger amounts of calcium are lost in feces and urine, and more phosphate is retained.

Influence of Calcitonin

Calcitonin, a hormone produced by the parafollicular cells of the thyroid gland, is released in response to rising blood calcium levels. Calcitonin targets bone, where it encourages deposit of calcium salts and inhibits bone reabsorption. Calcitonin is an antagonist of PTH, but its contribution to calcium homeostasis is minor.

Regulation of Magnesium Balance

Magnesium, the second most abundant intracellular cation, activates the coenzymes needed for carbohydrate and protein metabolism and plays an essential role in myocardial functioning, neurotransmission, and neuromuscular activity. Half of the magnesium in the body is in the skeleton. Most of the remainder is found intracellularly.

Control of magnesium balance is poorly understood, but a renal transport maximum for magnesium is known to exist. Under ordinary conditions, only 3–5% of the filtered magnesium is excreted; excesses and deficits are rapidly corrected.

Regulation of Anions

Chloride is the major anion accompanying sodium in the ECF and, like sodium, it helps maintain the osmotic pressure of the blood. When blood pH is within normal limits or is slightly alkaline, about 99% of filtered chloride ions are reabsorbed by passive transport. They simply follow sodium ions out of the filtrate and into the peritubular capillary blood. When acidosis occurs, fewer chloride ions accompany sodium because bicarbonate ion reabsorption is stepped up to restore blood pH to its normal range. Thus, the choice between chloride and bicarbonate ions serves acid-base regulation. Most other anions, such as sulfates and nitrates, have definite transport maximums, and when their concentrations in the filtrate exceed their renal thresholds, excesses spill over into urine.

ACID-BASE BALANCE

Because all functional proteins (enzymes, hemoglobin, cytochromes, and others) are influenced by hydrogen ion concentration, it follows that nearly all biochemical reactions are influenced by the pH of their fluid environment. Accordingly, the acid-base balance of body fluids is critical and closely regulated. (For a review of the basic principles of acid-base reactions and pH, see Chapter 2, pp. 40–42.)

The optimal pH of various body fluids differs, but not very much. The normal pH of arterial blood is 7.4, that of venous blood and interstitial fluid is 7.35, and that of intracellular fluid averages 7.0. The lower pH of cells and venous blood reflects their greater amounts of acidic metabolites (such as lactic acid) and carbon dioxide, which combines with water to form carbonic acid (H_2CO_3).

Whenever the pH of arterial blood rises above 7.45, a person is said to have **alkalosis** (al″kah-lo′sis). A drop in arterial pH to below 7.35 results in **acidosis** (as″ĭ-do′sis). Because a pH of 7.0 is neutral, chemically speaking, 7.35 is not acidic. However, it is a higher-than-optimal H^+ concentration for functioning of most cells, and any arterial pH between 7.35 and 7.0 is called **physiological acidosis.**

Although small amounts of acidic substances enter the body via ingested foods, most hydrogen ions originate as by-products or end products of cellular metabolism. For example (1) breakdown of phosphorus-containing proteins (and certain other molecules) releases *phosphoric acid* into the ECF, (2) anaerobic respiration of glucose produces *lactic acid*, (3) fat metabolism yields other organic acids, such as fatty acids, and *ketone bodies*, and (4) as described in Chapter 23, the loading and transport of carbon dioxide in the blood as bicarbonate liberates hydrogen ions. Finally, although hydrochloric acid produced by the stomach is not really *in* the body, it is a source of H^+ that must be buffered if digestion is to occur normally in the small intestine.

The concentration of H^+ in blood is regulated sequentially by (1) chemical buffer systems, (2) the respiratory center in the brain stem, and (3) renal mechanisms. Chemical buffers act within a fraction of a second to resist pH changes and are the first line of defense. Adjustments in respiratory rate and depth begin compensating for acidosis and alkalosis within 1–3 minutes. The kidneys, although the most potent of the acid-base regulatory systems, ordinarily require hours to a day or more to effect changes in blood pH.

Chemical Buffer Systems

Before examining the body's chemical buffer systems, let's review the definitions of strong and weak acids and bases. Recall that acids are *proton donors*, and that the acidity of a solution reflects only the *free* hydrogen ions, not those bound to anions. *Strong acids*, which dissociate completely and liberate all their H^+ in water (Figure 27.11a), can dramatically change a solution's pH. By contrast, *weak acids*, like carbonic and acetic acids, dissociate only partially (Figure 27.11b), and so have a much slighter effect on pH. However, weak acids are very efficient at preventing pH changes, and this characteristic allows them to play extremely important roles in the chemical buffer systems of the body.

Now, we will attend to the concept of strong and weak bases. Remember that bases are *proton acceptors*. Strong bases are those, like hydroxides, that dissociate easily in water and quickly tie up H^+. Conversely, bicarbonate ion (HCO_3^-) and ammonia (NH_3) are slower to accept protons and are considered weak bases.

Chemical acid-base buffers are systems of one or two molecules that act to prevent pronounced changes in H^+ concentration when a strong acid or base is added. They do this by binding to hydrogen ions whenever the pH of body fluids drops and releasing them when pH rises. The three major chemical buffer systems in the body are the *bicarbonate, phosphate,* and *protein buffer systems*, each of which is important in maintaining the pH in one or more fluid compartments. They all work together. Anything that causes a shift in hydrogen ion concentration in one compartment simultaneously causes a change in the others. Thus, the buffer systems actually buffer each other, so that any drifts in pH are resisted by the *entire* chemical buffering system.

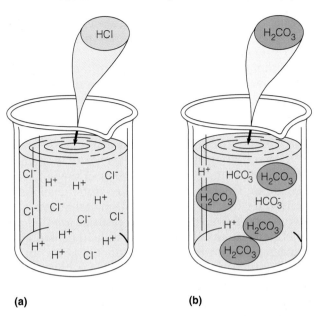

To prevent the pH shift that occurs in situation (a), would it be better to add a strong base or a weak base? Why?

(a)   (b)

FIGURE 27.11
Comparison of dissociation of strong and weak acids.
(a) When HCl, a strong acid, is added to water it dissociates completely into its ions (H^+ and Cl^-). **(b)** By contrast, dissociation of H_2CO_3, a weak acid, is very incomplete, and some molecules of H_2CO_3 remain undissociated (symbols shown in green circles) in solution.

Bicarbonate Buffer System

The **bicarbonate buffer system** is a mixture of carbonic acid (H_2CO_3) and its salt, sodium bicarbonate ($NaHCO_3$), in the same solution. Although it also buffers the ICF, it is the *only* important ECF buffer.

Carbonic acid, a weak acid, does not dissociate to any great extent in neutral or acidic solutions. Thus, when a strong acid, such as hydrochloric acid (HCl), is added to this system, most existing carbonic acid remains intact. However, the bicarbonate ions of the salt act as weak bases to tie up the H^+ released by the stronger acid, forming *more* carbonic acid:

$$HCl + NaHCO_3 \rightarrow H_2CO_3 + NaCl$$

strong acid   weak base   weak acid   salt

Because the strong acid HCl is converted to the weak acid H_2CO_3, it lowers the pH of the solution only slightly.

Similarly, if a strong base such as sodium hydroxide (NaOH) is added to the same buffered solution, a weak base such as sodium bicarbonate ($NaHCO_3$) will not dissociate under such (alkaline) conditions and so will not contribute to the rise in pH. On the other hand, carbonic acid will be forced to dissociate further by the presence of the base (and rising pH), donating more H^+ to tie up the OH^- released by the strong base:

$$NaOH + H_2CO_3 \rightarrow NaHCO_3 + H_2O$$

strong base   weak acid   weak base   water

The net result is replacement of a strong base (NaOH) by a weak one ($NaHCO_3$), so that the pH of the solution rises very little.

Although the bicarbonate salt in the example is sodium bicarbonate, the specific cation dissociated is unimportant. Other bicarbonate salts function in an identical way. Within cells, where little sodium is present, potassium and magnesium bicarbonates act as part of the bicarbonate buffer system.

The buffering power of this type of system is directly related to the concentrations of the buffering substances. Thus, if acids are poured into the blood at such a rate that all the available bicarbonate ions, often referred to as the **alkaline reserve**, are tied up, the buffer system becomes ineffective in resisting pH changes. The bicarbonate ion concentration in the ECF is normally around 25 mEq/L and is closely regulated by the kidneys. The concentration of carbonic acid is only about one-twentieth that of bicarbonate. However, the supply of carbonic acid (made available from the CO_2 released during cellular respiration) is almost limitless, so obtaining that member of the buffer pair is usually not a problem. The carbonic acid content of the blood is subject to respiratory controls.

Phosphate Buffer System

The operation of the **phosphate buffer system** is nearly identical to that of the bicarbonate buffer. Its components are the sodium salts of dihydrogen phosphate ($H_2PO_4^-$) and monohydrogen phosphate (HPO_4^{2-}). NaH_2PO_4 acts as a weak acid. Na_2HPO_4 acts as a weak base.

Again, hydrogen ions released by strong acids are tied up in weak acids:

$$HCl + Na_2HPO_4 \rightarrow NaH_2PO_4 + NaCl$$

strong acid   weak base   weak acid   salt

and strong bases are converted to weak bases:

$$NaOH + NaH_2PO_4 \rightarrow Na_2HPO_4 + H_2O$$

strong base   weak acid   weak base   water

Because the phosphate buffer system is present in low concentrations in the ECF (approximately one-sixth that of the bicarbonate buffer system), it is relatively unimportant for buffering blood plasma. However, it is a very effective buffer in urine and intracellular fluid where phosphate concentrations are usually higher.

Protein Buffer System

Proteins in plasma and within cells are the body's most plentiful and powerful source of buffers, and constitute the **protein buffer system.** In fact, at least three-quarters of all the buffering power of body flu-

ids resides within the cells, and most of this reflects the buffering activity of intracellular proteins.

As described in Chapter 2, proteins are polymers of amino acids. Some of the linked amino acids have free, or exposed, groups of atoms called *organic acid (carboxyl) groups (—COOH)*, which dissociate to release H^+ when the pH begins to rise:

$$R^* - COOH \rightarrow R - COO^- + H^+$$

Additionally, some amino acids have groups of atoms that can act as bases and accept protons. For example, an exposed $-NH_2$ group can bind with hydrogen ions, becoming $-NH_3^+$:

$$R - NH_2 + H^+ \rightarrow R - NH_3^+$$

Because this withdraws free hydrogen ions from solution, it prevents the solution from becoming too acidic. Consequently, the same protein molecules can function reversibly as either acids or bases depending on the pH of their environment. Molecules with this ability are called **amphoteric** (am″fo-ter′ik) **molecules.**

Hemoglobin of red blood cells is an excellent example of a protein that functions as an intracellular buffer. As explained earlier, carbon dioxide released from the tissues forms carbonic acid, which dissociates liberating hydrogen and bicarbonate ions in the blood. However, at the same time, hemoglobin is unloading oxygen, becoming reduced hemoglobin, which carries a negative charge. Because hydrogen ions rapidly bind to the hemoglobin anions, pH changes are minimized (see Chapter 23, p. 771). In this case, carbonic acid, a weak acid, is buffered by an even weaker acid, hemoglobin.

Respiratory System Regulation of Hydrogen Ion Concentration

As described in Chapter 23, the respiratory system eliminates carbon dioxide from the blood while replenishing its stores of oxygen. Carbon dioxide generated by cellular respiration enters erythrocytes in the circulation and is converted to bicarbonate ions for transport in the plasma as shown by the equation:

$$CO_2 + H_2O \underset{\text{carbonic}}{\overset{\text{carbonic anhydrase}}{\rightleftharpoons}} \underset{\text{acid}}{H_2CO_3} \rightleftharpoons H^+ + \underset{\text{ion}}{HCO_3^-}$$

There is a reversible equilibrium between dissolved carbon dioxide and water on the one hand and carbonic acid on the other, and also between carbonic acid and the hydrogen and bicarbonate ions. Consequently, an increase in any of these chemical species will push the reaction in the opposite direction. Notice also that the right side of the equation is equivalent to the bicarbonate buffer system.

---

*Note that R indicates the rest of the organic molecule, which contains many atoms.

In healthy individuals, carbon dioxide is expelled from the lungs at the same rate it is formed in the tissues. During carbon dioxide unloading, the reaction shifts to the left and H^+ generated from carbonic acid is reincorporated into water. Thus, H^+ produced by CO_2 transport is not allowed to accumulate and has little or no effect on blood pH. However, when hypercapnea occurs, it activates medullary chemoreceptors (via cerebrospinal fluid acidosis promoted by excessive accumulation of CO_2). The medullary chemoreceptors respond by increasing respiratory rate and depth (see Figure 23.24, p. 775). Additionally, a rising plasma H^+ concentration, resulting from any metabolic process, indirectly (via peripheral chemoreceptors) excites the respiratory center to stimulate deeper, more rapid respirations. As ventilation increases, more CO_2 is removed from the blood, pushing the reaction to the left and reducing the H^+ concentration. On the other hand, when blood pH begins to rise (alkalosis), the respiratory center is depressed. As the respiratory rate drops and respirations become more shallow, carbon dioxide accumulates; the equilibrium is pushed to the right, causing H^+ concentrations to increase. Again blood pH is restored to the normal range. These respiratory system–mediated corrections of blood pH (via regulation of the CO_2 content of the blood) are accomplished within a minute or so.

Respiratory system regulation of acid-base balance provides a *physiological, or functional, buffering system.* Although it acts more slowly than the chemical buffers, it has one to two times the buffering power of all the chemical buffers combined. Changes in alveolar ventilation can produce dramatic changes in blood pH—far more than is needed. For example, a doubling or halving of alveolar ventilation can raise or lower blood pH by about 0.2 pH unit. Because normal arterial pH is 7.4, a change of 0.2 pH unit would yield a blood pH of 7.6 or 7.2—both well beyond the normal limits of blood pH. Actually, alveolar ventilation can be increased about fifteenfold or reduced to zero. Thus, respiratory controls of blood pH have a tremendous reserve capacity.

Anything that impairs respiratory system functioning causes acid-base imbalances. For example, net carbon dioxide retention leads to acidosis; hyperventilation, which causes net elimination of CO_2, can cause alkalosis. When the cause of the pH imbalance is respiratory system problems, the resulting condition is either **respiratory acidosis** or **respiratory alkalosis** (see Table 27.2).

Renal Mechanisms of Acid-Base Balance

Chemical buffers can tie up excess acids or bases temporarily, but they cannot eliminate them from the body. And while the lungs can dispose of the **volatile acid** carbonic acid by eliminating CO_2, only the kidneys can rid the body of other acids generated by cellular metabolism: phosphoric, uric, and lactic acids,

and ketone bodies. These acids are sometimes referred to as **metabolic (fixed) acids,** and the acidosis resulting from their accumulation is called **metabolic acidosis.** This terminology is both unfortunate and incorrect because carbon dioxide (hence, carbonic acid) is also a product of metabolism. Additionally, only the kidneys have the power to regulate blood levels of alkaline substances and to renew the chemical buffers that are used up in regulating H^+ levels in the ECF. (HCO_3^-, which helps regulate H^+ levels, is lost to the body when CO_2 flushes from the lungs.) Thus, the ultimate acid-base regulatory organs are the kidneys, which act slowly but surely to compensate for acid-base imbalances resulting from enormous variations in diet or metabolism or from disease states.

The most important renal mechanisms for regulating acid-base balance of the blood involve (1) excreting bicarbonate ions and (2) conserving (reabsorbing) or generating new bicarbonate ions. If we look back at the equation for the operation of the carbonic acid–bicarbonate buffer system of the blood, it becomes obvious that losing a HCO_3^- from the body produces the same net effect as gaining a H^+ because it pushes the equation to the right. By the same token, generating and/or reabsorbing HCO_3^- is the same as losing H^+ because it pushes the equation to the left. Therefore, to reabsorb bicarbonate, H^+ has to be secreted, and when we excrete excess HCO_3^-, H^+ is retained (not secreted).

Since the mechanisms for regulating acid-base balance mentioned above depend on H^+ being secreted into the filtrate, we consider that process first. The tubule (and collecting duct) cells respond directly to the pH of the ECF and alter their rate of H^+ secretion accordingly. The hydrogen ions secreted are obtained from the dissociation of carbonic acid, which in turn comes from the combination of carbon dioxide and water within the tubule cells (Figure 27.12). For each H^+ actively secreted into the tubule lumen, one Na^+ is reabsorbed from the filtrate, maintaining the electrochemical balance.

The rate of H^+ secretion rises and falls with CO_2 levels in the ECF. The more CO_2 in the peritubular capillary blood, the faster the rate of H^+ secretion. Because CO_2 levels in the blood directly relate to blood pH, this system can respond to both rising and falling H^+ concentrations. Also notice that secreted H^+ can combine with bicarbonate ions (HCO_3^-) in the filtrate, generating CO_2 and water in the tubule lumen. In this case, H^+ is bound in water. The rising concentration of CO_2 in the filtrate creates a steep diffusion gradient for its entry into the tubule cell, where it promotes still more H^+ secretion.

Conserving Filtered Bicarbonate Ions: Bicarbonate Reabsorption

Bicarbonate ions (HCO_3^-) are an important part of the bicarbonate buffer system, the most important inorganic blood buffer. If this reservoir of base, or *alkaline reserve,* is to be maintained, the kidneys must do more than just eliminate enough hydrogen ions to counter rising blood H^+ levels. Depleted stores of HCO_3^- also must be replenished. This is more complex than it seems because the tubule cells are almost completely impermeable to bicarbonate ions present in the filtrate—they cannot reabsorb them. However, the kidneys can conserve filtered bicarbonate by a rather roundabout mechanism, also illustrated in Figure 27.12. As you can see, dissociation of carbonic acid liberates HCO_3^- as well as H^+. While the tubule cells cannot reclaim bicarbonate directly from the filtrate, they can, and do, shunt bicarbonate ions generated within them into the peritubular capillary blood. Accompanying HCO_3^- into the blood is the Na^+ that enters the tubule cell as H^+ is pumped out. Thus, reabsorption of bicarbonate depends on the secretion of H^+ into the filtrate and its combination there with filtered bicarbonate ions. For each filtered HCO_3^- that "disappears," an HCO_3^- generated within the tubule cells enters the blood—a one-for-one exchange. When large amounts of hydrogen ions are secreted, correspondingly large amounts of HCO_3^- enter the peritubular blood, and the net effect is that bicarbonate ions are almost completely removed from the filtrate.

Generating New Bicarbonate Ions

Generally speaking, two renal mechanisms generate *new* HCO_3^- that can be added to plasma. Both involve renal excretion of acid, via secretion *and excretion* of either hydrogen ions or ammonium ions in urine. Let's examine how these mechanisms differ.

Via Excretion of Buffered H^+. Notice that as long as *filtered bicarbonate* is reclaimed (Figure 27.12), the secreted H^+ is not *excreted* or lost from the body in urine. Instead, such hydrogen ions are buffered by HCO_3^- in the filtrate and ultimately become part of water molecules (most of which are reabsorbed).

However, once filtered HCO_3^- is "used up," any additional H^+ secreted begins to be excreted from the body in urine. More often than not, this is the case. Reclaiming filtered HCO_3^- simply restores the bicarbonate concentration of plasma that exists at the time. However, a normal diet introduces new H^+ into the body which must be counteracted by generating and adding new HCO_3^- (as opposed to filtered HCO_3^-) to the blood to counteract acidosis. These excreted hydrogen ions also must bind with buffers in the filtrate. Otherwise, a urine pH of approximately 1.4 would result—a situation incompatible with life. (H^+ secretion ceases when urine pH falls to 4.5.) The most important urine buffer of excreted H^+ is the *phosphate buffer system.*

Although the members of the phosphate buffer system filter freely into the tubules, their absorption is inhibited during acidosis. Therefore, the buffer pair

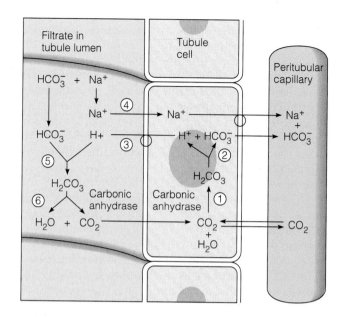

FIGURE 27.12

Reabsorption of filtered HCO_3^- is coupled to H^+ secretion. For each H^+ secreted into the filtrate, a Na^+ and a bicarbonate ion (HCO_3^-) are reabsorbed. Secreted H^+ can combine with HCO_3^- present in the tubular filtrate, forming carbonic acid (H_2CO_3). Thus, HCO_3^- disappears from the filtrate at the same rate that HCO_3^- (formed within the tubule cells) is entering the peritubular capillary blood. The H_2CO_3 formed in the filtrate dissociates to release carbon dioxide and water. Carbon dioxide then diffuses into the tubule cells, where it acts to trigger further H^+ secretion. Active transport processes are indicated by a circle beneath the reaction arrow. (Numbers by reaction lines indicate the sequence of events.)

becomes more and more concentrated as the filtrate moves through the renal tubules. As shown in Figure 27.13a, secreted H^+ combines with Na_2HPO_4, forming NaH_2PO_4, which then flows out in urine. Sodium ions released during this reaction move into the cells and are moved along with bicarbonate ions (generated within the tubule cells) into the peritubular capillary blood. Notice again that when H^+ is being excreted, "brand new" bicarbonate ions are added to the blood—over and above those reclaimed from the filtrate. Thus, in response to acidosis, the kidneys generate bicarbonate ions and add them to the blood (alkalinize the blood) while adding an equal amount of H^+ to the filtrate (acidify the urine).

Via NH_4^+ Excretion. The second mechanism, which comes into play during severe acidosis, utilizes the ammonia (NH_3) produced by metabolism of glutamine within the tubule cells. The ammonia is combined with H^+ to form ammonium ions (NH_4^+), which are weak acids that donate few H^+ at physiologic pH. These, in turn, are excreted in urine in combination with chloride ions (Figure 27.13b). As with the phosphate buffer system, this buffering mechanism replenishes the alkaline reserve of the blood,

FIGURE 27.13
Buffering of excreted hydrogen ions in urine. **(a)** Buffering of excreted H^+ by the phosphate buffer system. Sodium ions released during the reaction are reabsorbed along with the generated bicarbonate ions into the peritubular capillary blood, which also contributes to a rise in blood pH. **(b)** Buffering of excreted H^+ by ammonia. Tubule cells metabolize glutamine to NH_4^+ ($NH_3 + H^+$) and HCO_3^-, and then *actively* secrete the ammonium ions. Sodium ions reabsorbed from the filtrate take the place of ammonium ions in the tubule cells and subsequently enter the peritubular capillary blood along with produced bicarbonate ions. Note that active transport processes are indicated by a circle below the reaction arrow. (Numbers by reaction lines indicate the sequence of events.)

because as NH_4^+ is secreted the newly made sodium bicarbonate is reabsorbed.

Bicarbonate Ion Secretion

When the body is in alkalosis, certain intercalated cells of the collecting ducts exhibit net HCO_3^- secretion (rather than net HCO_3^- reabsorption) while reclaiming H^+ to acidify the blood. Overall the process can be visualized as the exact opposite of that illustrated in Figure 27.12. However, the predominant process in the nephrons and collecting ducts as a whole is HCO_3^- reabsorption, and even during alkalosis, the amount of HCO_3^- excreted is much less than the amount conserved.

Abnormalities of Acid-Base Balance

All cases of acidosis and alkalosis can be classed according to cause as *respiratory* or *metabolic.* The causes and consequences of acid-base disorders are summarized in Table 27.2. The methods for determining the cause of an acid-base disturbance and whether or not it is being compensated (whether the lungs or kidneys are taking steps to correct the imbalance) are described in *A Closer Look*.

Respiratory Acidosis or Alkalosis

Respiratory pH imbalances result from some failure of the respiratory system to perform its normal pH-balancing role. The partial pressure of carbon dioxide (P_{CO_2}) is the single most important indicator of the adequacy of respiratory function. When respiratory functioning is normal, the P_{CO_2} fluctuates between 35 and 45 mm Hg. Generally speaking, values above 45 mm Hg indicate respiratory acidosis, and values below 35 mm Hg indicate respiratory alkalosis.

Respiratory acidosis most often occurs when a person breathes shallowly or when gas exchange is hampered by diseases such as pneumonia, cystic fibrosis, or emphysema. Under such conditions, CO_2 accumulates in the blood. Thus, respiratory acidosis is predicted by a falling blood pH and a rising P_{CO_2}.

Respiratory alkalosis results when carbon dioxide is eliminated from the body faster than it is produced, causing the blood to become more alkaline. This is a common result of hyperventilation. Notice that respiratory acidosis is frequently associated with pathology, but respiratory alkalosis rarely is.

Metabolic Acidosis or Alkalosis

Metabolic pH imbalances include all abnormalities of acid-base imbalance, *except* those caused by too much or too little carbon dioxide in the blood. Bicarbonate ion levels above or below the normal range of 22–26 mEq/L are indicative of a metabolic acid-base imbalance.

The most common causes of **metabolic acidosis** are ingestion of too much alcohol (which is metabolized to acetaldehyde and then acetic acid) and excessive loss of HCO_3^- as might result from persistent

Table 27.2 Causes and Consequences of Acid-Base Imbalances

Condition and hallmark	Possible causes; comments
Metabolic acidosis uncompensated ($HCO_3^- < 22$ mEq/L; pH < 7.4)	*Severe diarrhea:* bicarbonate-rich intestinal (and pancreatic) secretions rushed through digestive tract before their solutes can be reabsorbed; bicarbonate ions are replaced by removal from blood *Renal disease:* failure of kidneys to rid body of acids formed by normal metabolic processes *Untreated diabetes mellitus:* lack of insulin or inability of tissue cells to respond to insulin, resulting in inability to use glucose; fats are used as primary energy fuel, and ketoacidosis occurs *Starvation:* lack of dietary nutrients for cellular fuels; body proteins and fat reserves are used for energy—both yield acidic metabolites as they are broken down for energy *Excess alcohol ingestion:* results in excess acids in blood *High ECF potassium concentrations:* potassium ions compete with H^+ for secretion in renal tubules; when ECF levels of K^+ are high, H^+ secretion is inhibited
Metabolic alkalosis uncompensated ($HCO_3^- > 26$ mEq/L; pH > 7.4)	*Vomiting or gastric suctioning of hydrogen chloride–containing gastric contents:* loss of stomach HCl requires that H^+ be withdrawn from blood to replace stomach acid; thus H^+ decreases and HCO_3^- increases proportionately *Selected diuretics:* cause K^+ depletion and H_2O loss. Low K^+ directly stimulates the tubule cells to secrete H^+. Reduced blood volume elicits the renin-angiotensin mechanism which stimulates Na^+ reabsorption and H^+ secretion. *Ingestion of excessive amount of sodium bicarbonate:* bicarbonate moves easily into ECF, where it enhances natural alkaline reserve *Constipation:* prolonged retention of feces, resulting in increased amounts of HCO_3^- being reabsorbed *Excess aldosterone (e.g., adrenal tumors):* promotes excessive reabsorption of Na^+, which pulls increased amount of H^+ into urine. Hypovolemia promotes the same relative effect because aldosterone secretion is increased to enhance Na^+ (and H_2O) reabsorption
Respiratory acidosis uncompensated ($Pco_2 > 45$ mm Hg; pH < 7.4)	*Any condition that impairs gas exchange or lung ventilation (chronic bronchitis, cystic fibrosis, emphysema):* increased airway resistance and decreased expiratory air flow, leading to retention of carbon dioxide *Rapid, shallow breathing:* tidal volume markedly reduced *Narcotic or barbiturate overdose or injury to brain stem:* depression of respiratory centers, resulting in hypoventilation and respiratory arrest
Respiratory alkalosis uncompensated ($Pco_2 < 35$ mm Hg; pH > 7.4)	*Direct cause is always hyperventilation:* hyperventilation in asthma, pneumonia, anxiety, and at high altitude represents effort to raise Po_2 at the expense of excessive carbon dioxide excretion *Brain tumor or injury:* abnormality of respiratory controls

diarrhea. It may also be due to an accumulation of lactic acid during exercise or shock or to the ketosis that occurs in diabetic crisis or starvation. Kidney failure, in which excess H^+ is not eliminated in urine, is an infrequent cause. Metabolic acidosis is recognized by blood pH and HCO_3^- levels below their homeostatic ranges.

Metabolic alkalosis, indicated by rising blood pH and HCO_3^- levels, is much less common. Typical causes are vomiting of the acidic contents of the stomach (or loss of those secretions through gastrointestinal suctioning), intake of excess base (antacids, for example), and constipation, in which more than the usual amount of HCO_3^- is reabsorbed by the colon.

Effects of Acidosis and Alkalosis

The absolute blood pH limits for life are a low of 7.0 and a high of 7.8. When blood pH falls below 7.0, the central nervous system is so depressed that the person goes into coma and death soon follows. In contrast, alkalosis overexcites the nervous system. Characteristic signs include muscle tetany, extreme nervousness, and convulsions. Death often results from respiratory arrest.

Respiratory and Renal Compensations

When an acid-base imbalance arises due to inadequate functioning of one of the physiological buffer systems (the lungs or kidneys), the other system tries to compensate. The respiratory system will attempt to compensate for metabolic acid-base imbalances, and the kidneys (although much slower) will work to correct imbalances caused by respiratory disease. These **respiratory** and **renal compensations** can be recognized by changes in plasma P_{CO_2} and bicarbonate ion concentrations (see *A Closer Look* on the facing page).

Respiratory Compensations. As a rule, changes in respiratory rate and depth are evident when the respiratory system is attempting to compensate for metabolic acid-base imbalances. In metabolic acidosis, the respiratory rate and depth are usually elevated—an indication that the respiratory centers are stimulated by the high H^+ levels. The blood pH is low (below 7.35) and the bicarbonate level is low (below 22 mEq/L). As the respiratory system "blows off" CO_2 to rid the blood of excess acid, the P_{CO_2} falls below the

Text continues on p. 950.

A CLOSER LOOK | **Sleuthing: Using Blood Values to Determine the Cause of Acidosis or Alkalosis**

Students, particularly nursing students, are often provided with blood values and asked to determine (1) whether the patient is in acidosis or alkalosis, (2) the cause of the condition (respiratory or metabolic), and (3) whether or not the condition is being compensated. Such determinations are not nearly as difficult as they may appear if they are approached systematically. When attempting to analyze a person's acid-base balance, scrutinize the blood values in the following order:

1. Note the pH. This tells you whether the person is in acidosis (pH < 7.35) or alkalosis (pH > 7.45), but it does *not* tell you the cause.

2. Next, check the P_{CO_2} to see if this is the cause of the acid-base imbalance. Because the respiratory system is a fast-acting system, an excessively high or low P_{CO_2} may indicate either that the condition is respiratory system–caused or that the respiratory system is compensating. For example, if the pH indicates acidosis and
   (a) the P_{CO_2} is over 45 mm Hg, the respiratory system *is the cause* of the problem and the condition is a respiratory acidosis;
   (b) the P_{CO_2} is below normal limits (below 35 mm Hg), the respiratory system is *not the cause but is compensating;*

   (c) the P_{CO_2} is within normal limits, the condition is *neither caused nor compensated* by the respiratory system.

3. Check the bicarbonate level. If step 2 proves that the respiratory system is not responsible for the imbalance, then the condition is metabolic and should be reflected in increased or decreased bicarbonate levels: Metabolic acidosis is indicated by HCO_3^- values below 22 mEq/L, and metabolic alkalosis by values over 26 mEq/L. Notice that whereas P_{CO_2} levels vary inversely with blood pH (P_{CO_2} rises as blood pH falls), HCO_3^- levels vary directly with blood pH (increased HCO_3^- results in increased pH).

Consider two examples of this approach:

Problem 1
Blood values given: pH 7.5; P_{CO_2} 24 mm Hg; HCO_3^- 24 mEq/L.
Analysis:

1. The pH is elevated = alkalosis.
2. The P_{CO_2} is very low = the cause of the alkalosis.
3. The HCO_3^- value is within normal limits.

Conclusion: This is a respiratory alkalosis not compensated by renal mechanisms, as might occur during short-term hyperventilation.

Problem 2
Blood values given: pH 7.48; P_{CO_2} 46 mm Hg; HCO_3^- 32 mEq/L.
Analysis:

1. The pH is elevated = alkalosis.
2. The P_{CO_2} is elevated = the cause of *acidosis,* not alkalosis; thus, the respiratory system is compensating and is not the cause.
3. The HCO_3^- is elevated = the cause of the alkalosis.

Conclusion: This is a metabolic alkalosis being compensated by respiratory acidosis (retention of CO_2 to restore blood pH to the normal range).

A simple chart to help you in your future determinations is provided below.

Normal range in plasma	pH 7.35–7.45	P_{CO_2} 35–45 mm Hg	HCO_3^- 22–26 mEq/L
Acid-base disturbance			
Respiratory acidosis	↓	↑	↑ if compensating
Respiratory alkalosis	↑	↓	↓ if compensating
Metabolic acidosis	↓	↓ if compensating	↓
Metabolic alkalosis	↑	↑ if compensating	↑

Making Connections

Systems Connections: Homeostatic Interrelationships Between the Urinary System and Other Body Systems

- Neural controls involved in micturition; sympathetic nervous system activity triggers the renin-angiotensin mechanism and during extreme stress reduces GFR

 Endocrine System

- Kidneys dispose of nitrogenous wastes; maintain fluid, electrolyte, and acid-base balance of blood; produce the hormone erythropoietin; renal regulation of Na^+ and water balance essential for blood pressure homeostasis; Na^+, K^+, and Ca^{2+} regulation maintain cardiac irritability and contractility

- ADH, aldosterone, ANF, and other hormones help regulate renal reabsorption of water and electrolytes

 Cardiovascular System

- Kidneys dispose of nitrogenous wastes; maintain fluid, electrolyte, and acid-base balance of blood; renal regulation of Na^+ and water balance essential for blood pressure homeostasis. Na^+, K^+, and Ca^{2+} regulation maintains cardiac irritability and contractility

- Systemic arterial blood pressure is the driving force for glomerular filtration; heart secretes atrial natriuretic factor; transports nutrients, oxygen, etc. to urinary organs

 Lymphatic System/Immunity

- Kidneys dispose of nitrogenous wastes; maintain fluid, electrolyte, and acid-base balance of blood

- By returning leaked plasma fluid to cardiovascular system, lymphatic vessels help assure normal systemic arterial pressure required for kidney function; immune cells protect urinary organs from infection, cancer, and other foreign substances

 Respiratory System

- Kidneys dispose of nitrogenous wastes; maintain fluid, electrolyte, and acid-base balance of blood

- Respiratory system provides oxygen required by kidney cells for their high metabolic activity; disposes of carbon dioxide; cells in the lungs convert angiotensin I to angiotensin II

 Digestive System

- Kidneys dispose of nitrogenous wastes; maintain fluid, electrolyte, and acid-base balance of blood; also, metabolize vitamin D to the active form needed for calcium absorption

- Digestive organs provide nutrients needed for kidney cell health; liver synthesizes most urea, a nitrogenous waste that must be excreted by the kidneys

 Reproductive System

- Kidneys dispose of nitrogenous wastes; maintain fluid, electrolyte, and acid-base balance of blood

 Integumentary System

- Kidneys dispose of nitrogenous wastes; maintain fluid, electrolyte, and acid-base balance of blood

- Skin provides external protective barrier; serves as site for water loss (via perspiration); vitamin D synthesis site

 Skeletal System

- Kidneys dispose of nitrogenous wastes; maintain fluid, electrolyte, and acid-base balance of blood

- Bones of rib cage provide some protection to kidneys

 Muscular System

- Kidneys dispose of nitrogenous wastes; maintain fluid, electrolyte, and acid-base balance of blood; renal regulation of Na^+, K^+, and Ca^{2+} content in ECF crucial for muscle excitability and contractility

- Muscles of pelvic diaphragm and external urethral sphincter function in voluntary control of micturation; creatinine is a nitrogenous waste product that must be excreted by the kidneys

 Nervous System

- Kidneys dispose of nitrogenous wastes; maintain fluid, electrolyte, and acid-base balance of blood; renal regulation of Na^+, K^+, and Ca^{2+} content in ECF essential for normal neural function

Closer Connections: The Urinary System and Interrelationships with the Cardiovascular, Endocrine, and Nervous Systems

A drink of water—such a simple thing. It quenches a powerful thirst, but that's not all. Inadequate hydration is a major cause of poor functioning, both mental and physical; fatigue; illness; and even death (if it exists during vigorous activity). The body also needs water to regulate its temperature via perspiration, to wash wastes and toxins out of the body in urine, to maintain proper blood volume and pressure, and to keep the skeletal muscles well hydrated (otherwise they feel weak and tire quickly, and even stop working all together). A drink provides that needed water, but it takes the kidneys to keep it pure so that all of these vital activities can continue to occur. Seemingly wise, the exceedingly tiny nephrons "know" which blood solutes are valuable, which disposable, and that alcohol and caffeine are diuretics and as such drain water from the body. Make no mistake about it, the kidneys are crucially important to the body—all systems, all cells. The body systems that most influence the kidneys' ability to do their life-sustaining work are the cardiovascular, endocrine, and nervous systems. Let's take a look.

Cardiovascular System

As important as they are, and as intricate their functioning, the kidneys cannot work without blood to process and blood pressure to drive filtrate through the glomerular filters. When we hemorrhage severely, the GFR drops and the kidneys stop functioning altogether. When blood pressure is normal, as both autoregulatory and systemic mechanisms try to keep it, it provides the driving force that allows the nephrons to perform their job. On the other hand, because the kidneys furnish the means for excreting or retaining water, they are indispensable for maintaining the blood volume that furnishes that filtration pressure.

Endocrine System and Nervous System

Although the kidneys have a whole "toolbox" of ways to ensure that their own blood pressure is normal, autoregulation can be augmented by hormonal mechanisms (the renin-angiotensin mechanism which calls aldosterone and ADH into service, and release of ANF by the heart). In addition, activity of sympathetic inputs makes sure that bodywide blood pressure is maintained within homeostatic limits. Alternatively, the kidneys' needs are overcome as necessary by the same sympathetic fibers to make sure that the heart and brain receive adequate blood perfusion in periods of dramatically falling blood pressure. Now that's flexibility!

Clinical Connections

Urinary System

Case study: Mr. Heyden, a somewhat stocky 72-year-old man, is brought in to the emergency room (ER) at the same time as Jimmy Chin. The paramedics report that his left arm and the left side of his body trunk were pinned beneath some of the wreckage, and that when he was freed, his left hypogastric and lumbar areas appeared to be compressed and his left arm was blanched and without sensation. At the time of admission, Mr. Heyden is alert, slightly cyanotic, and complaining of pain in his left side; he loses consciousness shortly thereafter. His vital signs are taken, blood is drawn for laboratory tests, and Mr. Heyden is catheterized and immediately scheduled for a CT scan of his left abdominal region.

Analyze the information that was subsequently recorded on Mr. Heyden's chart:

• Re vital signs: T° 102°F; BP 90/50 mm Hg and falling; HR 116 bpm and thready; RR 30 respirations/min

Given these values and his attendant cyanosis, what would you guess is Mr. Heyden's immediate problem? Explain your reasoning.

• Re CT scan: CT scan reveals a ruptured spleen and a large hematoma in the upper left abdominal quadrant. Mr. Heyden is scheduled for an immediate splenectomy.

Rupture of the spleen results in massive hemorrhage—much more so than when most other organs are severely damaged. Explain this observation. What problems (if any) may ensue from removal of Mr. Heyden's spleen?

• Re hematology data: Most blood tests yield normal results. However, renin, aldosterone, and ADH levels are elevated. Explain the cause and consequence of each of these findings.

• Re urinalysis: Some granular casts (particulate cell debris) are noted, and the urine is brownish-red in color; other values are normal, but urine output is very low. An order is given to force fluids.

What might account for the low volume of urine output? (Name at least two possibilities.) What might account for the casts and abnormal color of his urine? Can you see any possible relationship between his crush injury and these findings?

The next day, Mr. Heyden is awake and alert. He says that he now has feeling in his arm, but he is still complaining of pain. However, the pain site appears to have moved from the left upper quadrant to his lumbar region. His urine output is still low. He is scheduled once again for a CT scan, this time of his lumbar region. The order to force fluids is renewed and some additional and more specific blood tests are ordered. We will visit Mr. Heyden again shortly, but in the meantime be thinking about what these new findings may indicate.

normal range of 35–45 mm Hg. By contrast, in respiratory acidosis, the respiratory rate is typically depressed and *is the immediate cause of the acidosis* (with some exceptions such as COPD).

In metabolic alkalosis, on the other hand, respiratory compensation involves slow, shallow breathing, which allows carbon dioxide to accumulate in the blood. A metabolic alkalosis that is being compensated by respiratory mechanisms is revealed by a high pH (over 7.45), elevated bicarbonate levels (over 28 mEq/L), and a rising P_{CO_2} (over 45 mm Hg).

Renal Compensations. When the imbalance is of respiratory origin, renal mechanisms are stepped up to correct the imbalance. For example, a hypoventilating individual will exhibit acidosis. When renal compensation is occurring, both the P_{CO_2} and the bicarbonate levels are high. The high P_{CO_2} is the cause of the acidosis. The rising HCO_3^- levels indicate that the kidneys are retaining bicarbonate to offset the acidosis. Conversely, a person with renal-compensated respiratory alkalosis will have a high blood pH and a low P_{CO_2}. Bicarbonate ion levels begin to fall as the kidneys act to eliminate more bicarbonate from the body by failing to reclaim it or by actively secreting it. •

DEVELOPMENTAL ASPECTS OF FLUID, ELECTROLYTE, AND ACID-BASE BALANCE

An embryo and a very young fetus are over 90% water, but solids accumulate as fetal development continues. At birth an infant is 70% to 80% water. (The average value for adults is 58%.) Infants have proportionately more ECF than adults and, consequently, a much higher NaCl content in relation to potassium, magnesium, and phosphate salts. Distribution of body water begins to change about two months after birth and achieves the adult pattern when the child is 2 years old. Although plasma electrolyte concentrations are similar in infants and adults, potassium values are higher and magnesium, bicarbonate, and calcium levels are lower in the first few months of life than at any other time. At puberty, sex differences in body water content become obvious as males develop relatively greater amounts of skeletal muscle.

Problems with fluid, electrolyte, and particularly acid-base balance are most common in infancy, reflecting the following conditions:

1. The very low residual volume of the infant's lungs (approximately half that of adults relative to body weight). When respiration is altered, rapid and dramatic changes in the P_{CO_2} can result.

2. The high rate of fluid intake and output in infants (about seven times higher than that in adults). Infants may exchange fully half their ECF daily. Though infants have proportionately much more body water

than adults, this does not protect them from excessive fluid shifts. Even slight alterations in fluid balance can cause serious problems. Further, although adults can live without water for about ten days, infants can survive for only three to four days.

3. The relatively high metabolic rate of infants (about twice that of adults). The higher metabolic rate yields much larger amounts of metabolic wastes and acids that need to be excreted by the kidneys. This, along with buffer systems that are not yet fully effective, results in a tendency toward acidosis.

4. The high rate of insensible water loss in infants because of their larger surface area relative to body volume (about three times that of adults). Infants lose substantial amounts of water through their skin.

5. The inefficiency of the kidneys in infants. At birth, the kidneys are immature and only about half as proficient as adult kidneys at concentrating urine, and are notably inefficient in ridding the body of acids.

All these factors put newborns at risk for dehydration and acidosis, at least until the end of the first month when their kidneys achieve reasonable efficiency. Bouts of vomiting or diarrhea greatly amplify the risk. With such extreme variations in their internal environment, it is little wonder that mortality of premature infants in particular is so high.

In old age, total body water often decreases (the loss is largely from the intracellular compartment) because muscle mass progressively declines and body fat rises. Although few changes in solute concentrations of body fluids occur, the speed with which homeostasis of the internal environment is restored after being disrupted declines with age. Elders may also be unresponsive to thirst cues and thus are at risk for dehydration. Additionally, they are the most frequent prey of diseases that lead to severe fluid, electrolyte, or acid-base problems, such as congestive heart failure (and its attendant edema) and diabetes mellitus. Because most fluid, electrolyte, and acid-base imbalances occur when body water content is highest or lowest, the very young and the very old are the most frequent victims.

* * *

This chapter has examined the chemical and physiological mechanisms that provide the optimal internal environment for survival. Although the kidneys are the "Rolex" among homeostatic organs in regulating water, electrolyte, and acid-base balance, they do not and cannot act alone. Rather, their activity is made possible by a host of hormones and enhanced both by blood-borne buffers, which give the kidneys time to react, and by the respiratory system, which shoulders a substantial responsibility for acid-base balance of the blood. Now that we have discussed the topics relevant to renal functioning, we are ready to look more closely at how the urinary system interacts with other body systems in *Making Connections.*

RELATED CLINICAL TERMS

Acidemia (as″ĭ-de′me-ah) Arterial blood pH below 7.35.

Alkalemia (al″kah-le′me-ah) Arterial blood pH above 7.45.

Antacid An agent that counteracts acidity, such as sodium bicarbonate, aluminum hydroxide gel, and magnesium trisilicate; commonly used in the management of peptic ulcer.

Conn's disease Also called **primary aldosteronism;** a condition of hypersecretion of aldosterone by the adrenal cortical cells accompanied by excessive loss of potassium and generalized muscular weakness, hypernatremia, and hypertension; usual cause is adrenal tumor; usual treatment is adrenal-suppressing drugs prior to tumor removal.

Renal tubular acidosis A metabolic acidosis resulting from impaired renal reabsorption of bicarbonate; the urine is alkaline.

Syndrome of inappropriate ADH secretion (SIADH) A group of disorders associated with excessive ADH secretion in the absence of appropriate (osmotic or nonosmotic) stimuli; characterized by hyponatremia, concentrated urine, fluid retention, and weight gain. Usual causes are ectopic secretion of ADH by cancer cells (e.g., bronchogenic cancer cells) and brain disorders or trauma affecting the ADH-secreting hypothalamic neurons; temporary management involves water restriction.

CHAPTER SUMMARY

Body Fluids (pp. 928–930)

Body Water Content (p. 928)
1. Water accounts for 45% to 75% of body weight, depending on age, sex, and amount of body fat.

Fluid Compartments (p. 928)
2. About two-thirds (25 L) of body water is found within cells in the intracellular fluid (ICF) compartment; the balance (15 L) is in the extracellular fluid (ECF) compartment. The ECF includes plasma and interstitial fluid, considered to be in separate subcompartments.

Composition of Body Fluids (pp. 928–930)
3. Solutes dissolved in body fluids include electrolytes and nonelectrolytes. Electrolyte concentration is expressed in mEq/L.

4. Plasma contains more proteins than does interstitial fluid; otherwise, extracellular fluids are similar. The most abundant ECF electrolytes are sodium, chloride, and bicarbonate ions.

5. Intracellular fluids contain large amounts of protein anions and potassium, magnesium, and phosphate ions.

Movement of Fluids Among Compartments (p. 930)
6. Fluid exchanges between compartments are regulated by osmotic and hydrostatic pressures: (a) Filtrate is forced out of the capillaries by hydrostatic pressure and pulled back in by osmotic pressure; (b) water moves freely between the ECF and the ICF by osmosis, but solute movements are restricted by size, charge, and dependence on active transport; (c) water flows always follow changes in ECF osmolarity.

7. Plasma links the internal and external environments.

Water Balance (pp. 930–934)

1. Sources of body water are ingested foods and fluids and metabolic water.

2. Water leaves the body via the lungs, skin, gastrointestinal tract, and kidneys.

Regulation of Water Intake: The Thirst Mechanism (pp. 931–932)
3. Increased plasma osmolarity or decreased plasma volume triggers the thirst mechanism, mediated by hypothalamic osmoreceptors. Thirst, inhibited by distension of the gastrointestinal tract by ingested water and then by osmotic signals, may be damped before body needs for water are met.

Regulation of Water Output (p. 932)
4. Obligatory water loss is unavoidable and includes insensible water losses from the lungs, the skin, in feces, and about 500 ml of urine output daily.

5. Beyond obligatory water loss, the volume of urinary output depends on water intake and loss via other routes and reflects the influence of antidiuretic hormone and aldosterone on the renal tubules.

Disorders of Water Balance (pp. 932–934)
6. Dehydration occurs when water loss exceeds water intake over time. It is evidenced by thirst, dry skin, and decreased urine output.

7. Hypotonic hydration occurs when body fluids are excessively diluted and cells become swollen by water entry. The most serious consequence is cerebral edema.

8. Edema is an abnormal accumulation of fluid in the interstitial space, which may impair blood circulation.

Electrolyte Balance (pp. 934–940)

1. Most electrolytes (salts) are obtained from ingested foods and fluids. Salts, particularly NaCl, are often ingested in excess of need.

2. Electrolytes are lost in perspiration, feces, and urine. The kidneys are most important in regulating electrolyte balance.

The Central Role of Sodium in Fluid and Electrolyte Balance (p. 934)
3. Sodium salts are the most abundant solutes in ECF. They exert the bulk of ECF osmotic pressure and control water volume and distribution in the body.

4. Na^+ transport by the renal tubule cells is coupled to and helps regulate K^+, Cl^-, HCO_3^-, and H^+ concentrations in the ECF.

Regulation of Sodium Balance (pp. 935–937)
5. Sodium ion balance is linked to water balance and blood pressure regulation and involves both neural and hormonal controls.

6. Declining blood pressure and falling filtrate osmolarity stimulate the juxtaglomerular cells to release renin. Renin, via angiotensin II, enhances systemic blood pressure and aldosterone release.

7. Cardiovascular system baroreceptors sense changing arterial blood pressure, prompting changes in sympathetic vasomotor activity. Rising arterial pressure leads to vasodilation and enhanced Na^+ and water loss in urine. Falling arterial pressure promotes vasoconstriction and conserves Na^+ and water.

8. Atrial natriuretic factor, released by certain atrial cells in response to rising blood pressure (or blood volume), causes systemic vasodilation and inhibits renin, aldosterone, and ADH release. Hence, it enhances Na^+ and water excretion, reducing blood volume and blood pressure.

9. Estrogens and glucocorticoids increase renal retention of sodium. Progesterone promotes enhanced sodium and water excretion in urine.

Regulation of Potassium Balance (pp. 937–939)

10. About 90% of filtered potassium is reabsorbed by the proximal regions of the nephrons.

11. The main thrust of renal regulation of K^+ is to excrete it. Potassium ion secretion by the principal cells of the cortical collecting ducts is enhanced by increased plasma K^+ content and aldosterone. Collecting duct cells reabsorb small amounts of K^+ during K^+ deficit.

Regulation of Calcium Balance (p. 939–940)

12. Calcium balance is regulated primarily by parathyroid hormone, which targets the bones, intestine, and kidneys, thereby enhancing blood Ca^{2+} levels.

13. Calcitonin accelerates the deposit of Ca^{2+} in bone and inhibits its release from bone matrix. However, its influence on the kidneys is relatively minor.

Regulation of Magnesium Balance (p. 940)

14. Magnesium levels are regulated to counteract excesses or deficits in the ECF. The mechanism is unclear.

Regulation of Anions (pp. 940)

15. When blood pH is normal or slightly high, chloride is the major anion accompanying sodium reabsorption. In acidosis, chloride is replaced by bicarbonate.

16. Most other anions appear to be regulated by their T_m.

Acid-Base Balance (pp. 940–950)

1. Acids are proton (H^+) donors; bases are proton acceptors. Acids that dissociate completely in solution are strong acids; those that dissociate incompletely are weak acids. Strong bases are much more effective proton acceptors than weak bases.

2. The homeostatic pH range of arterial blood is 7.35 to 7.45. A higher pH represents alkalosis; a lower pH reflects acidosis.

3. Some acids enter the body in foods, but most are generated by breakdown of phosphorus-containing proteins, incomplete oxidation of fats or glucose, and the loading and transport of carbon dioxide in the blood.

4. Acid-base balance is achieved by renal regulation of bicarbonate ion (hence, hydrogen ion) concentration of body fluids.

Chemical Buffer Systems (pp. 941–942)

5. Chemical buffers are single or paired sets (a weak acid and its salt) of molecules that act rapidly to resist excessive shifts in pH by releasing or binding H^+.

6. Chemical buffers of the body include the bicarbonate, phosphate, protein, and ammonia buffer systems.

Respiratory System Regulation of Hydrogen Ion Concentration (pp. 942–943)

7. Respiratory regulation of acid-base balance of the blood utilizes the bicarbonate buffer system and the fact that carbon dioxide and water are in reversible equilibrium with H_2CO_3.

8. Acidosis activates the respiratory center to increase respiratory rate and depth, which eliminates more CO_2 and causes blood pH to rise. Alkalosis depresses the respiratory center, resulting in CO_2 retention and a fall in blood pH.

Renal Mechanisms of Acid-Base Balance (pp. 943–945)

9. The kidneys provide the major long-term mechanism for controlling acid-base balance by maintaining stable HCO_3^- levels in the ECF. Metabolic acids (organic acids other than carbonic acid) can be eliminated from the body only by the kidneys.

10. Secreted hydrogen ions come from the dissociation of carbonic acid generated within the tubule cells.

11. Tubule cells are impermeable to bicarbonate in the filtrate, but they can conserve bicarbonate ions generated within them by dissociation of carbonic acid to HCO_3^- and H^+. For each HCO_3^- (and Na^+) reabsorbed, one H^+ is secreted into the filtrate where it combines with HCO_3^-.

12. To generate and add new HCO_3^- to plasma to counteract acidosis

- secreted H^+, buffered by bases other than HCO_3^-, are excreted from the body in urine (the major urine buffer is the phosphate buffer system); or

- NH_4^+ derived from glutamine catabolism is excreted in urine.

13. To counteract alkalosis, bicarbonate ion is secreted into the filtrate and H^+ is reabsorbed.

Abnormalities of Acid-Base Balance (pp. 945–950)

14. Classification of acid-base imbalances as metabolic or respiratory indicates the cause of the acidosis or alkalosis.

15. Respiratory acidosis results from carbon dioxide retention; respiratory alkalosis occurs when carbon dioxide is eliminated faster than it is produced.

16. Metabolic acidosis occurs when fixed acids (lactic acid, ketone bodies, and others) accumulate in the blood or when bicarbonate is lost from the body; metabolic alkalosis occurs when bicarbonate levels are excessive.

17. Extremes of pH for life are 7.0 and 7.8.

18. Compensations occur when the respiratory system or kidneys act to reverse acid-base imbalances resulting from abnormal or inadequate functioning of the alternate system. Respiratory compensations involve changes in respiratory rate and depth. Renal compensations modify blood levels of HCO_3^-.

Developmental Aspects of Fluid, Electrolyte, and Acid-Base Balance (p. 950)

1. Factors that place infants at risk for dehydration and acidosis include low lung residual volume, high rate of fluid intake and output, high metabolic rate, relatively large body surface area, and functional immaturity of the kidneys at birth.

2. The elderly are at risk for dehydration because of their low percentage of body water and insensitivity to thirst cues. Diseases that promote fluid and acid-base imbalances (cardiovascular disease, diabetes mellitus, and others) are most common in the aged.

REVIEW QUESTIONS

Multiple Choice/Matching

1. Body water content is greatest in (a) infants, (b) young adults, (c) elderly adults.

2. Potassium, magnesium, and phosphate ions are the predominant electrolytes in (a) plasma, (b) interstitial fluid, (c) intracellular fluid.

3. Sodium balance is regulated primarily by control of amount(s) (a) ingested, (b) excreted in urine, (c) lost in perspiration, (d) lost in feces.

4. Water balance is regulated primarily by control of amount(s) (use choices in question 3).

5 through 10. Answer questions 5 through 10 by choosing a response from the following:

(a) ammonia (e) hydrogen ions (h) potassium
(b) bicarbonate (f) magnesium (i) sodium
(c) calcium (g) phosphate (j) water
(d) chloride

5. Three ionic substances regulated (at least in part) by the influence of aldosterone on the kidney tubules.

6. Two substances regulated by parathyroid hormone.

7. Two substances secreted into the distal convoluted tubules in exchange for sodium ions.

8. Part of an important chemical buffer system in plasma.

9. When being secreted by the tubule cells, it combines with H^+ to form a substance that cannot be reabsorbed and is, thus, excreted in urine.

10. Substance regulated by ADH's effects on the renal tubules.

11. Which of the following factors will enhance ADH release? (a) increase in ECF volume, (b) decrease in ECF volume, (c) decrease in ECF osmolarity, (d) increase in ECF osmolarity, (e) increase in blood pressure (f) decrease in blood pressure.

12. The pH of blood varies directly with (a) HCO_3^-, (b) P_{CO_2}, (c) neither of the above.

13. In an individual with metabolic acidosis, a clue that the respiratory system is compensating is provided by (a) high blood bicarbonate levels, (b) low blood bicarbonate levels, (c) rapid, deep breathing, (d) slow, shallow breathing.

Short Answer Essay Questions

14. Name the body fluid compartments, noting their locations and the approximate fluid volume in each.

15. Describe the thirst mechanism, noting how it is triggered and terminated.

16. Explain why and how sodium and water balance are jointly regulated.

17. Describe the role of the respiratory system in controlling acid-base balance.

18. Explain how the chemical buffer systems resist changes in pH.

19. Explain the relationship of the following to renal secretion and excretion of hydrogen ions: (a) plasma carbon dioxide levels, (b) phosphate, and (c) sodium bicarbonate reabsorption.

20. Note several factors that place newborn babies at risk for acid-base imbalances.

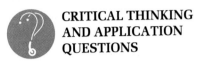

CRITICAL THINKING AND APPLICATION QUESTIONS

1. Mr. Jessup, a 55-year-old man is operated on for a cerebral tumor. About a month later, he appears at his physician's office complaining of excessive thirst. He claims to have been drinking about 20 liters of water daily for the past week and that he has been voiding nearly continuously. A urine sample is collected and its specific gravity is reported as 1.001. What is your diagnosis of Mr. Jessup's problem? What connection might exist between his previous surgery and his present problem?

2. For each of the following sets of blood values, name the acid-base imbalance (acidosis or alkalosis), determine its cause (metabolic or respiratory), decide whether the condition is being compensated, and cite at least one possible cause of the imbalance. *Problem 1:* pH 7.63; P_{CO_2} 19 mm Hg; HCO_3^- 19.5 mEq/L. *Problem 2:* pH 7.22; P_{CO_2} 30 mm Hg; HCO_3^- 12.0 mEq/L.

3. Explain how emphysema and congestive heart failure can lead to acid-base imbalance.

4. A 70-year-old woman is admitted to the hospital. Her history states that she has been suffering from diarrhea for three weeks. On admission, she complains of severe fatigue and muscle weakness. A blood chemistry study yields the following information: Na^+ 142 mEq/L; K^+ 1.5 mEq/L; Cl^- 92 mEq/L; P_{CO_2} 32 mm Hg. Which electrolytes are within normal limits? Which are so abnormal that the patient has a medical emergency? Which of the following represents the greatest danger to this patient? (a) a fall due to her muscular weakness, (b) edema, (c) cardiac arrhythmia and cardiac arrest.

28

The Reproductive System

CHAPTER OUTLINE AND STUDENT OBJECTIVES

1. Describe the common function of the male and female reproductive systems.

Anatomy of the Male Reproductive System (pp. 955–960)

2. Describe the structure and function of the testes, and explain the importance of their location in the scrotum.
3. Describe the location, structure, and function of the accessory organs of the male reproductive system.
4. Describe the structure of the penis, and note its role in the reproductive process.
5. Discuss the sources and functions of semen.

Physiology of the Male Reproductive System (pp. 960–969)

6. Define meiosis. Compare and contrast it to mitosis.
7. Outline the events of spermatogenesis.
8. Describe the phases of the male sexual response.
9. Discuss hormonal regulation of testicular function and the physiological effects of testosterone on male reproductive anatomy.

Anatomy of the Female Reproductive System (pp. 968–976)

10. Describe the location, structure, and function of the ovaries.

11. Describe the location, structure, and function of each of the organs of the female reproductive duct system.
12. Describe the anatomy of the female external genitalia.
13. Discuss the structure and function of the mammary glands.

Physiology of the Female Reproductive System (pp. 976–984)

14. Describe the process of oogenesis and compare it to spermatogenesis.
15. Describe the phases of the ovarian cycle, and relate them to events of oogenesis.
16. Describe the regulation of the ovarian and menstrual cycles.
17. Discuss the physiological effects of estrogens and progesterone.
18. Describe the phases of female sexual response.

Sexually Transmitted Diseases (pp. 984–987)

19. Describe the infectious agents and modes of transmission of gonorrhea, syphilis, chlamydia, and genital herpes.

Developmental Aspects of the Reproductive System: Chronology of Sexual Development (pp. 988–994)

20. Discuss the determination of genetic sex and prenatal development of male and female structures.
21. Note the significant events of puberty and menopause.

Most organ systems of the body function almost continuously to maintain the well-being of the individual. The **reproductive system,** however, appears to "slumber" until puberty. The **primary sex organs,** or **gonads** (go'nadz; "seeds"), are the *testes* in males and the *ovaries* in females. The gonads produce sex cells, or **gametes** (gam'ēts; "spouses"), and secrete **sex hormones.** The remaining diverse collection of reproductive structures—ducts, glands, and external genitalia (jen'ĭ-ta-le-ah)—are referred to as **accessory reproductive organs.**

Although male and female reproductive organs are quite different, their common purpose is to produce offspring.

The male's reproductive role is to manufacture male gametes called *sperm* and to deliver them to the female reproductive tract, where fertilization can occur. The mutually complementary role of the female is to produce female gametes, called *ova* or *eggs.* When these events are appropriately timed, a sperm and egg fuse to form a fertilized egg, the first cell of the new individual, from which all body

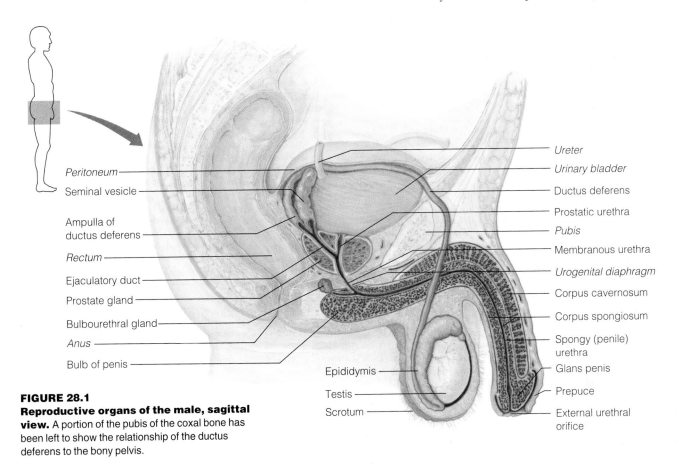

FIGURE 28.1
Reproductive organs of the male, sagittal view. A portion of the pubis of the coxal bone has been left to show the relationship of the ductus deferens to the bony pelvis.

Labels (left side, top to bottom):
Peritoneum
Seminal vesicle
Ampulla of ductus deferens
Rectum
Ejaculatory duct
Prostate gland
Bulbourethral gland
Anus
Bulb of penis

Labels (center bottom):
Epididymis
Testis
Scrotum

Labels (right side, top to bottom):
Ureter
Urinary bladder
Ductus deferens
Prostatic urethra
Pubis
Membranous urethra
Urogenital diaphragm
Corpus cavernosum
Corpus spongiosum
Spongy (penile) urethra
Glans penis
Prepuce
External urethral orifice

cells will arise. The male and female reproductive systems are equal partners in events leading up to fertilization, but once fertilization has occurred, the female uterus provides a protective environment in which the embryo develops until birth.

The sex hormones—androgens in males and estrogens and progesterone in females—play vital roles both in the development and function of the reproductive organs and in sexual behavior and drives. These gonadal hormones also influence the growth and development of many other organs and tissues of the body.

ANATOMY OF THE MALE REPRODUCTIVE SYSTEM

Figure 28.1 presents an overview of the male reproductive system. Males are males because they possess testes. The sperm-producing **testes,** or male gonads, lie within the *scrotum.* From the testes, the sperm are delivered to the body exterior through a system of ducts including (in order) the *epididymis,* the *ductus deferens,* and finally the *urethra,* which opens to the outside at the tip of the *penis.* The accessory sex glands, which empty their secretions into the ducts during ejaculation, are the *seminal vesicles, prostate gland,* and *bulbourethral glands.* Take a moment to trace the duct system and identify the accessory glands before continuing.

The Scrotum

The **scrotum** (skro'tum; "pouch") is a sac of skin and superficial fascia that hangs outside the abdominopelvic cavity at the root of the penis (Figure 28.2). The scrotum is covered with sparse hairs and with skin that is more heavily pigmented than that elsewhere on the body. The paired oval testes, or *testicles,* lie suspended in the scrotum. A midline septum divides the scrotum into right and left halves, providing one compartment for each testis. This location seems a rather vulnerable position for a man's testes, which contain his entire genetic heritage. However, viable sperm cannot be produced at core body temperature (36.2°C). Hence, the superficial location of the scrotum, which provides a temperature about 3°C lower, is an essential adaption. Furthermore, the scrotum responds to changes in temperature. For example, when it is cold, the testes are pulled closer to the warmth of the body wall, and the scrotum becomes shorter and heavily wrinkled to reduce heat loss. When it is warm, the scrotal skin is flaccid and loose to increase the surface area for cooling, and the testes hang lower. These changes in scrotal surface area help maintain a fairly constant intrascrotal temperature and reflect the activity of two sets of muscles. The **dartos** (dar'tos; "skinned") **muscle,** a layer of smooth muscle in the superficial fascia, wrinkles the scrotal skin. The **cremaster** (kre-mas'ter; "a suspender") **muscles,** bands of skeletal muscle that arise

Internal oblique muscle

Aponeurosis of external oblique muscle (cut)

Suspensory ligament of penis

Penis (cut)

Midline septum of scrotum

Cremaster muscle

External spermatic fascia

Scrotum — Superficial fascia containing dartos muscle

Skin

Superficial inguinal ring (end of inguinal canal)

Spermatic cord

Ductus (vas) deferens

Autonomic nerve fibers

Pampiniform plexus of testicular veins

Testicular artery

Epididymis

Double layered tunica vaginalis (from peritoneum)

Tunica albuginea of testis

Internal spermatic fascia

FIGURE 28.2
Relationships of the testis to the scrotum and spermatic cord. The scrotum has been opened and its anterior portion removed.

from the internal oblique muscle of the trunk, elevate the testes.

The Testes

Each olive-sized testis is approximately 4 cm (1.5 inches) long and 2.5 cm (1 inch) in diameter and is surrounded by two tunics. The outer tunic is the two-layered **tunica vaginalis** (vaj″ĭ-nal′is), derived from the peritoneum (see Figures 28.2 and 28.3). Deep to this is the **tunica albuginea** (al″bu-jin′e-ah; "white coat"), the fibrous capsule of the testis. Septal extensions of the tunica albuginea divide the testis into 250 to 300 wedge-shaped compartments or *lobules* (Figure 28.3). Each lobule contains one to four tightly coiled **seminiferous** (sem″ĭ-nif′er-us; "sperm-carrying") **tubules,** the actual "sperm factories."

The seminiferous tubules of each lobule converge to form a **tubulus rectus,** a straight tubule that conveys sperm into the **rete** (re′te) **testis,** a tubular network located on the posterior side of the testis. From the rete testis, sperm leave the testis through the *efferent ductules* and enter the *epididymis* (ep″ĭ-did′ĭ-mis), which hugs the external surface of the testis.

Lying in the soft connective tissue surrounding the seminiferous tubules are the **interstitial cells,** or *Leydig* (li′dig) *cells.* These functionally distinct cells produce androgens (most importantly, *testosterone*),

which they secrete into the surrounding interstitial fluid. Thus, the sperm-producing and hormone-producing functions of the testis are carried out by completely different cell populations.

The testes receive their arterial blood supply from the long **testicular arteries,** which branch from the abdominal aorta (see Figure 20.20c, p. 679). The **testicular veins,** which drain the testes, arise from a vinelike network called the **pampiniform** (pam-pin′ĭ-form; "tendril-shaped") **plexus** that surrounds the testicular artery (see Figure 28.2). This plexus absorbs heat from the arterial blood, cooling it before it enters the testes. Thus, it provides an additional avenue for maintaining the testes at their cool homeostatic temperature. The testes are served by both divisions of the autonomic nervous system. Associated sensory nerves transmit impulses that result in agonizing pain and nausea when the testes are hit forcefully. The nerve fibers are enclosed, along with the blood vessels and lymphatics, in a connective tissue sheath called the **spermatic cord** (see Figure 28.2).

Although *testicular cancer* is relatively rare (affecting 1 of every 20,000 males), it is the most common cancer in young men (ages of 15 to 35). A history of mumps or orchitis (inflammation of the testis) increases the risk, but the most important risk factor for this cancer is *cryptorchidism* (nondescent of the testes, see p. 991). Because the most common

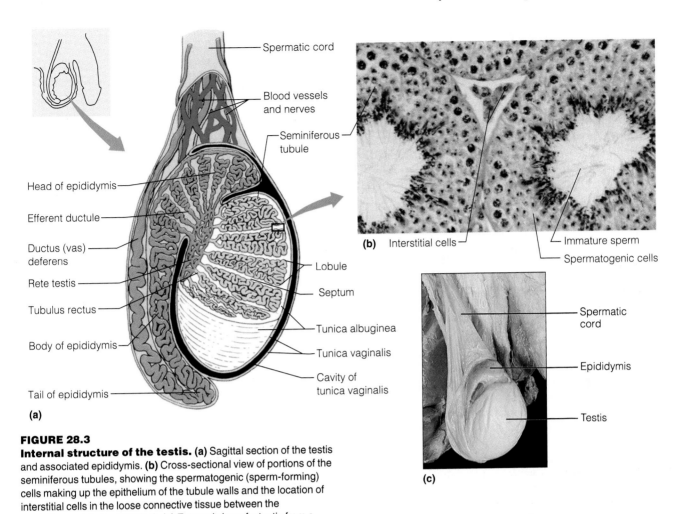

(b)   Interstitial cells   Immature sperm   Spermatogenic cells

(c)

Labels in part (a):
Spermatic cord
Blood vessels and nerves
Seminiferous tubule
Head of epididymis
Efferent ductule
Ductus (vas) deferens
Rete testis
Tubulus rectus
Body of epididymis
Tail of epididymis
Lobule
Septum
Tunica albuginea
Tunica vaginalis
Cavity of tunica vaginalis

(a)

Labels in part (c):
Spermatic cord
Epididymis
Testis

FIGURE 28.3
Internal structure of the testis. (a) Sagittal section of the testis and associated epididymis. **(b)** Cross-sectional view of portions of the seminiferous tubules, showing the spermatogenic (sperm-forming) cells making up the epithelium of the tubule walls and the location of interstitial cells in the loose connective tissue between the seminiferous tubules (1200×). **(c)** External view of a testis from a cadaver; same orientation as in part (a).

sign of testicular cancer is a painless solid mass in the testis, self-examination of the testes should be practiced by every male. If detected early, most testicular cancers are cured by surgical removal of the cancerous testis *(orchiectomy)* followed by radiation therapy or chemotherapy. •

The Male Duct System

As mentioned earlier, sperm travel from the testes to the outside of the body through a system of ducts. In order (proximal to distal), the **accessory ducts** are the epididymis, the ductus deferens, and the urethra.

The Epididymis

The comma-shaped **epididymis** (*epi* = beside; *didym* = the testes) is about 3.8 cm (1.5 inches) long (see Figures 28.1 and 28.3a, c). Its *head,* which contains and receives sperm from the efferent ductules, caps the superior aspect of the testis. Its *body* and *tail* regions, which lie on the posterolateral aspect of the testis, contain the highly coiled *duct of the*

epididymis (with a true uncoiled length of about 6 m [20 feet]). Some of the cells of the pseudostratified epithelium of its mucosa exhibit long, nonmotile microvilli called *stereocilia,* which absorb excess testicular fluid and pass nutrients to the sperm in the lumen.

The immature, nearly nonmotile sperm that leave the testis are moved slowly through the duct of the epididymis. During their transport along its tortuous course (a trip that takes about 20 days), the sperm gain the ability to swim. When a male is sexually stimulated and ejaculates, the smooth muscle in the walls of the epididymis contracts vigorously, expelling sperm from the tail portion into the next segment of the duct system, the ductus deferens. However, sperm can be stored in the epididymis for several months. If held longer, they are eventually phagocytized by the epithelial cells of the epididymis.

The Ductus Deferens

The **ductus deferens** (duk'tus def'er-ens; "carrying away"), or **vas deferens,** is about 45 cm (18 inches) long. It runs upward as part of the spermatic cord from the epididymis through the inguinal canal into the pelvic cavity (see Figure 28.1). It is easily palpated as it passes anterior to the pubic bone. It then arches medially over the ureter and descends along the posterior aspect of the bladder. Its terminus expands to form the **ampulla** and then joins with the duct of the seminal vesicle (a gland) to form the short **ejaculatory duct.** Each ejaculatory duct, in turn, passes into the prostate gland where it empties into the urethra. The ductus deferens propels live sperm from their storage sites, the epididymis and distal part of the ductus deferens, into the urethra. At the moment of ejaculation, the thick layers of smooth muscle in its walls create strong peristaltic waves that rapidly squeeze the sperm forward.

As Figure 28.3 illustrates, part of the ductus deferens lies in the scrotal sac. Some men opt to take full responsibility for birth control by having a **vasectomy** (vah-sek'to-me; "cutting the vas"). In this relatively minor operation, the physician makes a small incision into the scrotum and then cuts through and ligates (ties off) the ductus deferens. Although sperm continue to be produced for the next several years, they can no longer reach the body exterior. Eventually, they deteriorate and are phagocytized. Although vasectomy is simple and provides highly effective birth control (close to 100%), it is not risk free. Recent studies have raised the possibility that vasectomy is associated with increased risk of prostate cancer, and autoimmune reactions against the testes after vasectomy are well documented. (Since sperm are not produced until adolescence, the immune system does not recognize sperm antigens as self.)

The Urethra

The **urethra** is the terminal portion of the male duct system (see Figures 28.1 and 28.4). Since it conveys both urine and semen (at different times), it serves both the urinary and reproductive systems. Its three regions are (1) the *prostatic urethra,* the portion surrounded by the prostate gland; (2) the *membranous urethra* in the urogenital diaphragm; and (3) the *spongy (penile) urethra,* which runs through the penis and opens to the outside at the *external urethral orifice.* The spongy urethra is about 15 cm (6 inches) long and accounts for 75% of urethral length.

Accessory Glands

The **accessory glands** include the paired seminal vesicles and bulbourethral glands and the single prostate gland (Figure 28.1). These glands produce the bulk of *semen* (sperm plus accessory gland secretions).

The Seminal Vesicles

The **seminal** (sem'ĭ-nul) **vesicles** lie on the posterior wall of the bladder. These glands are fairly large, each about the shape and length (5 to 7 cm) of a little fin-

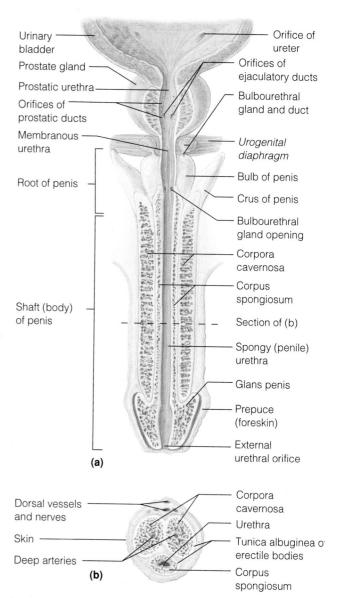

FIGURE 28.4
Structure of the penis. (a) Longitudinal (coronal) section of the penis. **(b)** Transverse section of the penis.

ger. Their secretion, which accounts for about 60% of the volume of semen, is a yellowish viscous alkaline fluid containing fructose sugar, ascorbic acid, a coagulating enzyme *(vesiculase),* and prostaglandins. As noted, the duct of each seminal vesicle joins that of the ductus deferens on the same side to form the ejaculatory duct. Sperm and seminal fluid mix in the ejaculatory duct and enter the prostatic urethra together during ejaculation.

The Prostate Gland

The **prostate** (pros'tāt) **gland** is a single gland about the size and shape of a chestnut (see Figures 28.1 and 28.4). It encircles the part of the urethra just inferior to the bladder. Enclosed by a thick connective tissue capsule, it is made up of 20 to 30 compound tubuloalveolar glands embedded in a mass (stroma) of smooth muscle and a dense connective tissue. The prostatic gland secretion, accounting for up to one-third of the semen volume, is a milky, slightly acid fluid that contains several enzymes (fibrinolysin and acid phosphatase) and plays a role in activating sperm. It enters the prostatic urethra via several ducts when the prostatic smooth muscle contracts during ejaculation.

The prostate gland has a reputation as a health destroyer (perhaps reflected in the common mispronunciation "prostrate"). Hypertrophy of the prostate gland, which affects nearly every elderly male, distorts the urethra. The more the man strains to urinate, the more the valvelike prostatic mass blocks the opening. This troublesome condition also enhances the risk of bladder infections (cystitis) and kidney damage. Treatment is usually surgical, but the "balloon option," in which a small balloon is inserted and inflated to compress the prostate tissue away from the prostatic urethra, is gaining popularity. *Prostatitis* (pros"tah-ti'tis), inflammation of the prostate, is the single most common reason for a man to consult a urologist, and prostatic cancer is the third most prevalent cancer in men. Screening for prostatic cancer typically involves digital examination of the size and texture of the prostate through the anterior wall of the rectum and assay of *prostate specific antigen (PSA)* levels in the blood. PSA is a tumor marker and its rising serum level follows the clinical disease course of prostate cancer. Additionally, elevated blood levels of acid phosphatase are usually diagnostic for prostatic cancer. When possible, prostatic cancer is treated surgically. Alternative therapies for metastasized cancers involve castration or drug therapy with antiandrogen drugs (flutamide), which block androgen receptors, or LHRH analogues (such as leuprolide), which inhibit gonadotropin release. Deprived of the stimulatory effects of androgens, the prostatic tissue regresses and urinary symptoms typically decline. •

The Bulbourethral Glands

The **bulbourethral** (bul"bo-u-re'thral) **glands** are pea-sized glands situated inferior to the prostate gland (Figures 28.1 and 28.4). They produce a thick, clear mucus that drains into the spongy urethra. This secretion, which is released prior to ejaculation, is believed to neutralize traces of acidic urine in the urethra.

The Penis

The **penis** ("tail") is a copulatory organ, designed to deliver sperm into the female reproductive tract (see Figure 28.4). The penis and scrotum (described earlier), which hang suspended from the perineum, make up the external reproductive structures, or **external genitalia,** of the male. The **male perineum** (per"ĭ-ne-um; "around the anus") is the diamond-shaped region located between the pubic symphysis anteriorly, the

coccyx posteriorly, and the ischial tuberosities laterally. The floor of the perineum is formed by muscles described in Chapter 10 (pp. 310–311).

The penis consists of an attached *root* and a free *shaft* or *body* that ends in an enlarged tip, the **glans penis.** The skin covering the penis is loose, and it slides distally to form a cuff of skin called the **prepuce** (pre'pūs), or **foreskin,** around the glans. Frequently, the foreskin is surgically removed shortly after birth, a procedure called *circumcision* ("cutting around").

Internally, the penis contains the spongy urethra and three long cylindrical bodies *(corpora)* of erectile tissue, each bound by fibrous tunica albuginea. *Erectile tissue* is a spongy network of connective tissue and smooth muscle riddled with vascular spaces. During sexual excitement, the vascular spaces fill with blood, causing the penis to enlarge and become rigid. This event, called *erection,* enables the penis to serve as a penetrating organ. The midventral erectile body, the **corpus spongiosum** (spon"je-o'sum; "spongy body") surrounds the urethra and expands distally to form the glans. Its proximal end is also enlarged, forming the part of the root called the **bulb of the penis.** The bulb is covered externally by the sheetlike bulbospongiosus muscle and is secured to the urogenital diaphragm. The paired dorsal erectile bodies, called the **corpora cavernosa** (kor'por-ah kă-ver-no'sah; "cavernous bodies"), make up most of the penis. Their proximal ends form the **crura** (kroo'rah; "legs") **of the penis** (singular, crus). Each crus is surrounded by an ischiocavernosus muscle and anchors to the pubic arch of the bony pelvis.

Semen

Semen (se'men) is a milky white, somewhat sticky mixture of sperm and accessory gland secretions. The liquid provides a transport medium and nutrients and contains chemicals that protect and activate the sperm and facilitate their movement. Mature sperm cells are streamlined cellular "missiles" containing very little cytoplasm or stored nutrients. The fructose in seminal vesicle secretion provides essentially all of their fuel. The prostaglandins in semen decrease the viscosity of mucus guarding the entry (cervix) of the uterus and cause reverse peristalsis in the uterus and the medial parts of the uterine tubes, facilitating the movement of sperm through the female reproductive tract. The presence of the hormone *relaxin* and certain enzymes in semen enhance sperm motility. The relative alkalinity of semen as a whole (pH 7.2–7.6) due to bases (spermine and others) helps neutralize the acid environment (pH 3.5–4) of the female's vagina. Thus, it protects the delicate sperm and enhances their motility. Sperm are very sluggish under acidic conditions (below pH 6). Semen also contains an antibiotic chemical called **seminalplasmin,** which destroys certain bacteria. Clotting factors (fibrinogen and others) found in semen coagulate it just after it is ejaculated. Then, its contained fibrinolysin liquefies the sticky mass, enabling the sperm to swim out and begin their journey through the female duct system.

The amount of semen propelled out of the male duct system during ejaculation is relatively small, only 2–5 ml, but there are between 50 and 100 million sperm per milliliter.

PHYSIOLOGY OF THE MALE REPRODUCTIVE SYSTEM

Male Sexual Response

The chief phases of the male sexual response are (1) *erection* of the penis, which allows it to penetrate the female vagina, and (2) *ejaculation,* which expels semen into the vagina.

Erection

Erection, enlargement and stiffening of the penis, results from engorgement of the erectile bodies with blood. When a man is not sexually aroused, the arterioles supplying the erectile tissue are constricted, and the penis is flaccid. However, during sexual excitement, a parasympathetic reflex is triggered that promotes release of nitric oxide locally that relaxes vascular smooth muscle causing these arterioles to dilate. As a result the vascular spaces of the erectile bodies fill with blood, causing the penis to become enlarged and rigidly erect. Expansion of the penis compresses its drainage veins, retarding blood outflow and maintaining engorgement. Erection of the penis is one of the rare examples of parasympathetic control of arterioles. Another parasympathetic effect is stimulation of the bulbourethral glands, which causes lubrication of the glans penis.

Erection is initiated by a variety of sexual stimuli, such as touching the genital skin, mechanical stimulation of the pressure receptors in the penis, and pleasurable sights, sounds, and smells. The CNS responds to such stimuli by sending impulses to the second through fourth sacral segments of the spinal cord, activating parasympathetic neurons that innervate the internal pudendal arteries serving the penis. Sometimes erection is induced solely by emotional or higher mental activity (the thought of a sexual encounter). Emotions and thoughts can also inhibit erection, causing vasoconstriction and resumption of the flaccid penile state.

Failure to attain erection is called *impotence.* Psychological factors, alcohol, and certain drugs can cause temporary impotence in healthy males. In some cases, impotence results from vascular or nervous system problems. Various injectable drugs and implantable penile devices are available to restore sexual activity to those with nonreversible impotence. •

Ejaculation

Ejaculation (*ejac* = to shoot forth) is the propulsion of semen from the male duct system. Whereas erection is under parasympathetic control, *ejaculation* is under sympathetic control. When impulses provoking erection reach a certain critical level, a spinal reflex is initiated, and a massive discharge of nerve impulses occurs over the sympathetic nerves (largely at the level of L_1 and L_2) serving the genital organs. As a result, (1) the reproductive ducts and accessory glands contract, emptying their contents into the urethra; (2) the bladder sphincter muscle constricts, preventing expulsion of urine or reflux of semen into the bladder; and (3) the bulbospongiosus muscles of the penis undergo a rapid series of contractions, propelling semen from the urethra. These rhythmic muscle contractions are accompanied by intense pleasure and many systemic changes, such as generalized muscle contraction, rapid heartbeat, and elevated blood pressure. The entire event is referred to as **climax** or **orgasm.** Orgasm is quickly followed by muscular and psychological relaxation and vasoconstriction of the penile arterioles, which allows the penis to become flaccid once again. After ejaculation, there is a latent period, ranging in time from minutes to hours, during which a man is unable to achieve another orgasm.

Spermatogenesis

Spermatogenesis (sper"mah-to-jen'ĕ-sis; "sperm formation") is the sequence of events in the seminiferous tubules of the testes that leads to the production of male gametes—sperm or spermatozoa. The process begins during puberty, around the age of 14 years in males, and continues throughout life. Every day, a healthy adult male makes about 400 million sperm. It seems that nature has made sure that the human species will not be endangered for lack of sperm.

Meiosis

Both spermatogenesis and oogenesis, its counterpart in the female, involve **meiosis** (mi-o'sis; "a lessening"), the unique kind of nuclear division that, for the most part, occurs only within the gonads. Recall that *mitosis* (the process by which most body cells divide) distributes replicated chromosomes equally between the two daughter cells (see Chapter 3). Consequently, each daughter cell receives a set of chromosomes identical to that of the mother cell. Meiosis, on the other hand, consists of two consecutive nuclear divisions, and its product is four daughter cells instead of two, each with half as many chromosomes as typical body cells. Mitosis and meiosis are compared in Figure 28.5.

The normal chromosome number in most body cells is referred to as the **diploid** (dip'loid) or **2n chromosomal number** of the organism. In humans, this

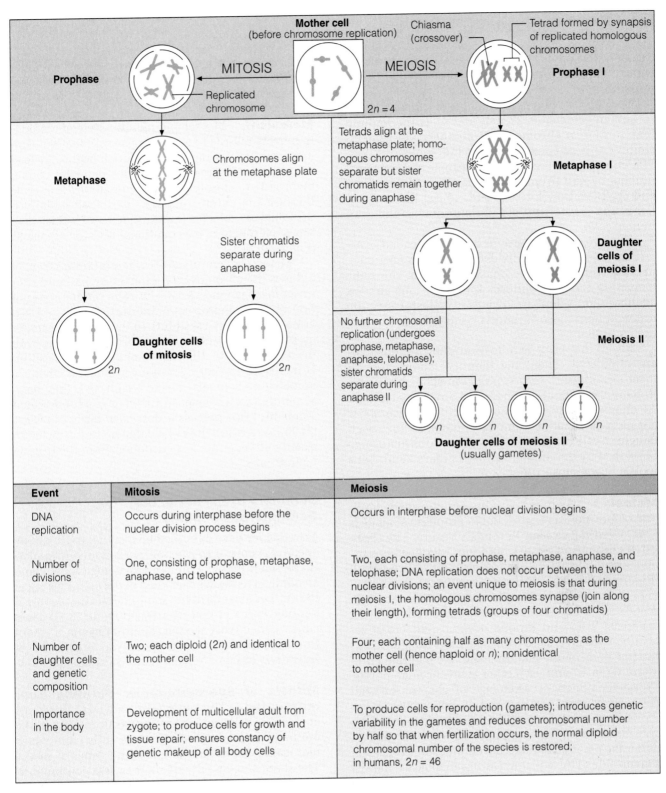

Event	Mitosis	Meiosis
DNA replication	Occurs during interphase before the nuclear division process begins	Occurs in interphase before nuclear division begins
Number of divisions	One, consisting of prophase, metaphase, anaphase, and telophase	Two, each consisting of prophase, metaphase, anaphase, and telophase; DNA replication does not occur between the two nuclear divisions; an event unique to meiosis is that during meiosis I, the homologous chromosomes synapse (join along their length), forming tetrads (groups of four chromatids)
Number of daughter cells and genetic composition	Two; each diploid (2n) and identical to the mother cell	Four; each containing half as many chromosomes as the mother cell (hence haploid or n); nonidentical to mother cell
Importance in the body	Development of multicellular adult from zygote; to produce cells for growth and tissue repair; ensures constancy of genetic makeup of all body cells	To produce cells for reproduction (gametes); introduces genetic variability in the gametes and reduces chromosomal number by half so that when fertilization occurs, the normal diploid chromosomal number of the species is restored; in humans, 2n = 46

FIGURE 28.5
Comparison of mitosis and meiosis in a mother cell with a diploid number (2n)
of 4. Mitosis is shown on the left, meiosis on the right. Not all the phases of mitosis and meiosis
are shown.

number is 46, and such diploid cells contain 23 pairs of similar chromosomes called **homologous** (ho-mol′ŏ-gus) **chromosomes** or **homologues.** One member of each pair is from the male parent (the *paternal chromosome*); the other is from the female parent (the *maternal chromosome*). The two homologues of each

chromosome pair look alike and carry genes that code for the same traits, though not necessarily for identical expression of those traits. (Consider, for example, the homologous genes controlling the expression of freckles; the paternal gene might code for an ample sprinkling of freckles and the maternal gene for no freckles.) In Chapter 30, we will consider how maternal and paternal genes interact to produce our visible traits.

In contrast, the number of chromosomes present in human gametes is 23, referred to as the **haploid** (hap'loid) or **n chromosomal number,** and gametes contain only one member of each homologous pair. The importance of reducing the gamete chromosomal number by half (from $2n$ to n) is clear. When sperm and egg fuse, they form a fertilized egg that reestablishes the typical diploid chromosomal number of human cells.

The two nuclear divisions of meiosis, called *meiosis I* and *meiosis II,* are divided into phases for convenience. Although these phases are given the same names as those of mitosis (prophase, metaphase, anaphase, and telophase), events of meiosis I are quite different from those of mitosis, as detailed below and in Figure 28.6.

Recall that prior to mitosis all the chromosomes are replicated. Then, the identical copies remain together as *sister chromatids* connected by a centromere throughout prophase and during metaphase. At anaphase, the centromeres split and the sister chromatids separate from each other so that each daughter cell inherits a copy of *every* chromosome possessed by the mother cell (see Figure 28.5). Let's look at how meiosis differs.

Meiosis I.

As in mitosis, the chromosomes replicate before meiosis begins. But in prophase of meiosis I, an event never seen in mitosis occurs. The replicated chromosomes seek out their homologous partners and align with them along their entire length (Figure 28.6). This intimate pairing of the homologues is called **synapsis,** and it produces little groups of four chromatids called **tetrads.** During synapsis, a second unique event called crossover occurs. **Crossovers** are formed within each tetrad as the free ends of one maternal and one paternal chromatid wrap around each other at one or more points. Crossover allows an exchange of genetic material between maternal and paternal chromosomes.

During metaphase I, the tetrads line up at the spindle equator. This alignment is random; that is, either the paternal or maternal chromosome can be on a given side of the equator. During anaphase I, the sister chromatids representing each homologue behave as a unit—almost as if replication had not occurred—and the *homologous chromosomes* (each still composed of two joined sister chromatids) are distributed to opposite ends of the cell.

Thus, when meiosis I is completed, the following conditions exist: Each daughter cell has (1) *two* copies of one member of each homologous pair (either the paternal or maternal) and none of the other, and (2) a diploid amount of DNA but a *haploid* chromosomal number because the still-united sister chromatids are considered to be a single chromo-

some. Since meiosis I reduces the chromosome number from $2n$ to n, it is sometimes called the **reduction division of meiosis.**

Meiosis II.

The second meiotic division, meiosis II, mirrors mitosis in every way, except that the chromosomes are *not* replicated before it begins. Instead, the chromatids present in the two daughter cells of meiosis I are simply parceled out among four cells. Because the chromatids are distributed equally to the daughter cells (as in mitosis), meiosis II is sometimes referred to as the **equational division of meiosis** (Figure 28.6).

Meiosis accomplishes two important tasks: (1) It reduces the chromosomal number by half and (2) it introduces genetic variability. The random orientation of the homologous pairs during meiosis I provides tremendous variability in the resulting gametes by scrambling genetic characteristics derived from the two parents in different combinations. Variability is increased further by crossover because when the homologues separate during anaphase I, they break at points of crossover and exchange chromosomal segments. (This process is described further in Chapter 30.) As a result, it is likely that no two gametes are exactly alike, and all are different from the original mother cells.

Summary of Events in the Seminiferous Tubules

Now that we have described meiosis, let us turn to the specific events of spermatogenesis which take place in the seminiferous tubules. A histological section of an adult testis shows that most of the cells making up the epithelial walls of the seminiferous tubules are in various stages of cell division (Figure 28.7). These cells, collectively called **spermatogenic** ("sperm forming") **cells,** give rise to sperm via the series of cellular divisions and transformations explained below.

Mitosis of Spermatogonia: Forming Spermatocytes.

The outermost and least differentiated tubule cells, which are in direct contact with the epithelial basal lamina, are stem cells called **spermatogonia** (sper"mah-to-go'ne-ah; "sperm seed"). The spermatogonia divide more or less continuously by *mitosis* and, until puberty, all the daughter cells become new spermatogonia. Spermatogenesis begins during puberty, and from then on, each mitotic division of a spermatogonium results in two distinctive daughter cells (Figure 28.7)—*types A* and *B.* The **type A daughter cell** remains at the basement membrane to maintain the germ cell line. The **type B** cell gets pushed toward the lumen, where it becomes a **primary spermatocyte** destined to produce four sperm.

Meiosis: Spermatocytes to Spermatids.

Each primary spermatocyte generated during the first phase

(1) Why is it important that the chromosomal number is reduced from 2n to n during meiosis? (2) What two events introduce variability in the daughter cells?

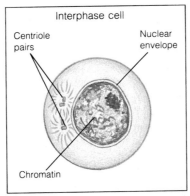

Interphase cell

Centriole pairs

Nuclear envelope

Chromatin

FIGURE 28.6
Meiotic cell division. This series of diagrams shows meiotic cell division for an animal cell with a diploid number (2*n*) of 4. The behavior of the chromosomes is emphasized.

Interphase events
As in mitosis, meiosis is preceded by events occurring during interphase that lead to DNA replication and other preparations needed for the division process. Just before meiosis begins, the replicated chromatids, held together by centromeres, are ready and waiting.

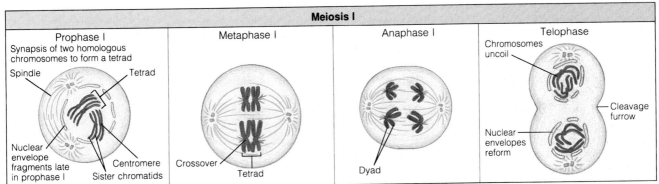

Meiosis I

Prophase I
Synapsis of two homologous chromosomes to form a tetrad

Spindle — Tetrad

Nuclear envelope fragments late in prophase I — Centromere — Sister chromatids

Metaphase I

Crossover — Tetrad

Anaphase I

Dyad

Telophase

Chromosomes uncoil

Cleavage furrow

Nuclear envelopes reform

Prophase I
As in prophase of mitosis, the chromosomes coil and condense, the nuclear membrane and nucleolus break down and disappear, and the spindle is formed. However, a unique event not seen in mitosis, called synapsis, occurs in prophase I of meiosis. Synapsis involves the coming together of homologous chromosomes, to form tetrads, little packets of four chromatids. While in synapsis, the "arms" of adjacent homologous chromatids become wrapped around each other, forming several points of crossover or chiasmata. Generally speaking, the longer the chromatids, the more chiasmata are formed. Prophase I is the longest period of meiosis, accounting for about 90% of the total period; by its end, the tetrads have attached to the spindle and are moving toward the spindle equator.

Metaphase I
During metaphase I, the tetrads align on the spindle equator in preparation for anaphase.

Anaphase I
Unlike the anaphase events of mitosis, the centromeres do not break during anaphase I of meiosis, and so the sister chromatids (dyads) remain firmly attached. However, the homologous chromosomes do separate from each other, and the dyads are moved toward opposite poles of the cell.

Telophase I
The nuclear membranes re-form around the chromosomal masses, the spindle breaks down, and the chromatin reappears as telophase and cytokinesis are completed, so that two daughter cells are formed. The daughter cells (now haploid) then enter a second interphase-like period called interkinesis, before meiosis II occurs. There is no second replication of DNA before meiosis II. During human spermatogenesis, the daughter cells remain interconnected by cytoplasmic extensions.

Meiosis II

| Prophase II | Metaphase II | Anaphase II | Telophase II and cytokinesis | Products of meiosis |

Haploid daughter cells

?   *What cell type results from meiosis?*

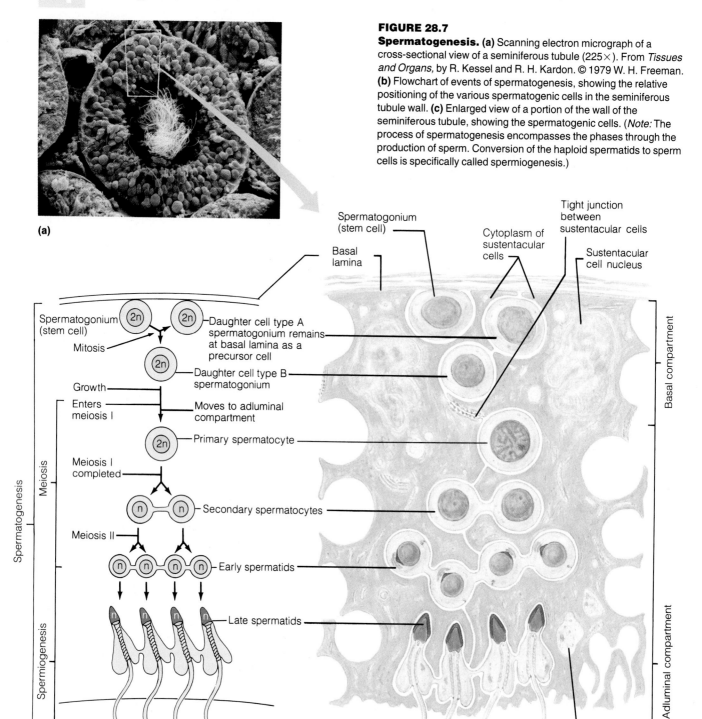

(a)

FIGURE 28.7
Spermatogenesis. (a) Scanning electron micrograph of a cross-sectional view of a seminiferous tubule (225×). From *Tissues and Organs,* by R. Kessel and R. H. Kardon. © 1979 W. H. Freeman. **(b)** Flowchart of events of spermatogenesis, showing the relative positioning of the various spermatogenic cells in the seminiferous tubule wall. **(c)** Enlarged view of a portion of the wall of the seminiferous tubule, showing the spermatogenic cells. (*Note:* The process of spermatogenesis encompasses the phases through the production of sperm. Conversion of the haploid spermatids to sperm cells is specifically called spermiogenesis.)

(b)

(c)

(a)

- Golgi apparatus
- Acrosomal vesicle
- Spermatid nucleus

1

2
- Centrioles

3
- Microtubules
- Flagellum

- Mitochondria

4

5
- Excess cytoplasm

- Acrosome
- Nucleus

6

7
- Midpiece
- Head
- Tail

(b)

FIGURE 28.8
Spermiogenesis: transformation of a spermatid into a functional sperm. (a) The stepwise process of spermiogenesis consists of (1) activity of the Golgi apparatus to package the acrosomal enzymes, (2) positioning of the acrosome at the anterior end of the nucleus and of the centrioles at the opposite end of the nucleus, (3) elaboration of microtubules to form the flagellum of the tail, (4) mitochondrial multiplication and their positioning around the proximal portion of the flagellum, and (5) sloughing off excess cytoplasm. (6) Structure of an immature sperm that has just been released from a sustentacular cell. (7) Structure of a fully mature sperm. **(b)** Scanning electron micrograph of mature sperm (430 ×).

undergoes meiosis I, forming two smaller haploid cells called **secondary spermatocytes.** The secondary spermatocytes continue on rapidly into meiosis II, and their daughter cells, called **spermatids** (sper'mah-tidz), can be seen as small round cells with large spherical nuclei closer to the lumen of the tubule.

Spermiogenesis: Spermatids to Sperm.

Although each spermatid has the correct chromosomal number for fertilization *(n),* it is nonmotile. It still must undergo a streamlining process called **spermiogenesis** (Figure 28.8a), during which it sheds its superfluous cytoplasmic baggage and fashions a tail. The resulting **sperm,** or **spermatozoon** (sper"mah-to-zo'on; "animal seed"), has three major regions: a head, a midpiece, and a tail, which correspond roughly to *genetic, metabolic,* and *locomotor regions,* respectively. The **head** of the sperm consists almost entirely of its flattened nucleus, which contains the DNA. Adhering to the top of the nucleus is a helmet-like **acrosome** (ak'ro-sōme; "tip piece"). The lyso-somelike acrosome is produced by the Golgi apparatus and contains hydrolytic enzymes (hyaluronidase and others) that enable the sperm to penetrate and enter an egg. The sperm **midpiece** contains mitochondria spiraled tightly around the contractile filaments of the tail. The **tail** is a typical flagellum elaborated by

a centriole. The mitochondria provide the metabolic energy (ATP) needed for the whiplike movements of the tail that will propel the sperm along its way in the female reproductive tract.

Role of the Sustentacular Cells.

Throughout the spermatogenic process, descendants of the same spermatogonium remain closely attached to one another by cytoplasmic bridges (see Figure 28.7). Additionally, they are surrounded by and connected to supporting cells of a special type, called **sustentacular cells** or **Sertoli cells,** which extend from the basal lamina to the lumen of the tubule (see Figure 28.7c). The sustentacular cells, bound to each other by tight junctions, form an unbroken layer within the seminiferous tubule, dividing it into two compartments (Figure 28.9). The **basal compartment** extends from the basal lamina to their tight junctions and contains spermatogonia and the earliest primary spermatocytes. The **adluminal compartment** lies internal to the tight junctions and includes the meiotically active cells and the tubule lumen.

The tight junctions between the sustentacular cells form the **blood-testis barrier.** This barrier prevents the membrane antigens (mostly proteins) of differentiating sperm from escaping through the basal

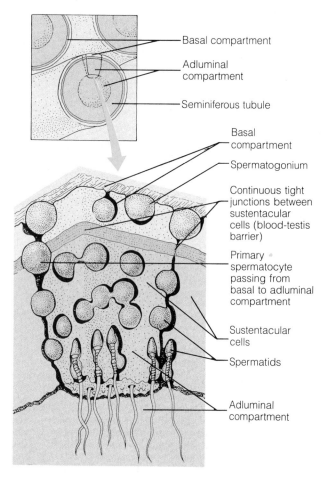

FIGURE 28.9
Schematic view of the relationship between a sustentacular cell and the spermatogenic cells and of the sustentacular cell's role in maintaining the blood-testis barrier. Continuous tight junctions, connecting sustentacular cells laterally at their bases, separate the basal compartment containing spermatogonia from the adluminal compartment containing cells in various stages of spermatogenesis.

lamina into the bloodstream. Since sperm are not formed until puberty, they are absent when the immune system is being programmed to recognize one's own tissues early in life. Moreover, all spermatogenic cells formed after meiosis I are genetically different from somatic body cells. Consequently, if the blood-testis barrier did not exist, sperm membrane antigens entering the blood might provoke an autoimmune response to one's own sperm and cause sterility. The spermatogonia, which are genetically identical to other body cells and are recognized as "self," are outside the barrier and can be influenced by blood-borne chemical messengers that prompt spermatogenesis. Following mitosis of the spermatogonia, the tight junctions of the sustentacular cells open to allow primary spermatocytes to pass into the

adluminal compartment—much as locks in a canal are opened to allow a boat to pass.

In the adluminal compartment, spermatocytes and spermatids are nearly enclosed in recesses in the sustentacular cells (see Figure 28.9). The sustentacular cells deliver nutrients to the dividing cells, move them along to the lumen, secrete **testicular fluid** (rich in androgens and metabolic acids) that provides the transport medium for sperm in the lumen, and dispose of the excess cytoplasm sloughed off the spermatids as they transform into sperm. As described shortly, the sustentacular cells also produce chemical mediators that help regulate spermatogenesis.

Spermatogenesis—from formation of a primary spermatocyte to release of immature sperm into the lumen—takes 64 to 72 days. Sperm in the lumen are unable to "swim" and are incapable of fertilizing an egg. They are pushed by the pressure of the testicular fluid through the tubular system of the testes into the epididymis. There they undergo further maturation, which results in increased motility and fertilizing power.

An alarming decline in male fertility has been observed in the past 40 years. Not only has the average volume of the ejaculate declined 20% (from about 3.40 ml to 2.75 ml), but average sperm count per ml has decreased more than 40% (from 113 million to 66 million). Some believe the main cause is environmental toxins, especially compounds with estrogenic effects now found in our meat supply as well as in the air. Common antibiotics such as tetracycline may suppress sperm formation; and radiation, lead, certain pesticides, marijuana, and excessive alcohol can cause abnormal (two-headed, multiple-tailed, etc.) sperm to be produced.

Male infertility may also be caused by anatomical obstructions and hormonal imbalances. One of the first series of tests done when a couple has been unable to conceive is *semen analysis.* Factors analyzed include sperm count, motility, and morphology (shape and maturity), and semen volume, pH, and fructose content. A low sperm count accompanied by a high percentage of immature sperm may hint that a man has a *varicocele* (var′ĭ-ko-sēl″), a condition that hinders drainage of the testicular vein, resulting in an elevated temperature in the scrotum that interferes with normal sperm development. •

Hormonal Regulation of Male Reproductive Function

The Brain-Testicular Axis

Hormonal regulation of spermatogenesis and testicular androgen production involves interactions between the hypothalamus, anterior pituitary gland, and testes, a relationship sometimes called the **brain-testicular axis.** The sequence of regulatory events, shown schematically in Figure 28.10, is as follows:

1. The hypothalamus releases **gonadotropin-releasing hormone (GnRH),** which controls the release of the anterior pituitary gonadotropins, **follicle-stimulating hormone (FSH)** and **luteinizing hormone (LH).** (As described in Chapter 17, both FSH and LH were named for their effects on the female gonad.) GnRH reaches the anterior pituitary cells via the blood of the hypophyseal portal system.

2. Binding of GnRH to pituitary cells (gonadotrophs) prompts them to secrete FSH and LH into the blood.

3. FSH stimulates spermatogenesis in the testes indirectly by stimulating the sustentacular cells to release **androgen-binding protein (ABP).** ABP prompts the spermatogenic cells to bind and concentrate **testosterone** which, in turn, stimulates spermatogenesis. Thus, FSH makes the cells receptive to testosterone's stimulatory effects.

4. LH binds to the interstitial cells and stimulates them to secrete testosterone (and a small amount of estrogen). LH is therefore sometimes called **interstitial cell–stimulating hormone (ICSH)** in males. Locally testosterone serves as the final trigger for spermatogenesis. Testosterone entering the bloodstream exerts a number of effects at other body sites.

5. Both the hypothalamus and the anterior pituitary are subject to feedback inhibition by blood-borne hormones. Testosterone inhibits hypothalamic release of GnRH and may act directly on the anterior pituitary to inhibit gonadotropin release. **Inhibin** (in-hib′in), a protein hormone produced by the sustentacular cells, serves as a barometer of the normalcy of spermatogenesis. When the sperm count is high, inhibin release increases and it inhibits anterior pituitary release of FSH and GnRH release by the hypothalamus. When the sperm count falls below 20 million per milliliter, inhibin secretion declines steeply.

As you can see, the amount of testosterone and sperm produced by the testes reflects a balance among three sets of hormones: (1) gonadotropins, which directly stimulate the testes; (2) GnRH, which indirectly stimulates the testes via its effect on FSH and LH release; and (3) testicular hormones (testosterone and inhibin), which exert negative feedback controls on the hypothalamus and anterior pituitary. Since the hypothalamus is also influenced by input from other brain areas, the whole axis is under CNS control. In the absence of GnRH and gonadotropins, the testes atrophy, and for all practical purposes, sperm and testosterone production ceases.

Development of male reproductive structures (discussed later in the chapter) depends on prenatal secretion of male hormones, and for a few months after birth, a male infant has plasma gonadotropin and testosterone levels nearly equal to those of a midpu-

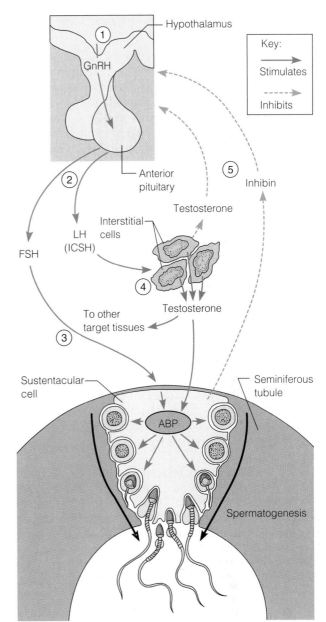

FIGURE 28.10

Hormonal regulation of testicular function, the brain-testicular axis. (1) The hypothalamus releases gonadotropin-releasing hormone (GnRH). (2) GnRH stimulates the anterior pituitary to release gonadotropins—follicle-stimulating hormone (FSH) and luteinizing hormone (LH), also called interstitial cell–stimulating hormone (ICSH). (3) FSH acts on the sustentacular cells, causing them to release androgen-binding protein (ABP). (4) LH acts on the interstitial cells, stimulating their release of testosterone. ABP binding of testosterone then enhances spermatogenesis. (5) Rising levels of testosterone and inhibin (released by the sustentacular cells) exert feedback inhibition on the hypothalamus and pituitary.

bertal boy. Shortly thereafter, blood levels of these hormones recede and they remain low throughout childhood. As puberty nears, the threshold for hypothalamic inhibition rises, and much higher levels of testosterone are required to suppress hypothalamic release of GnRH. As more GnRH is released, more testosterone is secreted by the testes, but the threshold for hypothalamic inhibition keeps rising until the adult pattern of hormone interaction is achieved. Maturation of the brain-testicular axis takes about three years, and once established, the balance between the interacting hormones remains relatively constant. Consequently, an adult male's sperm and testosterone production also remains fairly stable, whereas in females, cyclic swings in gonadotropin and female sex hormone levels are the normal condition.

Mechanism and Effects of Testosterone Activity

Testosterone, like all steroid hormones, is synthesized from cholesterol. It exerts its effects by activating specific genes to transcribe messenger RNA molecules, which results in enhanced synthesis of certain proteins in the target cells. (See Chapter 17.)

In some target cells, testosterone must be transformed into another steroid before it can exert its effects. In cells of the prostate gland, for example, testosterone must be converted to *dihydrotestosterone* before it can bind within the nucleus. In certain neurons of the brain, testosterone is converted to *estrogen* (es'tro-jen) to bring about its stimulatory effects. Thus, in that case at least, a "male" hormone is transformed into a "female" hormone to exert its masculinizing effects.

As puberty ensues, testosterone not only prompts spermatogenesis, but has multiple anabolic effects throughout the body (see Table 28.1, p. 983). It targets all accessory reproductive organs—ducts, glands, and the penis—causing them to grow and assume adult size and function. In adult males, normal plasma levels of testosterone are required to maintain these organs: When the hormone is deficient or absent, all accessory organs atrophy, semen volume declines markedly, and erection and ejaculation are impaired. Thus, a man becomes both sterile and impotent. This situation is easily rectified by testosterone replacement therapy.

Male secondary sex characteristics—that is, features induced in the *nonreproductive* organs by the male sex hormones (mainly testosterone)—make their appearance at puberty. These include the appearance of pubic, axillary, and facial hair, enhanced hair growth on the chest or other body areas in some men, and a deepening of the voice as the larynx enlarges. The skin thickens and becomes oilier (which predisposes young men to acne), bones grow and increase in density, and skeletal muscles increase in size and mass. The last two effects are often referred to as the *somatic effects* of testosterone (*soma* = body).

Testosterone also boosts basal metabolic rate and influences behavior. It is the basis of the sex drive (libido) in both males and females, be they heterosexual or homosexual. Thus, although testosterone is called a "male" sex hormone, it should not be specifically tagged as a promoter of male sexual activity. The masculinization of brain anatomy by testosterone is dealt with in Chapter 12.

The testes are not the only source of androgens; the adrenal glands of both sexes also release androgens. However, since the relatively small amounts of adrenal androgens are unable to support normal testosterone-mediated functions when the testes fail to produce androgens, it is the testosterone production by the testes that supports male reproductive function.

ANATOMY OF THE FEMALE REPRODUCTIVE SYSTEM

The reproductive role of the female is far more complex than that of a male. Not only must she produce gametes, but her body must prepare to nurture a developing embryo for a period of approximately nine months. **Ovaries, the female gonads,** are the primary reproductive organs of a female, and like the male testes, ovaries serve a dual purpose: Besides their gametogenic functions, they produce the female sex hormones, the **estrogens*** and **progesterone** (projes'tĕ-rōn). The accessory ducts (uterine tubes, uterus, and vagina) transport or otherwise serve the needs of the reproductive cells and/or the developing fetus.

As illustrated in Figure 28.11, the ovaries and duct system, collectively known as the **internal genitalia,** are mostly located in the pelvic cavity. The female's accessory ducts, from the vicinity of the ovary to the body exterior, are the *uterine tubes,* the *uterus,* and the *vagina.* The external sex organs of females are referred to as the **external genitalia** or *vulva.*

The Ovaries

The paired ovaries, which flank the uterus on each side (see Figure 28.11a), are shaped like almonds and about twice as large. Each ovary is held in place within the peritoneal cavity by several ligaments. The **ovarian ligament** anchors the ovary medially to the uterus; the **suspensory ligament** anchors it laterally to the pelvic wall; and the **mesovarium** (mez"o-va're-um) suspends it in between. Both the suspensory ligament and the mesovarium are part of the **broad ligament,** a peritoneal fold that "tents" over the uterus and supports the uterine tubes, uterus, and vagina. The fibrous ovarian ligaments are enclosed within the broad ligament.

The ovaries are served by the **ovarian arteries,** branches of the abdominal aorta (Figure 28.12), and by the *ovarian branch of the uterine arteries.* The ovarian blood vessels reach the ovaries by traveling through the suspensory ligaments and mesovaria.

Like a testis, the external surface of an ovary is surrounded by a fibrous **tunica albuginea** (Figure 28.13). The tunica albuginea is, in turn, covered

---

*Although the ovaries produce several different estrogens, the most important are *estradiol, estrone,* and *estriol.* Of these, estradiol is the most abundant and is most responsible for mediating estrogenic effects.

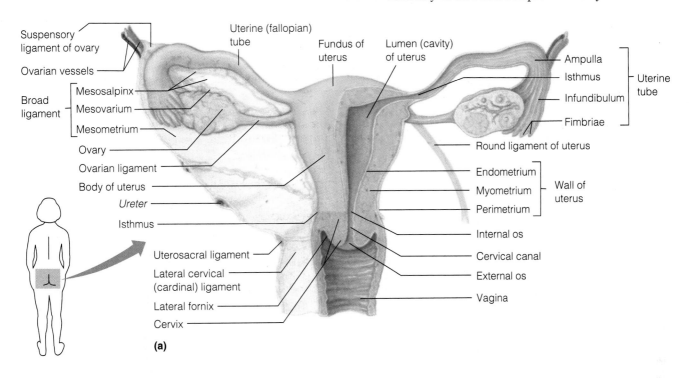

Suspensory
ligament of ovary

Ovarian vessels

Broad
ligament
  Mesosalpinx
  Mesovarium
  Mesometrium

Ovary

Ovarian ligament

Body of uterus

Ureter

Isthmus

Uterosacral ligament

Lateral cervical
(cardinal) ligament

Lateral fornix

Cervix

Uterine (fallopian)
tube

Fundus of
uterus

Lumen (cavity)
of uterus

Ampulla

Isthmus

Infundibulum

Fimbriae

Uterine
tube

Round ligament of uterus

Endometrium

Myometrium

Perimetrium

Wall of
uterus

Internal os

Cervical canal

External os

Vagina

(a)

Peritoneum

Uterosacral
ligament

Perimetrium

Rectouterine
pouch

Rectum

Posterior fornix

Cervix

Anterior fornix

Vagina

Anus

Urogenital diaphragm

Greater vestibular
(Bartholin's) gland

Infundibulum

Suspensory ligament
of ovary

Uterine tube

Fimbriae

Ovary

Uterus

Round ligament

Vesicouterine pouch

Urinary bladder

Symphysis pubis

Mons pubis

Urethra

Clitoris

External urethral
orifice

Hymen

Labium minus

Labium majus

(b)

FIGURE 28.11
Internal organs of the female reproductive system. (a) Posterior view of the female
reproductive organs. The posterior walls of the vagina, uterus, and uterine tubes and the broad
ligament have been removed on the right side to reveal the shape of the lumen of these organs.
(b) Midsagittal section of the female pelvis.

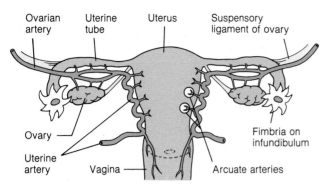

FIGURE 28.12
Arteries of the internal female genitalia (posterior view). Corresponding veins run with these arteries.

externally by a layer of cuboidal epithelial cells called the *germinal epithelium,* which is continuous with the peritoneum of the mesovarium. The term *germinal epithelium* is a misnomer because this layer does not give rise to ova. The ovary has an outer cortex, which houses the forming gametes, and an inner medullary region, containing the largest blood vessels and nerves, but the relative extent of each region is poorly defined.

Embedded in the highly vascular connective tissue of the ovary cortex are many tiny saclike struc-tures called **ovarian follicles.** Each follicle consists of an immature egg, called an **oocyte** (o'o-sīt; *oo* = egg), encased by one or more layers of very different cells. The surrounding cells are called **follicle cells** if a single layer is present, and **granulosa cells** when more than one layer is present. Follicles at different stages of maturation are distinguished by their structure. In a **primordial follicle,** one layer of squamouslike folli-cle cells surrounds the oocyte. A **primary follicle** has two or more layers of cuboidal or columnar-type gran-ulosa cells enclosing the oocyte; it becomes a **sec-ondary follicle** when fluid-filled spaces appear between the granulosa cells and then coalesce to form a central fluid-filled cavity called an *antrum.* At its most mature stage, when it is called a **vesicular,** or **Graafian** (graf'e-an) **follicle,** the oocyte "sits" on a stalk of granulosa cells at one side of the antrum and the follicle bulges from the surface of the ovary. Each month, in adult women, one of the ripening follicles ejects its oocyte from the ovary, an event called **ovu-lation.** After ovulation, the ruptured follicle is trans-formed into a very different looking structure called the **corpus luteum** (lu'te-um; plural, corpora lutea), which eventually degenerates. As a rule, most of these structures can be seen within the same ovary. In older women, the surfaces of the ovaries are scarred and pitted, revealing that many oocytes have been released.

FIGURE 28.13
Structure of an ovary. (a) The ovary has been sectioned to reveal the follicles in its interior.
Note that not all of these structures would appear in the ovary at the same time.
(b) Photomicrograph of a mature vesicular (Graafian) follicle (250×).

The Female Duct System

The Uterine Tubes

The **uterine** (u'ter-in) **tubes,** also called **fallopian tubes** and **oviducts,** form the initial part of the female duct system (Figure 28.11a). They receive the ovulated oocyte and provide a site where fertilization can occur. Each uterine tube is about 10 cm (4 inches) long and extends medially from the region of an ovary to empty into the superolateral region of the uterus via a constricted region called the **isthmus** (is'mus). The distal end of each uterine tube expands as it curves around the ovary, forming the **ampulla;** fertilization usually occurs in this region. The ampulla ends in the **infundibulum** (in″fun-dib'u-lum), an open, funnel-shaped structure bearing ciliated, fingerlike projections called **fimbriae** (fim'bre-e; "fringe") that drape over the ovary. Unlike the male duct system, which is continuous with the tubules of the testes, the uterine tubes have little or no actual contact with the ovaries. An ovulated oocyte is cast into the peritoneal cavity, and many oocytes are lost there. However, the uterine tube performs a complex sequence of movements to capture oocytes. Specifically, the infundibulum bends to cover the ovary while the fimbriae stiffen and sweep the ovarian surface. The beating cilia on the fimbriae then create currents in the peritoneal fluid that act to carry the oocyte into the uterine tube, where it begins its journey toward the uterus.

The structure of the uterine tube wall aids the progress of an oocyte. Its wall contains sheets of smooth muscle, and its thick, highly folded mucosa contains ciliated and nonciliated cells. The oocyte is carried toward the uterus by a combination of muscular peristalsis and the beating of the cilia. Nonciliated cells of the mucosa have dense microvilli and produce a secretion that keeps the oocyte (and sperm, if present) moist and nourished.

Externally, the uterine tubes are covered by visceral peritoneum and supported along their length by a short mesentery (part of the broad ligament) called the **mesosalpinx** (mez″o-sal'pinks; "mesentery of the trumpet"; *salpin* = trumpet), a reference to the trumpet-shaped uterine tube it supports (see Figure 28.11a).

The fact that the uterine tubes are not continuous distally with the ovaries places women at risk for *ectopic pregnancy* in which an ovum, fertilized in the peritoneal cavity, begins development there. Such pregnancies naturally abort, often with substantial bleeding. Another potential problem is infection spreading into the peritoneal cavity from other parts of the reproductive tract. Gonorrhea bacteria and other sexually transmitted microorganisms sometimes infect the peritoneal cavity in this way, causing an extremely severe inflammation called **pelvic inflammatory disease (PID).** Unless treated promptly, PID can cause scarring of the narrow uterine tubes and of the ovaries and lead to sterility, and even death.

Indeed, scarring and closure of the uterine tubes, which have an internal diameter as small as the width of a human hair in some regions, is one of the major causes of female infertility. •

The Uterus

The **uterus** (Latin for "womb") is located in the pelvis, anterior to the rectum and posterosuperior to the bladder (see Figure 28.11b). It is a hollow, thick-walled organ that functions to receive, retain, and nourish a fertilized ovum. In a premenopausal woman who has never been pregnant, the uterus is about the size and shape of an inverted pear, but it is usually somewhat larger in women who have borne children. Normally, the uterus is flexed anteriorly where it joins the vagina, causing the uterus as a whole to be inclined forward or *anteverted.* However, the organ is frequently turned backward, or *retroverted,* in older women.

The major portion of the uterus is referred to as the **body** (see Figure 28.11a and Figure 28.14). The rounded region superior to the entrance of the uterine tubes is the **fundus,** and the slightly narrowed region between the body and the cervix is the **isthmus.** The **cervix** of the uterus is its narrow neck, or outlet, which projects into the vagina inferiorly. The cavity of the cervix, called the **cervical canal,** communicates with the vagina via the *external os* (*os* = mouth) and with the cavity of the uterine body via the *internal os.* The mucosal lining of the cervical canal contains *cervical glands* that secrete a mucus that fills the cervical canal and covers the external os, presumably to block the spread of bacteria from the vagina into the uterus. Cervical mucus also blocks the entry of sperm, except at mid-cycle, when it becomes less viscous and allows the sperm to pass through.

Cancer of the cervix is common among women between the ages of 30 and 50. Risk factors include frequent cervical inflammations, sexually transmitted diseases including genital warts, and multiple pregnancies. The cancer cells arise from the epithelium covering the cervical tip. In a *Papanicolaou (Pap) smear,* or cervical smear test, some of these epithelial cells are scraped away and then examined for abnormalities. A Pap smear is the most effective way to detect this slow-growing cancer, and women are advised to have one every year. •

Supports of the Uterus. The uterus is supported laterally by the **mesometrium** ("mesentery of the uterus") portion of the broad ligament (Figure 28.11). More inferiorly, the **lateral cervical (cardinal) ligaments** extend from the cervix and superior part of the vagina to the lateral walls of the pelvis, and the paired **uterosacral ligaments** secure the uterus to the sacrum posteriorly. The uterus is bound to the anterior body wall by the fibrous **round ligaments,** which run through the inguinal canals to anchor in the subcutaneous tissue of the labia majora (the outer lips of

Fimbriae of
uterine tube

Mesosalpinx

Round
ligament of
uterus

Internal vaginal surface
(vaginal wall is cut and
reflected superiorly)

Left ovary

Fundus of uterus

Mesovarium

Uterine tube

Body of uterus

Broad ligament

Cervix

FIGURE 28.14
Anterior view of the internal reproductive organs from a female cadaver.
Compare this to the posterior view of the same organs in Figure 28.11a.

the vulva). These various ligaments allow the uterus a good deal of mobility, and its position changes as the rectum and bladder fill and empty.

Despite the above ligaments, the principal support of the uterus is provided by the muscles of the pelvic floor, namely the muscles of the urogenital and pelvic diaphragms (Table 10.7, pp. 310–311). These muscles are sometimes torn during childbirth. Subsequently, the unsupported uterus may sink inferiorly, until the tip of the cervix protrudes through the external vaginal opening. This condition is called **prolapse of the uterus.** •

The undulating course of the peritoneum around and over the various pelvic structures produces several cul-de-sacs, or blind-ended peritoneal pouches. The most important of these are the *vesicouterine* (ves″ĭ-ko-u′ter-in) *pouch* between the bladder and uterus, and the *rectouterine pouch* between the rectum and uterus (see Figure 28.11b).

The Uterine Wall.
The wall of the uterus is composed of three layers (see Figure 28.11a): the perimetrium, the myometrium, and the endometrium. The **perimetrium,** the outermost serous layer, is the visceral peritoneum. The **myometrium** (mi″o-me′tre-um; "muscle of the uterus") is the bulky middle layer, composed of interlacing bundles of smooth muscle. The myometrium contracts rhythmically during childbirth to expel the baby from the mother's body. The **endometrium** is the mucosal lining of the uterine cavity (Figure 28.15); it is a simple columnar epithelium underlain by a thick lamina propria of highly cellular connective tissue. Should fertilization occur, the young embryo burrows into the endometrium (implants) and resides there for the rest of its development. The endometrium has two chief *strata* (layers).

The **stratum functionalis** (fungk-shun-a′lis), or **functional layer,** undergoes cyclic changes in response to blood levels of ovarian hormones and is shed during menstruation (approximately every 28 days). The thin, deeper **stratum basalis** (ba-să′lis), or **basal layer,** shows little response to ovarian hormones and is responsible for forming a new functionalis after menstruation ends. The endometrium has numerous *uterine glands* that change in length as the endometrial thickness changes.

To understand the cyclic changes of the uterine endometrium (discussed later in the chapter), it is essential to understand the vascular supply of the uterus. The **uterine arteries** arise from the *internal iliacs* in the pelvis, ascend along the sides of the uterine body, and send branches into the uterine wall (Figure 28.12). These branches break into several **arcuate** (ar′ku-āt) **arteries** within the myometrium. The arcuate arteries send **radial branches** into the endometrium, where they, in turn, give off **straight arteries** to the stratum basalis and **spiral (coiled) arteries** to the stratum functionalis (see Figure 28.15b). The spiral arteries undergo repeated degeneration and regeneration, and it is their spasms that actually cause the shedding of the functionalis layer during menstruation. Veins in the endometrium are thin-walled and form an extensive network with occasional sinusoidal enlargements.

The Vagina

The **vagina** ("sheath") is a thin-walled tube, 8–10 cm (3 to 4 inches) long. It lies between the bladder and the rectum and extends from the cervix to the body exterior (see Figure 28.11). The urethra is embedded in its anterior wall. Often called the *birth canal,* the vagina provides a passageway for delivery of an

FIGURE 28.15
Structure of the endometrium and its blood supply.
(a) Photomicrograph of the endometrium, longitudinal section, showing its stratum functionalis and basalis regions (3×).
(b) Diagrammatic view of the endometrium, showing the straight arteries that serve the stratum basalis and the spiral arteries that serve the stratum functionalis. The thin-walled veins and venous sinusoids are also illustrated.

infant and for menstrual flow. Since it receives the penis (and semen) during sexual intercourse, it is the female organ of copulation.

The highly distensible wall of the vagina consists of three coats: an outer fibroelastic *adventitia,* a smooth muscle *muscularis,* and a *mucosa* marked by transverse ridges or *rugae,* which stimulate the penis during intercourse. The epithelium of the mucosa is a stratified squamous epithelium adapted to stand up to friction. Certain of the mucosal cells *(dendritic cells)* act as antigen-presenting cells and are thought to provide the route of HIV transmission from an infected male to the female during sexual intercourse. (AIDS, the immune deficiency disease caused by HIV, is the subject of *A Closer Look* on p. 738.) The vaginal mucosa has no glands; its lubrication is provided by cervical mucous glands. Its epithelial cells store large amounts of glycogen, which is anaerobically metabolized to lactic acid by resident bacteria; consequently, the pH of the vagina is normally quite acidic. This acidity helps keep the vagina healthy and free of infection, but it is also hostile to sperm.

Near the distal **vaginal orifice** (in virgins), the mucosa is elaborated, forming an incomplete partition called the **hymen** (hi'men) (Figure 28.16). The hymen is very vascular and tends to bleed when it is ruptured during the first coitus (sexual intercourse). However, its durability varies. In some females, it is ruptured during a sports activity, tampon insertion, or pelvic examination. Occasionally, it is so tough that it must be breached surgically if intercourse is to occur.

The upper end of the vaginal canal loosely surrounds the cervix of the uterus, giving rise to a vaginal recess called the **vaginal fornix.** The posterior part of this recess, the *posterior fornix,* is much deeper than the *lateral* and *anterior fornices* (see Figure 28.11a and b). Generally, the lumen of the vagina is quite small and, except where it is held open by the cervix, its posterior and anterior walls are in contact with one another. The vagina stretches considerably during copulation and childbirth, but its lateral distension is limited by the ischial spines and the sacrospinous ligaments.

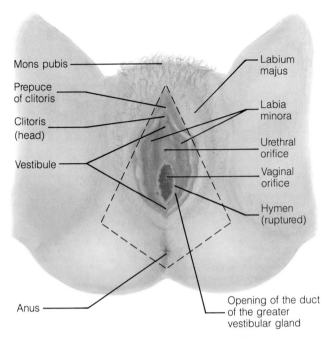

Labels (clockwise from top-left):
Mons pubis
Prepuce of clitoris
Clitoris (head)
Vestibule
Anus
Labium majus
Labia minora
Urethral orifice
Vaginal orifice
Hymen (ruptured)
Opening of the duct of the greater vestibular gland

FIGURE 28.16
The external genitalia (vulva) of the female. The region enclosed by the dashed lines is the perineum.

Because the uterus tilts away from the vagina, attempts by untrained persons to induce an abortion by entering the uterus with a surgical instrument may result in puncturing of the posterior wall of the vagina, followed by hemorrhage and—if the instrument is unsterile—subsequent peritonitis. •

The External Genitalia

As mentioned earlier, the female reproductive structures that lie external to the vagina are called the *external genitalia* (see Figure 28.16). The external genitalia, also called the **vulva** (vul′vah; "covering") or **pudendum** ("shameful"), include the mons pubis, labia, clitoris, and structures associated with the vestibule.

The **mons pubis** (mons pu′bis; "mountain on the pubis") is a fatty, rounded area overlying the pubic symphysis. After puberty, this area is covered with pubic hair. Running posteriorly from the mons pubis are two elongated, hair-covered fatty skin folds, the **labia majora** (la′be-ah mah-jor′ah; "larger lips"). These are the female counterpart, or *homologue,* of the male scrotum (that is, they derive from the same embryonic tissue). The labia majora enclose the **labia minora** (mi-nor′ah; "smaller"), two thin, hair-free skin folds, homologous to the ventral penis. The labia minora enclose a recess called the **vestibule,** which contains the external opening of the urethra more anteriorly followed by that of the vagina. Flanking the vaginal opening are the pea-size **greater vestibular glands** (not illustrated), homologous to the bulboure-

thral glands of males. These glands release mucus into the vestibule and help to keep it moist and lubricated, facilitating intercourse.

Just anterior to the vestibule is the **clitoris** (klit′o-ris; "hill"), a small, protruding structure, composed largely of erectile tissue, that is homologous to the penis of the male. It is hooded by a skin fold called the **prepuce of the clitoris,** formed by the junction of the labia minora folds. The clitoris is richly innervated with sensory nerve endings sensitive to touch, and it becomes swollen and erect with blood during tactile stimulation, contributing to a female's sexual arousal. Like the penis, the clitoris has dorsal erectile columns (corpora cavernosa); but it lacks a corpus spongiosum. In males, the urethra carries both urine and semen and runs through the penis, but the female urinary and reproductive tracts are completely separate, and neither runs through the clitoris.

The female **perineum** is a diamond-shaped region located between the pubic arch anteriorly, the coccyx posteriorly, and the ischial tuberosities laterally. The soft tissues of the perineum overlie the muscles of the pelvic outlet and the posterior ends of the labia majora overlie the *central tendon,* into which most muscles supporting the pelvic floor insert (see Chapter 10).

The Mammary Glands

The **mammary glands** are present in both sexes, but they normally function only in females (Figure 28.17). Since the biological role of the mammary glands is to produce milk to nourish a newborn baby, they are actually important only when reproduction has already been accomplished.

Developmentally, the mammal glands are modified sweat glands that are actually part of the *skin,* or *integumentary system.* Each mammary gland is contained within a rounded skin-covered breast anterior to the pectoral muscles of the thorax. Slightly below the center of each breast is a ring of pigmented skin, the **areola** (ah-re′o-lah), which surrounds a central protruding **nipple.** Large sebaceous glands in the areola make it slightly bumpy and produce sebum that reduces chapping and cracking of the skin of the nipple. Autonomic nervous system controls of smooth muscle fibers in the areola and nipple cause the nipple to become erect when stimulated by tactile or sexual stimuli and when exposed to cold.

Internally, each mammary gland consists of 15 to 25 **lobes** that radiate around and open at the nipple. The lobes are padded and separated from each other by fibrous connective tissue and fat. The interlobar connective tissue forms **suspensory ligaments** that attach the breast to the underlying muscle fascia and to the overlying dermis. As suggested by their name, the suspensory ligaments provide natural support for the breasts, like a built-in brassiere. Within the lobes are smaller units called **lobules,** which contain glandular **alveoli** that produce milk when a woman is lactating. These compound alveolar glands pass the milk

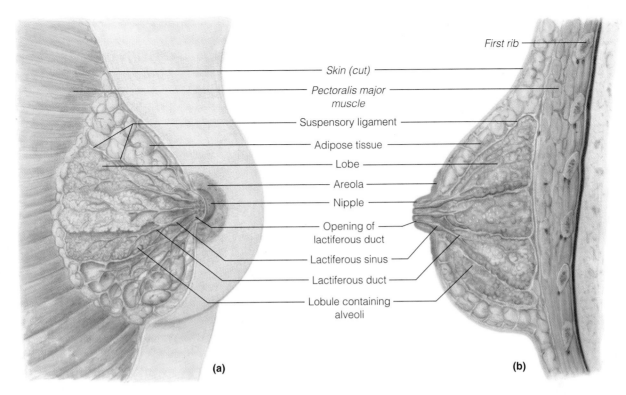

First rib

Skin (cut)

Pectoralis major muscle

Suspensory ligament

Adipose tissue

Lobe

Areola

Nipple

Opening of lactiferous duct

Lactiferous sinus

Lactiferous duct

Lobule containing alveoli

(a)

(b)

FIGURE 28.17
Structure of lactating mammary glands. (a) Anterior view of a partially dissected breast. **(b)** Sagittal section of a breast.

into the **lactiferous** (lak-tif′er-us) **ducts,** which open to the outside at the nipple. Just deep to the areola, each lactiferous duct has a dilated region called a **lactiferous sinus.** Milk accumulates in these sinuses during nursing. The process and regulation of lactation are described in Chapter 29.

The description of mammary glands given above applies only to those of nursing women or women in the last trimester of pregnancy. In nonpregnant women, the glandular structure of the breast is largely undeveloped and the duct system is rudimentary; hence breast size is largely due to the amount of fat deposition.

Breast Cancer

After lung cancer, cancer of the breast is a leading cause of death in American women. One woman in 8 will develop this condition (responsible for over 45,000 deaths in 1993). Breast cancer usually arises from the epithelial cells of the ducts, not from the alveoli. A small cluster of cancer cells grows into a lump in the breast from which cells eventually metastasize.

Risk factors for developing breast cancer include (1) early onset menses and late menopause; (2) no pregnancies or first pregnancy later in life; (3) overexposure to ionizing radiation (X rays); (4) cigarette smoking, excessive alcohol intake, and perhaps a high-fat diet; (5) advanced age; (6) previous history of breast cancer; and (7) familial history of breast cancer (especially in a sister or mother). Some 10% of breast cancers stem from hereditary defects and half of these can be traced to a dangerous mutation in a single gene, dubbed *BRCA1* (breast cancer 1), which virtually guarantees that its carriers will develop breast cancer. However, more than 70% of women who develop breast cancer have no known risk factors for the disease.

Breast cancer is often signaled by a change in skin texture, puckering, or leakage from the nipple. Early detection by breast self-examination and mammography is unquestionably the best way to increase one's chances of surviving breast cancer. Since most breast lumps are discovered by women themselves in routine monthly breast exams, this simple examination should be a health maintenance priority in every woman's life. Currently the American Cancer Society recommends scheduling **mammography**—X ray examination that detects breast cancers too small to feel (less than 1 cm)—every two years for women between 40 and 49 years old and yearly thereafter (Figure 28.18).

Once diagnosed, breast cancer is treated in various ways depending on specific characteristics of the lesion. Current therapies include (1) hormone therapy (the antiestrogen tamoxifen for those shown to have estrogen-sensitive tumors), (2) radiation therapy, (3) chemotherapy, and (4) surgery, often followed by irradiation or chemotherapy to destroy stray cancer cells. Until the 1970s, the standard treatment was **radical mastectomy** (mas-tek′to-me; "breast cutting"), removal of the entire affected breast, plus all underlying muscles, fascia, and associated lymph nodes. Medical records reveal that this painful and

(a)

(b) Normal breast

Malignancy

(c) Breast with malignant tumor

FIGURE 28.18
Mammograms. (a) Photograph of a woman undergoing mammography. **(b)** Normal breast.
(c) Breast with tumor.

disfiguring treatment is no more effective at halting the cancer than less extensive surgery. Hence, most physicians now recommend **lumpectomy,** in which only the cancerous part (lump) is excised, or **simple mastectomy,** removal of the breast tissue only (and perhaps some of the axillary lymph nodes).

Many mastectomy patients opt for breast reconstruction to replace the excised tissue. Although silicone gel implants initially appeared to be "just what the doctor ordered," their use was banned by the FDA in 1991 following evidence that implant ruptures that allowed gel leakage and distribution to other body sites were resulting in increased frequency of autoimmune disorders and cancers. Currently the patient's own tissues (tissue "flaps" containing muscle, fat, and skin taken from the abdomen or back) are providing acceptable alternatives for "sculpting" a natural-looking breast. •

PHYSIOLOGY OF THE FEMALE REPRODUCTIVE SYSTEM

Oogenesis

Gamete production in males begins at puberty and continues throughout life, but the situation is quite different in females. A female's total supply of eggs is already determined by the time she is born, and the time span during which she releases them extends from puberty to menopause (about the age of 50).

Meiosis, the specialized nuclear division that occurs in the testes to produce sperm, also occurs in the ovaries. In this case, female sex cells are produced, and the process is called **oogenesis** (o″o-jen′ĕ-sis; "the beginning of an egg"). The process of oogenesis (Figure 28.19) takes years to complete. First, in the fetal period, the **oogonia,** the diploid stem germ cells of the ovaries, multiply rapidly by mitosis, and then enter a growth phase and lay in nutrient reserves. Gradually, *primordial follicles* (Figure 28.19) begin to appear as the oogonia are transformed into **primary oocytes** and become surrounded by a single layer of flattened follicle cells. The primary oocytes begin the first meiotic division, but become "stalled" late in prophase I and do not complete it. By birth, a female's lifetime supply of primary oocytes, approximately 700,000 of them, is already in place in the cortical region of the immature ovary. Since they remain in their state of suspended animation all through childhood, the wait is a long one—10 to 14 years at the very least!

Beginning at puberty, a small number of primary oocytes are activated each month. However, only one is "selected" to continue meiosis I, ultimately producing two haploid cells (each with 23 replicated chromosomes) that are quite dissimilar in size. The smaller cell is called the **first polar body;** the larger cell, which contains nearly all the cytoplasm of the primary oocyte, is the **secondary oocyte.** The events of this first maturation division are interesting. A spindle forms at the very edge of the oocyte, (see Figure 28.19, left) and a little "nipple," into which the polar body chromosomes will be cast, appears at that edge. This sets up the polarity of the oocyte and

Meiotic Events

Follicle Development in Ovary

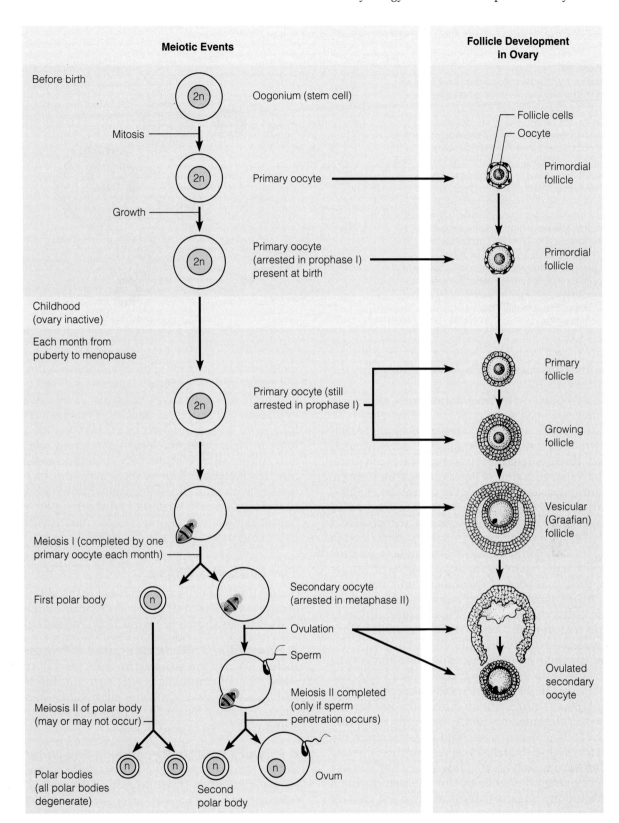

Before birth

Oogonium (stem cell)

Mitosis

Primary oocyte

Growth

Primary oocyte
(arrested in prophase I)
present at birth

Follicle cells
Oocyte

Primordial
follicle

Primordial
follicle

Childhood
(ovary inactive)

Each month from
puberty to menopause

Primary oocyte (still
arrested in prophase I)

Primary
follicle

Growing
follicle

Meiosis I (completed by one
primary oocyte each month)

Vesicular
(Graafian)
follicle

First polar body

Secondary oocyte
(arrested in metaphase II)

Ovulation

Sperm

Meiosis II of polar body
(may or may not occur)

Meiosis II completed
(only if sperm
penetration occurs)

Ovulated
secondary
oocyte

Polar bodies
(all polar bodies
degenerate)

Second
polar body

Ovum

FIGURE 28.19
Events of oogenesis. Left, flowchart of meiotic events. Right, correlation with follicle
development and ovulation in the ovary.

Which of the follicles shown contain primary oocytes? Which contain secondary oocytes?

FIGURE 28.20
The ovarian cycle: development and fate of ovarian follicles. The numbers on the diagram indicate the sequence of events in follicle development, *not* the movement of a developing follicle within the ovary. (1) Primordial follicle containing a primary oocyte surrounded by flattened cells. (2) A primary follicle containing a primary oocyte surrounded by cuboidal follicle cells. (3–4) The growing primary follicle. This follicle is secreting estrogen as it continues to mature. (5) The secondary follicle with its forming antrum. (6) The mature vesicular follicle, ready to be ovulated. Meiosis I, producing the secondary oocyte and first polar body, occurs in the mature follicle. (7) The ruptured follicle and ovulated secondary oocyte surrounded by its corona radiata of granulosa cells. (8) The corpus luteum, formed from the ruptured follicle under the influence of LH, produces progesterone (and estrogens). (9) The scarlike corpus albicans.

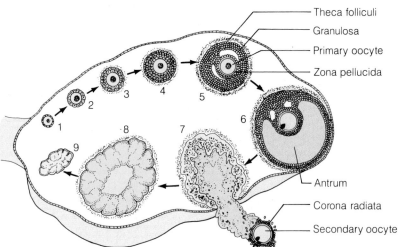

ensures that the polar body receives almost no cytoplasm or organelles.

The first polar body usually undergoes meiosis II, producing two even smaller polar bodies. However, in humans, the secondary oocyte arrests in metaphase II and it is this cell (not a functional ovum) that is ovulated. If an ovulated secondary oocyte is not penetrated by a sperm, it simply deteriorates. But, if sperm penetration does occur, it quickly completes meiosis II, yielding one large **ovum** and a tiny **second polar body** (see Figure 28.19). Completion of meiosis II and the union of the egg and sperm nuclei are described in Chapter 29. What you should realize now is that the end products of oogenesis are usually three tiny polar bodies, nearly devoid of cytoplasm, and one large ovum. All of these cells are haploid, but only the ovum is a *functional gamete.* This is quite different from spermatogenesis, where meiosis produces four viable gametes—spermatozoa.

The unequal cytoplasmic divisions that occur during oogenesis assure that a fertilized egg has ample nutrients for its seven-day journey to the uterus. Without nutrient-containing cytoplasm the polar bodies degenerate and die. Since the reproductive life of a female is at best about 45 years (from the age of 11 to approximately 55) and typically only one ovulation occurs each month, only 400 to 500 oocytes out of her potential of 700,000 are released during a woman's lifetime. Again, nature has provided us with a generous oversupply of sex cells.

The Ovarian Cycle

The monthly series of events associated with the maturation of an egg is called the **ovarian cycle.** The ovarian cycle is best described in terms of two consecutive phases. The **follicular phase** is the period of follicle growth, typically from the first to the fourteenth day of the cycle. The **luteal phase** is the period of corpus luteum activity, days 14–28. The "typical" ovarian cycle repeats at intervals of 28 days, with **ovulation** occurring midcycle. However, cycles as long as 40 days or as short as 21 days are not uncommon. In such cases, the length of the follicular phase and timing of ovulation vary, but the luteal phase remains constant: It is 14 days between the time of ovulation and the end of the cycle. Hormonal controls of these events will be described shortly; here we will concentrate on what happens each month within the ovary (Figure 28.20).

The Follicular Phase

Maturation of a primordial follicle to the mature state occupies the first half of the cycle and involves several events as shown in Figure 28.20, steps 1–6.

A Primordial Follicle Becomes a Primary Follicle. When the primordial follicles (1) are activated, the squamouslike cells surrounding the primary oocyte grow to become cuboidal cells and the oocyte enlarges. The follicle is now called a primary follicle (2).

A Primary Follicle Becomes a Secondary Follicle. Next the follicular cells proliferate until they form a stratified epithelium around the oocyte (3). As soon as more than one cell layer is present, the follicle cells take on the name *granulosa cells.*

In the next stage (4), a layer of connective tissue begins to condense around the follicle, forming the **theca folliculi** (the'kah fah-lik'u-li; "box around the follicle"). As the granulosa cells continue to divide and the follicle grows, the thecal and granulosa cells cooperate to produce estrogens (the inner thecal cells produce androgens, which the granulosa cells convert to estrogens). At the same time, the granulosa cells secrete a glycoprotein-rich substance that forms a thick transparent membrane, called the **zona pellucida** (pĕ-lu'sid-ah), around the oocyte.

In the next phase (5), clear liquid accumulates between the granulosa cells and eventually coalesces to form a fluid-filled cavity called the **antrum** ("cave"). The presence of an antrum distinguishes the new secondary follicle from the primary follicle.

A Secondary Follicle Becomes a Vesicular Follicle. The antrum continues to expand with fluid until it isolates the oocyte, along with its surrounding capsule of granulosa cells called a **corona radiata** ("radiating crown"), on a stalk on one side of the follicle. When a follicle attains full size (about 2.5 cm, or 1 inch, in diameter), it becomes a vesicular follicle (6) and bulges from the external ovarian surface like an "angry boil." This has usually taken place by day 14.

As one of the final events of follicle maturation, the primary oocyte completes meiosis I to form the secondary oocyte and first polar body (see Figure 28.19). Once this has occurred (6 in Figure 28.20), the stage is set for ovulation.

Ovulation

Ovulation occurs when the ballooning ovary wall ruptures and expels the secondary oocyte (still surrounded by its *corona radiata*) into the peritoneal cavity (7). Some women experience a twinge of abdominal pain in the lower abdomen when ovulation occurs. This phenomenon, called *mittelschmerz* (mit'el-shmärts; German for "middle pain"), is thought to be caused by the intense stretching of the ovarian wall during ovulation.

In the ovaries of adult females, there are always several follicles at different stages of maturation. As a rule, one follicle outstrips the others to become the *dominant follicle* and is at the peak stage of maturation when the hormonal (LH) stimulus is given for ovulation. How this follicle is selected, or selects itself, is still uncertain. The others degenerate.

In 1% to 2% of all ovulations, more than one oocyte is ovulated, which can result in multiple births. Since different oocytes are fertilized by different sperm, the siblings are *fraternal*, or nonidentical, twins. (Identical twins result from the fertilization of a single oocyte by a single sperm, followed by separation, in early development, of the fertilized egg's daughter cells.)

The Luteal Phase

After ovulation and discharge of antrum fluid, the ruptured follicle collapses, and the antrum fills with clotted blood (the *corpus hemorrhagicum*) which is eventually absorbed. The remaining granulosa cells increase in size and along with the internal thecal cells they form a new, quite different endocrine gland, the *corpus luteum* ("yellow body") (see Figure 28.20, step 8). Once formed, the corpus luteum begins to secrete progesterone and some estrogen. If pregnancy does not occur, the corpus luteum begins to degenerate in about ten days and its hormonal output ceases. In this case, all that ultimately remains is a scar (9) called the *corpus albicans* (al'bĭ-kans; "white body"). On the other hand, if the oocyte is fertilized and pregnancy ensues, the corpus luteum persists until the placenta is ready to take over its hormone-producing duties in about three months.

Hormonal Regulation of the Ovarian Cycle

Ovarian events are much more complicated than those occurring within the testes, but the hormonal controls set into motion at puberty are quite similar in the two sexes. Gonadotropin-releasing hormone (GnRH), the pituitary gonadotropins, and, in this case, ovarian estrogen and progesterone interact to produce the cyclic events occurring in the ovaries.

Establishment of the Ovarian Cycle

During childhood, the ovaries grow and continuously secrete small amounts of estrogens which inhibit hypothalamic release of GnRH. But as puberty nears, the hypothalamus becomes less sensitive to estrogen and begins to release GnRH in a rhythmic pulselike manner. GnRH, in turn, stimulates the anterior pituitary to release FSH and LH, which act on the ovaries.

Gonadotropin levels continue to increase for about four years, and during this time, the pubertal girl is anovulatory and hence incapable of becoming pregnant. Eventually, the adult cyclic pattern is achieved, and hormonal interactions stabilize. These events are heralded by the young woman's first menstrual period, referred to as **menarche** (mĕ-nar'ke; *men* = month, *arche* = first). Many cycles are still anovulatory in the one to two years that follow. Usually, it is not until the third year postmenarche that the cycle becomes regular.

Hormonal Interactions During the Ovarian Cycle

The waxing and waning of anterior pituitary gonadotropins (FSH and LH) and ovarian hormones and the positive and negative feedback interactions that regulate ovarian function appear to be as described next. Notice that events 1–8 in the following discussion directly correspond to the same numbered steps in Figure 28.21. A 28-day cycle is assumed.

1. On day 1 of the cycle, rising levels of GnRH from the hypothalamus stimulate increased production

Key:

Stimulates ⟶

Inhibits ⤏

Hypothalamus

① GnRH

Anterior pituitary

② FSH, LH

⑤ LH, FSH surge

③ Slightly elevated estrogen level

④ High estrogen level

⑧ Estrogen and Progesterone

Estrogen

③

Growing follicle

Mature follicle

⑥ Ovulation

⑦ Corpus luteum

FIGURE 28.21
Feedback interactions involved in the regulation of ovarian function. Numbers refer to events listed in the text. Events that follow step 8 (negative feedback inhibition of the hypothalamus and anterior pituitary by progesterone and estrogens) are not depicted, but involve a gradual deterioration of the corpus luteum and, therefore, a decline in ovarian hormone production. Ovarian hormones reach their lowest levels in the blood around day 28.

and release of follicle-stimulating hormone (FSH) and luteinizing hormone (LH) by the anterior pituitary.

2. **FSH and LH stimulate follicular growth and maturation and estrogen secretion.** FSH exerts its main effects on the follicle cells, whereas LH (at least initially) more specifically targets the thecal cells. (Why only *some* follicles respond to these hormonal stimuli is still a mystery. However, there is little doubt that enhanced responsiveness reflects the development of increased numbers of gonadotropin receptors.) As the follicles enlarge, estrogen secretion begins. LH prods the thecal cells to produce androgens. These diffuse through the basement membrane, where they are converted to estrogens by the FSH-primed granulosa cells. Only tiny amounts of ovarian androgens enter the blood, because they are almost completely converted to estrogens within the ovaries.

3. The rising estrogen levels in the plasma exert *negative feedback* on the anterior pituitary, inhibit-

ing its release of FSH and LH, while simultaneously prodding it to synthesize and accumulate these gonadotropins. Within the ovary, estrogen increases the output of estrogens by intensifying the effect of FSH on follicle growth and maturation. *Inhibin,* released by the granulosa cells, also exerts negative feedback controls of FSH release during this period.

4. While the initial small rise in estrogen blood levels inhibits the hypothalamic-pituitary axis as just described, high estrogen levels have the opposite effect. Once estrogen reaches a critical concentration in the blood, it exerts *positive feedback* on the brain and anterior pituitary.

5. The stimulatory effects of high estrogen levels set a cascade of events into motion. There is a sudden burstlike release of accumulated LH (and, to a lesser extent, FSH) by the anterior pituitary. This occurs about midcycle (also see Figure 28.22a).

6. The sudden flush of LH stimulates the primary oocyte of the dominant follicle to complete the first meiotic division. The secondary oocyte formed continues on to metaphase II. LH also triggers ovulation at or around day 14. Perhaps LH induces the synthesis of proteolytic enzymes, but whatever the mechanism, the blood stops flowing through the externally protruding part of the follicle wall and then, within 5 minutes, that region of the follicle wall bulges out, thins and oozes fluid, and then abruptly ruptures. The role (if any) of FSH in this process is unknown. Shortly after ovulation, estrogen levels decline. This probably reflects the damage to the dominant estrogen-secreting follicle during ovulation.

7. The LH surge also promotes transformation of the ruptured follicle into a corpus luteum (hence the name "luteinizing" hormone), and stimulates the newly formed endocrine gland to produce progesterone and estrogen almost immediately after it is formed.

8. As progesterone and estrogen levels rise in the blood, the combination exerts a powerful negative feedback (inhibitory) effect on anterior pituitary release of LH and FSH. As gonadotropins decline, development of new follicles is inhibited, and additional LH surges that might cause additional oocytes to be ovulated are prevented.

9. As LH blood levels decline, the stimulus for corpus luteum activity ends, and the corpus luteum begins to degenerate. As goes the corpus luteum, so go the levels of ovarian hormones, and blood estrogen and progesterone levels drop sharply. (However, if implantation of an embryo has occurred, the activity of the corpus luteum is maintained by an LH-like hormone *[human chorionic gonadotropin]* released by the developing embryo.)

10. A marked decline in ovarian hormones at the end of the cycle (days 26–28) ends their blockade of FSH and LH secretion, and the cycle starts anew.

The Uterine (Menstrual) Cycle

Although the uterus is the receptacle in which the young embryo implants and develops, it is receptive to implantation only for a very short period each month. Not surprisingly, this brief interval coincides exactly with the time when a developing embryo would normally begin implanting, approximately seven days after ovulation. The **uterine,** or **menstrual** (men'stroo-al), **cycle** is a series of cyclic changes that the uterine endometrium goes through, month after month, as it responds to changing levels of ovarian hormones in the blood. These endometrial changes are closely coordinated with the phases of the ovarian cycle, which in turn are dictated by gonadotropins released by the anterior pituitary.

The three phases of the uterine cycle are the (1) **menstrual,** (2) **proliferative,** and (3) **secretory.**

Basically, the first phase is a shedding and the second is a rebuilding of the endometrium. Both of these events occur during the period preceding ovulation. The third phase, which begins immediately after ovulation, enriches the blood supply and provides the nutrients that prepare the endometrium to receive an embryo.

Figure 28.22 describes the uterine cycle and illustrates how the ovarian and uterine cycles fit together. Notice that the menstrual and proliferative phases overlap the follicular stage and ovulation in the ovarian cycle, and that the uterine secretory phase corresponds to the ovarian luteal phase.

Extremely strenuous activity can delay menarche in girls and can disrupt the normal menstrual cycle in adult women, even causing *amenorrhea* (a-men"o-re'ah), cessation of menses. Part of the problem appears to be that female athletes have little body fat, and fat deposits aid in conversion of adrenal androgens to estrogens. In addition, hypothalamic controls seem to be blocked in some way by severe physical regimens. Although these effects are believed to be totally reversible when the athletic training is discontinued, a worrisome consequence of amenorrhea in young, healthy adult women is that they begin to suffer dramatic losses in bone mass usually seen only in old age. Once estrogen levels drop and the menstrual cycle stops (regardless of cause), bone loss begins. Currently, female athletes are encouraged to increase their daily calcium intake to 1.5 g, roughly the amount contained in a quart of milk. •

Although menses has traditionally been viewed as a somewhat messy way of discarding a uterine lining "fattened" in anticipation of a baby that was never conceived, its adaptive value and expense to the female body in terms of tissue, blood, and nutrient (particularly iron) loss have recently been questioned. Why not just keep the prepared endometrium for the next cycle? A radical and controversial view of menses proposed by Maggie Profit of the University of California at Berkeley may give you something to think about and debate. The uterus is a hospitable receptacle for bacteria and viruses delivered via the male penis and piggy-backing in semen. This being so, she theorizes that menses is an aggressive way of cleaning house. Not only does bleeding rid the body of the uterine lining where pathogens are likely to linger, but menstrual blood is loaded with macrophages which provide active protection. Additionally, since menstrual blood lacks clotting factors, flushing the uterus out appears to be the goal rather than the by-product of bleeding.

Extrauterine Effects of Estrogens and Progesterone

With a name meaning "generators of sexual activity," estrogens are analogous to the testosterone of males.

FIGURE 28.22
The female menstrual cycle: Structural and hormonal changes.
The time bar at the bottom of the figure, reading Days 1 to 28, applies to all four parts of this figure. **(a)** The fluctuating levels of pituitary gonadotropins in the blood (FSH = follicle-stimulating hormone; LH = luteinizing hormone). These hormones regulate the events of the ovarian cycle. **(b)** The fluctuating levels of ovarian hormones (estrogens and progesterone) that cause the endometrial changes of the uterine cycle. **(c)** Structural changes in the ovarian follicles during the 28-day ovarian cycle are correlated with **(d)** changes in the endometrium of the uterus during the uterine cycle.

The events of the three-stage uterine cycle, depicted in **(d)**, are as follows:

1. Days 1–5: Menstrual phase. In this phase, the uterus sheds all but the deepest part of its endometrium. (At the beginning of this stage, gonadotropins and ovarian hormones are at their lowest normal levels. Then FSH levels begin to rise.) The thick functional layer of the endometrium detaches from the uterine wall, a process that is accompanied by bleeding for 3–5 days. The detached tissue and blood pass out through the vagina as the menstrual flow. By day 5, the growing ovarian follicles are starting to produce more estrogen; see (b).

2. Days 6–14: Proliferative phase. In this phase, the endometrium rebuilds itself: Under the influence of rising blood levels of estrogen, the basal layer of the endometrium generates a new functional layer. This new layer thickens, its glands enlarge, and its spiral arteries increase in number (also see Figure 28.15). Consequently, the endometrium once again becomes velvety, thick, and well vascularized. All the changes in the endometrium in the proliferative phase are stimulated by estrogens. Estrogens also induce synthesis of progesterone receptors in the endometrial cells, readying them for interaction with progesterone.

Normally, the cervical mucus is thick and sticky, but rising estrogen levels cause it to thin and become crystalline, forming channels that facilitate the passage of sperm into the uterus. **Ovulation** occurs in the ovary at the end of this stage (day 14) in response to the sudden release of LH from the anterior pituitary. LH also converts the ruptured follicle to a corpus luteum.

3. Days 15–28: Secretory phase. In this phase, the endometrium prepares for implantation of an embryo. Rising levels of progesterone from the corpus luteum act on the estrogen-primed endometrium, causing the spiral arteries to elaborate and coil more

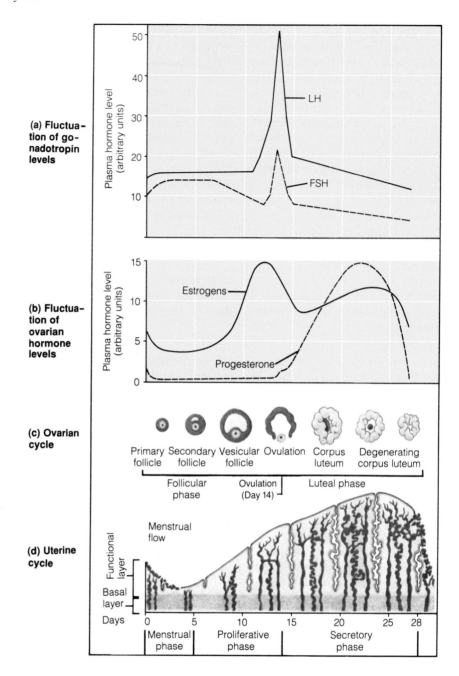

(a) Fluctuation of gonadotropin levels

(b) Fluctuation of ovarian hormone levels

(c) Ovarian cycle

(d) Uterine cycle

tightly and converting the functional area to a secretory mucosa. The uterine glands enlarge, coil, and begin secreting nutritious glycoproteins into the uterine cavity. These nutrients sustain the embryo until it has implanted in the blood-rich endometrial lining. All events of the secretory phase are caused by progesterone.

Increasing progesterone levels also cause the cervical mucus to become viscous again, forming the *cervical plug*, which blocks sperm entry and plays an important role in keeping the uterus "private" in the event an embryo has begun to implant. Rising progesterone (and estrogen) levels inhibit LH release by the anterior pituitary. If

fertilization has not occurred, the corpus luteum begins to degenerate toward the end of the secretory phase as LH blood levels decline. Progesterone levels fall, depriving the endometrium of hormonal support, and the spiral arteries kink and go into spasms. Denied oxygen and nutrients, the endometrial cells begin to die, and as their lysosomes rupture, the functional layer begins to "self-digest," setting the stage of menstruation to begin on day 28. The spiral arteries constrict one final time and then suddenly relax and open wide. As blood gushes into the weakened capillary beds, they fragment, causing the functional layer to slough off. The menstrual cycle starts over again on this first day of menstrual flow.

Table 28.1 Summary of Hormonal Effects of Gonadal Estrogens, Progesterone, and Testosterone

Stimulus/source/effects	Estrogens	Progesterone	Testosterone
Major source	Ovary: developing follicles and corpus luteum	Ovary: mainly the corpus luteum	Testes: interstitial cells
Stimulus for release	FSH (and LH)	LH	LH and declining levels of inhibin produced by the sustentacular cells
Feedback effects exerted	Both negative and positive feedback exerted on anterior pituitary release of gonadotropins	Negative feedback exerted on anterior pituitary release of gonadotropins	Negative feedback suppresses release of LH by the anterior pituitary (and perhaps release of GnRH by the hypothalamus)
Effects on reproductive organs	Stimulates growth and maturation of the internal and external genitalia and breasts at puberty; maintains adult size and function of the reproductive organs. Promotes the proliferative phase of the uterine (menstrual) cycle; rising levels stimulate production of watery (crystalline) cervical mucus and activity of the fimbriae and cilia of the uterine tubes. Promotes oogenesis and ovulation by stimulating the formation of FSH receptors on follicle cells and acts with FSH to induce formation of LH receptors on the follicle cells. Stimulates capacitation of sperm in the female reproductive tract via its effect on vaginal, uterine, and tubal secretions. During pregnancy stimulates mitoses of myometrial cells, growth of the uterus, and enlargement of the external genitalia and mammary glands.	Cooperates with estrogen in stimulating growth of breasts and in regulating the uterine cycle (promotes the secretory phase of the uterine cycle); stimulates production of viscous cervical mucus. During pregnancy, helps maintain and quiets the myometrium and acts with estrogen to cause mammary glands to achieve their mature milk-producing state (stimulates formation of alveoli).	Stimulates formation of male reproductive ducts, glands, and external genitalia. Promotes descent of the testes. Stimulates growth and maturation of the internal and external genitalia at puberty; maintains their adult size and function. Required for normal spermatogenesis via effects promoted by its binding to ABP on spermatogenic cells; suppresses mammary gland development.
Promotion of secondary sex characteristics and somatic effects	Stimulates lengthening of long bones and feminization of the skeleton (particularly the pelvis); inhibits bone reabsorption and then stimulates epiphyseal closure; promotes hydration of the skin; stimulates female pattern of fat deposit, and appearance of axillary and pubic hair. During pregnancy acts with relaxin (placental hormone) to induce softening and relaxation of the pelvic ligaments and pubic symphysis.		Stimulates the growth spurt at puberty; promotes increased bone mass and skeletal mass and then epiphyseal closure at the end of adolescence; promotes growth of the larynx and vocal cords and deepening of the voice; enhances sebum secretion and hair growth, especially on the face, axillae, genital region, and chest.
Metabolic effects	Generally anabolic effects; stimulates Na^+ reabsorption by the renal tubules, hence inhibits diuresis; enhances HDL (and reduces LDL) blood levels (cardiovascular sparing effect)	Promotes diuresis (antiestrogenic effect); increases body temperature	Generally anabolic effects; stimulates hematopoiesis; enhances the basal metabolic rate
Neural effects	Feminizes the brain		Responsible for sex drive (libido) in both sexes; masculinizes the brain; promotes aggressiveness

As estrogen levels rise during puberty, they (1) promote oogenesis and follicle growth in the ovary and (2) exert anabolic effects on the female reproductive tract (see Table 28.1). Consequently, the uterine tubes, uterus, and vagina grow larger and become functional—ready to support a pregnancy. The uterine tubes and uterus begin to exhibit enhanced motility; the vaginal mucosa thickens; and the external genitalia mature.

Estrogens also support the growth spurt at puberty that makes girls grow much more quickly than boys during the ages of 12 and 13. But this growth is short-lived because rising estrogen levels also cause earlier closure of the epiphyses of long bones, and females reach their full height between the ages of 15 and 17 years. In contrast, the aggressive growth of males continues until the age of 19 to 21 years.

The estrogen-induced secondary sex characteristics of females include (1) growth of the breasts; (2) increased deposit of subcutaneous fat, especially in the hips and breasts; (3) widening and lightening of the pelvis (adaptations for childbirth); (4) growth of axillary and pubic hair; and (5) several metabolic effects, including maintaining low blood cholesterol levels and facilitating calcium uptake, which helps sustain the density of the skeleton. (These metabolic effects, though initiated under estrogen's influence during puberty, are not true secondary sex characteristics.)

Progesterone works with estrogen to establish and then help regulate the uterine cycle and promotes changes in cervical mucus (see Figure 28.22d). Its other major effects are exhibited during pregnancy, when it inhibits the motility of the uterus and takes up where estrogen leaves off in preparing the breasts for lactation. Indeed, progesterone is named for these important roles (*pro* = for; *gestation* = pregnancy). However, the source of progesterone and estrogen during most of pregnancy is the placenta, not the ovaries.

Female Sexual Response

The **female sexual response** is similar to that of males in most respects. During sexual excitement, the clitoris, vaginal mucosa, and breasts become engorged with blood; the nipples erect; and increased secretory activity of the vestibular glands lubricates the vestibule and facilitates entry of the penis. These events, though more widespread, are analogous to the *erection* phase in men. Sexual excitement is promoted by touch and psychological stimuli and is mediated along the same autonomic nerve pathways as in males.

The final phase of the female sexual response, *orgasm,* is not accompanied by ejaculation, but muscle tension increases throughout the body, pulse rate and blood pressure rise, and the uterus begins to contract rhythmically. As in males, orgasm is accompanied by a sensation of intense pleasure and followed by relaxation. Orgasm in females is not followed by a refractory period; consequently, females may experience multiple orgasms during a single sexual experience. A man must achieve orgasm and ejaculate if fertilization is to occur, but female orgasm is not required for conception. Indeed, some women never experience orgasm, yet are perfectly able to conceive.

SEXUALLY TRANSMITTED DISEASES

Sexually transmitted diseases (STDs), also called *venereal diseases (VDs),* are infectious diseases spread through sexual contact. As a group, they are the single most important cause of reproductive disorders. Until recently, gonorrhea and syphilis, caused by bacterial infections, were the most common STDs, but within the past decade, viral diseases such as genital herpes and AIDS (mostly transmitted during sexual intercourse) have taken center stage. AIDS, caused by HIV, the virus that cripples the immune system, is described in Chapter 22. The important bacterial and viral STDs are described here. Condoms are effective in helping to prevent the spread of STDs, and their use is strongly urged since the advent of AIDS.

Gonorrhea

The causative agent of **gonorrhea** (gon"o-re'ah) is *Neisseria gonorrhoeae,* which invades the mucosae of the reproductive and urinary tracts. These bacteria are spread by genital contact, as well as by contact with anal and pharyngeal mucosal surfaces. Most cases occur in adolescents and young adults.

Commonly called "the clap," the most common symptom of gonorrhea in males is *urethritis,* accompanied by painful urination and discharge of pus from the penis (penile "drip"). Symptoms vary in women, ranging from none (about 20% of cases) to abdominal discomfort, vaginal discharge, abnormal uterine bleeding, and, occasionally, urethral symptoms similar to those seen in males.

Untreated gonorrhea can cause urethral constriction and inflammation of the entire male duct system. In women, it causes pelvic inflammatory disease and sterility. These consequences declined with the advent in the 1950s of penicillin, tetracycline, and certain other antibiotics. However, strains resistant to those antibiotics are becoming increasingly prevalent. Currently, ceftriaxone is the antibiotic agent most used for gonorrhea treatment.

Syphilis

Syphilis (sif′ĭ-lis), caused by *Treponema pallidum,* a corkscrew-shaped bacterium, is usually transmitted sexually. However, it can be contracted congenitally from an infected mother. Indeed, an increasing number of women trading sex for "crack" (a cocaine derivative) are passing syphilis on to their fetuses. Fetuses infected with syphilis are usually stillborn or die shortly after birth. This bacterium easily penetrates intact mucosae and abraded skin and enters the local lymphatics and the bloodstream. Within a few hours of exposure, an asymptomatic bodywide infection is in progress. The incubation period is typically two to three weeks, at the end of which a red, painless primary lesion called a *chancre* (shang′ker) appears at the site of bacterial invasion. In males, this is typically the penis, but in females the lesion is often undetected within the vagina or on the cervix. The primary lesion ulcerates and becomes crusty; then it heals spontaneously and disappears after one to a few weeks.

If syphilis is untreated, its secondary signs appear several weeks later. A pink skin rash all over the body is one of the first symptoms. Fever and joint pain are common. Anemia may develop, and the hair may fall out in clumps. These signs and symptoms disappear spontaneously in three to twelve weeks. Then the disease enters the *latent period* and is detectable only by a blood test. The latent stage may last a person's lifetime (or the bacteria may be killed by the immune system), or it may be followed by the signs of *tertiary syphilis.* Tertiary syphilis is characterized by *gummas* (gum′ahs), destructive lesions of the CNS, blood vessels, bones, and skin. Penicillin, which interferes with the ability of dividing bacteria to synthesize new cell walls, is still the treatment of choice for all stages of syphilis.

Chlamydia

Chlamydia (klah-mid′e-ah) is a largely unrecognized, silent epidemic that infects perhaps 3 to 5 million people yearly, making it the most common sexually transmitted disease in the United States. Chlamydia is responsible for 25% to 50% of all diagnosed cases of pelvic inflammatory disease (and, consequently, at least a 1 in 4 chance of ectopic pregnancy), and each year, more than 150,000 infants are born to infected mothers. About 20% of men and 30% of women infected with gonorrhea are also infected by *Chlamydia trachomatis,* the causative agent of chlamydia.

Chlamydia is a bacterium with a viruslike dependence on host cells. Its incubation period is about one week. Symptoms, which often go unrecognized, include urethritis; vaginal discharge; abdominal, rectal, or testicular pain; painful intercourse; and irregular menses. In men, it can cause arthritis as well as widespread urogenital tract infection. In women, its most severe consequence is sterility. Newborns infected in the birth canal tend to develop conjunctivitis and respiratory tract inflammations including pneumonia. The disease can be diagnosed by cell culture techniques and is easily treated with tetracycline.

Vaginitis

Vaginitis is typically a manifestation of a local infection with a flagellated protozoan (one-celled animal) called *Trichomonas vaginalis,* or by the bacterium *Gardnerella vaginalis,* but several microorganisms including *Gonococcus* and *Candida* can cause it. The form caused by *T. vaginalis* is as common in sexually active women as gonorrhea. Although there may be many symptoms, including painful intercourse, most common are severe genital itching and a copious green, foul-smelling vaginal discharge. The drug of choice for treating vaginitis is metronidazole given in a single oral dose. Both sexual partners must be treated simultaneously to prevent continual reinfection.

Genital Warts

The *human papillomavirus (HPV)*—actually a group of about 60 viruses—is responsible for the sexual transmission of **genital warts.** About a million Americans develop genital warts each year, and it appears that HPV infection increases the risk for certain cancers (penile, vaginal, cervical, and anal). Treatment is difficult and controversial. Some prefer to leave the warts untreated unless they become very widespread, whereas other clinicians recommend their removal by cryosurgery, laser therapy, and/or treatment with alpha interferon.

Genital Herpes

Human herpesviruses (*herpes simplex, Epstein-Barr virus,* and others) are among the most difficult human pathogens to control. They remain silent for weeks or years and then suddenly flare up, causing a burst of blisterlike lesions. Direct transmission of herpes simplex virus type 2, the common cause of **genital herpes** (her′pēz), is via infectious secretions. The resulting painful lesions that appear on the reproductive organs of infected adults are usually more of a nuisance than a threat to life. However, congenital herpes infections can cause severe malformations of a fetus, and herpes infections have been implicated as a cause of cervical cancer. Most people who have genital herpes do not know it, and it has been estimated that one-quarter to one-half of all adult Americans harbor the type 2 herpes simplex virus. The antiviral *acyclovir* is the drug of choice for treatment of symptoms. •

A CLOSER LOOK | **Contraception: To Be or Not To Be**

In a society such as ours, where many women opt for professional careers or must work for economic reasons, **contraception** (*contra* = against; *cept* = taking), or birth control, is often seen as a necessity. Although scientists across the country are making some headway in the search for a male contraceptive, and an extremely effective antisperm vaccine has recently been developed, thus far the burden for birth control has fallen on women's shoulders, and most birth control products are female directed.

The key to birth control is dependability. As shown by the red arrows in the accompanying flowchart, the birth control techniques and products currently available have many sites of action for blocking reproduction. Let's examine the relative advantages of a few of these more closely.

The most used contraceptive product in the United States is the *birth control pill,* or simply "the pill," a preparation containing minute amounts of estrogens and progestins (progesterone-like hormones) that is taken daily, except for the last five days of the 28-day cycle. The pill tricks the hypothalamic-pituitary axis and "lulls it to sleep," because the relatively constant blood levels of ovarian hormones make it appear that the woman is pregnant (both estrogen and progesterone are produced throughout pregnancy). Ovarian follicles do not develop and ovulation ceases. The endometrium does proliferate slightly and is sloughed off monthly when the pill is discontinued, but menstrual flow is much reduced. However, since hormonal balance in the body is one of the most precisely controlled of all body functions, some women simply cannot tolerate the changes caused by the pill—they become nauseated and/or hypertensive. For a while, the pill was suspected of increasing the incidence of breast and uterine cancer, but it now appears that the new

Flowchart of the events that must occur to produce a baby. Techniques or products that interfere with the process are indicated by colored arrows at the site of interference and act to prevent the next step from occurring.

very-low-dose preparations may actually help protect against ovarian and endometrial cancer. (The argument is less clear when it comes to breast cancer.) The incidence of serious cardiovascular side effects, such as strokes, heart attacks, and blood clots, that occurred (rarely) with earlier forms of the pill has also been reduced. Presently, well over 50 million women use the pill to prevent pregnancy. Its incidence of failure is less than six pregnancies per 100 women per year.

Though not approved by the FDA for this use, many combination birth control pills (marketed under various names including Ovral, Tetragynon, and Triphasil) are also being used for *postcoital contraception.* In common use in Europe and Canada, widely prescribed on our college campuses, and the therapy of choice for rape victims in U.S. emergency rooms, these *morning after pills (MAPs)* are one of the best kept secrets in the U.S.—most teenagers and women in their 30s and 40s have never heard of them. Taken within 72 hours of unprotected intercourse, the estrogen-progesterone combination "messes up" the normal hormonal signals so much that fertilization is prevented altogether or a fertilized egg is prevented from implanting. Within the past four years, Planned Parenthood Clinics have begun to publicize the availability of MAPs; however, since the therapy is not FDA approved, it cannot be dispensed in federally supported clinics.

Other approaches include a device that is implanted just under the skin and injections of synthetic progesterone. The Norplant implant, 6 tiny silicone rods that release a progestin hormone over a 5-year period, was approved late in 1990 and quickly gained advocates. Its failure rate (0.05%) is even lower than that of the pill, but there have been some problems with rod removal. *Depo-Provera,* a synthetic progesterone, has had the longest gestation period of any contraceptive in U.S. history. Developed 35 years before, it was finally approved for use as an injectable contraceptive in October 1992. Administered in a 150-mg dose once every three months, Depo-Provera's failure rate is only 0.4%.

For several years, the second most used contraceptive method was the *intrauterine device (IUD),* a plastic or metal device inserted into the uterus that prevented implantation of the fertilized egg in the endometrial lining. The failure rate of the IUD was nearly as low as that of the pill; however, IUDs were taken off the market in the United States because of occasional contraceptive failure, uterine perforation, or pelvic inflammatory disease. New IUD products are being marketed once again, however, and are particularly recommended for women who have given birth and are in monogamous relationships (i.e., who have a lower risk of developing PID).

Some methods, such as *tubal ligation* or *vasectomy* (cutting or cauterizing the uterine tubes or vas deferens, respectively) are nearly foolproof and are the choice of approximately 33% of couples of childbearing age in the United States. Both procedures can be done in the physician's office. However, these techniques are usually permanent, making them unpopular with individuals who still plan to have children but want to select the time.

Coitus interruptus, or withdrawal of the penis just before ejaculation, is simply against nature, and control of ejaculation is never assured. *Rhythm* or *fertility awareness methods* are based on recognizing the period of ovulation or fertility and avoiding intercourse during those intervals. This may be accomplished by (1) recording daily basal body temperatures (body temperature drops slightly [0.2°–0.6°F] immediately prior to ovulation and then rises slightly [0.2°–0.6°F] after ovulation) or (2) recording changes in the consistency of vaginal mucus (the mucus first becomes sticky and then clear and stringy, much like egg white, during the fertile period). Both of these rhythm techniques require accurate record keeping for several cycles before they can be used with confidence, but have a high success rate for those willing to take the trouble.

Barrier methods, such as diaphragms, cervical caps, condoms (male and female [vaginal pouch] versions), spermicidal foams, gels, and sponges, are quite effective, especially when used by both partners. But many avoid them because they can reduce the spontaneity of sexual encounters.

Several new products are presently undergoing clinical trials, including the following:

1. *RU 486 (mifepristone).* RU 486, the so-called *abortion pill* developed in France, may well be the next "big seller" in the U.S. A topic of bitter controversy among pro-choice and pro-life groups, it is under consideration for approval by the FDA. Although clinical tests for RU486 in the U.S. did not begin until 1994, it has been tested clinically for over a decade on thousands of women in other parts of the world and has proven to have a 96% to 98% success rate with virtually no side effects. RU 486 is an antihormone that, when taken during the first 7 weeks of pregnancy in conjunction with a tiny amount of prostaglandin to induce uterine contractions, induces miscarriage by blocking progesterone's quieting effect on the uterus.

2. *Inhibin.* Inhibin acts on the anterior pituitary gland to depress FSH secretion without changing levels of the other pituitary hormones that are often released in tandem (such as LH). Some researchers believe that it can provide an ideal contraceptive for both women and men.

3. *GnRH antagonist.* Clinical studies of GnRH antagonist drugs have demonstrated their effectiveness as both male and female contraceptives. Since they block anterior pituitary release of FSH and LH (ICSH), they block both sperm and testosterone production in males. Hence, periodic injections of testosterone are needed to maintain the male's ability to have an erection.

This summary barely touches the large number of experimental birth control drugs now awaiting clinical trials, and other methods are sure to be developed in the near future. In the final analysis, however, the only 100% effective means of birth control is the age-old one—*total abstinence.*

DEVELOPMENTAL ASPECTS OF THE REPRODUCTIVE SYSTEM: CHRONOLOGY OF SEXUAL DEVELOPMENT

Thus far, we have described the reproductive organs as they exist and operate in adults. Now we are ready to look at events that cause us to become reproductive individuals. These events begin long before birth and end, at least in women, in late middle age.

Embryological and Fetal Events

Determination of Genetic Sex

Genetic sex is determined at the instant the genes of a sperm combine with those of an ovum. The determining factor is the **sex chromosomes** each gamete contains. Of the 46 chromosomes in the fertilized egg, two (one pair) are sex chromosomes. The other 44 are called **autosomes.** Two types of sex chromosomes, quite different in size, exist in humans: the large **X chromosome** and the much smaller **Y chromosome.** The body cells of females have two X chromosomes and are designated XX; the ovum resulting from normal meiosis in a female always contains an X chromosome. Males have one X chromosome and one Y in each body cell (XY). Approximately half of the sperm produced by normal meiosis in males contain an X and the other half a Y. If the fertilizing sperm delivers an X chromosome, the fertilized egg and its daughter cells will contain the female (XX) composition, and the embryo will develop ovaries. If the sperm bears the Y, the offspring will be male (XY) and will develop testes. (A single gene on the Y chromosome—the *SRY* gene—initiates testis development and, hence, determines maleness.) Thus, the father determines the genetic sex of the offspring, and all subsequent events of sexual differentiation depend on which gonads are formed during embryonic life.

When meiosis distributes the sex chromosomes to the gametes improperly, an event called **nondisjunction,** abnormal combinations of sex chromosomes occur in the fertilized egg and cause striking abnormalities in sexual and reproductive system development. For example, females with a single X chromosome (XO), a condition called *Turner's syndrome,* never develop ovaries. Males with no X chromosome (YO) die during embryonic development. *Metafemales,* or females carrying XXX, XXXX, or other multiples of the X chromosome, have underdeveloped ovaries and limited fertility and as a rule are mentally retarded. *Klinefelter's syndrome,* which affects one out of 500 live male births, is the most common sex chromosome abnormality. Affected individuals usually have a single Y chromosome, two or more X chromosomes, and are sterile males. Although XXY males are normal (or only slightly below normal) intellectually, the incidence of mental retardation increases as the number of X sex chromosomes rises. Human males with an extra Y chromosome (XYY) appear to be normal healthy males but may be somewhat taller than average. •

Sexual Differentiation of the Reproductive System

The gonads of both males and females begin their development during week 5 of gestation as masses of mesoderm called the **gonadal ridges** (Figure 28.23). The gonadal ridges form bulges on the dorsal abdominal wall just medial to the mesonephros (a transient kidney system, see p. 920). The **paramesonephric,** or **Müllerian, ducts** (future female ducts) develop lateral to the **mesonephric ducts** (future male ducts), and both sets of ducts empty into a common chamber called the *cloaca.* At this stage of embryonic development, the embryo is said to be in the **sexually indifferent stage,** because the gonadal ridge tissue can develop into either male or female gonads and both duct systems are present.

Shortly after the gonadal ridges appear, **primordial germ cells** migrate to them from an embryonic structure called the *yolk sac* (see Figure 29.7) and seed the developing gonads with stem cells destined to become spermatogonia or oogonia. Once these cells are in residence, the gonadal ridges differentiate into testes or ovaries, depending on the genetic makeup of the embryo. The process begins in week 7 in male (XY) embryos. Seminiferous tubules form in the internal part of the gonadal ridges and join the mesonephric duct via the efferent ductules. Further development of the mesonephric duct produces the duct system of the male. The paramesonephric ducts play no part in male development and soon degenerate.

In female embryos (XX), the process begins slightly later, at about week 8. The outer, or cortical, part of the immature ovaries forms follicles. Shortly thereafter, the paramesonephric ducts differentiate into the structures of the female duct system, and the mesonephric ducts degenerate.

Like the gonads, the external genitalia arise from the same structures in both sexes (Figure 28.24). During the indifferent stage, all embryos exhibit a small projection called the **genital tubercle** on their external body surface. The urogenital sinus, which develops from subdivision of the cloaca (future urethra and bladder), lies deep to the tubercle. The **urethral groove,** which serves as the external opening of the urogenital sinus, is on the tubercle's inferior surface. The urethral groove is flanked laterally by the **urethral folds** and then the **labioscrotal swellings.**

During week 8, the external genitalia begin to develop rapidly. In males, the genital tubercle enlarges, forming the penis. The urethral folds fuse in the midline, forming the spongy urethra in the penis. Only the

FIGURE 28.23
Development of the internal reproductive organs.

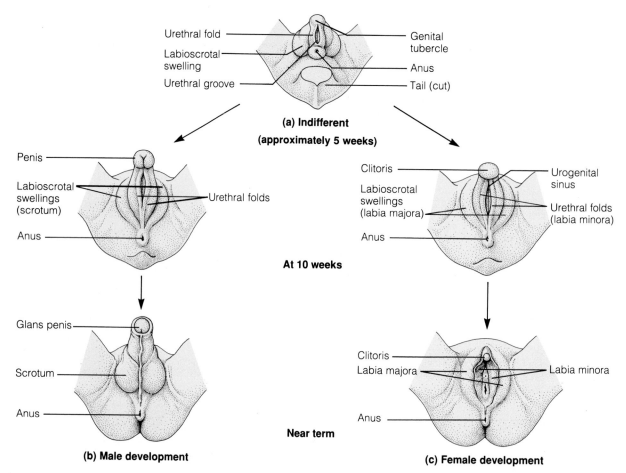

(a) Indifferent
(approximately 5 weeks)

At 10 weeks

Near term

(b) Male development

(c) Female development

FIGURE 28.24
Development of external genitalia in humans. (a) The external reproductive organs are undifferentiated until about the eighth week of gestation. During the indifferent stage, all embryos have a conical elevation called the genital tubercle, which has a ventral opening called the urethral groove. The groove is surrounded by urethral folds, which in turn are bounded by the labioscrotal swellings. **(b)** In males, under the influence of testosterone, the genital tubercle enlarges, forming the shaft of the penis, the urethral groove elongates and closes completely, and the urethral folds give rise to the spongy (penile) urethra. The labioscrotal swellings develop into the scrotum. **(c)** In females (or in the absence of testosterone), the genital tubercle gives rise to the clitoris, the urethral groove remains open as the vestibule, and the urethral folds become the labia minora. The labioscrotal swellings develop into the labia majora.

tips of the folds remain unfused to form the *urethral orifice* at the tip of the penis. The labioscrotal swellings also fuse in the body midline to form the scrotum. In females, the genital tubercle gives rise to the clitoris and the urethral groove persists as the vestibule. The unfused urethral folds become the labia minora, and the unfused labioscrotal folds become the labia majora.

Differentiation of accessory structures and the external genitalia as male or female structures is totally dependent on the presence or absence of testosterone. When testes are formed, they quickly begin to release testosterone, which causes the development of male accessory ducts and external genitalia. In the absence of testosterone, the female ducts and external genitalia develop.

Any interference with the normal pattern of sex hormone production in the embryo results in bizarre abnormalities. For example, if the embryonic testes fail to produce testosterone, a genetic male develops the female accessory structures and external genitalia. On the other hand, if a genetic female is exposed to testosterone (as might happen if the mother has an androgen-producing tumor of her adrenal gland), the embryo has ovaries but develops the male ducts and glands, as well as a penis and an empty scrotum. It appears that the female pattern of reproductive structures has an intrinsic ability to develop (is the default condition), and in the absence of testosterone, proceeds to do so, regardless of the embryo's genetic makeup.

Individuals with accessory reproductive structures that do not "match" their gonads are called *pseudohermaphrodites* (soo-do-her-maf′ro-dīts), to distinguish them from true *hermaphrodites,* rare individuals who possess both ovarian and testicular tissue. Many pseudohermaphrodites have sought sex-change operations to match their outer selves (external genitalia) with their inner selves (gonads). ●

Descent of the Gonads

About two months before birth, the testes begin their descent toward the scrotum, dragging their supplying blood vessels and nerves along behind them (Figure 28.25). They finally exit from the pelvic cavity via the inguinal canals, slanting passages through the oblique muscles of the inferior abdominal wall, and enter the scrotum. This migration is stimulated by testosterone made by the male fetus's testes, and is guided mechanically by a strong fibrous cord called the **gubernaculum** ("governor"), which extends from the testis to the floor of the scrotal sac. The *tunica vaginalis* covering of the testis that is pulled into the scrotum with the testis is derived from a fingerlike outpocketing of the parietal peritoneum, the *vaginal process.* The accompanying blood vessels, nerves, and fascial layers form part of the *spermatic cord,* which helps suspend the testis within the scrotum.

Like the testes, the ovaries descend during fetal development, but in this case only to about the level of the pelvic brim, where their progress is stopped by the tentlike broad ligament. Each ovary is guided in its descent by a gubernaculum (anchored in the labium majus) that later divides, becoming the ovarian and round ligaments that help support the internal genitalia in the pelvis.

Failure of the testes to make their normal descent leads to *cryptorchidism* (*crypt* = hidden, concealed; *orchi* = testicle). Because this condition causes sterility and increases the risk of testicular cancer, surgery is usually performed during early childhood to rectify this problem. •

Puberty

Puberty is the period of life, generally between the ages of 10 and 15 years, when the reproductive organs grow to their adult size and become functional. These changes occur in response to rising levels of gonadal hormones (testosterone in males and estrogen in females). The secondary sex characteristics and regulatory events of puberty were described earlier. But it is important to remember that puberty represents the earliest time that reproduction is possible.

The events of puberty occur in the same sequence in all individuals, but the age at which they occur varies widely. In males, the event that signals puberty's onset is enlargement of the testes and scrotum around the age of 13 years, followed by the appearance of pubic, axillary, and facial hair. Growth of the penis goes on over the next two years, and sexual maturation is evidenced by the presence of mature sperm in the semen. In the meantime, the young man has unexpected, and often embarrassing, erections and frequent nocturnal emissions ("wet dreams") as his hormones surge and the hormonal control axis struggles to achieve a normal balance.

The first sign of puberty in females is budding breasts, often apparent by the age of 11 years. Menar-

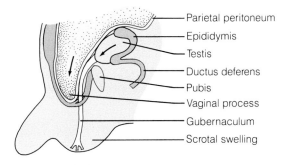

(a)   **7-month fetus**

Labels: Parietal peritoneum; Epididymis; Testis; Ductus deferens; Pubis; Vaginal process; Gubernaculum; Scrotal swelling

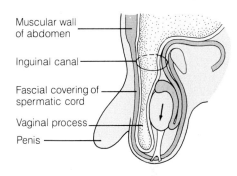

(b)   **8-month fetus**

Labels: Muscular wall of abdomen; Inguinal canal; Fascial covering of spermatic cord; Vaginal process; Penis

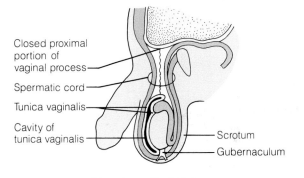

(c)   **1-month-old infant**

Labels: Closed proximal portion of vaginal process; Spermatic cord; Tunica vaginalis; Cavity of tunica vaginalis; Scrotum; Gubernaculum

FIGURE 28.25
Descent of the testes. (a) A testis begins to descend behind the peritoneum about two months before birth, and the vaginal process (a peritoneal extension) protrudes into the tissue that will become the scrotum (scrotal swellings). **(b)** By 8 months, the testis, accompanied by the vaginal process, has descended into the scrotum via the inguinal canal. **(c)** In the one-month-old infant, descent is complete. The lower part of the vaginal process becomes the tunica vaginalis covering of the testis. The proximal portion of the vaginal process is obliterated.

che usually occurs about two years later. Dependable ovulation and fertility await the maturation of the hormonal controls, which takes nearly two more years.

Menopause

Most women reach the peak of their reproductive abilities in their late 20s. After that, ovarian function declines gradually, presumably because the ovaries

Making Connections

Systems Connections: Homeostatic Interrelationships Between the Reproductive System and Other Body Systems

Muscular System
- Androgens promote increase in muscle mass
- Abdominal muscles active during childbirth; muscles of the pelvic floor support reproductive organs and aid erection of penis/clitoris

Nervous System
- Sex hormones masculinize or feminize the brain and influence sex drive
- Hypothalamus regulates timing of puberty; neural reflexes regulate events of sexual response

Endocrine System
- Gonadal hormones exert feedback effects on hypothalamic pituitary axis; placental hormones promote maternal hypermetabolism
- Gonadotropins (and GnRH) help regulate function of gonads

Cardiovascular System
- Estrogens lower blood cholesterol levels and promote cardiovascular health in premenopausal women; pregnancy increases workload of the cardiovascular system
- Cardiovascular system transports needed substances to organs of reproductive system; local vasodilation involved in erection; blood transports sex hormones

Lymphatic System/Immunity
- Developing embryo/fetus escapes immune surveillance (not rejected)
- Lymphatic vessels drain leaked tissue fluids; transport sex hormones; immune cells protect reproductive organs from disease; IgA is present in breast milk

Respiratory System
- Pregnancy impairs descent of the diaphragm, promotes dyspnea
- Respiratory system provides oxygen; disposes of carbon dioxide; vital capacity and respiratory rate increase during pregnancy

Integumentary System
- Androgens activate oil glands which lubricate skin and hair; gonadal hormones stimulate characteristic fat distribution and appearance of pubic and axillary hair; estrogen increases skin hydration; enhances facial skin pigmentation during pregnancy
- Skin protects all body organs by external enclosure; mammary gland secretions (milk) nourish the infant

Skeletal System
- Androgens masculinize the skeleton and increase bone density; estrogen feminizes skeleton and maintains bone mass in females
- The bony pelvis encloses some reproductive organs; if narrow, the bony pelvis may hinder vaginal delivery of an infant

Digestive System
- Digestive organs crowded by developing fetus; heartburn, constipation common during pregnancy
- Digestive system provides nutrients needed for health

Urinary System
- Hypertrophy of the prostate gland inhibits urination; compression of bladder during pregnancy leads to urinary frequency and urgency
- Kidneys dispose of nitrogenous wastes and maintain acid-base balance of blood of mother and fetus; semen discharged through the urethra of the male

Closer Connections: The Reproductive System and Interrelationships with the Endocrine, Skeletal and Muscular Systems

The reproductive system seems to be a particularly "self-ish" system—interested only in its own well-being. But when we reflect on the importance of reproduction and continuity in the scheme of things, that selfishness is a benefit, not a drawback. Indeed, the reproductive system assures (or tries to) that a person's gene pool passes on and, rather than directing its main energy to other body systems, it builds a whole new organism. Quite an incredible feat—don't you think?

Though reproductive system interactions with other body systems are relatively meager, one—that with the endocrine system—stands out and will receive the bulk of our attention. Indeed, these two systems are difficult to divorce from one another, particularly since the gonads themselves function as endocrine organs. Most other reproductive system interactions, such as those with the nervous and cardiovascular systems, are mediated through its hormones. For example, testosterone and estrogen imprint the brain as male or female, respectively, and estrogens help stave off atherosclerosis and help keep a woman's cardiovascular system (particularly her blood vessels) youthful. The gonadal hormones also play major roles in somatic development particularly at puberty, and these are explored below.

Endocrine System

First of all, specific endocrine organs of the body—the hypothalamus via its gonadotropin-releasing hormones and the anterior pituitary gland via FSH and LH—help orchestrate virtually all reproductive functions. Without them, the gonads would never mature to adult functional status during adolescence, gametes would not be produced,

and subsequent effects mediated by gonadal hormones would fail to occur. We would forever remain sexually infantile with a childlike reproductive system. On the other hand, if testosterone were not secreted by the tiny male fetal testes, the male reproductive tract would not be formed to begin with. Furthermore, gonadal hormones produced in response to gonadotropins also help to regulate gonadotropin release (via negative and positive feedback mechanisms), as well as that of GnRH. So what we have here is an interlocking cycle in which one part cannot function without the other.

  Skeletal and Muscular Systems

Once the reproductive system gonads are "up and running," they in turn start producing hormones that not only cause maturation of their own system's accessory organs and help maintain gametogenesis, but also are crucial for the incredible growth spurt that occurs during puberty that converts the child's body to an adult's. The most important effects are the anabolic effects exerted on bone and skeletal muscle. The skeleton becomes taller, heavier, and denser, and in females its pelvis is shaped to accommodate birth. All through a woman's reproductive years, estrogen helps maintain a healthy bone mass. (Its lack is quickly obvious after menopause.) The skeletal muscles, too, increase in size and mass, and become capable of great strength. Testosterone in particular is the muscle builder. Although the gonadal hormones do not act alone, and their effects are superimposed on those of growth hormone and thyroid hormone, they certainly promote adult stature and are responsible for the musculoskeletal changes that distinguish the sexes anatomically.

Clinical Connections

 Reproductive System

Case study: We are back to look in on Mr. Heyden today. Since we last saw him (Chapter 27), he has been to radiology to try to determine the cause of his back pain, and his blood test results have come in. The note recorded from X ray indicates:

• X irradiation of skeleton displays numerous carcinomatous metastases in his skull and lumbar vertebrae

The hematology note of interest here reads:

• Serum acid phosphatase levels abnormally high

1. What is carcinoma? What do you suppose is the primary source of the secondary carcinoma lesions in his skull and spine?

2. On what basis did you come to this conclusion?

3. What other tests might be of some diagnostic help here?

4. What type of therapy do you predict Mr. Heyden will be given to treat his carcinoma? Why?

become less and less responsive to gonadotropin signals. As estrogen production declines, many ovarian cycles become anovulatory, and menstrual periods become erratic and shorter in length. Eventually, ovulation and menses cease entirely. This normally occurs between the ages of 46 and 54 years, an event called menopause. **Menopause** is considered to have occurred when a whole year has passed without menstruation.

Although ovarian estrogen production continues for a while after menopause, the ovaries finally become nonfunctional as endocrine organs. Deprived of stimulatory effects of estrogen, the reproductive organs and breasts begin to atrophy. The vagina becomes dry; intercourse may become painful (particularly if infrequent); and vaginal infections become increasingly common. Other sequels to cessation of estrogen release include irritability and other mood changes (depression in some); intense vasodilation of the skin's blood vessels, which causes uncomfortable sweat-drenching "hot flashes"; gradual thinning of the skin and loss of bone mass; and slowly rising blood cholesterol levels, which places postmenopausal women at risk for cardiovascular disorders. Some physicians prescribe low-dose estrogen-progesterone (e.g., Premarin and Provera respectively) preparations to help women through this often difficult period and to prevent the skeletal and cardiovascular complications. (However, there is still controversy about whether the estrogen component increases the risk of breast cancer in postmenopausal women.)

Although some women's groups vocally urge rejection of hormone replacement therapy (HRT) because it "interferes with the natural events of a woman's life," it is important to recognize that women are living longer after their estrogen-synthesizing reproductive years than ever before. Consequently, the time span during which osteoporosis can take its toll and cause pathological fractures of the spine and hip is ever lengthening. Women must make informed choices about their options in this matter.

There is no equivalent of menopause in males. While aging men do exhibit a steady decline in testosterone secretion and a longer latent period after orgasm, a male's reproductive capability seems unending. Healthy men are able to father offspring well into their eighth decade of life.

*   *   *

The reproductive system is unique among organ systems in at least two ways: (1) It is nonfunctional during the first 10 to 15 years of life, and (2) it is capable of interacting with the complementary system of another person—indeed, it *must* do so to carry out its biological function. The events of this complex interaction culminate in pregnancy and birth. To be sure, having a baby is not always what the interacting partners have in mind, and we humans have devised a variety of techniques for preventing this outcome (see *A Closer Look* on p. 986).

The major goal of the reproductive system is ensuring the healthy function of its own organs so that conditions are optimal for producing offspring. However, as illustrated in *Making Connections,* gonadal hormones do influence other body organs, and the reproductive system depends on other body systems for oxygen and nutrients and to carry away and dispose of its wastes.

Now that we know how the reproductive system functions to prepare itself for childbearing, we are ready to consider the events of pregnancy and prenatal development of a new living being, the topics of Chapter 29.

RELATED CLINICAL TERMS

Dysmenorrhea (dis″men-ŏ-re′ah; *dys* = bad; *meno* = menses, a month) Painful menstruation; may reflect abnormally high prostaglandin activity during menses.

Endometriosis (en″do-me″tre-o′sis; *endo* = within; *metrio* = the uterus, womb) An inflammatory condition in which endometrial tissue occurs and grows atypically in the pelvic cavity; characterized by abnormal uterine or rectal bleeding, dysmenorrhea, and pelvic pain; may cause sterility.

Gynecology (gi″nĕ-kol′o-je; *gyneco* = woman; *ology* = study of) Specialized branch of medicine that deals with the diagnosis and treatment of female reproductive system disorders.

Hysterectomy (his″tĕ-reck′to-me; *hyster* = uterus; *ectomy* = cut out) Surgical removal of the uterus.

Inguinal hernia Protrusion of part of the intestine into the scrotum or through a separation in the abdominal muscles in the groin region; since the inguinal canals represent weak points in the abdominal wall, inguinal hernia may be caused by heavy lifting or other activities that increase intra-abdominal pressure.

Laparoscopy (lap″ah-ros′ko-pe; *lapar* = the flank; *scopy* = observation) Examination of the abdominopelvic cavity with a laparoscope, a viewing device at the end of a thin tube inserted through the anterior abdominal wall. Laparoscopy is often used to assess the condition of the pelvic reproductive organs of females.

Oophorectomy (o″of-o-rek′to-me; *oophor* = ovary) Surgical removal of the ovary.

Orchitis (or-ki′tis; *orcho* = testis) Inflammation of the testes, sometimes caused by the mumps virus.

Ovarian cancer Malignancy of the ovary; the fourth most common reproductive system cancer; incidence increases with age with the greatest risk between the ages of 50 and 60. Since early symptoms mimic GI disorders (abdominal discomfort, bloating, and flatulence), medical assessment is often delayed until after metastasis has occurred; five-year survival rate is 60% if the condition is diagnosed before metastasis.

Ovarian cysts The most common disorders of the ovary; some are tumors. Types include (1) *simple follicle retention cysts* in which single or clustered follicles become enlarged with a clear fluid; (2) *dermoid cysts,* which are filled with a thick yellow fluid and contain partially developed tissues of hair, teeth, bone, etc.; and (3) *chocolate cysts* filled with dark gelatinous material which are the result of endometriosis of the ovary. None of these is malignant, but the latter two may become so.

Salpingitis (sal″pin-ji′tis; *salpingo* = uterine tube) Inflammation of the uterine tubes.

Uterine prolapse Protrusion of the uterus through the vaginal orifice due to weakening of uterine supports.

CHAPTER SUMMARY

The function of the reproductive system is to produce offspring. The gonads produce gametes (sperm or ova) and sex hormones. All other reproductive organs are accessory organs.

Anatomy of the Male Reproductive System (pp. 955–960)

The Scrotum (pp. 955–956)
1. The scrotum contains the testes. It provides a temperature slightly lower than that of the body, as required for viable sperm production.

The Testes (pp. 956–957)
2. Each testis is covered externally by a tunica albuginea that extends internally to divide the testis into many lobules. Each lobule contains sperm-producing seminiferous tubules and interstitial cells that produce androgens.

The Male Duct System (pp. 957–958)
3. The epididymis hugs the external surface of the testis and serves as a site for sperm maturation and storage.

4. The ductus (vas) deferens, extending from the epididymis to the urethra, propels sperm into the urethra by peristalsis during ejaculation. Its terminus fuses with the duct of the seminal vesicle, forming the ejaculatory duct.

5. The urethra extends from the urinary bladder to the tip of the penis. It conducts semen and urine to the body exterior.

Accessory Glands (pp. 958–959)
6. The accessory glands produce the bulk of the semen, which contains fructose from the seminal vesicles, activating fluid from the prostate gland, and mucus from the bulbourethral glands.

The Penis (p. 959)
7. The penis, the male copulatory organ, is largely erectile tissue (corpus spongiosum and corpora cavernosa). Engorgement of the erectile tissue with blood causes the penis to become rigid, an event called erection.

8. The male perineum is the region encompassed by the pubic symphysis, ischial tuberosities, and coccyx.

Semen (pp. 959–960)
9. Semen is an alkaline fluid that dilutes and transports sperm. Important chemicals in semen are nutrients, prostaglandins, and seminalplasmin. An ejaculation contains 2–5 ml of semen, with 50 to 100 million sperm/ml in normal adult males.

Physiology of the Male Reproductive System (pp. 960–969)

Male Sexual Response (p. 960)
1. Erection is controlled by parasympathetic reflexes.

2. Ejaculation is expulsion of semen from the male duct system, promoted by the sympathetic nervous system. Ejaculation is part of male orgasm, which also includes pleasurable sensations and increased pulse and blood pressure.

Spermatogenesis (pp. 960–966)
3. Spermatogenesis, production of male gametes in the seminiferous tubules, begins at puberty.

4. Meiosis, the basis of gamete production, consists of two consecutive nuclear divisions without DNA replication in between. Meiosis reduces the chromosomal number by half and introduces genetic variability. Events unique to meiosis include synapsis and crossover of homologous chromosomes.

5. Spermatogonia divide by mitosis to maintain the germ cell line. Some of their progeny become primary spermatocytes, which undergo meiosis I to produce secondary spermatocytes. Secondary spermatocytes undergo meiosis II, each producing a total of four haploid *(n)* spermatids.

6. Spermatids are converted to functional sperm by spermiogenesis, during which superfluous cytoplasm is stripped away and an acrosome and a flagellum (tail) are produced.

7. Sustentacular cells form the blood-testis barrier, nourish spermatogenic cells, move them toward the lumen of the tubules, and secrete fluid for sperm transport.

Hormonal Regulation of Male Reproductive Function (pp. 966–968)
8. GnRH, produced by the hypothalamus, stimulates the anterior pituitary gland to release FSH and LH (ICSH). FSH stimulates spermatogenesis by causing sustentacular cells to produce androgen-binding protein (ABP). LH stimulates interstitial cells to release testosterone, which binds to ABP, stimulating spermatogenesis. Testosterone and inhibin (produced by sustentacular cells) feed back to inhibit the hypothalamus and anterior pituitary.

9. Maturation of hormonal controls occurs during puberty and takes about three years.

10. Testosterone stimulates maturation of the male reproductive organs and triggers the development of the secondary sex characteristics of the male. It exerts anabolic effects on the skeleton and skeletal muscles, stimulates spermatogenesis, and is responsible for sex drive.

Anatomy of the Female Reproductive System (pp. 968–976)

1. The female reproductive system produces gametes and sex hormones and houses a developing infant until birth.

The Ovaries (pp. 968–970)
2. The ovaries flank the uterus laterally and are held in position by the ovarian and suspensory ligaments and mesovaria.

3. Within each ovary are oocyte-containing follicles at different stages of development and corpora lutea.

The Female Duct System (pp. 971–974)
4. The uterine tube, supported by the mesosalpinx, extends from near the ovary to the uterus. Its fibriated and ciliated dis-

tal end creates currents that help move an ovulated oocyte into the uterine tube. Cilia of the uterine tube mucosa help propel the oocyte toward the uterus.

5. The uterus has fundus, body, and cervical regions. It is supported by the broad, lateral cervical, uterosacral, and round ligaments.

6. The uterine wall is composed of the outer perimetrium, the myometrium, and the inner endometrium. The endometrium consists of a functional layer (stratum functionalis), which sloughs off periodically unless an embryo has implanted, and an underlying basal layer (stratum basalis), which rebuilds the functional layer.

7. The vagina extends from the uterus to the exterior. It is the copulatory organ and allows passage of the menstrual flow and a baby.

The External Genitalia (p. 974)

8. The female external genitalia (vulva) include the mons pubis, labia majora and minora, clitoris, and the urethral and vaginal orifices. The labia majora house the mucus-secreting vestibular glands.

The Mammary Glands (pp. 974–976)

9. The mammary glands lie over the pectoral muscles of the chest and are surrounded by adipose and fibrous connective tissue. Each mammary gland consists of many lobules, which contain milk-producing alveoli.

Physiology of the Female Reproductive System (pp. 976–984)

Oogenesis (pp. 976–978)

1. Oogenesis, the production of eggs, begins in the fetus. Oogonia, the diploid stem cells of female gametes, are converted to primary oocytes before birth. The infant female's ovaries contain about 700,000 primordial follicles, each containing a primary oocyte arrested in prophase of meiosis I.

2. At puberty, meiosis resumes. Each month, one primary oocyte completes meiosis I, producing a large secondary oocyte and a tiny first polar body. Meiosis II of the secondary oocyte produces a functional ovum and a second polar body, but does not occur unless the secondary oocyte is penetrated by a sperm.

3. The ovum contains most of the primary oocyte's cytoplasm. The polar bodies are nonfunctional and degenerate.

The Ovarian Cycle (pp. 978–979)

4. During the follicular phase (days 1–14), several primary follicles begin to mature. The follicle cells proliferate and produce estrogens, and a connective tissue capsule (theca) is formed around the maturing follicle. Generally, only one follicle per month completes the maturation process and protrudes from the ovarian surface. Late in this phase, the oocyte in the dominant follicle completes meiosis I. Ovulation occurs, usually on day 14, releasing the secondary oocyte into the peritoneal cavity. Other developing follicles deteriorate.

5. In the luteal phase (days 15–28), the ruptured follicle is converted to a corpus luteum, which produces progesterone and estrogen for the remainder of the cycle. If fertilization does not occur, the corpus luteum degenerates in about ten days.

Hormonal Regulation of the Ovarian Cycle (pp. 979–981)

6. Beginning at puberty, the hormones of the hypothalamus, anterior pituitary, and ovaries interact to establish and regulate the ovarian cycle. Establishment of the mature cyclic pattern, indicated by menarche, takes about four years.

7. The hormonal events of each ovarian cycle are as follows: (1) GnRH stimulates the anterior pituitary to release FSH and LH, which stimulate follicle maturation and estrogen production. (2) When blood estrogen reaches a certain level, positive feedback exerted on the hypothalamic-pituitary axis causes a sudden release of LH that stimulates the primary oocyte to continue meiosis and triggers ovulation. LH then causes conversion of the ruptured follicle to a corpus luteum and stimulates its secretory activity. (3) Rising levels of progesterone and estrogen inhibit the hypothalamic-pituitary axis, the corpus luteum deteriorates, ovarian hormones drop to their lowest levels, and the cycle begins anew.

The Uterine (Menstrual) Cycle (p. 981)

8. Varying levels of ovarian hormones in the blood trigger events of the uterine cycle.

9. During the menstrual phase of the uterine cycle (days 1–5), the functional layer sloughs off in menses. During the proliferative phase (days 6–14), rising estrogen levels stimulate its regeneration, making the uterus receptive to implantation about one week after ovulation. During the secretory phase (days 15–28), the uterine glands secrete glycogen, and endometrial vascularity increases further.

10. Falling levels of ovarian hormones during the last few days of the ovarian cycle cause the spiral arteries to become spastic and cut off the blood supply to the functional layer, and the uterine cycle begins again with menstruation.

Extrauterine Effects of Estrogens and Progesterone (pp. 981–984)

11. Estrogen promotes oogenesis. At puberty, it stimulates the growth of the reproductive organs and the growth spurt and promotes the appearance of the secondary sex characteristics.

12. Progesterone cooperates with estrogen in breast maturation and regulation of the uterine cycle.

Female Sexual Response (p. 984)

13. The female sexual response is similar to that of males. Orgasm in females is not accompanied by ejaculation and is not necessary for conception.

Sexually Transmitted Diseases (pp. 984–985)

1. Sexually transmitted diseases (STDs) are infectious diseases spread via sexual contact. Gonorrhea, syphilis, chlamydia, and some forms of vaginitis are bacterial diseases; if untreated, they can cause sterility. Syphilis has broader consequences than most other sexually transmitted bacterial diseases since it can infect organs throughout the body. Genital herpes and genital warts, viral infections, are implicated in cervical cancer. AIDS, a condition of immune suppression, can also be transmitted sexually.

Developmental Aspects of the Reproductive System: Chronology of Sexual Development (pp. 988–994)

Embryological and Fetal Events (pp. 988–991)

1. Genetic sex is determined by the sex chromosomes: an X from the mother, an X or a Y from the father. If the fertilized egg contains XX, it is a female and develops ovaries; if it contains XY, it is a male and develops testes.

2. Gonads of both sexes arise from the mesodermal gonadal ridges. The mesonephric ducts produce the male accessory ducts and glands. The paramesonephric ducts produce the female duct system.

3. The external genitalia arise from the genital tubercle and associated structures. The development of male accessory structures and external genitalia depends on the presence of testosterone produced by the embryonic testes. In its absence, female structures develop.

4. The testes form in the abdominal cavity and descend into the scrotum.

Puberty (p. 991)

5. Puberty is the interval when reproductive organs mature and become functional. It begins in males with penile and scrotal growth and in females with breast development.

Menopause (pp. 991–994)

6. During menopause, ovarian function declines, and ovulation and menstruation cease. Hot flashes and mood changes may occur. Postmenopausal events include atrophy of the reproductive organs, bone mass loss, and increasing risk for cardiovascular disease.

REVIEW QUESTIONS

Multiple Choice/Matching

1. The structures that draw an ovulated oocyte into the female duct system are (a) cilia, (b) fimbriae, (c) microvilli, (d) stereocilia.

2. The usual site of embryo implantation is (a) the uterine tube, (b) the peritoneal cavity, (c) the vagina, (d) the uterus.

3. The male homologue of the female clitoris is (a) the penis, (b) the scrotum, (c) the penile urethra, (d) the testis.

4. Which of the following is correct relative to female anatomy? (a) The vaginal orifice is the most dorsal of the three openings in the perineum, (b) the urethra is between the vaginal orifice and the anus, (c) the anus is between the vaginal orifice and the urethra, (d) the urethra is the more ventral of the two orifices in the vulva.

5. Secondary sex characteristics are (a) present in the embryo, (b) a result of male or female sex hormones increasing in amount at puberty, (c) the testis in the male and the ovary in the female, (d) not subject to withdrawal once established.

6. Which of the following produces the male sex hormones? (a) seminal vesicles, (b) corpus luteum, (c) developing follicles of the testes, (d) interstitial cells.

7. Which will occur as a result of nondescent of the testes? (a) male sex hormones will not be circulated in the body, (b) sperm will have no means of exit from the body, (c) inadequate blood supply will retard the development of the testes, (d) viable sperm will not be produced.

8. The normal diploid number of human chromosomes is (a) 48, (b) 47, (c) 46, (d) 23, (e) 24.

9. Relative to differences between mitosis and meiosis, choose the statements that apply *only* to events of meiosis. (a) tetrads present, (b) produces two daughter cells, (c) produces four daughter cells, (d) occurs throughout life, (e) reduces the chromosomal number by half, (f) synapsis and crossover of homologues occur.

10. Match the key choices with the descriptive phrases below.

Key: **(a)** Androgen-binding   **(e)** Inhibin
                protein   **(f)** LH
       (b) Estrogens   **(g)** Progesterone
       (c) FSH   **(h)** Testosterone
       (d) GnRH

_____ , _____ **(1)** Hormones that directly regulate the ovarian cycle

_____ , _____ **(2)** Chemicals in males that inhibit the pituitary-testicular axis

_____ **(3)** Hormone that makes the cervical mucus viscous

_____ **(4)** Potentiates the activity of testosterone on spermatogenic cells

_____ , _____ **(5)** In females, exerts feedback inhibition on the hypothalamus and anterior pituitary

_____ **(6)** Stimulates the secretion of testosterone

11. The menstrual cycle can be divided into three continuous phases. Starting from the first day of the cycle, their consecutive order is (a) menstrual, proliferative, secretory, (b) menstrual, secretory, proliferative, (c) secretory, menstrual, proliferative, (d) proliferative, menstrual, secretory, (e) secretory, proliferative, menstrual.

12. Spermatozoa are to seminiferous tubules as oocytes are to (a) fimbriae, (b) corpus albicans, (c) ovarian follicles, (d) corpora lutea.

13. Which of the following does not add a secretion that makes a major contribution to semen? (a) prostate, (b) bulbourethral glands, (c) testes, (d) vas deferens.

14. The corpus luteum is formed at the site of (a) fertilization, (b) ovulation, (c) menstruation, (d) implantation.

15. The sex of a child is determined by (a) the sex chromosome contained in the sperm, (b) the sex chromosome contained in the oocyte, (c) the number of sperm fertilizing the oocyte, (d) the position of the fetus in the uterus.

16. FSH is to estrogen as estrogen is to (a) progesterone, (b) LH, (c) FSH, (d) testosterone.

17. A drug that "reminds the pituitary" to produce gonadotropins might be useful as (a) a contraceptive, (b) a diuretic, (c) a fertility drug, (d) an abortion stimulant.

Short Answer Essay Questions

18. Why is the term *urogenital system* more applicable to males than to females?

19. The spermatid is haploid, but it is not a functional gamete. Name and describe the process during which a spermatid is converted to a motile sperm, and describe the major structural (and functional) regions of a sperm.

20. Oogenesis in the female results in one functional gamete— the egg, or ovum. What other cells are produced? What is the significance of this rather wasteful type of gamete production—that is, production of a single functional gamete instead of four, as seen in males?

21. List three secondary sex characteristics of females.

22. Describe the events and possible consequences of menopause.

23. Define menarche. What does it indicate?

24. For three popular types of birth control—the pill, the diaphragm, and coitus interruptus—indicate (a) the point of blockage of the reproductive process, (b) the mode of action, (c) the relative efficiency or effectiveness, and (d) the inherent problems.

 25. Trace the pathway of a sperm from the male testes to the uterine tube of a female.

26. In menstruation, the stratum functionalis is shed from the endometrium. Explain the hormonal and physical factors responsible for this shedding. (Hint: See Figure 28.22.)

27. The epithelium of the vagina fights bacteria, and the cervical glands of the uterus prevent the spread of vaginal bacteria. Explain how each of these mechanisms works.

28. Some anatomy students were saying that the bulbourethral glands (and the urethral glands) of males act like city workers who come around and clear parked cars from the street before a parade. What did they mean by this analogy?

29. A man swam in a cold lake for an hour and then noticed that his scrotum was shrunken and wrinkled. His first thought was that he had lost his testicles. What had really happened?

 ## CRITICAL THINKING AND CLINICAL APPLICATION QUESTIONS

1. Gina, a 44 year-old mother of 8 children, visited her physician complaining of a "bearing down" sensation in her pelvis, low backache, and urinary incontinence. A vaginal examination showed that the external os of her cervix was just inside the vaginal orifice and her perineum exhibited large keloids. Her history revealed that she was a member of a commune located in the nearby mountains that shunned hospital births (if at all possible). What do you think Gina's problem is and what caused it? (Be anatomically specific.)

2. Harry, a sexually active adolescent, appeared in the emergency room complaining of a penile "drip" and pain on urination. An account of his recent sexual behavior was requested and recorded. (a) What do you think Harry's problem is? (b) What is the causative agent of this disorder? (c) How is the condition treated, and what may happen if it isn't treated?

3. A 36-year-old mother of four is considering tubal ligation as a means of ensuring that her family gets no larger. She asks the physician if she will become "menopausal" after the surgery. (a) How would you answer her question and explain away her concerns? (b) Explain what a tubal ligation is.

4. A 76-year-old gentleman, interested in a much younger woman and concerned about his age, asks his urologist if he will be able to father a child. What questions would a physician ask of this man, and what diagnostic tests would be ordered?

5. Lucy had both her left ovary and her right uterine tube removed surgically at age 17 because of a cyst and a tumor in these organs. Now, at age 32, she remains healthy and is expecting her second child. How could Lucy conceive a child with just one ovary and one uterine tube, widely separated on opposite sides of the pelvis like this?

Pregnancy and Human Development

29

CHAPTER OUTLINE AND STUDENT OBJECTIVES

From Egg to Embryo (pp. 1000–1007)

1. Describe the importance of capacitation to the ability of sperm to penetrate an oocyte.

2. Explain the mechanism of the fast and slow blocks to polyspermy.

3. Define fertilization.

4. Explain the process and product of cleavage.

5. Describe the processes of implantation and placenta formation, and list placental functions.

Events of Embryonic Development (pp. 1008–1014)

6. Describe the process of gastrulation and its consequence.

7. Name and describe the formation, location, and function of the embryonic membranes.

8. Define organogenesis and note the important roles of the three primary germ layers in this process.

9. Describe the unique features of the fetal circulation.

Events of Fetal Development (pp. 1014–1017)

10. Indicate the duration of the fetal period, and note the major events of fetal development.

Effects of Pregnancy on the Mother (pp. 1017–1019)

11. Describe changes in maternal reproductive organs and in cardiovascular, respiratory, and urinary system functioning during pregnancy.

12. Note the effects of pregnancy on maternal metabolism and posture.

Parturition (Birth) (pp. 1019–1021)

13. Explain how labor is initiated, and describe the three stages of labor.

Adjustments of the Infant to Extrauterine Life (pp. 1021–1022)

14. Outline the events leading to the first breath of a newborn.

15. Describe the changes that occur in the fetal circulation after birth.

Lactation (pp. 1022–1023)

16. Explain how the breasts are prepared for lactation.

ecause the birth of a baby is such a familiar event, we tend to lose sight of the wonder of this accomplishment: How does a single cell, the fertilized egg, grow to become an extremely complex human being consisting of trillions of cells? The details of this process can fill a good-sized book. Our intention here is simply to outline the important events of gestation and to consider briefly the events that occur immediately after birth.

But to get started, we need to define some terms. The term **pregnancy** refers to events that occur from the time of fertilization (conception) until the infant is born. The pregnant woman's developing offspring is called the **conceptus** (kon-sep′tus; "that which is conceived"). The time during which development occurs is referred to as the **gestation period** (*gestare* = to carry) and extends by convention from the last menstrual period until birth, approximately 280 days. Thus, at the moment of fertilization, the mother is officially (but illogically) two weeks pregnant! For two weeks following fertilization, the conceptus undergoes *preembryonic development* and is known informally as a **preembryo.** From the third through eighth weeks after fertilization, the *embryonic period,* the conceptus is called an **embryo,** and from the ninth week through birth, the *fetal period,* the conceptus is called a **fetus** ("the young in the womb"). At birth, it is an infant. Figure 29.1 shows the changing size and shape of the conceptus as it progresses from fertilization to the early fetal stage.

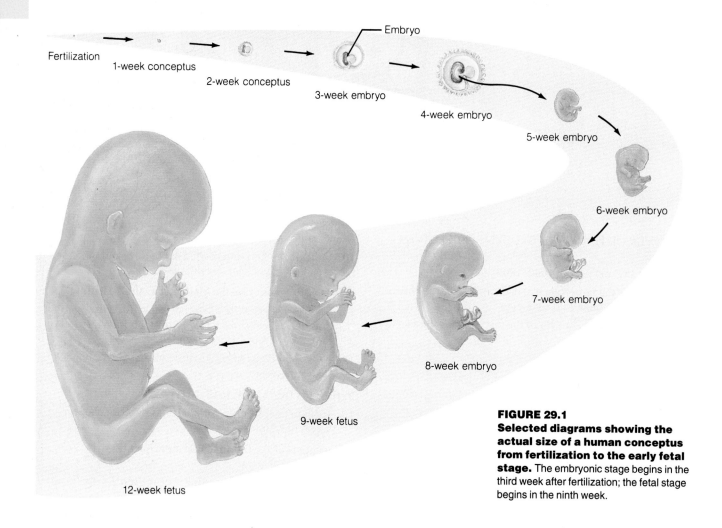

Fertilization

1-week conceptus

2-week conceptus

Embryo

3-week embryo

4-week embryo

5-week embryo

6-week embryo

7-week embryo

8-week embryo

9-week fetus

12-week fetus

FIGURE 29.1
Selected diagrams showing the actual size of a human conceptus from fertilization to the early fetal stage. The embryonic stage begins in the third week after fertilization; the fetal stage begins in the ninth week.

FROM EGG TO EMBRYO

Accomplishing Fertilization

Before fertilization can occur, sperm must reach the ovulated secondary oocyte. The oocyte is viable for 12 to 24 hours after it is cast out of the ovary. Although some "super sperm" are viable for 72 hours, most sperm retain their fertilizing power within the female reproductive tract for 12 to 48 hours after ejaculation. Consequently, for fertilization to occur, coitus must occur no more than 72 hours before ovulation and no later than 24 hours after, at which point the oocyte is approximately one-third of the way down the length of the uterine tube. **Fertilization** occurs when a sperm fuses with an egg to form a fertilized egg, or **zygote** (zi′gōt; "yoked together"), the first cell of the new individual. Let's look at the events leading to fertilization.

Sperm Transport and Capacitation

Sperm travel a treacherous path as they propel themselves through the female reproductive tract. Millions of them leak from the vagina almost immediately after being deposited there. Of those that remain, millions more are destroyed by the vagina's acidic environment and, unless the cervical mucus has been made fluid by estrogens, additional millions fail to make it through the cervix. Those that do manage to enter the uterus are subjected to forceful uterine contractions that act in a "washing machine–like" manner to disperse them throughout the uterine cavity, where thousands more are destroyed by resident phagocytic leukocytes. Only a few thousand (and sometimes fewer than 200) sperm, out of the millions in the male ejaculate, finally reach the uterine tubes, where the oocyte may be moving leisurely toward the uterus.

These difficulties aside, there is still another hurdle to be overcome. Sperm freshly deposited in the vagina are incapable of penetrating an oocyte. They must first be **capacitated;** that is, their membranes must become fragile so that the hydrolytic enzymes in their acrosomes can be released. While the exact mechanism of capacitation is still a mystery, we do know that as sperm swim through the cervical mucus, uterus, and uterine tubes, the cholesterol that keeps their acrosomal membranes "tough" and stable is depleted, and the sperm undergo a gradual capacitation over the next 6 to 8 hours. Thus, even though the sperm may actually reach the oocyte within a few

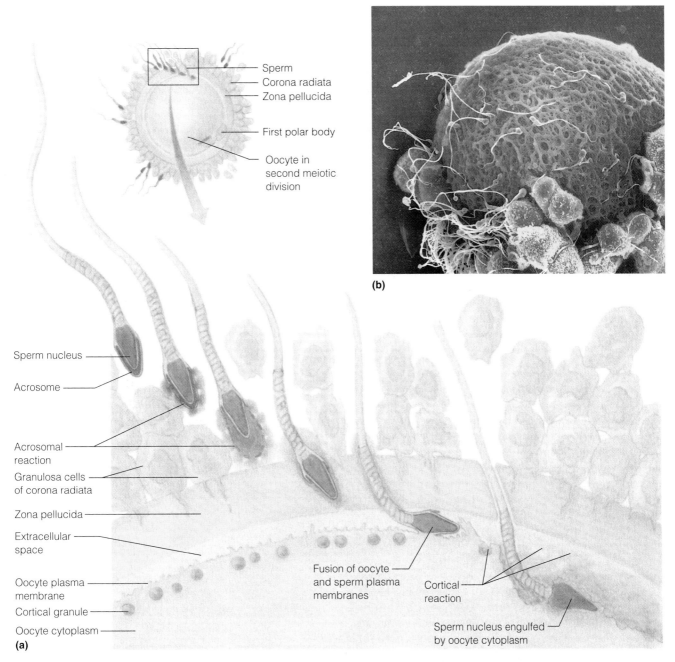

Sperm
Corona radiata
Zona pellucida
First polar body
Oocyte in second meiotic division

(b)

Sperm nucleus
Acrosome
Acrosomal reaction
Granulosa cells of corona radiata
Zona pellucida
Extracellular space
Oocyte plasma membrane
Cortical granule
Oocyte cytoplasm
(a)

Fusion of oocyte and sperm plasma membranes
Cortical reaction
Sperm nucleus engulfed by oocyte cytoplasm

FIGURE 29.2
Sperm penetration and the cortical reaction (slow block to polyspermy). (a) The sequential steps of oocyte penetration by a sperm are depicted from left to right. Sperm penetration through the corona radiata and zona pellucida surrounding the oocyte is accomplished by release of acrosomal enzymes by many sperm. Fusion of the plasma membrane of a single sperm with the oocyte membrane is followed by engulfment of the sperm head (nucleus) by the oocyte cytoplasm and the cortical reaction. The cortical reaction involves the release of the contents of the oocyte's cortical granules into the extracellular space, preventing the entry of more than one sperm.
(b) Scanning electron micrograph of human sperm surrounding a human oocyte (750×). The smaller spherical cells are granulosa cells of the corona radiata.

minutes, they must "wait around" (so to speak) for capacitation to occur. This is a pretty elaborate mechanism for preventing the spilling of acrosomal enzymes, but consider the alternative. If sperm had fragile acrosomal membranes while still within the male reproductive tract, they could rupture prematurely, causing some degree of autolysis (self-digestion) of the male reproductive system.

Acrosomal Reaction and Sperm Penetration

During the **acrosomal** (ak'ro-sōm-al) **reaction,** acrosomal enzymes (hyaluronidase, acrosin, proteases, and others) are released in the immediate vicinity of the oocyte (Figure 29.2). The ovulated oocyte is encapsulated by the corona radiata and, deep to that, the zona pellucida, both of which must be breached before the oocyte itself can be penetrated. Hundreds of acrosomes must rupture to break down the intercellular cement, rich in hyaluronic acid, that holds the granulosa cells together and to digest holes in the zona pellucida. This is one case that does not bear out the old adage, "The early bird catches the worm." A sperm that comes along later, after virtually hundreds of sperm have undergone acrosomal reactions to expose the oocyte membrane, is in the best position to be *the* fertilizing sperm.

Once a path has been cleared and a single sperm makes contact with the oocyte's membrane receptors, its nucleus is pulled into the oocyte cytoplasm (Figure 29.2a). Each sperm carries a special two-part binding apparatus on its surface. The *beta protein* part acts first as it finds and binds to a receptor on the oocyte membrane. This event engages the *alpha protein* part, causing it to insert into the membrane. This somehow causes the egg and sperm membranes to open and then fuse together with such perfect contact that the contents of both cells are combined within a single membrane—all without spilling a drop.

Blocks to Polyspermy

Although **polyspermy** (entry of several sperm into an egg) occurs in some animals, in humans only a single sperm is allowed to penetrate the oocyte. Two mechanisms ensure **monospermy,** the one-sperm condition. As soon as the plasma membrane of one sperm contacts the oocyte membrane, sodium channels open and ionic sodium diffuses into the oocyte from the extracellular space, causing its membrane to depolarize. This electrical event, called the *fast block to polyspermy,* prevents other sperm from fusing with the oocyte membrane. Then, once the sperm has entered, the **cortical reaction** occurs (see Figure 29.2a). The depolarization that serves as the fast block to polyspermy also causes ionic calcium (Ca^{2+}) to be released into the oocyte cytoplasm. The surge in intracellular Ca^{2+} activates the oocyte to prepare for cell division. It also causes the cortical granules, located just deep to the plasma membrane, to spill their contents into the extracellular space beneath the

zona pellucida. The spilled material binds water, and as it swells, it detaches all sperm still in contact with the oocyte membrane, accomplishing the permanent *slow block to polyspermy.* In rare cases of polyspermy that do occur, the embryos contain too much genetic material and are nonviable (die).

FIGURE 29.3
Events immediately following sperm penetration.
(a) Once a sperm has entered the secondary oocyte, the oocyte completes meiosis II and casts out the second polar body. **(b–c)** The ovum nucleus formed during meiosis II begins to swell, and the sperm and egg nuclei approach each other. When fully swollen, the nuclei are called pronuclei. **(d–g)** As the male and female pronuclei come together (constituting the act of fertilization), they immediately replicate their DNA, and then form chromosomes which attach to the mitotic spindle and undergo a mitotic division. This division is the first cleavage division and results in two daughter cells. **(h)** Scanning electron micrograph of a fertilized egg (zygote). Notice the second polar body protruding at the right. A single sperm is seen against the zygote's surface (500 ×).

Why is the multicellular blastocyst only slightly larger than the single-celled zygote?

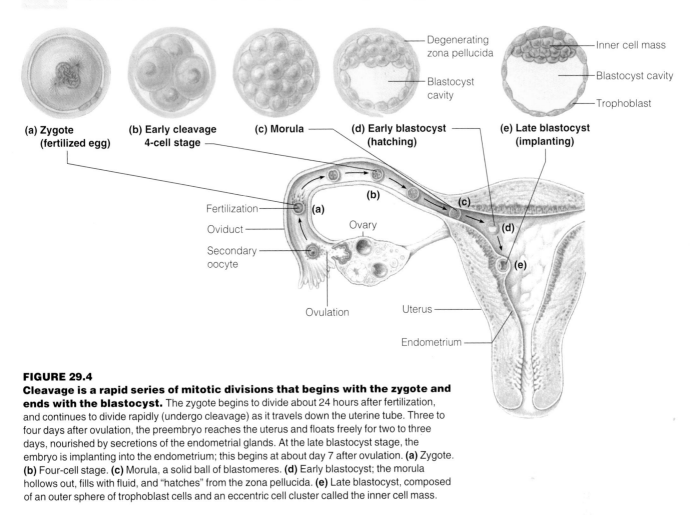

(a) Zygote (fertilized egg) **(b) Early cleavage 4-cell stage** **(c) Morula** **(d) Early blastocyst (hatching)** **(e) Late blastocyst (implanting)**

Degenerating zona pellucida — Inner cell mass — Blastocyst cavity — Trophoblast — Blastocyst cavity

Fertilization — (a) — Oviduct — Secondary oocyte — Ovary — Ovulation — (b) — (c) — (d) — (e) — Uterus — Endometrium

FIGURE 29.4
Cleavage is a rapid series of mitotic divisions that begins with the zygote and ends with the blastocyst. The zygote begins to divide about 24 hours after fertilization, and continues to divide rapidly (undergo cleavage) as it travels down the uterine tube. Three to four days after ovulation, the preembryo reaches the uterus and floats freely for two to three days, nourished by secretions of the endometrial glands. At the late blastocyst stage, the embryo is implanting into the endometrium; this begins at about day 7 after ovulation. **(a)** Zygote. **(b)** Four-cell stage. **(c)** Morula, a solid ball of blastomeres. **(d)** Early blastocyst; the morula hollows out, fills with fluid, and "hatches" from the zona pellucida. **(e)** Late blastocyst, composed of an outer sphere of trophoblast cells and an eccentric cell cluster called the inner cell mass.

Completion of Meiosis II and Fertilization

After a sperm enters the oocyte, it remains temporarily in the peripheral cytoplasm. What happens next is shown in Figure 29.3. The secondary oocyte, activated by the ionic calcium signal, now completes meiosis II to form the ovum nucleus and ejects the second polar body. The ovum and sperm nuclei swell, becoming **female** and **male pronuclei** (pronu'kle-i; *pro* = before), and approach each other as a mitotic spindle develops between them. The pronuclei membranes then rupture, releasing their chromosomes into the immediate vicinity of the spindle. The true moment of fertilization occurs as the maternal and paternal chromosomes combine and produce the diploid zygote.* Almost as soon as the male and female pronuclei come together, their chromosomes replicate. Then, the first mitotic division of the conceptus begins (Figure 29.3d–f).

* Some sources define the term "fertilization" simply as the act of oocyte penetration by the sperm. However, unless the chromosomes in the male and female pronuclei are actually joined, the zygote is never formed in humans.

Preembryonic Development

Preembryonic development begins with fertilization and continues as the preembryo travels through the uterine tube, floats free in the cavity of the uterus, and finally implants in the uterine wall. Significant events of the preembryonic period are *cleavage,* which results in the formation of the structure called a blastocyst, and *implantation* of the blastocyst.

Cleavage and Blastocyst Formation

Cleavage is a period of fairly rapid mitotic divisions of the zygote following fertilization. Since there is little time for *growth* between divisions, the daughter cells become smaller and smaller (Figure 29.4). Cleavage produces cells with a high surface-to-volume ratio, which enhances their uptake of nutrients and oxygen and the disposal of wastes. It also provides a large number of cells to serve as building blocks for constructing the embryo. Consider, for a moment, the difficulty of constructing a building from one huge block of granite. If you now consider how much easier your task would be if instead you could use hundreds of bricks, you will quickly grasp the importance of cleavage.

By about 36 hours after fertilization, the first cleavage division has produced two identical cells called *blastomeres.* These then divide to produce four cells, then eight, and so on. By 72 hours after fertilization, a berry-shaped cluster of 16 or more cells called the **morula** (mor'u-lah; "little mulberry") has been formed. All the while, transport of the preembryo toward the uterus continues. By the fourth or fifth day after fertilization, the preembryo consists of about 100 cells and is floating freely in the uterus. The zona pellucida now starts to break down and the inner structure, or blastocyst, escapes from it. The **blastocyst** (blas'to-sist) is a fluid-filled hollow sphere composed of a single layer of large, flattened cells called **trophoblast** (trof'o-blast) **cells** and a small cluster of rounded cells, called the **inner cell mass,** at one side. Trophoblast cells take part in placenta formation, a fact hinted at by the literal translation of "trophoblast" (nourishment generator). The inner cell mass becomes the **embryonic disc,** which forms the embryo proper.

Implantation

When the blastocyst reaches the uterus, it floats freely in the uterine cavity for two to three days, receiving nourishment from the uterine secretions. Then, about six days after ovulation, **implantation** begins. The blastocyst's outer layer, the trophoblast, tests the readiness of the endometrium for implantation and, if the mucosa is properly prepared, it implants high in the uterus. If the endometrium is not yet optimally mature, the blastocyst detaches and floats to a lower level, finally implanting when it finds a site with the proper chemical signals. The trophoblast cells overlying the inner cell mass adhere to the endometrium (Figure 29.5a and b) and begin to secrete digestive enzymes against the endometrial surface, which quickly thickens at the point of contact. The trophoblast then proliferates and forms two distinct layers (Figure 29.5c). The cells in the inner layer, called the **cytotrophoblast** (si"to-trof'o-blast), retain their cell boundaries. By contrast, the cells in the outer layer lose their plasma membranes and form a multinuclear cytoplasmic mass

(a)

Blastocyst
Uterine endometrial epithelium
Inner cell mass
Trophoblast
Blastocyst cavity
Lumen of uterus
(b)

(c)

Endometrial stroma with blood vessels and glands
Syncytiotrophoblast
Cytotrophoblast
Inner cell mass
Lumen of uterus
(d)

FIGURE 29.5
Implantation of the blastocyst.
(a) Diagrammatic view of a blastocyst that has just adhered to the uterine endometrium. **(b)** Scanning electron micrograph of a blastocyst as it begins to implant in the uterine endometrium. **(c)** Slightly later stage of an implanting embryo (approximately seven days after ovulation), depicting the cytotrophoblast and syncytiotrophoblast portions of the eroding trophoblast. **(d)** Light micrograph of an implanted blastocyst (approximately ten days after ovulation).

called the **syncytiotrophoblast** (sin-sit″e-o-trof′o-blast; *syn* = together, *cyt* = cell), which projects invasively into the endometrium and rapidly digests the uterine cells it contacts. As the endometrium is eroded, the blastocyst becomes burrowed into this thick, velvety lining and surrounded by a pool of blood leaked from degraded endometrial blood vessels. Shortly, the implanted blastocyst is covered over and sealed off from the uterine cavity by proliferation of the endometrial cells (Figure 29.5d).

Implantation takes about a week and is usually completed by the fourteenth day after ovulation—the exact time when the endometrium normally begins to slough off in menses. Obviously, menses would flush away the embryo as well and must be prevented if the pregnancy is to continue. Viability of the corpus luteum is maintained by an LH-like hormone called **human chorionic gonadotropin** (ko″re-on′ik go-nad″ o-trōp′in) **(hCG),** which is secreted by the trophoblast cells of the blastocyst. hCG bypasses the pituitary-ovarian controls at this critical time, and prompts the corpus luteum to continue secreting progesterone and estrogen. The *chorion,* which develops from the trophoblast after implantation, continues this hormonal stimulus; thus, the developing conceptus takes over the hormonal control of the uterus during this early phase of development. hCG is usually detectable in the mother's blood by the third week of gestation (one week after fertilization). Blood levels of hCG rise until the end of the second month and then decline sharply by 4 months to reach a low value, which persists for the remainder of gestation (Figure 29.6). Between the second and third month, the placenta (described below) assumes the role of progesterone and estrogen production for the remainder of the pregnancy. The corpus luteum then degenerates and the ovaries remain inactive until after birth. All pregnancy tests used today are antibody tests that detect hCG in a woman's blood or urine.

Initially, the implanted embryo obtains its nutrition by digesting the endometrial cells, but by the second month, the placenta is providing nutrients and oxygen to the embryo and carrying away embryonic metabolic wastes. Since placenta formation is a continuation of the events of implantation, we will consider it next, although we will be getting ahead of ourselves a little as far as embryonic development is concerned.

Placentation

Placentation (plas″en-ta′shun) refers to the formation of a **placenta** ("flat cake"), a temporary organ that originates from both embryonic (trophoblastic) and maternal (endometrial) tissues. When the proliferating trophoblast gives rise to a layer of extraembryonic mesoderm on its inner surface (Figure 29.7b), it becomes the **chorion.** The chorion develops finger-like **chorionic villi** (Figure 29.7c), which become

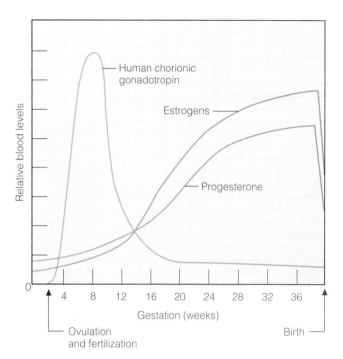

FIGURE 29.6
Relative change in maternal blood levels of human chorionic gonadotropin, estrogens, and progesterone during pregnancy. (Actual relative blood concentrations are not depicted.)

especially elaborate where they are in contact with maternal blood. Soon the mesodermal cores of the villi become richly vascularized by newly forming blood vessels, which extend to the embryo as the umbilical arteries and vein. Thus, the embryo's blood vessels are connected to the fetal (chorionic) portion of the placenta. The continuing erosion produces large, blood-filled **lacunae,** or **intervillus spaces,** in the stratum functionalis of the endometrium (see Figure 28.15, p. 973), and the villi come to lie in these spaces totally immersed in maternal blood (Figure 29.7d). The part of the endometrium that lies between the chorionic villi and the stratum basalis becomes the **decidua basalis** (de-sid′u-ah); whereas that surrounding the uterine cavity face of the implanted embryo forms the **decidua capsularis** (Figure 29.7d and f). Together, the chorionic villi and the decidua basalis form the pancake-shaped placenta.

The fetal side of the placenta is easily recognized because it is slick and smooth, and the umbilical cord projects from its surface (see Figure 29.18c on p. 1021). In contrast, the maternal side is "bumpy," revealing the shape of the chorionic villus masses.

The placenta detaches and sloughs off after the infant is born, so the name of the maternal portion—*decidua* ("that which falls off")—is very appropriate. The decidua capsularis expands to accommodate the growing fetus, which eventually fills and stretches

A CLOSER LOOK | **Baby Making: Popsicles, GIFTs, and Surrogate Moms**

In the summer of 1978, Louise Joy Brown was born. A cause for her parents to rejoice, for sure, but tiny Louise was unique. She was the first baby born who was conceived in a glass dish, or, more precisely, in an *in vitro* laboratory setting. Most who read of this event were overcome with amazement that a child could be conceived outside the body. For scientists in the field of reproductive physiology, Louise's birth was a stunning breakthrough that fueled the subsequent avalanche of new techniques to provide childless couples with offspring.

Making babies outside the privacy of the bedroom is quite a recent phenomenon. In the 1970s, the first and simplest of the so-called alternative forms of conception became available. This technique, *artificial insemination by donor (AID)* was directed at couples where the male was sterile, or nearly so, and at single women. Almost overnight, sperm banks that collected, froze, and stored sperm from anonymous donors began to spring up. Today, in the United States, there are several sperm banks with well over 100,000 frozen ejaculates for sale. The technique is simple by today's standards: All that is required is sperm, a syringe, and a fertile woman. The sperm are deposited in the woman's vagina or cervix at the appropriate time of the month, and

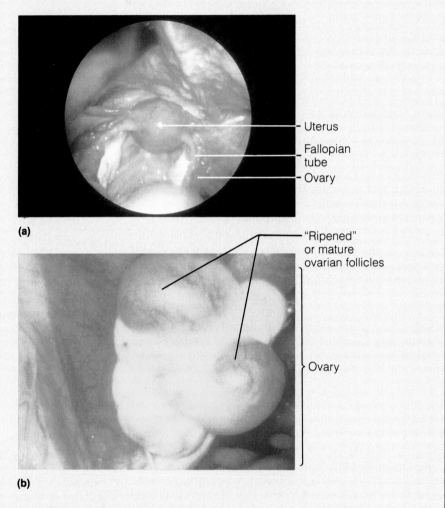

(a)

— Uterus
— Fallopian tube
— Ovary

— "Ripened" or mature ovarian follicles

— Ovary

(b)

Photographs of (a) an unstimulated ovary and (b) an ovary that has been stimulated with hormones to develop multiple mature follicles, which can be seen protruding from the ovary surface.

the uterine cavity. As the developing infant grows, the villi in the decidua capsularis are compressed and their blood supply is reduced; consequently, these villi degenerate. As this happens, the villi in the decidua basalis increase in number and branch even more profusely.

The placenta is usually fully formed and functional as a nutritive, respiratory, excretory, and endocrine organ by the end of the third month of pregnancy. However, well before this time, oxygen and nutrients are diffusing from maternal to embryonic blood, and embryonic metabolic wastes are passing in the opposite direction. The barriers to free passage of substances between the two blood supplies are embryonic barriers—the membranes of the chorionic villi and the endothelium of embryonic capillaries. Although the maternal and embryonic blood supplies are very close, they normally do not intermix.

While the placenta secretes hCG from the very beginning, the ability of its syncytiotrophoblast cells (the "hormone manufacturers") to produce the steroid hormones of pregnancy (estrogens and progesterone) matures much more slowly. If, for some reason, the placenta is producing inadequate amounts of these hormones when hCG levels wane, the endometrium degenerates and the pregnancy is aborted. Throughout pregnancy, blood levels of estrogens and progesterone continue to increase (see Figure 29.6), encouraging growth and further differentiation of the mammary glands and readying them for lactation. The placenta nature is allowed to take its course. Presently, AID accounts for over 20,000 American babies each year. It is an "oldie but goodie" that does what it claims to do.

Although the number of *test-tube babies* like Louise is swelling, they are still relatively few because only a few hundred test-tube clinics exists around the world. (The first U.S. test-tube clinic was opened in 1980.) *In vitro fertilization (IVF)* is an elegant, but tricky, procedure. The woman is primed with hormones (natural or synthetic gonadotropins) to promote the development of several oocytes in her ovaries. (The photographs show an unstimulated and stimulated ovary.) The oocytes are then sucked from the ovary through a small opening in the abdomen into which a viewing instrument called a *laparoscope* has been inserted. A few of these oocytes are fertilized with her partner's sperm in a glass receptacle, and after a few days of growth, all preembryos that show normal early development are implanted back into her uterus. IVF has an added benefit for couples whose families harbor genes for genetic abnormalities. In a technique called *preimplantation diagnosis,* one or two cells are plucked from the early (8-cell) conceptus and tested for the presence of the deleterious genes. Hence, the decision to implant or not can be made with some sense of security. The other oocytes are also fertilized and frozen "for spares" in case the first implantation is unsuccessful—hence, the catchy term *popsicle babies.* Since it is estimated that only 30% of natural fertilizations result in pregnancy and a healthy baby, the success rate of 15% to 20% reported by these clinics is actually very good, and the number in the popsicle baby club is beginning to become significant.

Meanwhile, the use of *surrogate* mothers had been growing by leaps and bounds. Surrogates (for a fee) provide ova and substitute uteri for women who have fertile husbands but who have been unsuccessful in becoming pregnant. The surrogate is artificially fertilized with the sponsor husband's sperm (as in AID), and the baby is eventually delivered to the sponsoring parents. Anyone who reads the newspapers is well aware that the use of surrogates is teeming with legal and ethical problems, primarily because some surrogate mothers have refused to relinquish the baby after birth. Whose baby is it?

Surrogates will no longer be needed when *embryo transfers* from the womb of one woman into that of another become more common. In this procedure, a conceptus is harvested from a donor, who has been artificially inseminated by the infertile recipient's mate, and then transferred into the infertile recipient's uterus. The harvesting procedure involves flushing the donor's uterus out during the first week of pregnancy through a soft catheter (plastic tube). As you can imagine, this procedure is even more rife with complications than *in vitro* fertilization, but the first successful transfer occurred in early 1984 with the birth of a healthy baby boy.

In 1985, another new technique was added to the roster, *gamete intrafallopian transfer (GIFT).* GIFT is an attempt to bypass the hazards (high acidity, unsuitable mucus, phagocytes, and others) that sperm encounter in a female's reproductive tract by bringing oocytes and sperm together in a woman's uterine tubes. As with the *in vitro* procedure, the woman is given ovulatory stimulant drugs, and the oocytes are harvested by vacuum aspiration. The oocytes and the partner's sperm are mixed and then immediately inserted into the woman's uterine tubes via the same laparoscope tubing. GIFT has a cost advantage over *in vitro* fertilization because everything is done as a single procedure.

These new scientific breakthroughs are good news for childless couples, but for some people they have raised the fear of a "brave new world" where babies will gestate in laboratory bottles and only those with the right gender or selected genetic traits will be chosen to live. This is the nature of every major change—intense joy in a vale of tears.

---

also produces other hormones, such as *human placental lactogen, human chorionic thyrotropin,* and *relaxin.* The effects of these hormones on the mother will be described shortly.

Since many potentially harmful substances can cross placental barriers and enter the fetal blood, a pregnant woman should be very much aware of what she is taking into her body, particularly during the embryonic period when the body's foundations are laid down. **Teratogens** (ter′ah-to-jenz; *terato* = monster), factors that may cause severe congenital abnormalities or even fetal death, include alcohol, nicotine, many drugs (anticoagulants, sedatives, antihypertensives, and some antibiotics), and maternal infections, particularly German measles. For example, when a woman imbibes alcohol, her fetus becomes inebriated as well. However, the fetal consequences may be much more lasting and result in the *fetal alcohol syndrome (FAS)* typified by microcephaly (small head), mental retardation, and abnormal growth. Nicotine hinders oxygen delivery to the fetus, impairing normal growth and development. The sedative **thalidomide** (thah-lid′o-mīd) was used by thousands of pregnant women in the 1960s to alleviate morning sickness. When taken during the period of limb bud differentiation (days 26–56), it sometimes resulted in tragically deformed infants with short flipperlike legs and arms. •

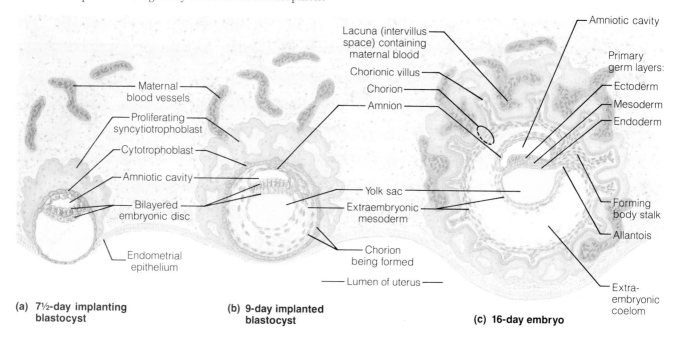

(a) 7½-day implanting blastocyst

(b) 9-day implanted blastocyst

(c) 16-day embryo

(d) 4½-week embryo

(e) 7-week embryo

EVENTS OF EMBRYONIC DEVELOPMENT

Having followed placental development into the fetal stage, we will now backtrack and consider development of the embryo during and after implantation. Even while implantation is occurring, the blastocyst is being converted to the next developmental stage, the **gastrula** (gas′troo-lah), in which the three primary germ layers are evident, and the embryonic membranes are developing.

Formation and Roles of the Embryonic Membranes

The **embryonic membranes** that form during the first two to three weeks of development include the amnion, yolk sac, allantois, and chorion (see Figure 29.7c). The **amnion** (am′ne-on) develops when cells at the dorsal surface of the *embryonic disc* fashion themselves into a transparent membranous sac. This sac, the amnion, becomes filled with **amniotic fluid.** Later, as the embryonic disc curves to form the tubular body (a process we

Placenta
Decidua basalis
Chorionic villi

Maternal arteries
Maternal veins

Myometrium

Stratum basalis of endometrium

Maternal portion of placenta (decidua basalis)

Fetal portion of placenta (chorion)

Yolk sac
Amnion
Amniotic cavity
Umbilical cord
Chorionic villus containing fetal capillaries
Maternal blood in lacuna (intervillus space)
Uterus
Lumen of uterus

Decidua capsularis
Extraembryonic coelom

Fetal arteriole
Fetal venule
Amnion
Umbilical cord

Umbilical arteries
Umbilical vein
Connection to yolk sac

(f) 13-week fetus

(g)

FIGURE 29.7
Events of placentation, early embryonic development, and formation of the embryonic membranes. Times given refer to the age of the conceptus, which is typically 2 weeks "younger" than the gestation age. **(a)** Implanting blastocyst. The erosion of the endometrium by the syncytiotrophoblast is ongoing, and cells of the embryonic disc are now separated by a fluid-filled space from the amnion. **(b)** Implantation is completed by the ninth day and extraembryonic mesoderm is beginning to form a discrete layer beneath the cytotrophoblast. **(c)** By 16

days, the cytotrophoblast and associated mesoderm has become the chorion, and chorionic villi are elaborating. The embryo now exhibits all three germ layers, a yolk sac (formed by endodermal cells), and an allantois, an outpocketing of the yolk sac that forms the structural basis of the body stalk, or umbilical cord. **(d)** At 4½ weeks, the decidua capsularis (placental portion enclosing the embryo on the uterine lumen face) and decidua basalis (placental portion encompassing the elaborate chorionic villi and maternal endometrium) are well formed. The chorionic villi lie in blood-filled intervillus spaces within the endometrium.

Organogenesis is occurring in the embryo, which is now receiving its nutrition via the umbilical vessels that connect it (via the body stalk) to the placenta. The amnion and yolk sac are well developed. **(e)** A 7-week embryo and the embryonic membranes that will contribute to the placenta (at right). **(f)** 13-week fetus. **(g)** Detailed anatomy of the vascular relationships in the mature decidua basalis. This state of development has been accomplished by the end of the third month of development.

will describe shortly), the amnion curves with it. Eventually, the sac extends all the way around the embryo, broken only by the umbilical cord (see Figure 29.7d).

Sometimes called the "bag of waters," the amnion provides a buoyant environment that protects the developing embryo against physical trauma, and helps maintain a constant homeostatic temperature. The fluid also prevents the rapidly growing embryonic parts from adhering and fusing together and allows the embryo considerable freedom of movement, thus aiding musculoskeletal development. Initially, amniotic fluid is derived from the maternal blood, but as the fetal kidneys become functional, fetal urine contributes to amniotic fluid volume.

The **yolk sac** (see Figure 29.7b) forms (at least in part) from cells on the surface of the embryonic disc opposite the forming amnion. These cells proliferate and fashion themselves into a sac that hangs from the ventral surface of the embryo (see Figure 29.7b). Thus, the amnion and yolk sac resemble two balloons touching one another with the embryonic disc at the point of contact. In many species, the yolk sac is the main source of nutrition for the embryo, but human eggs contain very little yolk and nutritive functions have been taken over by the placenta. Nevertheless, the yolk sac is important in humans because it (1) forms part of the *gut* (digestive tube), (2) produces the earliest blood cells, and (3) is the source of pri-

FIGURE 29.8

Gastrulation: formation of the three primary germ layers. (a) Surface view of an embryonic disc. Notice the correlation between the forming notochord and other areas of the embryonic disc with the body plan (see inset showing the baby at the upper right) of the developing infant. The solid blue lines indicate the path taken by surface cells as they migrate toward the median primitive streak. The broken lines indicate the path of the same cells as they enter the primitive streak and migrate laterally just beneath the surface cells. (b) Cross section of the embryonic disc, showing the germ layers resulting from cell migration. Arrows show the migratory pathway of the cells that have invaded the primitive streak. (c) Migratory behavior is over; the cells at the surface of the embryonic disc are ectodermal cells; those at the ventral surface endodermal cells; and the migratory cells that now occupy the middle position are mesodermal cells. This cross-sectional view is taken anterior to the primitive streak in the future thorax region.

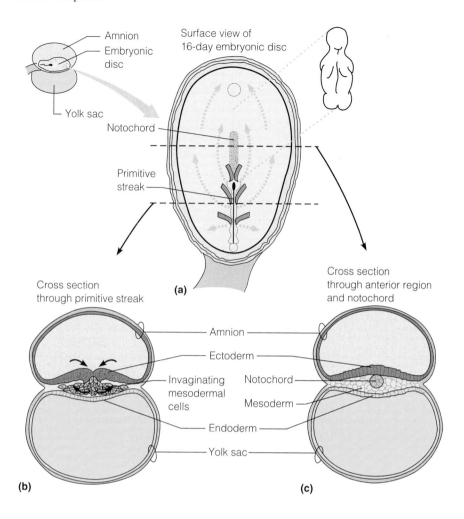

mordial germ cells that migrate into the embryo's body to seed the gonads.

The **allantois** (ah-lan'to-is) forms as a small out-pocketing at the caudal end of the yolk sac (see Figure 29.7c). In animals that develop within shelled eggs, the allantois is a disposal site for solid metabolic wastes (excreta). In humans, the allantois serves as a structural base for constructing the umbilical cord that links the embryo to the placenta, and becomes part of the urinary bladder. When the umbilical cord is fully formed, it contains a core of embryonic connective tissue (Wharton's jelly) and the umbilical arteries and vein, and is covered externally by amniotic membrane.

The *chorion*, which helps to form the placenta, has already been described (see Figure 29.7c). Since it is the outermost membrane, the chorion encloses the embryonic body and all other membranes.

Gastrulation: Germ Layer Formation

During the third week, the two-layered embryonic disc transforms into a three-layered *embryo* in which the **primary germ layers**—*ectoderm, mesoderm,* and *endoderm*—are present. This process, called **gastru-**

lation (gas"troo-la'shun), involves cellular rearrangements and widespread cell migrations. Shortly after the amnion forms, the embryonic disc elongates and broadens anteriorly, becoming a pear-shaped plate of cells. A raised groove, called the **primitive streak,** appears on its dorsal surface and establishes the longitudinal axis of the embryo (Figure 29.8a and b).

The cell migrations that follow appear rather frantic when observed microscopically. Surface cells of the embryonic disc (1) migrate medially across other cells, (2) enter the primitive streak, and then (3) push laterally between the cells at the upper and lower surfaces (see Figure 29.8a and b). When this migratory behavior ends (about the second week after fertilization), the cells at the dorsal boundary of the embryonic disc are the **ectoderm,** those at the ventral surface are **endoderm,** and the migratory cells that now occupy the middle of the "sandwich" form the **mesoderm.** The mesodermal cells immediately beneath the early primitive streak quickly aggregate, forming a rod of mesodermal cells called the **notochord** (no'to-kord), which serves as the first axial support of the embryo (Figure 29.8c). The conceptus, now called an embryo, is about 2 mm long.

The three primary germ layers differ in the arrangement of their cells and serve as the *primitive tissues* from which all body organs will derive. Ectoderm ("outer skin") goes on to fashion the structures of the nervous system and the skin epidermis. Endoderm ("inner skin") forms the epithelial linings of the digestive, respiratory, and urogenital systems, and associated glands. Mesoderm ("middle skin") forms virtually everything else. Both ectoderm and endoderm consist mostly of cells that are securely joined to each other and are considered *epithelia.* Mesoderm, by contrast, is a *mesenchyme* (literally, "poured into the middle [of the embryo]"). Notice, however, that the term **mesenchyme** indicates *any* embryonic tissue with starshaped cells that are free to migrate widely within the embryo. Table 29.1 (p. 1014) lists the germ layer derivatives; some of the details of the differentiation processes are described next.

Organogenesis: Differentiation of the Germ Layers

Gastrulation lays down the basic structural framework of the embryo and sets the stage for **organogenesis** (or″gah-no-jen′ĕ-sis), formation of body organs and organ systems. During organogenesis, the cells of the embryo continue to rearrange themselves, forming clusters, rods, or membranes that differentiate into definitive tissues and organs. By the end of the embryonic period, when the embryo is eight weeks old and about 22 mm (slightly less than 1 inch) long from head to buttocks (referred to as the *crown-rump measurement*), all the adult organ systems are recognizable. It is truly amazing how much organogenesis occurs in such a short time in such a small amount of living matter.

Specialization of the Ectoderm

The first major event in organogenesis is **neurulation,** the differentiation of ectoderm that gives rise to the brain and spinal cord (Figure 29.9). This process is *induced* (stimulated to happen) by chemical signals from the *notochord,* the axial rod of mesoderm mentioned earlier. The ectoderm overlying the notochord thickens, forming the **neural plate,** and then starts to fold inward as a **neural groove,** which forms prominent **neural folds** as it deepens. By the twenty-third day, the superior margins of the neural folds fuse, forming a **neural tube,** which soon detaches from the surface ectoderm to lie beneath it in the body midline. As described in Chapter 12, the anterior end of the neural tube becomes the brain and the rest becomes the spinal cord. The associated **neural crest cells** migrate widely and give rise to the cranial, spinal, and sympathetic ganglia (and associated nerves), to the medulla of the adrenal gland, and contribute to some connective tissues. By the end of the first month of development, the three primary brain vesicles (fore-, mid-, and hindbrain) are obvious. By

What germ layer gives rise to the neural tube?

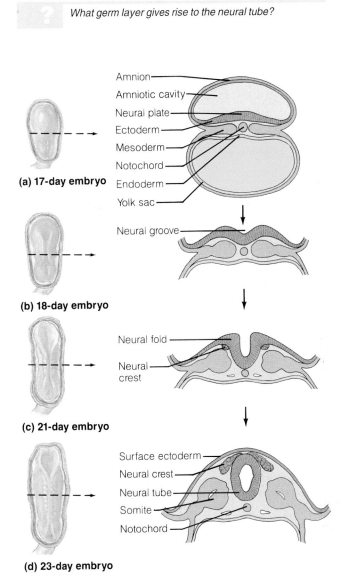

(a) 17-day embryo

(b) 18-day embryo

(c) 21-day embryo

(d) 23-day embryo

FIGURE 29.9

Events of neurulation. Dorsal surface views on the left; frontal sections on the right. **(a)** The embryonic disc, which has accomplished gastrulation. The notochord and neural plate have formed. **(b)** Formation of the neural folds by folding of the neural plate. **(c)** The neural folds begin to close. **(d)** The newly formed neural tube has detached from the surface ectoderm and lies between the surface ectoderm and the notochord; the neural crest is evident. While the neural tube is forming, the embryonic disc is folding to form the embryonic body, as shown in Figure 29.10.

the end of the second month, all brain flexures are evident, the cerebral hemispheres cover the top of the brain stem (see Figure 12.4), and brain waves can be recorded. Most of the remaining ectoderm forming the surface layer of the embryonic body differentiates into the epidermal layer of the skin. Other ectodermal derivatives are indicated in Table 29.1.

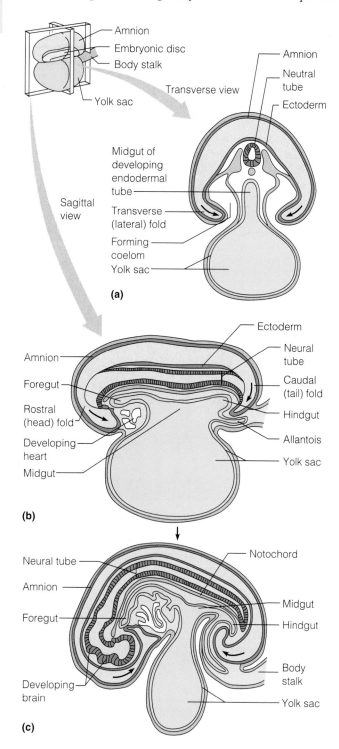

FIGURE 29.10
Folding of the embryonic body that produces the tubular body trunk. (a) Frontal view showing the lateral folding of the embryonic disc. Sagittal views of the (b) early and (c) late folding process, which begins simultaneously from the rostral and caudal ends of the embryo. Folding results in the formation of an internal endodermal tube (primitive gut) that constitutes the embryonic foregut, midgut, and hindgut.

Specialization of the Endoderm

As noted, the embryo starts off as a flat embryonic plate, but as it grows rapidly, it folds to achieve a cylindrical body shape (Figure 29.10). The folding occurs simultaneously on both sides *(lateral folds)* and from the rostral *(head fold)* and caudal *(tail fold)* ends, and progresses toward the central part of the embryonic body, where the yolk sac and umbilical vessels protrude. As the endoderm undercuts the embryo and its edges come together and fuse, it encloses part of the yolk sac. The tube of endoderm formed, called the **primitive gut,** forms the epithelial lining of the gastrointestinal tract (Figure 29.11). The organs of the GI tract (pharynx, esophagus, etc.) quickly become apparent, and then the oral and anal openings perforate. The mucosal lining of the respiratory tract forms as an outpocketing from the *foregut* (pharyngeal endoderm), and the glands that derive from endoderm arise as endodermal outpocketings at various points along the tract. For example, the thyroid, parathyroids, and thymus form from the pharyngeal endoderm, and the liver and pancreas arise from the intestinal mucosa *(midgut)* more inferiorly. Notice that while the glands mentioned form entirely from endodermal cells, the endoderm forms only the epithelium of the mucosal lining of the hollow organs of the digestive and respiratory tracts. Mesoderm forms the rest of their wall structure.

Specialization of the Mesoderm

Mesoderm forms all body parts except the nervous system, skin epidermis and derivatives, and the epithelium and glandular derivatives of mucosae. Since we have covered embryonic development of the various organ systems in earlier chapters, we will focus only on the very early events of mesodermal segregation and specialization here.

The first evidence of mesodermal differentiation is the appearance of the notochord in the embryonic disc (see Figure 29.8c). (Although the notochord is eventually replaced by the vertebral column, its remnants persist in the springy nucleus pulposus of the intervertebral discs until the second decade of life.) Shortly thereafter, mesodermal aggregates appear on either side of the notochord (Figure 29.12a). The largest of these, the *somites* (so'mīts), are a series of paired mesodermal blocks that hug the notochord on either side. All 40 pairs of somites are present by the end of the fourth week of development. Flanking the somites laterally are small clusters of mesoderm called the *intermediate mesoderm* and then double sheets of *lateral mesoderm.*

Each **somite** has three functional parts— *sclerotome, dermatome,* and *myotome.* Cells of the **sclerotome** (skle'ro-tōm; "hard piece") on either side migrate medially, gather around the notochord and neural tube, and produce the vertebra and rib at the

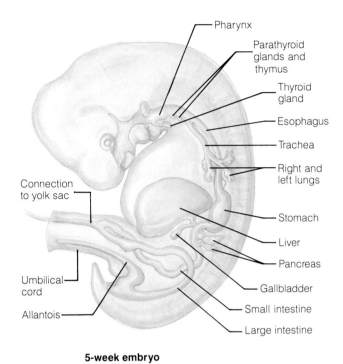

5-week embryo

FIGURE 29.11
Endodermal differentiation to form the epithelial linings of the digestive and respiratory tracts and associated glands.

Cells of the **somatic mesoderm** have three major roles: (1) They migrate beneath the surface ectoderm and help to form the dermis of the skin in the ventral body region; (2) they form the parietal serosa that lines the ventral body cavity; and (3) they produce the **limb buds** that give rise to the bones and contribute to the muscles of the limbs (see Figure 29.12b). **Splanchnic mesoderm** provides the mesenchymal cells that form cardiovascular system organs and most connective tissues of the body. Splanchnic mesodermal cells also collect around the endodermal mucosal linings, where they form the smooth muscle, connective tissues, and serosal coverings (in other words, nearly the entire wall) of the digestive and respiratory organs. As you can see in Figure 29.12b, folding of the embryonic body forms the ventral body cavity, called the **coelom** (se'lom), at this time. As already described, the lateral mesodermal layers cooperate to form the serosae of the coelom.

By the end of the embryonic period, ossification of the bones has begun and the skeletal muscles are well formed and contracting spontaneously. The metanephric kidneys are developing, the gonads are formed, and the lungs and digestive organs are attaining their final shape and body position. Blood delivery to and from the placenta via the umbilical vessels is constant and efficient. The heart and the liver are

associated level. The **dermatome** ("skin piece") cells, which form the outer wall of each somite, help form the dermis of the skin in the dorsal part of the body. The **myotome** (mi'o-tōm; "muscle piece") consists of somite cells that remain behind as the sclerotome and dermatome cells migrate away. The myotomes develop in conjunction with the vertebrae. They form the skeletal musculature of the neck, body trunk, and the bulk of the limbs.

Cells of the **intermediate mesoderm** form the gonads, kidneys, and adrenal cortex. The **lateral mesoderm** consists of paired mesodermal sheets: the *somatic mesoderm* and the *splanchnic mesoderm.*

FIGURE 29.12
Early mesodermal differentiation. (a) Segregation of the mesoderm (with the exception of notochord formation, which occurs earlier) takes place as neurulation is occurring. The notochord becomes flanked bilaterally by a somite, intermediate mesoderm, and lateral mesoderm successively. **(b)** Schematic view of the mesodermal divisions and relationships in an undercut (folded) embryo. The different regions of each somite—the sclerotome, dermatome, and myotome—contribute to the formation of the vertebrae, skin dermis, and skeletal muscles, respectively. The intermediate mesoderm forms the kidneys, gonads, and associated structures. The somatic mesoderm portion of the lateral mesoderm forms the limb buds and parietal serosa and contributes to the dermis. The splanchnic mesoderm forms the muscle, connective tissues, and serosae of the walls of the visceral organs, and the heart and blood vessels.

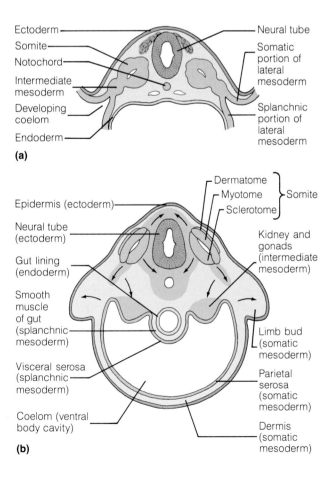

Table 29.1 Derivatives of the Primary Germ Layers		
Ectoderm	**Mesoderm**	**Endoderm**
All nervous tissue	Skeletal, smooth, and cardiac muscle	Epithelium of digestive tract (except that of oral and anal cavities)
Epidermis of skin and epidermal derivatives (hairs, hair follicles, sebaceous and sweat glands, nails)	Cartilage, bone, and other connective tissues	Glandular derivatives of digestive tract (liver, pancreas)
Cornea and lens of eye	Blood, bone marrow, and lymphoid tissues	
Epithelium of oral and nasal cavities, of paranasal sinuses, and of anal canal	Endothelium of blood vessels and lymphatics	Epithelium of respiratory tract, auditory tube, and tonsils
Tooth enamel	Serosae of ventral body cavity	Thyroid, parathyroid, and thymus glands
Epithelium of pineal and pituitary glands and adrenal medulla	Fibrous and vascular tunics of eyes	Epithelium of reproductive ducts and glands
Melanocytes: some cranial bones and branchial cartilages (derived from neural crest)	Synovial membranes of joint cavities	Epithelium of urethra and bladder
	Organs of urogenital system (ureters, kidneys, gonads, and reproductive ducts)	

competing with each other for space and form a conspicuous bulge on the ventral surface of the embryo's body. All this by the end of eight weeks in an embryo about 1 inch long from crown to rump!

Development of the Fetal Circulation.
Embryonic development of the cardiovascular system lays the groundwork for the fetal circulatory pattern, which is converted to the adult pattern at birth. The first blood cells arise in the yolk sac. Before the third week of development, tiny spaces appear within the splanchnic mesoderm. These are quickly lined by endothelial cells, covered with mesenchyme, and linked together into rapidly spreading vascular networks, destined to form the heart, blood vessels, and lymphatics. By the end of the third week, the embryo has a fairly elaborate system of paired blood vessels, and the two vessels forming the heart have fused and bent into an S shape (see Figure 19.22). By 3½ weeks, the miniature heart is pumping blood for an embryo less than a quarter inch long.

The **umbilical arteries** and **vein** and three *vascular shunts* are unique vascular modifications seen only during prenatal development (Figure 29.13). All of these structures are occluded at birth. The large umbilical vein carries freshly oxygenated blood returning from the placenta into the embryonic body, where it is conveyed to the liver. There, some of the returning blood percolates through the liver sinusoids and out the hepatic veins. Most of the blood coursing through the umbilical vein, however, enters the **ductus venosus** (duk'tus ve-no'sus), a venous shunt that bypasses the liver entirely. Both the hepatic veins and the ductus venosus empty into the inferior vena cava where the placental blood mixes with deoxygenated blood returning from the lower parts of the fetus's body. The vena cava in turn conveys this "mixed load" of blood directly to the right atrium of the heart. After birth, the liver plays an important role in nutrient processing, but during embryonic life these functions are performed by the mother's liver. Consequently, blood flow through the liver during development is important only to ensure viability of the liver cells.

Blood entering and leaving the heart encounters two more shunt systems, each serving to bypass the nonfunctional lungs. Some of the blood entering the right atrium flows directly into the left side of the heart via the **foramen ovale** ("oval hole"), an opening in the interatrial septum. Blood that enters the right ventricle is pumped out into the pulmonary trunk. However, the second shunt, the **ductus arteriosus,** transfers most of that blood directly into the aorta, again bypassing the pulmonary circuit. (The lungs *do* receive adequate blood to maintain their growth.) Blood tends to enter the two pulmonary bypass shunts because the heart chamber or vessel on the other side of each shunt is a lower-pressure area, owing to the low volume of venous return from the lungs. Blood flowing distally through the aorta eventually reaches the umbilical arteries, which are branches of the internal iliac arteries serving the pelvis. From here the largely deoxygenated blood, laden with metabolic wastes, is delivered back to the capillaries in the chorionic villi of the placenta. The changes in the circulatory plan that occur at birth are described on p. 1022 in Figure 29.13b.

EVENTS OF FETAL DEVELOPMENT

The main events of the fetal period—weeks 9 through 40—are listed chronologically in Table 29.2. The fetal period is a time of rapid growth of the body structures that were established in the embryo. The fetal period

FIGURE 29.13
Circulation in fetus and newborn.
Arrows indicate direction of blood flow.
(a) Special adaptations for embryonic
and fetal life. The umbilical vein carries
oxygen- and nutrient-rich blood from the
placenta to the fetus; the umbilical
arteries carry waste-laden blood from the
fetus to the placenta; the ductus
arteriosus and foramen ovale bypass the
nonfunctional lungs; and the ductus
venosus allows blood to partially bypass
the liver. **(b)** Changes in the
cardiovascular system at birth. The
umbilical vessels are occluded, as are
the liver and lung bypasses (ductus
venosus and arteriosus, and the foramen
ovale).

Table 29.2 Developmental Events of the Fetal Period

Time	Changes/accomplishments
8 weeks (end of embryonic period) 8 weeks	Head nearly as large as body; all major brain regions present; first brain waves Liver disproportionately large and begins to form blood cells Limbs present; digits are initially webbed, but fingers and toes are free by the end of this interval Ossification just begun; weak, spontaneous muscle contractions occur Cardiovascular system fully functional (heart has been pumping blood since the fourth week) All body systems present in at least rudimentary form Approximate crown-to-rump length: 30 mm (1.2 inches); weight: 1 gram (0.03 ounces)
9–12 weeks (third month) 12 weeks	Head still dominant, but body elongating; brain continues to enlarge, shows its general structural features; cervical and lumbar enlargements apparent in spinal cord; retina of eye is present Skin epidermis and dermis obvious; facial features present in crude form Liver prominent and bile being secreted; palate is fusing; most glands of endodermal origin are developed; walls of hollow visceral organs gaining smooth muscle Blood cell formation begins in bone marrow Notochord degenerating and ossification accelerating; limbs well molded Sex readily detected from the genitals Approximate crown-to-rump length at end of interval: 90 mm
13–16 weeks (fourth month) 16 weeks	Cerebellum becoming prominent; general sensory organs differentiated; eyes and ears assume characteristic position and shape; blinking of eyes and sucking motions of lips occur Face looks human and body beginning to outgrow head Glands developed in GI tract; meconium is collecting Kidneys attain typical structure Most bones are now distinct and joint cavities are apparent Approximate crown-to-rump length at end of interval: 140 mm
17–20 weeks (fifth month)	Vernix caseosa (fatty secretions of sebaceous glands) covers body; lanugo (silklike hair) covers skin Fetal position (body flexed anteriorly) assumed because of space restrictions Limbs reach near-final proportions Quickening occurs (mother feels spontaneous muscular activity of fetus) Approximate crown-to-rump length at end of interval: 190 mm
21–30 weeks (sixth and seventh months) At birth	Period of substantial increase in weight (may survive if born prematurely at 27–28 weeks, but hypothalamic temperature regulation and lung production of surfactant are still inadequate) Myelination of cord begins; eyes are open Distal limb bones are beginning to ossify Skin is wrinkled and red; fingernails and toenails are present; tooth enamel is forming on deciduous teeth Body is lean and well proportioned Bone marrow becomes sole site of blood cell formation Testes reach scrotum in seventh month (in males) Approximate crown-to-rump length at end of interval: 280 mm
30–40 weeks (term) (eight and ninth months)	Skin whitish pink; fat laid down in subcutaneous tissue (hypodermis) Approximate crown-to-rump length at end of interval: 350–400 mm (14–16 inches); weight: 2.7–4.1 kg (6–10 pounds)

FIGURE 29.14
Photographs of developing fetuses.
The major events of fetal development are growth and tissue specialization. All the organ systems are laid down, at least in rudimentary form, during the embryonic period of development. **(a)** Fetus of 14 weeks, approximately 6 cm long. **(b)** Fetus of 20 weeks, approximately 19 cm long. By birth the fetus is typically 35 cm in length crown to rump.

is more than just a time of growth, however, During the first half of this period, cells are still differentiating into specific cell types to form the body's distinctive tissues and are completing the fine details of body structure. During the fetal period, the developing fetus grows from a crown-to-rump length of about 30 mm (slightly more than 1 inch) and a weight of approximately 1 g (0.03 ounce) to about 360 mm (14 inches) and 2.7–4.1 kg (6–10 pounds) or more. (Total body length at birth is about 550 mm, or 22 inches.) As you might expect with such tremendous growth, the changes in fetal appearance are quite dramatic (Figure 29.14).

EFFECTS OF PREGNANCY ON THE MOTHER

Pregnancy can be a difficult time for the mother. Not only are there anatomical changes, but striking changes in her metabolism and physiology occur as well.

Anatomical Changes

As pregnancy progresses, the female reproductive organs become increasingly vascularized and engorged with blood, and the vagina develops a purplish hue *(Chadwick's sign).* This enhanced vascularity increases vaginal sensitivity and sexual intensity, and some women achieve orgasm for the first time when they are pregnant. The breasts, too, become engorged with blood, and prodded by rising levels of estrogen and progesterone, they enlarge and their areolae darken. Some women develop increased pigmentation of facial skin of the nose and cheeks, a condition called *chloasma* (klo-az′mah; "to be green") or the "mask of pregnancy."

The degree of uterine enlargement during pregnancy is remarkable. Starting as a fist-sized organ, the uterus fills most of the pelvic cavity by 16 weeks (Figure 29.15b). Though the fetus is only about 120 mm

long at this time, the placenta is fully formed, uterine muscle is hypertrophied, and amniotic fluid volume is increasing. As pregnancy continues, the uterus pushes higher and higher into the abdominal cavity, exerting pressure on both abdominal and pelvic organs (Figure 29.15c). As birth nears, the uterus reaches the level of the xiphoid process and occupies most of the abdominal cavity (Figure 29.15d). The crowded abdominal organs press superiorly against the diaphragm, which intrudes on the thoracic cavity. As a result, the ribs flare, causing the thorax to widen.

The increasing bulkiness of the anterior abdomen changes the woman's center of gravity, and many women develop an accentuated lumbar curvature (lordosis), and often backaches, during the last few months of pregnancy. Placental production of the hormone **relaxin** causes pelvic ligaments and the pubic symphysis to relax, widen, and become more flexible. This increased motility eases birth passage, but it may result in a waddling gait in the meantime.

A considerable weight gain occurs during a normal pregnancy. Because some women are over- or underweight before pregnancy begins, it is almost impossible to state the ideal or desirable weight gain. However, summing up the weight increases resulting from fetal and placental growth, growth of the maternal reproductive organs and breasts, and increased blood volume during pregnancy, a weight gain of approximately 13 kg (about 29 pounds) usually occurs.

Obviously, good nutrition is necessary all through pregnancy if the developing fetus is to have all the building materials (especially proteins, calcium, and iron) needed to form its tissues. Additionally, multivitamins containing folic acid seem to reduce the risk of having babies with neurological problems, including such birth defects as spina bifida and anencephaly. However, a pregnant woman only needs about 300 additional calories daily to sustain proper fetal growth. The emphasis should be on eating high-quality food, not just more food.

(a) before conception (b) 4 months (c) 7 months (d) 9 months

FIGURE 29.15
Relative size of the uterus before conception and during pregnancy. **(a)** Before conception, the uterus is the size of a fist and resides within the pelvis. **(b)** At 4 months, the fundus of the uterus is halfway between the pubic symphysis and the umbilicus. **(c)** At 7 months, the fundus is well above the umbilicus. **(d)** At 9 months, the fundus reaches the xiphoid process.

Metabolic Changes

As the placenta enlarges, it secretes increasing amounts of **human placental lactogen (hPL),** also called **human chorionic somatomammotropin (hCS),** which works cooperatively with estrogens and progesterone to stimulate maturation of the breasts for lactation. In addition, hPL has anabolic effects (promotes growth of the fetus) and exerts a glucose-sparing effect in the mother. Consequently, maternal cells metabolize more fatty acids and less glucose than usual, sparing glucose for use by the fetus. The placenta also releases **human chorionic thyrotropin (hCT),** a glycoprotein hormone similar to thyroid-stimulating hormone of the anterior pituitary. hCT activity increases the rate of maternal metabolism throughout the pregnancy, causing hypermetabolism. Because plasma levels of parathyroid hormone and activated vitamin D rise, pregnant women tend to be in positive calcium balance throughout pregnancy. This ensures that the developing fetus will have adequate calcium to mineralize its bones.

Physiological Changes

Gastrointestinal System

Many women suffer nausea, commonly called *morning sickness,* during the first few months of pregnancy, until their system adjusts to the elevated levels of progesterone and estrogens. (It is interesting to note that nausea is a side effect of many birth control pills.)

Reflux of stomach acid into the esophagus, causing *heartburn,* is common because the esophagus is displaced and the stomach is crowded by the growing uterus. *Constipation* occurs because motility of the digestive tract declines during pregnancy.

Urinary System

The kidneys produce more urine during pregnancy because they have the additional burden of disposing of fetal metabolic wastes. As the growing uterus compresses the bladder, urination becomes more frequent, more urgent, and sometimes uncontrollable *(stress incontinence).*

Respiratory System

The nasal mucosa responds to estrogens by becoming edematous and congested. Thus, nasal stuffiness and occasional nosebleeds may occur. Vital capacity and respiratory rate increase during pregnancy and hyperventilation is common. But residual volume declines, and many women exhibit *dyspnea* (disp-ne'ah), or difficult breathing, during the later stages of pregnancy.

Cardiovascular System

The most dramatic physiological changes occur in the cardiovascular system. Total body water rises; blood volume increases 25% to 40% by the thirty-second week, owing to increases in both formed elements and plasma volume to accommodate the additional needs of the fetus. The rise in blood volume also acts as a safeguard against blood loss during birth. Blood pressure and pulse typically rise and increase cardiac output by 20% to 40% at various stages of pregnancy. This helps propel the greater circulatory volume around the body. Because the uterus presses on the pelvic blood vessels, venous return from the lower limbs may be impaired somewhat, resulting in *varicose veins.*

Much to the chagrin of physically fit women who know that continuous regular exercise is necessary to retain fitness, many obstetricians limit the intensity and duration of exercise during pregnancy. However, recent studies indicate that although blood *is* diverted to the skeletal muscles during exercise, cardiovascular and respiratory system adjustments that occur during pregnancy compensate and ensure adequate blood delivery to and from the placenta in healthy women. Additionally, women who continue their exercise regimen during pregnancy not only remain fit themselves, but they give birth to infants weighing 5% to 10% more than babies of inactive moms. ●

PARTURITION (BIRTH)

Parturition (par″tu-rish′un; "bringing forth young") is the culmination of pregnancy—giving birth to the baby. It usually occurs within 15 days of the calculated due date (280 days from the last menstrual period). The series of events that expel the infant from the uterus are referred to collectively as **labor.**

Initiation of Labor

While the precise mechanism that triggers labor is not clear, several events and hormones are interlocked in this process. During the last few weeks of pregnancy, estrogens reach their highest levels in the mother's blood.* This has two important consequences: It stimulates the myometrial cells of the uterus to form abundant oxytocin receptors and it antagonizes progesterone's quieting influence on the uterine muscle. As a result, the myometrium becomes increasingly irritable, and weak, irregular uterine contractions begin to occur. These contractions, called *Braxton Hicks contractions,* have caused many women to go to the hospital, only to be told that they were in **false labor** and sent home.

As birth nears, two more chemical signals cooperate to convert these false labor pains into the real thing. Certain cells of the fetus begin to produce **oxy-**

tocin (ok″sĭ-to′sin), which in turn acts on the placenta causing it to release **prostaglandins** (pros″tah-glan′dinz). Both hormones are powerful uterine muscle stimulants, and since the myometrium is now highly sensitive to oxytocin, contractions become more frequent and more vigorous. At this point, the increasing emotional and physical stresses activate the mother's hypothalamus, which signals for oxytocin release by the posterior pituitary. The combined effects of elevated levels of oxytocin and prostaglandins trigger the rhythmic expulsive contractions of true labor. Once the hypothalamus is involved, a *positive feedback mechanism* is propelled into action—greater contractile force causes the release of more oxytocin, which causes greater contractile force, and so on (Figure 29.16).

Both oxytocin and prostaglandins are essential for initiating labor in humans. Untimely spurts of oxytocin may be responsible for some instances of premature birth, and interfering with production of either of these hormones will hinder onset of labor.

④ Hypothalamus sends efferent impulses to posterior pituitary, where oxytocin is stored

⑤ Posterior pituitary releases oxytocin to blood; oxytocin targets mother's uterine muscle

⑥ Uterus responds by contracting more vigorously

① Baby moves deeper into mother's birth canal

③ Afferent impulses to hypothalamus

② Pressoreceptors in cervix of uterus excited

Positive feedback mechanism continues to cycle until interrupted by birth of baby

FIGURE 29.16
The positive feedback mechanism by which oxytocin promotes labor contractions during birth.

---

* Some studies indicate that the fetus determines its own birth date. Rising levels of fetal adrenocortical hormones (especially cortisol) late in pregnancy have a major effect on stimulating the placenta to release such large amounts of estrogens.

For example, antiprostaglandin drugs such as aspirin and ibuprofen can inhibit the early stages of labor and such drugs are used occasionally to prevent preterm births.

Stages of Labor

Stage 1: Dilation Stage

The **dilation stage** (Figure 29.17a and b) is the time from labor's onset until the cervix is fully dilated by the baby's head (about 10 cm in diameter). As labor starts, weak but regular contractions (much like peristaltic contractions) begin in the upper part of the uterus and move downward toward the vagina. At first, only the superior uterine muscle is active. These initial contractions are 15–30 minutes apart and last for 10–30 seconds. As labor progresses, the contractions become more vigorous and more rapid, and the lower uterine segment gets involved. As the infant's head is forced against the cervix with each contraction, the cervix softens, becomes thinner (effaces), and dilates. Eventually, the amnion ruptures, releasing the amniotic fluid, an event commonly called "breaking the water." The dilation stage is the longest part of labor, lasting 6–12 hours (or more). Several events happen during this phase. *Engagement* occurs when the infant's head enters the true pelvis. As descent continues through the birth canal, the baby's head rotates so that its greatest dimension is in the anteroposterior line, which allows it to navigate the narrow dimensions of the pelvic outlet.

Stage 2: Expulsion Stage

The **expulsion stage** (Figure 29.17c) lasts from full dilation to delivery of the infant, or actual childbirth. Ordinarily, by the time the cervix is fully dilated, strong contractions are occurring every 2–3 minutes and lasting about 1 minute, and a mother undergoing labor without local anesthesia has an increasing urge to push or bear down with the abdominal muscles. Although this phase can take as long as 2 hours, it is typically 50 minutes in a first birth and around 20 minutes in subsequent births.

FIGURE 29.17
Parturition. **(a)** Dilation stage (early). The baby's head has entered the true pelvis and is engaged. The widest head dimension is along the left-right axis. **(b)** Late dilation. The baby's head rotates so that its greatest dimension is in the anteroposterior axis as it moves through the pelvic outlet. Dilation of the cervix is nearly complete. **(c)** Expulsion stage. The baby's head extends as it reaches the perineum and is delivered. **(d)** Placental stage. After the baby has been delivered, the placenta is detached by the continuing uterine contractions and is delivered.

FIGURE 29.18
Birth. (a) Crowning. The baby's head is distending the mother's vulva. **(b)** The expulsion stage of labor has progressed to delivery of the infant's head. **(c)** The placenta, once delivered, is examined for normal structure, and the number of blood vessels in the umbilical cord is counted.

Crowning occurs when the largest dimension of the baby's head is distending the vulva (Figure 29.18a). At this point, an *episiotomy* (e-piz″e-ot′o-me) may be performed to reduce tissue tearing. An episiotomy is an incision made to widen the vaginal orifice. The baby's head extends as it exits from the perineum, and once the head has been delivered, the rest of the baby's body is delivered much more easily. After birth, the umbilical cord is clamped and cut.

When the infant is in the usual *vertex* (head-first) *presentation,* the skull (its largest diameter) acts as a wedge to dilate the cervix. The head-first presentation also allows the baby to be suctioned free of mucus and to breathe even before it has completely exited from the birth canal (Figure 29.18b). In *breech* (buttock-first) and other nonvertex presentations, these advantages are lost and delivery is much more difficult, often requiring the use of forceps.

If a woman has a deformed or malelike pelvis, labor may be prolonged and difficult. This condition is called *dystocia* (dis-to′se-ah; *dys* = difficult; *toc* = birth). Besides extreme maternal fatigue, another possible consequence of dystocia is fetal brain damage (resulting in cerebral palsy or epilepsy) and decreased viability of the infant. To prevent these outcomes, a *cesarean* (sĕ-sa′re-an) *(C-) section* is performed in many such instances. A C-section is delivery of the infant through a surgical incision made through the abdominal and uterine walls. •

Stage 3: Placental Stage

The **placental stage** (Figure 29.17d), or the delivery of the placenta, is accomplished within 15 minutes after birth of the infant. The vigorous uterine contractions that continue after birth compress uterine blood vessels, limit bleeding, and cause the placenta to detach from the uterine wall. The placenta and its attached fetal membranes, collectively called the **afterbirth,** are then easily removed by a slight tug on the umbilical cord. It is very important that all placental fragments be removed to prevent continued uterine bleeding after birth *(postpartum bleeding).* The number of blood vessels in the severed umbilical cord is routinely counted after the placenta has been delivered (Figure 29.18c). This is done because absence of one of the umbilical arteries is often associated with cardiovascular disorders in the infant. •

ADJUSTMENTS OF THE INFANT TO EXTRAUTERINE LIFE

The **neonatal period** is the four-week period immediately after birth. Here we will be concerned with the events of just the first few hours after birth in a normal infant. As you might suspect, birth represents quite a shock to the infant. Exposed to physical trauma during the birth process, it is suddenly cast out of its watery, warm environment and its placental life supports are severed. Now it must do for itself all that the mother had been doing for it—respire, obtain nutrients, excrete, and maintain its body temperature.

At 1 and 5 minutes after birth, the infant's physical status is assessed based on five signs: heart rate, respiration, color, muscle tone, and reflexes (tested by slaps on the feet). Each observation is given a score of 0 to 2, and the total is called the **Apgar score.** An Apgar score of 8 to 10 indicates a healthy baby. Lower scores reveal problems in one or more of the physiological functions assessed.

Taking the First Breath

The crucial first requirement is to breathe. Once carbon dioxide is no longer removed by the placenta, it begins to accumulate in the baby's blood, causing central acidosis. This excites the respiratory control centers in the brain and triggers the first inspiration. The first breath requires a tremendous effort—the airways are tiny, and the lungs are collapsed. However, once the lungs have been inflated in full-term babies, lung surfactant in the alveolar fluid helps to reduce the surface tension in the alveoli, and breathing becomes easier. The rate of respiration is rapid (about 45 respirations per minute) during the first two weeks and then gradually declines to normal levels.

Keeping the lungs inflated is much more difficult for premature infants (those weighing less than 2500 g, or about 5.5 pounds, at birth) because surfactant production occurs during the last months of prenatal life. Consequently, preemies are usually put on respiratory assistance (a ventilator) until their lungs are mature enough to function on their own.

Occlusion of Special Fetal Blood Vessels and Vascular Shunts

After birth the special umbilical blood vessels and fetal shunts are no longer necessary (see Figure 29.13b). The umbilical arteries and vein constrict and become fibrosed. The proximal parts of the umbilical arteries persist as the *superior vesical arteries* that supply the urinary bladder, and their distal parts become the **medial umbilical ligaments.** The remnant of the umbilical vein becomes the **round ligament of the liver,** or **ligamentum teres,** that attaches the umbilicus to the liver. The ductus venosus collapses as blood stops flowing through the umbilical vein and is eventually converted to the **ligamentum venosum** on the liver's undersurface.

As the pulmonary circulation becomes functional, left heart pressure increases and right heart pressure decreases. These changing pressure relationships cause the pulmonary shunts to close. The flap of the foramen ovale is pushed to the closed position, and its edges fuse to the septal wall. Ultimately, only a slight depression, the **fossa ovalis,** marks its posi-

tion in adults. The ductus arteriosus constricts and is converted to the cordlike **ligamentum arteriosum,** which connects the aorta and pulmonary trunk.

Except for the foramen ovale, all of the special circulatory adaptations of the fetus are functionally occluded within 30 minutes after birth. Closure of the foramen ovale is usually complete within the year; however, the flap of the foramen ovale *never* fuses in about one-fourth of all people. This usually presents no problem, since normal blood pressure in the left atrium causes the "trapdoor" to stay in the closed position. As described in Chapter 19, failure of the ductus arteriosus or foramen ovale to close leads to congenital heart defects.

The Transitional Period

Infants pass through an unstable **transitional period** lasting 6–8 hours after birth, during which they adjust to extrauterine life. For the first 30 minutes, the baby is awake, alert, and active. Heart rate increases above the normal infant range of 120 to 160 beats per minute, respirations become more rapid and irregular, and body temperature falls. Then activity gradually diminishes, and the baby sleeps for 3 hours or so. A second period of activity then occurs, and the baby gags frequently as it regurgitates mucus and debris. After this, the infant sleeps again and then stabilizes, with waking periods (dictated by hunger) occurring every 3–4 hours.

LACTATION

Lactation is production of milk by the hormone-prepared mammary glands. Rising levels of (placental) estrogens, progesterone, and lactogen toward the end of pregnancy stimulate the hypothalamus to release prolactin-releasing hormone (PRH), and the anterior pituitary gland responds by secreting **prolactin.** (This mechanism is described in more detail in Chapter 17, p. 559.) After an initial two- to three-day delay, true milk production begins. During this delay (and during late gestation), a yellowish fluid called **colostrum** (ko-los'trum) is secreted. Colostrum has less lactose than milk and almost no fat, but it contains more protein, vitamin A, and minerals than true milk. Like milk, colostrum is rich in IgA antibodies. Since these antibodies are somewhat resistant to digestion in the stomach, they may help to protect the infant's digestive tract against bacterial infection. Additionally, some authorities claim that these IgA antibodies are absorbed by endocytosis and subsequently enter the bloodstream to provide even broader immunity.

After birth, prolactin release gradually wanes, and continual milk production depends on mechanical stimulation of the nipples, normally provided by the sucking infant. Mechanoreceptors in the nipple send afferent nerve impulses to the hypothalamus,

④ Hypothalamus sends efferent impulses to posterior pituitary, where oxytocin is stored

⑤ Posterior pituitary releases oxytocin to blood; oxytocin targets milk-producing glands in mother's breasts

⑥ Myoepithelial cells respond by contracting; alveolar glands release milk through ducts of nipples

① Baby sucks on mother's breast

② Pressoreceptors in mother's nipples activated

③ Afferent impulses to hypothalamus

Positive feedback mechanism continues to cycle until interrupted when baby stops sucking

FIGURE 29.19
Positive feedback mechanism of the milk let-down reflex.

prepregnant size. Breast milk also has advantages for the infant: (1) Its fats and iron are better absorbed and its amino acids are metabolized more efficiently than those of cow's milk; and (2) it has a natural laxative effect that helps to cleanse the bowels of **meconium** (mě-ko′ne-um), a tarry green-black paste containing sloughed off epithelial cells, bile, and other substances. Since meconium, and later feces, provides the route for eliminating bilirubin from the body, clearing meconium as quickly as possible helps to prevent *physiological jaundice* (see the Related Clinical Terms section on p. 1024). It also encourages bacteria (the source of vitamin K and some B vitamins) to colonize the large intestine.

When nursing is discontinued, the stimulus for prolactin release—and thus milk production—ends, and the mammary glands stop producing milk. Milk secretion can continue for several years if the child continues to nurse, but women who nurse their infants for six months or more lose a significant amount of calcium from their bones. While prolactin levels are high, the normal hypothalamic-pituitary controls of the ovarian cycle are damped, probably because stimulation of the hypothalamus by the infant's sucking causes it to release beta-endorphin, a peptide hormone that inhibits hypothalamic release of GnRH and hence the release of gonadotropins by the pituitary. Because of this prolactin-induced inhibition of ovarian function, nursing has been called natural birth control. Nonetheless, there is a good deal of "slippage" in these controls, and most women eventually begin to ovulate even while continuing to nurse their infants.

*   *   *

In this chapter, we have followed changes that occur during human *in utero* development. But the phenomenon of differentiation has barely been touched upon. How does an unspecialized cell that can become *anything* in the body develop into a specific *something* (a heart cell, for example)? And what paces the developmental sequence, so that if a particular process fails to occur at a precise time, it never occurs at all? Scientists are beginning to believe that there are master switches in the genes. Chapter 30, the final chapter of this book, describes a small part of the "how" as it examines the interaction of genes that determine who we finally become.

stimulating secretion of PRH. This results in a burst-like release of prolactin, which stimulates milk production for the next feeding.

The same afferent impulses also prompt hypothalamic release of oxytocin from the posterior pituitary via a *positive feedback mechanism.* Oxytocin causes the **let-down reflex,** the actual ejection of milk from the alveoli of the mammary glands (Figure 29.19). Let-down occurs when oxytocin binds to myoepithelial cells surrounding the glands, after which milk is ejected from *both* breasts, not just the suckled one. Many obstetricians recommend that mothers nurse because oxytocin also stimulates the recently emptied uterus to contract, helping it to return to (nearly) its

RELATED CLINICAL TERMS

Abortion (*abort* = born prematurely) Premature removal of the embryo or fetus from the uterus; may be spontaneous or induced.

Eclampsia (e-klamp′se-ah; *eclamp* = shine) Dangerous condition in which the pregnant woman becomes edematous and hypertensive, and proteinuria and seizures occur; formerly called toxemia of pregnancy.

Ectopic pregnancy (ek-top′ik; *ecto* = outside) A pregnancy in which the embryo implants in any site other than the uterus; most often the site is a uterine tube (tubal pregnancy); since the uterine tube (as well as most other ectopic sites) is unable to establish a placenta or accommodate growth, the uterine tube ruptures unless the condition is diagnosed early, or the pregnancy spontaneously aborts.

Hydatid (hydatidiform) mole (hi′-dah-tid; *hydat* = watery) Developmental abnormality of the placenta; the conceptus degenerates and the chorionic villi convert into a mass of vesicles that resemble tapioca; signs include vaginal bleeding, which contains some of the grapelike vesicles.

Physiological jaundice (jawn′dis) Jaundice sometimes occurring in normal newborns within three to four days after birth; fetal erythrocytes are short-lived, and they break down rapidly after birth; the infant's liver may be unable to process the bilirubin (breakdown product of hemoglobin pigment) fast enough to prevent its accumulation in blood and subsequent deposit in body tissues.

Placenta abruptio (ah-brup′she-o; *abrupt* = broken away from) Premature separation of the placenta from the uterine wall; if this occurs before labor, it can result in fetal death due to anoxia.

Placenta previa (pre′ve-ah) Placental formation adjacent to or across the internal os of the uterus; represents a problem because as the uterus and cervix stretch, tearing of the placenta may occur; additionally, the placenta precedes the infant during labor.

Ultrasonography (ul″trah-son-og′rah-fe) Noninvasive technique that uses sound waves to visualize the position and size of the fetus and placenta (see p. 19).

CHAPTER SUMMARY

1. The gestation period of approximately 280 days extends from the woman's last menstrual period to birth. The conceptus undergoes preembryonic development for about two weeks after fertilization, then embryonic development (weeks 3–8) and fetal development (week 9–birth).

From Egg to Embryo (pp. 1000–1007)

Accomplishing Fertilization (pp. 1000–1003)

1. An oocyte is fertilizable for up to 24 hours; sperm are viable within the female reproductive tract for up to 72 hours.

2. Sperm must survive the hostile environment of the vagina and become capacitated.

3. Hundreds of sperm must release their acrosomal enzymes to break down the egg's corona radiata and zona pellucida.

4. When one sperm penetrates the egg, it triggers first the fast block to polyspermy (membrane depolarization) and then the slow block (release of cortical granules).

5. Following sperm penetration, the secondary oocyte completes meiosis II. Then the ovum and sperm pronuclei fuse (fertilization), forming a zygote.

Preembryonic Development (pp. 1003–1007)

6. Cleavage, a rapid series of mitotic divisions without intervening growth, begins with the zygote and ends with a blastocyst. The blastocyst consists of the trophoblast and an inner cell mass. Cleavage produces a large number of cells with a favorable surface-to-volume ratio.

7. The trophoblast adheres to, digests, and implants in the endometrium. Implantation is completed when the blastocyst is entirely surrounded by endometrial tissue, about 14 days after ovulation.

8. hCG released by the blastocyst maintains hormone production by the corpus luteum, preventing menses. hCG levels decline after four months. Typically, the placenta is functional as an endocrine organ by the third month.

9. The placenta acts as the respiratory, nutritive, and excretory organ of the fetus and produces the hormones of pregnancy. It is formed from embryonic (chorionic villi) and maternal (endometrial decidua) tissues. The chorion develops when the trophoblast becomes associated with extraembryonic mesoderm.

Events of Embryonic Development (pp. 1008–1014)

Formation and Roles of the Embryonic Membranes (pp. 1008–1010)

1. The fluid-filled amnion forms from cells of the superior surface of the inner cell mass. It protects the embryo from physical trauma and adhesion formation, provides a constant temperature, and allows fetal movements.

2. The yolk sac forms from the endoderm; it is the source of primordial germ cells and early blood cells.

3. The allantois, a caudal outpocketing of the yolk sac, forms the structural basis of the umbilical cord.

4. The chorion is the outermost membrane and takes part in placentation.

Gastrulation: Germ Layer Formation (pp. 1010–1011)

5. Gastrulation involves cellular migrations that transform the inner cell mass into a three-layered embryo (gastrula) containing ectoderm, mesoderm, and endoderm. Cells destined to become mesoderm migrate to the middle layer from the surface of the embryonic disc by moving through the midline primitive streak.

Organogenesis: Differentiation of the Germ Layers (pp. 1011–1014)

6. Ectoderm forms the nervous system and the epidermis of the skin and its derivatives. The first event of organogenesis is neurulation, which produces the brain and spinal cord. By the eighth week, all major brain regions are formed.

7. Endoderm forms the mucosa of the digestive and respiratory systems, as well as all associated glands (thyroid, parathyroids, thymus, liver, pancreas). It becomes a continuous tube when the embryonic body undercuts and fuses ventrally.

8. Mesoderm forms all other organ systems and tissues. It segregates early into (1) a dorsal superior notochord, (2) paired somites that form the vertebrae, skeletal trunk muscles, and part of the dermis, and (3) paired masses of intermediate and lateral mesoderm. The intermediate mesoderm forms the kidneys and gonads. The somatic layer of the lateral mesoderm forms the dermis of skin, parietal serosa, and bones and muscles of the limbs; the splanchnic layer forms the cardiovascular system and the visceral serosae.

9. The fetal cardiovascular system is formed in the embryonic period. The umbilical vein delivers nutrient- and oxygen-rich blood to the embryo; the paired umbilical arteries return oxygen-poor, waste-laden blood to the placenta. The ductus venosus allows most of the blood to bypass the liver; the foramen ovale and ductus arteriosus are pulmonary shunts.

Events of Fetal Development (pp. 1014–1017)

1. All organ systems are laid down during the embryonic period; growth and tissue/organ specialization are the major events of the fetal period.

2. During the fetal period, fetal length increases from about 30 mm to 360 mm, and weight increases from less than an ounce to 6–10 pounds.

Effects of Pregnancy on the Mother (pp. 1017–1019)

Anatomical Changes (p. 1017)

1. Maternal reproductive organs and breasts become increasingly vascularized during pregnancy, and the breasts enlarge.

2. The uterus eventually occupies nearly the entire abdominopelvic cavity. Abdominal organs are pushed superiorly and encroach on the thoracic cavity, causing the ribs to flare.

3. The increased abdominal mass changes the woman's center of gravity; lordosis and backache are common. A waddling gait occurs as pelvic ligaments and joints are loosened by placental relaxin.

4. A typical weight gain during pregnancy in a woman of normal weight is 29 pounds.

Metabolic Changes (p. 1018)

5. Human placental lactogen has anabolic effects and promotes glucose sparing in the mother. Human chorionic thyrotropin results in maternal hypermetabolism.

Physiological Changes (pp. 1018–1019)

6. Many women suffer morning sickness, heartburn, and constipation during pregnancy.

7. The kidneys produce more urine, and pressure on the bladder may cause frequency, urgency, and stress incontinence.

8. Vital capacity and respiratory rate increase, but residual volume decreases. Dyspnea is common.

9. Total body water and blood volume increase dramatically. Heart rate and blood pressure rise, resulting in enhancement of cardiac output in the mother.

Parturition (Birth) (pp. 1019–1021)

1. Parturition encompasses a series of events called labor.

Initiation of Labor (pp. 1019–1020)

2. When estrogen levels are sufficiently high, they induce oxytocin receptors on the myometrial cells and inhibit progesterone's quieting effect on uterine muscle. Weak, irregular contractions begin.

3. Fetal cells produce oxytocin, which stimulates prostaglandin production by the placenta. Both hormones stimulate contraction of uterine muscle. Increasing stress activates the hypothalamus, causing oxytocin release from the posterior pituitary; this sets up a positive feedback loop resulting in true labor.

Stages of Labor (pp. 1020–1021)

4. The dilation stage is from the onset of rhythmic, strong contractions until the cervix is fully dilated. The head of the fetus rotates as it descends through the pelvic outlet.

5. The expulsion stage extends from full cervical dilation until the birth of the infant.

6. The placental stage is the delivery of the afterbirth (the placenta and attached fetal membranes).

Adjustments of the Infant to Extrauterine Life (pp. 1021–1022)

1. The infant's Apgar score is recorded immediately after birth.

Taking the First Breath (p. 1022)

2. Once the umbilical cord is clamped, carbon dioxide accumulates in the infant's blood, causing respiratory centers in the brain to trigger the first inspiration.

3. Once the lungs are inflated, breathing is eased by the presence of surfactant, which decreases the surface tension of the alveolar fluid.

Occlusion of Special Fetal Blood Vessels and Vascular Shunts (p. 1022)

4. Inflation of the lungs causes pressure changes in the circulation; as a result, the umbilical arteries and vein, ductus venosus, and ductus arteriosus collapse, and the foramen ovale closes. The occluded blood vessels are converted to fibrous cords; the site of the foramen ovale becomes the fossa ovalis.

The Transitional Period (p. 1022)

5. For the first 8 hours after birth, the infant is physiologically unstable and adjusting. After stabilizing, the infant wakes approximately every 3–4 hours in response to hunger.

Lactation (pp. 1022–1023)

1. The breasts are prepared for lactation during pregnancy by high blood levels of estrogen, progesterone, and placental lactogen.

2. Colostrum, a premilk fluid, is a fat-poor fluid that contains more protein, vitamin A, and minerals than true milk. It is produced toward the end of pregnancy and for the first two to three days after birth.

3. True milk is produced around day 3 in response to suckling, which stimulates the hypothalamus to prompt anterior pituitary release of prolactin and posterior pituitary release of oxytocin. Prolactin stimulates milk production; oxytocin triggers milk let-down. Continued breast-feeding is required for continued milk production.

4. Ovulation and menses are absent or irregular at first during nursing, but in most women the ovarian cycle is eventually reestablished while still nursing.

REVIEW QUESTIONS

Multiple Choice/Matching

1. Indicate whether each of the following statements is describing (a) cleavage or (b) gastrulation.

_____ **(1)** period during which a morula forms
_____ **(2)** period when vast amounts of cell migration occur
_____ **(3)** period when the three embryonic germ layers appear
_____ **(4)** period during which the blastocyst is formed

2. Most systems are operational in the fetus by four to six months. Which system is the exception to this generalization, impacting on premature infants? (a) the circulatory system, (b) the respiratory system, (c) the urinary system, (d) the digestive system.

3. The zygote contains chromosomes from (a) the mother only, (b) the father only, (c) both the mother and father, but half from each, (d) each parent and synthesizes others.

4. The outer layer of the blastocyst, which later attaches to the uterus, is the (a) decidua, (b) trophoblast, (c) amnion, (d) inner cell mass.

5. The fetal membrane that forms the basis of the umbilical cord is the (a) allantois, (b) amnion, (c) chorion, (d) yolk sac.

6. In the fetus, the ductus arteriosus carries blood from (a) the pulmonary artery to the pulmonary vein, (b) the liver to the inferior vena cava, (c) the right ventricle to the left ventricle, (d) the pulmonary trunk to the aorta.

7. Which of the following changes occur in the baby's cardio-vascular system after birth? (a) blood clots in the umbilical vein, (b) the pulmonary vessels dilate as the lungs expand, (c) the ductus venosus becomes obliterated, as does the ductus arteriosus, (d) all of these.

8. Following delivery of the infant, the delivery of the after-birth includes the (a) placenta only, (b) placenta and decidua, (c) placenta and attached (torn) fetal membranes, (d) chorionic villi.

9. Identical twins result from the fertilization of (a) one ovum by one sperm, (b) one ovum by two sperm, (c) two ova by two sperm, (d) two ova by one sperm.

10. The umbilical vein carries (a) waste products to the placenta, (b) oxygen and food to the fetus, (c) oxygen and food to the placenta, (d) oxygen and waste products to the fetus.

11. The germ layer from which the skeletal muscles, heart, and skeleton are derived is the (a) ectoderm, (b) endoderm, (c) mesoderm.

12. Which of the following cannot pass through placental bar-riers? (a) blood cells, (b) glucose, (c) amino acids, (d) gases, (e) antibodies.

13. The most important hormone in initiating and maintain-ing lactation after birth is (a) estrogen, (b) FSH, (c) prolactin, (d) oxytocin.

14. The initial stage of labor, during which the neck of the uterus is stretched, is the (a) dilation stage, (b) expulsion stage, (c) placental stage.

15. Match each embryonic structure in Column A with its adult derivative in Column B.

Column A	Column B
———— **(1)** notochord	**(a)** kidney
———— **(2)** ectoderm (not neural tube)	**(b)** ventral body cavity
———— **(3)** intermediate mesoderm	**(c)** pancreas, liver
———— **(4)** splanchnic mesoderm	**(d)** parietal serosa, dermis
———— **(5)** sclerotome	**(e)** nucleus pulposus
———— **(6)** coelom	**(f)** visceral serosa
———— **(7)** neural tube	**(g)** hair and epidermis
———— **(8)** somatic mesoderm	**(h)** brain
———— **(9)** endoderm	**(i)** ribs

Short Answer Essay Questions

16. Fertilization involves much more than a mere restoration of the diploid chromosome number. (a) What does the process of fertilization entail on the part of both the egg and sperm? (b) What are the effects of fertilization?

17. Cleavage is an embryonic event that mainly involves mitotic divisions. How does cleavage differ from mitosis occur-ring during life after birth, and what are its important functions?

18. The life span of the ovarian corpus luteum is extended for nearly three months after implantation, but otherwise it deteri-orates. (a) Explain why this is so. (b) Explain why it is impor-tant that the corpus luteum remain functional following implantation.

19. The placenta is a marvelous, but temporary, organ. Start-ing with a description of its formation, show how it is an inti-mate part of both fetal and maternal anatomy and physiology during the gestation period.

20. Why is it that only one sperm out of the hundreds (or thou-sands) available enters the oocyte?

21. What is the function of the gastrulation process?

22. (a) What is a breech presentation? (b) Cite two problems with this type of presentation.

23. What factors are believed to bring about uterine contrac-tions at the termination of pregnancy?

24. Explain how the flat embryonic disc takes on the cylindri-cal shape of a tadpole.

 CRITICAL THINKING AND CLINICAL APPLICATION QUESTIONS

1. A freshman in your dormitory tells you she just discov-ered that she is three months pregnant. She recently bragged that since she came to college she has been drinking alcohol heavily and experimenting with every kind of recreational drug she could find. From the following, select the advice you would give her, and explain why it is the best choice. (a) She must stop taking drugs, but they could not have affected her fetus during these first few months of her pregnancy. (b) Harm-ful substances usually cannot pass from mother to embryo, so she can keep using drugs. (c) There could be defects in the fetus, so she should stop using drugs and visit a doctor as soon as possible. (d) If she has not taken any drugs in the last week, she is okay.

2. During Mrs. Jones's labor, the obstetrician decided that it was necessary to perform an episiotomy. What is an episiotomy, and why is it done?

3. A woman in substantial pain called her doctor and explained (between sobs) that she was about to have her baby "right here." The doctor calmed her and asked how she had come to that conclusion. She said that her water had broken and that her husband could see the baby's head. (a) Was she right? If so, what stage of labor was she in? (b) Do you think that she had time to make it to the hospital 60 miles away? Why or why not?

4. Mary is a heavy smoker and has ignored a friend's advice to stop smoking during her pregnancy. On the basis of what you know about the effect of smoking on physiology, describe how Mary's smoking might affect her fetus.

5. While Mortimer was cramming for his anatomy test, he read that some parts of the mesoderm become segmented. He suddenly realized that he could not remember what segmenta-tion is. Define segmentation, and give two examples of seg-mented structures in the embryo.

Heredity

30

CHAPTER OUTLINE AND STUDENT OBJECTIVES

The Vocabulary of Genetics (pp. 1027–1028)

1. Define allele.

2. Differentiate clearly between genotype and phenotype.

Sexual Sources of Genetic Variation (pp. 1028–1030)

3. Describe events that lead to genetic variability of gametes.

Types of Inheritance (pp. 1030–1034)

4. Compare and contrast dominant-recessive inheritance with incomplete dominance and codominance.

5. Describe the mechanism of sex-linked inheritance.

6. Explain how polygene inheritance differs from that resulting from the action of a single pair of alleles.

The Influence of Environmental Factors on Gene Expression (p. 1034)

7. Provide examples illustrating how gene expression may be modified by environmental factors.

Nontraditional Inheritance (pp. 1034–1035)

8. Describe how genetic imprinting and extrachromosomal (mitochondrial) inheritance differ from classical Mendelian inheritance.

Genetic Screening, Counseling, and Therapy (pp. 1035–1038)

9. List and explain several techniques used to determine or predict genetic diseases.

10. Describe briefly some approaches of gene therapy.

The wondrous growth and development of a new individual is guided by the codes of the gene-bearing chromosomes it receives from its parents in the egg and sperm. As described in Chapter 3, individual *genes,* or DNA segments, contain the "recipes" or genetic blueprints for proteins, many of which are enzymes that dictate the synthesis of virtually all of the body's molecules. Consequently, genes are ultimately expressed in your hair color, sex, blood type, and so on. However, genes do not act as free agents. As you will see, the ability of a gene to prompt the development of a specific trait is enhanced or inhibited by interactions with other genes, as well as by environmental factors.

Although the science of **genetics,** which studies the mechanism of heredity (*genes* = give birth to), is still relatively young, our understanding of how human genes act and interact has advanced considerably since the rules of gene transmission were first proposed by the monk Gregor Mendel in the mid-1800s. Part of the problem in unraveling the complexities of human genetics is that, unlike the pea plants studied by Mendel, humans have long life spans, produce relatively few offspring, and cannot be mated experimentally just to exam-

ine the nature of their offspring. But the urge to understand human inheritance is a powerful one, and recent advances have enabled geneticists to manipulate and engineer human genes to examine their expression and treat or cure disease. Although we will touch upon some of these newer topics, we will concentrate on the principles of heredity proposed by Mendel over a century ago.

THE VOCABULARY OF GENETICS

The nuclei of all human cells except gametes contain the diploid number of chromosomes (46), consisting of 23 pairs of homologous chromosomes. Two of this set are **sex chromosomes** (X and Y) that determine genetic sex. The other 44 are the 22 pairs of **autosomes** that guide the expression of most other traits. The complete human **karyotype** (kar′e-o-tīp), or diploid chromosomal complement, is illustrated in Figure 30.1. The diploid **genome** (je′nōm), or genetic (DNA) makeup, actually represents two sets of genetic instructions—one from the egg and the other from the sperm.

(a) The slide is viewed with a microscope, and the chromosomes are photographed.

(b) The photograph is entered into a computer, and the chromosomes are electronically rearranged into pairs according to size and shape.

(c) The resulting display is the karyotype.

FIGURE 30.1
Preparing a human karyotype.
After lymphocytes are stimulated to divide and grow in culture for several days, they are treated with a drug that arrests mitosis in metaphase, a stage when the chromosomes are easily identified. Then the cells are harvested, treated with a solution that makes their chromosomes spread out, and prepared for microscopic examination. As illustrated in **(a),** the chromosomes are photographed, and the photograph is entered into a computer for analysis and arrangement of the chromosomes into homologous pairs **(b).** The completed karyotype is displayed for examination of chromosomal structure and number **(c).**

Gene Pairs (Alleles)

Since chromosomes are paired, it follows that the genes within them are paired as well. Consequently, each of us receives two genes, one inherited from each parent (for the most part), that interact to dictate a particular trait. These matched genes, which are at the same *locus* (location) on homologous chromosomes, are called **alleles** (ah-lēlz′). Alleles may code for the same or for alternative forms of a trait. For example, there are two alleles that dictate whether or not you have loose thumb ligaments. One variant codes for tight thumb ligaments; the other codes for loose ligaments (the so-called double-jointed thumb condition). When the two alleles controlling a single trait are exactly alike, a person is said to be **homozygous** (ho-mo-zi′gus) for that particular trait. When the two alleles are dissimilar and differ in their expression, the individual is **heterozygous** (het″er-o-zi′gus) for the trait.

Sometimes, one allele masks or suppresses the expression of its partner. Such an allele is said to be **dominant,** whereas the allele that is masked is said to be **recessive.** By convention, a dominant allele is represented by a capital letter (for example, *J*), and a recessive allele by a lowercase letter *(j).* Dominant alleles are expressed, or make themselves "known," when they are present in either single or double dose. But, for recessive alleles to be expressed, they must be present in double dose, the homozygous condition. Returning to our last example, a person whose genetic makeup includes either the gene pair *JJ* (the homozygous dominant condition) or *Jj* (the heterozygous condition) will have double-jointed thumbs. The combination *jj* (the homozygous recessive condition) is required to produce tight thumb ligaments.

A common misunderstanding is that dominant traits are automatically seen more often because they are expressed whether the allele is present in single or double dose. However, dominance and recessiveness alone do not determine the frequency of a trait in a population; this also depends on the frequency or relative abundance of the respective dominant or recessive alleles in that population.

Genotype and Phenotype

A person's genetic makeup (that is, whether one is homozygous or heterozygous for the various gene pairs) is referred to as his or her **genotype** (jen″o-tīp). The way that genotype is expressed in the body is called one's **phenotype** (fe′no-tīp). Thus, the double-jointed condition is the phenotype produced by a genotype of *JJ* or *Jj.*

SEXUAL SOURCES OF GENETIC VARIATION

Before we examine how genes interact, let us consider why each of us is one of a kind, with a unique genotype and phenotype. This variability reflects three phenomena that occur before we are even a twinkle in our parents' eyes: independent assortment of chromosomes, crossover of homologues, and random fertilization of eggs by sperm.

Segregation and Independent Assortment of Chromosomes

As described in Chapter 28 (p. 960), each pair of homologous chromosomes synapses during meiosis I, forming a tetrad. This happens during both spermatogenesis and oogenesis. Chance determines how the tetrads align on the metaphase I spindle, so maternal and paternal chromosomes are randomly distributed to the daughter nuclei. As illustrated in Figure 30.2, this simple event leads to an amazing amount of variation in the gametes that result. The cell in our example has a diploid chromosome number of 6, so three tetrads are formed. As you can see, the possible combinations of alignments of the three tetrads result in eight different types of gametes. Since the way each tetrad aligns is random, and many mother cells are undergoing meiosis simultaneously, each alignment and each type of gamete occurs with the same frequency as all others. Notice two important points here: (1) The members of the allele pair determining each trait are **segregated,** or distributed to different gametes, during meiosis; and (2) alleles on different pairs of homologous chromosomes are distributed independently of each other. The net result is that each gamete has a single allele for each trait, and that allele represents only one of the four possible parental alleles.

The number of different gamete types resulting from **independent assortment** of the homologues during meiosis I can be quickly calculated for any genome by the formula 2^n, where n is the number of homologous pairs. In our example, $2^n = 2^3$ (or $2 \times 2 \times 2$), for a total of eight different gamete types. The number of gamete types increases dramatically as chromosome number increases. A cell with six pairs of homologues would produce 2^6, or 64, kinds of gametes. In a man's testes, the number of gamete types that can be produced on the basis of independent assortment alone is 2^{23}, or about 8.5 million possibilities—an incredible variety. Since a human female's ovaries complete at most 500 reduction divisions in her lifetime, the number of different gamete types produced simultaneously is significantly less. Still, each ovulated oocyte will most likely be novel genetically because of the random assortment of chromosomes.

Crossover of Homologues and Gene Recombination

Additional variation results from the crossing over and exchange of chromosomal parts that occur during meiosis I. Genes are arranged linearly along a chromosome's length, and genes on the same chromosome

What event leads to the variability seen here?

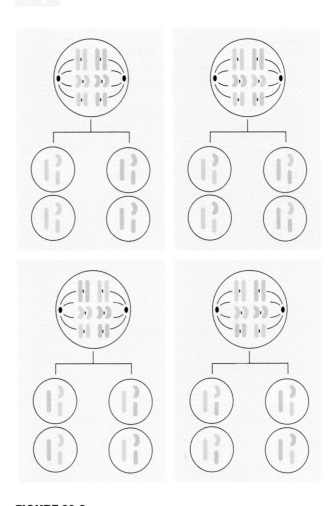

FIGURE 30.2
Production of variability in gametes by independent assortment of homologous chromosomes during metaphase of meiosis I. The large circles depict the possible metaphase I alignments of a mother cell with a diploid number of 6. The paternal homologues are depicted as the pink chromosomes; the maternal chromosomes are green. The small circles represent the genetic complements of the daughter cells (gametes) arising from each alignment. Some of the gametes contain all maternal or all paternal chromosomes; others have maternal and paternal chromosomes in varying combinations.

are said to be **linked** because they are transmitted as a unit to daughter cells during mitosis. However, during meiosis, paternal chromosomes can precisely exchange gene segments with the homologous maternal ones, giving rise to **recombinant chromosomes** with mixed contributions from each parent. In the hypothetical example shown in Figure 30.3, the genes for hair and eye color are linked. The paternal chromosome contains alleles coding for blond hair and blue eyes, while the maternal chromosomal alleles code for brown hair and brown eyes. In the **crossover,** or **chiasma,** shown, the break occurs between these

? *What would be the result if the crossover occurred at a different location?*

Key
H = allele for brown hair   **E** = allele for brown eyes
h = allele for blond hair   **e** = allele for blue eyes

▭ Paternal chromosome ⎤
▭ Maternal chromosome ⎦ — Homologous pair

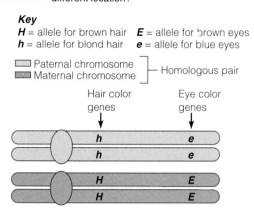

Hair color genes   Eye color genes

Homologous chromosomes synapse during prophase I of meiosis; each chromosome consists of two sister chromatids

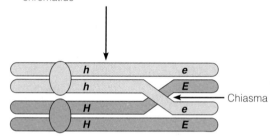

One chromatid segment exchanges positions with a homologous chromatid segment, crossing over occurs, with the formation of a chiasma

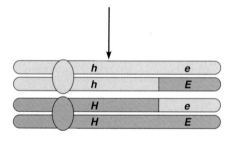

The chromatids forming the chiasma break and join their homologues

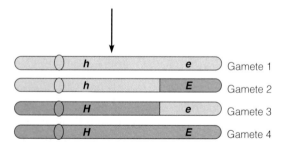

Gamete 1
Gamete 2
Gamete 3
Gamete 4

At the conclusion of meiosis, each haploid gamete has one of the four chromosomes shown; two of the chromosomes are recombinant; they carry new combinations of genes

FIGURE 30.3
Crossover and genetic recombination occurring during meiosis I introduce genetic variability in the gametes formed.

linked genes, resulting in some gametes with alleles for blond hair and brown eyes and others with alleles for brown hair and blue eyes. (If the chiasma formed at another position, other gene combinations would occur.) Thus, as a result of crossover, two of the four chromatids present in the tetrad end up with a mixed set of alleles—some maternal and some paternal. This means that when the chromatids segregate, each gamete will receive a unique and scrambled combination of parental genes.

Only two of the four chromatids in a tetrad appear to take part in crossing over and recombination, but these two may make many crossovers during synapsis. Furthermore, each crossover causes recombination of many genes, not just two as shown in our example. In general, crossovers occur at random points (a sort of molecular lottery), and the longer the chromosome, the greater the number of possible crossovers. Since humans have 23 tetrads, with crossovers going on in most of them during meiosis I, the variability resulting from this factor alone is tremendous.

Random Fertilization

At any point in time, gametogenesis is turning out gametes with all possible variations introduced by independent assortment and random crossovers. Compounding the variety still more is the fact that a single human egg will be fertilized by a single sperm on a totally haphazard basis. If we consider variation resulting only from independent assortment and random fertilization, any resulting offspring represents one out of the close to 72 trillion (8.5 million × 8.5 million) zygotes possible. The additional variation introduced by crossovers increases this number exponentially. Perhaps now you can understand why brothers and sisters are so different, and marvel at how they can also be so alike in many ways.

Once these sources of variability are understood, it is also easy to see that the concept that most people have of their inheritance is inaccurate. We often hear something like "I'm one-half German, one-quarter Scotch, and one-quarter Italian," which reveals a belief that genes from both sides of the family are parceled out in mathematically precise combinations. While it is true that we receive half of our genes from each parent, they may not (indeed, do not) contain one-quarter from each grandparent, or one-eighth from each great grandparent, and there are no such things as German or Italian genes.

TYPES OF INHERITANCE

Although a few visible traits, or phenotypes, in humans can be traced to a single gene pair (as described shortly), most such traits are very limited in nature, or reflect a variation in a single enzyme. Most human traits are determined by multiple alleles or by the interaction of several gene pairs.

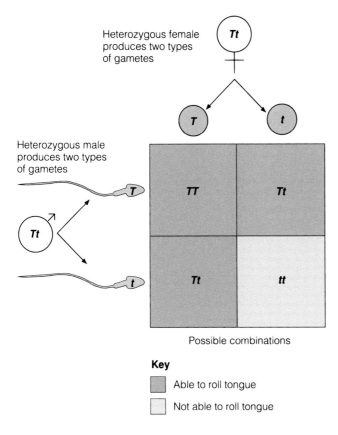

Heterozygous female produces two types of gametes

Heterozygous male produces two types of gametes

Possible combinations

Key

Able to roll tongue

Not able to roll tongue

FIGURE 30.4
Use of a Punnett square to determine probabilities of genotypes and phenotypes resulting from a mating of two heterozygous parents. The alleles carried by the mother are shown at the top; those carried by the father, along the side. The square shows all possible combinations of those alleles in the zygote. In this example, the *T* allele is dominant and determines the tongue-rolling ability; the *t* allele is recessive. Homozygous recessive individuals *(tt)* are unable to exhibit tongue rolling. The *TT* and *Tt* offspring are tongue rollers.

Dominant-Recessive Inheritance

Dominant-recessive inheritance reflects the interaction of dominant and recessive alleles. A simple diagram, called the **Punnett square,** is used to figure out the possible combinations of genes for a single trait that would result from the mating of parents of known genotypes (Figure 30.4). In the example shown, both parents can roll their tongues into a U because both are heterozygous for the dominant allele *(T)* that confers this ability. In other words, each parent has the genotype *Tt*. The gamete types (alleles) of one parent are indicated at the top of the Punnett square, and the gamete types for the other parent are shown along one side. The alleles are combined down and across to determine the possible gene combinations (genotypes) and their expected frequency in their offspring. As you can see from the completed Punnett square, the probability of these parents producing a homozygous dominant child *(TT)* is 25% (1 out of 4); of producing a heterozygous child *(Tt)*, 50% (2 out of 4); and of producing a homozygous recessive child, 25% (1 out of

4). Since the *T* allele is dominant, the *TT* and *Tt* offspring will be tongue rollers; only the *tt* offspring will be unable to roll their tongues.

Although the Punnett square allows the results of simple genetic crosses to be predicted quickly, it only predicts the *probability* of having a certain percentage of offspring with a particular genotype (and phenotype). The larger the number of offspring, the greater the likelihood that the ratios will conform to the predictions—just as the chances of getting half heads and half tails when we toss a coin increase with the number of tosses. If we toss only twice, we may well get heads both times. Likewise, if the couple in our example has only two children, it would not be surprising if both children had the genotype *Tt*.

What are the chances of having two children of the same genotype? To determine the probability of two events happening in succession, we must multiply the probabilities of the separate events happening. The probability of getting heads for one coin toss is ½, so the probability of getting two heads in a row is ½ × ½ = ¼. (In other words, out of a large number of double coin tosses, we will get two heads one-quarter of the time.) Now consider the chances of our couple having two children, both non–tongue rollers *(tt)*. The probability that one child will be *tt* is ¼, so the probability that both children will be *tt* is ¼ × ¼ = ¹⁄₁₆, or only slightly better than 6%. Remember though, the production of each child, like each coin toss in a series, is an *independent event* that does not influence the others. If you get heads on the first toss, the chance of getting heads the second time is still ½. Likewise, if our couple's first child is a non–tongue roller, they still have a ¼ chance of getting a non–tongue roller the next time.

Dominant Traits

Human traits known to be dictated by dominant alleles include dimples, freckles, and the condition of detached earlobes, in which the lobe hangs inferior to the point of attachment of the ear.

Genetic disorders caused by dominant genes are fairly uncommon because *lethal dominant genes* are almost always expressed and result in the death of the embryo, fetus, or child. Thus, the deadly genes are not usually passed along to successive generations. However, there are some dominant disorders where the person is less impaired or at least survives long enough to reproduce. One example is *achondroplasia* (a-kon″dro-pla′ze-ah), a rare type of dwarfism resulting from inability of the fetus to form cartilage bone. Another is *Huntington's disease,* a fatal nervous system disease involving degeneration of the basal nuclei. However, in this case, the gene is a *delayed-action gene* that is expressed when the affected individual is in his or her late 30s or early 40s. Offspring of a parent with Huntington's disease have a 50% chance of inheriting the lethal gene. (The parent is inevitably heterozygous, since the dominant homozygous condition is lethal to the fetus.) Many informed

Table 30.1 Traits Determined by Simple Dominant-Recessive Inheritance	
Phenotype due to expression of dominant genes (genotype *ZZ* or *Zz*)	**Phenotype due to expression of recessive genes (genotype *zz*)**
Tongue roller	Inability to roll tongue into a U shape
Free (unattached) earlobes	Attached earlobes
Farsightedness	Normal vision
Astigmatism	
Freckles	Absence of freckles
Dimples in cheeks	Absence of dimples
Feet with normal arches	Flat feet
PTC taster	PTC nontaster
Widow's peak	Straight hairline
Double-jointed thumb	Tight thumb ligaments
Broad lips	Thin lips
Polydactyly (extra fingers and toes)	Normal number of fingers and toes
Syndactyly (webbed digits)	Normal digits
Achondroplasia (heterozygous: dwarfism; homozygous: lethal)	Normal cartilage bone formation
Huntington's disease	Absence of Huntington's disease
Normal skin pigmentation	Albinism
Absence of Tay-Sachs disease	Tay-Sachs disease
Absence of cystic fibrosis	Cystic fibrosis
Normal mentation	Schizophrenia

offspring of such parents are opting not to become parents themselves. These and other dominant gene–determined traits are listed in Table 30.1.

Recessive Traits

Many examples of recessive inheritance cause no problems, and some are actually the more desirable genetic condition. For example, normal vision is dictated by recessive alleles, whereas farsightedness and astigmatism are prescribed by dominant alleles. However, many if not most genetic disorders are inherited as simple recessive traits. These include conditions as different as *albinism* (lack of skin pigmentation); *cystic fibrosis,* a condition of excessive mucus production which impairs lung and pancreatic functioning (see p. 780); and *Tay-Sachs disease,* a disorder of brain lipid metabolism, caused by an enzyme deficit that shows itself a few months after birth (see p. 80).

Recessive genetic disorders are more frequent than those caused by dominant alleles because those who carry a single recessive allele for a recessive genetic disorder do not themselves express the disease. However, they can pass the gene on to their offspring and, for this reason, such people are called **carriers** of the disorder. This understanding is acknowledged in the laws that prohibit **consanguineous** (kon″sang-gwi′ne-us) **marriages** (literally, "same blood" marriages)—those between close relatives such as siblings or first cousins. (The term *consanguineous* is a holdover from times when it was believed that inherited traits were carried by a person's blood.) The chance of inheriting two identical deleterious recessive genes, and thus expressing the disease they code for, is much higher in such matings than in matings between unrelated people. The greater incidence of stillbirth and severe genetic disorders seen in animals that are extremely inbred, such as show dogs, is ample proof of the truth of this statement.

Incomplete Dominance (Intermediate Inheritance)

As opposed to the rules of dominant-recessive inheritance described above, in which one allele variant completely masks the other, some traits exhibit **incomplete dominance,** or **intermediate inheritance.** In such instances, the heterozygote has a phenotype intermediate between those of homozygous dominant and homozygous recessive individuals. Incomplete dominance is very common in plants and some animals, but less so in humans.

Perhaps the best human example is inheritance of the *sickling gene (s),* which causes a substitution of one amino acid in the β chain of hemoglobin. Hemoglobin molecules containing the abnormal polypeptide chains crystallize and become sharp when the oxygen tension in blood is low, causing the erythrocytes to assume a sickle shape. The sickling gene is especially widespread among black people (those now living in the malaria belt of Africa or their descendants). Those with a double dose of the sickling allele *(ss)* have **sickle-cell anemia,** and any condition that lowers the oxygen level of their blood, such as respiratory difficulty or excessive exercise, can precipitate a *sickle-cell crisis.* The deformed erythrocytes jam up and fragment in small capillaries, causing intense pain, and vital organs may suffer ischemic damage. The only treatment for sickle-cell anemia is frequent blood transfusion to replace the sickling red blood cells with normal cells.

Individuals heterozygous for the sickling gene *(Ss)* make both normal and sickling hemoglobin. As a rule, these individuals are quite healthy, but they can suffer a crisis if there is prolonged reduction in blood oxygen levels, as might happen when traveling in high-altitude areas. It is estimated that 10% of African Americans have the heterozygous condition, known as **sickle-cell trait.** This high frequency is due to the fact that the heterozygous condition confers resistance to malaria—an important adaptation in some parts of Africa. *SS* homozygotes are normal.

Multiple-Allele Inheritance

Although we inherit only two alleles for each gene, some genes actually exhibit more than two alternate forms, leading to a phenomenon called **multiple-allele inheritance.** Inheritance of the ABO blood types is an example. There are three possible alleles that determine the ABO blood types in humans: I^A, I^B, and i. Each of us receives two of these. The I^A and I^B alleles are *codominant,* and both are expressed when present. The i allele is recessive to the other two alleles. Genotypes determining the four possible ABO blood groups are indicated in Table 30.2.

Sex-Linked Inheritance

Inherited traits determined by genes on the sex chromosomes are said to be **sex-linked.** The X and Y sex chromosomes are not homologous in the true sense. The Y chromosome, which contains the gene (or genes) that determines maleness, is only about one-third as large as the X chromosome and lacks many of the genes present on the X that code for nonsexual characteristics. For example, genes coding for certain clotting factors and cone pigments are present on the X chromosome but not the Y chromosome. A gene found only on the X chromosome is said to be **X-linked.**

When a male inherits an X-linked recessive allele (for example, for hemophilia [bleeder's disease] or for red-green color blindness), its expression is never masked or damped, because there is no corresponding allele on his Y chromosome. Consequently, the recessive gene is always expressed, even when present only in single dose. In contrast, females must have two X-linked recessive alleles to express such a disorder; as a result, very few females exhibit any of these X-linked conditions. X-linked traits are typically passed from mothers to their sons. (Since males receive no X chromosome from their fathers, X-linked

Table 30.2 ABO Blood Groups

Blood group (phenotype)	Genotype	Frequency (% U.S. population)		
		White	Black	Asian
O	*ii*	47	49	40
A	$I^A I^A$ or $I^A i$	41	27	28
B	$I^B I^B$ or $I^B i$	9	20	27
AB	$I^A I^B$	3	4	5

traits are never passed from father to son.) Of course, the mother can also pass the recessive allele to her daughter, but unless the daughter receives another such allele from her father, she will not express the trait.

It should also be noted that some segments of the Y chromosome have no counterpart on the X chromosome. Traits coded for by genes in these segments (including hairy ear pinnae) appear only in males and are passed from fathers to sons. This type of sex-linked gene transmission is referred to as **Y-linked inheritance.**

Polygene Inheritance

So far, we have considered only those traits inherited by mechanisms of classical Mendelian genetics, which are fairly easily understood. Such traits typically have two, or perhaps three, alternate forms. However, many phenotypes depend on several different gene pairs at different locations acting in tandem. **Polygene inheritance** results in *continuous,* or *qualitative,* phenotypic variation between two extremes and explains many human characteristics. Skin color, for instance, is controlled by three separately inherited genes, each existing in two allelic forms: *A, a; B, b;* and *C, c.* The *A, B,* and *C* alleles confer dark skin pigment, and their effects are additive. The *a, b,* and *c* alleles confer pale skin tone. Hence, an individual with an *AABBCC* genotype would be about as dark-skinned as a human can get, while an *aabbcc* person would be very fair. However, when individuals heterozygous for at least one of these gene pairs mate, a broad range of pigmentation is possible in their offspring. Such polygene inheritance results in a distribution of genotypes and phenotypes that, when plotted, yields a bell-shaped curve (Figure 30.5).

The amount of brown pigment in the iris (which determines eye color) is also regulated by polygenes, as are intelligence and height. Height is controlled by four gene pairs, and different combinations of the tallness or shortness alleles are reflected in differences in stature, much the same way as described for inheritance of skin tone. The phenomenon of polygene inheritance helps explain why parents of average height can produce very tall or very short offspring.

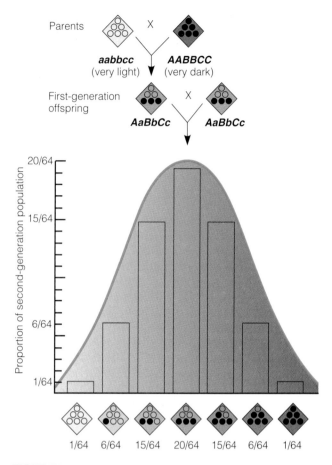

FIGURE 30.5
Polygene inheritance of skin color based on three separate gene pairs. Alleles for dark skin are incompletely dominant over those for light skin. Each dominant gene (*A, B,* or *C*) contributes one "unit" of darkness (indicated by a dark dot) to the phenotypes. In the example shown, the parents are homozygotes at opposite ends of the phenotype range. Each of their children inherits 3 "units" of darkness (is a heterozygote) and has intermediate pigmentation. When they mate, their offspring (second generation) may have a wide variation in pigmentation as shown by the histogram (plotted distribution) of skin colors.

THE INFLUENCE OF ENVIRONMENTAL FACTORS ON GENE EXPRESSION

There are many situations in which environmental factors override or at least influence gene expression. It appears that while our genotype (discounting mutations) is as unchanging as the Rock of Gibraltar, our phenotype is more like clay. If this were not the case, we would never get a tan, women body builders would never develop bulging muscles (Figure 30.6), and there would be no hope for treating genetic disorders.

Sometimes, maternal factors (drugs, pathogens, and others) alter normal gene expression during embryonic development. Take, for example, the case of the "thalidomide babies" (discussed on p. 1007). As a result of drug ingestion by their mothers, the embryos developed phenotypes other than that directed by their genes (flipperlike appendages developed to various degrees and lengths). Such environmentally produced phenotypes that mimic conditions that may be caused by genetic mutations (permanent transmissible changes in the DNA) are called **phenocopies.**

Equally significant are environmental factors that may influence genetic expression after birth, such as the effect of poor infant nutrition on subsequent brain growth, general body development, and height. In this way a person with "tall genes" can be stunted by insufficient nutrition. Furthermore, hormonal deficits during childhood can lead to abnormal skeletal growth and proportions as exemplified by cretinism, a type of dwarfism resulting from hypothyroidism. This is an example of genes (or genetic abnormalities), other than those dictating height, influencing the height phenotype. Hence, part of a gene's environment consists of the influence of other genes.

NONTRADITIONAL INHERITANCE

Mendel's writings underlie mainstream thinking about heredity, but there are additional factors that fail to fit Mendel's rules. Among these nontraditional types of inheritance are *genetic imprinting* and *extrachromosomal inheritance,* and the story is still unfolding.

Genetic Imprinting

Totally unrecognized by Mendel was the astonishing fact that the same allele can have a different effect depending on which parent it comes from. For example, victims of Prader-Willi syndrome are mildly to moderately mentally retarded, short, and grossly obese. Children with Angelman syndrome (called *marionette joyeuse* by the French) are severely retarded, unable to speak coherently, laugh uncontrollably, and exhibit jerky, lurching movements as if tied to a puppeteer's strings. The symptoms of these disorders are very different, but the genetic cause is the same—deletion of a particular region of chromosome 15. If the defective chromosome comes from the father, the result is Prader-Willi syndrome; the mother's defective chromosome confers Angelman syndrome. Thus, it seems that the genes of the deleted region normally behave differently depending on whether they are transmitted in the ovum or the sperm. The explanation for this is that during gametogenesis, certain genes in both sperm and eggs are modified by the addition of methyl ($-CH_3$) groups. This process, called **genetic imprinting,** somehow tags them as paternal or maternal, and confers impor-

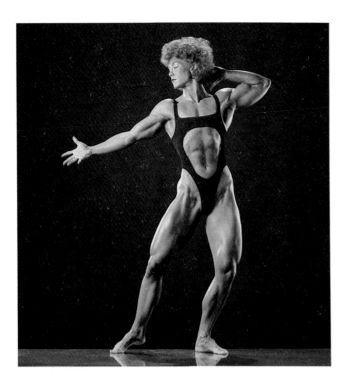

FIGURE 30.6
Although genes determine one's basic physique, body building can accentuate and develop one's muscular potential to the fullest extent.

tant functional differences in the resulting embryo. The developing embryo "reads" these tags, sometimes expressing the mother's gene while the father's version remains idle (or vice versa). The methylation process is reversible. Each generation, the old imprints are "erased" when new gametes are produced and all the chromosomes are newly imprinted according to the sex of the parents. Although not proven, many investigators suspect that *fragile X syndrome,* the most common form of mental retardation, is due to genetic imprinting.

Extrachromosomal (Mitochondrial) Inheritance

Although we have focused on the chromosomal basis of inheritance, remember that not all genes are in the cell's nucleus. Some are in mitochondria. Since the ovum donates essentially all the cytoplasm in the fertilized egg, mitochondrial genes are transmitted to the offspring exclusively by the mother. A growing list of disorders, all rare, is now being linked to errors in mitochondrial genes. Most involve unusual degenerative muscle disorders or neurological problems. Some researchers suggest that Parkinson's disease (see p. 489) may be among them.

GENETIC SCREENING, COUNSELING, AND THERAPY

Newborn infants are routinely screened for a number of anatomical disorders (congenital hip dysplasia, imperforate anus, and others), and phenylketonuria (PKU) testing is mandated by law in many states. These tests are performed much too late to allow any type of parental choice concerning whether or not to have the child, but they do alert the new parents that treatment is necessary to ensure the well-being of their infant. The anatomical defects are usually treated surgically, and PKU is managed by strict dietary measures that exclude most phenylalanine-containing foods. However, *genetic screening* and *genetic counseling* provide information and options for prospective parents not even dreamed of 100 years ago. Adult children of parents with Huntington's disease are obvious candidates for these services, but there are many other genetic conditions that place babies at risk. For example, a woman pregnant for the first time at the age of 35 may wish to know if her baby has trisomy-21 (Down syndrome), a chromosome abnormality with a high incidence in children of older mothers (Figure 30.7). Depending on the condition to be investigated, the screening process can occur before conception by carrier recognition or during fetal testing.

Carrier Recognition

When a prospective parent displays a recessive genetic disorder, but his or her partner does not, it is important to find out if the partner is heterozygous for the same recessive gene. If not, the offspring will receive only one such gene and will not express the trait. But if the other parent *is* a carrier, then the child's chance of having two harmful genes is 50%.

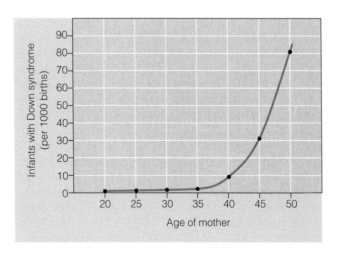

FIGURE 30.7
Maternal age and Down syndrome.

FIGURE 30.8
Large families: living laboratories of human genetics.
Here, Nancy Wexler, of Columbia University and the Hereditary
Disease Foundation, stands in front of a huge pedigree that traces
Huntington's disease though several generations of one large family.
Classical Mendelian analysis of this family, coupled with new
techniques of molecular biology, enabled scientists to develop a test
for the presence of the dominant allele that causes Huntington's
disease—before symptoms are evident. Dr. Wexler, who has studied
the afflicted family, is herself at risk for developing Huntington's
disease. Her mother died of the disorder, and there is a 50% chance
that Dr. Wexler inherited the dominant allele that causes the disease.

There are two major avenues for identifying carriers: pedigrees and blood tests. A **pedigree** traces a
particular genetic trait through several generations
and helps us predict the future (Figure 30.8). A
genetic counselor collects information on the phenotypes of as many family members as possible and uses
it to construct the pedigree. Figure 30.9a uses the rare
woolly hair trait of northern Europeans to illustrate
how a pedigree is constructed and read. Woolly hair,
resulting from the presence of a dominant allele *(W)*,
is fuzzy-textured hair that breaks easily; it is not the
same as the tightly curled hair of blacks. Looking at
the pedigree, we know that individuals with the
woolly hair phenotype (the colored symbols) have at
least one dominant gene *(WW* or *Ww)*, while those
with normal hair must be homozygous recessive
(ww). By working backward and applying the rules of
dominant-recessive inheritance, we can deduce the
genotypes of the parents. Since three of their offspring have normal hair *(ww)*, we know that each parent must have at least one recessive gene. The mother
has woolly hair, determined by the *W* gene, so her
genotype must be *Ww,* and the father with normal
hair is homozygous recessive. You should be able to
take it from here and figure out the most likely genotypes of the offspring. (Try it!) Figure 30.9b illustrates
a pedigree analysis for albinism, a recessive trait. See
what you can deduce about it. These pedigrees represent two of the simplest cases, because many human
traits are controlled by multiple alleles or polygenes
and are much more difficult to unsnarl.

Simple blood tests are used to screen for the sickling gene in heterozygotes, and sophisticated *blood
chemistry tests* and *DNA probes* (which use DNA
hybridization techniques to identify aberrant genes)
can ascertain the presence of other unexpressed
recessive genes. At present, carriers of the Tay-Sachs
and cystic fibrosis genes can be identified with such
tests.

(a) Pedigree of a dominant trait

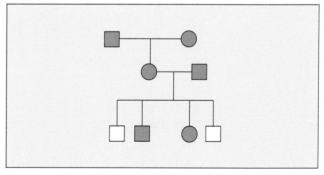

(b) Pedigree of a recessive trait

FIGURE 30.9
**Pedigree analysis is done to detect carriers of
particular genes.** Circles represent females; squares represent
males. Horizontal lines indicate a mating of the connected individuals;
vertical lines show their offspring. **(a)** A pedigree of inheritance of the
woolly hair gene in three generations of a family. Colored symbols
represent individuals expressing the dominant woolly hair trait. White
symbols represent those not expressing the trait; these individuals
are homozygous recessive *(ww)*. **(b)** Pedigree tracing the recessive
trait albinism (lack of skin pigmentation) through three generations.
Both parents in the second generation have pigmented skin (colored
symbols), and yet two of their four children have the albino trait (white
symbols). We can deduce that both of these parents are
heterozygous and have pigmented skin because the allele for that
trait is dominant.

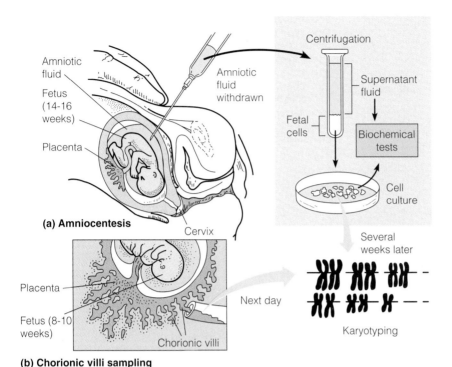

(a) Amniocentesis

(b) Chorionic villi sampling

FIGURE 30.10
Fetal testing. (a) In amniocentesis, ultrasound is used to locate the fetus, and a small amount of amniotic fluid is extracted for testing. Physicians can diagnose some disorders from chemicals in the fluid itself, while other disorders may show up in tests performed on cells cultured from fetal cells present in the fluid. These tests include biochemical tests, to detect the presence of certain enzymes, and karyotyping, to determine whether the chromosomes of the fetal cells are normal in number and microscopic appearance. **(b)** In chorionic villi sampling, a physician inserts a narrow tube through the cervix and suctions out a tiny sample of fetal tissue (chorionic villi) from the placenta. The fetal tissue sample is used immediately for karyotyping.

Fetal Testing

Fetal testing is used when there is a known risk of a genetic disorder. The most common type of fetal testing is **amniocentesis** (am″ne-o-sen-te′sis). In this fairly simple procedure, a wide-bore needle is inserted into the amniotic sac through the mother's abdominal wall (Figure 30.10a), and a small sample (about 10 ml) of fluid is withdrawn. Because there is a chance of injuring the fetus before ample amniotic fluid is present, this procedure is not normally done before the fourteenth week of pregnancy. The use of ultrasound to visualize the position of the fetus and the amniotic sac has dramatically reduced the risk of this procedure. Although the fluid is checked for the presence of chemicals (enzymes and others) that serve as markers for specific diseases, most tests are done on the sloughed-off fetal cells in the fluid. These cells are isolated and cultured (grown and proliferated) in laboratory dishes over a period of several weeks. Then the cells are examined for DNA markers of genetic disease and karyotyped (see Figure 30.1) to check for chromosomal abnormalities such as Down syndrome.

Chorionic villi sampling (CVS) snips off bits of the chorionic villi from the placenta for examination (Figure 30.10b). A small tube is inserted through the vagina and cervical canal and guided by ultrasound to an area where a piece of placental tissue can be removed. CVS allows earlier testing (at eight weeks but after the tenth week is usually recommended) than amniocentesis and is much faster. Karyotyping can be done almost immediately on the rapidly dividing chorionic cells.

Since both of these procedures are invasive, they carry with them an inherent risk to both fetus and mother. (For example, increased fetal risk of finger and toe defects is linked to CVS.) Although they are routinely ordered for pregnant women over the age of 35 (because of the enhanced risk of Down syndrome), they are performed on younger women only when the probability of finding a severe fetal disorder is greater than the probability of doing harm during the procedure. If a serious genetic or congenital defect is detected in the developing fetus, the parents must decide whether or not to continue the pregnancy.

Human Gene Therapy

As advances occur in diagnosis of human genetic diseases, new applications of "gene therapy" to alleviate or even cure the disorders have been quick to follow, particularly in cases traced to a single defective gene or protein. Indeed, genetic engineering has the potential to replace a defective gene with a normal version. One approach is to "infect" the defective cells with a virus into which a functional gene has been inserted (Figure 30.11); another is to inject the "corrected" DNA directly into the patient's cells. Such therapies have proven successful in treating cystic fibrosis and muscular dystrophy. However, genetic engineering processes are prohibitively expensive and raise some thorny ethical, religious, and societal questions: Who will pay? Who determines who will be treated with the new therapies? Are we playing God?

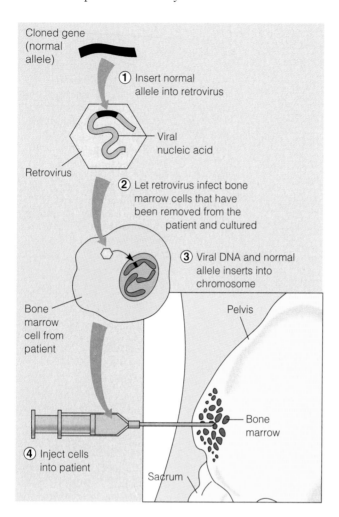

① Insert normal allele into retrovirus

Viral nucleic acid

Retrovirus

② Let retrovirus infect bone marrow cells that have been removed from the patient and cultured

③ Viral DNA and normal allele inserts into chromosome

Bone marrow cell from patient

Pelvis

Bone marrow

④ Inject cells into patient

Sacrum

Cloned gene (normal allele)

FIGURE 30.11
One type of gene therapy procedure. In this procedure, a harmless retrovirus is used as a vector to introduce a normal allele of a gene into the cells of a patient who lacks it. The method takes advantage of the fact that a retrovirus inserts a copy of its nucleic acid (actually a DNA transcript of its RNA genome) into the chromosomal DNA of its host cell. If its nucleic acid contains a foreign gene and that gene is expressed, the cell—and its mitotic descendants—will be cured. Cells that continue to reproduce throughout life, such as bone marrow cells, are ideal for gene therapy.

*   *   *

In this chapter, we have explored some of the most basic principles of genetics, the manner in which genes are expressed, and the means by which gene expression can be modified or thwarted. Considering the precision required to make perfect copies of genes and chromosomes, and considering the incredible mechanical events of meiotic division, it is amazing that genetic defects are as rare as they are. Perhaps, after reading this chapter, you have a greater sense of wonder that you turned out as well as you did.

RELATED CLINICAL TERMS

Deletion Chromosomal aberration in which part of a chromosome is lost.

Down syndrome Also called **mongolism,** this condition usually reflects the presence of an extra autosome (trisomy of chromosome 21); the child has slightly slanted eyes, flattened facial features, a large tongue, and a tendency toward short stature and stubby fingers; some, but not all, affected people are mentally retarded; the most important risk factor appears to be advanced maternal (or paternal) age.

Mutation (*mutare* = change) A permanent structural change in a gene; the mutation may or may not affect function, depending on the precise site and nature of the alteration.

Nondisjunction Abnormal segregation of chromosomes during meiosis, resulting in gametes receiving two or no copies of a particular parental chromosome; if the abnormal gamete participates in fertilization, the resulting zygote will have an abnormal chromosomal complement (monosomy or trisomy) for that particular chromosome (as in Down syndrome).

CHAPTER SUMMARY

Genetics is the study of heredity and mechanisms of gene transmission.

The Vocabulary of Genetics (pp. 1027–1028)

1. A complete diploid set of chromosomes is called the *karyotype* of an organism; the complete genetic complement is the *genome*. A person's genome consists of two sets of instructions, one from each parent.

Gene Pairs (Alleles) (p. 1028)

2. Genes coding for the same trait and found at the same locus on homologous chromosomes are called alleles.

3. Alleles may be the same or different in expression. When the allele pair is identical, the person is homozygous for that trait; when the alleles differ, the person is heterozygous.

Genotype and Phenotype (p. 1028)

4. The actual genetic makeup of cells is the genotype; phenotype is the manner in which those genes are expressed.

Sexual Sources of Genetic Variation (pp. 1028–1030)

Segregation and Independent Assortment of Chromosomes (p. 1029)

1. During meiosis I of gametogenesis, tetrads align randomly on the metaphase plate, and chromatids are randomly distributed to the daughter cells. This is called independent assortment of the homologues. Each gamete receives only one allele of each gene pair.

2. Each different metaphase I alignment produces a different assortment of parental chromosomes in the gametes, and all combinations of maternal and paternal chromosomes are equally possible.

Crossover of Homologues and Gene Recombination (pp. 1029–1030)

3. During meiosis I, two of the four chromatids (one maternal and the other paternal) may cross over at one or more points and exchange corresponding gene segments. The recombinant chromosomes contain new gene combinations, adding to the variability arising from independent assortment.

Random Fertilization (p. 1030)

4. The third source of genetic variation is random fertilization of eggs by sperm.

Types of Inheritance (pp. 1030–1034)

Dominant-Recessive Inheritance (pp. 1031–1032)

1. Dominant genes are expressed when present in single or double dose; recessive genes must be present in double dose to be expressed.

2. For traits following the dominant-recessive pattern, the laws of probability predict the outcome of a large number of matings.

3. Genetic disorders more often reflect the homozygous recessive condition than the homozygous dominant or heterozygous condition because dominant genes are expressed, and if they are lethal genes, the pregnancy is usually aborted. Genetic disorders caused by dominant alleles include achondroplasia and Huntington's disease; recessive disorders include cystic fibrosis and Tay-Sachs disease.

4. Carriers are heterozygotes who carry a deleterious recessive gene (but do not express the trait) and have the potential of passing it on to offspring. The chances of carriers of the same trait mating are higher in consanguineous marriages.

Incomplete Dominance (Intermediate Inheritance) (pp. 1032–1033)

5. In incomplete dominance, the heterozygote exhibits a phenotype intermediate between those of the homozygous dominant and recessive individuals. Inheritance of sickle-cell trait is an example of incomplete dominance.

Multiple-Allele Inheritance (p. 1033)

6. Multiple-allele inheritance involves genes that exist in more than two allelic forms in a population. Only two of the alleles are inherited, but on a random basis. Inheritance of ABO blood types is an example of multiple-allele inheritance in which the I^A and I^B alleles are codominant.

Sex-Linked Inheritance (p. 1033)

7. Traits determined by genes on the X and Y chromosomes are said to be sex-linked. The small Y chromosome lacks many genes present on the X chromosome. Recessive genes present only on the X chromosome are expressed in single dose in males. Examples of such X-linked conditions, passed from mother to son, include hemophilia and red-green color blindness. There are a few Y-linked genes, passed from father to son only.

Polygene Inheritance (pp. 1033–1034)

8. Polygene inheritance occurs when several gene pairs interact to produce phenotypes that vary qualitatively over a broad range. Height, eye color, and skin pigmentation are examples.

The Influence of Environmental Factors on Gene Expression (p. 1034)

1. Environmental factors may influence the expression of genotype.

2. Maternal factors that cross the placenta may alter expression of fetal genes. Environmentally provoked phenotypes that mimic genetically determined ones are called phenocopies. Nutritional deficits or hormonal imbalances may alter anticipated growth and development during childhood.

Nontraditional Inheritance (pp. 1034–1035)

Genetic Imprinting (pp. 1034–1035)

1. Genetic imprinting, which involves methylation of certain genes during gametogenesis, confers different effects and phenotypes on maternal and paternal genes. It is reversible, and occurs anew each generation.

Extrachromosomal (Mitochondrial) Inheritance (p. 1035)

2. Cytoplasmic (mitochondrial) genes pass to offspring via the ovum and help to determine certain characteristics. Deletions or mutations in mitochondrial genes are responsible for some rare genetic diseases.

Genetic Screening, Counseling, and Therapy (pp. 1035–1038)

Carrier Recognition (pp. 1035–1036)

1. The likelihood of an individual carrying a deleterious recessive gene may be assessed by constructing a pedigree. Some of these genes can be detected by various blood tests and DNA probes.

Fetal Testing (p. 1037)

2. Amniocentesis is fetal testing based on aspirated samples of amniotic fluid. Fetal cells in the fluid are cultured for several weeks, then examined for chromosomal defects (karyotyped) or for DNA markers of genetic disease. Amniocentesis cannot be performed until the fourteenth week of pregnancy.

3. Chorionic villi sampling is fetal testing based on a sample of the chorion. Because this tissue is rapidly mitotic, karyotyping can be done almost immediately. Samples may be obtained by the eighth week.

Human Gene Therapy (pp. 1037–1038)

4. Thus far, gene therapy has been particularly useful for correcting single-gene disorders. The most common approach involves transferring a corrected gene via a virus (or some other vector) to the affected cells to restore normal function.

REVIEW QUESTIONS

Multiple Choice/Matching

1. Match one of the following terms (a–i) with each of the appropriate descriptions below:

(a) alleles   **(d)** genotype   **(g)** phenotype
(b) autosomes   **(e)** heterozygote   **(h)** recessive allele
(c) dominant allele   **(f)** homozygote   **(i)** sex chromosomes

———— **(1)** genetic makeup
———— **(2)** how genetic makeup is expressed
———— **(3)** chromosomes that dictate most body characteristics
———— **(4)** alternate forms of the same gene
———— **(5)** an individual bearing two alleles that are the same for a particular trait
———— **(6)** an allele that is expressed, whether in single or double dose
———— **(7)** an individual bearing two alleles that differ for a particular trait
———— **(8)** an allele that must be present in double dose to be expressed.

2. Match the following types of inheritance (a–e) with the descriptions below:

(a) dominant-recessive   **(d)** polygene
(b) incomplete dominance   **(e)** sex-linked
(c) multiple-allele

———— **(1)** only sons show the trait
———— **(2)** homozygotes and heterozygotes have the same phenotype
———— **(3)** heterozygotes exhibit a phenotype intermediate between those of the homozygotes
———— **(4)** phenotypes of offspring may be more varied than those of the parents
———— **(5)** inheritance of ABO blood types
———— **(6)** inheritance of stature

Short Answer Essay Questions

3. Describe the important mechanisms that lead to genetic variations in gametes.

4. The ability to taste PTC (phenylthiocarbamide) depends on the presence of a dominant gene T; nontasters are homozygous for the recessive gene t. This is a situation of classical dominant-recessive inheritance. (a) Consider a mating between heterozygous parents producing three offspring. What proportion of the offspring will be tasters? What is the chance that all three offspring will be tasters? Nontasters? What is the chance that two will be tasters and one will be a nontaster? (b) Consider a mating between Tt and tt parents. What is the anticipated percentage of tasters? Nontasters? What proportion can be expected to be homozygous recessive? Heterozygous? Homozygous dominant?

5. Most albino children are born to normally pigmented parents. Albinos are homozygous for the recessive gene *(aa)*. What can you conclude about the genotypes of the nonalbino parents?

6. A woman with blood type A has two children. One has type O blood and the other has type B blood. What is the genotype of the mother? What are the genotype and phenotype of the father? What is the genotype of each child?

7. In skin color inheritance, what will be the relative range of pigmentation in offspring arising from the following parental matches: (a) *AABBCC* × *aabbcc*, (b) *AABBCC* × *AaBbCc*, (c) *AAbbcc* × *aabbcc*?

8. Compare and contrast amniocentesis and chorionic villi sampling as to the time at which they can be performed and the techniques used to obtain information on the fetus's genetic status.

 CRITICAL THINKING AND CLINICAL APPLICATION QUESTIONS

1. A color-blind man marries a woman with normal vision. The woman's father was also color-blind. (a) What is the chance that their first child will be a color-blind son? A color-blind daughter? (b) If they have four children, what is the chance that two will be color-blind sons? (Be careful on this one.)

2. Brian is a college student. His genetics assignment is to do a family pedigree for dimples in the cheeks. Absence of dimples is recessive; presence of dimples reflects a dominant allele. Brian has dimples, as do his three brothers. His mother and maternal grandmother are dimple-free, but his father and all other grandparents have dimples. Construct a pedigree spanning three generations for Brian's family. Show the phenotype and genotype for each person.

3. Mr. and Mrs. Lehman have sought genetic counseling. Mrs. Lehman is concerned because she is unexpectedly pregnant and her husband's brother died of Tay-Sachs disease. She can recall no incidence of Tay-Sachs disease in her own family. Do you think biochemical testing should be recommended to detect the deleterious gene in Mrs. Lehman? Explain your answer.

EPILOGUE

Well, we've spent nearly a year taking the human body apart (in the academic sense, of course). You have been asked to critically examine each organ system, often in minute detail, to learn about its contributions to body function and homeostasis. The problem with this traditional approach is that once the body has been "taken apart" for such an examination, it is never put back together again. Hence, the goal of this epilogue is to illustrate how seemingly simple everyday activities—like eating, eliminating urine, and walking—are brought about by scores of physiological events operating both independently and cooperatively.

A description of John's day and activities, from the time he wakes up until just before arousal the next morning is followed on the left-hand column both in pictures and in a simple narrative. You are sure to find nearly all of his activities very familiar (and part of your own daily routine). On the adjacent column is a replication of a computer print-out listing many of the physiological activities that are going on in John's body at that particular moment. Obviously this computer printout is not a complete listing. As long as you are alive, you are breathing, your heart is pumping, your mind is active, and your hormone levels are waxing and waning. Many of these activities are mentioned only when they need be enhanced, as during strenuous exercise. For the most part, our goal is to focus on specific activities and to indicate what other body systems are important in helping to effect or moderate those activities.

You are sure to be a bit overwhelmed with the number and kinds of processes that do (and must) occur to keep the body functioning smoothly and effectively as we go about our daily tasks. Even better, you will be amazed at how much you have learned as you worked your way through the course in A&P. Enjoy—it's time to see the forest instead of the trees!

A DAY in the LIFE

COMPLETE
WITH ComputerPrintout

7:00 AM AS JOHN'S EYES OPEN, HE CHECKS THE TIME, THEN CRAWLS DEEPER UNDER THE COVERS.

7:10 AM AFTER A FEW MINUTES OF TOSSING, HE REALIZES HE HAS TO URINATE.

7:12 AM ARISING, JOHN MAKES HIS WAY TO THE BATHROOM, URINATES, AND DECIDES TO EXERCISE.

Awakening occurs as: (pp.491–493)

1. Core body temperature rises.

2. EEG changes from stage 4 to stage 1 pattern.

3. Norepinephrine levels rise and serotonin (sleep neurotransmitter) levels decline in the brain; cortical activity rises. Neurons of dorsal raphe nuclei of midbrain reticular formation are firing at their maximal rate.

Full arousal and recognition of urge to urinate occurs as: (p. 920)

1. Accumulating urine distends the urinary bladder wall, initiating the micturition reflex. Detrussor muscle of bladder contracts and internal urethral sphincter relaxes allowing urine to enter the proximal (prostatic) urethra.

2. Afferent impulses sent to brain cause recognition of urge to urinate.

Blood Pressure homeostasis maintained while standing up: (pp. 653–655)

1. Blood pressure drops as erect posture is achieved.

2. Baroreceptors are activated, causing reflex activation of the sympathetic nervous system vasomotor center in the medulla. Sympathetic vasomotor fibers release norepinephrine, causing most arterioles of the body to constrict.

3. Blood pressure rises, restoring homeostasis.

Mobilization of voluntary muscles to walk to the bathroom: (pp. 263–267, 486–488)

1. Voluntary activity is initiated by precommand regions of the brain (cerebellum and basal nuclei).

2. Sitting, standing, and walking are monitored by the cerebellum, which receives continuous feedback on body balance and tension of muscles and tendons from visual, proprioceptor, and vestibular receptors. The cerebellum dispatches nerve impulses to the motor and premotor cortical regions to maintain balance and gait.

3. Locomotion and rhythmic activities of the limbs are regulated by control neurons in the brain stem which turn on the central pattern generators in the spinal cord. *

Blood supply to skeletal muscles increases: (pp. 661–663)

1. Sympathetic nervous system activity dilates arterioles in active skeletal muscles.

2. Precapillary sphincters open, allowing blood to enter the true capillaries to serve the muscle cells as their metabolic activity increases.

*All voluntary skeletal muscle activities involve this interplay of physiological events. From this point on they will be indicated by the letters VSMA (voluntary skeletal muscle activity).

7:30 AM BECAUSE HE HAS A BUSY DAY PLANNED, JOHN DECIDES TO GET TO HIS CYCLING EARLY. HE PULLS ON HIS CYCLING CLOTHES, STRETCHES, AND BEGINS SLOWLY TO GIVE HIS MUSCLES A CHANCE TO WARM UP.

Warmup: (p. 226)

1. Muscle fibers begin to contract and generate heat, increasing the efficiency of the muscle enzyme systems.

2. VSMA occurs.

3. The sympathetic nervous system promotes vasodilation in the working muscles; precapillary sphincters begin to open. Catecholamines are released and enhance the sensitivity of the stretch reflexes.

4. Skeletal muscle and respiratory pumps enhance venous return (hence, cardiac output and blood pressure).

Effects of training on muscle: (p. 274)

1. Sustained aerobic exercise produces muscle modifications that ultimately enhance endurance: more red nonfatiguable fibers; more capillaries, mitochondria, and myoglobin in the skeletal muscles.

2. High intensity (speed or resistance) exercise produces faster-acting, stronger muscles (by increasing muscle size and the numbers of white fibers).

Effects of training on the other organ systems (occur gradually): (p. 274)

1. Cardiovascular efficiency increases as the heart hypertrophies, venous return and stroke volume increase, and enhanced blood levels of LDLs clear fatty substances from the blood vessel walls.

2. Respiratory efficiency increases as VO_{max} increases.

3. The skeleton becomes stronger due to mechanical stresses of muscles pulling.

4. Neuromuscular coordination improves.

5. Lymphatic drainage improves due to the skeletal muscle pump.

6. Tissue cells become more responsive to insulin, helping to prevent diabetes mellitus.

Respiration increases to enhance gas exchange in the lungs: (pp. 777–778)

1. Respiratory rate rises as exercise begins, stabilizes, then remains high until oxygen debt is repaid after exercise.

Muscle pH homeostasis maintained: (p. 268)

1. During periods of intense activity, aerobic mechanisms are unable to keep pace and anaerobic glycolysis becomes the means of generating ATP.

2. Lactic acid is produced, moves from the muscles to the blood, and is sequestered by the liver. This prevents muscle and blood pH from falling too low during athletic activity.

Temperature homeostasis maintained: (pp. 888–890)

1. Heat generated by muscles warms the blood. Central temperature sensors in hypothalamus respond by activating sympathetic-mediated heat loss mechanisms: dermal blood vessels dilate to allow heat to radiate from skin surface, and sweat glands are activated to cool the body via evaporation of sweat.

7:40 AM JOHN, TRYING TO INCREASE HIS SPEED, ENDURANCE, AND STRENGTH, ALTERNATES BETWEEN CYCLING FLAT OUT (AS FAST AS HE POSSIBLY CAN), CRUISING AT A MODERATE PACE, AND PEDALING UPHILL IN A HIGH GEAR.

9:35 AM AFTER COOLING DOWN AT A SLOWER PACE, THEN STRETCHING TO MAINTAIN FLEXIBILITY AND PREVENT CRAMPING, JOHN HEADS FOR THE SHOWER.

9:45 AM AFTER DRYING OFF, JOHN AMBLES ON TO THE KITCHEN WHERE HE POURS HIMSELF A GLASS OF OJ AND A BOWL OF CEREAL AND BEGINS TO EAT.

Body temperature homeostasis maintained during showering: (pp. 888–890)

1. Hot shower washes away "skin-dwelling" bacteria and warms the skin surface.

2. Peripheral and central thermoreceptors are activated; sympathetic fibers dilate dermal blood vessels.

3. After the shower, radiation from the skin surface causes rapid heat loss.

4. Thermoreceptors initiate heat promoting mechanisms by hypothalamus. Sympathetic fibers stimulate vasoconstriction of cutaneous blood vessels and increase metabolic rate via released norepinephrine. Brain centers controlling muscle tone are activated. Shivering begins, generating large amounts of heat.

5. Temperature homeostasis is restored and shivering stops.

Ambulation and manipulation of food:

1. VSMA occurs.

Food intake activities: (pp. 802–804)

1. Salivation and secretion of stomach juices are initiated by sight of a liked food.

2. After voluntary activation of chewing muscles, mastication continues reflexively in response to pressure stimuli in the mouth.

3. Salivary amylase in saliva digests starch (in cereal) to simpler sugars.

4. Swallowing initiated voluntarily by tongue; beyond the oropharynx, swallowing occurs reflexively. Food propelled to the stomach by peristaltic contractions.

Digestion in stomach and intestine: (pp. 806–813, 828–829)

1. Rhythm of peristaltic contractions in the stomach initiated by local pacemaker cells.

2. Food in stomach activates pressure and chemical receptors which increase gastric mobilization and secretory activity.

3. HCl-activated pepsin digests cereal proteins; ingested food is converted to chyme.

4. Gastric gland secretion of mucus protects the gastric mucosa from self-digestion.

5. Chyme enters the small intestine and activates pressure and chemical receptors which reflexively cause secretion of intestinal juice, CCK and secretin. Bile and pancreatic juice enter the duodenum.

6. HCO_3-rich pancreatic juice provides the proper alkaline pH for digestion in small intestine. Pancreatic amylase, lipases, proteases, nucleases and intestinal brush border enzymes complete digestion.

7. Digested foodstuffs, minerals, vitamins, and water are absorbed as the chyme is mixed and moved along the length of the small intestine by segmentation.

8. Digestion is completed by end of ileum; peristaltic waves sweep undigested debris into the large intestine.

9. Foodstuff entering the large intestine is dehydrated; B and K vitamins made by enteric bacteria are absorbed.

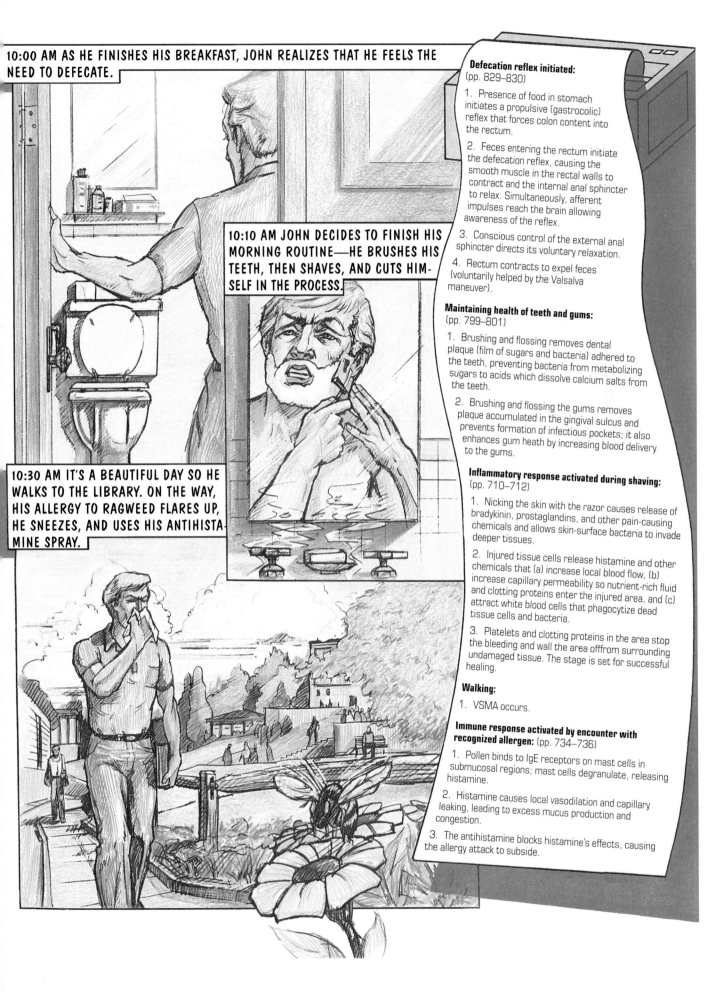

10:45 AM JOHN READS THE ASSIGNED CHAPTER, STUDIES *MAKING CONNECTIONS*, AND COMPLETES THE END-OF-CHAPTER QUESTIONS.

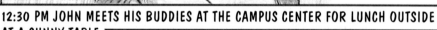

Reading the textbook: (pp. 515–526)

1. The pupils of the eyes are constricted by occulomotor nerves (III) to prevent entry of the most divergent light rays and increase clarity of vision.

2. The lens is bulged for close vision and the eyes are converged; the real image is focused on the fovea centralis of the retina.

3. Eyes move across lines of print (superior colliculi and extrinsic eye muscles involved).

4. Photoreceptors are activated; nerve impulses pass to the thalamus where synapse occurs; visual pathway continues to the visual cortex in the occipital lobes where vision occurs.

Comprehending and consolidating the material: (pp. 497–498)

1. Impulses are sent from the visual cortex to language areas of the brain for comprehension of the written words.

2. Comprehension requires retrieval of information previously learned and stored in long term memory depots in the cerebral cortex to provide a guideline or comparison point for current understanding.

3. Transfer of new information to long term memory and consolidation activate the hippocampus, amygdala, and frontal forebrain. These processes occur best when new material can be related to existing information.

Food intake and digestion occurring.

pH, water, and electrolyte balance of the blood is maintained: (pp. 930–942).

1. As nutrients enter the blood, blood buffers resist pH changes.

2. Renal mechanisms reabsorb or fail to reabsorb bicarbonate ions as necessary to maintain blood pH, and maintain water and electrolyte balance in response to hormones (particularly ADH, aldosterone, and ANF).

Body temperature maintained within physiological limits.

Keratinocytes protected from UV radiation: (p. 137)

1. UV rays of sunlight stimulate melanocytes to produce more melanin; keratinocytes engulf the melanin to protect their nuclei from UV damage.

2. UV exposure temporarily disables the immune response by inhibiting the antigen-presenting Langerhans' cells.

12:30 PM JOHN MEETS HIS BUDDIES AT THE CAMPUS CENTER FOR LUNCH OUTSIDE AT A SUNNY TABLE.

1:15 PM THE "GANG" DECIDES TO GO TO THE BEACH TO PLAY VOLLEYBALL. JOHN COMPETES AGGRESSIVELY IN THE MATCH.

Skeletal muscles vigorously exercised:
(pp. 452–454)

1. VSMA occurs.

2. Stretch reflexes are modified (suppressed) to allow John's arms to produce large movements to belt the ball over the net.

3. Conversely, leg muscles are being stretched as much and as quickly as possible to provide maximal force for John's jumps.

Temperature homeostasis is maintained.

Aggressiveness is enhanced during the match:
(p. 420).

1. Competitive thoughts provoke enhanced release of testosterone from the testes which increases John's aggressiveness during the match.

Maintaining water balance/preventing dehydration: (pp. 930–934)

1. Fluids are lost through sweating and frequent urination (ethyl alcohol in the beer acts as a diuretic by inhibiting ADH secretion).

2. Thirst reflex activated via hypothalamus reflex. (However, John continues to drink beer—no help.)

3. Aldosterone released in greater amounts to prompt kidneys to conserve Na^+ (and therefore water).

Keratinocytes protected from UV radiation.

Cerebellar activity impaired: (p. 369)

1. Alcohol affects the brain, particularly the cerebellum, leading to impaired neuromuscular coordination and some degree of ataxia (inaccurate movements).

BP homeostasis impaired: (p. 657)

1. Alcohol depresses the vasomotor center, causing vasodilation and a drop in systemic blood pressure. This accounts for John's flushed appearance and lightheadedness.

Blood pH maintained by the kidneys:
(pp. 908–912)

1. Alcohol is metabolized to acid end products by the liver, causing a drop in blood pH. The kidneys actively secrete H^+ and reabsorb HCO_3^- to restore physiological blood pH.

2:30 PM EVERYONE TAKES A BREAK TO "CATCH A FEW RAYS" AND QUENCH THEIR THIRST WITH SOME BEER AND SODA.

3:30 PM THE CRY GOES UP FOR ANOTHER VOLLEYBALL CHALLENGE, BUT NOW JOHN FINDS THAT HIS TIMING IS OFF.

4:00 PM JOHN LEAVES TO WALK HOME. HE TAKES A SHOWER, THEN CALLS HIS GIRLFRIEND CATHY AND ASKS HER TO MEET HIM AROUND 6:00 AFTER HE HAS A "SNOOZE" TO SLEEP IT OFF.

6:00 PM WHEN THEY MEET, JOHN COMPLAINS THAT HE'S SO HUNGRY HIS "BACKBONE IS TOUCHING HIS BELLYBUTTON." THEY GRAB A QUICK TACO BEFORE CATCHING A MOVIE.

7:00 PM JOHN AND CATHY GO TO THE MOVIES TO SEE A RECENT REMAKE OF "FRANKENSTEIN." BOTH WATCH WITH BATED BREATH AND SCREAM A LOT.

Events of postabsorptive state— Maintaining plasma glucose homeostasis: (pp. 873–878)

1. Blood glucose levels dropping. Brain continues to use glucose as its energy fuel; other body organs using fatty acids (glucose sparing).

2. Glucagon released; promotes glycogenolysis and gluconeogenesis which cause glucose (and fatty acids) to be released to the blood.

Absorptive period—Processing of nutrient-laden blood: (pp. 873–878)

1. Rising glucose and amino acid levels in plasma cause pancreatic beta cells to release insulin.

2. Blood draining from the digestive viscera is carried to the liver via the hepatic portal vein; liver cells respond to insulin by converting glucose to glycogen; liver sequesters amino acids to make plasma proteins.

3. Insulin accelerates glucose entry into tissue cells and speeds uptake of amino acids by tissue cells.

Vision and comprehension of viewed scenes.

Hearing: (pp. 530–535)

1. The sound reaches both ears at the same time. The eardrums vibrate, transmit the vibration to the ossicles, which in turn transmit the vibratory motion to the fluids of the cochlea. Hair cells (hearing receptors) are activated according to their position on the basilar membrane and the sound frequencies.

2. Impulses transmitted to the auditory cortex in the temporal lobes where interpretation of the tones as words, screams, and other sounds occurs.

Sensory inputs evoke emotional responses: (pp. 401–402)

1. Nearly all sensory pathways make synapses with limbic system structures where the sensory perception is coupled to emotional content on the basis of past experience. Hence, scenes recognized as threatening evoke screams or produce modifications of respiration (breath holding).

10:30 PM AFTER THE MOVIE, JOHN WALKS CATHY HOME. JOHN FINDS CATHY BEAUTIFUL AND EXCITING, AND AFTER A FEW KISSES, THEY DECIDE THAT THE BETTER PART OF WISDOM IS TO CALL IT A NIGHT.

11:30 PM AFTER HIS LONG AND BUSY DAY, JOHN IS REALLY TIRED AND DECIDES TO TURN IN. HE FALLS ASLEEP ALMOST AS SOON AS HIS HEAD HITS THE PILLOW.

Walking.

1. VSMA occurs.

Sexual arousal: (pp. 965–966)

1. Cathy's fragrance, and the feel of her body against his as they nuzzle and kiss, arouse John sexually. Parasympathetic fibers cause vasodilation of the penile blood vessels. As the corpora cavernosa begins to fill with blood, erection begins to occur.

2. As John leaves, interruption of sexually pleasurable stimuli results in vasoconstriction and resumption of the flaccid penile state.

Sleep: (pp. 491–493)

1. Initial drowsiness and floating feeling (indicated by alpha waves) gives way to sleep spindles, and finally delta wave sleep about 30 minutes later. During this progression of NREM sleep stages, vital signs (blood pressure, temperature, respiration rate, pulse) decline to lowest levels of the day. Gastric mobility increases during delta wave sleep; norepinephrine levels decline and serotonin levels rise in the brain.

2. About 90 minutes after sleep begins, REM occurs. The EEG backtracks to alpha waves, vital signs increase, and gastric mobility declines. Skeletal muscles, except the ocular muscles (which move rapidly under the lids) are temporarily paralyzed. Norepinephrine and ACh levels rise in the brain. Dreaming occurs. (Sweet dreams, John.)

3. NREM and REM sleep alternate throughout the night, with REM periods becoming closer together and body temperature rising as time of arousal nears.

Appendix A
The Metric System

MEASUREMENT	UNIT AND ABBREVIATION	METRIC EQUIVALENT	METRIC TO ENGLISH CONVERSION FACTOR	ENGLISH TO METRIC CONVERSION FACTOR
Length	1 kilometer (km)	$= 1000\ (10^3)$ meters	1 km = 0.62 mile	1 mile = 1.61 km
	1 meter (m)	$= 100\ (10^2)$ centimeters = 1000 millimeters	1 m = 1.09 yards 1 m = 3.28 feet 1 m = 39.37 inches	1 yard = 0.914 m 1 foot = 0.305 m
	1 centimeter (cm)	$= 0.01\ (10^{-2})$ meter	1 cm = 0.394 inch	1 foot = 30.5 cm 1 inch = 2.54 cm
	1 millimeter (mm)	$= 0.001\ (10^{-3})$ meter	1 mm = 0.039 inch	
	1 micrometer (μm) [formerly micron (μ)]	$= 0.000001\ (10^{-6})$ meter		
	1 nanometer (nm) [formerly millimicron (mμ)]	$= 0.000000001\ (10^{-9})$ meter		
	1 angstrom (Å)	$= 0.0000000001\ (10^{-10})$ meter		
Area	1 square meter (m²)	= 10,000 square centimeters	1 m² = 1.1960 square yards 1 m² = 10.764 square feet	1 square yard = 0.8361 m² 1 square foot = 0.0929 m²
	1 square centimeter (cm²)	= 100 square millimeters	1 cm² = 0.155 square inch	1 square inch = 6.4516 cm²
Mass	1 metric ton (t)	= 1000 kilograms	1 t = 1.103 ton	1 ton = 0.907t
	1 kilogram (kg)	= 1000 grams	1 kg = 2.205 pounds	1 pound = 0.4536 kg
	1 gram (g)	= 1000 milligrams	1 g = 0.0353 ounce 1 g = 15.432 grains	1 ounce = 28.35 g
	1 milligram (mg)	= 0.001 gram	1 mg = approx. 0.015 grain	
	1 microgram (μg)	= 0.000001 gram		
Volume (solids)	1 cubic meter (m³)	= 1,000,000 cubic centimeters	1 m³ = 1.3080 cubic yards 1 m³ = 35.315 cubic feet	1 cubic yard = 0.7646 m³ 1 cubic foot = 0.0283 m³
	1 cubic centimeter (cm³ or cc)	= 0.000001 cubic meter = 1 milliliter	1 cm³ = 0.0610 cubic inch	1 cubic inch = 16.387 cm³
	1 cubic millimeter (mm³)	= 0.000000001 cubic meter		
Volume (liquids and gases)	1 kiloliter (kl or kL)	= 1000 liters	1 kL = 264.17 gallons	1 gallon = 3.785 L
	1 liter (l or L)	= 1000 milliliters	1 L = 0.264 gallons 1 L = 1.057 quarts	1 quart = 0.946 L
	1 milliliter (ml or mL)	= 0.001 liter = 1 cubic centimeter	1 ml = 0.034 fluid ounce 1 ml = approx. $\frac{1}{4}$ teaspoon 1 ml = approx. 15–16 drops (gtt.)	1 quart = 946 ml 1 pint = 473 ml 1 fluid ounce = 29.57 ml 1 teaspoon = approx. 5 ml
	1 microliter (μl or μL)	= 0.000001 liter		
Time	1 second (s)	$= \frac{1}{60}$ minute		
	1 millisecond (ms)	= 0.001 second		
Temperature	Degrees Celsius (°C)		$°F = \frac{9}{5}°C + 32$	$°C = \frac{5}{9}(°F - 32)$

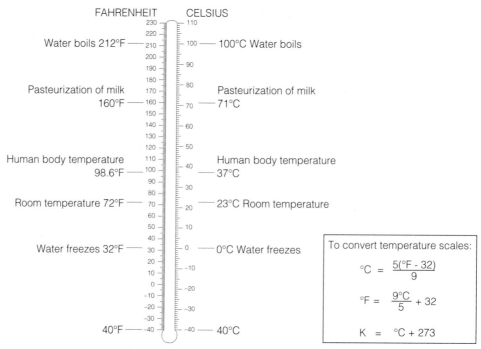

Fahrenheit and celsius scales compared

Appendix B
The Genetic Code: Codon Sheet

The genetic code. The three bases in an mRNA codon are designated as the first, second, and third, starting at the 5′ end. Each set of three specifies a particular amino acid, represented here by a three-letter abbreviation (see list below). The codon AUG (which specifies the amino acid methionine) is the usual start signal for protein synthesis. The word *stop* indicates the codons that serve as signals to terminate protein synthesis.

Abbreviation	Amino acid
Ala	alanine
Arg	arginine
Asn	asparagine
Asp	aspartic acid
Cys	cysteine
Glu	glutamic acid
Gln	glutamine
Gly	glycine
His	histidine
Ile	isoleucine
Leu	leucine
Lys	lysine
Met	methionine
Phe	phenylalanine
Pro	proline
Ser	serine
Thr	threonine
Try	tryptophan
Tyr	tyrosine
Val	valine

SECOND BASE

FIRST BASE	U	C	A	G	THIRD BASE
U	UUU UUC } Phe; UUA UUG } Leu	UCU UCC UCA UCG } Ser	UAU UAC } Tyr; UAA Stop; UAG Stop	UGU UGC } Cys; UGA Stop; UGG Trp	U C A G
C	CUU CUC CUA CUG } Leu	CCU CCC CCA CCG } Pro	CAU CAC } His; CAA CAG } Gln	CGU CGC CGA CGG } Arg	U C A G
A	AUU AUC } Ile; AUA; AUG Met or Start	ACU ACC ACA ACG } Thr	AAU AAC } Asn; AAA AAG } Lys	AGU AGC } Ser; AGA AGG } Arg	U C A G
G	GUU GUC GUA GUG } Val	GCU GCC GCA GCG } Ala	GAU GAC } Asp; GAA GAG } Glu	GGU GGC GGA GGG } Gly	U C A G

Appendix C
The Amino Acids

NONPOLAR

GLYCINE (Gly) ALANINE (Ala) VALINE (Val) LEUCINE (Leu) ISOLEUCINE (Ile)

METHIONINE (Met) PHENYLALANINE (Phe) TRYPTOPHAN (Trp) PROLINE (Pro)

POLAR

SERINE (Ser) THREONINE (Thr) CYSTEINE (Cys) TYROSINE (Tyr) ASPARAGINE (Asn) GLUTAMINE (Gln)

ELECTRICALLY CHARGED

ACIDIC

BASIC

ASPARTIC ACID (Asp) GLUTAMIC ACID (Glu) LYSINE (Lys) ARGININE (Arg) HISTIDINE (His)

Appendix D
Functional Groups in Organic Molecules

Functional Group	General Formula	Name of Compounds	Example	Where Else Found
Hydroxyl —OH (or HO—)	—O—H	Alcohols	Ethanol	Sugars; water-soluble vitamins
Carbonyl 〉CO	—C〈=O / H (aldehyde)	Aldehydes	Propanal	Some sugars; formaldehyde (a preservative)
	—C— with =O (ketone)	Ketones	Acetone	Some sugars; "ketone bodies" in urine (from fat breakdown)
Carboxyl —COOH	—C〈=O / OH	Carboxylic acids	Acetic acid	Amino acids; proteins; some vitamins; fatty acids
Amino —NH₂ (or H₂N —)	—N〈H / H	Amines	Methylamine	Amino acids; proteins; urea in urine (from protein breakdown)

Appendix E
Some Important Metabolic Pathways

Step 1 Two-carbon acetyl CoA is combined with oxaloacetic acid, a 4-carbon compound. The unstable bond between the acetyl group and CoA is broken as oxaloacetic acid binds and CoA is freed to prime another 2-carbon fragment derived from pyruvic acid. The product is the 6-carbon citric acid, for which the cycle is named.

Step 2 A molecule of water is removed, and another is added back. The net result is the conversion of citric acid to its isomer, isocitric acid.

Step 3 The substrate loses a CO_2 molecule, and the remaining 5-carbon compound is oxidized, forming α ketoglutaric acid and reducing NAD^+.

Step 4 This step is catalyzed by a multi-enzyme complex very similar to the one that converts pyruvic acid to acetyl CoA. CO_2 is lost; the remaining 4-carbon compound is oxidized by the transfer of electrons to NAD^+ to form NADH and is then attached to CoA by an unstable bond. The product is succinyl CoA.

Step 5 Substrate-level phosphorylation occurs in this step. CoA is displaced by a phosphate group, which is then transferred to GDP to form guanosine-triphosphate (GTP). GTP is similar to ATP, which is formed when GTP donates a phosphate group to ADP. The products of this step are succinic acid and ATP.

Step 6 In another oxidative step, two hydrogens are removed from succinic acid, forming fumaric acid, and transferred to FAD to form $FADH_2$. The function of this coenzyme is similar to that of NADH, but $FADH_2$ stores less energy. The enzyme that catalyzes this oxidation-reduction reaction is the only enzyme of the cycle that is embedded in the mitochondrial membrane. All other enzymes of the citric acid cycle are dissolved in the mitochondrial matrix.

Step 7 Bonds in the substrate are rearranged in this step by the addition of a water molecule. The product is malic acid.

Step 8 The last oxidative step reduces another NAD^+ and regenerates oxaloacetic acid, which accepts a 2-carbon fragment from acetyl CoA for another turn of the cycle.

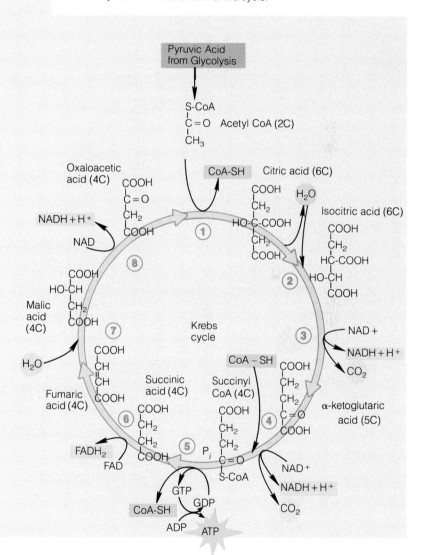

Events of the Krebs cycle.
Abbreviated version shown at top; detailed pathway shown at bottom. All but one of the steps (step 6) occur in the mitochondrial matrix. The preparation of pyruvic acid (by oxidation, decarboxylation, and reaction with coenzyme A) to enter the cycle as acetyl CoA is shown above the cycle. Acetyl CoA is picked up by oxaloacetic acid to form citric acid; and as it passes through the cycle, it is oxidized four more times (forming three molecules of reduced NAD [$NADH + H^+$] and one of reduced FAD [$FADH_2$]) and decarboxylated twice (releasing 2 CO_2). Energy is captured in the bonds of GTP, which then acts in a coupled reaction with ADP to benerate one molecule of ATP by substrate level phosphorylation.

Step 1 Glucose enters the cell and is phosphorylated by the enzyme hexokinase, which catalyzes the transfer of a phosphate group, indicated as P, from ATP to the number six carbon of the sugar producing glucose-6-phosphate. The electrical charge of the phosphate group traps the sugar in the cell because of the impermeability of the plasma membrane to ions. Phosphorylation of glucose also makes the molecule more chemically reactive. Although glycolysis is supposed to *produce* ATP, in step 1 ATP is actually consumed—an energy investment that will be repaid with dividends later in glycolysis.

Step 2 Glucose-6-phosphate is rearranged and converted to its isomer, fructose-6-phosphate. Isomers, remember, have the same number and types of atoms but in different structural arrangements.

Step 3 In this step, still another molecule of ATP is used to add a second phosphate group to the sugar, producing fructose 1,6-diphosphate. So far, the ATP ledger shows a debit of −2. With phosphate groups on its opposite ends, the sugar is now ready to be split in half.

Step 4 This is the reaction from which glycolysis gets its name. An enzyme cleaves the sugar molecule into two different 3-carbon sugars: glyceraldehyde 3-phosphate and dihydroxyacetone phosphate. These two sugars are isomers of one another.

Step 5 The isomerase enzyme interconverts the 3-carbon sugars, and if left alone in a test tube, the reaction reaches equilibrium. This does not happen in the cell, however, because the next enzyme in glycolysis uses only glyceraldehyde phosphate as its substrate and is unreceptive to dihydroxyacetone phosphate. This pulls the equilibrium between the two 3-carbon sugars in the direction of glyceraldehyde phosphate, which is removed as fast as it forms. Thus, the net result of steps 4 and 5 is cleavage of a 6-carbon sugar into two molecules of glyceraldehyde phosphate; each will progress through the remaining steps of glycolysis.

Step 6 An enzyme now catalyzes two sequential reactions while it holds glyceraldehyde phosphate in its active site. First, the sugar is oxidized by the transfer of H from the number one carbon of the sugar to NAD$^+$, forming NADH. Here we see in metabolic context the oxidation-reduction reaction described on page 820. This reaction releases substantial amounts of energy, and the enzyme capitalizes on this by coupling the reaction to the creation of a high-energy phosphate bond at the number one carbon of the oxidized substrate. The source of the phosphate is inorganic phosphate (P_i) always present in the cytosol. As products, the enzyme releases NADH and 1,3-diphosphoglyceric acid. Notice in the figure that the new phosphate bond is symbolized with a squiggle ($\sim$), which indicates that the bond is at least as energetic as the high-energy phosphate bonds of ATP.

The ten steps of glycolysis.
Each of the ten steps of glycolysis is catalyzed by a specific enzyme found dissolved in the cytoplasm. All steps are reversible. An abbreviated version of the three major phases of glycolysis appears in the lower right hand corner of the figure.

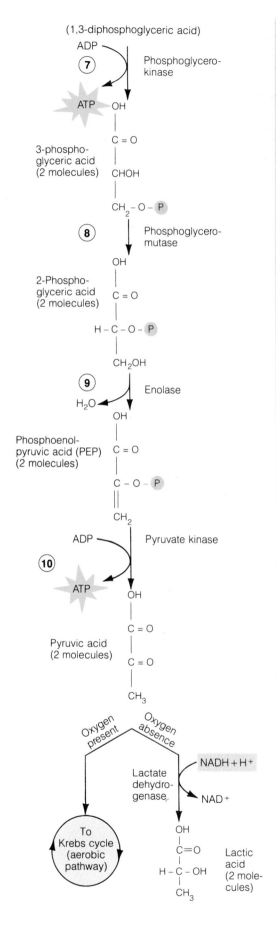

Step 7 Finally, glycolysis produces ATP. The phosphate group, with its high-energy bond, is transferred from 1,3-diphosphoglyceric acid to ADP. For each glucose molecule that began glycolysis, step 7 produces two molecules of ATP, because every product after the sugar-splitting step (step 4) is doubled. Of course, two ATPs were invested to get sugar ready for splitting. The ATP ledger now stands at zero. By the end of step 7, glucose has been converted to two molecules of 3-phosphoglyceric acid. This compound is not a sugar. The sugar was oxidized to an organic acid back in step 6, and now the energy made available by that oxidation has been used to make ATP.

Step 8 Next, an enzyme relocates the remaining phosphate group of 3-phosphoglyceric acid to form 2-phosphoglyceric acid. This prepares the substrate for the next reaction.

Step 9 An enzyme forms a double bond in the substrate by removing a water molecule from 2-phosphoglyceric acid to form phosphoenolpyruvic acid, or PEP. This results in the electrons of the substrate being rearranged in such a way that the remaining phosphate bond becomes very unstable; it has been upgraded to high-energy status.

Step 10 The last reaction of glycosis produces another molecule of ATP by transferring the phosphate group from PEP to ADP. Because this step occurs twice for each glucose molecule, the ATP ledger now shows a net gain of two ATPs. Steps 7 and 10 each produce two ATPs for a total credit of four, but a debt of two ATPs was incurred from steps 1 and 3. Glycolysis has repaid the ATP investment with 100% interest. In the meantime, glucose has been broken down and oxidized to two molecules of pyruvic acid, the compound produced from PEP in step 10.

Transamination and oxidative deamination of amino acids. (1) Transamination occurs when an amino acid transfers its amine group to α-ketoglutaric acid (one of the Krebs cycle intermediates). As α-ketoglutaric acid accepts the amine group, it becomes glutamic acid (a nonessential amino acid), which (2) easily unloads its amine group (as ammonia) to the urea cycle in the liver. (3) Although several steps are involved, urea is formed in the liver when ammonia is liberated from glutamic acid and combined with CO_2. Urea is excreted by the kidneys in urine. Deamination of glutamic acid regenerates α-ketoglutaric acid.

Appendix F
Periodic Table of the Elements

Legend:

1	Atomic number
H	Symbol
Hydrogen	Element
1.00794	Atomic weight

IA 1	IIA 2	IIIB 3	IVB 4	VB 5	VIB 6	VIIB 7	VIIIB 8	VIIIB 9	VIIIB 10	IB 11	IIB 12	IIIA 13	IVA 14	VA 15	VIA 16	VIIA 17	VIIIA 18
1 H Hydrogen 1.008																	2 He Helium 4.003
3 Li Lithium 6.941	4 Be Beryllium 9.012											5 B Boron 10.81	6 C Carbon 12.01	7 N Nitrogen 14.01	8 O Oxygen 16.00	9 F Fluorine 19.00	10 Ne Neon 20.18
11 Na Sodium 22.99	12 Mg Magnesium 24.31											13 Al Aluminum 26.98	14 Si Silicon 28.09	15 P Phosphorus 30.97	16 S Sulfur 32.06	17 Cl Chlorine 35.45	18 Ar Argon 39.95
19 K Potassium 39.10	20 Ca Calcium 40.08	21 Sc Scandium 44.96	22 Ti Titanium 47.88	23 V Vanadium 50.94	24 Cr Chromium 52.00	25 Mn Manganese 54.94	26 Fe Iron 55.85	27 Co Cobalt 58.93	28 Ni Nickel 58.70	29 Cu Copper 63.55	30 Zn Zinc 65.38	31 Ga Gallium 69.72	32 Ge Germanium 72.59	33 As Arsenic 74.92	34 Se Selenium 78.96	35 Br Bromine 79.90	36 Kr Krypton 83.80
37 Rb Rubidium 85.47	38 Sr Strontium 87.62	39 Y Yttrium 88.91	40 Zr Zirconium 91.22	41 Nb Niobium 92.91	42 Mo Molybdenum 95.94	43 Tc Technetium (98)	44 Ru Ruthenium 101.1	45 Rh Rhodium 102.9	46 Pd Palladium 106.4	47 Ag Silver 107.9	48 Cd Cadmium 112.4	49 In Indium 114.8	50 Sn Tin 118.7	51 Sb Antimony 121.8	52 Te Tellurium 127.6	53 I Iodine 126.9	54 Xe Xenon 131.3
55 Cs Cesium 132.9	56 Ba Barium 137.3	57 La* Lanthanum 138.9	72 Hf Hafnium 178.5	73 Ta Tantalum 180.9	74 W Tungsten 183.9	75 Re Rhenium 186.2	76 Os Osmium 190.2	77 Ir Iridium 192.2	78 Pt Platinum 195.1	79 Au Gold 197.0	80 Hg Mercury 200.6	81 Tl Thallium 204.4	82 Pb Lead 207.2	83 Bi Bismuth 209.0	84 Po Polonium (209)	85 At Astatine (210)	86 Rn Radon (222)
87 Fr Francium (223)	88 Ra Radium (226.0)	89 Ac** Actinium (227)	104 Rf Rutherfordium (261)	105 Ha Hahnium (262)	106 Unh Unnilhexium (263)	107 Uns Unnilseptium (262)	108 Uno Unniloctium (265)	109 Une Unnilennium (266)									

*Lanthanides

58 Ce Cerium 140.1	59 Pr Praseodymium 140.9	60 Nd Neodymium 144.2	61 Pm Promethium (145)	62 Sm Samarium 150.4	63 Eu Europium 152.0	64 Gd Gadolinium 157.3	65 Tb Terbium 158.9	66 Dy Dysprosium 162.5	67 Ho Holmium 164.9	68 Er Erbium 167.3	69 Tm Thulium 168.9	70 Yb Ytterbium 173.0	71 Lu Lutetium 175.0

**Actinides

90 Th Thorium 232.0	91 Pa Protactinium (231)	92 U Uranium 238.0	93 Np Neptunium (237)	94 Pu Plutonium (244)	95 Am Americium (243)	96 Cm Curium (247)	97 Bk Berkelium (247)	98 Cf Californium (251)	99 Es Einsteinium (252)	100 Fm Fermium (257)	101 Md Mendelevium (258)	102 No Nobelium (259)	103 Lr Lawrencium (260)

The periodic table arranges elements according to atomic number and atomic weight into horizontal rows called *periods* and eighteen vertical columns called *groups* or *families*. The elements in the groups are classified as being in either A or B classes.

Elements of each group of the A series have similar chemical and physical properties. This reflects the fact that members of a particular group have the same number of valence shell electrons, which is indicated by the number of the group. For example, group IA elements have one valence shell electron, group IIA elements have two, and group VA elements have five. In contrast, as you progress across a period from left to right, the properties of the elements change in discrete steps, varying gradually from the very metallic properties of groups IA and IIA elements to the nonmetallic properties seen in group VIIA (chlorine and others), and finally to the inert elements (noble gases) in group VIIIA. This change reflects the continual increase in the number of valence shell electrons seen in elements (from left to right) within a period.

Class B elements are referred to as *transition elements*. All transition elements are metals, and in most cases they have one or two valence shell electrons. (In these elements, some electrons occupy more distant electron shells before the deeper shells are filled.)

Element 110, discovered in November 1994, had not been named at time of press and is not included in this table. The 24 elements found in the human body are listed on p. 30 with their atomic symbols, names, and functions.

Appendix G
Reference Values for Selected Blood and Urine Studies

The reference values listed for the selected blood and urine studies are common ranges for adults, but specific "normals" are established by the laboratory performing the analysis. The values may be affected by a wide range of circumstances, including testing methods and equipment used, client age, body mass, sex, diet, activity level, medications, and extent of disease processes.

Reference values are identified in both standard or conventional units and in the system of international (SI) units.

SI units (given in parentheses) are measurements of amount per volume and are used in most countries and scientific journals. SI units are often given as moles or millimoles per liter. Most clinical laboratories and textbooks in the United States use conventional or standard units which measure mass per volume. These values are given as grams, milligrams, or milliequivalents per deciliter or liter. It is anticipated that the United States will eventually use SI units exclusively.

Blood Chemistry Studies		
Test (Sample)	Reference Values: Conventional (SI)	Physiologic Indication and Clinical Implications
Aspartate aminotransferase (ALT) or glutamic-oxaloacetic transaminase (SGOT) (S)	10–40 U/ml (5–30 U/L)	Cellular damage. Increased after myocardial infarction, acute liver disease, drug toxicity, muscle trauma. Decreased in ketoacidosis.
Ammonia (P)	15–120 µg/dL (12–65 µmol/L)	Liver and renal function. Increased values in liver disease, renal failure, newborn hemolytic disease, heart failure, cor pulmonale. Decreased values in hypertension.
Amylase (S)	56–190 IU/L (25–125 U/L)	Pancreatic function. Increased values in pancreatitis, mumps, obstruction of pancreatic duct, ketoacidosis. Decreased values in liver disease, perforated bowel, pulmonary infarct, toxemia of pregnancy.
Bilirubin (S)	Total: 0.1–1.0 mg/dl (5.1–17.0 µmol/L) Conjugated: <0.5 (<5.0 µmol/L) Unconjugated: 0.2–1.0 mg/dl (18–20 µmol/L) Newborn: 1.0–12.0 mg/dl (<200 µmol/L)	Liver function and red cell breakdown. Increased levels of conjugated in liver disease and biliary obstruction. Increased levels of unconjugated in hemolysis of red blood cells.
Blood urea nitrogen (S)	7–26 mg/dl (2.5–9.3 mmol/L)	Kidney function. Increased values in renal disease, dehydration, urinary obstruction, congestive heart failure, myocardial infarction, burns. Decreased values in liver failure, overhydration, impaired protein absorption, pregnancy.
Cholesterol	<200 mg/dl (<6.5 mmol/L)	Increased values in diabetes mellitus.
Creatine kinase (CK) (S)	Female: 30–135 U/L (10–55 U/ml) Male: 55–170 U/L (12–70 U/ml)	Cellular damage. Increased values in myocardial infarction, muscular dystrophy, hypothyroidism, pulmonary infarction, cerebral vascular accident (CVA), shock, tissue damage, and trauma.
Creatinine (S)	0.5–1.2 mg/dl (44–97 umol/L)	Renal function. Increased values in renal disease and acromegaly. Decreased in muscular dystrophy.

Test (Sample)	Reference Values: Conventional (SI)	Physiologic Indication and Clinical Implications
Gases (A)		Acid-base balance
Bicarbinate	22–26 mEq/L (22–26 mmol/L)	Increased values in metabolic alkalosis and respiratory acidosis. Decreased values in metabolic acidosis and respiratory alkalosis.
Carbon dioxide content	Arterial: 19–24 mEq/L (19–24 mmol/L) Venous: 22–30 mEq/L (22–30 mmol/L)	
Carbon dioxide partial pressure (P_{CO_2})	Arterial: 35–45 mm Hg (same) Venous: 45 mm Hg (same)	
Oxygen (O_2) saturation	95%–98% (same)	Increased values in polycythemia and decreased in pulmonary disease.
Oxygen partial pressure (P_{O_2})	80–105 mm Hg	Increased values in hyperventilation, polycythemia Decreased values in anemia, hypoxia.
pH	7.35–7.45 (same)	Increased values in metabolic and respiratory alkalosis. Decreased values in metabolic and respiratory acidosis.
Glucose (S)	Fasting: 70–120 mg/ml (3.9–6.1 mmol/L)	Metabolic function. Increased values in diabetes mellitus, Cushing's syndrome, liver disease, acute stress, and hyperpituitarism. Decreased levels in Addison's disease, insulinomas.
Immunoglobulins (S)		
IgG	560–1800 mg/dl (5.6–18 g/L)	Immune response. Increased levels in chronic infections, rheumatic fever, liver disease, rheumatoid arthritis. Decreased levels in amyloidosis, leukemia, and preeclampsia.
IgE	0.01–0.4 mg/dl (0.1–0.4 mg/L)	Allergic responses. Increased values in allergic responses. Decreased values in agammaglobulinemia.
IgA	85–563 mg/dl (0.85–5.6 g/L)	Immune integrity. Increased values in liver disease, rheumatic fever, cancer, autoimmune disorders. Decreased values in immunodeficiency disorders and inflammatory bowel disease.
IgM	55–375 mg/dl (0.5–3.8 g/L)	Immune integrity. Increased in autoimmune disease, rheumatoid arthritis, viral and fungal infections. Decreased in amyloidosis and leukemia.
IgD	0.5–3.0 mg/dl (5–30 mg/L)	Immune integrity. Increased values in myelomas and chronic infection.
Ketone bodies (S or P)	Negative Toxic level >20 mg/dl (0.2 g/L)	Fatty acid catabolism. Values increased in ketoacidosis, starvation, low-carbohydrate diet, dehydration, aspirin ingestion.
Lactic acid (lactate) (WB)	Arterial: 3–7 mg/dl (0.3–0.7 mmol/L) Venous: 5–20 mg/dl (0.5–2.0 mmol/L)	Anaerobic oxygenation of tissues. Increased values in congestive heart failure, shock, hemmorhage, strenuous exercise.
Lactate dehydrogenase (LDH) (S)	115–225 IU/L (0.4–1.7 µmol/L)	Tissue damage of organs or striated muscle. Increased in myocardial infarction, pulmonary infarction, liver disease, cerebral vascular accident, infectious mononucleosis, muscular dystrophy, fractures.
Lipoproteins (S)		
Total	400–800 mg/dl (4.0–8.0 g/L)	Metabolism—fat utilization. Increased values in diabetes mellitus, hypothyroidism, hyperlipidemia. Decreased values in hyperthyroidism and fat malabsorption.

(continued)

Test (Sample)	Reference Values: Conventional (SI)	Physiologic Indication and Clinical Implications
High-density lipoproteins (HDL)	25% of total Female: >55 mg/dl (>0.1 mmol/L) Male: >45 mg/dl (>0.1 mmol/L)	Increased levels in liver disease. Decreased levels in atherosclerotic heart disease, malnutrition.
Low-density lipoproteins (LDL)	75% of total 60–180 mg/dl (<3.2 mmol/L)	Increased values in hyperlipidemia, atherosclerotic heart disease. Decreased values in fat malabsorption and malnutrition.
Very low density lipoproteins (VLDL)	25%–50% of total (same)	Same
Osmolality (S)	285–295 mOsm/kg H_2O (285–295 mmol/kg H_2O)	Fluid and electrolyte balance. Increased levels in hypernatremia, dehydration, kidney disease, alcohol ingestion. Decreased levels in hyponatremia, overhydration, and syndrome of inappropriate ADH secretion (SIADH).
Phosphate (S) (phosphorus)	2.5–4.5 mg/dl (0.8–1.5 mmol/L)	Parathyroid function; bone disease. Increased levels in hypoparathyroidism, renal failure, bone metastasis, liver disease, hypocalcemia. Decreased values in hyperparathyroidism, hypercalcemia, alcoholism, vitamin D deficiency, ketoacidosis, osteomalacia.
Potassium (S)	3.5–5.1 mEq/L (3.5–5.1 mmol/L)	Fluid and electrolyte balance. Increased levels in renal disease, Addison's disease, ketoacidosis, burns and crush injuries. Decreased levels in vomiting, diarrhea, Cushing's syndrome, alkalosis.
Protein (S)		
Total	6.0–8.0 g/dl (60–80 g/L)	Osmotic pressure; immune system integrity. Increased values in chronic infections, dehydration, shock, hemoconcentration. Decreased values in protein malnutrition, burns, diarrhea, renal failure.
Albumin	3.2–5.0 g/dl (32–50 g/L)	Osmotic pressure. Increased levels in dehydration. Decreased levels in liver disease, malnutrition, Crohn's disease, nephrotic syndrome, systemic lupus erythematosus.
Sodium (S)	136–145 mEq/L (136–145 mmol/L)	Fluid and electrolyte balance. Increased values in dehydration, diabetes insipidus, Cushing's disease. Decreased values in vomiting, diarrhea, burns, Addison's disease, edema, congestive heart failure, overhydration, syndrome of inappropriate ADH secretion (SIADH).
Triglycerides	10–190 mg/dl (0.1–1.9 g/L)	Increased values in myocardial infarction, liver disease, nephrotic syndrome, pregnancy.
Uric acid (S)	Female: 2.0–7.3 mg/dl (0.09–0.36 nmol/L) Male: 2.1–8.5 mg/dl (0.15–0.48 nmol/L)	Renal function. Increased in lead poisoning, impaired renal function, gout, metastatic cancer, alcoholism, leukemia. Decreased in Wilson's disease.

Hematology Studies

Test (Sample)	Reference Values: Standard (SI)	Physiologic Indication and Clinical Implications
Hemoglobin (S)	Female: 12–16 g/dl (7.4–9.9 mmol/L) Male: 14–18 g/dl (8.7–11.2 mmol/L)	Oxygenation status. Increased values in dehydration, polycythemia, congestive heart failure, chronic obstructive pulmonary disease, high altitudes. Decreased levels in anemia, hemorrhage, cancer, renal disease, systemic lupus erythematosus, nutritional deficiency.

Test (Sample)	Reference Values: Standard (SI)	Physiologic Indication and Clinical Implications
Hematocrit (WB)	Female: 37%–47% (same) Male: 42%–54% (same)	Oxygenation status. Increased levels in polycythemia, dehydration, congestive heart failure, shock, surgery. Decreased levels in anemia, hemorrhage, bone marrow disease, malnutrition, cirrhosis, rheumatoid arthritis.
Partial thromboblastin time (activated) (PTT or APTT)	APTT: 30–40 sec (same) PTT: 60–70 sec (same)	Clotting mechanisms. Increased values in clotting factor deficiencies, cirrhosis, vitamin K deficiency, disseminated intravascular coagulation (DIC). Decreased values in early DIC, extensive cancer.
Platelet count (WB)	150,000–400,000/mm^3 (150–400 × 10^9/L)	Clotting mechanisms. Increased values in polycythemia, cancers, rheumatoid arthritis, cirrhosis, trauma. Decreased values in liver disease, hemolytic and pernicious anemia, disseminated intravascular coagulation (DIC), idiopathic thrombocytopenic purpura (ITP), systemic lupus erythematosus (SLE).
Prothrombin time (PT) (WB)	11–12.5 sec (same) 1.5–2 × control (evaluating anticoagulant treatment)	Clotting mechanisms. Increased values in liver disease, vitamin K deficiency, salicylate intoxication. Decreased values in disseminated intravascular coagulation (DIC), bile duct obstruction.
Red blood cell count (RBC) (WB)	Female: 4.2–5.4 million/mm^3 (4.2–5.4 × 10^{12}/L) Male: 4.7–6.1 million/mm^3 (4.7–6.1 × 10^{12}/L)	Oxygenation status. Increased values in high altitudes, polycythemia, hemoconcentration, cor pulmonale. Decreased values in hemorrhage, hemolysis, anemias, chronic illness, nutritional deficiencies, leukemia, overhydration.
Reticulocyte count	0.5%–2.0% (same) (WB)	Bone marrow function. Increased values in hemolytic anemia, sickle-cell anemia, leukemia, pregnancy. Decreased values in pernicious anemia, folic acid deficiency, cirrhosis, chronic infection, bone marrow depression or failure.
White blood cell count (WBC) (WB)		
Total	5,000–10,000/mm^3 (5–10 × 10^9/L)	Immune system integrity. Increased values in inflection, trauma, stress, tissue necrosis, inflammation. Decreased values in bone marrow depression or failure, drug toxicity, overwhelming infection, malnutrition.
White blood cell count, differential (WB)		
Neutrophils	55%–70% (same)	Immune system integrity. Increased values in stress, Cushing's syndrome, inflammatory disorders, ketoacidosis, gout. Decreased levels in aplastic anemia, bone marrow suppression, viral infections, severe bacterial infections, Addison's disease.
Lymphocytes	20%–40% (same)	Immune system integrity. Increased values in chronic bacterial infections, mumps, rubella, lymphocytic leukemia, infectious mononucleosis, infectious hepatitis. Decreased levels in leukemia, immunodeficiency, lupus erythemetosus, bone marrow depressive drugs.
Eosinophils	1%–4% (same)	Immune system integrity. Increased levels in allergic reactions, parasitic infections, leukemia, autoimmune diseases. Deceased levels in excess adrenosteroid production.
Monocytes	2%–8% (same)	Immune system integrity. Increased levels in inflammatory disorders, viral infections, tuberculosis. Decreased levels in steroid therapy.
Basophils	0.5%–1.0% (same)	Immune system integrity. Increased levels in myeloproliferative disorders, leukemia. Decreased levels in allergic reactions, hyperthyroidism, stress.

Urine Tests		
Test (Sample)	**Reference Values: Conventional (SI)**	**Physiologic Indication and Clinical Implications**
Amylase (24 hr)	3–35 IU/hr <5000 Somogyi units/24 hr (6.5–48 U/hr)	Pancreatic function. Increased values in pancreatic disease or obstruction, inflammation of the parotid or salivary glands, and cholecystitis.
Bilirubin (random)	Negative (same)	Liver function. Increased values in liver disease, extrahepatic obstruction (gallstones, tumor, inflammation).
Blood (random)	Negative (same)	Urinary system function. Increased values in cystitis, renal disease, hemolytic anemia, transfusion reaction, prostatitis, burns.
Osmolality (random or fasting)	50–1400 mOsm/kg H_2O (50–1400 mmol/kg H_2O) (random) <850 mOsm/kg H_2O (<850 mmol/kg H_2O) fluid restriction	Fluid and electrolyte balance, renal function, and endocrine function. Increased levels in hypernatremia, syndrome of inappropriate ADH secretion (SIADH), congestive heart failure (CHF), cirrhosis, acidosis. Decreased levels in diabetes insipidus, hypercalcemia, fluid intoxication, polynephritis, renal tubular necrosis, aldosteronism.
Phosphate (24 hr)	80%–90% reabsorbed (same)	Parathyroid function. Increased levels in hyperparathyroidism, uremia, osteomalacia, renal disease, autoimmune disease. Decreased levels in hypoparathyroidism.
Potassium (24 hr)	25–120 mEq/24 hr (25–120 mmol/24 hr)	Fluid and electrolyte balance. Increased values in renal disease, metabolic acidosis, dehydration, aldosteronism, Cushing's syndrome. Decreased values in Addison's disease, malabsorption, acute renal failure, syndrome of inappropriate ADH secretion (SIADH).
Protein (random)	<8 mg/dl (<0.8 mg/L)	Renal function. Increased levels in nephrotic syndrome, trauma, hyperthyroidism, diabetes mellitus, lupus erythematosus.
Sodium (24 hr)	40–220 mEq/24 hr (40–220 mmol/24 hr)	Fluid and electrolyte balance. Increased values in dehydration, ketoacidosis, syndrome of inappropriate ADH secretion (SIADH), adrenocortical insufficiency. Decreased levels in congestive heart failure (CHF), renal failure, diarrhea, aldosteronism.
Uric acid (24 hr)	0.4–1.0 g/24 hr (1.5–4.0 mmol/24 hr)	Renal function and metabolism. Increased in gout, leukemia, liver disease, ulcerative cholitis. Decreased in renal disease, alcoholism, lead toxicity.
Urinalysis (random)		
Color	Straw, yellow, amber	Fluid balance and renal function. Darker in dehydration. Lighter in overhydration, diabetes insipidus. Color varies with disease states, diet, and medications.
Odor	Aromatic	Metabolic function infection. Abnormal odors in infection, ketonuria, rectal fistula, hepatic failure, phenylketonuria.
Specific gravity	1.005–1.030	Kidney function. Increased levels in dehydration, syndrome of inappropriate ADH secretion (SIADH), fever, glycosuria, proteinuria, decreased renal blood flow (stenosis, heart failure). Decreased levels in renal disease.
Urobilinogen (24 hr)	<4 mg/24 hr	Liver function. Increased in hemolytic anemias, hepatitis A, cirrhosis, biliary disease. Decreased in renal disease, common bile duct obstruction.
Volume (24 hr)	1000–2000 ml/24 hr (1.0–2.0 L/24 hr)	Fluid and electrolyte balance, renal function. Increased values in diabetes insipidus, diabetes mellitus, renal disease. Decreased values in dehydration, syndrome of inappropriate ADH secretion (SIADH), renal disease.

Appendix H
Answers to Multiple Choice, Matching, and Key Figure Questions

Chapter 1
1. c; 2. a; 3. e; 4. a, d; 5. (a) wrist (b) hipbone (c) nose (d) toes (e) scalp; 6. neither c nor d would be visible in the median sagittal section; 7. (a) dorsal (b) ventral (c) dorsal (d) ventral; 8. b; 9. b; **Fig. 1.5** 1. The liver. 2. Declining blood sugar levels. 3. Rising blood glucose levels. **Fig. 1.6** This is a positive feedback mechanism because the response to the stimulus amplifies the stimulus. 2. The cascade ends when the break in the vessel is sealed by the clot. **Fig. 1.7** 1. Your armpit. 2. Your posterior skull region. 3. A finger.

Chapter 2
1. b, d; 2. d; 3. b; 4. a; 5. b; 6. a; 7. c, d; 8. b; 9. a; 10. a; 11. b; 12. a, c; 13. (1)a, (2)c; 14. c; 15. d; 16. e; 17. d; 18. d; 19. a; 20. b; 21. b; 22. c; **Fig. 2.8** In an XY covalent bond, one end of the molecule is slightly positive and one end is slightly negative. In an XX covalent bond the charge centers coincide. **Fig. 2.10** Reaction B, a decomposition reaction. **Fig. 2.18** Enzyme-substrate bonding.

Chapter 3
1. d; 2. a, c; 3. b; 4. d; 5. b; 6. e; 7. c; 8. d; 9. a; 10. a; 11. b; 12. d; 13. c; 14. b; 15. d; 16. a; 17. b; 18. d; **Fig. 3.1** Events occurring within membrane boundaries can take place unhampered by events occurring outside those membrane boundaries. **Fig. 3.2** Filaments of the cytoskeleton. **Fig. 3.11** Lungs, open to the external environment, collect dust and other airborne debris. In the lungs of smokers, carbon particles are added to this debris. **Fig. 3.12** 1. Both ions are being pumped against their concentration gradient. 2. Sodium ions are being pumped against their electrical gradient.

Chapter 4
1. a, c, d, b; 2. c, e; 3. b, f, a, d, g, d; 4. b; 5. c; 6. b **Fig. 4.5** The holocrine gland, because cells that are fragmented and secreted have to be replaced **Fig. 4.12** 1. Budding capillaries and soft connective tissue. 2. They bud from uninjured blood vessels in the area. 3. The epidermis would not be continuous. The injured region would be totally replaced by scar tissue.

Chapter 5
1. a; 2. c; 3. d; 4. d; 5. b; 6. b; 7. c; 8. c; 9. b; 10. b; 11. a; 12. d; 13. b; **Fig. 5.1** 1. The stratum basale or basal layer of the epidermis. 2. Adipose cells. **Fig. 5.2** The desmosomes connecting the keratinocytes are important to maintain continuity of the epidermis.

Chapter 6
1. e; 2. b; 3. c; 4. d; 5. e; 6. b; 7. c; 8. b; 9. e; 10. c; 11. b; 12. c; 13. a; 14. b; **Fig. 6.9** 1. Cartilage. 2. Because their avascular matrix is hardened by deposit of bone salts. **Fig. 6.10** Its shaft would be its original length and it would have two very elongated and enlarged ends. **Fig. 6.11** Calcium salts are deposited in bone and blood calcium levels fall.

Chapter 7
1. (1)b, g; (2)h; (3)d; (4)d, f; (5)e; (6)c; (7)a, b, d, h; (8)i; 2. (1)g, (2)f, (3)b, (4)a, (5)b, (6)c, (7)d, (8)e; 3. (1)b, (2)c, (3)e, (4)a, (5)h, (6)e, (7)f; **Fig. 7.1** Vertebra, rib, sternum. **Fig. 7.4** All other bones of the cranium articulate with the sphenoid bone. **Fig. 7.13** Because the lumbar region bears the greatest weight, its vertebrae are the sturdiest. **Fig. 7.23** You would look for the styloid process of the ulna which is on its medial aspect and for the two depressions on its lateral aspect, which receive the hand and the distal end of the radius.

Chapter 8
1. (1)c, (2)a, (3)a, (4)b, (5)c, (6)b, (7)b, (8)a, (9)c; 2. b; 3. d; 4. d; 5. b; 6. d; 7. d; **Fig. 8.3** Mobility.

Chapter 9
1. c; 2. b; 3. c; 4. (1)b, (2)a, (3)b, (4)a, (5)b, (6)a; 5. c; 6. a; 7. a; 8. d; 9. a; 10. (1)a; (2)a, c; (3)b; (4)c; (5)b; (6)b; 11. a; 12. c; 13. c; 14. c; 15. b; **Fig. 9.6** The H zone and the I zones. **Fig. 9.8** The sarcomeres would remain in their partially contracted state. **Fig 9.11** 1. Because calcium binding to troponin frees the actin active sites for myosin cross bridge binding. 2. The initial trigger is neurotransmitter release which generates the action potential along the sarcolemma.

Chapter 10
1. c; 2. (1)e, (2)c, (3)g, (4)f, (5)d; 3. a, c; 4. c; 5. d; 6. c; 7. c; 8. b; 9. d; 10. b; 11. a; 12. c; **Fig. 10.2** C. The third class lever. **Fig. 10.3** The sartorius and the biceps brachii could shorten most. The pectoralis major and the rectus femoris would be the most powerful because they are the most fleshy. **Fig. 10.5** The trapezius. The trapezius.

Chapter 11
1. b; 2. (1)d, (2)b, (3)f, (4)c, (5)a; 3. b; 4. c; 5. a; 6. c; 7. b; 8. d; 9. c; 10. c; 11. a; 12. (1)d, (2)b, (3)a, (4)c; **Fig. 11.3** The longer the neuron, the larger the cell body needed to service it. **Fig. 11.8** The negativity of the internal membrane surface. **Fig. 11.10** Those on the cell body that are closest to the axon hillock would have the greatest potential for producing a threshold stimulus. **Fig. 11.15** In a myelinated axon, voltage-gated sodium channels are located only at the nodes of Ranvier, as opposed to being located along the entire length of an unmyelinated axon. **Fig. 11.23** The term first messenger designates the original chemical messenger (the stimulus), which in this case is the neurotransmitter.

Chapter 12
1. a; 2. (1)c, (2)f, (3)e, (4)g, (5)b, (6)f, (7)i, (8)a; 3. d; 4. c; 5. a; 6. b; 7. c; 8. a; 9. (1)a, (2)b, (3)a, (4)a, (5)b, (6)a, (7)b, (8)b, (9)a; 10. d; **Fig. 12.4** Telencephalon, particularly the cerebral hemispheres. **Fig. 12.7** The growth of the cerebral hemisphere is restricted by the presence of the forming embryonic skull such that the cerebral hemispheres are forced to grow posteriorly and inferiorly. Hence their cavities (ventricles) become horn-shaped. **Fig. 12.10** Cental sulcus. **Fig. 12.11** Because the anatomical representations indicate the relative amount of the cerebral cortex dedicated to that particular body area. **Fig. 12.13** Because the fibers of the corona radiata running through them make them appear striped. **Fig. 12.23** Arachnoid villi.

Chapter 13

1. b; **2.** c; **3.** c; **4.** (1)f; (2)i; (3)b; (4)g, h, l; (5)e; (6)i; (7)c; (8)k; (9)l; (10)c, d, f, k; **5.** (1)b 6; (2)d 1, 8; (3)c 2; (4)c 5; (5)a 4; (6)a 3, 9; (7)a 7; (8)a 7; (9)d 1; **6.** b, 1; a, 3 and 5; a, 4; a, 2; c, 2; **7.** b; **Fig. 13.3** They act as phagocytes and reform the channel that guides axonal growth. **Fig. 13.5** The peripheral nerves serving the limbs arise in the lumbar and cervical regions. **Fig. 13.12** The fiber of the motor neuron.

Chapter 14

1. d; **2.** (1)S, (2)P, (3)P, (4)S, (5)S, (6)P, (7)P, (8)S, (9)P, (10)S, (11)P, (12)S; **Fig. 14.2** The axon of the preganglionic neuron spans the distance between the CNS and the autonomic ganglion, whereas the postganglionic neuron's axon lies distal to the ganglion.

Chapter 15

1. c; **2.** d; **3.** c; **4.** e; **5.** b; **6.** (1)d, (2)e, (3)d, (4)a; **Fig. 15.2** The smaller the two-point threshold, the more receptors there are in a given area, and the more sensitive the area. **Fig. 15.3** The middle level.

Chapter 16

1. d; **2.** a; **3.** d; **4.** c; **5.** d; **6.** b; **7.** c; **8.** d; **9.** a; **10.** b; **11.** c; **12.** d; **13.** b; **14.** a; **15.** b; **16.** b; **17.** b; **18.** d; **19.** b; **20.** c; **21.** d; **22.** b; **23.** b; **24.** e; **25.** b; **26.** c; **Fig. 16.2** Bitter. **Fig. 16.3** It serves as a dissolving medium for odor molecules. **Fig. 16.9** Ganglion. **Fig. 16.18** By having it in the discs you have increased surface area. **Fig. 16.21** The whole process will come to a halt because excitation depends on having the proper ionic concentrations on the two sides of the membrane. **Fig. 16.25** The tympanic membrane. The round membrane.

Chapter 17

1. b; **2.** (1)c, (2)b, (3)f, (4)d, (5)e, (6)g, (7)a, (8)h, (9)b and e, (10)a; **3.** a; **4.** c; **5.** d; **6.** d; **7.** c; **8.** b; **9.** d; **10.** b; **11.** d; **12.** b; **13.** c; **14.** d; **Fig. 17.1** See Table 17.4. **Fig. 17.2** Phototransduction in the eye. **Fig. 17.3** In the one illustrated here, the hormone (first messenger) enters the cell nucleus and directly stimulates the desired effect by acting on DNA. In Fig. 17.2, the hormone interacts with a plasma membrane receptor and its effects are mediated by an intracellular second messenger. **Fig. 17.12** In the zona glomerulosa the cells are in clusters. In the zona fasciculata the cells are in parallel cords. In the zona reticularis the cells have a netlike arrangement. **Fig. 17.13** The renin-angiotensin mechanism.

Chapter 18

1. c; **2.** c; **3.** b; **4.** b; **5.** d; **6.** a; **7.** a; **8.** b; **9.** c; **10.** d; **Fig. 18.6** Blood doping, which increases the number of red blood cells in the blood stream and thus increases the amount of oxygen being transported, would inhibit erythropoietin release. **Fig. 18.7** It would increase in the blood because liver bilirubin processing functions are impaired.

Chapter 19

1. a; **2.** c; **3.** b; **4.** c; **5.** b; **6.** b; **7.** c; **8.** d; **9.** b; **Fig. 19.1** The medial cavity of the thorax within the heart, great vessels, and trachea are found. **Fig. 19.4** Left ventricle. It's the systemic pump that has to pump blood through the entire systemic circulation against high resistance. **Fig. 19.9** Both valves operate in response to blood attempting to flow backwards. In the AV valves, rising ventricular pressure forces the valve flaps upward into the closed position, a condition maintained by the chordae tendonae. In the semilunar valves, blood flowing back toward the heart from the large vessels fills the valve cusps, closing the valves. No device is used to hold the valve in the closed position. **Fig. 19.14** Calcium entry.

Chapter 20

1. d; **2.** b; **3.** d; **4.** c; **5.** e; **6.** d; **7.** c; **8.** b; **9.** b; **10.** a; **11.** b; **12.** c; **Fig. 20.1** It forms an exceedingly thin diffusion membrane for the exchange of substances between the blood and the interstitial fluid. **Fig. 20.7** Arterial blood pressure initially drops, resulting in stimulation of the vasomotor and cardioacceleratory centers. The result is increased heart rate and vasoconstriction, which increases arterial blood pressure, restoring homeostasis.

Chapter 21

1. c; **2.** c; **3.** a, d; **4.** c; **5.** a; **6.** b; **7.** a; **8.** b; **9.** d; **Fig. 21.1** The arteries. It's not a problem because lymphatic fluid is formed by the blood capillary beds and is only moved in one direction, toward the heart. **Fig. 21.5** It causes lymphatic fluid to back up or accumulate somewhat in lymph nodes, allowing more time for its cleansing. **Fig. 21.6** The red pulp is the blood processing region; the white pulp has immune functions.

Chapter 22

1. c; **2.** a; **3.** d; **4.** d, e; **5.** a; **6.** d; **7.** b; **8.** c; **9.** d; **Fig. 22.2** This allows more filtrate containing oxygen, nutrients, blood-clotting proteins, and antibodies to enter the inflamed area where these substances are needed for defensive and repair processes. **Fig. 22.6** It allows them to come into contact with a broader spectrum of antigens and other body cells. **Fig. 22.13** Neutralization ties up the binding sites on the antigenic substance or pathogen so it can't bind body cells. Agglutination forms large clumps of the antigen which then precipitate and can't go anywhere, making it fair game for the phagocytes.

Chapter 23

1. b; **2.** a; **3.** c; **4.** c; **5.** b; **6.** d; **7.** d; **8.** b; **9.** c, d; **10.** c; **11.** b; **12.** b; **13.** b; **14.** c; **15.** b; **16.** b; **Fig. 23.1** The lungs. **Fig. 23.3** Because with increased turbulence, more debris (dust, bacteria) will be hurled into contact with the sticky mucous and prevented from going further. **Fig. 23.4** The epiglottis. **Fig. 23.13** They both decrease. **Fig. 23.18** They would be dilated. This response allows matching of blood flow to availability of oxygen. **Fig. 23.20** The same direction.

Chapter 24

1. d; **2.** d; **3.** b; **4.** b; **5.** a; **6.** d; **7.** d; **8.** b; **9.** c; **10.** c; **11.** a; **12.** d; **13.** d; **14.** b; **15.** c; **16.** a; **Fig. 24.1** The tongue, salivary gland, liver, gall bladder, pancreas. **Fig. 24.12** The presence of the stratified squamous epithelium indicates the esophagus is mainly a chute and thus must accommodate high friction, whereas the stomach has a secretory simple columnar epithelium, reflecting its role in chemical digestion. **Fig. 24.14** It has a third layer of smooth muscle in its muscularis in which the fibers run obliquely, allowing it to exhibit churning movements that physically digest the food. **Fig. 24.16** It would decrease it. **Fig. 24.28** They are activated in the small intestine where they work and where the cells exposed to them are protected by mucous. No such protection exists in the pancreas.

Chapter 25

1. a; **2.** c; **3.** c; **4.** d; **5.** b; **6.** c; **7.** a; **8.** d; **9.** d; **10.** a; **11.** b; **12.** d; **13.** c; **14.** d; **15.** a; **Fig. 25.2** Yes. He has both grain and beans, which together contain all the essential amino acids. **Fig. 25.6** 1. If oxygen was unavailable, the reduced coenzymes ($NADH + H^+$) would transfer their picked up H^+ to pyruvic acid to form lactic acid. 2. Glycolysis would come to a halt because the oxidase enzyme cannot hold onto the H^+ removed during substrate oxidation. If all the coenzymes are already reduced and can't release hydrogen, the oxidase enzyme couldn't continue to function. **Fig. 25.7** Decarboxylation, shown as removal of CO_2, and oxidation, shown as the reduction of the coenzymes, e.g., $NAD^+ \rightarrow NADH + H^+$. **Fig. 25.8** In substate level phosphorylation, a phosphate group is transferred directly from the substate to ADP, forming ATP. In oxidative phosphorylation, the substrates are oxidized by the removal of hydrogen, which is eventually transferred to molecular oxygen. The removed hydrogens contain the energy that is eventually used to generate the proton gradient, which provides the energy source for attaching phosphate to ADP, making ATP. **Fig. 25.12** Acetyl CoA. **Fig. 25.19** Insulin.

Chapter 26

1. d; **2.** b; **3.** c; **4.** d; **5.** c; **6.** b; **7.** a; **8.** c; **9.** a; **Fig. 26.4** It would go from the glomerular blood through the filtration membrane into Bowman's capsule, then through the renal tubule (PCT → Loop of Henle → DCT), then into the collecting duct which carries the urine through the cortex and medulla, and into the minor calyx, into the major calyx, and into the pelvis. **Fig. 26.7** The proximal convoluted tubule. The glomerulus. **Fig. 26.9** With liver disease you probably wouldn't have a normal supply of plasma proteins. Hence, more filtrate would be formed due to a lower osmotic pressure in the blood. **Fig. 26.12** The countercurrent multiplier is the loop of Henle. The countercurrent exchanger is the vasa recta.

Chapter 27

1. a; **2.** c; **3.** b; **4.** b; **5.** f, h, i; **6.** c, g; **7.** e, h; **8.** b; **9.** a; **10.** j; **11.** b, d, f; **12.** a; **13.** c; **Fig. 27.2** Na. K. Protein anions and $SO_4 2^-$. **Fig. 27.6** It would increase thirst because body fluids would become more concentrated. **Fig. 27.9** At increased water absorption. **Fig. 27.11** A weak base, because the weak base would act as a buffer.

Chapter 28

1. a and b; **2.** d; **3.** a; **4.** d; **5.** b; **6.** d; **7.** d; **8.** c; **9.** a, c, e, f; **10.** (1)c, f; (2)e, h; (3)g; (4)a; (5)b, g (and perhaps e); (6)f; **11.** a; **12.** c; **13.** d; **14.** b; **15.** a; **16.** b; **17.** c; **Fig. 28.6** 1. To reestablish the normal diploid number of the species when sperm and egg fuse. 2. Random alignment of tetrads at metaphase I and crossover. **Fig. 28.7** Spermatids. **Fig. 28.20** 1–5 contain primary oocytes; 6 contains secondary oocytes.

Chapter 29

1. (1)a, (2)b, (3)b, (4)a; **2.** b; **3.** c; **4.** b; **5.** a; **6.** d; **7.** d; **8.** c; **9.** a; **10.** b; **11.** c; **12.** a; **13.** c; **14.** a; **15.** (1)e, (2)g, (3)a, (4)f, (5)i, (6)b, (7)h, (8)d, (9)c; **Fig. 29.4** Because virtually no growth occurs between the successive divisions of cleavage. **Fig. 29.9** The ectoderm. **Fig. 29.15** As the pregnancy continues, the uterus pushes higher in the abdomen, eventually pressing on the diaphragm, inhibiting its downward movement.

Chapter 30

1. (1)d, (2)g, (3)b, (4)a, (5)f, (6)c, (7)e, (8)h; **2.** (1)e, (2)a, (3)b, (4)d, (5)c, (6)d; **Fig. 30.2** Crossover and exchange of chromosomal parts. **Fig. 30.3** You would get a different selection of linked genes in the resulting gametes.

Credits

Photograph Credits

Table 7.3; Figures 7.5.3, 7.6 a.2, 7.6 b.2, 7.7.3, 8.10 b, 8.12 c, 10.09 c, 10.10 c, 10.13 b.01, 12.1, 12.05 b, 12.18 a, 12.24 b, 12.24 c, 12.24 d, 14.04 b, 16.4, 16.7 b, 23.3 b, 23.4 c, 23.4 d, 23.10 b, 24.14 b, 24.20 b, 24.21 a, 24.24 a, 24.24 b, 24.30 b, 26.03 a, 28.03 c, 28.14, 29.7 e: from *A Stereoscopic Atlas of Human Anatomy* by David L. Bassett, M.D.

Chapter Openers
Frontispiece: ©Sidney Moulds/SPL/Photo Researchers, Inc. Chs. 1–4: ©CNRI/SPL/Photo Researchers, Inc. Chs. 11–17: ©Don Fawcett/Science Source/Photo Researchers, Inc. Chs. 18–27: ©Keith R. Porter/Photo Researchers, Inc. Chs. 28–30: ©Sidney Moulds/ SPL/Photo Researchers, Inc. Chs. 5–10: ©Prof. P. Motta/ Dept. of Anatomy, Univ. La Sapienza, Rome/SPL/Photo Researchers, Inc.

Chapter 1
"A Closer Look": ©Howard Sochurek. 1.8 a.2: ©Science Source/Photo Researchers, Inc. 1.8 b.2: ©Howard Sochurek. 1.8 c.2: ©Petit Format/Photo Researchers, Inc.

Chapter 2
2.21 c: Robert Langridge, Computer Graphics Laboratory, University of California, San Francisco.

Chapter 3
3.4 a: ©L. Orci and A. Perrelet, Freeze-Etch Histology. Heidelberg: Springer Verlag, 1975. 3.4 b: ©Douglas J. Kelly, *J. Cell Biol.* 28(196):51 by copyright permission of Rockefeller University Press. 3.4 c: ©C. Peracchia and A.F. Dulhunty, *J. Cell Biol.* 70(1976): 419 by copyright permission of Rockefeller University Press. 3.8 a: ©K.R.

Porter/Photo Researchers, Inc. 3.8 b: ©David M. Phillips/The Population Council/Science Source/Photo Researchers, Inc. 3.8 c: Courtesy of Dr. Mohandes Narlas/ Lawrence Livermore Laboratory. 3.14 b: Courtesy of N. Simionescu. 3.15 b: Dr. Barry F. King, Univ. of California, Davis, School of Medicine/Biological Photo Service. 3.16 b: G.T. Cole, Univ. of Texas-Austin/ Biological Photo Service. 3.18.2: R. Rodewald, Univ. of Virginia/Biological Photo Service. 3.20.1: Dr. John Heuser, Washington University Medical School. 3.21 b: W.L. Dentler, University of Kansas/ Biological Photo Service. 3.23 b: ©D.W. Fawcett/Photo Researchers, Inc. 3.24 a: D.E. Olins and A.L. Olins, *American Scientist* 66(1978): 704. Reprinted by permission of publisher. 3.28.1, 3.28.3, 3.28.5, 3.28.7, 3.28.9, 3.28.11: ©Ed Reschke.

Chapter 4
"A Closer Look": ©Allsport USA/Agence Vandystadt/ Laurent Zabulon, 1993. 4.2 a.3: Marian Rice. 4.2 b.3: ©Ed Reschke/Peter Arnold, Inc. 4.2 c.3: Marian Rice. 4.2 d.3, 4.2 e.3: ©Ed Reschke. 4.2 f.3: ©Bruce Iverson. 4.2 g.3: ©John D. Cunningham/Visuals Unlimited. 4.2 h.3: ©Ed Reschke. 4.3 a: ©Biophoto Associates/Photo Researchers, Inc. 4.8 a.2: ©Ed Reschke. 4.8 b.2: Marian Rice. 4.8 c.2, 4.8 D.2, 4.8 E.2, 4.8 F.2, 4.8 G.2, 4.8 H.2: ©Ed Reschke. 4.8 i.2: ©Biology Media/Photo Researchers, Inc. 4.8 j.2, 4.8 K.2: ©Ed Reschke. 4.10 a.2: ©Eric Grave/Photo Researchers, Inc. 4.10 b.2: ©Ed Reschke. 4.10 c.2: Department of Anatomy and Histology, University of California, San Francisco. 4.11.3: ©Ed Reschke.

Chapter 5
"A Closer Look": ©Scala/Art Resource, New York. 5.4: ©Science Photo Library/Photo Researchers, Inc. 5.5 e: Marian Rice. 5.9 a, 5.9 b: Courtesy of The Skin Cancer Foundation, New York, NY.

Chapter 6
6.5 b, 6.9.2: ©Ed Reschke. 6.14: Carolina Biological Supply.

Chapter 7
7.24 b: Department of Anatomy and Histology, University of California, San Francisco. 7.26 a, 7.26 b: William Thompson. 7.27 a.1, 7.27 a.2: BioMed Arts Associates, Inc.

Chapter 8
"A Closer Look": Courtesy of Rose Weibel. 8.3 b: ©Science Photo Library/Photo Researchers, Inc. 8.5: ©Duomo/Rick Rickman. 8.9 c: Courtesy of University of Kansas Medical Center; photo by Stephen Spector. 8.11 c: University of Kansas Medical Center, photo by Stephen Spector. 8.15: ©SIU/Peter Arnold, Inc.

Chapter 9
9.1 b: Marian Rice. 9.2 b: ©Ed Reschke. 9.6.1 a, 9.6.2 a, 9.6.3 a: Courtesy Dr. H.E. Huxley, Rosensteil Center, Brandeis University, Waltham, MA. 9.12 b: ©Eric Grave/Photo Researchers, Inc.

Chapter 10
10.4 a, 10.5 a: BioMed Arts Associates, Inc. 10.16 c: Courtesy of University of Kansas Medical Center; photo by Stephen Spector.

Chapter 11
"A Closer Look": ©Ormond Gigli/Photo Researchers, Inc. 11.3 a: ©Manfred Kage/Peter Arnold, Inc. 11.4 g: Courtesy of G.L. Scott, J.A. Feilbach, T.A. Duff. 11.17: Dr. E.R. Lewis, Y.Y. Zeevi, and T.E. Everhart.

Chapter 12
12.9.3: Lester V. Bergman and Associates. 12.18 c: ©Biophoto Associates, Science Source/ Photo Researchers, Inc.

Chapter 13
Table 13.2: William Thompson.

Chapter 15
15.4 a: ©Alexander Tsiaras/ Photo Researchers, Inc.

Chapter 16
16.8: Courtesy of Dr. Jerry Kuszak, Ph.D. 16.11: ©SIU/Photo Researchers, Inc. 16.14: ©Gregory K. Scott/ Photo Researchers, Inc. 16.22 b: Courtesy of University of Kansas Medical Center; photo by Stephen Spector. 16.35 c: Dr. I.M. Hunter-Duvar, Department of Otolaryngology, The Hospital for Sick Children, Toronto.

Chapter 17
"A Closer Look": ©Mike Neveux. 17.5 b: ©Biophoto Associates, Science Source/ Photo Researchers, Inc. 17.7: *American Journal of Medicine,* 20:133, 1956, with permission of Albert I. Mendeloff, M.D. 17.8 b: ©Ed Reschke. 17.10 b: From *Color Atlas of Histology,* by Leslie Gartner and James Hiatt. Williams and Wilkins ©1990. 17.12 b, 17.15 b: ©Ed Reschke.

Chapter 18
"A Closer Look": Courtesy of Tony Hunt/UCSF. 18.2 a, 18.2 b, 18.2 c, 18.2 d, 18.2 e, 18.2 f: Victor Eroschenko, University of Idaho. 18.12: ©Lennart Nilsson/Boehringer Ingelheim International GmbH. 18.13: Courtesy of Jack Scanlon, Holyoke Community College.

Chapter 19
"A Closer Look": Lennart Nilsson, *The Body Victorious.* ©Boehringer Ingelheim International GmbH. 19.4 b:

Courtesy of University of Kansas Medical Center; photo by Stephen Spector. 19.7 b, 19.7 c: ©Lennart Nilsson/ *Behold Man.* 19.11 a: ©Ed Reschke.

Chapter 20
"A Closer Look": ©Boehringer Ingelheim International GmbH. Photo: Lennart Nilsson. 20.18 c: ©Science Photo Library/Photo Researchers, Inc.

Chapter 21
21.3: ©Francis Leroy, Biocosmos, Science Photo Library, Science Source/Photo Researchers, Inc. 21.5 b, 21.6 c: ©Biophoto Associates, Science Source/Photo Researchers, Inc. 21.7, 21.8: ©John Cunningham/Visuals Unlimited. 21.9: ©Biophoto Associates/Science Source/ Photo Researchers, Inc.

Chapter 22
"A Closer Look": National Institute for Biological Standards and Control, United Kingdom. 22.1: Lennart Nilsson/Boehringer Ingelheim International GmbH. 22.11 c: ©Arthur J. Olson, The Scripps Research Institute. 22.16 b: ©Lennart Nilsson, Boehringer Ingelheim International GmbH.

Chapter 23
"A Closer Look": ©1985 Al Grotell. 23.1 b: Benjamin/ Cummings. 23.5 b: University of San Francisco. 23.6, 23.07 b: ©Science Photo Library/ Photo Researchers, Inc. 23.8 b: Kenneth Siegesmund.

Chapter 24
"A Closer Look": ©Hartley Photography. 24.8.3: R.G. Kessel and C.Y. Shih, *Scanning Electron Microscopy in Biology,* p. 277 (Springer-Verlag, 1974). 24.9 b: ©Science Photo Library/Photo Researchers, Inc. 24.12 a: ©Biophoto Associates/Photo Researchers, Inc. 24.12 b: From *Color Atlas of Histology,* by Leslie P. Gartner and James L. Hiatt. ©1990 Williams & Wilkins. 24.22 d: ©Manfred Kage/Peter Arnold, Inc. 24.25 b: ©M. Walker/Photo Researchers, Inc. 24.27 b: Tufts Medical School,

Department of Anatomy. 24.31 a: ©Ed Reschke/Peter Arnold, Inc.

Chapter 25
"A Closer Look": ©1994 Tom Raymond/TS Images. 25.22: ©William Thompson. 25.24: ©Mike Powell/AllSport.

Chapter 26
26.4 c: ©Biophoto Associates, Science Source/Photo Researchers, Inc. 26.8 B: ©David Phillips/Visuals Unlimited. 26.14: ©Biophoto Associates/Science Source/ Photo Researchers, Inc.

Chapter 27
"A Closer Look": ©David York/Medichrome.

Chapter 28
28.3 b: ©Ed Reschke. 28.8 B: ©Manfred Kage/Peter Arnold, Inc. 28.13 B: ©Ed Reschke. 28.15 A: ©Dr. Michael Ross. 28.18: ©1994 Richard D'Amico, M.D./Custom Medical Stock.

Chapter 29
"A Closer Look": Courtesy IVF Clinic, Stanford Medical Center 29.2 b: ©Lennart Nilsson/*A Child is Born.* 29.3 h: Courtesy of Dr. C.A. Ziomek, Worcester Fund for Experimental Biology, Shrewsbury, MA. 29.5 b: Courtesy of Dr. E.S.E. Hafez, Wayne State University, Detroit, MI. 29.5 d: Photographed for the Carnegie Collection by Dr. Allen C. Enders, University of California, Davis. 29.14 a, 29.14 b: Lennart Nilsson, *A Child is Born,* Dell Publishing Co. 29.18 a: ©Michael Alexander. 29.18 b, 29.18 c: ©Hal Stoezle.

Chapter 30
30.1 B: ©SIU/Visuals Unlimited. 30.1 C: ©Dept. of Clinical Cytogenetics, Addem-Brookes Hospital, Cambridge/ Science Photo Library/Photo Researchers, Inc. 30.06: ©John Balik. 30.08: Courtesy of Nancy Wexler, Columbia University.

Illustration Credits

Chapter 1
Figures 1.3, 1.5: adapted from Neil A. Campbell, *Biology,* 3rd ed. (Redwood City, CA: Benjamin/Cummings, 1993). ©1993, by The Benjamin/ Cummings Publishing Company.

Chapter 2
Figures 2.9, 2.11: adapted from Neil A. Campbell, *Biology,* 3rd ed. (Redwood City, CA: Benjamin/ Cummings, 1993). ©1993, by The Benjamin/ Cummings Publishing Company. Figures 2.12, 2.21.a, b: adapted from Neil A. Campbell, Lawrence G. Mitchell, Jane B. Reece, *Biology: Concepts and Connection* (Redwood City, CA: Benjamin/Cummings, 1994). ©1994, by The Benjamin/Cummings Publishing Company.

Chapter 3
A Closer Look 3, figures 3.2.2, 3.10, 3.11 a–c , 3.16 a, 3.16.1, 3.20.2–4, 3.22 a, 3.26, 3.29: adapted from Neil A. Campbell, *Biology,* 3rd ed. (Redwood City, CA: Benjamin/Cummings, 1993). ©1993, by The Benjamin/Cummings Publishing Company. Figures 3.3.1–5: from Neil A. Campbell, *Biology,* 3rd ed. (Redwood City, CA: Benjamin/ Cummings, 1993). ©1993, by The Benjamin/Cummings Publishing Company. Figures 3.15 a, 3.28.2–12: adapted from Neil A. Campbell, Lawrence G. Mitchell, Jane B. Reece, *Biology: Concepts and Connections* (Redwood City, CA: Benjamin/Cummings, 1994). ©1994, by The Benjamin/Cummings Publishing Company.

Chapter 6
Figure 6.12: Elizabeth Morales-Denney, from Elaine N. Marieb and Jon Mallatt, *Human Anatomy* (Redwood City, CA: Benjamin/ Cummings, 1992). ©1992, by The Benjamin/Cummings Publishing Company.

Chapter 7
Figures 7.1 a, b, 7.18 a, b, 7.18.1: Laurie O'Keefe, from Elaine N. Marieb and Jon Mallatt, *Human Anatomy* (Redwood City, CA: Benjamin/Cummings, 1992). ©1992, by The Benjamin/ Cummings Publishing Company. Figure 7.32.a: adapted from Neil A. Campbell, *Biology,* 3rd ed. (Redwood City, CA: Benjamin/Cummings, 1993). ©1993, by The Benjamin/ Cummings Publishing Company. Figure 7.32.b: from Neil A. Campbell, *Biology,* 3rd ed. (Redwood City, CA: Benjamin/Cummings, 1993). ©1993, by The Benjamin/ Cummings Publishing Company.

Chapter 8
Figure 8.14: Barbara Cousins, from Elaine N. Marieb and Jon Mallatt, *Human Anatomy* (Redwood City, CA: Benjamin/Cummings, 1992). ©1992, by The Benjamin/ Cummings Publishing Company.

Chapter 11
Figures 11.6, 11.20 a, b, c, d: from Neil A. Campbell, *Biology,* 3rd ed. (Redwood City, Benjamin/Cummings, 1993). ©1993, by The Benjamin/Cummings Publishing Company.

Chapter 12
Figures 12.6, 12.27: Raychel Ciemma, from Elaine N. Marieb and Jon Mallatt, *Human Anatomy* (Redwood City, CA: Benjamin/ Cummings, 1992). ©1992, by The Benjamin/Cummings Publishing Company. Figure 12.24 a: Stephanie McCann, from Elaine N. Marieb and Jon Mallatt, *Human Anatomy* (Redwood City, CA: Benjamin/Cummings, 1992). ©1992, by The Benjamin/ Cummings Publishing Company. Figure 12.25: adapted from Elaine N. Marieb and Jon Mallatt, *Human Anatomy* (Redwood City, CA: Benjamin/Cummings, 1992). ©1992, by The Benjamin/ Cummings Publishing Company.

Chapter 13

Figure 13.8c: Stephanie McCann, from Elaine N. Marieb and Jon Mallatt, *Human Anatomy* (Redwood City, CA: Benjamin/Cummings, 1992). ©1992, by The Benjamin/Cummings Publishing Company.

Chapter 16

Figures 16.25.1, 16.25.2: adapted from Neil A. Campbell, *Biology,* 3rd ed. (Redwood City, CA: Benjamin/Cummings, 1993). ©1993, by The Benjamin/Cummings Publishing Company. Figure 16.26: Cindie Wooley, from Elaine N. Marieb and Jon Mallatt, *Human Anatomy* (Redwood City, CA: Benjamin/Cummings, 1992). ©1992, by The Benjamin/Cummings Publishing Company.

Chapter 17

Figures 17.4 a, c: Elizabeth Morales-Denney, from Elaine N. Marieb and Jon Mallatt, *Human Anatomy* (Redwood City, CA: Benjamin/Cummings, 1992). ©1992, by The Benjamin/Cummings Publishing Company. Figure

17.4 b: Charles W. Hoffman and Elizabeth Morales-Denney, from Elaine N. Marieb and Jon Mallatt, *Human Anatomy* (Redwood City, CA: Benjamin/Cummings, 1992). ©1992, by The Benjamin/Cummings Publishing Company.

Chapter 19

Figures 19.22 a, b, c, d, e, 19.22.1, 19.23 a, b, c, A Closer Look 1: Barbara Cousins, from Elaine N. Marieb and Jon Mallatt, *Human Anatomy* (Redwood City, CA: Benjamin/Cummings, 1992). ©1992, by The Benjamin/Cummings Publishing Company.

Chapter 20

Figure 20.13: adapted from Neil A. Campbell, Lawrence G. Mitchell, Jane B. Reece, *Biology: Concepts and Connections* (Redwood City, CA: Benjamin/Cummings, 1994). ©1994, by The Benjamin/Cummings Publishing Company.

Chapter 21

Figure 21.5 a: from Alexander

P. Spence and Elliott B. Mason, *Human Anatomy and Physiology,* 3 ed. (Menlo Park, CA: Benjamin/Cummings, 1987). ©1987, by The Benjamin/Cummings Publishing Company.

Chapter 22

A Closer Look 2: adapted from Elaine N. Marieb, *Essentials of Human Anatomy and Physiology,* 4th ed. (Redwood City, CA: Benjamin/Cummings, 1994). ©1994 by The Benjamin/Cummings Publishing Company. Figure 22.9, Table 22.3: adapted from Neil A. Campbell, *Biology,* 3rd ed. (Redwood City, CA: Benjamin/Cummings, 1993). ©1993, by The Benjamin/Cummings Publishing Company. Figures 22.11 b: adapted from Gerard Tortora, Berdell Funke, Christine Case, *Microbiology: An Introduction,* 4th ed. (Redwood City, CA: Benjamin/Cummings, 1992). ©1992, by The Benjamin/Cummings Publishing Company.

Chapter 25

Figures 25.9, 25.25: from Neil A. Campbell, *Biology,* 3rd ed. (Redwood City, CA: Benjamin/Cummings, 1993). ©1993, by The Benjamin/Cummings Publishing Company.

Chapter 28

Figure 28.12: Raychel Ciemma, from Elaine N. Marieb and Jon Mallatt, *Human Anatomy* (Redwood City, CA: Benjamin/Cummings, 1992). ©1992, by The Benjamin/Cummings Publishing Company. Figure 28.22: Darwen and Vally Hennings, from Neil A, Campbell, *Biology* (Menlo Park, CA: Benjamin/Cummings, 1987). © 1987 by The Benjamin/Cummings Publishing Company.

Chapter 30

Figures 30.1 a, 30.9: from Neil A. Campbell, *Biology* 3rd ed. (Redwood City, CA: Benjamin/Cummings, 1993). ©1993, by The Benjamin/Cummings Publishing Company.

Glossary

Pronunciation Key:
' = Primary accent
" = Secondary accent
Pronounce:

a, fa, āt	as in	fate	o, no, ōt as in	note
a, hă, at		hat	ŏ, frˇ og	frog
ah		father	oo	soon
ar		tar	or	for
e, stre, ēt		street	ow	plow
ĕ, hĕ, en		hen	oy	boy
er		her	sh	she
ew		new	u, mu, ūt	mute
g		go	ŭ, sŭ, un	sun
i, bi, īt		bite	z	zebra
i, hi, im		him	zh	measure
ng		ring		

Abdomen (ab'do-men) Portion of the body between the diaphragm and the pelvis.

Abduct (ab-dukt') To move away from the midline of the body.

Abscess (ab'ses) Localized accumulation of pus and disintegrating tissue.

Absolute refractory period Period following stimulation during which no additional action potential can be evoked.

Absorption Process by which the products of digestion pass through the alimentary tube mucosa into the blood or lymph.

Accessory digestive organs Organs that contribute to the digestive process but are not part of the alimentary canal; include the tongue, teeth, salivary glands, pancreas, liver, and gallbladder.

Accommodation The process of increasing the refractive power of the lens of the eye; focusing.

Acetabulum (a"sĕ-tab'u-lum) Cuplike cavity on lateral surface of hipbone that receives the femur.

Acetylcholine (as"ĕ-til-ko'-lēn) Chemical transmitter substance released by some nerve endings.

Achilles tendon *See* Calcaneal tendon.

Acid Proton donor; substance capable of releasing hydrogen ions in solution.

Acid-base balance Situation in which the pH of the blood is maintained between 7.35 and 7.45.

Acidosis (as"ĭ-do'sis) State of abnormally high hydrogen ion concentration in the extracellular fluid.

Actin (ak'tin) A contractile protein of muscle.

Action potential A large transient depolarization event, including polarity reversal, that is conducted along the membrane of a muscle cell or a nerve fiber.

Activation energy The energy required to push reactants to the level necessary for interaction.

Active immunity Immunity produced by an encounter with an antigen; provides immunologic memory.

Active transport Membrane transport processes for which ATP is provided; e.g., solute pumping and endocytosis.

Adaptation (1) Any change in structure or response to suit a new environment; (2) decline in the transmission of a sensory nerve when a receptor is stimulated continuously and without change in stimulus strength.

Adduct (a-dukt') To move toward the midline of the body.

Adenohypophysis (ad"ĕ-no-hi-pof'ĭ-sis) Anterior pituitary; the glandular part of the pituitary gland.

Adenoids (ad'en-noids) Pharyngeal tonsils.

Adenosine triphosphate (ATP) (ah-den'o-sēn tri"fos'fāt) Organic molecule that stores and releases chemical energy for use in body cells.

Adipose (ad'ĭ-pōs) Fatty.

Adrenal glands (uh-drē'nul) Hormone-producing glands located superior to the kidneys; each consists of medulla and cortex areas.

Adrenergic fibers (ad"ren-er'jik) Nerve fibers that release norepinephrine.

Adrenocorticotropic hormone (ACTH) (ah-dre'no-kor"tĭ-ko-trō'pik) Anterior pituitary hormone that influences the activity of the adrenal cortex.

Adventitia (ad"ven-tish'e-ah) Outermost layer or covering of an organ.

Aerobic (a'er-ōb ik) Oxygen-requiring.

Aerobic (endurance) exercise Exercise such as biking, swimming, and jogging that causes more efficient muscle and general body metabolism resulting in greater endurance, strength, and resistance to fatigue.

Afferent (af'er-ent) Carrying to or toward a center.

Afferent neuron Nerve cell that carries impulses toward the central nervous system.

Agglutination (ah-gloo"tĭ-na'shun) Clumping of (foreign) cells; induced by cross-linking of antigen–antibody complexes.

AIDS Acquired immune deficiency syndrome; caused by human immunodeficiency virus (HIV); symptoms include severe weight loss, night sweats, swollen lymph nodes, opportunistic infections.

Albumin (al-bu'min) The most abundant plasma protein.

Aldosterone (al-dos'ter-ōn) Hormone produced by the adrenal cortex that regulates sodium ion reabsorption.

Alimentary canal (al"ĭ-men'tar-e) The continuous hollow tube extending from the mouth to the anus; its walls are constructed by the oral cavity, pharynx, esophagus, stomach, and small and large intestines.

Alkalosis (al″kah-lo′sis) State of abnormally low hydrogen ion concentration in the extracellular fluid.

Allantois (ah″lan′to-is) Embryonic membrane; its blood vessels develop into blood vessels of the umbilical cord.

Allergy (Hypersensitivity) Overzealous immune response to an otherwise harmless antigen.

Alopecia (al″o-pe′she-ah) Baldness.

Alveolus (al-ve′o-lus) One of the microscopic air sacs of the lungs.

Amino acid (ah-me′no) Organic compound containing nitrogen, carbon, hydrogen, and oxygen; building block of protein.

Amniocentesis A common form of fetal testing in which a small sample of fluid is removed from the amniotic cavity.

Amnion (am′ne-on) Fetal membrane that forms a fluid-filled sac around the embryo.

Amoeboid movement (ah-me′boyd) Process by which some cells move through tissue spaces by forming flowing cytoplasmic extensions that help them move along.

Amphiarthrosis (am″fe-ar-thro′sis) A slightly movable joint.

Ampulla (am-pul′lah) A localized dilation of a canal or duct.

Anabolism (ah-nab′o-lizm) Energy-requiring building phase of metabolism in which simpler substances are combined to form more complex substances.

Anaerobic (an-a′er-ōb-ik) Not requiring oxygen.

Anaphylaxis (an″ah-fi-lak′sis) A type of immediate hypersensitivity that is triggered when allergen molecules cross-link to IgE antibodies attached to mast cells or basophils causing the release of inflammatory substances.

Anastomosis (ah-nas″to-mo′sis) A union or joining of nerves, blood vessels, or lymphatics.

Anatomy (ah-nat′o-me) The study of the structure of living organisms and how those parts relate to one another.

Androgen (an′dro-jen) A hormone that controls male secondary sex characteristics, such as testosterone.

Anemia (ah-ne-me-ah) Reduced oxygen-carrying ability of blood resulting from too few erythrocytes or abnormal hemoglobin.

Aneurysm (an′u-rizm) Blood-filled sac in an artery wall caused by dilation or weakening of the wall.

Angina pectoris (an-ji′nah, an′jĭ-nah pek′tor-is) Severe suffocating chest pain caused by brief lack of oxygen supply to heart muscle.

Angiotensin II (an″je-o-ten′sin) A potent vasoconstrictor activated by renin; also triggers release of aldosterone.

Anion (an′i-on) An ion carrying one or more negative charges and therefore attracted to a positive pole.

Anorexia (an″ō-rek′sē-uh) Loss of appetite or desire for food.

Anoxia (an-nŏk′se-ah) Deficiency of oxygen.

Antagonist (an-tag′o-nist) Muscle that reverses, or opposes, the action of another muscle.

Anterior (an-tēr′e-er) The front of an organism, organ, or part; the ventral surface.

Anterior pituitary *See* Adenohypophysis.

Antibody A protein molecule that is released by a plasma cell (a daughter cell of an activated B lymphocyte) and that binds specifically to an antigen; an immunoglobulin.

Antidiuretic hormone (ADH) (an″tī-dī″yer-eh′tik) Hormone produced by the hypothalamus and released by the posterior pituitary; stimulates the kidneys to reabsorb more water, reducing urine volume.

Antigen (an′tĭ-jen) A substance or part of a substance (living or nonliving) that is recognized as foreign by the immune system, activates the immune system, and reacts with immune cells or their products.

Anus (a′nus) Distal end of the digestive tract; outlet of the rectum.

Aorta (a-or′tah) Major systemic artery; arises from the left ventricle of the heart.

Aortic body Receptor in the aortic arch sensitive to changing oxygen, carbon dioxide, and pH levels of the blood.

Apocrine gland (ap′o-krin) The less numerous type of sweat gland; produces a secretion containing water, salts, proteins, and fatty acids.

Aponeurosis (ap″o-nu-ro-sis) Fibrous or membranous sheet connecting a muscle and the part it moves.

Appendicitis (ap″ĕn-dĭ-si′tis) Inflammation of the appendix (wormlike sac attached to the cecum of the large intestine).

Aqueous humor (a′kwe-us) Watery fluid in the anterior chambers of the eye.

Arachnoid (ah-rak-noid) Weblike; specifically, the weblike middle layer of the three meninges.

Areola (ah-re′o-lah) Circular, pigmented area surrounding the nipple; any small space in a tissue.

Arrector pili (ah-rek′tor pi′li) Tiny, smooth muscles attached to hair follicles; cause the hair to stand upright when activated.

Arrhythmia (ah-rith′me-ah) Irregular heart rhythm caused by defects in the intrinsic conduction system.

Arteries Blood vessels that conduct blood away from the heart and into the circulation.

Arteriole (ar-tēr′e-ol) A minute artery.

Arteriosclerosis (ar-tēr′e-o-skler-o′sis) Any of a number of proliferative and degenerative changes in the arteries leading to their decreased elasticity.

Arthritis Inflammation of the joints.

Articular capsule Double-layered capsule composed of an outer fibrous capsule lined by synovial membrane; encloses the joint cavity of a synovial joint.

Articulation Joint; point where two bones meet.

Astigmatism (ah-stig′mah-tizm) A condition in which unequal curvatures in different parts of the lens (or cornea) of the eye lead to blurred vision.

Ataxia (ah-tak′se-ah) Disruption of muscle coordination resulting in inaccurate movements.

Atherosclerosis (a″ther-o″skler-o′sis) Changes in the walls of large arteries consisting of lipid deposits on the artery walls; the early stage of arteriosclerosis.

Atom Smallest particle of an elemental substance that exhibits the properties of that element; composed of protons, neutrons, and electrons.

Atomic mass number Sum of the number of protons and neutrons in the nucleus of an atom.

Atomic number Number of protons in an atom.

Atomic symbol A one- or two-letter symbol indicating a particular element.

Atomic weight Average of the mass numbers of all of the isotopes of an element.

Atrial natriuretic factor (a′tre-al na″tre-u-ret′ik) A hormone released by certain cells of the heart atria that reduces blood pressure and blood volume by inhibiting nearly all events that promote vasoconstriction and Na$^+$ and water retention.

Atrioventricular bundle (AV bundle) (a″tre-o-ven-tri′kyoo-ler) Bundle of specialized fibers that conduct impulses from the AV node to the right and left ventricles; also called bundle of His.

Atrioventricular node (AV node) Specialized mass of conducting cells located at the atrioventricular junction in the heart.

Atrophy (at′ro-fe) Reduction in size or wasting away of an organ or cell resulting from disease or lack of use.

Auditory ossicles (ah′sih-kulz) The three tiny bones serving as transmitters of vibrations and located within the middle ear: the malleus, incus, and stapes.

Auditory tube Tube that connects the middle ear and the pharynx. Also called eustachian tube.

Autoimmune response Production of antibodies or effector T cells that attack a person's own tissue.

Autonomic nervous system Efferent division of the peripheral nervous system that innervates cardiac and smooth muscles and glands; also called the involuntary or visceral motor system.

Autoregulation The automatic adjustment of blood flow to a particular body area in response to its current requirements.

Autosomes Chromosomes number 1 to 22; do not include the sex chromosomes

Axilla (ak-sih′luh) Armpit.

Axon Neuron process that carries impulses away from the nerve cell body; efferent process; the conducting portion of a nerve cell.

B cells Lymphocytes that oversee humoral immunity; their descendants differentiate into antibody-producing plasma cells. Also called B lymphocytes.

Baroreceptor (bayr″o-re-sep-tor) Pressoreceptor; receptor that is stimulated by pressure changes.

Basal metabolic rate (BMR) Rate at which energy is expended (heat produced) by the body per unit time under controlled (basal) conditions: 12 hours after a meal, at rest.

Basal nuclei Gray matter areas located deep within the white matter of the cerebral hemispheres. Also called basal ganglia.

Base Proton acceptor; substance capable of binding with hydrogen ions.

Basement membrane Extracellular material consisting of a basal lamina secreted by epithelial cells and a reticular lamina secreted by underlying connective tissue cells.

Basophil (ba′zo-fil) White blood cell whose granules stain deep blue with basic dye; has a relatively pale nucleus.

Benign (be-nin′) Not malignant.

Biceps (bi′seps) Two-headed, especially applied to certain muscles.

Bile Greenish-yellow or brownish fluid produced in and secreted by the liver, stored in the gallbladder, and released into the small intestine.

Bilirubin (bil″i-roo′bin) Red pigment of bile.

Biogenic amines (am′inz, ah′mēnz) Class of neurotransmitters, including catecholamines and indolamines.

Bipolar neuron Neuron with axon and dendrite that extend from opposite sides of the cell body.

Blastocyst (blas′to-sist) Stage of early embryonic development; the product of cleavage.

Blood-brain barrier Mechanism that inhibits passage of materials from the blood into brain tissues; reflects relative impermeability of brain capillaries.

Blood flow Amount of blood flowing through a vessel or organ at a particular time.

Blood pressure Force exerted by blood against a unit area of the blood vessel walls; differences in blood pressure between different areas of the circulation provide the driving force for blood circulation.

Bolus (bo′lus) A rounded mass of food prepared by the mouth for swallowing; any soft round mass.

Bone remodeling Process involving bone formation and destruction in response to hormonal and mechanical factors.

Bony thorax Bones that form the framework of the thorax; includes sternum, ribs, and thoracic vertebrae.

Bowman's capsule (bo-manz) *See* Glomerular capsule.

Bradycardia (brad″e-kar′deah) A heart rate below 60 beats per minute.

Brain stem Collectively the midbrain, pons, and medulla of the brain.

Brain ventricle Fluid-filled cavity of the brain.

Brain waves Patterns of electrical activity of the neurons of the brain, recordable with an electroencephalograph.

Branchial groove (brang′ke-al) An indentation of the surface ectoderm in the embryo; the external auditory canals develop from these.

Bronchus (brong′kus) One of the two large branches of the trachea that leads to the lungs.

Buffer Chemical substance or system that minimizes changes in pH by releasing or binding hydrogen ions.

Burn Tissue damage inflicted by intense heat, electricity, radiation, or certain chemicals, all of which denature cell proteins and cause cell death in the affected areas.

Bursa A fibrous sac lined with synovial membrane and containing synovial fluid; occurs between bones and muscle tendons (or other structures), where it acts to decrease friction during movement.

Calcaneal tendon (kal-ka″ne al) Tendon that attaches the calf muscles to the heelbone (calcaneus); also called the Achilles tendon.

Calcitonin (cal″sih-to′nin) Hormone released by the thyroid that promotes a decrease in calcium levels of the blood; also called thyrocalcitonin.

Calculus (kal′ku-lus) A stone formed within various body parts.

Callus (kal′lus) (1) Localized thickening of skin epidermis resulting from physical trauma. (2) Repair tissue (fibrous or bony) formed at fracture site.

Calorie (cal.) Amount of energy needed to raise the temperature of 1 gram of water 1° Celsius. Energy exchanges associated with biochemical reactions are usually reported in kilocalories (1 kcal = 1000 cal) or large calories (Cal).

Calyx (ka′liks) A cuplike extension of the pelvis of the kidney.

Canaliculus (kan″ah-lik′u-lus) Extremely small tubular passage or channel.

Cancer A malignant, invasive cellular neoplasm that has the capability of spreading throughout the body or body parts.

Capillaries (kap′il-layr″ēs) The smallest of the blood vessels and the sites of exchange between the blood and tissue cells.

Capping Proposed mechanism of B cell activation in which multivalent antigens bind to several adjacent receptors on a B lymphocyte and pull them into a continuous cluster.

Carbohydrate (kar″bo-hi-drat) Organic compound composed of carbon, hydrogen, and oxygen; includes starches, sugars, cellulose.

Carbonic anhydrase (kar-bon′ik an-hi′dras) Enzyme that facilitates the combination of carbon dioxide with water to form carbonic acid.

Carcinogen (kar-sĭ′no jin) Cancer-causing agent.

Cardiac cycle Sequence of events encompassing one complete contraction and relaxation of the atria and ventricles of the heart.

Cardiac muscle Specialized muscle of the heart.

Cardiac output Amount of blood pumped out of a ventricle in one minute.

Cardiovascular system Organ system which distributes the blood to deliver nutrients and remove wastes.

Carotid body (kar-rot′id) A receptor in the common carotid artery sensitive to changing oxygen, carbon dioxide, and pH levels of the blood.

Carotid sinus (si-nus) A dilation of a common carotid artery; involved in regulation of systemic blood pressure.

Cartilage (kar′tĭ-lij) White, semiopaque connective tissue.

Catabolism (kat-tab′o-lizm) Process in which living cells break down substances into simpler substances.

Catecholamines (kat″ĕ-kol′ah-menz) Epinephrine and norepinephrine.

Cation (kat′i-on) An ion with a positive charge.

Caudal (kaw′dul) Literally, toward the tail; in humans, the inferior portion of the anatomy.

Cecum (se′kum) The blind-end pouch at the beginning of the large intestine.

Cell The unit of structure and function in living organisms; the smallest unit capable of carrying out all the basic functions of life.

Cell membrane *See* Plasma membrane.

Cell-mediated immune response Immunity conferred by activated T cells, which directly lyse infected or cancerous body cells or cells of foreign grafts and release chemicals that regulate the immune response.

Cellular respiration Metabolic processes in which ATP is produced.

Cellulose (sel′u-lōs) A fibrous carbohydrate that is the main structural component of plant tissues.

Central (Haversian) canal (hah-ver′-shan) The canal in the center of each osteon that contains minute blood vessels and nerve fibers that serve the needs of the osteocytes.

Central nervous system (CNS) Brain and spinal cord.

Centriole (sen′tre-ol) Minute body found near the nucleus of the cell; active in cell division.

Centrosome (or cell center) A region near the nucleus which contains paired organelles called centrioles.

Cerebellum (ser″ĕ-bel′lum) Brain region most involved in producing smooth, coordinated skeletal muscle activity.

Cerebral aqueduct (ser″ĕ-bral, sĕ-re′bral) The slender cavity of the midbrain that connects the third and fourth ventricles; also called the aqueduct of Sylvius.

Cerebral cortex The outer gray matter region of the cerebral hemispheres.

Cerebral dominance Designates the hemisphere that is dominant for language.

Cerebrospinal fluid (ser″ĕ-bro-spi′nal) Plasmalike fluid that fills the cavities of the CNS and surrounds the CNS externally; protects the brain and spinal cord.

Cerebrum (ser′-ĕ-brum) The cerebral hemispheres and the structures of the diencephalon.

Cervix (ser′viks) The inferior necklike portion of the uterus.

Chemical bond An energy relationship holding atoms together; involves the interaction of electrons.

Chemical energy Energy stored in the bonds of chemicals.

Chemical reaction Process in which molecules are formed, changed, or broken down.

Chemoreceptor (ke′mo-re-sep″ter) Receptors sensitive to various chemicals in solution.

Chemotaxis (ke″mo-tak′sis) Movement of a cell, organism, or part of an organism toward or away from a chemical substance.

Cholecystokinin (CCK) (ko″le-sis″to-ki′nin) An intestinal hormone that stimulates gallbladder contraction and pancreatic juice release.

Cholesterol (ko-les′ter-ol″) Steroid found in animal fats as well as in most body tissues, made by the liver.

Cholinergic fibers (ko″lin-er′jik) Nerve endings that, upon stimulation, release acetylcholine.

Chondroblast (kon′dro-blast) Actively mitotic cell form of cartilage.

Chondrocyte (kon′dro-sit) Mature cell form of cartilage.

Chorion (kor′e-on) Outermost fetal membrane; helps form the placenta.

Chorionic villi sampling (ko″re-on′ik vil′i) Fetal testing procedure in which bits of the chorionic villi from the placenta are snipped off and the cells karyotyped. This procedure can be done as early as 8 weeks into the pregnancy.

Choroid (ko′roid) The vascular middle tunic of the eye.

Choroid plexus (kor′oid plek′sus) A capillary knot that protrudes into a brain ventricle; involved in forming cerebrospinal fluid.

Chromatin (kro′mah-tin) Structures in the nucleus that carry the hereditary factors (genes).

Chromosomes (kro′mo-somz) Barlike bodies of tightly coiled chromatin; visible during cell division.

Chyme (kīm′) Semifluid, creamy mass consisting of partially digested food and gastric juice.

Cilia (sil′e-ah) Tiny, hairlike projections on cell surfaces that move in a wavelike manner.

Circle of Willis An arterial anatomosis at the base of the brain.

Circumduction (ser″kum-duk′shun) Movement of a body part so that it outlines a cone in space.

Cirrhosis (si-ro′sis) Chronic disease, of the liver, characterized by an overgrowth of connective tissue or fibrosis.

Cisterna chyli (sis-ter′nah ki″ly) An enlarged sac at the base of the thoracic duct; the origin of the thoracic duct.

Cleavage An early embryonic phase consisting of rapid mitotic cell divisions without intervening growth periods; product is a blastocyst.

Clonal selection (klo′nul) Process during which a B cell or T cell becomes sensitized through binding contact with an antigen.

Clone Descendants of a single cell.

Cochlea (kok′le-ah) Snail-shaped chamber of the bony labyrinth that houses the receptor for hearing (the organ of Corti).

Coelom (se′lom) The ventral body cavity.

Coenzyme (ko-en′zim) Nonprotein substance associated with and activating an enzyme, typically a vitamin.

Cofactor Metal ion or organic molecule that is required for enzyme activity.

Collagen fibers The most abundant of the three fibers found in the matrix of connective tissue; constructed primarily of the fibrous protein collagen.

Colloid (kol′oid) A mixture in which the solute particles do not settle out readily and do not pass through natural membranes.

Colloidal osmotic pressure (kol′oid-ahl ahz-ma′tik) Pressure created in a fluid by large nondiffusible molecules, such as plasma proteins that are prevented from moving through a (capillary) membrane. Such substances tend to draw water to them.

Complement A group of blood-borne proteins, which, when activated, enhance the inflammatory and immune responses and may lead to cell lysis.

Complementarity of structure and function The relationship between a structure and its function; i.e., structure determines functions.

Complete blood count (CBC) Clinical test that includes a hematocrit, counts of all formed elements and clotting factors, and other indicators of normal blood function.

Compound Substance composed of two or more different elements, the atoms of which are chemically united.

Concentration gradient The difference in the concentration of a particular substance between two different areas.

Concussion Slight injury to the brain; the victim may lose consciousness briefly, but no permanent neurological damage is sustained.

Conductivity Ability to transmit an electrical impulse.

Cones One of the two types of photoreceptor cells in the retina of the eye; provide for color vision.

Congenital (kun-jeh′nih-tul) Existing at birth.

Congestive heart failure Condition in which the pumping efficiency of the heart is depressed so that circulation is inadequate to meet tissue needs.

Conjunctiva (kon″junk-ti′vah) Thin, protective mucous membrane lining the eyelids and covering the anterior surface of the eye itself.

Connective tissue A primary tissue; form and function vary extensively. Functions include support, storage, and protection.

Contraception The prevention of conception; birth control.

Contraction To shorten or develop tension, an ability highly developed in muscle cells.

Contralateral Opposite; acting in unison with a similar part on the opposite side of the body.

Contusion Brain injury in which marked tissue destruction results. Severe brain stem contusions always result in unconsciousness.

Convergence Turning toward a common point from different directions.

Cornea (kor′ne-ah) Transparent anterior portion of the eyeball; part of the fibrous tunic.

Corona radiata (kor-o′nah ra-de-ah′tah) (1) Arrangement of elongated follicle cells around a mature ovum; (2) Crownlike arrangement of nerve fibers radiating from the internal capsule of the brain to every part of the cerebral cortex.

Cortex (kor′teks) Outer surface layer of an organ.

Corticosteroids (kor″tĭ-ko-stĕ-roidz) Steroid hormones released by the adrenal cortex.

Cortisol (kor′tih-sol) Glucocorticoid produced by the adrenal cortex.

Covalent bond (ko-va′lent) Chemical bond created by electron sharing between atoms.

Cranial nerves The 12 nerve pairs that arise from the brain.

Creatine phosphate (kre′ah-tin fos-fāt) Compound that serves as an alternative energy source for muscle tissue.

Creatinine (kre-at′ĭ-nin) A nitrogenous waste molecule which is not reabsorbed by the kidney; this characteristic makes it useful for measurement of the GFR and glomerular function.

Crista ampullaris Sensory receptor organ within the ampulla of each semicircular canal of the inner ear; dynamic equilibrium receptor.

Cutaneous (ku-ta′ne-us) Pertaining to the skin.

Cyclic AMP Important intracellular second messenger that mediates hormonal effects; formed from ATP by the action of adenylate cyclase, an enzyme associated with the plasma membrane.

Cytochromes (si″to-krōmz) Brightly colored iron-containing proteins that form part of the inner mitochondrial membrane and function as electron carriers in oxidative phosphorylation.

Cytokinesis (si″to-ki-ne′sis) Division of cytoplasm that occurs after the cell nucleus has divided.

Cytoplasm (si′to-plazm) The cellular material surrounding the nucleus and enclosed by the plasma membrane.

Cytotoxic T cell Effector T cell that directly kills (lyses) foreign cells, cancer cells, or virus-infected body cells. Also called a killer T cell.

Deamination (de-am″ih-na′shun) Removal of an amine group from an organic compound.

Deafness Any degree of hearing loss.

Decibel (des′ĭ-bel) The unit used to measure relative sound intensity.

Defecation (def″ih-ka′shun) Elimination of the contents of the bowels (feces).

Deglutition (deg″loo-tish′un) Swallowing.

Dehydration (de″hi-dra′shun) Condition of excessive water loss.

Dehydration synthesis Process by which a large molecule is synthesized by covalently bonding smaller molecules together. One water molecule is removed for every bond formed.

Denatured Changed structure of a protein resulting from the rupture of hydrogen bonds subjected to stress such as heating.

Dendrite (den′drīt) Branching neuron process that serves as a receptive, or input, region; transmits the nerve impulse toward the cell body.

Deoxyribonucleic acid (DNA) (de-ok″sĭ-ri″bo-nu-kla″ik) A nucleic acid found in all living cells; carries the organism's hereditary information.

Depolarization (de-po″ler-ah-za′shun) Loss of a state of polarity; loss or reduction of negative membrane potential.

Dermatome (der′mah-tōm)   Portion of somite mesoderm that forms the dermis of the skin; also the area of skin innervated by the cutaneous branches of a single spinal nerve.

Dermis   Layer of skin deep to the epidermis; composed of dense irregular connective tissue.

Desmosome (dez′muh-sōm)   Cell junction composed of thickened plasma membranes joined by filaments.

Diabetes insipidus (di″ah-be′tez in-sih′pih-dus)   Disease characterized by passage of a large quantity of dilute urine plus intense thirst and dehydration caused by inadequate release of antidiuretic hormone (ADH).

Diabetes mellitus (meh-li′tus)   Disease caused by deficient insulin release, leading to inability of the body cells to use carbohydrates.

Dialysis (di-al′ah-sis)   Diffusion of solute(s) through a semipermeable membrane.

Diapedesis (di″ah-pě-de′sis)   Passage of blood cells through intact vessel walls into tissue.

Diaphragm (di′ah-fram)   (1) Any partition or wall separating one area from another; (2) a muscle that separates the thoracic cavity from the lower abdominopelvic cavity.

Diaphysis (di-af′ĭ-sis)   Elongated shaft of a long bone.

Diarthrosis (di″ar-thro′sis)   Freely movable joint.

Diastole (di-as′to-le)   Period of the cardiac cycle when either the ventricles or the atria are relaxing.

Diencephalon (di″ĕn-sŭ′lon)   That part of the forebrain between the cerebral hemispheres and the midbrain including the thalamus, the third ventricle, and the hypothalamus.

Diffusion (dĭ-fu′zhun)   The spreading of particles in a gas or solution with a movement toward uniform distribution of particles.

Digestion   Chemical or mechanical process of breaking down foodstuffs to substances that can be absorbed.

Digestive system   System that processes food into absorbable units and eliminates indigestible wastes.

Diploid chromosomal number   The chromosomal number characteristic of an organism symbolized as 2n; twice the chromosomal number(n) of the gamete; in humans, 2n = 46.

Disaccharide (di-sak′ah-rīd″, di-sak′ah-rid)   Literally, double sugar; e.g., sucrose, lactose.

Distal (dis′tul)   Away from the attached end of a limb or the origin of a structure.

Diuretics (di″u-ret′iks)   Chemicals that enhance urinary output.

Diverticulum (di″ver-tik′u-lum)   A pouch or sac in the walls of a hollow organ or structure.

Dorsal (dor′sul)   Pertaining to the back; posterior.

Down-regulation   Decreased response to hormonal stimulation; involves a loss in the number of receptors and effectively prevents the target cells from overreacting to persistently high hormone levels.

Duodenum (du″o-de′num)   First part of the small intestine.

Dura mater (du′rah ma′ter)   Outermost and toughest of the three membranes (meninges) covering the brain and spinal cord.

Dynamic equilibrium   Sense that reports on angular or rotatory movements of the head in space.

Ectoderm (ek′to-derm)   Embryonic germ layer; forms the epidermis of the skin and its derivatives, and nervous tissues.

Edema (ĕ-de′mah)   Abnormal accumulation of fluid in body parts or tissues; causes swelling.

Effector (ef-ek′ter)   Organ, gland, or muscle capable of being activated by nerve endings.

Efferent (ef′er-ent)   Carrying away or away from, especially a nerve fiber that carries impulses away from the central nervous system.

Elastic fibers   Fibers formed from the protein elastin, which gives a rubbery and resilient quality to the matrix of connective tissue.

Electrocardiogram (ECG) (e-lek″tro-car′de-o-gram″)   Graphic record of the electrical activity of the heart.

Electrochemical gradient   Distribution of ions involving both a chemical and an electrical gradient, which interact to determine the direction of diffusion.

Electroencephalogram (EEG) (e-lek″tro-en-sef′ah-lo-gram″)   Graphic record of the electrical activity of nerve cells in the brain.

Electrolyte (e-lek′tro-lit)   Chemical substances, such as salts, acids, and bases, that ionize and dissociate in water and are capable of conducting an electrical current.

Electron   Negatively charged subatomic particle; orbits the atomic nucleus.

Element   One of a limited number of unique varieties of matter that composes substances of all kinds; e.g., carbon, hydrogen, oxygen.

Embolism (em′bo-lizm)   Obstruction of a blood vessel by an embolus (blood clot, fatty mass, bubble of air, or other debris) floating in the blood.

Embryo (em′bre-o)   Developmental stage extending from gastrulation to the end of the eighth week.

Emesis   Reflexive emptying of the stomach through the esophagus and pharynx; also known as *vomiting.*

Encephalitis (en″seh-fuh-lī′tis)   Inflammation of the brain.

Endocardium (en″do-kar′de-um)   Endothelial membrane that lines the interior of the heart.

Endocrine glands (en′do-krin)   Ductless glands that empty their hormonal products directly into the blood.

Endocrine system   Body system that includes internal organs that secrete hormones.

Endocytosis (en″do-si-to′sis)   Means by which fairly large extra-cellular molecules or particles enter cells; e.g., phagocytosis, pinocytosis, receptor-mediated endocytosis.

Endoderm (en′do-derm)   Embryonic germ layer; forms the lining of the digestive tube and its associated structures.

Endometrium (en″do-me″tre-um)   Mucous membrane lining of the uterus.

Endomysium (en″do-mis′e-um)   Thin connective tissue surrounding each muscle cell.

Endoplasmic reticulum (en″do-plaz′mik rě-tik′u-lum)   Membranous network of tubular or saclike channels in the cytoplasm of a cell.

Endothelium (en″do-the′le-um)   Single layer of simple squamous cells that line the walls of the heart, blood vessels, and lymphatic vessels.

Energy   The capacity to do work; may be stored (potential energy) or in action (kinetic energy).

Enzyme (en′zīm)   A protein that acts as a biological catalyst to speed up chemical reactions.

Eosinophil (e″o-sin′o-filz)   Granular white blood cell whose granules readily take up a stain called eosin.

Epidermis (ep″ĭ-der′mis)   Superficial layer of the skin; composed of keratinized stratified squamous epithelium.

Epididymis (ep″ĭ-dĭ′dĭ-mis) That portion of the male duct system in which sperm mature. Empties into the ductus (or vas) deferens.

Epiglottis (eh″puh-glah′tis) Elastic cartilage at the back of the throat; covers the opening of the larynx (glottis) during swallowing.

Epimysium (ep″ĭ-mis′e-um) Sheath of fibrous connective tissue surrounding a muscle.

Epinephrine (ep″ĭ-nef′rin) Chief hormone produced by the adrenal medulla. Also called adrenalin.

Epiphyseal plate (e″pĭ-fis′e-ul) Plate of hyaline cartilage at the junction of the diaphysis and epiphysis that provides for growth in length of a long bone.

Epiphysis (e-pif′ĭ-sis) The end of a long bone, attached to the shaft.

Epithelial (ep″ĭ-the′le-ul) Pertaining to a primary tissue that covers the body surface, lines its internal cavities, and forms glands.

Erythrocytes (e-rith′ro-sits) Red blood cells.

Erythropoiesis (ĕ-rith″ro-poi-e′sis) Process of erythrocyte formation.

Erythropoietin (ĕ-rith″ro-poi′ĕ-tin) Hormone that stimulates production of red blood cells.

Estrogens (es′tro-jenz) Hormones that stimulate female secondary sex characteristics; female sex hormones.

Eustachian tube (u-sta′shan) *See* Auditory tube.

Excretion (ek-skre′shun) Elimination of waste products from the body.

Exocrine glands (ek′so-krin) Glands that have ducts through which their secretions are carried to a particular site.

Exocytosis (ek″so-si-to′sis) Mechanism by which substances are moved from the cell interior to the extracellular space as a secretory vesicle fuses with the plasma membrane.

Exogenous (ek-sah′jeh-nus) Developing or originating outside an organ or part.

Expiration Act of expelling air from the lungs, exhalation.

Exteroceptor (ek″ster-o-sep′ter) Sensory end organ that responds to stimuli from the external world.

Extracellular fluid Internal fluid located outside cells; includes plasma and interstitial fluid.

Extracellular matrix Substance secreted by connective tissue cells that determines the specialized function of each connective tissue type; typically includes ground substance (fluid to hard) and fibers (collagen, elastic, and/or reticular).

Extrinsic (ek-strin′sik) Of external origin.

Extrinsic eye muscles The six skeletal muscles which attach to and move each eye.

Exudate (ek′syoo-dāt) Material including fluid, pus, or cells that has escaped from blood vessels and has been deposited in tissues.

Fallopian tube (fah-lō′pē-un) *See* Uterine tube.

Fascia (fash′e-ah) Layers of fibrous tissue covering and separating muscles.

Fascicle (fas′ĭ-kl) Bundle of nerve or muscle fibers bound together by connective tissues.

Fatty acid Building block of fats.

Feces (fe′sēz) Material discharged from the bowel; composed of food residue, secretions, bacteria.

Fenestrated (fen′es-tra-tid) Pierced with one or more small openings.

Fertilization Fusion of the sperm and egg nuclei.

Fetus Developmental stage extending from the ninth week of development to birth.

Fibrin (fi′brin) Fibrous insoluble protein formed during blood clotting.

Fibrinogen (fi-brin′o-jin) A blood protein that is converted to fibrin during blood clotting.

Fibroblast (fi′bro-blast) Young, actively mitotic cell that forms the fibers of connective tissue.

Fibrocyte (fi′bro-sit) Mature fibroblast; maintains the matrix of fibrous types of connective tissue.

Filtrate A plasma-derived fluid that is processed by the renal tubules to form urine.

Filtration Passage of a solvent and dissolved substances through a membrane or filter.

Fissure (fih′zher) (1) A groove or cleft; (2) the deepest depressions or inward folds on the brain.

Fixator (fix′a-ter) Muscle that immobilizes one or more bones, allowing other muscles to act from a stable base.

Flagellum (flah-jel′lum) Long, whiplike extension of the plasma membrane of some bacteria and a sperm; propel the cell.

Fluid mosaic model A depiction of the structure of the membranes of a cell as phospholipid bilayers in which proteins are dispersed.

Follicle (fah′lih-kul) (1) Ovarian structure consisting of a developing egg surrounded by one or more layers of follicle cells; (2) colloid-containing structure of the thyroid gland.

Follicle-stimulating hormone (FSH) Hormone produced by the anterior pituitary that stimulates ovarian follicle production in females and sperm production in males.

Foramen (fo-ra′men) Hole or opening in a bone or between body cavities.

Forebrain Anterior portion of the brain consisting of the telencephalon and the diencephalon.

Formed elements Cellular portion of blood.

Fossa (fos′ah) A depression, often an articular surface.

Fovea (fo′ve-ah) A pit.

Fracture A break in a bone.

Frontal (coronal) plane Longitudinal plane that divides the body into anterior and posterior parts.

Fulcrum The fixed point on which a lever moves when a force is applied.

Fundus (fun′dus) Base of an organ; that part farthest from the opening of the organ.

Gallbladder Sac beneath the right lobe of the liver used for bile storage.

Gamete (gam′ēt) Sex cell; sperm or oocyte.

Gametogenesis (gam″eh-to-jen′eh-sis) Formation of gametes.

Ganglion (gang′gle-on) Collection of nerve cell bodies outside the CNS.

Gap junction A passageway between two adjacent cells; formed by transmembrane proteins called connexons.

Gastrulation (gas″troo-la′shun) Developmental process that produces the three primary germ layers (ectoderm, mesoderm, and endoderm).

Gene One of the biological units of heredity located in chromatin; transmits hereditary information.

Genetic code Information encoded in nucleotide base sequence.

Genotype (jen″o-tīp) One's genetic makeup or genes.

Germ layers Three cellular layers (ectoderm, mesoderm, and endoderm) that represent the initial specialization of cells in the embryonic body and from which all body tissues arise.

Gestation (jes-ta′shun) The period of pregnancy; about 280 days for humans.

Gland Organ specialized to secrete or excrete substances for further use in the body or for elimination.

Glomerular capsule (glō-mer yoo-ler) Double-walled cup at end of a renal tubule; encloses a glomerulus. Also called Bowman's capsule.

Glomerular filtration rate (GFR) (glō-mer′yoo-ler) Rate of filtrate formation by the kidneys.

Glomerulus (glo-mer′u-lus) Cluster of capillaries forming part of the nephron; forms filtrate.

Glottis (glah′tis) Opening between the vocal cords in the larynx.

Glucagon (gloo′kuh-gon) Hormone formed by alpha cells of islets of Langerhans in the pancreas; raises the glucose level of blood.

Glucocorticoids (gloo″ko-kor′tĭ-koidz) Adrenal cortex hormones that increase blood glucose levels and aid the body in resisting long-term stressors.

Gluconeogenesis (gloo″ko-ne″o-jen′ĕ-sis) Formation of glucose from noncarbohydrate molecules.

Glucose (gloo′kōs) Principal blood sugar, a hexose.

Glycerol (glis′er-ol) A sugar alcohol; a building block of fats.

Glycocalyx (gli″ko-kal′iks) Also called the cell coat; a layer of externally facing glycoproteins on a cell's plasma membrane that determine blood type, are involved in the cellular interactions of fertilization, embryonic development, and immunity, and act as an adhesive between cells.

Glycogen (glī′kō-jin) Main carbohydrate stored in animal cells; a polysaccharide.

Glycogenesis (gli″ko-jen′ĕ-sis) Formation of glycogen from glucose.

Glycogenolysis (gli″ko-jĕ-nol′ĭ-sis) Breakdown of glycogen to glucose.

Glycolysis (gli-kol′ĭ-sis) Breakdown of glucose to pyruvic acid—an anaerobic process.

Goblet cells Individual cells (unicellular glands) that produce mucus.

Gonad (go′nad) Primary reproductive organ; i.e., the testis of the male or the ovary of the female.

Gonadocorticoids (gon″ah-do-kor′tĭ-koidz) Sex hormones, primarily androgens, secreted by the adrenal cortex.

Gonadotropins (go-nad″o-trōp′inz) Gonad-stimulating hormones produced by the anterior pituitary.

Graafian follicle (grāf′e-an) *See* vesicular follicle.

Graded potential A local change in membrane potential that varies directly with the strength of the stimulus, declines with distance.

Gray matter Gray area of the central nervous system; contains cell bodies and unmyelinated fibers of neurons.

Growth hormone (GH) Hormone that stimulates growth in general; produced in the anterior pituitary; also called somatotropin (STH).

Growth Increase in size (typically due to an increase in cell number). Anabolic activities exceed catabolic ones.

Gustation (gus-ta′shun) Taste.

Gyrus (ji′rus) An outward fold of the surface of the cerebral cortex.

Hair follicle An epithelial structure surrounding a hair root from which a hair develops.

Hapten An incomplete antigen; has reactivity but not immunogenicity.

Haversian system (hah-ver′zhen) *See* Osteon.

Heart block Impaired transmission of impulses from atrium to ventricle resulting in dysrhythmia.

Heart murmur Abnormal heart sound (usually resulting from valve problems).

Heimlich maneuver Procedure in which the air in a person's own lungs is used to expel an obstructing piece of food.

Helper T cell Type of T lymphocyte that orchestrates cellular immunity by direct contact with other immune cells and by releasing chemicals called lymphokines; also helps to mediate the humoral response by interacting with B cells.

Hematocrit (hem″ah′to-krit) The percentage of erythrocytes to total blood volume.

Hematopoiesis (hem″ah-tō-poi-ē′sis) Blood cell formation; hemopoiesis.

Heme (hem) Iron-containing pigment that is essential to oxygen transport by hemoglobin.

Hemocytoblast (he″mo-si′to-blast) Bone marrow stem cell that gives rise to all formed elements.

Hemoglobin (he′muh-glo-bin) Oxygen-transporting component of erythrocytes.

Hemolysis (he-mah′lĕ-sis) Rupture of erythrocytes.

Hemophilia (he″mo-fil′e-ah) A term loosely applied to several different hereditary bleeding disorders that exhibit similar signs and symptoms.

Hemopoiesis (he″mo-poi-e′sis) Hematopoiesis.

Hemorrhage (hem′or-ij) Loss of blood from the vessels by flow through ruptured walls; bleeding.

Hemostasis (he″mo-sta′sis) Stoppage of bleeding.

Hepatic portal system (hĕ-pat′ik) Circulation in which the hepatic portal vein carries dissolved nutrients to the liver tissues for processing.

Hepatitis (hep″ah-ti′tis) Inflammation of the liver.

Hernia (her′ne-ah) Abnormal protrusion of an organ or a body part through the containing wall of its cavity.

Hilus (hi′lus) The indented region of an organ from which blood and/or lymph vessels and nerves enter and exit.

Histamine (his′tuh-mēn) Substance that causes vasodilation and increased vascular permeability.

Histology (his-tol′o-je) Branch of anatomy dealing with the microscopic structure of tissues.

Holocrine glands (hol′lo-krin) Glands that accumulate their secretions within their cells; secretions are discharged only upon rupture and death of the cell.

Homeostasis (ho″me-o-sta′sis) State of body equilibrium, maintenance of a stable internal environment of the body.

Homologous (ho-mol′ŏ-gus) Parts or organs corresponding in structure but not necessarily in function.

Hormones Steroidal or amino acid-based molecules released to the blood that act as chemical messengers to regulate specific body functions.

Humoral immune response (hu′mer-ul) Immunity conferred by antibodies present in blood plasma and other body fluids.

Hydrochloric acid (HCl) (hi″dro-klor′ik) Acid that aids protein digestion in the stomach; produced by parietal cells.

Hydrogen bond Weak bond in which a hydrogen atom forms a bridge between two electron-hungry atoms. An important intramolecular bond.

Hydrolysis (hi″drah-la′sis) Process in which water is used to split a substance into smaller particles.

Hydrophilic (hi″dro-fil′ik) Refers to molecules, or portions of molecules, that interact with water and charged particles.

Hydrophobic (hi″dro-fo-bik) Refers to molecules, or portions of molecules, that interact only with nonpolar molecules.

Hydrostatic pressure (hi″dro-stah′tic) Pressure of fluid in a system.

Hyperglycemic (hi″per-gli-se′mik) Term used to describe hormones such as glucagon that elevate blood glucose level.

Hyperopia A condition in which visual images are routinely focused behind the retina; commonly known as far-sightedness.

Hypersensitivity (allergy) An overreaction of the immune system in response to an allergen; results in inflammatory changes in tissue.

Hypertension (hi″per-ten′shun) High blood pressure.

Hypertonic (hi″per-ton′ik) Excessive, above normal, tone or tension.

Hypertrophy (hi-per′trah-fe) Increase in size of a tissue or organ independent of the body's general growth.

Hypodermis (hi″po-der′mis) Subcutaneous connective tissue; also called superficial fascia.

Hypoglycemic (hi″po-gli-se′mik) Term used to describe hormones such as insulin that decrease blood glucose level.

Hypoproteinemia (hi″po-pro″te-ĭ-ne′me-ah) A condition of unusually low levels of plasma proteins causing a reduction in colloid osmotic pressure; results in tissue edema.

Hypotension Low blood pressure.

Hypothalamic-hypophyseal tract (hi″po-thah-lam′ik— hi″po-fiz′e-al) Nerve bundles which run through the infundibulum and connect the neurohypophysis and the hypothalamus.

Hypothalamus (hi″po-thal′ah-mus) Region of the diencephalon forming the floor of the third ventricle of the brain.

Hypotonic (hi″po-ton′ik) Below normal tone or tension.

Hypoxia (hi-pok′se-ah) Condition in which inadequate oxygen is available to tissues.

Ileum (il′e-um) Terminal part of the small intestine; between the jejunum and the cecum of the large intestine.

Immune system A functional system whose components attack foreign substances or prevent their entry into the body.

Immunity (im″u-ni′te) Ability of the body to resist many agents (both living and nonliving) that can cause disease; resistance to disease.

Immunocompetence Ability of the body's immune cells to recognize (by binding) specific antigens; reflects the presence of plasma membrane–bound receptors.

Immunodeficiency disease Disease resulting from the deficient production or function of immune cells or certain molecules (complement, antibodies, and so on) required for normal immunity.

Immunoglobulin (im″u-no-glob′u-lin) *See* Antibody.

In vitro (in ve′tro) In a test tube, glass, or artificial environment.

In vivo (in ve′vo) In the living body.

Infarct (in′farkt) Region of dead, deteriorating tissue resulting from a lack of blood supply.

Inferior (caudal) Pertaining to a position near the tail end of the long axis of the body.

Inflammation (in″flah-ma′shun) A nonspecific defensive response of the body to tissue injury; includes dilation of blood vessels and an increase in vessel permeability; indicated by redness, heat, swelling, and pain.

Infundibulum (in″fun-dib′u-lum) A stalk of tissue which connects the pituitary gland to the hypothalamus; the distal end of the fallopian (uterine) tube.

Inguinal (ing′gwĭ-nal) Pertaining to the groin region.

Inner cell mass Accumulation of cells in the blastocyst from which the embryo develops.

Innervation (in″er-vā′shun) Supply of nerves to a body part.

Inorganic molecules Chemical substances that do not contain carbon, such as water and salts.

Insertion Movable attachment of a muscle.

Inspiration Drawing of air into the lungs, inhalation.

Insulin A hormone that enhances the carrier-mediated diffusion of glucose into tissue cells, thereby lowering blood glucose levels.

Integration The process by which the nervous system processes and interprets sensory input and makes decisions about what should be done at each moment.

Integumentary system (in-teg″u-men′tare) Skin (and its derivatives); provides the external protective covering of the body.

Intercalated discs (in-ter′kah-la″ted) Gap junctions connecting muscle cells of the myocardium.

Interferon (in-ter-fēr′on) Chemical that is able to provide some protection against virus invasion of the body; inhibits viral growth.

Internal capsule Band of projection fibers that runs between the basal nuclei and the thalamus.

Internal respiration Exchange of gases between blood and tissue fluid and between tissue fluid and cells.

Interoceptor (in″ter-o-sep′tor) Sensory receptor nerve ending in the viscera, which is sensitive to changes and stimuli within the body's internal environment; also called visceroceptor.

Interstitial cells (Leydig cells) Cells located in the loose connective tissue surrounding the seminiferous tubules; they produce androgens (most importantly testosterone), which are secreted into the surrounding interstitial fluid.

Interstitial fluid (in″ter-stish′al) Fluid between the cells.

Interstitial lamellae Incomplete lamellae that lie between intact osteons, fill the gaps between forming osteons, or represent the remnants of an osteon that has been cut through by bone remodeling.

Intervertebral discs (in″ter-ver′teh-brul) Discs of fibrocartilage between vertebrae.

Intracellular fluid (in″trah-sel′u-ler) Fluid within a cell.

Intrinsic (in-trin'sik) of internal origin.

Intrinsic factor Substance produced by the stomach that is required for vitamin B$_{12}$ absorption.

Ion (i'on) Atom with a positive or negative electric charge.

Ionic bond (i-ah'nik) Chemical bond formed by electron transfer between atoms.

Ipsilateral (ip"sih-la'ter-ul) Situated on the same side.

Irritability Ability to respond to a stimulus.

Ischemia (is-ke'me-ah) Local decrease in blood supply.

Isometric contraction (i"so-mĕ-trik) Contraction in which the muscle does not shorten (the load is too heavy) but its internal tension increases.

Isotonic contraction (i"so-tah'nik) Contraction in which muscle tension remains constant and the muscle shortens.

Isotopes (i'so-tōps) Different atomic forms of the same element. Isotopes vary only in the number of neutrons they contain, the heavier species tend to be radioactive.

Jejunum (jĕ-joo'num) The part of the small intestine between the duodenum and the ileum.

Joint Junction of two or more bones; an articulation.

Juxtaglomerular apparatus (juks"tah-glo-mer'ular) Cells of the distal tubule and afferent arteriole located close to the glomerulus that play a role in blood pressure regulation by releasing the enzyme renin.

Karyotype (kar'e-o-tīp) The diploid chromosomal complement, typically shown as homologous chromosome pairs arranged from longest to shortest (X and Y are arranged by size rather than paired).

Keratin (ker'ah-tin) Water-insoluble protein found in the epidermis, hair, and nails that makes those structures hard and water-repellent, precursor is keratohyalin.

Ketosis (kē-tō'sis) Abnormal condition during which an excess of ketone bodies is produced.

Killer T cell *See* Cytotoxic T cell.

Kilocalories *See* Calorie.

Krebs cycle Aerobic metabolic pathway occurring within mitochondria, in which food metabolites are oxidized and CO$_2$ is liberated, and coenzymes are reduced.

Labia (la'be-ah) Lips; singular labium.

Labyrinth (lab'ĭ-rinth") Bony cavities and membranes of the inner ear.

Lacrimal (lak'ri-mal) Pertaining to tears.

Lactation (lak-t'ashun) Production and secretion of milk.

Lacteal (lak'te-al) Special lymphatic capillaries of the small intestine that take up lipids.

Lactic acid (lak'tik) Product of anaerobic metabolism, especially in muscle.

Lacuna (lah-ku'ne) Little depression or space; the lacunae of bone or cartilage, lacunae are occupied by cells.

Lamella A layer, such as of bone matrix in Haversian systems of compact bone.

Lamina (lam'ĭ-nah) (1) A thin layer or flat plate; (2) the portion of a vertebra between the transverse process and the spinous process.

Larynx (lar'ingks) Cartilaginous organ located between the trachea and the pharynx; voice box.

Latent period Period of time between stimulation and the onset of muscle contraction.

Lateral Away from the midline of the body.

Leukocytes (loo'ko-sits) White blood cells; formed elements involved in body protection that take part in inflammatory and immune responses.

Leukocytosis An increase in the number of leukocytes (white blood cells); usually the result of a microbiological attack on the body.

Lever system Consists of a lever (bone), effort (muscle action), resistance (weight of object to be moved), and fulcrum (joint).

Ligament (lig'ah-ment) Band of regular fibrous tissue that connects bones.

Limbic system (lim'bik) Functional brain system involved in emotional response.

Lipid (lih'pid) Organic compound formed of carbon, hydrogen, and oxygen; examples are fats and cholesterol.

Lumbar (lum'bar) Portion of the back between the thorax and the pelvis.

Lumen (loo'min) Cavity inside a tube, blood vessel, or hollow organ.

Luteinizing hormone (LH) (lu'te-in-īz"ing) Anterior pituitary hormone that aids maturation of cells in the ovary and triggers ovulation in females. In males, causes the interstitial cells of the testis to produce testosterone.

Lymph (limf') Protein-containing fluid transported by lymphatic vessels.

Lymph node Small lymphatic organ that filters lymph; contains macrophages and lymphocytes.

Lymphatic system (lim'fa-tik) System consisting of lymphatic vessels, lymph nodes, and other lymphoid organs and tissues; drains excess tissue fluid from the extracellular space and provides a site for immune surveillance.

Lymphatics General term used to designate the lymphatic vessels which collect and transport lymph.

Lymphocyte Agranular white blood cell that arises from bone marrow and becomes functionally mature in the lymphoid organs of the body.

Lymphokines (lim'fo-kīn) Proteins involved in cell-mediated immune responses that enhance immune and inflammatory responses.

Lysosomes (li'so-sōmz) Organelles that originate from the Golgi apparatus and contain strong digestive enzymes.

Lysozyme (li'so-zīm) Enzyme in sweat, saliva, and tears that is capable of destroying certain kinds of bacteria.

Macrophage (mak'ro-fāj") Protective cell type common in connective tissue, lymphatic tissue, and certain body organs that phagocytizes tissue cells, bacteria, and other foreign debris; important as an antigen-presenter to T cells and B cells in the immune response.

Macula (mak'u-lah) (1) Static equilibrium receptor within the vestibule of the inner ear. (2) A colored area or spot.

Malignant (muh-lig'nent) Life threatening; pertains to neoplasms that spread and lead to death, such as cancer.

Mammary glands (mam'mer-e) Milk-producing glands of the breasts.

Mast cells Immune cells which function to detect foreign substances in the tissue spaces and initiate local inflammatory responses against them; typically found clustered deep to an epithelium or along blood vessels.

Mastication (mas"tĭ-ka-shun) Chewing.

Meatus (me-a'tus) External opening of a canal.

Mechanical advantage Condition that occurs when the load is close to the fulcrum and the effort is applied far from the fulcrum; allows a small effort exerted over a relatively large distance to move a large load over a small distance.

Mechanical disadvantage Condition that occurs when the load is far from the fulcrum and the effort is applied near the fulcrum; the effort applied must be greater than the load to be moved.

Mechanoreceptor (meh″kĕ-no-rē-sep-ter) Receptor sensitive to mechanical pressure such as touch, sound, or exerted by muscle contraction.

Medial (me-de ahl) Toward the midline of the body.

Medial lemniscal system (lem-nis′kul) The pathway to the cerebral cortex for discriminative touch, pressure, vibration, and conscious proprioception.

Mediastinum (me″de-ah-sti′-num) Region of the thoracic cavity between the lungs.

Medulla (mĕ-dul′ah) Central portion of certain organs.

Medulla oblongata (mĕ dul′ah ob″long-gah′tah) Inferior most part of the brain stem.

Meiosis (mi-o′sis) Nuclear division process that reduces the chromosomal number by half and results in the formation of four haploid (*n*) cells; occurs only in certain reproductive organs.

Melanin (mel′ah-nin) Dark pigment formed by cells called melanocytes; imparts color to the skin and hair.

Melatonin A hormone secreted by the pineal gland that inhibits secretion of GnRH by the hypothalamus; secretion peaks at night.

Memory The storage and retrieval of previous experience, or, more simply, the ability to recall our thoughts.

Memory cells Members of T cell and B cell clones that provide for immunologic memory.

Meninges (mĕ-nin′-jēz) Protective coverings of the central nervous system; from the most external to the most internal, the dura mater, arachnoid, and pia mater.

Meningitis (mĕ-nin-ji′tis) Inflammation of the meninges.

Menopause Period of life when, prompted by hormonal changes, ovulation and menstruation cease.

Menstruation (men″stroo-a′shun) The periodic, cyclic discharge of blood, secretions, tissue, and mucus from the mature female uterus in the absence of pregnancy.

Merocrine glands (mer′o-krin) Glands that produce secretions intermittently; secretions do not accumulate in the gland.

Mesencephalon (mes″en-sef′ah-lon) Midbrain.

Mesenchyme (meh′zin-kīm) Common embryonic tissue from which all connective tissues arise.

Mesenteries (mes″en-ter′ēz) Double-layered extensions of the peritoneum that support most organs in the abdominal cavity.

Mesoderm (mez′o-derm) Primary germ layer that forms the skeleton and muscles of the body.

Metabolic (fixed) acid Acid generated by cellular metabolism which must be eliminated by the kidneys.

Metabolic rate (mĕt″ah-bol′ik) Energy expended by the body per unit time.

Metabolism (mĕtab′o-lizm) Sum total of all the chemical reactions occurring in body cells, reactions that transform substances into energy or materials the body can use or store by means of anabolism or catabolism.

Metastasis (mĕ-tas′tah-sis) The spread of cancer from one body part or organ into another not directly connected to it.

Microvilli (mi″kro-vil′i) Tiny projections on the free surfaces of some epithelial cells; increase surface area for absorption.

Micturition (mik″tu-rish′un) Urination, or voiding; emptying the bladder.

Midbrain Region of the brain stem between the diencephalon and the pons.

Milliequivalents per liter The units used to measure electrolyte concentrations of body fluids; a measure of the number of electrical charges in 1 liter of solution.

Mineralocorticoid (min″er-al″ō-kor′tih-koyd) Steroid hormone of the adrenal cortex that regulates mineral metabolism and fluid balance.

Minerals Inorganic chemical compounds found in nature; salts.

Mitochondria (mi″to-kon′dre-ah) Cytoplasmic organelles responsible for ATP generation for cellular activities.

Mitosis (mi-to′sis) Process during which the chromosomes are redistributed to two daughter nuclei; nuclear division.

Mixed nerves Nerves containing the processes of motor and sensory neurons; their impulses travel to and from the central nervous system.

Mixture A substance consisting of particles dispersed together and in which the particles retain their unique properties; e.g., a solution, colloid, or suspension.

Molar (mo′lar) A solution concentration determined by mass of solute—one liter of solution contains an amount of solute equal to its molecular weight in grams.

Molecule Particle consisting of two or more atoms joined by chemical bonds.

Monoclonal antibodies (mon″o-klo′nal) Pure preparations of identical antibodies that exhibit specificity for a single antigen.

Monocyte (mon′o-sīt) Large single-nucleus white blood cell; agranular leukocyte.

Monosaccharide (mon″o-sak′ah-rīdz) Literally, one sugar; building block of carbohydrates; e.g., glucose, fructose.

Morula (mor′u-lah) The mulberry-like solid mass of blastomeres resulting from cleavage in the early conceptus.

Motor end plates Part of a muscle cell's sarcolemma in close contact with an expansions of an axonal terminal.

Motor nerves Nerves that carry impulses leaving the brain and spinal cord, and destined for effectors.

Motor unit A motor neuron and all the muscle cells it stimulates.

Mucous membranes Membranes that form the linings of body cavities open to the exterior (digestive, respiratory, urinary, and reproductive tracts).

Mucus (myoo′kus) A sticky, thick fluid, secreted by mucous glands and mucous membranes, that keeps the free surface of membranes moist.

Multipolar neuron Neuron that has one long axon and numerous dendrites.

Muscarinic receptors (mus″kah-rin′ik) Acetylcholine-binding receptors of the autonomic nervous system's target organs; named for activation by the mushroom poison muscarine.

Muscle fiber Muscle cell.

Muscle spindle Encapsulated receptor found in skeletal muscle that is sensitive to stretch.

Muscle tissue Primary tissue specialized to shorten or contract, thereby causing movement.

Muscle tone Sustained partial contraction of a muscle in response to stretch receptor inputs; keeps the muscle healthy and ready to act.

Muscular system The organ system consisting of the skeletal muscles of the body and their connective tissue attachments.

Myelencephalon (mi″el-en-sef′ah-lon) Lower part of the hindbrain, especially the medulla oblongata.

Myelin sheath (mi′ĕ-lin) Fatty insulating sheath that surrounds all but the smallest nerve fibers.

Myocardial infarction (mi″o-kar′de-al in-fark′shun) Condition characterized by dead tissue areas in the myocardium; caused by interruption of blood supply to the area.

Myocardium (mi″o-kar′de-um) Layer of the heart wall composed of cardiac muscle.

Myofibril (mi″o-fi′bril) Rodlike bundle of contractile filaments (myofilaments) found in muscle cells.

Myofilament (mi″o-fil′ah-ment) Filament that constitutes myofibrils. Of two types: actin and myosin.

Myoglobin (mi″o-glo′bin) Oxygen-binding pigment in muscle.

Myogram A graphic recording of mechanical contractile activity produced by an apparatus that measures muscle contraction.

Myometrium (mi″o-me′tre-um) Thick uterine musculature.

Myopia A condition in which visual images are focused in front of rather than on the retina; nearsightedness.

Myosin (mi′o-sin) One of the principal contractile proteins found in muscle.

Nares (na′rez) The nostrils.

Natrium Latin for sodium.

Necrosis (nĕ-kro′sis) Death or disintegration of a cell or tissues caused by disease or injury.

Negative feedback Feedback that tends to cause the levels of a variable to change in a direction opposite to that of an initial change.

Neonatal period The four-week period immediately after birth.

Neoplasm (ne′o-plazm) An abnormal mass of proliferating cells; benign neoplasms remain localized; malignant neoplasms are cancers, which can spread to other organs.

Nephron (nef′ron) Structural and functional unit of the kidney; consists of the glomerulus and renal tubule.

Nerve fiber Axon of a neuron.

Nerve impulse A self-propagating wave of depolarization; also called an action potential.

Nervous system Fast-acting control system that triggers muscle contraction or gland secretion.

Neural tube Fetal tissue which gives rise to the brain, spinal cord, and associated neural structures; formed from ectoderm by day 23 of embryonic development.

Neuroglia (nu-rog′le-ah) Nonexcitable cells of neural tissue that support, protect, and insulate the neurons.

Neurohypophysis (nu″ro-hi-pof′ĭ-sis) Posterior pituitary; portion of the pituitary gland derived from the brain.

Neuromuscular junction Region where a motor neuron comes into close contact with a skeletal muscle cell.

Neuron (nu-ron′) Cell of the nervous system specialized to generate and transmit nerve impulses.

Neuropeptides (nu″ro-pep′tīds) A class of neurotransmitters including beta-endorphins and enkephalins (which act as euphorics and reduce perception of pain) and gut-brain peptides.

Neurotransmitter Chemical released by neurons that may, upon binding to receptors of neurons or effector cells, stimulate or inhibit them.

Neutralization reaction A displacement reaction in which the mixing of an acid and a base forms water and a salt.

Neutron (nu′tron) Uncharged subatomic particle; found in the atomic nucleus.

Neutrophil (nu′trah-fil) Most abundant type of white blood cell.

Nicotinic receptors (nik″o-tin′ik) Acetylcholine-binding receptors of all autonomic postganglionic neurons and skeletal muscle neuromuscular junctions; named for activation by nicotine.

Nondisjunction Failure of sister chromatids to separate during mitosis or failure of homologous pairs to separate during meiosis; results in abnormal numbers of chromosomes in the resulting daughter cells.

Nonpolar molecules Electrically balanced molecules.

Norepinephrine (nor″ep-ĭ-nef′rin) A catecholamine (biogenic amine) neurotransmitter and adrenal medullary hormone, associated with sympathetic nervous system activation.

Nucleic acid (nu-kla′ik) Class of organic molecules that includes DNA and RNA.

Nucleoli (nu-kle′o-li) Dense spherical bodies in the cell nucleus involved with ribosomal subunit synthesis and storage.

Nucleoplasm (nu′kle-o-plazm″) A colloidal fluid, enclosed by the nuclear membrane, within which nucleoli and chromatin are suspended.

Nucleosome (nu′kle-o-sōm) Fundamental unit of chromatin; consists of a strand of DNA wound around a cluster of eight histone proteins.

Nucleotide (nu′kle-o-tīd) Building block of nucleic acids; consists of a sugar, a nitrogen-containing base, and a phosphate group.

Nucleus (nu′kle-is) Control center of a cell; contains genetic material.

Occlusion (ah-kloo′zhun) Closure or obstruction.

Olfaction (ol-fak′shun) Smell.

Olfactory epithelium Sensory receptor region in the nasal cavity containing olfactory neurons that respond to volatile chemicals that enter the nasal passages in air.

Oocyte (o′o-sit) Immature egg.

Oogenesis (o″o-jen′ĕ-sis) Process of ovum (female gamete) formation.

Ophthalmic (op-thal′mik) Pertaining to the eye.

Optic (op′tik) Pertaining to the eye or vision.

Optic chiasma (op′tik ki-az′muh) The partial crossover of fibers of the optic nerves.

Organ A part of the body formed of two or more tissues and adapted to carry out a specific function; e.g., the stomach.

Organ system A group of organs that work together to perform a vital body function; e.g., the nervous system.

Organelles (or″gah-nelz′) Small cellular structures (ribosomes, mitochondria, and others) that perform specific metabolic functions for the cell as a whole.

Organic Pertaining to carbon-containing molecules, such as proteins, fats, and carbohydrates.

Organism The living animal (or plant), which represents the sum total of all its organ systems working together to maintain life.

Origin Attachment of a muscle that remains relatively fixed during muscular contraction.

Osmolarity (oz″mo-lar′ĭ-te) The total concentration of all solute particles in a solution.

Osmoreceptor (oz″mo-re-sep′tor) Structure sensitive to osmotic pressure or concentration of a solution.

Osmosis (oz-mo′sis) Diffusion of a solvent through a membrane from a dilute solution into a more concentrated one.

Osmotic pressure Water-attracting ability of plasma proteins.

Ossicles (os′sik-kilz) *See* auditory ossicles.

Ossification (os″ĭ-fi-ka′shun) *See* Osteogenesis.

Osteoblasts (os′te-o-blasts) Bone-forming cells.

Osteoclasts (os′te-o-klasts) Large cells that resorb or break down bone matrix.

Osteocyte (os′te-o-sīt) Mature bone cell.

Osteogenesis (os″te-o-jen′e-sis) Process of bone formation, also called ossification.

Osteoid (os′te-oid) Unmineralized bone matrix.

Osteon (os′te-on) System of interconnecting canals in the microscopic structure of adult compact bone; unit of bone. Also called a Haversian system.

Osteoporosis (os″te-o-por-o′sis) Increased softening of the bone resulting from a gradual decrease in rate of bone formation.

Ovarian cycle (o-vayr′e-an) Monthly cycle of follicle development, ovulation, and corpus luteum formation in an ovary.

Ovary (o′var-e) Female sex organ in which ova (eggs) are produced; female gonad.

Ovulation (ov″u-la-shun) Ejection of an immature egg (oocyte) from the ovary.

Ovum (o′vum) Female gamete (germ cell); egg.

Oxidation (oks′i-da-shun) Process of substances combining with oxygen or the removal of hydrogen.

Oxidation-reduction reaction A reaction that couples the oxidation (loss of electrons) of one substance with the reduction (gain of electrons) of another substance.

Oxidative phosphorylation (ok′sĭ-da′tiv fos″for ĭ-la-shun) Process of ATP synthesis during which an inorganic phosphate group is attached to ADP; occurs via the electron transport chain within the mitochondria.

Oxygen debt The volume of oxygen required after exercise to oxidize the lactic acid formed during exercise.

Oxyhemoglobin (ok″sĭ-he″mo-glo′bin) Oxygen-bound form of hemoglobin.

Oxytocin (ok″sĭ-to′sin) Hormone secreted by hypothalamic cells that stimulates contraction of the uterus during childbirth and the ejection of milk during nursing.

Palate (pal′at) Roof of the mouth.

Pancreas (pan′kre-us) Gland located behind the stomach, between the spleen and the duodenum; produces both endocrine and exocrine secretions.

Pancreatic juice (pan″kre-at′ik) Bicarbonate-rich secretion of the pancreas containing enzymes for digestion of all food categories.

Papilla (pah-pil′ah) Small, nipplelike projection; e.g., dermal papillae are projections of dermal tissue into the epidermis.

Parasympathetic (par″ah-sim″pah-thet-ik) The division of the autonomic nervous system that oversees digestion, elimination, and glandular function; the resting and digesting subdivision.

Parathyroid glands (par″ah-thi′roid) Small endocrine glands located on the posterior aspect of the thyroid gland.

Parathyroid hormone (PTH) Hormone released by the parathyroid glands that regulates blood calcium level.

Parietal (pah-ri′ĕ-tal) Pertaining to the walls of a cavity.

Passive immunity Short-lived immunity resulting from the introduction of "borrowed antibodies" obtained from an immune animal or human donor; immunological memory is not established.

Passive transport Membrane transport processes that do not require cellular energy (ATP); e.g., diffusion, which is driven by kinetic energy.

Pathogen (path′o-jen) Harmful or disease-causing microorganism.

Pectoral (pek′tor-al) Pertaining to the chest.

Pectoral girdle Bones that attach the upper limbs to the axial skeleton; includes the clavicle and scapula.

Pelvic girdle Consists of the paired coxal bones that attach the lower limbs to the axial skeleton.

Pelvis (pel′vis) (1) Basin-shaped bony structure composed of the pelvic girdle, sacrum, and coccyx. (2) Expanded proximal portion of the ureter within the kidney.

Penis (pe′nis) Male organ of copulation and urination.

Pepsin Enzyme capable of digesting proteins in an acid pH.

Peptide bond (pep′tid) Bond joining the amine group of one amino acid to the acid carboxyl group of a second amino acid with the loss of a water molecule.

Perception Conscious recognition of a sensation.

Perforating canals Canals which run at right angles to the long axis of the bone, connecting the vascular and nerve supplies of the periosteum to those of the central canals and medullary cavity; also called Volkmann's canals.

Pericardium (per″ĭ-kar′de-um) Double-layered serosa enclosing the heart and forming its superficial layer.

Perichondrium (per″ĭ-kon′dre-um) Fibrous, connective-tissue membrane covering the external surface of cartilaginous structures.

Perimysium (per″ĭ-mis′e-um) Connective tissue enveloping bundles of muscle fibers.

Perineum (per″ĭ-ne′um) That region of the body spanning the region between the ischial tuberosities and extending from the anus to the scrotum in males and from the anus to the vulva in females.

Periosteum (per″e-os′te-um) Double-layered connective tissue that covers and nourishes the bone.

Peripheral nervous system (PNS) Portion of the nervous system consisting of nerves and ganglia that lie outside of the brain and spinal cord.

Peripheral resistance A measure of the amount of friction encountered by blood as it flows through the blood vessels.

Peristalsis (per″ĭ-stal′sis) Progressive, wavelike contractions that move foodstuffs through the alimentary tube organs (or that move other substances through other hollow body organs).

Peritoneum (per″ĭ-to-ne′um) Serous membrane lining the interior of the abdominal cavity and covering the surfaces of abdominal organs.

Peritonitis (per″ĭ-to-ni′tis) Inflammation of the peritoneum.

Permeability That property of membranes that permits passage of molecules and ions.

Petechiae (pe-te′ke-ah) Small, purplish skin blotches caused by widespread hemorrhage due to thrombocytopenia.

pH (pe-āch) The measure of the relative acidity or alkalinity of a solution: hydrogen ion concentration in moles per liter.

Phagocytosis (fag″o-si-to′sis) Engulfing of foreign solids by (phagocytic) cells.

Phagosome (fag′o-sōm) Vesicle formed as a result of phagocytosis; formed when an endocytic vesicle fuses with a lysosome.

Pharynx (fayr′inks) Muscular tube extending from the region posterior to the nasal cavities to the esophagus.

Phenotype (fe-no-tīp) Observable expression of the genotype.

Phospholipid (fos″fo-lip′id) Modified lipid containing phosphorus.

Photoreceptor (fo″to-re-sep′tor) Specialized receptor cells that respond to light energy.

Physiological acidosis (as″ĭ-do′sis) Arterial pH lower than 7.35 resulting from any cause.

Physiology (fiz″e-ol′o-je) The study of the function of living organisms.

Pineal gland (pin′e-al) A hormone-secreting part of the diencephalon of the brain thought to be involved in setting the biological clock and influencing reproductive function.

Pinocytosis (pe″no-si-to′sis) Engulfing of extracellular fluid by cells.

Pituitary gland (pĭ-tu′ih-tayr″e) Neuroendocrine gland located beneath the brain that serves a variety of functions including regulation of gonads, thyroid, adrenal cortex, lactation, and water balance.

Placenta (plah-sen′tah) Temporary organ formed from both fetal and maternal tissues that provides nutrients and oxygen to the developing fetus, carries away fetal metabolic wastes, and produces the hormones of pregnancy.

Plasma The nonliving fluid component of blood within which formed elements and various solutes are suspended and circulated.

Plasma cells Members of a B cell clone; specialized to produce and release antibodies.

Plasma membrane Membrane that encloses cell contents; outer limiting cell membrane.

Platelet (plāt′let) Cell fragment found in blood; involved in clotting.

Pleura (ploo′rah) Two-layered serous membrane that lines the thoracic cavity and covers the external surface of the lung.

Plexus (plek′sus) A network of converging and diverging nerve fibers, blood vessels or lymphatics.

Polar molecules Nonsymmetrical molecules that contain electrically unbalanced atoms.

Polarized State of the plasma membrane of an unstimulated neuron or muscle cell in which the inside of the cell is relatively negative in comparison to the outside; the resting state.

Polycythemia (pol″e-si-the′me-ah) An excessive or abnormal increase in the number of erythrocytes.

Polypeptide (pol″e-pep′tīd) A chain of amino acids.

Polysaccharide (pol″e-sak′ah-rīd) Literally, many sugars, a polymer of linked monosaccharides; e.g., starch, glycogen.

Pons (1) Any bridgelike structure or part; (2) the part of the brain stem connecting the medulla with the midbrain, providing linkage between upper and lower levels of the central nervous system.

Positive feedback Feedback that tends to cause the level of a variable to change in the same direction as an initial change.

Posterior (pos-tēr′e-or) The back of an organism, organ, or part; the dorsal surface.

Posterior pituitary *See* Neurohypophysis.

Postganglionic neuron (post″gan-gle-ah′nik) Autonomic motor neuron that has its cell body in a peripheral ganglion and projects its axon to an effector.

Preganglionic neuron Autonomic motor neuron that has its cell body in the central nervous system and projects its axon to a peripheral ganglion.

Presbyopia (pres″be-o′pe-ah) A condition that results in the loss of near focusing ability; typical onset is around age 40.

Pressoreceptor A nerve ending in the wall of the carotid sinus and aortic arch sensitive to vessel stretching.

Pressure gradient Difference in hydrostatic pressure that drives filtration.

Prime mover Muscle that bears the major responsibility for effecting a particular movement; agonist.

Process (1) Prominence or projection; (2) series of actions for a specific purpose.

Progesterone (pro-jes′ter-ōn) Hormone partly responsible for preparing the uterus for the fertilized ovum.

Prolactin (pro-lak′tin) Adenohypophyseal hormone that stimulates the breasts to produce milk.

Pronation (pro-na′shun) Inward rotation of the forearm causing the radius to cross diagonally over the ulna—palms face posteriorly.

Proprioceptor (pro″pre-o-sep′tor) Receptor located in a joint, muscle, or tendon; concerned with locomotion, posture and muscle tone.

Prostaglandin (pros″tah-glan′din) A lipid-based membrane-associated chemical messenger synthesized by most tissue cells that acts locally as a hormonelike substance.

Protein (pro′tēn) Complex nitrogenous substance; main building material of cells.

Proton (pro′ton) Subatomic particle that bears a positive charge; located in the atomic nucleus.

Proximal (prok′si-mul) Toward the attached end of a limb or the origin of a structure.

Pseudounipolar neuron (soo″do-u″nĭ-po′lar) Another term for unipolar neuron.

Puberty Period of life when reproductive maturity is achieved.

Pulmonary (pul′muh-nayr-e) Pertaining to the lungs.

Pulmonary circuit System of blood vessels that serves gas exchange in the lungs; i.e., pulmonary arteries, capillaries, and veins.

Pulmonary congestion Condition in which vascular pressure increases, resulting in tissue edema; caused by failure of the left side of the heart.

Pulmonary edema (ĕ-de′muh) Leakage of fluid into the air sacs and tissue of the lungs.

Pulmonary veins Vessels that deliver freshly oxygenated blood from the respiratory zones of the lungs to the heart.

Pulmonary ventilation   Breathing; consists of inspiration and expiration.

Pulse   Rhythmic expansion and recoil of arteries resulting from heart contraction; can be felt from outside the body.

Pupil   Opening in the center of the iris through which light enters the eye.

Purkinje fibers (pur-kin′je)   Modified cardiac muscle fibers of the conduction system of the heart.

Pus   Fluid product of inflammation composed of white blood cells, the debris of dead cells, and a thin fluid.

Pyloric sphincter (pi-lor′ik sfink′ter)   Valve of the distal end of the stomach that controls food entry into the duodenum.

Pyrogens   Fever-inducing chemicals secreted by macrophages, white blood cells, and injured tissue cells.

Radioactivity   The process of spontaneous decay seen in some of the heavier isotopes, during which particles or energy is emitted from the atomic nucleus; results in the atom becoming more stable.

Radioisotope (ra″de-o-i′so-tōp)   Isotope that exhibits radioactive behavior.

Ramus (ra′mus)   Branch of a nerve, artery, vein, or bone.

Receptor (re-sep′tor)   (1) A cell or nerve ending of a sensory neuron specialized to respond to particular types of stimuli. (2) Molecule that binds specifically with other molecules e.g., neurotransmitters, hormones, antigens, etc.

Receptor potential   A graded potential that occurs at a sensory receptor membrane.

Reduction   Chemical reaction in which electrons and energy are gained by a molecule (often accompanied by gain of hydrogen ions) or oxygen is lost.

Referred pain   Pain felt at a site other than the area of origin.

Reflex   Automatic reaction to stimuli.

Refractory period   Period during which an excitable cell is not responsive to a threshold stimulus.

Renal (re′nal)   Pertaining to the kidney.

Renin (re′nin)   Substance released by the kidneys that is involved with raising blood pressure.

Repolarization   Movement of the membrane potential to the initial resting (polarized) state.

Reproductive system   Organ system that functions to produce offspring.

Resistance exercise   High-intensity exercise in which the muscles are pitted against high resistance or immovable forces and, as a result, muscle cells increase in size.

Respiratory system   Organ system that carries out gas exchange; includes the nose, pharynx, larynx, trachea, bronchi, lungs.

Resting membrane potential   The voltage that exists across the plasma membrane during the resting state of an excitable cell; ranges from -50 to -200 millivolts depending on cell type.

Reticular fibers (rĕ-tik′u-lar)   Fine network of connective tissue fibers that form the internal supporting framework of lymphoid organs.

Reticular formation (ret-tik′u-lar)   Functional system that spans the brain stem; involved in regulating sensory input to the cerebral cortex, cortical arousal, and control of motor behavior.

Reticulocyte (rĕ-tik′u-lo-sīt)   Immature erythrocyte.

Retina (ret′ĭ-nah)   Neural tunic of the eyeball; contains photoreceptors (rods, cones).

Ribonucleic acid (RNA) (ri′bo-nu-kle′ik)   Nucleic acid that contains ribose; acts in protein synthesis.

Ribosomes (ri′bo-sōmz)   Cytoplasmic organelles at which proteins are synthesized.

Rods   One of the two types of photosensitive cells in the retina.

Rugae (ru′ge)   Elevations or ridges, as in the mucosa of the stomach.

Rule of eights   Atoms tend to interact in ways that result in their having eight electrons in their valence shells.

Rule of nines   Method of computing the extent of burns by dividing the body into a number of areas, each accounting for 9% of the total body area.

Sagittal plane (sa′jih-tul)   A longitudinal plane that divides the body or any of its parts into right and left portions.

Salt   Ionic compound that dissociates into charged particles (other than hydrogen or hydroxyl ions) when dissolved in water.

Saltatory conduction   Transmission of an action potential along a myelinated fiber in which the nerve impulse appears to leap from node to node.

Sarcomere (sar′ko-mēr)   The smallest contractile unit of muscle; extends from one Z line to the next.

Sarcoplasmic reticulum (sar″ko-plaz′mik rĕ-tik′u-lum)   Specialized endoplasmic reticulum of muscle cells.

Sclera (skle′rah)   White opaque portion of the fibrous tunic of the eyeball.

Scrotum (skro′tum)   External sac enclosing the testes.

Sebaceous gland (se-ba′shus)   Epidermal gland that produces an oily secretion called sebum.

Sebum (sé′bum)   Oily secretion of sebaceous glands.

Second messenger   Intracellular molecule generated by the binding of a chemical (hormone or neurotransmitter) to a plasma membrane receptor; mediates intracellular responses to the chemical messenger.

Secondary sex characteristics   Anatomic features, not directly involved in the reproductive process, that develop under the influence of sex hormones, e.g., male or female pattern of muscle development, bone growth, body hair distribution, etc.

Secretion (se-kre′shun)   (1) The passage of material formed by a cell to its exterior; (2) Cell product that is transported to the exterior of the cell.

Section   A cut through the body (or an organ) that is made along a particular plane; a thin slice of tissue prepared for microscopic study.

Segregation   During meiosis, the distribution of the members of the allele pair to different gametes.

Selectively permeable membrane   A membrane that selectively allows certain substances to pass while restricting the movement of others.

Semen (se′men)   Fluid mixture containing sperm and secretions of the male accessory reproductive glands.

Semilunar valves (sĕ″me-loo′ner)   Valves that prevent blood return to the ventricles after contraction.

Seminiferous tubules (sem″ĭ-nif′er-us)   Highly convoluted tubes within the testes; form sperm.

Sensation   Awareness of internal and external events.

Sensory input   Information gathered by millions of sensory receptors when monitoring changes occurring both inside and outside the body.

Sensory nerve Nerve that contains processes of sensory neurons and carries nerve impulses to the central nervous system.

Sensory neuron Neuron that initiates nerve impulses following receptor stimulation.

Sensory receptor Dendritic end organs, or parts of other cell types, specialized to respond to a stimulus.

Serous fluid (sēr′us) Clear, watery fluid secreted by cells of a serous membrane.

Serum (sēr′um) Amber-colored fluid that exudes from clotted blood as the clot shrinks and then no longer contains fibrinogen.

Sesamoid bones (ses′ah-moid) Short bones embedded in tendons, variable in size and number, many of which influence the action of muscles; the largest is the patella (kneecap).

Sex chromosomes The chromosomes, X and Y, that determine genetic sex (XX = female; XY = male); the 23rd pair of chromosomes.

Sinoatrial (SA) node (si″no-a′tre-al) Specialized myocardial cells in the wall of the right atrium; pacemaker of the heart.

Sinus (si′nus) (1) Mucous-membrane-lined, air-filled cavity in certain cranial bones; (2) dilated channel for the passage of blood or lymph.

Skeletal muscle Muscle composed of cylindrical multinucleate cells with obvious striations; the muscle(s) attached to the body's skeleton; voluntary muscle.

Skeletal system System of protection and support composed primarily of bone and cartilage.

Skull Bony protective encasement of the brain.

Smooth muscle Muscle consisting of spindle-shaped, unstriped (nonstriated) muscle cells; involuntary muscles.

Sol-gel transformation Reversible change of a colloid from a fluid (sol) to a more solid (gel) state.

Solute (sol′yoot) The substance that is dissolved in a solution.

Somatic nervous system (so-ma′tik) Division of the peripheral nervous system that provides the motor innervation of skeletal muscles.

Somatomedins (so″mah-to-me′dinz) Growth-promoting proteins produced by the liver and possibly by the kidneys and muscles as well.

Somite (so′mīt) A mesodermal segment of the body of an embryo that contributes to the formation of skeletal muscles, vertebrae, and dermis of skin.

Special senses The senses of taste, smell, vision, hearing, and equilibrium.

Spermatogenesis (sper″mah-to-jen′ĕ-sis) The process of sperm (male gamete) formation; involves meiosis.

Sphincter (sfink′ter) A circular muscle surrounding an opening; acts as a valve.

Spinal cord The bundle of nervous tissue that runs from the brain to the first to third lumbar vertebrae and provides a conduction pathway to and from the brain.

Spinal nerves The 31 nerve pairs that arise from the spinal cord.

Splanchnic circulation (splangk′nik) The blood vessels serving the digestive system.

Static equilibrium Sense of head position in space with respect to gravity.

Stenosis (stĕ-no′sis) Abnormal constriction or narrowing.

Steroids (stĕ′roidz) Group of chemical substances including certain hormones and cholesterol.

Stimulus (stim′u-lus) An excitant or irritant; a change in the environment that evokes a response.

Stressor Any stimulus that directly or indirectly causes the hypothalamus to initiate stress-reducing responses, such as the fight or flight response.

Stroke Condition in which brain tissue is deprived of a blood supply, as in blockage of a cerebral blood vessel; a cerebrovascular accident (CVA).

Stroke volume Amount of blood pumped out of a ventricle during one contraction.

Stroma (stro′mah) The basic internal structural framework of an organ.

Subcutaneous (sub″kyu-ta′ne-us) Beneath the skin.

Substrate A reactant on which an enzyme acts to cause a chemical reaction to proceed.

Sudoriferous gland (su″do-rif′er-us) Epidermal gland that produces sweat.

Sulcus (sul′kus) A furrow on the brain, less deep than a fissure.

Summation Accumulation of effects, especially those of muscular, sensory, or mental stimuli.

Superficial Located close to or on the body surface.

Superior Refers to the head or upper body regions.

Supination (soo″pĭ-na′shun) The outward rotation of the forearm causing palms to face anteriorly.

Suppressor T cells Regulatory T lymphocytes that suppress the immune response.

Surfactant (ser-fak′tant) Secretion produced by certain cells of the alveoli that reduces the surface tension of water molecules, thus preventing the collapse of the alveoli after each expiration.

Suture (soo′cher) An immovable fibrous joint; with one exception, all bones of the skull are united by sutures.

Sweat gland *See* Sudoriferous gland.

Sympathetic division Division of the autonomic nervous system that activates the body to cope with some stressor (danger, excitement, etc.); the fight, fright, and flight subdivision.

Sympathetic tone State of partial vasoconstriction of the blood vessels maintained by sympathetic fibers.

Symphysis (sim′fih-sis) A joint in which the bones are connected by fibrocartilage.

Synapse (sin′aps) Functional junction or point of close contact between two neurons or between a neuron and an effector cell.

Synapsis (sĭ-nap′sis) Pairing of homologous chromosomes during the first meiotic division.

Synaptic cleft (si-nap′tik) Fluid-filled space at a synapse.

Synaptic delay Time required for an impulse to cross a synapse between two neurons.

Synaptic knobs The bulbous distal endings of the telodendria; also known as boutons.

Synarthrosis (sin″ar-thro′sis) Immovable joint.

Synchondrosis (sin″kon-dro′sis) A joint in which the bones are united by hyaline cartilage.

Syndesmosis (sin″des-mos′sis) A joint in which the bones are united by a ligament or a sheet of fibrous tissue.

Synergist (sin′er-jist) Muscle that aids the action of a prime mover by effecting the same movement or by stabilizing joints across which the prime mover acts to prevent undesirable movements.

Synostosis (sin″os-to′sis) A completely ossified joint; a fused joint.

Synovial fluid (sĭ-no′ve-al) Fluid secreted by the synovial membrane; lubricates joint surfaces and nourishes articular cartilages.

Synovial joint (sĭ-no′ve-al) Freely movable joint exhibiting a joint cavity; also called a diarthrosis.

Systemic (sis-tem′ik) Pertaining to the whole body.

Systemic circuit System of blood vessels that serves gas exchange in the body tissues.

Systole (sis′to-le) Period when either the ventricles or the atria are contracting.

Systolic pressure (sis-tah′lik) Pressure exerted by blood on the blood vessel walls during ventricular contractions.

T cells Lymphocytes that mediate cellular immunity; include helper, killer, suppressor, and memory cells. Also called T lymphocytes.

T tubule Extension of the muscle cell plasma membrane (sarcolemma) that protrudes deeply into the muscle cell.

Target cell A cell that is capable of responding to a hormone because it bears receptors to which the hormone can bind.

Taste buds Sensory receptor organs that house gustatory cells, which respond to dissolved food chemicals.

Telencephalon (tel″en-seh′fuh-lon) Anterior subdivision of the primary forebrain that develops into olfactory lobes, cerebral cortex, and corporal striata.

Tendon (ten′dun) Cord of dense fibrous tissue attaching muscle to bone.

Testis (tes′tēz) Male primary sex organ that produces sperm; male gonad.

Tetanus (tet′ah-nus) (1) A smooth, sustained muscle contraction resulting from high-frequency stimulation; (2) an infectious disease caused by an anaerobic bacterium.

Thalamus (tha′luh-mis) A mass of gray matter in the diencephalon of the brain.

Thermogenesis (ther″mo-jen′ĕ-sis) Heat production.

Thermoreceptor (ther″mo-re-sep′ter) Receptor sensitive to temperature changes.

Thoracic duct Large duct that receives lymph drained from the entire lower body, the left upper extremity, and the left side of the head and thorax.

Thorax (tho′raks) That portion of the body trunk above the diaphragm and below the neck.

Threshold Stimulus Weakest stimulus capable of producing a response in an irritable tissue.

Thrombin (throm′bin) Enzyme that induces clotting by converting fibrinogen to fibrin.

Thrombocytes (throm′bo-sīts) Platelets; cell fragments that participate in blood coagulation.

Thrombocytopenia (throm″bo-si′to-pe′ne-ah) A reduction in the number of platelets circulating in the blood.

Thrombus (throm′bus) A clot that develops and persists in an unbroken blood vessel.

Thymus gland (thi′mus) Endocrine gland active in immune response.

Thyrocalcitonin (thi″ro-kal″sĭ-to′nin) *See* Calcitonin.

Thyroid gland (thi′roid) One of the largest of the body's endocrine glands; straddles the anterior trachea.

Thyroid-stimulating hormone Adenohypophyseal hormone that regulates secretion of thyroid hormones.

Thyroxine (thi-rok′sin) Also called T₄; iodine-containing hormone secreted by the thyroid gland; accelerates cellular metabolic rate in most body tissues.

Tight junction Area where plasma membranes of adjacent cells are fused.

Tissue A group of similar cells (and their intercellular substance) specialized to perform a specific function; primary tissue types of the body are epithelial, connective, muscle, and nervous tissue.

Tonicity (to-nis′ĭ-te) A measure of the ability of a solution to cause a change in cell shape or tone by promoting osmotic flows of water.

Tonsils A ring of lymphocyte tissue around the entrance to the pharynx; there are three pairs of tonsils, each named for its location.

Trabecula (trah-bek′u-lah) (1) Any of the fibrous bands extending from the capsule into the interior of an organ; (2) struts or thin plates of bone in spongy bone.

Trachea (tra′ke-ah) Windpipe; cartilage-reinforced tube extending from larynx to bronchi.

Tract A collection of nerve fibers in the central nervous system having the same origin, termination, and function.

Transduction (trans-duk′shun) The conversion of the energy of a stimulus into an electrical event.

Transepithelial transport (trans-ep″ĭ-the′le-al) Movement of substances through, rather than between, adjacent epithelial cells connected by tight junctions, such as absorpotion of nutrients in the small intestine.

Triglycerides (tri-glis′er-īdz) Fats and oils composed of fatty acids and glycerol; are the body's most concentrated source of energy fuel; also known as neutral fats.

Triiodothyronine (tri″i-o″do-thi′ro-nēn) Also known as T₃; secretion and function similar to those of thyroxine.

Trophoblast (tro′fo-blast) Outer sphere of cells of the blastocyst.

Tropic hormone (trōp′ik) A hormone that regulates the function of another endocrine organ.

Tubular reabsorption The movement of filtrate components from the renal tubules into the blood.

Tumor An abnormal growth of cells; a swelling; cancerous at times.

Tunica (too′nĭ-kah) A covering or tissue coat; membrane layer.

Twitch A single, rapid contraction of muscle in response to a stimulus.

Two-point discrimination test Test that determines how close together two points on the skin can be and still be perceived as two points when stimulated, rather than one.

Tympanic membrane (tim-pan′ik) Eardrum.

Ulcer (ul′ser) Lesion or erosion of the mucous membrane, such as gastric ulcer of stomach.

Umbilical cord (um-bĭ′lĭ-kul) Structure bearing arteries and veins connecting the placenta and the fetus.

Umbilicus (um-bĭ′lĭ-kus) Navel; marks site where umbilical cord was attached in fetal stage.

Unipolar neuron Neuron in which embryological fusion of the two processes leaves only one process extending from the cell body.

Unmyelinated fibers (un-mi′ĕ-lĭ-nāt″ed) Axons lacking a myelin sheath and therefore conducting impulses quite slowly.

Up-regulation   Increased target cell formation of receptors in response to increasingly higher levels of the hormones to which they respond.

Urea (u-re′ah)   Main nitrogen-containing waste excreted in urine.

Ureter (u′-re-ter)   Tube that carries urine from kidney to bladder.

Urethra (u-re′thrah)   Canal through which urine passes from the bladder to outside the body.

Urinary system   System primarily responsible for water, electrolyte, and acid-base balance and removal of nitrogenous wastes.

Uterine tube (u′-ter-in)   Tube through which the ovum is transported to the uterus. Also called fallopian tube.

Uterus (u′ter-us)   Hollow, thick-walled organ that receives, retains, and nourishes fertilized egg; site where embryo/fetus develops.

Uvula (u′vu-lah)   Tissue tag hanging from soft palate.

Vaccine   Preparation that provides artificially acquired active immunity.

Valence shell (va′lens)   Outermost energy level of an atom that contains electrons.

Vas (vaz′)   A duct; vessel.

Vasa recta (va′sah rek′tah)   Capillary branches that supply loops of Henle in the medulla region.

Vascular   Pertaining to blood vessels or richly supplied with blood vessels.

Vasoconstriction (vas″o-kon-strik′shun)   Narrowing of blood vessels.

Vasodilation (vas″o-di-la′shun)   Relaxation of the smooth muscles of the blood vessels producing dilation.

Vasomotion (vas″o-mo′shun)   Intermittent contraction or relaxation of the precapillary sphincter beds resulting in a staggered blood flow when tissue needs are not extreme.

Vasomotor center (vas″o-mo′ter)   Brain area concerned with regulation of blood vessel resistance.

Vasomotor fibers   Sympathetic nerve fibers that regulate the contraction of smooth muscle in the walls of blood vessels, thereby regulating blood vessel diameter.

Veins (vānz′)   Blood vessels that return blood toward the heart from the circulation.

Ventral   Pertaining to the front; anterior.

Ventricles (ven′trĭ-kulz)   (1) Paired, inferiorly located heart chambers that function as the major blood pumps (2) Cavities in the brain.

Venule (ven′ūl)   A small vein.

Vertebral column (ver′ti-brul)   The spine, formed of a number of individual bones called vertebrae and two composite bones (sacrum and coccyx).

Vesicle (vĕ′sĭ-kul)   A small liquid-filled sac or bladder.

Vesicular follicle   Mature ovarian follicle.

Vestibule   An enlarged area at the beginning of a canal, i.e., inner ear, nose, larynx.

Villus (vil′us)   Fingerlike projections of the small intestinal mucosa that tremendously increase its surface area for absorption.

Visceral (vis′er-al)   Pertaining to an internal organ of the body or the inner part of a structure.

Viscosity (vis-kos′ĭ-te)   State of being sticky or thick.

Vital capacity   The volume of air that can be expelled from the lungs by forcible expiration after the deepest inspiration; total exchangeable air.

Vitamins   Organic compounds required by the body in minute amounts.

Vocal folds   Mucosal folds that function in voice production (speech); also called the true vocal cords.

Volatile acid   An acid that can be eliminated by the lungs; carbonic acid is converted to CO_2, which diffuses into the alveoli.

Volkmann's canals   *See* Perforating canals

Voluntary muscle   Muscle under control of the will; skeletal muscle.

Vulva (vul′vuh)   Female external genitalia.

Wallerian degeneration (wal-er″ē-an)   A process of disintegration of an axon that occurs when it is crushed or severed and cannot receive nutrients from the cell body.

Water of oxidation (metabolic water)   Water produced from cellular metabolism (about 10% of our body's water).

White matter   White substance of the central nervous system; myelinated nerve fibers.

Yolk sac (yōk)   Endodermal sac that serves as the source for primordial germ cells.

Zygote (zi′gōt)   Fertilized egg.

Index

NOTE: Boldface page numbers indicate definitions. A *t* following a page number indicates tabular material and an *f* following a page number indicates a figure.

A bands, **252**
Abdomen
  arteries of, 678–679*t*
  muscles of, 293*f*
  veins of, 688–689*t*
Abdominal aorta, **672***t*, 673*f*
Abdominal aortic plexus, 464*f*, **468**
Abdominal cavity, 17*f*, **19**
Abdominal reflexes, **456**
Abdominal wall muscles, 308*t*, 309*f*
Abdominopelvic cavity, **17–19**
Abdominopelvic quadrants, 22
Abdominopelvic regions, 21
Abducens nerve, 435, 439*t*, 509
  nuclei of, 397, 398*f*
Abduction, **231**
Abductor pollicis longus
  muscle, 320*t*, 321*f*, 322*t*, 323*f*
ABO blood groups, **604–605**, 1033*t*
Abortion, **1023**
Abortion pill (RU486), 987
ABP. *See* Androgen-binding protein
Abscess, 712
Absolute refractory period, **358**, 627
Absorption, 789, 790, **791**, 834–837
  small intestine modifications for, 814–815
Absorptive cells, intestinal, 815
Absorptive state, **873**, 874–875
Accessory digestive organs, 789*f*, **790**
Accessory ducts, male, 957–958
Accessory glands, male, **958–959**
Accessory hemiazygos vein, **687***t*
Accessory nerve, 435, 441*t*
  nuclei of, 397*f*, 399
Accessory reproductive organs, **954**
Acclimatization, **778**
Accommodation, **517**
Accommodation pupillary reflex, **517**
Acetabular labrum, **236**
Acetabulum, **208**, 209*f*, 211*t*
Acetic acid, 869
Acetylcholine, 74, **258–259**, **366–367**, 368*t*, **462**, 469–470
  destruction of, 260–261, 367
  receptors for, 470–471, 470*t*
Acetylcholinesterase, **260**, **367**
Acetyl CoA, 858, 859*f*, **863**
ACh. *See* Acetylcholine
Achalasia, **479**
AChE. *See* Acetylcholinesterase
Achilles (calcaneal) tendon, 214

inflammation of (Achilles tendinitis), **338**
  rupture of, **338**
Achondroplasia, **173**, 1031
Acid-ash diet, urine pH affected by, 916–917
Acid-base balance, 41, 940–947
  abnormalities of, 943*t*, 946–950
  developmental aspects of, 950
  renal mechanisms in maintenance of, 944–946
  respiratory system in maintenance of, 942–943
Acid-base buffers, **42**, 941–942. *See also* Buffers
Acidemia, **951**
Acid group, 48
Acid hydrolases, 80
Acid mantle, 145, 708, 714*t*
Acidosis, 56, **940**
  blood values in, 947
  effects of, 946
  metabolic, 871, 943*t*, **944**, **946**
  physiological, **940**
  renal compensations in, **950**
  respiratory, 943*t*, **946**
  respiratory compensations in, **946–950**
Acids, **40**, 941
  pH of, 41
  strong and weak, **42**, 941
Acinar cells, 571
Acinar glands, **112**
Acne, 145, 149
Acoustic (auditory) meatus
  external, 182*f*, **184**, 185*f*, 188*t*, 527
  internal, 182*f*, 183*f*, **186**, 188*t*, 439*t*
Acquired immune deficiency syndrome (AIDS), **734**, 738–739
Acromegaly, **557**, 558*f*
Acromioclavicular joint, **203**, 224*t*
Acromion, **203**, 204*f*
Acrosomal reaction, **1001–1002**
Acrosome, **965**
ACTH. *See* Adrenocorticotropic hormone
Actin, 50*t*, 82, 124, 253*f*, **254**
Actin filaments. *See* Thin filaments
Action potential, 350, 352, **354–360**
  autorhythmic cardiac cells initiating, 627
  pacemaker, **627**
  postsynaptic potentials compared with, 364*t*
  in skeletal muscle fiber contraction, 257, 259–**260**
Activation energy, **52**, 862
Active humoral immunity, **722**
Active hyperemia, **662**
Active site, **53**
Active transport, 68*t*, **70–71**
  in absorption, 834

Active tubular reabsorption, **909–910**
Actomyosin, **601**
Acyclovir, 985
Adam's apple, 748
Adaptation, **429**
  dark, **523**
  light, **522–523**
  olfactory, 506
Adaptive relaxation, **810**
Addison's disease, 568, 569
  sodium balance and, 936
Adduction, **231**
Adductor brevis muscle, 325*f*, 326*t*, 336*t*
Adductor longus muscle, 325*f*, 326*t*, 336*t*
Adductor magnus muscle, 325*f*, 326*t*, 328*f*, 336*t*
Adductors, of thigh, 326*t*, 328*f*, 337*f*
Adductor tubercle, of femur, 212
Adenine, **54**
Adenine dinucleotide, **860**, 862
Adenocarcinoma of lung, **780**
Adenohypophysis, **553**
  hormones of, 554–560, 556–557*t*. *See also* *specific type*
Adenoids (pharyngeal tonsils), **704**, **747**
Adenoma, **132**
Adenosine, 908
Adenosine diphosphate. *See* ADP
Adenosine monophosphate. *See* AMP
Adenosine triphosphate. *See* ATP
Adenylate cyclase, **549**
ADH. *See* Antidiuretic hormone
Adhesions, 131
Adipocytes (fat cells), 114*f*, 115, **122**
Adipose capsule, 897, 898*f*
Adipose tissue (fat), 117*f*, **122**
  ANS affecting, 472*t*
Adluminal compartment, **965**, 966*f*
ADP, 58
  ATP production stimulated by, 866
  in hemostasis, 600
  phosphorylation of in muscle metabolism, 267–268, 269*f*
Adrenal cortex, **566–569**
  hormones of, 46*t*, 567–569, 570*t*
Adrenal glands, **566–571**, 897
Adrenaline. *See* Epinephrine
Adrenal medulla, **566**, **570–571**
  ANS affecting, 472*t*
  in blood pressure regulation, 656
  hormones of, 570–571, 570*t*
  sympathetic pathways with synapses in, 469
Adrenergic blocking drugs, 471
Adrenergic fibers, **470**
Adrenergic receptors, 470*t*, 471
Adrenocorticotropic hormone

(ACTH), 556*t*, **558**, **568**
Adult celiac disease, 837
Adult polycystic kidney disease, 923
Adventitia
  esophageal, **794**, 801, 802*f*
  tracheal, 750
  of ureter, 917
  vaginal, 973
Aerobic cellular respiration, 77, 863
  in muscle metabolism, **268**, 269*f*
Aerobic endurance, **270**
Aerobic exercise, muscles affected by, 274
Affective brain, 401. *See also* Limbic system
Affective language areas, **390**
Afferent arteriole, **901**, 907–908
Afferent lymphatic vessels, **699**
Afferent (sensory) division of PNS, **341**, 432
Afferent (sensory) nerves, **432**
Afferent (sensory) neurons, 343*f*, **349–350**
  in reflex arc, **451**
Afferent pathway, 10
Afterbirth, **1021**
After-discharge circuits, parallel, 372*f*, **373**
After-hyperpolarization, 356
Afterload, 634, **635–636**
Agglutination, by antibodies, **725**
Agglutinins, **604**
Agglutinogens, **604**
Aggregate field view, **386**
Aging, homeostatic imbalances and, 12
  of skin, 149–152
Agonist, **291**
Agranulocytes, 594, 595*t*, **596**
Ags. *See* Antigens
AHF. *See* Antihemophilic factor
AID. *See* Artificial insemination by donor
AIDS, **734**, 738–739
  pneumonia in, 784
Air-blood barrier (respiratory membrane), **753–754**
Air cells (mastoid sinuses), **184**
Air embolism, scuba diving and, 776
Alae
  of ilium, **208**, 209*f*
  nasal, 745
  sacral, **200**
Alar plate, **410**
Albinism, **152**, 1032
Albumin, 50*t*, **586**, 586*t*
Albuminuria, 917*t*
Alcohol
  blood pressure affected by, 657
  fetus affected by, 1007
Aldosterone, **567–568**, 570*t*
  blood pressure affected by, 657*t*, **658**
  in potassium balance, 939
  in sodium balance, **934–936**
  in tubular reabsorption, 911
Aldosteronism, 568, **951**

hyster-, hystero- *uterus or womb* hysterectomy, removal of the uterus; hysterodynia, pain in the womb

ile- *intestine* ileum, the last portion of the small intestine

im- *not* impermeable, not permitting passage, not permeable

inter- *between* intercellular, between the cells

intercal- *insert* intercalated discs, the end membranes between adjacent cardiac muscle cells

intra- *within, inside* intracellular, inside the cell

iso- *equal, same* isothermal, equal, or same, temperature

jugul- *throat* jugular veins, prominent vessels in the neck

juxta- *near, close to* juxtaglomerular apparatus, a cell cluster next to the glomeruli in the kidneys

karyo- *kernal nucleus* karyotype, the assemblage of the nuclear chromosomes

kera- *horn* keratin, the water-repellent protein of the skin

kilo- *thousand* kilocalories, equivalent to one thousand calories

kin, kines- *move* kinetic energy, the energy of motion

labi-, labri- *lip* labial frenulum, the membrane which joins the lip to the gum

lact- *milk* lactose, milk sugar

lacun- *space, cavity, lake* lacunae, the spaces occupied by cells of cartilage and bone tissue

lamell- *small plate* concentric lamellae, rings of bone matrix in compact bone

lamina *layer, sheet* basal lamina, part of the epithelial basement membrane

lat- *wide* latissimus dorsi, a broad muscle of the back

laten- *hidden* latent period of a muscle twitch

later- *side* lateral (directional term)

leuko- *white* leukocyte, white blood cell

leva- *raise, elevate* levator labii superioris, muscle that elevates upper lip

lingua- *tongue* lingual tonsil, adjacent to the tongue

lip-, lipo- *fat, lipid* lipophage, a cell that has taken up fat in its cytoplasm

lith- *stone* cholelithiasis, gallstones

luci- *clear* stratum lucidum, clear layer of the epidermis

lumen *light* lumen, center of a hollow structure

lut- *yellow* corpus luteum, a yellow, hormone-secreting structure in the ovary

lymph *water* lymphatic circulation, return of clear fluid to the bloodstream

macro- *large* macromolecule, large molecule

macula *spot* macula lutea, yellow spot on the retina

magn- *large* foramen magnum, largest opening of the skull

mal- *bad, abnormal* malfunction, abnormal functioning of an organ

mamm- *breast* mammary gland, breast

mast- *breast* mastectomy, removal of a mammary gland

mater *mother* dura mater, pia mater, membranes that envelop the brain

meat- *a passage* external auditory meatus, the ear canal

medi- *middle* medial (directional term)

medull- *marrow* medulla, the middle portion of the kidney, adrenal gland, and lymph node

mega- *large* megakaryocyte, large precursor cell of platelets

meio- *less* meiosis, nuclear division that halves the chromosome number

melan- *black* melanocytes, which secrete the black pigment melanin

men-, menstru- *month* menses, the cyclic menstrual flow

meningo- *membrane* meningitis, inflammation of the membranes of the brain

mer-, mero-, *a part* merocrine glands, the secretions of which do not include the cell

meso- *middle* mesoderm, middle germ layer

meta- *beyond, between, transition* metatarsus, the part of the foot between the tarsus and the phalanges

metro- *uterus* metroscope, instrument for examining the uterus

micro- *small* microscope, an instrument used to make small objects appear larger

mictur- *urinate* micturition, the act of voiding the bladder

mito- *thread, filament* mitochondria, small, filamentlike structures located in cells

mnem- *memory* amnesia

mono- *single* monospasm, spasm of a single limb

morpho- *form* morphology, the study of form and structure of organisms

multi- *many* multinuclear, having several nuclei

mural *wall* intramural ganglion, a nerve junction within an organ

muta- *change* mutation, change in the base sequence of DNA

myelo- *spinal cord, marrow* myeloblasts, cells of the bone marrow

myo- *muscle* myocardium, heart muscle

nano- *dwarf* nanometer, one billionth of a meter

narco- *numbness* narcotic, a drug producing stupor or numbed sensations

natri- *sodium* atrial natriuretic factor, a sodium-regulating hormone

necro- *death* necrosis, tissue death

neo- *new* neoplasm, an abnormal growth

nephro- *kidney* nephritis, inflammation of the kidney

neuro- *nerve* neurophysiology, the physiology of the nervous system

noci- *harmful* nociceptors, receptors for pain

nom- *name* innominate artery; innominate bone

noto- *back* notochord, the embryonic structure that precedes the vertebral column

nucle- *pit, kernel, little nut* nucleus

nutri- *feed, nourish* nutrition

ob- *before, against* obstruction, impeding or blocking up

oculo- *eye* monocular, pertaining to one eye

odonto- *teeth* orthodontist, one who specializes in proper positioning of the teeth in relation to each other

olfact- *smell* olfactory nerves

oligo- *few* oligodendrocytes, neuroglial cells with few branches

onco- *a mass* oncology, study of cancer

oo- *egg* oocyte, precursor of female gamete

ophthalmo- *eye* ophthalmology, the study of the eyes and related disease

orb- *circular* orbicularis oculi, muscle that encircles the eye

orchi- *testis* cryptorchidism, failure of the testes to descend into the scrotum

org- *living* organism

ortho- *straight, direct* orthopedic, correction of deformities of the musculoskeletal system

osm- *smell* anosmia, loss of sense of smell

osmo- *pushing* osmosis

osteo- *bone* osteodermia, bony formations in the skin

oto- *ear* otoscope, a device for examining the ear

ov-, ovi- *egg* ovum, oviduct

oxy- *oxygen* oxygenation, the saturation of a substance with oxygen

pan- *all, universal* panacea, a cure-all

papill- *nipple* dermal papillae, projections of the dermis into the epidermal area

para- *beside, near* paraphrenitis, inflammation of tissues adjacent to the diaphragm

pect-, pectus *breast* pectoralis major, a large chest muscle

pelv- *a basin* pelvic girdle, which cradles the pelvic organs

peni- *a tail* penis; penile urethra

penna- *a wing* unipennate, bipennate muscles, whose fascicles have a feathered appearance

pent- *five* pentose, a 5-carbon sugar

pep-, peps-, pept- *digest* pepsin, a digestive enzyme of the stomach; peptic ulcer

per-, permea- *through* permeate; permeable

peri- *around* perianal, situated around the anus

phago- *eat* phagocyte, a cell that engulfs and digests particles or cells

pheno- *show, appear* phenotype, the physical appearance of an individual

phleb- *vein* phlebitis, inflammation of the veins

pia *tender* pia mater, delicate inner membrane around the brain and spinal cord

pili *hair* arrector pili muscles of the skin, which make the hairs stand erect

pin-, pino- *drink* pinocytosis, the process of a cell in small particles

platy- *flat, broad* platysma, broad, flat muscle of the neck

pleur- *side, rib* pleural serosa, the membrane that lines the thoracic cavity and covers the lungs

plex-, plexus *net, network* brachial plexus, the network of nerves that supplies the arm

pneumo *air, wind* pneumothorax, air in the thoracic cavity

pod- *foot* podiatry, the treatment of foot disorders

poly- *multiple* polymorphism, multiple forms

post- *after, behind* posterior, places behind (a specific) part

pre-, pro- *before, ahead of* prenatal, before birth

procto- *rectum, anus* proctoscope, an instrument for examining the rectum

pron- *bent forward* prone; pronate

propri- *one's own* proprioception, awareness of body parts and movement

pseudo- *false* pseudotumor, a false tumor

psycho- *mind, psyche* psychogram, a chart of personality traits

ptos- *fall* renal ptosis, a condition in which the kidneys drift below their normal positon

pub- *of the pubis* puberty

pulmo- *lung* pulmonary artery, which brings blood to the lungs

pyo- *pus* pyocyst, a cyst that contains pus

pyro- *fire* pyrogen, a substance that induces fever

quad-, quadr- *four-sided* quadratus lumborum, a muscle with a square shape

re- *back, again* reinfect

rect- *straight* rectus abdominis, rectum

ren- *kidney* renal, renin, an enzyme secreted by the kidney

retin, retic- *net, network* endoplasmic reticulum, a network of membranous sacs within a cell

retro- *backward, behind* retrogression, to move backward in development

rheum- *watery flow, change, or flux* rheumatoid arthritis, rheumatic fever

rhin-, rhino- *nose* rhinitis, inflammation of the nose

ruga- *fold, wrinkle* rugae, the folds of the stomach, gallbladder, and urinary bladder

sagitt- *arrow* sagittal (directional term)

salta- *leap* saltatory conduction, the rapid conduction of impulses along myelinated neurons

sanguin- *blood* consanguineous, indicative of a genetic relationship between individuals

sarco- *flesh* sarcomere, unit of contraction in skeletal muscle

saphen- *visible, clear* great saphenous vein, superficial vein of the thigh and leg

sclero- *hard* sclerodermatitis, inflammatory thickening and hardening of the skin

seb- *grease* sebum, the oil of the skin

semen *seed, sperm* semen, the discharge of the male reproductive system

semi- *half* semicircular, having the form of half a circle

sens- *feeling* sensation; sensory

septi- *rotten* sepsis, infection; antiseptic

septum *fence* nasal septum

sero- *serum* serological tests, which assess blood conditions

serrat- *saw* serratus anterior, a muscle of the chest wall that has a jagged edge

sin-, sino- *a hollow* sinuses of the skull

soma- *body* somatic nervous system

somnus *sleep* insomnia, inability to sleep

sphin- *squeeze* sphincter

splanchn- *organ* splanchnic nerve, autonomic supply to abdominal viscera

spondyl- *vertebra* ankylosing spondylitis, rheumatoid arthritis affecting the spine

squam- *scale, flat* squamous epithelium, squamous suture of skull

steno- *narrow* stenocoriasis, narrowing of the pupil

strat- *layer* strata of the epidermis, stratified epithelium

stria- *furrow, streak* striations of skeletal and cardiac muscle tissue

stroma *spread out* strome, the connective tissue framework of some organs

sub- *beneath, under* sublingual, beneath the tongue

sucr- *sweet* sucrose, table sugar

sudor- *sweat* sudoriferous glands, the sweat glands

super- *above, upon* superior, quality or state of being above others or a part

supra- *above, upon* supracondylar, above a condyle

sym-, syn- *together, with* synapse, the region of communication between two neurons

synerg- *work together* synergism

systol- *contraction* systole, contraction of the heart

tachy- *rapid* tachycardia, abnormally rapid heartbeat

tact- *touch* tactile sense

telo- *the end* telophase, the end of mitosis

templ-, tempo- *time* temporal summation of nerve impulses

tens- *stretched* muscle tension

tertius *third* peroneus tertius, one of three peroneus muscles

tetan- *rigid, tense* tetanus of muscles

therm- *heat* thermometer, an instrument used to measure heat

thromb- *clot* thrombocyte; thrombus

thyro- *a shield* thyroid gland

tissu- *woven* tissue

tono- *tension* tonicity; hypertonic

tox- *poison* antitoxic, effective against poison

trab- *beam, timber* trabeculae, spicules of bone in spongy bone tissue

trans- *across, through* transpleural, through the pleura

trapez- *table* trapezius, the four-sided muscle of the upper back

tri- *three* trifurcation, division into three branches